Y0-ABE-779
ACURA
Through
VOLVO

1993 MITCHELL® AIR CONDITIONING & HEATING SERVICE & REPAIR

IMPORTED CARS, LIGHT TRUCKS & VANS

Mitchell®

The Leader in Professional Estimating and Repair Information.

Mitchell International

ACKNOWLEDGMENT

Mitchell International thanks the domestic and import automobile and light truck manufacturers, distributors, and dealers for their generous cooperation and assistance which make this manual possible.

MARKETING

Director
Robert Gradijan

Brand Managers
Catherine Smith
Daniel D. Fleming

EDITORIAL

Manager, Annual Data Editorial
Thomas L. Landis

Manager, Special Product Editorial
Ronald E. Garrett

Senior Editors
Chuck Vedra
Ramiro Gutierrez
John M. Fisher
Tom L. Hall
James A. Hawes
Serge G. Pirino

Technical Editors
Scott A. Olsen
Bob Reel
David W. Himes
Alex A. Solis
Donald T. Pellettera
Michael C. May
Scott A. Tiner
James R. Warren
James D. Boxberger
Bobby R. Gifford
Linda M. Murphy
Tim P. Lockwood
Dave L. Skora
Donald Lawler
Wayne D. Charbonneau
Sal Caloca
Charles "Bud" Gardner
Dan Hankins
Robert L. Eller
Nick DiVerde
Trang Nguyen
Julia A. Kinneer

WIRING DIAGRAMS

Manager
Matthew M. Krimple

TECHNICAL LIBRARIAN

Charlotte Norris

PRODUCT SUPPORT

Manager
Eddie Santangelo

Senior Product Specialist
Robert L. Rothgery

Product Specialists
James A. Wafford

Diagnostic Support Specialist
Jeffrey H. Lenzkes

GRAPHICS

Manager
Judie LaPierre

Supervisor
Ann Klimetz

Published By

MITCHELL INTERNATIONAL
9889 Willow Creek Road
P.O. Box 26260
San Diego, CA 92196-0260

ISBN 0-8470-1012-0

Printed in U.S.A.

Customer Service Numbers:

Subscription/Billing Information:
1-800-648-8010 or 619-578-6550

Technical Information:
1-800-854-7030 or 619-578-6550

Or Write: P.O. Box 26260, San Diego, CA 92196-0260

CONTENTS:

- **HEATER SYSTEMS**
- **MANUAL A/C HEATER SYSTEMS**
- **AUTOMATIC A/C HEATER SYSTEMS**

HOW TO FIND THE INFORMATION
3 Quick Steps

1 If you turn back one page, you'll find the Contents of this manual arranged according to manufacturer. Locate the manufacturer of the vehicle you're working on...notice it has a Black square next to it.

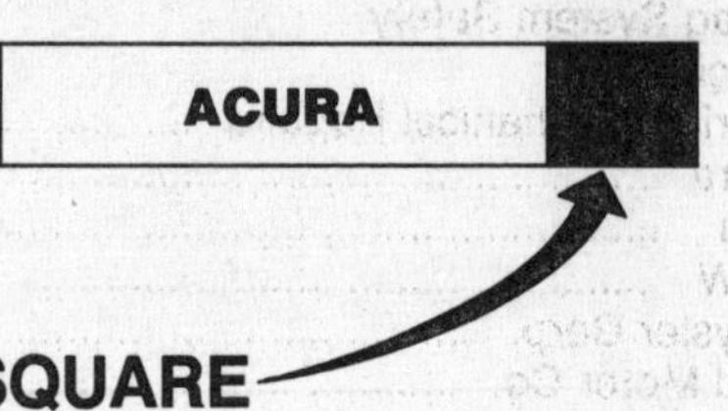
ACURA

THUMB INDEX SQUARE

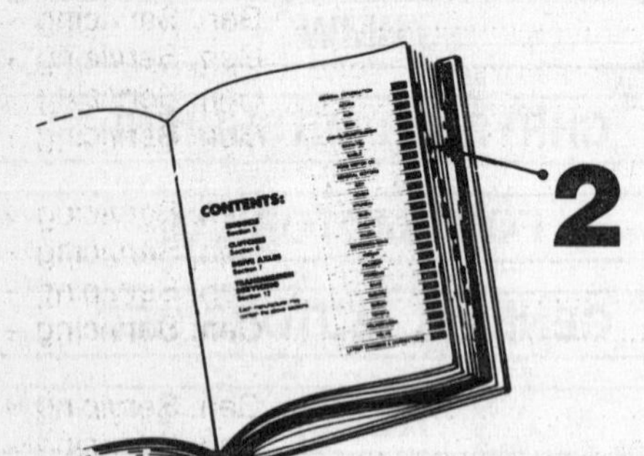
CONTENTS:

2 Looking along the right-hand edge of the manual, you'll notice additional Black squares. Match the Black square of the appropriate manufacturer with the Black squares in line with it on the manual's edge. Turn directly to the first page (Contents Page) of that manufacturer's "section".

3 Scan the Subjects listed in the Contents page; then turn to the page indicated for the Specific Information you desire.

1993 GENERAL SERVICING
Contents

1993 GENERAL SERVICING
Air Bag System Safety

WARNING: To avoid injury from accidental air bag deployment, read and carefully follow all SERVICE PRECAUTIONS and DISABLING & ACTIVATING AIR BAG SYSTEM procedures.

NOTE: References to SRS and SIR by manufacturers refer to Supplemental Restraint Systems (SRS) and Supplemental Inflatable Restraints (SIR).

SPECIAL CARE DURING MECHANICAL REPAIRS

NOTE: For information on air bag DIAGNOSIS & TESTING or DISPOSAL PROCEDURES, see MITCHELL® AIR BAG SERVICE & REPAIR MANUAL, DOMESTIC & IMPORTED MODELS.

In some instances, it may be necessary to remove steering column or instrument panel to gain access to blower motor housing, heater assembly, evaporator assembly, or other A/C-heater system related component. Observe manufacturer service precautions when working on vehicle with air bag system. See appropriate SERVICE PRECAUTIONS.

Electrical sources should never be allowed near inflator on back of air bag module. Never probe air bag system electrical wires with analog volt-ohmmeter or test light. Always disable air bag system before servicing vehicle. See appropriate DISABLING & ACTIVATING AIR BAG SYSTEM procedure. Failure to do so could result in accidental air bag deployment and possible personal injury.

If air bag system is not fully functional for any reason, DO NOT drive vehicle until system is repaired and is again operational. DO NOT remove bulbs, modules, sensors or other components, or in any way disable system from operating normally. If air bag system is not functional, park vehicle until system is repaired and functions properly.

ACURA

SYSTEM OPERATION CHECK

When ignition is turned on, SRS indicator light should come on and then go out after about 6 seconds. If indicator light does not come on, comes on while driving or does not go out after about 6 seconds, inspect system as soon as possible.

SERVICE PRECAUTIONS

Observe these precautions when working with air bag systems:

- Disable SRS before servicing any SRS or steering column component. Failure to do so could result in accidental air bag deployment and possible personal injury. See DISABLING & ACTIVATING AIR BAG SYSTEM.
- Air bag system retains voltage for about 3 MINUTES after it is disabled. Wait at least 3 MINUTES after system is disabled before servicing, as air bag may accidentally deploy, causing personal injury.
- After an accident, inspect all SRS components, including harness and brackets. Replace any damaged or bent components, even if a deployment did not occur. Check steering column, knee bolster, instrument panel steering column reinforcement plate and lower brace for damage. DO NOT service any component or wiring. Replace any damaged or defective components or wiring.
- After repairs, turn ignition on from passenger side of vehicle (on single air bag models). Verify SRS indicator light works properly and no system faults are indicated. See SYSTEM OPERATION CHECK.
- Always wear safety glasses when servicing or handling air bag.
- Air bag module must be stored in its original special container until ready for service. Store air bag module and container in clean, dry place, away from extreme heat, sparks and sources of high electrical energy.
- When placing live air bag module on bench or other surface, always face air bag and trim cover up, away from surface. This will reduce motion of module if it is accidentally deployed.
- Never allow any electrical source near inflator on back of air bag module.
- When carrying live air bag module, point trim cover away from your body to minimize injury in case of accidental air bag deployment.
- DO NOT probe through wire insulator; this will damage wire and eventually cause failure due to corrosion.
- When performing electrical tests, always use test harnesses recommended by manufacturer. DO NOT use test probes directly on component connector pins or wires.
- DO NOT use electrical equipment not specified by manufacturer.
- If SRS is not fully functional for any reason, DO NOT operate vehicle until system is repaired. DO NOT remove any component or in any way disable system from operating normally. If SRS is not functional, park vehicle until repairs can be made.

DISABLING & ACTIVATING AIR BAG SYSTEM

WARNING: Air bag system maintains voltage for about 3 MINUTES after battery is disconnected. Wait at least 3 MINUTES after system is disabled before servicing, as air bag may accidentally deploy, causing personal injury.

Disabling System – 1) Turn ignition off. Disconnect battery cables. Wait at least 3 MINUTES to allow capacitor in back-up circuit to discharge. This will prevent malfunction of seat belt pretensioner. Remove access panel from under driver-side air bag. Remove Red shorting connector.

2) Unplug 3-pin connector between driver-side air bag and clockspring. Connect Red shorting connector to driver-side air bag connector. Connect SRS Shorting Connector "A" (07MAZ-SP00200) to clockspring connector. *See Fig. 1.*

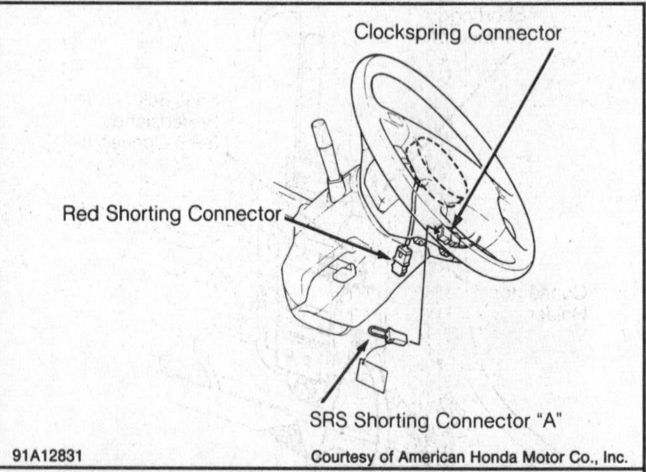
Clockspring Connector
Red Shorting Connector
SRS Shorting Connector "A"
91A12831
Courtesy of American Honda Motor Co., Inc.

Fig. 1: Installing Shorting Connector For Driver-Side Air Bag (Legend Shown; Vigor Is Similar)

3) Remove glove box. Unplug connector between passenger-side air bag and SRS main harness. Connect Red shorting connector to passenger-side air bag connector. *See Fig. 2.* Connect SRS Shorting Connector "A" to SRS main harness 3-pin connector.

4) On Legend, remove quarter trim panel. Remove Red shorting connectors from connector holders. Unplug seat belt pretensioner connectors. Connect Red shorting connectors to seat belt pretensioner connectors. *See Fig. 3.*

Activating System – 1) Remove shorting connectors from passenger-side air bag connector and SRS main harness connector. Reconnect passenger-side air bag connector to SRS main harness connector. Reinstall glove box.

2) Remove shorting connectors from driver-side air bag connector and clockspring connector. Reconnect driver-side air bag connector to clockspring connector. Attach shorting connector to access panel. Reinstall access panel.
3) On Legend, remove shorting connectors from seat belt pretensioner connectors. Attach shorting connectors to their holders. Reconnect side wire connector to right pretensioner connector.
4) Reconnect main wire to left pretensioner connector. Reinstall quarter trim panel. On all models, reconnect battery. Verify system is functioning properly. See SYSTEM OPERATION CHECK.

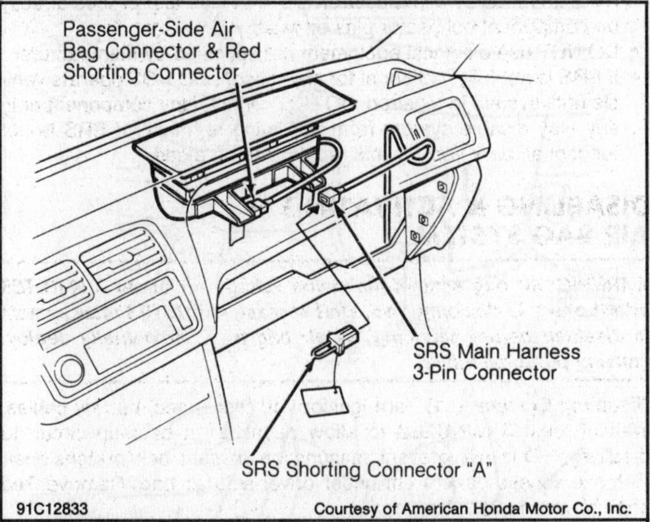
Passenger-Side Air
Bag Connector & Red
Shorting Connector
SRS Main Harness
3-Pin Connector
SRS Shorting Connector "A"
91C12833
Courtesy of American Honda Motor Co., Inc.

Fig. 2: Installing Shorting Connectors For Passenger-Side Air Bag (Legend Shown; Vigor Is Similar)

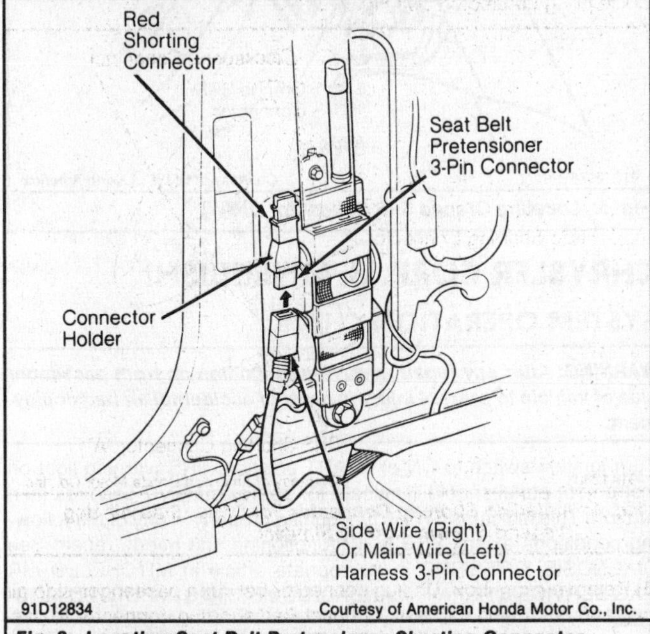
Red
Shorting
Connector
Seat Belt
Pretensioner
3-Pin Connector
Connector
Holder
Side Wire (Right)
Or Main Wire (Left)
Harness 3-Pin Connector
91D12834
Courtesy of American Honda Motor Co., Inc.

Fig. 3: Locating Seat Belt Pretensioner Shorting Connector (Legend)

AUDI

SYSTEM OPERATION CHECK

Turn ignition switch to ON position. AIR BAG indicator light should come on for about 10 seconds and then go out. If light remains on, system diagnosis is required. If light does not come on, check bulb. If bulb is okay, diagnose system.

SERVICE PRECAUTIONS

Observe these precautions when working with air bag systems:

- Before disconnecting battery cable(s) and disabling air bag system, obtain radio security code from vehicle owner.
- Before installing computer memory saver on vehicles with electronic radio lock, disconnect air bag voltage supply connector. See DISABLING & ACTIVATING AIR BAG SYSTEM. Failure to do so may cause air bag activation.
- Disable air bag system before servicing any air bag system or steering column component. See DISABLING & ACTIVATING AIR BAG SYSTEM.
- Because of critical operating requirements of system, DO NOT attempt to service any air bag system component.
- DO NOT leave air bag parts unattended. Install air bag parts in vehicle immediately after they are obtained.
- DO NOT use air bag components that have been dropped from heights of approximately 18" or higher.
- DO NOT allow chemical cleaners, oil or grease to contact vinyl covering on air bag unit.
- DO NOT place stickers or covers on steering wheel.
- Disable SRS before performing electric welding on vehicle.
- SRS can only be tested using Diagnostic Tester (VAG 1551) and Adapter Test Harness (VAG 1551/1). DO NOT use Air Bag Tester (VAG 1619). Never use test light, ohmmeter or voltmeter to test air bag system.
- DO NOT expose air bag unit to temperatures greater than 212°F (100°C).

DISABLING & ACTIVATING AIR BAG SYSTEM

Disabling System – Disconnect and shield negative battery cable. Disconnect voltage supply Red connector. On 100, connector is located in passenger-side footwell, above electronic box (marked with a warning tag). *See Fig. 4*. On 90, voltage supply Red connector is located on a clip behind inspection cover, on driver-side lower instrument panel cover.
Activating System – Reconnect negative battery cable and voltage supply connector. Perform system operation check to ensure system is functioning properly. See SYSTEM OPERATION CHECK.

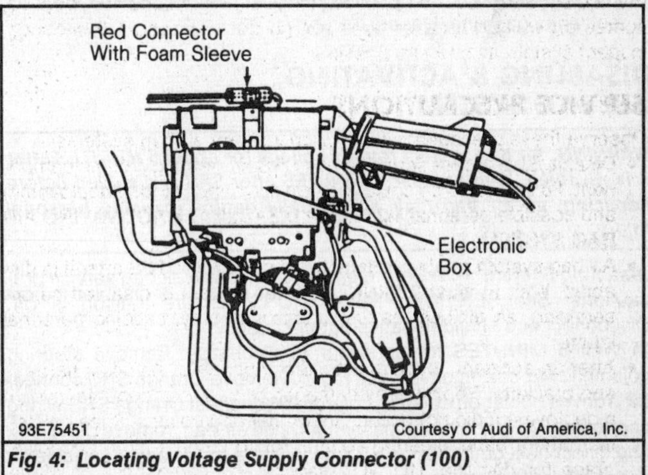
Red Connector
With Foam Sleeve
Electronic
Box
93E75451
Courtesy of Audi of America, Inc.

Fig. 4: Locating Voltage Supply Connector (100)

BMW

NOTE: For information on air bag DIAGNOSIS & TESTING or DISPOSAL PROCEDURES, see MITCHELL® AIR BAG SERVICE & REPAIR MANUAL, DOMESTIC & IMPORTED MODELS.

SYSTEM OPERATION CHECK

Turn ignition switch to ON position. SRS warning light should illuminate and then go out after 6-10 seconds if no fault codes are pre-

1993 GENERAL SERVICING
Air Bag System Safety (Cont.)

sent. The following conditions indicate SRS is malfunctioning; SRS fault code will be stored in control unit memory.

- SRS light does not illuminate when ignition is turned on.
- SRS light does not go out after 6-10 seconds.
- SRS light remains on after engine is started.
- SRS light comes on or flickers while driving.

To read SRS fault code(s), see DIAGNOSIS & TESTING in appropriate article in MITCHELL® AIR BAG SERVICE & REPAIR MANUAL, DOMESTIC & IMPORTED MODELS.

SERVICE PRECAUTIONS

Observe these precautions when working with air bag systems:

- When working around steering column and before any repairs are performed, disable SRS. See DISABLING & ACTIVATING AIR BAG SYSTEM.
- Before performing body damage straightening or electrical arc-welding, disable SRS. See DISABLING & ACTIVATING AIR BAG SYSTEM. Disconnect front sensors.
- Air bag system retains voltage for at least 5 MINUTES after it is disabled. Wait at least 5 MINUTES after system is disabled before servicing, as air bag may accidentally deploy, causing personal injury.
- Always wear safety glasses and gloves when handling a deployed air bag module. Air bag module may contain sodium hydroxide deposits which are irritating to the skin.
- Always use caution when handling any sensors. Never strike or jar sensors. All sensors and mounting bracket bolts must be carefully torqued to ensure proper sensor operation.
- Never use any SRS component that has been dropped from 3 feet or more.
- To avoid air bag deployment when trouble shooting SRS, DO NOT use self-powered electrical test equipment such as battery-powered or AC-powered voltmeter, ohmmeter, etc. DO NOT perform any repair on any portion of SRS wiring circuit.
- Always handle air bag module with trim cover away from your body. Always place air bag module on workbench with trim cover up, away from loose objects.
- Never expose SRS components to temperatures greater than 212°F (100°C).
- Never expose any SRS components to cleaning agents such as solvents, gasoline, lye, etc.

DISABLING & ACTIVATING AIR BAG SYSTEM

WARNING: Air bag system retains voltage for about 5 MINUTES after it is disabled. Wait at least 5 MINUTES after SRS is disabled before servicing, as air bag may accidentally deploy, causing personal injury.

Disabling System – 1) Before proceeding, follow air bag service precautions. See SERVICE PRECAUTIONS. Ensure ignition is off. Disconnect and shield negative battery cable.

2) Wait 5 MINUTES for capacitor to discharge. Remove steering column lower casing cover. *See Fig. 5*. Remove Orange SRS connector from its holder on steering column. Disconnect Orange SRS wiring connector. On models with passenger-side air bag, remove glove box and disconnect both Orange SRS connectors from passenger-side air bag module. System is now disabled.

3) An alternate method for disabling system is to disconnect and shield negative battery cable. Wait 5 MINUTES for capacitor to discharge. Locate SRS control unit under dash, and disconnect SRS control unit Orange connector(s). System is now disabled.

NOTE: Using alternate method to disable system will set a fault code that must be cleared before vehicle is driven.

Activating System – 1) Ensure ignition switch is in OFF position. Reconnect all Orange SRS connectors that were disconnected. Position Orange SRS connector back into holder on steering column. On models equipped with passenger-side air bag, place Orange SRS connectors back into position near passenger air bag module.

2) Install glove box. On all models, install steering column lower casing cover. Connect negative battery cable. System is now activated. Perform system operation check to ensure system is functioning properly. See SYSTEM OPERATION CHECK.

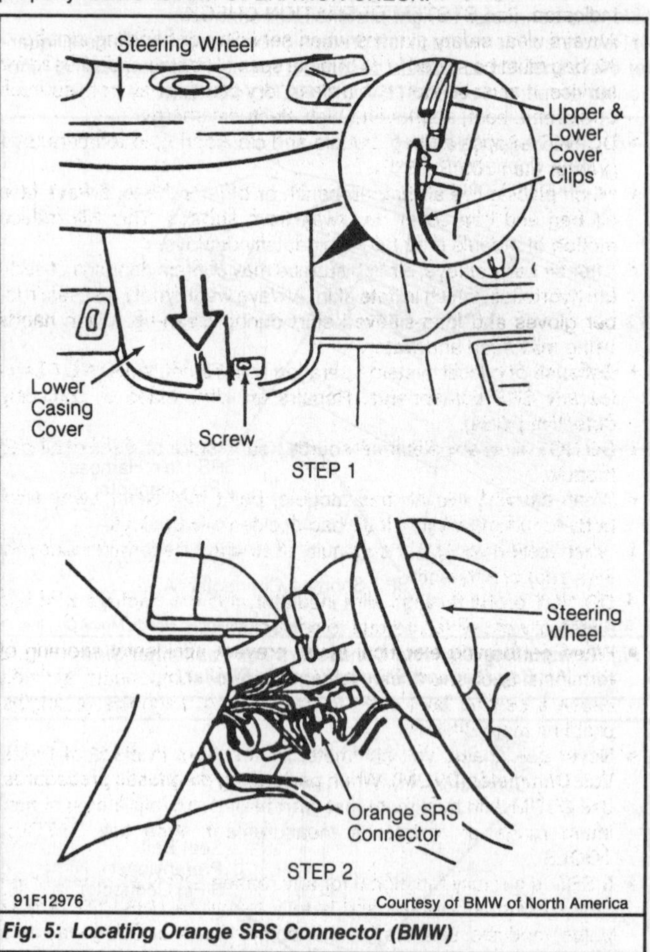
Steering Wheel
Upper & Lower Cover Clips
Lower Casing Cover
Screw
STEP 1
Steering Wheel
Orange SRS Connector
STEP 2
91F12976
Courtesy of BMW of North America

Fig. 5: Locating Orange SRS Connector (BMW)

CHRYSLER CORP. & MITSUBISHI

SYSTEM OPERATION CHECK

WARNING: After any repair, always turn ignition on from passenger side of vehicle to prevent injury in event of accidental air bag deployment.

Turn ignition switch to ON or START position. SRS warning light on instrument panel should illuminate for approximately 7 seconds then turn off. This indicates SRS is functioning properly. If any of the following conditions exists, SRS is malfunctioning and needs repair. See DIAGNOSIS & TESTING in appropriate article in MITCHELL® AIR BAG SERVICE & REPAIR MANUAL, DOMESTIC & IMPORTED MODELS.

- SRS warning light does not illuminate as described.
- SRS warning light stays on for more than 7 seconds.
- SRS warning light illuminates while driving.

SERVICE PRECAUTIONS

Observe these precautions when working with air bag systems:

- Disable SRS before servicing any SRS or steering column component. Failure to do this may result in accidental air bag deployment and possible personal injury. See DISABLING & ACTIVATING AIR BAG SYSTEM.

1993 GENERAL SERVICING
Air Bag System Safety (Cont.)

- Wait at least 60 seconds after disabling air bag system. SRS retains enough voltage, for a short time after system is disabled, to deploy air bag.
- After repairs, always turn ignition on from passenger side to prevent injury in event of accidental air bag deployment. Ensure SRS warning light is working properly and no system faults are indicated. See SYSTEM OPERATION CHECK.
- Always wear safety glasses when servicing or handling air bag.
- Air bag must be stored in its original special container until used for service. It must be stored in a clean, dry place, away from sources of extreme heat, sparks and high electrical energy.
- DO NOT expose air bag module and clockspring to temperatures greater than 200°F (93°C).
- When placing live air bag on bench or other surface, always face air bag and trim cover up, away from surface. This will reduce motion of module if air bag accidentally deploys.
- After air bag deploys, air bag surface may contain deposits of sodium hydroxide, which irritate skin. Always wear safety glasses, rubber gloves and long-sleeved shirt during clean-up. Wash hands using mild soap and water.
- Because of critical system operating requirements, DO NOT service any SRS components. Repairs are only made by replacing defective part(s).
- DO NOT allow any electrical source near inflator on back of air bag module.
- When carrying live air bag module, point trim cover away from body to minimize injury if air bag accidentally deploys.
- When testing voltage or continuity at air bag, use terminal side (not wire end) of connector.
- DO NOT probe through wire insulator; this will damage wire and eventually cause failure due to corrosion.
- When performing electrical tests, prevent accidental shorting of terminals. Such shorts can damage fuses or components, and may cause a second fault code to set, making diagnosis of original problem more difficult.
- Never use analog volt-ohmmeter or test light in place of Digital Volt-Ohmmeter (DVOM). When performing diagnostic procedures, use DVOM with maximum test current of 2 mA (milliamps) at minimum range of resistance measurement. Also see SPECIAL TOOLS.
- If SRS is not fully functional for any reason, DO NOT drive vehicle until system is repaired and is fully functional. DO NOT remove bulbs, modules, sensors or other components, or in any way disable system from operating normally. If SRS is not functional, park vehicle until repairs are made.

SPECIAL TOOLS

To avoid air bag deployment when working on SRS, DO NOT use electrical test equipment such as test lights, battery or A/C-powered volt-ohmmeter, or any type of electrical equipment other than those specified by manufacturer.

SRS RECOMMENDED TOOLS

Tool Name	Tool Number
Digital Volt-Ohmmeter (DVOM)	[1]
Multi-Use Tester	MB991341
ROM Pack [2]	MB991423
SRS Check Harness	MB991349

[1] – DVOM should have maximum test current of 2 mA (milliamps) at minimum range of resistance measurement.
[2] – ROM pack is used with multi-use tester.

DISABLING & ACTIVATING AIR BAG SYSTEM

WARNING: System reserve capacitor retains SRS voltage for about 60 seconds after battery is disconnected. Wait at least 60 seconds after negative battery cable is disconnected before servicing SRS, as air bag may accidentally deploy, causing personal injury.

To disable system, turn ignition switch to OFF position. Disconnect negative battery cable, and tape cable end. To activate system, reconnect negative battery cable.

FORD MOTOR CO.

SYSTEM OPERATION CHECK

NOTE: Capri is manufactured with either an early or late design air bag system. On early production models (built before July 1992), an external back-up power supply is used. On late production models (built after July 1992), back-up power supply is built into diagnostic monitor.

1) Check for faults in SRS at completion of each circuit test and whenever performing system operation check. To check system, turn ignition switch to RUN position. If AIR BAG light illuminates for 4-8 seconds then goes out, SRS is functioning properly and no fault codes exist.
2) If fault code is detected in SRS during system operation check, AIR BAG light will remain off, stay on continuously or flash code sequence. If AIR BAG light flashes, count number of flashes after fault code has cycled twice. Number of flashes represents fault code used to diagnose SRS.
3) If fault code exists and AIR BAG light fails to illuminate, an audible tone will be heard, indicating AIR BAG light is out and service is required.

NOTE: For information on air bag DIAGNOSIS & TESTING or DISPOSAL PROCEDURES, see MITCHELL® AIR BAG SERVICE & REPAIR MANUAL, DOMESTIC & IMPORTED MODELS.

SERVICE PRECAUTIONS

Observe these precautions when working with air bag systems:

- Disable SRS before servicing SRS or steering column components. Failure to do so could result in accidental air bag deployment and personal injury. See DISABLING & ACTIVATING AIR BAG SYSTEM.
- Unplug back-up power supply before servicing system. Back-up power supply retains deployment charge for minimum of 15 MINUTES after battery is disconnected. Failure to unplug back-up power supply could result in accidental air bag deployment and personal injury.
- Because of critical operating requirements of system, DO NOT service sensors, clockspring, diagnostic monitor, back-up power supply or air bag module. Corrections are made by replacement only.
- After servicing SRS, ensure AIR BAG light does not indicate any faults. Perform system operation check. See SYSTEM OPERATION CHECK.
- If a part is replaced and new part does not correct condition, reinstall original part, and perform diagnostic procedure again.
- Always wear safety glasses when servicing vehicles with air bag or when handling air bag.
- When carrying a live air bag module, point air bag module and trim cover away from your body. This minimizes chance of injury in event of an accidental deployment.
- When placing live air bag module on bench or other surface, always face air bag module and trim cover up, away from surface. This will reduce motion of module if it is accidentally deployed.
- After deployment, air bag surface may contain deposits of sodium hydroxide, which may irritate skin. Sodium hydroxide is a product of gas generant combustion. Always wear gloves and safety glasses when handling deployed air bag. Wash hands using mild soap and water.
- Never probe connectors on air bag module. Doing so may deploy air bag, causing personal injury.
- The instruction to DISCONNECT always refers to a connector. DO NOT disconnect a component from vehicle when instructed to DISCONNECT.

1993 GENERAL SERVICING
Air Bag System Safety (Cont.)

DISABLING & ACTIVATING AIR BAG SYSTEM

WARNING: On early production models, back-up power supply must be unplugged before any service is performed to system. Back-up power supply will hold a deployment charge for minimum of 15 minutes after battery is disconnected. Servicing SRS before 15-minute period or failure to unplug back-up power supply could result in accidental air bag deployment and personal injury. On late production models, back-up power supply will hold a deployment charge for approximately one minute after positive battery cable is disconnected. Servicing SRS before one-minute period may cause accidental air bag deployment and possible personal injury. The following disabling sequence is only for component replacement purposes. If vehicle was involved in a collision and air bag did not deploy, or SRS is not functioning properly, and vehicle needs to be driven, complete system deactivation is required. For information on COMPLETE SYSTEM DEACTIVATION, see MITCHELL® AIR BAG SERVICE & REPAIR MANUAL, DOMESTIC & IMPORTED MODELS.

Disabling System (Early Production Models) – **1)** Before proceeding, follow air bag service precautions. See SERVICE PRECAUTIONS. Disconnect and shield negative battery cable. Unplug back-up power supply 3-way harness connector. System is now disabled.
2) Back-up power supply is mounted to inside of instrument panel, left of glove box opening. Glove box door must be opened past its stops and lowered toward floor to access back-up power supply.
Disabling System (Late Production Models) – Disconnect negative and then positive battery cables. Shield both cables. Air bag system contains a back-up power supply built into air bag diagnostic monitor. Wait a minimum of one minute before servicing any air bag system components. System is now disabled.
Activating System (All Models) – To activate SRS, on early production models, reconnect back-up power supply connector. On all models, connect negative battery cable. From passenger side of vehicle, turn ignition switch to RUN position. System is now activated. Verify system is functioning properly. See SYSTEM OPERATION CHECK.

GEO

SYSTEM OPERATION CHECK

Turn ignition on. If system is functioning normally, INFLATABLE RESTRAINT indicator light should flash 7-9 times and then go off. The following conditions may indicate system failure:

- Light remains off.
- Light comes on while driving.
- Light flashes 7 times and remains on.
- Light does not flash but illuminates continuously with ignition on.
- Light flashes Code 12.

SIR system faults are usually due to a disconnected/loose electrical connector caused by previous service on vehicle. Always check Orange connector at base of steering column.

SERVICE PRECAUTIONS

Observe these precautions when working with air bag systems:

- Disable SIR system before servicing any SIR system or steering column component. Failure to do this could result in accidental air bag deployment and possible personal injury. See DISABLING & ACTIVATING AIR BAG SYSTEM.
- System retains voltage for about 10 MINUTES after it is disabled. Wait about 10 MINUTES after SIR system is disabled before servicing, as air bag may accidentally deploy, causing personal injury.
- After repairs, turn ignition on from passenger side of vehicle to prevent injury in event of accidental air bag deployment. Ensure INFLATABLE RESTRAINT indicator light is working properly and no system faults are indicated. See SYSTEM OPERATION CHECK.
- Always wear safety glasses when servicing or handling air bag.
- Inflator module must be stored in its original special container until used for service. It must be stored in a clean, dry place, away from sources of extreme heat, sparks or high electrical energy.
- When placing live inflator module (air bag module) on bench or other surface, always face air bag and trim cover up, away from surface. This will reduce motion of module if accidentally deployed.
- After deployment, air bag surface may contain deposits of sodium hydroxide, which can irritate skin. Always wear safety glasses, rubber gloves and long-sleeved shirt during clean-up. Wash hands using mild soap and water.
- Never allow any electrical source near inflator on back of inflator module.
- When carrying live inflator module, point trim cover away from your body to minimize injury in case of accidental deployment.
- DO NOT probe through wire insulator; this will damage wire and eventually cause failure due to corrosion.
- Replace coil assembly whenever air bag deploys.
- When performing electrical tests, prevent accidental shorting of terminals. Such mistakes can damage fuses or components and may cause a second fault code to set, making diagnosis of original problem more difficult.
- When using diagnostic charts to diagnose SIR system, DO NOT use volt-ohmmeter, test light or any type of electrical equipment not specified by manufacturer.
- If SIR system is not fully functional for any reason, DO NOT drive vehicle until system is repaired. DO NOT remove bulbs, modules, sensors or other components, or in any way disable system from operating normally. If SIR system is not functional, park vehicle until repairs can be made.

DISABLING & ACTIVATING AIR BAG SYSTEM

WARNING: System retains voltage for about 10 MINUTES after it is disabled. Wait about 10 MINUTES after SIR system is disabled before servicing, as air bag may accidentally deploy, causing personal injury.

Disabling System (Metro) – Turn ignition switch to OFF position. Disconnect negative battery cable. Remove access cover at back of steering wheel to access Yellow 2-pin SIR connector. *See Fig. 6.* Remove Connector Position Assurance (CPA) clip on Yellow 2-pin connector at back of steering wheel. Disconnect Yellow 2-pin connector. Wait 10 MINUTES before working on vehicle.
Activating System – Turn ignition switch to OFF position. Connect Yellow 2-pin connector and CPA clip at back of steering wheel. Connect negative battery cable. Install access cover at back of steering wheel. Turn ignition switch to ON position. Verify system is functioning properly. See SYSTEM OPERATION CHECK.

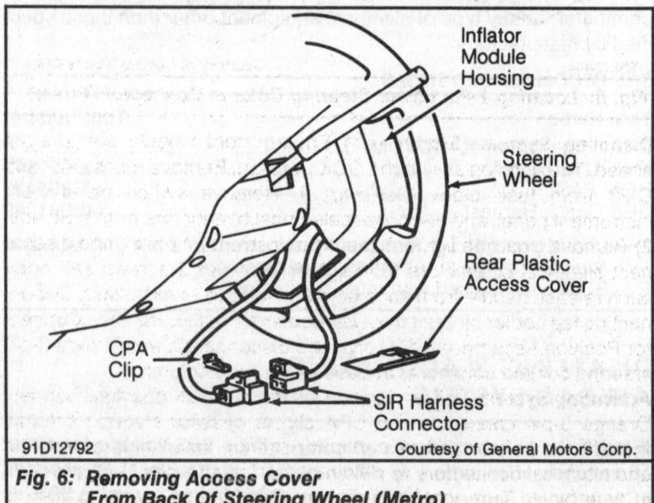
Inflator Module Housing
Steering Wheel
Rear Plastic Access Cover
CPA Clip
SIR Harness Connector
91D12792
Courtesy of General Motors Corp.

Fig. 6: Removing Access Cover From Back Of Steering Wheel (Metro)

1993 GENERAL SERVICING
Air Bag System Safety (Cont.)

Disabling System (Prizm) – Ensure front wheels face straight ahead. Turn ignition switch to LOCK. Remove CIG and RADIO fuse and IGN fuse from junction block. *See Fig. 7.* Remove Connector Position Assurance (CPA) clip and disconnect 2-pin SIR lower steering column connector. *See Fig. 8.*

Activating System – To activate SIR system, turn ignition switch to LOCK position. Connect 2-pin connector and CPA clip at base of steering column. Install IGN, CIG and RADIO fuses to junction block. Turn ignition switch to ACC or ON position. Verify system is functioning properly. See SYSTEM OPERATION CHECK.

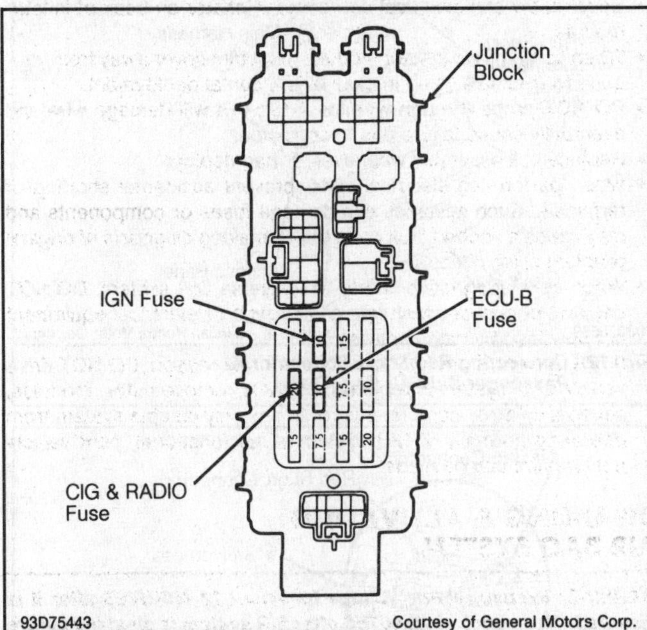
Junction
Block
IGN Fuse
ECU-B
Fuse
CIG & RADIO
Fuse
93D75443
Courtesy of General Motors Corp.

Fig. 7: Locating IGN, CIG & RADIO Fuses (Prism)

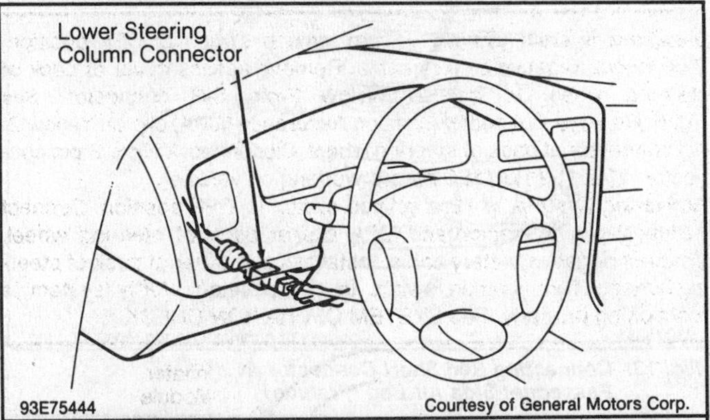
Lower Steering
Column Connector
93E75444
Courtesy of General Motors Corp.

Fig. 8: Locating 2-Pin Lower Steering Column Connector (Prism)

Disabling System (Storm) – 1) Ensure front wheels are straight ahead. Turn ignition switch to LOCK position. Remove fuses C-22 and C-23 from fuse block. *See Fig. 9.* Remove switch bezel from instrument panel, and disconnect electrical connectors from switches. **2)** Remove cigarette lighter bezel from instrument panel, and disconnect electrical connectors from lighter. Remove 2 screws and hood latch release handle from knee bolster. Remove knee bolster, disconnecting lap cooler air duct from lap cooler air outlet. Remove Connector Position Assurance (CPA) clip, and disconnect lower Orange 3-pin steering column connector at base of steering column.

Activating System – Turn ignition switch to LOCK position. Connect Orange 3-pin connector and CPA clip at base of steering column. Install knee bolster and related components. Install cigarette lighter and electrical connectors to switch bezel. Install fuses C-22 and C-23 in fuse block. Turn ignition switch to ON position. Verify system is functioning properly. See SYSTEM OPERATION CHECK.

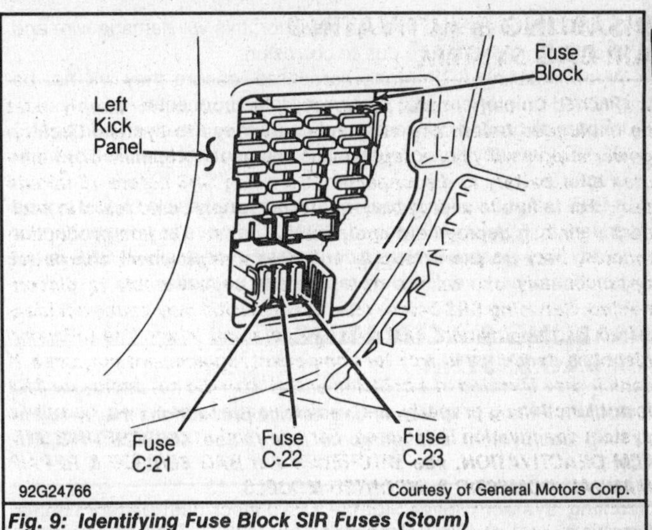
Fuse
Block
Left
Kick
Panel
Fuse
C-21
Fuse
C-22
Fuse
C-23
92G24766
Courtesy of General Motors Corp.

Fig. 9: Identifying Fuse Block SIR Fuses (Storm)

HONDA

SYSTEM OPERATION CHECK

When ignition is turned on, SRS indicator light should come on and then go off after about 6 seconds. If indicator light does not come on as indicated or comes on while driving, inspect system as soon as possible.

SERVICE PRECAUTIONS

NOTE: On models with theft protection system, obtain 5-digit stereo theft security from vehicle owner before disconnecting battery cable.

Observe these precautions when working with air bag systems:

- Disable SRS before servicing any SRS or steering column component. Failure to do this could result in accidental air bag deployment and possible personal injury. See DISABLING & ACTIVATING AIR BAG SYSTEM.
- After an accident, all SRS components, including harness and brackets, must be inspected. If any components are damaged or bent, they must be replaced, even if a deployment did not occur. Check steering column, knee bolster, instrument panel steering column reinforcement plate and lower brace for damage. DO NOT service any component or wiring. If components or wiring are damaged or defective, replacement is necessary. DO NOT use components from another vehicle. Only use new replacement parts.
- After repairs, turn ignition on while ensuring any accidental air bag deployment will not cause injury. Ensure SRS indicator light is working properly and no system faults are indicated. See SYSTEM OPERATION CHECK.
- Always wear safety glasses when servicing or handling an air bag.
- Air bag module must be stored in its original special container until used for service. It must be stored in a clean, dry place, away from sources of extreme heat, sparks and high electrical energy.
- When placing a live air bag module on a bench or other surface, always face air bag and trim cover up, away from surface. This will reduce motion of module if it is accidentally deployed.
- After deployment, air bag surface may contain deposits of sodium hydroxide, which can irritate skin. Always wear safety glasses, rubber gloves and long-sleeved shirt during clean-up, and wash hands using mild soap and water. Follow correct disposal procedures. See DISPOSAL PROCEDURES in MITCHELL® AIR BAG SERVICE & REPAIR MANUAL, DOMESTIC & IMPORTED MODELS.
- Never allow any electrical source near inflator on back of air bag module.
- When carrying a live air bag module, trim cover should be pointed away from your body to minimize injury in case of deployment.

1993 GENERAL SERVICING
Air Bag System Safety (Cont.)

- DO NOT probe a wire through insulator; this will damage wire and eventually cause failure due to corrosion.
- When installing SRS wiring harnesses, ensure they will not be pinched or interfere with other vehicle components.
- Inspect all ground connections. Ensure they are clean and tight.
- DO NOT use any type of electrical equipment not specified by manufacturer.
- If SRS is not fully functional for any reason, vehicle should not be driven until system is repaired. DO NOT remove any component or in any way disable system from operating normally. If SRS is not functional, park vehicle until repairs can be made.

DISABLING & ACTIVATING AIR BAG SYSTEM

WARNING: Failure to follow air bag service precautions may result in air bag deployment and personal injury. See SERVICE PRECAUTIONS.

Disabling System (Driver Side) – Disconnect both battery cables. Remove access panel from steering wheel. *See Fig. 10.* Remove Red short connector, located on inside of access panel. Disconnect air bag connector from cable reel connector. Connect Red short connector to air bag connector.

Disabling System (Passenger Side) – Disable driver-side air bag. Open glove box (remove it on Accord and Civic). Disconnect air bag connector from main harness connector. *See Figs. 11-13.*

Connect Red shorting connector to air bag connector.

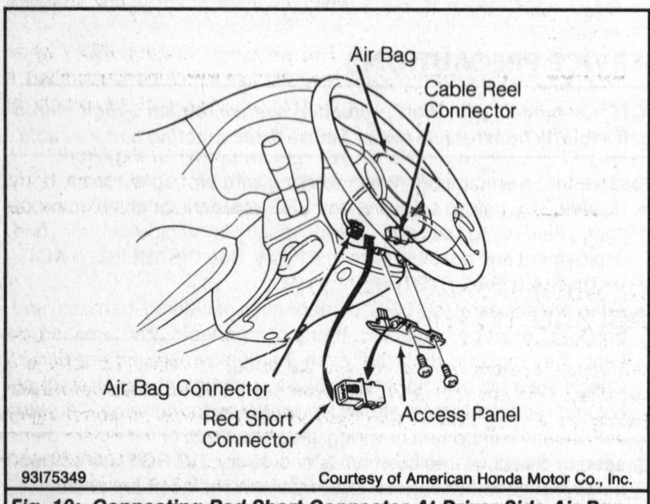
Air Bag
Cable Reel Connector
Air Bag Connector
Red Short Connector
Access Panel
93I75349
Courtesy of American Honda Motor Co., Inc.

Fig. 10: Connecting Red Short Connector At Driver-Side Air Bag

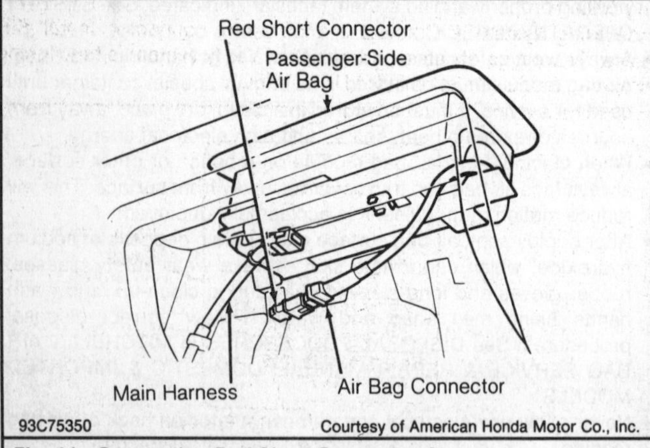
Red Short Connector
Passenger-Side Air Bag
Main Harness
Air Bag Connector
93C75350
Courtesy of American Honda Motor Co., Inc.

Fig. 11: Connecting Red Short Connector At Passenger-Side Air Bag (Accord)

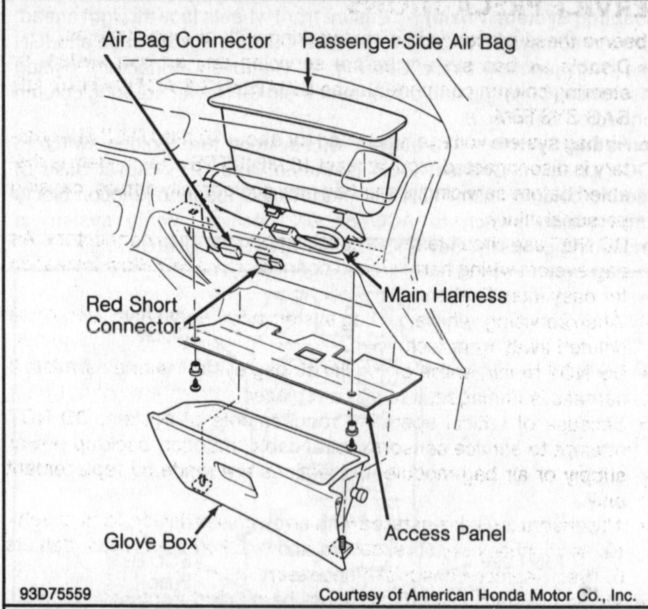
Air Bag Connector
Passenger-Side Air Bag
Red Short Connector
Main Harness
Glove Box
Access Panel
93D75559
Courtesy of American Honda Motor Co., Inc.

Fig. 12: Connecting Red Short Connector At Passenger-Side Air Bag (Civic)

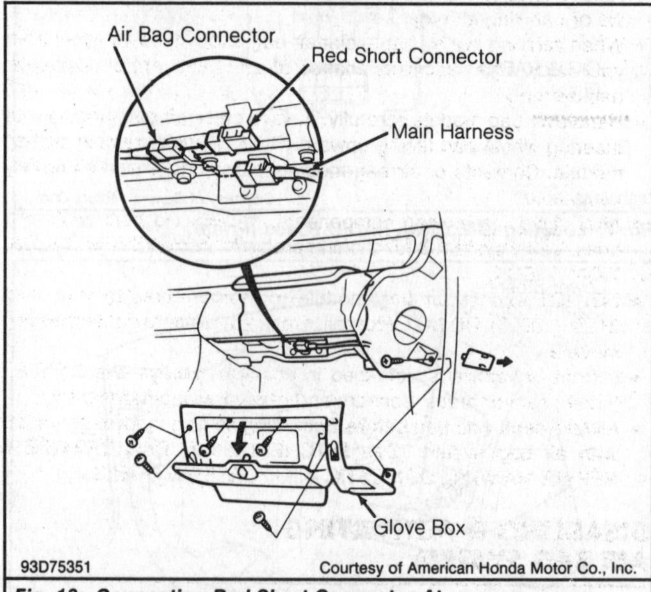
Air Bag Connector
Red Short Connector
Main Harness
Glove Box
93D75351
Courtesy of American Honda Motor Co., Inc.

Fig. 13: Connecting Red Short Connector At Passenger-Side Air Bag (Prelude)

Activating System – Remove Red short connector(s) that were installed at air bag(s) during disabling procedure. Reconnect air bag connector to cable reel connector and/or main harness connector. Return Red short connector to storage location. Check AIR BAG indicator light to ensure system is functioning properly. See SYSTEM OPERATION CHECK.

INFINITI

NOTE: For information on air bag DIAGNOSIS & TESTING or DISPOSAL PROCEDURES, see MITCHELL® AIR BAG SERVICE & REPAIR MANUAL, DOMESTIC & IMPORTED MODELS.

SYSTEM OPERATION CHECK

When ignition switch is turned to ON or START position, the AIR BAG warning light should come on for about 7 seconds and then go off, indicating system is operational.

1993 GENERAL SERVICING
Air Bag System Safety (Cont.)

SERVICE PRECAUTIONS

Observe these precautions when working with air bag systems:

- Disable air bag system before servicing any air bag system or steering column component. See DISABLING & ACTIVATING AIR BAG SYSTEM.
- Air bag system voltage is retained for about 10 MINUTES after battery is disconnected. Wait at least 10 MINUTES after system is disabled before servicing, as air bag may accidentally deploy, causing personal injury.
- DO NOT use circuit tester to check air bag harness connectors. Air bag system wiring harness and connectors have Yellow insulation for easy identification.
- When servicing vehicle, air bag system and related parts should be pointed away from technician.
- DO NOT repair, splice or modify air bag system wiring harness. If harness is damaged, it must be replaced.
- Because of critical operating requirements of system, DO NOT attempt to service sensors, spiral cable, monitor, back-up power supply or air bag module. Corrections are made by replacement only.
- All sensors must be installed with arrow marks facing front of vehicle. Also, check sensors, covers and brackets for cracks, defects or rust. Replace sensor(s) if necessary.
- Air bag system spiral cable must be aligned in neutral position, since its rotation ability is limited. DO NOT turn steering wheel or column after removal of steering gear.
- Always wear safety glasses when servicing air bag-equipped vehicle or handling air bag.
- When carrying live air bag, point air bag and trim cover away from your body. This minimizes chance of injury in event of accidental deployment.
- Handle air bag module carefully. Always place air bag module with steering wheel pad facing upward. DO NOT disassemble air bag module. Contents of air bag module is poisonous and extremely flammable.
- After removing air bag components, replace old bolts with new ones. Verify system is functioning properly. See SYSTEM OPERATION CHECK.
- DO NOT expose air bag module to temperatures greater than 212°F (100°C). DO NOT allow oil, grease or water to contact air bag module.
- If front of vehicle is damaged in collision, always check impact (crash) sensor areas, sensors and related wiring harnesses.
- Always deploy air bag before discarding air bag module or vehicle with air bag system. See MITCHELL® AIR BAG SERVICE & REPAIR MANUAL, DOMESTIC & IMPORTED MODELS.

DISABLING & ACTIVATING AIR BAG SYSTEM

WARNING: Air bag system voltage is retained for about 10 MINUTES after it is disabled. Wait at least 10 MINUTES after system is disabled before servicing, as air bag may accidentally deploy, causing personal injury.

Disabling System – Turn ignition switch to OFF position. Disconnect and shield negative battery cable. Wait at least 10 MINUTES before working on or near air bag components.

Activating – Reconnect battery. From passenger side of vehicle, turn ignition switch to RUN position. Verify system is functioning properly. See SYSTEM OPERATION CHECK.

ISUZU

SYSTEM OPERATION CHECK

WARNING: After repairs, turn ignition on from passenger side of vehicle to avoid injury in case of accidental air bag deployment.

Turn ignition switch to ON position. INFL REST indicator light should flash 7-9 times then go off, indicating SIR system is functioning properly. Following conditions indicate SIR system is malfunctioning and requires service.

- INFL REST indicator light does not illuminate as described.
- During engine cranking, INFL REST indicator light does not remain on steady.
- After starting engine, INFL REST indicator light does not blink 7-9 times then goes out.
- After starting engine, INFL REST indicator light flashes Code 12.

NOTE: For information on air bag TESTING & DIAGNOSIS or DISPOSAL PROCEDURES, see MITCHELL® AIR BAG SERVICE & REPAIR MANUAL, DOMESTIC & IMPORTED MODELS.

SERVICE PRECAUTIONS

Observe these precautions when working with air bag systems:

- Disable SIR system. See DISABLING & ACTIVATING AIR BAG SYSTEM. Failure to do this could result in accidental air bag deployment and personal injury.
- After repairs, turn ignition on from passenger side of vehicle to prevent injury in event of accidental air bag deployment. Ensure INFL REST indicator light is working properly and no system faults are indicated. See SYSTEM OPERATION CHECK.
- After air bag deployment, air bag surface may contain deposits of sodium hydroxide, which can irritate skin. Always wear safety glasses, rubber gloves and long-sleeved shirt during cleanup. Wash hands using mild soap and water.
- Never strike or jar sensor. All sensors and mounting bracket bolts must be carefully torqued to ensure proper sensor operation.
- Never apply power to SIR system if sensor is not rigidly attached to vehicle.
- To avoid air bag deployment and possible personal injury when trouble shooting SIR system, only use test equipment specified in diagnostic charts. Never use battery-powered test equipment or test light. Carefully follow all instructions.
- DO NOT perform repairs on any portion of SIR wiring circuit.
- Always carry air bag module with trim cover away from body. Always place inflatable module on workbench with trim cover up, away from loose objects.

DISABLING & ACTIVATING AIR BAG SYSTEM

WARNING: System retains voltage for about 10 MINUTES after it is disabled. Wait about 10 MINUTES after system is disabled before servicing, as air bag may accidentally deploy, causing personal injury.

Disabling System – Ensure ignition switch is off. Disconnect negative battery cable and tape cable end. Remove 3 SIR fuses (C-21, C-22 and C-23) from bottom of fuse block, located behind left kick panel. *See Fig. 14*. Disconnect Orange 3-wire connector near base of steering column.

Activating System – Connect Orange 3-wire connector. Install SIR fuses. Reconnect negative battery cable. Verify system is functioning properly. See SYSTEM OPERATION CHECK.

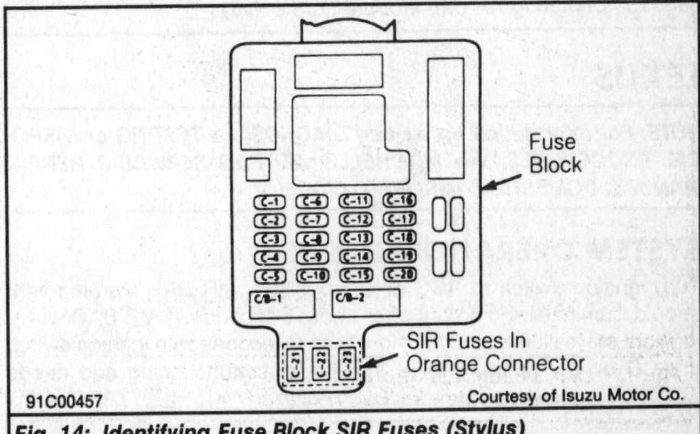
Fuse
Block
C-1
C-2
C-3
C-4
C-5
C-6
C-7
C-8
C-9
C-10
C-11
C-12
C-13
C-14
C-15
C-16
C-17
C-18
C-19
C-20
C/B-1
C/B-2
SIR Fuses In
Orange Connector
91C00457
Courtesy of Isuzu Motor Co.

Fig. 14: Identifying Fuse Block SIR Fuses (Stylus)

1993 GENERAL SERVICING
Air Bag System Safety (Cont.)

JAGUAR

SERVICE PRECAUTIONS

Observe these precautions when working with air bag systems:

- Disable air bag system before servicing any air bag system or steering column component. See DISABLING & ACTIVATING AIR BAG SYSTEM.
- Because of critical operating requirements of system, DO NOT attempt to service air bag components.
- DO NOT attempt to dismantle air bag module. DO NOT puncture, incinerate or bring into contact with electricity or electrical devices.
- DO NOT remove steering column mountings or steering wheel from vehicle before disarming and removing air bag module.
- Air bag module must be stored in its original special container until used for service. It must be stored in a clean, dry place, away from sources of extreme heat, sparks and high electrical energy.
- To prevent inadvertently arming module, DO NOT tamper with safety shaft in center on rear of module after removal.
- DO NOT cut open inflator/sensor assembly or in any way repair module.
- DO NOT hit module or apply force on steering wheel.
- DO NOT install module to steering wheel and arm module until column and wheel are firmly installed into vehicle.
- DO NOT store module at temperatures above 168° F (75° C).

DISABLING & ACTIVATING AIR BAG SYSTEM

Disabling System – Disconnect negative battery cable. To disable air bag module, open disarming mechanism cover on back of steering wheel. Using Torx screwdriver, turn arming screw counterclockwise until it stops (approximately 12 turns). *See Fig. 15.* Air bag module is now disabled.

Activating System – Turn arming screw clockwise approximately 12 turns until it stops. Tighten arming screw to 8-18 INCH lbs. (1-2 N.m). Reconnect negative battery cable.

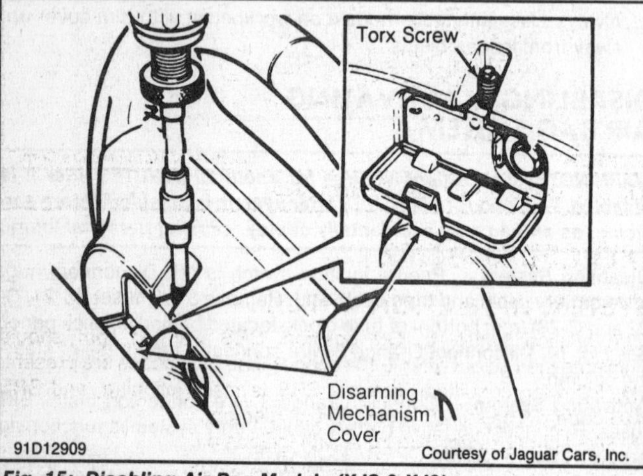
Torx Screw
Disarming
Mechanism
Cover
91D12909
Courtesy of Jaguar Cars, Inc.

Fig. 15: Disabling Air Bag Module (XJS & XJ6)

LEXUS

NOTE: For information on air bag DIAGNOSIS & TESTING or DISPOSAL PROCEDURES, see MITCHELL® AIR BAG SERVICE & REPAIR MANUAL, DOMESTIC & IMPORTED MODELS.

SYSTEM OPERATION CHECK

Turn ignition switch to ACC or ON position. AIR BAG warning light should illuminate and go out after about 6 seconds. If AIR BAG warning light stays illuminated for more than 6 seconds with ignition switch in ACC or ON position, SRS system is malfunctioning and needs repair. If AIR BAG warning light illuminates with ignition off, check for short circuit in AIR BAG warning light circuit.

SERVICE PRECAUTIONS

Observe these precautions when working with air bag systems:

- Disable SRS before servicing any SRS or steering column component. Failure to do this could result in accidental air bag deployment and possible personal injury. See DISABLING & ACTIVATING AIR BAG SYSTEM.
- When trouble shooting SRS, always check for diagnostic codes before disconnecting battery.
- SRS is equipped with back-up power source, which retains voltage for about 20 seconds after negative battery cable is disconnected. To prevent accidental air bag deployment, wait at least 20 seconds after turning ignition switch to LOCK position and disconnecting negative battery cable before working on SRS.
- In a minor collision in which air bag does not deploy, front air bag sensors and steering wheel pad should be inspected.
- Never use air bag parts from another vehicle. Replace air bag parts with NEW parts.
- Remove air bag sensors if shocks are likely to be applied to sensors during repairs.
- Center air bag sensor assembly contains mercury. After replacement, DO NOT destroy old part. When scrapping vehicle or replacing center air bag sensor assembly, remove center air bag sensor assembly and dispose of as toxic waste.
- Never disassemble or repair front air bag sensors, center air bag sensor assembly or steering wheel pad.
- If front air bag sensors, center air bag sensor assembly or steering wheel pad is dropped, or if there are cracks, dents or other defects in case, bracket or connector, replace parts with NEW parts.
- DO NOT expose front air bag sensors, center air bag sensor assembly or steering wheel pad directly to hot air or flame.
- Use volt-ohmmeter with high impedance (10,000 ohm minimum) to trouble shoot electrical circuit.
- Information labels are attached to air bag components. Follow all instructions on labels.
- After work on SRS is completed, verify system is functioning properly. See SYSTEM OPERATION CHECK.
- Always wear safety glasses when servicing or handling air bag.
- When placing live air bag on bench or other surface, always face air bag and trim cover up, away from surface. This will reduce motion of module if accidentally deployed.
- After deployment, air bag surface may contain deposits of sodium hydroxide, a product of gas generant combustion, which can irritate skin. Always wear safety glasses, rubber gloves and long-sleeved shirt during clean-up. Wash hands using mild soap and water.
- When carrying live air bag module, point trim cover away from your body to minimize injury in case of accidental deployment.
- If SRS is not fully functional for any reason, DO NOT drive vehicle until system is repaired and is again operational. DO NOT remove bulbs, modules, sensors or other components, or in any way disable system from operating normally. If SRS is not functional, park vehicle until it is repaired and functions properly.

DISABLING & ACTIVATING AIR BAG SYSTEM

WARNING: System retains voltage for a short period of time after power is disconnected. Wait at least 90 seconds after SRS is disabled before servicing, as air bag may accidentally deploy, causing personal injury.

Disabling & Activating System – To disable SRS, turn ignition switch to LOCK position, and disconnect negative battery cable. Wait 90 seconds before working on system. To activate SRS, reconnect negative battery cable. Perform SYSTEM OPERATION CHECK.

1993 GENERAL SERVICING
Air Bag System Safety (Cont.)

MAZDA

SYSTEM OPERATION CHECK

Turn ignition switch on. AIR BAG warning light in instrument cluster should come on for about 6 seconds then go out, indicating system is functioning properly. If any of the following conditions exists, system is malfunctioning and needs repair.

- AIR BAG warning light does not come on as described.
- AIR BAG warning light stays on for more than 6 seconds.
- AIR BAG warning light comes on while driving.

If air bag system components are replaced for any reason, check system for proper operation after repair. If system does not function properly, repair as necessary. If system functions properly, check horn operation. If horn does not sound, remove air bag module, and check air bag module and horn switch connections. Follow service precautions, and deactivate air bag system before servicing. See SERVICE PRECAUTIONS and DISABLING & ACTIVATING AIR BAG SYSTEM.

SERVICE PRECAUTIONS

Observe these precautions when working with air bag systems:

- Disable air bag system before servicing any air bag system or steering column component. See DISABLING & ACTIVATING AIR BAG SYSTEM.
- System voltage is retained for about 10 MINUTES after system is disabled. Wait about 10 MINUTES after system is disabled before servicing, as air bag may accidentally deploy, causing personal injury.
- Obtain radio code number from customer, and deactivate radio anti-theft function before disconnecting battery.
- Because of critical system operating requirements, DO NOT service any air bag system component. Corrections are made by replacement only.
- DO NOT use ohmmeter to check resistance of air bag module, as it may cause air bag deployment.
- When carrying live (undeployed) air bag module, point trim cover away from your body. This minimizes chance of injury in event of accidental air bag deployment.
- When placing live air bag module on any surface, always face trim cover upward to reduce motion of module if it is accidentally deployed.
- If an open circuit is present, replace entire wiring harness. DO NOT repair wire.
- Impact sensors must be installed with arrows facing front of vehicle. Check sensors for cracks, defects or rust before installing. Replace impact sensor(s) if necessary. After a collision, inspect crash sensor mounting surface. If surface is deformed or damaged, restore it to original shape.
- Air bag system clockspring must be aligned in neutral position, since its rotation ability is limited. DO NOT turn steering wheel or column after removal of steering gear.
- A double-lock mechanism is used on clockspring connectors. DO NOT use excessive force when disconnecting connectors, as damage to connector may occur.

DISABLING & ACTIVATING AIR BAG SYSTEM

WARNING: System voltage is retained for about 10 MINUTES after system is disabled. Wait about 10 MINUTES after system is disabled before servicing, as air bag may accidentally deploy, causing personal injury.

Disabling System – 1) Obtain radio code number from customer, and deactivate audio anti-theft function. Turn ignition switch off. Disconnect and shield negative battery cable. On all models except 929, remove cover panel below left side of instrument panel. Disconnect clockspring lower connector. *See Fig. 16.*

2) On 929, disconnect diagnostic module connector, and connect Short Circuit Connector (49-H066-004) to harness connectors. *See Fig. 17.*

Activating System – On all models except 929, reconnect clockspring lower connector. Install cover panel. On 929, remove short circuit connector from harness connector. Reconnect diagnostic module connector to diagnostic module. On all models, connect negative battery cable. Turn ignition switch on. Check AIR BAG warning light to ensure system is operating properly. See SYSTEM OPERATION CHECK.

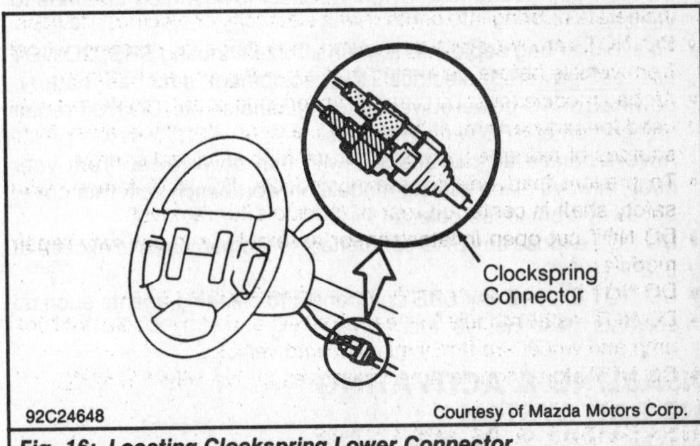
Clockspring
Connector
92C24648
Courtesy of Mazda Motors Corp.

Fig. 16: Locating Clockspring Lower Connector (Miata Shown; MX-6, RX7 & 626 Are Similar)

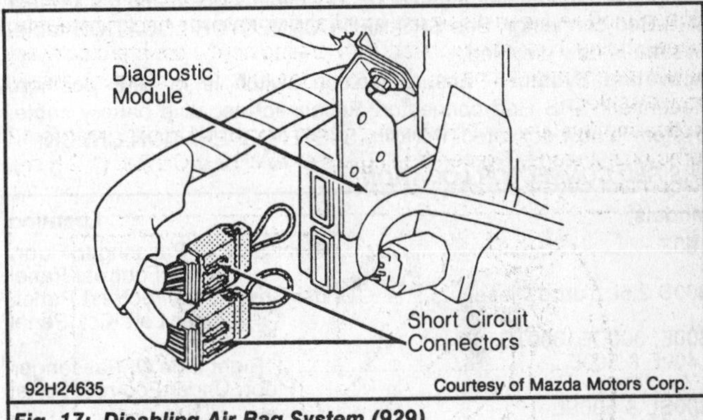
Diagnostic
Module
Short Circuit
Connectors
92H24635
Courtesy of Mazda Motors Corp.

Fig. 17: Disabling Air Bag System (929)

MERCEDES-BENZ

SYSTEM OPERATION CHECK

Turn ignition switch to ON position. SRS warning light should illuminate then go out after 4-10 seconds if no fault codes are present. The following conditions indicate SRS is malfunctioning, and SRS fault code will be stored in control unit memory.

- SRS light does not illuminate with ignition on.
- SRS light does not go out after 4-10 seconds.
- SRS light does not go out after engine is started.
- SRS light comes on or flickers while driving.

To retrieve SRS fault code(s), see DIAGNOSIS & TESTING in appropriate article in MITCHELL® AIR BAG SERVICE & REPAIR MANUAL, DOMESTIC & IMPORTED MODELS.

SERVICE PRECAUTIONS

Observe these precautions when working with air bag systems:

- When working around steering column components and before any repairs are performed, disable air bag system. See DISABLING & ACTIVATING AIR BAG SYSTEM.
- Always ensure radio is in OFF position before disconnecting battery. This will prevent damage to radio microprocessor.

1993 GENERAL SERVICING
Air Bag System Safety (Cont.)

- Before straightening any damage to body, or before performing electrical arc-welding, disable air bag system. See DISABLING & ACTIVATING AIR BAG SYSTEM.
- Always wear safety glasses and gloves when handling a deployed air bag module. Air bag module may contain sodium hydroxide deposits which are irritating to the skin.
- Use caution when handling sensors. Never strike or jar sensors. All sensors and mounting bracket bolts must be carefully torqued to ensure proper sensor operation.
- DO NOT apply voltage to SRS if a sensor is not rigidly attached to vehicle.
- To avoid air bag deployment when trouble shooting SRS, DO NOT use self-powered electrical test equipment such as battery-powered or AC-powered voltmeter, ohmmeter, etc. DO NOT repair any portion of SRS wiring harness.
- Always handle air bag module with trim cover away from your body. Always place air bag module on workbench with trim cover up, away from loose objects.
- DO NOT expose any SRS component to temperatures in excess of 212°F (100°C).
- DO NOT expose any SRS component to cleaning agents such as solvents, gasoline, lye, etc.

DISABLING & ACTIVATING AIR BAG SYSTEM

Disabling System – Before proceeding, follow air bag service precautions. See SERVICE PRECAUTIONS. Ensure ignition is off. Disconnect and shield negative battery cable. Locate and disconnect SRS Red connector. See SRS RED CONNECTOR LOCATION table. System is now disabled.

Activating System – Ensure ignition switch is in OFF position. Reconnect SRS Red connector. Reconnect negative battery cable. System is now activated. Perform SYSTEM OPERATION CHECK.

SRS RED CONNECTOR LOCATION [1]

Models	Location
190E	Right Side Of Passenger Floor, Under Footrest Panel
300D 2.5L Turbo Diesel	Under Driver-Side Footrest Panel, Near Left Kick Panel
300E, 300CE, 300TE, 400E & 500E	Right Side Of Passenger Floor, Under Footrest Panel
300SL & 500SL (Convertibles)	Far Right Side Of Passenger Floor, Under Footrest Panel
300SD Turbo, 300SE, 400SE, 500SEL & 600SEL [2]	Left Side Of Passenger Floor, Under Footrest Panel

[1] – SRS Red connector is a 10-pin connector for all models EXCEPT 300SD Turbo, 300SE, 400SE, 500SEL & 600SEL.

[2] – SRS Red connector is a 12-pin connector for 300SD Turbo, 300SE, 400SE, 500SEL & 600SEL models. A separate ETR connector (X11/17) is connected to SRS 12-pin Red connector.

MITSUBISHI

Diamante & 3000GT – See CHRYSLER CORP. & MITSUBISHI.

NISSAN

NOTE: For information on air bag DIAGNOSIS & TESTING or DISPOSAL PROCEDURES, see MITCHELL® AIR BAG SERVICE & REPAIR MANUAL, DOMESTIC & IMPORTED MODELS.

SYSTEM OPERATION CHECK

When ignition switch is turned to ON or START position, AIR BAG warning light should come on for about 7 seconds then go off, indicating system is operational.

SERVICE PRECAUTIONS

Observe these precautions when working with air bag systems:

- Disable air bag system before servicing any air bag system or steering column component. See DISABLING & ACTIVATING AIR BAG SYSTEM.
- System voltage is retained for about 10 MINUTES after system is disabled. Wait about 10 MINUTES after system is disabled before servicing, as air bag may accidentally deploy, causing personal injury.
- Air bag will operate only when ignition switch is in ON or START position. Ensure ignition switch is in LOCK position when working under the hood or inside vehicle.
- When servicing vehicle, air bag system and related parts should be pointed away from technician.
- DO NOT use circuit tester to check air bag harness connectors. Air bag system wiring harness and connectors have Yellow insulation for easy identification.
- DO NOT repair, splice or modify air bag system wiring harness. If harness is damaged, it must be replaced.
- Impact sensors must be installed with arrows facing front of vehicle. Check sensors for cracks, defects or rust before installing. Replace impact sensor(s) if necessary.
- Air bag system spiral cable must be aligned in neutral position, since its rotation ability is limited. DO NOT turn steering wheel or column after removal of steering gear.
- Handle air bag module carefully. Always place air bag module with steering wheel pad facing upward. DO NOT disassemble air bag module.
- After removing air bag components, replace old bolts with new ones. Verify system is functioning properly. See SYSTEM OPERATION CHECK.
- DO NOT expose air bag module to temperatures greater than 212°F (100°C). DO NOT allow oil, grease or water to contact module.

DISABLING & ACTIVATING AIR BAG SYSTEM

WARNING: System voltage is retained for about 10 MINUTES after system is disabled. Wait about 10 MINUTES after system is disabled before servicing, as air bag may accidentally deploy, causing personal injury.

Disabling System – Turn ignition switch to OFF position. Disconnect and shield battery negative cable. Wait 10 minutes before working on or near air bag components.

Activating System – Reconnect battery. Turn ignition switch to RUN position. Verify system is functioning properly. See SYSTEM OPERATION CHECK.

PORSCHE

SYSTEM OPERATION CHECK

Turn ignition switch to ON position. AIR BAG light on instrument panel should come on for about 5 seconds and then go off. If AIR BAG light fails to come on, remains on longer than 5 seconds or comes on while driving, air bag system needs servicing.

SERVICE PRECAUTIONS

Observe these precautions when working with air bag systems:

- Disable air bag system before servicing any air bag or steering column component. See DISABLING & ACTIVATING AIR BAG SYSTEM.
- System voltage is retained for about 20 MINUTES after system is disabled. Wait 20 MINUTES after system is disabled before servicing, as air bag may accidentally deploy, causing personal injury.

1993 GENERAL SERVICING
Air Bag System Safety (Cont.)

- Because of critical operating requirements of system, DO NOT service any air bag component. Corrections are made by replacement only.
- DO NOT allow grease, oil, cleaning solutions or similar substances to contact air bag units.
- DO NOT subject air bag units to temperatures warmer than 195°F (90°C).
- Replace air bag units, impact sensors and control units that have been dropped from a height of 1.5 feet or more.
- DO NOT install additional trim, labels or stickers on steering wheel or in area of passenger-side air bag.
- DO NOT repair or modify air bag system wiring.
- Air bag system must be disabled before electric welding can be performed on vehicle.
- DO NOT route wires from other electrical equipment in vicinity of air bag wire harness.
- Wash hands thoroughly after handling deployed air bags.

DISABLING & ACTIVATING AIR BAG SYSTEM

WARNING: System voltage is retained for about 20 MINUTES after system is disabled. Wait about 20 MINUTES after system is disabled before servicing, as air bag may accidentally deploy, causing personal injury.

Disabling & Activating System – To disable system, turn ignition off. Disconnect and shield negative battery cable. To activate system, reconnect negative battery cable. Verify system is functioning properly. See SYSTEM OPERATION CHECK.

SAAB

SYSTEM OPERATION CHECK

1) Turn ignition on. If SRS warning light comes on for about 6 seconds and then goes out, system is operating properly. If light remains on, a fault exists in system.

2) If fault occurs in system while ignition is on, SRS warning light will flash for about 10 MINUTES on 900 or about 5 MINUTES on 9000, and then stay lit. If air bag is deployed, SRS warning light will flash for about 5 seconds and then stay lit.

SERVICE PRECAUTIONS

Observe these precautions when working with air bag systems:

- Disable SRS before servicing any SRS or steering column component. See DISABLING & ACTIVATING AIR BAG SYSTEM.
- System retains voltage for about 20 MINUTES after battery is disconnected. Wait about 20 MINUTES after system is disabled before servicing, as air bag may accidentally deploy, causing personal injury.
- Because of critical operating requirements of system, DO NOT attempt to service air bag components. Corrections are made by replacement only.
- Always wear safety glasses when servicing or handling an air bag.
- Handle air bag components carefully. Avoid exposing components to impact, heat, moisture, etc.
- Air bag module must be installed immediately after it is taken out of storage. If work is interrupted, module must be returned to storage. Air bag modules must never be left out of storage unattended.
- Air bag module is a sealed unit. DO NOT attempt to dismantle or repair it.
- When placing live air bag module on bench or other surface, always face air bag and trim cover up, away from surface. This will reduce motion of module if accidentally deployed.
- After deployment, air bag surface may contain deposits of sodium hydroxide, which can irritate skin. Always wear safety glasses, rubber gloves and long-sleeved shirt during clean-up. Wash hands using mild soap and water.
- Never allow any electrical source near inflator on back of air bag module.
- When carrying live air bag module, point trim cover away from your body to minimize injury in case of accidental deployment.
- Never apply grease to SRS connectors.

DISABLING & ACTIVATING AIR BAG SYSTEM

WARNING: System retains voltage for about 20 MINUTES after battery is disconnected. Wait about 20 MINUTES after system is disabled before servicing, as air bag may accidentally deploy, causing personal injury.

Disabling & Activating System – To disable SRS, disconnect and shield negative battery cable. Wait 20 MINUTES before working on vehicle. To activate system, reconnect battery negative cable. Verify system is functioning properly. See SYSTEM OPERATION CHECK.

SUBARU

NOTE: For information on air bag DIAGNOSIS & TESTING or DISPOSAL PROCEDURES, see MITCHELL® AIR BAG SERVICE & REPAIR MANUAL, DOMESTIC & IMPORTED MODELS.

SYSTEM OPERATION CHECK

Legacy & SVX – Turn ignition switch to ON position. AIR BAG warning light in instrument cluster should come on and go out after about 8 seconds. If AIR BAG warning light stays on for more than 8 seconds with ignition on, SRS is malfunctioning and needs repair. See DIAGNOSIS & TESTING in appropriate article in MITCHELL® AIR BAG SERVICE & REPAIR MANUAL, DOMESTIC & IMPORTED MODELS.

SERVICE PRECAUTIONS

Observe these precautions when working with air bag systems:

- Disable SRS before servicing any SRS or steering column component. Failure to disable system could result in accidental air bag deployment and possible personal injury. See DISABLING & ACTIVATING AIR BAG SYSTEM.
- System reserve capacitor retains voltage for about 10 MINUTES after battery is disconnected. Wait about 10 MINUTES after negative battery cable is disconnected before servicing SRS, as air bag may accidentally deploy, causing personal injury.
- When trouble shooting SRS, always check for diagnostic codes before disconnecting battery.
- In a minor collision in which air bag does not deploy, front air bag impact sensors and steering wheel pad should be inspected.
- DO NOT use air bag parts from another vehicle. Replace air bag parts with NEW parts.
- Remove front impact sensors if shocks are likely to be applied to sensors during repairs.
- DO NOT disassemble or repair of front impact sensors or steering wheel pad.
- If front impact sensors, control unit or steering wheel pad is dropped, or if there are cracks, dents or other defects in case or connector, replace parts with NEW parts.
- DO NOT expose front impact sensors, control unit or steering wheel pad to temperatures greater than 194°F (90°C).
- Use digital volt-ohmmeter with high impedance (10 k/ohm minimum) to trouble shoot electrical circuit.
- Information labels are attached to air bag components. Follow all instructions on labels.
- After work on SRS is completed, verify system is functioning properly. See SYSTEM OPERATION CHECK.
- Always wear safety glasses when servicing or handling air bag.
- DO NOT check air bag module continuity with air bag removed from vehicle.

1993 GENERAL SERVICING
Air Bag System Safety (Cont.)

- When placing live air bag on bench or other surface, always face air bag and trim cover up, away from surface. This will reduce motion of module if it is accidentally deployed.
- After deployment, air bag surface may contain deposits of sodium hydroxide, a product of gas generant combustion, which can irritate skin. Always wear safety glasses, rubber gloves and long-sleeved shirt during clean-up. Wash hands using mild soap and water.
- When carrying live air bag module, point trim cover away from your body to minimize injury in case of accidental deployment.
- If SRS is not fully functional for any reason, DO NOT drive vehicle until system is repaired and is again operational. DO NOT remove bulbs, modules, sensors or other components, or in any way disable system from operating normally. If SRS is not functional, park vehicle until it is repaired and functions properly.

DISABLING & ACTIVATING AIR BAG SYSTEM

WARNING: System reserve capacitor retains voltage for about 10 MINUTES after battery is disconnected. Wait about 10 MINUTES after negative battery cable is disconnected before servicing SRS, as air bag may accidentally deploy, causing personal injury.

Disabling & Activating System – To disable SRS, turn ignition switch to OFF position. Disconnect and shield negative then positive battery cables. After battery cables have been disconnected, wait about 10 MINUTES before servicing SRS. To activate SRS, reconnect positive and then negative battery cables. Verify system is functioning properly. See SYSTEM OPERATION CHECK.

TOYOTA

SYSTEM OPERATION CHECK

Turn ignition switch to ACC or ON position. AIR BAG/SRS warning light in instrument cluster should come on and go out after about 6 seconds. If AIR BAG/SRS warning light stays on for more than 6 seconds with ignition switch in ACC or ON position, SRS system is malfunctioning and needs repair. If AIR BAG/SRS warning light comes on with ignition off, check for a short circuit in AIR BAG/SRS warning light circuit.

SERVICE PRECAUTIONS

Observe these precautions when working with air bag systems:

- Disable SRS before servicing any SRS or steering column component. Failure to do this could result in accidental air bag deployment and possible personal injury. See DISABLING & ACTIVATING AIR BAG SYSTEM.
- When trouble shooting SRS, always check for diagnostic codes before disconnecting battery.
- SRS is equipped with back-up power source, which retains voltage for 90 seconds after negative battery cable is disconnected. Before working on SRS, wait at least 90 seconds after turning ignition switch to LOCK position and disconnecting negative battery cable, as air bag may accidentally deploy, causing personal injury.
- In a minor collision in which air bag does not deploy, front air bag sensors and steering wheel pad should be inspected.
- Never use air bag parts from another vehicle. Replace air bag parts with NEW parts.
- Remove air bag sensors if shocks are likely to be applied to sensors during repairs.
- Center air bag sensor contains mercury. After replacement, DO NOT destroy old part. When scrapping vehicle or replacing center air bag sensor, remove center air bag sensor and dispose of as toxic waste.
- Never disassemble or repair front air bag sensors, center air bag sensor or steering wheel pad.
- If front air bag sensors, center air bag sensor or steering wheel pad is dropped, or if cracks, dents or other defects exist in case, bracket or connector, replace parts with NEW parts.
- DO NOT expose front air bag sensors, center air bag sensor or steering wheel pad directly to hot air or flame.
- Use volt-ohmmeter with high impedance (10 k/ohm minimum) to trouble shoot electrical circuit.
- Information labels are attached to air bag components. Follow all instructions on labels.
- After work on SRS is completed, verify system is functioning properly. See SYSTEM OPERATION CHECK.
- Always wear safety glasses when servicing or handling air bag.
- When placing live air bag on bench or other surface, always face air bag and trim cover up, away from surface. This will reduce motion of module if accidentally deployed.
- After deployment, air bag surface may contain deposits of sodium hydroxide, a product of gas generant combustion, which can irritate skin. Always wear safety glasses, rubber gloves and long-sleeved shirt during clean-up. Wash hands using mild soap and water.
- When carrying live air bag module, point trim cover away from your body to minimize injury in case of accidental deployment.
- If SRS is not fully functional for any reason, DO NOT drive vehicle until system is repaired and is again operational. DO NOT remove bulbs, modules, sensors or other components, or in any way disable system from operating normally. If SRS is not functional, park vehicle until it is repaired and functions properly.

DISABLING & ACTIVATING AIR BAG SYSTEM

WARNING: Back-up power supply retains voltage for about 90 seconds after battery is disconnected. Wait about 90 seconds after SRS is disabled before servicing, as air bag may accidentally deploy, causing personal injury.

Disabling & Activating System – To disable SRS, turn ignition switch to LOCK position, and disconnect negative battery cable. Wait about 90 seconds before working on system. To activate SRS, reconnect negative battery cable. Verify system is functioning properly. See SYSTEM OPERATION CHECK.

VOLKSWAGEN

SYSTEM OPERATION CHECK

Two lights pertaining to air bag system are located directly above air bag symbol in instrument cluster. Control light is used to indicate readiness of system. With ignition on, control light comes on for about 5-8 seconds then goes out, while diagnosis unit in air bag control unit performs an electronic test cycle of system.

If control light does not function as described, a fault probably exists in system. If fault occurs while ignition is on, it will be stored in fault memory. Warning light will then come on, and air bag system will be switched off. If warning light comes on or flickers while driving, air bag system should be tested. See DIAGNOSIS & TESTING in appropriate article in MITCHELL® AIR BAG SERVICE & REPAIR MANUAL, DOMESTIC & IMPORTED MODELS.

SERVICE PRECAUTIONS

Observe these precautions when working with air bag systems:

- DO NOT use computer memory saver tool. Using computer memory tool will keep air bag system active and may cause accidental deployment of air bag unit.
- Disable air bag system before servicing any air bag system or steering column component. See DISABLING & ACTIVATING AIR BAG SYSTEM.

1993 GENERAL SERVICING
Air Bag System Safety (Cont.)

- Because of critical operating requirements of system, DO NOT attempt to service any air bag system component.
- DO NOT leave air bag parts unattended. Install parts in vehicle immediately after obtaining.
- DO NOT use air bag components that have been dropped from height of more than 18 inches.
- DO NOT allow chemical cleaners, oil and grease to contact vinyl covering on air bag unit.
- DO NOT place stickers or covers on steering wheel.
- Always disable air bag system before performing electric welding on vehicle.
- Air bag system can only be tested using Diagnostic Tester (VAG 1551) and Multimeter (US-1119). Never use test light on air bag system.
- DO NOT expose air bag unit to temperatures greater than 194°F (90°C).

DISABLING & ACTIVATING AIR BAG SYSTEM

WARNING: System voltage is retained for about 20 MINUTES after system is deactivated. Wait about 20 MINUTES after system is disabled before servicing, as air bag may accidentally deploy, causing personal injury.

Disabling & Activating System – To disable system, disconnect negative battery cable. Wait 20 MINUTES before working on vehicle. To activate system, reconnect negative battery cable. Verify system is functioning properly. See SYSTEM OPERATION CHECK.

VOLVO

NOTE: For information on air bag DIAGNOSIS & TESTING or DISPOSAL PROCEDURES, see MITCHELL® AIR BAG SERVICE & REPAIR MANUAL, DOMESTIC & IMPORTED MODELS.

SYSTEM OPERATION CHECK

Turn ignition switch to ON position (engine off). If no fault codes are present, SRS warning light should come on and go out after 10 seconds. Following conditions indicate SRS system is malfunctioning, and SRS fault code will be stored in crash sensor memory.

- SRS light does not illuminate.
- SRS light does not go out after 10 seconds.
- SRS light does not go out after engine is started.
- SRS light comes on while driving.

SERVICE PRECAUTIONS

Observe these precautions when working with air bag systems:

- Always disable SRS before performing any air bag repairs. See DISABLING & ACTIVATING AIR BAG SYSTEM.
- Always ensure radio is in OFF position before disconnecting battery. This will prevent damage to radio microprocessor.
- Always wear safety glasses and gloves when handling a deployed air bag module. Air bag module may contain sodium hydroxide deposits, which can irritate skin.
- Use caution when handling sensors. Never strike or jar sensors. All sensors and mounting bracket bolts must be tightened carefully to ensure proper sensor operation.
- Never apply power to SRS if a sensor is not securely attached to vehicle.
- Never make any measurement directly on air bay module(s) or seat belt tensions (if equipped).
- To avoid accidental air bag deployment when trouble shooting SRS, DO NOT use self-powered electrical test equipment such as battery- or AC-powered voltmeter, ohmmeter, etc. DO NOT repair any portion of SRS wiring circuit.
- Always handle air bag module with trim cover away from your body. Always place air bag module on workbench with trim cover facing up, away from loose objects.

DISABLING & ACTIVATING AIR BAG SYSTEM

WARNING: Never disconnect crash sensor connector or standby power unit to disable SRS system.

Disabling System (240) – **1)** Before proceeding, follow air bag service precautions. See SERVICE PRECAUTIONS. Before performing any repairs, turn ignition off, and disconnect and shield negative battery cable.

2) Remove carpet from driver-side of center console. Locate and disconnect Orange SRS disabling connector near Yellow harness connector. *See Fig. 18.* DO NOT disconnect crash sensor connector or standby power unit to disable system. This action could cause air bag to deploy.

Activating System – After repairs are performed, ensure all wiring and component connectors are connected. Connect Orange SRS disabling connector on driver side of center console, near Yellow harness connector. Install carpet. Reconnect negative battery cable. Check SRS warning light to ensure system is functioning properly. See SYSTEM OPERATION CHECK.

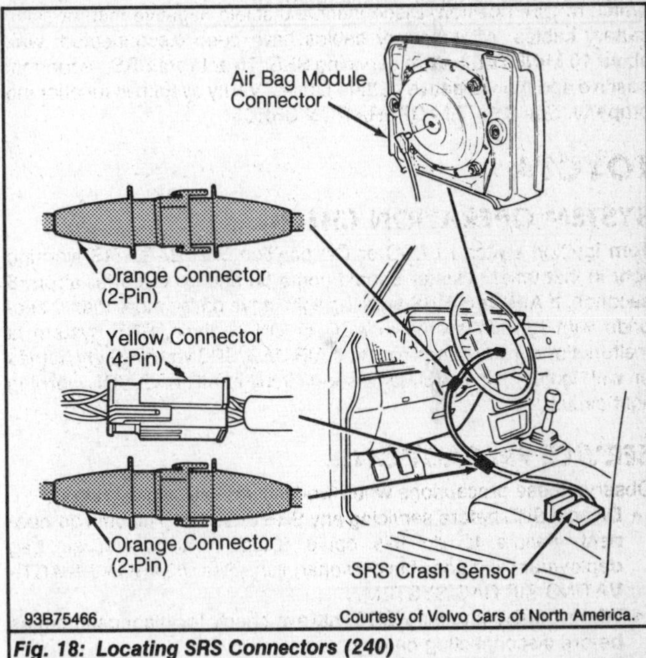
Air Bag Module
Connector
Orange Connector
(2-Pin)
Yellow Connector
(4-Pin)
Orange Connector
(2-Pin)
SRS Crash Sensor
93B75466
Courtesy of Volvo Cars of North America.

Fig. 18: Locating SRS Connectors (240)

Disabling System (850, 940 & 960) – **1)** Before proceeding, see SERVICE PRECAUTIONS. Before performing any repairs, turn ignition switch to OFF position. Disconnect and shield negative battery cable.

2) Locate and disconnect Orange air bag module and seat belt tensioner connectors and Violet passenger-side air bag module connector (850 and 960). DO NOT disconnect crash sensor connector or standby power unit to disable system. This action could cause air bag to deploy. *See Figs. 19 and 20.*

Activating System – After repairs are performed, ensure all wiring and component connectors are connected. Turn ignition switch to ON position. Connect negative battery cable. Ensure vehicle is not occupied when connecting battery cable. Ensure system is functioning properly. See SYSTEM OPERATION CHECK.

1993 GENERAL SERVICING
Air Bag System Safety (Cont.)

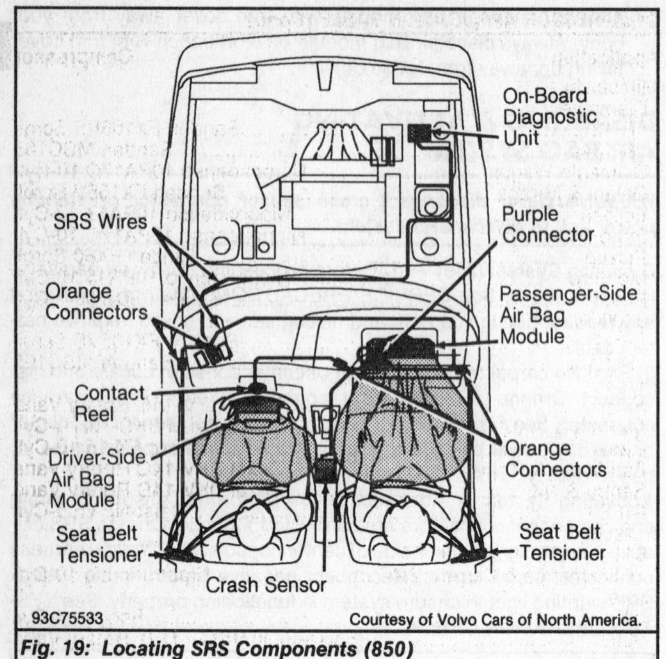
On-Board
Diagnostic
Unit
SRS Wires
Purple
Connector
Orange
Connectors
Passenger-Side
Air Bag
Module
Contact
Reel
Orange
Connectors
Driver-Side
Air Bag
Module
Seat Belt
Tensioner
Seat Belt
Tensioner
Crash Sensor
93C75533
Courtesy of Volvo Cars of North America.

Fig. 19: Locating SRS Components (850)

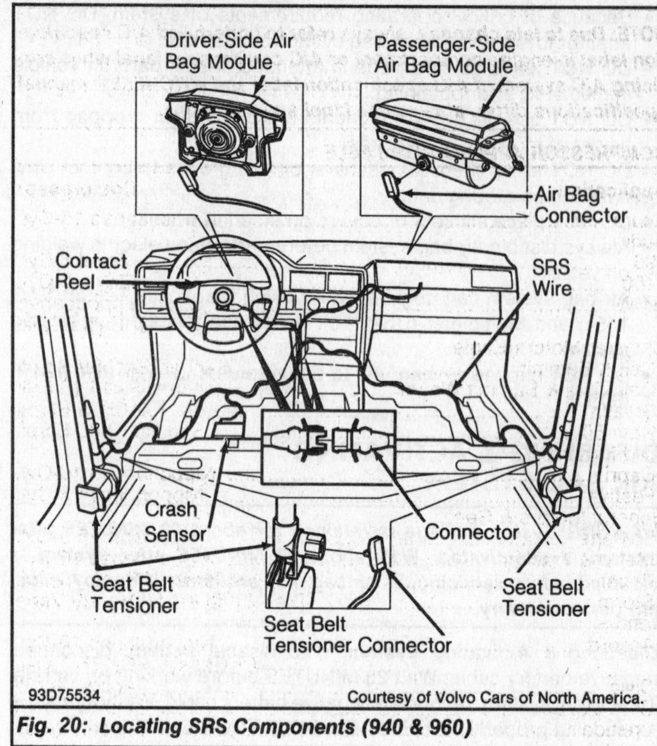
Driver-Side Air
Bag Module
Passenger-Side
Air Bag Module
Air Bag
Connector
Contact
Reel
SRS
Wire
Crash
Sensor
Connector
Seat Belt
Tensioner
Seat Belt
Tensioner
Seat Belt
Tensioner Connector
93D75534
Courtesy of Volvo Cars of North America.

Fig. 20: Locating SRS Components (940 & 960)

1993 GENERAL SERVICING
Compressor Applications

NOTE: Due to late changes, always refer to underhood A/C specification label in engine compartment or A/C compressor label while servicing A/C system. If A/C specification label and MITCHELL® manual specifications differ, always use label specifications.

COMPRESSOR APPLICATION TABLE

Application	Compressor
Acura	Nippondenso 10-Cyl.
Audi	
90	Zexel 6-Cyl.
100	Zexel 6-Cyl.
BMW	Nippondenso Or Seiko-Seiki
Chrysler Motors/Eagle	
Colt & Summit	Sanden FX105V Scroll
Colt Vista & Summit Wagon	Nippondenso 10PA15 10-Cyl.
Stealth	Sanden FX105VS Scroll
Ram-50	Sanden FX80 Scroll
Ford Motor Co.	
Capri	Nippondenso 10-Cyl.
Festiva	Nippondenso 6-Cyl.
General Motors & Geo	
LeMans	Harrison V5 5-Cyl.
Metro & Tracker	Nippondenso 10-Cyl.
Prizm	Nippondenso 10PA15 10-Cyl.
Storm	Diesel Kiki KC-50 Rotary Vane
Honda	
Accord	Nippondenso 10-Cyl. Or Hadsys RC-17S 7-Cyl.
Civic	Sanden Scroll
Civic Del Sol	Sanden Scroll
Prelude	Sanden Scroll
Hyundai	
Elantra	Sanden TRF-090 Scroll
Excel	Sanden SD-709 7-Cyl.
Scoupe	Nippondenso 10PA15C 10-Cyl.
Sonata	Ford FX-15 10-Cyl.
Infiniti	
G20	Atsugi NVR 140S Rotary Vane
J30	Calsonic V6 6-Cyl.
Q45	Calsonic V5 5-Cyl.
Isuzu (R-12)	
Amigo	Diesel Kiki DKS-13CH 6-Cyl.
Pickup	
4-Cylinder	Diesel Kiki DKS-13CH 6-Cyl.
V6	Harrison R4 4-Cyl. Radial
Stylus	Diesel Kiki DKV-14D Rotary Vane
Rodeo	
4-Cylinder	Diesel Kiki DKS-17CH 6-Cyl.
V6	Diesel Kiki DKV-14D Rotary Vane
Trooper	Diesel Kiki DKV-14D Rotary Vane
Isuzu (R-134a Option) [1]	
Amigo, Pickup, Rodeo & Trooper	
2.3L & 2.6L Engine	Zexel R-134a 6-Cyl.
3.1L Engine	Harrison R-134a R-4 4-Cyl. Radial
3.2L Engine	Zexel R-134a Rotary Vane
Jaguar	
XJS	Sanden SD-709 7-Cyl.
XJ6	Sanden SD-7H15 7-Cyl.
Lexus	Nippondenso 10PA20 10-Cyl.
Mazda	
B2200 & B2600i	Sanden 5-Cyl.
Miata	Nippondenso TV12 Rotary Vane
MPV	Nippondenso 10-Cyl.
MX-6 & 626	Panasonic Rotary Vane
Navajo	Ford FX-15 10-Cyl.
MX-3, Protege & 323	Panasonic Rotary Vane
929	Panasonic Rotary Vane
RX7	Nippondenso TV12 Rotary Vane
Mercedes-Benz	
190E	Nippondenso 10PA15 10-Cyl.
300D/E, 400E & 500E	Nippondenso 10PA17 10-Cyl.
300SE/SD, 400SE & 500SEL	Nippondenso 10PA20 10-Cyl.

[1] – Standard equipment on some models built after 5/1/93.

COMPRESSOR APPLICATION TABLE (Cont.)

Application	Compressor
Mitsubishi	
Diamante	
R-12	Sanden FX105VS Scroll
R-134a	Sanden MSC105
Diamante Wagon	Nippondenso 10PA17C 10-Cyl.
Galant & Mirage	Sanden FX105V Scroll
Eclipse	Nippondenso 10PA17 10-Cyl.
Expo/Expo LRV	Nippondenso 10PA17C 10-Cyl.
Pickup	Sanden FX80 Scroll
Montero	Nippondenso 10PA15 10-Cyl.
Precis	Sanden SD-709 7-Cyl.
3000GT	
R-12	Sanden FX105VS Scroll
R-134a	Sanden MSC105
Nissan	
Altima	Zexel DKV-14C Rotary Vane
Maxima & 300ZX	Zexel DKS-16H 6-Cyl.
Quest	Ford FX-15 10-Cyl.
Pathfinder & Pickup	Zexel DKV-14C Rotary Vane
Sentra & NX	Zexel DKV-14D Rotary Vane
240SX	Calsonic V5 5-Cyl.
Porsche	
911 America Roadster, RS America & Carrera 2/4	Nippondenso 10-Cyl.
Saab	
900	Sanden 5-Cyl.
9000	Seiko-Seiki SS121 DN1 Rotary Vane
Subaru	
Impreza	Zexel Rotary Vane
Legacy	Zexel DKS-15CH 5-Cyl. Calsonic V5-15C 5-Cyl.
Loyale	Hitachi MJS170-5DP 6-Cyl.
SVX	Calsonic V5 5-Cyl.
Suzuki	Nippondenso 10-Cyl.
Toyota	
Camry	Nippondenso 10PA17C 10-Cyl.
Celica	
4A-FE Engine	Nippondenso 10PA15C 10-Cyl.
3S-GTE & 5S-FE Engine	Nippondenso 10PA17C/VC 10-Cyl.
Corolla	Nippondenso 10PA15 10-Cyl.
Land Cruiser	Nippondenso 10PA17 10-Cyl.
MR2	Nippondenso 10P13C 10-Cyl.
Paseo	Matsushita Rotary Vane
Pickup & 4Runner	Nippondenso 10-Cyl.
Previa	Nippondenso 10PA17E 10-Cyl.
Supra	Nippondenso 10-Cyl.
Tercel	Matsushita TV10B Rotary Vane
T100	Nippondenso 10PA15 10-Cyl.
Volkswagen	
Cabriolet	Sanden SD-508 5-Cyl. Or SD-709 7-Cyl.
Corrado SLC	Sanden SD-709 7-Cyl.
EuroVan	Sanden SD7H15 7-Cyl.
Golf, GTI & Jetta	Sanden SD7-V16/SD7-V16L 7-Cyl.
Fox	Nippondenso 6-Cyl.
Passat	Sanden SD7-V16/SD7-V16L 7-Cyl.
Volvo	
240	Seiko-Seiki SS-121DS5
850	Zexel DKS-15CH 6-Cyl.
940 & 960	Sanden SD-510 5-Cyl., Sanden SD-709 7-Cyl. Or Seiko-Seiki SS-121DS5

1993 GENERAL SERVICING
Refrigerant Oil & Refrigerant Specifications

NOTE: Due to late changes, always refer to underhood A/C specification label in engine compartment or A/C compressor label while servicing A/C system. If A/C specification label and MITCHELL® manual specifications differ, always use label specifications.

REFRIGERANT OIL & REFRIGERANT CAPACITY

Application	[1] Oil Ounces	Refrigerant Ounces
Acura		
Integra	[2] 2.0-3.4	32-34
Legend		
Sedan	[2] 4.7-5.2	[3] 24.7-26.5
Coupe	6.0	24.7-26.5
Vigor	[2] 4.7-4.9	26.5-28.0
Audi		
90	7.8-9.2	[4] 23.0-24.8
100	7.8-9.2	[4] 21.0-22.8
BMW		
318 & 325 Series	3.4-4.8	[5] 35-36
525i & 535i	4.7-6.1	[5] 53.0-55.5
740i & 740iL	4.7-6.1	[5] 53.0-55.5
Chrysler Motors/Eagle		
Colt & Summit	[2] 4.4-5.1	26-30
Colt Vista & Summit Wagon	[2] 2.0-3.4	30
Ram-50	[2] 4.4-5.1	30
Stealth	[2] 4.6-6.0	29
Ford Motor Co.		
Capri	2.4-3.0	23-27
Festiva	10	25
General Motors & Geo		
LeMans	8.0	35
Metro	2.7	18
Prizm & Prizm LSi	6.0	25
Storm	5.1	21
Tracker	2.7	21
Honda		
Accord		
Nippondenso	3.0-4.1	28-30
Hadsys	4.1-4.3	28-30
Civic	4.0-4.7	21-23
Civic Del Sol	4.0-4.7	21-23
Prelude	[6] 4.3-5.0	21-23
Hyundai		
Excel	8.1	30-32
Scoupe	2-3	28-32
Elantra	4.0	32
Sonata	6.9-7.7	30-32
Infiniti		
G20	6.8	24-29
J30	8.5	[7] 24-26
Q45	9.7	38-42

[1] – Total system capacity, unless otherwise noted.
[2] – Compressor refrigerant oil capacity.
[3] – Use R-134a refrigerant and ND-Oil 8 (Part No. 38899-PR7-003).
[4] – Use R-134a refrigerant and Polyalkylene Glycol (PAG) oil.
[5] – Use R-134a and Poyalkylene Glycol Oil (Part No. 81-22-9-407-724).
[6] – Use R-134a refrigerant and PAG Refrigerant Oil (Part No. 38899-P13-003).
[7] – Use R-134a refrigerant and Type "S" Oil (Part No. KLH00-PAGS0).

REFRIGERANT OIL & REFRIGERANT CAPACITY (Cont.)

Application	[1] Oil Ounces	Refrigerant Ounces
Isuzu (R-12)		
Amigo	5.0	26
Pickup		
2.3L & 2.6L Engine	5.0	26
3.1L Engine	6.0	26
Rodeo		
2.6L Engine	5.0	26
3.2L Engine	5.0	26
Stylus	5.0	21
Trooper	5.0	30
Isuzu (R-134a Option) [3]		
Amigo & Pickup		
2.3L & 2.6L Engine	5.0	23
3.1L Engine	7.5-8.5	23
Rodeo	5.0	23
Trooper	5.0	26
Jaguar		
XJS	[2] 4.6	40
XJ6	[2] 4.5	[4] 40
Lexus		
ES300	[2] 3.5	32-35
GS300	[2] 4.0	[5] 28-32
LS400	[2] 2.8-3.5	[5] 32
SC300 & SC400	[2] 4.0	32-35
Mazda		
B2200 & B2600i	[2] 4.5	28
Miata	[2] 2.7-3.3	28
MPV		
Dual Unit	[2] 2.7-3.3	51
Single Unit	[2] 2.7-3.3	37
MX-3	[2] 5.0	28
MX-6 & 626	[2] 4.3	26
Protege & 323	[2] 3.9-4.6	28
Navajo	7.0	28-29
929	3.6	28
RX7	3.4-4.7	21
Mercedes-Benz		
190E	[2] 4.0	36
300D/E, 400E & 500E	[2] 5.4	[6] 36
300SE/SD, 400SE & 500SEL	[2] 5.4	[7] 43

[1] – Total system capacity, unless otherwise noted.
[2] – Compressor refrigerant oil capacity.
[3] – Standard equipment on some models built after 5/1/93. Use R-134a Swash Plate Compressor Oil (Part No. 2-90188-300-0) on 2.3L and 2.6L engine. Use R-134a R-4 Compressor Oil (Part No. 2-90222-320-0) on 3.1L engine. Use R-134a Rotary Vane Compressor Oil (Part No. 2-90188-301-0) on 3.2L engine.
[4] – Use R-134a refrigerant and PAG SP20 refrigerant oil.
[5] – Use R-134a refrigerant and ND-Oil 8 (Part No. 38899-PR7-003).
[6] – Use R-134a refrigerant and Densooil 8 (Part No. A 001 989 08 03).
[7] – Use R-134a refrigerant and Densooil 8 (Part No. A 001 989 08 03). Use 50 ounces if equipped with rear passenger compartment A/C-heater system.

1993 GENERAL SERVICING
Refrigerant Oil & Refrigerant Specifications (Cont.)

REFRIGERANT OIL & REFRIGERANT CAPACITY (Cont.)

Application	[1] Oil Ounces	Refrigerant Ounces
Mitsubishi		
Diamante		
R-12	5.4-6.0	34-38
R-134a	[3] 5.7-6.4	26-28
Diamante Wagon	5.4	28
Eclipse	[2] 2.0-3.4	33
Expo/Expo LRV		
1.8L	[2] 3.4-4.0	30
2.4L	[2] 2.0-3.4	30
Galant	[2] 5.0-5.7	33
Mirage	[2] 4.4-5.1	26-30
Pickup	[2] 4.4-5.1	30
Montero	[2] 2.0-3.4	28
Precis	8.1	30-32
3000GT		
R-12	4.7-6.0	29
R-134a	[3] 4.7-6.0	26-28
Nissan		
Altima	[4] 6.8	25-28
Maxima	[5] 6.8	30-33
Pathfinder & Pickup	[4] 6.8	26-30
Quest		
Front A/C	7.0	36
Front & Rear A/C	10	56
Sentra & NX	6.8	23-26
240SX	8.0	29-32
300ZX	6.8	26-30
Porsche		
911 America Roadster, RS America & Carrera 2/4	4.6	[6] 29.5
Saab		
900	5.9	34-36
9000	6.6	[3] 33-34
Subaru		
Impreza	6.1	23-26
Legacy		
Zexel	[2] 2.4	29-32
Calsonic	[2] 3.2	29-32
Loyale	[2] 2.4	26-28
SVX	[2] 2.4	[7] 22-23

[1] – Total system capacity, unless otherwise noted.
[2] – Compressor refrigerant oil capacity.
[3] – Use SUN PAG 56 refrigerant oil.
[4] – Use R-134a refrigerant and Type "R" Oil (Part No. KLH00-PAGR0).
[5] – Use R-134a refrigerant and Type "S" Oil (Part No. KLH00-PAGS0).
[6] – Use R-134a refrigerant and Nippondenso ND8 refrigerant oil.
[7] – Use R-134a refrigerant and ZXL100 PG (DH-PS) Type "S" Oil (Part No. K0010PS000).

REFRIGERANT OIL & REFRIGERANT CAPACITY (Cont.)

Application	[1] Oil Ounces	Refrigerant Ounces
Suzuki		
Samurai	2.0-3.4	18
Sidekick	2.0-3.4	21-23
Swift	2.0-3.4	18
Toyota		
Camry	[2] 3.5	32-35
Celica	3.4-4.1	24-27
Corolla	3.4-4.1	25-28
Land Cruiser	3.4-4.1	30-34
MR2	3.4-4.1	28-32
Paseo	3.4-4.1	25-28
Pickup	3.4-4.1	24-29
Previa		
Without Rear A/C	3.4-4.7	32-35
With Rear A/C	3.4-4.1	41-44
Supra	[2] 4.1	[3] 23-27
Tercel	3.4-4.1	25-28
T100	3.4-4.1	[3] 21-25
4Runner	3.4-4.1	27-30
Volkswagen		
Cabriolet	4.6	30.0-31.8
Corrado SLC	3.9-4.4	35.0-36.8
EuroVan		
Without Rear A/C	4.6	[4] 34-35
With Rear A/C	8.2	[4] 48-49
Fox	5.7	41-42
Golf, GTI & Jetta	3.9	[4] 28-30
Passat	3.9-4.4	[4] 41.0-42.8
Volvo		
240	7.4	[5] 26
850		
Cold Climates	7.0	[5] 29
Hot Climates	7.0	[5] 26
940 & 960		
Sanden SD-510	4.8	[6] 32-34
Sanden SD-709	8.5	[6] 32-34
Seiko-Seiki	7.8	[6] 32-34

[1] – Total system capacity, unless otherwise noted.
[2] – Compressor refrigerant oil capacity.
[3] – Use R-134a refrigerant and ND-Oil 8 (Part No. 38899-PR7-003).
[4] – Use R-134a refrigerant and SP-10 PAG Oil (Part No. G 052 154 A2).
[5] – Use R-134a refrigerant and ZXL 100 PG Oil (Part No. 8708581-7).
[6] – Use R-134a refrigerant and PAG Oil (Part No. 8708581-9).

1993 GENERAL SERVICING
Compressor Refrigerant Oil Checking

NOTE: For compressor applications, see COMPRESSOR APPLICATIONS article in GENERAL SERVICING. DO NOT exceed A/C system refrigerant oil capacity, when servicing system. See REFRIGERANT OIL & REFRIGERANT SPECIFICATIONS article in GENERAL SERVICING.

REFRIGERANT OIL

Only NEW, moisture-free refrigerant oil should be used in the air conditioning system. This oil is highly refined and dehydrated so moisture content is less than 10 parts per million. The oil container must be tightly closed at all times when not in use, or moisture from the air will be absorbed into the refrigerant oil.

SERVICING PRECAUTIONS

DISCHARGING SYSTEM

Discharge A/C system using approved refrigerant recovery/recycling equipment. Always follow recovery/recycling equipment manufacturer's instructions. After refrigerant recovery process is completed, the amount of compressor oil removed must be measured and the same amount added to A/C system.

DISCONNECTING LINES & FITTINGS

After system is discharged, carefully clean area around all fittings to be opened. Always use 2 wrenches when tightening or loosening fittings. Some refrigerant lines are connected with a coupling. Special tools may be required to disconnect lines. Cap or plug all openings as soon as lines are removed. DO NOT remove caps until connections of lines and fittings are completed.

CONNECTING LINES & FITTINGS

NOTE: All R-134a based systems use 1/2-16 ACME threaded fittings. Ensure all replacement parts match the connections of the system being worked on.

Always use a new gasket or "O" ring when connecting lines or fittings. Coat "O" ring with refrigerant oil and ensure it is not twisted during installation. Always use 2 wrenches to prevent damage to lines and fittings.

PLACING SYSTEM IN OPERATION

After component service or replacement has been completed and all connections have been made, evacuate system thoroughly with a vacuum pump. Charge system with proper amount of refrigerant and perform leak test. See REFRIGERANT OIL & REFRIGERANT SPECIFICATIONS article in GENERAL SERVICING for system capacities. Check all fittings that have been opened. After system has been leak tested, check system performance.

NOTE: Most compressors are pre-charged with a fixed amount of refrigerant (shipping) oil. Drain compressor oil from new compressor and add refrigerant oil to new compressor according to amount removed from old compressor. Always refer to underhood A/C specification label or A/C compressor label while servicing A/C system.

ATSUGI

ROTARY VANE

1) Before checking and adjusting oil level, operate engine at 1200 RPM. Set controls at maximum cooling and high blower motor speed for 10 minutes to return oil to compressor.

2) Stop engine. Discharge refrigerant and remove compressor from vehicle. See SERVICING PRECAUTIONS. Drain compressor oil through compressor discharge port and measure oil amount.

3) If amount drained is less than 3 ounces, conduct leak tests at system connections. Repair or replace faulty parts as necessary. Check purity of oil and adjust oil level as follows.

4) If amount drained is 3 ounces or more, oil level is okay. Fill with same amount drained, using new oil. If amount drained is less than 3 ounces, pour in 3 ounces of new refrigerant oil.

COMPONENT REFRIGERANT OIL CAPACITIES (ATSUGI ROTARY VANE)

Component	Ounces
Condenser	1.0-1.7
Evaporator	1.5-2.5
Receiver-Drier	0.5-0.8
Refrigerant Lines [1]	1.0-1.7

[1] – Add only if a refrigerant oil leak is indicated.

BOSCH

6-CYLINDER

1) Before checking and adjusting oil level, operate compressor at engine idle speed, and set controls at maximum cooling and high blower motor speed for 20-30 minutes to return oil to compressor.

2) Stop engine and discharge refrigerant. See SERVICING PRECAUTIONS. Remove refrigerant oil level inspection plug on side of compressor. Oil should be at lower lip of threaded hole. If oil level is low, add new refrigerant oil as necessary. Replace inspection plug and tighten to 10-12 ft. lbs. (14-16 N.m).

CALSONIC

V5 5-CYLINDER & V6 6-CYLINDER

Infiniti & Nissan – 1) Before checking and adjusting oil level, operate engine at 1200 RPM. Set controls at maximum cooling and high blower motor speed for 10 minutes to return oil to compressor.

2) Stop engine. Discharge refrigerant. See SERVICING PRECAUTIONS. Measure the amount of oil drained/discharged into refrigerant recovery/recycling equipment.

3) Remove compressor from vehicle. Drain compressor oil from compressor drain plug and measure oil amount. Add this amount to amount drained in step **2)**, to obtain total amount drained.

4) Fill compressor with total amount drained, using new oil. If any major components of the system were also replaced, determine the amount of additional oil needed. See appropriate COMPONENT REFRIGERANT OIL CAPACITIES table for specified amount.

COMPONENT REFRIGERANT OIL CAPACITIES (CALSONIC V5)

Component	Ounces
Condenser	1.0-1.7
Evaporator	1.5-2.5
Receiver-Drier	0.5-0.8
Refrigerant Lines [1]	1.0-1.7

[1] – Add only if a refrigerant oil leak is indicated.

COMPONENT REFRIGERANT OIL CAPACITIES (CALSONIC V6)

Component	Ounces
Condenser	2.5
Evaporator	2.5
Receiver-Drier	0.2
Refrigerant Lines [1]	1.0

[1] – Add only if a refrigerant oil leak is indicated.

Subaru – 1) Before checking and adjusting oil level, operate engine at 1000-1500 RPM. Set controls at maximum cooling and high blower motor speed for 20 minutes to return oil to compressor.

2) Stop engine. Discharge refrigerant and remove compressor from vehicle. See SERVICING PRECAUTIONS. Drain compressor oil from compressor drain plug and measure oil amount.

3) Fill compressor with total amount drained, using new oil. If any major components of the system were also replaced, determine the amount of additional oil needed. See appropriate SUBARU COMPONENT REFRIGERANT OIL CAPACITIES table for specified amount.

1993 GENERAL SERVICING
Compressor Refrigerant Oil Checking (Cont.)

SUBARU COMPONENT REFRIGERANT OIL CAPACITIES (LEGACY)

Component	Ounces
Compressor	2.4
Condenser	1.7
Evaporator	2.4
Refrigerant Lines [1]	1.7

[1] – Add only if a refrigerant oil leak is indicated.

SUBARU COMPONENT REFRIGERANT OIL CAPACITIES (SVX)

Component	Ounces
Compressor	2.4
Condenser	1.7
Evaporator	2.4
Refrigerant Lines [1]	1.7

[1] – Add only if a refrigerant oil leak is indicated.

DIESEL KIKI

ROTARY VANE

1) Before checking and adjusting oil level, operate engine at 800-1000 RPM. Set controls at maximum cooling and high blower motor speed for 20 minutes to return oil to compressor.
2) Stop engine. Discharge refrigerant and remove compressor from vehicle. See SERVICING PRECAUTIONS. Remove oil drain plug and measure amount of oil drained.
3) If amount drained is less than 3 ounces (1.7 ounces on Geo Storm), conduct leak tests at system connections. Repair or replace faulty parts as necessary.
4) If amount drained is more 3 ounces (1.7 ounces on Geo Storm), oil level is okay. Fill compressor with same amount drained, using new oil. If amount drained is less than 3 ounces (1.7 ounces on Geo Storm), pour in 3 (1.7) ounces of new refrigerant oil.
5) When replacing other A/C system components, add the following amount(s) of refrigerant oil. See COMPONENT REFRIGERANT OIL CAPACITIES (DIESEL KIKI ROTARY VANE) table.

COMPONENT REFRIGERANT OIL CAPACITIES (DIESEL KIKI ROTARY VANE)

Component	Ounces
Condenser	1.7
Evaporator	1.0
Receiver-Drier	1.0
Refrigerant Lines	0.3

5 & 6-CYLINDER

1) Before checking and adjusting oil level, operate engine at 800-1000 RPM. Set controls at maximum cooling and high blower motor speed for 20 minutes to return oil to compressor.
2) Stop engine. Discharge refrigerant and remove compressor from vehicle. See SERVICING PRECAUTIONS. Remove oil drain plug and measure amount of oil drained.
3) If amount drained is less than 3 ounces, conduct leak tests at system connections. Repair or replace faulty parts as necessary.
4) If amount drained is more 3 ounces, oil level is okay. Fill compressor with same amount drained, using new oil.
5) When replacing other A/C system components, add the following amount(s) of refrigerant oil. See COMPONENT REFRIGERANT OIL CAPACITIES (DIESEL KIKI 5 & 6-CYLINDER) table.

COMPONENT REFRIGERANT OIL CAPACITIES (DIESEL KIKI 5 & 6-CYLINDER)

Component	Ounces
Condenser	1.0
Evaporator	1.7
Receiver-Drier	1.0
Refrigerant Lines	0.3

FORD

FX-15 10-CYLINDER

1) Slowly discharge system. See SERVICING PRECAUTIONS. Remove A/C compressor. Drain compressor oil from suction and discharge ports. Measure amount drained and discard oil.
2) If amount drained from removed (old) compressor is between 3 and 5 ounces, add drained amount of new refrigerant oil into the NEW compressor through suction port.
3) If amount drained is less than 3 ounces, add 3 ounces to the NEW compressor. If amount drained is more than 5 ounces, add 5 ounces. Use new "O" rings on refrigerant lines. Install A/C compressor. Evacuate and recharge system. Perform leak test.
4) When replacing other A/C system components, add the following amount(s) of refrigerant oil. See COMPONENT REFRIGERANT OIL CAPACITIES (FX-15 10-CYLINDER) table.

COMPONENT REFRIGERANT OIL CAPACITIES (FX-15 10-CYLINDER)

Component	Ounces
Condenser	1.0
Evaporator	3.0
Receiver-Drier	[1] 2.0
Refrigerant Lines	[2] 1.0

[1] – On Hyundai Sonata and Mazda Navajo, drain oil from old receiver-drier. Add amount drained to amount specified.
[2] – Add only if a large oil leak is indicated.

HADSYS

7-CYLINDER

Honda (Accord) – 1) Discharge system. See SERVICING PRECAUTIONS. Remove compressor from vehicle. Drain all oil from NEW compressor and fill compressor with 4 ounces of clean refrigerant oil.
2) Add one ounce of refrigerant oil when replacing evaporator. Add 1/2 ounce when replacing condenser. When replacing receiver-drier or hoses, add 1/3 ounce per component replaced.

HARRISON

R4 4-CYLINDER

1) Before checking and adjusting oil level, operate engine at 800-1000 RPM. Set controls at maximum cooling and high blower motor speed for 20 minutes to return oil to compressor.
2) Stop engine. Discharge refrigerant and remove compressor from vehicle. See SERVICING PRECAUTIONS. Remove oil drain plug and measure amount of oil drained.
3) If amount drained is less than one ounce, conduct leak tests at system connections. Repair or replace faulty parts as necessary. Fill compressor with 2 ounces, using new refrigerant oil.
4) If amount drained is more one ounce, oil level is okay. Fill compressor with same amount drained, using new oil.
5) When replacing other A/C system components, add the following amount(s) of refrigerant oil. See COMPONENT REFRIGERANT OIL CAPACITIES (HARRISON R4 4-CYLINDER) table.

COMPONENT REFRIGERANT OIL CAPACITIES (HARRISON R4 4-CYLINDER)

Component	Ounces
Condenser	1.0
Evaporator	1.7
Receiver-Drier	1.0
Refrigerant Lines	0.3

V5 5-CYLINDER

1) If system is operable, run A/C system for several minutes to stabilize system. Turn off engine. Discharge system and remove compressor. See SERVICING PRECAUTIONS. Remove drain plug and measure oil.

1993 GENERAL SERVICING
Compressor Refrigerant Oil Checking (Cont.)

2) If one ounce or more is drained, add same amount. If less than one ounce is drained, add 2 ounces of new refrigerant oil to compressor.
3) If condenser is replaced, add one ounce. Add 3.5 ounces if accumulator is replaced. If evaporator is replaced or if a large refrigerant leak occurred, add 3 ounces of new refrigerant oil.

HITACHI

6-CYLINDER

1) Before checking and adjusting oil level, operate compressor at 1000-1500 engine RPM, and set controls at maximum cooling and high blower motor speed for about 10 minutes to return oil to compressor.
2) Stop engine. Discharge refrigerant and remove compressor from vehicle. See SERVICING PRECAUTIONS. Drain oil from compressor through suction port. Measure amount of oil drained.
3) If amount drained is 2.4 ounces or more, fill with same amount using new oil. If amount drained is less than 2.4 ounces, fill with 2.4 ounces. Install compressor and recharge.
4) If A/C components are replaced, add refrigerant oil to system. Add 1.7 ounces if condenser is replaced. Add 2.4 ounces if evaporator is replaced. Oil does not need to be added if receiver-drier is replaced. Add 1.7 ounces of refrigerant oil only if a refrigerant oil leak is indicated.

MATSUSHITA

ROTARY VANE

Geo (Prizm) – 1) If system is operable, run A/C system for several minutes to stabilize system. Turn off engine. Discharge system and remove compressor. See SERVICING PRECAUTIONS. Remove drain plug and measure oil.
2) If one ounce or more is drained, add same amount. If less than one ounce is drained, add 2 ounces of new refrigerant oil to compressor.
3) If condenser is replaced, add one ounce. Add 3.5 ounces if receiver-drier is replaced. If evaporator is replaced or if a large refrigerant leak occurred, add 3 ounces of new refrigerant oil.
Toyota – Discharge system. See SERVICING PRECAUTIONS. Remove compressor from vehicle. Drain oil from compressor through inlet and outlet ports. Fill compressor with 3.4-4.1 ounces of oil through suction port. Add 0.7 ounces if receiver-drier was replaced. When replacing condenser or evaporator, add 1.4-1.7 ounces of refrigerant oil.

NIPPONDENSO

ROTARY VANE

1) Before checking and adjusting oil level, operate compressor at engine idle speed, and set controls at maximum cooling and high blower motor speed for 20-30 minutes to return oil to compressor.
2) Stop engine. Discharge refrigerant and remove compressor from vehicle. See SERVICING PRECAUTIONS. Drain compressor oil through compressor intake and discharge ports. Measure amount drained.
3) Fill compressor with same amount as drained, plus one ounce. When replacing condenser, add one ounce. When replacing evaporator, add 1 1/2 ounces. When replacing receiver-drier, add 1/3 ounce of new refrigerant oil.

6 & 10-CYLINDER

NOTE: Porsche and Suzuki compressor oil checking procedures are not available from manufacturer.

Acura & Honda – 1) Discharge system. See SERVICING PRECAUTIONS. Remove compressor from vehicle. Drain all oil from NEW compressor and fill compressor with 3-4 ounces of clean refrigerant oil.
2) On Accord, add 5/6 ounce of refrigerant oil when replacing evaporator. Add 1/3 ounce when replacing condenser. When replacing receiver-drier or hoses, add 1/3 ounce per component replaced.
3) On Legend, add 2 ounces of refrigerant oil when replacing evaporator. Add one ounce when replacing condenser. When replacing receiver-drier or hoses, add 1/3 ounce per component replaced.
4) On Integra, add one ounce of refrigerant oil when replacing evaporator. When replacing condenser, receiver-drier or hoses, add 1/3 ounce per component replaced.
5) On Vigor, add 1/2 ounce of refrigerant oil when replacing evaporator. Add 2/3 ounce when replacing condenser. When replacing receiver-drier or hoses, add 1/3 ounce per component replaced.
Chrysler Corp. (Colt Vista/Summit Wagon) – Add 2 ounces of refrigerant oil when replacing evaporator. Add one ounce when replacing condenser. When replacing receiver-drier or hoses, add 1/3 ounce per component replaced.
Ford Motor Co. – On Capri, add 2-3 ounces when replacing compressor. Add one ounce of refrigerant oil when replacing condenser or evaporator. When replacing receiver-drier, add 1/2 ounce. On Festiva, drain and measure oil from receiver-drier. Add the amount drained plus one ounce. Add one ounce when replacing condenser. Add 3 ounces of refrigerant oil when replacing evaporator.
Geo, Hyundai & Mazda – Add one ounce of refrigerant oil when replacing condenser. Add 1-1 1/2 ounce when replacing evaporator. When replacing receiver-drier or hoses, add 1/3 ounce per component replaced.
Lexus & Toyota – The use of refrigerant recovery/recycling is recommended by manufacturer. After refrigerant recovery process is completed, the amount of compressor oil removed must be measured and the same amount added to A/C system. Add 1 1/2 ounces of refrigerant oil when replacing condenser. Add 1 1/2 ounces when replacing evaporator. When replacing receiver-drier or hoses, add 1/2 ounce per component replaced.
Mercedes-Benz – Add 2/3 ounce of refrigerant oil when replacing condenser. Add 1 1/3 ounces when replacing evaporator. When replacing receiver-drier or hoses, add 1/3 ounce per component replaced. If A/C system line has broken (sudden discharge), add 1 1/3 ounces of refrigerant oil.

NOTE: On Mercedes-Benz vehicles with rear A/C, add 2/3 ounce of refrigerant oil when replacing rear condenser. When replacing rear A/C lines, add 1/3 ounce per line replaced.

Mitsubishi – 1) On Eclipse, add 2/3 ounce of refrigerant oil when replacing condenser. Add one ounce when replacing evaporator. When replacing receiver-drier or hoses, add 1/3 ounce per component replaced.
2) On Expo/Expo LRV and Montero, add one ounce of refrigerant oil when replacing condenser. Add 2 ounces when replacing evaporator. When replacing receiver-drier or hoses, add 1/3 ounce per component replaced.
Volkswagen (Fox) – 1) The use of refrigerant recovery/recycling is recommended by manufacturer. After refrigerant recovery process is completed, the amount of compressor oil removed must be measured and the same amount added to A/C system.
2) Add 1 1/2 ounce of refrigerant oil when replacing evaporator. When replacing condenser, add 1 1/3 ounce of refrigerant oil. Add one ounce of refrigerant oil when replacing receiver-drier (1 1/2 ounces if relief valve on receiver-drier has burst).

PANASONIC

ROTARY VANE

Mazda – Add 1 1/3 ounce of refrigerant oil when replacing condenser (1/2 ounce on MX-6 and 626). Add 2 ounces when replacing evaporator. When replacing receiver-drier or hoses, add 1/3 ounce of refrigerant oil.

1993 GENERAL SERVICING
Compressor Refrigerant Oil Checking (Cont.)

SANDEN

SCROLL

Chrysler/Mitsubishi – 1) On Colt, Galant, Mirage, Pickup, Ram-50 and Summit, add 1/2 ounce of refrigerant oil when replacing condenser. Add 1 1/2 ounces when replacing evaporator. When replacing receiver-drier or hoses, add 1/3 ounce per component replaced.
2) On Stealth and 3000GT, add 1/2 ounce of refrigerant oil when replacing condenser. Add 2 ounces when replacing evaporator. When replacing receiver-drier or low-pressure hose, add 1/3 ounce per component replaced.
Honda – 1) Discharge system. See SERVICING PRECAUTIONS. Remove compressor from vehicle. Drain all oil from NEW compressor and fill compressor with 4 ounces of clean refrigerant oil.
2) On Civic and Civic Del Sol, add 1 1/2 ounce of refrigerant oil when replacing evaporator. Add 2/3 ounce when replacing condenser. When replacing receiver-drier or hoses, add 1/3 ounce per component replaced.
3) On Prelude, add one ounce of refrigerant oil when replacing evaporator. When replacing other A/C components, add 1/3 ounce per component replaced (including hoses).
Hyundai – Add 1 1/2 ounces of refrigerant oil when replacing evaporator. Add one ounce when replacing condenser. When replacing receiver-drier, add 1/3 ounce of refrigerant oil.

5-CYLINDER

Mazda – Add one ounce of refrigerant oil when replacing condenser. Add 1 2/3 ounce when replacing evaporator. When replacing receiver-drier, add 1/2 ounce of refrigerant oil.

NOTE: Saab and Volvo (Sanden 5 or 7-cylinder) compressor oil checking procedures are not available from manufacturer.

7-CYLINDER

Hyundai & Mitsubishi (Excel & Precis) – 1) Before checking and adjusting oil level, operate compressor at engine idle speed, and set controls at maximum cooling and high blower motor speed for 20-30 minutes to return oil to compressor.
2) Stop engine. Discharge refrigerant and remove compressor from vehicle. See SERVICING PRECAUTIONS. Remove oil drain plug and drain oil. Measure amount of oil drained. Install drain plug with new "O" ring.
3) If amount drained is 2.3 ounces or more, fill compressor with same amount using new oil. If amount drained is less than 2.3 ounces, fill with 2.3 ounces. Install filler plug. Install compressor and recharge system.

COMPONENT REFRIGERANT OIL CAPACITIES (SANDEN 7-CYLINDER – EXCEL & PRECIS)

Component	Ounces
Condenser	1.0
Evaporator	3
Receiver-Drier	1

Jaguar (XJS) – 1) Operate engine at idle speed for 10 minutes, to return refrigerant oil to compressor. Stop engine. Discharge refrigerant. See SERVICING PRECAUTIONS. Clean area around compressor filler plug and remove plug slowly.
2) Determine angle at which compressor is mounted. Insert compressor dipstick diagonally until stop on dipstick contacts filler plug surface. *See Fig. 1.* Remove dipstick and note oil fill level. Each increment on dipstick represents one ounce of oil.
3) Determine amount of oil needed according to mounting angle. See COMPRESSOR OIL CAPACITIES (JAGUAR XJS) table for specified amount.
4) If necessary, correct compressor oil level. Install compressor oil plug, and tighten it to 72-108 INCH lbs. (8-12 N.m). Evacuate and recharge A/C system. Perform leak test.

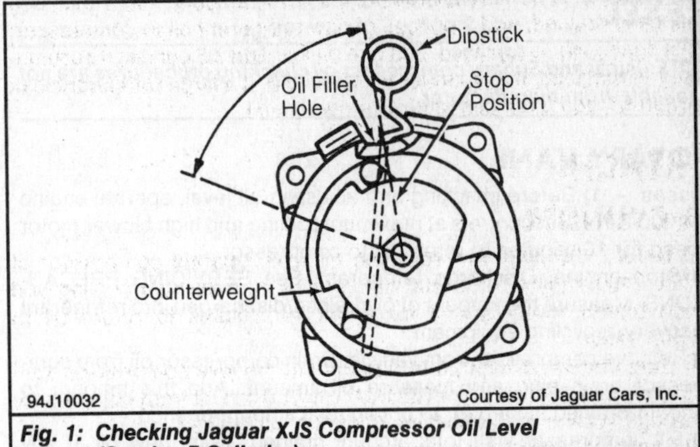
Dipstick
Oil Filler
Hole
Stop
Position
Counterweight
94J10032
Courtesy of Jaguar Cars, Inc.

Fig. 1: Checking Jaguar XJS Compressor Oil Level (Sanden 7-Cylinder)

COMPRESSOR OIL CAPACITIES (JAGUAR XJS)

Mounting Angle (In Degrees)	Oil Level In Increments
0	3-5
10	4-6
20	5-7
30	6-8
40	7-9
50	8-10
60	9-11
90	10-12

Volkswagen – 1) The use of refrigerant recovery/recycling is recommended by manufacturer. After refrigerant recovery process is completed, the amount of compressor oil removed must be measured and the same amount added to A/C system.
2) On Cabriolet, add 2/3 ounce of refrigerant oil when replacing evaporator. When replacing condenser or receiver-drier, add 1/3 ounce of refrigerant oil per component replaced.
3) On Corrado SLC, Golf, GTI, Jetta and Passat, add 2/3 ounce of refrigerant oil when replacing evaporator. When replacing condenser or receiver-drier, add 1/3 ounce of refrigerant oil per component replaced.
4) On EuroVan, add one ounce of refrigerant oil when replacing evaporator. Add 1/2 ounce when replacing condenser (2/3 ounce on vehicles with rear A/C). When replacing receiver-drier, add 1/3 ounce (2/3 ounce on vehicles with rear A/C).

SEIKO-SEIKI

ROTARY VANE

Saab (9000) – The A/C system is filled with 6.6 ounces of compressor oil. The compressor must be topped off with the specified amount. See COMPONENT REFRIGERANT OIL CAPACITIES (SEIKO-SEIKI ROTARY VANE) table. Topping off should be carried out on the high pressure side of the compressor.

COMPONENT REFRIGERANT OIL CAPACITIES (SEIKO-SEIKI ROTARY VANE)

Component	Ounces
Compressor	[1] 2.3
Condenser	1.3
Expansion Valve	0.6
Evaporator	1.3
Receiver-Drier	1.3
Refrigerant Lines	0.6

[1] – To avoid an excessive amount of oil in the A/C system, oil must be drained from the compressor before it is installed.

1993 GENERAL SERVICING
Compressor Refrigerant Oil Checking (Cont.)

ZEXEL

NOTE: Isuzu and Subaru compressor oil checking procedures are not available from manufacturer.

ROTARY VANE

Nissan – 1) Before checking and adjusting oil level, operate engine at 1200 RPM. Set controls at maximum cooling and high blower motor speed for 10 minutes to return oil to compressor.
2) Stop engine. Discharge refrigerant. See SERVICING PRECAUTIONS. Measure the amount of oil drained/discharged into refrigerant recovery/recycling equipment.
3) Remove compressor from vehicle. Drain compressor oil from compressor drain plug and measure oil amount. Add this amount to amount drained in step **2)**, to obtain total amount drained.
4) Fill compressor with total amount drained, using new oil. If any major components of the system were also replaced, determine the amount of additional oil needed. See COMPONENT REFRIGERANT OIL CAPACITIES (ZEXEL ROTARY VANE & 6-CYLINDER) table for specified amount.

COMPONENT REFRIGERANT OIL CAPACITIES (ZEXEL ROTARY VANE & 6-CYLINDER)

Component	Ounces
Condenser	
Altima & Maxima	2.5
NX, Pickup, Sentra & 300ZX	1.0-1.7
Evaporator	
Altima & Maxima	2.5
NX, Pickup, Sentra & 300ZX	1.5-2.5
Receiver-Drier	
Altima & Maxima	0.2
NX, Pickup, Sentra & 300ZX	0.5-0.8
Refrigerant Lines [1]	1.0

[1] – Add only if a refrigerant oil leak is indicated.

6-CYLINDER

Audi – 1) The use of refrigerant recovery/recycling is recommended by manufacturer. After refrigerant recovery process is completed, the amount of compressor oil removed must be measured and the same amount added to A/C system.
2) Add one ounce of refrigerant oil when replacing accumulator. When replacing condenser, add amount drained from condenser plus 1/3 ounce of refrigerant oil. When replacing evaporator, add amount drained from evaporator plus 2/3 ounce of refrigerant oil.
Nissan – 1) Before checking and adjusting oil level, operate engine at 1200 RPM. Set controls at maximum cooling and high blower motor speed for 10 minutes to return oil to compressor.
2) Stop engine. Discharge refrigerant. See SERVICING PRECAUTIONS. Measure the amount of oil drained/discharged into refrigerant recovery/recycling equipment.
3) Remove compressor from vehicle. Drain compressor oil from compressor drain plug and measure oil amount. Add this amount to amount drained in step **2)**, to obtain total amount drained.
4) Fill compressor with total amount drained, using new oil. If any major components of the system were also replaced, determine the amount of additional oil needed. See COMPONENT REFRIGERANT OIL CAPACITIES (ZEXEL ROTARY VANE & 6-CYLINDER) table for specified amount.
Volvo (850) – 1) Discharge refrigerant. See SERVICING PRECAUTIONS. Remove compressor from vehicle. Drain compressor oil from compressor drain plug and measure oil amount. Add the same amount of oil as was drained from the old compressor.
2) Add 1 2/3 ounce of refrigerant oil when replacing evaporator. When replacing condenser or hoses, add 2/3 ounce of refrigerant oil per component replaced. Add 3 ounce of refrigerant oil when replacing receiver-drier.

1993 GENERAL SERVICING
Compressor Servicing

NOTE: Due to variety of clutch and shaft seal configurations, obtain appropriate A/C compressor service tools for compressor being serviced.

ATSUGI ROTARY VANE

CLUTCH COIL

Removal – When replacing compressor clutch, be careful not to scratch shaft or bend pulley. When removing center bolt, hold clutch disc with Clutch Holder (KV99231010). Using Hub Puller (KV998VR001), remove clutch disc. When removing pulley, remove lock nut with Hub Socket (KV99235160).

Installation – 1) Tighten center bolt to 81-104 INCH lbs. (9.1-11.8 N.m). Tighten lock nut to 21-29 ft. lbs. (29-39 N.m). Using feeler gauge, ensure clearance between clutch disc and pulley is .012-.024" (.30-.60 mm).

2) If clearance is not correct, replace adjustment shim(s). *See Fig. 1.* Break-in clutch by engaging and disengaging clutch about 30 times.

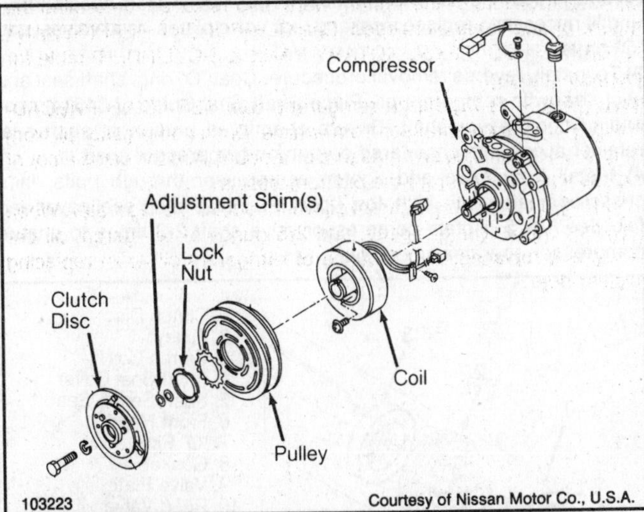
Compressor
Adjustment Shim(s)
Lock
Nut
Clutch
Disc
Coil
Pulley
103223
Courtesy of Nissan Motor Co., U.S.A.

Fig. 1: Exploded View Of Compressor (Atsugi Rotary Vane)

BOSCH 6-CYLINDER

CLUTCH COIL

Removal – 1) Hold clutch plate and remove shaft nut. Using Clutch Plate Remover (64 5 00), remove clutch plate. Using snap ring pliers, remove circlip and remove pulley assembly.

2) If pulley bearing is being replaced, remove circlip at rear of pulley. Press bearing and spacer from pulley. Press in new bearing with spacer and replace circlip.

Installation – 1) Clean all surfaces. Install pulley assembly on compressor and install circlip. Ensure clutch plate shim is in place on shaft. Install clutch plate and nut. Tighten nut to 13-15 ft. lbs. (18-20 N.m).

2) Using a feeler gauge, check clutch plate-to-pulley clearance. Clearance should be .028-.051" (.7-1.3 mm). If clearance is not correct, remove clutch plate and replace clutch plate shim. *See Fig. 2.*

SHAFT SEAL

Removal – Remove clutch plate. Remove shaft key and circlip. Using Seal Seat Remover/Installer (64 5 030), remove seal seat. Using Seal Remover/Installer (64 5 040), turn seal slightly clockwise to disengage tangs and pull out shaft seal. Remove "O" ring seal.

Installation – 1) Coat new "O" ring seal with refrigerant oil and install. Coat new shaft seal with refrigerant oil and install seal on Seal Remover/Installer
(64 5 040). Ensure shaft seal and shaft machine surfaces align. Insert shaft seal and turn slightly counterclockwise to secure on shaft.

2) Using sleeve from Seal Seat Remover/Installer (64 5 030), push seal seat into compressor and install circlip. Install shaft key and clutch plate. Check compressor oil level before charging system.

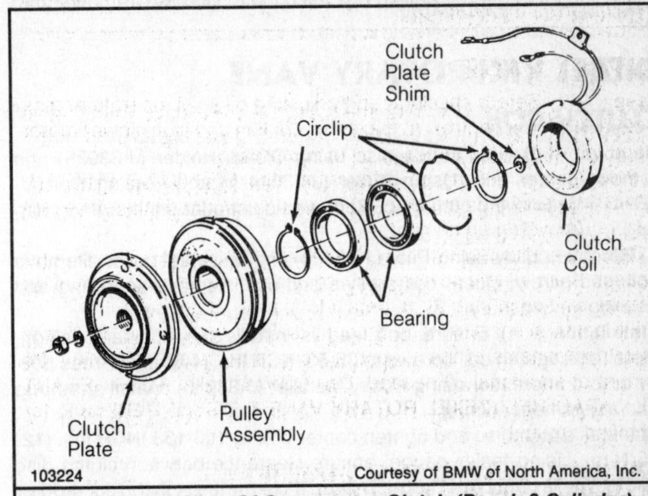
Clutch
Plate
Shim
Circlip
Clutch
Coil
Bearing
Pulley
Assembly
Clutch
Plate
103224
Courtesy of BMW of North America, Inc.

Fig. 2: Exploded View Of Compressor Clutch (Bosch 6-Cylinder)

CALSONIC V5 & V6

NOTE: Calsonic V6 compressor servicing procedure is not available from manufacturer.

CLUTCH COIL

Removal – 1) Remove shaft nut while holding clutch plate with Clutch Disc Wrench (J-39072). Install clutch disc Puller Set (J-39073-4, J-33013-1, J-33013-3) and remove clutch plate.

2) Remove snap ring. Use a universal gear puller to remove clutch pulley. *See Fig. 3.* Remove screw from clutch coil lead. Use puller to remove clutch coil.

Installation – 1) To install clutch coil, reverse removal procedure. Ensure coil lead is installed in original position. Using puller set and Coil Jig (J-39073-1), carefully press clutch coil into place.

2) Install a new clutch pulley snap ring, being careful not to damage shaft seal. Press clutch plate into place. Install shaft nut and torque to 89-106 INCH lbs. (10-12 N.m).

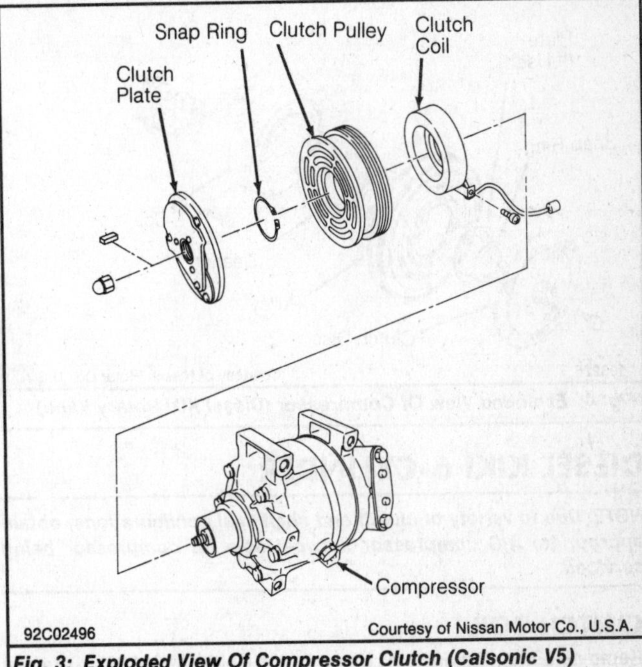
Snap Ring
Clutch Pulley
Clutch
Coil
Clutch
Plate
Compressor
92C02496
Courtesy of Nissan Motor Co., U.S.A.

Fig. 3: Exploded View Of Compressor Clutch (Calsonic V5)

1993 GENERAL SERVICING
Compressor Servicing (Cont.)

3) Use a feeler gauge to check clutch plate-to-pulley clearance. Clearance should be .012-.024" (.30-.60 mm). If clearance is too large, remove shaft nut and again press in clutch plate. If clearance is too small, increase gap by pulling up clutch plate. DO NOT remove shaft nut.

DIESEL KIKI ROTARY VANE

CLUTCH COIL

Removal - 1) Hold clutch disc using Clutch Holder (J-33939) and remove center bolt. Using Puller (J-33944-A) and Forcing Bolt (J-33944-4), remove clutch disc. Remove adjustment shim(s) and snap ring.

2) Remove pulley using Pilot (J-38424) and universal puller. Remove coil lead screw, clutch coil screws and coil. Remove snap ring and bearing if necessary.

Installation - 1) Ensure coil lead is installed in original position. Install and tighten coil screws to 35-53 INCH lbs. (4-6 N.m). Press pulley onto compressor using Pulley Installer (J-33940). Install snap ring and adjustment shim(s).

2) Install clutch disc and tighten center bolt to 106-133 INCH lbs. (12-15 N.m). Using feeler gauge, ensure clearance between clutch disc and pulley is .012-.024" (.30-.60 mm). If clearance is incorrect, add or remove shim(s) as necessary. Break-in clutch by engaging and disengaging clutch 30 times.

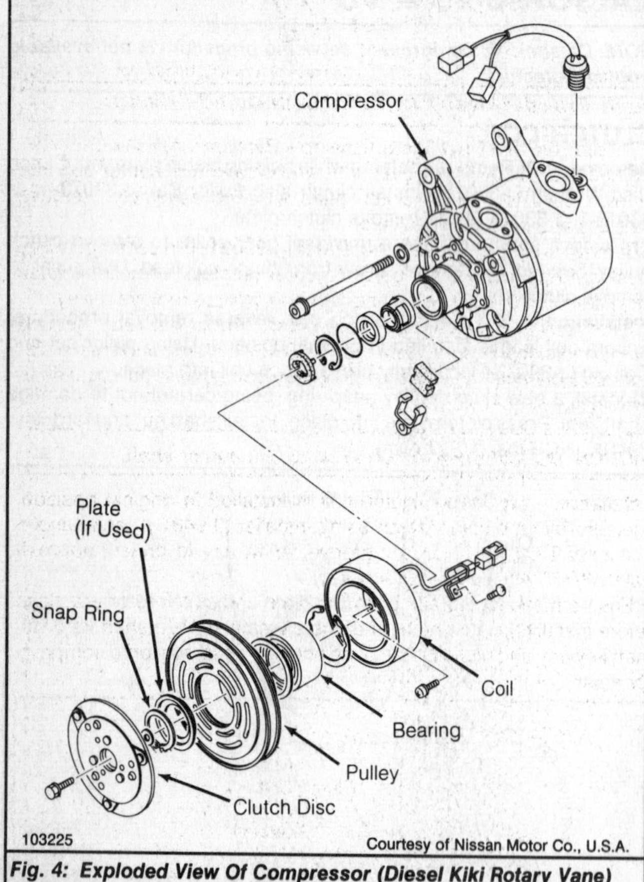
Compressor
Plate
(If Used)
Snap Ring
Coil
Bearing
Pulley
Clutch Disc
103225
Courtesy of Nissan Motor Co., U.S.A.

Fig. 4: Exploded View Of Compressor (Diesel Kiki Rotary Vane)

DIESEL KIKI 6-CYLINDER

NOTE: Due to variety of clutch and shaft seal configurations, obtain appropriate A/C compressor service tools for compressor being serviced.

CLUTCH COIL

Removal & Installation - 1) Using Clutch Holder (J-33939) to prevent clutch disc from rotating, remove shaft bolt. Using Clutch Disc Puller (J-33944-A) and Forcing Bolt (J-33944-4), remove clutch disc. Remove shim(s) from compressor drive shaft or clutch disc. *See Fig. 5.*

2) Remove snap ring, cover and pulley. With Puller Guide (J-33943-A) in center of pulley, attach Crossbar (J-8433) to outside diameter of pulley. Tighten crossbar bolt against puller guide to remove pulley. Remove coil lead, screws, and coil.

3) To install, reverse removal procedure. Install cover snap ring with beveled side facing out. Install clutch disc and tighten center bolt to 133 INCH lbs. (15 N.m).

4) Using feeler gauge, ensure clearance between clutch disc and pulley is .012-.024" (.30-.60 mm). If clearance is incorrect, add or remove shim(s) as necessary.

SHAFT SEAL

Removal & Installation - 1) Remove clutch coil. Remove and discard felt. Using Shaft Seal Cover Remover/Installer (J-33942), push down and turn remover clockwise to engage tangs to cover. Slowly remove seal cover from bore.

2) Remove shaft seal snap ring. Use Shaft Seal Remover (J-33942-B) to remove seal. Remove compressor through bolts, front head and "O" ring. If necessary, replace front and rear valve plates, reed valves, and "O" rings.

3) To install, reverse removal procedure. Coat "O" ring, shaft seal and seal seat with refrigerant oil. Place Shaft Seal Guide (J-34614) over end of compressor shaft. Ensure chamfered portion of shaft seal retainer aligns with chamfered portion on compressor shaft.

4) Install front head and tighten compressor through bolts, in a crisscross pattern, to 16 ft. lbs. (22 N.m). Install shaft seal cover and felt. *See Fig. 5.* Rotate compressor drive shaft 2-3 times to ensure compressor operates smoothly.

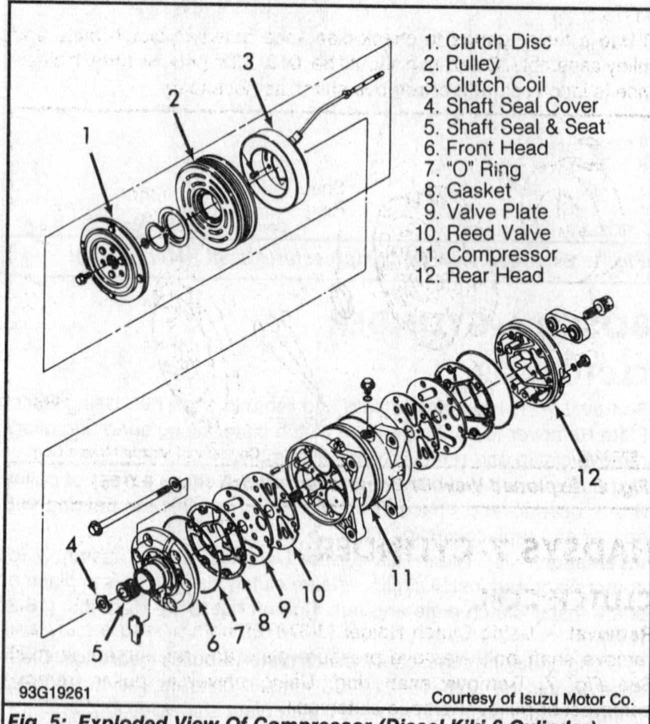
1. Clutch Disc
2. Pulley
3. Clutch Coil
4. Shaft Seal Cover
5. Shaft Seal & Seat
6. Front Head
7. "O" Ring
8. Gasket
9. Valve Plate
10. Reed Valve
11. Compressor
12. Rear Head
93G19261
Courtesy of Isuzu Motor Co.

Fig. 5: Exploded View Of Compressor (Diesel Kiki 6-Cylinder)

FORD FX-15

CLUTCH COIL

Removal - 1) Using Clutch Holder (000 41 0812 05), remove clutch plate bolt. Using an 8-mm bolt threaded into clutch plate, remove clutch plate and shim(s). *See Fig. 6.*

2) Remove snap ring and pulley assembly. Install Shaft Protector (49 UN01 047) over shaft seal opening. Use a 2-jaw puller to remove clutch coil from compressor.

Installation - 1) Ensure clutch coil mounting surface is clean. Use Coil Installer (49 UN01 046) and 2-jaw puller engaged to rear side of compressor front mounts to press coil into place.
2) Install pulley assembly. Install pulley assembly snap ring with bevel side of snap ring facing out. Install shim(s) and clutch plate. Install a new clutch plate bolt and tighten to 97-115 INCH lbs. (11-13 N.m).
3) Use a feeler gauge to check clearance between clutch plate and pulley assembly. Clearance should be .018-.033" (.46-.84 mm). If clearance is incorrect, add or remove shims as necessary.

SHAFT SEAL

Removal - 1) Using Clutch Holder (000 41 0812 05), remove clutch plate bolt. Using an 8-mm bolt threaded into clutch plate, remove clutch plate and shim(s). *See Fig. 6.*
2) Remove shaft felt seal. Thoroughly clean seal area of compressor. Remove shaft seal snap ring. Position Shaft Seal Remover (49 UN01 044) over compressor shaft.
3) Push shaft seal remover downward against seal. Ensure end of shaft seal remover is engaged with inside of seal. Rotate shaft seal remover clockwise to expand remover tip inside seal. Pull shaft seal from compressor.
Installation - 1) Lubricate shaft seal protector and shaft seal with refrigerant oil. Install shaft seal on shaft seal protector so lip seal is toward compressor (large end of shaft seal protector).
2) Install shaft seal protector on compressor shaft. Using Shaft Seal Installer (49 UN01 043), push shaft seal down seal protector until seal is seated.
3) Remove shaft seal installer and protector. Install a new shaft seal retaining snap ring and shaft seal felt. Install shim(s) and clutch plate. Install a new clutch plate retaining bolt and tighten to 97-115 INCH lbs. (11-13 N.m).
4) Use a feeler gauge to check clearance between clutch plate and pulley assembly. Clearance should be .018-.033" (.46-.84 mm). If clearance is incorrect, add or remove shims as necessary.

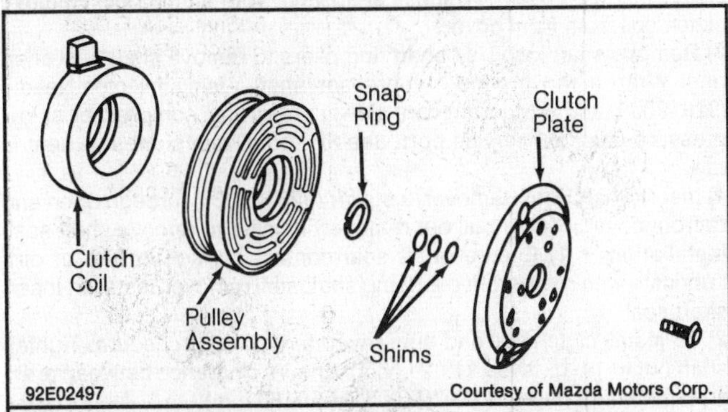
Snap Ring
Clutch Plate
Clutch Coil
Pulley Assembly
Shims
92E02497
Courtesy of Mazda Motors Corp.

Fig. 6: Exploded View Of Compressor Clutch (Ford FX-15)

HADSYS 7-CYLINDER

CLUTCH COIL

Removal - Using Clutch Holder (J-37872), hold pressure plate and remove shaft bolt. Remove pressure plate and adjustment shim(s). *See Fig. 7.* Remove snap ring. Using universal puller, remove compressor pulley. Remove clutch coil.
Installation - Install clutch coil in reverse order of removal. Ensure snap ring is properly seated. Apply locking compound to shaft bolt and tighten it to 62 INCH lbs. (7 N.m). Ensure clearance between pressure plate and pulley is 0.012-0.024" (.30-.60 mm). If clearance is incorrect, add or remove shim(s) as necessary.

HARRISON R4 4-CYLINDER

CLUTCH COIL & BEARING

Removal - 1) Clamp Holding Fixture (J-25008-A) in vise. Attach compressor to holding fixture. Use Clutch Hub Holder (J-33027) to hold clutch and remove shaft nut.

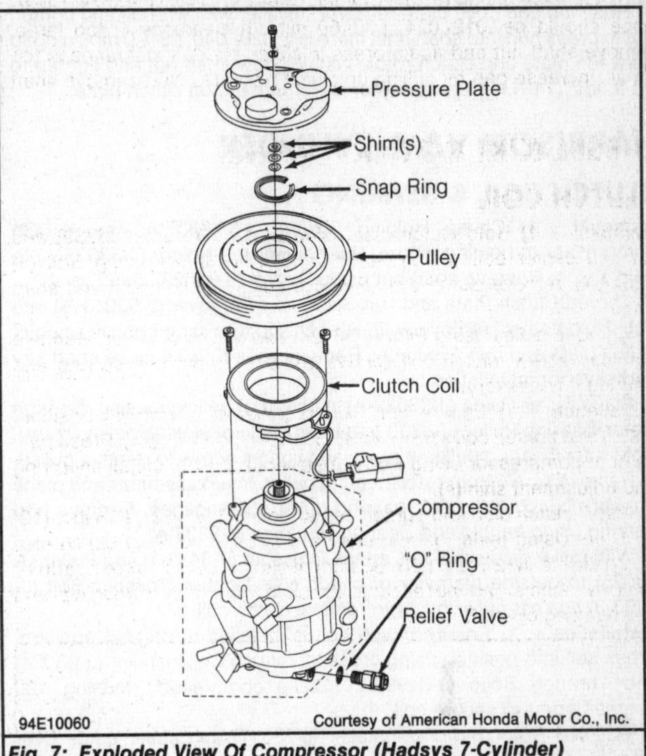
Pressure Plate
Shim(s)
Snap Ring
Pulley
Clutch Coil
Compressor
"O" Ring
Relief Valve
94E10060
Courtesy of American Honda Motor Co., Inc.

Fig. 7: Exploded View Of Compressor (Hadsys 7-Cylinder)

2) Thread Hub and Drive Plate Assembly Remover/Installer (J-37707) into hub. Hold body of remover with wrench and turn center bolt into remover body to remove clutch plate and hub assembly. Remove shaft key and save for installation.
3) Remove snap ring. Place Puller Guide (J-25031-1) in center of pulley housing. Engage universal puller to outer diameter of pulley (clutch rotor). *See Fig. 8.* Hold puller and tighten screw to remove pulley.
4) Invert pulley and place on work bench. Press out rotor bearing using handle and Bearing Remover (J-9398-A). Attach universal puller to outside diameter of clutch coil. Tighten bolt against puller guide to remove clutch coil.

CAUTION: DO NOT drive or pound on clutch hub or shaft.

Installation - 1) Ensure clutch coil is installed in original position. Press pulley onto compressor using Installer (J-9481-A) and handle. Install shaft key into hub key groove. Allow key to project approximately 3/16" (4.8 mm) out of keyway.
2) Ensure frictional surface of clutch plate and clutch rotor are clean before installing clutch plate and hub assembly. Align shaft key with shaft keyway and place clutch plate and hub assembly onto compressor shaft.

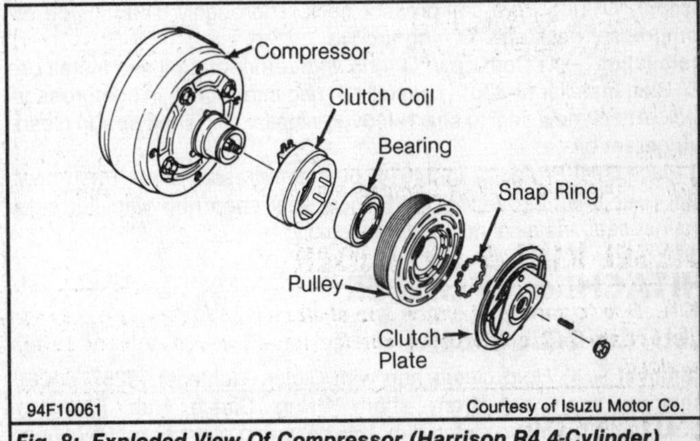
Compressor
Clutch Coil
Bearing
Snap Ring
Pulley
Clutch Plate
94F10061
Courtesy of Isuzu Motor Co.

Fig. 8: Exploded View Of Compressor (Harrison R4 4-Cylinder)

1993 GENERAL SERVICING
Compressor Servicing (Cont.)

3) Hold hub and drive plate remover/installer with wrench and tighten nut to press hub into shaft until there is a .020-.040" (.5-1.0 mm) air gap between plate and clutch rotor. Install a new shaft nut and tighten to 10 ft. lbs. (14 N.m). Ensure rotor is not rubbing on clutch plate.

HARRISON V5 5-CYLINDER

CLUTCH COIL & BEARING

Removal - 1) Clamp Holding Fixture (J-34992) in vise. Attach compressor to holding fixture. Use Clutch Hub Holder (J-33027-A) to hold clutch. Remove shaft nut using Socket (J-33022). *See Fig. 9.*
2) Thread Clutch Plate and Hub Assembly Remover (J-33013-B) into hub. Hold body of remover with wrench and turn center bolt to remove clutch plate and hub assembly. Remove snap ring. Remove shaft key and save for installation.
3) Place Puller Guide (J-33023-A) in center of pulley housing. Engage Rotor/Bearing Puller (J-33020) to inner circle of slots in pulley (rotor). Hold rotor/bearing puller in place and tighten screw to remove pulley.
4) Remove screw from rotor/bearing puller. Invert assembly and place on work bench with rotor/bearing puller still engaged. Remove hub bearing using handle and Bearing Remover (J-9398-A).
5) With puller guide in place, attach Crossbar (J-8433-1) and Puller (J-33025) to outside diameter of clutch coil. Tighten crossbar Bolt (J-8433-3) against puller guide to remove clutch coil.
Installation - 1) Ensure clutch coil is installed in original position. Press coil into position using crossbar, clutch Coil Installer (J-33024) and Through Bolts (J-34992-2). Stake compressor housing 120 degrees apart to secure coil.
2) Position Rotor/Bearing Installer (J-33017) and puller guide over inner race of bearing. Using through bolts, assemble crossbar over puller pilot and tighten through bolts onto holding fixture. Tighten crossbar bolt to press pulley/bearing assembly onto compressor.
3) Install shaft key into hub key groove. Allow key to project approximately 1/8" (3.2 mm) out of keyway. Align shaft key with shaft keyway and place clutch plate and hub assembly onto compressor shaft.

CAUTION: Do not drive or pound on clutch hub or compressor shaft, as compressor could be damaged internally.

4) Hold hex portion of Hub Installer (J-33013) with a wrench. Tighten center screw to press hub into shaft until there is .020-.030" (.50-.76 mm) air gap between frictional plate and clutch rotor.
5) Install new shaft nut with small diameter boss of nut against crankshaft shoulder. Use Socket (J-33022) and Clutch Hub Holder (J-33027-A). Tighten shaft nut to 12 ft. lbs. (16 N.m). Ensure pulley does not rub on clutch plate. *See Fig. 9.*

SHAFT SEAL

Removal - Remove clutch plate and hub assembly. Remove shaft seal snap ring. Thoroughly clean inside of compressor neck area around shaft and seal. Engage tangs of Seal Remover/Installer (J-23128-A) into recessed portion of seal and remove seal. Remove and discard "O" ring from compressor neck. Thoroughly clean inside of compressor neck and "O" ring groove.
Installation - 1) Coat new "O" ring with refrigerant oil and install on "O" Ring Installer (J-33011). Install "O" ring into groove in compressor neck. Attach new seal to seal remover/installer. Dip shaft seal in clean refrigerant oil.
2) Place Seal Protector (J-34614) over compressor shaft. Push new seal over shaft protector. Install new seal snap ring with flat side against seal. Install clutch plate assembly.

HITACHI 6-CYLINDER

CLUTCH COIL & SEAL

Removal - 1) Hold clutch hub with Clutch Tightener (925770000). Remove shaft nut from shaft. Using Clutch Hub Remover (926130000), remove clutch hub. Use snap ring pliers to remove inner snap ring.

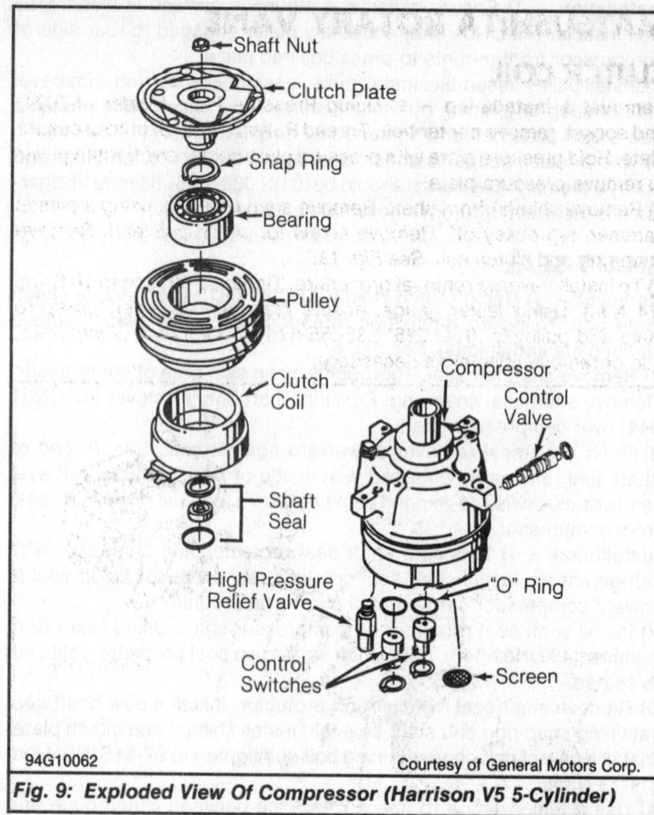
Shaft Nut
Clutch Plate
Snap Ring
Bearing
Pulley
Clutch
Coil
Compressor
Control
Valve
Shaft
Seal
High Pressure
Relief Valve
"O" Ring
Control
Switches
Screen
94G10062
Courtesy of General Motors Corp.

Fig. 9: Exploded View Of Compressor (Harrison V5 5-Cylinder)

2) Remove pulley and bearing assembly. Remove screws securing clutch coil lead. Remove inner snap ring from clutch coil. Remove clutch coil from front cover.
3) Remove shaft key. Use snap ring pliers to remove shaft seal snap ring. Wrap a rag around compressor shaft. Using Injector Needle (92619000) and refrigerant can, slowly pressurize compressor at low pressure (suction) service port. *See Fig. 10.* Catch shaft seal seat in rag.
4) Insert Shaft Seal Remover/Installer (926120000) through open end of front cover. Slowly pull out remover/installer to remove shaft seal.
Installation - 1) Ensure shaft seal contact surface is free of dirt. Lubricate with refrigerant oil. Using shaft seal remover/installer, insert shaft seal.
2) To install clutch coil and hub, reverse removal procedure. Tighten shaft nut to 14-15 ft. lbs. (19-21 N.m). Ensure clearance between pressure plate and pulley is 0.020-0.031" (.50-.80 mm).

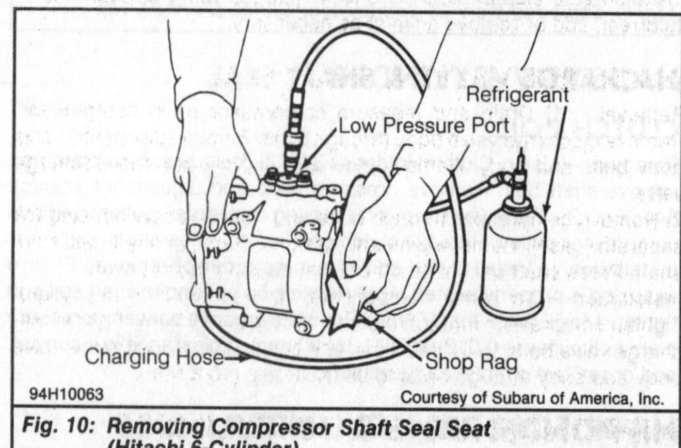
Refrigerant
Low Pressure Port
Charging Hose
Shop Rag
94H10063
Courtesy of Subaru of America, Inc.

Fig. 10: Removing Compressor Shaft Seal Seat (Hitachi 6-Cylinder)

MATSUSHITA ROTARY VANE

CLUTCH COIL

Removal & Installation – 1) Using Pressure Plate Holder (J-7624) and socket, remove center bolt. Thread Puller (J-34878) onto pressure plate. Hold pressure plate with pressure plate holder and tighten puller to remove pressure plate.

2) Remove shim(s) from shaft. Remove snap ring and, using a plastic hammer, tap pulley off. Remove screw for clutch coil lead. Remove snap ring and clutch coil. *See Fig. 11.*

3) To install, reverse removal procedure. Tighten shaft bolt to 10 ft. lbs (14 N.m). Using feeler gauge, ensure clearance between pressure plate and pulley is .014-.026" (.35-.65 mm). If clearance is incorrect, add or remove shim(s) as necessary.

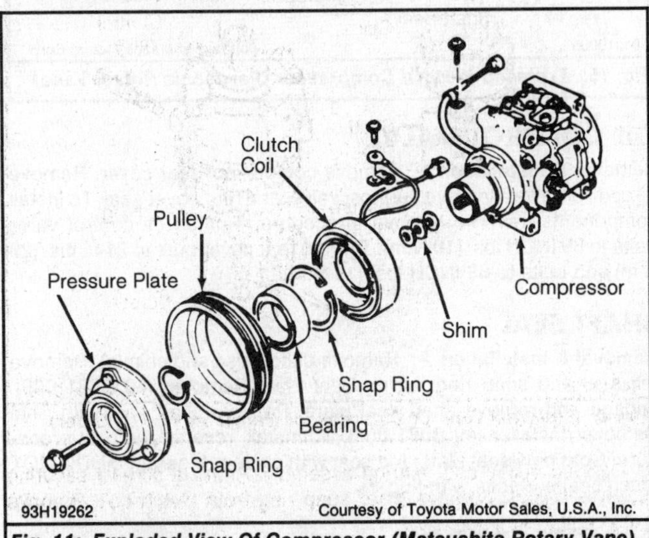
Clutch Coil
Pulley
Pressure Plate
Compressor
Shim
Snap Ring
Bearing
Snap Ring
93H19262
Courtesy of Toyota Motor Sales, U.S.A., Inc.

Fig. 11: Exploded View Of Compressor (Matsushita Rotary Vane)

NIPPONDENSO TV12 ROTARY VANE

CLUTCH COIL

Removal – 1) Hold clutch disc with Clutch Holder (00007-10331) and remove shaft nut. Install Clutch Disc Remover (4992-02-020) and remove clutch disc and shims. *See Fig. 12.*

2) Remove pulley snap ring and tap pulley (with bearing) off of compressor with plastic hammer. Remove screw for clutch coil lead. Remove snap ring and clutch coil.

Installation – To install, reverse removal procedure. Ensure pulley-to-clutch disc clearance is .016-.024" (.40-.60 mm). If clearance is incorrect, add or remove shim(s) as necessary.

DISCHARGE VALVE & SHAFT SEAL

Removal – 1) Drain and measure compressor oil in compressor. Remove discharge valve body through bolts. Remove discharge valve body bolts and body. Remove discharge valve plate and discharge valve.

2) Remove compressor through bolts and front and rear housing (oil separator case). Remove pins and gaskets. Remove shaft seal from shaft. Press shaft seal plate off of front housing (head cover).

Installation – To install components, reverse removal procedure. Tighten compressor through bolts to 19 ft. lbs. (26 N.m). Tighten discharge valve bolts to 41 INCH lbs. (4.6 N.m). Tighten discharge valve body and body through bolts to 96 INCH lbs. (10.8 N.m).

NIPPONDENSO 6 & 10-CYLINDER

***NOTE:* Due to variety of clutch and shaft seal configurations, obtain appropriate A/C compressor service tools for compressor being serviced.**

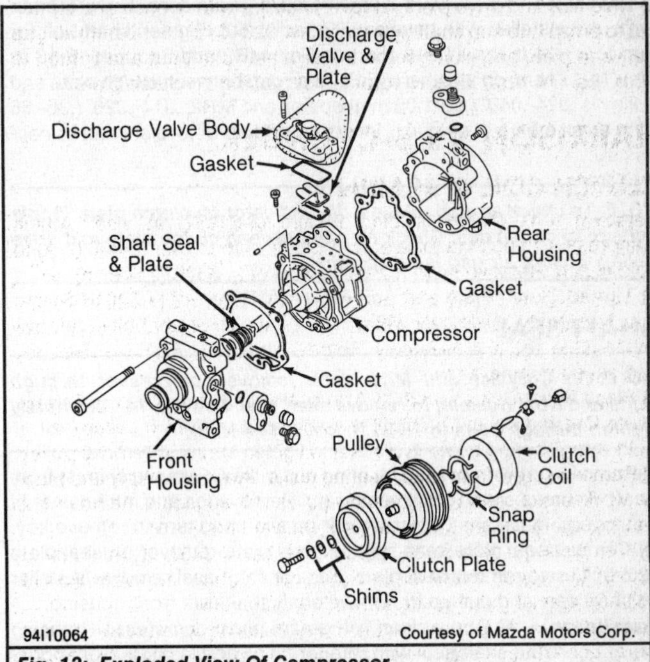
Discharge Valve & Plate
Discharge Valve Body
Gasket
Rear Housing
Shaft Seal & Plate
Gasket
Compressor
Gasket
Front Housing
Pulley
Clutch Coil
Snap Ring
Clutch Plate
Shims
94I10064
Courtesy of Mazda Motors Corp.

Fig. 12: Exploded View Of Compressor (Nippondenso TV12 Rotary Vane)

CLUTCH COIL & BEARING

Removal – 1) Hold clutch plate stationary and remove shaft bolt (or nut). Remove clutch plate using puller. Remove shim(s) from shaft and snap ring. Tap pulley off shaft with plastic hammer. If pulley cannot be removed by hand, use commercially available puller.

2) Remove snap ring, bearing, and seal (if equipped) from pulley. *See Fig. 13.* Remove screw for clutch coil lead. Remove snap ring and clutch coil.

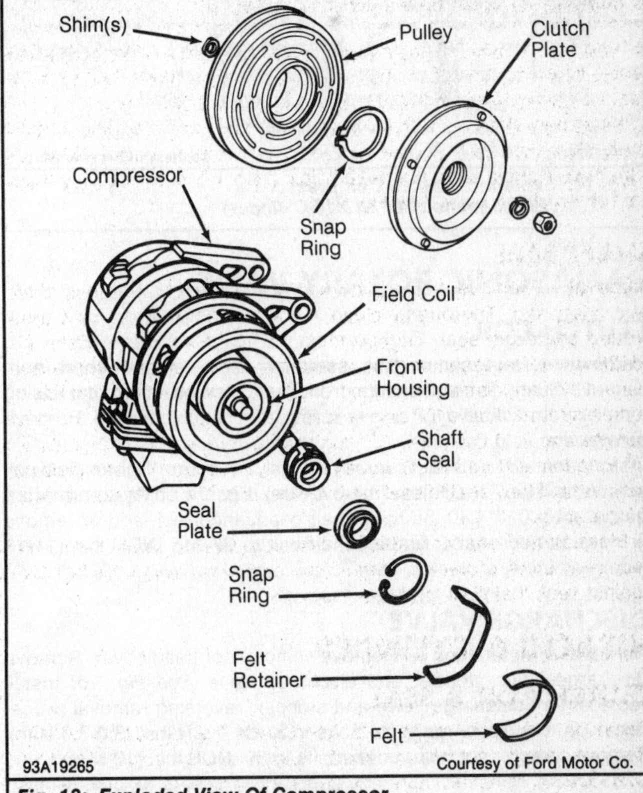
Shim(s)
Pulley
Clutch Plate
Compressor
Snap Ring
Field Coil
Front Housing
Shaft Seal
Seal Plate
Snap Ring
Felt Retainer
Felt
93A19265
Courtesy of Ford Motor Co.

Fig. 13: Exploded View Of Compressor (Nippondenso 10-Cylinder)

1993 GENERAL SERVICING
Compressor Servicing (Cont.)

Installation – To install, reverse removal procedure. Ensure snap rings are installed with beveled side facing out. Tighten shaft bolt (or nut) to 13-14 ft. lbs. (17-19 N.m) on Fox, MR2 and Scoupe; 10-13 ft. lbs. (14-17 N.m) on all others. Ensure air gap between clutch plate and pulley is .024-.040" (.60-1.00 mm) on Fox and MR2; .014-.026" (.36-.66 mm) on all others. If air gap is incorrect, add or remove shim(s) as necessary.

NOTE: To check air gap, place a dial indicator on clutch plate. Apply voltage to clutch coil. Check air gap between clutch plate and drive pulley. Ensure air gap is as specified.

SHAFT SEAL

NOTE: On Chrysler and Mitsubishi, remove compressor through bolts and front housing to remove shaft seal. See Fig. 14. Alternately tighten through bolts to 18-21 ft. lbs. (24-28 N.m).

Removal – **1)** Remove clutch plate and pulley. Remove shim(s) from shaft. Remove clutch coil if necessary. Remove felt and felt retainer (if equipped). Place shaft key remover on shaft and turn to remove key.
2) Remove seal plate snap ring. Engage plate remover on seal plate and pull up to remove seal plate. Engage shaft seal remover/installer to shaft seal and pull up to remove shaft seal from front housing.
Installation – **1)** Apply clean refrigerant oil to compressor housing bore. Lubricate shaft seal with refrigerant oil and install in front housing. Lubricate seal plate and install in front housing.
2) Install shaft key, snap ring, felt retainer and felt. With clutch plate installed, ensure air gap between clutch plate and pulley is .024-.040" (.60-1.00 mm) on Fox and MR2; .014-.026" (.36-.66 mm) on all others. If air gap is incorrect, add or remove shim(s) as necessary.

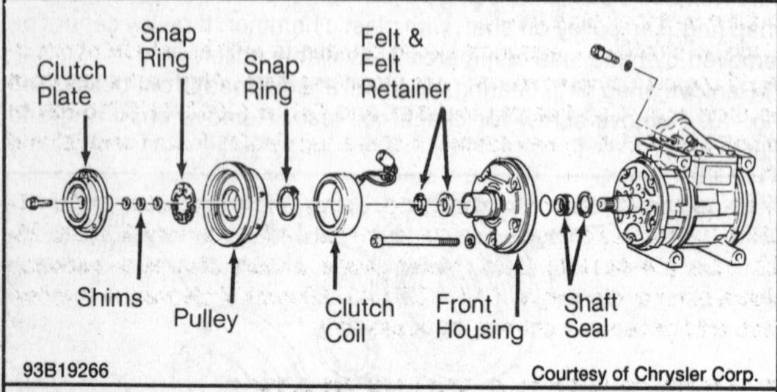
Snap Ring
Felt & Felt Retainer
Clutch Plate
Snap Ring
Shims
Pulley
Clutch Coil
Front Housing
Shaft Seal
93B19266
Courtesy of Chrysler Corp.

Fig. 14: Exploded View Of Compressor (Nippondenso 10PA15 10-Cylinder)

PANASONIC ROTARY VANE

CLUTCH COIL

Removal – Hold clutch disc stationary and remove shaft bolt. Remove clutch disc and shim(s) from shaft. Remove snap ring. Using a puller, remove pulley. Remove screw from clutch coil lead. Remove screws and field coil.
Installation – To install, reverse removal procedure. Tighten field coil screws to 30-57 INCH lbs. (3.4-6.4 N.m). Ensure pulley-to-armature gap is .016-.020" (.40-.50 mm). If air gap is incorrect, add or remove shim(s) as necessary. Tighten shaft bolt to 97-115 INCH lbs. (11-13 N.m).

DISCHARGE VALVE

Removal & Installation – Remove compressor head cover. Remove discharge valve stopper and discharge valve. *See Fig. 15.* Install replacement discharge valve and stopper, reversing removal procedure. Tighten discharge valve bolts to 27-34 INCH lbs. (3.0-3.8 N.m). Tighten compressor head cover bolts to 89 INCH lbs. (10 N.m).

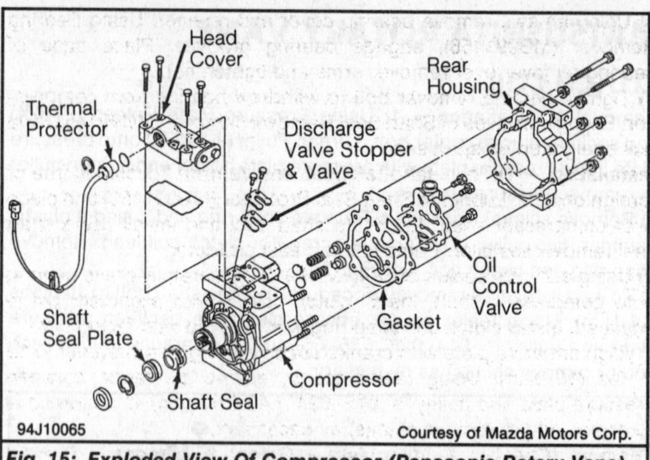
Head Cover
Rear Housing
Thermal Protector
Discharge Valve Stopper & Valve
Oil Control Valve
Gasket
Shaft Seal Plate
Compressor
Shaft Seal
94J10065
Courtesy of Mazda Motors Corp.

Fig. 15: Exploded View Of Compressor (Panasonic Rotary Vane)

OIL CONTROL VALVE

Removal & Installation – Remove compressor rear cover. Remove oil control valve. Remove springs, valve, and rear cover seal. To install components, reverse removal procedure. Tighten oil control valve bolts to 89 INCH lbs. (10 N.m). Tighten rear cover nuts to 21 ft. lbs. (29 N.m) and bolts to 89 INCH lbs. (10 N.m).

SHAFT SEAL

Removal & Installation – Remove clutch disc and shim(s). Remove felt seal and snap ring. Using Seal Plate Remover (49 B061 005), engage and remove shaft seal plate. Remove shaft seal with Seal Remover/Installer (49 B061 006). To install, reverse removal procedure. Coat new seal plate and seal with clean refrigerant oil. DO NOT touch seal surfaces with fingers.

SANDEN SCROLL

CLUTCH COIL & SHAFT SEAL

NOTE: Due to variety of clutch and shaft seal configurations, obtain appropriate A/C compressor service tools for compressor being serviced.

Removal (Chrysler & Mitsubishi – Except Galant & Mirage) – **1)** Remove drive belt pulley (if equipped). Hold clutch plate using Pliers (MB991367) and Bolts (MB991386). Use a ratchet and socket to remove clutch hub nut.
2) Remove clutch plate. Remove snap ring with internal snap ring pliers. Remove clutch hub (rotor). Remove snap ring and clutch coil.

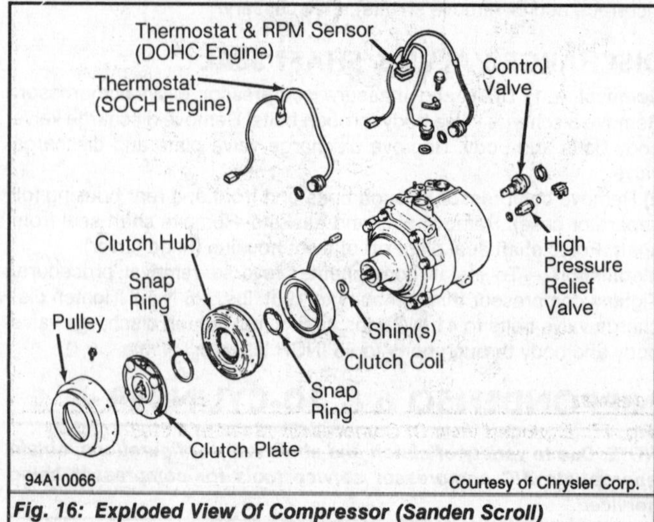
Thermostat & RPM Sensor (DOHC Engine)
Thermostat (SOCH Engine)
Control Valve
Clutch Hub
Snap Ring
Pulley
High Pressure Relief Valve
Shim(s)
Clutch Coil
Snap Ring
Clutch Plate
94A10066
Courtesy of Chrysler Corp.

Fig. 16: Exploded View Of Compressor (Sanden Scroll)

1993 GENERAL SERVICING
Compressor Servicing (Cont.)

3) Using an awl, remove bearing cover and retainer. Using Bearing Remover (MB991456), engage bearing grooves. Place base of bearing remover over remover arms and tighten nut.
4) Tighten bearing remover bolt to withdraw bearing from compressor. Engage grooves of Shaft Seal Remover/Installer (MB991458) and pull straight up on shaft seal.
Installation - 1) To install shaft seal, ensure front housing is free of foreign objects. Lubricate Shaft Seal Protector (MB991459) and place over compressor shaft. Lubricate shaft seal and install using shaft seal remover/installer. Remove shaft seal protector.
2) Using a 21 mm socket or Drift (MB991301), carefully press bearing onto compressor shaft. Install clutch coil so that alignment pin is engaged. Install clutch coil snap ring with tapered side facing out.
3) Align armature plate with crankshaft spline. Tighten shaft nut to 12 ft. lbs (16 N.m). Using feeler gauge, ensure clearance between pressure plate and pulley is .016-.024" (.40-0.60 mm). If clearance is incorrect, add or remove shim(s) as necessary.
Removal (Chrysler & Mitsubishi - Galant & Mirage) - 1) Hold clutch plate by securing 2 box-end wrenches with two 6-mm bolts, 1" (25 mm) or longer. Holding bow-end wrenches, use a ratchet and socket to remove clutch hub nut.
2) Remove clutch plate. *See Fig. 17*. Remove snap ring with internal snap ring pliers. Remove clutch hub. Remove snap ring and clutch coil.
3) Remove front housing bolts. Remove front housing and "O" ring from compressor. Remove shaft seal from shaft. Remove snap ring from back side of front housing. Remove seal plate. Use brass drift and hammer to lightly tap shaft bearing from front housing. Remove felt seal.

NOTE: DO NOT touch sealing surfaces of shaft seal carbon ring and shaft seal plate.

Installation - 1) Lubricate shaft seal with compressor oil. Align notches on shaft seal with notches on shaft. Install shaft seal plate on front housing. Install front seal housing to compressor.
2) Use Drift (MB991301) to install felt into front housing. Ensure metal ring on felt faces up. Use drift to press bearing into front housing.
3) Align and install clutch coil. Install snap ring so tapered surface faces outward. Install clutch hub. Install snap ring. Align clutch plate mark with shaft; where there are no splines on shaft.
4) Tighten clutch hub nut to 12 ft. lbs. (16 N.m). Using feeler gauge, measure clutch plate-to-clutch hub gap. If gap is not .012-.024" (.30-.60 mm), remove clutch assembly and add or remove shim(s).

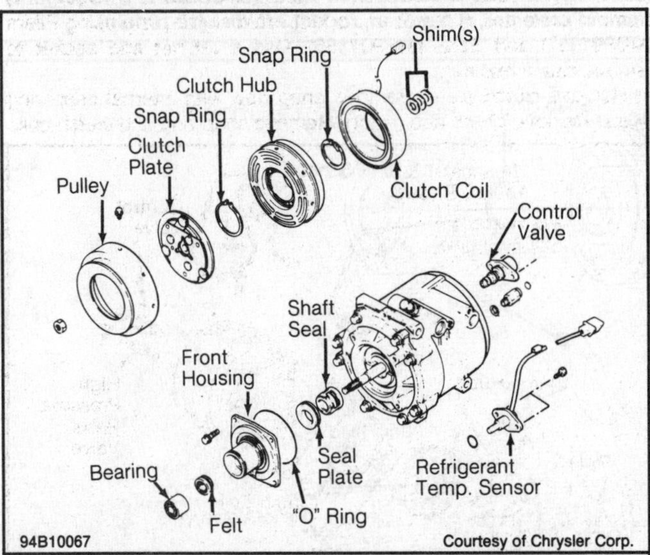
Shim(s)
Snap Ring
Clutch Hub
Snap Ring
Clutch Plate
Pulley
Clutch Coil
Control Valve
Shaft Seal
Front Housing
Bearing
Felt
"O" Ring
Seal Plate
Refrigerant Temp. Sensor
94B10067
Courtesy of Chrysler Corp.
Fig. 17: Exploded View Of Compressor (Sanden FX105V Scroll)

Removal & Installation (Honda & Hyundai) - 1) Remove shaft nut while holding clutch plate with Armature Holder (J-37872). Using Puller (07935-8050003), remove pressure plate and shim(s). *See Fig. 16*. Remove snap ring.
2) Place Seal Driver (07945-4150200) in center of pulley. Engage universal puller to outer diameter of pulley. DO NOT engage puller on belt area. Hold puller in place and tighten screw to remove pulley. Remove screw for clutch coil lead. Remove snap ring and clutch coil.
3) To install clutch coil, reverse removal procedure. Align lug on clutch coil with hole in compressor. Install snap rings with chamfered side facing out. Tighten shaft nut to 12-14 ft. lbs. (16-19 N.m). Using feeler gauge, ensure clearance between pressure plate and pulley is .014-.026" (.35-.65 mm). If clearance is incorrect, add or remove shim(s) as necessary.

NOTE: Shaft seal removal and installation procedures not available from Honda or Hyundai.

SANDEN 5-CYLINDER

CLUTCH COIL

Removal - 1) Hold clutch plate, using Holder (0000-41-0809-01), and remove shaft nut. Remove clutch plate using Puller (0000-41-0809-02). Remove shaft key and shim(s). Remove external front housing snap ring and internal bearing snap ring (if used).
2) Install Clutch Pilot (0000-41-0810-77), Pulley/Clutch Remover (0000-41-0810-76), and Puller (0000-41-0804-51/57) to remove pulley assembly. Remove snap ring and drive bearing out of pulley. Remove screw for clutch coil lead. Remove snap ring and clutch coil.
Installation - 1) Install new bearing, ensuring Bearing Installer (000-41-0804-43) contacts outer race of bearing. Install snap ring and ensure bearing turns freely.
2) Install clutch coil, ensuring lug on coil aligns with hole in front housing. Support compressor on rear mounting ears. Align rotor on front housing hub. Use bearing installer and Driver (0000-41-0810-59) to install pulley. With pulley seated, install snap ring(s). Install shim(s) and shaft key.
3) Place clutch plate over shaft and, using Shaft Protector (0000-41-0809-10), tap clutch plate into place. Install and tighten shaft nut to 25-32 ft. lbs. (34-44 N.m). Using feeler gauge, ensure clearance between clutch plate and pulley is .016-.032" (.40-.80 mm). If clearance is incorrect, add or remove shim(s) as necessary.

CYLINDER HEAD & VALVE PLATE

Removal & Installation - Remove compressor cylinder head (rear cover) bolts. Carefully pry cylinder head of compressor. Remove reed valve plate and gasket. To install components, reverse removal procedure. Tighten compressor cylinder head bolts, in a crisscross pattern, to 21-29 ft. lbs. (29-39 N.m).

SHAFT SEAL

Removal - Remove shaft nut and clutch plate. Remove shaft key and shim(s). Carefully remove felt ring. Remove shaft seal seat snap ring. Using Seal Seat Remover/Installer (0000-41-0810-73), carefully remove seal seat. Using Shaft Seal Remover/Installer (0000-41-0812-11), carefully remove shaft seal.
Installation - 1) Install Seal Protector (0000-41-0812-13) over shaft. Place new seal on remover/installer. DO NOT touch carbon sealing surface with fingers. Dip seal in refrigerant oil and install. Remove seal installer by turning counterclockwise.
2) Coat seal seat with refrigerant oil. Install seal seat using remover/installer. Install seal seat snap ring (with flat side down). Install shim(s), felt ring and shaft key. Install shaft nut and clutch plate. Ensure clearance between clutch plate and pulley is .016-.032" (.40-.80 mm). If clearance is incorrect, add or remove shim(s) as necessary.

1993 GENERAL SERVICING
Compressor Servicing (Cont.)

SANDEN 7-CYLINDER

NOTE: Due to variety of clutch and shaft seal configurations, obtain appropriate A/C compressor service tools for compressor being serviced.

CLUTCH COIL & BEARING

Removal – 1) Install two 6-mm bolts, 1" (25 mm) or longer, in clutch plate holes. Using 2 box-end wrenches to hold bolts and to prevent clutch plate from turning, remove shaft nut.

2) Remove clutch plate using Clutch Plate Puller (09977-21100). Remove clutch shim(s) and bearing dust cover. Remove external front housing snap ring. *See Fig. 18.*

3) Remove pulley using universal puller. Detach clutch coil lead from compressor housing. Remove clutch coil snap ring and clutch coil. If necessary, remove snap ring and bearing.

Installation – 1) Align clutch coil lug with hole in compressor housing, and install clutch coil. Install clutch coil snap ring. Install drive pulley using Drive Pulley Installer (09977-21811).

2) Install external bearing snap ring. Using Seal Installer (09977-21800), install bearing dust cover. After dust cover installation, ensure there is no contact between cover and front housing.

3) Install clutch shim(s) and clutch plate. Tighten shaft nut to 13-14 ft. lbs. (17-19 N.m). Using a dial indicator, check air gap between clutch plate and drive pulley. Apply voltage to clutch coil. Ensure air gap is .016-.032" (.40-.80 mm). If clearance is incorrect, add or remove shim(s) as necessary.

NOTE: If compressor valve plate is serviced, tighten compressor cylinder head bolts to 25-26 ft. lbs. (34-35 N.m).

SHAFT SEAL

NOTE: Check compressor refrigerant oil level when replacing seals. See COMPRESSOR REFRIGERANT OIL CHECKING article in GENERAL SERVICING.

Removal – 1) Remove clutch plate, shim(s) and bearing dust cover. Tap shaft key out of slot in compressor shaft. Remove seal retainer felt ring.

2) Remove shaft seal seat snap ring. Insert Seal Seat Remover/Installer (09977-21400) into front housing and turn to engage tangs on seat. Lift seal seat out.

3) Insert Seal Remover/Installer (09977-21510) into front housing and turn to engage tangs on seal. Carefully lift shaft seal out without scratching compressor shaft.

Installation – 1) Install Shaft Seal Guide Sleeve (09977-21700) over compressor shaft. Dip seal in refrigerant oil and install seal on sleeve. Using seal remover/installer, rotate seal clockwise until seal is engaged. Remove seal remover/installer by turning it counterclockwise.

2) Coat seal seat with refrigerant oil and install seal with seal seat remover/installer. Remove shaft seal guide sleeve. Install snap ring with beveled edge facing out. Install seal retainer felt ring using seal seat remover/installer.

3) Install shaft key and clutch plate. Tighten shaft nut to 13-14 ft. lbs. (17-19 N.m). Using a dial indicator, check air gap between clutch plate and drive pulley. Apply voltage to clutch coil. Ensure air gap is .016-.032" (.40-.80 mm). If clearance is incorrect, add or remove shim(s) as necessary.

SEIKO-SEIKI ROTARY VANE

NOTE: Volvo Seiko-Seiki compressor servicing procedure is not available from manufacturer.

ZEXEL ROTARY VANE

CLUTCH COIL & BEARING

Removal – 1) Hold clutch disc using Clutch Disc Wrench (KV99231260) and remove center bolt. Using Clutch Disc Puller (KV99232340), remove drive plate and adjustment shim(s).

2) Remove snap ring. Remove pulley using Pilot (J-39023) and universal puller. Remove clutch coil. If necessary, remove snap ring and bearing. *See Fig. 19.*

Installation – 1) Ensure coil lead is installed in original position. Install and tighten coil screws. Press pulley onto compressor using Pulley Installer (J-33940). Install snap ring and adjustment shim(s).

2) Install clutch disc and tighten center bolt to 11-13 ft. lbs. (15-18 N.m). Using feeler gauge, ensure clearance between clutch disc and pulley is .012-.024" (.30-.60 mm). If clearance is incorrect, add or remove shim(s) as necessary. Break-in clutch by engaging and disengaging clutch 30 times.

NOTE: Shaft seal assembly servicing procedure is not available from manufacturer. Use exploded view as a guide. See Fig. 19. Tighten thermal protector, if removed, to 11-13 ft. lbs. (15-18 N.m).

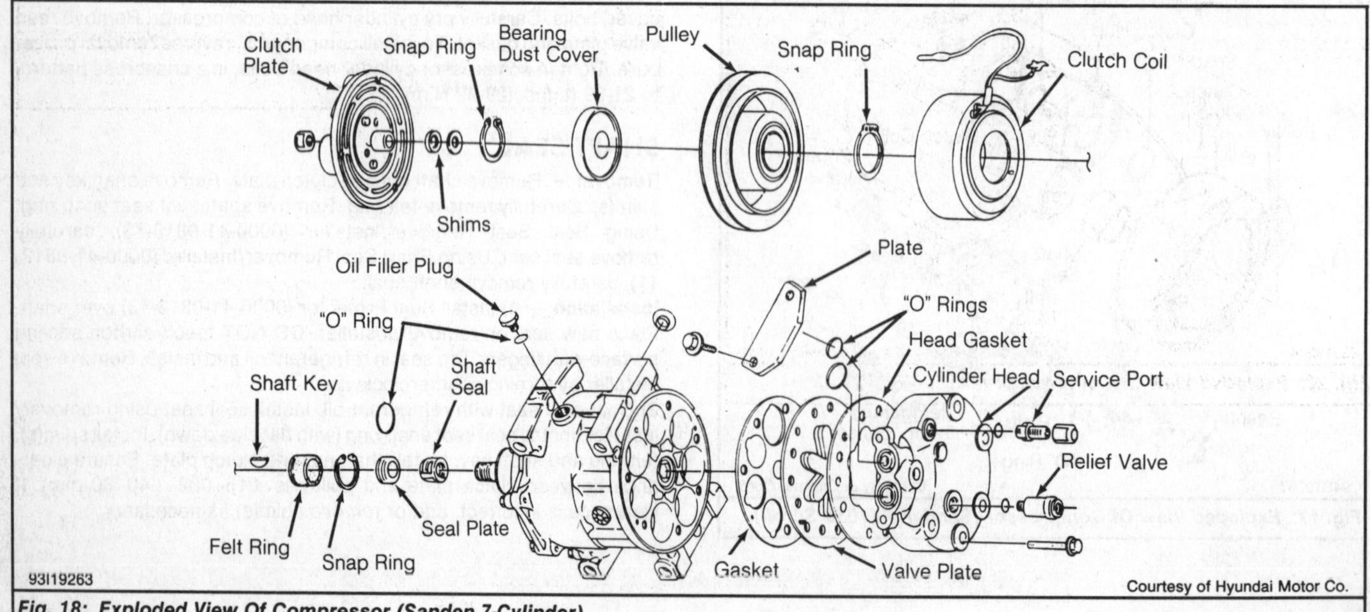
Clutch Plate
Snap Ring
Bearing Dust Cover
Pulley
Snap Ring
Clutch Coil
Shims
Plate
Oil Filler Plug
"O" Ring
"O" Rings
Head Gasket
Cylinder Head
Service Port
Shaft Key
Shaft Seal
Relief Valve
Seal Plate
Felt Ring
Snap Ring
Gasket
Valve Plate
93I19263
Courtesy of Hyundai Motor Co.

Fig. 18: Exploded View Of Compressor (Sanden 7-Cylinder)

1993 GENERAL SERVICING
Compressor Servicing (Cont.)

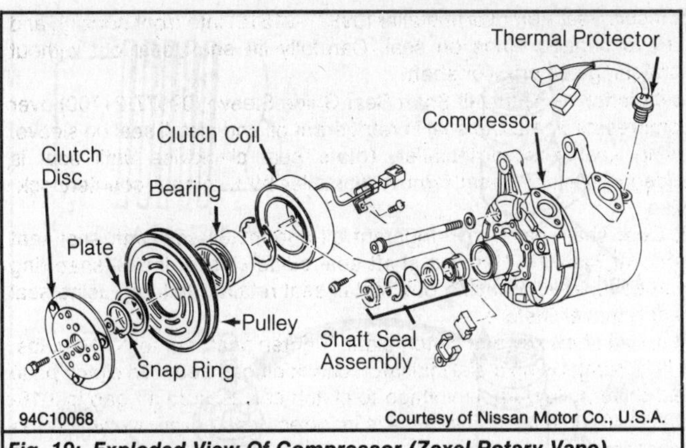
Thermal Protector
Compressor
Clutch Coil
Clutch Disc
Bearing
Plate
Pulley
Shaft Seal Assembly
Snap Ring
94C10068
Courtesy of Nissan Motor Co., U.S.A.

Fig. 19: Exploded View Of Compressor (Zexel Rotary Vane)

ZEXEL 6-CYLINDER

NOTE: Volvo Zexel compressor servicing procedure is not available from manufacturer.

CLUTCH COIL & BEARING

Removal (Audi) – 1) Using Spanner Wrench (44-4), hold clutch hub stationary and remove shaft bolt. Remove clutch plate and shim(s) using Puller (VAG 1719) and Spanner Wrench (3212). *See Fig. 20.* Remove snap ring.

2) Place Spacer (VAG 1719/1) in center of pulley cavity. Attach Puller (US 1078) to outer diameter of pulley and remove pulley. Remove snap ring, bearing, and clutch coil as necessary.

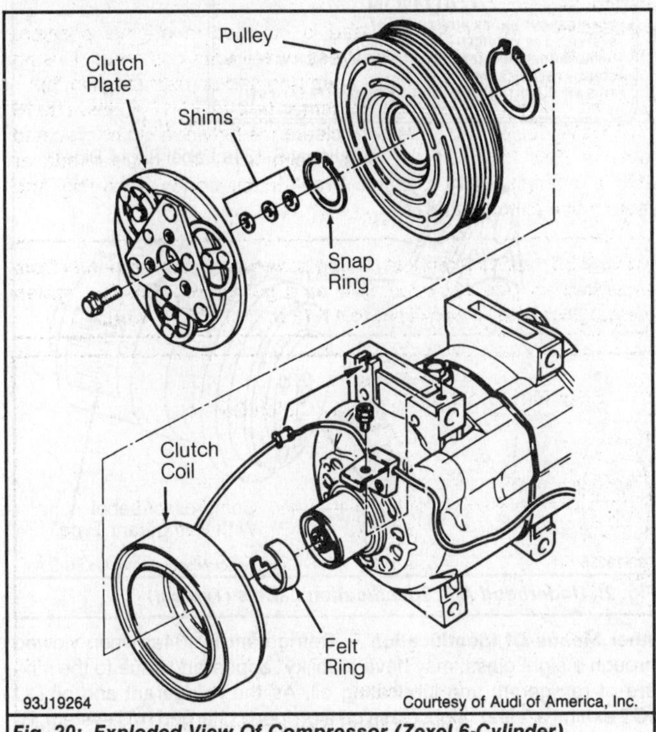
Pulley
Clutch Plate
Shims
Snap Ring
Clutch Coil
Felt Ring
93J19264
Courtesy of Audi of America, Inc.

Fig. 20: Exploded View Of Compressor (Zexel 6-Cylinder)

Installation – Ensure clutch coil lug fits into hole on compressor housing. Using Installer (VAG 1719/2), press on pulley and install snap ring. Install shim(s) and clutch plate. Tighten shaft bolt to 11 ft. lbs. (15 N.m). Using feeler gauge, ensure air gap between pulley and clutch disc is .012-.024" (.30-.60 mm). If clearance is incorrect, add or remove shim(s) as necessary.

Removal (Nissan) – 1) Using Clutch Disc Wrench (J-37877), hold clutch hub stationary and remove shaft nut. Remove adjustment shim(s) and clutch disc using Clutch Disc Puller (J-26571-A).

2) Bend lock washer away from lock nut. *See Fig. 21.* Remove lock nut with Wrench (J-37882). Remove pulley by hand or, if difficult to remove, use Pilot (J-26720-A) and universal puller. Remove snap ring, bearing, and clutch coil as necessary.

Installation – 1) Ensure key is installed in compressor shaft keyway. Install pulley, lock washer and pulley. Tighten lock nut to 25-29 ft. lbs. (34-39 N.m). Bend lock washer against lock nut.

2) Install clutch disc and tighten shaft nut to 10-12 ft. lbs (14-16 N.m). Using feeler gauge, ensure air gap between pulley and clutch disc is .012-.024" (.30-.60 mm). If clearance is incorrect, add or remove shim(s) as necessary. Break-in compressor clutch assembly by engaging and disengaging clutch 30 times.

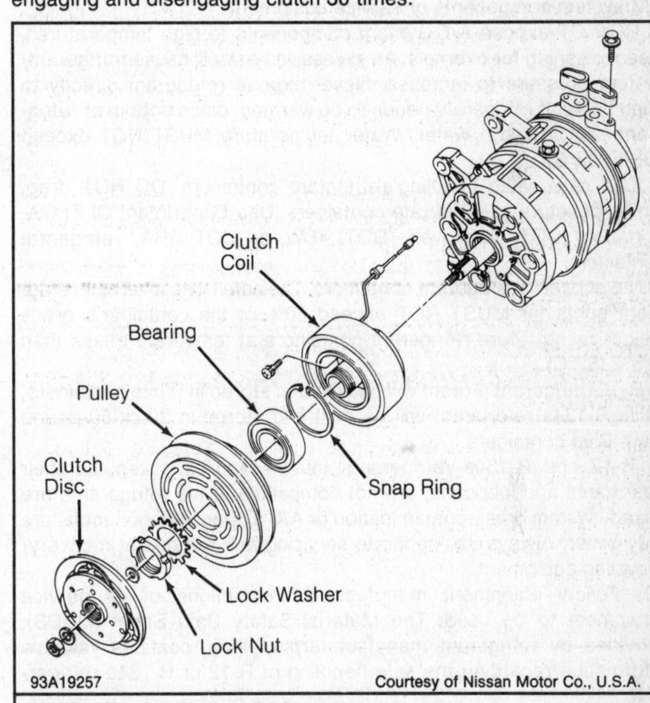
Clutch Coil
Bearing
Pulley
Clutch Disc
Snap Ring
Lock Washer
Lock Nut
93A19257
Courtesy of Nissan Motor Co., U.S.A.

Fig. 21: Exploded View Of Compressor (Zexel DKS-16H 6-Cylinder)

1993 GENERAL SERVICING
General Servicing Procedures

USING R-12 & R-134a REFRIGERANT

HANDLING/SAFETY PRECAUTIONS

1) Always work in a well-ventilated, clean area. Refrigerant R-134a is colorless and is invisible as a gas. Refrigerant (R-12 or R-134a) is heavier than oxygen and will displace oxygen in a confined area. Avoid breathing refrigerant vapors. Exposure may irritate eyes, nose and throat.

2) The system's high pressure can cause severe injury to eyes and skin if a hose were to burst. Always wear eye protection when working around A/C system and refrigerant. If necessary, wear rubber gloves or other protective clothing.

3) Refrigerant evaporates quickly when exposed to atmosphere, freezing anything it contacts. If liquid refrigerant contacts eyes or skin, DO NOT rub eyes or skin. Immediately flush affected area with cool water for 15 minutes and consult a doctor or hospital.

4) Never use R-134a in combination with compressed air for leak testing. Pressurized R-134a in the presence of oxygen (air concentrations greater than 60% by volume) may form a combustible mixture. DO NOT introduce compressed air into R-134a containers (full or empty), A/C system components or service equipment.

5) DO NOT expose A/C system components to high temperatures, steam cleaning for example, as excessive heat will cause refrigerant/system pressure to increase. Never expose refrigerant directly to open flame. If refrigerant needs to be warmed, place bottom of refrigerant tank in warm water. Water temperature MUST NOT exceed 125°F (52°C).

6) Use care when handling refrigerant containers. DO NOT drop, strike, puncture or incinerate containers. Use Department Of Transportation (DOT) approved, DOT 4BW or DOT 4BA, refrigerant containers.

7) Never overfill refrigerant containers. The safe filling level of a refrigerant container MUST NOT exceed 60% of the container's gross weight rating. Store refrigerant containers at temperature less than 125°F (52°C).

8) R-12 refrigerant (Freon) will be sold and stored in White containers, while R-134a refrigerant will be sold and stored in 30 or 50-pound Light Blue containers.

9) R-12 and R-134a refrigerants must never be mixed, as their desiccants and lubricants are not compatible. If the refrigerants are mixed, system cross-contamination or A/C system component failure may occur. Always use separate servicing and refrigerant recovery/recycling equipment.

10) Follow equipment manufacturer instructions of all service equipment to be used. The Material Safety Data Sheet (MSDS), provided by refrigerant manufacturer/suppliers, contains valuable information regarding the safe handling of R-12 or R-134a refrigerants.

IDENTIFYING R-134a SYSTEMS & COMPONENTS

To prevent refrigerant cross-contamination, use following methods to identify R-134a based systems and components.

Fittings & "O" Rings – All R-134a based A/C systems use 1/2" - 16" ACME threaded fittings (identifiable by square threads) and quick-connect service couplings. *See Fig. 1.* Besides the use of these fittings, most manufacturers will use Green colored "O" rings in R-134a systems.

Underhood A/C Specification Labels – Most R-134a based systems will be identified through the use of Green or Light Blue underhood labels, or with R-134a refrigerant clearly printed on labels. *See Fig. 2.* Some manufacturers will identify R-12 based systems with White, Red, Silver or Gold underhood labels. Before servicing an A/C system, always determine which refrigerant is being used.

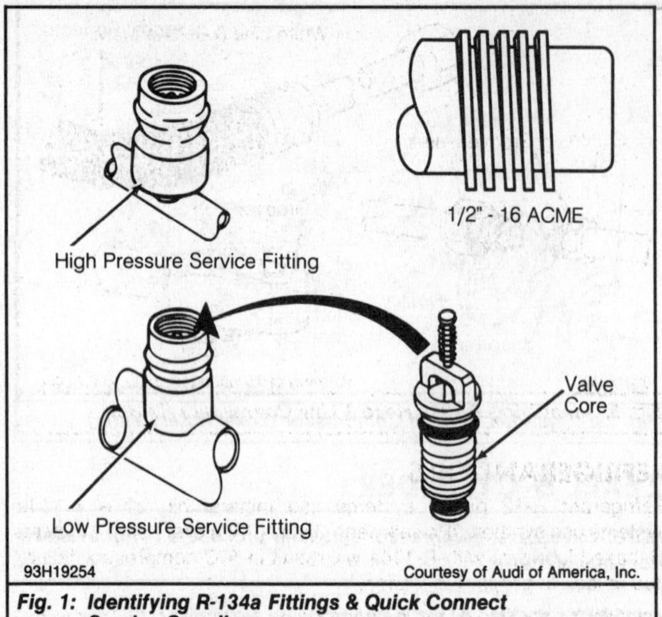
1/2" - 16 ACME
High Pressure Service Fitting
Valve
Core
Low Pressure Service Fitting
93H19254
Courtesy of Audi of America, Inc.

Fig. 1: Identifying R-134a Fittings & Quick Connect Service Couplings

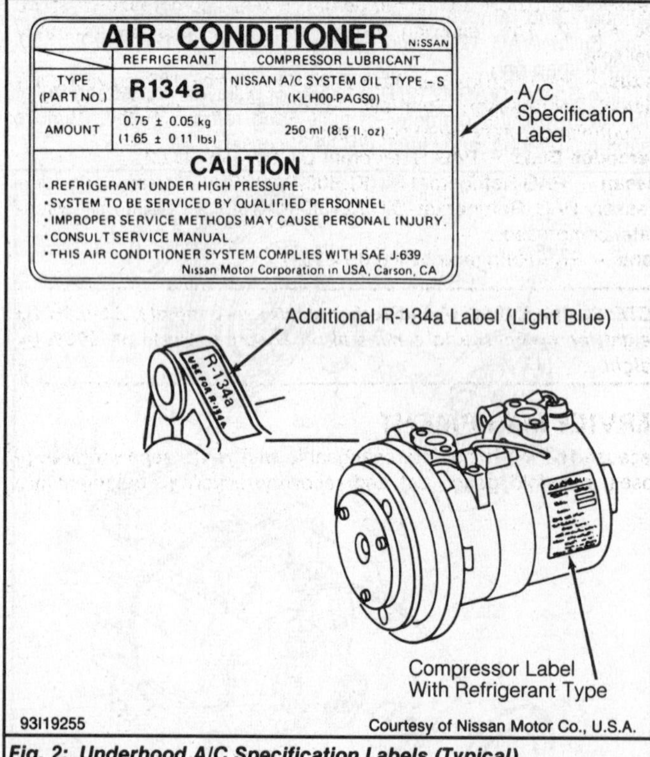
AIR CONDITIONER
NISSAN
REFRIGERANT
COMPRESSOR LUBRICANT
TYPE
(PART NO.)
R134a
NISSAN A/C SYSTEM OIL TYPE - S
(KLH00-PAGS0)
AMOUNT
0.75 ± 0.05 kg
(1.65 ± 0.11 lbs)
250 ml (8.5 fl. oz)
CAUTION
• REFRIGERANT UNDER HIGH PRESSURE
• SYSTEM TO BE SERVICED BY QUALIFIED PERSONNEL
• IMPROPER SERVICE METHODS MAY CAUSE PERSONAL INJURY.
• CONSULT SERVICE MANUAL
• THIS AIR CONDITIONER SYSTEM COMPLIES WITH SAE J-639
Nissan Motor Corporation in USA, Carson, CA
A/C
Specification
Label
Additional R-134a Label (Light Blue)
Compressor Label
With Refrigerant Type
93I19255
Courtesy of Nissan Motor Co., U.S.A.

Fig. 2: Underhood A/C Specification Labels (Typical)

Other Means Of Identification – Refrigerant R-134a, when viewed through a sight glass, may have a "milky" appearance due to the mixture of refrigerant and lubricating oil. As the refrigerant and oil DO NOT exhibit a "clear" sight glass on a properly charged A/C system, R-134a systems have no sight glass.

Audi, Mercedes-Benz and Volkswagen use Green bands/labels on condenser, refrigerant lines, receiver-drier and expansion valve. Lexus A/C system hoses and line connectors have a groove, a White line and "R-134a" marked on them. *See Fig. 3.*

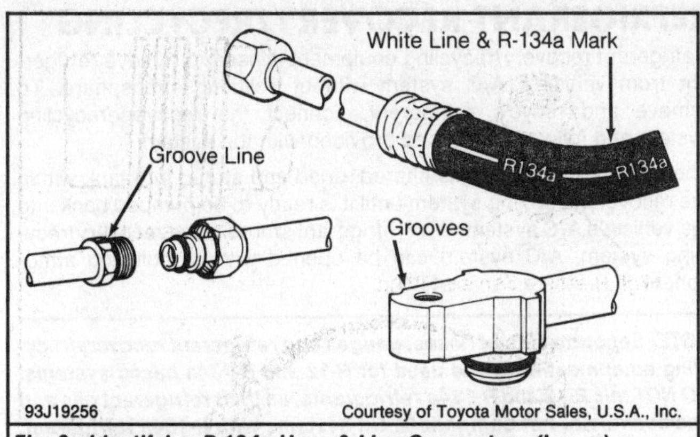
White Line & R-134a Mark
Groove Line
R134a
R134a
Grooves
93J19256
Courtesy of Toyota Motor Sales, U.S.A., Inc.

Fig. 3: Identifying R-134a Hose & Line Connectors (Lexus)

REFRIGERANT OILS

Refrigerant R-12 based systems use mineral oil, while R-134a systems use synthetic/Polyalkylene Glycol (PAG) oils. Using a mineral oil based lubricant with R-134a will result in A/C compressor failure due to lack of proper lubrication.

Use ONLY specified oil for the appropriate system and A/C compressor. Always check the underhood A/C specification label or A/C compressor label before adding refrigerant oil to A/C compressor/system. *See Fig. 2.* The following R-134a refrigerant oils are currently available.

Lexus - PAG Refrigerant Oil (ND-OIL 8) with 10P/10PA swashplate (piston) compressor. Synthetic Refrigerant Oil (ND-OIL 9) with through-vane (rotary vane) compressor.

Mercedes-Benz - PAG Refrigerant Oil (001 989 08 03).

Nissan - PAG Refrigerant Oil (KLH00-PAGR0) with rotary vane compressor. PAG Refrigerant Oil (KLH00-PAGS0) with piston (swashplate) compressor.

Saab - PAG Refrigerant Oil (40 74 787).

NOTE: Synthetic/PAG oils absorb moisture very rapidly, 2.3-5.6% by weight, as compared to a mineral oil absorption rate of .005% by weight.

SERVICE EQUIPMENT

Because R-134a is not interchangeable with R-12, separate sets of hoses, manifold gauge set and recovery/recycling equipment are required to service vehicles. This is necessary to avoid cross-contaminating and damaging system.

All equipment used to service systems using R-134a must meet SAE standard J1991. The service hoses on the manifold gauge set must have manual (turn wheel) or automatic back-flow valves at the service port connector ends. This will prevent refrigerant from being released into the atmosphere.

For identification purposes, R-134a service hoses must have a Black stripe along its length and be clearly labeled SAE J2196/R-134a. The low pressure test hose is Blue with a Black stripe. The high pressure test hose is Red with a Black stripe, and the center test hose is Yellow with a Black stripe.

NOTE: Refrigerant R-12 service hoses will ONLY be labeled SAE J2196.

R-134a manifold gauge sets can be identified by one or all of the following.

- Labeled FOR USE WITH R-134a on set
- Labeled HFC-134 or R-134a on gauge face
- Light Blue color on gauge face

In addition, pressure/temperature scales on R-134a gauge sets are different from R-12 manifold gauge sets.

SYSTEM SERVICE VALVES

SCHRADER-TYPE VALVES

NOTE: Although similar in construction and operation to a tire valve, NEVER replace a Schrader-type valve with a tire valve.

Schrader valve is similar in construction and operation to a tire valve. When a test gauge hose with built-in valve core depressor is attached, Schrader stem is pushed inward to the open position and allows system pressure to reach gauge.

If test hose does not have a built-in core depressor, an adapter must be used. Never attach hose or adapter to Schrader valve unless it is first connected to manifold gauge set.

Refrigerant R-12 Schrader-type valve cores have TV5 thread size. Refrigerant R-134a Schrader-type valve cores use M6 (Metric) threads. R-134a valve cores can be easily identified by use of "O" rings and external spring. *See Fig. 1.*

1993 GENERAL SERVICING
General Servicing Procedures (Cont.)

SERVICE VALVE LOCATIONS

SERVICE VALVE LOCATIONS

Vehicle	High	Low
Audi	12	13
Acura	2	3
BMW	4	5
Chrysler, Eagle & Mitsubishi		
Colt, Mirage & Summit	10	5
Colt Vista & Summit Wagon	10	11
Diamante	4	5
Eclipse & Expo	10	11
Galant	10	11
Montero	11	11
Pickup & Ram-50	10	11
Precis	10	10
Stealth & 3000GT		
R-12	1	1
R-134a	1	5
Ford Motor Co.	4	5
General Motors	12	12
Geo	4	5
Honda	4	5
Hyundai		
Elantra & Scoupe	4	5
Excel & Sonata	10	10
Infiniti	4	5
Isuzu	4	5
Jaguar	4	5
Lexus	4	5
Mazda		
B2200 & B2600i	8	8
Miata, MPV Protege & 323	4	5
Navajo	6	7
All Others	1	1
Mercedes-Benz	4	5
Nissan	4	5
Porsche	8	8
Saab	8	8
Subaru		
Impreza	1	1
Legacy & Loyale	4	5
SVX	9	9
Suzuki	4	5
Toyota		
Pickup & 4Runner	11	11
All Others	4	5
Volkswagen	4	5
Volvo		
240, 940 & 960	4	5
850	1	5

1 – Information is not available from manufacturer.
2 – On high pressure line (near top of condenser on Integra; near receiver-drier on Legend; on receiver-drier on Vigor). Use High-Side Adapter (J-25498).
3 – On low pressure line (near battery on Integra; near right rear of engine on Legend; near compressor on Vigor).
4 – On high pressure (discharge) hose/line.
5 – On low pressure (suction) hose/line.
6 – On high pressure line, between compressor and condenser.
7 – On suction accumulator/drier.
8 – On low and high pressure hoses, behind compressor.
9 – On receiver/drier and low pressure hose (near compressor).
10 – On compressor discharge hose and accumulator.
11 – On compressor discharge and suction ports.
12 – Front of condenser on right side.
13 – Towards rear of compressor.

REFRIGERANT RECOVERY/RECYCLING

Refrigerant recovery/recycling equipment is used to remove refrigerant from vehicle's A/C system without polluting atmosphere. To remove and recycle refrigerant, connect the recovery/recycling system and follow instructions provided with the system.

The removed refrigerant is filtered, dried and stored in a tank within the recovery/recycling system until it is ready to be pumped back into the vehicle's A/C system. With refrigerant stored in the recovery/recycling system, A/C system can be opened without polluting atmosphere.

NOTE: Separate sets of hoses, gauges and refrigerant recovery/recycling equipment MUST be used for R-12 and R-134a based systems. DO NOT mix R-12 and R-134a refrigerants, as their refrigerant oils and desiccants are not compatible. On systems with R-134a refrigerant, use Polyalkylene Glycol (PAG) wax-free refrigerant oil.

1993 GENERAL SERVICING
General Diagnostic Procedures

Diagnosis is an important first step in A/C system servicing. To save time and effort, systems should be carefully checked to identify the causes of poor performance. By using the following diagnostic charts, defective components or system problems can be quickly located. To identify problems that are specific to one system, refer to the repair section of this manual. The charts in this section apply to all systems.

PREPARATION FOR TESTING

1) Attach Low and High pressure gauges.
2) Start engine and allow to warm up.
3) Set system to COOL and blower to HIGH.
4) Open car doors and hood.
5) Run engine at fast idle for 2-3 minutes.

Air Conditioning System Performance Check

PERFORM TESTS:	SHOULD BE:	IF:
Temperature Check		**Temperature Check Is**
• Switch to LOW blower.		
• Close doors.		Too warm – Check control lever operation, heater water valve, cooling system and gauge readings.
• Check outlet temperature.	35-45° F	
Visual Check		**Visual Check Shows:**
• Compressor	Quiet with no leaks	Noisy – Check belts, oil level, seals, gaskets, reed valves.
• Condenser	Free of obstructions	Blocked – Clean off. Plugged – Flush or replace.
• Receiver-Drier	Dry and warm to touch	Frosty – Check for restriction, replace desiccant.
• Sight Glass	Clear or few bubbles	Bubbly, foamy or streaks – Check gauge readings.
• High Side Lines	Dry and warm to touch	Frosty or very hot – Check for restriction or overcharge.
• Low Side Lines	Dry and cool to touch	Frosty or warm – Check for restriction, low charge or bad valve.
• Expansion Valve	Dry	Frosty – Check for moisture or restriction. Check sensing bulb.
• STV	Dry and cool to touch	Frosty or warm – Check gauge readings for valve malfunction.
• Evaporator	Dry and cold to touch	Freezing or warm – Check expansion valve, STV or thermoswitch.
Gauge Readings		**Gauge Readings are:**
• High Side Gauge	See Pressure Chart	Above or below normal – See A/C Diagnosis on next page.
• Low Side Gauge	See Pressure Chart	Above or below normal – See A/C Diagnosis on next page.

AMBIENT TEMPERATURE/PRESSURE (R-12)

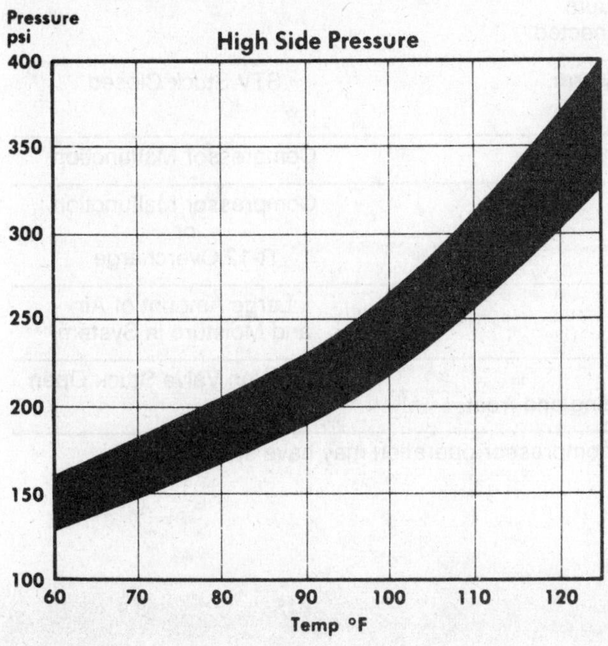
Pressure psi
High Side Pressure
400
350
300
250
200
150
100
60
70
80
90
100
110
120
Temp °F
103240

EVAPORATOR TEMPERATURE/PRESSURE (R-12)

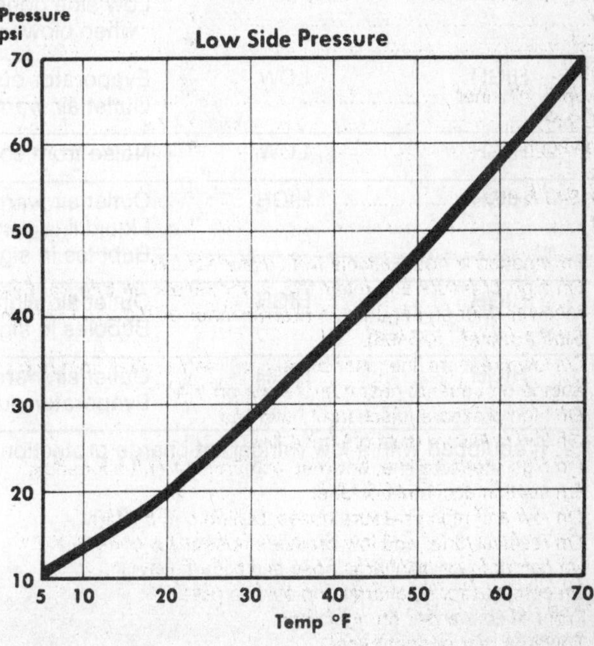
Pressure psi
Low Side Pressure
70
60
50
40
30
20
10
5
10
20
30
40
50
60
70
Temp °F
103241

1993 GENERAL SERVICING
General Diagnostic Procedures (Cont.)

Air Conditioning Diagnosis With Gauges
For Systems With Insufficient or No Cooling

Low Side Gauge	High Side Gauge	Other Symptoms [1]	Diagnosis
NORMAL	NORMAL	No or few bubbles in sight glass. High side gauge may go high. Low side gauge does not fluctuate with compressor on/off cycle.	Some Air and Moisture in System
NORMAL	NORMAL	Cools okay in morning but not during hot part of day. Bubbles in sight glass. Discharge air warm when low side gauge drops into vacuum.	Excessive Moisture in System
NORMAL	NORMAL	Thermostatic switch system only – compressor cycles off and on too rapidly.	Defective Thermostatic Switch
NORMAL to HIGH	NORMAL	Cycling clutch systems only – compressor doesn't turn on soon enough. Discharge air becomes warm as low side pressure rises.	Misadjusted Thermostatic Switch or Defective Pressure Sensing Switch
LOW	LOW	Bubbles in sight glass. Outlet air slightly cool.	Low R-12 Charge
LOW	LOW	Sight glass clear. Outlet air very warm.	Excessively Low R-12 Charge
LOW	LOW	Outlet air slightly cool. Sweating or frost at expansion valve.	Expansion Valve Stuck Closed Screen Plugged or Sensing Bulb Malfunction
LOW	LOW	Outlet air slightly cool. High side line cool to touch. Sweating or frost on high side.	Restriction on High Side
LOW	HIGH	Evaporator outlet pipe cold. Low side goes into vacuum when blower is disconnected.	STV Stuck Open
HIGH	LOW	Evaporator outlet pipe warm. Outlet air warm.	STV Stuck Closed
HIGH	LOW	Noise from compressor.	Compressor Malfunction
HIGH	HIGH	Outlet air warm. Liquid line very hot. Bubbles in sight glass.	Compressor Malfunction or R-12 Overcharge
HIGH	HIGH	Outlet air slightly cool. Bubbles in sight glass.	Large Amount of Air and Moisture in System
HIGH	HIGH	Outlet air warm. Evaporator outlet sweating and frost.	Expansion Valve Stuck Open

[1] – If equipped with a low refrigerant charge protection system, compressor operation may have stopped.

1993 GENERAL SERVICING
General Trouble Shooting

AIR CONDITIONING

CONDITION & POSSIBLE CAUSE	CONDITION & POSSIBLE CAUSE
Compressor Not Working • Compressor clutch circuit open. • Compressor clutch coil inoperative. • Poor clutch ground connection. • Fan belts loose. • Thermostatic switch inoperative. • Thermostatic switch not adjusted. • Ambient temperature switch open. • Superheat fuse blown. **Excessive Noise or Vibration** • Missing or loose mounting bolts. • Bad idler pulley bearings. • Fan belts not tightened correctly. • Compressor clutch contacting body. • Excessive system pressure. • Compressor oil level low.	**Excessive Noise or Vibration (Cont.)** • Damaged clutch bearings. • Damaged reed valves. • Damaged compressor. **Insufficient or No Cooling; Compressor Working** • Expansion valve inoperative. • Heater control valve stuck open. • Low system pressure. • Blocked condenser fins. • Blocked evaporator fins. • Vacuum system leak. • Vacuum motors inoperative. • Control cables improperly adjusted. • Restricted air inlet. • Mode doors binding. • Blower motor inoperative. • Temperature above system capacity.

HEATERS

CONDITION & POSSIBLE CAUSE	CONDITION & POSSIBLE CAUSE
Insufficient, Erratic, or No Heat • Low coolant level. • Incorrect thermostat. • Restricted coolant flow through heater core. • Heater hoses plugged. • Misadjusted control cable. • Sticking heater control valve. • Vacuum hose leaking. • Vacuum hose blocked. • Vacuum motors inoperative. • Blocked air inlet. • Inoperative heater blower motor. • Oil residue on heater core fins. • Dirt on heater core fins. **Too Much Heat** • Improperly adjusted cables. • Sticking heater control valve. • No vacuum to heater control valve. • Temperature door stuck open.	**Airflow Changes During Acceleration** • Vacuum system leak. • Bad check valve or reservoir. **Air From Defroster At All Times** • Vacuum system leak. • Improperly adjusted control cables. • Inoperative vacuum motor. **Blower Does Not Operate Correctly** • Blown fuse. • Blower motor windings open. • Resistors burned out. • Motor ground connection loose. • Wiring harness connections loose. • Blower motor switch inoperative. • Blower relay inoperative. • Fan binding or foreign object in housing. • Fan blades broken or bent.

1993 ACURA CONTENTS

GENERAL SERVICING

ALL MODELS

HEATER SYSTEMS

INTEGRA

MANUAL A/C-HEATER SYSTEMS

INTEGRA & LEGEND

MANUAL A/C-HEATER SYSTEMS (Cont.)

INTEGRA & LEGEND (Cont.)

VIGOR

1993 ACURA CONTENTS (Cont.)

MANUAL A/C-HEATER SYSTEMS (Cont.)

AUTOMATIC A/C-HEATER SYSTEMS

1993 HEATER SYSTEMS
Integra

DESCRIPTION

The heater system delivers fresh or recirculated air to the passenger compartment. Airflow passes through the heater unit and is warmed and distributed to selected passenger compartment outlets. The outlets are chosen by function control buttons or a lever. The temperature control knob regulates temperature of delivered air. The blower motor is controlled by turning the fan speed dial to any of 4 positions. *See Fig. 1.*

OPERATION

TEMPERATURE CONTROL DIAL

Turning the temperature control dial clockwise increases air temperature by mechanically opening the heater control valve and air mix mode door. *See Fig. 2*. On LS and GS models, the air mix door is electrically operated. Air passes through the heater core, is warmed, and distributed to selected passenger compartment outlets.

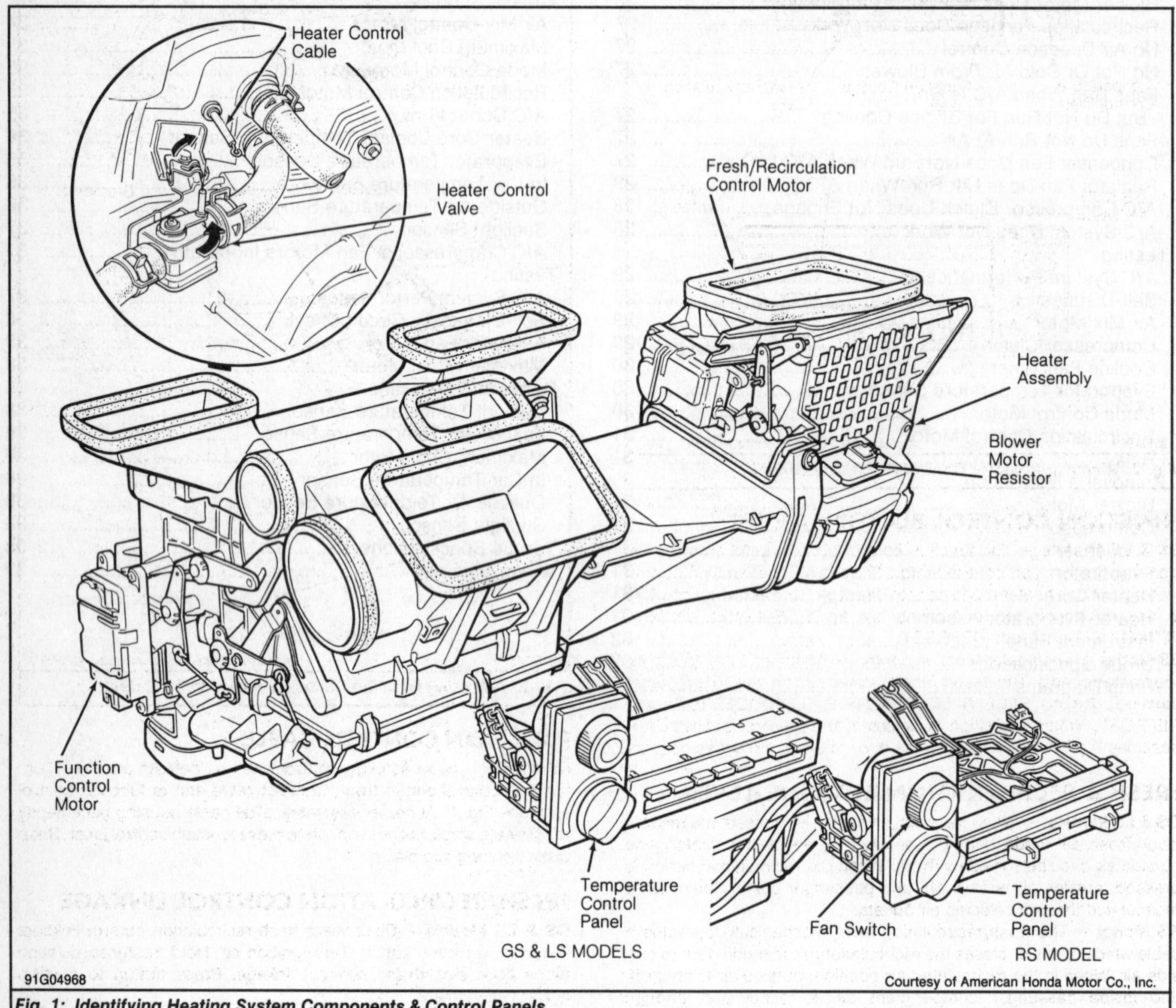
Heater Control
Cable
Heater Control
Valve
Fresh/Recirculation
Control Motor
Heater
Assembly
Blower
Motor
Resistor
Function
Control
Motor
Temperature
Control
Panel
GS & LS MODELS
Fan Switch
Temperature
Control
Panel
RS MODEL
91G04968
Courtesy of American Honda Motor Co., Inc.

Fig. 1: Identifying Heating System Components & Control Panels

1993 HEATER SYSTEMS
Integra (Cont.)

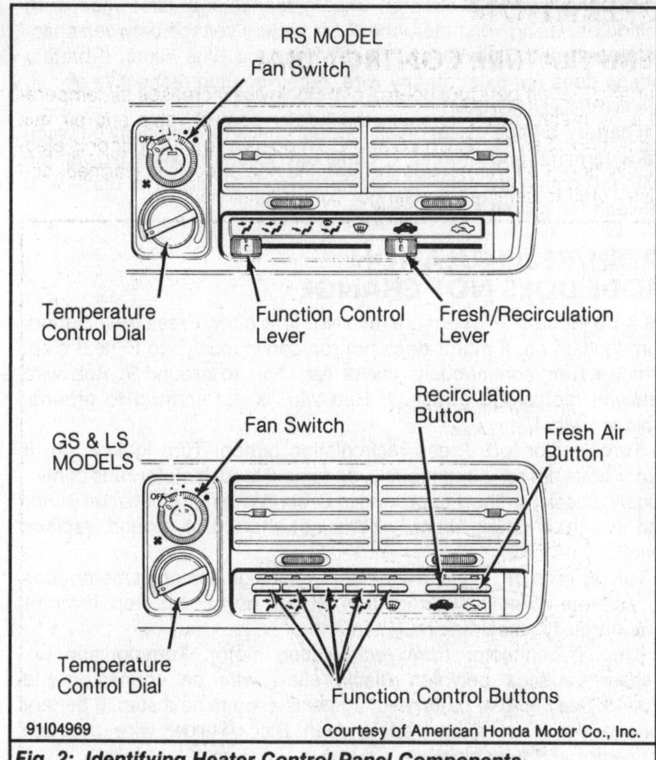
RS MODEL
Fan Switch
Temperature Control Dial
Function Control Lever
Fresh/Recirculation Lever
GS & LS MODELS
Fan Switch
Recirculation Button
Fresh Air Button
Temperature Control Dial
Function Control Buttons
91I04969
Courtesy of American Honda Motor Co., Inc.

Fig. 2: Identifying Heater Control Panel Components

FUNCTION CONTROL BUTTONS/LEVER

GS & LS Models – The function control buttons send an electrical signal to the function control motor. *See Fig. 2.* The function control motor positions heater mode door to direct air to selected outlets. The 5 heater function control buttons are FACE, BI-LEVEL, FLOOR, FLOOR/DEFROST, and DEFROST.

RS Model – The heater function control lever controls the flow of air to selected outlets. The heater function lever can be moved to 5 heater function positions: FACE, BI-LEVEL, FLOOR, FLOOR/DEFROST, and DEFROST. When a position is selected, the function control cable positions the function control mode door to direct airflow as desired.

FRESH & RECIRCULATION BUTTONS/LEVER

GS & LS Models – When the fresh air button is pressed, the recirculation/fresh air mode door is operated by an electric motor, and outside air circulates inside vehicle. When the recirculation button is pressed, outside air is shut off, and passenger compartment air is recirculated through selected air outlets.

RS Model – The fresh/recirculation lever mechanically operates a cable which opens or closes the recirculation/fresh mode door to outside air. When in the recirculated air position, outside air is shut off, and inside passenger compartment air is recirculated through selected air outlets.

ADJUSTMENTS

AIR MIX CABLE

Set temperature control dial to cold. Move air mix door shaft arm toward front of vehicle. Connect end of air mix cable to arm. Gently slide cable outer housing back enough to take up slack in cable, but not enough to move arm. Snap cable housing into clamp. Adjust heater valve cable. See HEATER VALVE CABLE.

HEATER VALVE CABLE

Set temperature control dial to cold. Connect end of heater valve cable to heater valve control arm. *See Fig. 3.* At heater control valve, gently slide cable housing back enough to eliminate slack, but not enough to move temperature control dial. Snap cable housing into clamp.

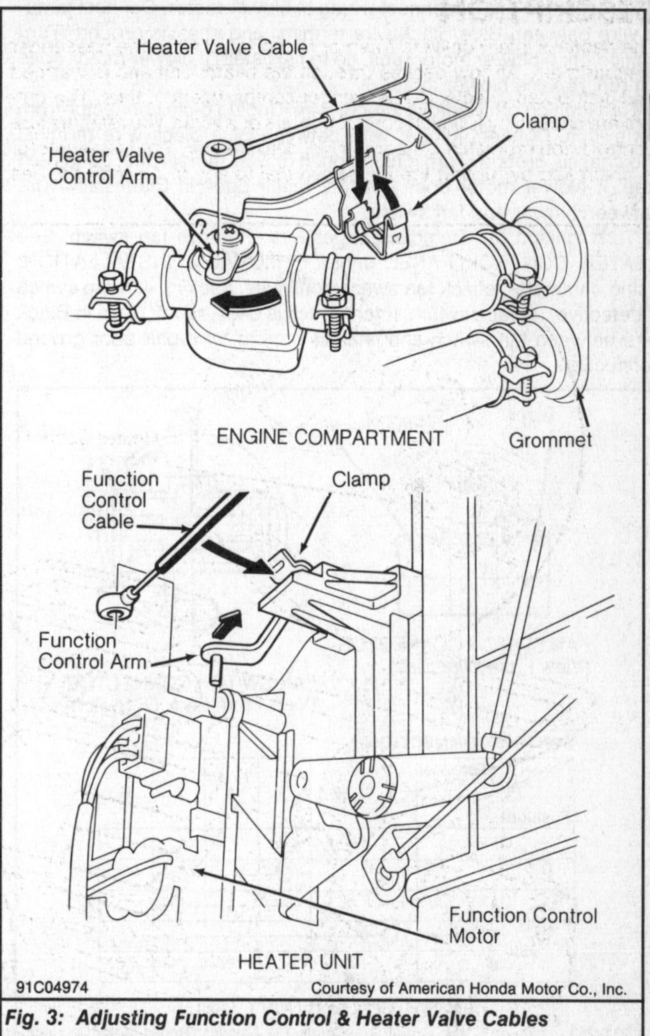
Heater Valve Cable
Clamp
Heater Valve Control Arm
ENGINE COMPARTMENT
Grommet
Function Control Cable
Clamp
Function Control Arm
Function Control Motor
HEATER UNIT
91C04974
Courtesy of American Honda Motor Co., Inc.

Fig. 3: Adjusting Function Control & Heater Valve Cables

FUNCTION CONTROL CABLE

RS Model – Slide function control lever to defrost position. Turn function control arm to front. Connect cable end to function control arm. *See Fig. 3.* At heater assembly, slide cable housing back gently to eliminate slack, but not enough to move function control lever. Snap cable housing into clamp

FRESH/RECIRCULATION CONTROL LINKAGE

GS & LS Models – Disconnect fresh/recirculation control linkage. Press recirculation button. Turn ignition on. Hold fresh/recirculation mode door closed and connect linkage. Press button to confirm correct adjustment.

FRESH/RECIRCULATION CONTROL MOTOR

GS & LS Models – If motor has been replaced or if linkage is binding, check motor positioning. Attach motor and all linkage. Apply battery voltage and observe door movement. If linkage binds or is pulled too far, loosen motor mounting screws and reposition motor.

TROUBLE SHOOTING

BLOWER MOTOR DOES NOT RUN

1) If heater blower fuse No. 25 (40-amp) is okay, unplug connector at blower motor. Turn ignition on. Measure voltage between Blue/White wire terminal on harness connector and chassis ground. If battery voltage exists, go to next step. If battery voltage does not exist, repair open in Blue/White wire between blower and ignition switch. See WIRING DIAGRAM.

1993 HEATER SYSTEMS
Integra (Cont.)

2) Turn ignition off. Reconnect wiring to blower motor. Connect jumper wire between Blue/Black wire terminal and chassis ground. Turn ignition on. If blower motor runs, go to next step. If blower motor does not run, replace blower motor.

3) Turn ignition off. Remove jumper wire. Unplug 6-pin connector from fan switch. Connect jumper wire between Blue/Black wire terminal and chassis ground. Turn ignition on. If blower motor runs, go to next step. If blower motor does not run, repair open in Blue/Black wire between blower and fan switch.

4) Turn ignition off. Remove jumper wire. Remove fan switch. See HEATER CONTROL PANEL under REMOVAL & INSTALLATION. Using ohmmeter, check fan switch continuity. *See Fig. 4*. If fan switch is defective, replace switch. If fan switch is okay, repair open in Black wire between fan switch and chassis ground, or repair poor ground connection.

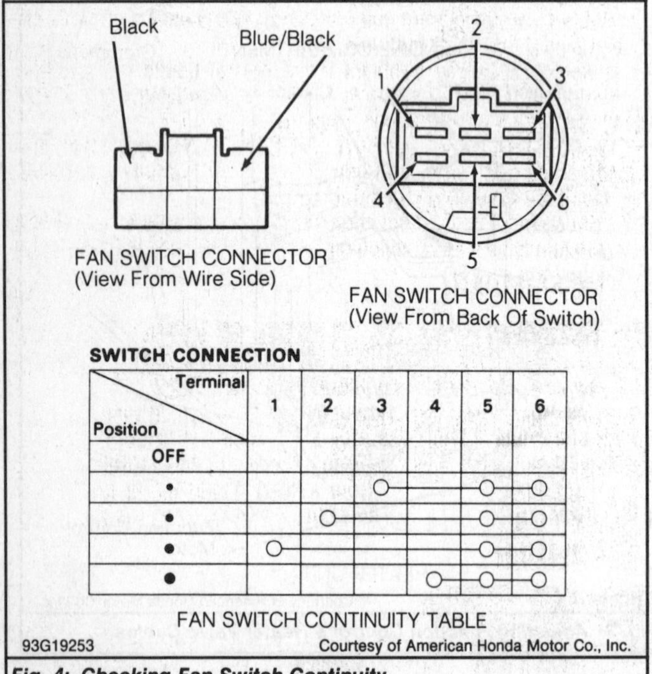
Black
Blue/Black
1
2
3
4
5
6
FAN SWITCH CONNECTOR
(View From Wire Side)
FAN SWITCH CONNECTOR
(View From Back Of Switch)
SWITCH CONNECTION

Position \ Terminal	1	2	3	4	5	6
OFF						
•			O		O	O
•		O			O	O
•	O				O	O
•				O	O	O

FAN SWITCH CONTINUITY TABLE

93G19253 Courtesy of American Honda Motor Co., Inc.

Fig. 4: Checking Fan Switch Continuity

BLOWER MOTOR RUNS AT ONE SPEED ONLY

1) Remove glove box. Unplug connector at blower motor resistor. Using ohmmeter, check for continuity between terminals No. 2 and 4. *See Fig. 5*. If continuity exists, go to next step. If continuity does not exist, replace resistor.

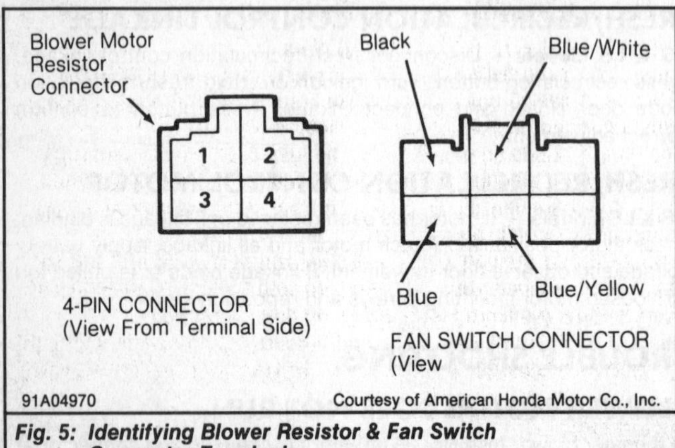
Blower Motor
Resistor
Connector
1
2
3
4
4-PIN CONNECTOR
(View From Terminal Side)
Black
Blue/White
Blue
Blue/Yellow
FAN SWITCH CONNECTOR
(View

91A04970 Courtesy of American Honda Motor Co., Inc.

Fig. 5: Identifying Blower Resistor & Fan Switch Connector Terminals

2) Reconnect wiring to resistor. Unplug connector at fan switch. Turn ignition on. Using voltmeter, check for battery voltage between chassis ground and Blue/Yellow, Blue/White, and Blue wires. If battery voltage does not exist on any wire, repair open in respective circuit. See WIRING DIAGRAM.

3) If battery voltage exists on all 3 wires, check for continuity between Black terminal and ground. If continuity exists, replace blower fan switch. If continuity does not exist, repair open circuit in Black wire between fan switch and chassis.

FRESH/RECIRCULATION MODE DOES NOT CHANGE

GS & LS Models – 1) Ensure fuse No. 17 is okay. Press fresh button. Turn ignition on. If motor does not run continuously, go to next step. If motor runs continuously, check for short to ground in Red wire between motor and switch. If Red wire is not shorted to ground, replace switch.

2) Turn ignition off. Press recirculation button. Turn ignition on. If motor does not run continuously, go to next step. If motor runs continuously, check for short to ground in Green/White wire between motor and switch. If Green/White wire is not shorted to ground, replace switch.

3) Turn ignition off. Press fresh button. Turn ignition on. If motor does not operate normally, turn ignition off and go to next step. If motor runs normally, check recirculation door.

4) Unplug connector from recirculation motor. Turn ignition on. Measure voltage between Black/Yellow wire on connector and ground. *See Fig. 6*. If battery voltage exists, go to next step. If battery voltage does not exist, repair open Black/Yellow wire between connector and fuse block.

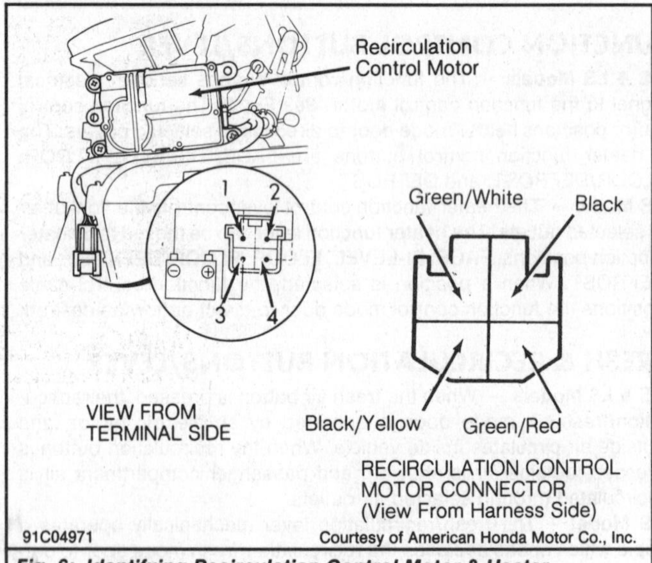
Recirculation
Control Motor
1
2
3
4
Green/White
Black
VIEW FROM
TERMINAL SIDE
Black/Yellow
Green/Red
RECIRCULATION CONTROL
MOTOR CONNECTOR
(View From Harness Side)

91C04971 Courtesy of American Honda Motor Co., Inc.

Fig. 6: Identifying Recirculation Control Motor & Heater Control Connector Terminals

5) Turn ignition off. Check for continuity between Black wire on terminal and ground. If continuity exists, go to next step. If no continuity exists, repair Black wire between connector and ground.

6) Press fresh button. Check for continuity between Green/White wire on terminal and ground. If continuity exists, go to next step. If no continuity exists, repair Green/White wire between connector and control panel.

7) Press recirculation button. Check for continuity between Green/Red wire on terminal and ground. If continuity exists, replace recirculation control motor. If no continuity exists, repair Green/Red wire between connector and control panel. If Green/Red wire is okay, inspect control panel for possible damage, and repair or replace as required.

8) Check for continuity between chassis ground and Blue/White, Green/White, Yellow, Yellow/Red and Yellow/Blue wires. If continuity does not exist, go to next step. If continuity exists, repair short to ground in affected wire(s).

NOTE: A short to ground in any wire will prevent function control motor from changing positions.

9) Turn ignition on. Check for voltage between chassis ground and Blue/White, Green/White, Yellow, Yellow/Red, and Yellow/Blue wires. If voltage does not exist, go to next step. If voltage exists, repair short to power in affected wire(s). Inspect heater control panel for possible damage, and repair or replace as required.
10) Check for continuity between Black wire and ground. If continuity exists, replace heater control panel. If continuity does not exist, repair open in Black wire between heater control panel and chassis ground.

FUNCTION CONTROL MOTOR DOES NOT RUN

GS & LS Models - 1) Check fuse No. 17 (7.5-amp). If fuse is okay, disconnect 8-pin connector from function control motor.
2) Turn ignition on. Measure voltage between Black/Yellow terminal and chassis ground. If battery voltage exists, go to next step. If battery voltage does not exist, repair open in Black/Yellow wire between function control motor and fuse block. See WIRING DIAGRAM.
3) Turn ignition off. Check for continuity between Black wire and ground. If continuity exists, go to next step. If continuity does not exist, repair open between Black wire and chassis ground.
4) Inspect function control motor. See FUNCTION CONTROL MOTOR under TESTING. If function control motor is defective, replace motor. If function control motor is okay, go to next step.
5) Unplug 14-pin connector from heater control panel. Check continuity of Blue/White, Green/White, Yellow, Yellow/Red, and Yellow/Blue wires between 14-pin and 8-pin connectors. *See Fig. 7.* If continuity exists, go to next step. If continuity does not exist, repair open circuit in affected wire(s).

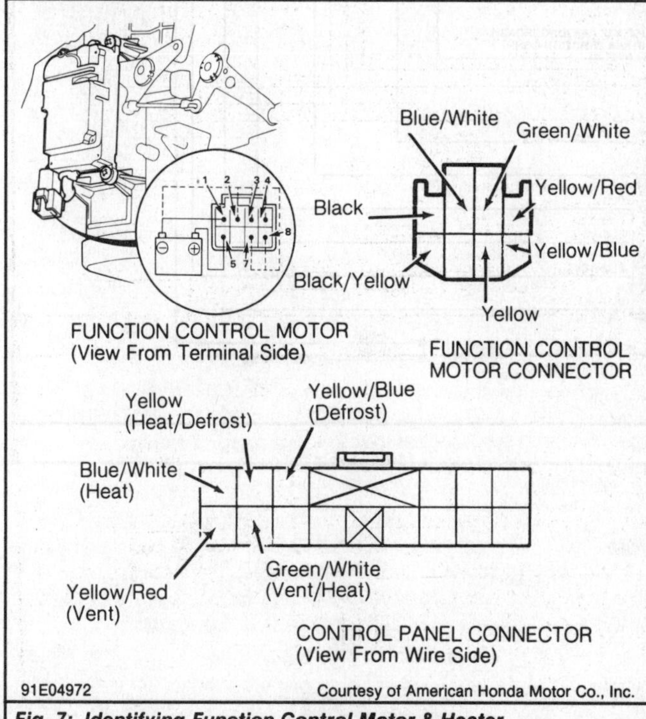
Blue/White
Green/White
Yellow/Red
Black
Yellow/Blue
Black/Yellow
Yellow
FUNCTION CONTROL MOTOR
(View From Terminal Side)
FUNCTION CONTROL
MOTOR CONNECTOR
Yellow
(Heat/Defrost)
Yellow/Blue
(Defrost)
Blue/White
(Heat)
Green/White
(Vent/Heat)
Yellow/Red
(Vent)
CONTROL PANEL CONNECTOR
(View From Wire Side)
91E04972
Courtesy of American Honda Motor Co., Inc.

Fig. 7: Identifying Function Control Motor & Heater Control Connector Terminals

6) Using ohmmeter, check continuity between chassis ground and Blue/White, Green/White, Yellow, Yellow/Red and Yellow/Blue wires. If continuity does not exist, go to next step. If continuity exists, repair short to ground in affected wire(s).

NOTE: A short to ground in any wire will prevent function control motor from changing positions.

7) Turn ignition on. Check for voltage between chassis ground and Blue/White, Green/White, Yellow, Yellow/Red and Yellow/Blue wires. If voltage does not exist, go to next step. If voltage exists, repair short to power in affected wire(s). Inspect heater control panel for possible damage, and repair or replace as required.
8) Using ohmmeter, check for continuity between Black wire and ground. If continuity exists, replace heater control panel. If continuity does not exist, repair open in Black wire between heater control panel and chassis ground.

TESTING

RECIRCULATION CONTROL MOTOR

GS & LS Models - 1) Unplug connector from recirculation control motor. Connect battery voltage to terminal No. 3 on recirculation control motor. *See Fig. 6.* Ground terminal No. 2. Using jumper wire, connect terminals No. 1 and 2 together. With fresh/recirculation door in recirculated position, motor should rotate 1/2 turn and stop.
2) Connect terminals No. 2 and 4 together. With fresh/recirculation door in fresh position, motor should rotate 1/2 turn and stop. If motor operation is not as specified, replace recirculation control motor.

FUNCTION CONTROL MOTOR

Unplug connector from function control motor. Connect battery voltage to terminal No. 5 of motor. Ground motor terminal No. 1. *See Fig. 7.* Using jumper wire, connect terminal No. 1 in turn to terminals No. 2, 3, 4, 7, and 8. Motor should run each time connection is made. If motor does not perform as specified, replace function control motor.

REMOVAL & INSTALLATION

BLOWER MOTOR

Removal & Installation - Remove passenger-side lower dashboard panel. Remove glove box. Remove right kick panel. Remove motorized shoulder belt control unit. Remove knee bolster. Remove heater duct. Unplug connector from blower motor. Remove 3 mounting bolts and blower unit. To install, reverse removal procedure. Check for air leaks.

HEATER CONTROL PANEL

Removal & Installation - Remove instrument cluster trim panel. Remove left and right lower dashboard panels. Remove front console and radio. Disconnect control cables/linkage. Remove retaining screws, pull out control panel, and disconnect harness connector. Remove heater control panel. To install, reverse removal procedure.

HEATER ASSEMBLY

Removal - 1) Disconnect negative battery cable. Drain radiator coolant. Place drip pan under heater hoses. Disconnect heater hoses at firewall. Disconnect heater valve cable from heater valve. Remove heater mounting nut on engine side of firewall.
2) Slide seats back fully. Remove left and right lower instrument panel covers. Remove front console. Remove knee bolster. Unplug wiring from instrument panel connectors and fuse block. Lower steering column. Disconnect ground cable at right side of steering column.
3) Remove radio/cassette player. Unplug transmission range and shift lock connectors (A/T) models. On all models, remove clock. Remove side defroster trim. Remove instrument panel mounting bolts. Lift and remove instrument panel.
4) Remove heater duct. Disconnect air mix cable from heater. Remove heater mounting bolts. On GS and LS models, unplug connector from function control motor. On all models, remove heater assembly.

1993 HEATER SYSTEMS
Integra (Cont.)

Installation – To install, reverse removal procedure. Ensure electrical harness and heater control cables are not pinched when replacing instrument panel. Apply sealant to grommets. DO NOT interchange inlet and outlet hoses. Secure hose clamps. Loosen radiator bleed bolt. Refill radiator and reservoir tank with coolant. Tighten bleed bolt after trapped air has escaped. Connect cables and adjust as necessary. See AIR MIX CABLE, HEATER VALVE CABLE and FUNCTION CONTROL CABLE under ADJUSTMENTS.

TORQUE SPECIFICATIONS

TORQUE SPECIFICATIONS

Application	Ft. Lbs. (N.m)
Heater Lower Mounting Nut	16 (22)
	INCH Lbs. (N.m)
Blower Motor Bolt	88 (10)
Heater Bolt	88 (10)
Instrument Panel Bolt	88 (10)

WIRING DIAGRAM

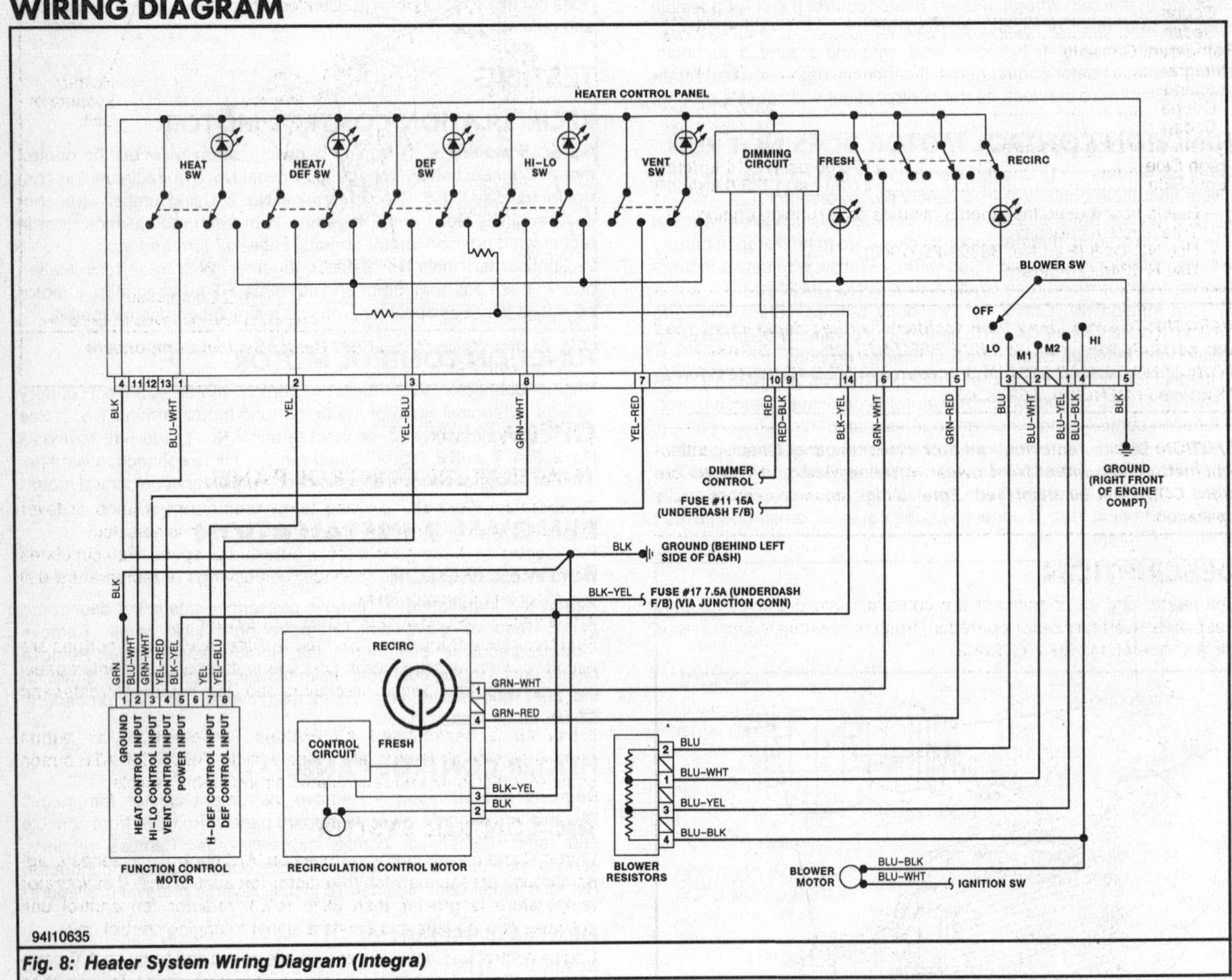
HEATER CONTROL PANEL
HEAT SW
HEAT/ DEF SW
DEF SW
HI-LO SW
VENT SW
DIMMING CIRCUIT
FRESH
RECIRC
BLOWER SW
OFF
LO
M1
M2
HI
BLK
BLU-WHT
YEL
YEL-BLU
GRN-WHT
YEL-RED
RED
RED-BLK
BLK-YEL
GRN-WHT
GRN-RED
BLU
BLU-WHT
BLU-YEL
BLU-BLK
BLK
GROUND (RIGHT FRONT OF ENGINE COMPT)
DIMMER CONTROL
FUSE #11 15A (UNDERDASH F/B)
GROUND (BEHIND LEFT SIDE OF DASH)
BLK-YEL
FUSE #17 7.5A (UNDERDASH F/B) (VIA JUNCTION CONN)
GRN
BLU-WHT
GRN-WHT
YEL-RED
BLK-YEL
YEL
YEL-BLU
GROUND
HEAT CONTROL INPUT
HI-LO CONTROL INPUT
VENT CONTROL INPUT
POWER INPUT
H-DEF CONTROL INPUT
DEF CONTROL INPUT
FUNCTION CONTROL MOTOR
RECIRC
CONTROL CIRCUIT
FRESH
GRN-WHT
GRN-RED
BLK-YEL
BLK
RECIRCULATION CONTROL MOTOR
BLU
BLU-WHT
BLU-YEL
BLU-BLK
BLOWER RESISTORS
BLOWER MOTOR
BLU-BLK
BLU-WHT
IGNITION SW
94I10635

Fig. 8: Heater System Wiring Diagram (Integra)

1993 MANUAL A/C-HEATER SYSTEMS
Integra & Legend

SPECIFICATIONS

Compressor Type	Nippondenso 10-Cyl.
Compressor Belt Deflection	
Integra	
New Belt [1]	3/16-1/4" (4.5-6.5 mm)
Used Belt	9/32-11/32" (7.0-9.0 mm)
Legend	
New Belt [1]	13/64-1/4" (5.0-6.5 mm)
Used Belt	5/16-25/64" (8.0-10.0 mm)
Compressor Oil Capacity	
Integra	2.0-3.4 ozs.
Legend	
Coupe	[2] 6.0 ozs.
Sedan	[3] 4.7-5.2 ozs.
Refrigerant Capacity	
Integra	32-34 ozs.
Legend	
Coupe	24.7-26.5 ozs.
Sedan	[4] 24.7-26.5 ozs.
System Operating Pressures	
High Side	170-200 psi (12-14 kg/cm²)
Low Side	21-28 psi (1.5-2.0 kg/cm²)

[1] – Belt is new if used less than 5 minutes on a running engine.
[2] – Total system capacity.
[3] – Use ND-Oil 8 (Part No. 38899-PR7-003).
[4] – Use R-134a refrigerant.

WARNING: To avoid injury from accidental air bag deployment, read and carefully follow all SERVICE PRECAUTIONS and DISABLING & ACTIVATING AIR BAG SYSTEM procedures in AIR BAG SYSTEM SAFETY article in GENERAL SERVICING.

CAUTION: Before removing radio or disconnecting battery, obtain anti-theft code number from owner. After servicing, turn radio on. Word CODE will be displayed. Enter 5-digit code to restore radio operation.

DESCRIPTION

The heater and air conditioner are combined into one system. Only fresh air is used for heater operation; fresh or recirculated air is used for A/C operation. *See Fig. 1 or 2.*

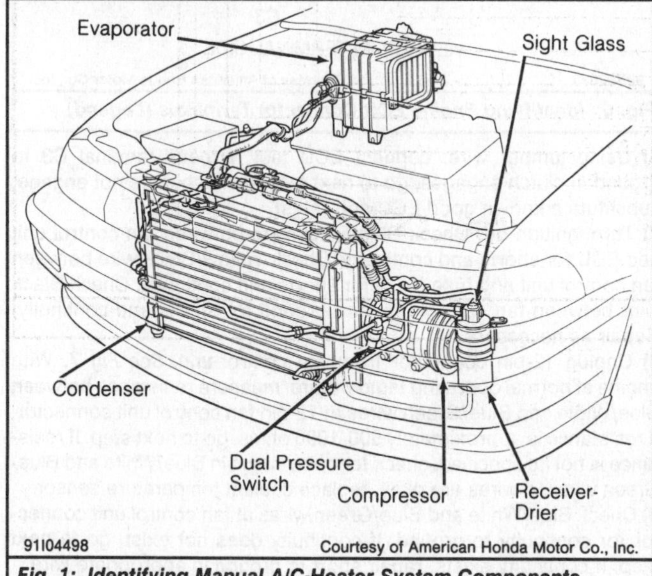
Evaporator
Sight Glass
Condenser
Dual Pressure Switch
Compressor
Receiver-Drier
91I04498
Courtesy of American Honda Motor Co., Inc.

Fig. 1: Identifying Manual A/C-Heater System Components (Integra)

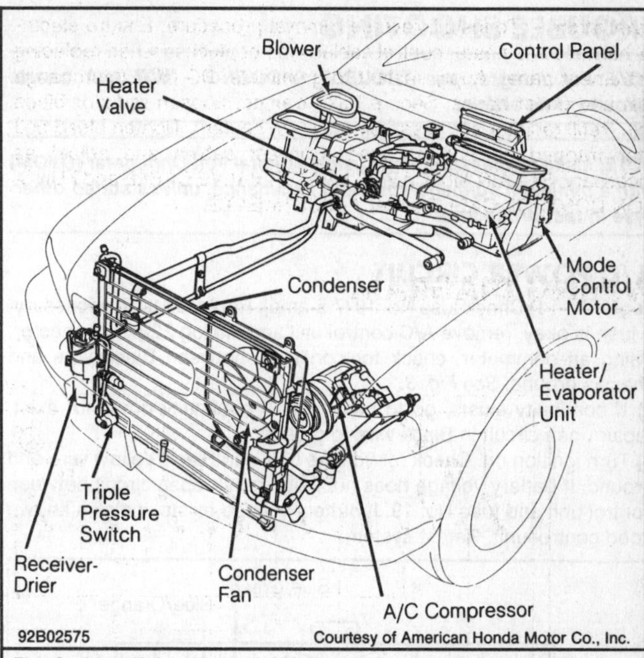
Blower
Control Panel
Heater Valve
Condenser
Mode Control Motor
Heater/ Evaporator Unit
Triple Pressure Switch
Receiver-Drier
Condenser Fan
A/C Compressor
92B02575
Courtesy of American Honda Motor Co., Inc.

Fig. 2: Identifying Manual A/C-Heater System Components (Legend)

OPERATION

TEMPERATURE CONTROL PANEL

Temperature Control – Moving temperature control knob or lever makes air warmer when the appropriate function is selected.

Fan Control – Moving fan control adjusts fan speed. Fan circulates warm, cool, or outside air depending on settings of temperature dial and function buttons or lever.

A/C Switch – A/C switch activates A/C system.

Function/Mode Buttons – On Integra, either a lever or 5 buttons are used to control function motor. On Legend, temperature control panel has 5 mode buttons which direct air to and from heater, defroster and vents.

Fresh Air & Recirculated Air Buttons – The FRESH air button permits outside air to circulate inside vehicle. RECIRCULATE button shuts off outside air and recirculates air inside the vehicle.

A/C CONTROL SYSTEM

With A/C and blower motor switches on, A/C control unit sends a signal through pressure switch to radiator fan control unit. If evaporator temperature is greater than 39°F (4°C), radiator fan control unit activates cooling fans and sends a signal to engine control unit.

Engine control unit increases engine idle speed and turns on A/C compressor. When evaporator sensor temperature drops to less than 37°F (3°C), sensor signals engine control unit to turn off cooling fans and compressor. If refrigerant pressure becomes too high or too low, pressure switch signals cooling fan control unit, which inhibits A/C system operation.

When refrigerant pressure is too high because of heavy use in high temperatures, pressure switch is activated to increase cooling fan speed. A/C system is shut off if coolant temperature reaches 228°F (109°C).

1993 MANUAL A/C-HEATER SYSTEMS
Integra & Legend (Cont.)

TROUBLE SHOOTING

NOTE: For Integra, see TROUBLE SHOOTING – INTEGRA charts following this article.

NOTE: Make all measurements using a Digital Volt-Ohmmeter (DVOM) with a minimum 10-megohms input impedance, unless stated otherwise in test procedure.

A/C POWER CIRCUIT

Legend – 1) Check fuse No. 19 (7.5-amp). Replace fuse if necessary. If fuse is okay, remove A/C control unit and unplug 22-pin connector. Using an ohmmeter, check for continuity between Black wire and chassis ground. *See Fig. 3*.

2) If continuity exists, go to next step. If continuity does not exist, repair open circuit in Black wire to ground.

3) Turn ignition on. Check for voltage between Black/Yellow wire and ground. If battery voltage does not exist, repair open circuit between control unit and fuse No. 19. If battery voltage exists, install a known good control unit. Retest system.

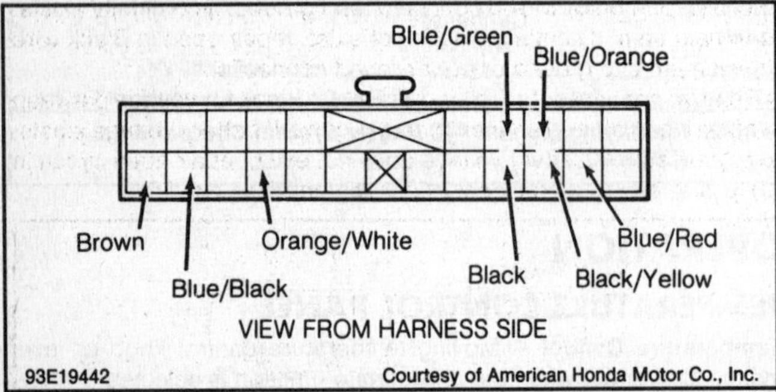
Blue/Green
Blue/Orange
Brown
Orange/White
Blue/Red
Black
Black/Yellow
Blue/Black
VIEW FROM HARNESS SIDE
93E19442
Courtesy of American Honda Motor Co., Inc.

Fig. 3: Identifying A/C Control Unit Connector Terminals (Legend)

A/C COMPRESSOR CLUTCH INOPERATIVE

Legend – 1) Remove A/C compressor clutch relay from underhood relay box, located in right rear corner of the engine compartment. *See Fig. 4*. Turn ignition on. Check for voltage between ground and terminals No. 2 and 3. If battery voltage exists, go to next step. If battery voltage does not exist, repair open circuit between relay and fuse No. 3 (15-amp).

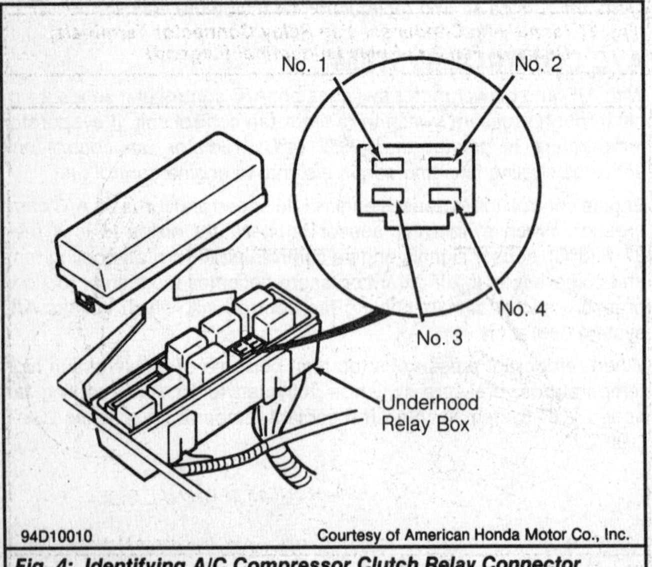
No. 1
No. 2
No. 4
No. 3
Underhood
Relay Box
94D10010
Courtesy of American Honda Motor Co., Inc.

Fig. 4: Identifying A/C Compressor Clutch Relay Connector Terminals (Legend)

2) Using a jumper wire, connect terminals No. 3 and 4. If compressor clutch engages, go to next step. If clutch does not engage, repair open circuit in Red wire between relay and clutch. If wire is okay, check clutch air gap and clutch. See COMPRESSOR CLUTCH under TESTING. Repair as necessary.

3) Connect ohmmeter leads to terminals "C" and "D" of A/C compressor clutch relay. *See Fig. 5*. If continuity does not exist, replace relay. If continuity exists, go to next step.

4) Connect ohmmeter leads to relay terminals "A" and "B". Connect relay terminal "C" to battery voltage. Connect relay terminal "D" to ground. Relay should click and ohmmeter should indicate continuity. If relay functions as specified, go to next step. If relay does not function as specified, replace relay.

5) Turn ignition off. Unplug connectors from Electronic Control Unit (ECU). Connect ECU Test Harness (07AJ-PT3010A). Turn ignition on. Turn A/C off. Measure voltage between terminal A15 of ECU test harness and ground. *See Fig. 6*. If battery voltage exists, go to next step. If battery voltage does not exist, repair open circuit in Red/Blue wire between clutch relay and ECU.

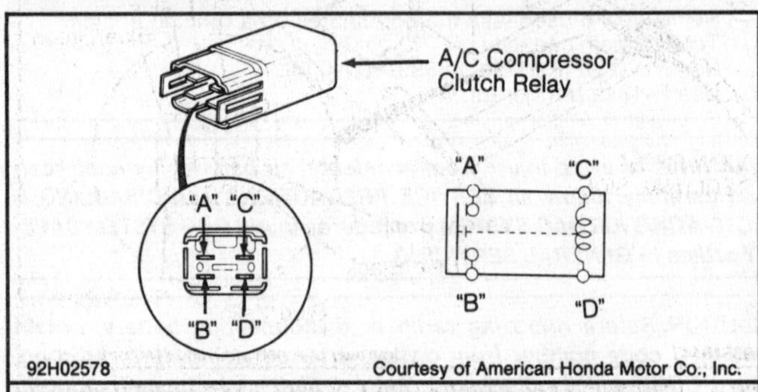
A/C Compressor
Clutch Relay
"A"
"C"
"A" "C"
"B" "D"
"B"
"D"
92H02578
Courtesy of American Honda Motor Co., Inc.

Fig. 5: Identifying Compressor Clutch Relay Terminals; Blower Motor & Fan Relays Are Similar (Legend)

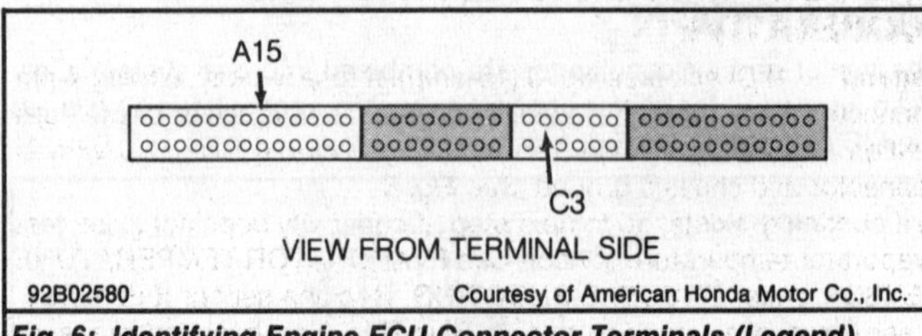
A15
C3
VIEW FROM TERMINAL SIDE
92B02580
Courtesy of American Honda Motor Co., Inc.

Fig. 6: Identifying Engine ECU Connector Terminals (Legend)

6) Using jumper wire, connect ECU test harness terminal C3 to ground. If clutch engages, go to next step. If clutch does not engage, substitute a known good ECU and retest.

7) Turn ignition off. Check Blue/Black wire between fan control unit and ECU for shorts and continuity. Check Yellow/Black wire between fan control unit and fuse No. 3 for shorts and continuity. Check Black wire between fan control unit and ground for shorts and continuity. Repair as necessary.

8) Unplug 12-pin connector from fan control unit. *See Fig 7*. With engine at normal operating temperature, measure resistance between Blue/White and Blue/Green wires at 12-pin fan control unit connector. If resistance is approximately 500-1000 ohms, go to next step. If resistance is not as specified, check for open circuit in Blue/White and Blue/Green wires. If wires are okay, replace coolant temperature sensor.

9) Check Blue/White and Blue/Green wires at fan control unit connector for continuity to ground. If continuity does not exist, go to next step. If continuity exists, repair short to ground in appropriate wire.

10) Reconnect wiring to fan control unit and coolant temperature sensor. Unplug connector from pressure switch. Turn ignition on. Check for battery voltage at Light Blue wire at pressure switch connector. If battery voltage exists, go to next step. If battery voltage does not exist, repair open circuit in Light Blue wire between pressure switch and fan control unit. If wire is okay, substitute a known good fan control unit.

11) Turn ignition off. Check for continuity between terminals No. 1 and 2 on pressure switch (Blue/Red and Light Blue wires on mating connector). If continuity exists, go to next step. If continuity does not exist, check A/C system pressure. If pressure is okay, replace pressure switch. If pressure is not okay, perform leak test and repair as necessary.

12) Reconnect wiring to pressure switch. Unplug 22-pin connector from A/C control unit. Turn ignition on. Check for battery voltage at Blue/Red wire on control unit harness connector. If battery voltage exists, replace control unit. If battery voltage does not exist, repair open circuit in Blue/Red wire between control unit and pressure switch.

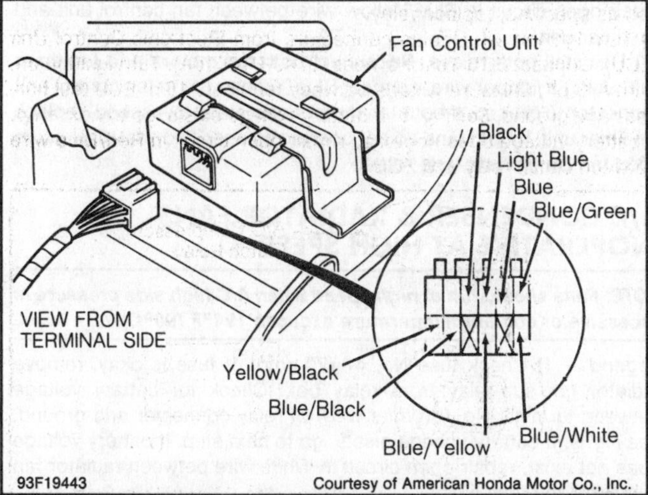
Fan Control Unit
Black
Light Blue
Blue
Blue/Green
VIEW FROM TERMINAL SIDE
Yellow/Black
Blue/Black
Blue/Yellow
Blue/White
93F19443
Courtesy of American Honda Motor Co., Inc.

Fig. 7: Identifying Fan Control Unit Connector Terminals (Legend)

A/C COMPRESSOR & FAN MOTORS INOPERATIVE

Legend - 1) Check fuse No. 3 (15-amp). If fuse is okay, unplug 4-pin connector from pressure switch, located near receiver-drier. Turn ignition and A/C on. Check for continuity between Blue/Red wire in connector and chassis ground. *See Fig. 8.*

2) If continuity exists, go to next step. If continuity does not exist, test evaporator temperature sensor. See EVAPORATOR TEMPERATURE SENSOR under TROUBLE SHOOTING. Replace sensor if defective. If sensor is okay, repair open in Blue/Red wire between pressure switch and A/C control unit. If wire is okay, install a known good control unit and retest.

3) Turn ignition off. Check for continuity between terminals No. 1 (Blue/Red wire) and No. 2 (Black wire) of pressure switch. If continuity exists, go to next step. If continuity does not exist, check A/C system pressure. If pressure is okay, replace switch. If pressure is low, check system for leaks. Repair as required.

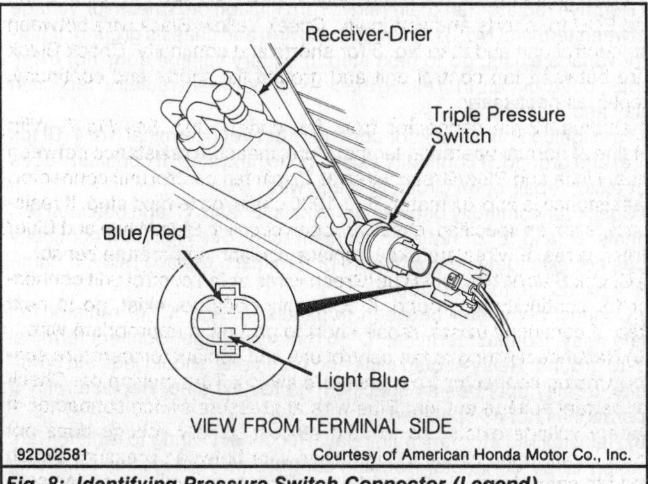
Receiver-Drier
Triple Pressure Switch
Blue/Red
Light Blue
VIEW FROM TERMINAL SIDE
92D02581
Courtesy of American Honda Motor Co., Inc.

Fig. 8: Identifying Pressure Switch Connector (Legend)

4) Unplug 12-pin connector from fan control unit. Check for continuity between Black wire in connector and chassis ground. *See Fig. 7.* If continuity exists, go to next step. If continuity does not exist, repair open circuit in Black wire.

5) Turn ignition on. Check for voltage between Yellow/Black wire in 12-pin connector and chassis ground. If battery voltage exists, go to next step. If battery voltage does not exist, repair open circuit in Yellow/Black wire between fuse No. 3 and fan control unit.

6) Turn ignition off. Using a jumper wire, connect Light Blue wire in pressure switch connector to ground. Check for continuity between Light Blue wire in 12-pin connector and ground. If continuity does not exist, repair open circuit between pressure switch and fan control unit. If continuity exists, install a known good fan control unit, and retest.

A/C CONDENSER FAN & RADIATOR COOLING FAN INOPERATIVE

Legend - 1) Check fuses No. 15 (7.5-amp) and No. 50 (20-amp). If fuses are okay, unplug radiator fan 2-pin connector. Check for continuity between Black wire in connector and ground. If continuity exists, go to next step. If continuity does not exist, repair open in Black wire between fan and ground or poor ground connection.

2) Remove condenser fan relay. *See Fig. 9.* Check for voltage between terminal No. 4 of relay connector and ground. If battery voltage exists, go to next step. If battery voltage does not exist, repair open circuit in White wire between condenser fan relay and fuse No. 50.

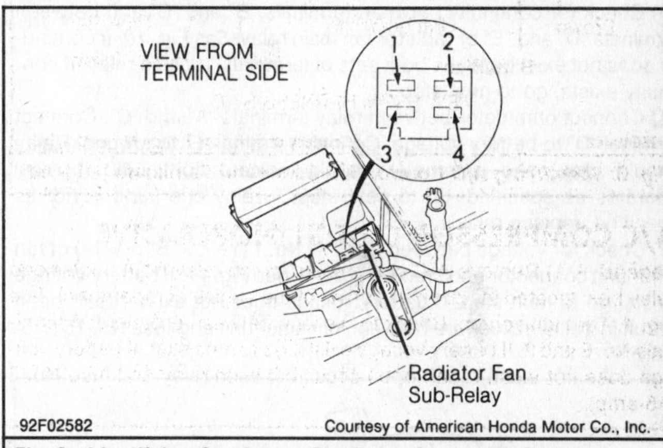
VIEW FROM TERMINAL SIDE
1
2
3
4
Radiator Fan Sub-Relay
92F02582
Courtesy of American Honda Motor Co., Inc.

Fig. 9: Identifying Condenser Fan Relay Connector Terminals; Radiator Fan Sub-Relay Is Identical (Legend)

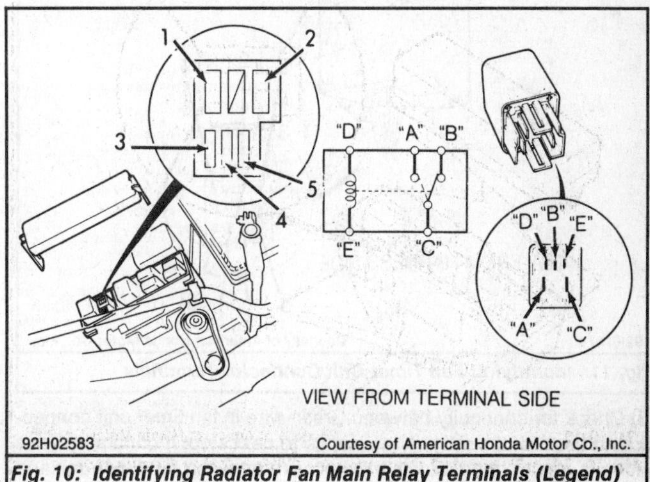
1
2
3
4
5
"D"
"A"
"B"
"E"
"C"
VIEW FROM TERMINAL SIDE
92H02583
Courtesy of American Honda Motor Co., Inc.

Fig. 10: Identifying Radiator Fan Main Relay Terminals (Legend)

1993 MANUAL A/C-HEATER SYSTEMS
Integra & Legend (Cont.)

3) Unplug 2-pin connector at condenser fan. Connect battery voltage to Blue wire in fan connector. Connect Black wire to ground. If fan operates, go to next step. If fan does not operate, replace condenser fan motor.
4) Remove radiator fan main relay. *See Fig. 10.* Check for continuity between terminal No. 4 (White wire) of relay connector and radiator fan. If continuity exists, go to next step. If continuity does not exist, repair open in White wire between relay and fan motor.
5) Unplug 2-pin connector at radiator fan. Connect battery voltage to Blue wire in fan connector. Connect Black wire to ground. If fan operates, go to next step. If fan does not operate, replace radiator fan motor.
6) Check for continuity between condenser fan relay connector terminal No. 3 (Pink wire) and condenser fan. If continuity exists, go to next step. If continuity does not exist, repair open circuit between condenser fan relay and condenser fan.
7) Connect ohmmeter leads to terminals "C" and "D" of condenser fan relay. *See Fig. 5.* If continuity does not exist, replace relay. If continuity exists, go to next step.
8) Connect ohmmeter leads to terminals "A" and "B" on relay. Connect relay terminal "C" to battery voltage. Connect relay terminal "D" to ground. Relay should click and ohmmeter should indicate continuity. If relay functions as specified, go to next step. If relay does not function as specified, replace relay.
9) Check for continuity between radiator fan main relay terminal No. 5 (White/Green wire) and condenser fan. If continuity exists, go to next step. If continuity does not exist, repair open circuit in White/Green wire between radiator fan main relay and condenser fan.
10) Check for continuity between terminals "B" and "C" and between terminals "D" and "E" of radiator fan main relay. *See Fig. 10.* If continuity does not exist between both sets of terminals, replace relay. If continuity exists, go to next step.
11) Connect ohmmeter between relay terminals "A" and "C". Connect terminal "D" to battery voltage. Connect terminal "E" to ground. Relay should click, and ohmmeter should indicate continuity. If relay operates as specified, go to next step. If relay operation is not as specified, replace relay.
12) Check for voltage between terminal No. 1 (Yellow/Blue wire) of fan timer unit connector and chassis ground. *See Fig. 11.* If battery voltage exists, go to next step. If battery voltage does not exist, repair open circuit in Yellow/Blue wire between fan timer unit and fuse No. 15 (7.5-amp).

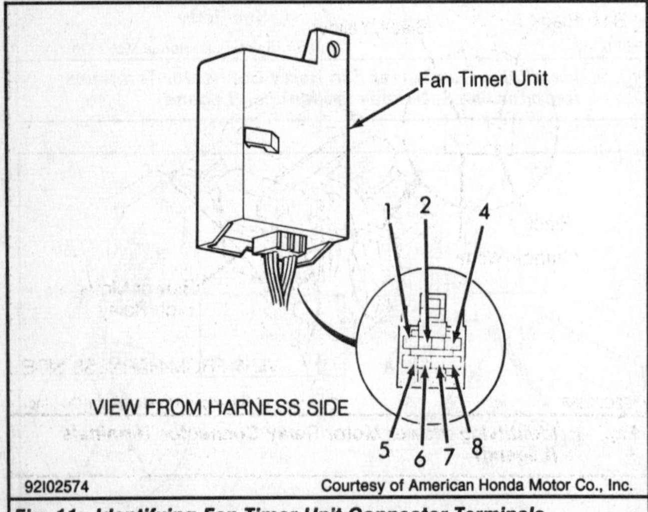
Fan Timer Unit
1
2
4
VIEW FROM HARNESS SIDE
5
6
7
8
92I02574
Courtesy of American Honda Motor Co., Inc.

Fig. 11: Identifying Fan Timer Unit Connector Terminals

13) Check for continuity between Green wire in fan timer unit connector and ground. If continuity exists, go to next step. If continuity does not exist, repair short circuit in Green wire between fan timer unit and condenser fan relay.
14) Using a jumper wire, connect terminal No. 2 of condenser fan relay connector to ground. Check for continuity in Green wire between fan timer unit and ground. If continuity exists, go to next step. If continuity does not exist, repair open circuit in Green wire between fan timer unit and condenser fan relay.
15) Check for continuity between condenser fan relay terminal No. 2 (Blue/Red wire) and fan timer unit. If continuity exists, go to next step. If continuity does not exist, repair open circuit in Blue/Red wire between condenser fan relay and fan timer unit.
16) Unplug 12-pin connector from fan control unit. Check continuity in Blue/Yellow wire between fan timer unit and fan control unit. *See Fig. 7.* If continuity exists, go to next step. If continuity does not exist, repair open circuit in Blue/Yellow wire between fan control unit and fan timer unit.
17) Reinstall both relays. Reconnect both fan motors and fan timer unit. Using a jumper wire, connect Blue/Yellow wire in fan control unit connector to ground. If both fan motors operate at low speed, replace fan timer unit. If both fans do not operate as specified, install a known good fan control unit, and retest.

A/C CONDENSER & RADIATOR FANS INOPERATIVE AT HIGH SPEED

NOTE: Fans should run at high speed when A/C high side pressure is excessive or coolant temperature exceeds 194°F (90°C).

Legend - 1) Check fuse No. 47 (20-amp). If fuse is okay, remove radiator fan sub-relay from relay box. Check for battery voltage between terminal No. 3 (White wire) of relay connector and ground. *See Fig. 9.* If battery voltage exists, go to next step. If battery voltage does not exist, repair open circuit in White wire between radiator fan sub-relay and fuse No. 47.
2) Turn ignition on. Check for voltage between terminal No. 4 (Yellow/Black wire) and chassis ground. If battery voltage exists, go to next step. If battery voltage does not exist, repair open circuit in Yellow/Black wire between radiator fan sub-relay and fuse No. 3 (15-amp).
3) Turn ignition off. Connect ohmmeter leads to terminals "C" and "D" of radiator fan sub-relay. *See Fig. 5.* If continuity does not exist, replace relay. If continuity exists, go to next step.
4) Connect ohmmeter to terminals "A" and "B" of sub-relay. Connect relay terminal "C" to battery voltage. Connect terminal "D" to ground. Relay should click and ohmmeter should indicate continuity. If relay functions as specified, go to next step. Replace relay if it does not function as specified.
5) Unplug connector from radiator fan motor. Check for continuity between terminal No. 1 (White/Blue wire) of radiator fan sub-relay and radiator fan connector. If continuity exists, go to next step. If continuity does not exist, repair open circuit in White/Blue wire between radiator fan sub-relay and radiator fan.
6) Remove radiator fan main relay. Turn ignition on. Check for voltage between terminal No. 3 (Yellow/Black wire) and chassis ground. If battery voltage exists, go to next step. If battery voltage does not exist, repair open circuit in Yellow/Black wire between radiator fan main relay and fuse No. 3.
7) Turn ignition off. Check for continuity between terminal No. 4 (Black wire) and ground. If continuity exists, go to next step. If continuity does not exist, repair open circuit in Black wire.
8) Check for continuity between terminals "B" and "C" and between terminals "D" and "E" of radiator fan main relay. *See Fig. 10.* If continuity does not exist between both sets of terminals, replace relay. If continuity exists, go to next step.
9) Connect ohmmeter between terminals "A" and "C" of radiator fan main relay. Connect terminal "D" to battery voltage. Connect terminal "E" to ground. Relay should click and ohmmeter should indicate continuity. If relay operates as specified, go to next step. Replace relay if operation is not as specified.
10) Reinstall radiator fan main relay. Reconnect wiring to radiator fan. Unplug 12-pin connector from fan control unit. Turn ignition on. Using jumper wires, connect Blue and Blue/Yellow wire terminals to ground. *See Fig. 7.*

11) If both fans run at high speed, go to next step. If both fans do not run at high speed, repair open circuit in Blue wire between fan control unit and radiator fan main and sub-relays.
12) With engine at normal operating temperature, measure resistance between Blue/White and Blue/Green wires in fan control unit connector. If resistance is not approximately 500-1200 ohms, go to step **14)**. If resistance is as specified, go to next step.
13) Unplug coolant temperature sensor. Check for continuity between ground and Blue/White and Blue/Green wires. If continuity exists in either wire, repair short to ground in affected wire. If continuity does not exist in either wire, replace fan control unit.
14) With engine at normal operating temperature, measure resistance across sensor terminals. If resistance is not 500-1200 ohms, replace coolant temperature sensor. If resistance is as specified, check for high resistance in Blue/White or Blue/Green wire between fan control unit and coolant temperature sensor. Repair as required.

A/C CONDENSER & RADIATOR FANS INOPERATIVE AT LOW SPEED

***NOTE:* Both fans operate at high speed and compressor clutch engages when A/C is turned on.**

Legend – 1) Unplug 12-pin connector from fan control unit. Turn ignition on. Using a jumper wire, connect Blue/Yellow wire to ground. *See Fig. 7.* If both fans run at low speed, go to step **3)**. If both fans do not run at low speed, unplug 8-pin connector from fan timer unit.
2) Check Blue/Yellow wire for continuity between fan control unit and terminal No. 2 of fan timer unit. *See Fig. 11.* If continuity does not exist, repair open circuit in Blue/Yellow wire. If continuity exists, install a known good fan timer unit, and retest.
3) Test coolant temperature sensor. See COOLANT TEMPERATURE SENSOR TEST table. If sensor is okay, go to next step. If sensor is faulty, replace sensor.

COOLANT TEMPERATURE SENSOR TEST

Coolant Temperature °F (°C)	Ohms
183 (84)	1047-1255
194 (90)	872-1024
226 (108)	519-573
230 (110)	489-541

4) Check Blue/White and Blue/Green wires for continuity between fan control unit and coolant temperature sensor. If continuity exists, go to next step. If continuity does not exist, repair open circuit in affected wire.
5) Check Blue/White and Blue/Green wires for continuity to ground. If continuity exists, repair short circuit in affected wire between fan control unit and coolant temperature sensor. If continuity does not exist, install a known good fan control unit, and retest.

AIR MIX CONTROL MOTOR

Legend – 1) Unplug 6-pin connector from air mix control motor. Test motor. See AIR MIX CONTROL MOTOR under TESTING. If motor is okay, go to next step. If motor is faulty, replace motor.
2) Remove A/C control unit. Unplug 22-pin connector. Unplug connector from air mix motor. *See Fig. 12.* Check for continuity between ground and Green/Red, Green/White, Red/Yellow, and Red/White wires. If continuity does not exist for any wire, go to next step. If continuity exists for any wire, repair short circuit between control unit and air mix motor.
3) Check each wire for continuity between control unit and air mix motor. If continuity does not exist for any wire, repair open circuit. If continuity exists on all wires, install a known good control unit, and retest.

BLOWER MOTOR DOES NOT RUN

Legend – 1) Check fuses No. 37 (40-amp) and No. 19 (7.5-amp). If fuses are okay, unplug connectors from blower relay and blower high relay. *See Fig. 13.*

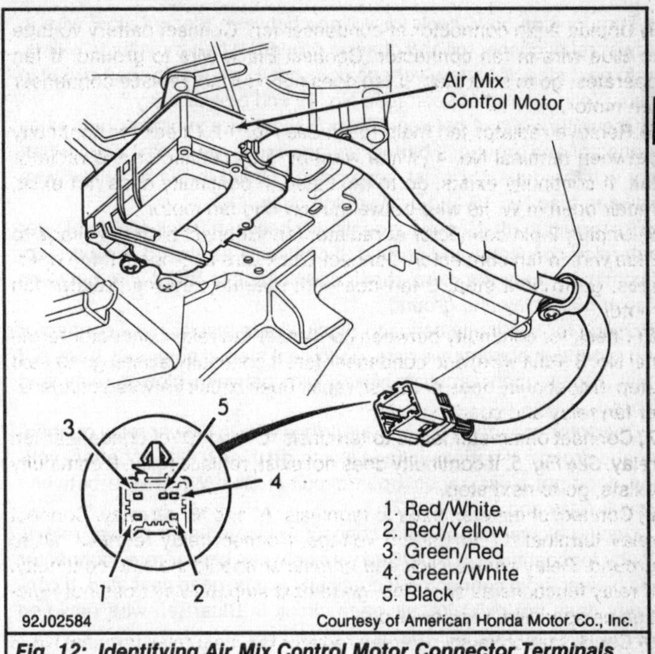
Air Mix
Control Motor
3
5
4
1
2
1. Red/White
2. Red/Yellow
3. Green/Red
4. Green/White
5. Black
92J02584
Courtesy of American Honda Motor Co., Inc.

Fig. 12: Identifying Air Mix Control Motor Connector Terminals (Legend)

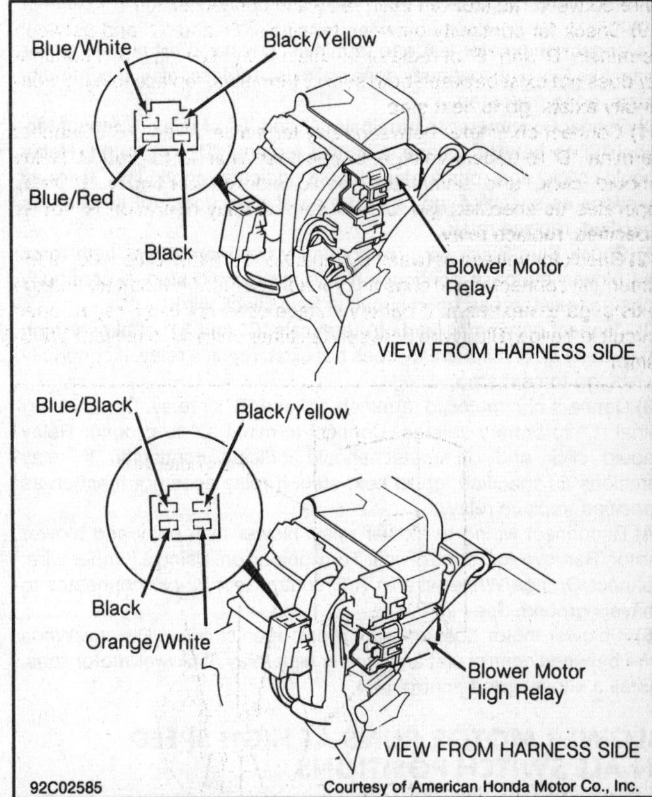
Blue/White
Black/Yellow
Blue/Red
Black
Blower Motor
Relay
VIEW FROM HARNESS SIDE
Blue/Black
Black/Yellow
Black
Orange/White
Blower Motor
High Relay
VIEW FROM HARNESS SIDE
92C02585
Courtesy of American Honda Motor Co., Inc.

Fig. 13: Identifying Blower Motor Relay Connector Terminals (Legend)

1993 MANUAL A/C-HEATER SYSTEMS Integra & Legend (Cont.)

2) Turn ignition on. Check for voltage between Black/Yellow wire in blower relay connector and chassis ground. If battery voltage exists, go to next step. If battery voltage does not exist, repair open circuit in Black/Yellow wire between fuse No. 19 and blower relay.

3) Check for voltage between Black/Yellow wire in blower high relay connector and ground. If battery voltage exists, go to next step. If battery voltage does not exist, repair open circuit in Black/Yellow wire between fuse No. 19 and blower high relay.

4) Turn ignition off. Check for continuity between Black wire in blower high relay connector and ground. If continuity exists, go to next step. If continuity does not exist, repair open circuit in Black wire between blower high relay and ground.

5) Check for continuity between Black wire in blower relay connector and ground. If continuity exists, go to next step. If continuity does not exist, repair open circuit in Black wire between blower relay and ground.

6) Check for voltage between Blue/White wire in blower relay connector and ground. If battery voltage exists, go to next step. If battery voltage does not exist, repair open circuit in Blue/White wire between blower relay and fuse No. 37.

7) Unplug blower motor 2-pin connector, located near blower relays. Check for continuity in Blue/Red wire between blower relay connector and blower 2-pin connector. If continuity exists, go to next step. If continuity does not exist, repair open circuit in Blue/Red wire between blower relay and blower motor.

8) Connect battery voltage to Blue wire in blower motor connector. Connect Black wire in blower motor connector to ground. If blower motor runs, go to next step. If blower motor does not run, replace motor.

9) Connect ohmmeter leads to terminals "C" and "D" of blower motor relay. *See Fig. 5.* If continuity does not exist, replace relay. If continuity exists, go to next step.

10) Connect ohmmeter to terminals "A" and "B" of relay. Connect terminal "C" to battery voltage. Connect terminal "D" to ground. Relay should click and ohmmeter should indicate continuity. If relay functions as specified, go to next step. If relay does not function as specified, replace relay.

11) Check Blue/Black wire for continuity between blower high relay and blower motor. If continuity exists, go to next step. If continuity does not exist, repair open circuit in Blue/Black wire.

12) Connect ohmmeter leads to terminals "C" and "D" of blower high relay. *See Fig. 5.* If continuity does not exist, replace relay. If continuity exists, go to next step.

13) Connect ohmmeter to terminals "A" and "B" of relay. Connect terminal "C" to battery voltage. Connect terminal "D" to ground. Relay should click and ohmmeter should indicate continuity. If relay functions as specified, go to next step. If relay does not function as specified, replace relay.

14) Reconnect wiring to blower relay, blower high relay and blower motor. Remove A/C control unit. Turn ignition on. Using a jumper wire, connect Orange/White wire in A/C control unit 22-pin connector to chassis ground. *See Fig. 3.*

15) If blower motor does not run, repair open circuit in Orange/White wire between control unit and blower high relay. If blower motor runs, install a known good control unit.

BLOWER MOTOR RUNS AT HIGH SPEED IN ALL SWITCH POSITIONS

Legend – 1) Turn ignition on. Remove blower motor high relay. *See Fig. 13.* If blower motor does not stop, go to step **5)**. If blower motor stops, turn ignition off.

2) Connect ohmmeter to terminals "C" and "D" of blower high relay. *See Fig. 5.* If continuity does not exist, replace relay. If continuity exists, go to next step.

3) Connect ohmmeter terminals to "A" and "B" of relay. Connect terminal "C" to battery voltage. Connect terminal "D" to ground. Relay should click and ohmmeter should indicate continuity. If relay functions as specified, go to next step. If relay does not function as specified, replace relay.

4) Check for short circuit in Orange/White wire between blower motor high relay and A/C control unit. If wire is okay, install a known good control unit, and retest.

5) Unplug power transistor connector on A/C control unit. If blower motor stops, go to next step. If blower motor does not stop, repair short circuit in Blue/Black wire between control unit, power transistor, blower motor high relay and blower motor. If wire is okay, install a known good control unit, and retest.

6) Measure voltage between Light Green/Black wire in power transistor connector and ground. *See Fig. 14.* If voltage is less than 7 volts, replace power transistor. If voltage is greater than 7 volts, install a known good control unit, and retest.

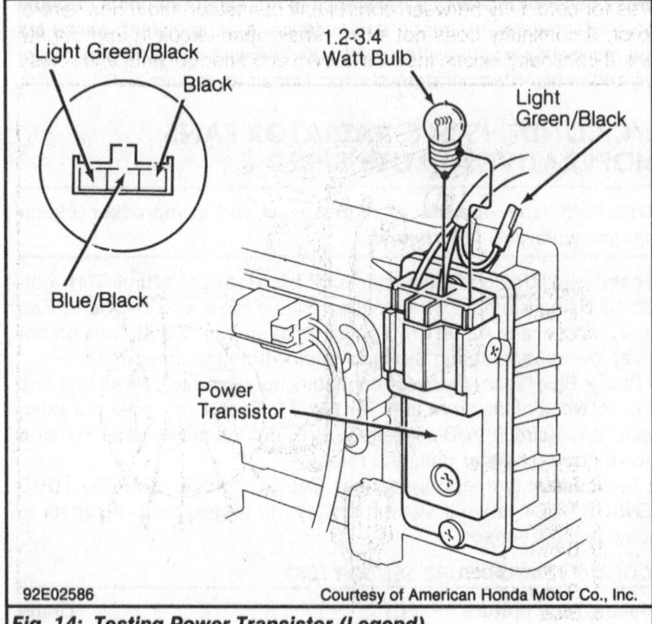
Light Green/Black
1.2-3.4
Watt Bulb
Black
Light
Green/Black
Blue/Black
Power
Transistor
92E02586
Courtesy of American Honda Motor Co., Inc.

Fig. 14: Testing Power Transistor (Legend)

BLOWER MOTOR RUNS ONLY IN HIGH POSITION

Legend – 1) Connect a jumper wire between Blue/Black wire of power transistor and chassis ground. *See Fig. 14.* Turn ignition on. If blower motor runs at high speed, go to next step. If blower motor does not run at high speed, repair open circuit in Blue/Black wire between power transistor and blower motor.

2) Connect a jumper wire between Blue/Black and Black wires at power transistor. If blower motor runs at high speed, go to next step. If blower motor does not run at high speed, repair open in Black wire between power transistor and ground.

3) Turn ignition off. Remove Light Green/Black wire from power transistor connector. Connect a 1.2-3.4 watt test bulb between Blue/Black wire and open power transistor terminal. *See Fig. 14.* If blower motor runs at less than high speed, go to next step. If blower motor runs at high speed, repair short in Light Green/Black wire between power transistor and control unit.

4) Turn ignition off. Remove A/C control unit. Turn ignition on. Using a jumper wire, connect Blue/Black wire of control unit connector to ground. If blower motor runs at high speed, go to next step. If blower motor does not run at high speed, repair open circuit in Blue/Black wire between control unit and blower motor.

5) Repair open circuit in Light Green/Black wire between power transistor and control unit. If wire is okay, install a known good control unit, and retest.

MODE CONTROL MOTOR

Legend – 1) Unplug 8-pin connector from mode control motor. Check for continuity between Black wire in connector and chassis

ground. *See Fig. 15.* If continuity exists, go to next step. If continuity does not exist, repair open circuit in Black wire or ground connection.
2) Turn ignition on. Check for voltage between Black/Yellow wire and ground. If battery voltage exists, go to next step. If battery voltage does not exist, repair open circuit in Black/Yellow wire between motor and fuse No. 19.
3) Turn ignition off. Remove A/C control unit. Unplug 22-pin connector. Check for continuity between ground and Gray, Brown, Blue, Yellow, Blue/Red and Yellow/Green wires in control unit connector. If continuity does not exist, go to next step. If continuity exists, repair short circuit in appropriate wire.
4) Check Gray, Brown, Blue, Yellow, Blue/Red and Yellow/Green wires for continuity between control unit connector and mode control motor. If continuity does not exist, repair open circuit in appropriate wire. If continuity exists, install a known good control unit, and retest.

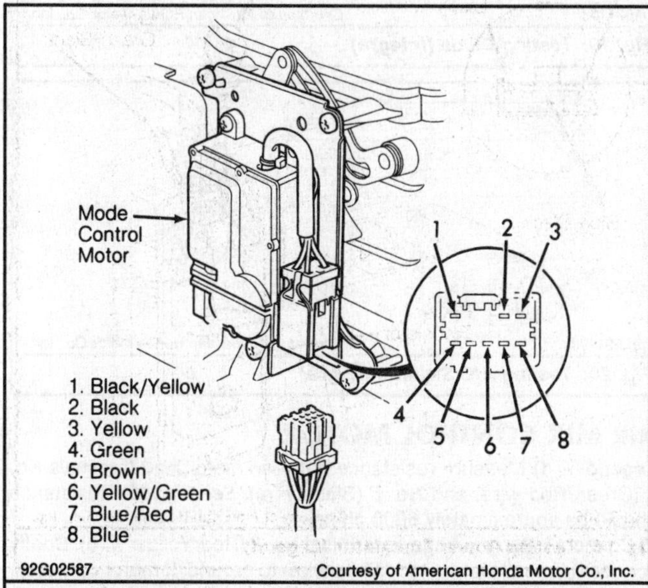
Mode Control Motor
1
2
3
4
5
6
7
8
1. Black/Yellow
2. Black
3. Yellow
4. Green
5. Brown
6. Yellow/Green
7. Blue/Red
8. Blue
92G02587
Courtesy of American Honda Motor Co., Inc.

Fig. 15: Identifying Mode Control Motor Connector Terminals (Legend)

RECIRCULATION CONTROL MOTOR

Legend – 1) Remove instrument panel lower cover. Unplug recirculation motor 4-pin connector. *See Fig. 16.* Turn ignition on. Check for voltage between Black/Yellow wire and ground. If battery voltage exists, go to next step. If battery voltage does not exist, repair open circuit between fuse No. 19 and recirculation control motor.
2) Turn ignition off. Test recirculation control motor. See RECIRCULATION CONTROL MOTOR under TESTING. If motor is okay, go to next step. If motor is defective, replace motor. Check recirculation control door. Repair as required. Remove A/C control unit. See A/C CONTROL UNIT under REMOVAL & INSTALLATION.
3) Unplug 22-pin connector from A/C control unit. Check for continuity between recirculation control motor and Blue/Orange and Blue/Green wires at control unit connector. *See Figs. 3 and 16.* If continuity exists, go to next step. If continuity does not exist, repair open circuit in appropriate wire.
4) Check for continuity between chassis ground and Blue/Orange and Blue/Green wires at control unit connector. If continuity exists, repair short circuit in appropriate wire. If continuity does not exist, install a known good control unit, and retest. If condition no longer exists, replace control unit.

EVAPORATOR TEMPERATURE SENSOR

Unplug connector from evaporator temperature sensor, located at evaporator housing. *See Fig. 17.* Measure sensor resistance at temperatures specified in table. See EVAPORATOR TEMPERATURE SENSOR TEST table. If resistance is not approximately as specified, replace sensor.

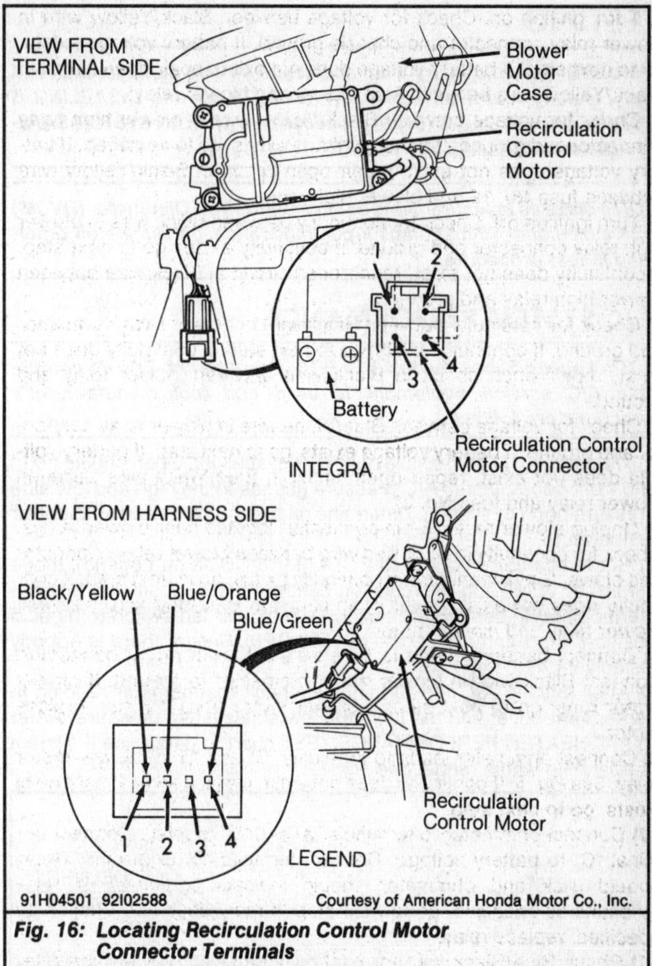
VIEW FROM TERMINAL SIDE
Blower Motor Case
Recirculation Control Motor
1
2
3
4
Battery
Recirculation Control Motor Connector
INTEGRA
VIEW FROM HARNESS SIDE
Black/Yellow
Blue/Orange
Blue/Green
1
2
3
4
Recirculation Control Motor
LEGEND
91H04501 92I02588
Courtesy of American Honda Motor Co., Inc.

Fig. 16: Locating Recirculation Control Motor Connector Terminals

CAUTION: To avoid damage to sensor, use an ohmmeter with a measuring current of one milliamp or less.

EVAPORATOR TEMPERATURE SENSOR TEST

Coolant Temperature °F (°C)	Ohms
32 (0)	4800
50 (10)	2900
68 (20)	1800
86 (30)	1300

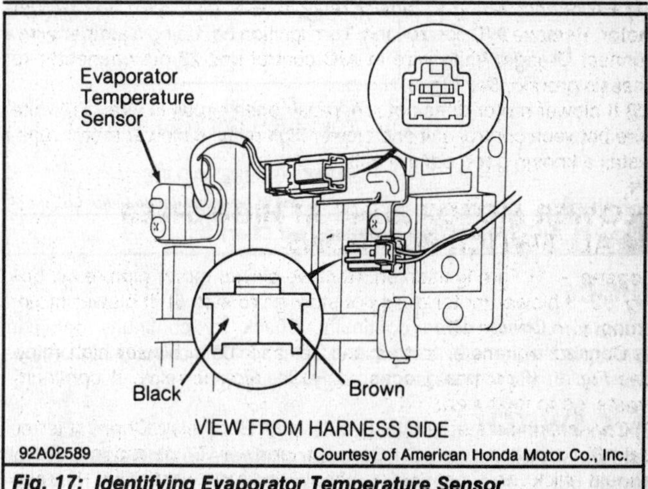
Evaporator Temperature Sensor
Black
Brown
VIEW FROM HARNESS SIDE
92A02589
Courtesy of American Honda Motor Co., Inc.

Fig. 17: Identifying Evaporator Temperature Sensor Connector Terminals (Legend)

1993 MANUAL A/C-HEATER SYSTEMS
Integra & Legend (Cont.)

TESTING

WARNING: To avoid injury from accidental air bag deployment, read and carefully follow all SERVICE PRECAUTIONS and DISABLING & ACTIVATING AIR BAG SYSTEM procedures in AIR BAG SYSTEM SAFETY article in GENERAL SERVICING.

NOTE: Make all measurements using a Digital Volt-Ohmmeter (DVOM) with a minimum 10-megohms input impedance, unless stated otherwise in test procedure.

A/C SYSTEM PERFORMANCE

NOTE: Legend Sedan models use R-134a refrigerant. Ensure compatible A/C service equipment is used and tool manufacturer's directions are followed.

All Models – 1) Park vehicle out of direct sunlight. Open engine hood and front doors. Install A/C pressure gauges to the high and low side pressure ports of system. Determine relative humidity and ambient air temperature.

2) Set temperature control to COOL (MAX COOL on Legend), mode control to VENT and recirculation control to REC positions. Insert a thermometer in center vent outlet. Turn blower fan switch to highest position. Start and run engine at 1500 RPM. Ensure there is nobody inside vehicle.

3) After running A/C for 10 minutes, check thermometer reading in center vent outlet and the high and low side system pressure. Refer to A/C-HEATER PERFORMANCE TEST chart to determine if system is operating within range. *See Fig. 18.*

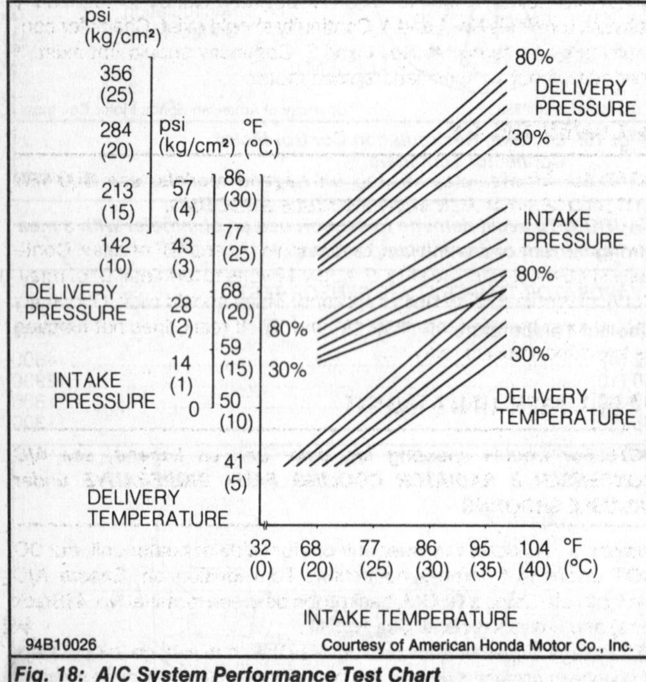
psi
(kg/cm²)
356
(25)
284
(20)
213
(15)
142
(10)
DELIVERY
PRESSURE
14
(1)
INTAKE
PRESSURE
0
psi
(kg/cm²)
57
(4)
43
(3)
28
(2)
°F
(°C)
86
(30)
77
(25)
68
(20)
59
(15)
50
(10)
41
(5)
DELIVERY
TEMPERATURE
80%
DELIVERY
PRESSURE
30%
INTAKE
PRESSURE
80%
30%
80%
30%
DELIVERY
TEMPERATURE
32 (0)
68 (20)
77 (25)
86 (30)
95 (35)
104 (40)
°F (°C)
INTAKE TEMPERATURE
94B10026
Courtesy of American Honda Motor Co., Inc.
Fig. 18: A/C System Performance Test Chart

DIODE

Integra – Check diode continuity. Check for continuity between terminals No. 1 and 2, 1 and 3, and 2 and 3 in both directions. Continuity should exist in one direction only. *See Fig. 19.*

A/C SWITCH

Integra – Pull out screw hole cover. Remove retaining screw. Pull switch out. Unplug connector and remove A/C switch. Test for continuity between switch terminals. *See Fig. 20.*

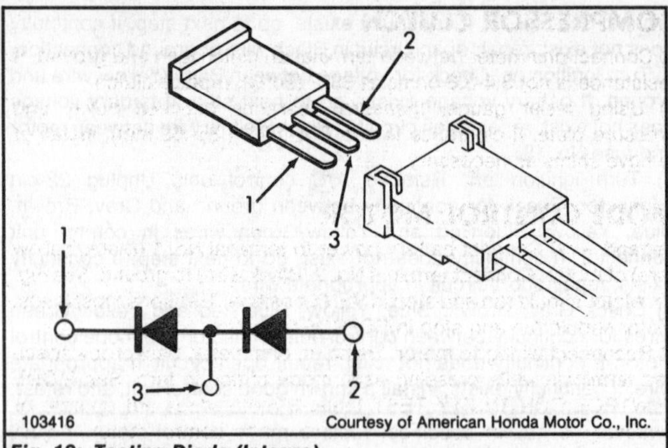
2
1
3
1
3
2
103416
Courtesy of American Honda Motor Co., Inc.
Fig. 19: Testing Diode (Integra)

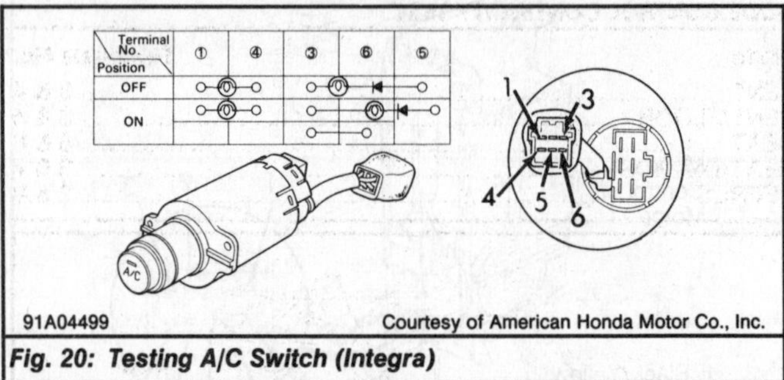
Terminal No.
Position
OFF
ON
1
3
4
5
6
91A04499
Courtesy of American Honda Motor Co., Inc.
Fig. 20: Testing A/C Switch (Integra)

AIR MIX CONTROL MOTOR

Legend – 1) Measure resistance between motor lead terminals No. 3 (Green/Red wire) and No. 5 (Black wire). *See Fig. 12.* Resistance should be approximately 6000 ohms.

2) Connect battery voltage to terminal No. 2 (Red/Yellow wire). Briefly connect terminal No. 1 (Red/White wire) to ground. If motor operates, transpose leads. Replace motor if it does not run in both directions.

CAUTION: Remove power immediately after motor moves to avoid damaging motor.

3) Connect ohmmeter leads to terminals No. 4 (Green/White wire) and No. 5 (Black wire). Resistance should be approximately 4800 ohms with air mix door in HEAT position, and approximately 1200 ohms with door in COOL position. Replace air mix motor if it does not operate as specified. Adjust air mix door rod as required. *See Fig. 21.*

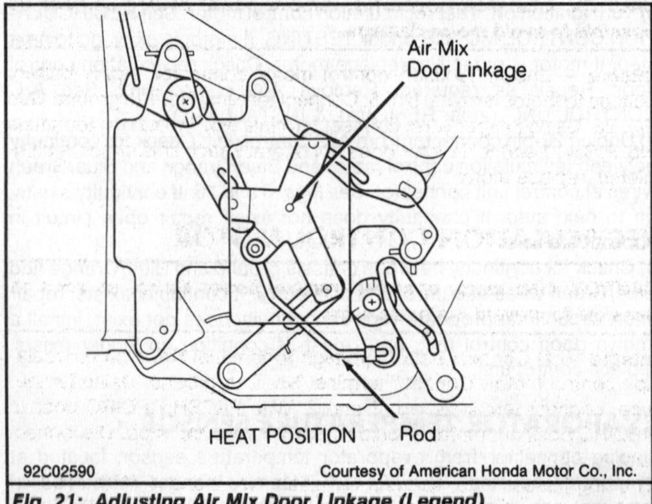
Air Mix
Door Linkage
HEAT POSITION
Rod
92C02590
Courtesy of American Honda Motor Co., Inc.
Fig. 21: Adjusting Air Mix Door Linkage (Legend)

COMPRESSOR CLUTCH

1) Connect ohmmeter between terminal on clutch lead and ground. If resistance is not 3.4-3.8 ohms at 68°F (20°C), replace clutch.
2) Using feeler gauge, measure clearance between pulley and pressure plate. If clearance is not .014-.026" (.35-.65 mm), install or remove shims as necessary.

MODE CONTROL MOTOR

Legend – 1) Connect battery power to terminal No. 1 (Black/Yellow wire) of motor. Connect terminal No. 2 (Black wire) to ground. *See Fig. 15.* Motor should run and stop in VENT position. Transpose test leads. Motor should run and stop in DEFROST position.
2) Reconnect wiring to motor. Using an ohmmeter, backprobe specified terminals while pressing each mode button in turn. See MODE CONTROL CONTINUITY TEST table. If motor does not operate or continuity is not as specified, replace mode control motor. Adjust mode door linkage as required. *See Fig. 22.*

MODE CONTROL CONTINUITY TEST

Mode	Terminals No.
VENT	3 & 4
VENT/FLOOR	3 & 5
HEAT	3 & 6
HEAT/DEFROST	3 & 7
DEFROST	3 & 8

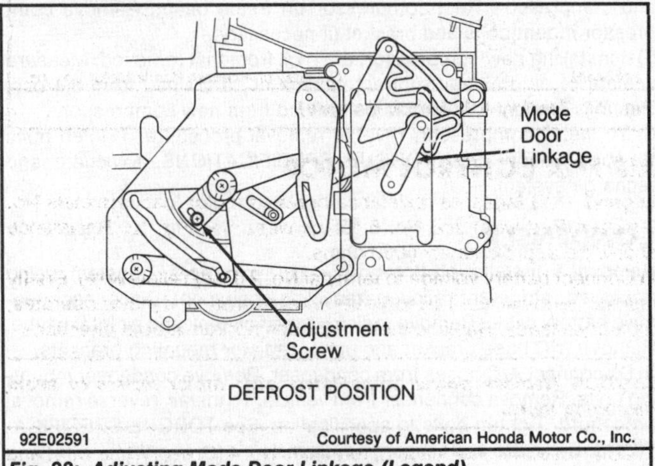
Mode
Door
Linkage
Adjustment
Screw
DEFROST POSITION
92E02591
Courtesy of American Honda Motor Co., Inc.

Fig. 22: Adjusting Mode Door Linkage (Legend)

FUNCTION CONTROL MOTOR

CAUTION: After motor operates, remove power source as soon as possible to avoid motor damage.

Integra – Unplug function control motor connector. Apply battery voltage to motor terminal No. 5. Connect terminal No. 1 to ground. *See Fig. 23.* Using jumper wire, connect terminal No. 1 in turn to terminals No. 2, 3, 4, 7 and 8. If motor does not operate each time circuit is completed, replace motor.

RECIRCULATION CONTROL MOTOR

CAUTION: After motor operates, remove power source as soon as possible to prevent motor damage.

Integra – 1) Connect battery voltage to terminal No. 1 on recirculation control motor. Connect terminal No. 2 to ground. Using jumper wire, connect terminals No. 1 and 2. With FRESH/RECIRC door in RECIRC position, motor should rotate 1/2 turn and stop. Disconnect jumper wire.
2) Using jumper wire, connect terminals No. 2 and 4. With FRESH/RECIRC door in FRESH position, motor should rotate 1/2 turn and stop. If motor operation is not as specified, replace recirculation control motor. *See Fig. 16.*

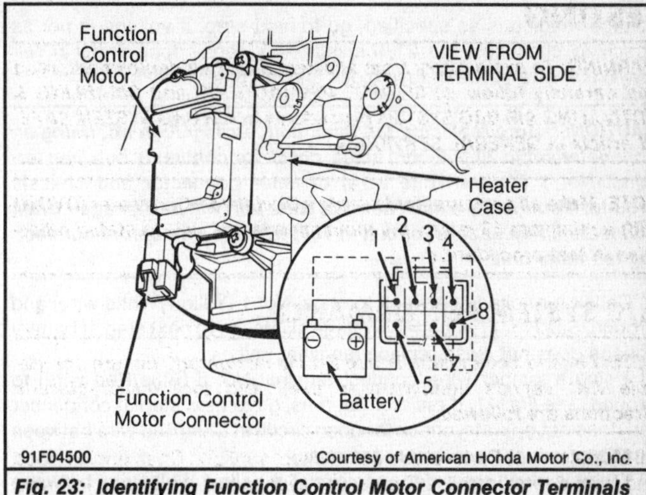
Function
Control
Motor
VIEW FROM
TERMINAL SIDE
Heater
Case
1
2
3
4
8
5
7
Function Control
Motor Connector
Battery
91F04500
Courtesy of American Honda Motor Co., Inc.

Fig. 23: Identifying Function Control Motor Connector Terminals (Integra)

Legend – 1) Unplug recirculation control motor connector. Using jumper wires, apply positive battery voltage to terminal No. 1. Connect terminal No. 2 to ground. *See Fig. 16.* If motor does not operate, transpose jumper wires. If motor operates, go to next step. If motor still does not operate, replace motor.
2) Check for continuity between terminals No. 1 and 2. With recirculation door in FRESH position, continuity should exist. Check continuity between terminals No. 1 and 4. With recirculation door in FRESH position, continuity should not exist.
3) Set recirculation door to RECIRC position. Check for continuity between terminals No. 1 and 4. Continuity should exist. Check for continuity between terminals No. 1 and 2. Continuity should not exist. If continuity is not as specified, replace motor.

BLOWER RELAY

NOTE: For blower relay testing on Legend models, see BLOWER MOTOR DOES NOT RUN under TROUBLE SHOOTING.

Integra – Connect ohmmeter to terminals "A" and "B" of relay. Continuity should not exist. *See Fig. 5.* Apply 12 volts to terminal "C" of relay. Connect terminal "D" of relay to ground. Relay should click. Continuity should exist between terminals "A" and "B". If relay does not function as specified, replace relay.

FAN TIMER UNIT INPUT

NOTE: For trouble shooting fan timer unit on Legend, see A/C CONDENSER & RADIATOR COOLING FANS INOPERATIVE under TROUBLE SHOOTING.

Integra – 1) Locate fan timer unit on right side of heater unit, but DO NOT disconnect harness connector. Turn ignition on. Ensure A/C switch is off. Using a DVOM, backprobe between terminal No. 4 (Black wire) and chassis ground. *See Fig. 11.*
2) If voltage is greater than zero but less than one volt, go to next step. If voltage is greater than one volt, repair open circuit or poor connection in Black wire between fan timer unit and ground.
3) Check for voltage between terminal No. 6 (White wire) and ground. *See Fig. 11.* If battery voltage exists, go to next step. If battery voltage does not exist, check fuse No. 20. If fuse is okay, repair open circuit in White wire between fuse block and fan timer unit.
4) Check for voltage between terminal No. 7 (Black/Yellow wire) and ground. *See Fig. 11.* Battery voltage should exist with ignition on. If voltage is as specified, go to next step. If voltage is not as specified, check fuse No. 24. If fuse is okay, repair open circuit in Black/Yellow wire between fuse block and fan timer unit.
5) Check for voltage between terminal No. 2 (Yellow/Black wire) and ground. *See Fig. 11.* Battery voltage should exist with ignition on. If

1993 MANUAL A/C-HEATER SYSTEMS
Integra & Legend (Cont.)

voltage reading is as specified, go to next step. If voltage is not as specified, check fuse No. 21. If fuse is okay, repair open circuit in Yellow/Black wire between fuse block and fan timer unit.

CAUTION: Before replacing fan timer unit, turn ignition off. Using an ohmmeter set to 20,000-ohm scale, check for continuity between terminal No. 1 (Yellow/White wire) of timer connector and chassis ground. If continuity exists, new fan timer unit will be damaged when connected. Repair short circuit in Yellow/White wire before connecting fan timer unit.

6) Check for voltage between terminal No. 1 (Yellow/White wire) and ground. *See Fig. 11*. If battery voltage exists, go to next step. If battery voltage does not exist, replace fan timer unit.
7) Using a jumper wire, connect terminal No. 8 (Blue/Red wire) to ground. *See Fig. 11*. If radiator fan runs, go to next step. If condenser fan does not operate, check for open circuit in Blue/Red wire between fan timer unit and condenser fan relay.
8) If wire is okay, check for open circuit in Yellow/White wire between fan timer unit and 2-pin connector (located near radiator), and Black/Yellow wire between 2-pin connector and condenser fan relay. If wiring is okay, test condenser fan relay. See TROUBLE SHOOTING - INTEGRA charts following this article.
9) Check for voltage between terminal No. 5 (White/Green wire) and ground. *See Fig. 11*. With engine oil temperature less than 226°F (108°C), voltage should be approximately 11 volts. If voltage is not as specified, check for short to ground in White/Green wire. If wire is okay, check oil temperature switch. If oil temperature switch is okay, install a known good fan timer unit. Retest system.

REMOVAL & INSTALLATION

WARNING: To avoid injury from accidental air bag deployment, read and carefully follow all SERVICE PRECAUTIONS and DISABLING & ACTIVATING AIR BAG SYSTEM procedures in AIR BAG SYSTEM SAFETY article in GENERAL SERVICING.

NOTE: For removal and installation procedures not covered in this article, see appropriate HEATER SYSTEMS article.

A/C CONTROL UNIT

NOTE: Before removing radio, obtain anti-theft code number from customer. After servicing, turn radio on. Word CODE will be displayed. Enter 5-digit code to restore radio operation.

Removal & Installation (Integra) - Remove instrument cluster trim panel. Remove left and right lower panels. Remove front console and radio. Disconnect control cables/linkage. Remove retaining screws, pull control panel out, and unplug harness connector. Remove heater control panel. To install, reverse removal procedure.
Removal & Installation (Legend) - Remove radio. Remove control unit retaining screws. Using a thin screwdriver, release 2 clips located above dash vents. Pull control unit outward. Unplug harness connectors. Remove control unit. To install, reverse removal procedure.

BLOWER MOTOR

NOTE: For removal and installation procedure on Legend models, see HEATER-EVAPORATOR under REMOVAL & INSTALLATION.

Removal & Installation (Integra) - Remove passenger-side lower panel. Remove glove box. Remove right kick panel. Remove motorized shoulder belt control unit. Remove knee bolster. Remove heater duct. Unplug connectors from blower motor. Remove mounting bolts and blower unit. To install, reverse removal procedure. Check for air leaks.

COMPRESSOR

Removal & Installation (Integra) - **1)** Run engine at idle speed. Operate A/C system for about 2 minutes before removing compressor. Stop engine. Disconnect negative battery cable. Discharge A/C system, using approved refrigerant recovery/recycling equipment.
2) Remove power steering pump. Unplug compressor clutch connector. Disconnect suction and discharge hoses from compressor. Remove condenser fan shroud. Remove compressor belt. Remove compressor mounting bolts and compressor.
3) If installing new compressor, drain oil from that removed. Measure volume of oil drained. Subtract volume of oil drained from 2.7 ozs. Result is amount that should be drained from new compressor.
4) To install compressor, reverse removal procedure. Tighten bolts to specification. See TORQUE SPECIFICATIONS. Evacuate and recharge system.
Removal & Installation (Legend) - **1)** Run engine at idle speed. Operate air conditioner for about 2 minutes before removing compressor. Stop engine. Disconnect negative battery cable.
2) Raise and support vehicle. Remove grille, spoiler, bumper, and right front wheel. Remove engine splash shield. Remove right radius rod.
3) Unplug compressor clutch connector. Discharge A/C system, using approved refrigerant recovery/recycling equipment. Disconnect suction and discharge hoses from compressor. Loosen lock nut and compressor adjuster bolt.
4) Remove A/C compressor belt. Remove compressor mounting bolts and compressor. Rest compressor on frame beam. Remove compressor mount bolts and bracket (if necessary).
5) If installing new compressor, drain oil from that removed. Measure volume of oil drained. Subtract volume of oil drained from 3.4 ozs. Result is amount that should be drained from new compressor.
6) To install compressor, reverse removal procedure. Tighten bolts to specification. See TORQUE SPECIFICATIONS. Evacuate and recharge system.

CONDENSER

Removal & Installation (Integra) - **1)** Discharge A/C system, using approved refrigerant recovery/recycling equipment. Disconnect negative battery cable. Remove radiator reservoir tank and air intake tube. Remove A/C hose bracket and upper radiator mounting brackets.
2) Disconnect A/C hoses from condenser. Remove condenser mounting bolts. Remove condenser from vehicle. To install, reverse removal procedure. Tighten bolts to specification. See TORQUE SPECIFICATIONS. Evacuate and recharge system.
Removal & Installation (Legend) - **1)** Discharge A/C system, using approved refrigerant recovery/recycling equipment. Remove battery and battery tray. Remove engine intake air duct. Remove throttle cable cover, and disconnect throttle cables.
2) Disconnect refrigerant lines. Remove receiver-drier. Remove underhood relay box. Remove condenser fan. Remove upper condenser mounting brackets. Remove condenser mounting nuts and condenser. To install, reverse removal procedure. Tighten bolts to specification. See TORQUE SPECIFICATIONS. Evacuate and recharge system.

HEATER-EVAPORATOR

Removal & Installation (Integra) - **1)** Disconnect negative battery cable. Discharge A/C system, using approved refrigerant recovery/recycling equipment. Disconnect receiver-drier line and suction hose from evaporator.
2) Remove left and right lower instrument panel covers. Remove glove box screws, bolt, and frame. Remove console box and bracket. Remove right knee bolster.
3) Unplug thermostat connector. Remove 2 A/C retaining bands. Remove evaporator. *See Fig. 24*. To install, reverse removal procedure. Tighten bolts to specification. See TORQUE SPECIFICATIONS. Evacuate and recharge system.

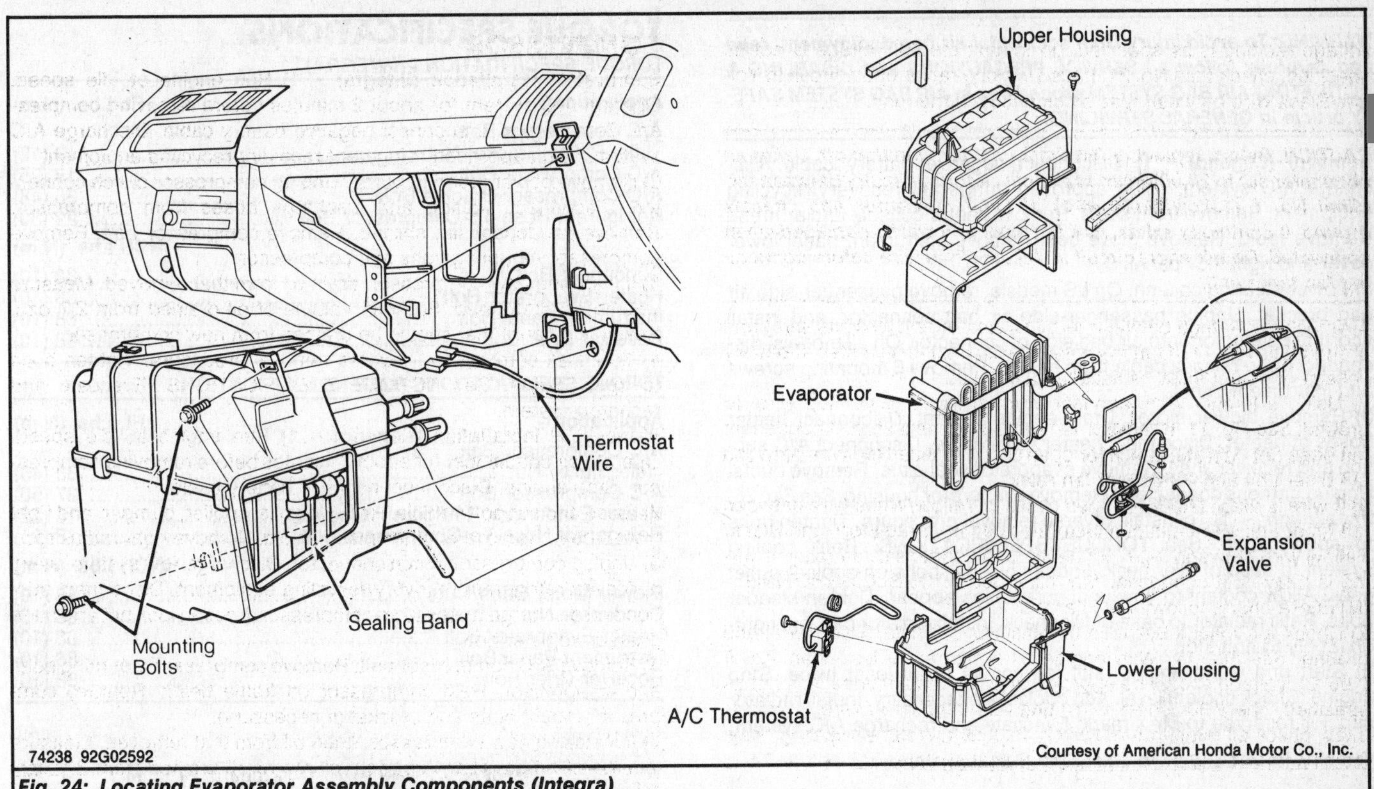
Upper Housing
Evaporator
Thermostat Wire
Expansion Valve
Sealing Band
Mounting Bolts
Lower Housing
A/C Thermostat
74238 92G02592
Courtesy of American Honda Motor Co., Inc.

Fig. 24: Locating Evaporator Assembly Components (Integra)

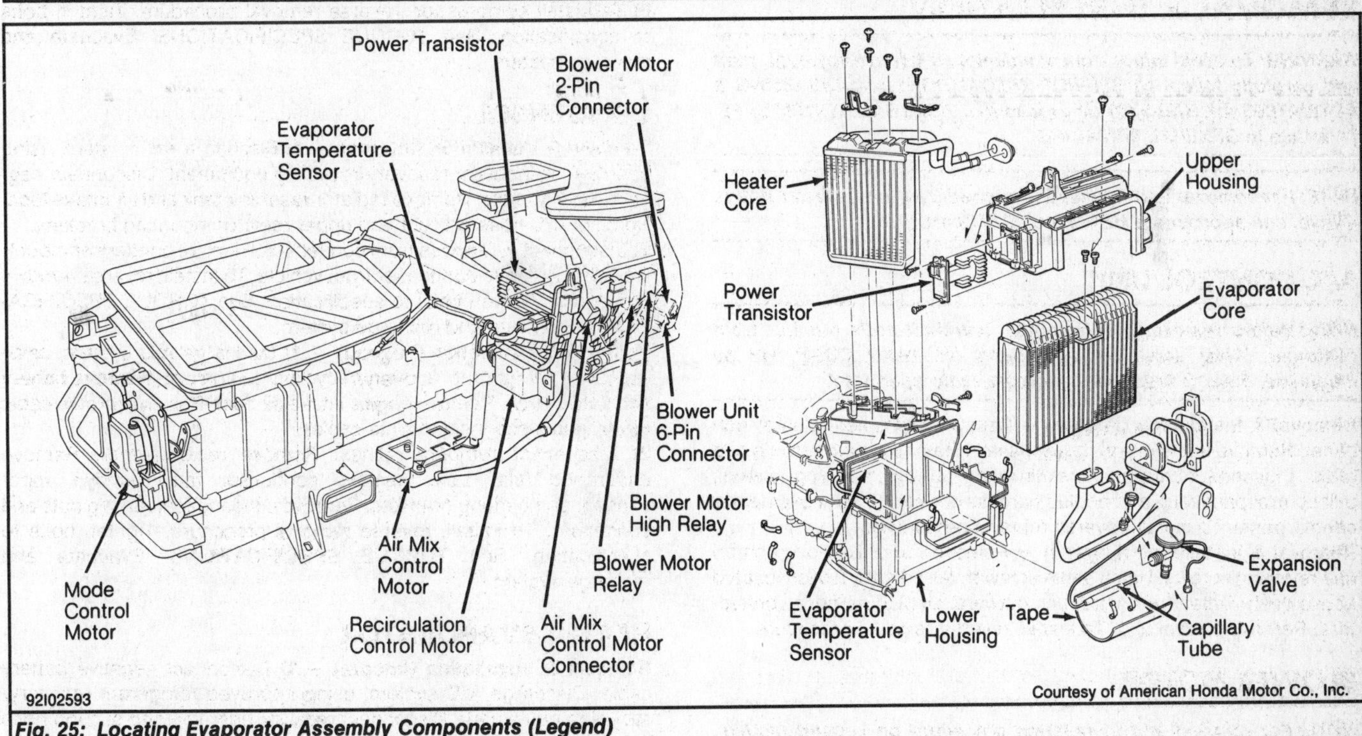
Power Transistor
Blower Motor 2-Pin Connector
Evaporator Temperature Sensor
Heater Core
Upper Housing
Power Transistor
Evaporator Core
Blower Unit 6-Pin Connector
Blower Motor High Relay
Blower Motor Relay
Air Mix Control Motor
Mode Control Motor
Recirculation Control Motor
Air Mix Control Motor Connector
Evaporator Temperature Sensor
Lower Housing
Tape
Capillary Tube
Expansion Valve
92I02593
Courtesy of American Honda Motor Co., Inc.

Fig. 25: Locating Evaporator Assembly Components (Legend)

1993 MANUAL A/C-HEATER SYSTEMS
Integra & Legend (Cont.)

WARNING: To avoid injury from accidental air bag deployment, read and carefully follow all SERVICE PRECAUTIONS and DISABLING & ACTIVATING AIR BAG SYSTEM procedures in AIR BAG SYSTEM SAFETY article in GENERAL SERVICING.

Removal (Legend) - 1) Disconnect negative battery cable. Discharge A/C system, using approved refrigerant recovery/recycling equipment. Remove front seats. Remove center console and armrest. Remove radio. Remove glove box. Remove instrument panel lower cover and right kick panel.

2) Lower steering column. On LS models, remove passenger-side air bag bracket. Unplug passenger-side air bag connector, and install shorting connector onto air bag side of connector. On all models, disconnect hood release cable from handle. Remove 6 mounting screws and instrument panel.

3) Remove blower motor. Drain engine coolant. Disconnect heater hoses at heater. Disconnect heater valve cable. Disconnect A/C suction and receiver lines. Remove evaporator seal plate. Remove ducts. Unplug harness connectors. Remove evaporator housing. *See Fig. 25.*

Installation - 1) To install, reverse removal procedure. Tighten bolts to specification. See TORQUE SPECIFICATIONS. Refill cooling system to base of filler neck. Loosen bleeder bolts on coolant outlet neck. Allow coolant to flow until no bubbles appear. Tighten bleeder bolts. Refill radiator to base of filler neck. Install radiator cap, but tighten it only to first stop.

2) Start and warm engine until fan comes on at least twice. Stop engine. Check coolant level. Add coolant as necessary. Install radiator cap. Fill reservoir to MAX mark. Evacuate and recharge A/C system.

TORQUE SPECIFICATIONS

TORQUE SPECIFICATIONS (INTEGRA)

Application	Ft. Lbs. (N.m)
A/C Compressor Belt	
Idler Pulley Bracket Nut	13 (18)
A/C Compressor Bolt	18 (25)
A/C Compressor Bracket Bolt	35 (48)
Refrigerant Hose-To-Compressor Bolt	22 (30)
	INCH Lbs. (N.m)
Condenser Bolt	88 (10)
Heater-Evaporator Bolt	88 (10)
Instrument Panel Bolt	88 (10)
Receiver-Drier Bolt	88 (10)

TORQUE SPECIFICATIONS (LEGEND)

Application	Ft. Lbs. (N.m)
A/C Compressor Belt	
Idler Pulley Nut	33 (45)
A/C Compressor Bolt	37 (50)
Heater-Evaporator Refrigerant Line Nut	16 (22)
Refrigerant Hose-To-Compressor Bolt	18 (25)
	INCH Lbs. (N.m)
Blower Motor Bolts/Nuts	88 (10)
Condenser Nut	88 (10)
Heater-Evaporator Bolt	88 (10)
Instrument Panel Bolt	88 (10)
Receiver-Drier Bolt	88 (10)

1993 MANUAL A/C-HEATER SYSTEMS
Integra & Legend (Cont.)

WIRING DIAGRAMS

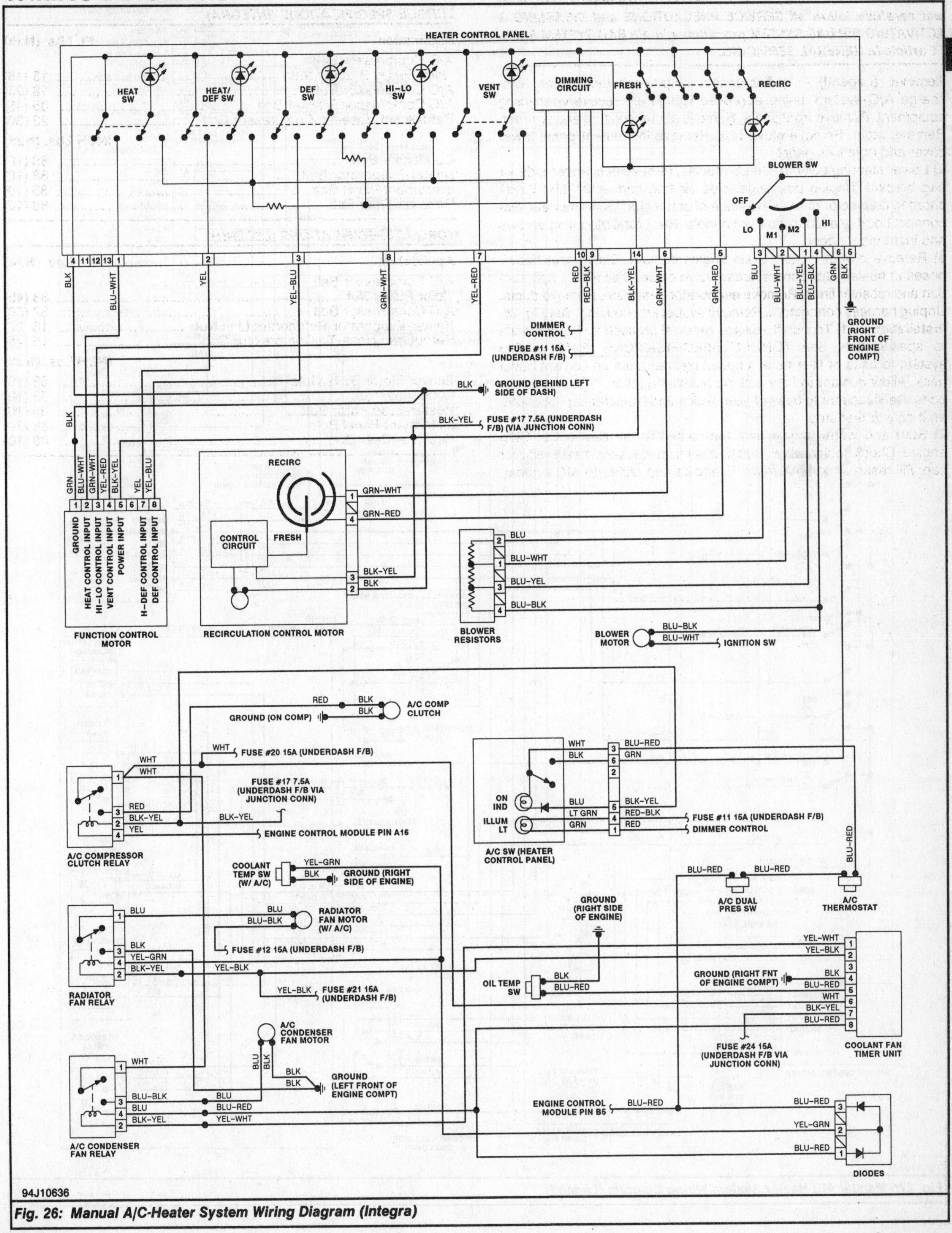

HEATER CONTROL PANEL
HEAT SW
HEAT/ DEF SW
DEF SW
HI-LO SW
VENT SW
DIMMING CIRCUIT
FRESH
RECIRC
BLOWER SW
OFF
LO
M1
M2
HI
4 11 12 13 1
2
3
8
7
10 9
14
6
5
3 2 1 4 6 5
BLK
BLU-WHT
YEL
YEL-BLU
GRN-WHT
YEL-RED
RED
RED-BLK
BLK-YEL
GRN-WHT
GRN-RED
BLU
BLU-WHT
BLU-YEL
BLU-BLK
GRN
BLK
GROUND (RIGHT FRONT OF ENGINE COMPT)
DIMMER CONTROL
FUSE #11 15A (UNDERDASH F/B)
BLK
GROUND (BEHIND LEFT SIDE OF DASH)
BLK-YEL
FUSE #17 7.5A (UNDERDASH F/B) (VIA JUNCTION CONN)
BLK
GRN
BLU-WHT
YEL-RED
BLK-YEL
YEL
YEL-BLU
1 2 3 4 5 6 7 8
GROUND
HEAT CONTROL INPUT
HI-LO CONTROL INPUT
VENT CONTROL INPUT
POWER INPUT
H-DEF CONTROL INPUT
DEF CONTROL INPUT
FUNCTION CONTROL MOTOR
RECIRC
FRESH
CONTROL CIRCUIT
GRN-WHT
GRN-RED
BLK-YEL
BLK
RECIRCULATION CONTROL MOTOR
BLU
BLU-WHT
BLU-YEL
BLU-BLK
BLOWER RESISTORS
BLOWER MOTOR
BLU-BLK
BLU-WHT
IGNITION SW
RED
BLK
BLK
GROUND (ON COMP)
A/C COMP CLUTCH
WHT
FUSE #20 15A (UNDERDASH F/B)
WHT
WHT
FUSE #17 7.5A (UNDERDASH F/B VIA JUNCTION CONN)
RED
BLK-YEL
YEL
BLK-YEL
ENGINE CONTROL MODULE PIN A16
A/C COMPRESSOR CLUTCH RELAY
WHT
BLK
BLU-RED
GRN
ON IND
ILLUM LT
BLU
LT GRN
GRN
BLK-YEL
RED-BLK
RED
FUSE #11 15A (UNDERDASH F/B)
DIMMER CONTROL
A/C SW (HEATER CONTROL PANEL)
COOLANT TEMP SW (W/ A/C)
YEL-GRN
BLK
GROUND (RIGHT SIDE OF ENGINE)
BLU-RED
BLU-RED
BLU-RED
A/C DUAL PRES SW
A/C THERMOSTAT
GROUND (RIGHT SIDE OF ENGINE)
BLU
BLU
BLU-BLK
RADIATOR FAN MOTOR (W/ A/C)
FUSE #12 15A (UNDERDASH F/B)
BLK
YEL-GRN
BLK-YEL
YEL-BLK
RADIATOR FAN RELAY
YEL-BLK
FUSE #21 15A (UNDERDASH F/B)
OIL TEMP SW
BLK
BLU-RED
YEL-WHT
YEL-BLK
GROUND (RIGHT FNT OF ENGINE COMPT)
BLK
BLU-RED
WHT
BLK-YEL
BLU-RED
FUSE #24 15A (UNDERDASH F/B VIA JUNCTION CONN)
COOLANT FAN TIMER UNIT
A/C CONDENSER FAN MOTOR
BLU
BLK
BLK
BLK
GROUND (LEFT FRONT OF ENGINE COMPT)
WHT
BLU-BLK
BLU
BLK-YEL
BLU
BLU-RED
YEL-WHT
A/C CONDENSER FAN RELAY
ENGINE CONTROL MODULE PIN B5
BLU-RED
BLU-RED
YEL-GRN
BLU-RED
DIODES
94J10636

Fig. 26: Manual A/C-Heater System Wiring Diagram (Integra)

1993 MANUAL A/C-HEATER SYSTEMS
Integra & Legend (Cont.)

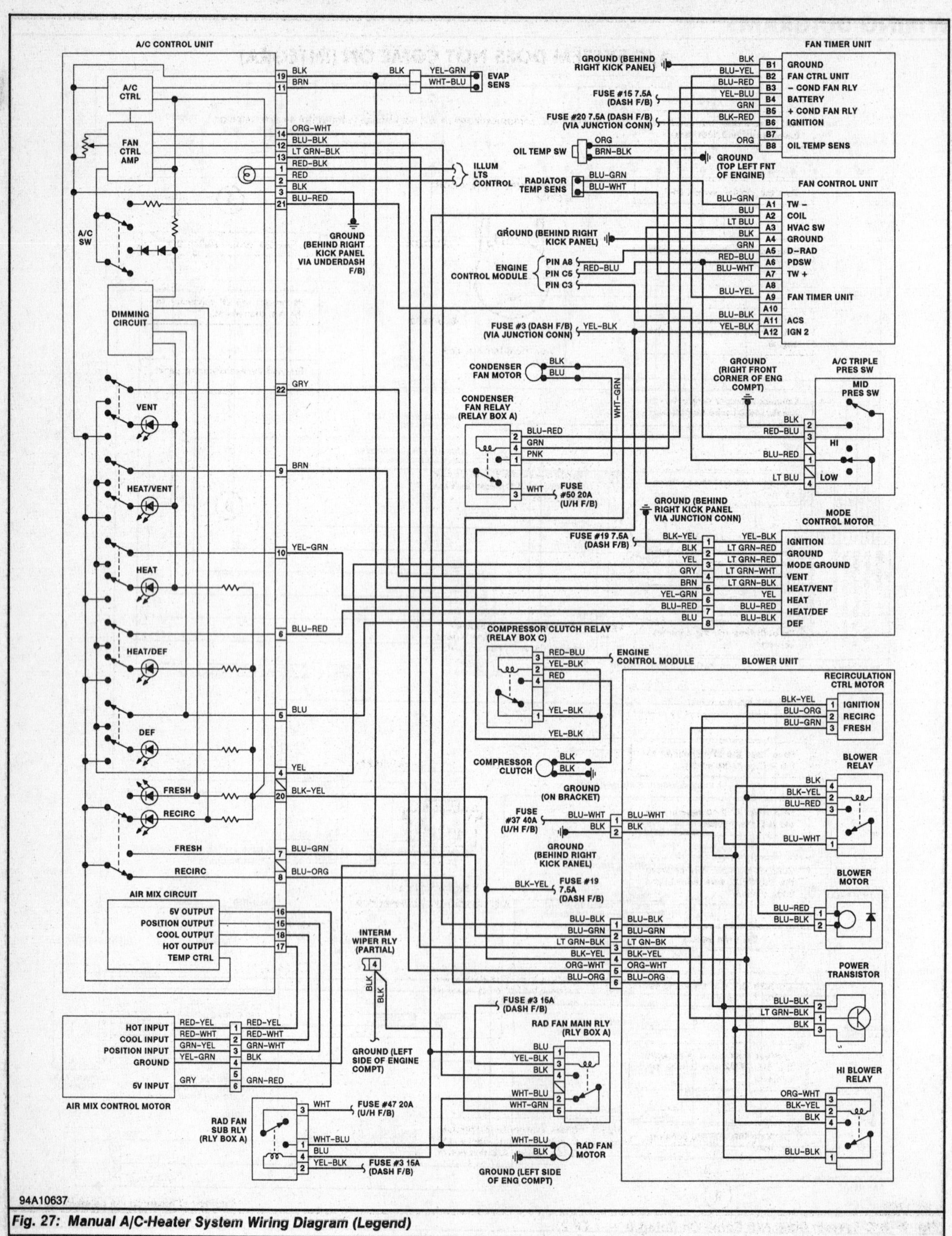
A/C CONTROL UNIT
A/C CTRL
FAN CTRL AMP
A/C SW
DIMMING CIRCUIT
VENT
HEAT/VENT
HEAT
HEAT/DEF
DEF
FRESH
RECIRC
AIR MIX CIRCUIT
5V OUTPUT
POSITION OUTPUT
COOL OUTPUT
HOT OUTPUT
TEMP CTRL
EVAP SENS
ILLUM LTS CONTROL
GROUND (BEHIND RIGHT KICK PANEL VIA UNDERDASH F/B)
FAN TIMER UNIT
GROUND (BEHIND RIGHT KICK PANEL)
FUSE #15 7.5A (DASH F/B)
FUSE #20 7.5A (DASH F/B) (VIA JUNCTION CONN)
OIL TEMP SW
GROUND (TOP LEFT FNT OF ENGINE)
B1 GROUND
B2 FAN CTRL UNIT
B3 - COND FAN RLY
B4 BATTERY
B5 + COND FAN RLY
B6 IGNITION
B7
B8 OIL TEMP SENS
RADIATOR TEMP SENS
FAN CONTROL UNIT
A1 TW -
A2 COIL
A3 HVAC SW
A4 GROUND
A5 D-RAD
A6 PDSW
A7 TW +
A8
A9 FAN TIMER UNIT
A10
A11 ACS
A12 IGN 2
GROUND (BEHIND RIGHT KICK PANEL)
ENGINE CONTROL MODULE
PIN A8
PIN C5
PIN C3
FUSE #3 (DASH F/B) (VIA JUNCTION CONN)
CONDENSER FAN MOTOR
CONDENSER FAN RELAY (RELAY BOX A)
FUSE #50 20A (U/H F/B)
GROUND (RIGHT FRONT CORNER OF ENG COMPT)
A/C TRIPLE PRES SW
MID PRES SW
HI
LOW
GROUND (BEHIND RIGHT KICK PANEL VIA JUNCTION CONN)
FUSE #19 7.5A (DASH F/B)
MODE CONTROL MOTOR
IGNITION
GROUND
MODE GROUND
VENT
HEAT/VENT
HEAT
HEAT/DEF
DEF
COMPRESSOR CLUTCH RELAY (RELAY BOX C)
ENGINE CONTROL MODULE
BLOWER UNIT
RECIRCULATION CTRL MOTOR
IGNITION
RECIRC
FRESH
COMPRESSOR CLUTCH
GROUND (ON BRACKET)
BLOWER RELAY
FUSE #37 40A (U/H F/B)
GROUND (BEHIND RIGHT KICK PANEL)
FUSE #19 7.5A (DASH F/B)
BLOWER MOTOR
POWER TRANSISTOR
INTERM WIPER RLY (PARTIAL)
GROUND (LEFT SIDE OF ENGINE COMPT)
FUSE #3 15A (DASH F/B)
RAD FAN MAIN RLY (RLY BOX A)
HI BLOWER RELAY
HOT INPUT
COOL INPUT
POSITION INPUT
GROUND
5V INPUT
AIR MIX CONTROL MOTOR
RAD FAN SUB RLY (RLY BOX A)
FUSE #47 20A (U/H F/B)
FUSE #3 15A (DASH F/B)
RAD FAN MOTOR
GROUND (LEFT SIDE OF ENG COMPT)
94A10637

Fig. 27: Manual A/C-Heater System Wiring Diagram (Legend)

1993 MANUAL A/C-HEATER SYSTEMS
Trouble Shooting – Integra

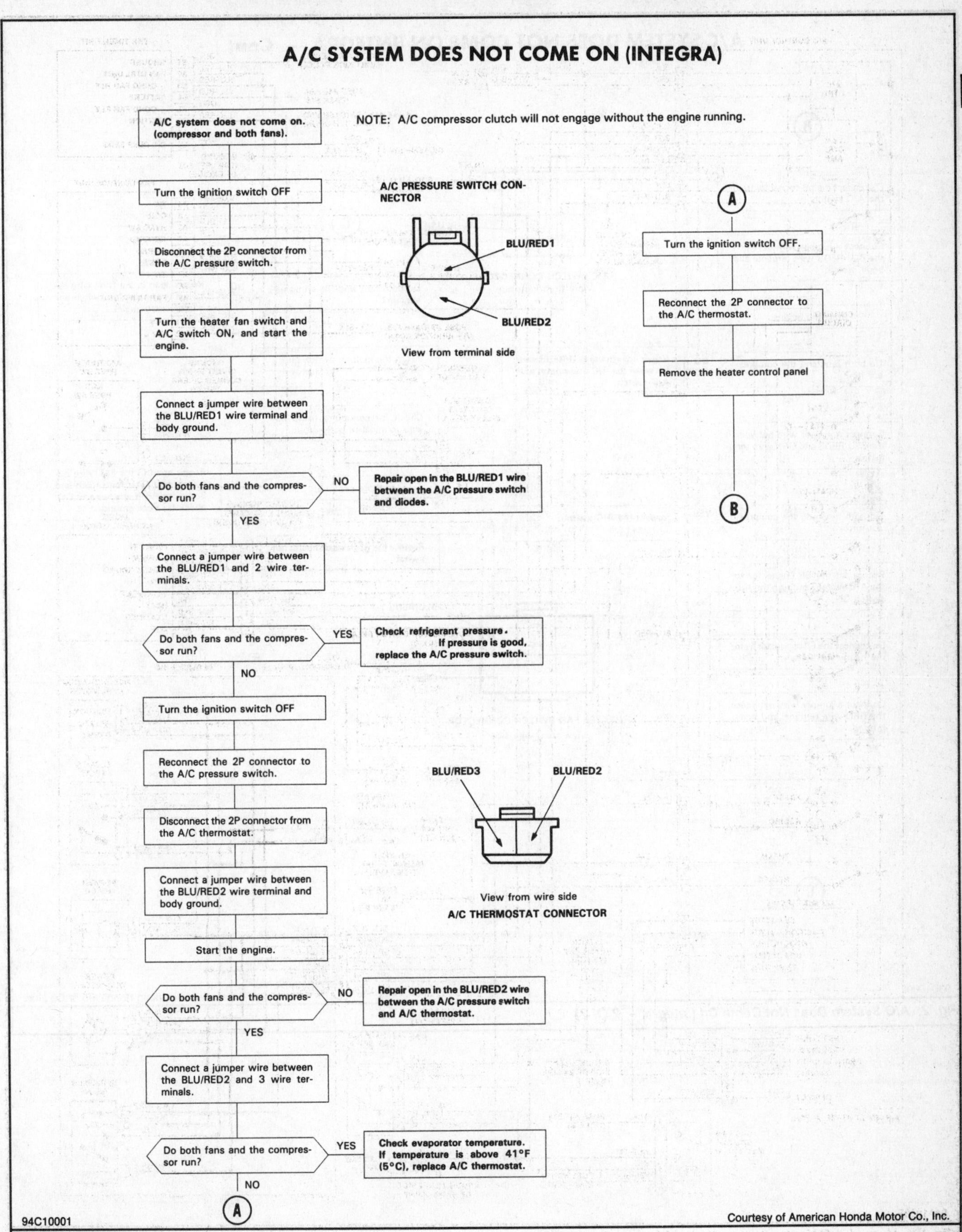
A/C SYSTEM DOES NOT COME ON (INTEGRA)
A/C system does not come on. (compressor and both fans).
NOTE: A/C compressor clutch will not engage without the engine running.
Turn the ignition switch OFF
A/C PRESSURE SWITCH CONNECTOR
BLU/RED1
BLU/RED2
View from terminal side
Disconnect the 2P connector from the A/C pressure switch.
Turn the heater fan switch and A/C switch ON, and start the engine.
Connect a jumper wire between the BLU/RED1 wire terminal and body ground.
Do both fans and the compressor run?
NO
Repair open in the BLU/RED1 wire between the A/C pressure switch and diodes.
YES
Connect a jumper wire between the BLU/RED1 and 2 wire terminals.
Do both fans and the compressor run?
YES
Check refrigerant pressure. If pressure is good, replace the A/C pressure switch.
NO
Turn the ignition switch OFF
Reconnect the 2P connector to the A/C pressure switch.
Disconnect the 2P connector from the A/C thermostat.
Connect a jumper wire between the BLU/RED2 wire terminal and body ground.
Start the engine.
Do both fans and the compressor run?
NO
Repair open in the BLU/RED2 wire between the A/C pressure switch and A/C thermostat.
YES
Connect a jumper wire between the BLU/RED2 and 3 wire terminals.
Do both fans and the compressor run?
YES
Check evaporator temperature. If temperature is above 41°F (5°C), replace A/C thermostat.
NO
A
BLU/RED3
BLU/RED2
View from wire side
A/C THERMOSTAT CONNECTOR
A
Turn the ignition switch OFF.
Reconnect the 2P connector to the A/C thermostat.
Remove the heater control panel
B
94C10001
Courtesy of American Honda Motor Co., Inc.

Fig. 1: A/C System Does Not Come On (Integra – 1 Of 2)

1993 MANUAL A/C-HEATER SYSTEMS
Trouble Shooting – Integra (Cont.)

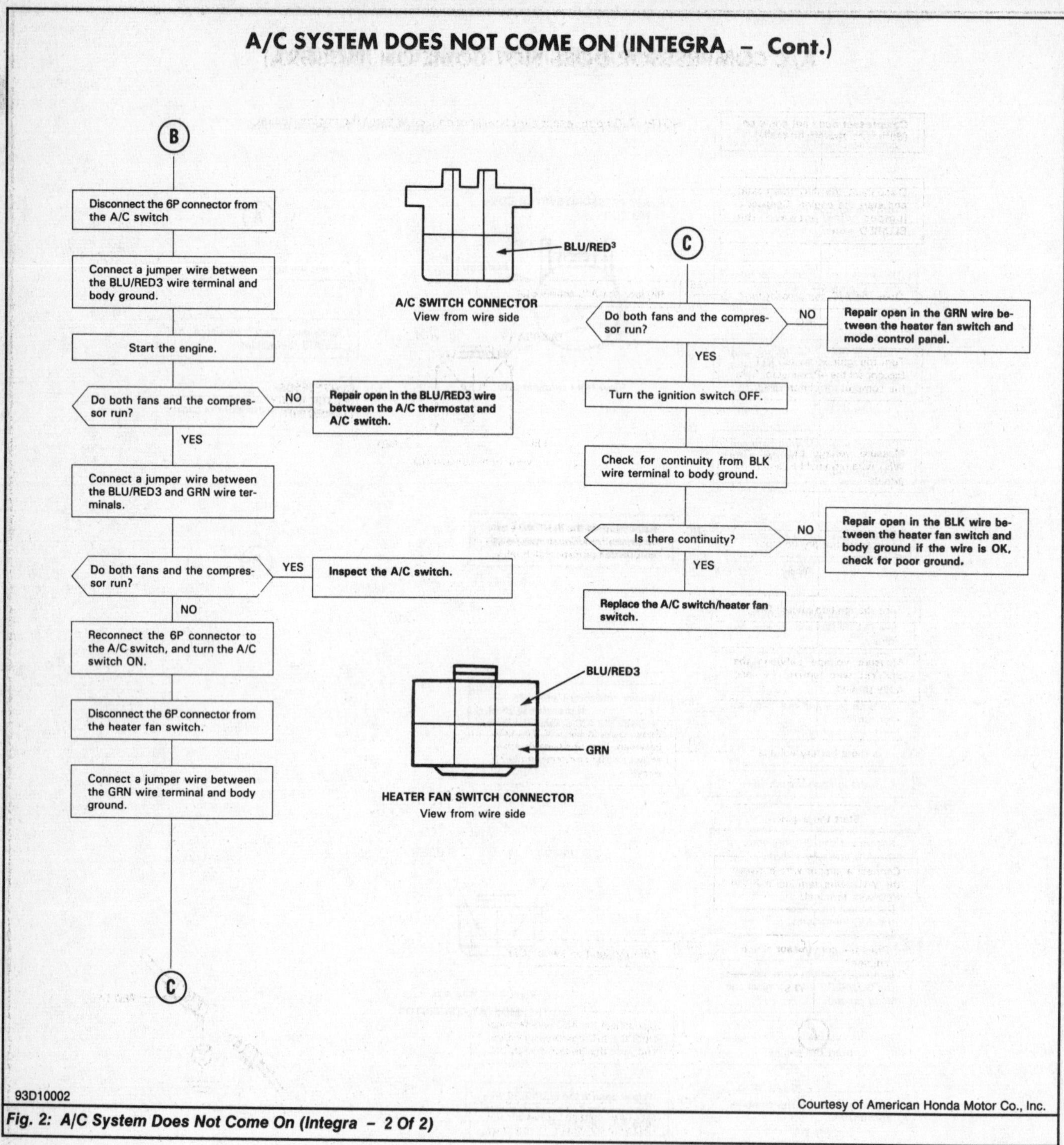
A/C SYSTEM DOES NOT COME ON (INTEGRA – Cont.)
B
Disconnect the 6P connector from the A/C switch
Connect a jumper wire between the BLU/RED3 wire terminal and body ground.
Start the engine.
Do both fans and the compressor run?
NO
Repair open in the BLU/RED3 wire between the A/C thermostat and A/C switch.
YES
Connect a jumper wire between the BLU/RED3 and GRN wire terminals.
Do both fans and the compressor run?
YES
Inspect the A/C switch.
NO
Reconnect the 6P connector to the A/C switch, and turn the A/C switch ON.
Disconnect the 6P connector from the heater fan switch.
Connect a jumper wire between the GRN wire terminal and body ground.
C
BLU/RED3
A/C SWITCH CONNECTOR
View from wire side
BLU/RED3
GRN
HEATER FAN SWITCH CONNECTOR
View from wire side
C
Do both fans and the compressor run?
NO
Repair open in the GRN wire between the heater fan switch and mode control panel.
YES
Turn the ignition switch OFF.
Check for continuity from BLK wire terminal to body ground.
Is there continuity?
NO
Repair open in the BLK wire between the heater fan switch and body ground if the wire is OK, check for poor ground.
YES
Replace the A/C switch/heater fan switch.
93D10002
Courtesy of American Honda Motor Co., Inc.

Fig. 2: A/C System Does Not Come On (Integra – 2 Of 2)

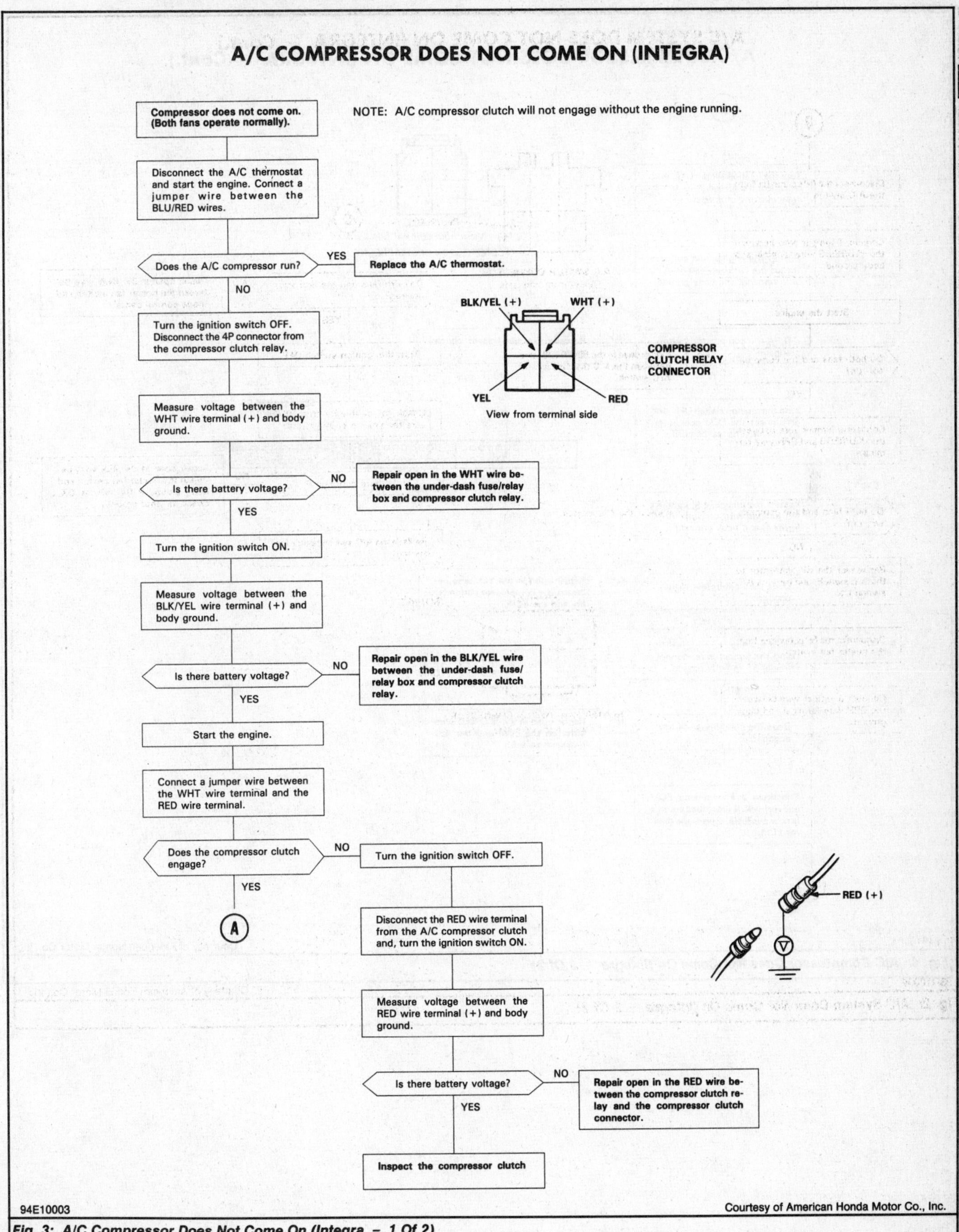
A/C COMPRESSOR DOES NOT COME ON (INTEGRA)
Compressor does not come on. (Both fans operate normally).
NOTE: A/C compressor clutch will not engage without the engine running.
Disconnect the A/C thermostat and start the engine. Connect a jumper wire between the BLU/RED wires.
Does the A/C compressor run?
YES
Replace the A/C thermostat.
NO
Turn the ignition switch OFF. Disconnect the 4P connector from the compressor clutch relay.
BLK/YEL (+)
WHT (+)
COMPRESSOR CLUTCH RELAY CONNECTOR
YEL
RED
View from terminal side
Measure voltage between the WHT wire terminal (+) and body ground.
Is there battery voltage?
NO
Repair open in the WHT wire between the under-dash fuse/relay box and compressor clutch relay.
YES
Turn the ignition switch ON.
Measure voltage between the BLK/YEL wire terminal (+) and body ground.
Is there battery voltage?
NO
Repair open in the BLK/YEL wire between the under-dash fuse/relay box and compressor clutch relay.
YES
Start the engine.
Connect a jumper wire between the WHT wire terminal and the RED wire terminal.
Does the compressor clutch engage?
NO
Turn the ignition switch OFF.
YES
A
Disconnect the RED wire terminal from the A/C compressor clutch and, turn the ignition switch ON.
RED (+)
Measure voltage between the RED wire terminal (+) and body ground.
Is there battery voltage?
NO
Repair open in the RED wire between the compressor clutch relay and the compressor clutch connector.
YES
Inspect the compressor clutch
94E10003
Courtesy of American Honda Motor Co., Inc.

Fig. 3: A/C Compressor Does Not Come On (Integra – 1 Of 2)

1993 MANUAL A/C-HEATER SYSTEMS
Trouble Shooting – Integra (Cont.)

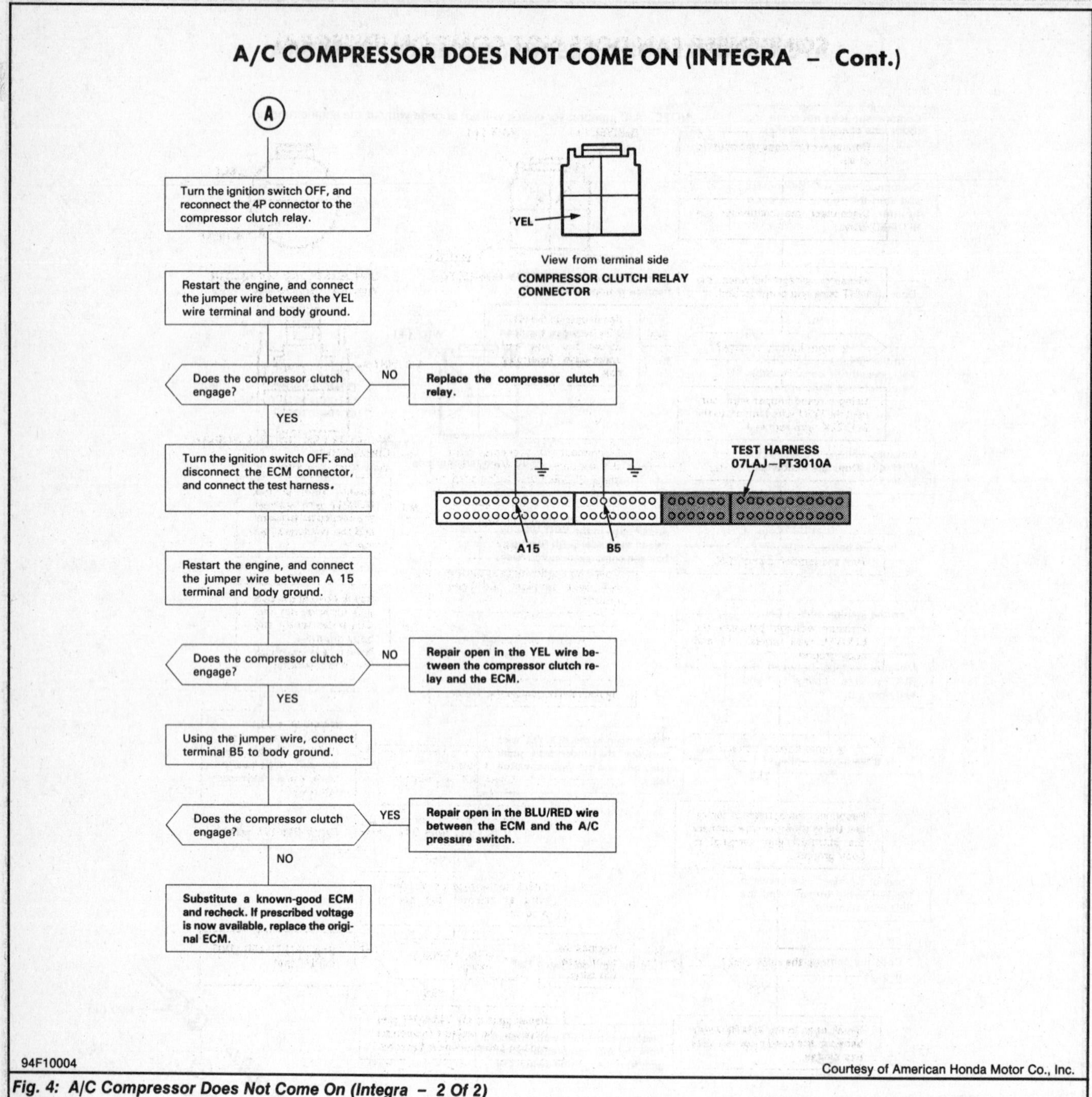
A/C COMPRESSOR DOES NOT COME ON (INTEGRA – Cont.)
A
Turn the ignition switch OFF, and reconnect the 4P connector to the compressor clutch relay.
YEL
View from terminal side
COMPRESSOR CLUTCH RELAY CONNECTOR
Restart the engine, and connect the jumper wire between the YEL wire terminal and body ground.
Does the compressor clutch engage?
NO
Replace the compressor clutch relay.
YES
Turn the ignition switch OFF. and disconnect the ECM connector, and connect the test harness.
TEST HARNESS 07LAJ–PT3010A
A15
B5
Restart the engine, and connect the jumper wire between A 15 terminal and body ground.
Does the compressor clutch engage?
NO
Repair open in the YEL wire between the compressor clutch relay and the ECM.
YES
Using the jumper wire, connect terminal B5 to body ground.
Does the compressor clutch engage?
YES
Repair open in the BLU/RED wire between the ECM and the A/C pressure switch.
NO
Substitute a known-good ECM and recheck. If prescribed voltage is now available, replace the original ECM.
94F10004
Courtesy of American Honda Motor Co., Inc.

Fig. 4: A/C Compressor Does Not Come On (Integra – 2 Of 2)

1993 MANUAL A/C-HEATER SYSTEMS
Trouble Shooting – Integra (Cont.)

CONDENSER FAN DOES NOT COME ON (INTEGRA)

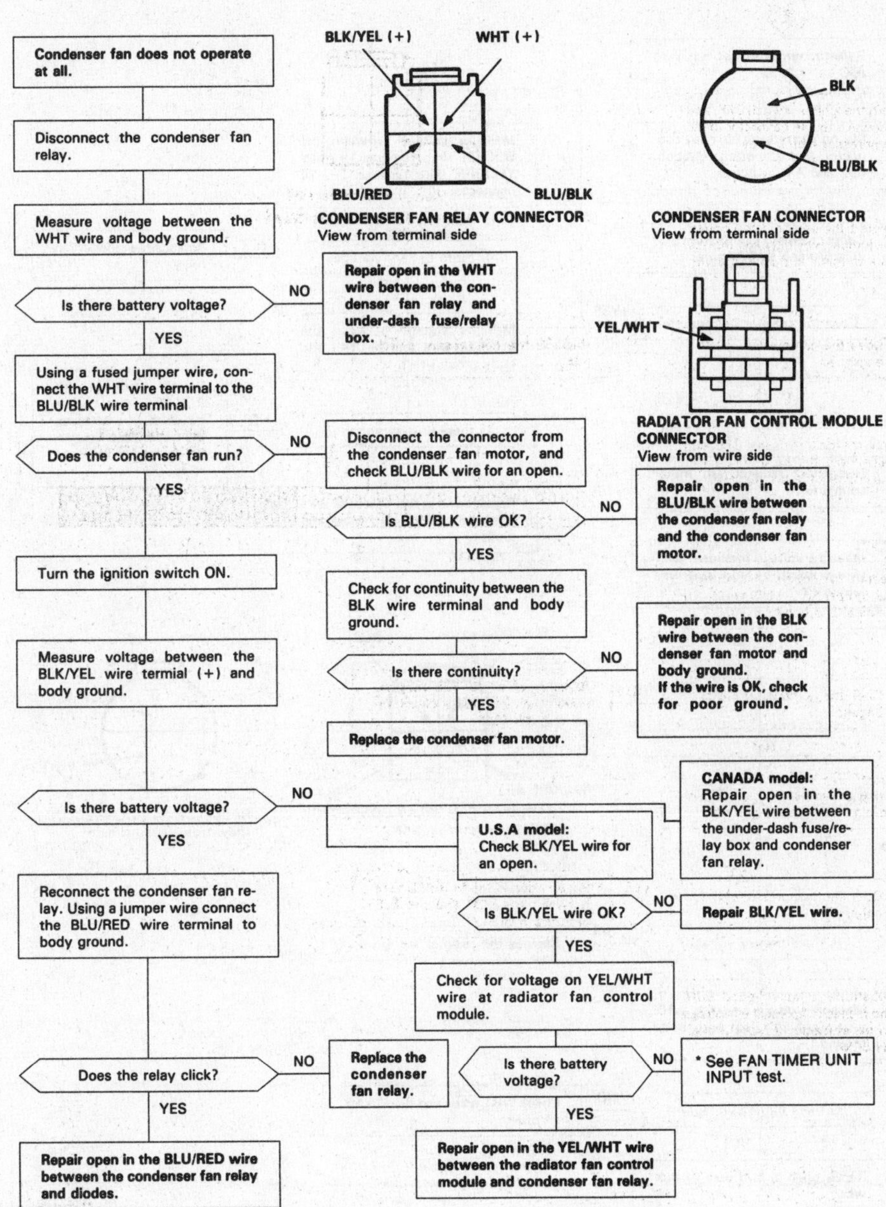
Condenser fan does not operate at all.
Disconnect the condenser fan relay.
Measure voltage between the WHT wire and body ground.
Is there battery voltage?
NO
Repair open in the WHT wire between the condenser fan relay and under-dash fuse/relay box.
YES
Using a fused jumper wire, connect the WHT wire terminal to the BLU/BLK wire terminal
Does the condenser fan run?
NO
Disconnect the connector from the condenser fan motor, and check BLU/BLK wire for an open.
Is BLU/BLK wire OK?
NO
Repair open in the BLU/BLK wire between the condenser fan relay and the condenser fan motor.
YES
Check for continuity between the BLK wire terminal and body ground.
Is there continuity?
NO
Repair open in the BLK wire between the condenser fan motor and body ground. If the wire is OK, check for poor ground.
YES
Replace the condenser fan motor.
YES
Turn the ignition switch ON.
Measure voltage between the BLK/YEL wire termial (+) and body ground.
Is there battery voltage?
NO
CANADA model: Repair open in the BLK/YEL wire between the under-dash fuse/relay box and condenser fan relay.
U.S.A model: Check BLK/YEL wire for an open.
Is BLK/YEL wire OK?
NO
Repair BLK/YEL wire.
YES
Check for voltage on YEL/WHT wire at radiator fan control module.
Is there battery voltage?
NO
* See FAN TIMER UNIT INPUT test.
YES
Repair open in the YEL/WHT wire between the radiator fan control module and condenser fan relay.
YES
Reconnect the condenser fan relay. Using a jumper wire connect the BLU/RED wire terminal to body ground.
Does the relay click?
NO
Replace the condenser fan relay.
YES
Repair open in the BLU/RED wire between the condenser fan relay and diodes.
BLK/YEL (+)
WHT (+)
BLU/RED
BLU/BLK
CONDENSER FAN RELAY CONNECTOR
View from terminal side
BLK
BLU/BLK
CONDENSER FAN CONNECTOR
View from terminal side
YEL/WHT
RADIATOR FAN CONTROL MODULE CONNECTOR
View from wire side

* See TESTING in INTEGRA & LEGEND MANUAL A/C-HEATER SYSTEMS article.

94G10005

Fig. 5: Condenser Fan Does Not Come On (Integra)

1993 MANUAL A/C-HEATER SYSTEMS
Trouble Shooting – Integra (Cont.)

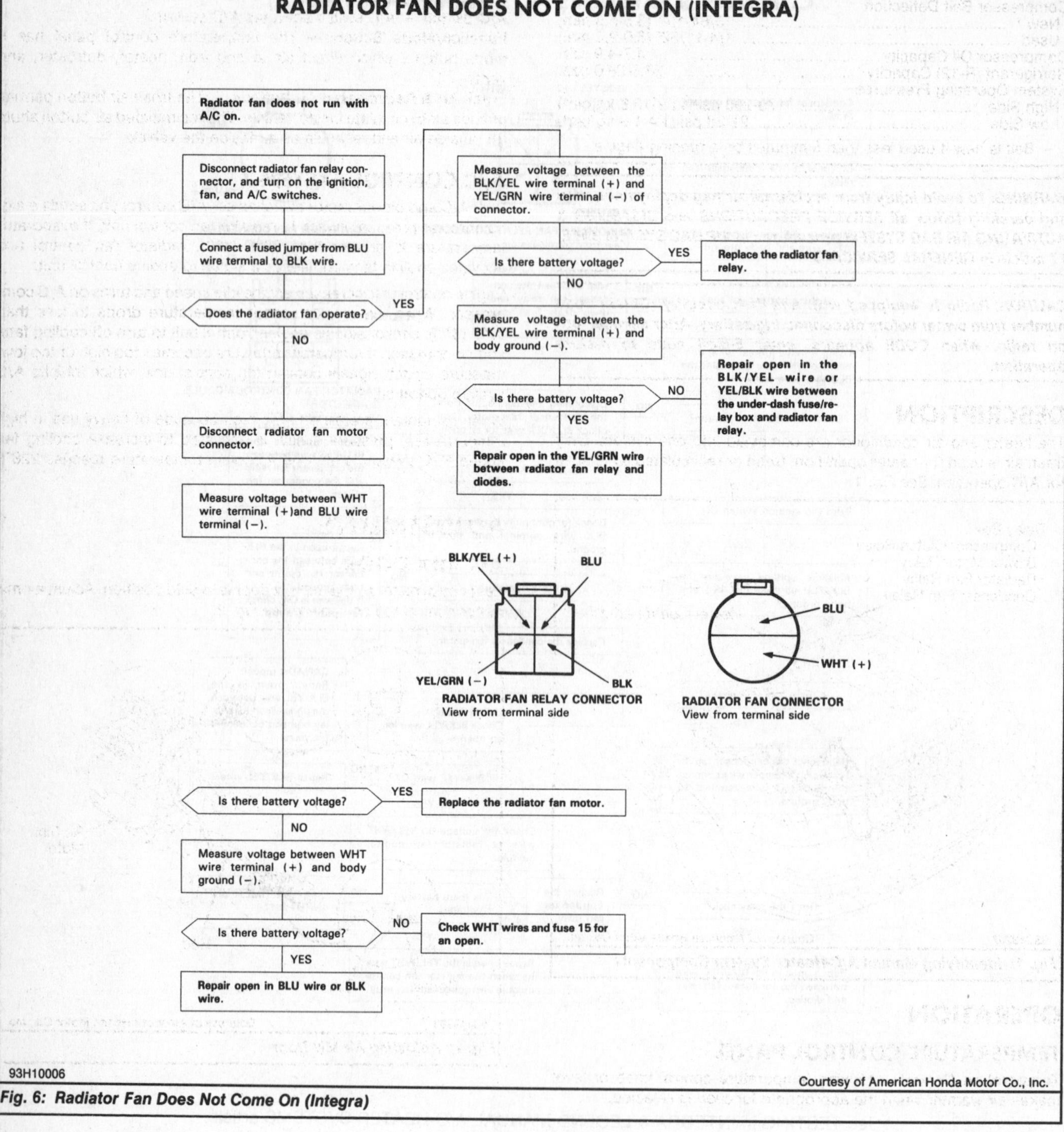
RADIATOR FAN DOES NOT COME ON (INTEGRA)
Radiator fan does not run with A/C on.
Disconnect radiator fan relay connector, and turn on the ignition, fan, and A/C switches.
Connect a fused jumper from BLU wire terminal to BLK wire.
Does the radiator fan operate?
YES
NO
Measure voltage between the BLK/YEL wire terminal (+) and YEL/GRN wire terminal (–) of connector.
Is there battery voltage?
YES
Replace the radiator fan relay.
NO
Measure voltage between the BLK/YEL wire terminal (+) and body ground (–).
Is there battery voltage?
NO
Repair open in the BLK/YEL wire or YEL/BLK wire between the under-dash fuse/relay box and radiator fan relay.
YES
Repair open in the YEL/GRN wire between radiator fan relay and diodes.
Disconnect radiator fan motor connector.
Measure voltage between WHT wire terminal (+)and BLU wire terminal (–).
BLK/YEL (+)
BLU
YEL/GRN (–)
BLK
RADIATOR FAN RELAY CONNECTOR
View from terminal side
BLU
WHT (+)
RADIATOR FAN CONNECTOR
View from terminal side
Is there battery voltage?
YES
Replace the radiator fan motor.
NO
Measure voltage between WHT wire terminal (+) and body ground (–).
Is there battery voltage?
NO
Check WHT wires and fuse 15 for an open.
YES
Repair open in BLU wire or BLK wire.
93H10006
Courtesy of American Honda Motor Co., Inc.

Fig. 6: Radiator Fan Does Not Come On (Integra)

1993 MANUAL A/C-HEATER SYSTEMS
Vigor

SPECIFICATIONS

Compressor Type .... Nippondenso 10-Cyl.
Compressor Belt Deflection
  New [1] .... 13/64-1/4" (3.5-5.5 mm)
  Used .... 1/4-11/32" (6.0-9.0 mm)
Compressor Oil Capacity .... 4.7-4.9 ozs.
Refrigerant (R-12) Capacity .... 26.5-28.0 ozs.
System Operating Pressures
  High Side .... 170-200 psi (11.9-13.8 kg/cm²)
  Low Side .... 21-28 psi (1.4-1.9 kg/cm²)

[1] - Belt is new if used less than 5 minutes on a running engine.

WARNING: To avoid injury from accidental air bag deployment, read and carefully follow all SERVICE PRECAUTIONS and DISABLING & ACTIVATING AIR BAG SYSTEM procedures in AIR BAG SYSTEM SAFETY article in GENERAL SERVICING.

CAUTION: Radio is equipped with anti-theft circuitry. Obtain code number from owner before disconnecting battery. After service, turn on radio. When CODE appears, enter 5-digit code to restore operation.

DESCRIPTION

The heater and air conditioner are combined into one system. Only fresh air is used for heater operation; fresh or recirculated air is used for A/C operation. *See Fig. 1.*

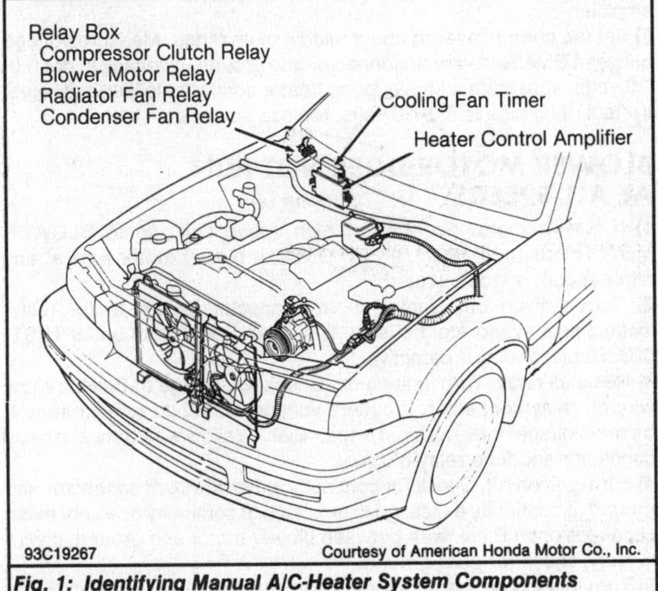
Relay Box
Compressor Clutch Relay
Blower Motor Relay
Radiator Fan Relay
Condenser Fan Relay
Cooling Fan Timer
Heater Control Amplifier
93C19267
Courtesy of American Honda Motor Co., Inc.

Fig. 1: Identifying Manual A/C-Heater System Components

OPERATION

TEMPERATURE CONTROL PANEL

Temperature Control - Moving temperature control knob or lever makes air warmer when the appropriate function is selected.

Fan Control - Moving fan control adjusts fan speed. Fan circulates warm, cool, or outside air depending on settings of temperature dial and function buttons or lever.

A/C Switch - A/C switch activates A/C system.

Function/Mode Buttons - The temperature control panel has 5 mode buttons which direct air to and from heater, defroster, and vents.

Fresh Air & Recirculated Air Buttons - The fresh air button permits outside air to circulate inside vehicle. The recirculated air button shuts off outside air and recirculates air inside the vehicle.

A/C CONTROL SYSTEM

With A/C and blower motor switches on, A/C control unit sends a signal through pressure switch to radiator fan control unit. If evaporator temperature is greater than 39°F (4°C), radiator fan control unit activates cooling fans and sends a signal to engine control unit.

Engine control unit increases engine idle speed and turns on A/C compressor. When evaporator sensor temperature drops to less than 37°F (3°C), sensor signals engine control unit to turn off cooling fans and compressor. If refrigerant pressure becomes too high or too low, pressure switch signals cooling fan control unit, which inhibits A/C system operation.

When refrigerant pressure is too high because of heavy use in high temperatures, pressure switch is activated to increase cooling fan speed. A/C system is shut off if coolant temperature reaches 228°F (109°C).

ADJUSTMENTS

AIR MIX DOOR

Set control panel so that air mix door is in cold position. Adjust air mix motor control rod as shown. *See Fig. 2.*

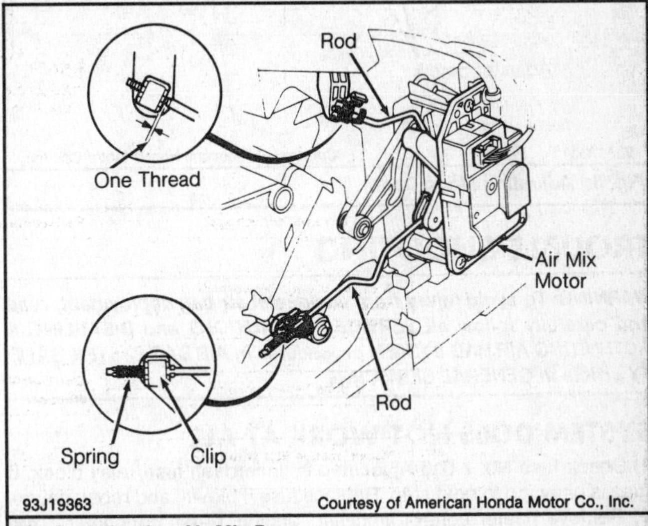
Rod
One Thread
Air Mix
Motor
Rod
Spring
Clip
93J19363
Courtesy of American Honda Motor Co., Inc.

Fig. 2: Adjusting Air Mix Door

1993 MANUAL A/C-HEATER SYSTEMS
Vigor (Cont.)

MODE DOOR

Hold door guide plate with pin. *See Fig. 3.* Secure rod with clip. Rotate adjuster screws as necessary.

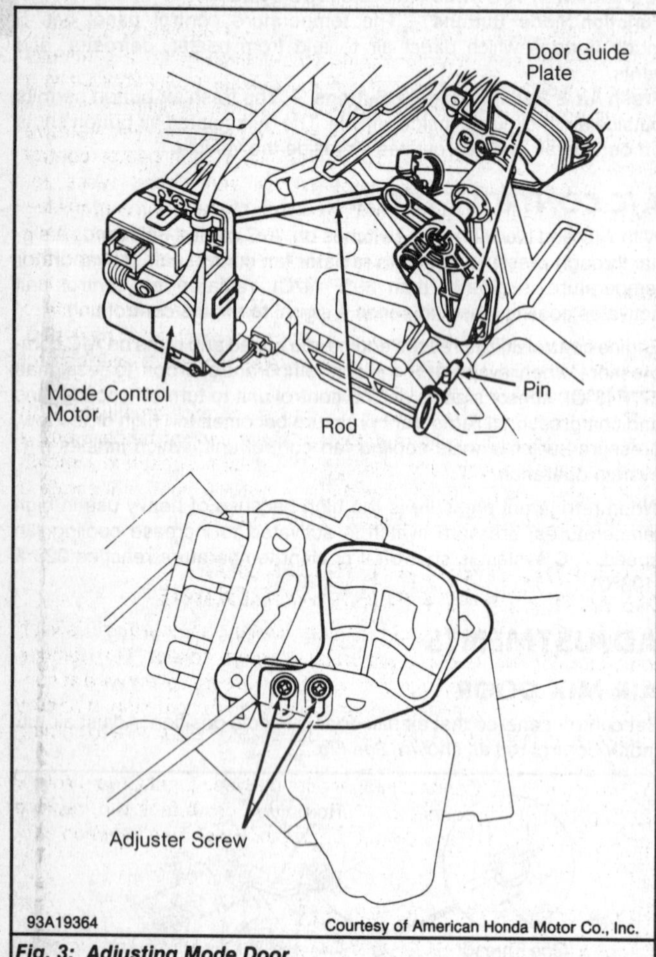
Door Guide
Plate
Mode Control
Motor
Rod
Pin
Adjuster Screw
93A19364
Courtesy of American Honda Motor Co., Inc.

Fig. 3: Adjusting Mode Door

TROUBLE SHOOTING

WARNING: To avoid injury from accidental air bag deployment, read and carefully follow all SERVICE PRECAUTIONS and DISABLING & ACTIVATING AIR BAG SYSTEM procedures in AIR BAG SYSTEM SAFETY article in GENERAL SERVICING.

SYSTEM DOES NOT WORK AT ALL

1) Check fuse No. 7 (7.5 A) located in underdash fuse/relay block. If fuse is okay, go to next step. Replace fuse if blown, and repair cause.
2) Remove heater control amplifier. Unplug 14-pin connector. Turn ignition on. Using a DVOM, check for battery voltage at Black/Yellow wire terminal and ground. If battery voltage exists, go to next step. If battery voltage does not exist, repair Black/Yellow wire between fuse No. 7 and heater control amplifier connector.
3) Turn ignition off. Check for continuity between Black wire on connector and ground. If continuity does not exist, check for open Black wire between connector and ground. If wire is okay, check for poor ground. If continuity exists, substitute a known good heater control amplifier. Retest system.

BLOWER MOTOR DOES NOT RUN AT ALL

1) Check fuses No. 7 (7.5 A) and 17 (30 A), located in underdash fuse/relay block. If fuses are okay, go to next step. Replace fuse if is blown, and repair cause.
2) Disconnect 2-pin connector from blower motor. Turn ignition on. Check for battery voltage at Blue/White wire at connector. If battery voltage exists, go to next step. If battery voltage does not exist, test blower motor relay. See RELAY under TESTING.
3) Turn ignition off. Reconnect blower motor connector. Turn ignition on. Connect jumper wire between Blue wire of blower motor and ground. If blower motor runs, repair open Blue wire. If blower motor does not run, replace blower motor.

BLOWER MOTOR RUNS AT HIGH SPEED ONLY

1) Turn ignition off. Unplug 3-pin connector from power transistor, located on evaporator housing. Connect jumper wire between Blue wire on connector and ground. Turn ignition on. If motor runs at high speed, go to next step. If motor does not run at high speed, repair open Blue wire between power transistor and blower motor.
2) Connect jumper wire between Blue and Black wires of power transistor connector. If motor runs at high speed, go to next step. If motor does not run at high speed, repair open circuit between power transistor connector and ground.
3) Turn ignition off. Remove heater control amplifier. Disconnect 22-pin connector from heater control amplifier. Check continuity in Blue/Red wire between power transistor and heater control amplifier. If continuity exists, go to next step. If continuity does not exist, check for open Blue/Red wire between power transistor and heater control amplifier.
4) Turn ignition on. Measure voltage between Blue wire terminal of heater control amplifier 22-pin connector and ground. If battery voltage is present, go to next step. If battery voltage is not present, repair open Blue wire between the blower motor and heater control amplifier.
5) Set fan control lever to about middle of its range. Measure voltage between Blue/Red wire at connector and ground. If voltage is not 6.0-7.0 volts, substitute a known good heater control amplifier and retest system. If voltage is 6.0-7.0 volts, replace power transistor.

BLOWER MOTOR DOES NOT RUN AT ALL SPEEDS

1) If blower motor operates at high speed only, go to BLOWER MOTOR RUNS AT HIGH SPEED ONLY. If blower motor runs at any other speed, go to next step.
2) Turn ignition off. Unplug 4-pin connector blower motor relay, located near evaporator housing. Test relay. See RELAY under TESTING. Replace relay if defective.
3) Reinstall relay. Turn ignition on. Check for voltage at Black/Yellow wire on relay connector. If battery voltage exists, go to next step. If battery voltage does not exist, repair Black/Yellow wire between relay connector and fuse/relay block.
4) Turn ignition off. Check for continuity in Black wire at connector and ground. If continuity exists, go to next step. If continuity does not exist, check for open Black wire between blower motor and ground. If wire is okay, check for poor ground.
5) Turn ignition on. Using jumper wire, connect Blue and Black wires at connector. If blower runs, go to next step. If blower does not run, repair open Blue wire between blower high speed relay and blower motor connector.
6) Unplug connector from blower motor high speed relay, located on side of blower unit. Test relay. See RELAY under TESTING. Replace relay if defective. Reinstall blower motor relay. Remove heater control amplifier and disconnect 14-pin connector.
7) Using jumper wire, connect Green wire at heater control amplifier to ground. If blower runs, go to next step. If blower does not run, repair open Green wire between heater control amplifier and blower motor high speed relay.
8) Turn ignition off. Remove heater control panel and heater control amplifier. Unplug 14-pin connector from heater control panel. Check Green/Blue, Green/Black and Green/White wires for continuity between heater control panel and heater control amplifier. If continuity exists, go to next step. If continuity does not exist for any wire, repair open circuit in affected wire.
9) Reconnect connector to heater control amplifier. Turn ignition on. Measure voltage between Green/Blue wire at heater control panel connector and ground. If meter indicates about 5 volts, substitute a

1993 MANUAL A/C-HEATER SYSTEMS Vigor (Cont.)

known good heater control panel. If meter does not indicate about 5 volts, substitute a known good heater control amplifier. Retest system.

RECIRCULATION FUNCTION DOES NOT WORK

1) Turn ignition off. Unplug 7-pin connector from recirculation control motor, located on side of A/C-heater unit. Test recirculation control motor. See RECIRCULATION CONTROL MOTOR under TESTING. Check door for freedom of movement. If motor and door are okay, go to next step. Replace motor if defective.
2) Remove heater control amplifier. Unplug 22-pin connector from heater control amplifier. Check Yellow/Red, Yellow, Green/Black, Yellow/Green and Yellow/Blue wires for continuity between heater control amplifier and recirculation control motor. If all wires are okay, go to next step. Repair any defective wire.
3) Check Yellow/Red, Yellow, Green/Black, Yellow/Green and Yellow/Blue wires for continuity to ground and to each other. If continuity to ground or each other does not exist, go to next step. If continuity exists for any wire, repair shorted wires.
4) Unplug 14-pin connector from heater control amplifier. Remove heater control panel. Unplug 14-pin connector from heater control panel. Check Orange wire at connector for continuity between heater control panel and heater control amplifier. If continuity exists, go to next step. If continuity does not exist, repair Orange wire.
5) Check for continuity between Orange wire and ground. If continuity does not exist, go to next step. If continuity exists, repair short circuit in Orange wire between heater control amplifier and heater control panel.
6) Reconnect 14-pin connector to heater control panel. Press recirculation button. Check for continuity between Orange wire and ground. If continuity exists, substitute a known good heater control amplifier. If continuity does not exist, substitute a known good heater control panel. Retest system.

NO AIR DIRECTION CONTROL

1) Turn ignition off. Unplug 7-pin connector from mode control motor, located on side of A/C-heater unit. Test mode control motor and ensure doors move freely. See MODE CONTROL MOTOR under TESTING. If motor is okay, go to next step. Replace motor if defective.
2) Remove heater control amplifier. Unplug 22-pin connector. Check White/Red, White/Blue, White/Green, White/Yellow, Green/Black, Brown/White and Red/White wires for continuity between mode control motor and heater control amplifier. If continuity exists, go to next step. If continuity does not exist for any wire, repair open circuit in associated wire.
3) Check White/Red, White/Blue, White/Green, White/Yellow, Green/Black, Brown/White and Red/White wires for continuity to ground and to each other. If continuity does not exist, go to next step. If continuity exists for any wire, repair shorted wires.
4) Unplug 14-pin connector from heater control amplifier. Remove heater control panel. Unplug 14-pin connector from heater control panel. Check Orange/White and Green wires for continuity between heater control panel and heater control amplifier. If continuity exists, go to next step. If no continuity exists, repair appropriate wire.
5) Check Orange/White and Green wires for continuity to ground and to each other. If continuity does not exist, go to next step. If continuity exists, repair short in wire(s) between heater control amplifier and heater control panel.
6) Reconnect 14-pin connector to heater control amplifier. Turn ignition on. Measure voltage between Green wire at heater control panel connector and ground. If voltage is 4-6 volts, substitute a known good heater control panel. If voltage is not 4-6 volts, substitute a known good heater control amplifier. Retest system.

NO HOT OR COLD AIR FROM BLOWER

1) Turn ignition off. Unplug 7-pin connector from air mix motor. Test air mix motor. See AIR MIX MOTOR under TESTING. Ensure air mix door moves freely. If air mix motor is okay, go to next step. Replace air mix motor if defective.
2) Remove heater control amplifier. Unplug 22-pin connector. Check Green/Blue, Red/Blue, Green/Black, Red/Yellow and Red/Black wires for continuity between air mix motor and heater control amplifier. If continuity exists, go to next step. If continuity does not exist for any wire, repair open circuit in associated wire.
3) Check Green/Blue, Red/Blue, Green/Black, Red/Yellow and Red/Black wires for continuity to ground and to each other. If continuity does not exist, go to next step. If continuity exists, repair shorted wire between air mix control motor and heater control amplifier.
4) Unplug 14-pin connector from heater control amplifier. Remove heater control panel. Unplug 14-pin connector from heater control panel. Check Green/Yellow, Green/White and Green wires for continuity between heater control panel and heater control amplifier. If continuity exists, go to next step. If continuity does not exist, check for open in wire(s) between heater control amplifier and heater control panel.
5) Check Green/Yellow, Green/White and Green wires for continuity to ground and to each other. If continuity does not exist, go to next step. If continuity exists, repair any short in wire(s) between heater control amplifier and heater control panel.
6) Reconnect 14-pin connector to heater control amplifier. Turn ignition on. Measure voltage between Green wire at heater control panel connector and ground. If voltage is 4-6 volts, substitute a known good heater control panel. If voltage is not 4-6 volts, substitute a known good heater control amplifier. Retest system.

FANS RUN WHEN A/C IS ON, BUT DO NOT RUN FOR ENGINE COOLING

1) Turn ignition off. Unplug engine coolant temperature switch connector, located near coolant outlet hose on radiator. Turn ignition on. Check for battery voltage between Light Green/Yellow wire at connector and ground. If battery voltage exists, go to next step. If battery voltage does not exist, repair open Light Green/Yellow wire to cooling fan switch.
2) Turn ignition off. Connect jumper wire between Light Green/Yellow and Black wires at connector. Turn ignition on. If fans run, replace cooling fan switch. If fans do not run, repair Black wire between connector and ground.

FANS DO NOT RUN AT ALL

1) Check fuses No. 8 (7.5 A), 34 (15 A) and 38 (15 A). If fuses are okay, go to next step. Replace fuse if blown, and repair cause.
2) Turn ignition off. Remove cooling fan timer, located behind instrument panel on passenger side. Unplug 8-pin connector from timer. Turn ignition on. Check for battery voltage at Yellow/Black wire on connector. If battery voltage exists, go to next step. If battery voltage does not exist, repair Yellow/Black wire between fuse block and timer.
3) Turn ignition off. Reconnect wiring to timer. Turn ignition on. Backprobe Yellow/White and Yellow wires at connector. If battery voltage exists, go to next step. If battery voltage does not exist, replace cooling fan timer.
4) Turn ignition off. Unplug connectors from Electronic Control Module (ECM), located under right footwell. Connect ECM Test Harness (07LAJ-PT3010A) to wire harness only. DO NOT connect test harness to ECM.
5) Turn ignition on. Using jumper wire, connect test harness terminal A12 to ground. If radiator and condenser fans do not run, go to next step. If both fans run, substitute a known good ECM. Retest system.
6) Check for battery voltage at test harness terminal A12. If battery voltage exists, repair open Black wire between fan motors and ground. If battery voltage does not exist, repair open Light Green wire between relay box and ECM.

CONDENSER FAN DOES NOT RUN WHEN A/C IS ON

1) Check fuse No. 34 (15 A). If fuse is okay, go to next step. Replace fuse if blown, and repair cause.

1993 MANUAL A/C-HEATER SYSTEMS Vigor (Cont.)

2) Turn ignition off. Remove condenser fan relay from underdash relay box. Check for battery voltage at terminal No. 1 (White/Green wire) of relay socket. If battery voltage exists, go to next step. If battery voltage does not exist, repair White wire between underdash relay box and underhood fuse/relay block.
3) Turn ignition on. Check for battery voltage at terminal No. 2 (Light Green/Yellow wire) of relay socket and ground. If battery voltage exists, go to step **5)**. If battery voltage does not exist, go to next step.
4) Turn ignition off. Unplug 8-pin connector from fan timer. Check for continuity of Yellow/White wire between fan timer and relay box. If continuity exists, test cooling fan timer. See COOLING FAN TIMER under TESTING. If continuity does not exist, repair open Yellow/White wire between cooling fan timer and relay box.
5) Turn ignition off. Unplug condenser fan relay, located in relay box under instrument panel. Test relay. See RELAY under TESTING. Replace relay if defective.
6) Reinstall relay. Turn ignition off. Unplug connectors from Electronic Control Module (ECM), located under right footwell. Connect ECM Test Harness (07LAJ-PT3010A) to wire harness only. DO NOT connect test harness to ECM.
7) Turn ignition on. Using jumper wire, connect test harness terminal A12 to ground. If condenser fan does not run, go to next step. If condenser fan runs, substitute a known good ECM. Retest system.
8) Check for battery voltage on test harness terminal A12. If battery voltage exists, go to next step. If battery voltage does not exist, repair open Light Green/Yellow wire between relay box and ECM.
9) Turn ignition off. Connect jumper wire between test harness terminal A12 and ground. Unplug connector from condenser fan motor. Turn ignition on. Check for voltage at White/Green wire at motor terminal connector. If battery voltage exists, go to next step. If battery voltage does not exist, repair open White/Green wire between relay box and fan motor connector.
10) Turn ignition off. Apply battery voltage to Blue wire terminal on condenser fan motor. Connect Black wire terminal to ground. If fan motor runs, repair Black wire between fan motor connector and ground. If motor does not run, replace fan motor.

RADIATOR FAN DOES NOT RUN WHEN A/C IS ON

1) Turn ignition off. Remove condenser fan from underdash relay box. Check for battery voltage at terminal No. 1 (White wire) of relay socket. If battery voltage exists, go to next step. If battery voltage does not exist, repair White wire between underdash relay box and underhood fuse/relay block.
2) Turn ignition on. Check for battery voltage at terminal No. 2 (Light Green/Yellow wire) of relay socket. If battery voltage does not exist, go to next step. If battery voltage exists, go to step **4)**.
3) Turn ignition off. Unplug 8-pin connector from fan timer. Check Yellow wire for continuity between cooling fan timer and relay box. If continuity exists, test cooling fan timer. See COOLING FAN TIMER under TESTING. If continuity does not exist, repair open Yellow wire between cooling fan timer and relay box.
4) Turn ignition off. Remove condenser fan relay, located in relay box under instrument panel. Test relay. See RELAY under TESTING. Replace relay if defective.
5) Reinstall relay. Turn ignition off. Unplug connectors from Electronic Control Module (ECM), located under right footwell. Connect ECM Test Harness (07LAJ-PT3010A) to wire harness only. DO NOT connect test harness to ECM.
6) Turn ignition on. Using jumper wire, connect test harness terminal A12 to ground. If condenser fan does not run, go to next step. If condenser fan runs, substitute a known good ECM. Retest system.
7) Check for battery voltage at test harness terminal A12. If battery voltage exists, go to next step. If battery voltage does not exist, repair open Light Green/Yellow wire between relay box and ECM.
8) Turn ignition off. Connect jumper wire between test harness terminal A12 and ground. Unplug connector from radiator fan motor. Turn ignition on. Check for voltage at White/Blue wire at motor terminal connector. If battery voltage exists, go to next step. If battery voltage does not exist, repair open White/Blue wire between relay box and fan motor connector.
9) Turn ignition off. Apply battery voltage to Blue wire terminal on condenser fan motor. Connect Black wire terminal to ground. If fan motor runs, repair Black wire between fan motor connector and ground. Replace motor if it does not run.

A/C COMPRESSOR CLUTCH DOES NOT ENGAGE

1) Remove A/C compressor clutch relay from underdash relay box. Turn ignition on. Check for battery voltage between relay socket terminals No. 1 (Red wire) and 2 (Red/Blue wire). If battery voltage does not exist, repair Yellow/Black wire between relay box and fuse No. 8 in underhood fuse/relay block.
2) If battery voltage exists, turn ignition switch off. Test compressor clutch relay. See RELAY under TESTING. Replace relay if defective.
3) Unplug connector from compressor clutch. Check continuity between compressor clutch relay terminal No. 3 (Yellow/Black wire) and compressor clutch connector. If continuity exists, go to next step. If continuity does not exist, repair open Yellow/Black wire.
4) Reconnect wire to compressor clutch. Connect jumper wire between terminals No. 1 (Red wire) and 3 (Yellow/Black wire) of relay socket. Turn ignition on. If compressor clutch engages, go to next step. If compressor clutch does not engage, see COMPRESSOR CLUTCH under TESTING.
5) Turn ignition off. Reinstall compressor clutch relay. Unplug connectors from Electronic Control Module (ECM), located under right footwell. Connect ECM Test Harness (07LAJ-PT3010A) to wire harness only. DO NOT connect test harness to ECM.
6) Turn ignition on. Using jumper wire, connect test harness terminal A15 to ground. If compressor clutch does not engage, repair Red/Blue wire between compressor clutch relay and ECM. If compressor clutch engages, substitute a known good ECM. Retest system.

A/C SYSTEM DOES NOT WORK

1) Check fuses No. 7 (7.5 A), 34 (15 A) and 38 (15 A). If fuses are okay, go to next step. Replace fuse if blown, and repair cause. Check self-diagnostic circuit, see SELF-DIAGNOSTICS under TESTING. If Code 1 is not indicated, go to next step. If Code 1 is indicated, see EVAPORATOR TEMPERATURE SENSOR under TESTING.
2) Turn ignition off. Remove heater control amplifier. Unplug 14-pin connector. Turn ignition on. Check for battery voltage at Pink wire at connector. If battery voltage exists, go to next step. If battery voltage does not exist, go to step **4)**.
3) Turn ignition off. Check for continuity between Black wire on connector and ground. If continuity does not exist, repair open Black wire between connector and ground. If continuity exists, substitute a known good heater control amplifier. Retest system.
4) Turn ignition off. Unplug connectors from Electronic Control Module (ECM), located under right footwell. Connect ECM Test Harness (07LAJ-PT3010A) to wire harness only. DO NOT connect test harness to ECM.
5) Turn ignition on. Check for voltage at test harness terminal B5 and ground. If battery voltage exists, go to step **7)**. If battery voltage does not exist, go to next step.
6) Using jumper wire, connect test harness terminal A12 to ground. If fans run, go to next step. If fans do not run, go to FANS DO NOT RUN AT ALL.
7) Turn ignition on. Using jumper wire, connect test harness terminal A15 to ground. If compressor clutch does not engage, go to A/C COMPRESSOR CLUTCH DOES NOT ENGAGE. If compressor clutch engages, substitute a known good ECM. Retest system.
8) Turn ignition off. Reconnect wiring to ECM. Unplug connector from pressure switch. Turn ignition on. Check for voltage at Blue/Black wire terminal at pressure switch connector. If battery voltage exists, go to next step. If battery voltage does not exist, repair Blue/Black wire between pressure switch and ECM.
9) Check for continuity between pressure switch terminals. If continuity exists, repair open Pink wire between pressure switch and heater control amplifier. If continuity does not exist, check A/C system pressure. If pressure is okay, replace A/C pressure switch.

TESTING

WARNING: To avoid injury from accidental air bag deployment, read and carefully follow all SERVICE PRECAUTIONS and DISABLING & ACTIVATING AIR BAG SYSTEM procedures in AIR BAG SYSTEM SAFETY article in GENERAL SERVICING.

A/C SYSTEM PERFORMANCE

1) Park vehicle out of direct sunlight. Open engine hood and front doors. Install A/C pressure gauges to the high and low side pressure ports of system. Determine relative humidity and ambient air temperature.

2) Set temperature control to maximum cool, mode control to vent and recirculation control to recirculate positions. Insert thermometer in center vent outlet. Turn blower fan switch to highest position. Start and run engine at 1500 RPM. Ensure there is nobody inside vehicle.

3) After running A/C for 10 minutes, check thermometer reading in center vent outlet and the high and low side system pressure. Determine if A/C system is operating within range. *See Fig. 4.*

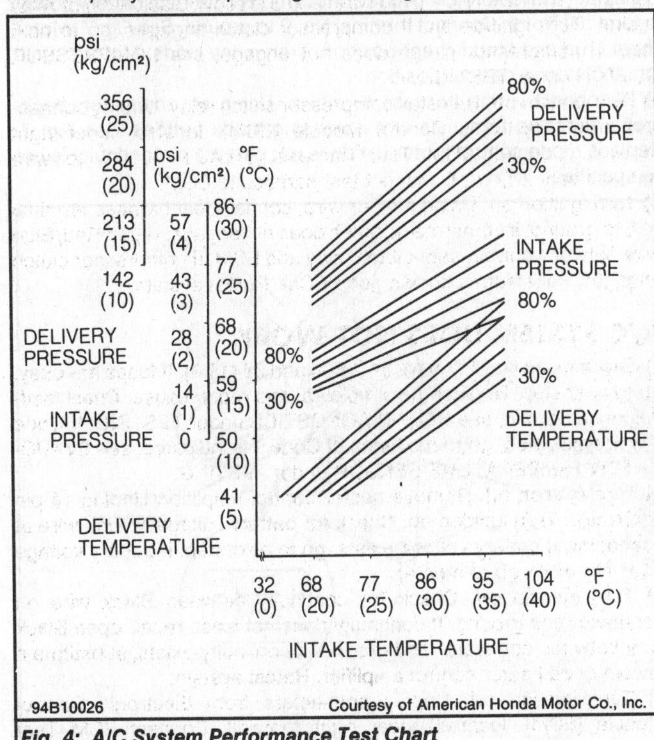
psi
(kg/cm²)
356
(25)
284
(20)
213
(15)
142
(10)
DELIVERY
PRESSURE
psi
(kg/cm²)
57
(4)
43
(3)
28
(2)
14
(1)
0
INTAKE
PRESSURE
°F
(°C)
86
(30)
77
(25)
68
(20)
59
(15)
50
(10)
41
(5)
DELIVERY
TEMPERATURE
80%
DELIVERY
PRESSURE
30%
INTAKE
PRESSURE
80%
80%
30%
30%
DELIVERY
TEMPERATURE
32
(0)
68
(20)
77
(25)
86
(30)
95
(35)
104
(40)
°F
(°C)
INTAKE TEMPERATURE
94B10026
Courtesy of American Honda Motor Co., Inc.

Fig. 4: A/C System Performance Test Chart

SELF-DIAGNOSTICS

Retrieving Codes – 1) Turn ignition off. Set temperature control lever to maximum heat position. Set fan control lever to OFF position. Press recirculated air button.

2) Turn ignition on. Within 5 seconds of turning ignition on, alternately press recirculated air and fresh air buttons 3 times. A/C indicator light will come on momentarily, then go out. Wait at least one minute.

3) Any code stored will be indicated by flashes of A/C indicator light. The number of times light flashes indicates code stored. See TROUBLE CODES table. If 2 or more codes exist simultaneously, only the lowest code will be displayed. If no code exists, see appropriate symptom under TROUBLE SHOOTING. To exit self-diagnostics, turn ignition off.

TROUBLE CODES

Code Number	Affected Circuit
1	Evaporator Temperature Sensor
2	Air Mix Control Motor
3	Mode Control Motor
4	Recirculation Control Motor
5	Blower Motor

AIR MIX MOTOR

1) Measure resistance between motor lead terminals No. 3 and 5. *See Fig. 5.* Resistance should be approximately 10,000 ohms.

CAUTION: Remove battery voltage immediately after motor operates to avoid damaging motor.

2) Connect battery voltage to terminal No. 2. Briefly connect terminal No. 1 to ground. If motor operates, transpose leads. Replace motor if it does not run in both directions.

3) Connect battery voltage to terminal No. 2. Connect terminal No. 1 to ground. Measure resistance between terminals No. 4 and 5. Resistance should be approximately 4800 ohms with air mix door in hot position, and approximately 1200 ohms with door in cool position. Replace air mix motor if it does not operate as specified.

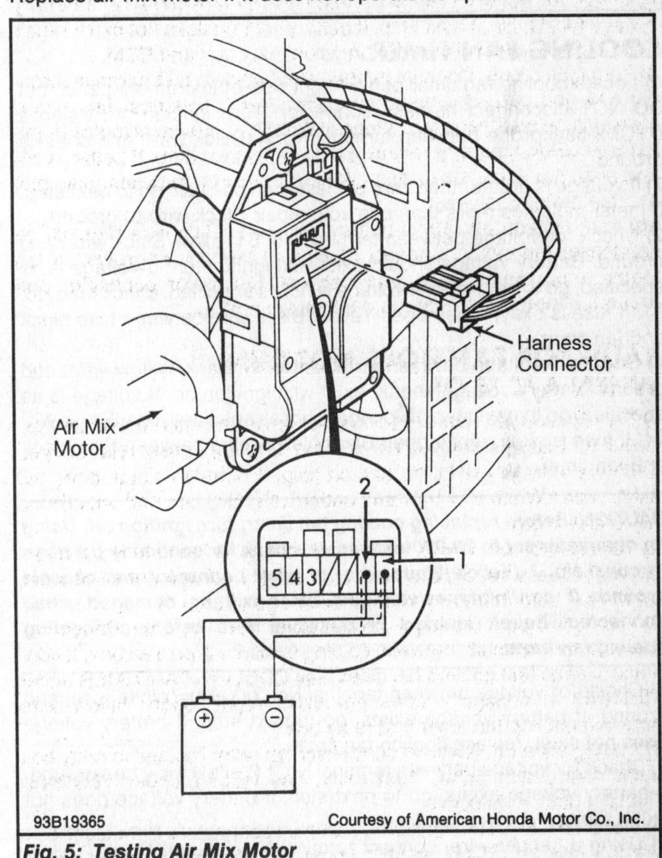
Harness
Connector
Air Mix
Motor
2
1
5
4
3
93B19365
Courtesy of American Honda Motor Co., Inc.

Fig. 5: Testing Air Mix Motor

COMPRESSOR CLUTCH

Connect ohmmeter between terminal on clutch lead and ground. *See Fig. 6.* If resistance is not 3.4-3.8 ohms at 68°F (20°C), replace clutch. Using feeler gauge, measure clearance between pulley and pressure plate. If clearance is not .014-.026" (.35-.65 mm), repair clutch.

1993 MANUAL A/C-HEATER SYSTEMS
Vigor (Cont.)

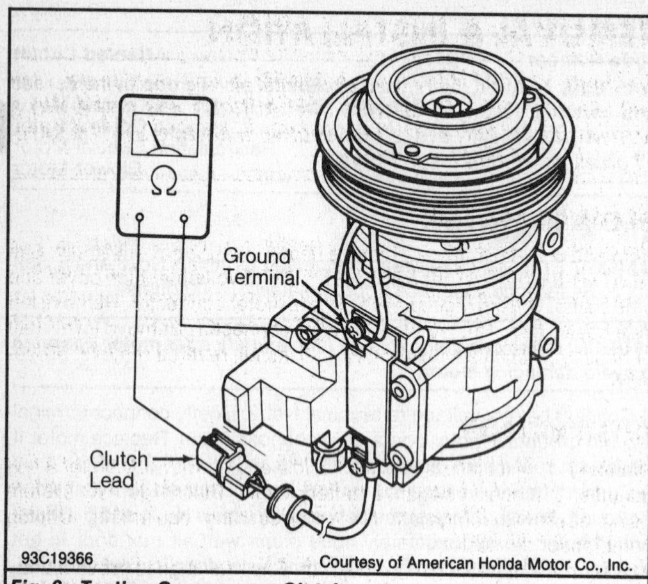
Ω
Ground
Terminal
Clutch
Lead
93C19366

Courtesy of American Honda Motor Co., Inc.

Fig. 6: Testing Compressor Clutch

COOLING FAN TIMER

1) Locate cooling fan timer behind right side of instrument panel, but DO NOT disconnect harness connector. Turn ignition on. Using a DVOM, backprobe between terminal No. 4 (Black wire) and chassis ground.

2) If voltage is greater than zero but less than one volt, go to next step. If meter indicates more than one volt, repair Black wire to ground.

3) Check for voltage between terminal No. 8 (Yellow/Black wire) and ground. Battery voltage should exist with ignition on. If voltage is as specified, go to next step. If voltage is not as specified, check fuse No. 21. If fuse is okay, repair open Yellow/Black wire between fuse block and fan timer.

4) Check for voltage between terminal No. 2 (Black/Yellow wire) and ground. Battery voltage should exist with ignition on. If voltage is as specified, go to next step. If voltage is not as specified, check fuse No. 24. If fuse is okay, repair open Black/Yellow wire between fuse block and fan timer.

CAUTION: Before replacing cooling fan timer, turn ignition off. Using an ohmmeter set to 20,000-ohm scale, check for continuity between terminal No. 1 (Yellow/White wire) of timer connector and chassis ground. If continuity exists, new timer will be damaged when connected. Repair shorted Yellow/White wire before connecting cooling fan timer.

5) Check for voltage between terminal No. 3 (Yellow/White wire) and ground. If battery voltage exists, go to next step. If battery voltage does not exist, replace cooling fan timer.

6) Check for voltage between terminal No. 1 (Yellow wire) and ground. If battery voltage exists, go to next step. If battery voltage does not exist, replace cooling fan timer.

7) Using a jumper wire, connect terminal No. 8 (Light Green/Yellow wire) to ground. If condenser fan runs, go to next step. If condenser fan does not operate, check Light Green/Yellow wire for an open circuit between cooling fan timer and condenser fan relay.

8) If wire is okay, check Yellow/White wire for an open circuit between cooling fan timer and 2-pin connector (located near radiator), and Black/Yellow wire between 2-pin connector and condenser fan relay. If wiring is okay, test condenser fan relay. See RELAY under TESTING.

9) Check for voltage between terminal No. 5 (White/Green wire) and ground. With engine oil temperature less than 226°F (108°C), meter should indicate approximately 11 volts. If voltage is not as specified, White/Green wire for short to ground. If wire is okay, temporarily substitute a known good oil temperature switch. If oil temperature switch is okay, install a known good cooling fan timer. Retest system.

EVAPORATOR TEMPERATURE SENSOR

CAUTION: To avoid damage to sensor, use an ohmmeter with a measuring current of one milliamp or less.

Unplug connector from evaporator temperature sensor, located at evaporator housing. Measure sensor resistance at temperatures specified in table. See EVAPORATOR TEMPERATURE SENSOR TEST table. If resistance is not approximately as specified, replace sensor.

EVAPORATOR TEMPERATURE SENSOR TEST

Coolant Temperature °F (°C)	Ohms
32 (0)	6400
50 (10)	4100
68 (20)	2600
86 (30)	1700

MODE CONTROL MOTOR

1) Unplug connector from mode control motor. Connect battery power to terminal No. 1. Connect terminal No. 2 to ground. *See Fig. 7.* Motor should run and stop in vent position. Transpose leads. Motor should run and stop in defrost position.

2) Reconnect wiring harness to motor. Using an ohmmeter, backprobe specified terminals while pressing mode buttons. *See Fig. 7.* Replace mode control motor if it does not operate or continuity is not as specified.

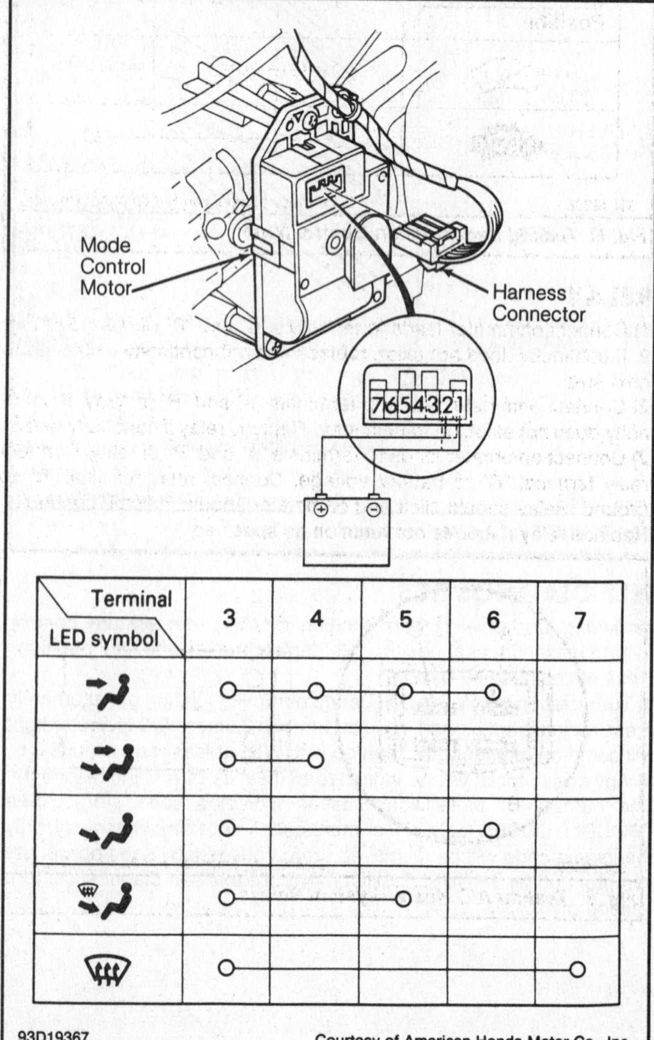
Mode
Control
Motor
Harness
Connector
7654321
Terminal
LED symbol
3
4
5
6
7
93D19367

Courtesy of American Honda Motor Co., Inc.

Fig. 7: Testing Mode Control Motor

RECIRCULATION CONTROL MOTOR

1) Remove heater-evaporator assembly. See HEATER-EVAPORATOR ASSEMBLY under REMOVAL & INSTALLATION. Unplug motor connector. Remove motor. *See Fig. 8.*

2) Connect battery voltage to motor terminal No. 1. Connect terminal No. 2 to ground. Motor should rotate 1/2 turn and stop. If motor does not run, transpose battery leads. If motor runs, repeat step. Replace motor if it does not run in both directions.

3) Check for continuity between terminals with motor in positions specified. *See Fig. 8*. Replace motor if continuity is not as specified.

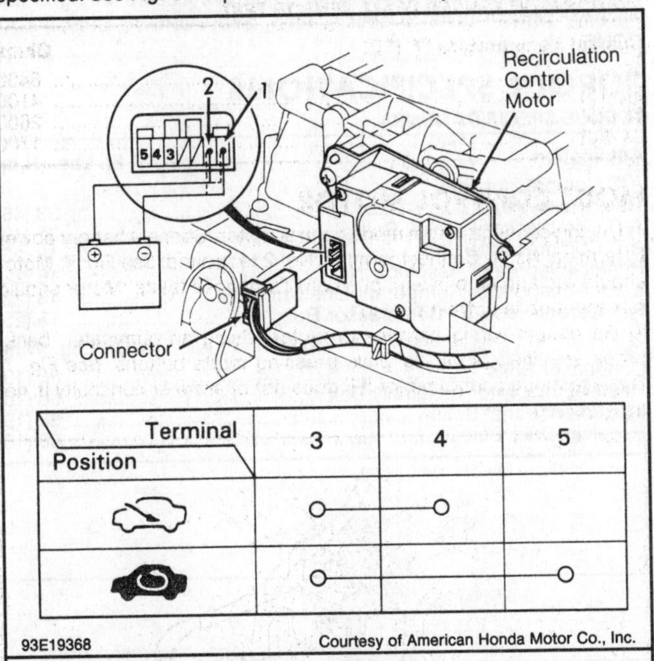
Recirculation
Control
Motor
2
1
5 4 3
Connector
Terminal
Position
3
4
5
93E19368

Courtesy of American Honda Motor Co., Inc.

Fig. 8: Testing Recirculation Control Motor

RELAY

1) Connect ohmmeter leads to terminals "C" and "D" of relay. *See Fig. 9.* If continuity does not exist, replace relay. If continuity exists, go to next step.

2) Connect ohmmeter leads to terminals "A" and "B" of relay. If continuity does not exist, go to next step. Replace relay if continuity exists.

3) Connect ohmmeter leads to terminals "A" and "B" of relay. Connect relay terminal "C" to battery voltage. Connect relay terminal "D" to ground. Relay should click and ohmmeter should indicate continuity. Replace relay if it does not function as specified.

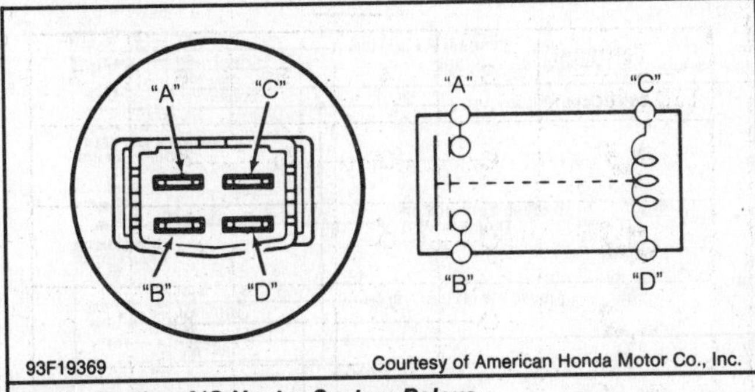
"A"
"C"
"B"
"D"
"A"
"C"
"B"
"D"
93F19369

Courtesy of American Honda Motor Co., Inc.

Fig. 9: Testing A/C Heater System Relays

REMOVAL & INSTALLATION

WARNING: To avoid injury from accidental air bag deployment, read and carefully follow all SERVICE PRECAUTIONS and DISABLING & ACTIVATING AIR BAG SYSTEM procedures in AIR BAG SYSTEM SAFETY article in GENERAL SERVICING.

BLOWER MOTOR

Removal & Installation – Remove heater-evaporator assembly. See HEATER-EVAPORATOR ASSEMBLY. Remove heater pipe cover and pipe clamp. Unplug recirculation control motor connector. Remove left side heater duct. Unplug blower motor connector. Remove lower half of housing. Remove blower motor. To install, reverse removal procedure.

COMPRESSOR

Removal – **1)** If compressor works, idle engine with A/C on for a few minutes. Disconnect negative battery cable. Discharge A/C system using approved refrigerant recovery/recycling equipment. Unplug compressor connector.

2) Disconnect hoses from compressor. Cap openings to prevent entry of moisture and dirt. Loosen idler pulley. Remove power steering pump belt. Remove compressor.

3) If installing new compressor, drain oil from removed compressor. Measure volume of oil drained. Subtract volume of oil drained from 4.7 ozs. Result is amount that should be drained from new compressor.

Installation – To install compressor, reverse removal procedure. Tighten bolts to specification. See TORQUE SPECIFICATIONS. Evacuate and recharge system.

CONDENSER

Removal – Discharge A/C system, using approved refrigerant recovery/recycling equipment. Unplug connector from radiator fan motor. Remove radiator fan shroud. Unplug connector from condenser fan motor. Remove condenser fan shroud. Remove upper radiator mount brackets. Remove receiver-drier. Disconnect refrigerant line from condenser. Remove condenser.

Installation – To install condenser, reverse removal procedure. Install new "O" rings. Tighten bolts to specification. See TORQUE SPECIFICATIONS. Evacuate and recharge system.

EVAPORATOR

Removal & Installation – Remove heater-evaporator assembly. See HEATER-EVAPORATOR ASSEMBLY. Remove heater pipe cover and heater pipe clamp. Remove left heater duct. Remove blower high relay. Unplug connector from power transistor. Carefully separate housing halves. Remove evaporator. To install, reverse removal procedure.

HEATER CORE

Removal & Installation – Remove heater-evaporator assembly. See HEATER-EVAPORATOR ASSEMBLY. Remove heater pipe cover and heater pipe clamp. Detach clip from mode control motor rod. Remove mode control motor. Remove evaporator temperature sensor. Remove mode door arms. Remove left side cover. Remove heater core cover and heater core. To install, reverse removal procedure.

HEATER-EVAPORATOR ASSEMBLY

Removal – **1)** Remove instrument panel. See INSTRUMENT PANEL. Allow engine to cool. Drain coolant. Place pan under heater inlet and outlet fittings. Disconnect hoses at heater inlet and outlet fittings. Note locations of hoses for installation reference.

2) Discharge A/C system using approved refrigerant recovery/recycling equipment. Disconnect refrigerant lines from evaporator. Remove heater-evaporator nut from engine side of firewall. Remove air duct. Unplug electrical connectors. Remove bolts and heater-evaporator assembly.

1993 MANUAL A/C-HEATER SYSTEMS Vigor (Cont.)

Installation – 1) To install, reverse removal procedure. Install new "O" rings. Tighten bolts to specification. See TORQUE SPECIFICATIONS. Connect heater hoses to proper fittings.

2) Refill cooling system to base of filler neck. Loosen 2 bleeder bolts on top of engine. Allow coolant to flow until no bubbles appear. Tighten bleeder bolts. Refill radiator to base of filler neck. Install radiator cap, but tighten it only to first stop.

3) Start and warm engine until fan comes on at least twice. Stop engine. Check coolant level and add coolant as necessary. Install radiator cap. Fill reservoir to MAX mark. Evacuate and recharge A/C system.

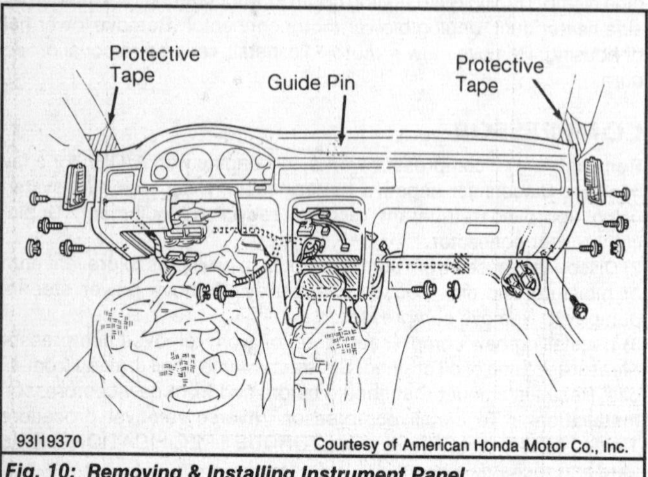
Protective Tape
Guide Pin
Protective Tape
93I19370
Courtesy of American Honda Motor Co., Inc.

Fig. 10: Removing & Installing Instrument Panel

INSTRUMENT PANEL

Removal & Installation – 1) Disable air bag system. Remove front seats, console, and console panel. Remove instrument panel lower cover, knee bolster, and kick panel. Lower steering column. Protect steering column with shop towels.

2) Remove air vents from each side of instrument panel. *See Fig. 10.* Unplug electrical connectors. Protect bottom of front pillar trim with tape. Remove 6 bolts. Carefully lift instrument panel from vehicle.

3) To install instrument panel, reverse removal procedure. Ensure instrument panel fits properly onto guide pin. Ensure wiring is not pinched. Tighten bolts to specification. See TORQUE SPECIFICATIONS.

TORQUE SPECIFICATIONS

TORQUE SPECIFICATIONS

Application	Ft. Lbs. (N.m)
A/C Compressor Belt Idler Pulley Nut	33 (45)
A/C Compressor Bracket Bolt	35 (48)
A/C Compressor Bolts	18 (25)
Heater-Evaporator Assembly Nut	16 (22)
Heater-Evaporator Refrigerant Line Nut	16 (22)
Refrigerant Hose-To-Compressor Bolt	18 (25)
	INCH Lbs. (N.m)
Condenser Bolts	88 (10)
Heater-Evaporator Assembly Bolt	88 (10)
Instrument Panel Bolts	88 (10)
Receiver-Drier Bolt	88 (10)

WIRING DIAGRAMS

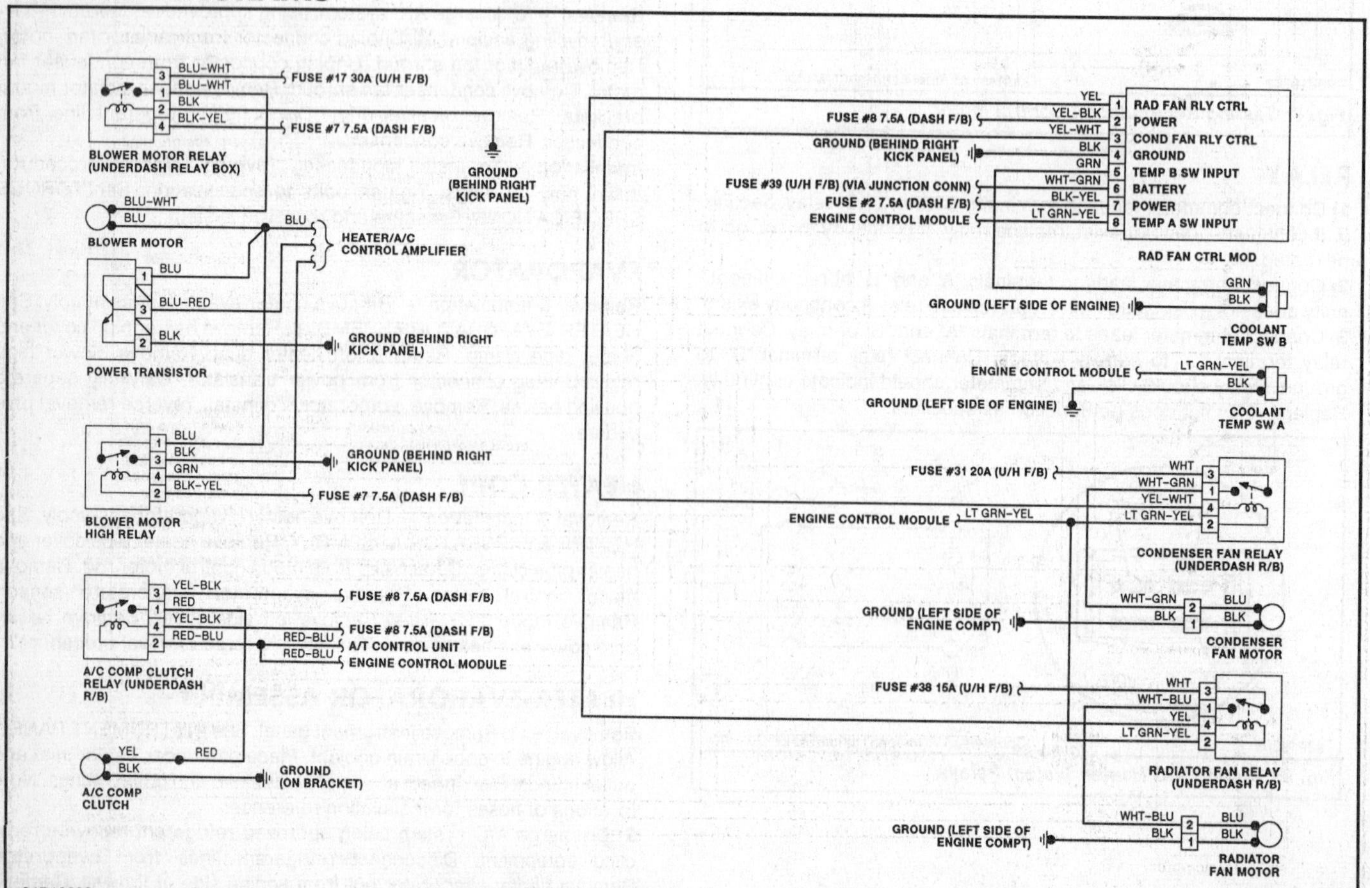

BLOWER MOTOR RELAY (UNDERDASH RELAY BOX)
FUSE #17 30A (U/H F/B)
FUSE #7 7.5A (DASH F/B)
GROUND (BEHIND RIGHT KICK PANEL)
BLOWER MOTOR
HEATER/A/C CONTROL AMPLIFIER
POWER TRANSISTOR
BLOWER MOTOR HIGH RELAY
A/C COMP CLUTCH RELAY (UNDERDASH R/B)
FUSE #8 7.5A (DASH F/B)
A/T CONTROL UNIT
ENGINE CONTROL MODULE
GROUND (ON BRACKET)
A/C COMP CLUTCH
RAD FAN CTRL MOD
FUSE #39 (U/H F/B) (VIA JUNCTION CONN)
FUSE #2 7.5A (DASH F/B)
GROUND (LEFT SIDE OF ENGINE)
COOLANT TEMP SW B
COOLANT TEMP SW A
FUSE #31 20A (U/H F/B)
CONDENSER FAN RELAY (UNDERDASH R/B)
GROUND (LEFT SIDE OF ENGINE COMPT)
CONDENSER FAN MOTOR
FUSE #38 15A (U/H F/B)
RADIATOR FAN RELAY (UNDERDASH R/B)
RADIATOR FAN MOTOR
94B10638

Fig. 11: Manual A/C-Heater System Wiring Diagram (Vigor – 1 Of 2)

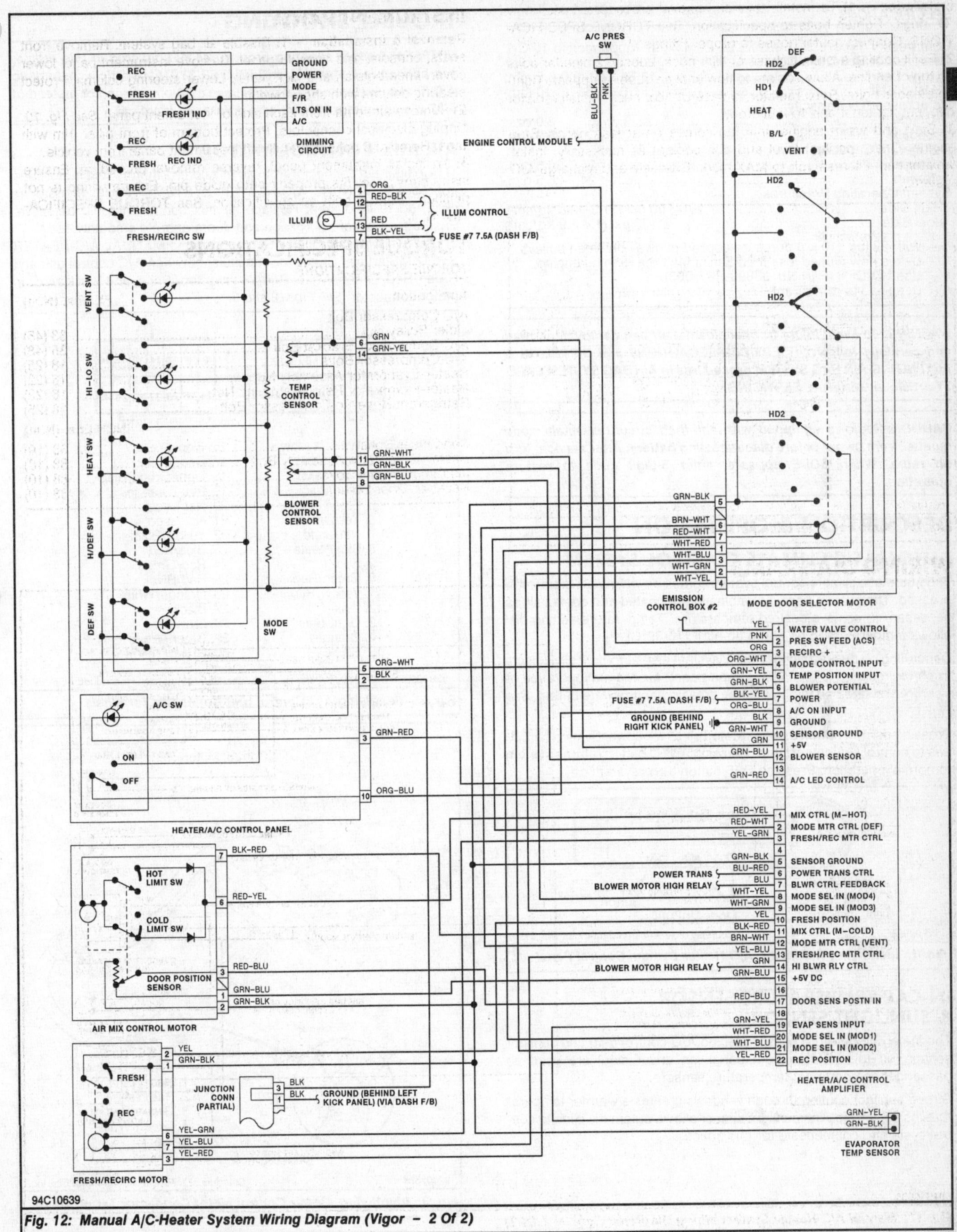

REC
FRESH
FRESH IND
REC
REC IND
FRESH
REC
FRESH
FRESH/RECIRC SW
GROUND
POWER
MODE
F/R
LTS ON IN
A/C
DIMMING CIRCUIT
ILLUM
ORG
RED-BLK
RED
BLK-YEL
ILLUM CONTROL
FUSE #7 7.5A (DASH F/B)
A/C PRES SW
BLU-BLK
PNK
ENGINE CONTROL MODULE
DEF
HD2
HD1
HEAT
B/L
VENT
VENT SW
HI-LO SW
HEAT SW
H/DEF SW
DEF SW
MODE SW
GRN
GRN-YEL
TEMP CONTROL SENSOR
GRN-WHT
GRN-BLK
GRN-BLU
BLOWER CONTROL SENSOR
GRN-BLK
BRN-WHT
RED-WHT
WHT-RED
WHT-BLU
WHT-GRN
WHT-YEL
MODE DOOR SELECTOR MOTOR
EMISSION CONTROL BOX #2
ORG-WHT
BLK
A/C SW
ON
OFF
GRN-RED
ORG-BLU
HEATER/A/C CONTROL PANEL
YEL
PNK
ORG
ORG-WHT
GRN-YEL
GRN-BLK
BLK-YEL
ORG-BLU
BLK
GRN-WHT
GRN
GRN-BLU
GRN-RED
WATER VALVE CONTROL
PRES SW FEED (ACS)
RECIRC +
MODE CONTROL INPUT
TEMP POSITION INPUT
BLOWER POTENTIAL
POWER
A/C ON INPUT
GROUND
SENSOR GROUND
+5V
BLOWER SENSOR
A/C LED CONTROL
FUSE #7 7.5A (DASH F/B)
GROUND (BEHIND RIGHT KICK PANEL)
BLK-RED
HOT LIMIT SW
RED-YEL
COLD LIMIT SW
DOOR POSITION SENSOR
RED-BLU
GRN-BLU
GRN-BLK
AIR MIX CONTROL MOTOR
RED-YEL
RED-WHT
YEL-GRN
GRN-BLK
BLU-RED
BLU
WHT-YEL
WHT-GRN
YEL
BLK-RED
BRN-WHT
YEL-BLU
GRN
GRN-BLU
RED-BLU
GRN-YEL
WHT-RED
WHT-BLU
YEL-RED
MIX CTRL (M-HOT)
MODE MTR CTRL (DEF)
FRESH/REC MTR CTRL
SENSOR GROUND
POWER TRANS CTRL
BLWR CTRL FEEDBACK
MODE SEL IN (MOD4)
MODE SEL IN (MOD3)
FRESH POSITION
MIX CTRL (M-COLD)
MODE MTR CTRL (VENT)
FRESH/REC MTR CTRL
HI BLWR RLY CTRL
+5V DC
DOOR SENS POSTN IN
EVAP SENS INPUT
MODE SEL IN (MOD1)
MODE SEL IN (MOD2)
REC POSITION
POWER TRANS
BLOWER MOTOR HIGH RELAY
BLOWER MOTOR HIGH RELAY
HEATER/A/C CONTROL AMPLIFIER
GRN-YEL
GRN-BLK
EVAPORATOR TEMP SENSOR
YEL
GRN-BLK
FRESH
REC
JUNCTION CONN (PARTIAL)
BLK
BLK
GROUND (BEHIND LEFT KICK PANEL) (VIA DASH F/B)
YEL-GRN
YEL-BLU
YEL-RED
FRESH/RECIRC MOTOR
94C10639

Fig. 12: Manual A/C-Heater System Wiring Diagram (Vigor – 2 Of 2)

1993 AUTOMATIC A/C-HEATER SYSTEMS
Legend

SPECIFICATIONS

Compressor Type	Nippondenso 10-Cyl.
Compressor Belt Deflection [1]	
New Belt [2]	13/64-1/4" (5.0-6.5 mm)
Used Belt	5/16-25/64" (8-10 mm)
Compressor Oil Capacity	
Coupe	6.0 ozs.
Sedan	[3] 4.7-5.2 ozs.
Refrigerant Capacity	
Coupe	24.7-26.5 ozs.
Sedan	[4] 24.7-26.5 ozs.
System Operating Pressures	
High Side	170-200 psi (11.9-13.8 kg/cm²)
Low Side	21-28 psi (1.4-1.9 kg/cm²)

[1] – With 22 lbs. (10 kg) pressure applied midway between pulleys.
[2] – Belt is new if used less than 5 minutes on a running engine.
[3] – Use ND-Oil 8 (Part No. 38899-PR7-003).
[4] – Use R-134a refrigerant.

WARNING: To avoid injury from accidental air bag deployment, read and carefully follow all SERVICE PRECAUTIONS and DISABLING & ACTIVATING AIR BAG SYSTEM procedures in AIR BAG SYSTEM SAFETY article in GENERAL SERVICING.

CAUTION: Radio is equipped with anti-theft circuitry. Obtain code number from owner before disconnecting battery. After service, turn on radio. When CODE appears, enter 5-digit code to restore operation.

DESCRIPTION & OPERATION

AUTOMATIC CLIMATE CONTROL SYSTEM

The automatic climate control system comes on when AUTO button is pressed. The system uses a combination of heated and cooled air as necessary to achieve desired temperature. Temperature setting dial allows temperature to be set to 60-90°F (16-32°C).

Depending on desired temperature, system also automatically selects fresh/recirculated (passenger compartment) air. Manual operation of fresh/recirculated air is obtained by pressing appropriate button. *See Fig. 1.*

Pressing defrost button directs treated air to windows. System continues to control set temperature. Pressing AUTO button returns system to normal operation. Pressing OFF button turns system off.

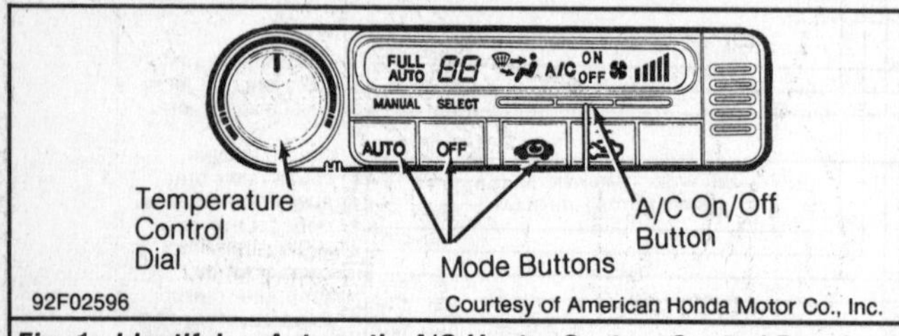
FULL AUTO
A/C
ON OFF
MANUAL
SELECT
AUTO
OFF
Temperature Control Dial
Mode Buttons
A/C On/Off Button
92F02596
Courtesy of American Honda Motor Co., Inc.

Fig. 1: Identifying Automatic A/C-Heater System Control Panel

IN-CAR TEMPERATURE SENSOR & SUNLIGHT SENSOR

The in-car temperature sensor (behind A/C control unit) and sunlight sensor (on top of instrument panel, on driver side) are used as passenger compartment temperature sensors.

Strong sunlight coming through windows creates a warmer temperature inside vehicle. The sunlight sensor allows automatic climate control system to compensate for this effect.

TROUBLE SHOOTING

NOTE: For trouble shooting procedures not covered in this article, see appropriate MANUAL A/C-HEATER SYSTEMS article. Automatic A/C-heater system control panel uses a 30-pin connector instead of a 22-pin connector. Circuit wire colors are identical.

AIR MIX CONTROL MOTOR

1) Unplug 6-pin connector from air mix control motor. Test motor. See appropriate MANUAL A/C-HEATER SYSTEMS article. If motor is okay, go to next step. Replace air mix control motor if defective. Ensure air mix control linkage and doors operate smoothly.

2) Remove A/C control unit. See appropriate MANUAL A/C-HEATER SYSTEMS article. Check for continuity between A/C control unit and Green/Red, Green/White, Red/Yellow, Red/White, and Black wires in motor connector. *See Figs. 2 and 3.*

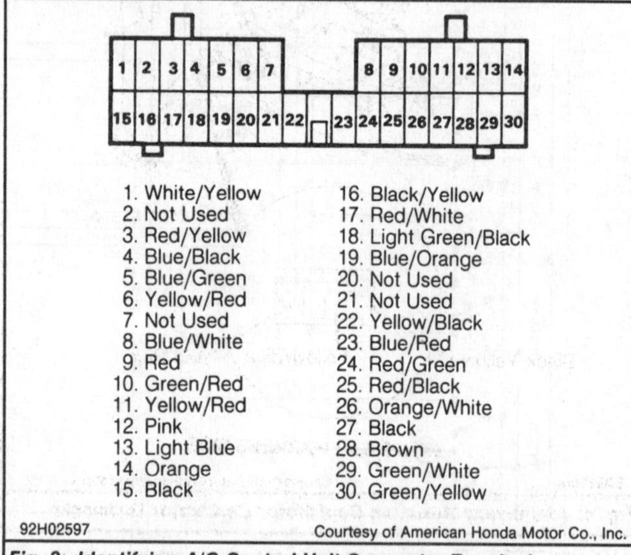
1 2 3 4 5 6 7 8 9 10 11 12 13 14
15 16 17 18 19 20 21 22 23 24 25 26 27 28 29 30
1. White/Yellow
2. Not Used
3. Red/Yellow
4. Blue/Black
5. Blue/Green
6. Yellow/Red
7. Not Used
8. Blue/White
9. Red
10. Green/Red
11. Yellow/Red
12. Pink
13. Light Blue
14. Orange
15. Black
16. Black/Yellow
17. Red/White
18. Light Green/Black
19. Blue/Orange
20. Not Used
21. Not Used
22. Yellow/Black
23. Blue/Red
24. Red/Green
25. Red/Black
26. Orange/White
27. Black
28. Brown
29. Green/White
30. Green/Yellow
92H02597
Courtesy of American Honda Motor Co., Inc.

Fig. 2: Identifying A/C Control Unit Connector Terminals

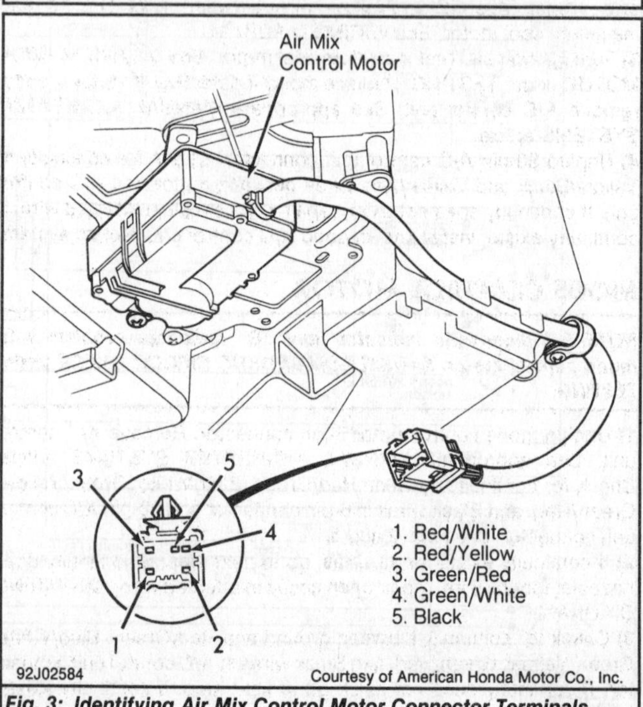
Air Mix Control Motor
3
5
4
1
2
1. Red/White
2. Red/Yellow
3. Green/Red
4. Green/White
5. Black
92J02584
Courtesy of American Honda Motor Co., Inc.

Fig. 3: Identifying Air Mix Control Motor Connector Terminals

1993 AUTOMATIC A/C-HEATER SYSTEMS
Legend (Cont.)

3) If continuity exists on all wires, go to next step. If continuity does not exist on any wire, repair open circuit between A/C control unit and air mix control motor. See WIRING DIAGRAM.
4) Check each wire for continuity between ground and air mix control motor. If continuity exists for any wire, repair short circuit between air mix control motor and A/C control unit. If continuity does not exist on any wire, install a known good A/C control unit. Retest system.

MAXIMUM COOL MOTOR

1) Remove glove box lower panel. Unplug 4-pin connector from maximum cool motor. Turn ignition on. Check voltage between Black/Yellow wire in harness connector and ground. *See Fig. 4.*

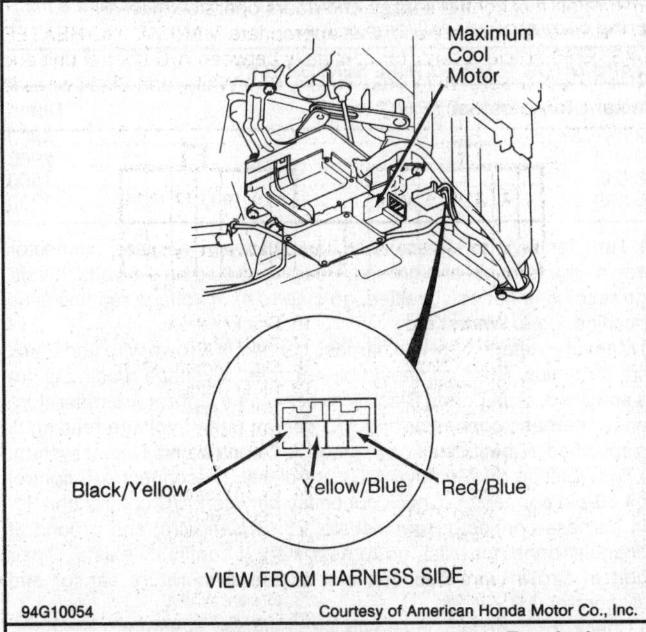
Maximum
Cool
Motor
Black/Yellow
Yellow/Blue
Red/Blue
VIEW FROM HARNESS SIDE
94G10054
Courtesy of American Honda Motor Co., Inc.

Fig. 4: Identifying Maximum Cool Motor Connector Terminals

2) If battery voltage exists, go to next step. If battery voltage does not exist, repair open Black/Yellow wire between fuse No. 19 and maximum cool motor. See WIRING DIAGRAM.
3) Turn ignition off. Test maximum cool motor. See MAXIMUM COOL MOTOR under TESTING. Replace motor if defective. If motor is okay, remove A/C control unit. See appropriate MANUAL A/C-HEATER SYSTEMS article.
4) Unplug 30-pin A/C control unit connector. Check for continuity in Yellow/Black and Yellow/Red wires between motor and A/C control unit. If continuity does not exist, repair open circuit in affected wire. If continuity exists, install known good A/C control unit. Retest system.

MODE CONTROL MOTOR

NOTE: Self-diagnostic indicator light "G" indicates problem with mode control motor. See SELF-DIAGNOSTIC CIRCUIT CHECK under TESTING.

1) Unplug mode control motor 6-pin connector. Remove A/C control unit. See appropriate MANUAL A/C-HEATER SYSTEMS article. Check for continuity between Red/Green, Blue/White, Green/Yellow, Green/Red, and Black wires in 6-pin connector and 30-pin A/C control unit connector. *See Figs. 2 and 5.*
2) If continuity exists for all wires, go to next step. If continuity does not exist for any wire, repair open circuit in affected wire. See WIRING DIAGRAM.
3) Check for continuity between ground and Red/Green, Blue/White, Green/Yellow, Green/Red, and Black wires in A/C control unit connector. If continuity does not exist, go to next step. If continuity exists, repair short circuit to ground in affected wire.
4) Test mode control motor. See appropriate MANUAL A/C-HEATER SYSTEMS article. Replace motor if defective. If motor is okay, install a known good A/C control unit. Retest system.

RECIRCULATION CONTROL MOTOR

1) Remove glove box lower cover. Unplug recirculation motor 4-pin connector. Turn ignition on. Check for voltage between Black/Yellow wire and ground. If battery voltage exists, go to next step. If battery voltage does not exist, repair open Black/Yellow wire between fuse No. 19 and recirculation control motor.

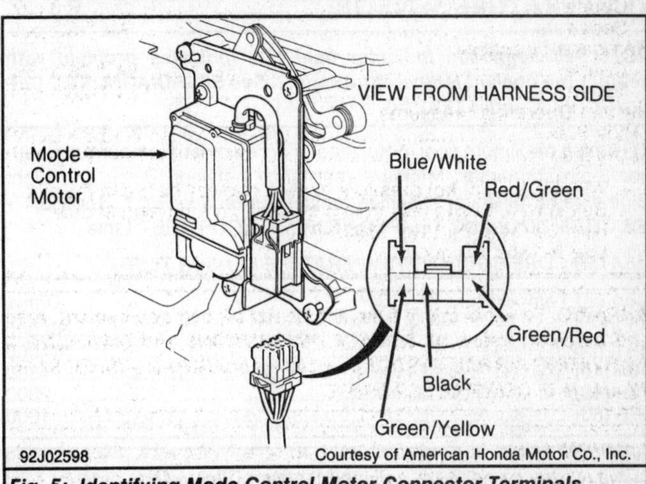
VIEW FROM HARNESS SIDE
Mode
Control
Motor
Blue/White
Red/Green
Green/Red
Black
Green/Yellow
92J02598
Courtesy of American Honda Motor Co., Inc.

Fig. 5: Identifying Mode Control Motor Connector Terminals

2) Turn ignition off. Test recirculation control motor. See appropriate MANUAL A/C-HEATER SYSTEMS article. If motor is okay, go to next step. If motor is faulty, replace motor. Check recirculation control door and linkage for smooth operation. Repair as required.
3) Unplug A/C control panel 30-pin connector. Check Blue/Orange and Blue/Green wires for continuity between recirculation control motor and A/C control unit connector. *See Figs. 2 and 6.* If continuity exists, go to next step. If continuity does not exist, repair open circuit in affected wire.
4) Check for continuity between chassis ground and Blue/Orange and Blue/Green wires at A/C control unit connector. If continuity exists, repair short circuit in affected wire. If continuity does not exist, install a known good A/C control unit. Retest system.

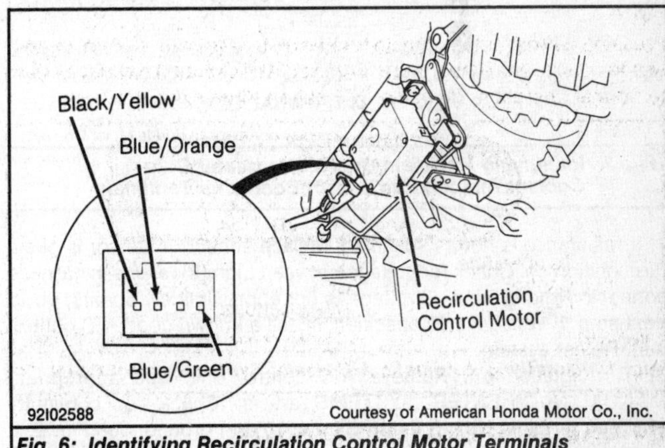
Black/Yellow
Blue/Orange
Recirculation
Control Motor
Blue/Green
92I02588
Courtesy of American Honda Motor Co., Inc.

Fig. 6: Identifying Recirculation Control Motor Terminals

A/C CONTROL UNIT

1) Check fuses No. 19 and 56. Replace fuses if necessary, and check for short circuit. If fuses are okay, remove A/C control unit. See appropriate MANUAL A/C–HEATER SYSTEMS article.
2) Unplug A/C control panel 30-pin connector. Check for continuity between terminal No. 27 (Black wire) and chassis ground. *See Fig. 2.* If continuity exists, go to next step. If continuity does not exist, repair open Black wire to ground.
3) Check for voltage between terminal No. 1 (White/Yellow wire) and ground. If battery voltage exists, go to next step. If battery voltage does not exist, repair open circuit between A/C control unit and fuse No. 56.

1993 AUTOMATIC A/C-HEATER SYSTEMS
Legend (Cont.)

4) Turn ignition on. Check for voltage between terminal No. 16 (Black/Yellow wire) and ground. If battery voltage does not exist, repair open circuit between A/C control unit and fuse No. 19. If battery voltage exists, install a known good A/C control unit. Retest system.

HEATER CORE COOLANT TEMPERATURE SENSOR

NOTE: Self-diagnostic indicator light "D" indicates problem with heater core coolant temperature sensor. See SELF-DIAGNOSTIC CIRCUIT CHECK under TESTING.

1) Unplug maximum cool motor/heater core coolant temperature sensor 8-pin connector. Measure resistance between Black and Light Blue wire terminals at specified temperatures. *See Fig. 7.* See HEATER CORE COOLANT TEMPERATURE SENSOR TEST table.

HEATER CORE COOLANT TEMPERATURE SENSOR TEST

Coolant Temperature °F (°C)	Ohms
32 (0)	30,000
68 (20)	10,000
104 (40)	4500
140 (60)	2000
176 (80)	1000

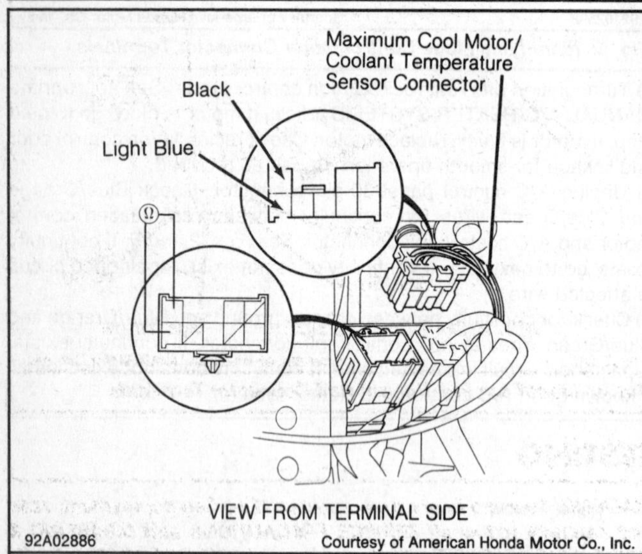
Maximum Cool Motor/
Coolant Temperature
Sensor Connector
Black
Light Blue
VIEW FROM TERMINAL SIDE
92A02886
Courtesy of American Honda Motor Co., Inc.

Fig. 7: Identifying Maximum Cool Motor/Heater Core Coolant Temperature Sensor Connector Terminals

2) If resistance is not as specified, replace sensor. If sensor is okay, turn ignition on. Check for voltage between Light Blue wire in harness connector and ground. If voltage is not approximately 5 volts, go to next step. If voltage is as specified, install a known good A/C control unit. Retest system.
3) Turn ignition off. Remove A/C control unit. See appropriate MANUAL A/C-HEATER SYSTEMS article. Check for continuity between terminal No. 13 (Light Blue wire) and ground. *See Fig. 2.* If continuity does not exist, go to next step. If continuity exists, repair short between heater core coolant temperature sensor and A/C control unit.
4) Check for continuity between terminal No. 13 (Light Blue wire) and heater core coolant temperature sensor. If continuity does not exist, repair open circuit between sensor and A/C control unit. If continuity exists, install a known good A/C control unit. Retest system.

EVAPORATOR TEMPERATURE SENSOR

NOTE: Self-diagnostic indicator light "E" indicates problem with evaporator temperature sensor. See SELF-DIAGNOSTIC CIRCUIT CHECK under TESTING.

1) Unplug 2-pin connector from evaporator temperature sensor, located at evaporator housing. Measure sensor resistance at temperatures specified. See EVAPORATOR TEMPERATURE SENSOR TEST table. If resistance is not as specified, replace sensor. If resistance is as specified, go to next step.

CAUTION: To avoid damage to sensor, use an ohmmeter with a measuring current of one milliamp or less.

EVAPORATOR TEMPERATURE SENSOR TEST

Coolant Temperature °F (°C)	Ohms
32 (0)	4800
50 (10)	2900
68 (20)	1800
86 (30)	1300

2) Turn ignition on. Measure voltage between harness connector Brown wire terminal and ground. Reading should be 4-6 volts. If voltage reading is not as specified, go step to **4)**. If voltage reading is as specified, go to next step.
3) Measure voltage between harness connector Brown wire and Black wire terminals. Reading should be 4-6 volts. If voltage reading is not as specified, repair open Black wire between evaporator temperature sensor harness connector and A/C control unit. If voltage reading is as specified, substitute a known good A/C control unit. Retest system.
4) Turn ignition off. Remove A/C control unit. Disconnect A/C control unit 30-pin connector. Check continuity between A/C control unit 30-pin harness connector terminal No. 28 (Brown wire) and ground. If continuity does not exist, go to next step. If continuity exists, repair short in Brown wire between evaporator temperature sensor and A/C control unit.
5) Check for continuity in Brown wire between evaporator temperature sensor and A/C control unit. If continuity does not exist, repair open Brown wire between evaporator temperature sensor and A/C control unit. If continuity exists, install a known good A/C control unit. Retest system.

IN-CAR TEMPERATURE SENSOR

NOTE: Self-diagnostic indicator light "A" indicates problem with in-car temperature sensor. See SELF-DIAGNOSTIC CIRCUIT CHECK under TESTING.

Measure sensor resistance temperatures specified. See IN-CAR TEMPERATURE SENSOR TEST table. If resistance is not as specified, replace sensor.

IN-CAR TEMPERATURE SENSOR TEST

In-Car Air Temperature °F (°C)	Ohms
32 (0)	5800
50 (10)	3300
68 (20)	2000
86 (30)	1400
104 (40)	1000

OUTSIDE AIR TEMPERATURE SENSOR

NOTE: Self-diagnostic indicator light "B" indicates problem with outside air temperature sensor. See SELF-DIAGNOSTIC CIRCUIT CHECK under TESTING.

1) Unplug connector from outside air temperature sensor, located beneath condenser. Measure sensor resistance at specified temperatures. See OUTSIDE AIR TEMPERATURE SENSOR TEST table.

CAUTION: To avoid damage to sensor, use an ohmmeter with a measuring current of one milliamp or less.

OUTSIDE AIR TEMPERATURE SENSOR TEST

Outside Air Temperature °F (°C)	Ohms
32 (0)	6000
50 (10)	3800
68 (20)	2300
86 (30)	1700
104 (40)	1000
122 (50)	800

2) If resistance is not as specified, replace sensor. If sensor resistance is okay, turn ignition on. Measure voltage between Pink wire in harness connector and ground. Voltage should be 4-6 volts. If voltage is not as specified, go to step **4)**. If voltage is 4-6 volts, go to next step.
3) Measure voltage between Pink wire Black wire terminals. Voltage should be 4-6 volts. If voltage is not as specified, repair open Black wire between sensor and A/C control unit. If voltage is as specified, install a known good A/C control unit. Retest system.
4) Turn ignition off. Remove A/C control unit. See appropriate MANUAL A/C-HEATER SYSTEMS article. Unplug A/C control unit 30-pin connector. Check for continuity between terminal No. 12 (Pink wire) and ground. *See Fig. 2.* If continuity does not exist, go to next step. If continuity exists, repair short in Pink wire between A/C control unit and outside air temperature sensor.
5) Using a jumper wire, connect Pink wire in sensor harness connector to ground. Check for continuity between Pink wire in A/C control unit connector and ground. If continuity does not exist, repair open Pink wire between A/C control unit and sensor. If continuity exists, install a known good A/C control unit. Retest system.

SUNLIGHT SENSOR

NOTE: Self-diagnostic indicator light "C" indicates problem with sunlight sensor. See SELF-DIAGNOSTIC CIRCUIT CHECK under TESTING.

1) Carefully pry sunlight sensor from instrument panel. Unplug 2-pin connector from sunlight sensor. Measure voltage between sensor terminals while sensor is out of direct sunlight. Voltage reading should be 1.2-1.6 volts. If voltage reading is as specified, go to next step. If voltage is not as specified, replace sensor.
2) Remove A/C control unit. Disconnect 30-pin connector from A/C control unit. See appropriate MANUAL A/C-HEATER SYSTEMS article. Check for continuity in Green/Red wire between sunlight sensor and A/C control unit. If continuity exists, go to next step. If continuity does not exist, repair open Green/Red wire between A/C control unit and sensor.
3) Check for continuity in Green/Red wire between sunlight sensor and ground. If continuity exists, repair short in Green/Red wire between sensor and A/C control unit. If continuity does not exist, go to next step.
4) Check for continuity in Orange wire between sunlight sensor and A/C control unit. If continuity exists, install a known good A/C control unit. Retest system. If continuity does not exist, repair open Orange wire between sunlight sensor and A/C control unit.

A/C COMPRESSOR & FAN MOTORS INOPERATIVE

1) Check fuse No. 3. If fuse is okay, unplug 4-pin connector from triple pressure switch, located near receiver-drier. Turn ignition and A/C on. Check for continuity between Blue/Red wire in connector and chassis ground. If continuity exists, go to step **4)**.
2) If continuity does not exist, perform self-diagnostic circuit check. See SELF-DIAGNOSTIC CIRCUIT CHECK under TESTING. If self-diagnostic indicator lights come on, trouble shoot affected circuits.
3) If self-diagnostic check is okay, repair open Blue/Red wire between triple pressure switch and A/C control unit. If wire is okay, install a known good A/C control unit. Retest system.
4) Turn ignition off. Check for continuity between terminals No. 1 (Blue/Red wire) and No. 2 (Black wire) of triple pressure switch, located next to receiver-drier. If continuity exists, go to next step. If continuity does not exist, check A/C system pressure. If pressure is okay, replace switch. If pressure is low, check system for leaks. Repair as required.
5) Unplug 12-pin connector from fan control unit. Check for continuity between Black wire in connector and chassis ground. *See Fig. 8.* If continuity exists, go to next step. If continuity does not exist, repair open Black wire to ground.
6) Turn ignition on. Check for voltage between Yellow/Black wire in 12-pin connector and chassis ground. If battery voltage exists, go to next step. If battery voltage does not exist, repair open Yellow/Black wire between fan control unit and fuse No. 3.
7) Turn ignition off. Using a jumper wire, connect Light Blue wire in triple pressure switch connector to ground. Check for continuity between Light Blue wire in 12-pin connector and ground. If continuity does not exist, repair open circuit between triple pressure switch and fan control unit. If continuity exists, install a known good fan control unit. Retest system.

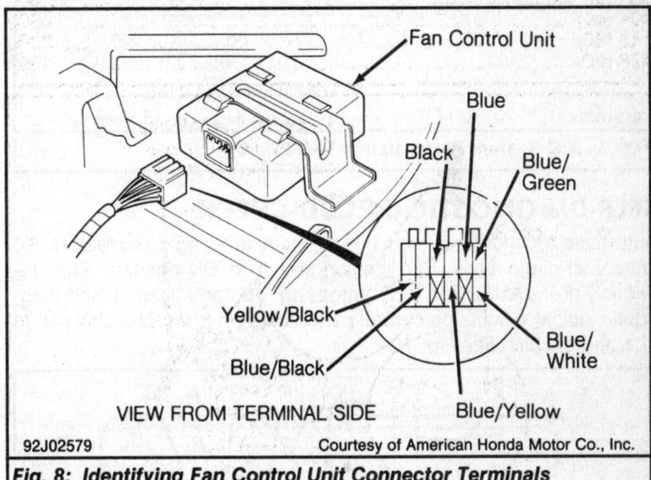
Fan Control Unit
Blue
Black
Blue/
Green
Yellow/Black
Blue/
White
Blue/Black
VIEW FROM TERMINAL SIDE
Blue/Yellow
92J02579
Courtesy of American Honda Motor Co., Inc.

Fig. 8: Identifying Fan Control Unit Connector Terminals

TESTING

WARNING: To avoid injury from accidental air bag deployment, read and carefully follow all SERVICE PRECAUTIONS and DISABLING & ACTIVATING AIR BAG SYSTEM procedures in AIR BAG SYSTEM SAFETY article in GENERAL SERVICING.

NOTE: For information not covered in this article, see appropriate MANUAL A/C-HEATER SYSTEMS article.

A/C SYSTEM PERFORMANCE

All Models – 1) Park vehicle out of direct sunlight. Open engine hood and front doors. Install A/C pressure gauges to the high and low side pressure ports of system. Determine relative humidity and ambient air temperature.
2) Set temperature control to maximum cooling, mode control to vent and recirculation control to recirculated air positions. Insert a thermometer in center vent outlet. Turn blower fan switch to highest position. Start and run engine at 1500 RPM. Ensure there is nobody inside vehicle.
3) After running A/C for 10 minutes, check thermometer reading in center vent outlet and the high and low side system pressure. Determine if system is operating within range. *See Fig. 9.*

1993 AUTOMATIC A/C-HEATER SYSTEMS
Legend (Cont.)

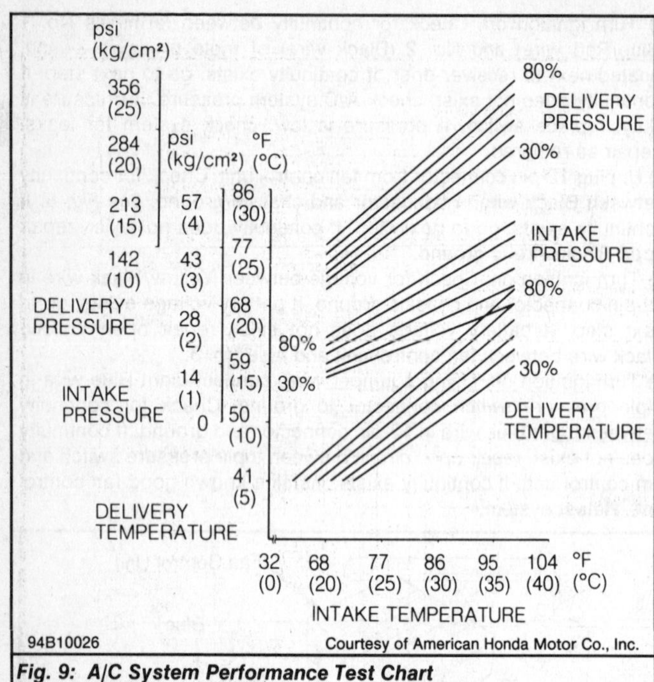
psi
(kg/cm²)
356
(25)
284
(20)
213
(15)
142
(10)
DELIVERY
PRESSURE
psi
(kg/cm²)
57
(4)
43
(3)
28
(2)
14
(1)
0
INTAKE
PRESSURE
°F
(°C)
86
(30)
77
(25)
68
(20)
59
(15)
50
(10)
41
(5)
DELIVERY
TEMPERATURE
80%
DELIVERY
PRESSURE
30%
INTAKE
PRESSURE
80%
30%
80%
30%
DELIVERY
TEMPERATURE
32 (0) 68 (20) 77 (25) 86 (30) 95 (35) 104 (40) °F (°C)
INTAKE TEMPERATURE
94B10026
Courtesy of American Honda Motor Co., Inc.

Fig. 9: A/C System Performance Test Chart

SELF-DIAGNOSTIC CIRCUIT CHECK

Automatic A/C-heater system has a built-in self-diagnostic feature. To enter self-diagnostics, turn ignition switch to ON position. Simultaneously press AUTO and OFF buttons on A/C control panel. Self-diagnostic indicator lights on control panel come on to direct technician to affected circuits. *See Fig. 10.*

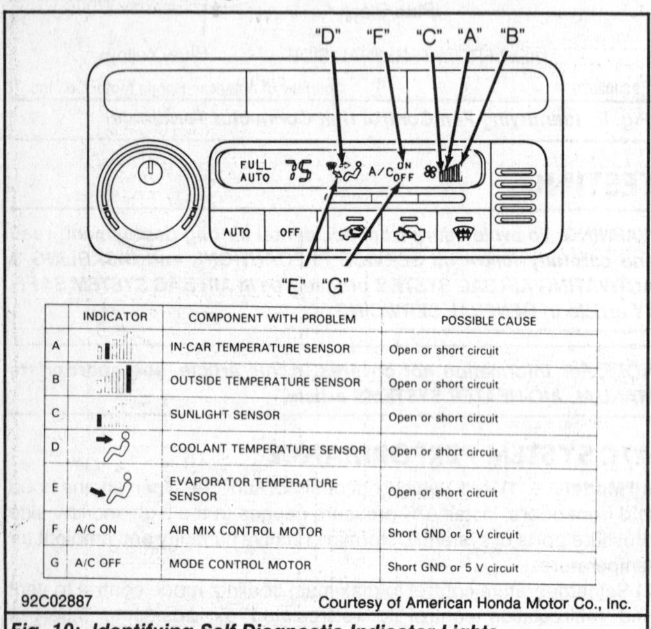
"D"
"F"
"C"
"A"
"B"
FULL AUTO
75
A/C ON OFF
AUTO
OFF
"E"
"G"

	INDICATOR	COMPONENT WITH PROBLEM	POSSIBLE CAUSE
A		IN-CAR TEMPERATURE SENSOR	Open or short circuit
B		OUTSIDE TEMPERATURE SENSOR	Open or short circuit
C		SUNLIGHT SENSOR	Open or short circuit
D		COOLANT TEMPERATURE SENSOR	Open or short circuit
E		EVAPORATOR TEMPERATURE SENSOR	Open or short circuit
F	A/C ON	AIR MIX CONTROL MOTOR	Short GND or 5 V circuit
G	A/C OFF	MODE CONTROL MOTOR	Short GND or 5 V circuit

92C02887
Courtesy of American Honda Motor Co., Inc.

Fig. 10: Identifying Self-Diagnostic Indicator Lights

ASPIRATOR FAN MOTOR

Remove A/C control unit. See appropriate MANUAL A/C-HEATER SYSTEMS article. Disconnect and remove aspirator fan from A/C control unit. Apply battery voltage to Blue wire. Connect White/Black wire to ground. If aspirator fan motor does not run, replace motor.

MAXIMUM COOL MOTOR

1) Using jumper wires at motor harness connector, connect battery voltage to Black/Yellow wire. Connect Yellow/Black wire to ground. *See Fig. 4.* If motor does not operate, disconnect jumper wire from Yellow/Black wire. Connect Yellow/Red wire to ground.

2) If motor now operates, run motor to end of travel. Disconnect jumper wire from Yellow/Red wire. Connect Yellow/Black wire to ground. Motor should operate in reverse direction. Replace motor if it does not operate as specified.

REMOVAL & INSTALLATION

WARNING: To avoid injury from accidental air bag deployment, read and carefully follow all SERVICE PRECAUTIONS and DISABLING & ACTIVATING AIR BAG SYSTEM procedures in AIR BAG SYSTEM SAFETY article in GENERAL SERVICING.

NOTE: For removal of A/C-heater system components not covered in this article, see appropriate MANUAL A/C-HEATER SYSTEMS article.

COOLANT TEMPERATURE SENSOR

Removal & Installation – Remove dashboard lower panel. Unplug maximum cool motor 7-pin connector. Remove screw from sensor harness clamp. Pull out sensor retaining clip. Remove sensor. To install, reverse removal procedure.

EVAPORATOR TEMPERATURE SENSOR

Removal & Installation – Unplug sensor harness connector. Remove clips, sensor screws, and sensor. To install, reverse removal procedure.

MAXIMUM COOL MOTOR

Removal & Installation – Remove lower dash panel. Remove air mix control motor screws, air mix motor, and mounting bracket. Remove maximum cool motor from air mix control motor bracket. Unplug harness connector. Remove motor. To install, reverse removal procedure.

IN-CAR TEMPERATURE SENSOR

Removal & Installation – 1) Remove A/C control unit. See appropriate MANUAL A/C-HEATER SYSTEMS article. Remove screws and separate front panel from control unit. Unplug sensor connector from side of A/C control unit.

2) Remove air intake tube from between A/C control unit and aspirator fan. Pull sensor harness from tube. Release sensor detent and remove sensor from front of control panel. To install, reverse removal procedure.

OUTSIDE AIR TEMPERATURE SENSOR

Removal & Installation – Remove screw and outside air temperature sensor from lower edge of condenser. Unplug wiring harness, and remove sensor. To install, reverse removal procedure.

SUNLIGHT SENSOR

Removal & Installation – Carefully pry sensor from instrument panel. Unplug connector. To install, reverse removal procedure.

TORQUE SPECIFICATIONS

TORQUE SPECIFICATIONS

Application	Ft. Lbs. (N.m)
A/C Compressor Belt Idler Pulley Nut	33 (45)
A/C Compressor Bolts	37 (50)
Heater-Evaporator Refrigerant Line Nut	16 (22)
Refrigerant Hose-To-Compressor Bolt	18 (25)
	INCH Lbs. (N.m)
Blower Motor Bolts/Nuts	88 (10)
Condenser Nut	88 (10)
Heater-Evaporator Mounting Bolt	88 (10)
Instrument Panel Bolt	88 (10)
Receiver-Drier Bolt	88 (10)

WIRING DIAGRAM

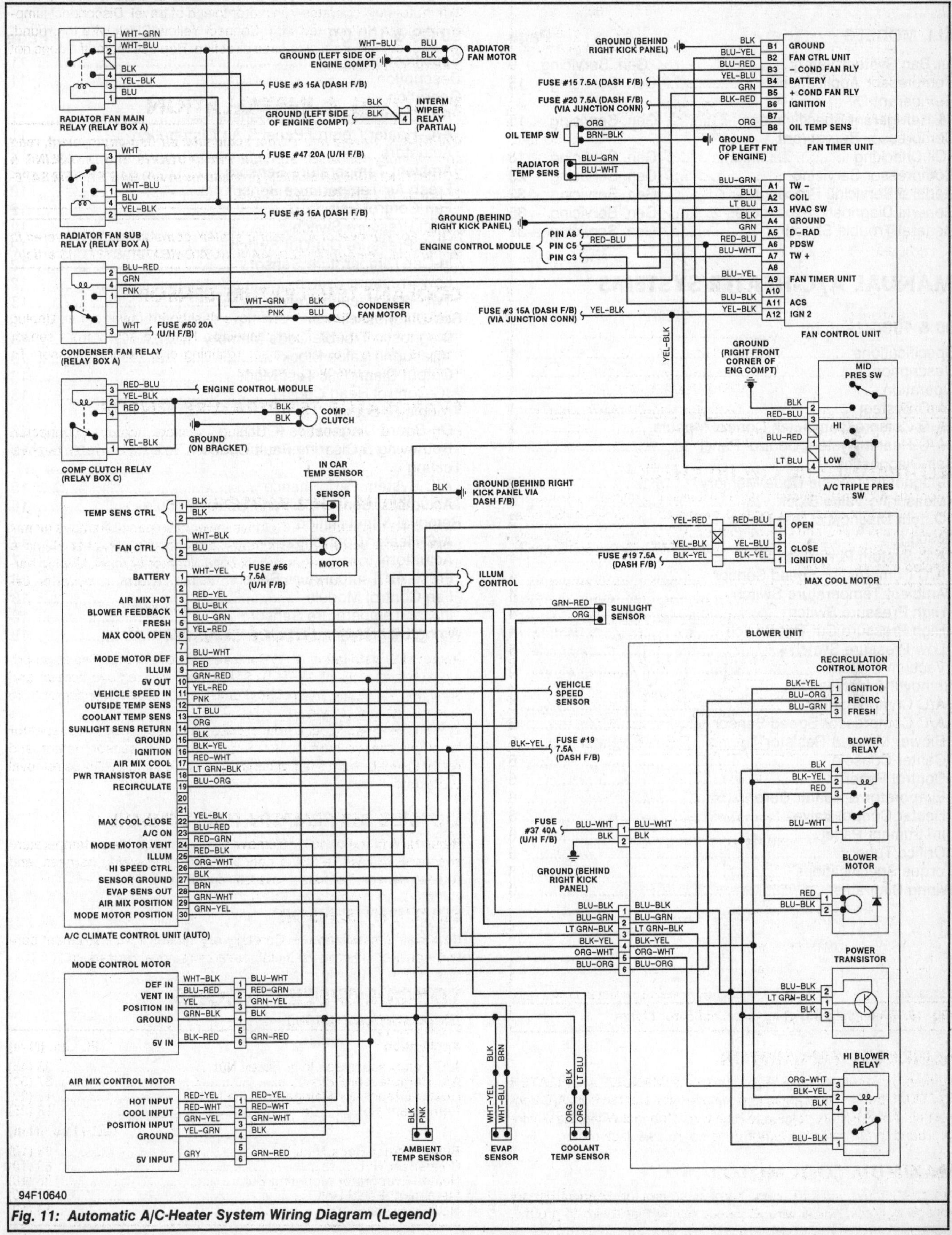

Fig. 11: Automatic A/C-Heater System Wiring Diagram (Legend)

1993 AUDI CONTENTS

GENERAL SERVICING

ALL MODELS

MANUAL A/C-HEATER SYSTEMS

90 & 100

AUTOMATIC A/C-HEATER SYSTEMS

90 CS & 100 CS — Page

1993 MANUAL A/C-HEATER SYSTEMS
90 & 100

SPECIFICATIONS

Compressor Type	Zexel 6-Cyl.
Compressor Belt Tension [2]	....
Refrigerant (R-134a) Capacity	
90	23.0-24.8 ozs.
100	21.0-22.8 ozs.
System Oil Capacity	[1] 7.8-9.2 ozs.
System Operating Pressures [3]	
Low Side	26-29 psi (1.8-2.0 kg/cm²)
High Side	290 psi (20.4 kg/cm²)

[1] – Use Polyalkylene Glycol (PAG) oil.
[2] – Belt tension is automatically adjusted by belt tensioner.
[3] – Measured at 77°F (25°C). High side pressure increases from base pressure (engine off) to a maximum of 290 psi (20.4 kg/cm²).

WARNING: To avoid injury from accidental air bag deployment, read and carefully follow all SERVICE PRECAUTIONS and DISABLING & ACTIVATING AIR BAG SYSTEM procedures in AIR BAG SYSTEM SAFETY article in GENERAL SERVICING.

CAUTION: When battery is disconnected, radio will go into anti-theft protection mode. Obtain radio anti-theft protection code from owner prior to servicing vehicle.

DESCRIPTION

The A/C system uses a variable displacement compressor. The A/C compressor does not cycle when the A/C system is on. System components include accumulator, A/C compressor clutch control module, compressor, condenser, evaporator, restrictor (orifice tube), control panel, and vacuum reservoir. *See Fig. 1 or 2.*

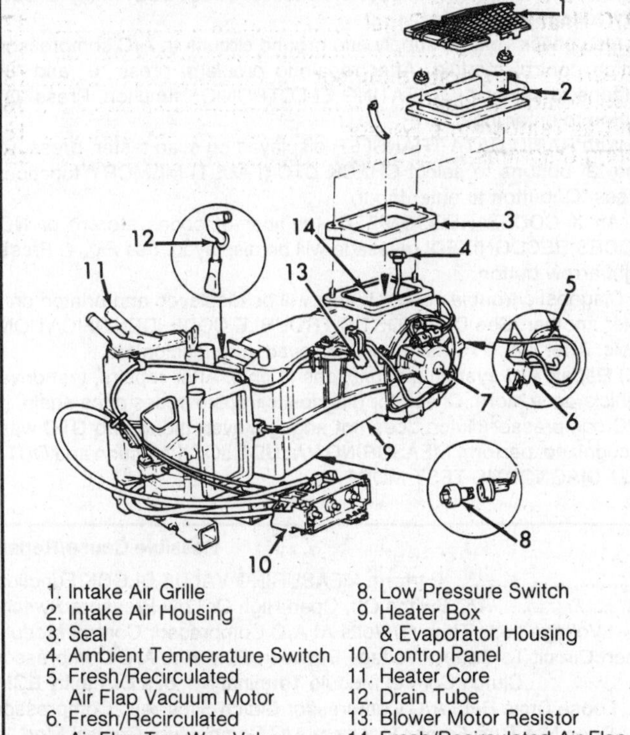
1
2
3
4
5
6
7
8
9
10
11
12
13
14
1. Intake Air Grille
2. Intake Air Housing
3. Seal
4. Ambient Temperature Switch
5. Fresh/Recirculated Air Flap Vacuum Motor
6. Fresh/Recirculated Air Flap Two-Way Valve
7. Blower Motor
8. Low Pressure Switch
9. Heater Box & Evaporator Housing
10. Control Panel
11. Heater Core
12. Drain Tube
13. Blower Motor Resistor
14. Fresh/Recirculated Air Flap
94B10141
Courtesy of Audi of America, Inc.

Fig. 1: Identifying A/C-Heater System Components (90)

OPERATION

A/C SYSTEM

The A/C system control panel uses 3 knobs (switches) to control fan speed, temperature, and air distribution. One switch controls the A/C compressor, one the blower motor, and the remaining switch opens or closes the recirculation door.

The A/C compressor clutch control module controls the A/C compressor clutch. The module checks operation of A/C compressor clutch, supply voltage, engine and compressor speed, and other inputs. The module's fault memory is erased when ignition is turned off.

A/C COMPRESSOR CLUTCH CONTROL MODULE

The A/C compressor clutch control module, located on auxiliary relay panel, is equipped with an On-Board Diagnostic (OBD) system. If a malfunction occurs in a monitored sensor or component, Diagnostic Trouble Code (DTC) is stored in control module memory.

A/C-HEATER SYSTEM CONTROL PANEL

Air Distribution Control Knob – Placing control knob at downward pointing arrow distributes air flow to footwells. To direct full air flow to footwells, the center and side instrument panel outlets must be manually closed. With control knob in defrost position, air is directed to windshield. A bi-level and center/side vent position is also available.

A/C Switch – A Green indicator light comes on when air conditioning system is switched on.

Fan Control Knob – The fan control knob may be placed in 4 manually controlled positions. With control knob placed on the fan symbol, the fan automatically runs at low speed.

Recirculation Switch – The recirculated air mode works only when the A/C system is turned on. A Green indicator light comes on when the system is operating in recirculated air mode. In this setting, no fresh air enters the vehicle (interior air is recirculated continuously).

Temperature Control Knob – Turning control knob increases or decreases temperature.

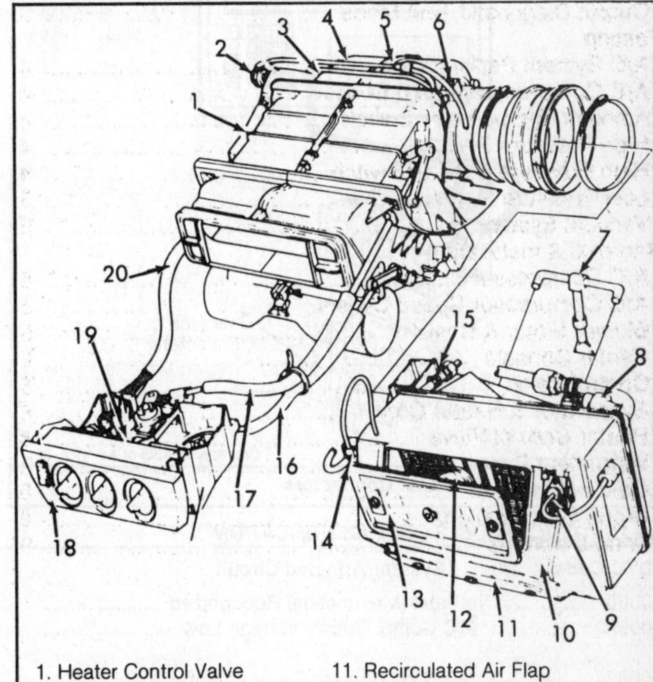
1
2
3
4
5
6
7
8
9
10
11
12
13
14
15
16
17
18
19
20
1. Heater Control Valve
2. Vacuum Reservoir & Check Valve
3. Blower Motor Resistor
4. Blower Motor
5. Heater Box
6. Coolant Two-Way Vacuum Valve
7. Evaporator Drain Hose
8. A/C Refrigerant Low Pressure Switch
9. Outside Temperature Switch
10. Evaporator Housing
11. Recirculated Air Flap
12. Fresh/Recirculated Air Flap Vacuum Motor
13. Fresh Air Flap
14. Fresh/Recirculated Air Flap Two-Way Valve
15. Orifice Tube
16. Footwell/Defroster & Instrument Panel Vent Control Cable
17. Temperature Control Cable
18. Control Panel
19. Coolant Cut-Off Valve Switch
20. Wiring Harness
94C10142
Courtesy of Audi of America, Inc.

Fig. 2: Identifying A/C-Heater System Components (100)

1993 MANUAL A/C-HEATER SYSTEMS
90 & 100 (Cont.)

SELF-DIAGNOSTICS

NOTE: Scan Tester (VAG 1551) must be used to make full use of the system's self-diagnostic capabilities.

Hard Failures – If A/C-heater system malfunctions are present for more than 5 seconds, they are stored as Diagnostic Trouble Codes (DTCs). The A/C compressor control module distinguishes data between 6 different trouble codes and stores malfunctions until ignition is turned off (volatile memory).

Intermittent Failures – If a malfunction occurs intermittently, they are stored and considered to be "sporadic" (intermittent) failures. When displayed on scan tester, intermittent malfunctions will have "SP" (sporadic) on right side of display.

DIAGNOSTIC TROUBLE CODE MEMORY

NOTE: Diagnostic trouble code memory is cleared when ignition is turned off. DO NOT turn ignition off after driving vehicle, as this will erase fault codes.

Retrieving & Clearing Codes – **1)** Ensure all fuses are okay. Drive vehicle for at least 5 minutes with the A/C system on. Without turning off ignition or A/C system, connect Scan Tester (VAG 1551) to Data Link Connectors (DLC) located in plenum chamber (fuse/relay block). *See Fig. 3.* DO NOT use Blue connector.

2) If display does not appear on scan tester, check DLC terminals for battery voltage and ground. Also check DLC wiring for open/short circuits to battery voltage or ground.

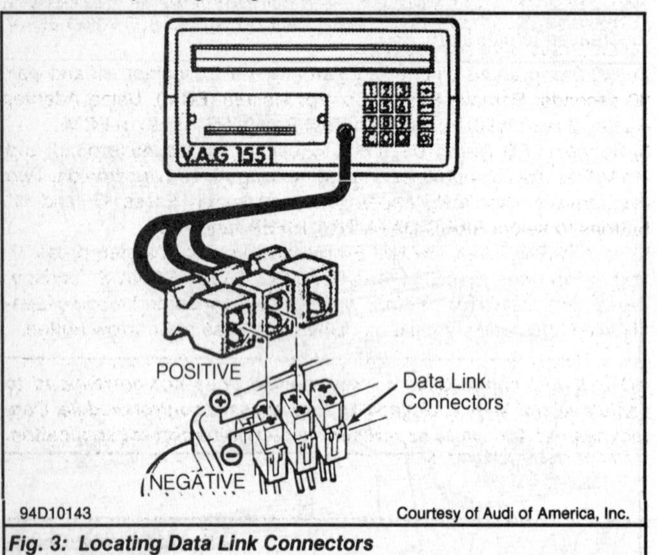
V.A.G 1551
POSITIVE
Data Link Connectors
NEGATIVE
94D10143
Courtesy of Audi of America, Inc.

Fig. 3: Locating Data Link Connectors

3) Two displays will alternately appear on scan tester. If necessary, press right arrow button on scan tester to maneuver through program sequence. Press PRINT button to turn on scan tester printer. Press "1" button to select RAPID DATA TRANSFER function.

4) With RAPID DATA TRANSFER displayed on scan tester, press "0" and "8" buttons to select A/C/HEATING ELECTRONICS function. Press "Q" button to enter input. A/C compressor control module identification and coding should be displayed.

NOTE: If A/C compressor control module does not correspond to vehicle and/or engine, replace A/C compressor control module. Contact nearest Audi parts department to determine correct application.

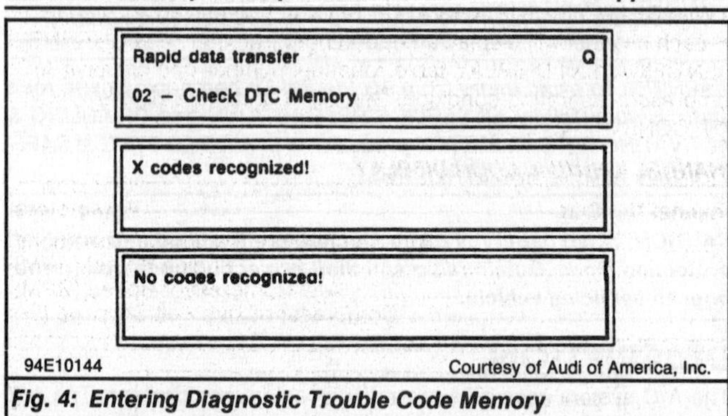
Rapid data transfer Q
02 – Check DTC Memory
X codes recognized!
No codes recognized!
94E10144
Courtesy of Audi of America, Inc.

Fig. 4: Entering Diagnostic Trouble Code Memory

5) If CONTROL MODULE (UNIT) DOES NOT ANSWER!, K WIRE DOES NOT SWITCH TO GROUND/POSITIVE, or if FAULT (MALFUNCTION) IN COMMUNICATION SET-UP is displayed, press HELP button to print out a list of possible causes. Check DLC wiring for battery voltage and ground.

6) Also check voltage supply and ground circuits to A/C compressor clutch control module. After repairing problem, press "0" and "8" buttons to select A/C/HEATING ELECTRONICS function. Press "Q" button to enter input.

7) With RAPID DATA TRANSFER displayed on scan tester, press "0" and "2" buttons to select CHECK DTC (FAULT) MEMORY function. Press "Q" button to enter input.

8) An X CODES RECOGNIZED! (number of codes stored) or NO CODES RECOGNIZED! message will be displayed. *See Fig. 4.* Press right arrow button.

9) Diagnostic trouble codes, if any, will be displayed and printed one after another. See DIAGNOSTIC TROUBLE CODE IDENTIFICATION table. After last DTC has been displayed, turn ignition off.

10) Repair A/C system malfunctions (if any). After repairs, test drive vehicle once more. Check for diagnostic trouble codes once again. If A/C compressor clutch does not engage, even though no DTC was recognized, perform MEASURING VALUE BLOCK function and OUTPUT DIAGNOSTIC TEST MODE.

DIAGNOSTIC TROUBLE CODE IDENTIFICATION

DTC Code	System/Affected Circuit	Possible Cause/Repair
0000	No Fault (Malfunction) Recognized	Perform MEASURING VALUE BLOCK Function
00532	A/C Comp. Supply Voltage Low	A/C Switch Off, Open High Or Low Pressure Switch, [1] Voltage Less Than 10 Volts At A/C Compressor Control Module
00624	A/C Compressor Engagement	Short Circuit To Battery Voltage Between ECM And A/C Compressor Clutch Control Module Terminal No. 87a Or Faulty ECM
01270	A/C Comp. Clutch Speed Deviation	Loose Drive Belt, A/C Compressor Clutch Slips, A/C Compressor Does Not Turn Freely, Incorrect A/C Compressor Control Module
01270	A/C Compressor Clutch Break	[2] A/C Compressor Does Not Turn Freely, Faulty A/C Compressor, Or Open Circuit Between A/C Compressor And A/C Compressor Control Module
01270	A/C Comp. Clutch Mechanical Fault	A/C Compressor Clutch Stuck On, Short Circuit To Battery Voltage Between A/C Compressor And A/C Compressor Control Module Terminal "K" Or Faulty Module
00529	No Engine Speed (RPM) Information [3]	Open Circuit Between Instrument Cluster And A/C Compressor Control Module Or Faulty Module

[1] – Check wiring harness for an open circuit to A/C compressor control module terminal No. 30 and 75.

[2] – Check A/C compressor clutch and speed sensor. Check wiring (open/shorted circuit) between A/C compressor control module and A/C compressor clutch and/or speed sensor.

[3] – This malfunction is only recognized during OUTPUT DIAGNOSTIC TEST MODE. No additional message is displayed.

1993 MANUAL A/C-HEATER SYSTEMS 90 & 100 (Cont.)

MEASURING VALUE BLOCK

1) Check Diagnostic Trouble Code (DTC) memory. See DIAGNOSTIC TROUBLE CODE MEMORY. Repair A/C system malfunctions (if any). After checking DTC memory, keep engine running and turn on A/C system.

2) Ensure scan tester is in A/C/HEATING ELECTRONICS function. With RAPID DATA TRANSFER displayed on scan tester, press "0" and "8" button to select READ MEASURING VALUE BLOCK function. Press "Q" button to enter input.

3) With INPUT DISPLAY GROUP NUMBER displayed on scan tester, press "0" and "1" buttons to select group number. *See Fig. 5.* Press "Q" button to enter input.

4) With READ MEASURING VALUE BLOCK 1 displayed on scan tester, each channel will display an operating parameter. See CHANNEL IDENTIFICATION DISPLAY table. Channel number one displays A/C compressor operating condition. See A/C COMPRESSOR SWITCH-OFF CONDITIONS table.

CHANNEL IDENTIFICATION DISPLAY

Channel Number	Parameters
1	A/C Compressor Switch-Off Conditions
2	Engine Speed (RPM)
3	A/C Compressor Speed (RPM)
4	Compressor Drive Belt Slippage (%)

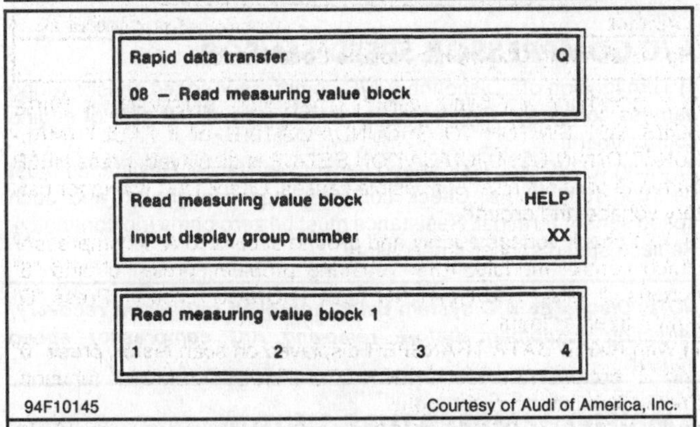

Rapid data transfer Q
08 – Read measuring value block

Read measuring value block HELP
Input display group number XX

Read measuring value block 1
1 2 3 4

94F10145 Courtesy of Audi of America, Inc.

Fig. 5: Entering Measuring Value Block Function

OUTPUT DIAGNOSTIC TEST MODE

1) Entering Output Diagnostic Test Mode – Check Diagnostic Trouble Code (DTC) memory. See DIAGNOSTIC TROUBLE CODE MEMORY. Perform measuring value block function. See MEASURING VALUE BLOCK. Repair A/C system malfunctions (if any).

2) Turn on A/C system. Ensure scan tester is in A/C/HEATING ELECTRONICS function. With RAPID DATA TRANSFER displayed on scan tester, press "0" and "3" button to select OUTPUT DIAGNOSTIC TEST MODE (DMT) function. Press "Q" button to enter input.

NOTE: On Audi 100, OUTPUT CHECK DIAGNOSIS and OUTPUT CHECK : 0270 may be displayed on scan tester.

3) Scan tester should display either AIR CONDITIONING COMPRESSOR ENGAGEMENT or OUTPUT DTM : 0270. Go to A/C COMPRESSOR CLUTCH ENGAGEMENT only if one or more of the following conditions exist:

- A/C COMPRESSOR ENGAGEMENT – SHORT CIRCUIT TO POSITIVE message appears on scan tester
- A/C compressor clutch does not engage and Code 5 is displayed in Channel 1 of MEASURING VALUE BLOCK function
- Engine RPM fluctuates or is irregular during A/C system operation
- Idle speed too high, Idle Air Control (IAC) valve value too high

4) If none of the above listed conditions exist, press right arrow button. Scan tester should display A/C COMPRESSOR (MAGNETIC) CLUTCH – N 25. The A/C compressor clutch is switched on and off in 3 second intervals.

5) If FUNCTION IS UNKNOWN OR CURRENTLY CANNOT BE CARRIED OUT is displayed in scan tester after A/C compressor clutch switches on, check DTC memory once again. A malfunction exists which is only recognized during output diagnostic test mode. Press right arrow button.

6) If A/C compressor clutch does not engage or A/C compressor does not rotate when clutch engages, ensure A/C compressor is not seized or repair clutch as necessary. Also check voltage to A/C compressor clutch. Press right arrow button.

7) A/C Compressor Clutch Engagement – Turn ignition off and wait 30 seconds. Remove Engine Control Module (ECM). Using Adapter Cables (VAG 1598/11), connect Test Box (VAG 1598) to ECM.

8) Connect LED Tester (US 1115) to test box pin No. 45 (ground) and Pin No. 11 (A/C compressor engagement input). Turn ignition on. Two displays will alternately appear on scan tester. Press "0" and "1" buttons to select RAPID DATA TRANSFER function.

9) With RAPID DATA TRANSFER displayed on scan tester, press "0" and "8" buttons to select A/C/HEATING ELECTRONICS function. Press "Q" button to enter input. A/C compressor control module identification and coding should be displayed. Press right arrow button.

NOTE: If A/C compressor control module does not correspond to vehicle and/or engine, replace A/C compressor control module. Contact nearest Audi parts department to determine correct application.

A/C COMPRESSOR SWITCH-OFF CONDITIONS

Code No. (Condition)	Affected Circuit/Cause
0 [1] (A/C Compressor On)	Switch-Off Condition Not Recognized
1 (A/C Compressor Off)	No Output Speed Signal From Instrument Cluster, Engine Speed Not Recognized Or Too Low (600 RPM Or Less), Or Open Circuit Between Instrument Cluster And A/C Compressor Control Module
2 (A/C Compressor Off)	[2] A/C Compressor Control Module Voltage At Terminal No. 75 Less Than 3 Volts Or [3] A/C Compressor Control Module Voltage At Terminal No. 30 Less Than 10 Volts
3 (A/C Compressor Off)	Terminal "R" Of Electronic Thermoswitch Closed, Or A/C Compressor Control Module Terminal "HLS" Shorted To Ground
4 (A/C Compressor Off)	No Voltage At Terminal "87a" Of A/C Compressor Control Module, Or Engine Control Module (ECM) Has Switched To Ground
5 (A/C Compressor Off)	A/C Compressor Does Not Turn Freely (Seized), Belt Tension Too Loose, Incorrect A/C Compressor Control Module Installed, Or [4] A/C Compressor Speed Signal Not Recognized
6 (A/C Compressor Off)	A/C Compressor Off For 12 Seconds After Kickdown Switch Closes
7 (Kickdown Switch Closed)	No Voltage At Terminal "U" Of A/C Compressor Control Module, Or Transmission Control Module Has Switched Input To Ground

[1] – If A/C Compressor Does Not Come On, Perform OUTPUT DIAGNOSTIC TEST MODE.

[2] – Ensure A/C switch is on. Ensure that ambient temperature switch and high pressure switch are not open. Check wiring harness for an open circuit.

[3] – Ensure low pressure switch is not open. Check wiring harness for an open circuit or high resistance.

[4] – Correct condition number 2 first. Check A/C compressor clutch and speed sensor. Check wiring (open/shorted circuit) between A/C compressor control module and A/C compressor clutch and/or speed sensor.

1993 MANUAL A/C-HEATER SYSTEMS 90 & 100 (Cont.)

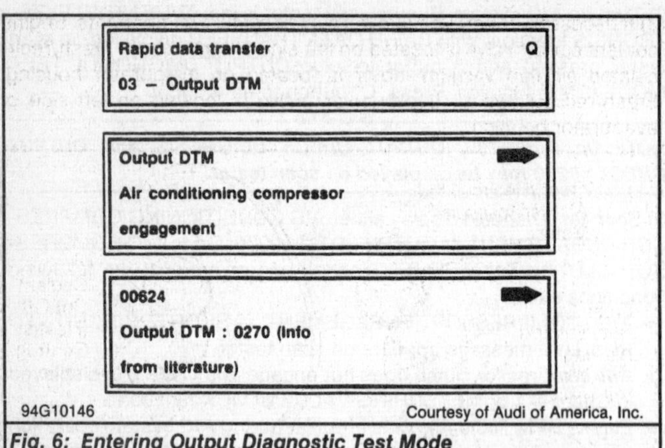

Rapid data transfer Q
03 – Output DTM

Output DTM
Air conditioning compressor engagement

00624
Output DTM : 0270 (Info from literature)

94G10146 Courtesy of Audi of America, Inc.

Fig. 6: Entering Output Diagnostic Test Mode

10) Press "0" and "3" buttons to select OUTPUT DTM function. Press "Q" button to enter input. *See Fig. 6*. Scan tester should display either AIR CONDITIONING COMPRESSOR ENGAGEMENT or OUTPUT DTM : 0270. LED tester should blink on and off in 3 second intervals.
11) If LED tester does not blink, check wiring harness between A/C compressor control module and ECM connector for an open/short circuit. Repair wiring harness as necessary.
12) Press right arrow button. Scan tester should display A/C COMPRESSOR (MAGNETIC) CLUTCH – N 25. The A/C compressor clutch is switched on and off in 3 second intervals. Press right arrow button to end procedure.

TESTING

WARNING: To avoid injury from accidental air bag deployment, read and carefully follow all SERVICE PRECAUTIONS and DISABLING & ACTIVATING AIR BAG SYSTEM procedures in AIR BAG SYSTEM SAFETY article in GENERAL SERVICING.

A/C SYSTEM PERFORMANCE

1) Park vehicle out of direct sunlight. Ensure condenser and radiator are free of obstructions. Close engine hood. Ensure compressor drive belt is in good condition. Ensure engine is at normal operating temperature.
2) Start engine and run it at 2000 RPM. Turn A/C system on and press recirculation button on. Indicator lights on A/C switch and recirculation button should be on.
3) Set temperature control knob to maximum cold position. Open all instrument panel air outlets. Place blower motor knob on high speed (IIII position). Set air distribution control knob so that air flows out of instrument panel vents.
4) Close doors, windows, and sun roof. Record ambient temperature and check outlet air temperature at center instrument panel vent after A/C system has run for 5 minutes. See A/C SYSTEM PERFORMANCE SPECIFICATIONS table.

A/C SYSTEM PERFORMANCE SPECIFICATIONS

Ambient Temperature °F (°C)	Outlet Air Temperature °F (°C)
59 (15)	37-43 (3-6)
68 (20)	37-43 (3-6)
77 (25)	37-43 (3-6)
86 (30)	37-43 (3-6)
95 (35)	39-45 (4-7)
104 (40)	41-48 (5-8)

5) If outlet air temperature is not as specified, remove low pressure switch and jumper connector terminals. Remove high pressure cut-out switch, leaving its wiring harness connected.
6) Connect manifold gauge set to high and low pressure service valves. Start engine and connect Scan Tester (VAG 1551) to Data Link Connectors (DLC) located in plenum chamber (fuse/relay block). *See Fig. 3.*
7) Select READ MEASURING VALUE BLOCK function and monitor A/C system. Repeat A/C system performance test. Check A/C system pressures and scan data from channel No. 1 on scan tester display.
8) High side (discharge) pressure should increase from base pressure (engine off) to a maximum of 290 psi (20.4 kg/cm²). The high pressure switch should switch cooling fan to second speed between 190-254 psi (13.4-17.9 kg/cm²). If cooling fan does not switch to second speed, check cooling fan circuit.
9) Low side (suction) pressure should be as specified in A/C SYSTEM LOW SIDE PRESSURE SPECIFICATIONS. If both high and low side pressures are okay, A/C system cooling performance is okay. Check low pressure and high pressure switches as necessary.
10) If high and low side pressures are incorrect, check refrigerant and A/C system for malfunctions (low refrigerant charge, faulty A/C compressor, kinked/plugged A/C hose, etc.).

A/C SYSTEM LOW SIDE PRESSURE SPECIFICATIONS

Ambient Temp. °F (°C)	psi (kg/cm²)
50 (10)	30-32 (2.1-2.2)
59 (15)	29-32 (2.0-2.2)
68 (20)	28-30 (1.9-2.1)
77 (25)	26-29 (1.8-2.0)
86 (30)	25-29 (1.7-2.0)
95 (35)	25-30 (1.7-2.1)
104 (40)	28-33 (1.9-2.3)

A/C COMPRESSOR SPEED SENSOR

1) Turn ignition off. Disconnect A/C compressor speed sensor wiring harness connector. Connector is located in front, left side of engine compartment.
2) Using a DVOM, check speed sensor resistance. Resistance must be 1000-1500 ohms. Check continuity between ground and each speed sensor terminal. Resistance must be zero ohms (no continuity). Replace speed sensor if necessary.

NOTE: Discharge A/C system using approved refrigerant recovery/recycling equipment before removing A/C compressor speed sensor.

AMBIENT TEMPERATURE SWITCH

1) Remove right side plenum tray. Remove glove box. Remove switch from intake air duct, on right side of heater box (evaporator housing on Audi 100). Place switch in freezer.
2) Using a DVOM, check switch resistance. Switch resistance must be infinite (no continuity) below 30°F (–1°C). Allow switch to warm above 45°F (7°C). Switch resistance must be zero ohms (continuity). Replace switch if necessary.

HIGH PRESSURE SWITCH

Locate high pressure switch on refrigerant line (on left side of condenser on Audi 100). Switch is identified by its Green housing. Ensure switch closes at 190.0-254.0 psi (13.36-17.86 kg/cm²). Ensure switch opens at 153.7-217.5 psi (10.81-15.29 kg/cm²). Replace switch if necessary.

NOTE: High pressure switch, high pressure cut-out switch, and low pressure switch may be removed without discharging A/C system.

HIGH PRESSURE CUT-OUT SWITCH

1) High pressure cut-out switch is located on right/left side of condenser. Switch is identified by its Red housing. Ensure switch opens at 409.0-449.5 psi (28.76-31.60 kg/cm²).
2) Ensure switch closes at 149.0-251.0 psi (10.45-17.65 kg/cm²). Difference between opening and closing points must be at least 29.0 psi (2.04 kg/cm²). Replace switch if necessary.

LOW PRESSURE SWITCH

1) On Audi 90, locate low pressure switch between heater housing and passenger side of firewall. Ensure switch opens at 21.0-23.2 psi (1.48-1.63 kg/cm²).

2) Ensure switch closes at 42.0-46.4 psi (2.95-3.26 kg/cm²). Difference between opening and closing points must be 20.3-23.2 psi (1.43-1.63 kg/cm²). Replace switch if necessary.

3) On Audi 100, locate switch on right side of plenum chamber. Ensure switch opens at 23.2-24.7 psi (1.63-1.74 kg/cm²). Ensure switch closes at 45.0-52.2 psi (3.16-3.67 kg/cm²). Replace switch if necessary.

VACUUM SYSTEM

90 – 1) To test vacuum reservoir, connect hand-held vacuum pump and apply 20 in. Hg to vacuum supply line. Vacuum reservoir may be accessed by removing left front wheel housing liner. *See Fig. 7.*

2) Vacuum must hold steady and not drop more than 10 percent (3 in. Hg) in 2 minutes. If necessary, apply vacuum to vacuum system components, hoses, and vacuum "T" fittings to check for leaks.

3) To test fresh/recirculated air flap, remove right side plenum tray and air intake grille. Start engine and allow it to idle. Turn A/C system on. Push recirculation switch on. Fresh/recirculated air flap must close to outside air.

4) If fresh/recirculated air flap does not close, check voltage to two-way valve (Black/Green wire). Valve is located on right side of heater box. Repair Black/Green wire as necessary.

5) To test fresh/recirculated air flap vacuum motor, remove passenger side lower instrument panel cover. Locate fresh/recirculated air flap vacuum motor on right side of heater box.

6) Disconnect vacuum hose from vacuum motor. Connect hand-held vacuum pump and apply 20 in. Hg to vacuum motor. Fresh/recirculated air flap must move to stop. Vacuum must hold steady and not drop more than 10 percent in 2 minutes.

7) If fresh/recirculated air flap does not operate as specified, replace vacuum motor. The heater box and evaporator housing must be removed to replace vacuum motor.

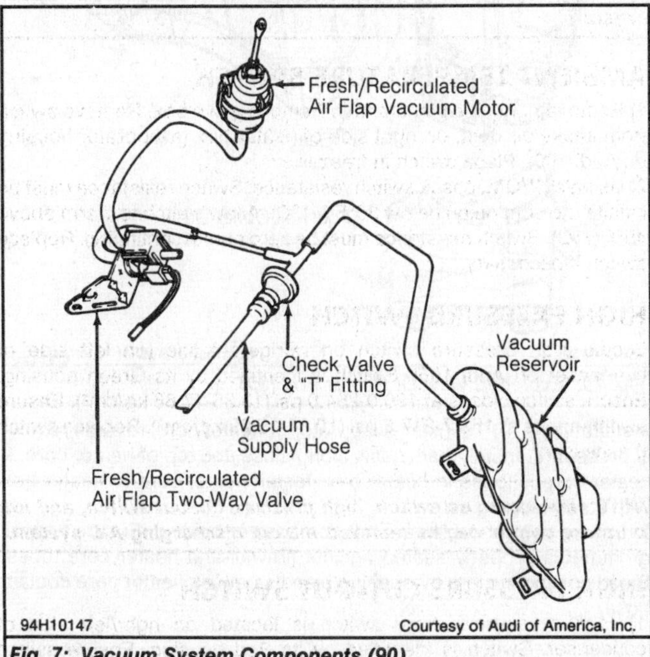

Fresh/Recirculated
Air Flap Vacuum Motor
Check Valve
& "T" Fitting
Vacuum
Reservoir
Vacuum
Supply Hose
Fresh/Recirculated
Air Flap Two-Way Valve
94H10147
Courtesy of Audi of America, Inc.

Fig. 7: Vacuum System Components (90)

100 – 1) To test reservoir, locate vacuum reservoir. Vacuum reservoir is located on left side of heater box. Remove vacuum outlet line, from reservoir, leading to two-way valve. *See Fig. 8.*

2) Connect vacuum gauge to vacuum reservoir vacuum outlet line. Start and run engine for one minute. Turn engine off. Vacuum must hold steady and not drop more than 10 percent (3 in. Hg) in 2 minutes.

3) If necessary, apply vacuum to vacuum system components. Engine coolant cut-off valve is located on left side of heater box. Fresh/recirculated air flap vacuum motor is located on evaporator housing. Fresh/recirculated air flap two-way valve is located on left side of evaporator housing.

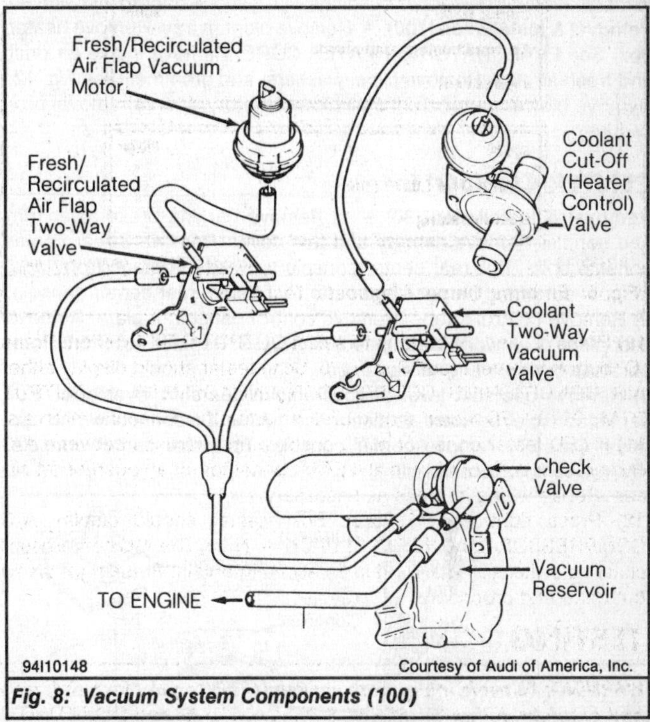

Fresh/Recirculated
Air Flap Vacuum
Motor
Fresh/
Recirculated
Air Flap
Two-Way
Valve
Coolant
Cut-Off
(Heater
Control)
Valve
Coolant
Two-Way
Vacuum
Valve
Check
Valve
Vacuum
Reservoir
TO ENGINE
94I10148
Courtesy of Audi of America, Inc.

Fig. 8: Vacuum System Components (100)

REMOVAL & INSTALLATION

WARNING: To avoid injury from accidental air bag deployment, read and carefully follow all SERVICE PRECAUTIONS and DISABLING & ACTIVATING AIR BAG SYSTEM procedures in AIR BAG SYSTEM SAFETY article in GENERAL SERVICING.

A/C COMPRESSOR

Removal & Installation (90) – 1) Mark direction of drive belt. Loosen drive belt tensioner and remove drive belt. Remove oil filter. Clamp shut oil cooler coolant hoses. Remove coolant hoses from oil cooler. Remove oil cooler.

2) Discharge A/C system using approved refrigerant recovery/recycling equipment. Disconnect A/C compressor clutch connector. Remove bolts and A/C compressor. To install compressor, reverse removal procedure.

Removal & Installation (100) – 1) Mark direction of drive belt. Loosen drive belt tensioner and remove drive belt. Remove clamp bolt and pull refrigerant line upward.

2) Discharge A/C system using approved refrigerant recovery/recycling equipment. Remove A/C compressor bracket bolts. Disconnect A/C compressor clutch connector. Remove bolts and A/C compressor. To install compressor, reverse removal procedure.

A/C COMPRESSOR SPEED SENSOR

Removal & Installation – Discharge A/C system using approved refrigerant recovery/recycling equipment. Disconnect speed sensor connector. Remove screws and sensor. To install sensor, reverse removal procedure.

BLOWER MOTOR & RESISTOR

Removal (90) – 1) Remove glove box. Mark location of blower motor wires and disconnect wires. Remove 4 screws and loosen blower motor. Disengage 3 rubber bushings.

1993 MANUAL A/C-HEATER SYSTEMS 90 & 100 (Cont.)

2) Detach plate and blower motor from heater box. Turn plate inward and pull out connector. Remove blower motor. To remove resistor, disconnect wiring harness from resistor. Remove screws and resistor.
Installation – To install components, reverse removal procedure. Coat sealing surface of blower motor plate with silicone sealant prior to installation. Spray rubber bushings with silicone prior to installation.
Removal & Installation (100) – Remove plenum tray. Remove heater box. See EVAPORATOR & HEATER CORE. Remove intake air duct and fresh air flap. Remove clips, washers, and grommet. *See Fig. 12.* Remove blower motor. To install blower motor, reverse removal procedure.

CENTER CONSOLE

Removal & Installation (90) – **1)** Remove parking brake lever trim and handle. Remove ashtray and trim cover. Remove 3 rear center console bolts. Pull rear center console upward to detach from lugs. Disconnect wiring harness and carefully remove rear center console.
2) Remove control knobs. Remove control panel trim plate. Remove filler piece downward (if equipped). *See Fig. 9.* Remove automatic temperature control panel (if equipped).
3) Remove gearshift lever knob. Remove gearshift lever boot. Pull center console rearward, to disengage guides. Disconnect wiring harness. Carefully remove center console. To install center console, reverse removal procedure.

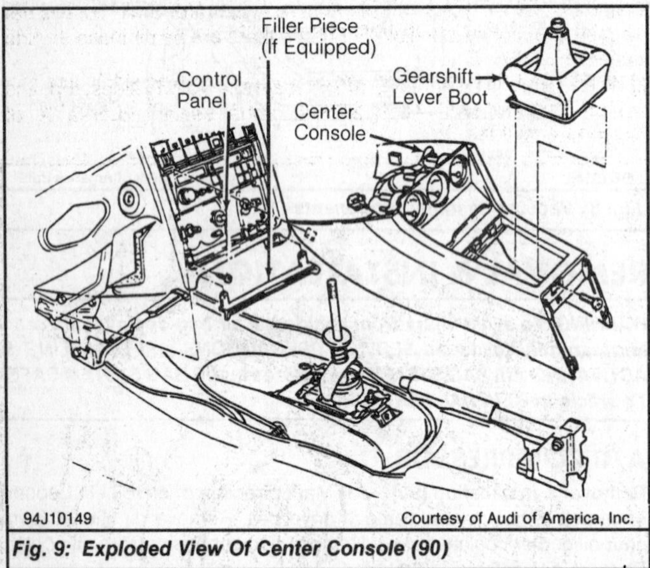
Filler Piece
(If Equipped)
Control
Panel
Gearshift
Lever Boot
Center
Console
94J10149
Courtesy of Audi of America, Inc.

Fig. 9: Exploded View Of Center Console (90)

Removal & Installation (100) – **1)** Disconnect negative battery cable. Obtain radio anti-theft protection code. Remove gearshift lever knob. Remove screw and gearshift lever boot.
2) Remove parking brake lever handle. Remove cigarette lighter and trim cover. Move driver's seat and passenger's seat all the way forward. Remove rear center console bolts. Carefully remove rear center console (forward and at an angle).
3) Remove control panel knobs (if equipped). Remove control panel trim plate. Remove A/C-heater system control panel and radio. Remove ashtray, trim, and center air vent. Remove nuts along exterior sides of center console.
4) Remove screws from interior opening of center console. Carefully remove center console (rearward and at an angle). To install center console, reverse removal procedure.

CONTROL PANEL

Removal – Remove control panel knobs (if equipped). Remove control panel trim plate. On Audi 90 with manual A/C-heater system, remove center console. See CENTER CONSOLE. On all models, remove A/C-heater system control panel. Carefully detach cables from retaining clips (if equipped).

Installation – To install control panel, reverse removal procedure. Footwell/defroster flap cable has a White retainer. Central flap cable has a Black retainer. Temperature flap cable has a Red retainer. If cable locking tabs break off, use self-tapping screws to secure cables.

EVAPORATOR & HEATER CORE

Removal (90) – **1)** Obtain radio anti-theft protection code. Disconnect negative battery cable. Disable air bag system. Remove center console and instrument panel. See CENTER CONSOLE and INSTRUMENT PANEL.
2) Discharge A/C system using approved refrigerant recovery/recycling equipment. Drain cooling system. Clamp shut heater core coolant hoses. Remove coolant hoses from heater core.
3) Loosen refrigerant line clamp and remove lines from evaporator. Remove right side plenum tray. Remove intake air duct grille. Remove ambient temperature switch. Remove screws and intake air duct.
4) Remove evaporator housing nuts from engine compartment side of firewall. Remove vacuum hose from fresh/recirculated air flap two-way valve. Remove evaporator housing drain hose.
5) Remove control module from bottom of evaporator housing. Remove heater box and evaporator housing assembly. Remove evaporator or heater core as necessary. *See Figs. 10 and 11.*

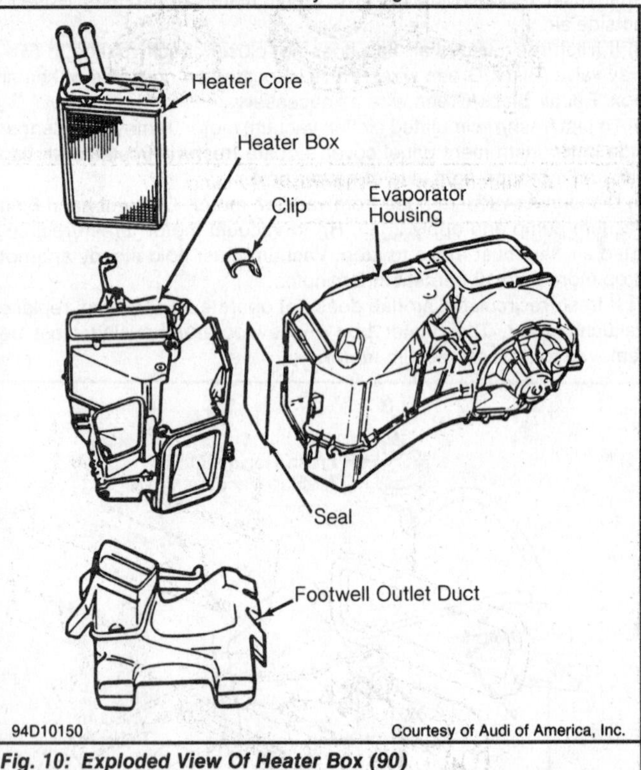
Heater Core
Heater Box
Clip
Evaporator
Housing
Seal
Footwell Outlet Duct
94D10150
Courtesy of Audi of America, Inc.

Fig. 10: Exploded View Of Heater Box (90)

Installation – **1)** To install evaporator or heater core, reverse removal procedure. Install foam seals along sides and top of heater core. If heater core is loose in heater box, fasten heater core to heater box with 2 self-tapping screws.
2) Ensure control cables are not damaged or binding. Ensure firewall grommet is properly seated against firewall and heater core tubes. Bleed cooling system by opening bleed screw on heater core coolant hose.

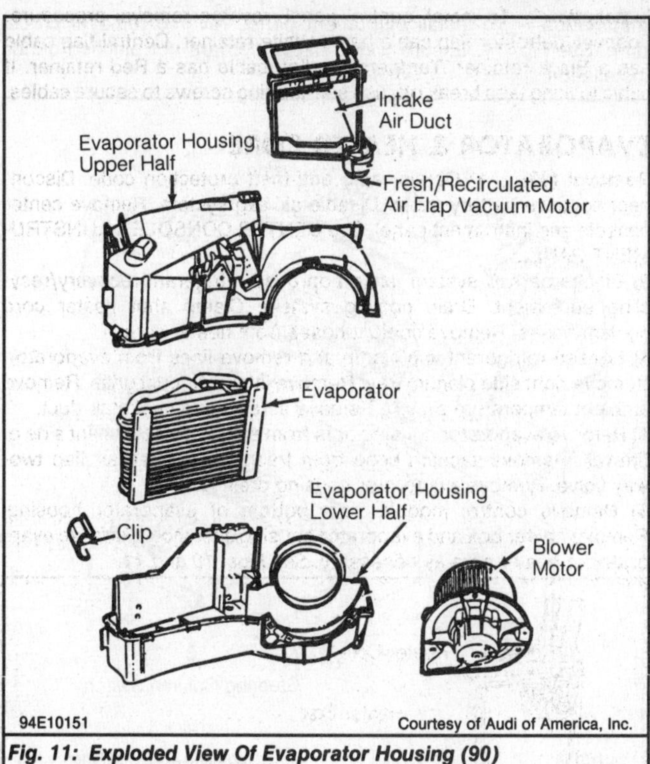
Intake
Air Duct
Evaporator Housing
Upper Half
Fresh/Recirculated
Air Flap Vacuum Motor
Evaporator
Evaporator Housing
Lower Half
Clip
Blower
Motor
94E10151
Courtesy of Audi of America, Inc.

Fig. 11: Exploded View Of Evaporator Housing (90)

Removal (100) – 1) Disable air bag system. If removing evaporator housing, discharge A/C system using approved refrigerant recovery/recycling equipment. Remove glove box. Remove 4 screws and evaporator cover.

2) Remove plenum tray. Disconnect refrigerant lines to evaporator. Disconnect wiring harnesses and cables attached to evaporator housing. Remove evaporator housing from vehicle. Evaporator housing must be replaced as an assembly.

3) If removing heater core, remove plenum tray. Entirely remove windshield wiper motor and linkage assembly. Remove center console. See CENTER CONSOLE. Remove glove box and driver's side tray. Remove control panel.

4) On manual A/C-heater system, remove footwell air outlet on driver and passenger side. Remove rubber grommet between heater box and evaporator housing. Remove hoses and bellows to rear heater duct.

5) Remove tensioning strap. Disconnect wiring harnesses and cables between heater box, evaporator housing, and vehicle. Drain cooling system. Disconnect heater core coolant hoses from heater box.

6) Attach Engine Support Bridge (10-222 A/1) and Claw (2075) to lip of heater box. Tighten wing nut on bridge, until heater box is loosened. Remove engine support bridge and heater box. Disassemble heater box and remove heater core.

Installation – 1) When installing evaporator, replace seal between evaporator housing and vehicle. Ensure evaporator drain hose is not pinched shut during installation. Ensure there are no air leaks around evaporator housing.

2) When installing heater core, attach foam seals along sides, top, and bottom of heater core. Apply silicone rubber sealant to area "A" of heater box. *See Fig. 12.*

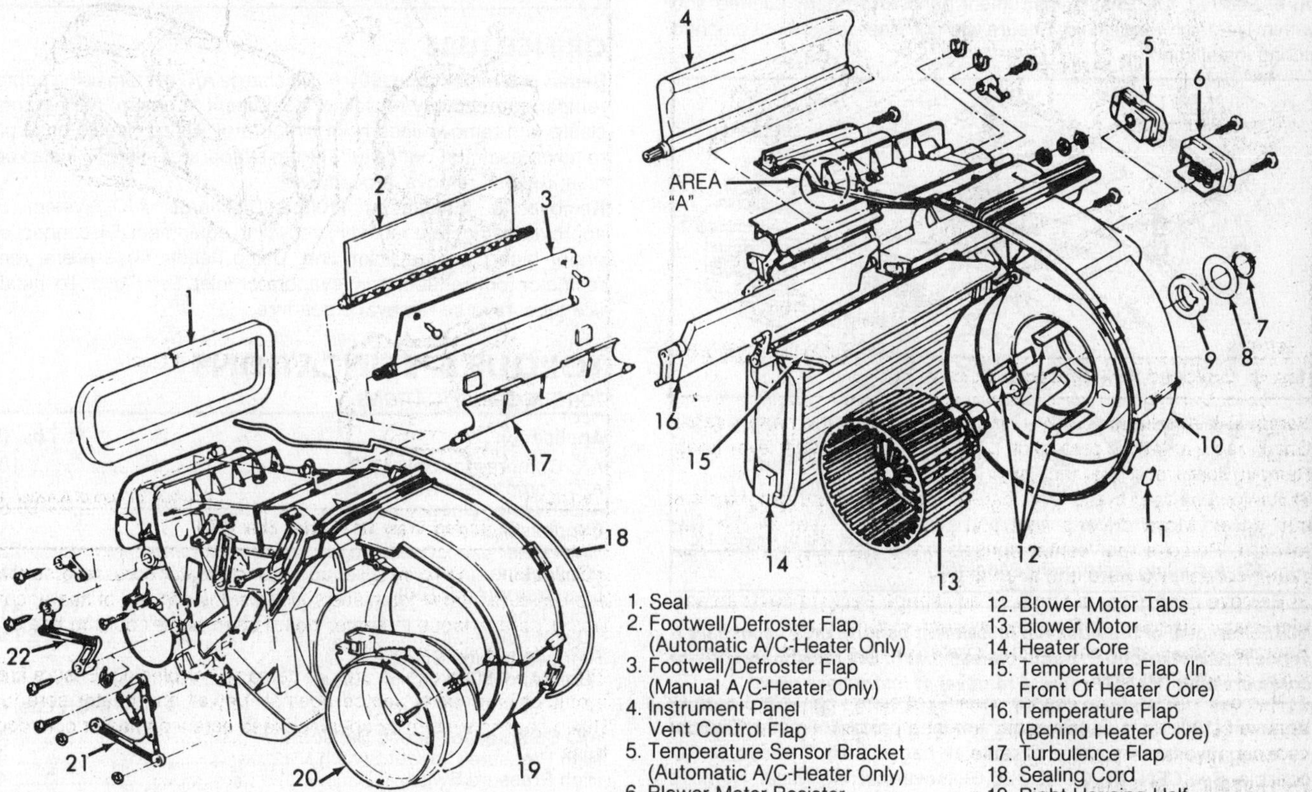

AREA "A"

1. Seal
2. Footwell/Defroster Flap (Automatic A/C-Heater Only)
3. Footwell/Defroster Flap (Manual A/C-Heater Only)
4. Instrument Panel Vent Control Flap
5. Temperature Sensor Bracket (Automatic A/C-Heater Only)
6. Blower Motor Resistor
7. Snap Ring
8. Washer
9. Grommet
10. Left Housing Half
11. Clip
12. Blower Motor Tabs
13. Blower Motor
14. Heater Core
15. Temperature Flap (In Front Of Heater Core)
16. Temperature Flap (Behind Heater Core)
17. Turbulence Flap
18. Sealing Cord
19. Right Housing Half
20. Intake Duct
21. Temperature Lever Flap
22. Footwell/Defroster & Instrument Panel Vent Flap (Manual A/C-Heater Only)

94F10152

Courtesy of Audi of America, Inc.

Fig. 12: Exploded View Of Heater Box (100)

1993 MANUAL A/C-HEATER SYSTEMS 90 & 100 (Cont.)

3) Use Aligning Plate (2076 A) to align instrument panel vent control flap, temperature flaps, and footwell/defroster control flap (automatic A/C system only). Assemble heater box, and apply silicone rubber sealant around heater core tubes. To complete installation, reverse removal procedure.

HEATER CONTROL VALVE

Removal & Installation (100) – Remove plenum tray. Drain cooling system. Disconnect heater core coolant hoses. Loosen heater control valve hose clamps. Remove screw and heater control valve. To install valve, reverse removal procedure.

INSTRUMENT PANEL

Removal (90) – **1)** Obtain radio anti-theft protection code. Disconnect negative battery cable. Disable air bag system. Remove center console. See CENTER CONSOLE. Remove passenger side instrument panel lower cover. Pry up cover and disconnect air bag wiring harness connectors. Pry off driver side lower instrument panel cover.
2) Remove bolts and driver side knee bar. Disconnect wiring harness connectors from instrument panel and along center console tunnel. Remove ground lead on relay and relay plate with fuse block.
3) Remove steering wheel. Insert Phillips head screwdriver into steering column cover opening and loosen clamp on cover. Release steering column cover by firmly pulling up on upper half of cover, then repeat procedure at bottom. Remove steering wheel cover.
4) Remove screws and instrument cluster. Disconnect wiring harness and remove instrument cluster. Remove radio. Remove instrument panel nut through radio opening. Remove instrument panel bolts on sides and along center console tunnel.
Installation – To install instrument panel, reverse removal procedure. *See Fig. 13*. Ensure instrument panel is properly aligned and within 1/4" from windshield. Ensure wiring harnesses are not pinched during installation.

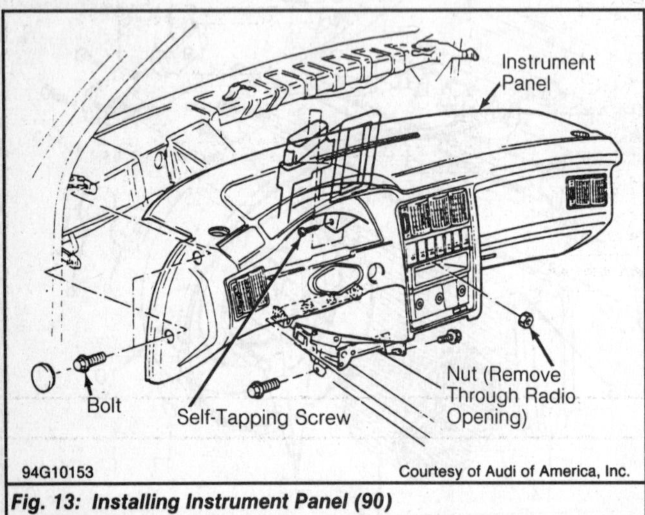
Instrument
Panel
Bolt
Self-Tapping Screw
Nut (Remove
Through Radio
Opening)
94G10153
Courtesy of Audi of America, Inc.

Fig. 13: Installing Instrument Panel (90)

NOTE: Removal of the Audi 100 instrument panel is only necessary if servicing air distribution ducts beneath dash. Evaporator and heater core servicing DO NOT require removal of instrument panel.

Removal (100) – **1)** Obtain radio anti-theft protection code. Disconnect negative battery cable. Disable air bag system. Remove center console. See CENTER CONSOLE. Remove steering wheel. Remove steering column switch assembly.
2) Remove trim strip and instrument cluster. Remove ignition switch trim ring. Remove instrument panel side covers. Remove fuse block. Remove instrument panel bolts on sides and along center console tunnel.

Installation – To install instrument panel, reverse removal procedure. *See Fig. 14*. Ensure wiring harnesses are not pinched during installation.

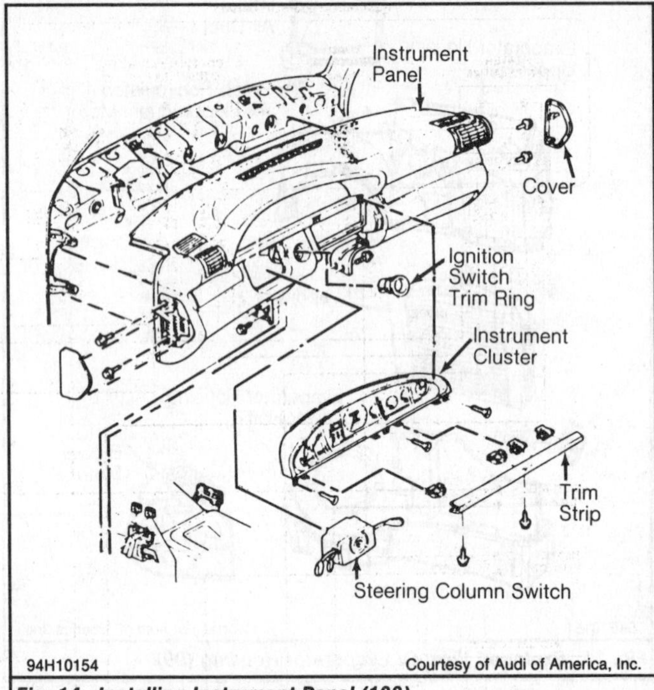
Instrument
Panel
Cover
Ignition
Switch
Trim Ring
Instrument
Cluster
Trim
Strip
Steering Column Switch
94H10154
Courtesy of Audi of America, Inc.

Fig. 14: Installing Instrument Panel (100)

ORIFICE TUBE

Removal & Installation (90) – Discharge A/C system using approved refrigerant recovery/recycling equipment. Loosen refrigerant line clamp and remove lines from evaporator. Using needle nose pliers, remove restrictor (orifice tube) from evaporator inlet. To install orifice tube, reverse removal procedure.
Removal & Installation (100) – Discharge A/C system using approved refrigerant recovery/recycling equipment. Disconnect evaporator high pressure (inlet) line. Using needle nose pliers, remove restrictor (orifice tube) from evaporator inlet. *See Fig. 2*. To install orifice tube, reverse removal procedure.

TORQUE SPECIFICATIONS

TORQUE SPECIFICATIONS

Application	Ft. Lbs. (N.m)
A/C Compressor Bolts	18 (25)
A/C Compressor Bracket Bolts	18 (25)
Accumulator Lines	29.5 (40)
Condenser	
Inlet Line	22 (30)
Outlet Line	11 (15)
Evaporator (Audi 100)	
Inlet Line	11 (15)
Outlet Line	29.5 (40)
Refrigerant Line Clamp	
Bolt (Audi 90)	11 (15)
	INCH Lbs. (N.m)
A/C Compressor Speed Sensor	44 (5)
High Pressure Cut-Out Switch [1]	44 (5)
High Pressure Switch [1]	44 (5)
Low Pressure Switch [1]	44 (5)
Instrument Panel Bolts & Nut	44 (5)

[1] – High pressure switch, high pressure cut-out switch, and low pressure switch may be removed without discharging A/C system.

WIRING DIAGRAMS

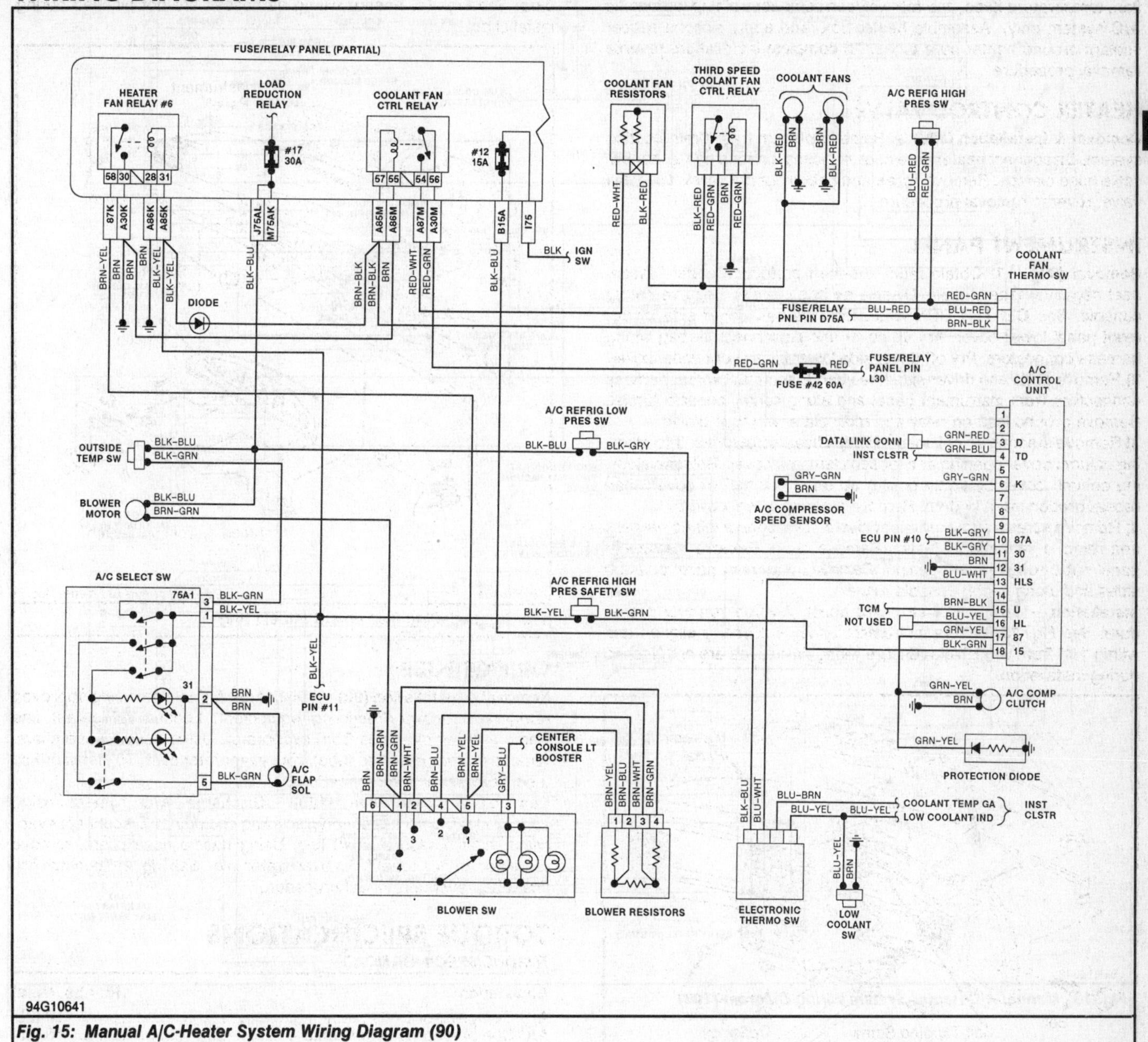
FUSE/RELAY PANEL (PARTIAL)
HEATER FAN RELAY #6
LOAD REDUCTION RELAY
COOLANT FAN CTRL RELAY
#17 30A
#12 15A
COOLANT FAN RESISTORS
THIRD SPEED COOLANT FAN CTRL RELAY
COOLANT FANS
A/C REFIG HIGH PRES SW
IGN SW
DIODE
COOLANT FAN THERMO SW
FUSE/RELAY PNL PIN D75A
FUSE/RELAY PANEL PIN L30
FUSE #42 60A
A/C CONTROL UNIT
A/C REFRIG LOW PRES SW
OUTSIDE TEMP SW
DATA LINK CONN
INST CLSTR
BLOWER MOTOR
A/C COMPRESSOR SPEED SENSOR
ECU PIN #10
A/C SELECT SW
A/C REFRIG HIGH PRES SAFETY SW
TCM
NOT USED
ECU PIN #11
A/C COMP CLUTCH
A/C FLAP SOL
CENTER CONSOLE LT BOOSTER
PROTECTION DIODE
COOLANT TEMP GA
LOW COOLANT IND
INST CLSTR
BLOWER SW
BLOWER RESISTORS
ELECTRONIC THERMO SW
LOW COOLANT SW
94G10641

Fig. 15: Manual A/C-Heater System Wiring Diagram (90)

1993 MANUAL A/C-HEATER SYSTEMS
90 & 100 (Cont.)

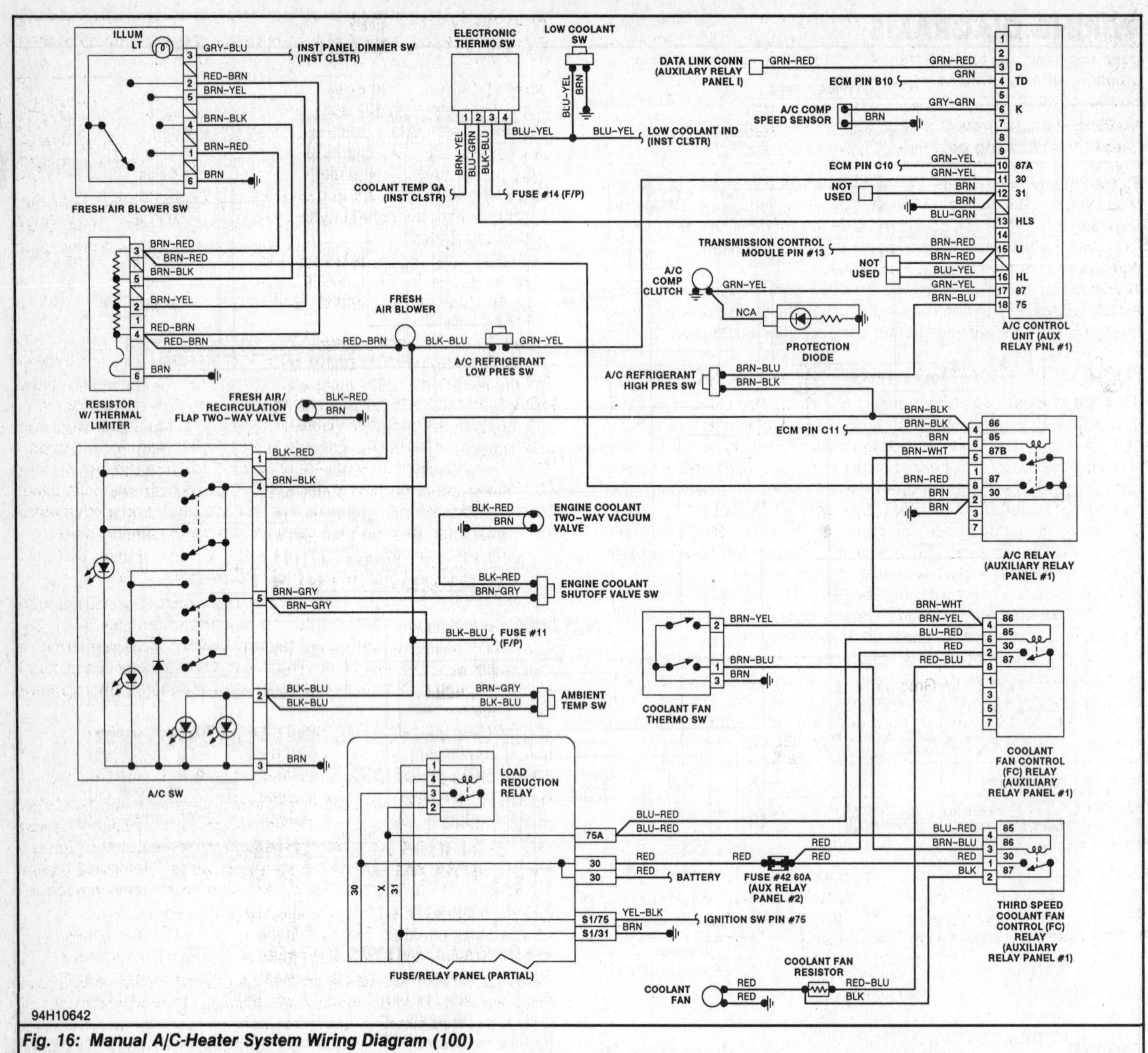
ILLUM LT
GRY-BLU
INST PANEL DIMMER SW (INST CLSTR)
RED-BRN
BRN-YEL
BRN-BLK
BRN-RED
BRN
FRESH AIR BLOWER SW
ELECTRONIC THERMO SW
LOW COOLANT SW
BLU-YEL
BLU-YEL
LOW COOLANT IND (INST CLSTR)
COOLANT TEMP GA (INST CLSTR)
FUSE #14 (F/P)
DATA LINK CONN (AUXILARY RELAY PANEL I)
GRN-RED
ECM PIN B10
A/C COMP SPEED SENSOR
ECM PIN C10
NOT USED
TRANSMISSION CONTROL MODULE PIN #13
A/C COMP CLUTCH
NCA
PROTECTION DIODE
A/C CONTROL UNIT (AUX RELAY PNL #1)
RESISTOR W/ THERMAL LIMITER
FRESH AIR BLOWER
A/C REFRIGERANT LOW PRES SW
FRESH AIR/ RECIRCULATION FLAP TWO-WAY VALVE
A/C REFRIGERANT HIGH PRES SW
ECM PIN C11
A/C RELAY (AUXILIARY RELAY PANEL #1)
ENGINE COOLANT TWO-WAY VACUUM VALVE
ENGINE COOLANT SHUTOFF VALVE SW
FUSE #11 (F/P)
AMBIENT TEMP SW
COOLANT FAN THERMO SW
COOLANT FAN CONTROL (FC) RELAY (AUXILIARY RELAY PANEL #1)
A/C SW
LOAD REDUCTION RELAY
BATTERY
FUSE #42 60A (AUX RELAY PANEL #2)
IGNITION SW PIN #75
THIRD SPEED COOLANT FAN CONTROL (FC) RELAY (AUXILIARY RELAY PANEL #1)
FUSE/RELAY PANEL (PARTIAL)
COOLANT FAN RESISTOR
COOLANT FAN
94H10642

Fig. 16: Manual A/C-Heater System Wiring Diagram (100)

SPECIFICATIONS

Compressor Type .... Zexel 6-Cyl.
Compressor Belt Tension [1]
System Oil Capacity .... [2] 7.8-9.2 ozs.
Refrigerant (R-134a) Capacity
90 .... 23.0-24.8 ozs.
100 .... 21.0-22.8 ozs.
System Operating Pressures [3]
Low Side .... 26-29 psi (1.8-2.0 kg/cm²)
High Side .... 79.8 psi (5.61 kg/cm²)

[1] - Belt tension is automatically adjusted by belt tensioner.
[2] - Use Polyalkylene Glycol (PAG) oil.
[3] - Measured at 77°F (25°C). High side pressure increases from base pressure (engine off) to a maximum of 290 psi (20.4 kg/cm²).

WARNING: To avoid injury from accidental air bag deployment, read and carefully follow all SERVICE PRECAUTIONS and DISABLING & ACTIVATING AIR BAG SYSTEM procedures in AIR BAG SYSTEM SAFETY article in GENERAL SERVICING.

DESCRIPTION

The A/C-heater control panel has buttons to control system. Blower speed is controlled automatically according to difference between selected temperature and interior temperature. Blower speed can also be controlled manually.

The A/C-heater control panel left side display shows selected temperature and automatic functions. *See Fig. 1.* The right side display indicates manual functions. The A/C-heater system microprocessor, located within the A/C-heater control panel, has a self-diagnostic feature.

The A/C-heater system automatically maintains temperatures from 64°F (18°C) to 85°F (29°C). If a temperature greater than 85°F (29°C) is selected, the word HI appears in temperature display. If a temperature less than 64°F (18°C) is selected, the word LO is displayed. Selection of these temperatures overrides automatic climate control system.

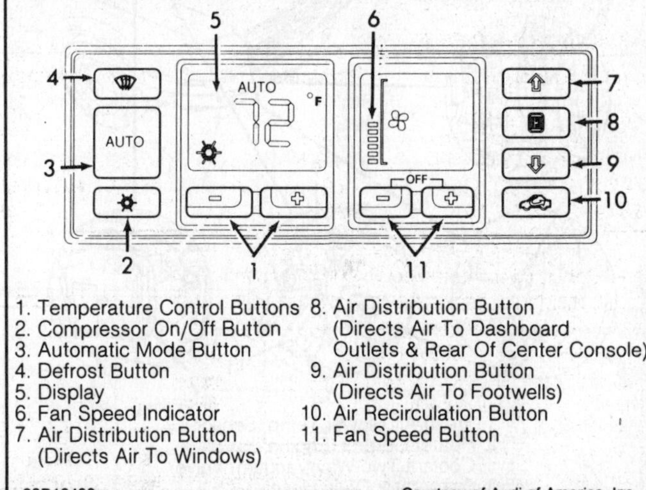
AUTO
72 °F
AUTO
OFF
1
2
3
4
5
6
7
8
9
10
11
1. Temperature Control Buttons
2. Compressor On/Off Button
3. Automatic Mode Button
4. Defrost Button
5. Display
6. Fan Speed Indicator
7. Air Distribution Button (Directs Air To Windows)
8. Air Distribution Button (Directs Air To Dashboard Outlets & Rear Of Center Console)
9. Air Distribution Button (Directs Air To Footwells)
10. Air Recirculation Button
11. Fan Speed Button
93D19490
Courtesy of Audi of America, Inc.

Fig. 1: Identifying A/C-Heater Control Panel

OPERATION

A/C COMPRESSOR SPEED SENSOR

Sensor is located on compressor and determines A/C compressor speed. A/C-heater control panel then compares compressor speed to engine speed and calculates belt slippage (as a percentage). If slippage is excessive, control panel switches compressor off.

A/C-HEATER CONTROL PANEL & AIR DISTRIBUTION

A/C-Heater Control Panel - A/C-heater control panel has a digital microprocessor that compares values from various sensors. Microprocessor then activates appropriate adjustment motor and A/C compressor clutch to maintain desired temperature. A/C clutch, blower speed, temperature/blend air door position, and mode doors are all controlled by A/C-heater control panel.

Air Distribution - Three buttons control air distribution. *See Fig. 1.* When selected, uppermost air distribution button directs air to windows. When middle air distribution button is selected, air is directed to dashboard outlets and rear of center console. When lowermost air distribution button is selected, air is directed to footwells.

Automatic Mode - In this setting, air temperature, air delivery and air distribution are regulated automatically to achieve and maintain desired interior temperature. All previously selected settings are cancelled.

Blower Speed Settings - Blower speed buttons can be used to raise or lower blower speed in all operating modes. Blower speed plus (+) button is used to raise blower speed. Minus (-) button lowers blower speed. If minus (-) button is pushed after blower speed is set at its lowest setting, climate control system will be deactivated.

Climate control system will also be deactivated if minus (-) and plus (+) buttons are pushed simultaneously. To reactivate system, press AUTO button, defrost button, one of temperature control buttons or blower speed plus (+) button.

Compressor On/Off Button - This button controls compressor operation.

Defrost Mode - In this setting, recirculation door is open. Blower runs at highest speed and temperature is automatically regulated. All air is directed toward windshield.

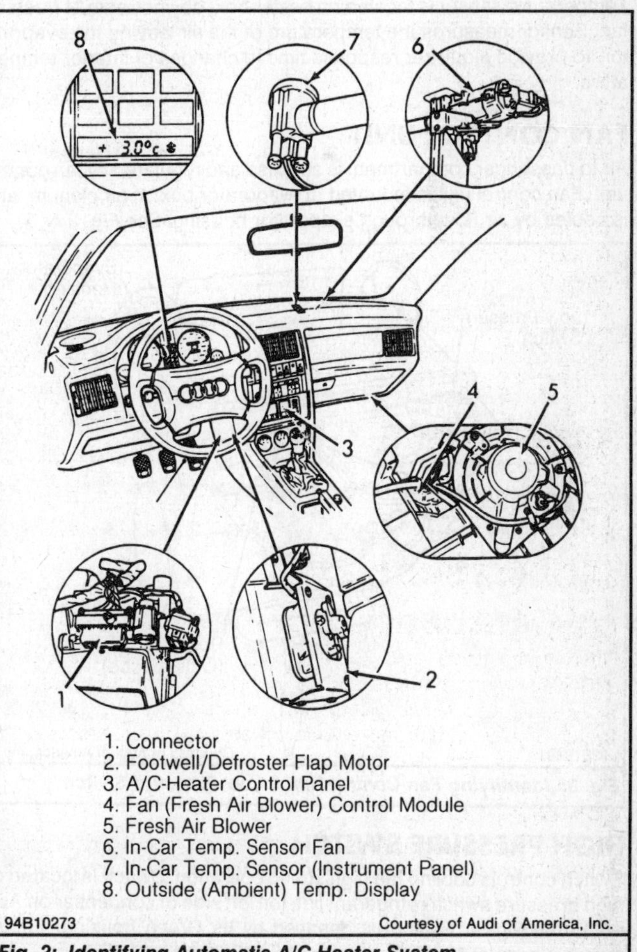
8
7
6
+ 3.0°c
4
5
3
1
2
1. Connector
2. Footwell/Defroster Flap Motor
3. A/C-Heater Control Panel
4. Fan (Fresh Air Blower) Control Module
5. Fresh Air Blower
6. In-Car Temp. Sensor Fan
7. In-Car Temp. Sensor (Instrument Panel)
8. Outside (Ambient) Temp. Display
94B10273
Courtesy of Audi of America, Inc.

Fig. 2: Identifying Automatic A/C-Heater System Components (90 CS)

1993 AUTOMATIC A/C-HEATER SYSTEMS 90 CS & 100 CS (Cont.)

ACTUATORS

Central Air Distribution Flap Motor – This actuator (motor) is located on front of heater box. The central air distribution flap is used to distribute air flow to instrument panel vents or to footwell/defroster outlets. A potentiometer, inside motor, indicates the position of the air distribution flap to the A/C-heater control panel as a feedback value.

Footwell/Defrost Flap Motor – This actuator (motor) is located on front of heater box. *See Fig. 2.* The footwell/defrost flap distributes air to footwell or defroster outlets depending on mode selected. A potentiometer, inside motor, indicates the position of the air distribution flap to the A/C-heater control panel as a feedback value.

Temperature Regulator Flap Motor – This actuator (motor) is mounted on left side of heater box. *See Fig. 4.* A potentiometer, inside motor, indicates the position of the air distribution flap to the A/C-heater control panel as a feedback value.

The temperature regulator flap is used to control air temperature in vehicle passenger compartment. Air temperature regulation is accomplished by using two flaps, one flap before and one flap after heater core. The temperature-regulating flap actuating mechanism also operates the turbulence flap.

AMBIENT TEMPERATURE SENSORS

Two sensors measure outside air temperature and send input signals to A/C-heater control panel. A/C-heater control panel measures sensor readings and lowest temperature value to calculate correction factor for interior temperature regulation. One sensor is located in front of vehicle, behind lower air grille. Second sensor is located in evaporator, next to fresh air flap.

FRESH AIR TEMPERATURE SENSOR

Temperature sensor is located on heater box, downstream of fresh air fan. Sensor measures the temperature of the air leaving the evaporator, to provide a quicker response time to changes of interior temperature.

FAN CONTROL UNIT

Air to passenger compartment is supplied and regulated by fan control unit. Fan control unit is mounted to evaporator box, in air plenum, and is cooled by air flow through evaporator housing. *See Fig. 2 or 3.*

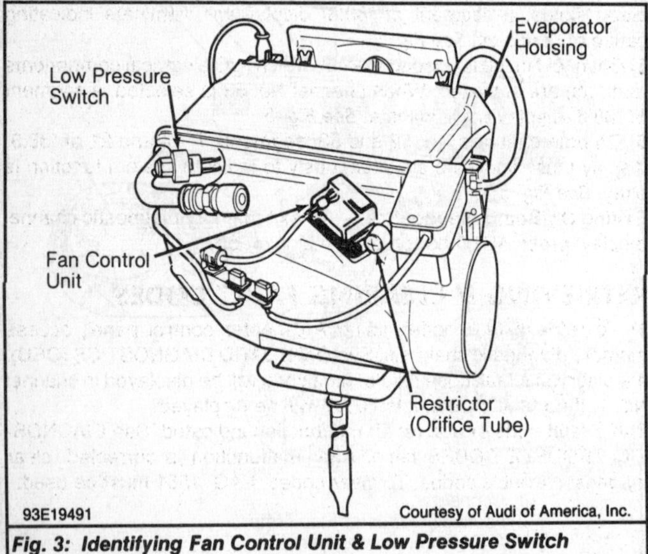
Evaporator Housing
Low Pressure Switch
Fan Control Unit
Restrictor (Orifice Tube)
93E19491
Courtesy of Audi of America, Inc.

Fig. 3: Identifying Fan Control Unit & Low Pressure Switch

HIGH PRESSURE SWITCH

Switch controls cooling fan high speed operation. Switch is located on high pressure switch refrigerant line (on left side of condenser on Audi 100). *See Fig. 4.* Switch is identified by its Green housing. Ensure switch closes at 190.0-254.0 psi (13.36-17.86 kg/cm²). Ensure switch opens at 153.7-217.5 psi (10.81-15.29 kg/cm²). Switch can be removed without discharging system.

HIGH PRESSURE CUT-OUT SWITCH

Switch is identified by Red housing and located on right/left side of condenser. *See Fig. 4.* Cut-out switch turns off A/C compressor clutch when refrigerant pressure reaches 409.0-449.5 psi (28.76-31.60 kg/cm²). Switch can be replaced without discharging system.

IN-CAR TEMPERATURE SENSORS

In-car temperature sensors measure interior air temperature and send signals to A/C-heater control panel. *See Fig. 2.* A small fan drives air over instrument panel sensor to ensure accurate measurement. One sensor is mounted on top of instrument panel and a second sensor is located next to front dome light.

LOW PRESSURE SWITCH

Refrigerant low pressure switch disengages A/C compressor clutch if refrigerant pressure drops below specified pressure. On Audi 90, ensure switch opens at 21.0-23.2 psi (1.48-1.63 kg/cm²). On Audi 100, ensure switch opens at 23.2-24.7 psi (1.63-1.74 kg/cm²).

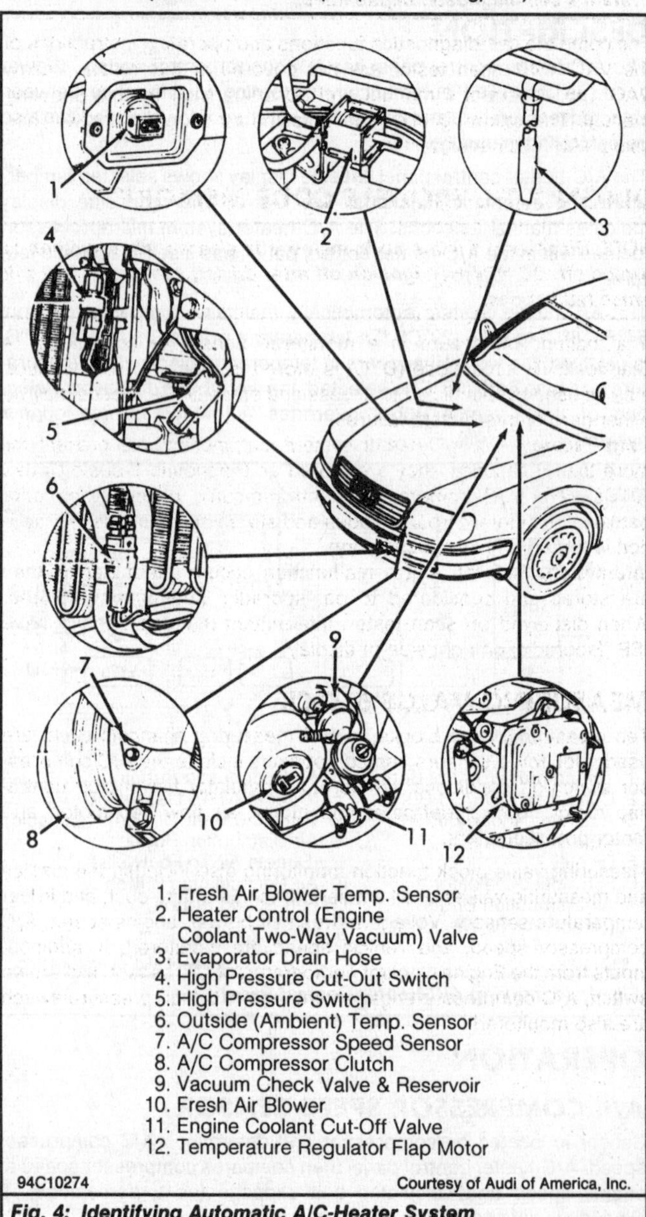
1
2
3
4
5
6
7
8
9
10
11
12
1. Fresh Air Blower Temp. Sensor
2. Heater Control (Engine Coolant Two-Way Vacuum) Valve
3. Evaporator Drain Hose
4. High Pressure Cut-Out Switch
5. High Pressure Switch
6. Outside (Ambient) Temp. Sensor
7. A/C Compressor Speed Sensor
8. A/C Compressor Clutch
9. Vacuum Check Valve & Reservoir
10. Fresh Air Blower
11. Engine Coolant Cut-Off Valve
12. Temperature Regulator Flap Motor
94C10274
Courtesy of Audi of America, Inc.

Fig. 4: Identifying Automatic A/C-Heater System Components (100 CS)

TWO-WAY VACUUM VALVES

Fresh/Recirculated Air Flap – This two-way vacuum valve is used to control the vacuum applied to fresh/recirculated air flap door vacuum servo. Valve is located on left side of evaporator assembly, in air plenum.

Two-way vacuum valve is electrically controlled by signals from A/C-heater control panel. When vacuum is applied to fresh/recirculated air flap door vacuum servo, the flap door closes and no fresh air enters vehicle.

Heater Control Valve – This vacuum valve is located on right side of heater box, in air plenum. *See Fig. 4*. Two-way vacuum valve is electrically controlled by signals from A/C-heater control panel and directs or vents vacuum to heater control valve. When vacuum is applied to heater control valve, no coolant flows through heater core.

SELF-DIAGNOSTICS

NOTE: Scan Tester (VAG 1551) must be used to make full use of the system's self-diagnostic capabilities.

The complete self-diagnostics functions and operating instructions of the VAG 1551 scan tester are not covered in this article. Follow VAG 1551 operator's manual and accompanying trouble shooting manual. The following text highlights the functions available when using VAG 1551 scan tester.

DIAGNOSTIC TROUBLE CODE MEMORY

NOTE: Diagnostic trouble code memory is cleared when ignition is turned off. DO NOT turn ignition off after driving vehicle, as this will erase fault codes.

If a malfunction occurs in a monitored sensor or component, a Diagnostic Trouble Code (DTC) is stored in memory. This function may be used by technician to access and erase DTCs. Codes may be either hard or intermittent failures.

Hard Failures – If A/C-heater system malfunctions are present for more than 5 seconds, they are stored as Diagnostic Trouble Codes (DTCs). The A/C compressor control module distinguishes data between 19 different trouble codes and stores malfunctions until ignition is turned off (volatile memory).

Intermittent Failures – If a malfunction occurs intermittently, they are stored and considered to be "sporadic" (intermittent) failures. When displayed on scan tester, intermittent malfunctions will have "SP" (sporadic) on right side of display.

MEASURING VALUE BLOCK

Ten measuring value blocks, with 4 measuring channels each, are used. Monitored sensors and components include the A/C compressor switch-off conditions, temperature regulator flap motor, central flap motor, footwell/defroster flap motor, air flow flap motor, and motor potentiometers.

Measuring value block function monitoring also includes the display and measuring values of all ambient, fresh air intake duct, and in-car temperature sensors. Voltage at fresh air blower, engine speed, A/C compressor speed, and vehicle speed are monitored. In addition, inputs from the Engine Coolant Temperature (ECT) sensor, kick-down switch, A/C compressor engagement, and A/C high pressure switch are also monitored.

OUTPUT DIAGNOSTIC TEST MODE

Since the VAG 1551 scan tester is a bi-directional tester, it may be used to actuate a number of A/C-heater system components. The output diagnostic test mode may be used to actuate A/C compressor clutch, fresh air blower, temperature sensor blower fan, and cooling fan.

The A/C-heater control panel segment displays, outside temperature indicator (display), and Idle Air Control (IAC) may also be actuated.

In addition, the temperature regulator flap motor, central flap motor, footwell/defroster flap motor, air flow flap motor, and fresh/recirculated air flap two-way valve may also be actuated.

A/C CONTROL HEAD CODING

Replacement A/C control heads (A/C-heater control panel) are sold with Code 000 and must be properly coded after installation. Contact nearest Audi parts department to determine correct application.

TROUBLE SHOOTING

ON-BOARD DIAGNOSTICS (OBD)

NOTE: While OBD information is being displayed on A/C-heater control panel, A/C system operation does not take place (A/C compressor, radiator fan, etc. are not controlled).

Accessing Memory Diagnostic Channels – **1)** Turn ignition switch on or start engine. Simultaneously press and hold down air recirculation button and air distribution (up arrow) button. *See Fig. 1*. Release both buttons. Display panel should read "01c", indicating diagnostic channel No. 1.

2) Pressing temperature plus (+) button will advance display of diagnostic channel by one. Display panel should read "02c", indicating diagnostic channel No. 2. Each time plus (+) button is pressed, system will advance to next diagnostic channel until last number is reached; display will then return to channel No. 1.

3) Memory diagnostic channels identify individual circuits, and are not fault codes. See MEMORY DIAGNOSTIC CHANNELS table. To retrieve information about a particular channel, select desired channel then press air recirculation button.

4) If channel No. 52 is selected and an A/C compressor switch-off condition exists, a segment of "88.8" display will illuminate indicating cause of condition. *See Fig. 5*.

5) Channel No. 53 is used to identify which A/C electrical components (outputs) are activated. When channel No. 53 is selected, a segment of "88.8" display will illuminate. *See Fig. 5*.

6) On both channels No. 52 and 53, segments 7, 14 and 21 of "88.8" display must illuminate simultaneously to indicate system function is okay. *See Fig. 5*.

Exiting On-Board Diagnostics – To exit memory diagnostic channel display, press AUTO button or turn ignition off.

RETRIEVING & CLEARING FAULT CODES

1) To retrieve fault codes using A/C-heater control panel, access memory diagnostic channels. See ON-BOARD DIAGNOSTICS (OBD). If a diagnostic fault code exists, fault code will be displayed in channel No. 1. If no fault code exists, "00.0" will be displayed.

2) If a fault code exists, repair malfunction indicated. See DIAGNOSTIC TROUBLE CODES table. After malfunction is corrected, clear diagnostic trouble codes. To clear codes, VAG 1551 must be used.

MEMORY DIAGNOSTIC CHANNELS

Diagnostic Channel No.	Display
1	System Malfunction -- Displayed As Diagnostic Trouble Code (See DIAGNOSTIC TROUBLE CODES table)
2	Digital Value Of In-Car Temperature Sensor (Headliner)
3	Digital Value Of In-Car Temperature Sensor (Instrument Panel)
4	Digital Value Of Fresh Air Intake Duct Temperature Sensor
5	Digital Value Of Outside (Ambient) Temperature Sensor (Front)
6	Digital Value Of Outside (Ambient) Temperature Sensor
7	Digital Value Of Ambient Temperature Sensor At Fresh Air Blower
8	Digital Value Of Temperature Regulator Flap Motor Potentiometer
9	Delta Value Of Temperature Regulator Flap
10	Non-Corrected Specified Value Of Temperature Regulator Flap
11	Digital Value Of Central Flap Motor Potentiometer
12	Specified Value Of Central Flap
13	Digtal Value Of Footwell/Defroster Flap Motor Potentiometer
14	Specified Value Of Footwell/Defroster Flap
15	Digital Value Of Air Flow Flap Motor Potentiometer
16	Specified Value Of Air Flow Flap
17	Vehicle Speed (Kilometers Per Hour)
18	Actual Fresh Air Blower Voltage
19	Specified Fresh Air Blower Voltage
20	A/C Compressor Clutch Voltage
21	Number Of Low Voltage Occurrences (Non-Transient)
22	Cycle Condition Of A/C Refrigerant High Pressure Switch
23	Cycling Of A/C Refrigerant High Pressure Switch
24	Cycling Of Switches, Absolute & Non-Fluctuating
25	Kick-Down Switch Analog/Digital Value
26	Engine Coolant Temperature (ECT) Sensor Warning Light Analog/Digital Value
27	Coding Value
28	Engine Speed (RPM)
29	A/C Compressor Speed In RPM (Equals Engine Speed x 1.28)
30	Software Version
31	Segment Display Check (All Segments Of A/C-Heater Control Panel Light Up)
32	Temperature Regulator Flap Potentiometer Malfunction Counter
33	Central Flap Potentiometer Malfunction Counter
34	Footwell/Defroster Flap Potentiometer Malfunction Counter
35	Air Flow Flap Potentiometer Malfunction Counter
36	Temperature Regulator Flap Motor Potentiometer Feedback Value (Cold End Stop)
37	Temperature Regulator Flap Motor Potentiometer Feedback Value (Hot End Stop)
38	Central Flap Motor Potentiometer Feedback Value (Cold End Stop)
39	Central Flap Motor Potentiometer Feedback Value (Hot End Stop)
40	Footwell/Defroster Flap Motor Potentiometer Feedback Value (Cold End Stop)
41	Footwell/Defroster Flap Motor Potentiometer Feedback Value (Hot End Stop)
42	Air Flow Flap Motor Potentiometer Feedback Value (Cold End Stop)
43	Air Flow Flap Motor Potentiometer Feedback Value (Hot End Stop)
44	Vehicle Operation Cycle Counter
45	Calculated Interior Temperature, In Digits (Internal Software)
46	Outside (Ambient) Temperature, Filtered For Regulation (Internal Software)
47	Outside (Ambient) Temperature, Unfiltered In Degrees °C (Internal Software)
48	Outside (Ambient) Temperature, Unfiltered In Digits
49	Malfunction Counter For Speedometer (Vehicle Speed) Signal
50	Standing Time (In Minutes)
51	Engine Coolant Temperature (ECT) In Degrees °C
52	[1] Graphics Channel Number 1 Through 88.8
53	[1] Graphics Channel Number 1 Through 88.8
54	Control Characteristics
55	Outside (Ambient) Temperature, In Degrees °F Or °C, Depending On A/C-Heater Control Panel Setting
56	In-Car Temperature Sensor Temperature In Degrees °C (Headliner)
57	In-Car Temperature Sensor Temperature In Degrees °C (Instrument Panel)
58	Fresh Air Duct Temperature Sensor Temperature In Degrees °C
59	Front Outside (Ambient) Temperature Sensor Temperature In Degrees °C
60	Fresh Air Blower Ambient Temperature Sensor Temperature In Degrees °C
61	Software Version (Latest)

[1] – When diagnostic channel No. 52 or 53 is selected, "— — . —" is displayed first. The A/C compressor switch-off conditions are identified by the illuminated segments of display. See Fig. 5.

1993 AUTOMATIC A/C-HEATER SYSTEMS
90 CS & 100 CS (Cont.)

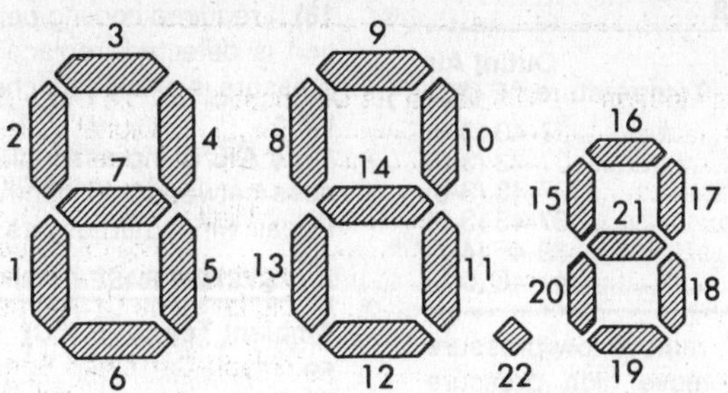
3
9
2
4
8
10
7
14
16
15
21
17
1
5
13
11
20
18
6
12
22
19

CHANNEL 52
1. High Pressure Occurrences More Than 30 Times
2. Ambient Temperature Sensor At Fresh Air Blower Less Then 27° (-3C°)
3. Not Used
4. Off Selected
5. Ambient Temperature Too Low
6. Engine Management System (Compressor Will Remain Off For 3-12 Seconds)
7. * System Function Okay
8. A/C Refrigerant High Pressure Switch
9. A/C Manually Switched Off (A/C Standby Cancelled)
10. Low Voltage
11. Kickdown Switch (Via Transmission Control Module, Compressor Off For 12 Seconds Maximum)
12. Engine Coolant Temperature Warning Light Switch
13. A/C Refrigerant Low Pressure Switch
14. * System Function Okay
15. Not Used
16. Slippage Or Blockage
17. Engine Speed At 200-500 RPM
18. Not Used
19. Engine Speed Greater Than 6000 RPM
20. Not Used
21. * System Function Okay
22. Visible With A/C Compressor On Not Visible With A/C Compressor Off

CHANNEL 53
1. Temperature Flap In Cold Air Position
2. Temperature Flap In Warm Air Position
3. Not Used
4. Central Flap In Instrument Panel Outlet Position
5. Central Flap In Footwell Outlet/Defrost Position
6. Not Used
7. * System Function Okay
8. Footwell/Defroster Flap In Defrost Position
9. Not Used
10. Airflow Flap Open
11. Airflow Flap Closed
12. Not Used
13. Footwell/Defroster Flap In Footwell Position
14. * System Function Okay
15. First Speed Of Coolant Fan On
16. Fan For In-Car Temperature Sensor
17. Fresh Air/Recirculation Flap Closed
18. Heater Valve Closed
19. Be-Directional Wiring Harness
20. A/C Compressor On
21. * System Function Okay
22. Not Used

* Segments 7, 14 and 21 must illuminate simultaneously to indicate system function is okay.

93H19494

Courtesy of Audi of America, Inc.

Fig. 5: Identifying Diagnostic Channel No. 52 & 53

DIAGNOSTIC TROUBLE CODES

Diagnostic Trouble Code	Affected Circuit
00.0	No Malfunctions
02.1-02.4	In-Car Temp. Sensor (Headliner)
03.1-03.4	In-Car Temp. Sensor (Instrument Panel)
04.1-04.4	Fresh Air Intake Duct Temp. Sensor
05.1-05.4	Outside (Ambient) Temp. Sensor (Front)
06.1-06.4	Engine Coolant Temp. (ECT) Sensor
07.1-07.4	Fresh Air Blower Ambient Temp. Sensor
08.1-08.7	[1] Temp. Regulator Flap Motor Potentiometer
11-1-11.7	[1] Central Flap Motor Potentiometer
13.1-13.7	[1] Footwell/Defroster Flap Motor Potentiometer
15.1-15.7	Air Flow Flap Motor Potentiometer
17.0	Vehicle Speed Signal
18.1-18.3	Fresh Air Blower (Incorrect Voltage)
20.1-20.3	[2] A/C Compressor (Incorrect Voltage)
22.1-22.5	[3] A/C High Pressure Switch
29.1-29.4	A/C Belt Slip

[1] – Motors will no longer be controlled automatically.
[2] – The A/C compressor remains off until voltage is greater than 10.8 volts for at least 25 seconds.
[3] – The A/C compressor remains off until switch closes.

TESTING

WARNING: To avoid injury from accidental air bag deployment, read and carefully follow all SERVICE PRECAUTIONS and DISABLING & ACTIVATING AIR BAG SYSTEM procedures in AIR BAG SYSTEM SAFETY article in GENERAL SERVICING.

A/C SYSTEM PERFORMANCE

1) Park vehicle out of direct sunlight. Ensure condenser and radiator are free of obstructions. Ensure compressor drive belt is in good condition. Ensure engine is at normal operating temperature. Close engine hood.

2) Start engine and run it at 2000 RPM. Turn A/C system on and press AUTO mode button. *See Fig. 1*. Press minus (-) button until "LO" temperature setting is displayed.

3) Press air recirculation button until recirculated air symbol is displayed. Press compressor on/off button until ice crystal symbol is displayed. *See Fig. 1*.

4) Open all instrument panel air outlets. Ensure cooling fan and A/C compressor run. Ensure blower motor runs on high speed and air flows out of instrument panel vents.

5) Using VAG 1551 scan tester, check DTC memory. Close doors, windows, and sun roof. Record ambient temperature and check outlet air temperature at center instrument panel vent after A/C system has run for 5 minutes. See A/C SYSTEM PERFORMANCE SPECIFICATIONS table.

NOTE: If A/C compressor clutch disengages during performance test, go to step 11).

1993 AUTOMATIC A/C-HEATER SYSTEMS 90 CS & 100 CS (Cont.)

A/C SYSTEM PERFORMANCE SPECIFICATIONS

Ambient Temperature °F (°C)	Outlet Air Temperature °F (°C)
59 (15)	37-43 (3-6)
68 (20)	37-43 (3-6)
77 (25)	37-43 (3-6)
86 (30)	37-43 (3-6)
95 (35)	39-45 (4-7)
104 (40)	41-48 (5-8)

6) If outlet air temperature is not as specified, remove low pressure switch and jumper connector terminals. Remove high pressure switch, leaving its wiring harness connected. Connect manifold gauge set to high and low pressure service valves.

7) Repeat A/C system performance test. High side (discharge) pressure should increase from base pressure (engine off) to a maximum of 290 psi (20.4 kg/cm²). See A/C SYSTEM BASE (HIGH SIDE) PRESSURE SPECIFICATIONS table.

8) The high pressure switch should switch cooling fan to second speed between 190-254 psi (13.4-17.9 kg/cm²). If cooling fan does not switch to second speed, check cooling fan circuit.

9) Low side (suction) pressure should be as specified in A/C SYSTEM LOW SIDE PRESSURE SPECIFICATIONS table. If both high and low side pressures are okay, A/C system cooling performance is okay. Check low pressure and high pressure switches as necessary.

10) If either high and low side pressures are incorrect, check refrigerant and A/C system for malfunctions (low refrigerant charge, faulty A/C compressor, kinked/plugged A/C hose, etc.).

A/C SYSTEM LOW SIDE PRESSURE SPECIFICATIONS

Ambient Temp. °F (°C)	Pressure psi (kg/cm²)
50 (10)	30-32 (2.1-2.2)
59 (15)	29-32 (2.0-2.2)
68 (20)	28-30 (1.9-2.1)
77 (25)	26-29 (1.8-2.0)
86 (30)	25-29 (1.7-2.0)
95 (35)	25-30 (1.7-2.1)
104 (40)	28-33 (1.9-2.3)

11) Check Diagnostic Trouble Code (DTC) memory. See DIAGNOSTIC TROUBLE CODE MEMORY. Repair A/C system malfunctions (if any). Erase DTC memory. End session using RAPID DATA TRANSFER, leaving VAG 1551 connected. Repeat A/C system performance test.

12) Ensure scan tester is in A/C/HEATING ELECTRONICS function. With RAPID DATA TRANSFER displayed on scan tester, press "0" and "8" button to select READ MEASURING VALUE BLOCK function. Press "Q" button to enter input.

13) With INPUT DISPLAY GROUP NUMBER displayed on scan tester, press "0" and "1" buttons to select COMPRESSOR SWITCH-OFF CONDITIONS. Press "Q" button to enter input.

14) Read display group No. 1, channel No. 1. If Code 2 (high pressure cut-out switch) is displayed, go to next step. If Code 3 (low pressure switch) is displayed, go to step **20)**. If other codes are displayed, go to MEASURING VALUE BLOCK under SELF-DIAGNOSTICS.

15) End session using RAPID DATA TRANSFER. Remove high pressure cut-out switch, leaving its wiring harness connected. Connect manifold gauge set to high pressure cut-out switch Schrader valve.

16) Repeat A/C system performance test and check A/C system high side pressure. High side (discharge) pressure should increase from base pressure (engine off) to a maximum of 290 psi (20.4 kg/cm²). See A/C SYSTEM BASE (HIGH SIDE) PRESSURE SPECIFICATIONS table.

17) The high pressure switch should switch cooling fan to second speed between 190-254 psi (13.4-17.9 kg/cm²). If cooling fan does not switch to second speed, check cooling fan circuit.

18) If required cooling performance is attained and no other malfunction is detected, replace high pressure cut-out switch. If high side pressure is exceeded, check refrigerant and A/C system for malfunctions.

19) If A/C compressor clutch still does not engage, check wiring harness between A/C control panel and high pressure cut-out switch. Repair wiring harness as necessary.

A/C SYSTEM BASE (HIGH SIDE) PRESSURE SPECIFICATIONS

Ambient Temp. °F (°C)	[1] psi (kg/cm²)
59 (15)	56.5 (3.97)
68 (20)	68.2 (4.79)
77 (25)	79.8 (5.61)
86 (30)	95.7 (6.73)
95 (35)	108.8 (7.65)
104 (40)	127.6 (8.97)
113 (45)	142.1 (9.99)

[1] – Pressures listed are with engine off.

20) End session using RAPID DATA TRANSFER. Remove low pressure switch and jumper connector terminals. Connect manifold gauge set to low pressure switch Schrader valve.

21) Repeat A/C system performance test and check A/C system low side pressure. Low side (suction) pressure should be as specified in A/C SYSTEM LOW SIDE PRESSURE SPECIFICATIONS table.

22) If required cooling performance is attained and no other malfunction is detected, replace low pressure switch. If low side pressure is incorrect, check refrigerant and A/C system for malfunctions (low refrigerant charge, faulty A/C compressor, kinked/plugged A/C hose, etc.).

23) If A/C compressor clutch disengages during test, check wiring harness between A/C control panel and low pressure switch. Repair wiring harness as necessary.

24) If A/C compressor clutch doe not disengage during test, check heater box and evaporator assembly for air leaks. If no leaks are found, A/C system may be low on refrigerant. Check refrigerant lines and components for leaks. Repair leaks as necessary.

ACTUATORS, SENSORS & FAN CONTROL MODULE

NOTE: On 100, manufacturer recommends the use of VAG 1551 scan tester for circuit and component testing.

90 – 1) Ensure all fuses are okay. Turn ignition off. Remove A/C-heater control panel. Connect Adapter Harness (VAG 1598/11) and Adapter Harness (VAG 1598/12) to A/C-heater control panel wiring harness.

2) Leave A/C-heater control panel disconnected. While performing tests, DO NOT connect adapter harnesses to A/C-heater control panel. The A/C-heater control panel will be damaged.

3) Adapter harnesses cannot be connected simultaneously to Test Box (VAG 1598). Set measuring range on DVOM before connecting it to test box sockets, as damage to components may result.

CAUTION: When using Adapter Harness (VAG 1598/11), test box socket terminal numbers and A/C-heater control panel wiring harness terminal numbers are not the same. Connector "A" terminals No. 1-12 are identified as socket terminals No. 41-52 on test box. See Fig. 6. Connector "B" terminals No. 1-20 are identified as socket terminals No. 21-40. Connector "C" and "D" terminal No. 1-16 are identified as socket terminals No. 1-16.

AUTOMATIC A/C-HEATER SYSTEM COMPONENT TESTING (AUDI 90 CS)

Component Being Tested (VAG 1598 Pin No.)	Test Condition	Resistance Voltage Value
In-Car Temp. Sensor – Headliner (43 & 52 [1])	Ambient Temp. At Sensor	[2] 3513 Ohms @ 68°F (20°C)
In-Car Temp. Sensor – Dash (50 & 52 [1])	Ambient Temp. At Sensor [3]	[2] 3513 Ohms @ 68°F (20°C)
Fresh Air Temp. Sensor (47 & 52 [1])	Ambient Temp. At Sensor	[2] 1250 Ohms @ 68°F (20°C)
Ambient Temp. Sensor (48 & 52 [1])	Ambient Temp. At Sensor	[2] 1250 Ohms @ 68°F (20°C)
Temp. Regulator Flap Mtr. (2 & 10 [4])	....	20-100 Ohms
Central Air Dist. Flap Mtr. (4 & 12 [4])	....	20-100 Ohms
Footwell/Defroster Flap Mtr. (3 & 11 [4])	....	20-100 Ohms
Fan Control Module (16 & Ground [5])	Ignition On	Less Than 0.5 Volt (Blower Motor Off)
Blower Motor Voltage Supply (14 & Ground [5])	Ignition On	Battery Voltage
Fan Control Module Voltage Supply (& Ground [5])	Ignition On	Battery Voltage
Fan Control Module (13 & 16 [6])	Ignition On	LED Tester Lights Up (Blower Motor On)

[1] – Connect Adapter Harness (VAG 1598/11) to Test Box (VAG 1598). Set DVOM to 20,000 ohm range.
[2] – See AMBIENT, IN-CAR & FRESH AIR TEMPERATURE SENSOR RESISTANCE VALUES table for complete temperature range specifications.
[3] – Check temperature sensor fan using DIAGNOSTIC TEST MODE (DTM) under SELF-DIAGNOSTICS.
[4] – Connect Adapter Harness (VAG 1598/12) to Test Box (VAG 1598). Set DVOM to 200 ohm range.
[5] – Connect Adapter Harness (VAG 1598/11) to Test Box (VAG 1598). Set DVOM to 20 volt range.
[6] – Connect Adapter Harness (VAG 1598/11) to Test Box (VAG 1598) and use LED Tester (US 1115).

AMBIENT, IN-CAR & FRESH AIR TEMPERATURE SENSOR RESISTANCE VALUES

Temp.°F (°C) At Sensor	Ambient & Fresh Air Temp. Sensors (Ohms)	In-Car Temp. Sensors (Ohms)
14 (–10)	5591	1,6159
32 (0)	3281	9406
41 (5)	2544	7273
50 (10)	1991	5666
59 (15)	1571	4446
68 (20)	1250	3513
77 (25)	998	2795
86 (30)	804	2237
95 (35)	652	1801
104 (40)	533	1459
113 (45)	437	1188
122 (50)	361	972
131 (55)	300	803
140 (60)	250	667
149 (65)	556	556
158 (70)	466	466

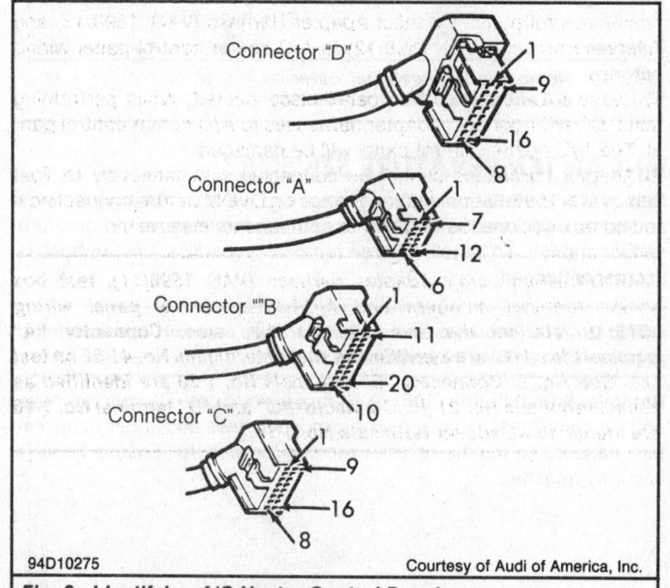
Connector "D"
1
9
16
8
Connector "A"
1
7
12
6
Connector "B"
1
11
20
10
Connector "C"
1
9
16
8
94D10275
Courtesy of Audi of America, Inc.

Fig. 6: Identifying A/C-Heater Control Panel Wiring Harness Terminals

REMOVAL & INSTALLATION

WARNING: To avoid injury from accidental air bag deployment, read and carefully follow all SERVICE PRECAUTIONS and DISABLING & ACTIVATING AIR BAG SYSTEM procedures in AIR BAG SYSTEM SAFETY article in GENERAL SERVICING.

NOTE: For removal and installation of components not covered in this article, see MANUAL A/C-HEATER SYSTEMS article.

A/C-HEATER CONTROL PANEL

Removal & Installation – Turn ignition off. Carefully pry off A/C-heater control panel trim. Remove A/C-heater control panel. To install, reverse removal procedure.

ACTUATORS

Removal & Installation (90) – **1)** Remove center console. See CENTER CONSOLE in MANUAL A/C-HEATER SYSTEM article. Remove glove box, driver's side tray, and ashtray. Remove instrument panel center support. Remove screws and footwell air outlets.

2) To remove central air distribution flap motor, disconnect wiring harness Black connector and linkage at motor. *See Fig. 7.* Remove screws and flap motor.

3) To remove footwell/defroster flap motor, disconnect wiring harness Red connector and linkage at motor. *See Fig. 8.* Remove screws and flap motor.

4) To remove temperature regulator flap motor, disconnect wiring harness Brown connector and linkage at motor. *See Fig. 9.* Remove screws and flap motor. To install motors, reverse removal procedure.

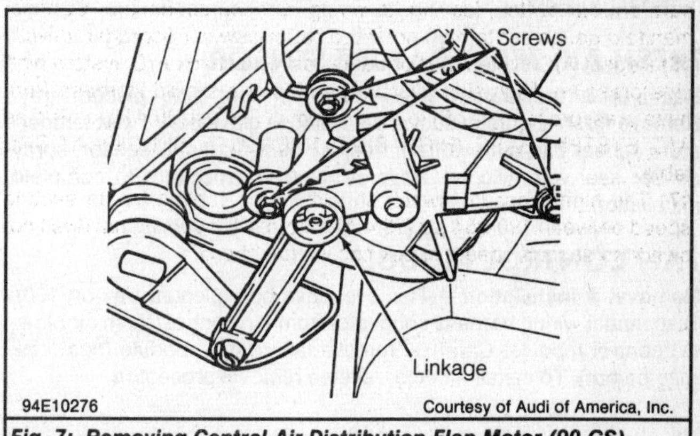
Screws
Linkage
94E10276
Courtesy of Audi of America, Inc.

Fig. 7: Removing Central Air Distribution Flap Motor (90 CS)

1993 AUTOMATIC A/C-HEATER SYSTEMS
90 CS & 100 CS (Cont.)

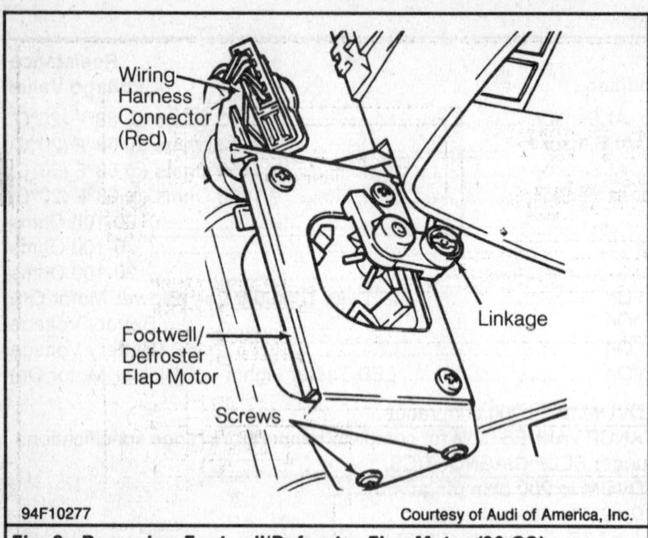
Wiring
Harness
Connector
(Red)
Linkage
Footwell/
Defroster
Flap Motor
Screws
94F10277
Courtesy of Audi of America, Inc.

Fig. 8: Removing Footwell/Defroster Flap Motor (90 CS)

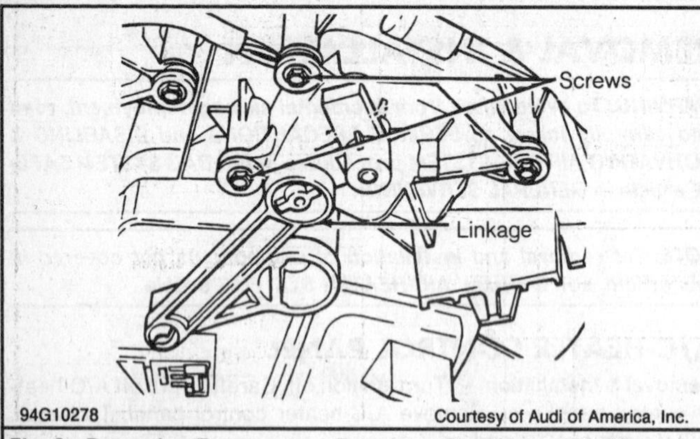
Screws
Linkage
94G10278
Courtesy of Audi of America, Inc.

Fig. 9: Removing Temperature Regulator Flap Motor (90 CS)

Removal & Installation (100) – **1)** To remove temperature regulator flap motor, remove plenum tray. Entirely remove windshield wiper motor and linkage assembly. Remove cover and temperature regulator flap motor.

2) To remove central flap and footwell/defroster flap motor, remove center console. See CENTER CONSOLE in MANUAL A/C-HEATER SYSTEM article. Remove glove box and driver's side tray. Remove defroster hoses from left and right sides of heater box.

3) Remove central flap and footwell/defroster flap motor support tray screws from left and right sides of heater box. Disconnect wiring harness Blue connector at central flap motor. *See Fig. 10.*

4) Disconnect wiring harness Red connector at footwell/defroster flap motor. Remove central flap and footwell/defroster flap motor support tray. Remove motor(s) from support tray. To install motors, reverse removal procedure.

FRESH AIR TEMPERATURE SENSOR

Removal & Installation (90) – Remove right side plenum tray. Remove fresh air intake duct grille. Remove glove box. Twist temperature sensor and remove from fresh air duct. To install sensor, spray sensor seal with silicone. Reverse removal procedure to complete installation.

FAN CONTROL MODULE

Removal & Installation – Remove glove box (plenum tray on 100). Disconnect wiring harness connector from fan control (fresh air blower) control module. Carefully remove fan control module (heat sink may be hot). To install module, reverse removal procedure.

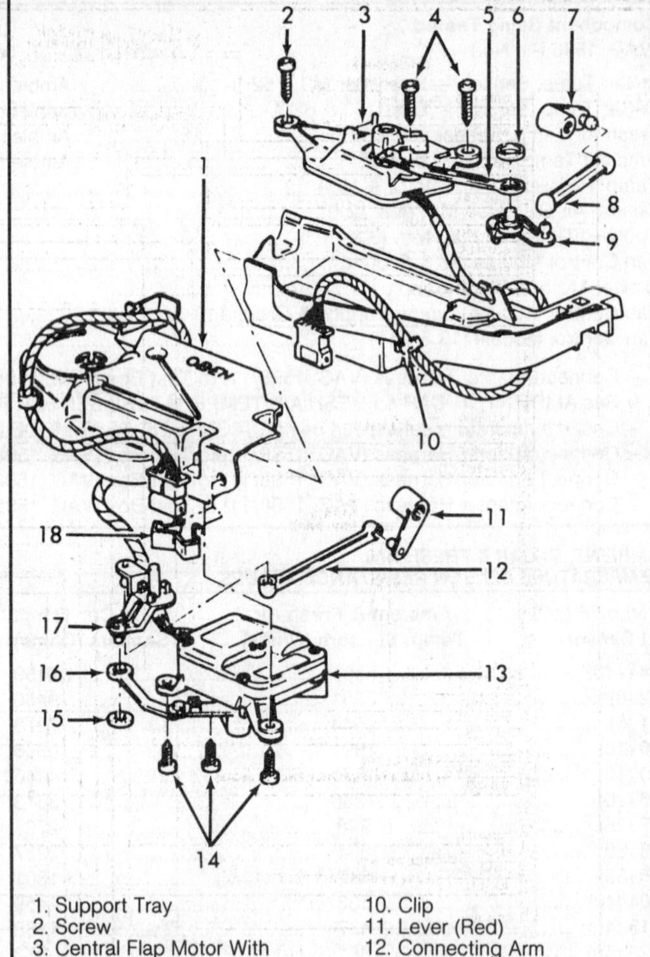
1
2
3
4
5
6
7
8
9
10
11
12
13
14
15
16
17
18

1. Support Tray
2. Screw
3. Central Flap Motor With Potentiometer (Blue Connector)
4. Screw
5. Connecting Arm
6. Retaining Washer
7. Lever (Blue)
8. Connecting Arm
9. Relay Lever
10. Clip
11. Lever (Red)
12. Connecting Arm
13. Footwell/Defroster Flap Motor With Potentiometer (Red Connector)
14. Screw
15. Retaining Washer
16. Connecting Arm
17. Relay Lever
18. Retaining Clip

93I19495 Courtesy of Audi of America, Inc.

Fig. 10: Removing Footwell/Defroster & Central Flap Motors (100 CS)

IN-CAR TEMPERATURE SENSOR

Removal & Installation (90) – Remove glove box. Remove screws and hose. Disconnect wiring harness connector. Remove temperature sensor and fan. To install, reverse removal procedure. Ensure hose is securely attached.

NOTE: On 100 models, in-car temperature sensor fan servicing requires the removal of instrument cluster.

Removal & Installation (100) – Remove glove box. Disconnect hose and wiring harness from sensor. Remove screws and in-car temperature sensor. To install, reverse removal procedure. Ensure hose is securely attached.

1993 AUTOMATIC A/C-HEATER SYSTEMS 90 CS & 100 CS (Cont.)

WIRING DIAGRAMS

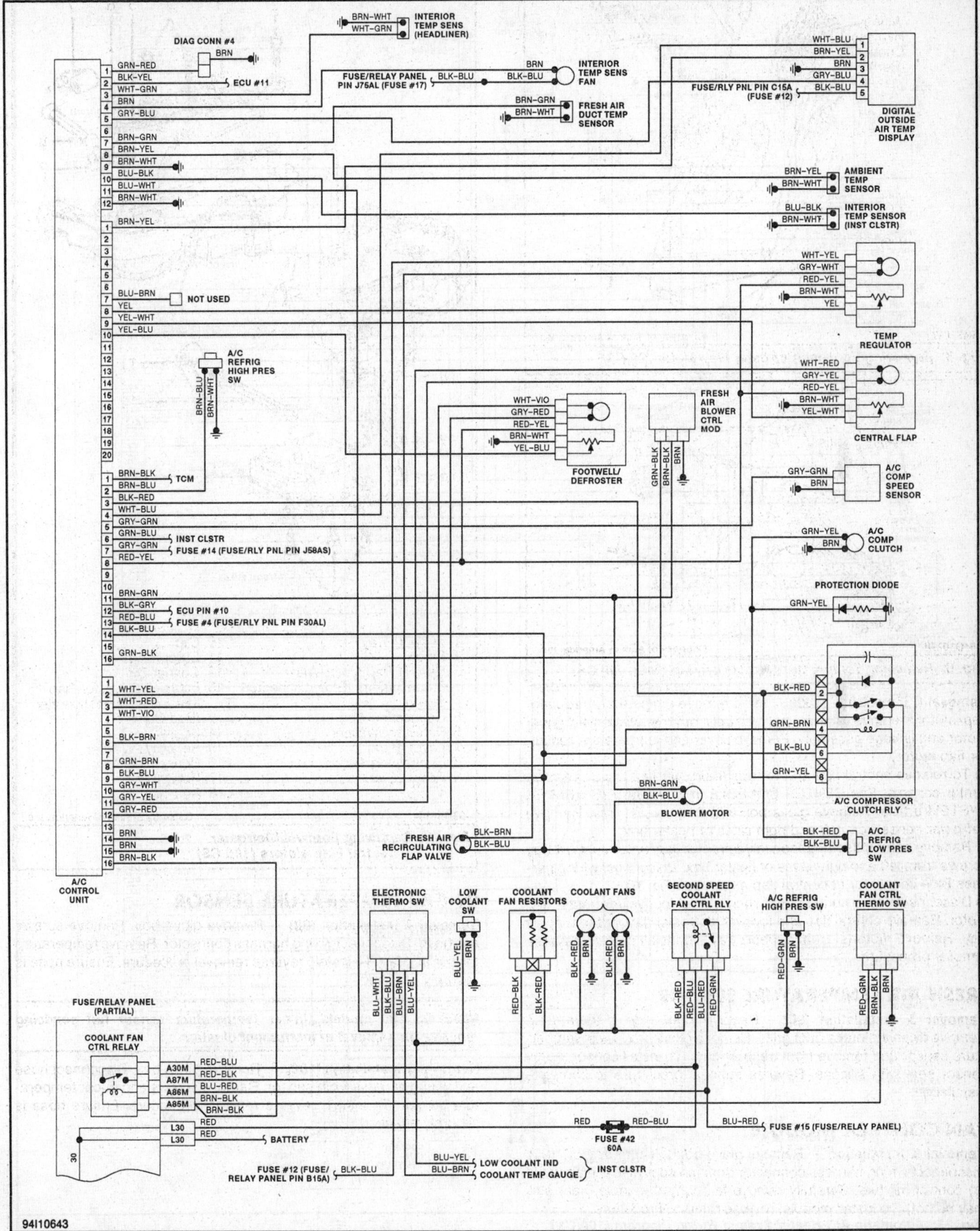

INTERIOR TEMP SENS (HEADLINER)
DIAG CONN #4
ECU #11
FUSE/RELAY PANEL PIN J75AL (FUSE #17)
INTERIOR TEMP SENS FAN
FRESH AIR DUCT TEMP SENSOR
FUSE/RLY PNL PIN C15A (FUSE #12)
DIGITAL OUTSIDE AIR TEMP DISPLAY
AMBIENT TEMP SENSOR
INTERIOR TEMP SENSOR (INST CLSTR)
NOT USED
TEMP REGULATOR
A/C REFRIG HIGH PRES SW
CENTRAL FLAP
FRESH AIR BLOWER CTRL MOD
FOOTWELL/ DEFROSTER
TCM
A/C COMP SPEED SENSOR
INST CLSTR
FUSE #14 (FUSE/RLY PNL PIN J58AS)
A/C COMP CLUTCH
PROTECTION DIODE
ECU PIN #10
FUSE #4 (FUSE/RLY PNL PIN F30AL)
BLOWER MOTOR
A/C COMPRESSOR CLUTCH RLY
FRESH AIR RECIRCULATING FLAP VALVE
A/C REFRIG LOW PRES SW
A/C CONTROL UNIT
ELECTRONIC THERMO SW
LOW COOLANT SW
COOLANT FAN RESISTORS
COOLANT FANS
SECOND SPEED COOLANT FAN CTRL RLY
A/C REFRIG HIGH PRES SW
COOLANT FAN CTRL THERMO SW
FUSE/RELAY PANEL (PARTIAL)
COOLANT FAN CTRL RLY
FUSE #42 60A
FUSE #15 (FUSE/RELAY PANEL)
BATTERY
LOW COOLANT IND
COOLANT TEMP GAUGE
INST CLSTR
FUSE #12 (FUSE/ RELAY PANEL PIN B15A)
94I10643

Fig. 11: Automatic A/C-Heater System Wiring Diagram (90 CS)

1993 AUTOMATIC A/C-HEATER SYSTEMS 90 CS & 100 CS (Cont.)

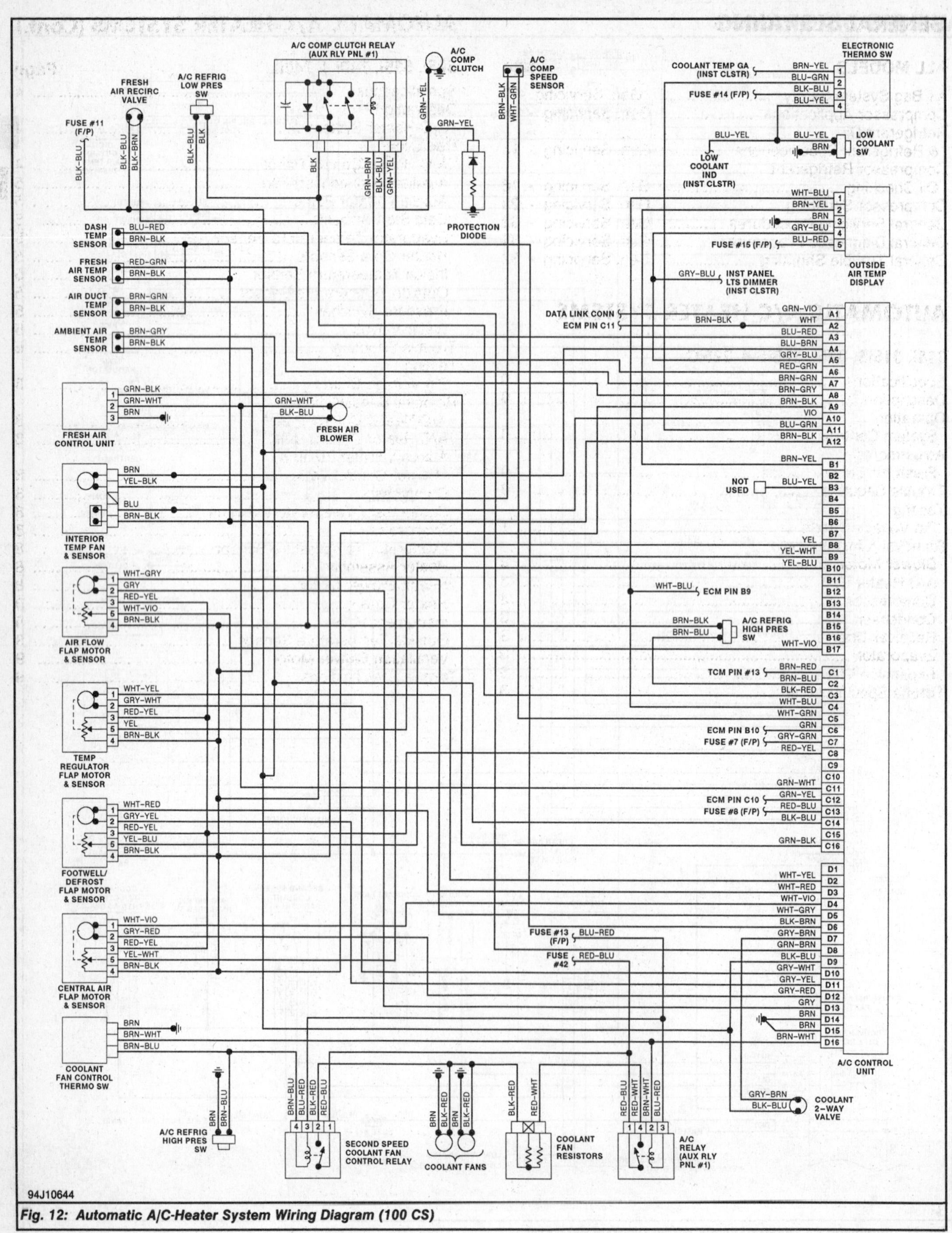
A/C COMP CLUTCH RELAY (AUX RLY PNL #1)
A/C COMP CLUTCH
A/C COMP SPEED SENSOR
ELECTRONIC THERMO SW
FRESH AIR RECIRC VALVE
A/C REFRIG LOW PRES SW
FUSE #11 (F/P)
COOLANT TEMP GA (INST CLSTR)
FUSE #14 (F/P)
LOW COOLANT SW
LOW COOLANT IND (INST CLSTR)
PROTECTION DIODE
DASH TEMP SENSOR
FRESH AIR TEMP SENSOR
AIR DUCT TEMP SENSOR
AMBIENT AIR TEMP SENSOR
FUSE #15 (F/P)
OUTSIDE AIR TEMP DISPLAY
INST PANEL LTS DIMMER (INST CLSTR)
DATA LINK CONN
ECM PIN C11
FRESH AIR CONTROL UNIT
FRESH AIR BLOWER
NOT USED
INTERIOR TEMP FAN & SENSOR
ECM PIN B9
A/C REFRIG HIGH PRES SW
AIR FLOW FLAP MOTOR & SENSOR
TCM PIN #13
TEMP REGULATOR FLAP MOTOR & SENSOR
ECM PIN B10
FUSE #7 (F/P)
ECM PIN C10
FUSE #8 (F/P)
FOOTWELL/ DEFROST FLAP MOTOR & SENSOR
CENTRAL AIR FLAP MOTOR & SENSOR
FUSE #13 (F/P)
FUSE #42
COOLANT FAN CONTROL THERMO SW
A/C CONTROL UNIT
COOLANT 2-WAY VALVE
A/C REFRIG HIGH PRES SW
SECOND SPEED COOLANT FAN CONTROL RELAY
COOLANT FANS
COOLANT FAN RESISTORS
A/C RELAY (AUX RLY PNL #1)
94J10644

Fig. 12: Automatic A/C-Heater System Wiring Diagram (100 CS)

1993 BMW CONTENTS

GENERAL SERVICING

ALL MODELS

AUTOMATIC A/C-HEATER SYSTEMS

318i, 318iS, 325i, 325iS & 325iC

AUTOMATIC A/C-HEATER SYSTEMS (Cont.)

525i, 535i, 740i & 740iL

1993 AUTOMATIC A/C-HEATER SYSTEMS 318i, 318iS, 325i, 325iS & 325iC

SPECIFICATIONS

Compressor Type .... Nippondenso Or Seiko Seiki
Compressor Belt Deflection
All Models .... [1]
Refrigerant (R-134a) Capacity
All Models .... 35-36 ozs.
System Oil Capacity [2]
All Models .... 3.4-4.8 ozs.
System Operating Pressures [3]
High Side .... 164-215 psi (11.5-15.1 kg/cm²)
Low Side .... 36-42 psi (2.5-3.0 kg/cm²)

[1] – Information is not available from manufacturer.
[2] – Uses Poyalkylene Glycol (PAG) oil (Part No. 81-22-9-407-724).
[3] – Specification is with ambient temperature at 80°F (27°C) and relative humidity at 50-70 percent.

WARNING: To avoid injury from accidental air bag deployment, read and carefully follow all SERVICE PRECAUTIONS and DISABLING & ACTIVATING AIR BAG SYSTEM procedures in AIR BAG SYSTEM SAFETY article under GENERAL SERVICING.

DESCRIPTION

The A/C-heater (IHKR) system automatically adjusts passenger compartment temperatures via a control unit and A/C-heater control panel. *See Fig. 1.* A/C-heater control unit regulates heater operation through 2 electromagnetic water valves. Each electromagnetic water valve controls flow rate through 2 separate heater cores.

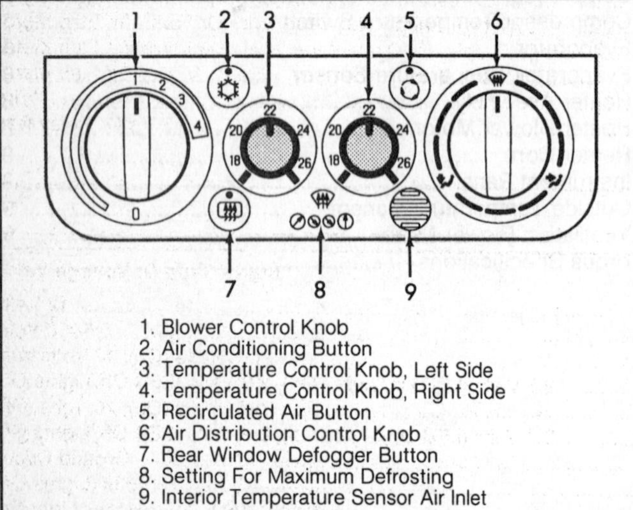
1
2
3
4
5
6
7
8
9
0
1
2
3
4
22
20
24
18
26
22
20
24
18
26
1. Blower Control Knob
2. Air Conditioning Button
3. Temperature Control Knob, Left Side
4. Temperature Control Knob, Right Side
5. Recirculated Air Button
6. Air Distribution Control Knob
7. Rear Window Defogger Button
8. Setting For Maximum Defrosting
9. Interior Temperature Sensor Air Inlet
93H19403
Courtesy of BMW of North America, Inc.

Fig. 1: Identifying A/C-Heater Control Panel

Air temperature is regulated by mixing varying ratios of cold and heated air through a cable operated temperature mixing flap. Temperature and air distribution for driver-side and front passenger-side can be controlled separately. All outlets can supply heated, cooled or fresh air according to temperature control knob setting. *See Fig. 2.*

System uses 6 input sensors for operation: outside temperature sensor, inside temperature sensor, heater core temperature sensor (driver and passenger-side), evaporator temperature sensor and interior temperature sensor. Temperature sensors continuously input information to A/C-heater control unit. A/C-heater control unit processes sensor signals and adjusts system temperature accordingly.

OPERATION

SYSTEM CONTROLS

NOTE: Refer to illustration for identification of A/C-heater control knobs and buttons. See Fig. 1.

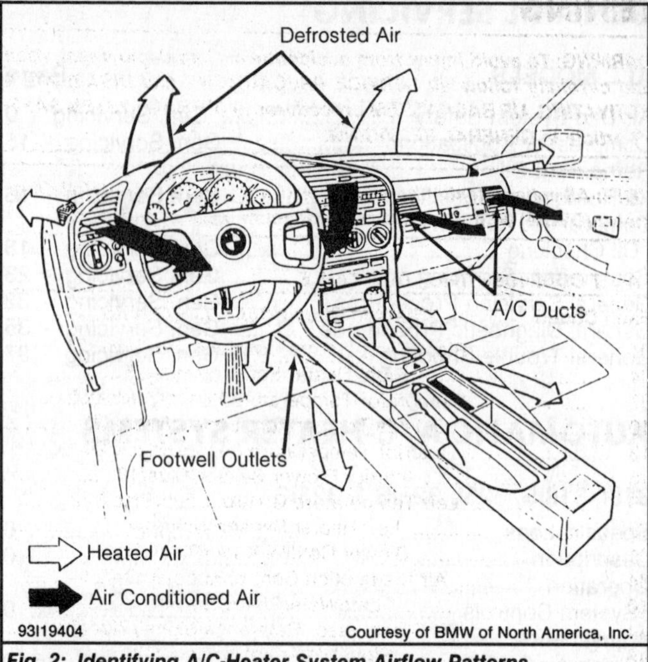
Defrosted Air
A/C Ducts
Footwell Outlets
Heated Air
Air Conditioned Air
93I19404
Courtesy of BMW of North America, Inc.

Fig. 2: Identifying A/C-Heater System Airflow Patterns

Air Conditioning Button – Air conditioning is switched on by push button located to right of blower control knob. A/C system will operate only at temperatures greater than 37°F (3°C) with engine on. At least one air outlet must be open when operating A/C system, to prevent evaporator freeze-up.

Air Distribution Control Knob – Rotary motion of control knob varies amount of air to defroster, footwell and instrument panel outlets. Defrost is controlled by temperature and blower controls. An illustration below temperature control knobs shows settings for maximum defrost.

Blower Control Knob – Blower control knob allows volume of air entering passenger compartment to be varied. Air flow increases as knob is turned clockwise. Air flow decreases automatically, at speeds greater than 50 MPH. When A/C switch is turned on with blower control knob in "0" position, a small amount of air will continue to enter passenger compartment. Blower control knob has 5 positions, and allows 4 different blower motor speed settings.

Recirculated Air Button – Pushing recirculated air button cuts off outside air flow.

Temperature Control Knob – Temperature control knobs determine temperature of air entering driver-side or passenger-side compartment. Turning control knob clockwise will increase air temperature. Selected air temperature will stabilize within passenger compartment shortly thereafter.

ADJUSTMENTS

FRESH AIR CABLES

Remove right and left side trim panels. Remove glove box. Place blower control knob in "4" position. Holding blower control knob in position, push back on upper clip lever to release internal wire in air cable. Set blower control knob to "0" position and release upper clip lever.

TROUBLE SHOOTING

NOTE: A/C control unit is capable of storing intermittent or permanent defects in memory. Diagnosis of such defects can be found using BMW Service Tester (Sun 2013 Engine Analyzer) and applicable BMW diagnostic software.

1993 AUTOMATIC A/C-HEATER SYSTEMS 318i, 318iS, 325i, 325iS & 325iC (Cont.)

TESTING

WARNING: To avoid injury from accidental air bag deployment, read and carefully follow all SERVICE PRECAUTIONS and DISABLING & ACTIVATING AIR BAG SYSTEM procedures in AIR BAG SYSTEM SAFETY article in GENERAL SERVICING.

NOTE: All voltage tests should be performed with a Digital Volt-Ohmmeter (DVOM) with a minimum 10-megohm input impedance.

PIN VOLTAGE CHARTS

Pin voltage charts are supplied to reduce diagnostic time. Checking pin voltages at the A/C-heater control unit determines whether it is receiving and transmitting proper voltage signals. Charts may also help determine if A/C-heater control unit wiring harness has a short or open circuit.

FAULT CODE IDENTIFICATION TABLE

Fault Codes	Affected Circuit/Connector/Pin No.	Probable Cause Or Defect
01	Right Temperature Control Knob/Black/21	Voltage Supply Not Okay, Wire Or Control Knob
04	Right Heater Sensor/White/25	Voltage Supply Not Okay, Wire Or Right Heater Sensor
07	Evaporator Temperature Sensor/White/22	Voltage Supply Not Okay, Wire Or Evaporator Sensor
10	Outside Temperature Sensor/White/23	Voltage Supply Not Okay, Wire Or Outside Temperature Sensor
13	Interior Temperature Sensor/Black/24	Voltage Supply Not Okay, Wire Or Interior Temperature Sensor
16	Interior Blower Sensor/Blue/18	Wire Or Interior Blower Sensor
25	Left Temperature Control Knob/Black/22	Voltage Supply Not Okay, Wire Or Control Knob
28	Left Heater Sensor/White/24	Voltage Supply Not Okay, Wire Or Left Heater Sensor
31	Blower Control Knob/Black/23	Voltage Supply Not Okay, Wire Or Control Knob
34	Air Distribution Control Knob/White/21	Voltage Supply Not Okay, Wire Or Mixing Air Control Knob
40	Left Water Valve/Black/5	Wire, Operating Unit Or Left Water Valve
44	A/C Compressor Reference Signal/Blue/22	Wire, [1] DME Control Unit Or Fan Relay
46	Right Water Valve/Black/12	Wire, Operating Unit Or Right Water Valve
47	A/C Signal To DME/Black/18	Wire Or Decoupling Relay
48	Rear Window Relay/Blue/20	Wire Or Rear Window Defogger Relay
52	Fresh Air Flap Motor/Blue/10, 11, 12 & 13	Voltage Supply Not Okay, Wire Or Fresh Air Flap Motor
55	Air Recirculation Flap Motor/Blue/6, 7, 8 & 9	Voltage Supply Not Okay, Wire Or Air Recirculation Flap Motor
61	Mixing Air Flap Motor/Blue/23, 24, 25 & 26	Voltage Supply Not Okay, Wire Or Mixing Air Flap Motor
92	Terminal No. 50/Black/1	Wire
94	Independent Heating & Ventilation/White/17 & 20	Wire Or Relay Box

[1] – Digital Engine Electronics.

A/C-HEATER SWITCHING UNIT PIN ASSIGNMENTS [1]

Pin No.	Function/Description	Signal Type Or Voltage Value
1	A/C-Heater Control Unit Reference Signal	12 Volts
3	Air Flow Control Knob, Nominal Value	0.6-4.0 Volts
5	A/C Push Button	Zero Volts (On); 10 Volts (Off)
6	A/C Indicator Light	2.7 Volts (LED On/Lights Off); 8.9 Volts (LED Off/Lights Off)
7	Air Recirculation Button	Zero Volts (On); 10 Volts (Off)
8	Air Recirculation Indicator Light	2.7 Volts (LED On/Lights Off); 8.9 Volts (LED Off/Lights Off)
9	Control Knob Lights	Ground Circuit
10	Indicator Lights Voltage Supply	10 Volts (Lights Off) 4 Volts (Lights On/Indicator Light On) 6 Volts (Lights On/Indicator Light Off)
11	Control Knob Lights & Indicator Lights	Input Signal
14	Water Valves Reference Signal	12 Volts
15	Interior Sensor Blower Activation	Zero Volts (Ignition On); [2] 12 Volts (Ignition Off)
16	Control Knob Reference Signal	5 Volts
17	Control Knobs & Interior Temperature Sensor	Ground Circuit
18	Nominal Temperature Sensor (Left)	0.5-4.2 Volts At 61-90°F (16-32°C)
19	Nominal Temperature Sensor (Right)	0.5-4.2 Volts At 61-90°F (16-31°C)
21	Interior Temperature Sensor	1.7-3.4 Volts At 50-104°F (10-40°C)
22	Ventilation Flap Switch	Zero Volts (On); 10 Volts (Off)
23	Rear Window Defogger Push Button	Zero Volts (On); 10 Volts (Off)
24	Rear Window Defogger Indicator Light	2.7 Volts (LED On/Lights Off)
25	Push Buttons & Ventilation Flap Switch	Ground Circuit

[1] – Pin assignments not listed are not used.
[2] – Reading is obtained after ignition is off for 3 minutes.

1993 AUTOMATIC A/C-HEATER SYSTEMS 318i, 318iS, 325i, 325iS & 325iC (Cont.)

A/C-HEATER CONTROL UNIT PIN ASSIGNMENTS (BLACK CONNECTOR) [1]

Pin No.	Function/Description	Signal Type Or Voltage Value
1	Terminal No. 50	12 Volts (When Starting)
2	Terminal No. 61 (Unloader Relay)	Zero Volts (Engine Off); 12 Volts (Engine Running)
4	A/C-Heater Control Unit Reference Signal	12 Volts
5	Left Water Valve Activation	0-100% (0-12 Volts)
9	Terminal No. 15 (Independent Ventilation)	12 Volts
12	Right Water Valve Activation	0-100% (0-12 Volts
14 & 15	A/C-Heater Control Unit Reference Signal	12 Volts
16 & 17	Load Circuit	Ground Circuit
18	[2] DME Activation (Anti-Stall)	Zero Volts (Off); 12 Volts (On)
21	Nominal Temperature Value (Right)	0.5-4.2 Volts At 61-90°F (16-32°C)
22	Nominal Temperature Value (Left)	0.5-4.2 Volts At 61-90°F (16-32°C)
23	Nominal Air Flow Value	0.6-4.0 Volts
24	Interior Temperature Sensor	1.7-3.4 Volts 50-104°F (10-40°C)
26	Terminal No. 31 (Electronics)	Ground Circuit

[1] – Pin assignments not listed are not used.
[2] – Digital Engine Electronics.

A/C-HEATER CONTROL UNIT PIN ASSIGNMENTS (BLUE CONNECTOR) [1]

Pin No.	Function/Description	Signal Type Or Voltage Value
1	Air Recirculation Flap Motor Reference Signal	11 Volts
2	Air Distribution Flap Motor Reference Signal	11 Volts
3	Fresh Air Flap Motor Reference Signal	11 Volts
6-9	Air Recirculation Flap Motor Activation	0-100% (11 Volts When Motor Is Off)
10-13	Fresh Air Flap Motor Activation	0-100% (11 Volts When Motor Is Off)
14	Control Knobs Reference Signal	5 Volts
15	Diagnostic Initiation Line (R x D)	Input Signal
16	Diagnostic Data Line (T x D)	Output Signal
17	Ventilation Flap Switch	Zero Volts (On); 10 Volts (Off)
18	Interior Blower Sensor Activation	Zero Volts (Ignition On); [2] 10 Volts (Ignition Off)
20	Rear Window Defogger Activation	Zero Volts (On); 12 Volts (Off)
22	A/C Compressor Fan (Stage 1)	Zero Volts (On); 12 Volts (Off)
23-26	Mixing Flap Motor	0-82% (Vent Flap Switch Off); 100% (Vent Flap Switch On) 11 Volts (Motor Off)

[1] – Pin assignments not listed are not used.
[2] – Reading is obtained after ignition is off for 3 minutes.

A/C-HEATER CONTROL UNIT PIN ASSIGNMENTS (WHITE CONNECTOR) [1]

Pin No.	Function/Description	Signal Type Or Voltage Value
1	Air Recirculation Indicator Light	2.7 Volts (LED On/Lights Off); 8.9 Volts (LED Off/Lights Off)
3	Rear Window Defogger Indicator Light	2.7 Volts (LED On/Lights Off); 8.9 Volts (LED Off/Lights Off)
4	A/C Indicator Light	2.7 Volts (LED On/Lights Off); 8.9 Volts (LED Off/Lights Off)
5	Rear Window Defogger Push Button	Zero Volts (On); 10 Volts (On)
6	Air Recirculation Push Button	Zero Volts (On); 10 Volts (On)
7	A/C Push Button	Zero Volts (On); 10 Volts (On)
9	Push Button, Vent Flap Switch & Indicator Lights	Ground Circuit
10	Air Distribution Control	Ground Circuit
11	Temperature Sensor	Ground Circuit
12	Control Knobs & Interior Temp. Sensor	Ground Circuit
13	Air Distribution Control Reference Signal	4.7 Volts
14	Indicator Light Voltage Supply	10 Volts (Lights Off) 4 Volts (Lights On/Indicator Light On) 6 Volts (Lights On/Indicator Light Off)
15	Terminal 58K	12 Volts (Lights On)
17	Independent Heating	Zero Volts (On); 11 Volts (Off)
18	Engine Speed Signal	Input Signal (Ignition On/Engine Off)
19	Road Speed Signal	Input Signal
20	Independent Ventilation	Zero Volts (On); 11 Volts (Off)
21	Nominal Mixing Value	1.6-2.7 Volts; 0-100%
22	Evaporator Temperature Sensor	[2] 1.6-3.4 Volts At 25-79°F (–5-26°C)
23	Outside Temperature Sensor	[2] 0.6-4.5 Volts At –32-104°F (–40-40°C)
24	Left Heater Temperature Sensor	[2] 0.7-4.3 Volts At 32-194°F (0-90°C)
25	Right Heater Temperature Sensor	[2] 0.7-4.3 Volts At 32-194°F (0-90°C)

[1] – Pin assignments not listed are not used.
[2] – Reading should be 5 volts with temperature sensor disconnected.

1993 AUTOMATIC A/C-HEATER SYSTEMS 318i, 318iS, 325i, 325iS & 325iC (Cont.)

REMOVAL & INSTALLATION

WARNING: To avoid injury from accidental air bag deployment, read and carefully follow all SERVICE PRECAUTIONS and DISABLING & ACTIVATING AIR BAG SYSTEM procedures in AIR BAG SYSTEM SAFETY article in GENERAL SERVICING.

BLOWER MOTOR

NOTE: If blower motor replacement is necessary, replace blower motor, shafts and wheels as an assembly.

Removal - 1) Disconnect negative battery cable. Pull rubber sealing strip from firewall. Remove screws attaching wiring harness to heater cover, and pull wiring aside.

2) Remove heater cover bolts, and remove heater cover. Disconnect wiring connectors from blower. Disengage clamp, and carefully lift out blower motor and fan without damaging flap.

Installation - To install, reverse removal procedure. Ensure all seals are installed correctly.

A/C-HEATER UNIT

Removal - 1) Remove instrument panel trim. Discharge A/C system using approved refrigerant recovery/recycling equipment. Disconnect negative battery cable. Pull rubber sealing strip from firewall. Remove screws attaching wiring harness to heater cover, and pull wiring out of way.

2) Remove heater cover bolts, and remove heater cover. Drain cooling system, and disconnect heater hoses. Disconnect heater system wiring harness connector. Unscrew nut and bolt, and remove heater bracket. Disconnect and plug refrigerant lines.

3) Remove connector between heater and rear area heater duct on right and left sides. Unscrew nuts, and remove A/C-heating unit with by-pass flaps closed.

Installation - To install, reverse removal procedure. Ensure all seals are installed correctly. Check oil level. Check system for proper operation.

COMPRESSOR

Removal - Disconnect negative battery cable. Discharge A/C system using approved refrigerant recovery/recycling equipment. Remove engine splash shield. Disconnect compressor clutch electrical connectors. Compress A/C belt tensioner to relieve tension, and remove A/C belt. Remove refrigerant hose couplings. Plug refrigerant lines. Remove compressor bolts, and remove compressor.

Installation - To install, reverse removal procedure. Check compressor oil level. Charge A/C system, and then operate and check for leaks and proper cooling.

CONDENSER

NOTE: Use Pulley Holder (11 5 050 on 318 Series or 11 5 030 on 325 Series) to hold radiator (cooling) fan pulley. Turn 32-mm Wrench (11 5 040) clockwise to remove cooling fan. Cooling fan nut uses left-hand threads.

Removal - Remove radiator fan. Remove radiator from vehicle. Remove radiator right grille section. Discharge A/C system using approved refrigerant recovery/recycling equipment. Disconnect and cap refrigerant lines at condenser. Remove condenser bolts. Remove condenser from above.

Installation - To install condenser, reverse removal procedure. Use new line coupling seals. Charge A/C system, and check for proper operation. Tighten cooling fan pulley nut to 22 ft. lbs. (30 N.m) if using 32-mm Wrench (11 5 040). Tighten nut to 29 ft. lbs. (40 N.m) if a conventional 32-mm wrench is used.

RECEIVER-DRIER

Removal - 1) Discharge A/C system using approved refrigerant recovery/recycling equipment. Remove windshield washer reservoir. Remove screws, and remove necessary trim to access receiver-drier. Disconnect and plug refrigerant lines at receiver-drier.

2) Cap receiver-drier fittings to prevent moisture from saturating desiccant bag. Disconnect plug on safety switches. Unscrew bolts, and remove receiver-drier.

Installation - To install, reverse removal procedure. Check and/or replace refrigerant line coupling seals. Install safety switches with locking compound. Check system oil level. Charge A/C system, and check for proper operation.

EVAPORATOR

Removal - 1) Disconnect negative battery cable. Remove package tray. Remove instrument panel trim on left side. Discharge A/C system using approved refrigerant recovery/recycling equipment. Open glove box. Unscrew bolt, and remove glove box trim.

2) Disconnect pins of straps. Loosen nuts, and remove glove box. Disconnect refrigerant lines from evaporator and plug. Remove blower motor cover.

3) Disconnect temperature switch and capillary tube sensor connectors from evaporator. Unscrew evaporator assembly bolts. Simultaneously remove temperature switch and sensor from evaporator housing. Pull evaporator from housing.

Installation - To install, reverse removal procedure. Use new line coupling seals. Wrap refrigerant lines with insulating tape after installation.

EXPANSION VALVE

Removal - 1) Disconnect negative battery cable. Remove package tray. Remove instrument panel trim on left side. Discharge A/C system using approved refrigerant recovery/recycling equipment. Open glove box and remove screws and remove trim.

2) Disconnect pins of glove box straps. Loosen nuts, and remove glove box. Disconnect refrigerant lines from evaporator, and cap both sides of refrigerant lines.

3) Remove bolts, and remove blower motor cover. Remove foam rubber cover. Unscrew pipe connections, and remove expansion valve.

Installation - To install, reverse removal procedure. Use NEW line coupling seals.

TORQUE SPECIFICATIONS

TORQUE SPECIFICATIONS

Application	Ft. Lbs. (N.m)
A/C Compressor Bolts	16 (22)
A/C Compressor Clutch Spring Plate	15 (20)
Cooling Fan Pulley Nut	[1] 22 (30)
Pressure Safety Switch	
High Pressure	[2] 18 (25)
Low Pressure	[2] 14 (19)
	INCH Lbs. (N.m)
Heater Core Stud Nuts	27 (3.0)
Heater-To-Body Screw	40 (4.5)
Temperature Sensor Screw	4.4 (0.5)

[1] - Using 32-mm Wrench (11 5 040). Torque specification is 29 ft. lbs. (40 N.m) if using conventional wrench.

[2] - Apply Loctite to threads.

WIRING DIAGRAM

NOTE: Information is not available from manufacturer.

1993 AUTOMATIC A/C-HEATER SYSTEMS
525i, 535i, 740i & 740iL

SPECIFICATIONS

Compressor Type .... Nippondenso Or Seiko Seiki
Compressor Belt Deflection .... [1]
Refrigerant (R-134a) Capacity
525i, 535i
740i & 740iL .... 53.0-55.5 ozs.
System Oil Capacity [2] ....
525i, 535i,
740i & 740iL .... 4.7-6.1 ozs.
System Operating Pressures [3]
High Side .... 164-215 (11.5-15.1 kg/cm²)
Low Side .... 36-42 (2.5-3.0 kg/cm²)

[1] – Information is not available from manufacturer.
[2] – Uses Poyalkylene Glycol (PAG) oil (Part No. 81-22-9-407-724).
[3] – Specification is with ambient temperature at 80°F (27°C) and relative humidity at 50-70 percent.

WARNING: To avoid injury from accidental air bag deployment, read and carefully follow all SERVICE PRECAUTIONS and DISABLING & ACTIVATING AIR BAG SYSTEM procedures in AIR BAG SYSTEM SAFETY article in GENERAL SERVICING.

DESCRIPTION

A/C-HEATER SYSTEM

The A/C-heater system automatically adjusts passenger compartment temperatures via a control panel and A/C-heater control unit. The A/C-heater control unit regulates heater operation through 2 electromagnetic water valves. Temperature sensors continuously input information to A/C-heater control unit.

Temperature and air distribution for driver's side and front passenger's side can be controlled separately. Air distribution flaps are operated by stepper motors responding to program selected at A/C-heater control panel. Outside air is drawn through a microfilter to filter pollen and dust.

System uses 5 input sensors for operation: outside temperature sensor, inside temperature sensor, heater core temperature sensor (driver's side), heater core temperature sensor (passenger's side), and evaporator temperature sensor. A/C-heater control unit processes sensor signals and adjusts system temperatures accordingly.

Each electromagnetic water valve controls flow rate through 2 separate heater cores. Auxiliary circuits adjust heater output in relation to air volume and different air/water temperatures. An additional water pump is used to maintain a minimum pressure level to water valves. This additional water pump will only operate with heater on.

OPERATION

A/C-HEATER CONTROL PANEL

A/C Button – On 525i and 535i, pressing A/C button will activate the compressor and auxiliary (evaporator) fan as long as the blower control knob is turned to at least "1" position.

For maximum cooling, the fresh air flaps will close to 30 percent and the recirculated air flaps will fully open. As the passenger compartment cools, the recirculated air flaps close and the fresh air flaps will open depending on fan speed and vehicle speed.

On 740i and 740iL, pressing A/C button will operate the A/C system when temperatures are more than 34°F (1°C). When cooling with maximum power, the system automatically recirculates inside air (with little fresh air admission) and the defroster outlets close automatically.

Air Distribution Controls – On 525i and 535i, the top and center sliding levers operate cables which control the defrost (windshield air) and face (fresh air) outlets. *See Fig. 1.* The bottom sliding lever is a potentiometer which controls the footwell and rear seat heating outlets.

On 740i and 740iL, the air distribution buttons control airflow to either footwell outlets or to face and footwell outlets. *See Fig. 2.* The AUTO button in the middle controls airflow to windshield defroster outlets, front side windows, instrument panel grille openings, center console grille, and footwell outlets.

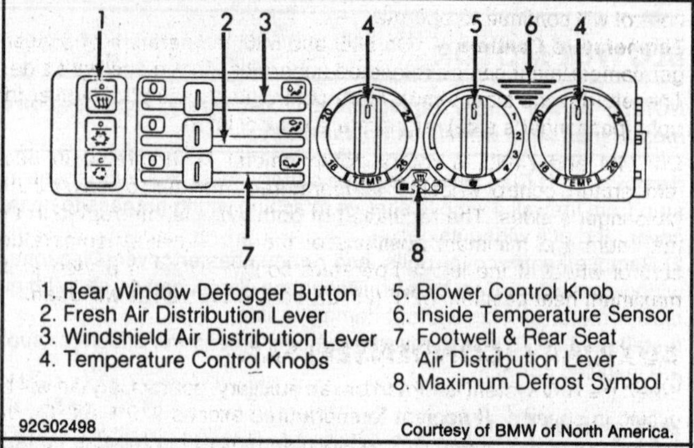
1
2 3
4
5 6 4
7
8
1. Rear Window Defogger Button
2. Fresh Air Distribution Lever
3. Windshield Air Distribution Lever
4. Temperature Control Knobs
5. Blower Control Knob
6. Inside Temperature Sensor
7. Footwell & Rear Seat Air Distribution Lever
8. Maximum Defrost Symbol
92G02498
Courtesy of BMW of North America.

Fig. 1: Identifying A/C-Heater Control Panel (525i & 535i)

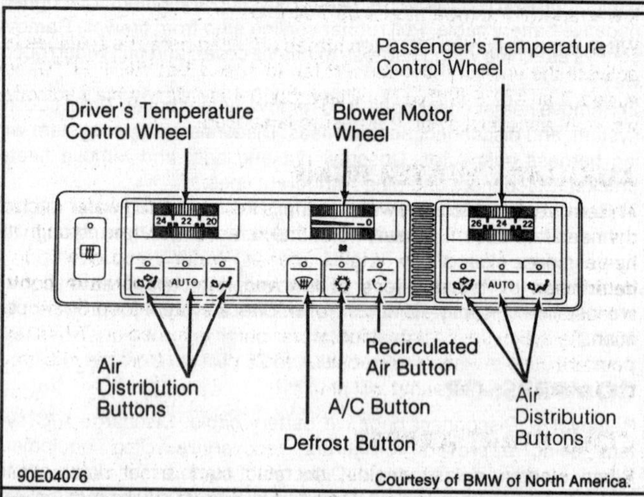
Passenger's Temperature Control Wheel
Driver's Temperature Control Wheel
Blower Motor Wheel
AUTO
AUTO
Recirculated Air Button
Air Distribution Buttons
A/C Button
Air Distribution Buttons
Defrost Button
90E04076
Courtesy of BMW of North America.

Fig. 2: Identifying A/C-Heater Control Panel (740i & 740iL)

Blower Control Knob (525i & 535i) – Blower motor is operated through a 4-speed rotary fan switch. In "0" position, the fresh air, recirculated air and footwell flaps are closed.

With knob at start of variable speed (wedge) position, the fresh air flaps are opened 40 percent. The footwell flaps are opened depending on the position of the sliding potentiometer (air distribution levers) and the recirculated air flaps are either open or closed depending on the position of the recirculated air switch.

Turning knob through the variable speed position will continue to open the fresh air flaps until they are 100 percent open in fan speed "1" position. The blower motor operates at low speed while knob is in variable speed position.

Blower Motor Wheel (740i & 740iL) – One rotary potentiometer wheel is used to control air volume to driver's and passenger's sides. System is switched off in the "0" position, except in defrost mode. The blower will run using about 4.5 volts in the first detent of the blower control wheel. In the maximum position, a relay is activated and the blower operates at full battery voltage.

Defrost Button (740i & 740iL) – Pressing the defrost button will activate the automatic defrost mode. This program has priority over other programs (including indicator lights of previously operated buttons). Entire air volume is supplied to defroster nozzles. Pressing button a second time resumes program selected before defrost was activated.

1993 AUTOMATIC A/C-HEATER SYSTEMS 525i, 535i, 740i & 740iL (Cont.)

Rear Defogger Button (525i & 535i) – Pressing the rear defogger button will activate the rear defogger grid for 10 minutes. After 10 minutes, the rear defogger operates on a timed basis of 40 seconds on and 80 seconds off.

Recirculated Air Button – Pressing the recirculated air button will stop fresh air intake and recirculate inside air. Automatic temperature control will continue to operate.

Temperature Controls – On 525i and 535i temperature of passenger compartment can be regulated separately on left and right sides. The left (driver's side) temperature control knob has priority over the right (passenger's side) temperature control knob.

On 740i and 740iL, a rotary potentiometer is integrated in each temperature control wheel for temperature adjustment on driver's and passenger's sides. The regulation of both sides is interrupted in the maximum and minimum positions of the left (driver's) temperature control wheel. If the left temperature control wheel is placed at its maximum heat position, 82°F (28°C), both water valves will open.

AUXILIARY (CONDENSER) FAN

When the A/C system is turned on, an auxiliary (condenser) fan will be cycled in speed 1. If coolant temperatures exceed 210°F (98°C), the fan will operate at speed 2. Auxiliary (condenser) fan will also operate when evaporator sensor has switched off the compressor because of low evaporator temperatures 35°F (1.6°C)

When the A/C system has been turned off, 2 temperature switches will activate the auxiliary (condenser) fan to speed 1 at 196°F (91°C) and speed 2 at 210°F (98°C). Auxiliary (condenser) fan is also activated when an abnormal system pressure is sensed.

AUXILIARY WATER PUMP

An auxiliary (electric type) water pump is installed in the water inlets of the heater cores. This ensures a sufficient water flow rate through the heater cores even at low engine speeds. Water pump operation is determined by the positions of left and right temperature control wheels. When temperature control wheels are positioned 30 percent from the maximum cool position, water pump is turned on. When temperature control wheels are positioned 25 percent from the maximum cool position, water pump will shut off.

COLD START ARREST

When starting a cold engine, the cold start arrest automatically controls the air distribution flaps to full defrost position to prevent drafts inside the passenger compartment. Blower runs with a minimum voltage of 3 volts and the A/C compressor and auxiliary water pump are switched off.

EVAPORATOR TEMPERATURE SENSOR

After A/C button is pushed, compressor is controlled by an evaporator temperature sensor, which will switch the compressor off once evaporator temperatures fall to less than 35°F (1.6°C). This prevents evaporator freezing. When evaporator temperature reaches more than 37°F (2.7°C), compressor is turned on.

HEATER CORE SENSORS

The heater core sensors are located behind the 2 heater cores. These sensors constantly monitor heater core temperatures. The auxiliary control circuits use signals from sensors to regulate temperature.

INSIDE TEMPERATURE SENSOR

The inside temperature sensor, located in the control panel, must be ventilated to measure actual inside temperatures. Ventilation is accomplished with a radial-type blower (located in rear section of control panel).

OUTSIDE TEMPERATURE SENSOR

Outside temperatures are monitored by an outside sensor, located in the air inlet opening for the blower. This sensor (a resistor) is attached on the right side of inlet opening and is a one-piece wire harness lead.

Outside sensor causes a slight increase in passenger compartment temperature by switching the inside temperatures a few degrees above current outside temperature. If outside temperature is 32°F (0°C), inside temperature is increased about 9°F (–13°C). If outside temperature is 68°F (20°C), inside temperature is increased about 2°F (–17°C).

PRESSURE SWITCHES

High Pressure Switch – A high pressure switch (located on receiver-drier) disengages compressor clutch when system pressures have increased to 441 psi (31 kg/cm²). Compressor will reactivate when system pressures have decreased to 338 psi (23 kg/cm²).

Low Pressure Switch – A low pressure switch (located on receiver-drier) disengages the compressor clutch when system pressures have decreased to less than 17 psi (1.2 kg/cm²). Compressor will reactivate when system pressures have increased to 32 psi (2.2 kg/cm²).

Medium Pressure Switch – Depending upon system pressures, a medium pressure switch causes the auxiliary (condenser) fan to operate in speed 2 when system pressures are at 257 psi (18 kg/cm²). Auxiliary (condenser) fan operation will shut off when system pressures stabilize at 213 psi (15 kg/cm²).

WATER VALVES

Two electromagnetic water valves control the water flow rate through the heater cores. Both valves are operated by ground pulses from the A/C-heater control unit. Each valve is spring-loaded open and powered closed for safety reasons. When the driver's side temperature control wheel is in either the maximum heating or minimum cooling positions, it has priority over the position of the passenger's side temperature control wheel. This is accomplished through electronics in the A/C-heater control unit and final stage switch, which is part of the circuit.

TROUBLE SHOOTING

NOTE: The A/C-heater control unit is capable of storing intermittent or permanent defects in memory. Diagnosis of such defects can be found using BMW Service Tester (Sun 2013 Engine Analyzer) and applicable BMW diagnostic software.

TESTING

WARNING: To avoid injury from accidental air bag deployment, read and carefully follow all SERVICE PRECAUTIONS and DISABLING & ACTIVATING AIR BAG SYSTEM procedures in AIR BAG SYSTEM SAFETY article in GENERAL SERVICING.

NOTE: The 525i and 535i may be equipped with either a dial-type or push-button type control panel. See Figs. 1 and 2. The 525i and 535i testing information in this article only pertains to the A/C-heater system with a dial type control panel.

PIN VOLTAGE CHARTS

Pin voltage charts are supplied to reduce diagnostic time. Checking pin voltages at A/C-heater control unit determines whether it is receiving and transmitting proper voltage signals. Charts may also help determine if A/C-heater control unit wiring harness has a short or open circuit.

1993 AUTOMATIC A/C-HEATER SYSTEMS
525i, 535i, 740i & 740iL (Cont.)

A/C-HEATER CONTROL UNIT PIN ASSIGNMENTS (BLACK CONNECTOR – 525 & 535 SERIES)

Pin No. [1]	Function/Description	Signal Type Or Voltage Value
1	Electronics	Ground Circuit
3	Inside Temperature Sensor	1.7-3.4 Volts At 50-104°F (10-40°C)
4	Nominal Air Flow Value	0.6-4.0 Volts
5	Left Nominal Temperature Value	0.5-4.2 Volts At 61-90°F (16-32°C)
6	Right Nominal Temperature Value	0.5-4.2 Volts At 61-90°F (16-32°C)
9	Auxiliary Fan Signal	Zero Volts (On); 12 Volts (Off)
10	Electronics	Ground Circuit
12 & 13	Control Unit Reference Signal	12 Volts
15	Right Water Valve Activation	0-100% (0-12 Volts)
18	Terminal No. 15 (Independent Ventilation)	12 Volts
22	Left Water Valve Activation	0-100% (0-12 Volts)
23	Control Unit Reference Signal	12 Volts
25	Terminal No. 61 (Unloader Relay)	Zero Volts (Engine Off); 12 Volts (Engine Running)
26	Terminal No. 30H	12 Volts (When Starting)

[1] – Pin assignments not listed are not used.

A/C-HEATER CONTROL UNIT PIN ASSIGNMENTS (BLUE CONNECTOR – 525 & 535 SERIES)

Pin No. [1]	Function/Description	Signal Type Or Voltage Value
1 & 2	Air Recirculation Flap Motor Reference Signal	11 Volts
6-9	Footwell Flap Motor Activation	0-100% (11 Volts When Motor Is Off)
10-13	Fresh Air Flap Motor Activation	0-100% (11 Volts When Motor Is Off)
14	Control Switch Knobs Reference Signal	5 Volts
15	Diagnostic Initiation Line (R x D)	Input Signal
16	Diagnostic Data Line (T x D)	Output Signal
18	Switching Unit Sensor, Fan Activation	Zero Volts (Ignition On); [2] 12 Volts (Ignition Off)
19	Auxiliary Water Pump Activation Relay	Ground Circuit
20	Rear Window Defogger Relay	Zero Volts (On); 12 Volts (Off)
22	A/C Compressor Activation ([3] DME Control Unit)	Zero Volts (On); 12 Volts (Off)
23-26	Mixing Flap Motor Activation	0-82% (Vent Flap Switch Off), 100% (Vent Flap Switch On); 11 Volts (Motor Off)

[1] – Pin assignments not listed are not used.
[2] – Reading is obtained after ignition is off for 3 minutes.
[3] – Digital Engine Electronics.

A/C-HEATER CONTROL UNIT PIN ASSIGNMENTS (WHITE CONNECTOR – 525 & 535 SERIES)

Pin No. [1]	Function/Description	Signal Type Or Voltage Value
2	Right Heater Temperature Sensor	[2] 0.7-4.3 Volts (0-90°C)
3	Left Heater Temperature Sensor	[2] 0.7-4.3 Volts At 32-194°F (0-90°C)
4	Outside Temperature Sensor	[2] 0.5-4.5 Volts –32-104°F (–40-40°C)
5	Evaporator Temperature Sensor	[2] 1.6-3.4 Volts At 5-79°F (–5-26°C)
6	Nominal Mixing Value	1.6-2.7 Volts; 0-100%
7	Independent Ventilation	Zero Volts (On); 11 Volts (Off)
8	Vehicle Speed Signal	Input Signal
10	Independent Heating	Zero Volts (On); 11 Volts (Off)
12	Terminal No. 58K	12 Volts (Lights On)
13	Indicator Light Voltage Supply	10 Volts (Lights Off); 4 Volts (Lights On/Indicator Light On); 6 Volts (Lights On/Indicator Light Off)
14	Air Distribution Control Reference Signal	4.7 Volts
15	Control Knobs & Inside Temperature Sensor	Ground Circuit
16	Temperature Sensors	Ground Circuit
17	Air Distribution Control	Ground Circuit
18	Switches & Indicator Lights	Ground Circuit
20	A/C Push Button	Zero Volts (On); 10 Volts (Off)
21	Air Recirculation Push Button	Zero Volts (On); 10 Volts (Off)
22	Rear Window Defogger Push Button	Zero Volts (On); 10 Volts (Off)
23	A/C Indicator Light	2.7 Volts (LED On/Lights Off); 8.9 Volts (LED Off/Lights Off)
24	Rear Window Defogger Indicator Light	2.7 Volts (LED On/Lights Off); 8.9 Volts (LED Off/Lights Off)
25	Air Recirculation Indicator Light	2.7 Volts (LED On/Lights Off); 8.9 Volts (LED Off/Lights Off)
26	Air Recirculation Control Indicator Light	2.7 Volts (LED On/Lights Off); 8.9 Volts (LED Off/Lights Off)

[1] – Pin assignments not listed are not used.
[2] – Reading should be 5 volts with temperature sensor disconnected.

1993 AUTOMATIC A/C-HEATER SYSTEMS 525i, 535i, 740i & 740iL (Cont.)

A/C-HEATER CONTROL UNIT PIN ASSIGNMENTS (BLUE CONNECTOR – 740 Series)

Pin No. [1]	Function/Description	Signal Type Or Voltage Value
1 & 2	Control Unit	Ground Circuit
4	Left Set Temperature Value	Input Signal
5	Set Air Volume Value	Input Signal
6	Inside Sensor Blower	Ground Circuit
7	Outside Temperature Sensor	Input & Output Signals
8	Right Set Temperature Value	Input Signal
9	Evaporator Temperature Sensor	Input Signal
10 & 11	Stepper Motors Reference Signal	Output Signal
12 & 13	Ignition On (Terminal No. 15)	Input Signal
14 & 15	Control Unit	Ground Circuit
16	Sensors & Control Knobs	Ground Circuit
17	Mixing Control Knob	Input Signal
18	Left Heater Sensor	Input & Output Signals
19	Starter Terminal No. 50 (30H)	Input Signal
20	Contol Unit 5-Volt Supply	Output Signal
21	Inside Temperature Value	Input & Output Signals
22	Right Heater Sensor	Input & Output Signals
23 & 24	Stepper Motors Reference Signal	Output Signal
25 & 26	Ignition On (Terminal No. 15)	Input Signal

[1] – Pin assignments not listed are not used.

A/C-HEATER CONTROL UNIT PIN ASSIGNMENTS (GREEN CONNECTOR – 740 Series)

Pin No. [1]	Function/Description	Signal Type Or Voltage Value
1	Left Footwell Flap Motor	Output Signal
2-5	Left Mixing Flap Motor	Output Signal
6-9	Fresh Air Flap Motor	Output Signal
14-16	Left Footwell Flap Motor	Output Signal
17-20	Left Footwell Flap Motor	Output Signal
21-24	Left Vent Flap Motor	Output Signal

[1] – Pin assignments not listed are not used.

A/C-HEATER CONTROL UNIT PIN ASSIGNMENTS (YELLOW CONNECTOR – 740 Series)

Pin No. [1]	Function/Description	Signal Type Or Voltage Value
1-4	Right Footwell Flap Motor	Output Signal
5	Rear Compartment Air Circulation Switch	Input Signal
6	Rear Window, Airflow Left & Bottom Left (Switch)	Input Signal
7	Defroster, Independent Ventilation & Heating (Switch)	Input Signal
8	Airflow Right & Bottom Right (Switch)	Input Signal
9	Speed "A" Signal	Input Signal
10	Diagnostic Initiation Line (R x D)	Input Signal
11	Rear Compartment, Rear Window Independent Heating (Switch)	Output Signal
12	Independent Ventilation, Max Left & Right Air Circulation (Switch)	Output Signal
13	Climate Control, Bottom Left, Defrost, Bottom Right (Switch)	Output Signal
14-17	Right Ventilation Flap Motor	Output Signal
18-21	Right Mixing Flap Motor	Output Signal

[1] – Pin assignments not listed are not used.

1993 AUTOMATIC A/C-HEATER SYSTEMS 525i, 535i, 740i & 740iL (Cont.)

A/C-HEATER CONTROL UNIT PIN ASSIGNMENTS (WHITE CONNECTOR - 740 Series)

Pin No. [1]	Function/Description	Signal Type Or Voltage Value
1-4	Footwell Flap Motor (Rear)	Output Signal
5	Blower Output Stage	Output Signal
6	A/C Motronic Relay	Output Signal
7	Rear Defogger Relay	Output Signal
8	Climate Control Relay	Output Signal
12 & 13	Terminal No. 30 Continuous Reference Signal	Input Signal
14-17	Air Circulation Flap Motor	Output Signal
18	Control Unit Indicator Lamp	Output Signal
19	Rear Window Switch Indicator Lamp	Output Signal
20	Diagnostic Data Line (T x D)	Output Signal
21	Left Water Valve	Output Signal
22	Front Defogger (Relay)	Output Signal
23	Right Water Valve	Output Signal
24	Auxiliary Water Pump (Relay)	Output Signal
25 & 26	Terminal No. 30 Continuous Reference Signal	Input Signal

[1] - Pin assignments not listed are not used.

REMOVAL & INSTALLATION

WARNING: To avoid injury from accidental air bag deployment, read and carefully follow all SERVICE PRECAUTIONS and DISABLING & ACTIVATING AIR BAG SYSTEM procedures in AIR BAG SYSTEM SAFETY article in GENERAL SERVICING.

A/C-HEATER CONTROL PANEL

Removal & Installation (525i & 535i) - 1) Remove radio. Squeeze retainer on left side of control panel through radio opening and pull out control panel from left side.

2) Detach cable and wiring harness connectors. Remove blower switch, ensuring catch lever and spring do not slide out. Remove screws and control panel.

3) Lift cover retainers and remove sensor blower cover. Disconnect wiring connector, and remove sensor blower. Remove control panel cover. To install, reverse removal procedure.

Removal & Installation (740i & 740iL) - 1) Carefully remove left side of control panel, and disconnect wiring connectors. Lift cover retainers and remove sensor blower cover. Disconnect wiring connector, and remove sensor blower. Remove control panel cover. Pry out control wheel pins.

2) Push back on micro switches and remove control panel (printed circuit board). If removing light diode, mark installed position and then unsolder diode. To install, reverse removal procedure. Ensure correct position of control wheel to potentiometer.

A/C-HEATER CONTROL UNIT

Removal & Installation - Remove screws and pull off trim on right and left sides of center console. Disconnect wiring from left and right sides of A/C-heater control unit. Fold down glove box. Remove screws and fold down ventilation duct. Press down retainer and pull out A/C-heater control unit from right side. To install, reverse removal procedure.

AUXILIARY WATER PUMP & HEATER CONTROL VALVE

Removal & Installation - Drain coolant, and disconnect heater hoses. Disconnect coolant hose at auxiliary water pump. Disconnect pump wiring. Remove nuts and lift out heater control valve and pump. Remove clamp and bolt. Remove auxiliary water pump assembly. To install, reverse removal procedure.

COMPRESSOR

Removal & Installation - 1) Discharge A/C system using approved refrigerant recovery/recycling equipment. Loosen hose clamp. Remove nut and air cleaner. Cut wiring straps, and disconnect compressor clutch lead. Disconnect suction hose and pressure hose. Cap all openings.

2) Raise vehicle on hoist, and remove engine splash shield. Loosen compressor mounting bolts, remove drive belt and remove compressor. To install, reverse removal procedure.

COMPRESSOR TEMPERATURE SWITCH

Removal & Installation - Loosen hose clamp. Remove nut and air cleaner. Cut wiring straps and disconnect switch lead. Remove compressor temperature switch. To install, reverse removal procedure.

EVAPORATOR

Removal & Installation - 1) Discharge A/C system using approved refrigerant recovery/recycling equipment. Pull off rubber trim along engine compartment firewall. Remove wiring and drain hose from expansion tank. Remove expansion tank, and set it aside. DO NOT bend coolant hose.

2) Cut 5 wiring straps along firewall. Remove screws and pull up cover. Remove nut, 2 screws and bolt. Remove wiring. Cut and discard wire straps. Disconnect wiring and gas cylinder rod from left side of glove box. Pull off trim, detach clips and remove glove box.

3) Detach clips and lift out holder. Remove 3 screws and evaporator cover. Remove screw and lift out pipe. Remove expansion valve and evaporator. To install, reverse removal procedure.

EVAPORATOR TEMPERATURE SENSOR

Removal & Installation - Remove screw and pull off trim on left side of center console. Disconnect wiring, and lift out evaporator sensor. To install, reverse removal procedure.

HEATER ASSEMBLY

Removal & Installation - 1) Drain coolant, and discharge A/C system using approved refrigerant recovery/recycling equipment. Remove instrument panel. See INSTRUMENT PANEL. Remove rubber trim along engine compartment firewall. Remove wiring and drain hose from expansion tank. Remove expansion tank, and set it aside. DO NOT bend coolant hose.

2) Cut wiring straps (on firewall). Tie wiring harness and, if necessary, carefully bend down brake and fuel pipes. Remove screws and pull up cover. Disconnect 3 heater hoses from heater assembly. Remove 5 bolts and nut from heater assembly (engine compartment side).

3) Remove 3 bolts from heater assembly. Lift out left and right side ventilation ducts. Remove heater assembly. To install, reverse removal procedure.

HEATER BLOWER MOTOR

Removal & Installation - 1) Disconnect negative battery cable. Pull off rubber trim. Remove wiring and drain hose from expansion tank. Remove expansion tank, and set it aside. DO NOT bend coolant hose. Cut 5 wiring straps from firewall. Remove screws and pull up cover.

2) Disconnect control cable, and unclip cable from cover. Open plastic retainer and remove cover. Unplug blower motor connectors. Lift out metal retainer and remove heater blower motor. To install, reverse removal procedure.

HEATER CORE

Removal & Installation (525i & 535i) – 1) Drain coolant. Remove center console. Remove glove box. Remove 3 bolts from heater assembly. Remove 2 bolts and lift out right holder. Remove front ventilation drive motor. Disconnect both temperature sensors.

2) Remove screws, loosen wire straps and clips, and remove cover. Remove 8 bolts and heater pipes. Remove heater core from right side. To install, reverse removal procedure. Use new "O" rings on heater pipes.

Removal & Installation (740i & 740iL) – Remove instrument panel. See INSTRUMENT PANEL. Drain coolant. Remove drain hose from expansion tank. Remove expansion tank, and set it aside. DO NOT bend coolant hose. Remove bolts from heater assembly. Remove screws, loosen wire straps and clips, and remove cover. Remove 8 bolts and heater pipes. Remove heater core from right side. To install, reverse removal procedure. Use new "O" rings on heater pipes.

INSTRUMENT PANEL

WARNING: To avoid injury from accidental air bag deployment, read and carefully follow all SERVICE PRECAUTIONS and DISABLING & ACTIVATING AIR BAG SYSTEM procedures in AIR BAG SYSTEM SAFETY article in GENERAL SERVICING.

Removal (525i & 535i) – 1) Disable air bag system. Using Torx TX30 bit with long shank, remove air bag module Torx screws from rear of steering wheel. Lift off air bag module enough to unplug wiring connector from rear of module. Place air bag module in a secure area, away from work area (preferably in trunk).

2) Position module with trim cover pad facing upward. Remove steering wheel nut and washer. Mark position of steering wheel on shaft, and remove steering wheel using puller. Remove center console. Remove glove box. Pry top of instrument cluster out slightly.

3) Pull cluster up to steering column and then fold down. Press tabs next to connectors and disconnect cluster wiring. Remove instrument cluster, and set it aside. Disconnect connector for radio speaker, if necessary. Remove left and right rubber door seals.

4) Remove "A" pillar trim on left and right side. Disconnect wiring harnesses as necessary. Remove screws from left and right sides of instrument panel. Disconnect air ducts as necessary. Carefully remove instrument panel.

Installation – To install instrument panel, reverse removal procedure. Tighten air bag module Torx screws and steering wheel hub nut to specification. See TORQUE SPECIFICATIONS. Activate air bag system and ensure air bag system is functioning properly. See SYSTEM OPERATION CHECK in AIR BAG SYSTEM SAFETY article in GENERAL SERVICING.

Removal (740i & 740iL) – 1) Disable air bag system. Using Torx TX30 bit with long shank, remove air bag module Torx screws from rear of steering wheel. Lift off air bag module enough to unplug wiring connector from rear of module. Place air bag module in a secure area, away from work area (preferably in trunk).

2) Position module with trim cover pad facing upward. Remove steering wheel nut and washer. Mark position of steering wheel on shaft, and remove steering wheel using puller. Disconnect wiring and gas cylinder rod from left side of glove box. Pull off trim, detach clips and remove glove box.

3) Remove center console. Pry top of instrument cluster out slightly. Pull cluster up to steering column and then fold down. Press tabs next to connectors and disconnect cluster wiring. Remove instrument cluster, and set it aside. Remove radio, if necessary.

4) Remove rubber door seal. Remove "A" pillar trim on left and right side. Disconnect wiring harnesses. If necessary, open lock tabs on some connectors to disconnect harnesses. Lift out speaker balance control, and disconnect wiring. Remove screw, and pull off trim and lead at glove box light.

5) Remove dashboard trim plate and 3 bolts on top of dash. Cut straps retaining heater wiring harness to dash (located in instrument cluster opening). Disconnect wiring to vent duct potentiometers. Remove bolts and instrument cluster.

Installation – To install instrument panel, reverse removal procedure. Tighten air bag module Torx screws and steering wheel hub nut to specification. See TORQUE SPECIFICATIONS. Activate air bag system and ensure air bag system is functioning properly. See SYSTEM OPERATION CHECK in AIR BAG SYSTEM SAFETY article in GENERAL SERVICING.

OUTSIDE TEMPERATURE SENSOR

Removal – 1) Pull off rubber trim along engine compartment firewall. Remove wiring and drain hose from expansion tank. Remove expansion tank, and set it aside. DO NOT bend coolant hose. Cut 5 wiring straps along firewall.

2) Remove screws and pull up cover. Cut sensor lead 1 1/4" (32 mm) away from sensor. Strip insulation rubber about 1 1/2" (38 mm) away from sensor. Remove outside temperature sensor.

Installation – 1) Place small diameter shrink tubing over each wire. Place large diameter shrink tubing over insulation rubber. Connect ends of new sensor to existing wiring. Solder ends of wiring.

2) Slide small diameter shrink tubing over solder points. Apply heat to shrink tubing using heat gun. Slide large diameter shrink tubing over solder points. Apply heat to shrink tubing using heat gun. Install outside temperature sensor.

VENTILATION BLOWER MOTOR

Removal & Installation – Remove screw and pull off trim on left side of center console. Fold down glove box. Remove screws and fold down ventilation duct. Disconnect wiring from A/C-heater control unit and ventilation blower fan. Remove microfilter cover and microfilter. Remove ventilation blower motor screws, and remove ventilation blower motor. To install, reverse removal procedure.

TORQUE SPECIFICATIONS

TORQUE SPECIFICATIONS

Application	Ft. Lbs. (N.m)
A/C Compressor Bolt	16 (22)
A/C Compressor Clutch Spring Plate	15 (20)
Steering Wheel Hub Nut	58 (80)
	INCH Lbs. (N.m)
Driver-Side Air Bag Module (Torx Screws)	70 (8)
Heater Core Stud Nut	27 (3)
Heater-To-Body Screw	40 (4.5)
Temperature Sensor Screw	4.4 (0.5)

WIRING DIAGRAM

NOTE: Information is not available from manufacturer.

1993 CHRYSLER MOTORS/MITSUBISHI CONTENTS

NOTE: For Mitsubishi Precis information, see Hyundai section.

GENERAL SERVICING

ALL MODELS

HEATER SYSTEMS

COLT, MIRAGE & SUMMIT

COLT VISTA, SUMMIT WAGON & EXPO

HEATER SYSTEMS (Cont.)

COLT VISTA, SUMMIT WAGON & EXPO (Cont.)

ECLIPSE & GALANT

MONTERO, PICKUP & RAM-50

1993 CHRYSLER MOTORS/MITSUBISHI CONTENTS (Cont.)

HEATER SYSTEMS (Cont.)

MONTERO, PICKUP & RAM-50 (Cont.)

MANUAL A/C-HEATER SYSTEMS

COLT, MIRAGE & SUMMIT

MANUAL A/C-HEATER SYSTEMS (Cont.)

COLT VISTA, SUMMIT WAGON & EXPO

1993 CHRYSLER MOTORS/MITSUBISHI CONTENTS (Cont.)

MANUAL A/C-HEATER SYSTEMS (Cont.)

ECLIPSE & GALANT (Cont.)

MONTERO, PICKUP & RAM-50

MANUAL A/C-HEATER SYSTEMS (Cont.)

MONTERO, PICKUP & RAM-50 (Cont.)

STEALTH & 3000GT

1993 CHRYSLER MOTORS/MITSUBISHI CONTENTS (Cont.)

AUTOMATIC A/C-HEATER SYSTEMS

AUTOMATIC A/C-HEATER SYSTEMS (Cont.)

1993 HEATER SYSTEMS
Colt, Mirage & Summit

DESCRIPTION

Heater control system incorporates a sliding air selector lever and individual temperature and mode selector knobs. Heater unit is located at center of dashboard, and blower motor is located beneath glove box. System incorporates the blend-air principle.

OPERATION

Air taken in by blower motor is passed through ducting and routed to heater unit. At right of heater unit is the blend-air door, which is controlled by temperature control knob.

Temperature control knob setting regulates temperature by varying amount of air passing through heater core. The airflow is controlled by position of mode selector door.

SYSTEM CONTROLS

Fresh/Recirculated Air Selector Lever – When air selector lever is placed in fresh air position, fresh/recirculated air door closes recirculation air inlet, leaving outside air inlet open. When lever is moved to recirculated air position, fresh/recirculated air door closes outside air inlet passage, leaving recirculated air inlet passage open.

Air Outlet Selector Knob – Depending on position selected, air can be directed to both front and rear of passenger compartment. Airflow selection capabilities include individual areas or a combination of windshield, upper body, knee and/or foot area. Rear passenger air distribution is limited to foot area only.

Temperature Control Knob – When temperature control knob is rotated toward cool air position, upper side of heater core is blocked by blend-air door. As a result, all air from blower motor by-passes heater core and flows into passenger compartment as cool air.

When temperature control knob is rotated toward warm air position, blend-air door will block cool air path. Cool air from blower motor now passes through heater core for maximum heating.

With temperature knob in middle position, blend-air door will split air stream into 2 branches, one passing through heater core and one by-passing heater core. Various combinations of warm and cool air are available to meet various temperature requirements.

ADJUSTMENTS

AIR MIXING DAMPER CABLE

1) Set temperature control knob on heater control panel to maximum heat setting. Set air mixing damper lever at bottom of heater unit to MAX HOT position, and install cable. *See Fig. 1.*

2) Push outer cable in direction of arrow, ensuring there is no looseness. Secure outer cable with clip.

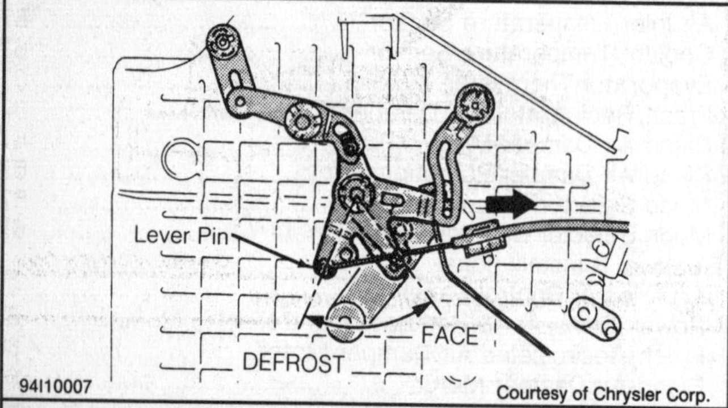
Lever Pin
FACE
DEFROST
94I10007
Courtesy of Chrysler Corp.

Fig. 1: Adjusting Air Mixing Damper Cable

AIR OUTLET SELECTOR DAMPER CABLE

Set air outlet selector knob on heater control panel to defrost setting. Set air outlet selector damper lever of heater unit to DEFROST position, and install cable to lever pin. *See Fig. 2.* Push outer cable in direction of arrow, ensuring there is no looseness. Secure cable with clip.

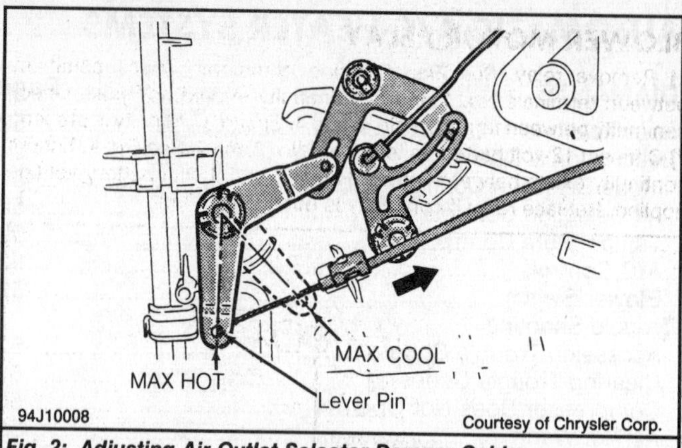
MAX COOL
MAX HOT
Lever Pin
94J10008
Courtesy of Chrysler Corp.

Fig. 2: Adjusting Air Outlet Selector Damper Cable

FRESH/RECIRCULATED AIR SELECTOR DAMPER CABLE

Set air selector lever to recirculated air setting. Move damper lever of blower motor to RECIRCULATED AIR position, and install cable. *See Fig. 3.* Pull outer cable in direction of arrow, ensuring there is no looseness. Secure cable with clip.

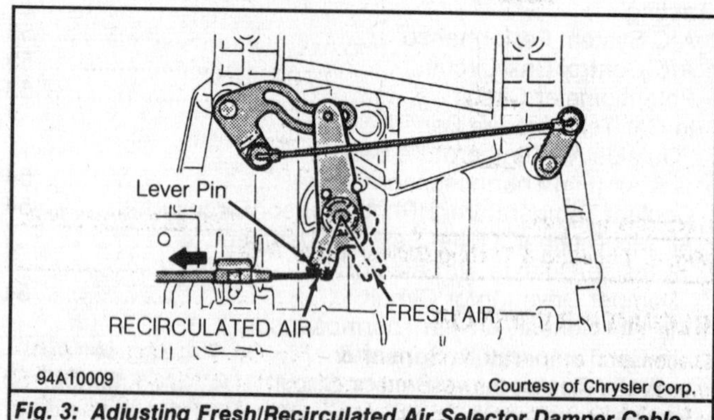
Lever Pin
FRESH AIR
RECIRCULATED AIR
94A10009
Courtesy of Chrysler Corp.

Fig. 3: Adjusting Fresh/Recirculated Air Selector Damper Cable

TROUBLE SHOOTING

INSUFFICIENT HEAT

Check component in the order listed, and repair or replace as necessary: obstructed heater outlets and/or hoses; binding or improperly adjusted air mixing dampers; faulty thermostat; improperly adjusted control cables; or plugged heater core.

NO VENTILATION EVEN WHEN AIR OUTLET SELECTOR IS OPERATED

Check component in the order listed, and repair or replace as necessary: air outlet selector dampers incorrectly adjusted; air outlet selector damper cable incorrectly installed; or ducts crushed, bent, clogged or incorrectly connected.

BLOWER MOTOR INOPERATIVE

Check component in the order listed, and repair or replace as necessary; blown fuse; poor grounding; faulty blower switch; faulty resistor; faulty blower motor; or faulty relay.

TESTING

BLOWER MOTOR

Apply battery voltage to blower motor terminals. Blower motor should operate. Ensure there is no abnormal noise.

1993 HEATER SYSTEMS
Colt, Mirage & Summit (Cont.)

BLOWER MOTOR RELAY

1) Remove relay. *See Fig. 4*. Using ohmmeter, check continuity between terminals No. 1 and 3. Continuity should not exist. Check continuity between terminals No. 2 and 4. Ensure continuity is present.
2) Connect 12-volt battery to terminals No. 2 and 4. *See Fig. 4*. Ensure continuity exists between terminals No. 1 and 3 with battery voltage applied. Replace relay if continuity is not as specified.

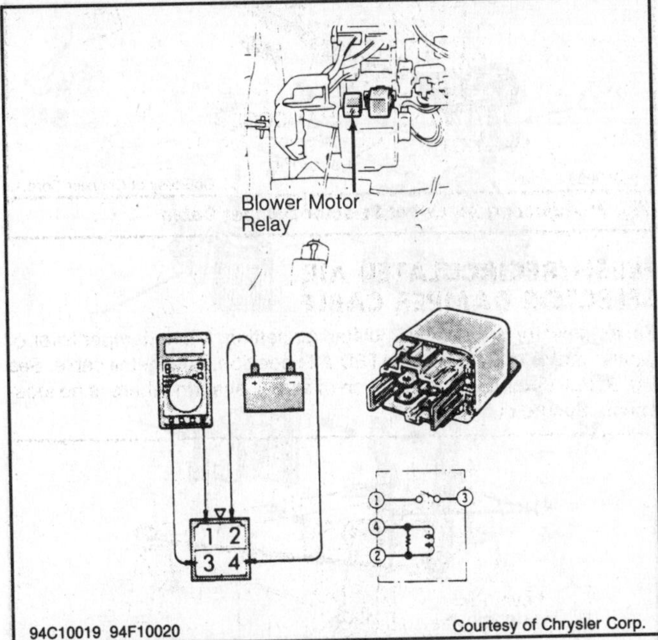
Blower Motor
Relay
1 2
3 4
94C10019 94F10020
Courtesy of Chrysler Corp.

Fig. 4: Locating & Testing Blower Motor Relay

BLOWER RESISTOR

Disconnect connector from resistor. *See Fig. 5*. Using ohmmeter, measure resistance between indicated resistor terminals. See BLOWER MOTOR RESISTOR RESISTANCE table. *See Fig. 6*. If resistance is not as specified, replace blower resistor.

BLOWER MOTOR RESISTOR RESISTANCE

Terminal No.	Ohms
3 & 2	2.21
3 & 4	0.97
3 & 1	0.35

BLOWER SWITCH

Disconnect blower switch harness. Using ohmmeter, check continuity between specified terminals, with switch in indicated position. See BLOWER SWITCH CONTINUITY TEST table. *See Fig. 7*. If continuity is not as specified, replace switch.

BLOWER SWITCH CONTINUITY TEST

Switch Position	Terminal No.	Continuity
Off		No
Low	6 & 7, 2 & 3	Yes
Medium Low	6 & 8, 2 & 3	Yes
Medium High	6 & 9, 2 & 3, 3 & 4	Yes
High	6 & 10, 2 & 3, 3 & 4	Yes

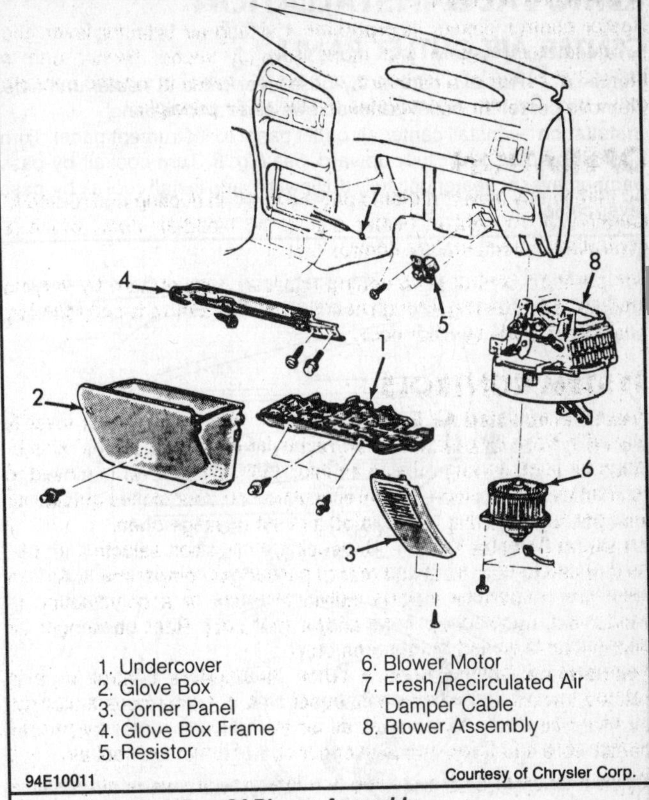
1. Undercover
2. Glove Box
3. Corner Panel
4. Glove Box Frame
5. Resistor
6. Blower Motor
7. Fresh/Recirculated Air Damper Cable
8. Blower Assembly
94E10011
Courtesy of Chrysler Corp.

Fig. 5 Exploded View Of Blower Assembly

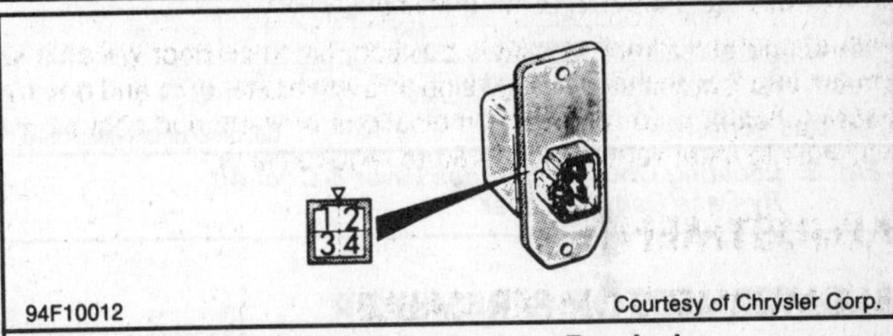
1 2
3 4
94F10012
Courtesy of Chrysler Corp.

Fig. 6: Identifying Blower Motor Resistor Terminals

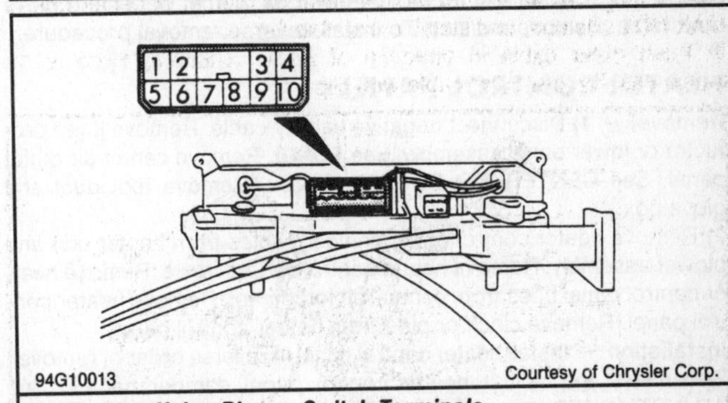
1 2 3 4
5 6 7 8 9 10
94G10013
Courtesy of Chrysler Corp.

Fig. 7: Identifying Blower Switch Terminals

1993 HEATER SYSTEMS
Colt, Mirage & Summit (Cont.)

REMOVAL & INSTALLATION

CENTER AIR OUTLET PANEL

Removal – Remove cool air by-pass lever cable at heater unit side. Remove center air outlet panel screws and remove panel.

Installation – Install center air outlet panel to instrument panel. Turn cool air by-pass lever fully upward. *See Fig. 8*. Turn cool air by-pass damper lever at heater unit fully downward, and install cool air by-pass lever cable.

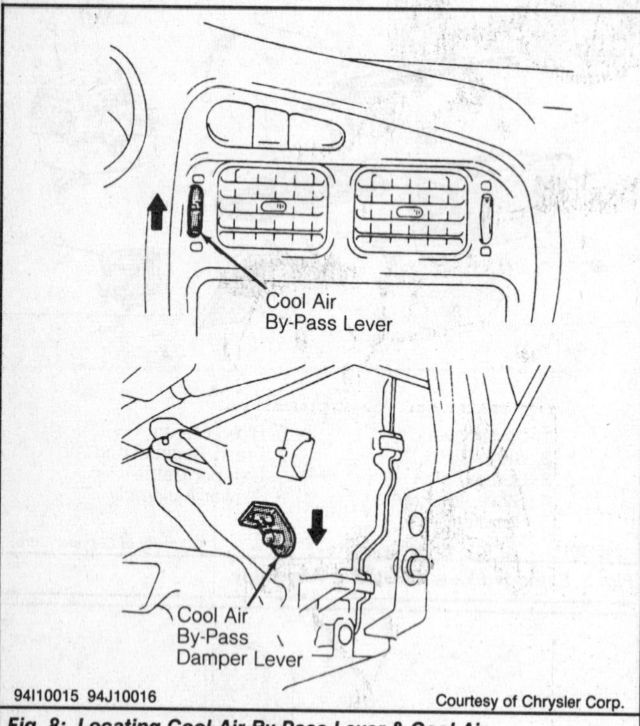
Cool Air
By-Pass Lever
Cool Air
By-Pass
Damper Lever
94I10015 94J10016
Courtesy of Chrysler Corp.

Fig. 8: Locating Cool Air By-Pass Lever & Cool Air By-Pass Damper Lever

BLOWER MOTOR & RESISTOR

Removal & Installation – Remove undercover. *See Fig. 5*. Remove blower motor assembly. Remove glove box, corner panel and glove box frame. Remove resistor. To install, reverse removal procedure.

HEATER CONTROL PANEL

Removal – **1)** Disconnect negative battery cable. Remove knee protector or lower panel assembly. *See Fig. 10*. Remove center air outlet panel. See CENTER AIR OUTLET PANEL. Remove foot duct and glove box.

2) Remove heater control panel damper cables from heater unit and blower assembly. Remove heater control panel screws. Remove heater control panel boss from center reinforcement. Remove heater control panel. Remove clock or plug from heater control panel.

Installation – Install heater control panel in reverse order of removal. Reconnect and adjust heater control panel damper cables. See ADJUSTMENTS. To complete installation, reverse removal procedure.

HEATER UNIT & HEATER CORE

Removal & Installation – Drain cooling system. Disconnect heater hoses. *See Fig. 9*. Remove instrument panel. See INSTRUMENT PANEL. Remove floor console box. Remove joint duct and foot duct. Remove center reinforcement. Remove center ventilation duct. Remove heater unit and heater core. To install, reverse removal procedure.

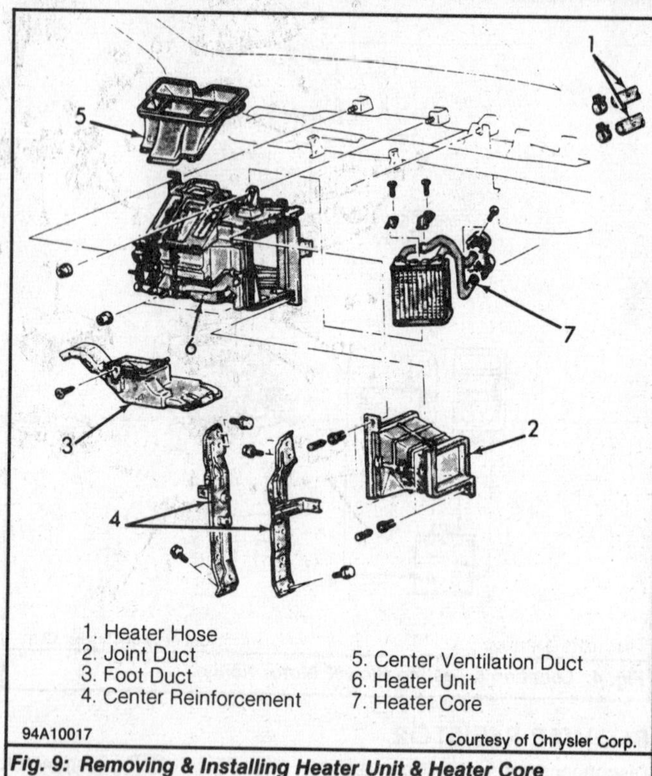
1
2
3
4
5
6
7
1. Heater Hose
2. Joint Duct
3. Foot Duct
4. Center Reinforcement
5. Center Ventilation Duct
6. Heater Unit
7. Heater Core
94A10017
Courtesy of Chrysler Corp.

Fig. 9: Removing & Installing Heater Unit & Heater Core

INSTRUMENT PANEL

Removal & Installation – **1)** Remove floor console. Remove knee protector or lower panel assembly. *See Fig. 10*. Remove sun glass pocket. Remove column cover and instrument cluster bezel. Remove remote control mirror switch, rheostat or plug. Remove coin box or rear wiper/washer switch. Remove air outlet panel assembly and ashtray.

2) Remove center air outlet panel. See CENTER AIR OUTLET PANEL. Remove radio plug and cup holder. Remove undercover, glove box and corner panel. Remove heater control panel. See HEATER CONTROL PANEL. Remove speaker. Remove side defroster grilles. Remove hood lock release handle. Remove steering column bolts.

3) Remove adapter lock from instrument panel. Pull speedometer cable slightly into passenger compartment, and remove adapter. Remove harness connector. Remove instrument panel. Remove ashtray panel and bracket. To install, reverse removal procedure. Tighten steering column bolts to 106 INCH lbs. (12 N.m).

1993 HEATER SYSTEMS
Colt, Mirage & Summit (Cont.)

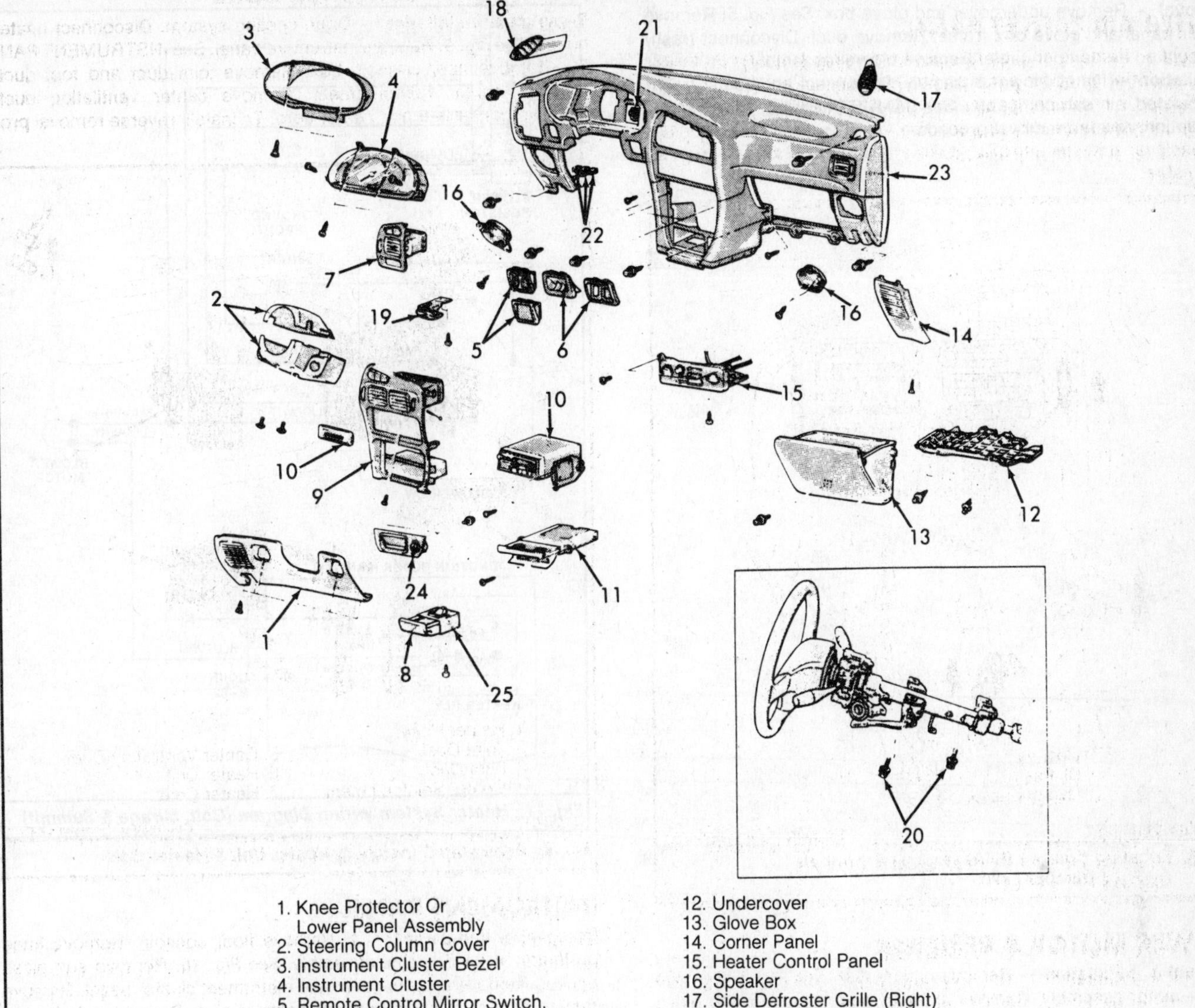
18
3
21
4
17
23
16
22
7
2
19
5
6
16
14
10
15
10
9
12
13
24
11
1
8
25
20

1. Knee Protector Or Lower Panel Assembly
2. Steering Column Cover
3. Instrument Cluster Bezel
4. Instrument Cluster
5. Remote Control Mirror Switch, Rheostat Or Plug
6. Coin Box Or Rear Wiper/Washer Switch
7. Air Outlet Panel
8. Ashtray
9. Center Air Outlet Panel
10. Radio Or Plug
11. Cup Holder
12. Undercover
13. Glove Box
14. Corner Panel
15. Heater Control Panel
16. Speaker
17. Side Defroster Grille (Right)
18. Side Defroster Grille (Left)
19. Hood Release Handle
20. Steering Column Bolts
21. Adapter
22. Harness Connector
23. Instrument Panel
24. Ashtray Panel
25. Ashtray Bracket

Courtesy of Chrysler Corp.

94H10014

Fig. 10: Exploded View Of Instrument Panel

1993 HEATER SYSTEMS
Colt, Mirage & Summit (Cont.)

BLOWER ASSEMBLY

Removal – Remove undercover and glove box. *See Fig. 5.* Remove corner panel and glove box frame. Remove duct. Disconnect fresh/recirculated air damper cable. Remove blower assembly.

Installation – Install blower assembly. Reconnect and adjust fresh/recirculated air damper cable. See ADJUSTMENTS. To complete installation, reverse removal procedure.

WIRING DIAGRAM

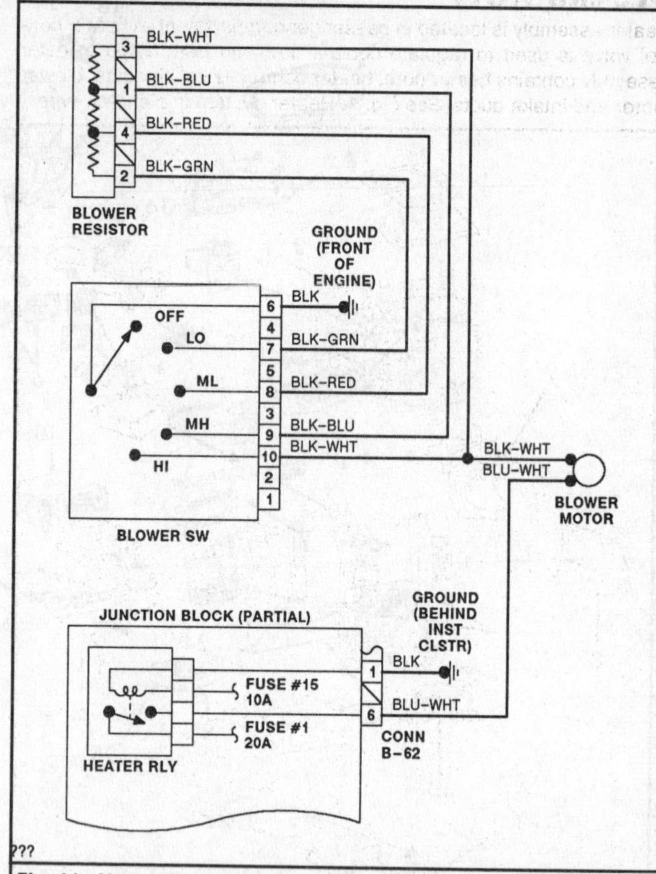
BLK-WHT
BLK-BLU
BLK-RED
BLK-GRN
BLOWER RESISTOR
GROUND (FRONT OF ENGINE)
BLK
OFF
LO
ML
MH
HI
BLK-GRN
BLK-RED
BLK-BLU
BLK-WHT
BLOWER SW
BLK-WHT
BLU-WHT
BLOWER MOTOR
GROUND (BEHIND INST CLSTR)
JUNCTION BLOCK (PARTIAL)
BLK
FUSE #15 10A
FUSE #1 20A
BLU-WHT
HEATER RLY
CONN B-62
???

Fig. 11: Heater System Wiring Diagram (Colt, Mirage & Summit)

1993 HEATER SYSTEMS
Colt Vista, Summit Wagon & Expo

DESCRIPTION

Heater assembly is located in passenger compartment. A heater control valve is used to regulate coolant flow and heat output. Heater assembly contains heater core, heater control valve, air ducts, blower motor and intake ducts. *See Fig. 1.* Heater system is blend-air type.

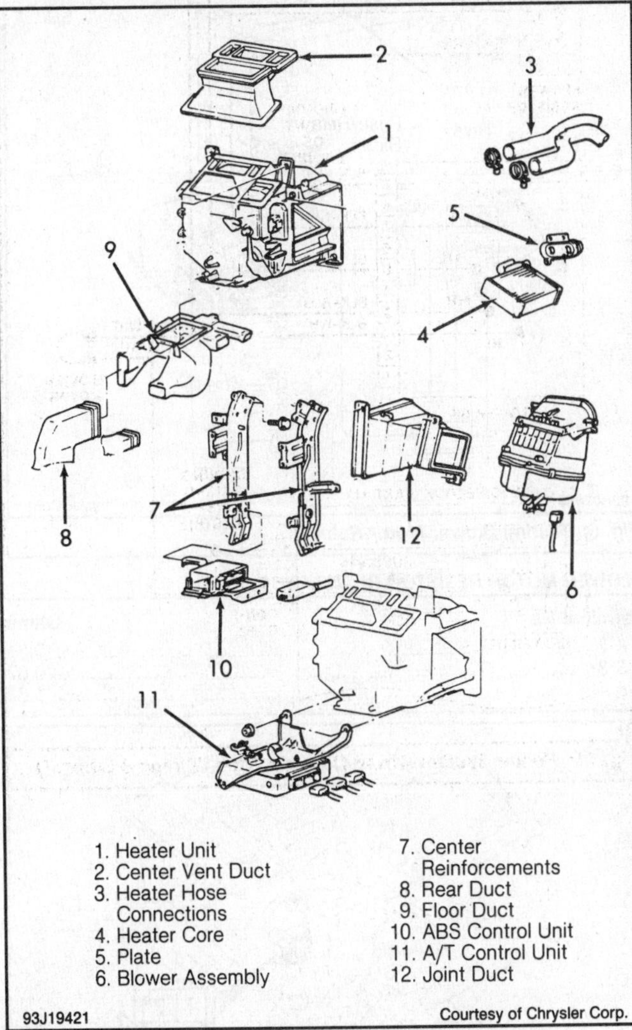
1. Heater Unit
2. Center Vent Duct
3. Heater Hose Connections
4. Heater Core
5. Plate
6. Blower Assembly
7. Center Reinforcements
8. Rear Duct
9. Floor Duct
10. ABS Control Unit
11. A/T Control Unit
12. Joint Duct
93J19421
Courtesy of Chrysler Corp.

Fig. 1: Exploded View Of Heater System Components

OPERATION

Heater and fresh air operations are controlled by a control lever. Temperature and air outlet functions are controlled by knobs. Multi-setting blower switch controls blower motor speed.

The temperature control knob opens and closes heater control valve and damper, which determines heat output. Heater mode control directs heated air to windshield when at defrost setting, to floor when at heat setting, or to center ventilation ducts when at vent setting.

TEMPERATURE CONTROL KNOB

Temperature level is selected by turning knob left or right. Highest heat setting is when control knob is turned to warm setting. With temperature knob turned to cool setting, ambient air is used for ventilating.

AIR SELECTOR LEVER

This lever is used to select source of airflow into vehicle. With lever at fresh air setting, outside air is allowed to enter and/or pass through heater. With lever at recirculated air setting, air is recirculated inside passenger compartment.

BLOWER SWITCH

The blower can be operated at different fan speeds to regulate amount of air forced through vehicle. Fan speed will increase as switch is turned to the right.

MODE SELECTOR KNOB

Depending on position selected, air can be directed to different areas of passenger compartment. Airflow selection capabilities include individual areas or a combination of windshield, upper body, knee and/or foot area.

ADJUSTMENTS

AIR MIXING DAMPER CABLE

Turn temperature control knob to maximum heat setting. Move air mixing damper lever of heater unit to MAXIMUM HEAT position, and install cable. *See Fig. 2.*

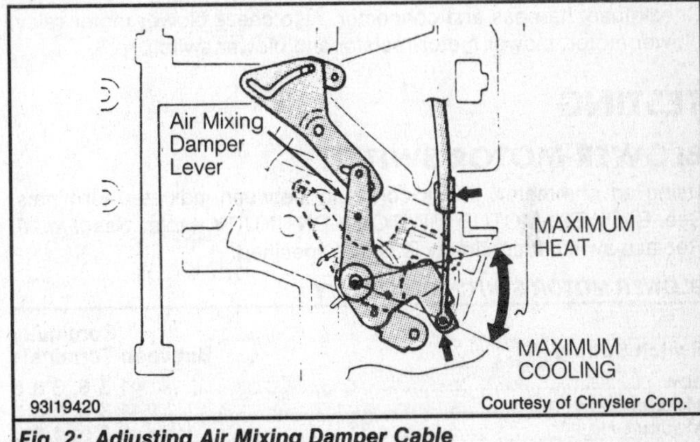
Air Mixing
Damper
Lever
MAXIMUM
HEAT
MAXIMUM
COOLING
93I19420
Courtesy of Chrysler Corp.

Fig. 2: Adjusting Air Mixing Damper Cable

FRESH/RECIRCULATED AIR SELECTOR DAMPER CABLE

1) Move air selector lever to fresh air setting. Turn damper lever in direction of arrow until it touches stopper. *See Fig. 3.* Connect inner wire of damper cable to damper lever. Insert outer wire of damper cable into clamp, and lightly pull outer wire from heater control panel side.

2) Slide air selector lever back and forth 2-3 times, and then set it at the fresh air setting. Check if damper lever is touching stopper. *See Fig. 3.* If damper lever is not touching stopper, readjust cable.

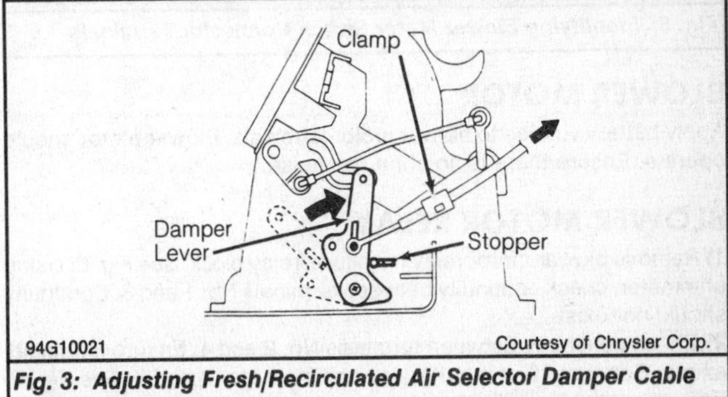
Clamp
Damper
Lever
Stopper
94G10021
Courtesy of Chrysler Corp.

Fig. 3: Adjusting Fresh/Recirculated Air Selector Damper Cable

AIR OUTLET SELECTOR DAMPER CABLE

Turn air outlet selector knob to defrost position. Move air outlet selector damper lever to DEFROST position. Install cable. *See Fig. 4.*

1993 HEATER SYSTEMS
Colt Vista, Summit Wagon & Expo (Cont.)

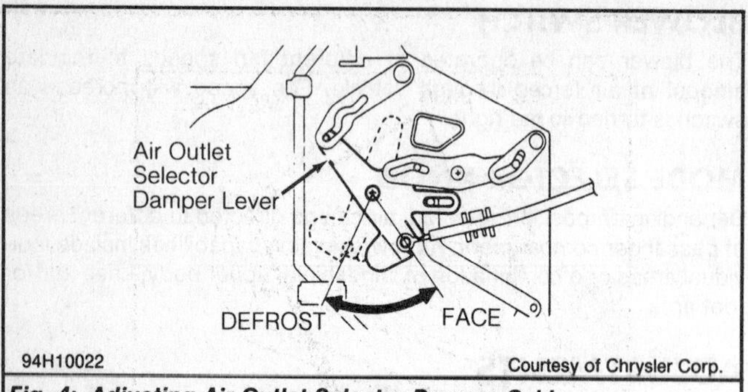
Air Outlet
Selector
Damper Lever
DEFROST
FACE
94H10022
Courtesy of Chrysler Corp.

Fig. 4: Adjusting Air Outlet Selector Damper Cable

TROUBLE SHOOTING

BLOWER MOTOR INOPERATIVE

Check fuse, harness and connector. Also check blower motor relay, blower motor, blower motor resistor and blower switch.

TESTING

BLOWER MOTOR SWITCH

Using an ohmmeter, check continuity between indicated terminals. See BLOWER MOTOR SWITCH CONTINUITY table. *See Fig. 5.* Replace switch if continuity is not as specified.

BLOWER MOTOR SWITCH CONTINUITY

Switch Setting	Continuity Between Terminals
Low	1 & 8, 3 & 5
Medium-Low	1 & 8, 5 & 6
Medium-High	1 & 4, 2 & 5, 4 & 8
High	1 & 4, 4 & 8, 5 & 7

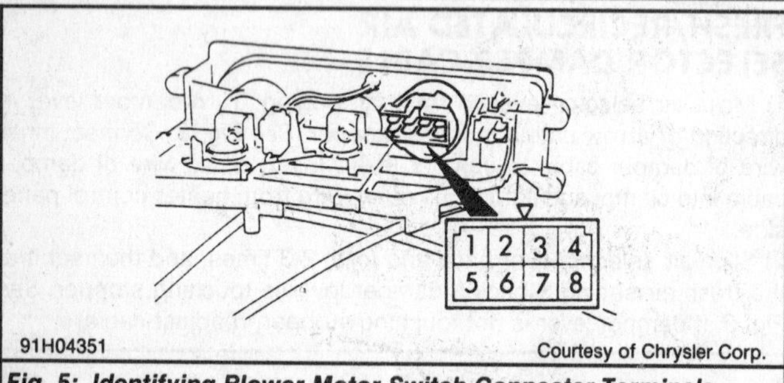
1 2 3 4
5 6 7 8
91H04351
Courtesy of Chrysler Corp.

Fig. 5: Identifying Blower Motor Switch Connector Terminals

BLOWER MOTOR

Apply battery voltage to blower motor terminals. Blower motor should operate. Ensure there is no abnormal noise.

BLOWER MOTOR RELAY

1) Remove blower motor relay from fuse/relay block. *See Fig. 6.* Using ohmmeter, check continuity between terminals No. 1 and 3. Continuity should not exist.

2) Check continuity between terminals No. 2 and 4. Ensure continuity exists. Connect 12-volt battery to terminals No. 2 and 4. *See Fig. 6.* Ensure continuity exists between terminals No. 1 and 3. If continuity is not as specified, replace relay.

BLOWER MOTOR RESISTOR

Disconnect harness connector from resistor. *See Fig. 7.* Using an ohmmeter, check resistance between indicated terminals. See BLOWER MOTOR RESISTOR RESISTANCE table. If resistance is not as specified, replace resistor.

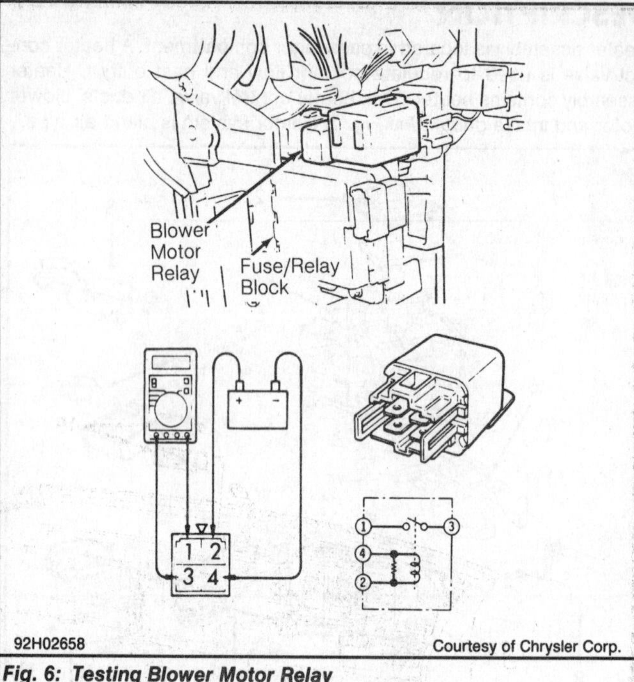
Blower
Motor
Relay
Fuse/Relay
Block
1 2
3 4
92H02658
Courtesy of Chrysler Corp.

Fig. 6: Testing Blower Motor Relay

BLOWER MOTOR RESISTOR RESISTANCE

Terminal No	Ohms
1 & 2	0.31
1 & 3	0.87
1 & 4	1.83

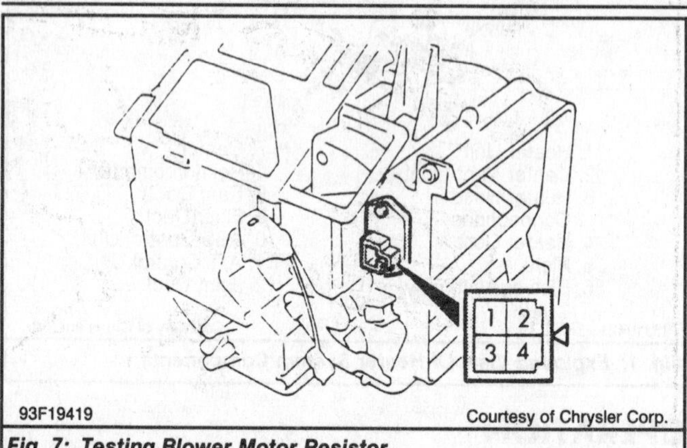
1 2
3 4
93F19419
Courtesy of Chrysler Corp.

Fig. 7: Testing Blower Motor Resistor

REMOVAL & INSTALLATION

BLOWER ASSEMBLY

Removal & Installation – Remove instrument panel. See INSTRUMENT PANEL. Remove clip from heater unit by pushing it at the center. Remove joint duct. *See Fig. 1.* Remove blower assembly. To install, reverse removal procedure.

BLOWER MOTOR & RESISTOR

Removal & Installation – 1) Remove lap heater duct under glove box. *See Fig. 9.* Remove screws at bottom of glove box. Pull glove box pass stopper to remove.

CAUTION: DO NOT remove stopper before removing screws. Glove box may drop out, damaging glove box hinge.

2) Remove resistor and speaker cover. Remove glove box frame. Remove blower motor. To install, reverse removal procedure.

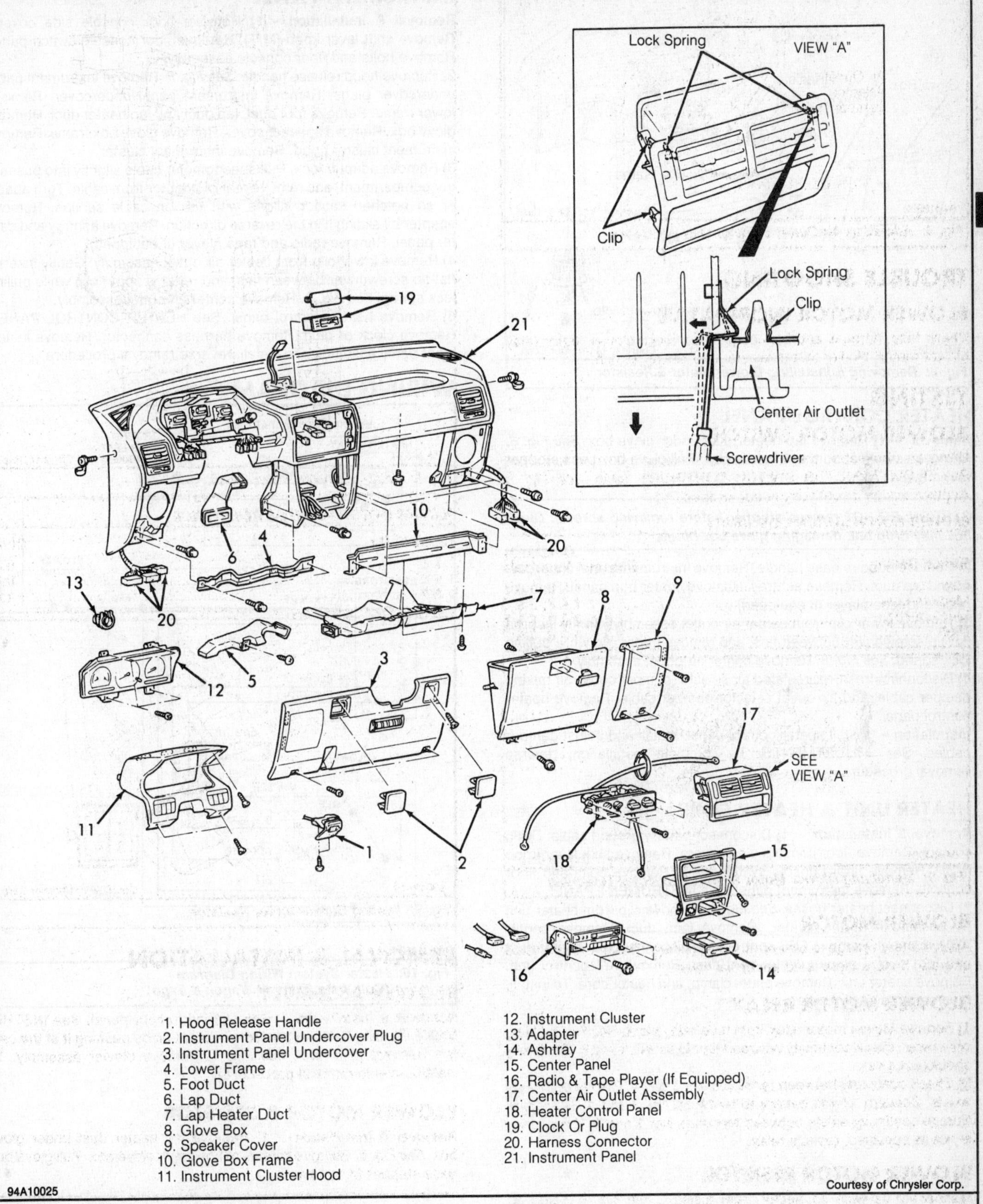
Lock Spring
VIEW "A"
Clip
Lock Spring
Clip
Center Air Outlet
Screwdriver
SEE VIEW "A"
1. Hood Release Handle
2. Instrument Panel Undercover Plug
3. Instrument Panel Undercover
4. Lower Frame
5. Foot Duct
6. Lap Duct
7. Lap Heater Duct
8. Glove Box
9. Speaker Cover
10. Glove Box Frame
11. Instrument Cluster Hood
12. Instrument Cluster
13. Adapter
14. Ashtray
15. Center Panel
16. Radio & Tape Player (If Equipped)
17. Center Air Outlet Assembly
18. Heater Control Panel
19. Clock Or Plug
20. Harness Connector
21. Instrument Panel
94A10025
Courtesy of Chrysler Corp.

Fig. 8: Exploded View Of Instrument Panel

1993 HEATER SYSTEMS
Colt Vista, Summit Wagon & Expo (Cont.)

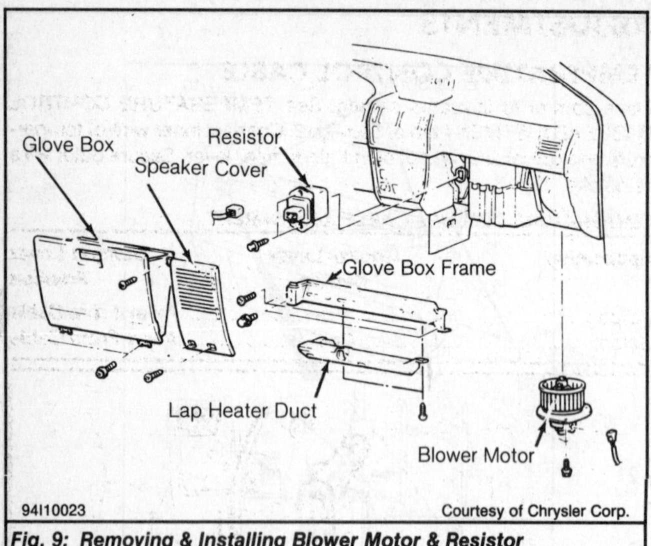
Glove Box
Resistor
Speaker Cover
Glove Box Frame
Lap Heater Duct
Blower Motor
94I10023
Courtesy of Chrysler Corp.

Fig. 9: Removing & Installing Blower Motor & Resistor

HEATER CONTROL PANEL

Removal - 1) Remove lap heater duct under glove box. *See Fig. 8.* Remove screws at bottom of glove box. Pull glove box pass stopper to remove.

CAUTION: DO NOT remove stopper before removing screws. Glove box may drop out, damaging glove box hinge.

2) Remove hood release handle. Remove instrument panel undercover and lap duct. Remove ashtray. Remove center trim panel. Remove radio and tape player (if equipped).
3) Remove lower clip from center air outlet assembly. Gently insert a flat-tip screwdriver between fins, and remove upper clip while pulling lock spring. *See Fig. 8.* Remove center air outlet assembly.
4) Disconnect fresh/recirculated air selector damper cable, air mixing damper cable, and air outlet selector damper cable. Remove heater control panel.
Installation - Install heater control panel. Install and adjust damper cables. See ADJUSTMENTS. To complete installation, reverse removal procedure.

HEATER UNIT & HEATER CORE

Removal & Installation - 1) Disconnect battery ground cable. Drain coolant. Remove floor console side covers. Remove shift lever knob (M/T). Remove floor console switch panel. Remove bolts and floor console. Remove instrument panel. See INSTRUMENT PANEL.
2) Disconnect heater hoses. *See Fig. 1.* Remove clip from heater unit by pushing it at the center. Remove joint duct. Remove center reinforcement. Remove ABS control unit. Disconnect rear heater duct and foot duct. Remove center vent duct. Remove A/T control unit. Remove heater unit. Remove plate, clamp, and heater core. To install, reverse removal procedure.

INSTRUMENT PANEL

Removal & Installation - 1) Remove floor console side covers. Remove shift lever knob (M/T). Remove floor console switch panel. Remove bolts and floor console assembly.
2) Remove hood release handle. *See Fig. 8.* Remove instrument panel undercover plugs. Remove instrument panel undercover. Remove lower frame. Remove foot duct, lap duct and lap heater duct. Remove glove box. Remove speaker cover. Remove glove box frame. Remove instrument cluster hood. Remove instrument cluster.
3) Remove adapter lock. Pull speedometer cable slightly into passenger compartment, and remove rear of adapter from cable. Turn adapter so notched section aligns with tab on cable section. Remove adapter by sliding it in the reverse direction. Remove ashtray and center panel. Remove radio and tape player (if equipped).
4) Remove lower clip from center air outlet assembly. Gently insert a flat-tip screwdriver between fins, and remove upper clip while pulling lock spring. *See Fig. 8.* Remove center air outlet assembly.
5) Remove heater control panel. See HEATER CONTROL PANEL. Remove clock or plug. Remove harness connector. Remove instrument panel assembly. To install, reverse removal procedure.

WIRING DIAGRAM

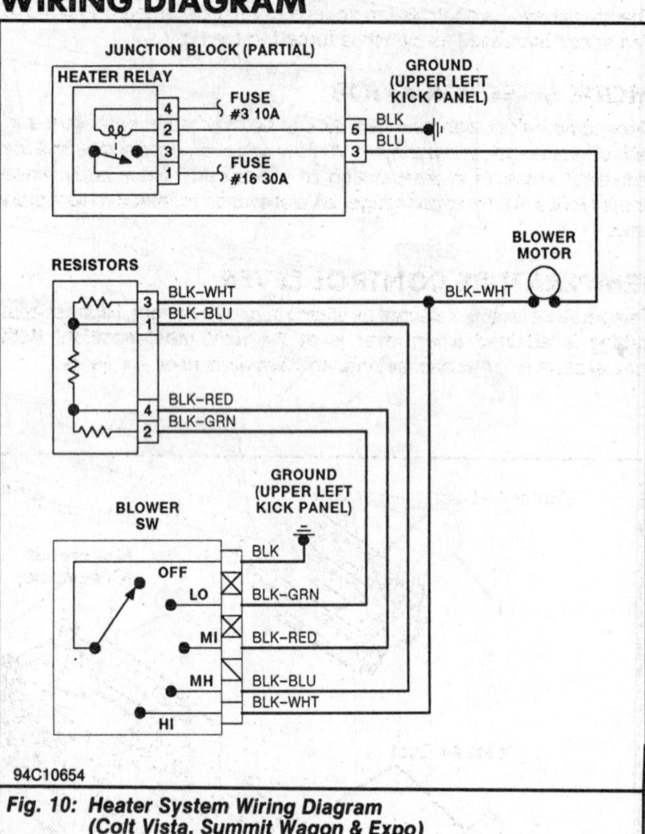
JUNCTION BLOCK (PARTIAL)
HEATER RELAY
4
2
3
1
FUSE
#3 10A
FUSE
#16 30A
5
3
BLK
BLU
GROUND
(UPPER LEFT
KICK PANEL)
BLOWER
MOTOR
RESISTORS
3
1
4
2
BLK-WHT
BLK-BLU
BLK-RED
BLK-GRN
BLK-WHT
GROUND
(UPPER LEFT
KICK PANEL)
BLOWER
SW
OFF
LO
MI
MH
HI
BLK
BLK-GRN
BLK-RED
BLK-BLU
BLK-WHT
94C10654

Fig. 10: Heater System Wiring Diagram (Colt Vista, Summit Wagon & Expo)

1993 HEATER SYSTEMS
Eclipse & Galant

DESCRIPTION

Heater assembly on all models is located in passenger compartment. A heater control valve is used to regulate coolant flow and heat output. Heater assembly contains heater core, heater control valve, air ducts, blower motor and intake ducts. *See Fig. 1*. Heater systems are blend-air type.

OPERATION

Air selector control regulates airflow source. The temperature control lever opens and closes heater control valve, which determines heat output. Mode selector lever directs airflow to appropriate outlet based on the selection.

AIR SELECTOR CONTROL

This control is used to select source of airflow. With control at fresh air setting, outside air is allowed to enter and/or pass through heater. With control at recirculated air setting, air is recirculated inside passenger compartment.

BLOWER SWITCH

The blower switch controls fan speeds to regulate amount of airflow. Fan speed increases as switch is turned to the right.

MODE SELECTOR KNOB

Depending on position selected, air can be directed to both front and rear of passenger compartment. Airflow selection capabilities include individual areas or a combination of windshield, upper body, knee and/or foot area. Rear passenger air distribution is limited to foot area only.

TEMPERATURE CONTROL LEVER

Temperature level is selected by sliding lever left or right. Highest heat setting is attained when lever is at the right most position. With temperature lever at cool setting, ambient air is used for vents.

ADJUSTMENTS

TEMPERATURE CONTROL CABLE

Place control to indicated setting. See TEMPERATURE CONTROL CABLE ADJUSTMENT table. *See Fig. 2*. Connect inner wire of temperature control cable to end of blend-air damper lever. Secure outer wire using clip.

TEMPERATURE CONTROL CABLE ADJUSTMENT

Application	Control Lever Setting	Damper Lever Position
Eclipse	Hot	Away From Cable
Galant	Cool	Away From Cable

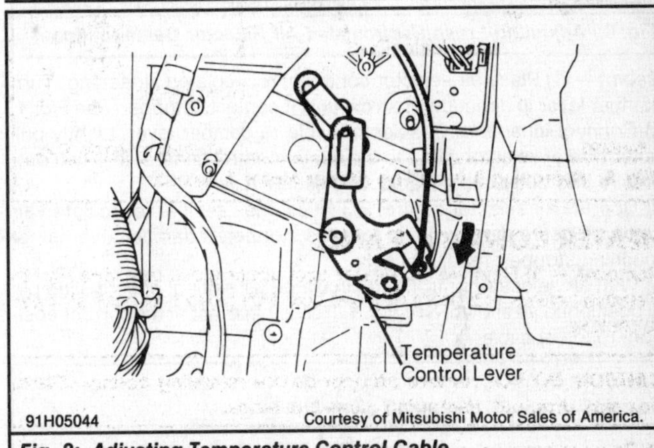
Temperature
Control Lever
91H05044
Courtesy of Mitsubishi Motor Sales of America.

Fig. 2: Adjusting Temperature Control Cable (Eclipse Shown; Galant Similar)

FRESH/RECIRCULATED AIR SELECTOR CABLE

Eclipse – Place lever at recirculated air setting. Move control lever until it touches stopper. *See Fig. 3*. Connect inner wire of selector cable to end of control lever. Secure outer wire using clip.

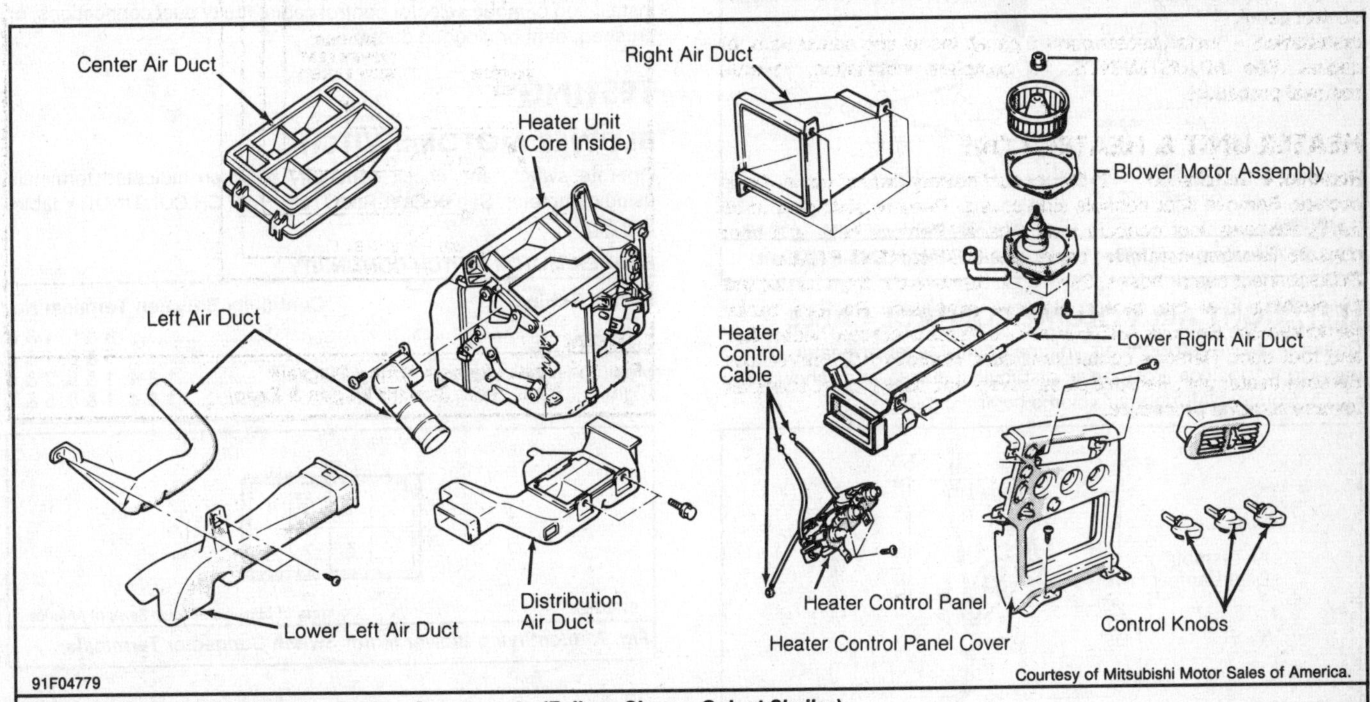
Center Air Duct
Right Air Duct
Heater Unit
(Core Inside)
Blower Motor Assembly
Left Air Duct
Heater
Control
Cable
Lower Right Air Duct
Distribution
Air Duct
Lower Left Air Duct
Heater Control Panel
Heater Control Panel Cover
Control Knobs
91F04779
Courtesy of Mitsubishi Motor Sales of America.

Fig. 1: Exploded View Of Heater System Components (Eclipse Shown; Galant Similar)

1993 HEATER SYSTEMS
Eclipse & Galant (Cont.)

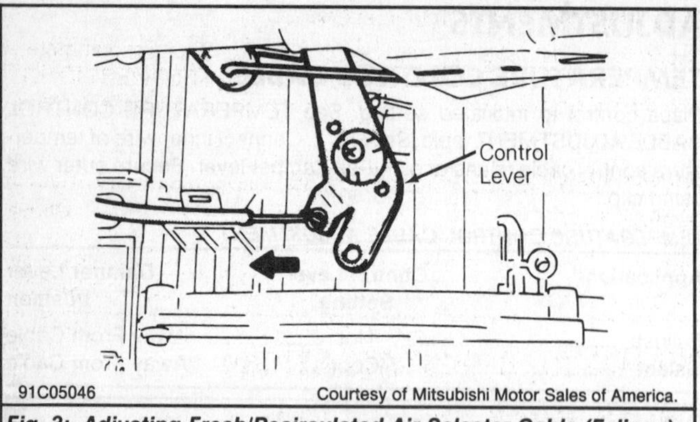
Control
Lever
91C05046
Courtesy of Mitsubishi Motor Sales of America.

Fig. 3: Adjusting Fresh/Recirculated Air Selector Cable (Eclipse)

Galant – **1)** Place air selector control at recirculated air setting. Turn damper lever in direction of arrow until it contacts stopper. *See Fig. 4.*
2) Connect inner wire of selector cable to damper lever. Lightly pull outer wire of selector cable to the heater control panel side. Push outer wire into outer cable clamp, and secure it.
3) Operate air selector control 2-3 times, then set it at recirculated air setting. Ensure damper lever touches stopper. If damper lever is not touching stopper, readjust cable.
4) With air selector control at recirculated air setting, ensure slide pin is positioned as shown. *See Fig. 4.* If slide pin is not at the correct position, readjust cable.

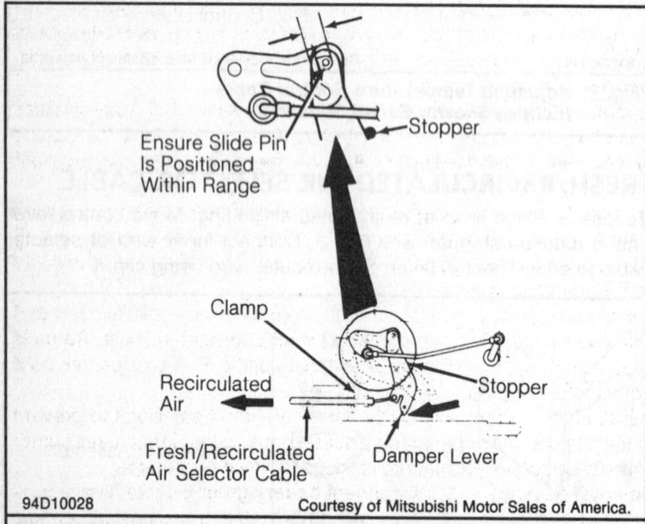
Stopper
Ensure Slide Pin
Is Positioned
Within Range
Clamp
Recirculated
Air
Stopper
Fresh/Recirculated
Air Selector Cable
Damper Lever
94D10028
Courtesy of Mitsubishi Motor Sales of America.

Fig. 4: Adjusting Fresh/Recirculated Air Selector Cable (Galant)

LEFT/RIGHT AIR VOLUME CONTROL CABLE

Galant – Move left/right air volume control lever in heater control panel to "L" position. Position air distribution duct lever as shown. *See Fig. 5.* Connect left/right air volume control cable.

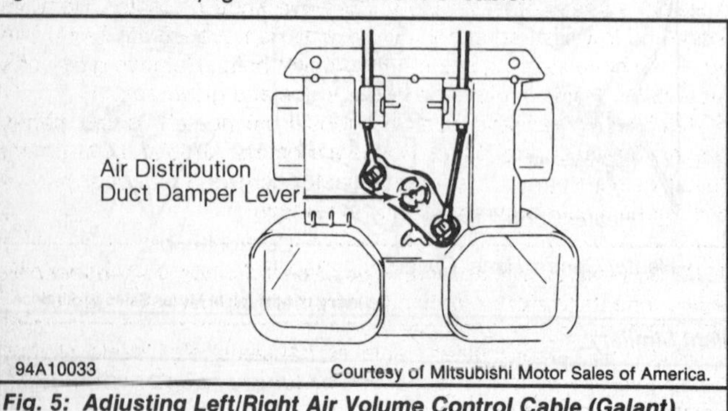
Air Distribution
Duct Damper Lever
94A10033
Courtesy of Mitsubishi Motor Sales of America.

Fig. 5: Adjusting Left/Right Air Volume Control Cable (Galant)

MODE SELECTOR CABLE

Place mode selector lever at defrost setting. Press damper lever inward, in direction of arrow. *See Fig. 6.* Connect inner wire of mode selector cable to end of damper lever. Secure outer wire using clip.

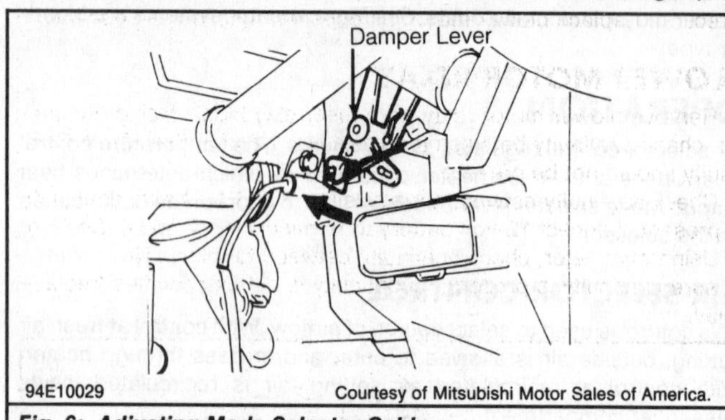
Damper Lever
94E10029
Courtesy of Mitsubishi Motor Sales of America.

Fig. 6: Adjusting Mode Selector Cable (Eclipse Shown; Galant Similar)

TROUBLE SHOOTING

BLOWER INOPERATIVE

Check for blown fuse, blower motor improperly grounded, defective switch, defective blower motor, faulty blower motor resistor, or faulty blower motor relay.

INSUFFICIENT HEAT

Check for obstructed heater outlets, bound or improperly adjusted blend-air dampers, faulty thermostat, obstructed heater hoses, improperly adjusted temperature control cable, or plugged heater core.

NO VENTILATION

Check for improper adjustment of mode selector dampers, incorrect installation of mode selector control cable, faulty duct connections, or crushed, bent or clogged ducts.

TESTING

BLOWER MOTOR SWITCH

Operate switch, and check continuity between indicated terminals using ohmmeter. See BLOWER MOTOR SWITCH CONTINUITY table. *See Fig. 7.*

BLOWER MOTOR SWITCH CONTINUITY

Switch Setting	Continuity Between Terminal No.
Low	3 & 5, 1 & 8
Medium-Low	5 & 6, 1 & 8
Medium-High	1 & 4, 1 & 8, 2 & 5
High	1 & 4, 1 & 8, 5 & 7

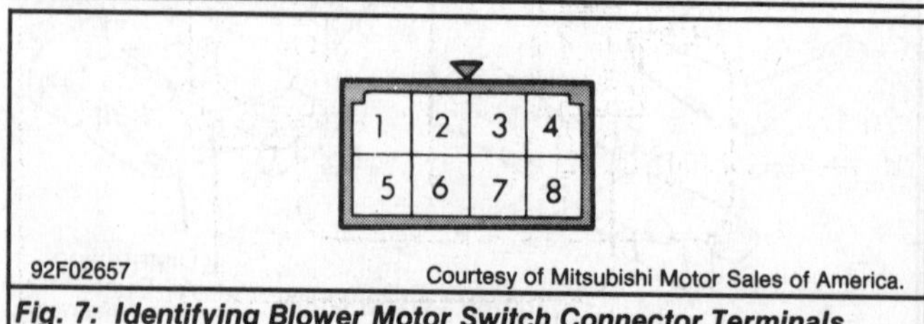
1
2
3
4
5
6
7
8
92F02657
Courtesy of Mitsubishi Motor Sales of America.

Fig. 7: Identifying Blower Motor Switch Connector Terminals

1993 HEATER SYSTEMS
Eclipse & Galant (Cont.)

BLOWER MOTOR

Disconnect blower motor connector. Connect battery directly to blower motor terminals. Ensure blower motor operates smoothly. Reverse polarity, and ensure blower motor operates smoothly in the reverse direction. Replace blower motor if it does not function as specified.

BLOWER MOTOR RELAY

1) Remove blower motor relay from fuse/relay block. Using ohmmeter, check continuity between terminals No. 1 and 3. *See Fig. 8*. Continuity should not be present.
2) Check continuity between terminals No. 2 and 4. Ensure continuity is present. Connect 12-volt battery to terminals No. 2 and 4. *See Fig. 8*. Using ohmmeter, check continuity between terminals No. 1 and 3. Ensure continuity is present. If continuity is not as specified, replace relay.

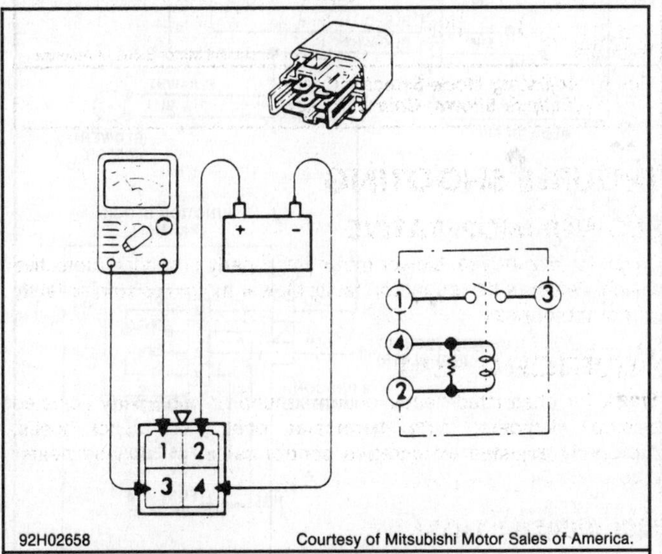
1
2
3
4
92H02658
Courtesy of Mitsubishi Motor Sales of America.

Fig. 8: Identifying Blower Relay Terminals

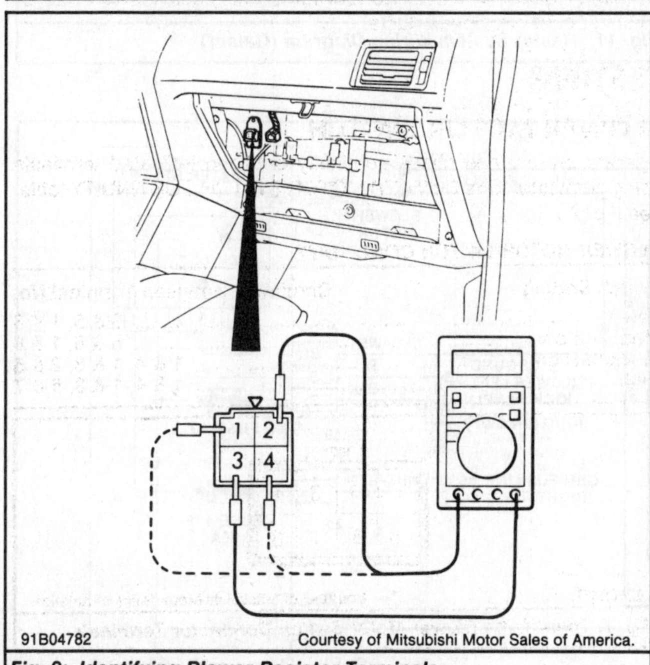
1
2
3
4
91B04782
Courtesy of Mitsubishi Motor Sales of America.

Fig. 9: Identifying Blower Resistor Terminals

BLOWER MOTOR RESISTOR

Disconnect resistor harness connector. *See Fig. 9*. Using ohmmeter, check resistance between indicated terminals. See BLOWER MOTOR RESISTOR RESISTANCE table. If resistance is not as specified, replace resistor.

BLOWER MOTOR RESISTOR RESISTANCE

Terminal No.	Ohms
2 & 3	1.70-1.96
3 & 4	0.81-0.93
1 & 3	0.29-0.33

REMOVAL & INSTALLATION

HEATER UNIT & HEATER CORE

Removal (Eclipse) – **1)** Disconnect battery ground cable. Drain coolant and remove heater hoses. Remove console side covers and trim. Remove shift knob (M/T models). Remove cup holder, lift carpet, and remove console screws. Disconnect console electrical connections. Remove PWR/ECO (power/economy) selector switch connector (A/T models). Remove shoulder belt guide ring and bracket. Remove console.
2) Remove knee protector plugs and knee protector. Remove hood release handle. Remove upper and lower steering column covers. Remove instrument cluster cover. Remove radio panel cover and radio.
3) Using flat-blade screwdriver, disconnect center air outlet assembly tabs. Use trim stick to remove center air outlet assembly. Remove control knobs from heater control panel. *See Fig. 1*. Remove heater control panel cover. Remove glove box door stops and glove box. Remove instrument cluster.
4) Disconnect speedometer cable at transaxle. Pull speedometer cable slightly toward vehicle interior, and release lock by turning adapter either left or right. Remove speedometer cable adapter. Remove speaker covers.
5) Remove instrument panel center console bracket. Remove heater control panel screws. Remove left air ducts. Remove lower-left air duct. Remove steering shaft bolt. Remove instrument panel screw and bolt. Remove instrument panel.
6) Remove center support brackets. Remove lower-right air duct and distribution duct. Remove center air duct and right air duct. Remove heater unit. Remove heater core cover plate. Remove heater core from heater unit.
Installation – Carefully insert heater core into heater unit to prevent damaging core fin or pad. Install heater core cover plate. Install heater unit. To complete installation, reverse removal procedure.
Removal (Galant) – **1)** Disconnect battery ground cable. Drain coolant, and remove heater hoses. Remove front seats. Remove console side covers and trim. Remove shift knob (M/T models). Remove transaxle spacer (A/T models). Remove parking brake side panel. Remove console switch panel or box.
2) Remove radio panel cover. Remove radio and bracket. Disconnect electrical connections. Remove shoulder belt guide rings. Remove console box.
3) Remove knee protector plugs. Remove knee protector. Remove upper and lower steering column covers. Remove left air ducts. *See Fig. 1*. Remove steering column tilt bracket bolts. Remove glove box undercover. Remove glove box door stops and glove box.
4) Remove ashtray and control knobs from heater control panel. Remove heater control panel. Remove tripmeter knob and instrument cluster bezel. Remove instrument cluster screws. Pull upper part of instrument cluster outward slightly to remove.

NOTE: On vehicles with automatic position indicator, disconnect harness connector before removing instrument cluster. See step 6).

5) Disconnect speedometer cable at transaxle. Pull cable slightly toward vehicle interior. Release lock by turning adapter left or right. Remove speedometer cable adapter.
6) Using flat-tip screwdriver, open instrument cluster connector tab. Disconnect instrument cluster harness connector. Remove dash

1993 HEATER SYSTEMS
Eclipse & Galant (Cont.)

speaker covers and clock. Remove speaker covers and clock. Remove heater control panel screws. Remove instrument panel bolts. Disconnect electrical connections. Remove instrument panel.

7) Remove instrument panel center support. Remove right air ducts, center air duct, distribution air duct and rear air ducts. Remove heater unit. Remove heater core cover plate. Remove heater core from heater unit.

Installation – Carefully insert heater core into heater unit to prevent damaging core fin or pad. Install heater core cover plate. Install heater unit. To complete installation, reverse removal procedure.

HEATER CONTROL PANEL

Removal (Eclipse) – **1)** Remove radio panel cover. Remove radio and bracket. Remove glove box door stops and glove box. Disconnect fresh/recirculated air selector control cable. *See Fig. 3*. Remove control knobs from heater control panel. *See Fig. 1*. Using flat-blade screwdriver, disengage center air outlet assembly tabs. Use trim stick to remove center air outlet assembly.

2) Remove instrument cluster cover. Remove heater control panel cover. Remove knee protector plugs and knee protector. Remove hood release handle. Remove left air ducts. Disconnect mode selector cable and temperature control cable. *See Figs. 2 and 6*. Remove heater control panel.

Installation – To install, reverse removal procedure. Adjust cables as necessary. See ADJUSTMENTS.

Removal (Galant) – **1)** Remove glove box door stops and glove box. Disconnect fresh/recirculated air selector cable and temperature control cable. *See Figs. 2 and 4*. Remove ashtray. Remove heater control panel knobs and heater control panel cover. *See Fig. 1*.

2) Remove left air duct and nozzle. Disconnect mode selector cable. *See Fig. 6*. Remove radio panel cover and radio. Disconnect left/right air volume control cable at left side of air distribution duct lever. *See Fig. 5*. Remove heater control panel and lever assembly.

Installation – To install, reverse removal procedure. Adjust cables as necessary. See ADJUSTMENTS.

BLOWER MOTOR

Removal & Installation (Eclipse) – Remove lower-right duct. Remove blower motor hose and blower motor. *See Fig. 1*. Remove blower motor packing. Remove blower motor fan nut and fan. To install, reverse removal procedure.

Removal & Installation (Galant) – Remove glove box door stops and glove box. Remove glove box undercover. Remove lower-right air duct. *See Fig. 1*. Disconnect electrical connections. Remove glove box frame. Remove cowl side trim and engine control module. Remove duct clips. Remove blower assembly. Remove blower motor and fan assembly. Remove blower case. To install, reverse removal procedure.

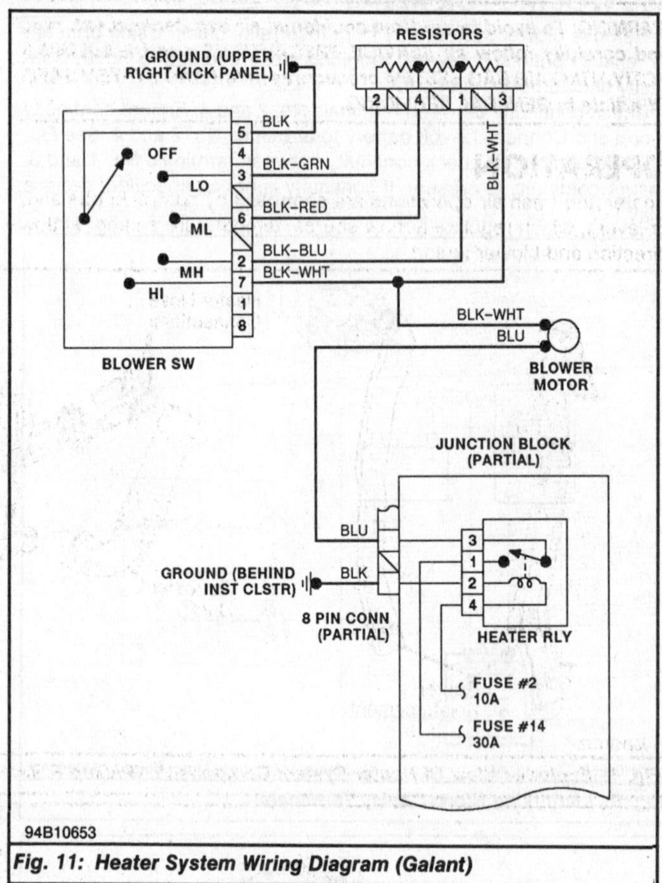
RESISTORS
GROUND (UPPER
RIGHT KICK PANEL)
2 4 1 3
BLK
BLK-WHT
OFF
LO
ML
MH
HI
BLK-GRN
BLK-RED
BLK-BLU
BLK-WHT
5 4 3 6 2 7 1 8
BLOWER SW
BLK-WHT
BLU
BLOWER
MOTOR
JUNCTION BLOCK
(PARTIAL)
BLU
GROUND (BEHIND
INST CLSTR)
BLK
8 PIN CONN
(PARTIAL)
3 1 2 4
HEATER RLY
FUSE #2
10A
FUSE #14
30A
94B10653

Fig. 11: Heater System Wiring Diagram (Galant)

WIRING DIAGRAMS

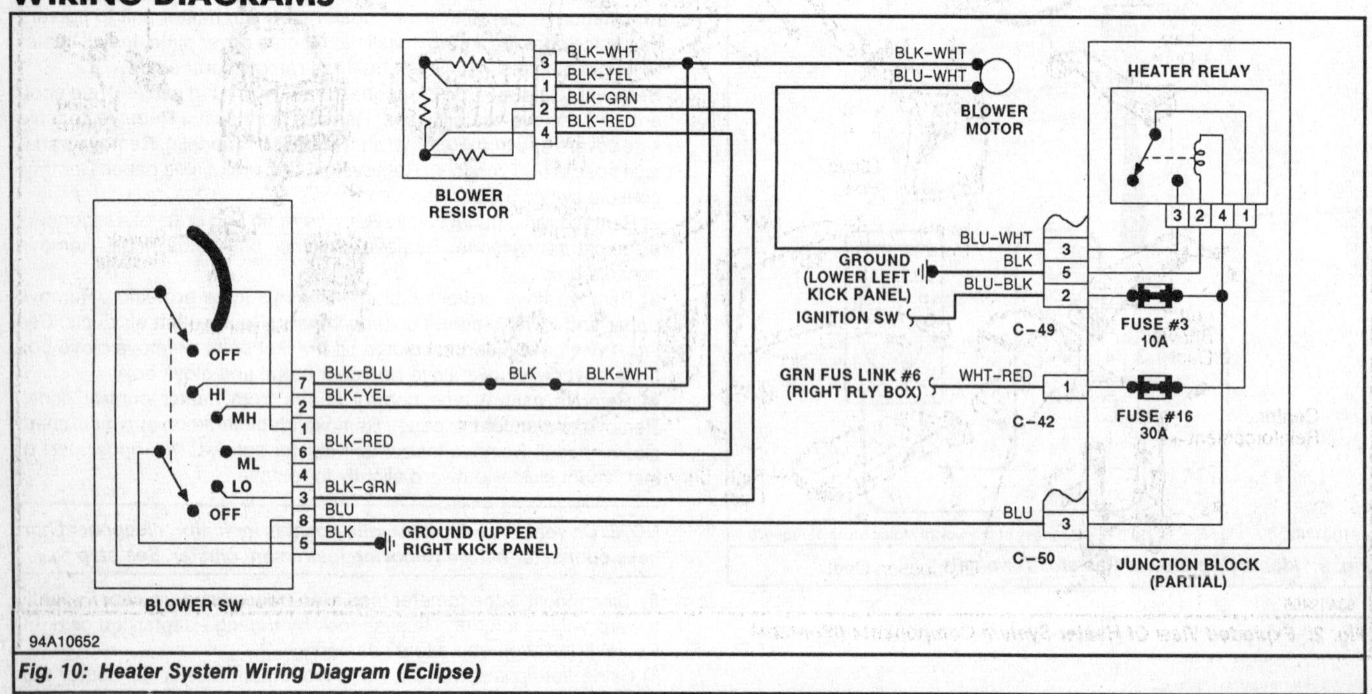
BLK-WHT
BLK-YEL
BLK-GRN
BLK-RED
3 1 2 4
BLOWER
RESISTOR
BLK-WHT
BLU-WHT
BLOWER
MOTOR
HEATER RELAY
3 2 4 1
BLU-WHT
BLK
BLU-BLK
GROUND
(LOWER LEFT
KICK PANEL)
IGNITION SW
C-49
FUSE #3
10A
GRN FUS LINK #6
(RIGHT RLY BOX)
WHT-RED
C-42
FUSE #16
30A
BLU
C-50
JUNCTION BLOCK
(PARTIAL)
OFF
HI
MH
ML
LO
OFF
BLK-BLU
BLK-YEL
BLK
BLK-WHT
BLK-RED
BLK-GRN
BLU
BLK
7 2 1 6 3 8 5
GROUND (UPPER
RIGHT KICK PANEL)
BLOWER SW
94A10652

Fig. 10: Heater System Wiring Diagram (Eclipse)

1993 HEATER SYSTEMS
Montero, Pickup & Ram-50

DESCRIPTION

Heater assembly is located in passenger compartment. A heater control valve is used to regulate coolant flow and heat output. Heater assembly contains heater core, heater control valve, air ducts, blower motor and intake ducts. *See Fig. 1 or 2.* Heater systems are blend-air type.

WARNING: To avoid injury from accidental air bag deployment, read and carefully follow all SERVICE PRECAUTIONS and DISABLING & ACTIVATING AIR BAG SYSTEM procedures in AIR BAG SYSTEM SAFETY article in GENERAL SERVICING.

OPERATION

Heater and fresh air operations are controlled by control knobs and/or levers, which regulate airflow source, temperature setting, airflow direction and blower speed.

AIR SELECTOR LEVER

This lever is used to select source of airflow. With lever at fresh air setting, outside air is allowed to enter and/or pass through heater. With lever at recirculated air setting, air is recirculated inside passenger compartment.

BLOWER SWITCH

The blower switch controls fan speeds to regulate amount of airflow. Fan speed increases as switch is turned/moved to the right.

COOL AIR BY-PASS KNOB

Montero – With heater in floor, defrost/floor or defrost mode, turning knob to the left allows cool air to enter passenger compartment through center vent.

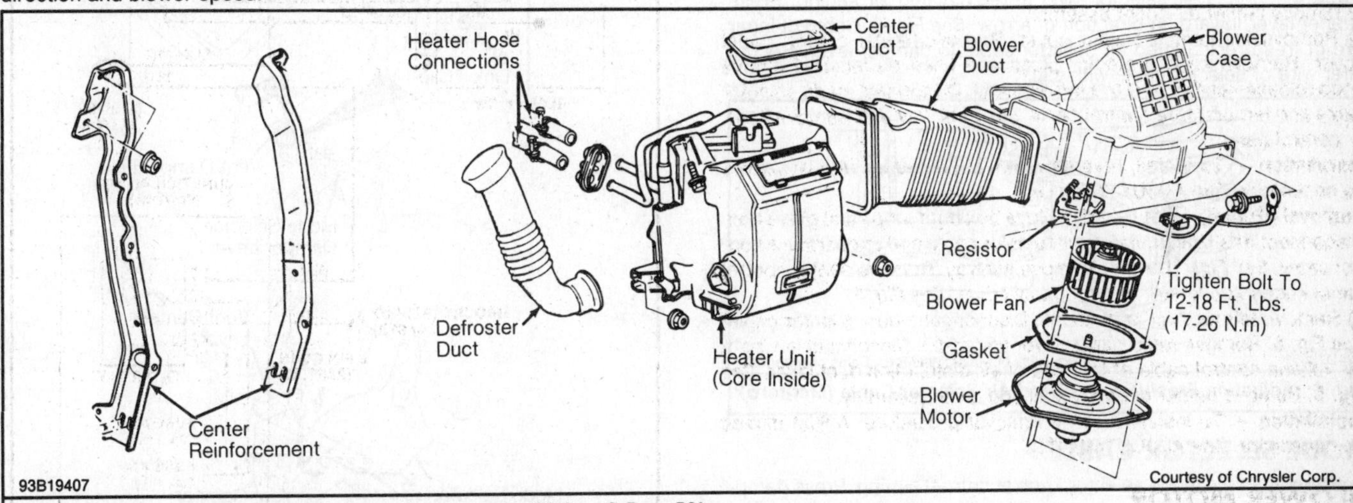
Heater Hose Connections
Center Duct
Blower Duct
Blower Case
Resistor
Tighten Bolt To 12-18 Ft. Lbs. (17-26 N.m)
Blower Fan
Gasket
Blower Motor
Defroster Duct
Heater Unit (Core Inside)
Center Reinforcement
93B19407
Courtesy of Chrysler Corp.

Fig. 1: Exploded View Of Heater System Components (Pickup & Ram-50)

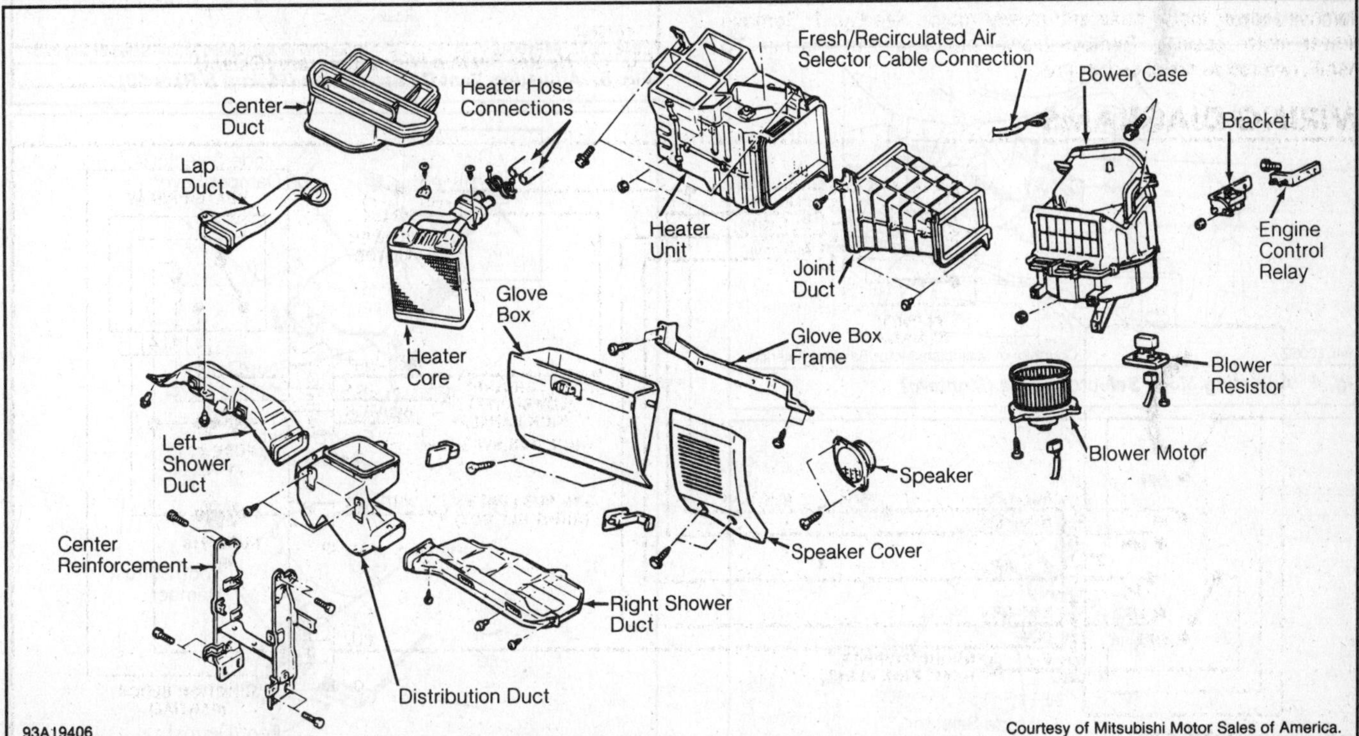
Fresh/Recirculated Air Selector Cable Connection
Bower Case
Bracket
Center Duct
Heater Hose Connections
Lap Duct
Heater Unit
Joint Duct
Engine Control Relay
Glove Box
Heater Core
Glove Box Frame
Blower Resistor
Left Shower Duct
Blower Motor
Speaker
Center Reinforcement
Speaker Cover
Right Shower Duct
Distribution Duct
93A19406
Courtesy of Mitsubishi Motor Sales of America.

Fig. 2: Exploded View Of Heater System Components (Montero)

1993 HEATER SYSTEMS
Montero, Pickup & Ram-50 (Cont.)

MODE SELECTOR KNOB/LEVER

Depending on position selected, airflow can be directed to different areas of passenger compartment. Airflow selection capabilities include individual areas or a combination of windshield, upper body, knee and/or foot area.

TEMPERATURE CONTROL LEVER/KNOB

Temperature level is selected by moving lever or turning knob left or right. The temperature control cable opens and closes heater control valve, which determines heat output. Highest heat setting is attained when lever/knob is at right most position. With temperature lever/knob at cool setting, ambient air is used for ventilating.

ADJUSTMENTS

FRESH/RECIRCULATED AIR SELECTOR CABLE

Montero – Place air selector lever at recirculated air setting. Press damper lever inward, in direction of arrow. *See Fig. 3*. Connect inner wire of fresh/recirculated air selector cable to damper lever. Secure outer wire of selector cable with clip.

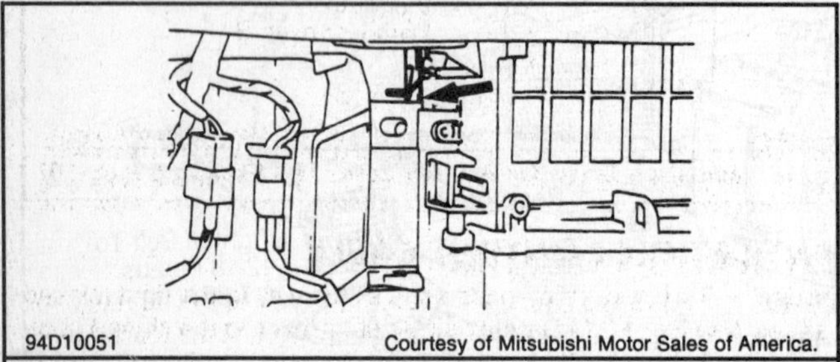

94D10051 Courtesy of Mitsubishi Motor Sales of America.

Fig. 3: Adjusting Fresh/Recirculated Air Selector Cable (Montero)

MODE SELECTOR CABLE

Montero – Place mode selector knob at defrost setting. Press damper lever inward, in direction of arrow. *See Fig. 4*. Connect inner cable of mode selector cable to damper lever. Secure outer wire of selector cable with clip.

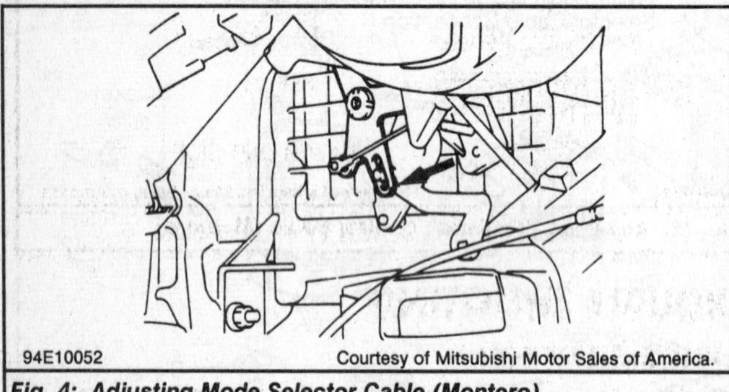

94E10052 Courtesy of Mitsubishi Motor Sales of America.

Fig. 4: Adjusting Mode Selector Cable (Montero)

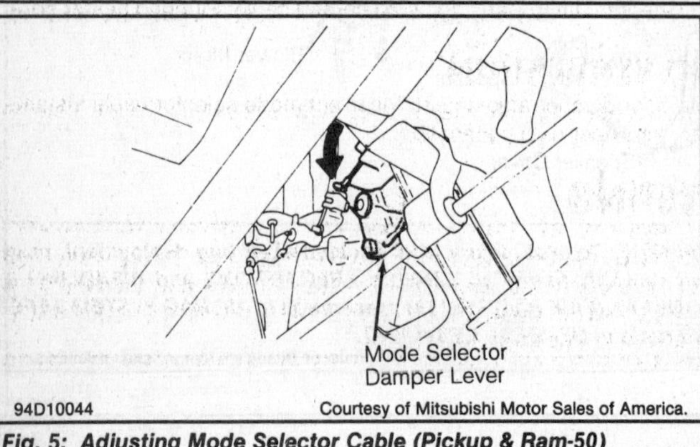
Mode Selector
Damper Lever

94D10044 Courtesy of Mitsubishi Motor Sales of America.

Fig. 5: Adjusting Mode Selector Cable (Pickup & Ram-50)

MODE SELECTOR LEVER

Mode Selector Cable (Pickup & Ram-50) – **1)** Turn blower on. Move mode selector lever to each position, and check airflow. If airflow is not correct, disconnect driver-side defrost duct from heater unit.

2) Disconnect mode selector cable from mode selector damper lever and heater unit clip. Move mode selector lever to defrost/heat setting. Turn mode selector damper lever in direction of arrow. *See Fig. 5*. Connect mode selector cable to damper lever and heater unit clip.

CAUTION: Ensure damper lever does not move when connecting selector cable to heater unit clip.

3) Move mode selector lever to each position, and check airflow. Ensure airflow is correct and lever moves smoothly. Connect driver-side defrost duct to heater unit.

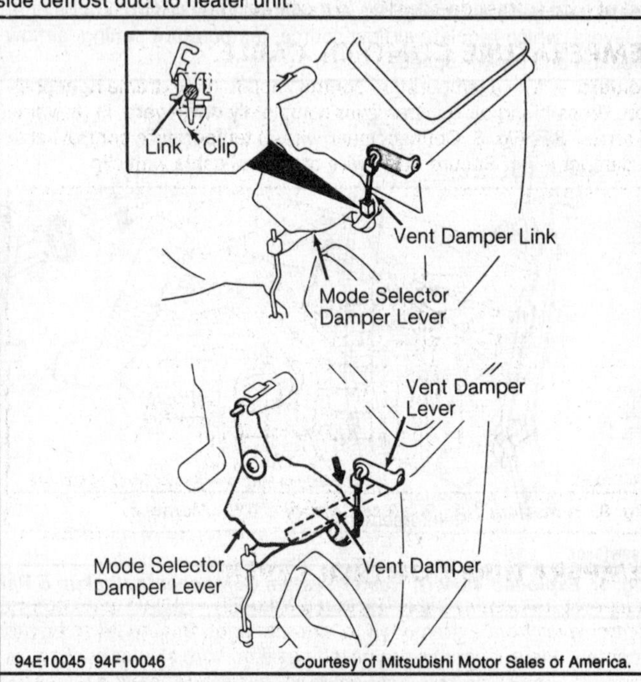
Link
Clip
Vent Damper Link
Mode Selector
Damper Lever
Vent Damper
Lever
Mode Selector
Damper Lever
Vent Damper

94E10045 94F10046 Courtesy of Mitsubishi Motor Sales of America.

Fig. 6: Adjusting Vent Damper Lever (Pickup & Ram-50)

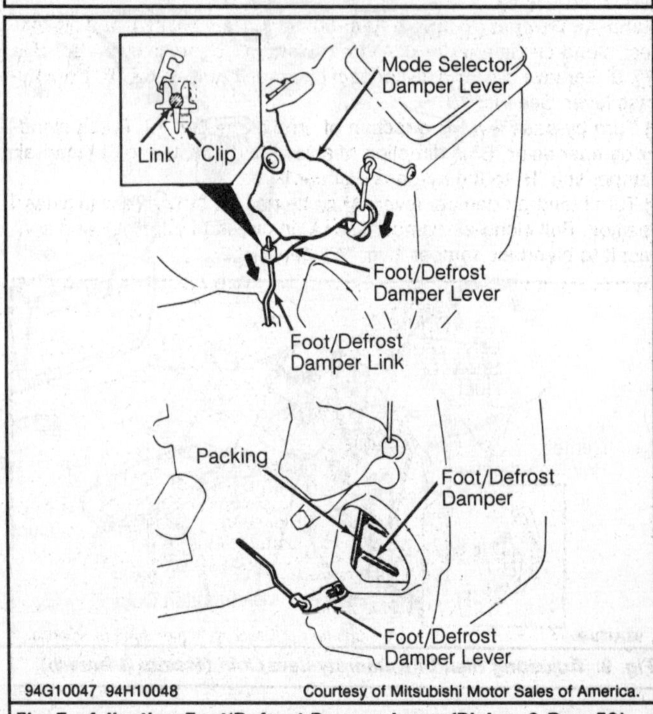
Mode Selector
Damper Lever
Link
Clip
Foot/Defrost
Damper Lever
Foot/Defrost
Damper Link
Packing
Foot/Defrost
Damper
Foot/Defrost
Damper Lever

94G10047 94H10048 Courtesy of Mitsubishi Motor Sales of America.

Fig. 7: Adjusting Foot/Defrost Damper Lever (Pickup & Ram-50)

Vent Damper Lever (Pickup & Ram-50) – Remove clip, and disconnect vent damper link from mode selector damper lever. *See Fig. 6.* Turn mode selector damper lever in direction of arrow. Pull vent damper link downward completely, and position vent damper as shown. Connect end of vent damper link to mode selector lever.

Foot/Defrost Damper Lever – **1)** Remove clip, and disconnect foot/defrost damper link from mode selector damper lever. *See Fig. 7.* Turn mode selector damper lever in direction of arrow. Pull foot/defrost damper lever downward completely, and position foot/defrost damper as shown. Ensure packing contacts case.

NOTE: With defrost duct disconnected, ensure foot/defrost damper is raised upward through heater unit defrost outlet.

2) Pull foot/defrost damper lever in direction of arrow, and connect end of foot/defrost damper link to mode selector lever.

TEMPERATURE CONTROL CABLE

Montero – Move temperature control knob to the extreme right position. Press blend-air damper lever completely downward, in direction of arrow. *See Fig. 8.* Connect inner wire of temperature control cable to damper lever. Secure outer wire of control cable with clip.

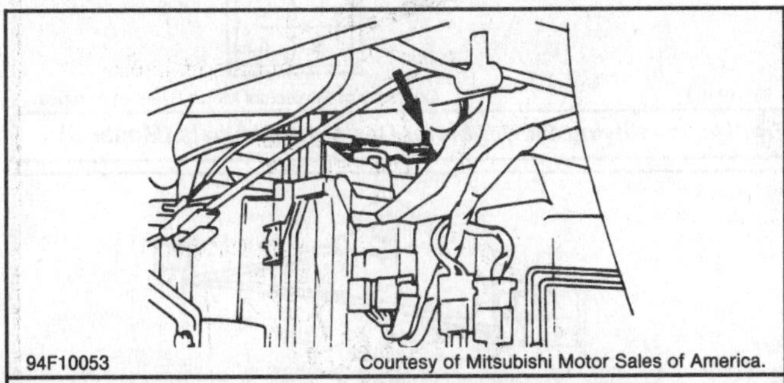

94F10053 Courtesy of Mitsubishi Motor Sales of America.

Fig. 8: Adjusting Temperature Control Cable (Montero)

TEMPERATURE CONTROL LEVER

Temperature Control Cable (Pickup & Ram-50) – Move temperature control lever from extreme left to extreme right. Ensure lever moves smoothly. Place lever at extreme left position. Turn blower on. Ensure warm air does come out. If airflow is not correct, reposition temperature control cable.

Blend-Air Damper (Pickup & Ram-50) – **1)** Remove clip, and disconnect blend-air damper link "A" from blend-air damper lever "A". *See Fig. 9.* Remove clip, and disconnect blend-air damper link "B" from by-pass lever. *See Fig. 10.*

2) Turn by-pass lever in direction of arrow. *See Fig. 10.* Press blend-air damper lever "B" in direction of arrow, and attach end of blend-air damper link "B" to the by-pass damper lever.

3) Turn blend-air damper lever "A" so heater control valve is in closed position. Pull blend-air damper link "A" in direction of arrow, and connect it to blend-air damper lever "A". *See Fig. 9.*

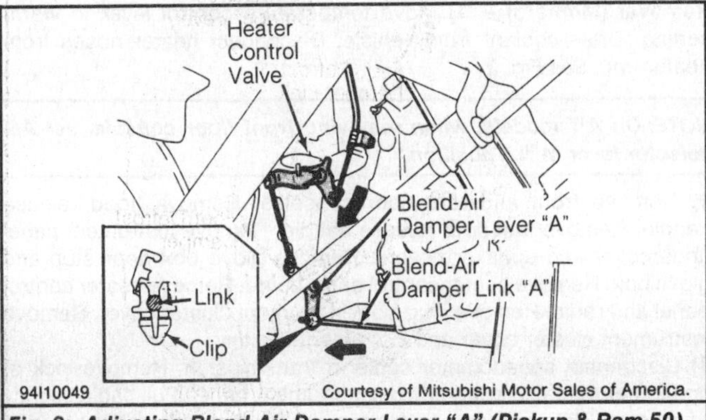

Heater Control Valve
Blend-Air Damper Lever "A"
Blend-Air Damper Link "A"
Link
Clip

94I10049 Courtesy of Mitsubishi Motor Sales of America.

Fig. 9: Adjusting Blend-Air Damper Lever "A" (Pickup & Ram-50)

4) Turn heater control valve lever in direction of arrow until heater control valve is in closed position. *See Fig. 9.* Connect temperature control cable to heater control valve lever and heater unit clip.

CAUTION: Ensure heater control valve lever does not move when connecting temperature control cable to heater unit clip.

5) Ensure temperature control lever moves smoothly. Place lever in extreme left position. Turn blower on. Ensure warm air does not come out.

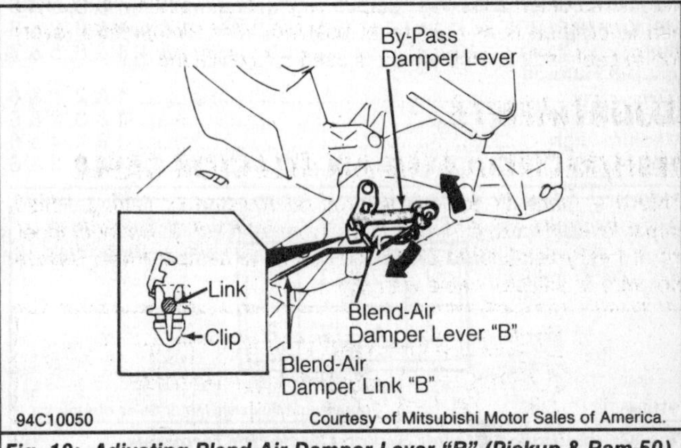

By-Pass Damper Lever
Link
Clip
Blend-Air Damper Lever "B"
Blend-Air Damper Link "B"

94C10050 Courtesy of Mitsubishi Motor Sales of America.

Fig. 10: Adjusting Blend-Air Damper Lever "B" (Pickup & Ram-50)

VENTILATION CONTROL CABLE

Montero – Turn cool air by-pass knob all the way to the right (closed position). *See Fig. 11.* Move cool air by-pass lever to the closed position. Lever should slightly touch stopper. Connect ventilation control cable, and secure with clip.

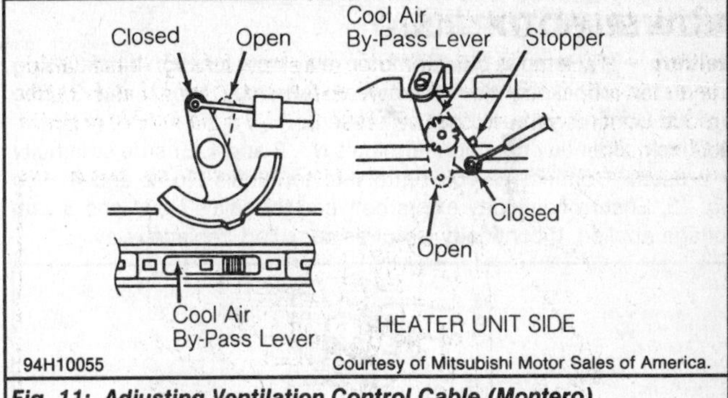

Closed
Open
Cool Air By-Pass Lever
Stopper
Closed
Open
Cool Air By-Pass Lever
HEATER UNIT SIDE

94H10055 Courtesy of Mitsubishi Motor Sales of America.

Fig. 11: Adjusting Ventilation Control Cable (Montero)

TROUBLE SHOOTING

INSUFFICIENT HEAT

Obstructed floor outlets or heater hoses. Bound or improperly adjusted dampers. Improperly adjusted control cable. Plugged heater core.

NO VENTILATION

Improper damper adjustment. Incorrect mode selector cable installation. Improper duct connection.

TESTING

WARNING: To avoid injury from accidental air bag deployment, read and carefully follow all SERVICE PRECAUTIONS and DISABLING & ACTIVATING AIR BAG SYSTEM procedures in AIR BAG SYSTEM SAFETY article in GENERAL SERVICING.

1993 HEATER SYSTEMS
Montero, Pickup & Ram-50 (Cont.)

BLOWER SWITCH

Operate switch, and check continuity between indicated terminals using ohmmeter. See BLOWER SWITCH CONTINUITY table. *See Fig. 12.*

BLOWER SWITCH CONTINUITY

Switch Position	Continuity Between Terminal No.
Montero	
Low	1 & 8, 3 & 5
Medium-Low	1 & 8, 5 & 6
Medium-High	1 & 4, 1 & 8, 2 & 5
High	1 & 4, 1 & 8, 5 & 7
Pickup & Ram-50	
Low	1 & 2, 2 & 6
Medium-Low	1 & 3, 3 & 6
Medium-High	1 & 4, 4 & 6
High	1 & 5, 5 & 6

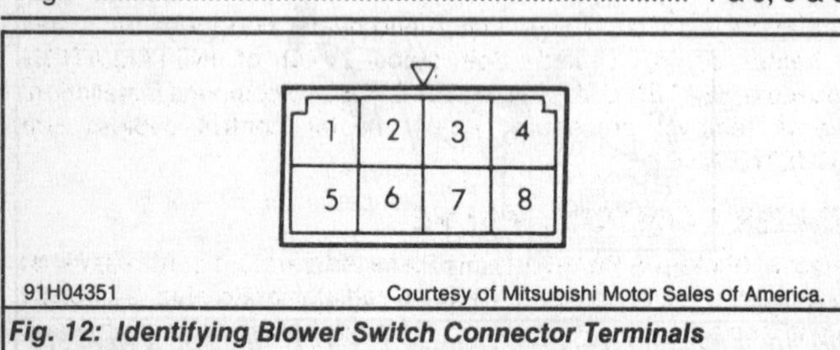
1
2
3
4
5
6
7
8
91H04351
Courtesy of Mitsubishi Motor Sales of America.

Fig. 12: Identifying Blower Switch Connector Terminals

BLOWER MOTOR

Disconnect blower motor connector. Connect battery directly to blower motor terminals. Ensure blower motor operates smoothly. Reverse polarity, and ensure blower motor operates smoothly in the reverse direction. Replace blower motor if it does not function as specified.

BLOWER MOTOR RELAY

Montero – 1) Remove blower motor relay from junction block. Using ohmmeter, check continuity between terminals No. 1 and 3. *See Fig. 13.* Continuity should not be present.

2) Check continuity between terminals No. 2 and 4. Ensure continuity is present. Connect 12-volt battery to terminals No. 2 and 4. *See Fig. 13.* Ensure continuity exists between terminals No. 1 and 3 with voltage applied. If continuity is not as specified, replace relay.

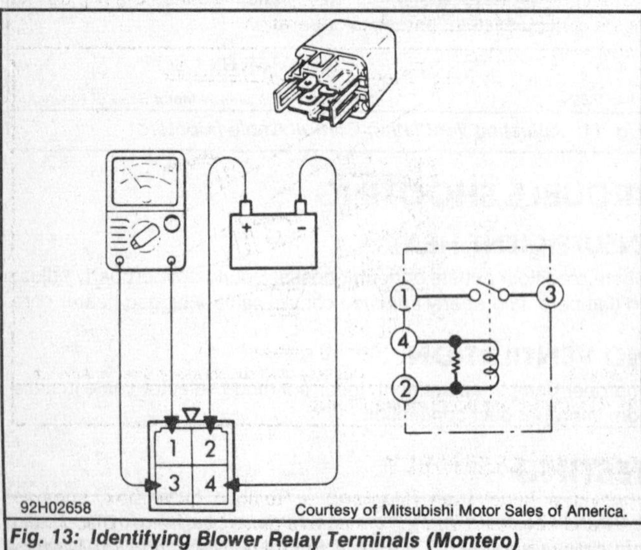
1
2
3
4
92H02658
Courtesy of Mitsubishi Motor Sales of America.

Fig. 13: Identifying Blower Relay Terminals (Montero)

BLOWER MOTOR RESISTOR

Disconnect harness connector from resistor, located in blower assembly. *See Fig. 1 or 2.* Using ohmmeter, check resistance between indicated terminals. See BLOWER MOTOR RESISTOR RESISTANCE table. *See Fig. 14 or 15.* If resistance is not as specified, replace resistor.

BLOWER MOTOR RESISTOR RESISTANCE

Terminal No.	Ohms
Montero	
1 & 2	0.88-1.02
2 & 3	0.31-0.35
2 & 4	1.82-2.10
Pickup & Ram-50	
1 & 2	1.19
1 & 3	0.50
1 & 4	2.33
1 & 5	0

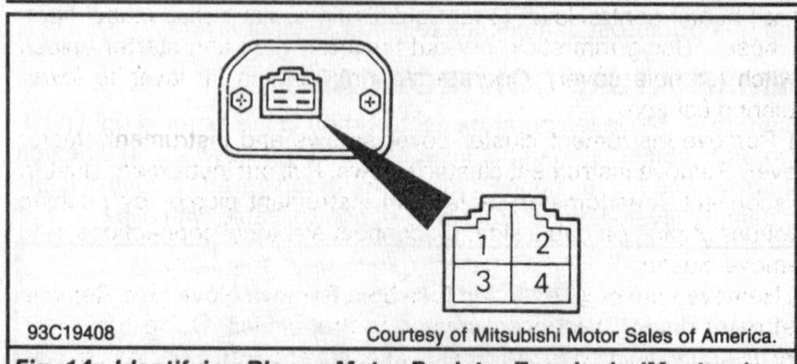
1
2
3
4
93C19408
Courtesy of Mitsubishi Motor Sales of America.

Fig. 14: Identifying Blower Motor Resistor Terminals (Montero)

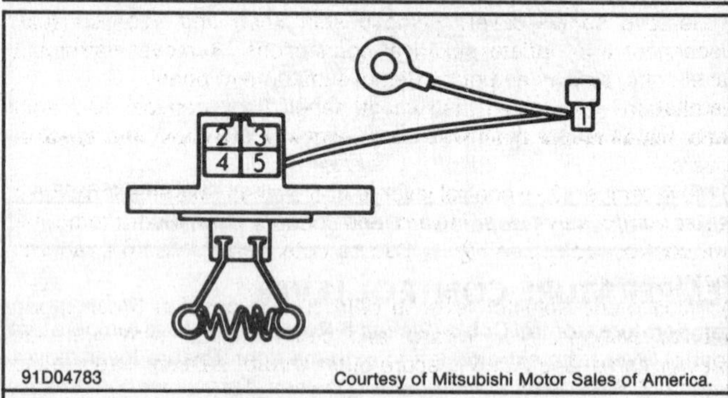
1
2
3
4
5
91D04783
Courtesy of Mitsubishi Motor Sales of America.

Fig. 15: Identifying Blower Motor Resistor Terminals (Pickup & Ram-50)

REMOVAL & INSTALLATION

WARNING: To avoid injury from accidental air bag deployment, read and carefully follow all SERVICE PRECAUTIONS and DISABLING & ACTIVATING AIR BAG SYSTEM procedures in AIR BAG SYSTEM SAFETY article in GENERAL SERVICING.

HEATER UNIT & HEATER CORE

Removal (Montero) – 1) Move temperature control lever to warm setting. Drain coolant from vehicle. Disconnect heater hoses from heater unit. *See Fig. 2.*

NOTE: On A/T models, when removing front floor console, set A/T selector lever in "L" position.

2) Remove front and rear floor consoles. Remove hood release handle. Remove fuel door release handle. Remove instrument panel undercover and speaker covers. Remove glove box door stop and glove box. Remove heater control panel cover. Remove heater control panel and radio. Remove plug from instrument cluster cover. Remove instrument cluster cover and instrument cluster.

3) Disconnect speedometer cable at transmission. Remove lock of speedometer cable adapter from instrument panel. Pull cable slightly toward vehicle's interior, and remove cable adapter. Remove steering column cover. Remove clock or plug. Remove side defroster covers. Remove side mirror control switch.

4) Remove front speakers. Remove rheostat, rear wiper/washer switch, and door lock switch. Disconnect ventilation control cable and harness connector. Remove steering column bolts and instrument panel.
5) Remove shower ducts, lap duct, joint duct and center duct. *See Fig. 2.* Remove center reinforcement. Remove heater unit. Remove distribution duct. Remove heater core.
Installation – Install heater core, distribution duct, heater unit and center reinforcement. Install remaining ducts in reverse order of removal. Install instrument panel. Tighten steering column bolts to 16 ft. lbs. (22 N.m). Install and adjust ventilation control cable. See ADJUSTMENTS. To complete installation, reverse removal procedure.
Removal (Pickup & Ram-50) – 1) Disconnect battery ground cable. Place heater control lever to far right. Drain coolant. Disconnect heater hoses. Using trim stick, pry out hazard switch and starter unlock switch (or hole cover). Operate steering column tilt lever to lower steering column.
2) Remove instrument cluster cover screws and instrument cluster cover. Remove instrument cluster screws. Pull out instrument cluster. Disconnect speedometer cable from instrument cluster by pushing stopper of plug on cable side. Disconnect electrical connections, and remove cluster.
3) Remove fuse box cover and fuse box. Remove glove box. Remove defroster ducts. Disconnect heater control cables. Using trim stick, pry up spring section to remove speaker covers. Remove clock or coin box in center of dash. Remove center dash hole cover (above clock).
4) Remove center cover. Remove shift knob and floor console. Disconnect appropriate electrical connections. Remove instrument panel bolts, screws and nuts. Remove instrument panel.
Installation – 1) Install instrument panel, floor console and shift knob. Install center dash hole cover, clock or coin box, and speaker covers.
2) Move temperature control lever to cool setting (extreme left). Push heater control valve lever inward, and connect inner wire of temperature control cable. *See Fig. 9.* Secure outer wire of control cable to heater unit clip.
3) Place mode selector lever in defrost/heat position. Push mode selector damper lever inward, and connect inner wire of mode selector cable. *See Fig. 5.* Secure outer wire of selector cable using clip.
4) Place air selector lever at fresh air setting. Push air selector damper lever against stopper, in direction of arrow. *See Fig. 16.* Connect inner wire of air selector cable to damper lever. Lightly pull outer wire of selector cable toward heater control panel side, and attach it to clamp. Operate mode selector lever 2-3 times, and set it at fresh air setting. Check if damper lever is touching stopper. If damper lever is not touching stopper, readjust cable.
5) To complete installation, reverse removal procedure. Securely clamp heater hoses to pipes to prevent leaks. When filling radiator with coolant, first open heater control valve fully, and then run engine to circulate coolant and discharge air from inside heater and engine cooling system. Stop engine, and top off coolant. Adjust heater control cables. See ADJUSTMENTS. Apply sealant to heater hose grommets.

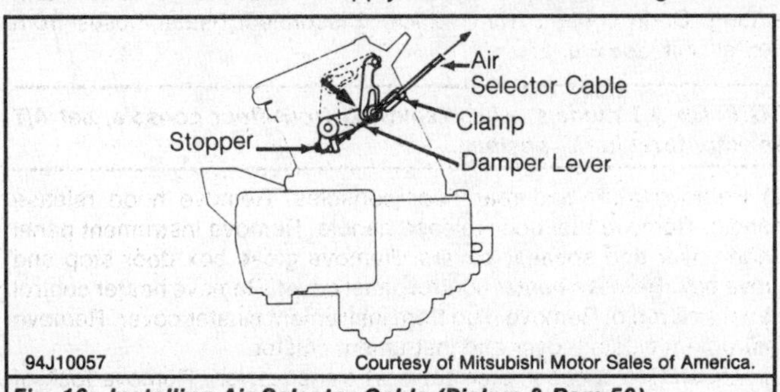
Air
Selector Cable
Clamp
Stopper
Damper Lever
94J10057
Courtesy of Mitsubishi Motor Sales of America.
Fig. 16: Installing Air Selector Cable (Pickup & Ram-50)

HEATER CONTROL PANEL

Removal & Installation (Montero) – 1) Remove glove box door stops. Disconnect fresh/recirculated air selector cable and temperature control cable. Remove knee protector. Remove lap duct and left shower duct. *See Fig. 2.* Disconnect mode selector wire.
2) Remove heater control panel cover and panel. Remove heater control panel bezel and knobs. Remove blower switch. Using a screwdriver, remove wire clip. Remove heater control cables from heater control panel. To install, reverse removal procedure. Adjust heater control cables while installing. See ADJUSTMENTS.
Removal (Pickup & Ram-50) – Remove glove box door stops, and pull glove box outward. Disconnect air selector cable at heater unit. Remove heater control panel knobs and cover. Remove defroster duct. *See Fig. 1.* Disconnect mode selector cable and temperature control cable at heater unit. Remove heater control panel and blower switch.
Installation – Install blower switch and heater control panel. Install all heater control cables. See steps **2) - 4)** of INSTALLATION procedure HEATER UNIT & HEATER CORE. To complete installation, reverse removal procedure. Adjust heater control cables. See ADJUSTMENTS.

HEATER CONTROL VALVE

Removal (Pickup & Ram-50) – 1) Place temperature control lever at warm setting (extreme right). Remove radiator drain plug, and drain engine coolant. Remove air filter. Remove heater hose clamp and heater hose.
2) Disconnect temperature control cable from heater control valve and heater unit clip. Remove blend-air lever clip, and disconnect blend-air damper link from blend-air damper lever. *See Fig. 9.* Remove joint hose cover and clamp. Cut joint hose. Remove heater control valve.
Installation – 1) Install joint hose and clamp to pipe on heater core side. Position joint hose clamp as shown, otherwise hose cover cannot be installed. *See Fig. 17.* Install heater control valve. Adjust blend-air damper, and attach blend-air damper link to blend-air damper lever. See TEMPERATURE CONTROL CABLE under ADJUSTMENTS.

CAUTION: Ensure heater control valve lever does not move when attaching temperature control cable to clip.

2) Connect temperature control cable to heater control valve lever, and secure cable to heater unit clip. Install radiator drain plug, fill engine cooling system, and check operation.

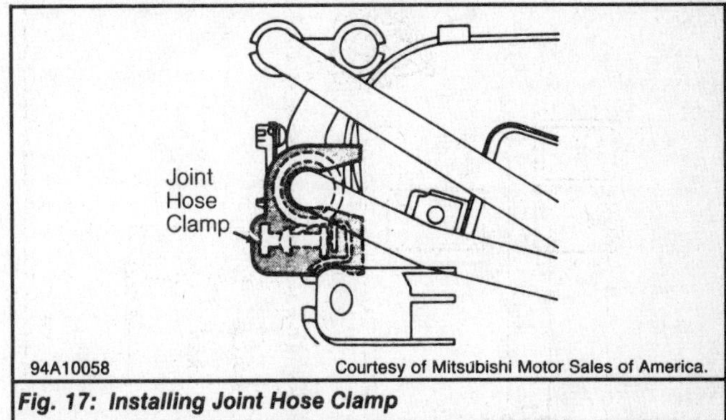
Joint
Hose
Clamp
94A10058
Courtesy of Mitsubishi Motor Sales of America.
Fig. 17: Installing Joint Hose Clamp

BLOWER ASSEMBLY

Removal & Installation (Montero) – Remove glove box, speaker cover and speaker. *See Fig. 2.* Remove glove box frame. Disconnect right shower duct. Remove engine control relay and bracket. Disconnect fresh/recirculated air selector cable and joint duct. Remove blower assembly. To install, reverse removal procedure. Adjust air selector cable. See ADJUSTMENTS.

1993 HEATER SYSTEMS
Montero, Pickup & Ram-50 (Cont.)

Removal (Pickup & Ram-50) – Remove glove box door stops, and pull glove box outward. Remove glove box frame. Disconnect air selector cable and blower duct. Remove blower assembly.

Installation – **1)** Install blower assembly and blower duct. Place air selector lever at fresh air setting. Push air selector damper lever against stopper, in direction of arrow. *See Fig. 16*. Connect inner wire of air selector cable to damper lever. Lightly pull outer wire of selector cable toward heater control panel side, and attach it to clamp. Operate mode selector lever 2-3 times, and set it at fresh air setting. Check if damper lever is touching stopper. If damper lever is not touching stopper, readjust cable. To complete installation, reverse removal procedure.

WIRING DIAGRAMS

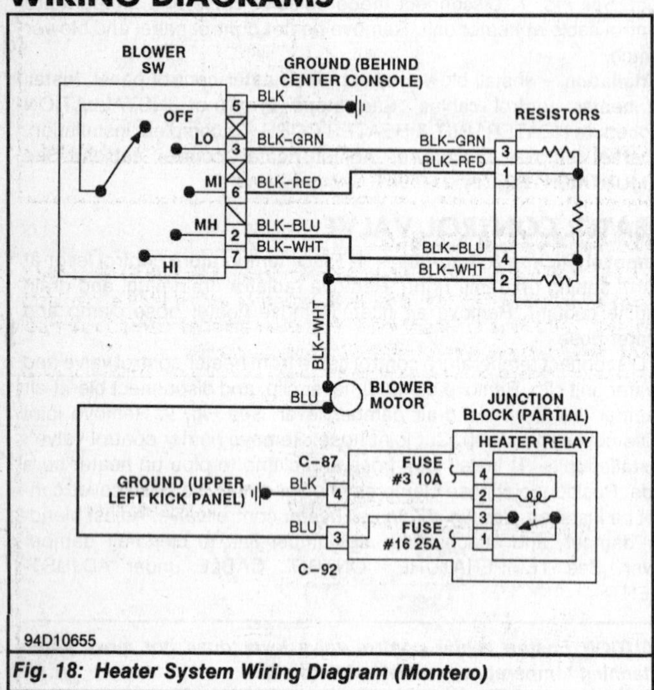
BLOWER SW
GROUND (BEHIND CENTER CONSOLE)
BLK
RESISTORS
OFF
LO
MI
MH
HI
5
3
6
2
7
BLK-GRN
BLK-RED
BLK-BLU
BLK-WHT
3
1
4
2
BLK-WHT
BLU
BLOWER MOTOR
JUNCTION BLOCK (PARTIAL)
HEATER RELAY
C-87
GROUND (UPPER LEFT KICK PANEL)
FUSE #3 10A
FUSE #16 25A
4
3
1
C-92
94D10655

Fig. 18: Heater System Wiring Diagram (Montero)

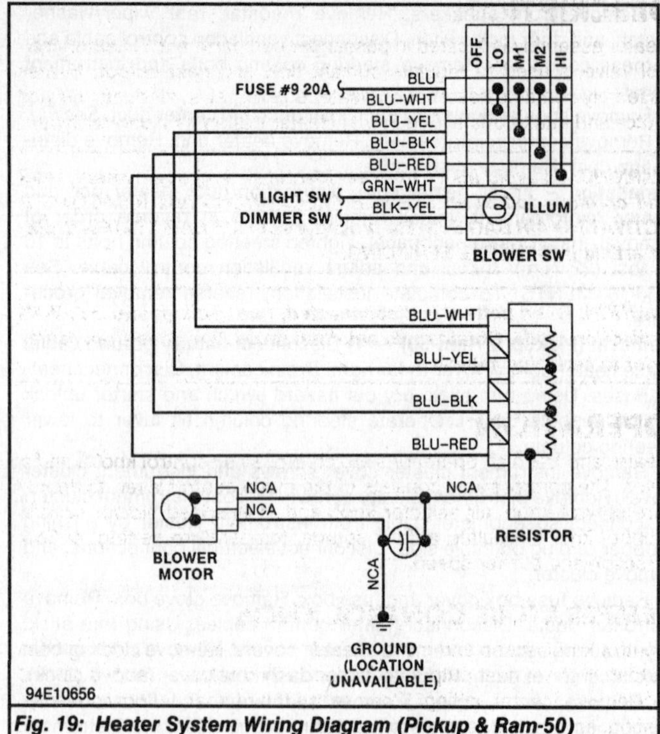
OFF
LO
M1
M2
HI
FUSE #9 20A
BLU
BLU-WHT
BLU-YEL
BLU-BLK
BLU-RED
GRN-WHT
BLK-YEL
LIGHT SW
DIMMER SW
ILLUM
BLOWER SW
NCA
BLOWER MOTOR
RESISTOR
GROUND (LOCATION UNAVAILABLE)
94E10656

Fig. 19: Heater System Wiring Diagram (Pickup & Ram-50)

DESCRIPTION

Heater assembly is located in passenger compartment. A heater control valve is used to regulate coolant flow and heat output. Heater assembly contains heater core, heater control valve, air ducts, blower motor and intake ducts. *See Fig. 1*. Heater system is blend-air type.

WARNING: To avoid injury from accidental air bag deployment, read and carefully follow all SERVICE PRECAUTIONS and DISABLING & ACTIVATING AIR BAG SYSTEM procedures in AIR BAG SYSTEM SAFETY article in GENERAL SERVICING.

CAUTION: When battery is disconnected, radio will go into anti-theft protection mode. Obtain radio anti-theft protection code from owner prior to servicing vehicle.

OPERATION

Heater and fresh air operations are controlled by control knobs and a lever. The control panel consists of the mode control lever, temperature control knob, air selector knob and multi-speed blower switch. Control knobs regulate airflow source, temperature setting, airflow direction and blower speed.

TEMPERATURE CONTROL KNOB

Control knob opens and closes heater control valve, regulating heat output. Highest heat output is obtained when selector knob is turned clockwise to warm setting. When temperature knob is turned to cool setting, ambient air is used for ventilation.

FRESH/RECIRCULATED AIR SELECTOR LEVER

This lever is used to select source of airflow. With lever at fresh air setting, outside air is allowed to enter and/or pass through heater. With lever at recirculated air setting, inside air is recirculated through passenger compartment.

BLOWER SWITCH

The blower can be operated at different fan speeds to regulate amount of air forced through vehicle. Fan speed will increase as switch is turned to the right.

MODE SELECTOR KNOB

Depending on position selected, airflow can be directed to different areas of passenger compartment. Airflow selection capabilities include individual areas or a combination of windshield, upper body, knee and/or foot area.

ADJUSTMENTS

TEMPERATURE CONTROL CABLE

Position temperature control knob at warm setting (extreme right). Move blend-air damper lever completely downward, in direction of arrow, and connect inner wire of temperature control cable to damper lever. *See Fig. 2*. Secure outer wire of control cable using clip.

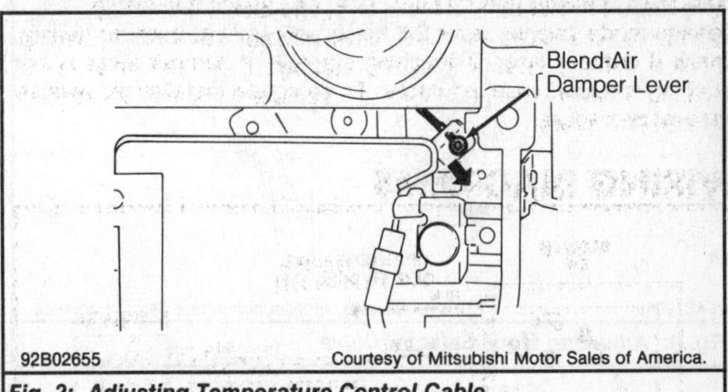
Blend-Air
Damper Lever
92B02655
Courtesy of Mitsubishi Motor Sales of America.

Fig. 2: Adjusting Temperature Control Cable

AIR SELECTOR CABLE

Position fresh/recirculated air selector knob at recirculated air setting. Move air selector damper lever in direction of arrow until in contacts stopper. *See Fig. 3*. Connect inner wire of air selector cable to damper lever. Secure outer wire of selector cable using clip.

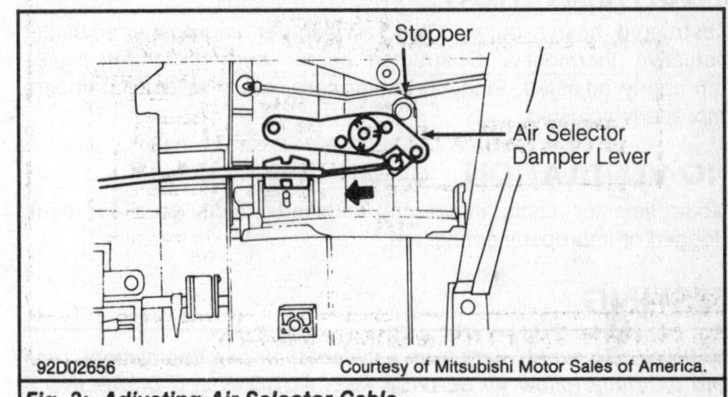
Stopper
Air Selector
Damper Lever
92D02656
Courtesy of Mitsubishi Motor Sales of America.

Fig. 3: Adjusting Air Selector Cable

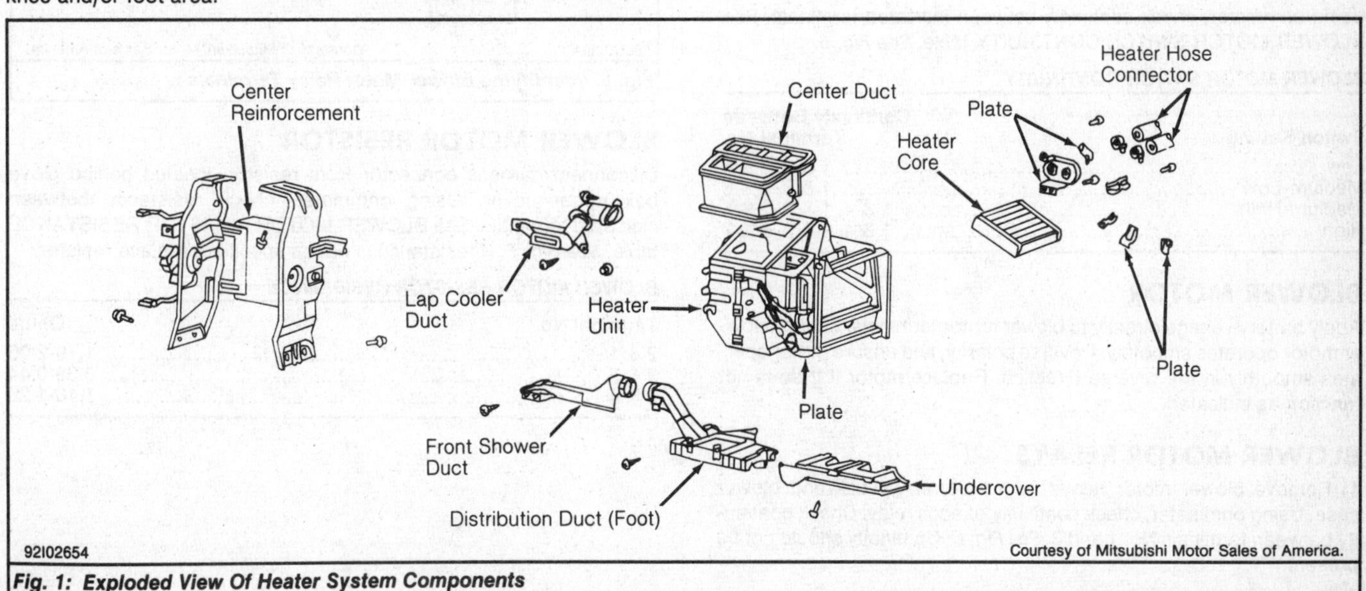
Center
Reinforcement
Center Duct
Plate
Heater Hose
Connector
Heater
Core
Lap Cooler
Duct
Heater
Unit
Plate
Plate
Front Shower
Duct
Distribution Duct (Foot)
Undercover
92I02654
Courtesy of Mitsubishi Motor Sales of America.

Fig. 1: Exploded View Of Heater System Components

1993 HEATER SYSTEMS
Stealth & 3000GT (Cont.)

MODE SELECTOR CABLE

Place mode selector lever at defrost setting. Move mode selector damper lever in direction of arrow, and connect inner wire of mode selector cable to damper lever. *See Fig. 4.* Secure outer wire of selector cable using clip.

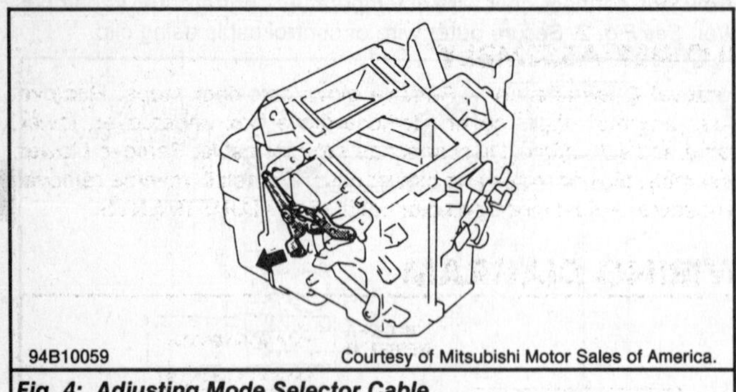
94B10059
Courtesy of Mitsubishi Motor Sales of America.

Fig. 4: Adjusting Mode Selector Cable

TROUBLE SHOOTING

BLOWER INOPERATIVE

Blown fuse. Blower motor improperly grounded. Defective switch, blower motor relays or resistor.

INSUFFICIENT HEAT

Obstructed heater outlet. Blend-air damper improperly adjusted. Defective thermostat. Obstructed heater hoses. Control cables improperly adjusted. Plugged heater core. Mode selector dampers improperly adjusted.

NO VENTILATION

Mode selector cable incorrectly installed. Ducts crushed, bent, clogged or improperly connected.

TESTING

WARNING: To avoid injury from accidental air bag deployment, read and carefully follow all SERVICE PRECAUTIONS and DISABLING & ACTIVATING AIR BAG SYSTEM procedures in AIR BAG SYSTEM SAFETY article in GENERAL SERVICING.

BLOWER MOTOR SWITCH

Using ohmmeter, check continuity between indicated terminals. See BLOWER MOTOR SWITCH CONTINUITY table. *See Fig. 5.*

BLOWER MOTOR SWITCH CONTINUITY

Switch Setting	Continuity Between Terminal No.
Low	1 & 8, 3 & 5
Medium-Low	1 & 8, 5 & 6
Medium-High	1 & 4, 1 & 8, 2 & 5
High	1 & 4, 1 & 8, 5 & 7

BLOWER MOTOR

Apply battery voltage directly to blower motor terminals. Ensure blower motor operates smoothly. Reverse polarity, and ensure motor operates smoothly in the reverse direction. Replace motor if it does not function as indicated.

BLOWER MOTOR RELAYS

1) Remove blower motor relays from fuse/relay block and blower case. Using ohmmeter, check continuity of each relay. Check continuity between terminals No. 1 and 3. *See Fig. 6.* Continuity should not be present.

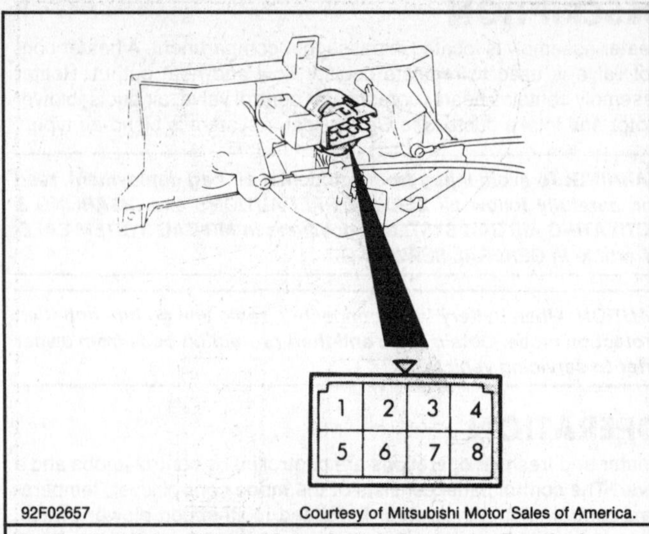
1
2
3
4
5
6
7
8
92F02657
Courtesy of Mitsubishi Motor Sales of America.

Fig. 5: Identifying Blower Motor Switch Connector Terminals

2) Check continuity between terminals No. 2 and 4. Continuity should be present. Connect 12-volt battery to terminals No. 2 and 4. *See Fig. 6.* Ensure continuity exists between terminals No. 1 and 3 with battery voltage applied. If continuity is not as specified, replace defective relay.

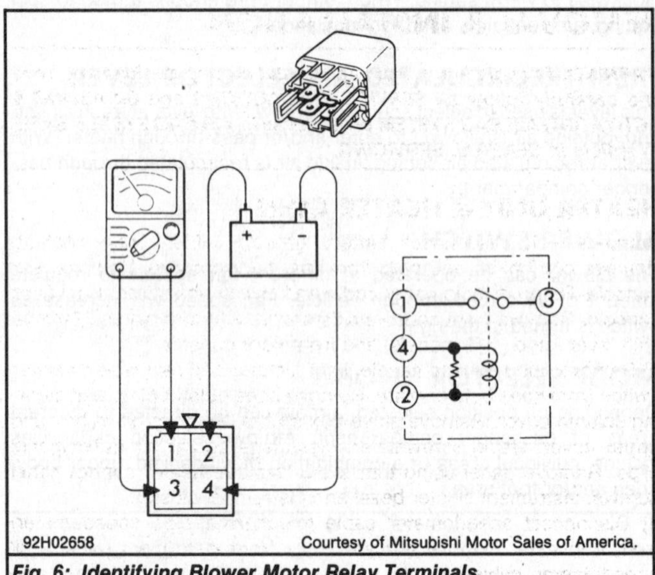
+
-
1
3
4
2
1
2
3
4
92H02658
Courtesy of Mitsubishi Motor Sales of America.

Fig. 6: Identifying Blower Motor Relay Terminals

BLOWER MOTOR RESISTOR

Disconnect harness connector from resistor, located behind glove box upper cover. Using ohmmeter, check resistance between indicated terminals. See BLOWER MOTOR RESISTOR RESISTANCE table. *See Fig. 7.* If resistance is not as specified, replace resistor.

BLOWER MOTOR RESISTOR RESISTANCE

Terminal No.	Ohms
2 & 1	1.79-2.06
2 & 3	0.38-0.44
2 & 4	1.10-1.26

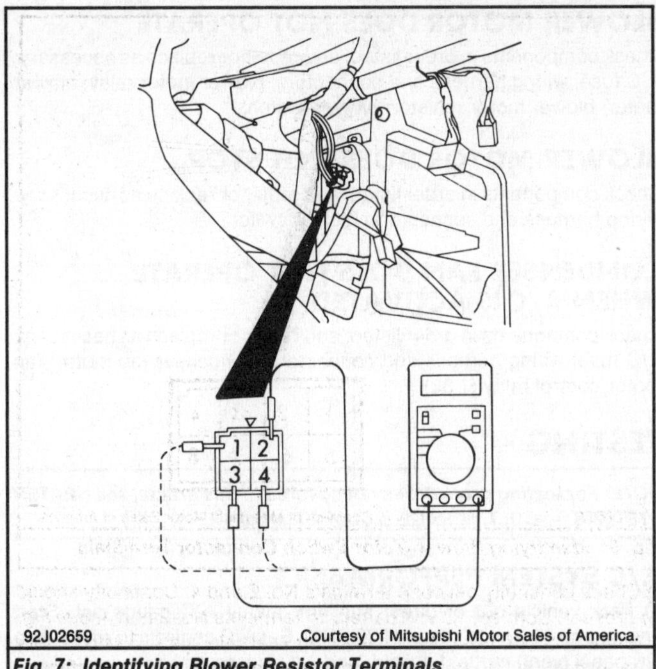
1
2
3
4
92J02659
Courtesy of Mitsubishi Motor Sales of America.

Fig. 7: Identifying Blower Resistor Terminals

REMOVAL & INSTALLATION

WARNING: To avoid injury from accidental air bag deployment, read and carefully follow all SERVICE PRECAUTIONS and DISABLING & ACTIVATING AIR BAG SYSTEM procedures in AIR BAG SYSTEM SAFETY article in GENERAL SERVICING.

HEATER UNIT & HEATER CORE

Removal - 1) Disconnect battery ground cable. Drain coolant. Remove cup holder and plug from rear floor console. Remove rear console. Remove radio panel, radio and switch panel from front floor console. Remove front console side covers and trim plates. Remove shift lever knob (M/T models) and front floor console.

2) Remove hood release handle, light dimmer and rear wiper/washer switch from knee bolster plate. Remove knee bolster plate and steering column cover. Remove glove box striker. Remove glove box and upper cover. Using screwdriver, disengage center air outlet panel clips. Remove panel using trim stick. Remove heater control panel screws, instrument cluster bezel and instrument cluster.

3) Disconnect speedometer cable (mechanical-type speedometer) from transaxle. Remove adapter locks from instrument panel. Pull speedometer cable slightly toward passenger compartment, and remove adapter. Remove speakers or plugs. Disconnect electrical wiring harness connectors. Remove steering column bolts and instrument panel.

4) Disconnect heater hoses. Remove center reinforcement and glove box undercover. Remove air distribution ducts. Remove heater unit. Remove heater core cover plate. Remove heater core from heater unit. *See Fig. 1*.

Installation - To install, reverse removal procedure. Ensure heater hose clamps are fully secured to prevent leaks.

HEATER CONTROL PANEL

Removal & Installation - 1) Disconnect battery ground cable. Drain coolant. Remove cup holder and plug from rear floor console. Remove rear console. Remove radio panel, radio and switch panel from front floor console. Remove front console side covers and trim plates. Remove shift lever knob (M/T models) and front floor console. Remove glove box door stops. Remove glove box upper cover.

2) Disconnect air selector cable. Remove hood release handle, light dimmer and rear wiper/washer switch from knee bolster plate. Remove knee bolster plate and foot shower duct. *See Fig. 1*. Disconnect mode selector cable and temperature control cable. Using screwdriver, disengage center air outlet panel clips. Remove panel using trim stick. Remove heater control panel. To install, reverse removal procedure. Adjust heater control cables. See ADJUSTMENTS.

BLOWER ASSEMBLY

Removal & Installation - Remove glove box door stops. Remove glove box and upper cover. Remove glove box undercover, lower frame and side frame. Disconnect air selector cable. Remove blower assembly, blower motor and blower case. To install, reverse removal procedure. Adjust mode selector cable. See ADJUSTMENTS.

WIRING DIAGRAM

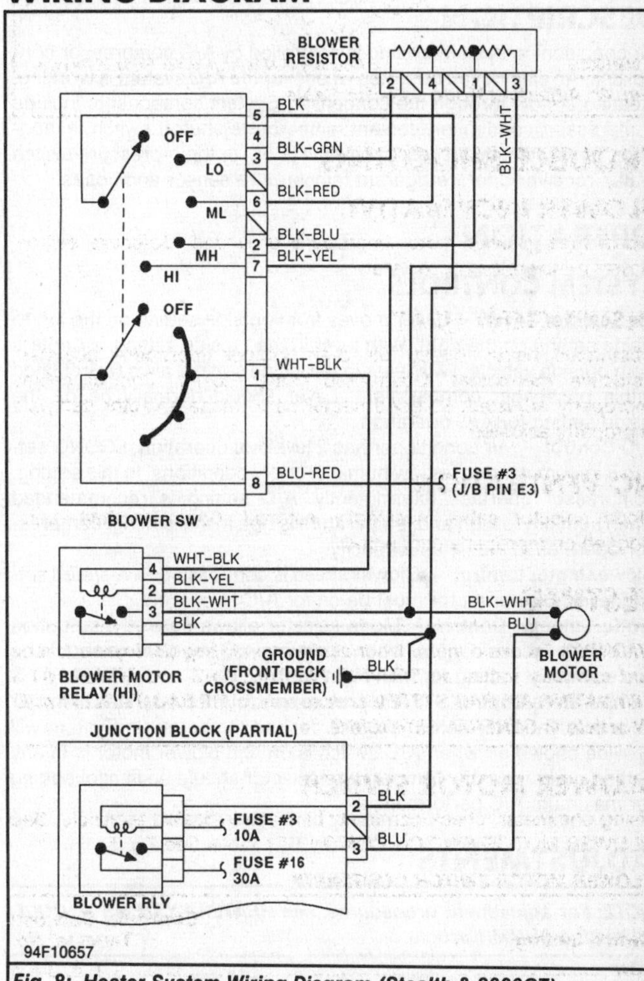
BLOWER
RESISTOR
2
4
1
3
BLK-WHT
5
4
3
6
2
7
1
8
BLK
OFF
BLK-GRN
LO
BLK-RED
ML
BLK-BLU
MH
BLK-YEL
HI
OFF
WHT-BLK
BLU-RED
FUSE #3
(J/B PIN E3)
BLOWER SW
WHT-BLK
BLK-YEL
BLK-WHT
BLK
BLK-WHT
BLU
GROUND
(FRONT DECK
CROSSMEMBER)
BLK
BLOWER MOTOR
RELAY (HI)
BLOWER
MOTOR
JUNCTION BLOCK (PARTIAL)
BLK
FUSE #3
10A
BLU
FUSE #16
30A
BLOWER RLY
94F10657

Fig. 8: Heater System Wiring Diagram (Stealth & 3000GT)

1993 MANUAL A/C-HEATER SYSTEMS
Colt, Mirage & Summit

SPECIFICATIONS

Compressor Type	Sanden FX105V Scroll
Compressor Belt Deflection	
1.5L	
New	.20-.24" (5.0-6.0 mm)
Used	.24-.28" (6.0-7.0 mm)
1.8L	
New	.22-.24" (5.5-6.0 mm)
Used	.24-.28" (6.0-7.0 mm)
Compressor Oil Capacity	4.4-5.1 ozs.
Refrigerant (R-12) Capacity	26-30 ozs.
System Operating Pressures [1]	
Low Side	20-30 psi (1.4-2.1 kg/cm²)
High Side	105-148 psi (7.3-10.4 kg/cm²)

[1] – Specification is with ambient temperature at about 80°F (27°C).

DESCRIPTION

Air conditioning system cycling is controlled by A/C compressor control unit. An electric fan operates whenever the A/C system is working, creating airflow through the condenser. System components include compressor, condenser, coolant temperature shutoff switch, evaporator, fan switch, dual-pressure switch (1.5L) or triple-pressure switch (1.8L), receiver-drier, refrigerant temperature sensor and hoses.

OPERATION

SYSTEM CONTROLS

Air Selector Lever – Lever moves from outside setting on the left to inside setting on the right. With lever in the outside setting, air enters from outside vehicle. With lever in the inside setting, air is recirculated within passenger compartment. Lever should normally be on the inside setting for A/C operation.

A/C Control – Air conditioner has 2 levels of operation. ECONO setting is recommended for low humidity or dry conditions. In this setting, compressor operates intermittently. A/C setting is recommended when humidity is high and temperature is hot. In this setting, compressor operates at maximum capacity.

Blower Motor Control – Blower speed is controlled by a 4-speed setting lever. Blower motor must be on for A/C to operate.

Mode Selector Control – Mode selector allows desired distribution of air from various outlets. When operating A/C, mode knob should be placed in vent setting for maximum cooling.

Temperature Control – Temperature control knob operates blend air door in A/C-heater unit to achieve desired temperature. System will provide cooled air when A/C switch is on and blower motor is in any setting other than off. Temperature selector should be in cool setting for maximum A/C performance.

ADJUSTMENTS

NOTE: For adjustment procedures, see HEATER SYSTEMS – COLT, MIRAGE & SUMMIT article.

TROUBLE SHOOTING

COMPRESSOR DOES NOT OPERATE

Check components in order listed, and repair or replace as necessary: A/C fuse; wiring harness and connectors; A/C compressor clutch relay; magnetic clutch; refrigerant charge; pressure switch; A/C switch; blower switch; air thermo sensor; A/C compressor control unit; drive belt; refrigerant temperature switch; engine control module.

AIR NOT COOL

Check components in order listed, and repair or replace as necessary: refrigerant charge; pressure switch; air thermo sensor; A/C compressor control unit; refrigerant temperature switch; engine control module.

BLOWER MOTOR DOES NOT OPERATE

Check components in order listed, and repair or replace as necessary: A/C fuse; wiring harness and connectors; blower motor relay; blower motor; blower motor resistor; blower switch.

BLOWER MOTOR DOES NOT STOP

Check components in order listed, and repair or replace as necessary: wiring harness and connectors; blower switch.

CONDENSER FAN DOES NOT OPERATE WHEN A/C IS ACTIVATED

Check components in order listed, and repair or replace as necessary: A/C fuse; wiring harness and connectors; condenser fan motor; fan motor control relay (1.8L).

TESTING

NOTE: For testing procedures not covered in this article, see HEATER SYSTEMS – COLT, MIRAGE & SUMMIT article.

A/C SYSTEM PERFORMANCE

1) Park vehicle out of direct sunlight. Install A/C gauge set. Start engine and allow it to idle at 1000 RPM. Set A/C controls to recirculate air, panel (vent) mode, full cold, and A/C button on.

2) Set blower/fan on high speed and close doors and windows. Insert thermometer in center vent. Operate system for 20 minutes to allow system to stabilize. Measure temperature. Temperature must be 37-42°F (3-6°C) at center vent, with high side and low side pressures within specification. See SPECIFICATIONS table at beginning of article.

A/C SWITCH

Disconnect A/C switch harness. A/C switch is located at left center of A/C-heater control panel. Using an ohmmeter, measure resistance between switch terminals. *See Fig. 1.* If resistance is not as specified, replace switch. See A/C SWITCH SPECIFICATIONS table.

A/C SWITCH SPECIFICATIONS

Switch Setting	Terminals	Continuity
OFF	[1]	No
ECONO	1 & 4	Yes
	1 & 5	[2] Yes
A/C	1, 2 & 4	Yes
	1 & 5	[2] Yes

[1] – Continuity should not exist between any terminals.
[2] – Continuity should exist in one direction only.

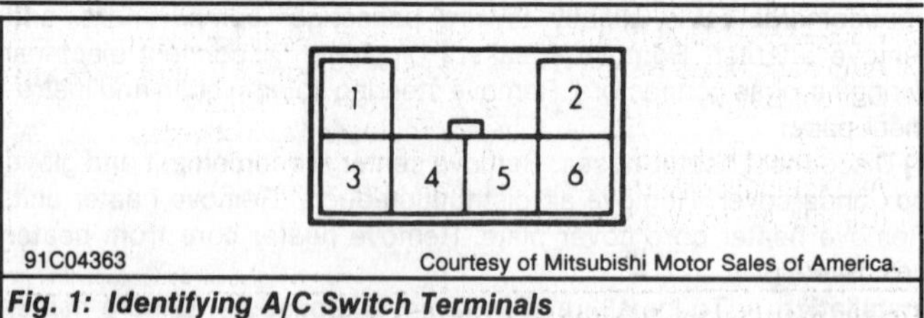
1
2
3
4
5
6
91C04363
Courtesy of Mitsubishi Motor Sales of America.

Fig. 1: Identifying A/C Switch Terminals

AIR THERMO SENSOR

1) Remove sensor connector from A/C compressor control unit (located above evaporator housing). *See Fig. 2.* Using an ohmmeter, measure continuity between connector terminals. Resistance should be within specification. See AIR THERMO SENSOR RESISTANCE table.

2) If resistance is not within specification, sensor is faulty and must be replaced. If resistance is within specification and all other components test okay, replace A/C compressor control unit.

AIR THERMO SENSOR RESISTANCE

Sensor Temperature	Approximate Ohms
32°F (0°C)	11,000
50°F (10°C)	7000
68°F (20°C)	5000
86°F (30°C)	3000
104°F (40°C)	2500

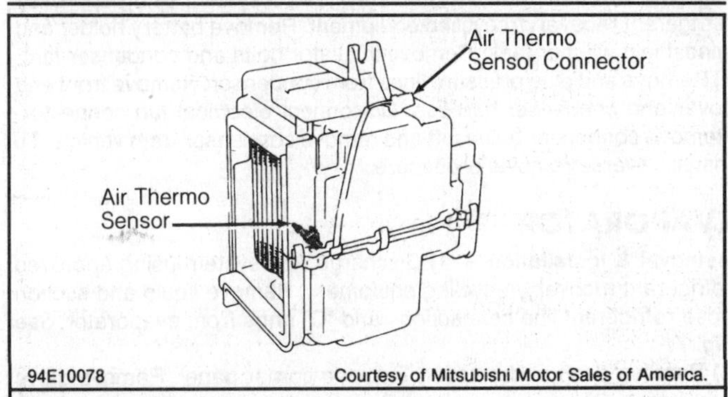

Air Thermo
Sensor Connector
Air Thermo
Sensor
94E10078
Courtesy of Mitsubishi Motor Sales of America.

Fig. 2: Locating A/C Air Thermo Sensor

COMPRESSOR

1) Install manifold gauge set. Start engine and operate at idle speed. Turn A/C control to HIGH setting. If pressure on suction side of gauge is 43-57 psi (3-4 kg/cm²), and 284 psi (20 kg/cm²) on discharge side, air in system is indicated. Evacuate system and recharge with refrigerant.

2) If pressure on suction side of gauge is negative, and 85-142 psi (6-10 kg/cm²) on discharge side, water in system is indicated. Check for leaks. Replace receiver-drier. Evacuate and recharge system.

3) If pressure on suction side of gauge is 71 psi (5 kg/cm²), and 128 psi (9 kg/cm²) on discharge side, compressor failure is indicated. Discharge A/C system using approved refrigerant recovery/recycling equipment. Replace compressor and receiver-drier. Evacuate and recharge system.

DUAL-PRESSURE SWITCH

1) With engine off, disconnect harness connector at dual-pressure switch (located on receiver-drier). Connect a jumper wire across harness connector. *See Fig. 3.* Turn A/C switch and blower switch on. Momentarily turn ignition on while listening for compressor clutch to engage.

2) If compressor clutch does not engage, connect manifold gauge set to system, and check operating pressures. Dual-pressure switch should allow compressor operation if system pressures are between 30-384 psi (2-27 kg/cm²). If dual-pressure switch does not operate within specified pressure range, discharge A/C system using approved refrigerant recovery/recycling equipment and replace switch.

3) After replacing switch, recharge system and monitor pressures for proper compressor function. If dual-pressure switch cuts power to compressor clutch while driving, even though temperatures inside vehicle have not yet decreased, it is possible that high pressure side of dual-pressure switch has been activated. Go to next step.

4) Discharge A/C system using approved refrigerant recovery/recycling equipment. Replace dual-pressure switch, and recharge system. Ensure compressor clutch is operating within pressure range given in step **2)**, and check for sufficient system cooling.

MAGNETIC CLUTCH

Disconnect compressor clutch wiring harness connector. Apply battery voltage to compressor clutch wiring harness connector terminals. If compressor clutch engages, clutch is okay. If compressor clutch does not engage, pulley and armature are not making contact. Repair as required.

TRIPLE-PRESSURE SWITCH

1) With engine off, disconnect harness connector at triple-pressure switch (located on receiver-drier). Turn A/C switch and blower switch

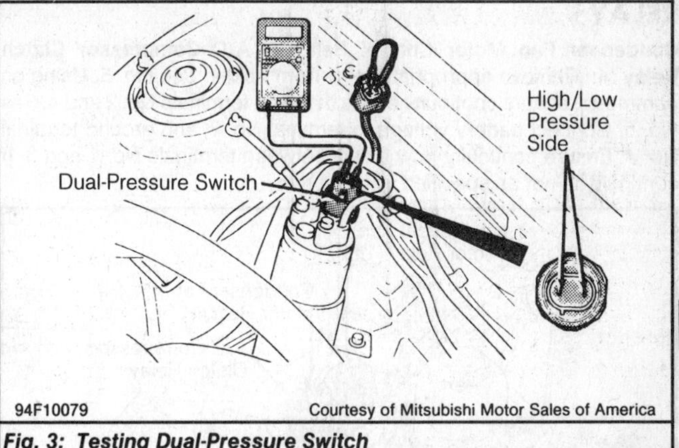

High/Low
Pressure
Side
Dual-Pressure Switch
94F10079
Courtesy of Mitsubishi Motor Sales of America

Fig. 3: Testing Dual-Pressure Switch

on. Jumper wires on harness side of connector. Momentarily turn ignition on and listen for compressor clutch engagement. If clutch does not engage, check fuse and other components wired in series with compressor clutch.

2) With triple-pressure switch connector removed, connect the high/low pressure side terminals on harness. *See Fig. 4*. Install gauge manifold to high pressure side service valve of refrigerant line.

3) When high/low and medium pressure side of triple-pressure switch is at operation pressure (ON), condition is normal if there is continuity between the respective terminals. If there is no continuity, replace switch. See PRESSURE SWITCH SPECIFICATIONS table.

PRESSURE SWITCH SPECIFICATIONS [1]

Application	Pressure psi (kg/cm²)
High Pressure	
On	299 (21)
Off	384 (27)
Low Pressure	
On	30 (2.10)
Off	33 (2.35)
Medium Pressure	
On	199 (14)
Off	256 (18)

[1] – With ambient temperature in engine compartment at least 80°F (27°C).

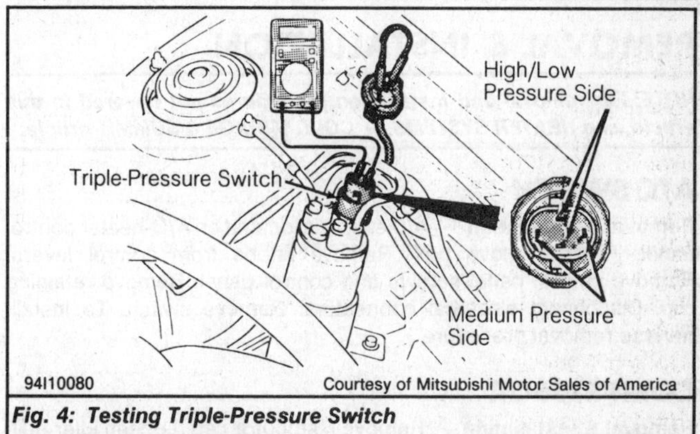

High/Low
Pressure Side
Triple-Pressure Switch
Medium Pressure
Side
94I10080
Courtesy of Mitsubishi Motor Sales of America

Fig. 4: Testing Triple-Pressure Switch

RECEIVER-DRIER

Operate A/C system, and check temperature of tubes entering and leaving receiver-drier. If temperature is different from side to side, receiver-drier is restricted. Repair as required.

REFRIGERANT TEMPERATURE SENSOR

Remove refrigerant temperature sensor connector (located on compressor). Using an ohmmeter, measure resistance between 2 bottom terminals. Resistance should be approximately 80,500 ohms at 77°F (25°C). If resistance is not as specified, replace refrigerant temperature sensor.

1993 MANUAL A/C-HEATER SYSTEMS
Colt, Mirage & Summit (Cont.)

RELAYS

Condenser Fan Motor Control Relay & A/C Compressor Clutch Relay – Remove appropriate relay from holder. *See Fig. 5.* Using an ohmmeter, ensure continuity exists between terminals No. 2 and 4. *See Fig. 6.* Connect battery voltage to terminal No. 2, and ground terminal No. 4. Ensure continuity now exists between terminals No. 1 and 3. If continuity is not as specified, replace relay.

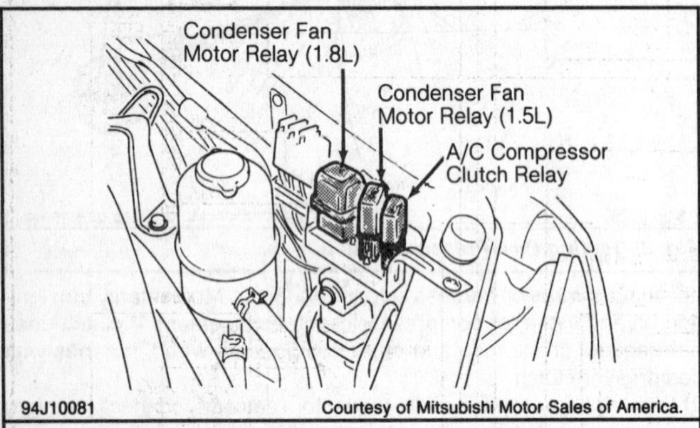
Condenser Fan
Motor Relay (1.8L)
Condenser Fan
Motor Relay (1.5L)
A/C Compressor
Clutch Relay
94J10081
Courtesy of Mitsubishi Motor Sales of America.

Fig. 5: Locating & Identifying Relays

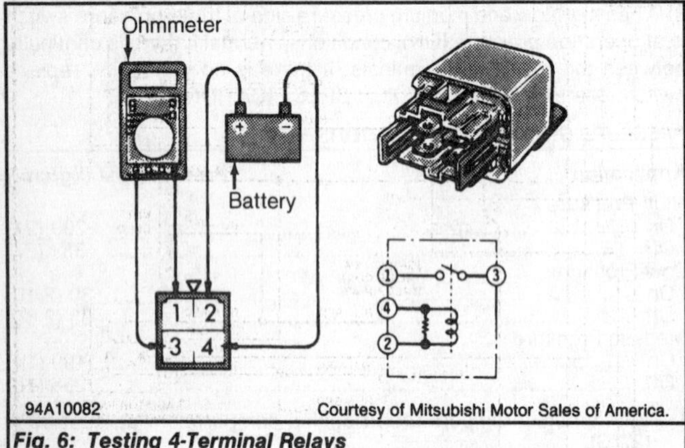
Ohmmeter
Battery
1
2
3
4
94A10082
Courtesy of Mitsubishi Motor Sales of America.

Fig. 6: Testing 4-Terminal Relays

REMOVAL & INSTALLATION

NOTE: For removal and installation procedures not covered in this article, see HEATER SYSTEMS – COLT, MIRAGE & SUMMIT article.

A/C SWITCH

Removal & Installation – A/C switch is located on A/C-heater control panel. Remove glove box. Remove knobs from control levers. Remove control panel screws and control panel. Remove retaining clip. Disconnect electrical connectors. Remove switch. To install, reverse removal procedure.

COMPRESSOR

Removal & Installation – Remove distributor cap. Loosen idler pulley, and remove belt. Disconnect compressor clutch connector. Discharge A/C system using approved refrigerant recovery/recycling equipment. Remove high and low pressure lines and "O" rings from compressor. Remove compressor bolts and compressor. To install, reverse removal procedure.

CONDENSER

Removal & Installation – 1) Discharge A/C system using approved refrigerant recovery/recycling equipment. Remove battery holder and windshield washer tank. Remove insulator bolts and condenser fan.

2) Remove and plug pressure lines from condenser. Remove front end cover and condenser harness. Disconnect electrical fan connector. Remove condenser bolts. Lift and remove condenser from vehicle. To install, reverse removal procedure.

EVAPORATOR

Removal & Installation – 1) Discharge A/C system using approved refrigerant recovery/recycling equipment. Remove liquid and suction hose refrigerant line connections and "O" rings from evaporator. *See Fig. 7.*

2) Remove dash under cover. Remove corner panel. Remove glove box frame. Remove glove box. Remove drain hose. Remove heater and blower duct joints. Disconnect A/C switch harness connector. Disconnect main harness connector.

CAUTION: If installing new evaporator, fill unit with 2.0 ounces of compressor oil before installing in vehicle.

3) Remove evaporator nuts and evaporator unit. To install, reverse removal procedure.

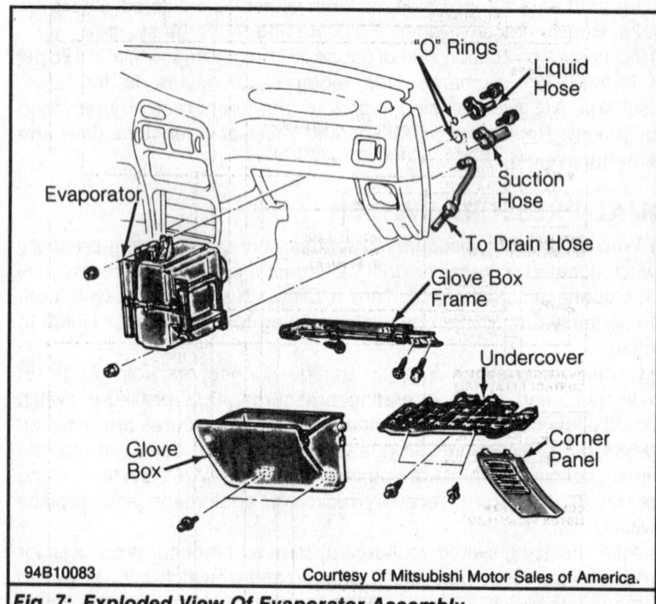
"O" Rings
Liquid
Hose
Suction
Hose
Evaporator
To Drain Hose
Glove Box
Frame
Undercover
Glove
Box
Corner
Panel
94B10083
Courtesy of Mitsubishi Motor Sales of America.

Fig. 7: Exploded View Of Evaporator Assembly

WIRING DIAGRAM

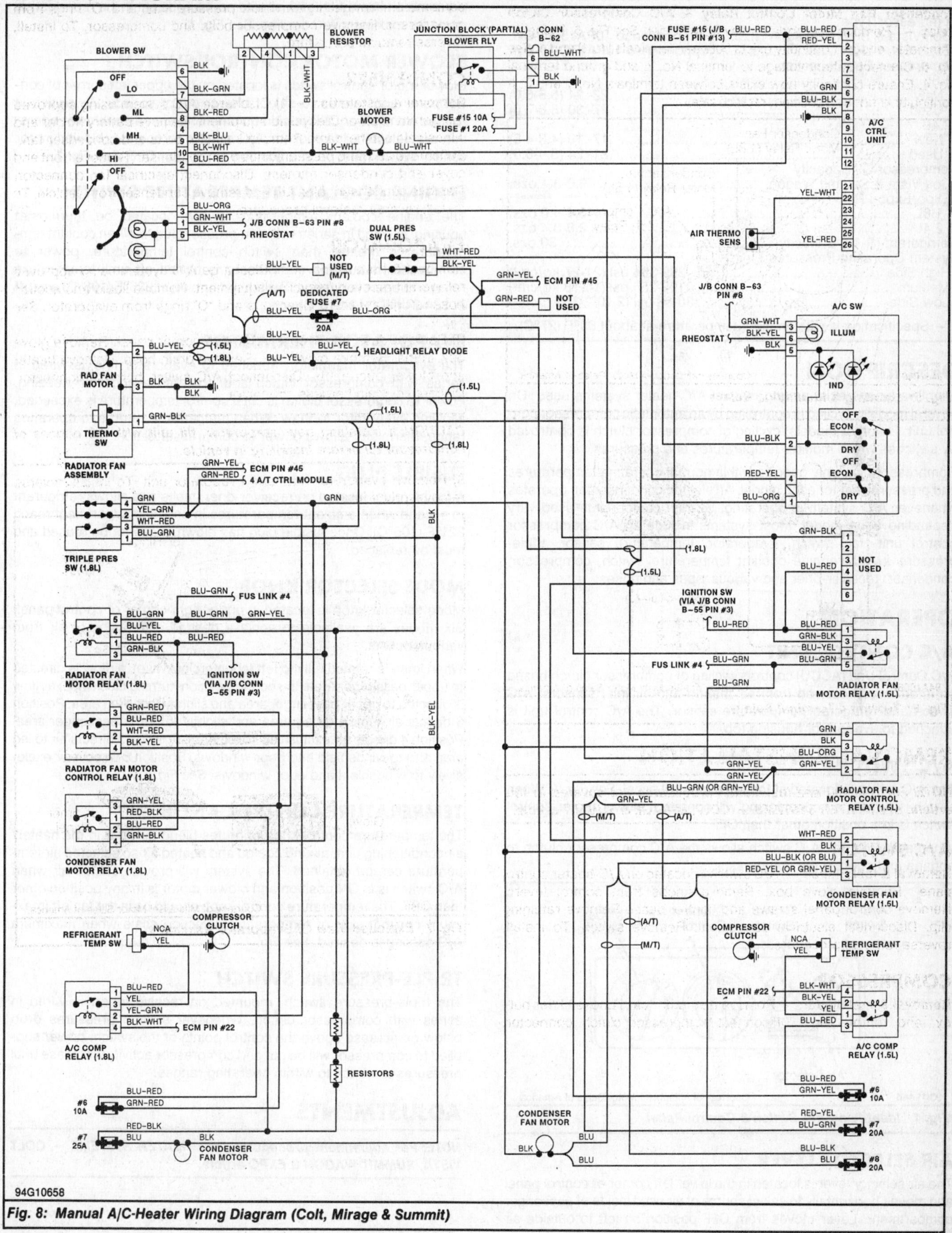
BLOWER SW
OFF
LO
ML
MH
HI
OFF
BLK
BLK-GRN
BLK-RED
BLK-BLU
BLK-WHT
BLU-RED
BLU-ORG
GRN-WHT
BLK-YEL
J/B CONN B-63 PIN #8
RHEOSTAT
BLOWER RESISTOR
BLK-WHT
JUNCTION BLOCK (PARTIAL)
BLOWER RLY
CONN B-62
BLU-WHT
BLOWER MOTOR
FUSE #15 10A
FUSE #1 20A
BLU-WHT
FUSE #15 (J/B CONN B-61 PIN #13)
BLU-RED
RED-YEL
GRN
BLU-BLK
A/C CTRL UNIT
YEL-WHT
AIR THERMO SENS
YEL-RED
DUAL PRES SW (1.5L)
WHT-RED
BLK-YEL
BLU-YEL
NOT USED (M/T)
(A/T)
DEDICATED FUSE #7 20A
BLU-ORG
GRN-YEL
ECM PIN #45
GRN-RED
NOT USED
J/B CONN B-63 PIN #8
A/C SW
GRN-WHT
RHEOSTAT
ILLUM
IND
OFF
ECON
DRY
BLU-BLK
RED-YEL
BLU-ORG
RAD FAN MOTOR
(1.5L)
(1.8L)
HEADLIGHT RELAY DIODE
THERMO SW
GRN-BLK
RADIATOR FAN ASSEMBLY
ECM PIN #45
4 A/T CTRL MODULE
YEL-GRN
WHT-RED
BLU-GRN
TRIPLE PRES SW (1.8L)
NOT USED
IGNITION SW (VIA J/B CONN B-55 PIN #3)
FUS LINK #4
RADIATOR FAN MOTOR RELAY (1.8L)
RADIATOR FAN MOTOR RELAY (1.5L)
RADIATOR FAN MOTOR CONTROL RELAY (1.8L)
RADIATOR FAN MOTOR CONTROL RELAY (1.5L)
BLU-GRN (OR GRN-YEL)
(M/T)
(A/T)
RED-BLK
CONDENSER FAN MOTOR RELAY (1.8L)
CONDENSER FAN MOTOR RELAY (1.5L)
BLU-BLK (OR BLU)
RED-YEL (OR GRN-YEL)
BLK-YEL
REFRIGERANT TEMP SW
NCA
YEL
COMPRESSOR CLUTCH
ECM PIN #22
BLK-WHT
A/C COMP RELAY (1.8L)
A/C COMP RELAY (1.5L)
RESISTORS
#6 10A
#7 25A
#7 20A
#8 20A
BLU
CONDENSER FAN MOTOR
94G10658

Fig. 8: Manual A/C-Heater Wiring Diagram (Colt, Mirage & Summit)

1993 MANUAL A/C-HEATER SYSTEMS
Colt Vista, Summit Wagon & Expo

SPECIFICATIONS

Compressor Type
 Colt Vista & Summit Wagon .... Nippondenso 10PA15 10-Cyl.
 Expo/Expo LRV .... Nippondenso 10PA17C 10-Cyl.
Compressor Belt Deflection
 1.8L
  New .... .22-.24 (5.5-6.0)
  Used .... .27-.30 (6.8-7.6)
 2.4L
  New .... .17-.19 (4.3-4.8)
  Used .... .21-.24 (5.4-6.0)
Compressor Oil Capacity
 Colt Vista & Summit Wagon .... 2.0-3.4 ozs.
 Expo/Expo LRV
  1.8L .... 3.4-4.0 ozs.
  2.4L .... 2.0-3.4 ozs.
Refrigerant (R-12) Capacity .... 30 ozs.
System Operating Pressures [1]
 High Side .... 299-384 psi (21-27 kg/cm²)
 Medium .... 199-256 psi (14-18 kg/cm²)
 Low Side .... 30-33 psi (2.10-2.35 kg/cm²)

[1] – Specification is with ambient temperature at about 80°F (27°C).

DESCRIPTION

Slight variations exist among manual A/C-heater systems used. On several models, cycling is controlled by an automatic compressor control unit. On other models, cycling of compressor clutch is controlled by switches which monitor temperatures and pressures.

Compressors will only operate within normal operating temperatures and pressures set for each model. An electric condenser fan operates whenever A/C system is operating. System components used vary depending upon model. Most systems include an A/C compressor control unit, fan switch, evaporator, temperature sensor, triple-pressure switch, engine coolant temperature switch, compressor, condenser, receiver-drier and various pipes and hoses.

OPERATION

A/C CONTROL UNIT

A/C Control Unit (ACCU) controls cycling of compressor clutch based on information received from air thermo and air inlet sensors, A/C switch and refrigerant temperature sensor. The A/C control unit is attached to evaporator housing top.

A/C SWITCH

The A/C switch is located at top left of control panel. *See Fig. 1.* When switch is turned, air conditioning will operate if blower motor control switch is in a position other than OFF.

When activated, the A/C switch allows the A/C compressor clutch to engage and operate the compressor.

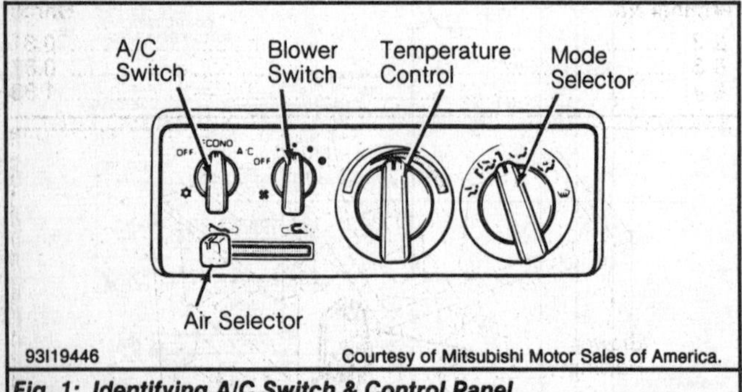
A/C Switch
Blower Switch
Temperature Control
Mode Selector
Air Selector
93I19446
Courtesy of Mitsubishi Motor Sales of America.

Fig. 1: Identifying A/C Switch & Control Panel

AIR SELECTOR LEVER

The air selector lever is located in the lower left corner of control panel and moves horizontally to select source of air used inside of passenger compartment. Lever moves from OFF position on left to outside air mode, to mixture of outside and inside air, and to recirculation (inside air) mode on the right. Lever should normally be set in the recirculation mode for maximum A/C cooling. *See Fig. 1.*

BLOWER MOTOR CONTROL SWITCH

Blower motor control switch is located on the upper left corner of control panel and rotates to select blower motor speeds. As switch is rotated from left or OFF position, increasing speeds of blower operation are selected. In order for A/C system to operate, blower motor control switch must be in a position other than OFF. *See Fig. 1.*

ENGINE COOLANT TEMPERATURE SWITCH

The engine coolant temperature switch, located on thermostat housing, is wired in series with compressor clutch. When coolant temperature is greater than switch control temperature, power to compressor is cut and compressor is turned off until temperature returns to operating range. Switch will turn on at 226°F (108°C) and off at 234-244°F (112-118°C).

EVAPORATOR THERMISTOR

The evaporator thermistor, attached to evaporator fins, is wired in series with compressor clutch and prevents evaporator freezing. Power to compressor clutch is cut if control temperature is exceeded, allowing evaporator to thaw. When temperature returns to operating range, thermistor allows power to compressor clutch.

FUSIBLE PLUG

A fusible plug, located on receiver-drier, melts and allows refrigerant to escape when ambient temperatures in engine compartment reach 221°F (105°C). Once fusible plug has blown, it cannot be reused and must be replaced.

MODE SELECTOR KNOB

Mode selector knob is located in upper right corner of control panel. Six modes are available to achieve desired distribution of air from various outlets.

When knob is rotated fully to left (counterclockwise), airflow is directed to upper passenger area. In second position (turning clockwise) airflow is directed to upper passenger area and slightly to the leg area. Position 3 directs air mostly to leg area and slightly to upper passenger area. Position 4 directs air exclusively to leg area. Position 5 directs air to leg area and to windshield and door windows. Position 6 directs air exclusively to windshield and door windows. *See Fig. 1.*

TEMPERATURE CONTROL KNOB

The temperature control knob operates blend-air door in the heater/air conditioning unit, mixing cooled and heated air so selected air temperature can be obtained. The system will provide cooled air when A/C switch is in ON position and blower motor is in any position other than OFF. The temperature control knob should be in the far left (maximum cooling) side of temperature selection scale when maximum A/C cooling is desired. *See Fig. 1.*

TRIPLE-PRESSURE SWITCH

The triple-pressure switch, mounted on receiver/drier, is wired in series with compressor clutch. Whenever system pressures drop below or increase above the control points of the switch, power supplied to compressor will be cut and compressor activity will cease until pressures are back to within operating ranges.

ADJUSTMENTS

NOTE: For adjustment procedures, see HEATER SYSTEMS – COLT VISTA, SUMMIT WAGON & EXPO article.

TROUBLE SHOOTING

COMPRESSOR DOES NOT OPERATE

Check components in order listed, and repair or replace as necessary: A/C fuse; wiring harness and connectors; A/C compressor clutch relay; magnetic clutch; refrigerant charge; pressure switch; engine coolant temperature switch (1.8L); A/C switch; blower switch; air inlet and air thermo sensors; A/C control unit; drive belt; Engine Control Module (ECM); belt lock controller (1.8L); compressor revolution pickup.

AIR NOT COOL

Check components in order listed, and repair or replace as necessary: refrigerant charge; pressure switch; air inlet and air thermo sensor; A/C control unit; refrigerant temperature switch; Engine Control Module (ECM).

BLOWER MOTOR DOES NOT OPERATE

Check components in order listed, and repair or replace as necessary: A/C fuse; wiring harness and connectors; heater relay; blower motor; blower motor resistor; blower switch.

BLOWER MOTOR DOES NOT STOP

Check components in order listed, and repair or replace as necessary: wiring harness and connectors; blower switch.

CONDENSER FAN DOES NOT OPERATE WHEN A/C IS ACTIVATED

Check components in order listed, and repair or replace as necessary: A/C fuse; wiring harness and connectors; condenser fan motor relay; condenser fan motor; pressure switch.

TESTING

NOTE: For testing procedures not covered in this article, see HEATER SYSTEMS - COLT VISTA, SUMMIT WAGON & EXPO article.

A/C SYSTEM PERFORMANCE

1) Park vehicle out of direct sunlight. Install A/C gauge set. Start engine and allow it to idle at 1000 RPM. Set A/C controls to recirculate air, panel (vent) mode, full cold, and A/C button on.

2) Set blower/fan on high speed and close doors and windows. Insert thermometer in center vent. Operate system for 20 minutes to allow system to stabilize. Measure temperature. Temperature must be 37-42°F (3-6°C) at center vent, with high side and low side pressures within specification. See SPECIFICATIONS table at beginning of article.

A/C SWITCH

1) Disconnect A/C switch harness connector. Using wiring diagram as a guide, jumper appropriate terminals of A/C switch wiring harness connector. See WIRING DIAGRAM.

2) Turn blower on and momentarily turn ignition on without starting engine. Listen for compressor clutch engagement. If compressor clutch does not engage, check fuse and other components wired in series with compressor clutch.

3) Using an ohmmeter, check continuity of switch. If continuity does not match table, replace switch. See A/C SWITCH CONTINUITY TEST table. *See Fig. 2.*

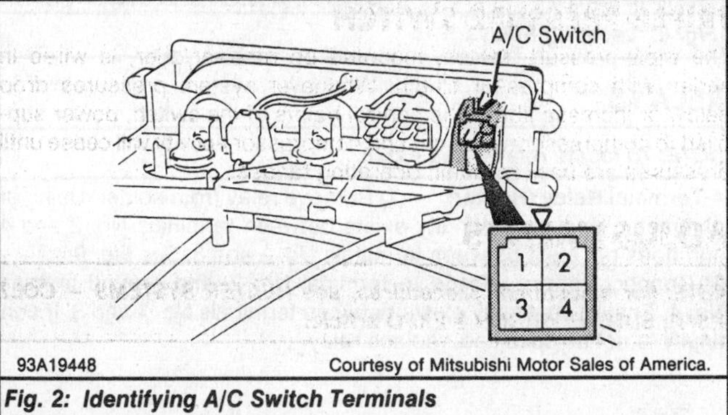
A/C Switch
1
2
3
4
93A19448
Courtesy of Mitsubishi Motor Sales of America.

Fig. 2: Identifying A/C Switch Terminals

A/C SWITCH CONTINUITY TEST

Switch Position	Terminal No.	Continuity
OFF	1 & Ground	No
ECONO	1 & 3	Yes
A/C	1 & 4	Yes

AIR THERMO & AIR INLET SENSORS

1) Disconnect sensor connector at evaporator case. Using an ohmmeter, measure resistance between sensor terminals. See AIR THERMO & AIR INLET SENSOR SPECIFICATIONS table.

2) If resistance is not within specification, sensor is faulty and must be replaced. If resistance is within specification and all other components are okay, replace A/C compressor control unit (if equipped). *See Fig. 3.*

AIR THERMO & AIR INLET SENSOR SPECIFICATIONS

Sensor Temperature	Ohms
32°F (0°C)	4800
50°F (10°C)	2800
68°F (20°C)	1800
86°F (30°C)	1000
104°F (40°C)	800

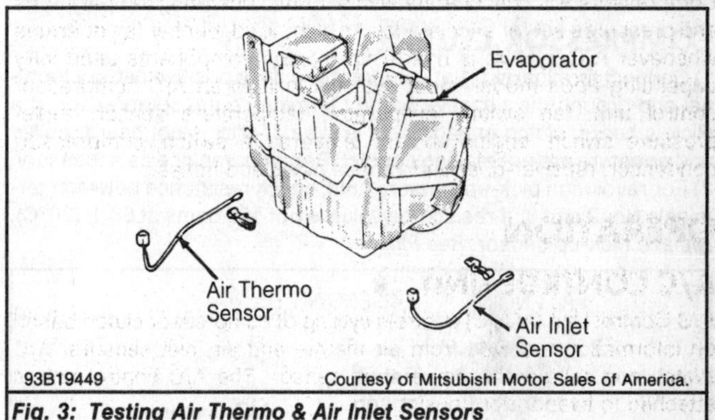
Evaporator
Air Thermo Sensor
Air Inlet Sensor
93B19449
Courtesy of Mitsubishi Motor Sales of America.

Fig. 3: Testing Air Thermo & Air Inlet Sensors

BLOWER RESISTOR

Disconnect blower resistor connector. Using an ohmmeter, measure resistance between terminals indicated in BLOWER RESISTOR RESISTANCE table. *See Fig. 4.*

BLOWER RESISTOR RESISTANCE

Terminal No.	Ohms
1 & 2	0.31
1 & 3	0.87
1 & 4	1.83

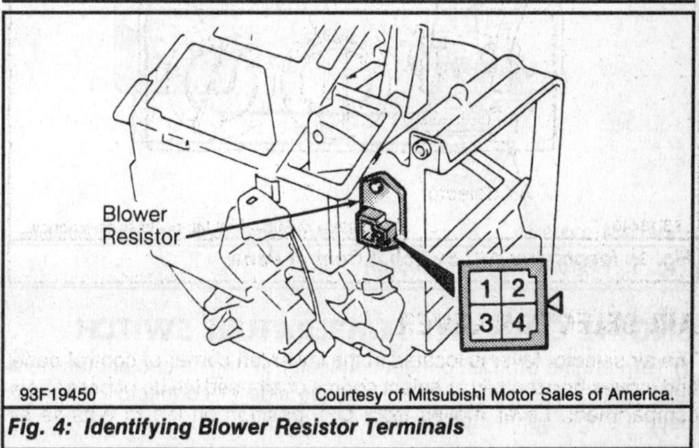
Blower Resistor
1
2
3
4
93F19450
Courtesy of Mitsubishi Motor Sales of America.

Fig. 4: Identifying Blower Resistor Terminals

1993 MANUAL A/C-HEATER SYSTEMS
Colt Vista, Summit Wagon & Expo (Cont.)

BLOWER SWITCH

With blower switch in position indicated in BLOWER SWITCH CONTINUITY TEST table, ensure continuity exists between terminals listed. *See Fig. 5.*

BLOWER SWITCH CONTINUITY TEST

Switch Position	Terminal No.	Continuity
OFF	1 & Ground	No
Low	1 & 8; 3 & 5	Yes
Medium 1	1 & 8; 5 & 6	Yes
Medium 2	1, 4 & 8; 2 & 5	Yes
High	1, 4 & 8; 5 & 7	Yes

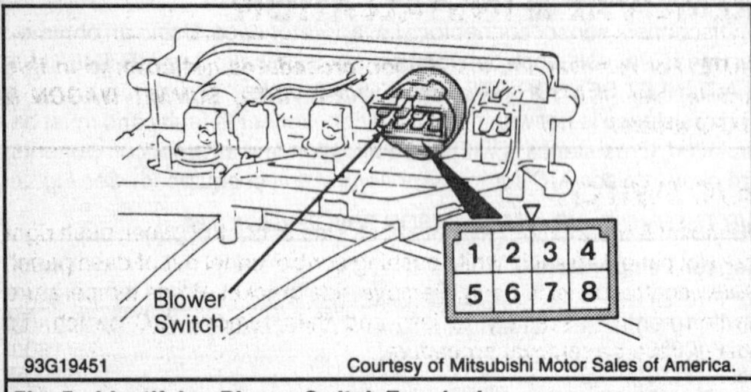
1 2 3 4
5 6 7 8
Blower Switch
93G19451
Courtesy of Mitsubishi Motor Sales of America.

Fig. 5: Identifying Blower Switch Terminals

COMPRESSOR CLUTCH

1) Connect terminal No. 1 at compressor side to positive battery terminal and ground the negative battery terminal to the compressor. If a click is heard, clutch engagement is okay. If click is not heard, pulley and armature are not making contact. Repair or replace as necessary.
2) For revolution pick-up sensor (1.8L), check resistance between terminals No. 2 and 3. If resistance value is not 185 ohms at 68°F (20°C), replace pick-up sensor. *See Fig. 6.*

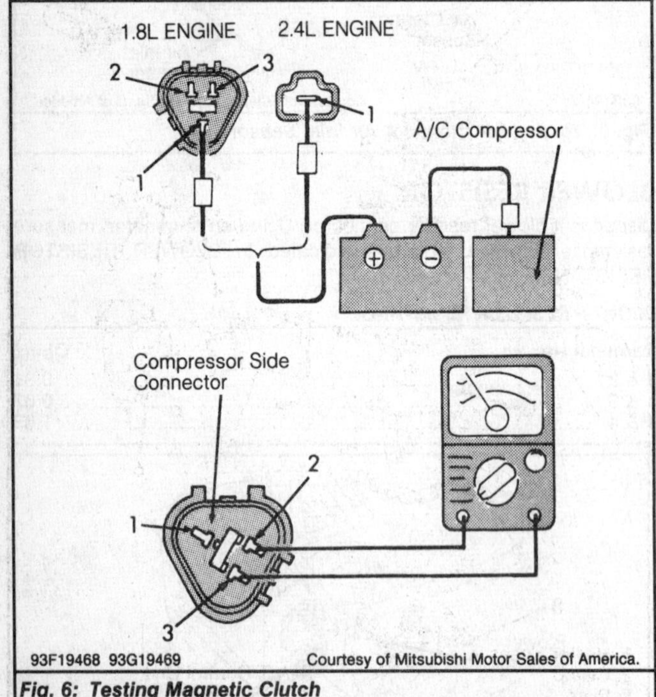
1.8L ENGINE
2.4L ENGINE
2
3
1
1
A/C Compressor
Compressor Side Connector
1
2
3
93F19468 93G19469
Courtesy of Mitsubishi Motor Sales of America.

Fig. 6: Testing Magnetic Clutch

ENGINE COOLANT TEMPERATURE SWITCH

1) Turn engine off. Disconnect connector at engine coolant temperature switch. Jumper wires on harness side of connector. If vehicle uses a single connector, ground connector.
2) Press A/C switch to ON position, and turn on blower switch. Momentarily turn ignition on and listen for compressor clutch engagement. Clutch should engage. If clutch does not engage, check fuse and other components wired in series with compressor clutch.
3) Immerse engine coolant temperature switch in oil. *See Fig. 7.* With an ohmmeter, check continuity as the oil temperature changes under heat. Switch will turn on at 226°F (108°C) and off at 234-244°F (112-118°C). Replace switch if it fails to operate in normal ranges.

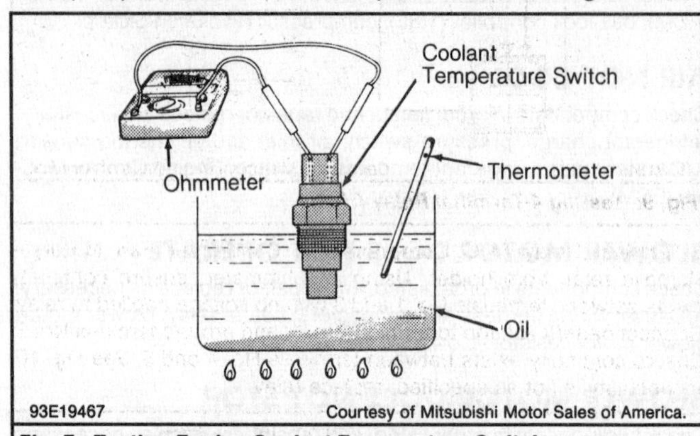
Coolant Temperature Switch
Ohmmeter
Thermometer
Oil
93E19467
Courtesy of Mitsubishi Motor Sales of America.

Fig. 7: Testing Engine Coolant Temperature Switch

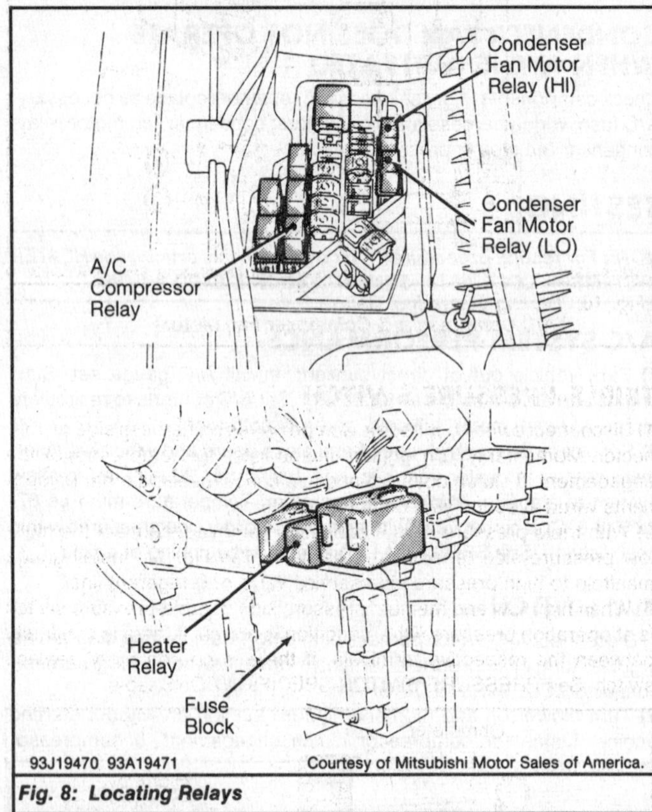
Condenser Fan Motor Relay (HI)
Condenser Fan Motor Relay (LO)
A/C Compressor Relay
Heater Relay
Fuse Block
93J19470 93A19471
Courtesy of Mitsubishi Motor Sales of America.

Fig. 8: Locating Relays

RELAYS

NOTE: To locate relays, see Fig. 8.

4-Terminal Relay (Heater) – 1) Remove relay from holder. Using an ohmmeter, ensure continuity exists between terminals No. 2 and 4, and does not exist between terminals No. 1 and 3. *See Fig. 9.*
2) Connect battery voltage to terminal No. 2, and ground terminal No. 4. Ensure continuity exists between terminals No. 1 and 3. If continuity is not as specified, replace relay.

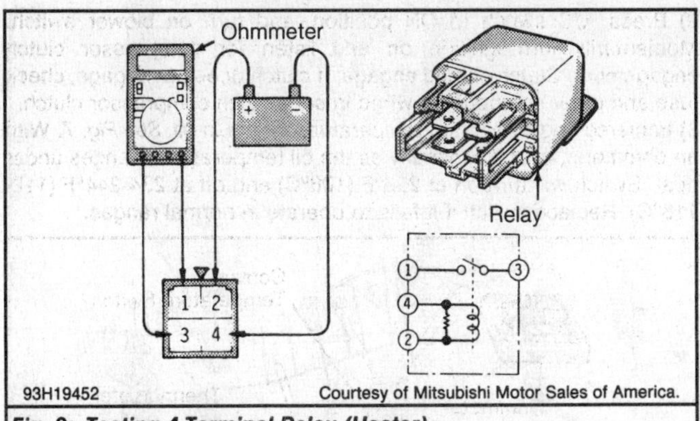

Ohmmeter
Relay
1 2
3 4
93H19452
Courtesy of Mitsubishi Motor Sales of America.

Fig. 9: Testing 4-Terminal Relay (Heater)

5-Terminal Relay (A/C Compressor & Condenser Fan Motor) – Remove relay from holder. Using an ohmmeter, ensure continuity exists between terminals No. 1 and 3 with no voltage applied to relay. Connect battery voltage to terminal No. 1, and ground terminal No. 3. Ensure continuity exists between terminals No. 4 and 5. *See Fig. 10*. If continuity is not as specified, replace relay.

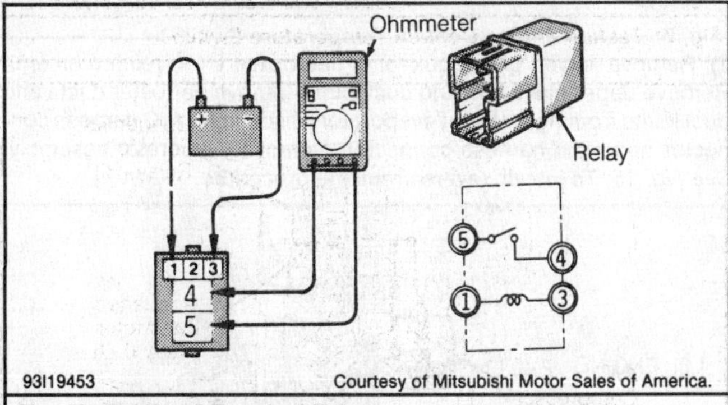

Ohmmeter
Relay
1 2 3
4
5
93I19453
Courtesy of Mitsubishi Motor Sales of America.

Fig. 10: Testing 5-Terminal Relay (A/C Compressor & Condenser Fan Motor)

TRIPLE-PRESSURE SWITCH

1) Disconnect switch connector. Jumper wires on harness side of connector. Momentarily turn ignition on and listen for compressor clutch engagement. If clutch does not engage, check fuse and other components wired in series with compressor clutch.
2) With triple-pressure switch connector removed, connect the high/low pressure side terminals on harness. *See Fig. 11*. Install gauge manifold to high pressure side service valve of refrigerant line.
3) When high/low and medium pressure side of triple-pressure switch is at operation pressure (ON), condition is normal if there is continuity between the respective terminals. If there is no continuity, replace switch. See PRESSURE SWITCH SPECIFICATIONS table.

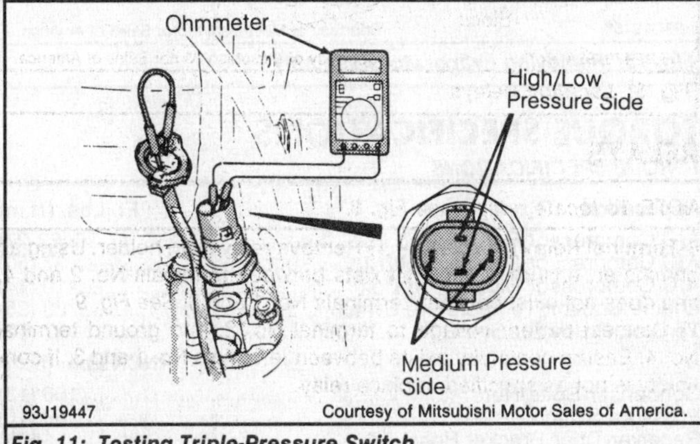

Ohmmeter
High/Low
Pressure Side
Medium Pressure
Side
93J19447
Courtesy of Mitsubishi Motor Sales of America.

Fig. 11: Testing Triple-Pressure Switch

PRESSURE SWITCH SPECIFICATIONS [1]

Application	Pressure psi (kg/cm²)
High Pressure	
On	299 (21)
Off	384 (27)
Low Pressure	
On	30 (2.10)
Off	33 (2.35)
Medium Pressure	
On	199 (14)
Off	256 (18)

[1] – Specification is with ambient temperature at about 80°F (27°C).

REMOVAL & INSTALLATION

NOTE: For removal and installation procedures not covered in this article, see HEATER SYSTEMS - COLT VISTA, SUMMIT WAGON & EXPO article.

A/C SWITCH

Removal & Installation – From back side of control panel, push right control panel clip aside while pushing control panel out of dash panel. Allow control panel to hang. Remove side bracket. Press temperature switch control assembly to left, and then remove A/C switch. To install, reverse removal procedure.

BLOWER MOTOR & RESISTOR

Removal & Installation – **1)** Remove glove box. Resistor is visible with glove box removed. Remove 2 screws, and remove resistor.
2) Remove right speaker cover, cowl trim, knee protector and glove box frame. Disconnect ventilator outlet at right side of blower housing. Disconnect electrical connector at blower motor. Remove engine control unit. Remove 3 screws, and remove blower motor assembly. *See Fig. 12*. To install, reverse removal procedure.

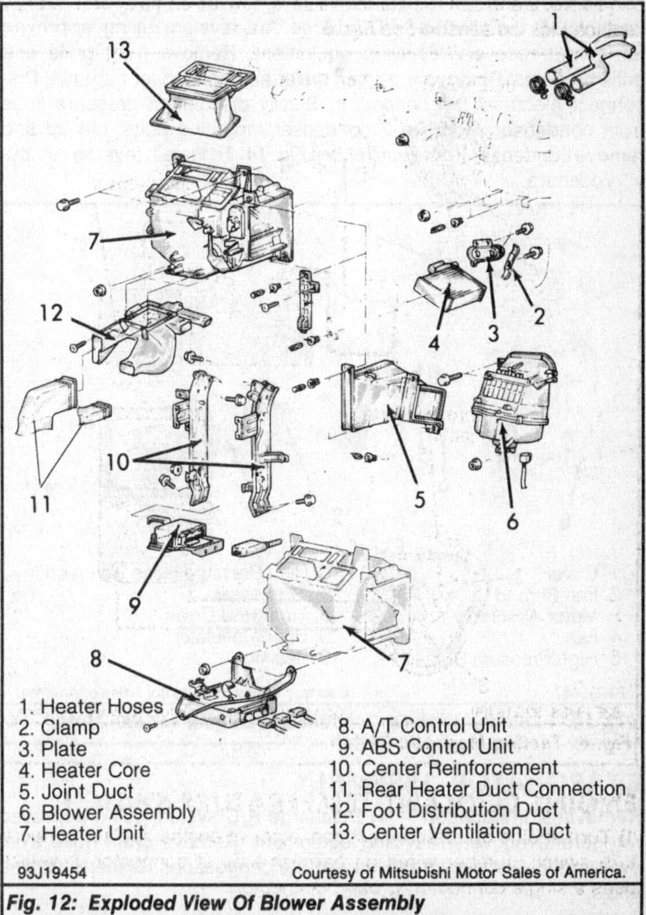

1
13
7
12
4
3
2
10
11
5
6
9
8
7
1. Heater Hoses
2. Clamp
3. Plate
4. Heater Core
5. Joint Duct
6. Blower Assembly
7. Heater Unit
8. A/T Control Unit
9. ABS Control Unit
10. Center Reinforcement
11. Rear Heater Duct Connection
12. Foot Distribution Duct
13. Center Ventilation Duct
93J19454
Courtesy of Mitsubishi Motor Sales of America.

Fig. 12: Exploded View Of Blower Assembly

1993 MANUAL A/C-HEATER SYSTEMS
Colt Vista, Summit Wagon & Expo (Cont.)

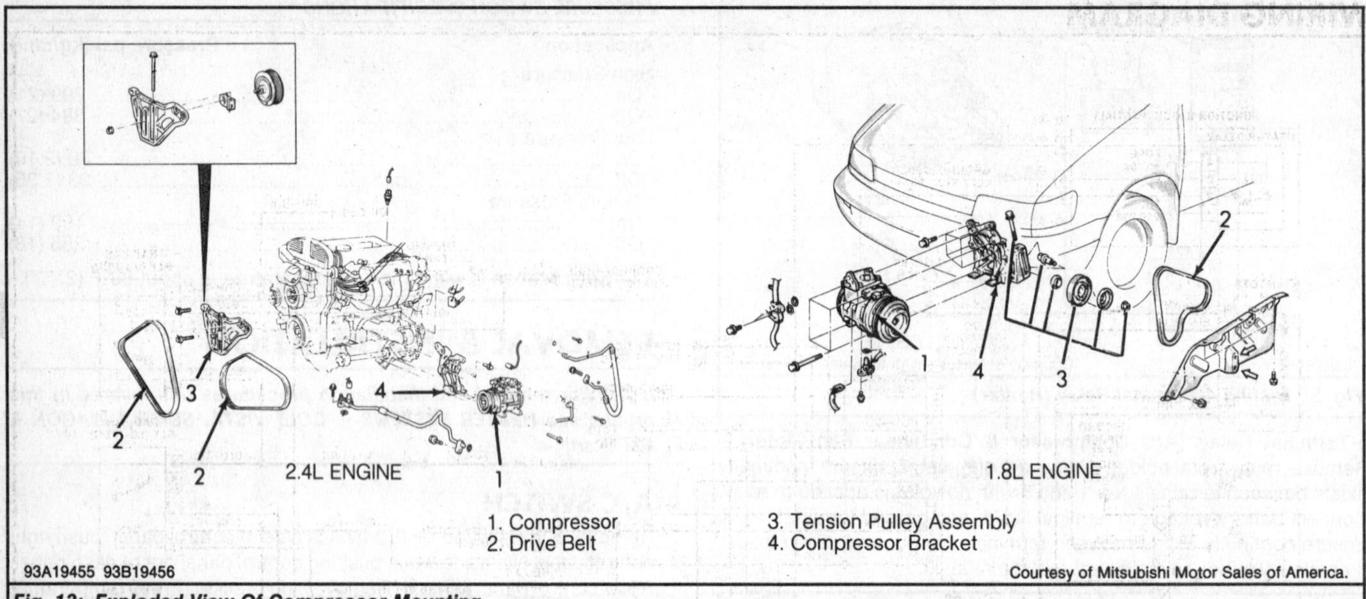
2.4L ENGINE
1.8L ENGINE
1. Compressor
2. Drive Belt
3. Tension Pulley Assembly
4. Compressor Bracket
93A19455 93B19456
Courtesy of Mitsubishi Motor Sales of America.

Fig. 13: Exploded View Of Compressor Mounting

COMPRESSOR

Removal & Installation - Discharge A/C system using approved refrigerant recovery/recycling equipment. Disconnect high tension cable from ignition coil. Remove distributor cap. Loosen idler pulley adjusting bolt, and remove belt. *See Fig. 13*. Disconnect compressor electrical connector. Remove high and low pressure lines and "O" rings from compressor. Remove compressor mounting bolts. Remove compressor. To install, reverse removal procedure.

CONDENSER

Removal & Installation - Discharge A/C system using approved refrigerant recovery/recycling equipment. Remove front grille and grille brackets. Remove front end cover and condenser harness. Disconnect electrical fan connector. Slowly disconnect pressure lines from condenser. Remove 2 condenser mounting bolts. Lift up and remove condenser from vehicle. *See Fig. 14*. To install, reverse removal procedure.

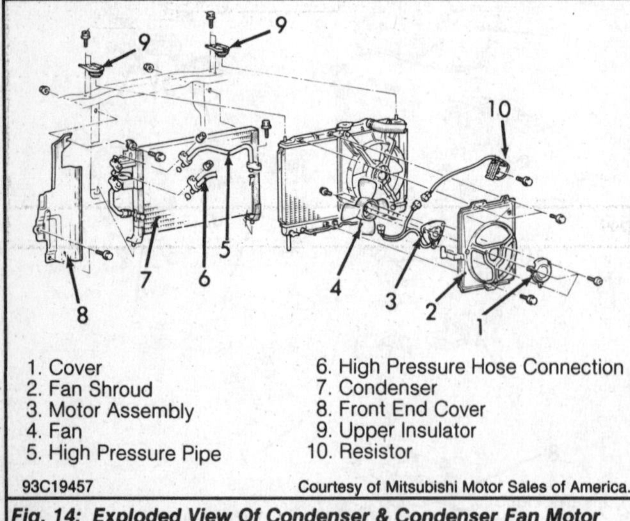
1. Cover
2. Fan Shroud
3. Motor Assembly
4. Fan
5. High Pressure Pipe
6. High Pressure Hose Connection
7. Condenser
8. Front End Cover
9. Upper Insulator
10. Resistor
93C19457
Courtesy of Mitsubishi Motor Sales of America.

Fig. 14: Exploded View Of Condenser & Condenser Fan Motor

EVAPORATOR ASSEMBLY

Removal & Installation - **1)** Discharge A/C system using approved refrigerant recovery/recycling equipment. Remove drain hose from evaporator. Disconnect refrigerant line connections. Discard "O" ring seals.

2) Remove lower glove box and dash insert (or reinforcement). Remove upper glove box and duct joint. Remove defroster ducts and duct joints from right side of evaporator. Disconnect A/C harness connector and main harness connector. Remove evaporator assembly. *See Fig. 15*. To install, reverse removal procedure.

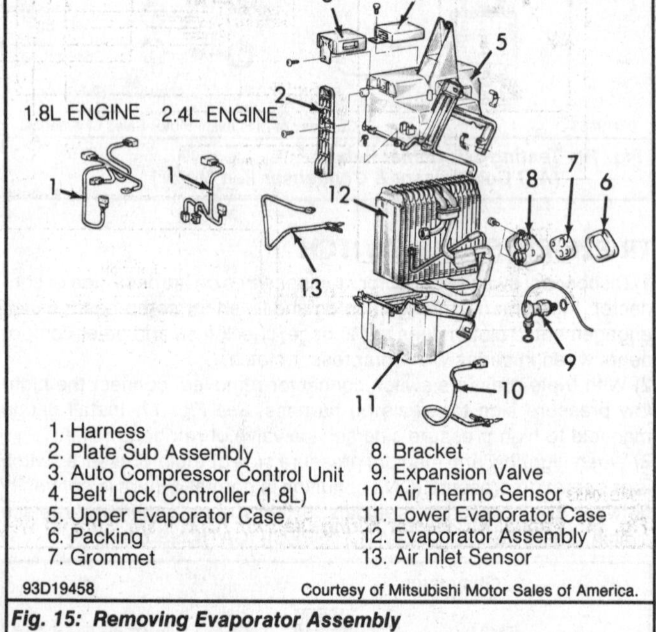
1.8L ENGINE
2.4L ENGINE
1. Harness
2. Plate Sub Assembly
3. Auto Compressor Control Unit
4. Belt Lock Controller (1.8L)
5. Upper Evaporator Case
6. Packing
7. Grommet
8. Bracket
9. Expansion Valve
10. Air Thermo Sensor
11. Lower Evaporator Case
12. Evaporator Assembly
13. Air Inlet Sensor
93D19458
Courtesy of Mitsubishi Motor Sales of America.

Fig. 15: Removing Evaporator Assembly

TORQUE SPECIFICATIONS

TORQUE SPECIFICATIONS

Application	Ft. Lbs. (N.m)
A/C Compressor Bolt/Nut	17-20 (23-27)
A/C Compressor Bracket Bolt/Nut	37 (50)
A/C Compressor Clutch Hub Bolt	10 (14)
Engine Coolant Temperature Switch	26 (35)
Tension Pulley Bracket Bolt	37 (50)
	INCH Lbs. (N.m)
Condenser Bolts/Nuts	106 (12)
Pressure Switch	89 (10)
Receiver-Drier Bracket Bolts	44 (5)

WIRING DIAGRAM

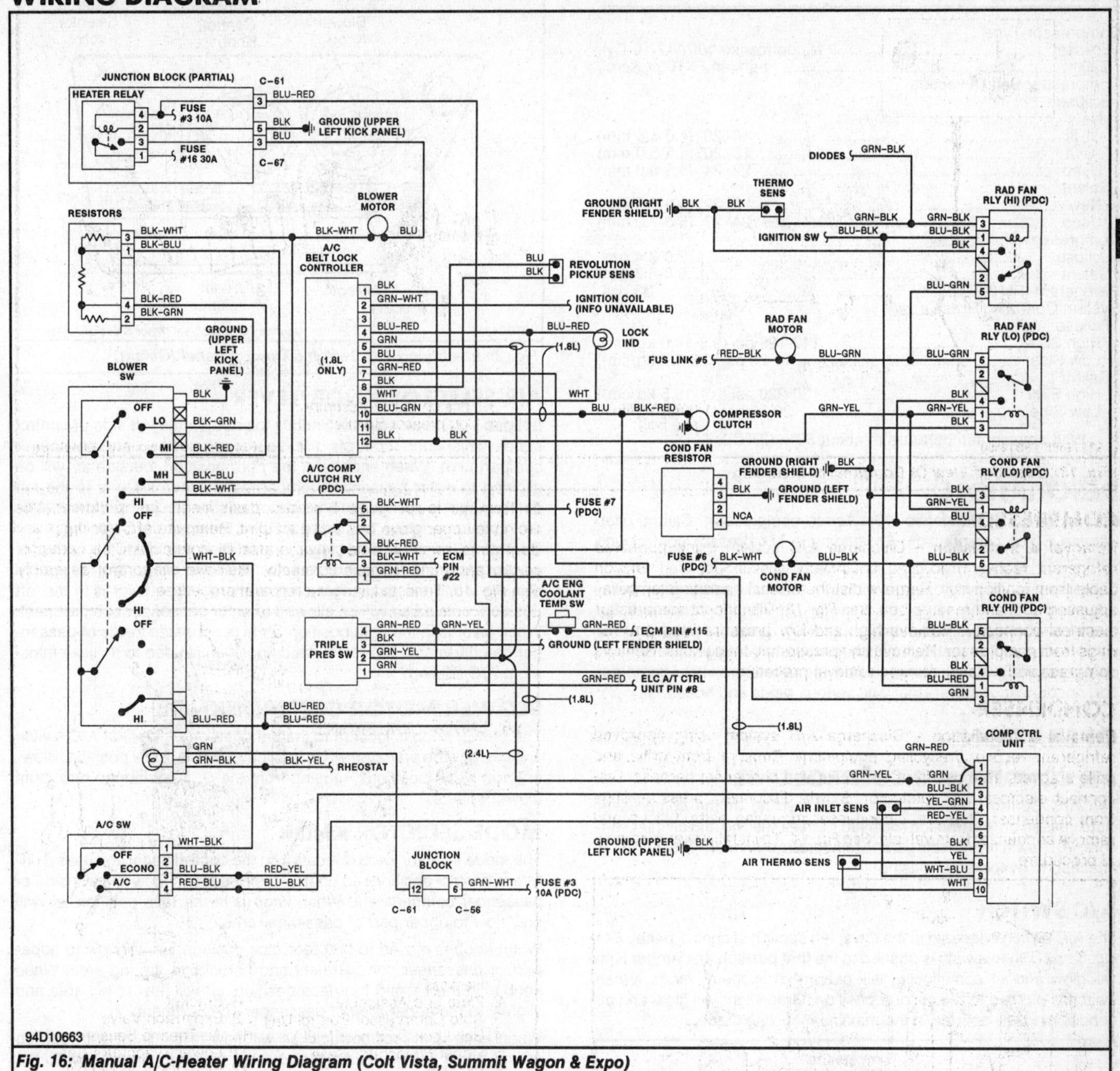

Fig. 16: Manual A/C-Heater Wiring Diagram (Colt Vista, Summit Wagon & Expo)

1993 MANUAL A/C-HEATER SYSTEMS
Eclipse & Galant

SPECIFICATIONS

Compressor Type
- Eclipse .... Nippondenso 10PA17 10-Cyl.
- Galant .... Sanden FX105V Scroll

Compressor Belt Deflection
- Eclipse
  - New
    - 1.8L .... .16-.20" (4.0-5.0 mm)
    - 2.0L .... .18-.20" (4.5-5.0 mm)
  - Used .... .22-.24" (5.5-6.0 mm)
- Galant
  - New .... .20-.22" (5.0-5.5 mm)
  - Used .... .24-.27" (6.0-7.0 mm)

Compressor Oil Capacity
- Eclipse .... 2.0-3.4 ozs.
- Galant .... 5.0-5.7 ozs.

Refrigerant (R-12) Capacity .... 33 ozs.

System Operating Pressures [1]
- Eclipse
  - High Side .... 142-199 psi (9.9-14.0 kg/cm²)
  - Low Side .... 11-26 psi (0.8-1.8 kg/cm²)
- Galant
  - High Side .... 130-220 psi (9.1-15.5 kg/cm²)
  - Low Side .... 20-26 psi (1.4-1.8 kg/cm²)

[1] – With ambient temperature at about 80°F (27°C).

DESCRIPTION

Eclipse uses Nippondenso 10-cylinder compressor; Galant uses Sanden Scroll compressor. An automatic compressor control unit controls cycling.

Compressors will only operate within the normal operating temperatures and pressures set for each model. An electric condenser fan operates whenever A/C system is operating. Systems include an A/C compressor control unit, fan switch, evaporator, temperature sensor, dual-pressure switch, engine coolant temperature switch, compressor, condenser, receiver-drier and various pipes and hoses.

OPERATION

AIR CONDITIONER CONTROL UNIT

The A/C Control Unit (ACCU) controls cycling of the compressor clutch based on information received from air thermo and air inlet sensors, A/C switch and refrigerant temperature sensor. The ACCU is attached to evaporator housing.

A/C SWITCH

The A/C switch is located in the lower left section of control panel. *See Fig. 1 or 2*. When switch is pushed to the first position, the Amber light will glow and air conditioning will operate in economy mode. When switch is pushed to the second position, Green light will glow and air conditioning will operate in the maximum cooling mode.

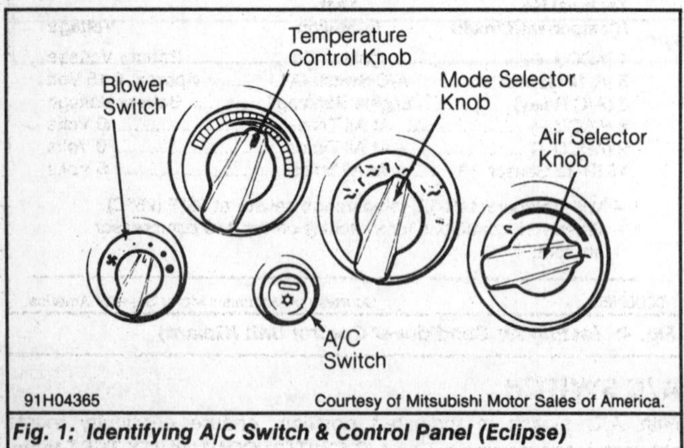
Temperature Control Knob
Blower Switch
Mode Selector Knob
Air Selector Knob
A/C Switch
91H04365
Courtesy of Mitsubishi Motor Sales of America.

Fig. 1: Identifying A/C Switch & Control Panel (Eclipse)

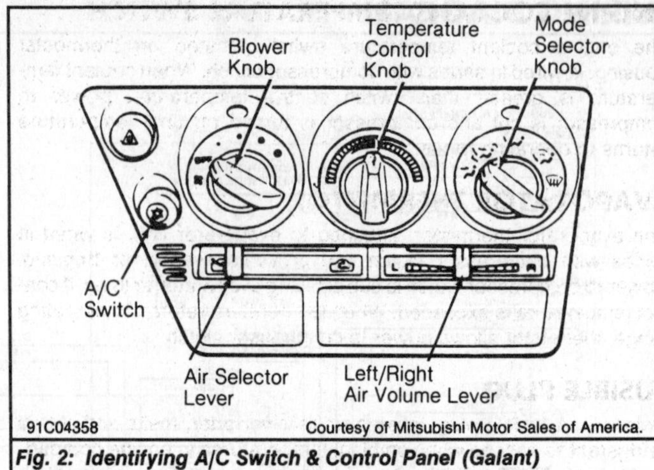
Blower Knob
Temperature Control Knob
Mode Selector Knob
A/C Switch
Air Selector Lever
Left/Right Air Volume Lever
91C04358
Courtesy of Mitsubishi Motor Sales of America.

Fig. 2: Identifying A/C Switch & Control Panel (Galant)

AIR SELECTOR KNOB/LEVER

Eclipse – The air selector knob is located on the left side of control panel. This knob controls the source of airflow into passenger compartment. When knob is in the right position, outside air will be allowed to enter passenger compartment. When knob is in the left position, air is recirculated inside of passenger compartment. The recirculation position is used to achieve maximum A/C cooling.

Galant – The air selector lever is located in the lower left corner of control panel and moves horizontally. This lever will control the source of airflow into the passenger compartment. When lever is in the left position, outside air will be allowed to enter passenger compartment. When lever is in the right position, air is recirculated inside of passenger compartment. The recirculation position is used to achieve maximum A/C cooling.

BLOWER MOTOR CONTROL KNOB

The blower knob is located to the right (left on Eclipse) of A/C switch and can only be operated when ignition switch is in ON position. Blower knob has 5 positions, ranging from the OFF position to maximum blower speed.

MODE SELECTOR KNOB

The mode selector knob is located on the control panel and uses 6 different control positions to control the directional flow of air inside of passenger compartment. When knob is in the face position, air will only flow to upper part of passenger area.

When knob is moved to first foot/face position, air will flow to upper part of passenger compartment and partially to the leg area. When knob is in the second foot/face position, air will flow to leg area and slightly to the upper area of passenger compartment.

When knob is in foot position, air will flow to the front and rear leg areas. When knob is in the foot/defrost position, air will flow to the front and rear leg areas and to the front windshield and door windows. When the knob is in the defrost position, air is directed only to windshield and door windows for defrosting of windows.

TEMPERATURE CONTROL KNOB

The temperature control knob is located in the center of control panel (left side on Eclipse) and is used to select the desired temperature level by turning it clockwise or counterclockwise. Turning knob clockwise will gradually warm temperature as desired.

DUAL-PRESSURE SWITCH

The dual-pressure switch, located in the refrigerant line near condenser, is wired in series with compressor clutch. Whenever system pressures decrease to less than or increase to more than the control point of the switch, power supplied to compressor will be cut and compressor activity will cease until pressures are back to within operating ranges.

ENGINE COOLANT TEMPERATURE SWITCH

The engine coolant temperature switch, located on thermostat housing, is wired in series with compressor clutch. When coolant temperature is greater than switch control temperature, power to compressor is cut and compressor is turned off until temperature returns to operating range.

EVAPORATOR THERMISTOR

The evaporator thermistor, attached to evaporator fins, is wired in series with compressor clutch and prevents evaporator freezing. Power to compressor clutch is cut, allowing evaporator to thaw, if control temperature is exceeded. When temperature returns to operating range, thermistor allows power to compressor clutch.

FUSIBLE PLUG

Galant – A fusible plug, located on receiver-drier, melts and allows refrigerant to escape when ambient temperatures in engine compartment reach 221°F (105°C). Once fusible plug has blown, it cannot be reused and must be replaced.

REFRIGERANT TEMPERATURE SWITCH

Galant – The refrigerant temperature switch, located on rear of compressor, detects refrigerant temperature discharged from compressor. A/C Control Unit (ACCU) uses this information to control compressor clutch cycling.

ADJUSTMENTS

NOTE: For adjustment procedures, see HEATER SYSTEMS – ECLIPSE & GALANT article.

TROUBLE SHOOTING

AIR NOT COOL

1) Ensure compressor clutch is operating. If compressor clutch is not operating, check fuses and relay. Check A/C switch. Check high and low pressure switches and dual-pressure switch. Check thermistor, thermo relay or Electronic Cycling Clutch Switch (ECCS). Check blower switch and relay. Check A/C compressor clutch coil.

2) Ensure system is properly charged with correct amount of refrigerant. Add refrigerant or evacuate and recharge system as necessary. Ensure receiver-drier is not clogged. Check compressor belt for proper tension. Check for clogged expansion valve. Check compressor operation. Repair or replace compressor as necessary.

INSUFFICIENT AIRFLOW

Check for air leakage at air duct joint. Check for frost on evaporator. Ensure blower motor is operating properly. Check for obstructed air intake.

INSUFFICIENT COOLING

Ensure system is properly charged with correct amount of refrigerant and free of air and moisture. Add refrigerant or evacuate and recharge system as necessary. Ensure receiver-drier is not clogged. Ensure sufficient airflow through condenser exists. Check compressor belt for proper tension. Check compressor operation. Repair or replace compressor as necessary. Check for clogged expansion valve. Replace expansion valve as necessary.

INTERMITTENT COOL AIR

Check for air or moisture in system. Evacuate and recharge system as necessary. Check for expansion valve malfunction. Replace expansion valve if necessary. Check compressor belt for proper tension.

TESTING

A/C SYSTEM PERFORMANCE

1) Park vehicle out of direct sunlight. Install A/C gauge set. Start engine and allow it to idle at 1000 RPM. Set A/C controls to recirculate air, panel (vent) mode, full cold, and A/C button on.

2) Set blower/fan on high speed and close doors and windows. Insert thermometer in center vent. Operate system for 20 minutes to allow system to stabilize. Measure temperature. Temperature must be 37-42°F (3-6°C) at center vent, with high side and low side pressures within specification. See SPECIFICATIONS table at beginning of article.

AIR CONDITIONER CONTROL UNIT

1) Disconnect A/C Control Unit (ACCU), and inspect connector and wiring for damage. Turn ignition on. Turn A/C switch to ON position.

2) Turn temperature control to maximum cooling setting and blower switch to high setting. Using a DVOM set to appropriate test function, inspect wiring harness side of connector. *See Fig. 3 or 4.* If all test readings are as specified, replace control unit.

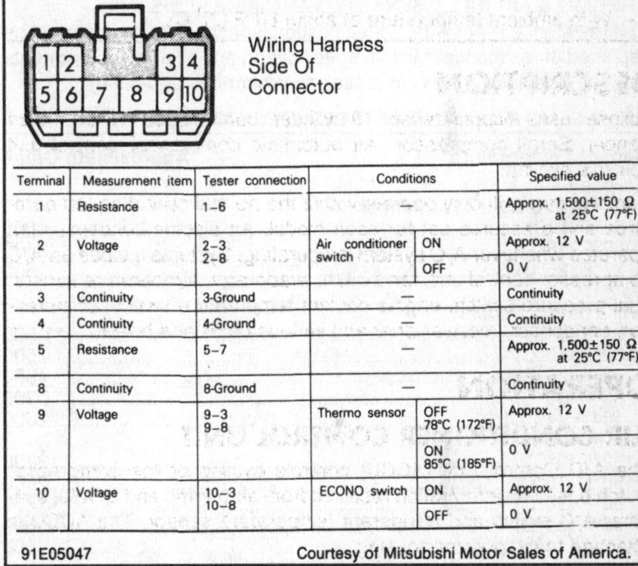
1 2 3 4
5 6 7 8 9 10
Wiring Harness
Side Of
Connector

Terminal	Measurement item	Tester connection	Conditions		Specified value
1	Resistance	1–6	—		Approx. 1,500±150 Ω at 25°C (77°F)
2	Voltage	2–3 2–8	Air conditioner switch	ON	Approx. 12 V
				OFF	0 V
3	Continuity	3-Ground	—		Continuity
4	Continuity	4-Ground	—		Continuity
5	Resistance	5–7	—		Approx. 1,500±150 Ω at 25°C (77°F)
8	Continuity	8-Ground	—		Continuity
9	Voltage	9–3 9–8	Thermo sensor	OFF 78°C (172°F)	Approx. 12 V
				ON 85°C (185°F)	0 V
10	Voltage	10–3 10–8	ECONO switch	ON	Approx. 12 V
				OFF	0 V

91E05047 Courtesy of Mitsubishi Motor Sales of America.

Fig. 3: Testing Air Conditioner Control Unit (Eclipse)

GALANT AIR CONDITIONER CONTROL UNIT (ACCU) TEST

Terminal No. (Component/Circuit)	Test Condition	Voltage
1 (ACCU +)	Ignition On	Battery Voltage
5 (R-12 Sensor –)	A/C Switch Off [1]	Approx. 0.15 Volt
6 (A/C Relay)	Engine Running [2]	Battery Voltage
8 (ACCU –)	At All Times	0 Volts
9 (ACCU –)	At All Times	0 Volts
12 (R-12 Sensor +)	At All times	5 Volts

[1] – With refrigerant (R-12) temperature sensor at 58°F (25°C).
[2] – When ALL conditions for switching on the A/C compressor are met.

92D02661 Courtesy of Mitsubishi Motor Sales of America.

Fig. 4: Testing Air Conditioner Control Unit (Galant)

A/C SWITCH

With A/C switch in indicated position, ensure continuity exists between listed terminals. See A/C SWITCH CONTINUITY TEST table. *See Fig. 5.*

1993 MANUAL A/C-HEATER SYSTEMS
Eclipse & Galant (Cont.)

A/C SWITCH CONTINUITY TEST

Switch Position [1]	Terminal No.	Continuity
OFF	1, 2 & 4	No
ECONOMY	1 & 4	Yes
A/C	1, 2 & 4	Yes

[1] – Terminals No. 3 and 6 should have continuity in all positions (light bulb circuit).

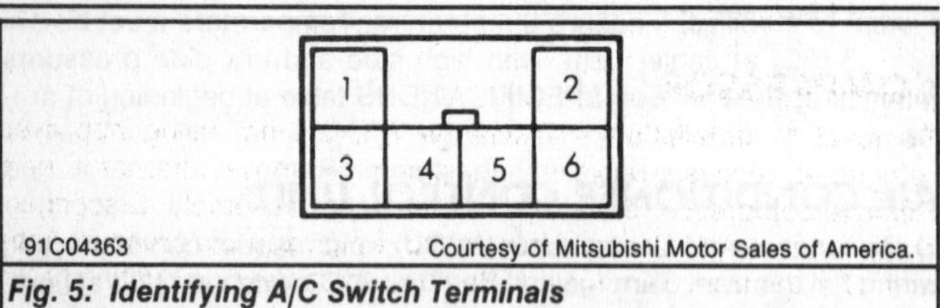
1
2
3
4
5
6

91C04363 Courtesy of Mitsubishi Motor Sales of America.

Fig. 5: Identifying A/C Switch Terminals

AIR THERMO & AIR INLET SENSORS

1) Disconnect sensor connector at top of evaporator case. Using an ohmmeter, measure continuity between sensor terminals. See AIR THERMO & AIR INLET SENSORS SPECIFICATIONS table.
2) If resistance is not within specification, sensor is faulty and must be replaced. If resistance is within specification and all other components are okay, replace A/C compressor control unit (if equipped).

AIR THERMO & AIR INLET SENSORS SPECIFICATIONS

Sensor Temperature	Approximate Ohms
Eclipse	
Air Thermo & Air Inlet Sensor	
32°F (0°C)	4800
59°F (15°C)	2400
77°F (25°C)	1500
Galant	
Air Thermo Sensor	
32°F (0°C)	11,500
50°F (10°C)	7500
68°F (20°C)	4800
86°F (30°C)	3300
104°F (40°C)	2300
Air Inlet Sensor	
32°F (0°C)	3300
50°F (10°C)	2000
68°F (20°C)	1250
86°F (30°C)	800
104°F (40°C)	500

BLOWER RESISTOR

Disconnect blower resistor connector. Using an ohmmeter, measure resistance between terminals indicated in BLOWER RESISTOR RESISTANCE table. *See Fig. 6.*

BLOWER RESISTOR RESISTANCE

Terminal No.	Approximate Ohms
1 & 3	.29-.33
2 & 3	1.70-1.95
3 & 4	.81-.93

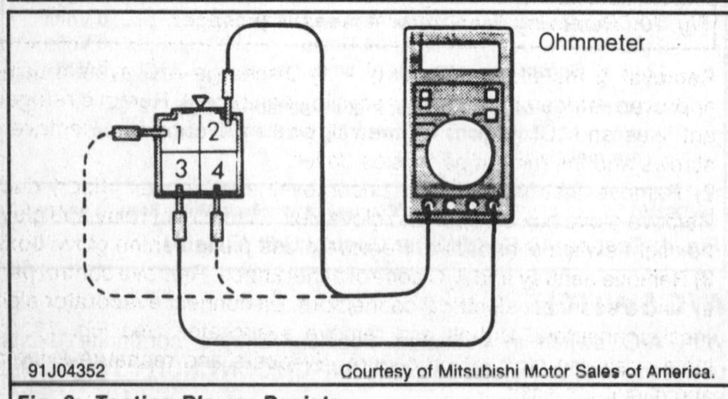
Ohmmeter
1
2
3
4

91J04352 Courtesy of Mitsubishi Motor Sales of America.

Fig. 6: Testing Blower Resistor

BLOWER SWITCH

With blower switch in position indicated in BLOWER SWITCH CONTINUITY TEST table, ensure continuity exists between listed terminals. *See Fig. 7.*

BLOWER SWITCH CONTINUITY TEST

Switch Position	Terminal No.	Continuity
OFF	[1]	No
Low	1 & 8; 3 & 5	Yes
Medium 1	1 & 8; 5 & 6	Yes
Medium 2	1, 4 & 8; 2 & 5	Yes
High	1, 4 & 8; 5 & 7	Yes

[1] – Continuity should not exist between any terminals.

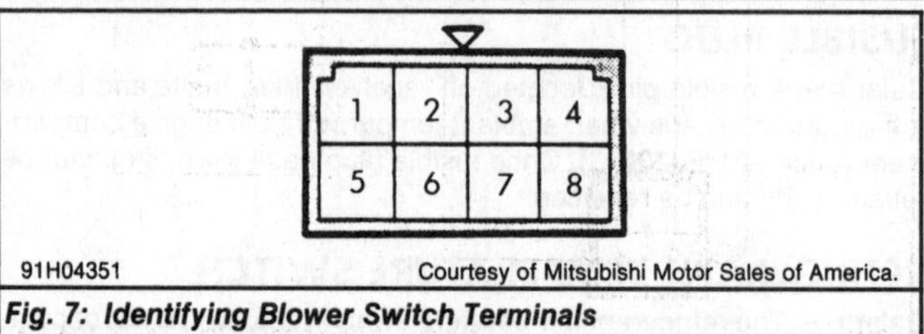
1
2
3
4
5
6
7
8

91H04351 Courtesy of Mitsubishi Motor Sales of America.

Fig. 7: Identifying Blower Switch Terminals

DUAL-PRESSURE SWITCH

1) Turn engine off. Disconnect harness connector at dual-pressure switch (located near condenser). Jumper harness connector. Turn A/C switch and blower switch to ON positions. Momentarily turn ignition on and listen for compressor clutch engagement.
2) If compressor clutch does not engage, check evaporator thermistor and engine coolant temperature switch. Check for a faulty fuse. Repair or replace components as necessary. If compressor clutch engages, go to next step.
3) Connect manifold gauge set to system, and check operating pressures. Dual-pressure switch should allow compressor operation if system pressure is 30-384 psi (2-27 kg/cm²). If dual-pressure switch does not operate within specified pressure range, discharge system using approved refrigerant recovery/recycling equipment and replace switch.
4) After replacing switch, recharge system and monitor pressures for proper compressor operation. If dual-pressure switch cuts power to compressor clutch during driving even though inside temperatures have not yet decreased, high pressure side of dual-pressure switch has possibly been activated. Go to next step.
5) Discharge system using approved refrigerant recovery/recycling equipment. Replace switch, and recharge system. Ensure compressor clutch operates within 30-384 psi (2-27 kg/cm²). Check for sufficient system cooling.

ENGINE COOLANT TEMPERATURE SWITCH

1) Turn engine off. Disconnect connector at engine coolant temperature switch. Jumper wires on harness side of connector. If vehicle uses a single connector, ground connector.
2) Press A/C switch to ON position, and turn blower switch to ON position. Momentarily turn ignition on and listen for compressor clutch engagement. Clutch should engage. If clutch does not engage, check fuse and other components wired in series with compressor clutch.

COMPRESSOR CLUTCH

Disconnect wiring to compressor clutch. Connect battery voltage directly to A/C compressor clutch wiring harness connector terminals. If click is heard, clutch engagement is okay. If click is not heard, pulley and armature are not making contact. Repair or replace compressor clutch as necessary.

REFRIGERANT TEMPERATURE SENSOR

Disconnect refrigerant temperature sensor electrical connector. Using an ohmmeter, measure resistance between terminals. At 77°F (25°C), resistance should be about 80,470 ohms. If resistance deviates greatly, replace sensor.

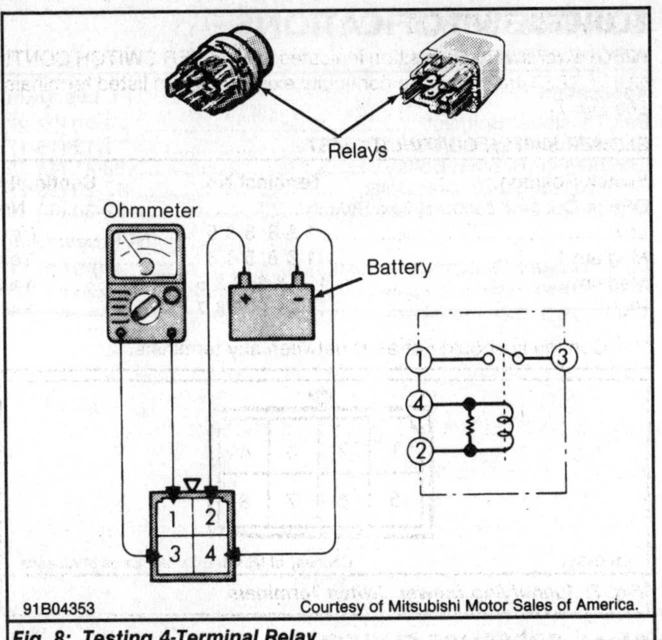
Relays
Ohmmeter
Battery
1
2
3
4
91B04353
Courtesy of Mitsubishi Motor Sales of America.

Fig. 8: Testing 4-Terminal Relay

RELAYS

4-Terminal Relay - 1) Relays may be round or square. Testing is same for either type. Remove relay from holder. Using an ohmmeter, ensure continuity exists between terminals No. 2 and 4 and does not exist between terminals No. 1 and 3. *See Fig. 8.*

2) Connect battery voltage to terminal No. 2, and ground terminal No. 4. Ensure continuity exists between terminals No. 1 and 3. If continuity is not as specified, replace relay.

5-Terminal Relay (Eclipse) - Remove relay from holder. Using an ohmmeter, ensure continuity exists between terminals No. 1 and 4 and terminals No. 3 and 5 and does not exist between terminals No. 1 and 2. Connect battery voltage to terminal No. 3, and ground terminal No. 5. Ensure continuity exists between terminals No. 1 and 2. *See Fig. 9.* If continuity is not as specified, replace relay.

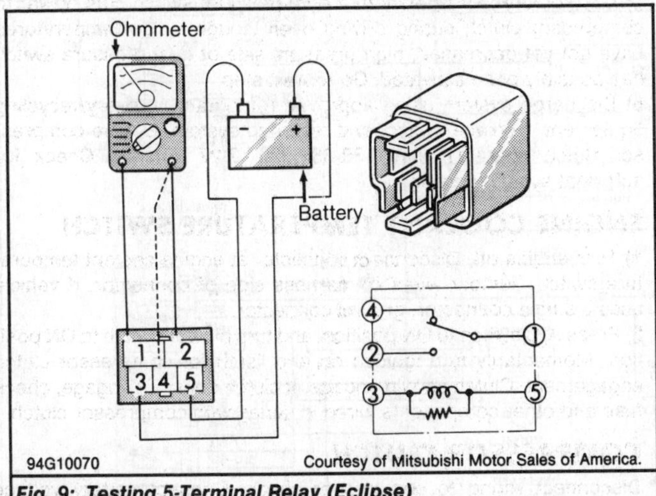
Ohmmeter
Battery
1
2
3
4
5
94G10070
Courtesy of Mitsubishi Motor Sales of America.

Fig. 9: Testing 5-Terminal Relay (Eclipse)

REMOVAL & INSTALLATION

NOTE: For removal and installation procedures not covered in this article, see appropriate HEATER SYSTEMS article.

A/C SWITCH

Removal & Installation (Eclipse) - Remove radio. Insert hand into radio opening and push A/C switch out of dash. Remove electrical connector and A/C switch. To install, reverse removal procedure.

Removal & Installation (Galant) - Remove ashtray. Remove air selector and right/left air volume lever knobs. Remove 4 screws and heater control panel. Disconnect A/C switch electrical connector. Remove 2 screws and A/C switch. To install A/C switch, reverse removal procedure.

COMPRESSOR

Removal & Installation - Discharge A/C system using approved refrigerant recovery/recycling equipment. Remove alternator belt. Remove compressor drive belt and tensioner assembly. Disconnect compressor electrical connector. Remove high and low pressure lines and "O" rings from compressor. Remove compressor mounting bolts. Remove compressor. To install, reverse removal procedure.

CONDENSER

Removal & Installation - Discharge A/C system using approved refrigerant recovery/recycling equipment. Remove air inlet hose. Remove condenser fan assembly (if necessary). Disconnect refrigerant lines from condenser. Remove upper radiator mounting bolts. Remove power relay assembly with mount. Slide condenser out of vehicle. To install, reverse removal procedure.

EVAPORATOR ASSEMBLY

Removal & Installation (Eclipse) - 1) Discharge A/C system using approved refrigerant recovery/recycling equipment. Remove refrigerant lines and "O" rings from firewall side of evaporator. Remove glove box stopper and glove box. *See Fig. 10.* Remove lower glove box frame.

2) Remove right shower (floor) duct (if equipped). Disconnect evaporator electrical connectors. Unbolt and remove evaporator. To install, reverse removal procedure. Evacuate and recharge system, and check for leaks.

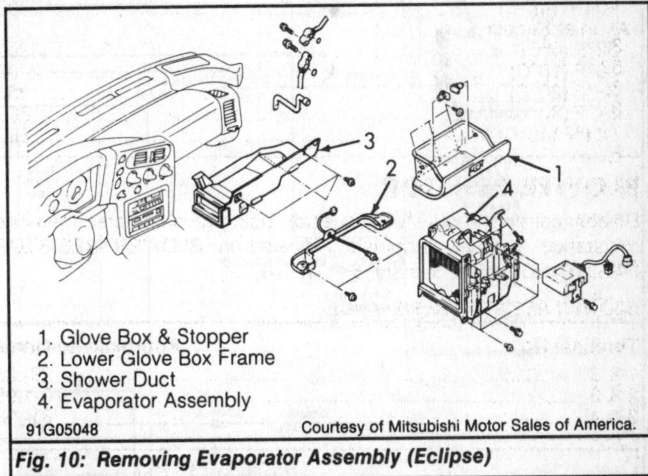
1
2
3
4
1. Glove Box & Stopper
2. Lower Glove Box Frame
3. Shower Duct
4. Evaporator Assembly
91G05048
Courtesy of Mitsubishi Motor Sales of America.

Fig. 10: Removing Evaporator Assembly (Eclipse)

Removal & Installation (Galant) - 1) Discharge A/C system using approved refrigerant recovery/recycling equipment. Remove refrigerant lines and "O" rings from firewall side of evaporator. Remove 3 screws and instrument panel side cover.

2) Remove instrument panel undercover and shower (floor) duct. Remove glove box stopper and glove box. Disconnect relay and glove box light switch connectors. Remove cross piece behind glove box.

3) Remove ashtray and A/C control panel knobs. Remove control panel, and disconnect electrical connectors. Disconnect evaporator electrical connectors. Unbolt and remove evaporator. *See Fig. 11.* To install, reverse removal procedure. Evacuate and recharge system, and check for leaks.

1993 MANUAL A/C-HEATER SYSTEMS
Eclipse & Galant (Cont.)

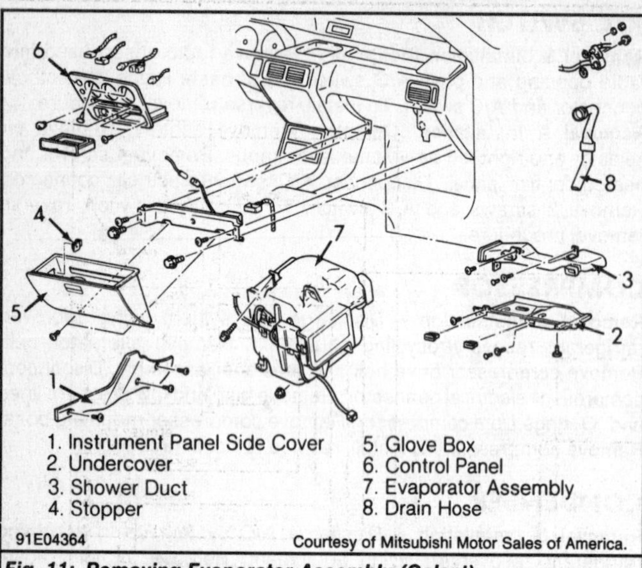
1. Instrument Panel Side Cover
2. Undercover
3. Shower Duct
4. Stopper
5. Glove Box
6. Control Panel
7. Evaporator Assembly
8. Drain Hose
91E04364
Courtesy of Mitsubishi Motor Sales of America.

Fig. 11: Removing Evaporator Assembly (Galant)

TORQUE SPECIFICATIONS

TORQUE SPECIFICATIONS

Application	Ft. Lbs. (N.m)
Belt Tensioner Bolt/Nut	17-20 (23-27)
Clutch Mounting Bolt/Nut	11-13 (15-17)
Compressor Bracket Bolts	33-41 (45-55)
Compressor-To-Bracket Bolts	17-20 (23-27)
Engine Coolant Temperature Switch	22-30 (30-40)
	INCH Lbs. (N.m)
Dual Pressure Switch	80-97 (9-11)
Duct Screws	13-22 (1.5-2.5)

WIRING DIAGRAMS

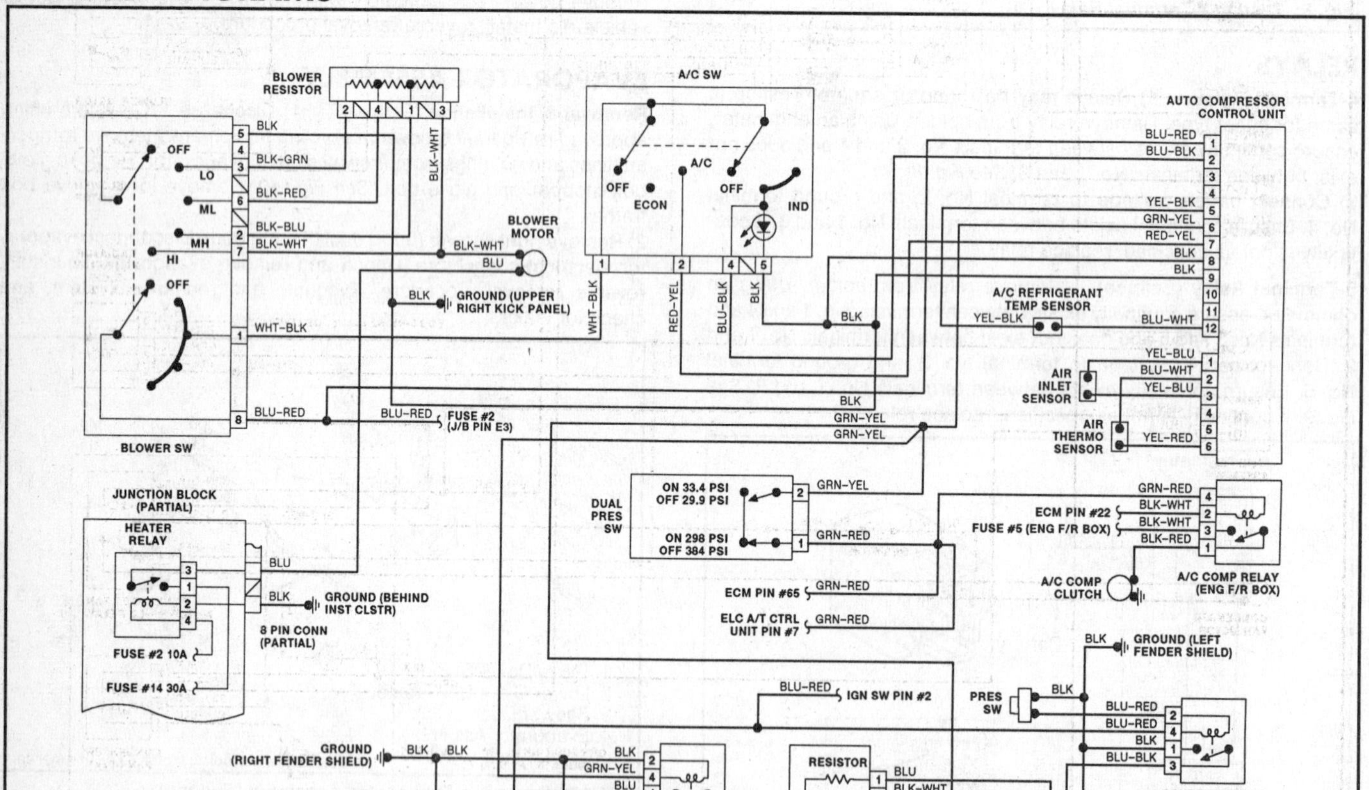

94H10659

Fig. 12: Manual A/C-Heater System Wiring Diagram (Galant)

1993 MANUAL A/C-HEATER SYSTEMS
Eclipse & Galant (Cont.)

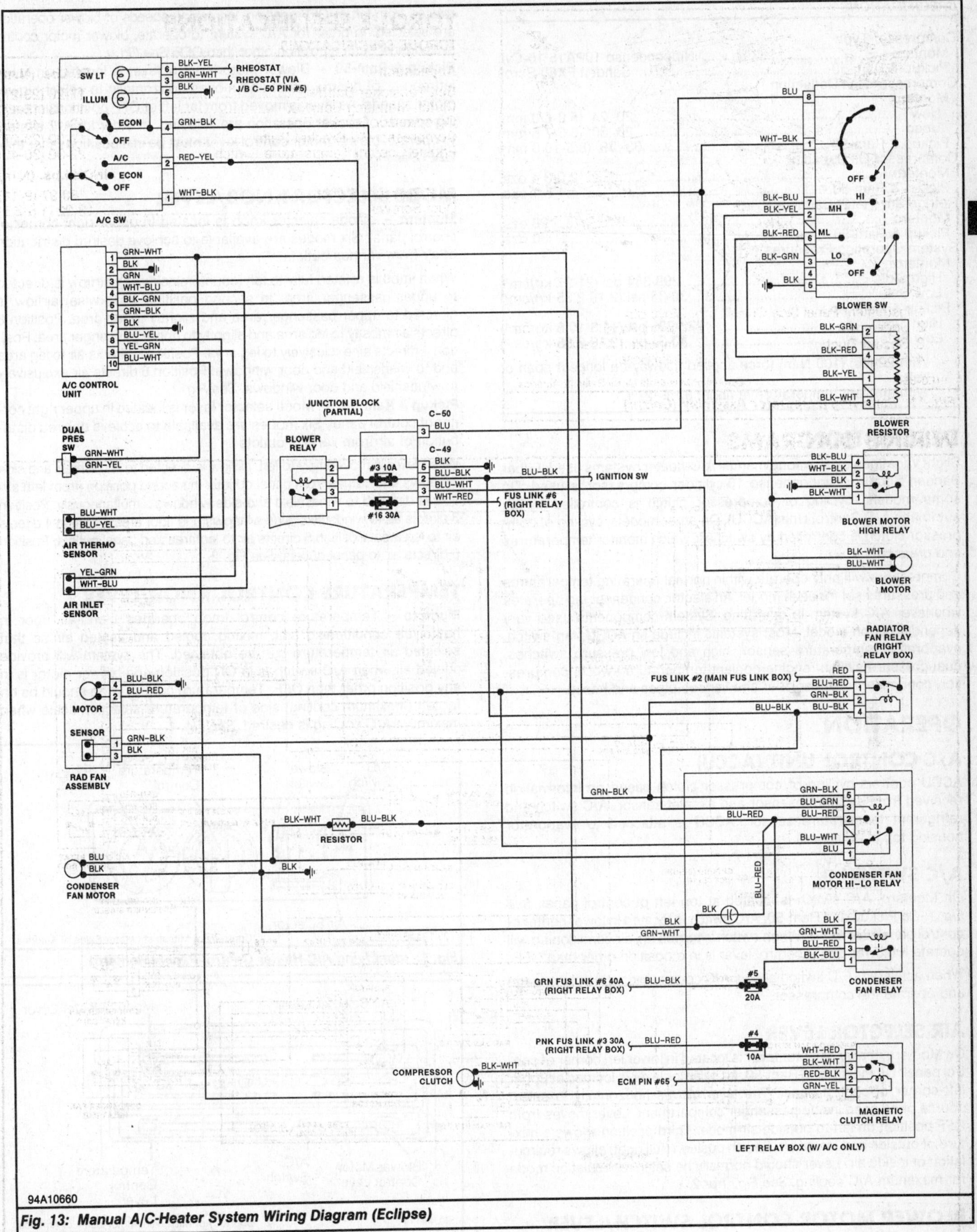
SW LT
ILLUM
ECON
OFF
A/C
ECON
OFF
A/C SW
BLK-YEL
GRN-WHT
BLK
GRN-BLK
RED-YEL
WHT-BLK
RHEOSTAT
RHEOSTAT (VIA J/B C-50 PIN #5)
A/C CONTROL UNIT
GRN-WHT
BLK
GRN
WHT-BLU
BLK-GRN
GRN-BLK
BLK
BLU-YEL
YEL-GRN
BLU-WHT
DUAL PRES SW
GRN-WHT
GRN-YEL
BLU-WHT
BLU-YEL
AIR THERMO SENSOR
YEL-GRN
WHT-BLU
AIR INLET SENSOR
JUNCTION BLOCK (PARTIAL)
BLOWER RELAY
C-50
BLU
C-49
BLK
BLU-BLK
BLU-WHT
WHT-RED
#3 10A
#16 30A
BLU-BLK
IGNITION SW
FUS LINK #6 (RIGHT RELAY BOX)
MOTOR
SENSOR
BLU-BLK
BLU-RED
GRN-BLK
BLK
RAD FAN ASSEMBLY
BLK-WHT
BLU-BLK
RESISTOR
BLU
BLK
CONDENSER FAN MOTOR
COMPRESSOR CLUTCH
BLK-WHT
BLU
WHT-BLK
OFF
HI
BLK-BLU
BLK-YEL
MH
BLK-RED
ML
BLK-GRN
LO
OFF
BLK
BLOWER SW
BLK-GRN
BLK-RED
BLK-YEL
BLK-WHT
BLOWER RESISTOR
BLK-BLU
WHT-BLK
BLK
BLK-WHT
BLOWER MOTOR HIGH RELAY
BLK-WHT
BLU-WHT
BLOWER MOTOR
RADIATOR FAN RELAY (RIGHT RELAY BOX)
FUS LINK #2 (MAIN FUS LINK BOX)
RED
BLU-RED
GRN-BLK
BLU-BLK
BLU-BLK
GRN-BLK
GRN-BLK
BLU-GRN
BLU-RED
BLU-RED
BLU-WHT
BLU
CONDENSER FAN MOTOR HI-LO RELAY
BLU-RED
BLK
BLK
GRN-WHT
BLK
GRN-WHT
BLU-RED
BLK-BLU
CONDENSER FAN RELAY
GRN FUS LINK #6 40A (RIGHT RELAY BOX)
BLU-BLK
#5
20A
PNK FUS LINK #3 30A (RIGHT RELAY BOX)
BLU-RED
#4
10A
WHT-RED
BLK-WHT
RED-BLK
GRN-YEL
ECM PIN #65
MAGNETIC CLUTCH RELAY
LEFT RELAY BOX (W/ A/C ONLY)
94A10660

Fig. 13: Manual A/C-Heater System Wiring Diagram (Eclipse)

1993 MANUAL A/C-HEATER SYSTEMS
Montero, Pickup & Ram-50

SPECIFICATIONS

Compressor Type
- Montero ..... Nippondenso 10PA15 10-Cyl.
- Pickup & Ram-50 ..... Sanden FX80 Scroll

Compressor Belt Deflection [1]
- Montero
  - New ..... .20-.24" (5.0-6.0 mm)
  - Used ..... .26-.30" (6.5-7.5 mm)
- Pickup & Ram-50 ..... .33-.39" (8.5-10.0 mm)

Compressor Oil Capacity
- Montero ..... 2.0-3.4 ozs.
- Pickup & Ram-50 ..... 4.4-5.1 ozs.

Refrigerant (R-12) Capacity
- Montero ..... 28 ozs.
- Pickup & Ram-50 ..... 30 ozs.

System Operating Pressures [2]
- Montero
  - High Side ..... 299-384 psi (21-27 kg/cm^2)
  - Low Side ..... 30-33 psi (2.10-2.35 kg/cm^2)
- Pickup & Ram-50
  - High Side ..... 222-235 psi (11.3-10.8 kg/cm^2)
  - Low Side ..... 30-33 psi (2.10-2.35 kg/cm^2)

[1] – With 22 lbs. (100 N.m) force applied midway on longest span of belt.

[2] – With ambient temperature at about 80°F (27°C).

DESCRIPTION

Slight variations exist among manual A/C-heater systems used. Either Sanden Scroll or Nippondenso 10-cylinder compressor is used. On some models, cycling of compressor clutch is controlled by an automatic A/C Control Unit (ACCU). On other models, cycling of compressor clutch is controlled by switches, which monitor temperatures and pressures.

Compressors will only operate within normal operating temperatures and pressures set for each model. An electric condenser fan operates whenever A/C system is operating. System components used vary depending upon model. Most systems include an ACCU, fan switch, evaporator, temperature sensor, high and low pressure switches, dual-pressure switch, engine coolant temperature switch, compressor, condenser, receiver-drier and various pipes and hoses.

OPERATION

A/C CONTROL UNIT (ACCU)

ACCU controls cycling of compressor clutch based on information received from air thermosensor and air inlet sensor, A/C switch and refrigerant temperature sensor. ACCU is attached to evaporator housing top (if equipped).

A/C SWITCH

On Montero, A/C switch is located at top left of control panel. *See Fig. 1.* On Pickup and Ram-50, A/C switch is located in lower center of control panel. *See Fig. 2.* When switch is turned on, air conditioning will operate if blower motor control lever is in a position other than OFF.

When activated, A/C switch allows A/C compressor clutch to engage and operate the compressor.

AIR SELECTOR LEVER

On Montero, the air selector lever is located in lower left corner of control panel. On Pickup and Ram-50, air selector lever is located at upper left corner of control panel. The lever moves horizontally to select source of air used inside passenger compartment. Lever moves from OFF position on left to outside air mode. Third position allows a mixture of outside and inside air. Fourth position (full right) allows recirculation of inside air. Lever should normally be set in recirculation mode for maximum A/C cooling. *See Fig. 1 or 2.*

BLOWER MOTOR CONTROL SWITCH/LEVER

Montero – Blower motor control switch is located on upper left corner of control panel and rotates to select blower motor speeds. As switch is rotated from left or OFF position, increasing speeds of blower operation are selected. In order for A/C system to operate, blower motor control switch must be in a position other than OFF. *See Fig. 1.*

Pickup & Ram-50 – Blower motor control lever is located on lower left corner of control panel and moves horizontally to select blower motor speeds. As lever is moved from far left or OFF position, increasing speeds of blower operation are selected. In order for A/C system to operate, blower motor control lever must be in a position other than OFF. *See Fig. 2.*

MODE SELECTOR KNOB/LEVER

Montero – Mode selector knob is located in upper right corner of control panel. Six modes are available to achieve desired distribution of air from various outlets.

When knob is rotated fully to left (counterclockwise), airflow is directed to upper passenger area. In second position (clockwise) airflow is directed to upper passenger area and slightly to leg area. Position 3 directs air mostly to leg area and slightly to upper passenger area. Position 4 directs air exclusively to leg area. Position 5 directs air to leg area and to windshield and door windows. Position 6 directs air exclusively to windshield and door windows. *See Fig. 1.*

Pickup & Ram-50 – Mode selector lever is located in upper right corner of control panel. Six modes are available to achieve desired distribution of air from various outlets.

When lever is moved fully to left, airflow is directed to windshield and side windows and comes from panel outlets. In second position (from left) airflow is directed to windshield and side windows simultaneously. Position 3 directs air to windshield, side windows and floor area. Position 4 directs air to leg area. Position 5 directs air to leg area and panel outlets. Position 6 directs air to panel outlets. *See Fig. 2.*

TEMPERATURE CONTROL KNOB/LEVER

Montero – Temperature control knob operates blend-air door in heater/air conditioning unit, mixing cooled and heated air so that selected air temperature can be obtained. The system will provide cooled air when A/C switch is in ON position and blower motor is in any position other than OFF. Temperature control knob should be on far left (maximum cooling) side of temperature selection scale when maximum A/C cooling is desired. *See Fig. 1.*

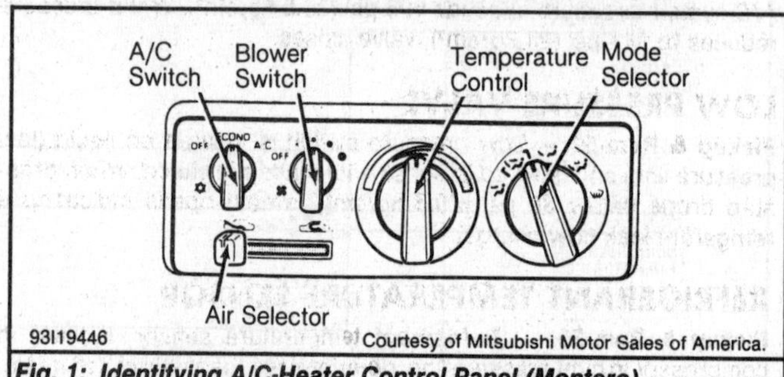
A/C
Switch
Blower
Switch
Temperature
Control
Mode
Selector
OFF
Air Selector
93I19446
Courtesy of Mitsubishi Motor Sales of America.

Fig. 1: Identifying A/C-Heater Control Panel (Montero)

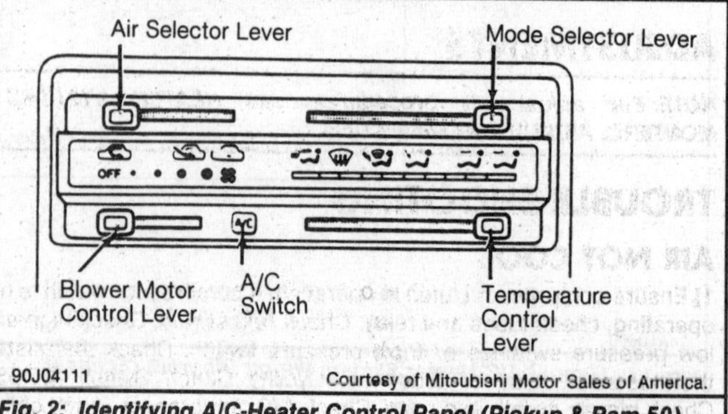
Air Selector Lever
Mode Selector Lever
OFF
Blower Motor
Control Lever
A/C
Switch
Temperature
Control
Lever
90J04111
Courtesy of Mitsubishi Motor Sales of America.

Fig. 2: Identifying A/C-Heater Control Panel (Pickup & Ram-50)

Pickup & Ram-50 - Temperature control lever is located at lower right of control panel. Temperature control lever operates blend-air door in heater/air conditioning unit, mixing cooled air and heated air so that selected air temperature can be obtained. System will provide cooled air when A/C switch is in ON position and blower motor is in any position other than OFF. Temperature control lever should be at far left for maximum A/C cooling. *See Fig. 2.*

DUAL-PRESSURE SWITCH

Montero - The dual-pressure switch, mounted on receiver-drier, is wired in series with compressor clutch. Whenever system pressures drop below or increase above control points of switch, power supplied to compressor will be cut and compressor function will cease, until pressures are back to normal operating ranges.

ENGINE COOLANT TEMPERATURE SWITCH

The engine coolant temperature switch, located on thermostat housing, is wired in series with compressor clutch. When coolant temperature is greater than switch control temperature, power to compressor is cut and compressor is turned off until temperature returns to operating range. Switch will turn on at 226°F (108°C) and off at 234-244°F (112-118°C).

EVAPORATOR THERMISTOR

The evaporator thermistor, attached to evaporator fins, is wired in series with compressor clutch and prevents evaporator freezing. Power to compressor clutch is cut if control temperature is exceeded, allowing evaporator to thaw. When temperature returns to operating range, thermistor again allows power to compressor clutch.

FUSIBLE PLUG

A fusible plug, located on receiver-drier, melts and allows refrigerant to escape when ambient temperature in engine compartment reaches 221°F (105°C). Once fusible plug has blown, it cannot be reused and must be replaced.

HIGH PRESSURE RELIEF VALVE

Pickup & Ram-50 - High pressure relief valve, located on compressor, is a safety feature which vents refrigerant to atmosphere when A/C system pressure exceeds 505 psi (35.5 kg/cm²). When pressure reduces to 341 psi (24 kg/cm²), valve closes.

LOW PRESSURE VALVE

Pickup & Ram-50 - Low pressure switch is located on liquid (low pressure line) and is wired in series with magnetic clutch. When pressure drops below 30 psi (20.6 kg/cm²), switch opens indicating a refrigerant leak (low charge).

REFRIGERANT TEMPERATURE SENSOR

Pickup & Ram-50 - Refrigerant temperature sensor, located at compressor in high pressure line, de-energizes magnetic clutch if temperature exceeds 347°F (175°C) due to a problem in system.

ADJUSTMENTS

***NOTE:* For adjustment procedures, see HEATER SYSTEMS - MONTERO, PICKUP & RAM-50 article.**

TROUBLE SHOOTING

AIR NOT COOL

1) Ensure compressor clutch is operating. If compressor clutch is not operating, check fuses and relay. Check A/C switch. Check high and low pressure switches or triple-pressure switch. Check thermistor, thermosensor relay or Electronic Cycling Clutch Switch (ECCS). Check blower switch and relay. Check A/C compressor clutch coil.

2) Ensure system is properly charged with correct amount of refrigerant. Add refrigerant or evacuate and recharge system as necessary. Ensure receiver-drier is not clogged. Check compressor belt for proper tension. Check for clogged expansion valve. Check compressor operation. Repair or replace components as necessary.

INSUFFICIENT AIRFLOW

Check for air leakage at air duct joint. Check for frost on evaporator. Ensure blower motor is operating properly. Check for obstructed air intake.

INSUFFICIENT COOLING

Ensure system is properly charged with correct amount of refrigerant and free of air and moisture. Add refrigerant or evacuate and recharge system as necessary. Ensure receiver-drier is not clogged. Ensure sufficient airflow through condenser exists. Check compressor belt for proper tension. Check compressor operation. Repair or replace compressor as necessary. Check for clogged expansion valve. Replace expansion valve as necessary.

INTERMITTENT COOL AIR

Check for air or moisture in system. Evacuate and recharge system as necessary. Check for expansion valve malfunction. Replace expansion valve if necessary. Check compressor belt for proper tension.

TESTING

***NOTE:* For testing procedures not covered in this article, see HEATER SYSTEMS - MONTERO, PICKUP & RAM-50 article.**

A/C SYSTEM PERFORMANCE

1) Park vehicle out of direct sunlight. Install A/C gauge set. Start engine and allow it to idle at 1000 RPM. Set A/C controls to recirculate air, panel (vent) mode, full cold, and A/C button on.

2) Set blower/fan on high speed and close doors and windows. Insert thermometer in center vent. Operate system for 20 minutes to allow system to stabilize. Measure temperature. Temperature must be 37-42°F (3-6°C) at center vent, with high side and low side pressures within specification. See SPECIFICATIONS table at beginning of article.

A/C CONTROL UNIT (ACCU)

Montero - Disconnect ACCU, found on top of evaporator case, and conduct tests on wire harness side of connector. *See Fig. 3.* Testing is done with ignition on, A/C switch on, temperature control lever at MAX COOL and blower switch on HI. If voltage is not as specified, replace control unit. See A/C CONTROL UNIT (ACCU) VOLTAGE TESTS (MONTERO) table.

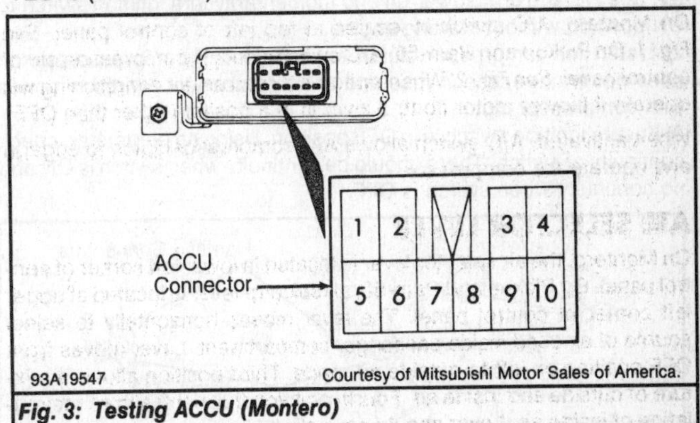
1
2
3
4
ACCU Connector
5
6
7
8
9
10
93A19547
Courtesy of Mitsubishi Motor Sales of America.

Fig. 3: Testing ACCU (Montero)

1993 MANUAL A/C-HEATER SYSTEMS
Montero, Pickup & Ram-50 (Cont.)

A/C CONTROL UNIT (ACCU) VOLTAGE TESTS (MONTERO)

Terminal No.	Terminal Voltage
1 (A/C Output)	Battery Voltage
3 (A/C Switch)	Battery Voltage
4 (Air Inlet Sensor +)	5.5 Volts
5 (A/C Switch: ECONO Or A/C)	Battery Voltage
6 (Lever Position Switch)	Zero Volts
7 (ACCU Ground)	Zero Volts
8 (Air Thermosensor -)	3.6 Volts
9 (Air Inlet Sensor -)	1.5 Volts
10 (Air Thermosensor +)	5.5 Volts

A/C SWITCH

Montero - 1) Disconnect A/C switch harness connector. Using wiring diagram as a guide, jumper appropriate terminals of A/C switch wiring harness connector. See WIRING DIAGRAMS.

2) Turn blower on and momentarily turn ignition on without starting engine. Listen for compressor clutch engagement. If compressor clutch does not engage, check fuse and other components wired in series with compressor clutch.

3) Using an ohmmeter, check continuity of switch. *See Fig. 4.* If continuity is not as specified, replace switch. See A/C SWITCH CONTINUITY TEST (MONTERO) table.

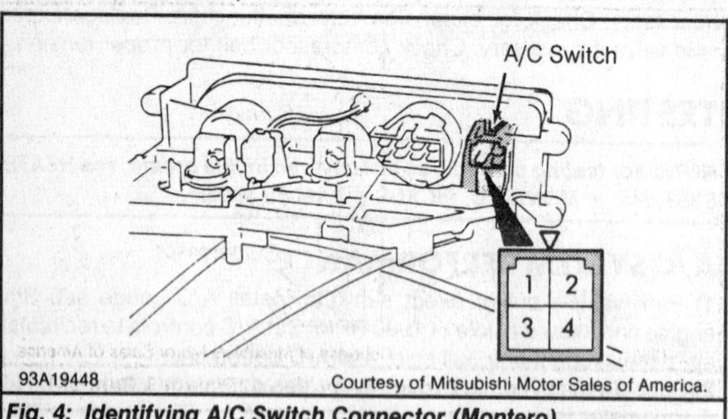
A/C Switch
1
2
3
4
93A19448
Courtesy of Mitsubishi Motor Sales of America.

Fig. 4: Identifying A/C Switch Connector (Montero)

A/C SWITCH CONTINUITY TEST (MONTERO)

Switch Position	Terminal No.	Continuity
OFF	[1]	No
ECONO	1 & 3	Yes
A/C	1, 3 & 4	Yes

[1] - Continuity should not exist between any terminals.

Pickup & Ram-50 - 1) Disconnect A/C switch harness connector. Jumper appropriate terminals of A/C switch wiring harness connector. *See Fig. 5.* Turn blower on and momentarily turn ignition switch to ON position without starting engine.

2) Listen for compressor clutch engagement. If compressor clutch does not engage, check fuse and other components wired in series with compressor clutch.

3) Ensure ignition switch is in OFF position. Using an ohmmeter, check continuity of switch. There should be continuity when switch is ON and no continuity when switch is OFF.

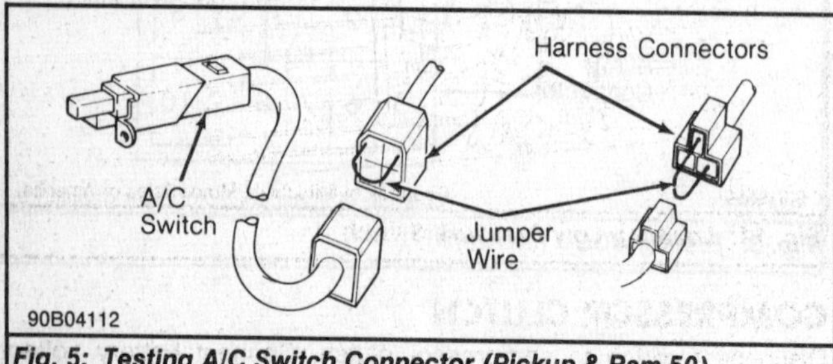
Harness Connectors
A/C
Switch
Jumper
Wire
90B04112

Fig. 5: Testing A/C Switch Connector (Pickup & Ram-50)

AIR THERMOSENSOR & AIR INLET SENSOR

Montero - 1) Disconnect sensor connector at evaporator case. Using an ohmmeter, measure resistance between sensor terminals. See AIR THERMOSENSOR & AIR INLET SENSOR SPECIFICATIONS (MONTERO) table.

2) If resistance is not within specifications, faulty sensor must be replaced. If resistance is within specifications and all other components are okay, replace A/C compressor control unit. *See Fig. 23.*

AIR THERMOSENSOR & AIR INLET SENSOR SPECIFICATIONS (MONTERO)

Sensor Temperature °F (°C)	Ohms
-20 (-4)	12,000
32 (0)	4800
50 (10)	2800
68 (20)	1800
86 (30)	1000
104 (40)	800

BLOWER RESISTOR

Disconnect blower resistor connector. Using an ohmmeter, measure resistance between terminals indicated in BLOWER RESISTOR RESISTANCE table. *See Figs. 6 and 7.*

BLOWER RESISTOR RESISTANCE

Terminal No.	Approximate Ohms
Montero	
1 & 2	0.95
2 & 3	0.33
2 & 4	1.96
Pickup & Ram-50	
1 & 2	1.19
1 & 3	0.50
1 & 4	2.33
1 & 5	0

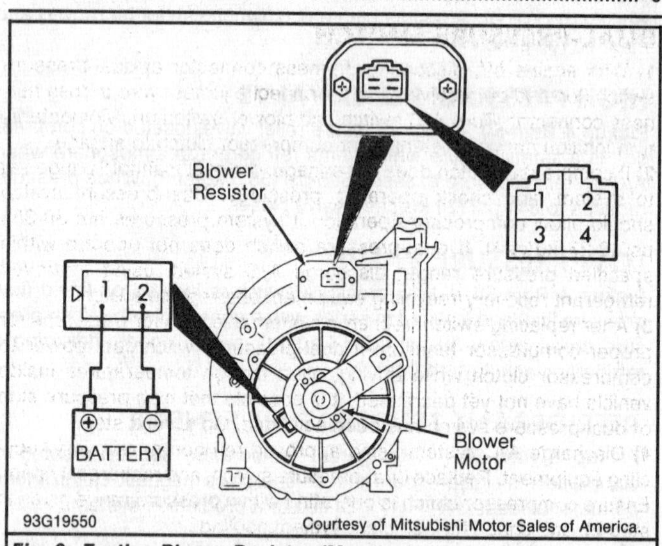
Blower
Resistor
1
2
3
4
BATTERY
Blower
Motor
93G19550
Courtesy of Mitsubishi Motor Sales of America.

Fig. 6: Testing Blower Resistor (Montero)

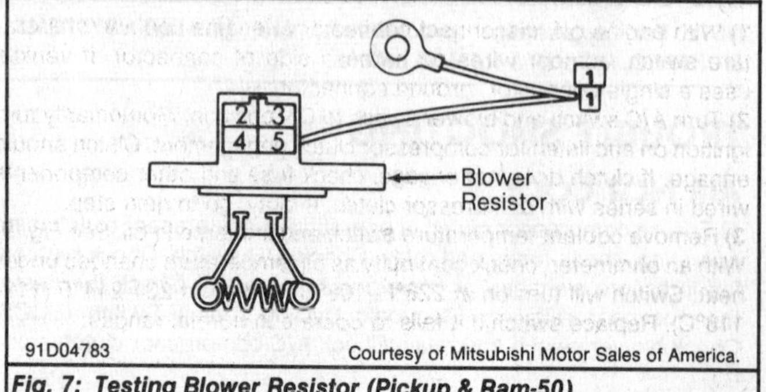
1
2 3
4 5
Blower
Resistor
91D04783
Courtesy of Mitsubishi Motor Sales of America.

Fig. 7: Testing Blower Resistor (Pickup & Ram-50)

BLOWER SWITCH

With blower switch in position indicated in BLOWER SWITCH CONTINUITY TEST table, ensure continuity exists between terminals listed. *See Fig. 8.*

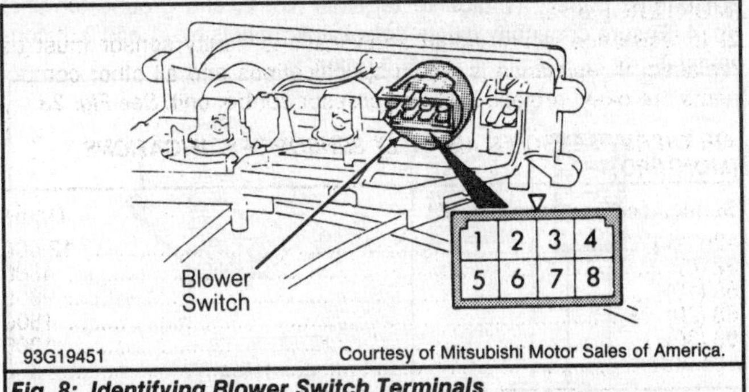
1 2 3 4
5 6 7 8
Blower
Switch
93G19451
Courtesy of Mitsubishi Motor Sales of America.

Fig. 8: Identifying Blower Switch Terminals

BLOWER SWITCH CONTINUITY TEST

Switch Position	Terminal No.
Montero	
OFF	[1]
Low	1 & 8; 3 & 5
Medium 1	1 & 8; 5 & 6
Medium 2	1, 4 & 8; 2 & 5
High	1, 4 & 8; 5 & 7
Pickup & Ram-50	
OFF	[1]
Low	1, 2 & 6
Medium 1	1, 3 & 6
Medium 2	1, 4 & 6
High	1, 5 & 6

[1] - Continuity should not exist between any terminals.

DUAL-PRESSURE SWITCH

1) With engine off, disconnect harness connector at dual-pressure switch (located on receiver-drier). Connect a jumper wire across harness connector. Turn A/C switch and blower switch on. Momentarily turn ignition on while listening for compressor clutch to engage.

2) If compressor clutch does not engage, connect manifold gauge set to system, and check operating pressures. Dual-pressure switch should allow compressor operation if system pressures are 30-384 psi (2-27 kg/cm²). If dual-pressure switch does not operate within specified pressure range, discharge A/C system using approved refrigerant recovery/recycling equipment and replace switch.

3) After replacing switch, recharge system and monitor pressures for proper compressor function. If dual-pressure switch cuts power to compressor clutch while driving, even though temperatures inside vehicle have not yet decreased, it is possible that high pressure side of dual-pressure switch has been activated. Go to next step.

4) Discharge A/C system using approved refrigerant recovery/recycling equipment. Replace dual-pressure switch, and recharge system. Ensure compressor clutch is operating within pressure range given in step **2)**, and check for sufficient system cooling.

A/C COOLANT TEMPERATURE SWITCH

1) With engine off, disconnect connector at engine coolant temperature switch. Jumper wires on harness side of connector. If vehicle uses a single connector, ground connector.

2) Turn A/C switch and blower switch to ON position. Momentarily turn ignition on and listen for compressor clutch engagement. Clutch should engage. If clutch does not engage, check fuse and other components wired in series with compressor clutch. If okay, go to next step.

3) Remove coolant temperature switch and immerse in oil. *See Fig. 9.* With an ohmmeter, check continuity as oil temperature changes under heat. Switch will turn on at 226°F (108°C) and off at 234-244°F (112-118°C). Replace switch if it fails to operate in normal ranges.

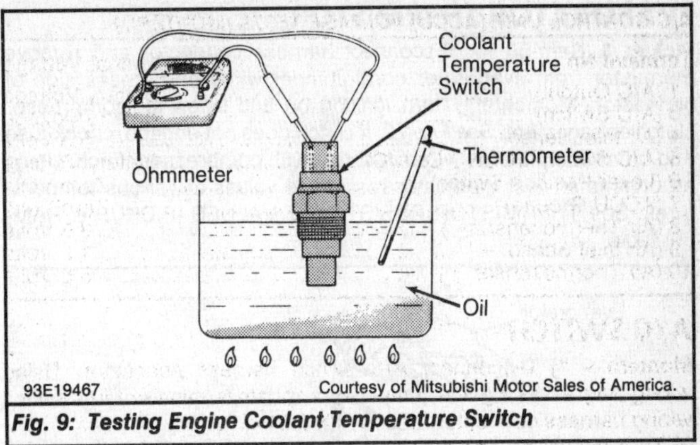
Coolant
Temperature
Switch
Thermometer
Ohmmeter
Oil
93E19467
Courtesy of Mitsubishi Motor Sales of America.

Fig. 9: Testing Engine Coolant Temperature Switch

HIGH PRESSURE RELIEF VALVE

Pickup & Ram-50 - Pressure relief valve opens at 505 psi (35.5 kg/cm²) and closes at 341 psi (24 kg/cm²). If a leak is detected at "A", replace relief valve. If a leak is detected at "B", tighten valve. If leak persists at "B", renew packing and retighten. *See Fig. 10.*

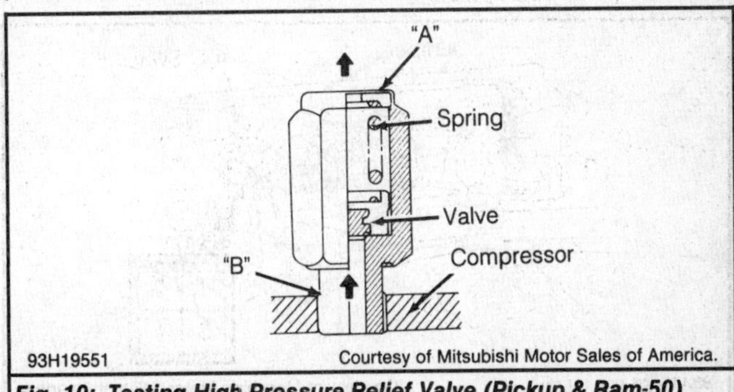
"A"
Spring
Valve
"B"
Compressor
93H19551
Courtesy of Mitsubishi Motor Sales of America.

Fig. 10: Testing High Pressure Relief Valve (Pickup & Ram-50)

LOW PRESSURE SWITCH

Pickup & Ram-50 - 1) Low pressure switch is wired in series with magnetic clutch and opens circuit if line pressure drops to less than 30 psi (20.6 kg/cm²). If low pressure switch is suspect, jumper the wire leads and turn A/C switch and blower switch ON. *See Fig. 11.* Momentarily turn ignition switch ON and listen for compressor clutch engaging.

2) If magnetic clutch does not engage, the fin thermostat, water temperature switch or fuse may be faulty. If clutch engages, connect manifold gauge set and read pressure. Switch must activate clutch at 30 psi (20.6 kg/cm²) or above. If pressure is less than 30 psi (20.6 kg/cm²), refrigerant system is low and must be recharged.

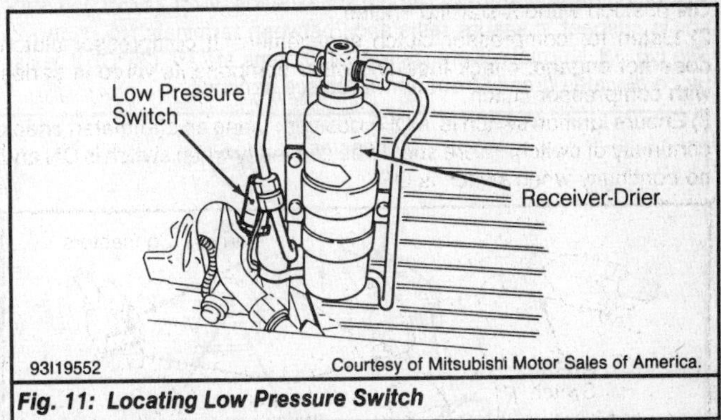
Low Pressure
Switch
Receiver-Drier
93I19552
Courtesy of Mitsubishi Motor Sales of America.

Fig. 11: Locating Low Pressure Switch

COMPRESSOR CLUTCH

Disconnect wiring to compressor clutch. Connect battery voltage directly to A/C compressor clutch wiring harness terminals. If click is heard, clutch engagement is okay. If click is not heard, pulley and armature are not making contact. Repair or replace as necessary.

1993 MANUAL A/C-HEATER SYSTEMS Montero, Pickup & Ram-50 (Cont.)

EVAPORATOR THERMISTOR

Pickup & Ram-50 – Disconnect harness connector and remove thermistor from evaporator core. Jumper wires on harness side of connector. Momentarily turn ignition on and listen for compressor clutch engagement. *See Fig. 12.* If clutch does not engage, check fuse and other components wired in series with compressor clutch. Using an ohmmeter, test thermistor resistance values at various temperatures. See THERMISTOR RESISTANCE VALUES (PICKUP & RAM-50) table.

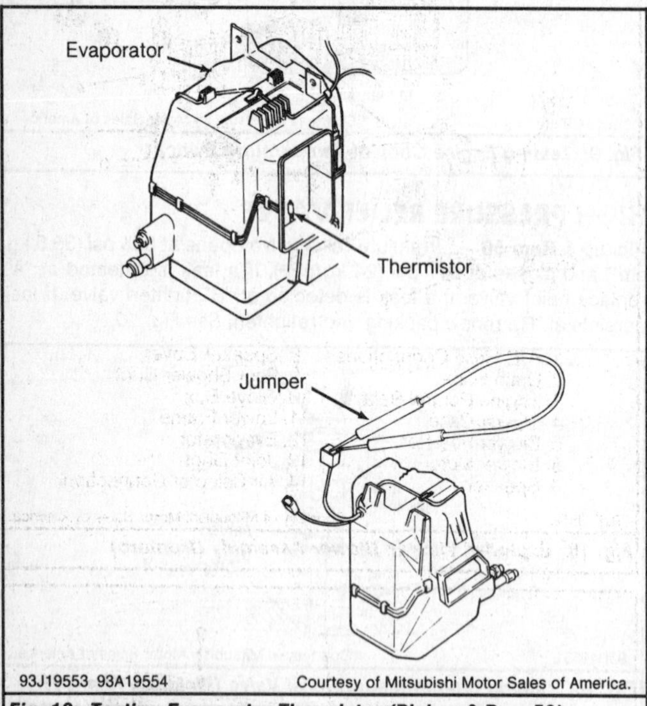
Evaporator
Thermistor
Jumper
93J19553 93A19554
Courtesy of Mitsubishi Motor Sales of America.

Fig. 12: Testing Evaporator Thermistor (Pickup & Ram-50)

THERMISTOR RESISTANCE VALUES (PICKUP & RAM-50)

Temperature °F (°C)	Approximate Ohms
32 (0)	10,000
50 (10)	4800
68 (20)	2200
86 (30)	1300
104 (40)	1000

REFRIGERANT TEMPERATURE SENSOR

Refrigerant temperature sensor should open and de-energize magnetic clutch if temperature of refrigerant exceeds 347°F (175°C). If sensor is suspect, measure resistance between terminals No. 1 and 2. *See Fig. 13.* Normal resistance is 80,470 ohms at 77°F (25°C). If resistance deviates greatly from norm, replace sensor.

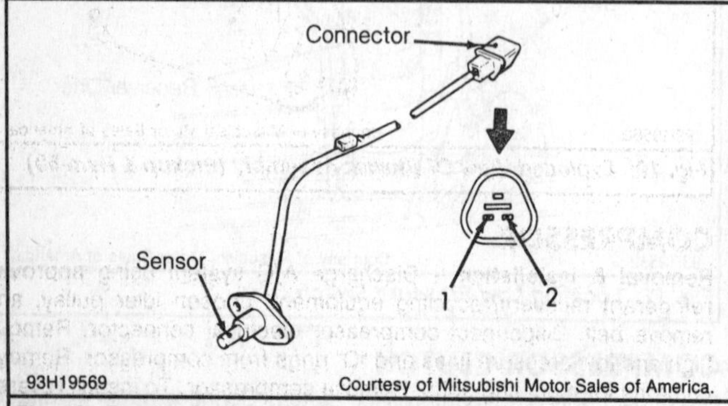
Connector
Sensor
1
2
93H19569
Courtesy of Mitsubishi Motor Sales of America.

Fig. 13: Testing Refrigerant Temperature Sensor

RELAYS

1) Remove relay from relay box located in engine compartment. Using an ohmmeter, ensure continuity exists between terminals No. 2 and 4 and does not exist between terminals No. 1 and 3. *See Fig. 14.*

2) Connect battery voltage to terminal No. 2, and ground terminal No. 4. Ensure continuity exists between terminals No. 1 and 3. If continuity is not as specified, replace relay.

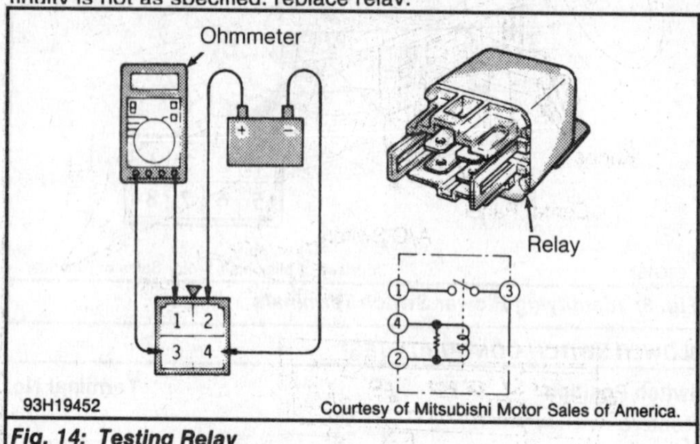
Ohmmeter
Relay
1 2
3 4
93H19452
Courtesy of Mitsubishi Motor Sales of America.

Fig. 14: Testing Relay

REMOVAL & INSTALLATION

NOTE: For removal and installation procedures not covered in this article, see HEATER SYSTEMS - MONTERO, PICKUP & RAM-50 article.

A/C CONTROL UNIT (ACCU)

Removal & Installation – Remove 2 clips on top of evaporator and remove ACCU. Disconnect wiring harness from ACCU. To install, reverse removal procedure. *See Fig. 15.*

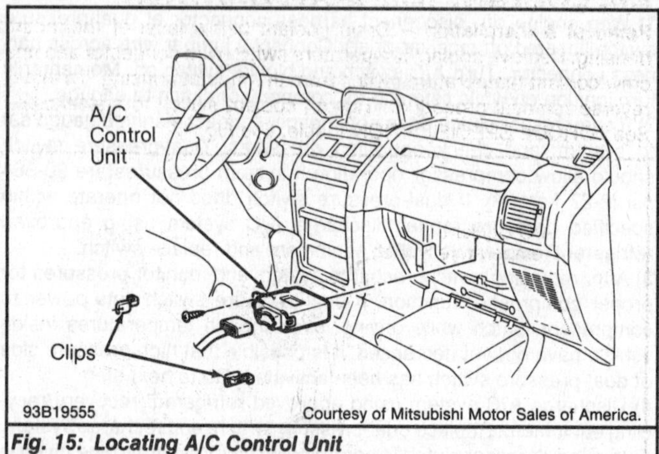
A/C
Control
Unit
Clips
93B19555
Courtesy of Mitsubishi Motor Sales of America.

Fig. 15: Locating A/C Control Unit

A/C SWITCH

Removal & Installation (Montero) – From back side of control panel, push right control panel clip aside while pushing control panel out of dash panel. Allow control panel to hang. Remove side bracket. Push temperature switch control assembly to left, and then remove A/C switch. To install, reverse removal procedure.

Removal & Installation (Pickup & Ram-50) – Remove heater control knobs. Remove glove box. Remove center panel mounting screws. Using a trim stick, remove upper side of panel. Remove A/C switch assembly mounting screws. Pull switch assembly away from panel. Remove switch. To install, reverse removal procedure. *See Fig. 16.*

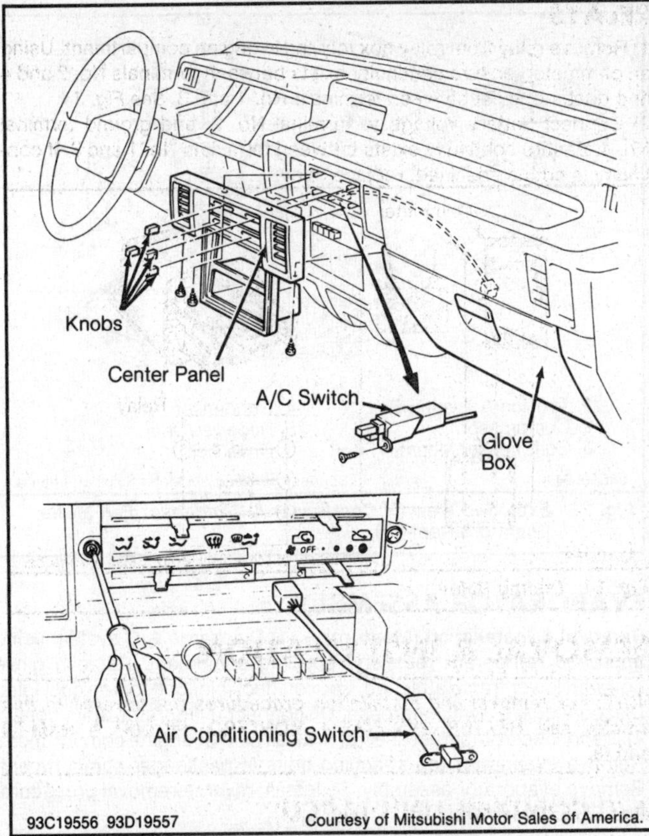
Knobs
Center Panel
A/C Switch
Glove
Box
Air Conditioning Switch
93C19556 93D19557
Courtesy of Mitsubishi Motor Sales of America.

Fig. 16: Removing A/C Switch (Pickup & Ram-50)

A/C COOLANT TEMPERATURE SWITCH

Removal & Installation - Drain coolant below level of thermostat housing. Remove coolant temperature switch wire connector and unscrew coolant temperature switch from thermostat housing. To install, reverse removal procedure. Tighten coolant switch to specification. See TORQUE SPECIFICATIONS table. *See Fig. 17.*

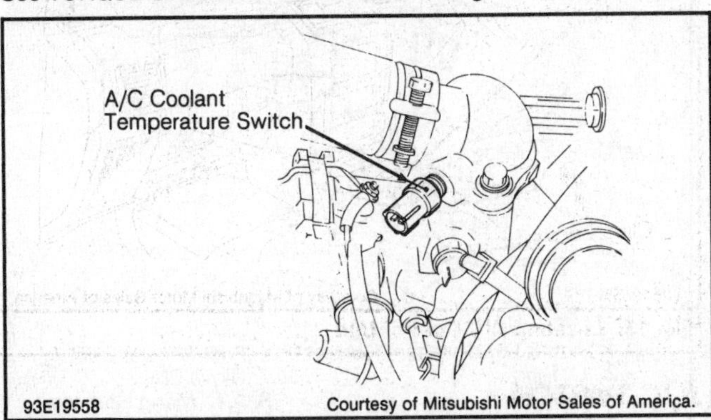
A/C Coolant
Temperature Switch
93E19558
Courtesy of Mitsubishi Motor Sales of America.

Fig. 17: Locating A/C Coolant Temperature Switch

BLOWER MOTOR & RESISTOR

Removal & Installation - **1)** Remove glove box. Resistor is visible with glove box removed. Remove 2 screws, and remove resistor. *See Fig. 18 or 19.*

2) Remove right speaker cover, cowl trim, knee protector and glove box frame. Disconnect ventilator outlet at right side of blower housing. Disconnect electrical connector at blower motor. Remove engine control unit. Remove 3 screws, and remove blower motor assembly. To install, reverse removal procedure.

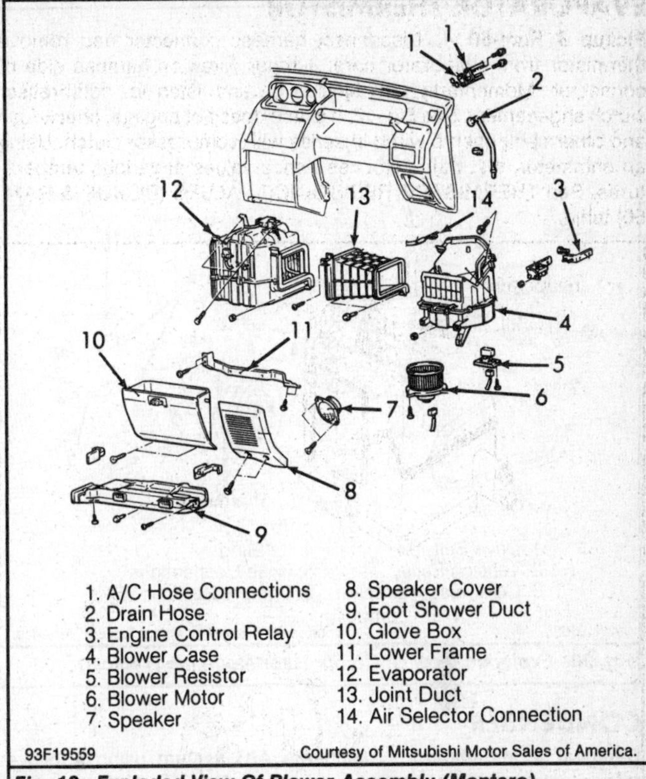
1. A/C Hose Connections
2. Drain Hose
3. Engine Control Relay
4. Blower Case
5. Blower Resistor
6. Blower Motor
7. Speaker
8. Speaker Cover
9. Foot Shower Duct
10. Glove Box
11. Lower Frame
12. Evaporator
13. Joint Duct
14. Air Selector Connection
93F19559
Courtesy of Mitsubishi Motor Sales of America.

Fig. 18: Exploded View Of Blower Assembly (Montero)

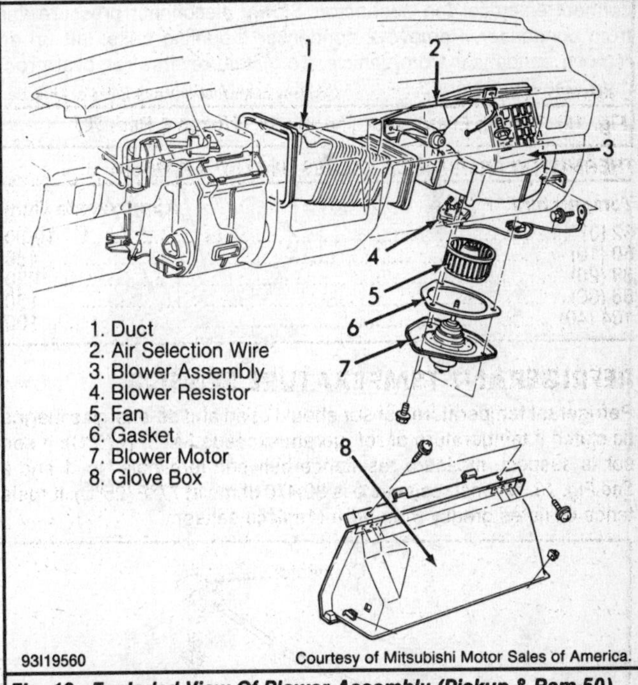
1. Duct
2. Air Selection Wire
3. Blower Assembly
4. Blower Resistor
5. Fan
6. Gasket
7. Blower Motor
8. Glove Box
93I19560
Courtesy of Mitsubishi Motor Sales of America.

Fig. 19: Exploded View Of Blower Assembly (Pickup & Ram-50)

COMPRESSOR

Removal & Installation - Discharge A/C system using approved refrigerant recovery/recycling equipment. Loosen idler pulley, and remove belt. Disconnect compressor electrical connector. Remove high and low pressure lines and "O" rings from compressor. Remove compressor mounting bolts. Remove compressor. To install, reverse removal procedure. *See Fig. 20.*

1993 MANUAL A/C-HEATER SYSTEMS
Montero, Pickup & Ram-50 (Cont.)

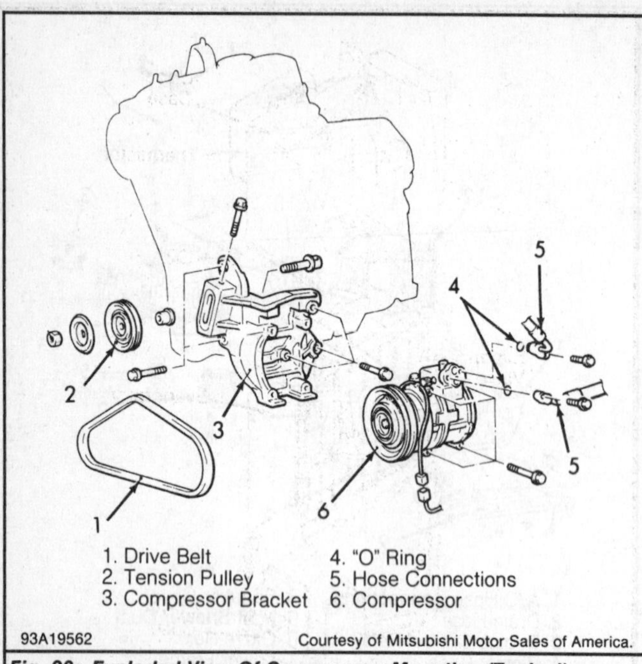
1. Drive Belt
2. Tension Pulley
3. Compressor Bracket
4. "O" Ring
5. Hose Connections
6. Compressor
93A19562
Courtesy of Mitsubishi Motor Sales of America.

Fig. 20: Exploded View Of Compressor Mounting (Typical)

CONDENSER

Removal & Installation - Discharge A/C system using approved refrigerant recovery/recycling equipment. Remove front grille and grille brackets. Remove front end cover and condenser harness. Disconnect electrical fan connector. Slowly disconnect pressure lines from condenser. Remove 2 condenser mounting bolts. Lift up and remove condenser from vehicle. To install, reverse removal procedure. *See Fig. 21 or 22.*

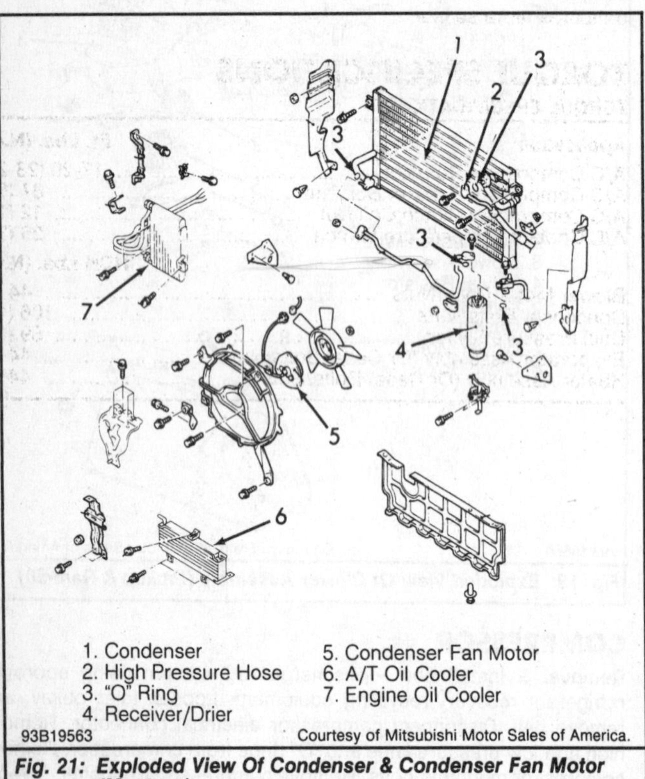
1. Condenser
2. High Pressure Hose
3. "O" Ring
4. Receiver/Drier
5. Condenser Fan Motor
6. A/T Oil Cooler
7. Engine Oil Cooler
93B19563
Courtesy of Mitsubishi Motor Sales of America.

Fig. 21: Exploded View Of Condenser & Condenser Fan Motor (Montero)

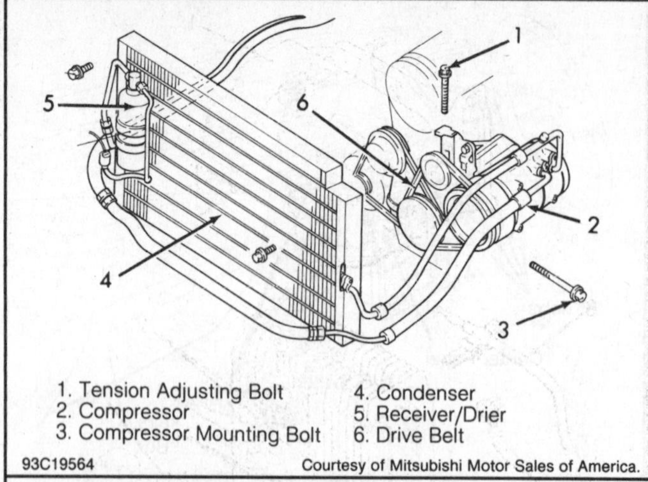
1. Tension Adjusting Bolt
2. Compressor
3. Compressor Mounting Bolt
4. Condenser
5. Receiver/Drier
6. Drive Belt
93C19564
Courtesy of Mitsubishi Motor Sales of America.

Fig. 22: Exploded View Of Condenser & Condenser Fan Motor (Pickup & Ram-50)

EVAPORATOR ASSEMBLY

Removal & Installation (Montero) - **1)** Discharge A/C system using approved refrigerant recovery/recycling equipment. Remove glove box with lower frame attached. Loosen duct joint bolt to free duct joint. Disconnect A/C switch harness. Disconnect evaporator drain hose.

2) Disconnect refrigerant lines at firewall side of engine compartment. Remove evaporator top attaching bolts in passenger compartment. Remove evaporator assembly. To install, reverse removal procedure. *See Figs. 23 and 24.*

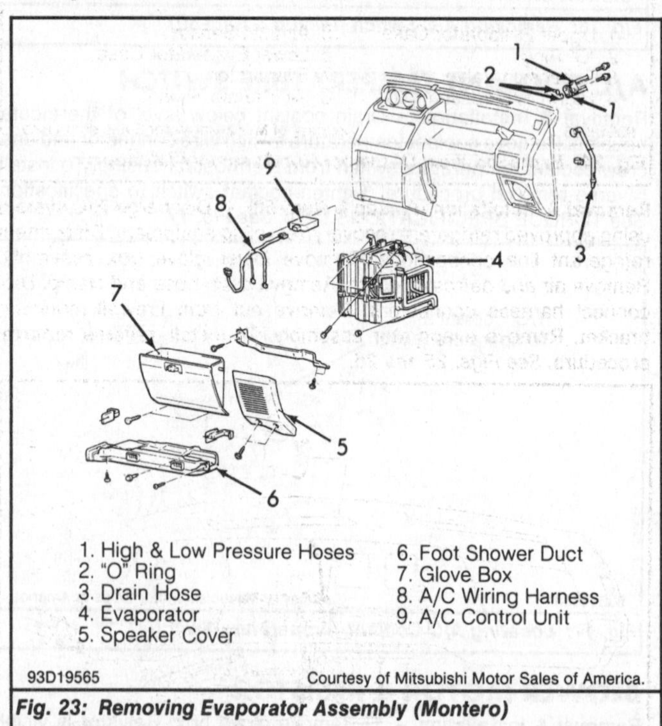
1. High & Low Pressure Hoses
2. "O" Ring
3. Drain Hose
4. Evaporator
5. Speaker Cover
6. Foot Shower Duct
7. Glove Box
8. A/C Wiring Harness
9. A/C Control Unit
93D19565
Courtesy of Mitsubishi Motor Sales of America.

Fig. 23: Removing Evaporator Assembly (Montero)

1993 MANUAL A/C-HEATER SYSTEMS
Montero, Pickup & Ram-50 (Cont.)

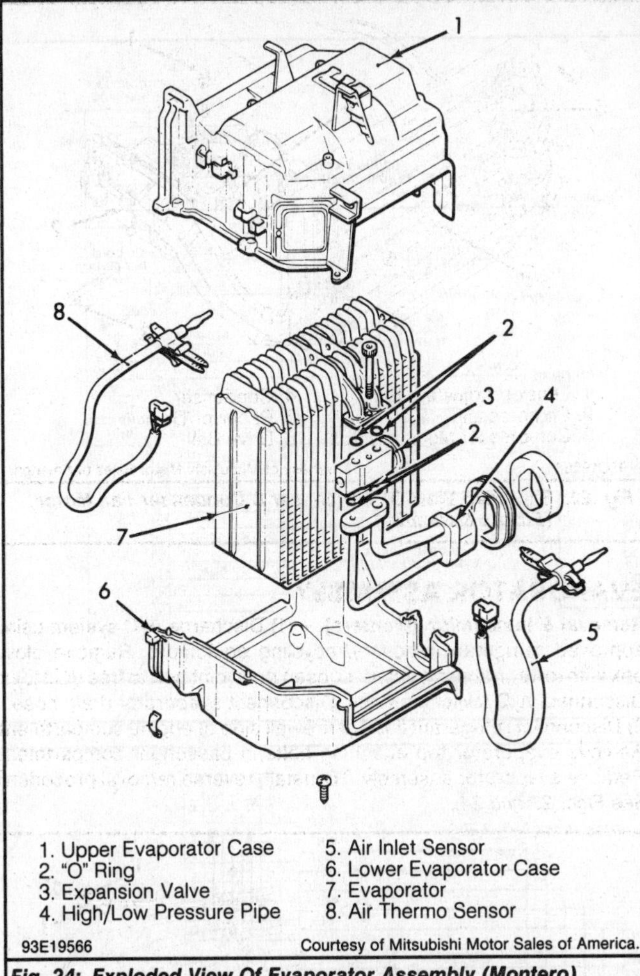
1
2
3
4
2
5
6
7
8
1. Upper Evaporator Case
2. "O" Ring
3. Expansion Valve
4. High/Low Pressure Pipe
5. Air Inlet Sensor
6. Lower Evaporator Case
7. Evaporator
8. Air Thermo Sensor
93E19566
Courtesy of Mitsubishi Motor Sales of America.

Fig. 24: Exploded View Of Evaporator Assembly (Montero)

Removal & Installation (Pickup & Ram-50) - Discharge A/C system using approved refrigerant recovery/recycling equipment. Disconnect refrigerant line connections. Remove lower glove box assembly. Remove air and defroster ducts. Remove drain hose and clamp. Disconnect harness connectors. Remove nut from firewall mounting bracket. Remove evaporator assembly. To install, reverse removal procedure. *See Figs. 25 and 26.*

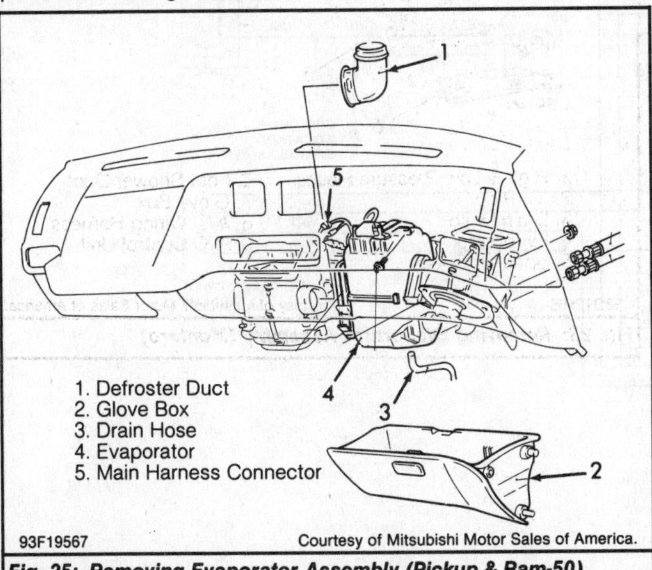
1
5
4
3
2
1. Defroster Duct
2. Glove Box
3. Drain Hose
4. Evaporator
5. Main Harness Connector
93F19567
Courtesy of Mitsubishi Motor Sales of America.

Fig. 25: Removing Evaporator Assembly (Pickup & Ram-50)

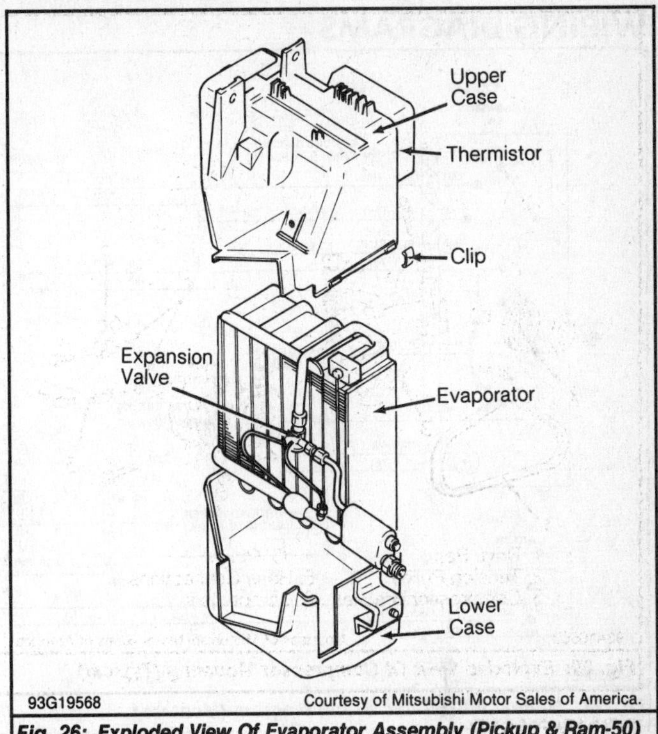
Upper
Case
Thermistor
Clip
Expansion
Valve
Evaporator
Lower
Case
93G19568
Courtesy of Mitsubishi Motor Sales of America.

Fig. 26: Exploded View Of Evaporator Assembly (Pickup & Ram-50)

REFRIGERANT TEMPERATURE SENSOR

Removal & Installation - Discharge A/C system using approved refrigerant recovery/recycling equipment. Disconnect refrigerant temperature sensor wiring connector. Remove 2 bolts securing temperature sensor to compressor. Remove temperature sensor from compressor. To install, reverse removal procedure using new "O" ring on temperature sensor.

TORQUE SPECIFICATIONS

TORQUE SPECIFICATIONS

Application	Ft. Lbs. (N.m)
A/C Compressor Bolt/Nut	17-20 (23-27)
A/C Compressor Bracket Bolt/Nut	37 (50)
A/C Compressor Clutch Coil Nut	12 (16)
A/C Coolant Temperature Switch	26 (35)
	INCH Lbs. (N.m)
Blower Motor Bolts/Nuts	44 (5)
Condenser Bolts/Nuts	106 (12)
Dual Pressure Switch	89 (10)
Evaporator Assembly (Or Case) Bolts/Nuts	44 (5)
Heater Assembly (Or Case) Bolts/Nuts	44 (5)

1993 MANUAL A/C–HEATER SYSTEMS
Montero, Pickup & Ram-50 (Cont.)

WIRING DIAGRAMS

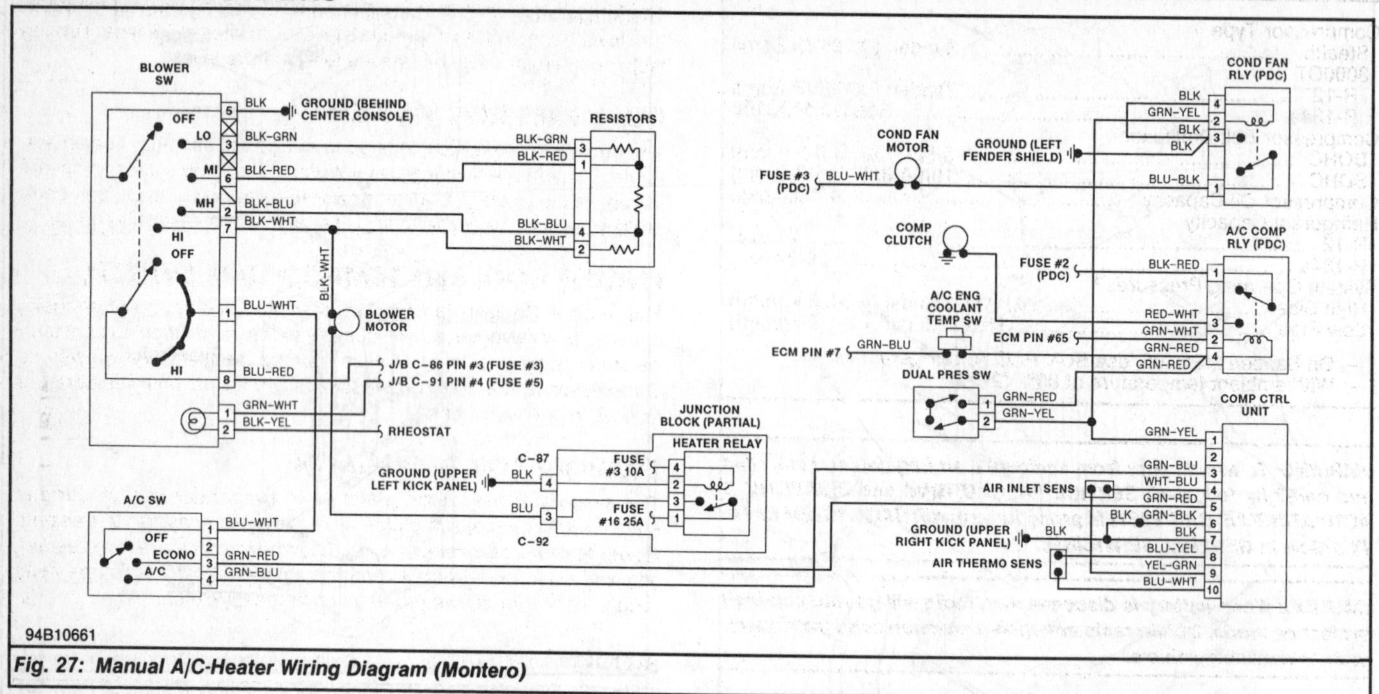
BLOWER SW
OFF
LO
MI
MH
HI
OFF
HI
BLK
GROUND (BEHIND CENTER CONSOLE)
BLK-GRN
BLK-RED
BLK-BLU
BLK-WHT
BLU-WHT
BLU-RED
GRN-WHT
BLK-YEL
RESISTORS
BLOWER MOTOR
J/B C-86 PIN #3 (FUSE #3)
J/B C-91 PIN #4 (FUSE #5)
RHEOSTAT
JUNCTION BLOCK (PARTIAL)
HEATER RELAY
C-87
GROUND (UPPER LEFT KICK PANEL)
FUSE #3 10A
FUSE #16 25A
BLU
C-92
A/C SW
ECONO
A/C
GRN-RED
GRN-BLU
COND FAN MOTOR
GROUND (LEFT FENDER SHIELD)
FUSE #3 (PDC)
COND FAN RLY (PDC)
GRN-YEL
BLU-BLK
COMP CLUTCH
FUSE #2 (PDC)
A/C COMP RLY (PDC)
A/C ENG COOLANT TEMP SW
ECM PIN #65
ECM PIN #7
RED-WHT
DUAL PRES SW
COMP CTRL UNIT
AIR INLET SENS
WHT-BLU
GROUND (UPPER RIGHT KICK PANEL)
GRN-BLK
BLU-YEL
YEL-GRN
AIR THERMO SENS
94B10661

Fig. 27: Manual A/C-Heater Wiring Diagram (Montero)

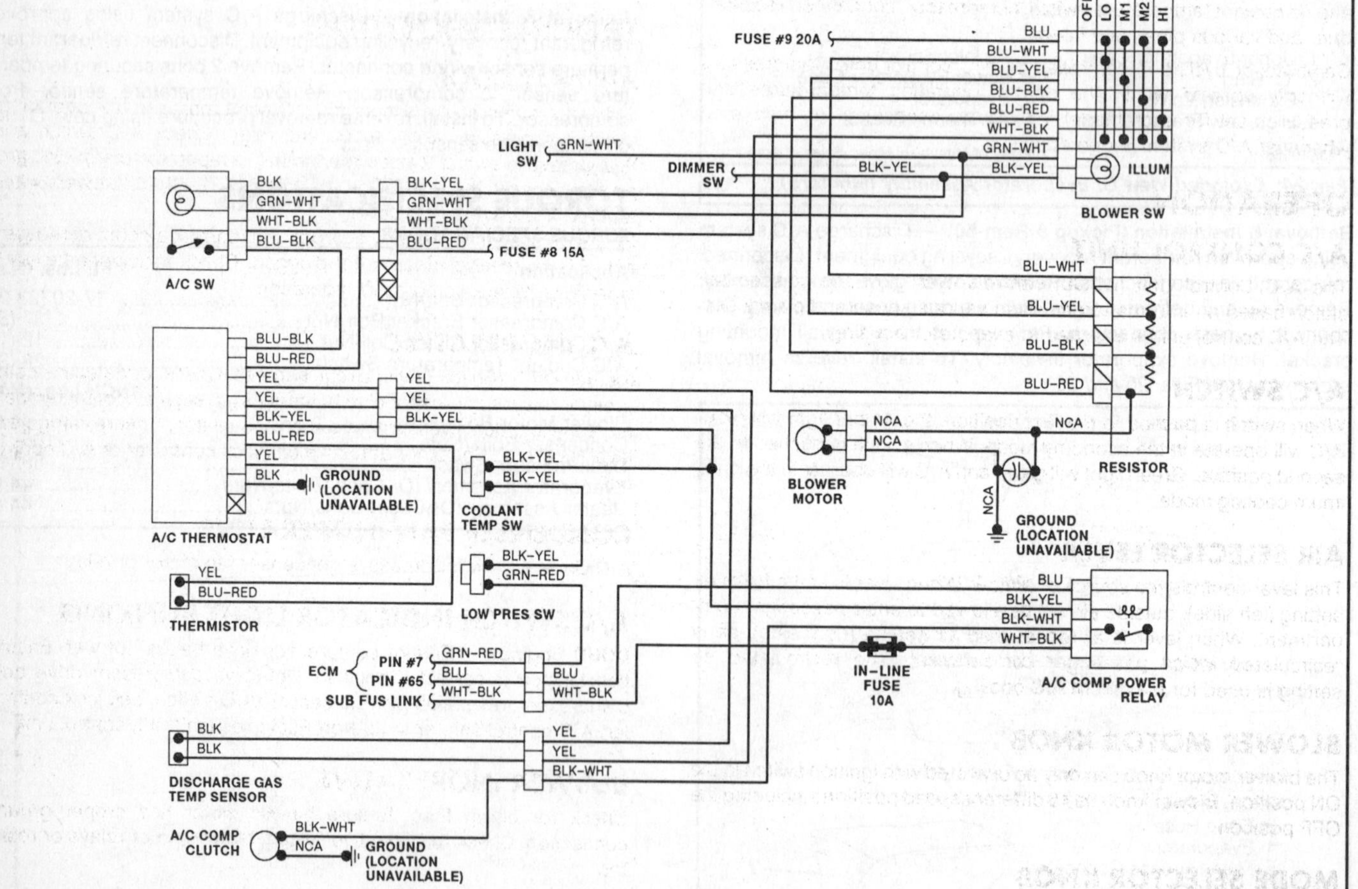

FUSE #9 20A
OFF LO M1 M2 HI
BLU
BLU-WHT
BLU-YEL
BLU-BLK
BLU-RED
WHT-BLK
GRN-WHT
BLK-YEL
LIGHT SW
DIMMER SW
ILLUM
BLOWER SW
A/C SW
BLK
FUSE #8 15A
A/C THERMOSTAT
YEL
GROUND (LOCATION UNAVAILABLE)
COOLANT TEMP SW
GRN-RED
LOW PRES SW
THERMISTOR
RESISTOR
NCA
BLOWER MOTOR
A/C COMP POWER RELAY
BLK-WHT
IN-LINE FUSE 10A
ECM
PIN #7
PIN #65
SUB FUS LINK
DISCHARGE GAS TEMP SENSOR
A/C COMP CLUTCH
94C10662

Fig. 28: Manual A/C-Heater Wiring Diagram (Pickup & Ram-50)

1993 MANUAL A/C-HEATER SYSTEMS
Stealth & 3000GT

SPECIFICATIONS

Compressor Type	
Stealth	Sanden FX105VS Scroll
3000GT	
R-12	Sanden FX105VS Scroll
R-134a	Sanden MSC105
Compressor Belt Deflection	
DOHC	5/32-7/32" (4.0-5.5 mm)
SOHC	19/64-3/8" (7.5-9.5 mm)
Compressor Oil Capacity [1]	4.7-6.0 ozs.
Refrigerant Capacity	
R-12	29 ozs.
R-134a	26-28 ozs.
System Operating Pressures [2]	
High Side	111-118 psi (7.8-8.3 kg/cm²)
Low Side	18.5-27.5 psi (1.3-1.9 kg/cm²)

1 – On Sanden MSC105, use SUN PAG 56 refrigerant oil.
2 – With ambient temperature at 80°F (27°C).

WARNING: To avoid injury from accidental air bag deployment, read and carefully follow all SERVICE PRECAUTIONS and DISABLING & ACTIVATING AIR BAG SYSTEM procedures in AIR BAG SYSTEM SAFETY article in GENERAL SERVICING.

CAUTION: When battery is disconnected, radio will go into anti-theft protection mode. Obtain radio anti-theft protection code from owner prior to servicing vehicle.

DESCRIPTION

A/C system consists of A/C control unit, fan switch, evaporator, engine coolant temperature switch, compressor, condenser, receiver-drier and various pipes and hoses.

Compressor cycling is controlled by A/C control unit. Compressors will only operate within the normal operating temperatures and pressures set for each model. An electric condenser fan comes on whenever A/C system is operating.

OPERATION

A/C CONTROL UNIT

The A/C Control Unit (ACCU) controls cycling of the compressor clutch based on information received various sensors and switches. The A/C control unit is attached to evaporator housing.

A/C SWITCH

When switch is pushed to the first position, the Amber light will glow, A/C will operate in the economy mode. When switch is pushed to the second position, Green light will glow, and A/C will operate in the maximum cooling mode.

AIR SELECTOR LEVER

This lever controls the source of airflow. When lever is at the fresh air setting (left side), outside air will be allowed to enter passenger compartment. When lever is at recirculated air setting (right side), air is recirculated inside passenger compartment. The recirculated air setting is used for maximum A/C cooling.

BLOWER MOTOR KNOB

The blower motor knob can only be operated with ignition switch in the ON position. Blower knob has 5 different speed positions including the OFF position.

MODE SELECTOR KNOB

Depending on position selected, airflow can be directed to different areas of passenger compartment. Airflow selection capabilities include individual areas or a combination of windshield, upper body, knee and/or foot area.

TEMPERATURE CONTROL KNOB

The temperature control knob is used for selecting desired temperature level. To increase temperature level, turn knob clockwise. Turning knob counterclockwise decreases temperature level.

DUAL-PRESSURE SWITCH

The dual-pressure switch, located in refrigerant line near condenser, is wired in series with compressor clutch. Whenever system pressure is outside the operating range, power to compressor is cut and compressor activity will cease until pressure is within operating range.

ENGINE COOLANT TEMPERATURE SWITCH

The engine coolant temperature switch, located on thermostat housing, is wired in series with compressor clutch. When coolant temperature is greater than switch control temperature, power to compressor is cut and compressor is turned off until temperature returns to operating range.

EVAPORATOR THERMISTOR

The evaporator thermistor, attached to evaporator fins, is wired in series with compressor clutch and prevents evaporator freezing. Power to compressor clutch is cut if control temperature is exceeded, allowing evaporator to thaw. When temperature returns to operating range, thermistor allows power to compressor clutch.

ADJUSTMENTS

NOTE: For adjustment procedures of basic A/C-heater system components, see appropriate HEATER SYSTEMS article.

TROUBLE SHOOTING

AIR NOT COOL

1) Ensure compressor is operating. If compressor is not operating, check compressor clutch, fuses and relay. Check A/C switch and dual-pressure switch. Check thermostat, evaporator thermistor and air inlet sensor. Check A/C Control Unit (ACCU). Check blower switch and relay. Check liquid pipe.

2) Ensure system is properly charged with correct amount of refrigerant. Ensure receiver-drier is not clogged. Check for clogged expansion valve. Check compressor operation.

A/C INOPERATIVE

Ignition On – Check power circuit harness. Check for defective compressor relay, compressor clutch, thermostat, engine coolant temperature switch, dual-pressure switch or A/C switch. Ensure refrigerant level is correct. Check for defective belt lock controller or A/C control unit.

CONDENSER FAN INOPERATIVE

A/C On – Check for defective condenser fan motor or relay.

A/C SWITCH INDICATOR LIGHT BLINKING

DOHC Engines – Ensure compressor drive belt is not wet. Ensure belt tension is correct. Check for defective compressor drive belt, compressor, revolution pick-up sensor, A/C switch, belt lock controller, A/C control unit, or Multi-Port Fuel Injection (MFI) control unit.

BLOWER INOPERATIVE

Check for blown fuse. Ensure blower motor has proper ground connection. Check for defective switch, blower motor relays or resistor.

1993 MANUAL A/C-HEATER SYSTEMS Stealth & 3000GT (Cont.)

INSUFFICIENT HEAT

Check for obstructed heater outlet or heater hoses. Ensure blend-air damper, mode selector damper and control cables are properly adjusted. Check for defective thermostat or plugged heater core.

NO VENTILATION

Ensure mode selector cable is correctly installed. Check duct connections, and ensure ducts are not crushed, bent or clogged.

TESTING

WARNING: To avoid injury from accidental air bag deployment, read and carefully follow all SERVICE PRECAUTIONS and DISABLING & ACTIVATING AIR BAG SYSTEM procedures in AIR BAG SYSTEM SAFETY article in GENERAL SERVICING.

A/C SYSTEM PERFORMANCE

R-12 - 1) Park vehicle out of direct sunlight. Connect a tachometer. Turn adapter valve all the way back, and install adapter valves to high-pressure and low-pressure service valves. Connect manifold gauge to service valves. Tighten adapter valve handle, and open service valves.
2) Start engine. Set mode selector lever at face position, and temperature control lever at maximum cool setting. Move air selector lever to recirculated air setting. Turn A/C on. Operate blower fan in high speed. Adjust engine speed to 1000 RPM with compressor clutch engaged. Close all doors and windows. Ensure hood is open.

NOTE: If clutch cycles, take temperature reading before clutch disengages.

3) Insert thermometer in center vent. Run engine for 20 minutes, and note discharge air temperature on thermometer. Ensure discharge temperature and system low-side and high-side pressures are within specification. See A/C SYSTEM PERFORMANCE SPECIFICATIONS table.

R-134a - 1) Park vehicle away from direct sunlight. Close high-pressure and low-pressure valves of manifold gauge. Connect manifold gauge to A/C system. Start engine.
2) Set mode selector lever at face position. Set temperature control lever at maximum cool setting, and air selector lever at recirculated air setting. Turn A/C on. Operate blower fan in high speed. Adjust engine speed to 1000 RPM with compressor clutch engaged. Close all doors and windows. Ensure hood is open.

NOTE: If clutch cycles, take temperature reading before clutch disengages.

3) Insert thermometer in center vent. Run engine for 20 minutes, and note discharge air temperature on thermometer. Ensure discharge temperature and system low-side and high-side pressures are within specification. See A/C SYSTEM PERFORMANCE SPECIFICATIONS table.

A/C SYSTEM PERFORMANCE SPECIFICATIONS

Application	[1] Specification
Discharge Air Temperature	33.8-39.2°F (1.0-4.0°C)
Low-Side Pressure	18.5-27.5 psi (1.30-1.93 kg/cm²)
High-Side Pressure	110.9-118.1 psi (7.80-8.30 kg/cm²)

[1] - Specification listed with ambient temperature at 80°F (27°C).

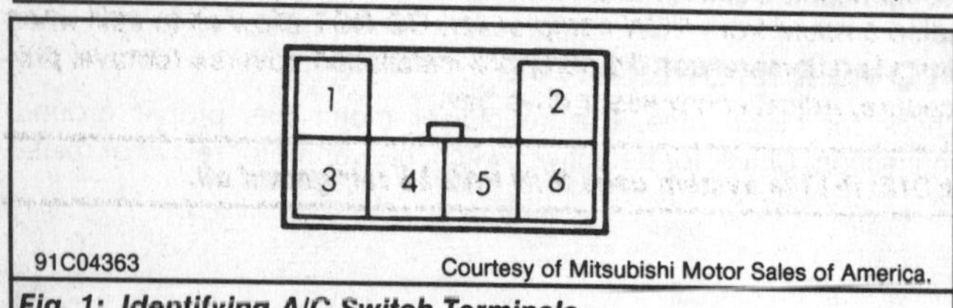
1
2
3
4
5
6
91C04363
Courtesy of Mitsubishi Motor Sales of America.

Fig. 1: Identifying A/C Switch Terminals

A/C SWITCH

Operate A/C switch, and check continuity between indicated terminal using ohmmeter. See A/C SWITCH CONTINUITY table. *See Fig. 1.* Replace switch if continuity is not as specified.

A/C SWITCH CONTINUITY

Switch Position	Terminal No. [1]	Continuity
Economy [2]	1 & 4	Yes
Maximum Cooling [3]	1 & 2, 1 & 4	Yes

[1] - Terminals No. 3 and 6 are for light bulb circuits and should always have continuity.
[2] - Amber indicator light on A/C switch.
[3] - Green indicator light on A/C switch.

EVAPORATOR THERMISTOR & AIR INLET SENSOR

Disconnect evaporator thermistor or air inlet sensor at evaporator case. Using ohmmeter, check component resistance at indicated temperatures. See EVAPORATOR THERMISTOR & AIR INLET SENSOR SPECIFICATIONS table. Resistance value should be within 10 percent of specified value. If resistance is not as specified, replace A/C control unit.

EVAPORATOR THERMISTOR & AIR INLET SENSOR SPECIFICATIONS

Component Temp. °F (°C)	Ohms
32 (0)	4800
41 (5)	3800
50 (10)	3000
59 (15)	2300
68 (20)	2800
77 (25)	1500

BLOWER MOTOR

Apply battery voltage directly to blower motor terminals. Ensure blower motor operates smoothly. Reverse polarity, and ensure blower motor operates smoothly in the reverse direction.

BLOWER RESISTOR

Disconnect blower resistor connector. Using ohmmeter, measure resistance between indicated terminals. See BLOWER RESISTOR RESISTANCE table. *See Fig. 2.* Replace resistor if readings are not within specification.

BLOWER RESISTOR RESISTANCE

Terminal No.	Ohms
1 & 2	Approx. 1.79-2.06
2 & 3	Approx. 0.38-0.44
2 & 4	Approx. 1.10-1.26

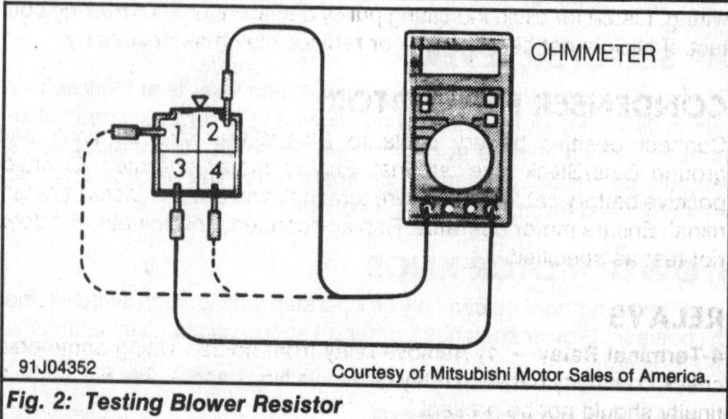
OHMMETER
1
2
3
4
91J04352
Courtesy of Mitsubishi Motor Sales of America.

Fig. 2: Testing Blower Resistor

BLOWER SWITCH

Operate switch, and check continuity between indicated terminals using ohmmeter. See BLOWER SWITCH CONTINUITY table. *See Fig. 3*. If continuity is not as specified, replace switch.

BLOWER SWITCH CONTINUITY

Switch Position	Terminal No.	Continuity
Low	1 & 8, 3 & 5	Yes
Medium-Low	1 & 8, 5 & 6	Yes
Medium-High	1 & 4, 1 & 8, 2 & 5	Yes
High	1 & 4, 1 & 8, 5 & 7	Yes

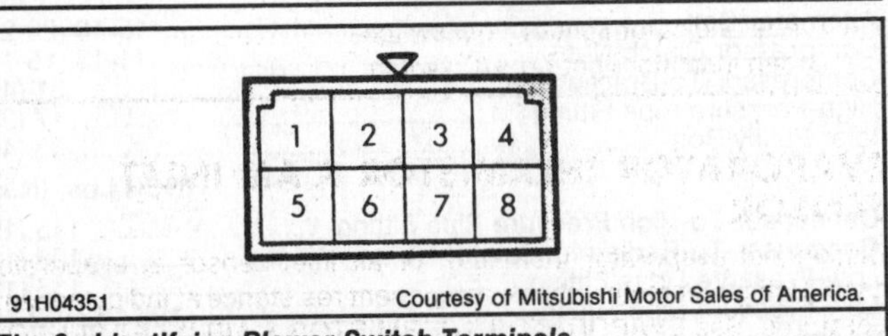
1
2
3
4
5
6
7
8
91H04351
Courtesy of Mitsubishi Motor Sales of America.

Fig. 3: Identifying Blower Switch Terminals

DUAL-PRESSURE SWITCH

1) Turn adapter valve handle all the way back, and connect it to low-pressure service valve. Close low-pressure service valve, and connect high-pressure charging hose of manifold gauge to adapter valve. Tighten adapter valve handle, and open service valve.
2) Check continuity between switch terminals. On R-12 system, continuity should exist when low-side pressure is 30-33 psi (2.1-2.3 kg/cm²). On R-134a system, continuity should exist when low-side pressure is 28-32 psi (2.0-2.2 kg/cm²). If continuity is not as specified, replace faulty dual-pressure switch.

RECEIVER-DRIER

Operate unit. Touch temperature at receiver-drier outlet and inlet. If there is a difference in temperatures, replace restricted receiver-drier.

ENGINE COOLANT TEMPERATURE SWITCH

WARNING: Stir engine oil well while heating. DO NOT allow engine oil temperature to exceed 244°F (118°C).

Immerse switch in engine oil. Heat engine oil to increase temperature. Ensure switch is turned off when engine oil temperature reaches 223-244°F (112-118°C).

COMPRESSOR CLUTCH

Disconnect wiring to compressor clutch. Connect negative battery cable to compressor body. Connect positive battery cable to clutch wiring. Listen for click, indicating pulley and armature are making contact. If click is not heard, repair or replace clutch as necessary.

CONDENSER FAN MOTOR

Connect positive battery cable to Blue/White wire terminal, and ground Blue/Black wire terminal. Ensure motor operates. Connect positive battery cable to Blue wire terminal, and ground Black wire terminal. Ensure motor operates. Replace condenser fan motor if it does not test as specified.

RELAYS

4-Terminal Relay – 1) Remove relay from holder. Using ohmmeter, check continuity between relay terminals No. 1 and 3. *See Fig. 4*. Continuity should not be present.
2) Check continuity between relay terminals No. 2 and 4. Ensure continuity is present. Apply battery voltage to terminals No. 2 and 4. Ensure continuity is present between terminals No. 1 and 3 with voltage applied. If continuity is not as specified, replace relay.

NOTE: Terminal No. 2 on 5-terminal relay is not used.

5-Terminal Relay – 1) Remove relay from holder. Using ohmmeter, check continuity between relay terminals No. 4 and 5. *See Fig. 4*. Continuity should not be present.
2) Check continuity between relay terminals No. 1 and 3. Ensure continuity is present. Apply battery voltage to terminals No. 1 and 3. Ensure continuity is present between terminals No. 4 and 5 with voltage applied. If continuity is not as specified, replace relay.

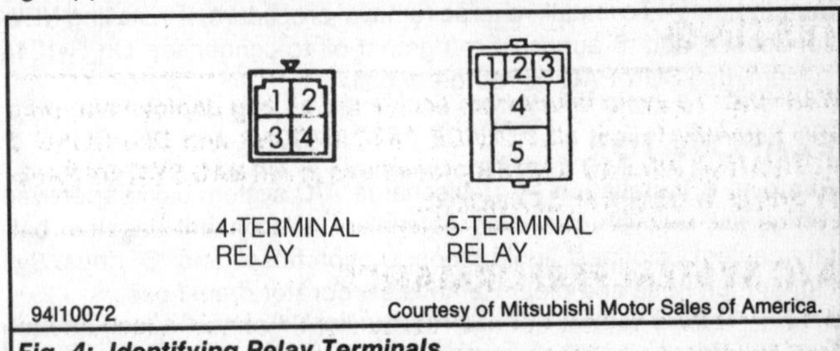
1
2
3
4
1
2
3
4
5
4-TERMINAL RELAY
5-TERMINAL RELAY
94I10072
Courtesy of Mitsubishi Motor Sales of America.

Fig. 4: Identifying Relay Terminals

REMOVAL & INSTALLATION

WARNING: To avoid injury from accidental air bag deployment, read and carefully follow all SERVICE PRECAUTIONS and DISABLING & ACTIVATING AIR BAG SYSTEM procedures in AIR BAG SYSTEM SAFETY article in GENERAL SERVICING.

CAUTION: When battery is disconnected, radio will go into anti-theft protection mode. Obtain radio anti-theft protection code from owner prior to servicing vehicle.

NOTE: For removal and installation procedures not covered in this article, see appropriate HEATER SYSTEMS article.

A/C SWITCH

Removal & Installation – Using flat-tip screwdriver, disengage clips from center air outlet panel. Remove center air outlet panel using trim stick. Insert hand through air outlet panel opening, and disconnect A/C switch electrical connector from back of A/C control panel. Push out A/C switch. To install, reverse removal procedure.

COMPRESSOR

Removal – 1) Discharge A/C system using approved refrigerant recovery/recycling equipment. Remove compressor drive belt. On DOHC engines, remove condenser fan motor assembly and alternator.
2) On all models, disconnect and cap refrigerant hoses. Disconnect compressor electrical connectors. Cover brake tubes with shop towel, and remove compressor. On DOHC engines, remove idler pulley.
3) On all models, remove compressor bracket. Remove bolt and tension pulley assembly from compressor bracket. Remove compressor mounting bolts and compressor.
Installation – 1) Install tension pulley assembly and compressor bracket. On DOHC engines, install idler pulley. On all models, cover brake tubes with shop towels.
2) If installing NEW compressor, measure amount of oil (ounces) in old compressor. Subtract this amount from 5.4 ounces. Remove calculated amount from NEW compressor. DO NOT allow oil to spill when installing compressor. To complete installation, reverse removal procedure. Adjust compressor drive belt.

NOTE: R-134a system uses SUN PAG 56 refrigerant oil.

1993 MANUAL A/C-HEATER SYSTEMS
Stealth & 3000GT (Cont.)

CONDENSER

Removal – 1) Discharge A/C system using approved refrigerant recovery/recycling equipment. On DOHC engines, remove alternator. On all models, disconnect condenser and cooling fan motor electrical connectors.

2) Remove condenser fan motor assembly. Remove condenser fan and motor. Remove condenser fan shroud and cooling fan motor assembly. Remove condenser-to-radiator insulator bolts. Remove liquid pipes. Remove condenser and bushings.

Installation – To install, reverse removal procedure. If installing NEW condenser, add .5 ounce of refrigerant oil to condenser. On R-134a system, use SUN PAG 56 refrigerant oil.

EVAPORATOR

Removal & Installation – 1) Discharge A/C system using approved refrigerant recovery/recycling equipment. Disconnect negative battery cable. Disconnect liquid pipes, suction hoses and "O" rings. *See Fig. 5.* Plug hose and pipe. Remove evaporator drain hose.

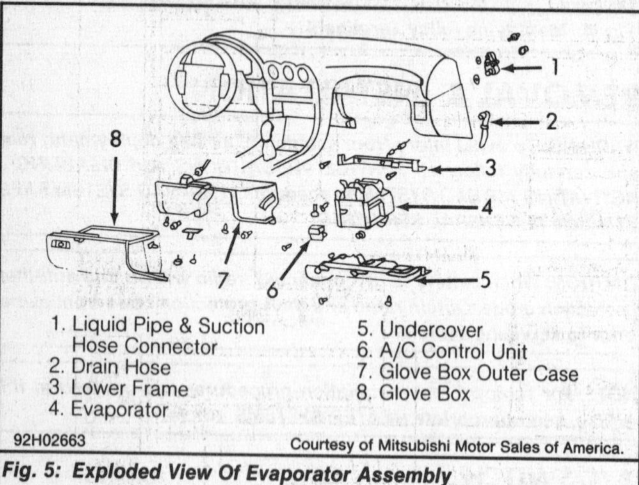
1
2
3
4
5
6
7
8
1. Liquid Pipe & Suction Hose Connector
2. Drain Hose
3. Lower Frame
4. Evaporator
5. Undercover
6. A/C Control Unit
7. Glove Box Outer Case
8. Glove Box
92H02663
Courtesy of Mitsubishi Motor Sales of America.

Fig. 5: Exploded View Of Evaporator Assembly

2) Remove glove box door stops and glove box. Remove glove box outer case. Remove glove box undercover and bracket. Disconnect electrical connectors. Remove A/C control unit and evaporator. To install, reverse removal procedure. On 3000GT, if installing NEW evaporator, add 2 ounces of refrigerant oil to evaporator. On R-134a system, use SUN PAG 56 refrigerant oil.

TORQUE SPECIFICATIONS

TORQUE SPECIFICATIONS

Application	Ft. Lbs. (N.m)
Alternator Bolt	15-18 (20-25)
Compressor Clutch Nut	11-13 (15-17)
Compressor-To-Bracket Bolts	31 (42)
High-Pressure Pipe Fitting	17 (23)
Idler Pulley Bolt	33 (45)
	INCH Lbs. (N.m)
Condenser-To-High Pressure Pipe Fitting	115 (13)
Condenser-To-Radiator Insulator Bolts	106 (12)
Low-Pressure Hose Fitting	115 (13)
Low-Pressure Pipe Fitting	106-132 (12-15)

1993 MANUAL A/C-HEATER SYSTEMS
Stealth & 3000GT (Cont.)

WIRING DIAGRAM

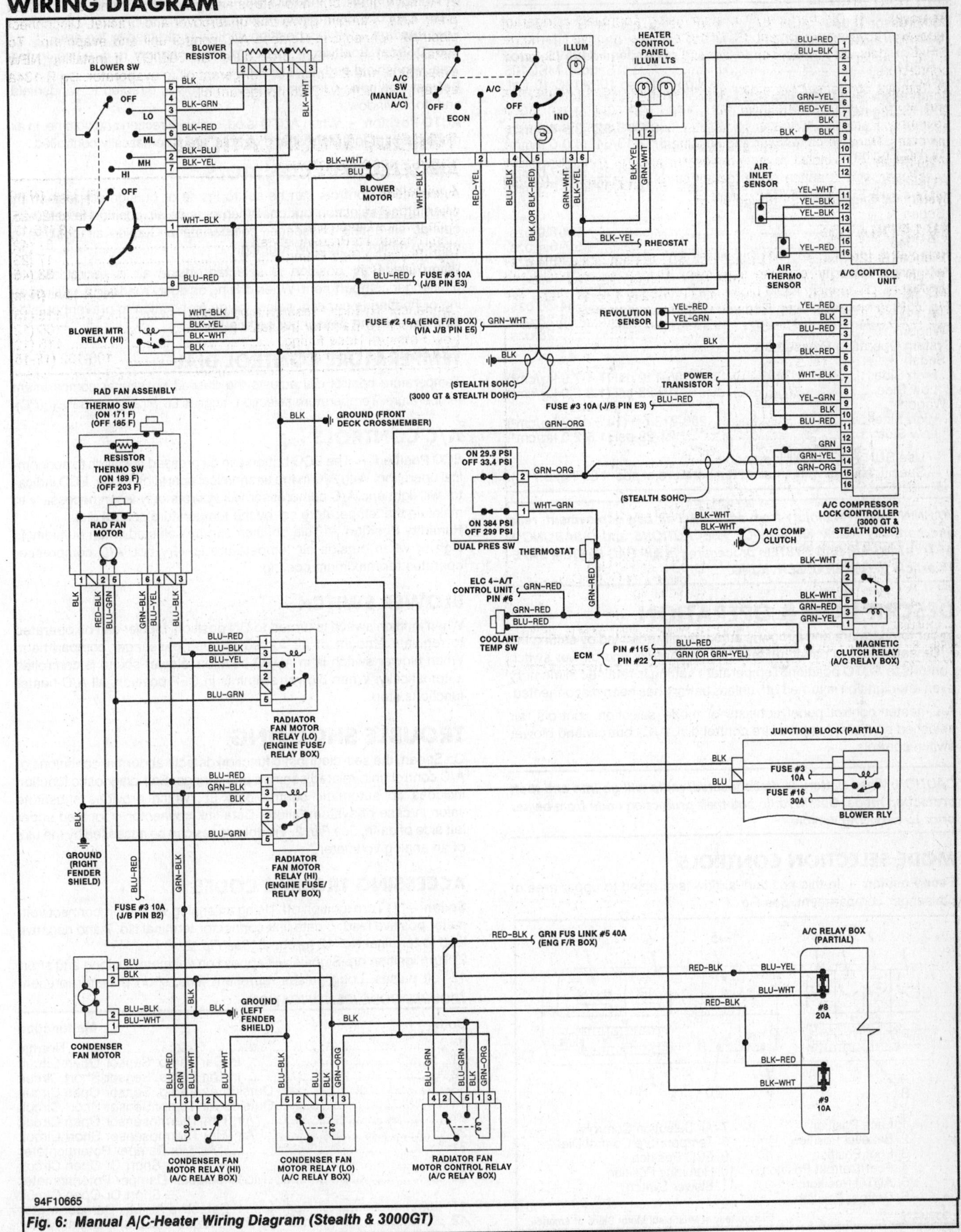
BLOWER SW
BLOWER RESISTOR
BLOWER MOTOR
BLOWER MTR RELAY (HI)
A/C SW (MANUAL A/C)
ILLUM
HEATER CONTROL PANEL ILLUM LTS
A/C CONTROL UNIT
AIR INLET SENSOR
AIR THERMO SENSOR
RHEOSTAT
REVOLUTION SENSOR
POWER TRANSISTOR
FUSE #3 10A (J/B PIN E3)
FUSE #2 15A (ENG F/R BOX) (VIA J/B PIN E5)
(STEALTH SOHC)
(3000 GT & STEALTH DOHC)
GROUND (FRONT DECK CROSSMEMBER)
RAD FAN ASSEMBLY
THERMO SW (ON 171 F) (OFF 185 F)
RESISTOR
THERMO SW (ON 189 F) (OFF 203 F)
RAD FAN MOTOR
ON 29.9 PSI OFF 33.4 PSI
ON 384 PSI OFF 299 PSI
DUAL PRES SW
THERMOSTAT
A/C COMP CLUTCH
A/C COMPRESSOR LOCK CONTROLLER (3000 GT & STEALTH DOHC)
ELC 4-A/T CONTROL UNIT PIN #6
COOLANT TEMP SW
ECM
PIN #115
PIN #22
MAGNETIC CLUTCH RELAY (A/C RELAY BOX)
RADIATOR FAN MOTOR RELAY (LO) (ENGINE FUSE/ RELAY BOX)
RADIATOR FAN MOTOR RELAY (HI) (ENGINE FUSE/ RELAY BOX)
JUNCTION BLOCK (PARTIAL)
FUSE #3 10A
FUSE #16 30A
BLOWER RLY
GROUND (RIGHT FENDER SHIELD)
FUSE #3 10A (J/B PIN B2)
GRN FUS LINK #5 40A (ENG F/R BOX)
A/C RELAY BOX (PARTIAL)
#8 20A
#9 10A
CONDENSER FAN MOTOR
GROUND (LEFT FENDER SHIELD)
CONDENSER FAN MOTOR RELAY (HI) (A/C RELAY BOX)
CONDENSER FAN MOTOR RELAY (LO) (A/C RELAY BOX)
RADIATOR FAN MOTOR CONTROL RELAY (A/C RELAY BOX)
94F10665

Fig. 6: Manual A/C-Heater Wiring Diagram (Stealth & 3000GT)

1993 AUTOMATIC A/C-HEATER SYSTEMS
Diamante

SPECIFICATIONS

Compressor Type
- Sedan
  - R-12 .... Sanden FX105VS Scroll
  - R-134a .... Sanden MSC105
- Wagon .... Nippondenso 10PA17C 10-Cyl.

Compressor Belt Deflection
- DOHC Engine
  - New .... 9/64-5/32" (3.5-4.0 mm)
  - Used .... 5/32-13/64" (4.0-5.0 mm)
- SOHC Engine
  - New .... 17/64-9/32" (6.5-7.0 mm)
  - Used .... 9/32-11/32" (7.0-8.5 mm)

System Oil Capacity
- Sedan
  - R-12 .... 5.4-6.0 ozs.
  - R-134a .... [1] 5.7-6.4 ozs.
- Wagon (R-12) .... 5.4 ozs.

Refrigerant Capacity
- Sedan
  - R-12 .... 34-38 ozs.
  - R-134a .... 26-28 ozs.
- Wagon .... 28 ozs.

System Operating Pressures [2]
- Sedan
  - High Side .... 105-112 psi (7.4-7.9 kg/cm²)
  - Low Side .... 19-28 psi (1.3-2.0 kg/cm²)
- Wagon
  - High Side .... 206-213 psi (14.5-15.0 kg/cm²)
  - Low Side .... 21-28 psi (1.5-2.0 kg/cm²)

[1] – Use SUN PAG 58 refrigerant oil.
[2] – Specification is with ambient temperature at about 80°F (26.7°C).

WARNING: To avoid injury from accidental air bag deployment, read and carefully follow all SERVICE PRECAUTIONS and DISABLING & ACTIVATING AIR BAG SYSTEM procedures in AIR BAG SYSTEM SAFETY article in GENERAL SERVICING.

DESCRIPTION & OPERATION

In-car temperature and airflow is automatically adjusted by setting the A/C-heater control panel mode selection controls and blower switch controls to AUTO position. Temperature setting is retained in memory even after ignition is turned off, unless battery has been disconnected.

A/C-heater control panel consists of mode selection controls, air selection controls, temperature control dial, A/C controls and blower switch controls.

CAUTION: When battery is disconnected, radio will go into anti-theft protection mode. Obtain radio anti-theft protection code from owner prior to servicing vehicle.

MODE SELECTION CONTROLS

Face Position – In this position, airflow is directed to upper area of passenger compartment. *See Fig. 1.*

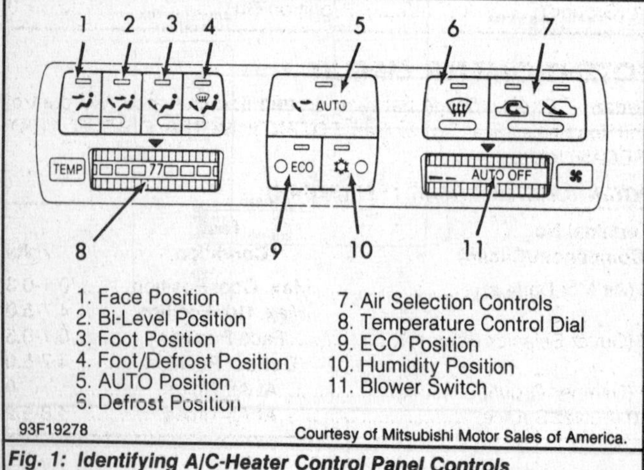

1
2
3
4
5
6
7
AUTO
TEMP
77
ECO
AUTO OFF
8
9
10
11
1. Face Position
2. Bi-Level Position
3. Foot Position
4. Foot/Defrost Position
5. AUTO Position
6. Defrost Position
7. Air Selection Controls
8. Temperature Control Dial
9. ECO Position
10. Humidity Position
11. Blower Switch
93F19278
Courtesy of Mitsubishi Motor Sales of America.

Fig. 1: Identifying A/C-Heater Control Panel Controls

Bi-Level Position – In this position, airflow is directed to leg area and upper area of passenger compartment.
Foot Position – In this position, airflow is directed to leg area.
Foot/Defrost Position – In this position, airflow is directed to leg area, windshield and door windows.
Defrost Position – In this position, airflow is directed to windshield and door windows.
AUTO Position – When AUTO is on, airflow direction and volume, in all modes except foot/defrost and defrost, are automatically controlled.

AIR SELECTION CONTROLS

Air selection controls can be set to inside or outside air position by pressing air selection button. When outside air position is selected, outside air enters passenger compartment. Outside air position is used to minimize window fogging.

When inside air position is selected, inside air is recirculated in passenger compartment. When driving on dusty roads or if quick cooling or heating is desired, select inside air position to prevent outside air from entering passenger compartment.

TEMPERATURE CONTROL DIAL

Temperature control dial adjusts the desired passenger compartment temperature. Temperature selection range is 68°F (20°C) to 86°F (30°C).

A/C CONTROLS

ECO Position – The ECO button can be pressed to switch to economical operation. With A/C in the economical operation mode, ECO indicator will light and A/C compressor will operate only when necessary to maintain the temperature set by the temperature control dial.
Humidity Position – This position can be selected when humidity is high or when outside air temperature is very hot. A/C compressor operates for maximum cooling.

BLOWER SWITCH

When ignition switch is turned to ON position, blower can be operated to regulate amount of air forced through passenger compartment. When blower switch is in AUTO position, blower speed is controlled automatically. When blower switch is in OFF position, all A/C-heater functions stop.

TROUBLE SHOOTING

On Sedan, the self-diagnostic function detects abnormal conditions of A/C control unit, related sensors and wirings. Self-diagnostic function includes an automatic control back-up, which provides substitute value in case of system failure. Data link connector is located under left side of dash. *See Fig. 2.* Trouble codes can be accessed by the use of an analog voltmeter.

ACCESSING TROUBLE CODES

Sedan – 1) Turn ignition off. Using an analog voltmeter, connect voltmeter positive lead to data link connector terminal No. 7 and negative lead to terminal No. 12 (ground). *See Fig. 2.*
2) Turn ignition on. Signals will appear on voltmeter as long and short 12-volt pulses. Long pulses represent tens; short pulses represent

TROUBLE CODE IDENTIFICATION

Code	Malfunction
0	Normal
11	In-Car Temp. Sensor Open Circuit
12	In-Car Temp. Sensor Short Circuit
13	Outside Air Temp. Sensor Open Circuit
14	Outside Air Temp. Sensor Short Circuit
21	Air (Fin) Thermosensor Open Circuit
22	Air (Fin) Thermosensor Short Circuit
31	Air Mix Damper Potentiometer Short Or Open Circuit
32	Mode Selector Damper Potentiometer Short Or Open Circuit
41	Defective Air Mix Damper Motor
42	Defective Mode Selector Damper Motor

ones. For example, 4 long pulses and one short pulse indicates Code 41. A constant repetition of short 12-volt pulses indicates Code 0, system is normal. If more than 2 abnormal conditions are present, code numbers are alternately displayed in numerical order until ignition switch is turned off. See TROUBLE CODE IDENTIFICATION table.

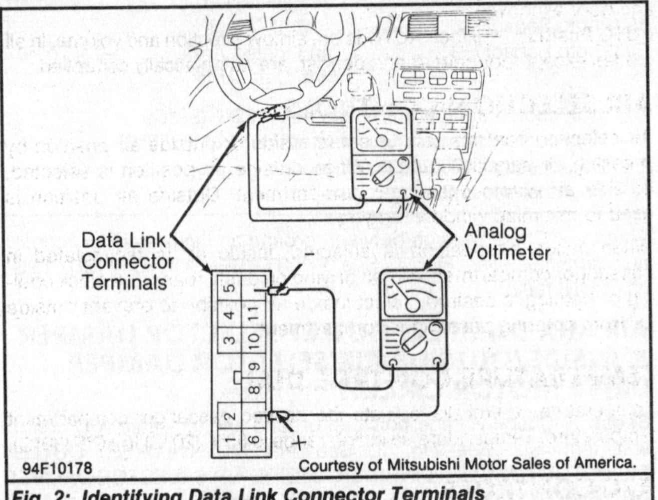
Data Link Connector Terminals
Analog Voltmeter
5
4
11
3
10
9
8
2
1
6
94F10178
Courtesy of Mitsubishi Motor Sales of America.

Fig. 2: Identifying Data Link Connector Terminals

CLEARING TROUBLE CODES

Sedan – To clear trouble codes from memory, turn ignition off. Disconnect negative battery cable for at least 10 seconds. Reconnect negative battery cable and recheck codes. Normal code (Code 0) should now be displayed. A normal code indication is a continuous voltmeter sweep pattern.

COMPRESSOR DOES NOT OPERATE

Wagon – Check components in order listed, and repair or replace as necessary: A/C fuse; refrigerant charge; wiring harness and connectors; compressor relay; magnetic clutch; dual-pressure switch; sensors; A/C-heater control panel; A/C control unit; engine control module.

AIR NOT WARM

Wagon – Check components in order listed, and repair or replace as necessary: wiring harness and connectors; sensors; air mix damper motor and potentiometer; A/C-heater control panel; A/C control unit.

AIR NOT COOL

Wagon – Check components in order listed, and repair or replace as necessary: A/C fuse; refrigerant charge; wiring harness and connectors; sensors; air mix damper motor and potentiometer; A/C-heater control panel; A/C control unit

BLOWER MOTOR DOES NOT OPERATE

Wagon – Check components in order listed, and repair or replace as necessary: A/C fuse; blower motor; heater relay; power transistor; wiring harness and connectors; A/C-heater control panel; A/C control unit.

BLOWER MOTOR DOES NOT STOP

Wagon – Check components in order listed, and repair or replace as necessary: wiring harness and connectors; blower motor relay; power transistor; A/C-heater control panel; A/C control unit.

INSIDE/OUTSIDE AIR SELECTOR DAMPER DOES NOT OPERATE

Wagon – Check components in order listed, and repair or replace as necessary: wiring harness and connectors; inside/outside air selector damper motor; A/C-heater control panel; A/C control unit.

MODE SELECTION DAMPER DOES NOT OPERATE

Wagon – Check components in order listed, and repair or replace as necessary: wiring harness and connectors; outlet selector damper motor and potentiometer; sensors; A/C-heater control panel; A/C control unit.

CONDENSER FAN DOES NOT OPERATE WHEN A/C IS ACTIVATED

Wagon – Check components in order listed, and repair or replace as necessary: A/C fuse; condenser fan relay; condenser fan motor; sensors; wiring harness and connectors; A/C control unit.

TESTING

***WARNING:** To avoid injury from accidental air bag deployment, read and carefully follow all SERVICE PRECAUTIONS and DISABLING & ACTIVATING AIR BAG SYSTEM procedures in AIR BAG SYSTEM SAFETY article in GENERAL SERVICING.*

A/C SYSTEM PERFORMANCE

1) Park vehicle out of direct sunlight. Connect manifold gauge set. Start engine and allow it to idle at 1000 RPM. Set A/C controls to recirculate air, panel (vent) mode, full cold, and A/C button on.

2) Set blower/fan on high speed and close doors and windows. Insert thermometer in center vent. Operate system for 20 minutes to allow system to stabilize. Measure temperature. Temperature must be 37-42°F (3-6°C) at center vent, with high side and low side pressures within specification. See SPECIFICATIONS table at beginning of article.

A/C CONTROL UNIT CIRCUIT

Sedan – Check voltage between ground and indicated A/C control unit terminals. *See Fig. 3.* See A/C CONTROL UNIT CIRCUIT TEST (SEDAN) table.

A/C CONTROL UNIT CIRCUIT TEST (SEDAN)

Terminal No. (Component/Circuit)	Test Condition	Volts
3 (Back-Up Power)	At All Times	12
35 (Ground)	At All Times	0
36 (Power Source)	Ignition On	12

Wagon) – Check voltage between ground and indicated A/C control unit terminals. *See Fig. 4.* See A/C CONTROL UNIT CIRCUIT TEST (WAGON) table.

A/C CONTROL UNIT CIRCUIT TEST (WAGON)

Terminal No. (Component/Circuit)	Test Condition	Volts
1 (Power Source)	Ignition On	12
11 (Ground)	Ignition On	0

POTENTIOMETER CIRCUIT

Sedan – Check voltage between ground and indicated A/C control unit terminals. *See Fig. 3.* See POTENTIOMETER CIRCUIT TEST (SEDAN) table.

POTENTIOMETER CIRCUIT TEST (SEDAN)

Terminal No. (Component/Circuit)	Test Condition	Volts
6 (Air Mix Damper)	Max. Cool Position	0.1-0.3
	Max. Hot Position	4.7-5.0
7 (Outlet Selector Damper)	Face Position	0.1-0.5
	Defrost Position	4.7-5.0
8 (Damper Ground)	At All Times	0
10 (Power Source)	At All Times	4.8-5.2

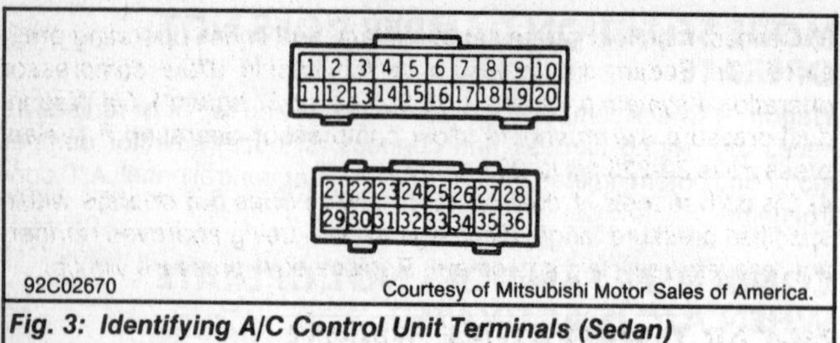
1 2 3 4 5 6 7 8 9 10
11 12 13 14 15 16 17 18 19 20
21 22 23 24 25 26 27 28
29 30 31 32 33 34 35 36
92C02670
Courtesy of Mitsubishi Motor Sales of America.

Fig. 3: Identifying A/C Control Unit Terminals (Sedan)

Wagon – Check voltage between ground and indicated A/C control unit terminals. *See Fig. 4.* See POTENTIOMETER CIRCUIT TEST (WAGON) table.

POTENTIOMETER CIRCUIT TEST (WAGON)

Terminal No. (Component/Circuit)	Test Condition	Volts
10 (Power Source)	Ignition On	4.8-5.2
12 (Damper Ground)	Ignition On	0
13 (Outlet Selector Damper)	Face Position	3.8-4.2
	Defrost Position	0.9-1.1
14 (Air Mix Damper)	Max. Cool Position	0.9-1.1
	Max. Hot Position	3.8-4.2

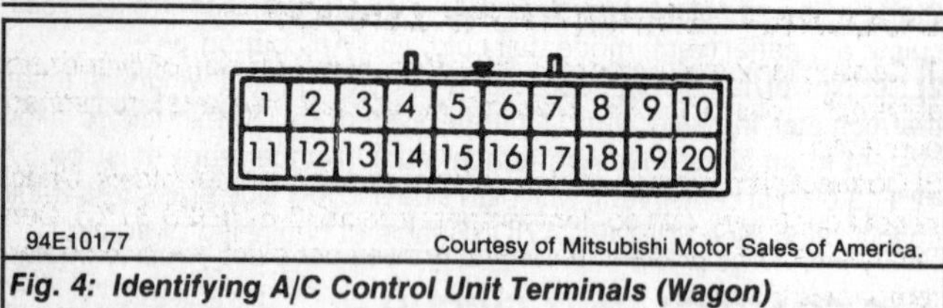
1 2 3 4 5 6 7 8 9 10
11 12 13 14 15 16 17 18 19 20
94E10177
Courtesy of Mitsubishi Motor Sales of America.

Fig. 4: Identifying A/C Control Unit Terminals (Wagon)

IN-CAR TEMPERATURE SENSOR, OUTSIDE AIR TEMPERATURE SENSOR & AIR (FIN) THERMOSENSOR CIRCUIT

Sedan – Check voltage between ground and indicated A/C control unit terminals. *See Fig. 3.* See IN-CAR TEMPERATURE SENSOR, OUTSIDE AIR TEMPERATURE SENSOR & AIR (FIN) THERMOSENSOR CIRCUIT TEST table.

IN-CAR TEMPERATURE SENSOR, OUTSIDE AIR TEMPERATURE SENSOR & AIR (FIN) THERMOSENSOR CIRCUIT TEST

Terminal No. (Component/Circuit)	Test Condition	Volts
5 (Outside Air Temp. Sensor)	[1] 77°C (25°C)	2.3-2.6
10 (Sensor Power Source)	At All Times	4.8-5.2
16 (In-Car Temp. Sensor)	[1] 77°C (25°C)	2.5-2.7
17 (Air/Fin Thermosensor)	[1] [2] 77°C (25°C)	2.5-2.7

[1] – Sensor resistance should be 4000 ohms.
[2] – Measured with A/C system off.

COOLANT TEMPERATURE & PHOTO SENSOR CIRCUIT

Sedan – Check voltage between ground and indicated A/C control unit terminals. *See Fig. 3.* See COOLANT TEMPERATURE SENSOR & PHOTO SENSOR CIRCUIT TEST (SEDAN) table.

PHOTO SENSOR CIRCUIT TEST (WAGON)

Terminal No. (Component/Circuit)	Test Condition	Volts
10 (Photo Sensor +)	Ignition On	4.8-5.2
16 (Photo Sensor –)	[1] In Lighted Area	0.06-2.0
	[2] In Dark Area	0.06

[1] – Brightness at 100,000 lux or more.
[2] – Brightness less than zero lux.

COOLANT TEMPERATURE SENSOR & PHOTO SENSOR CIRCUIT TEST (SEDAN)

Terminal No. (Component/Circuit)	Test Condition	Volts
9 (Coolant Temp. Sensor)	[1] Ignition Off	1.2
	[2] Ignition On	0
19 (Photo Sensor –)	At All Times	0
20 (Photo Sensor +)	[3] In Lighted Area	–0.1 To –0.2
	[4] In Dark Area	0

[1] – With coolant temperature less than 122°F (50°C).
[2] – With coolant temperature greater than 122°F (50°C).
[3] – Brightness at 100,000 lux or more.
[4] – Brightness less than zero lux.

Wagon – Check voltage between ground and indicated A/C control unit terminals. *See Fig. 4.* See PHOTO SENSOR CIRCUIT TEST (WAGON) table.

AIR MIX DAMPER, OUTLET SELECTOR DAMPER & INSIDE/OUTSIDE AIR SELECTOR DAMPER DRIVE MOTOR CIRCUIT

Sedan – Check voltage between ground and indicated A/C control unit terminals. *See Fig. 3.* See AIR MIX DAMPER, OUTLET SELECTOR DAMPER & INSIDE/OUTSIDE AIR SELECTOR DAMPER DRIVE MOTOR CIRCUIT TEST (SEDAN) table.

AIR MIX DAMPER, OUTLET SELECTOR DAMPER, INSIDE/OUTSIDE AIR SELECTOR DAMPER DRIVE MOTOR CIRCUIT TEST (SEDAN)

Terminal No. (Component/Circuit)	Test Condition	Volts
23 (Outlet Selector Motor –)	[1] Face Position	0.5
	[2] Defrost Position	10-12
25 (Air Mix Motor +)	[3] 63°F (17°C)	0.5
	[4] 90.5°F (32.5°C)	10-12
31 (Air Mix Motor –)	[3] 63°F (17°C)	10-12
	[4] 90.5°F (32.5°C)	0.5
32 (Out Selector Motor +)	[1] Face Position	10-12
	[2] Defrost Position	0.5

[1] – Output turns off 40 seconds after damper moves to face position.
[2] – Output turns off 40 seconds after damper moves to defrost position.
[3] – With temperature set as specified, output turns off 40 seconds after damper moves to maximum cool position.
[4] – With temperature set as specified, output turns off 40 seconds after damper moves to maximum hot position.

Wagon – Check voltage between ground and indicated A/C control unit terminals. *See Fig. 4.* See AIR MIX DAMPER & DAMPER DRIVE MOTOR CIRCUIT TEST (WAGON) table.

AIR MIX DAMPER & DAMPER DRIVE MOTOR CIRCUIT TEST (WAGON)

Terminal No. (Component/Circuit)	Test Condition	Volts
25 (Air Mix Motor +)	[3] Max. Cool	0-1.0
	[4] Max. Hot	10-12
26 (Outlet Selector Motor –)	[1] Face Position	10-12
	[2] Defrost Position	1-1.0
31 (Air Mix Motor –)	[3] Max. Cool	10-12
	[4] Max. Hot	0-1.0
32 (Out Selector Motor +)	[1] Face Position	10-12
	[2] Defrost Position	0-1.0

[1] – Output turns off 40 seconds after damper moves to face position.
[2] – Output turns off 40 seconds after damper moves to defrost position.
[3] – With temperature set as specified, output turns off 40 seconds after damper moves to maximum cool position.
[4] – With temperature set as specified, output turns off 40 seconds after damper moves to maximum hot position.

AIR INLET SENSOR, AIR/FIN THERMOSENSOR, IN-CAR TEMPERATURE SENSOR, & WATER TEMPERATURE SENSOR CIRCUIT

Wagon - Check voltage between ground and indicated A/C control unit terminals. *See Fig. 4.* See AIR INLET SENSOR, AIR (FIN) THERMOSENSOR, IN-CAR TEMPERATURE SENSOR, & WATER TEMPERATURE SENSOR CIRCUIT TEST (WAGON) table.

AIR INLET SENSOR, AIR/FIN THERMOSENSOR, IN-CAR TEMPERATURE SENSOR & WATER TEMPERATURE SENSOR CIRCUIT TEST (WAGON)

Terminal No. (Component/Circuit)	Test Condition	Volts
3 (Water Temp. Sensor)	77°F (25°C)	2.7-3.0
4 (Air/Fin Thermosensor)	[1] 77°F (25°C)	2.6-3.1
5 (Air Inlet Sensor)	77°F (25°C)	2.6-3.1
6 (In-Car Temp. Sensor)	77°F (25°C)	2.7-3.1
12 (Sensor Ground)	Ignition On	0

[1] - Measured with A/C system off.

POWER TRANSISTOR & BLOWER MOTOR HI RELAY CIRCUIT

Sedan - Check voltage between ground and indicated A/C control unit terminals. *See Fig. 3.* See POWER TRANSISTOR & BLOWER MOTOR HI RELAY CIRCUIT TEST (SEDAN) table.

POWER TRANSISTOR & BLOWER MOTOR HI RELAY CIRCUIT TEST (SEDAN)

Terminal No. (Component/Circuit)	Blower Sw. Position	Volts
1 (Power Transistor Collector)	OFF	12
	LO	Approx. 7
	HI	0
2 (Power Transistor Base)	OFF	0
	LO	Approx. 1.3
	HI	Approx. 1.2
21 (Blower Motor HI Relay)	HI	0-1.5
	MED	12
	LO	12
	OFF	12

Wagon - Check voltage between ground and indicated A/C control unit terminals. *See Fig. 4.* See POWER TRANSISTOR & BLOWER MOTOR HI RELAY CIRCUIT TEST (WAGON) table.

POWER TRANSISTOR & BLOWER MOTOR HI RELAY CIRCUIT TEST (WAGON)

Terminal No. (Component/Circuit)	Blower Sw. Position	Volts
52 (Blower Motor Hi Relay)	HI	1.5 Or Less
	MED	12
	LO	12
	OFF	12
58 (Power Transistor Collector)	OFF	12
	LO	Approx. 9
	HI	0
66 (Power Transistor Base)	OFF	0

DUAL-PRESSURE SWITCH

1) Turn engine off. Disconnect harness connector at dual-pressure switch (located near condenser). Jumper harness connector. Turn A/C switch and blower switch to ON position. Momentarily turn ignition on and listen for compressor clutch engagement.
2) If compressor clutch does not engage, check evaporator thermistor and engine coolant temperature switch. Check for a faulty fuse. Repair or replace components as necessary. If compressor clutch engages, go to next step.
3) Connect manifold gauge set to system, and check operating pressures. On Sedan, dual-pressure switch should allow compressor operation if system pressure is 30-384 psi (2-27 kg/cm²). On Wagon, dual-pressure switch should allow compressor operation if system pressure is 30-225 psi (2-22 kg/cm²).
4) On both models, if dual-pressure switch does not operate within specified pressure range, discharge system using approved refrigerant recovery/recycling equipment. Replace dual-pressure switch.

IN-CAR TEMPERATURE SENSOR

In-car temperature sensor is located on headliner. Connect ohmmeter to in-car temperature sensor terminals. Measure resistance value of sensor at 77°F (25°C). Resistance should be about 4000 ohms (Sedan) or 15,000 ohms (Wagon). Replace sensor if resistance is not as specified.

OUTSIDE TEMPERATURE SENSOR

Sedan - Outside temperature sensor is located on top of blower motor assembly. Connect ohmmeter to outside temperature sensor terminals. Measure resistance value of sensor at 77°F (25°C). Resistance should be about 4000 ohms. Replace sensor if resistance is not as specified.

COOLANT TEMPERATURE SENSOR

1) Coolant temperature sensor is located on top left side of evaporator assembly. *See Fig.* 22. Disconnect coolant temperature sensor connector.
2) Connect ohmmeter to coolant temperature sensor terminals. Check sensor continuity with coolant temperature at 73-87°F (23-31°C). Continuity should be present. If continuity does not exist, replace coolant temperature sensor.

AIR/FIN THERMOSENSOR

1) Air/fin thermosensor is located on left side of evaporator assembly. Connect ohmmeter to air/fin thermosensor terminals.
2) Measure resistance with sensor's sensing temperature at 77°F (25°C). Resistance should be about 4000 ohms (Sedan) or 15,000 ohms (Wagon). Replace air/fin thermosensor if resistance largely deviates from specified resistance.

INSIDE/OUTSIDE AIR DAMPER MOTOR

Sedan - **1)** Ensure damper is not in recirculated air or fresh air position. Disconnect inside/outside air damper motor connector. *See Fig. 5.* Apply battery voltage and ground to motor connector terminals No. 1 and 2. Motor should operate when battery voltage is applied. Check wiring or replace defective motor if it does not operate.
2) Reverse battery polarity on motor connector terminals. Motor should operate in opposite direction. DO NOT continue applying battery voltage if motor does not operate. Check wiring or replace defective motor if it does not operate.
Wagon - **1)** Ensure damper is not in recirculated air or fresh air position. Disconnect inside/outside air damper motor connector. *See Fig. 5.* Apply battery voltage to motor connector terminal No. 1 and ground terminal No. 2. Motor should operate when battery voltage is applied. DO NOT continue applying battery voltage if motor does not operate. Check wiring or replace defective motor if it does not operate.
2) Apply battery voltage to motor connector terminal No. 1 and ground terminal 4. Motor should operate when battery voltage is applied. DO NOT continue applying battery voltage if motor does not operate. Check wiring or replace defective motor if it does not operate.

1993 AUTOMATIC A/C-HEATER SYSTEMS
Diamante (Cont.)

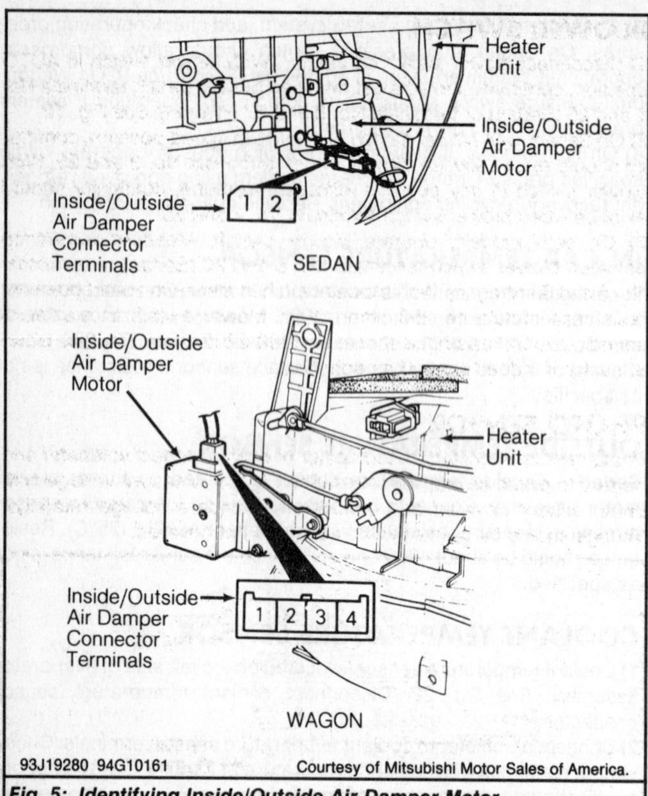
Heater Unit
Inside/Outside Air Damper Motor
Inside/Outside Air Damper Connector Terminals
1 2
SEDAN
Inside/Outside Air Damper Motor
Heater Unit
Inside/Outside Air Damper Connector Terminals
1 2 3 4
WAGON
93J19280 94G10161
Courtesy of Mitsubishi Motor Sales of America.

Fig. 5: Identifying Inside/Outside Air Damper Motor

AIR MIX DAMPER MOTOR

1) Ensure damper is not in maximum hot or maximum cool position. Disconnect air mix damper motor connector. *See Fig. 6.* Apply battery voltage and ground to motor connector terminals No. 2 and 6 (Sedan) or terminals No. 1 and 3 (Wagon). Motor should operate when battery voltage is applied.

2) Reverse battery polarity on motor connector terminals. Motor should operate in opposite direction. DO NOT continue applying battery voltage if motor does not operate. Check wiring or replace defective motor if it does not operate.

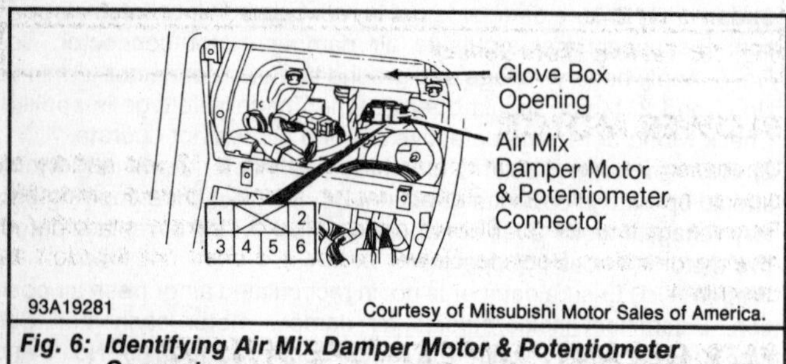
Glove Box Opening
Air Mix Damper Motor & Potentiometer Connector
1 2
3 4 5 6
93A19281
Courtesy of Mitsubishi Motor Sales of America.

Fig. 6: Identifying Air Mix Damper Motor & Potentiometer Connector

AIR MIX DAMPER POTENTIOMETER

1) Connect ohmmeter across air mix damper motor connector terminals No. 3 and 4 (Sedan) or terminals No. 2 and 5 (Wagon). *See Fig. 6.* Resistance should gradually change as damper is moved from maximum hot to maximum cool position.

2) On Sedan, resistance should be 200 ohms at maximum hot position and 4900 ohms at maximum cool position. On Wagon, resistance should be 4800 ohms at maximum hot position and 1200 ohms at maximum cool position. On both models, replace air mix damper potentiometer if resistance readings are not as specified.

OUTLET SELECTOR DAMPER MOTOR

1) Ensure damper is not in defrost or face position. Disconnect outlet selector damper motor connector. Apply battery voltage and ground to motor connector terminals No. 2 and 6 (Sedan) or terminals No. 1 and 3 (Wagon). *See Fig. 7.* Motor should operate when battery voltage is applied.

2) Reverse battery polarity on motor connector terminals. Motor should operate in opposite direction. DO NOT continue applying battery voltage if motor does not operate. Check wiring or replace defective motor if it does not operate.

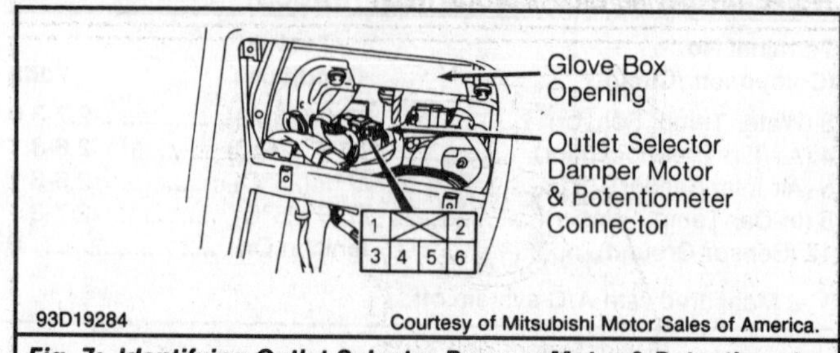
Glove Box Opening
Outlet Selector Damper Motor & Potentiometer Connector
1 2
3 4 5 6
93D19284
Courtesy of Mitsubishi Motor Sales of America.

Fig. 7: Identifying Outlet Selector Damper Motor & Potentiometer Connector

OUTLET SELECTOR DAMPER POTENTIOMETER

1) Connect ohmmeter across air mix damper motor connector terminals No. 3 and 4 (Sedan) or terminals No. 2 and 4 (Wagon). *See Fig. 7.* Resistance should gradually change as damper is moved from defrost to face position.

2) On Sedan, resistance should be 2000 ohms in defrost position and 4300 ohms in face position. On Wagon, resistance should be 900 ohms in defrost position and 3600 ohms in face position. On both models, replace outlet selector damper potentiometer if resistance readings are not as specified.

A/C-HEATER RELAYS

1) Disconnect each relay. *See Figs. 8-10.* Check continuity of each relay as follows. Connect negative battery lead to relay terminal No. 4 and positive lead to terminal No. 2. *See Fig. 11.* Using an ohmmeter, ensure continuity exists between relay terminals No. 1 and 3.

2) Disconnect battery. Ensure continuity does not exist between relay terminals No. 1 and 3. Continuity should exist between relay terminals No. 2 and 4. Replace relay if it does not test as specified.

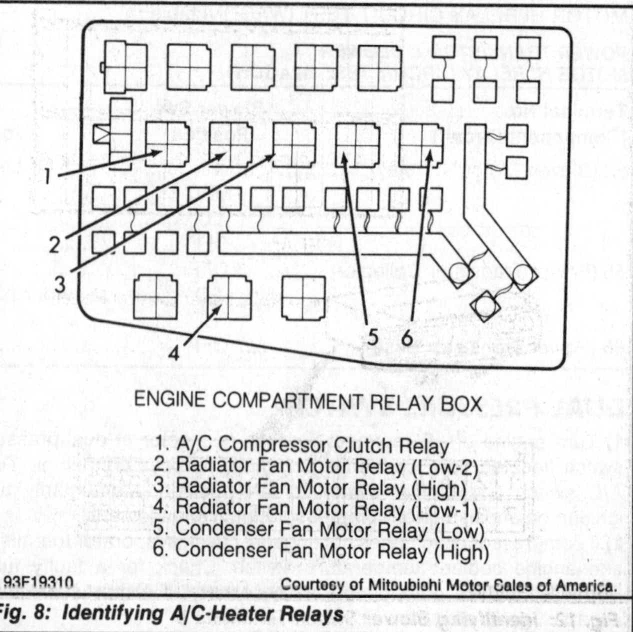
1
2
3
4
5 6
ENGINE COMPARTMENT RELAY BOX
1. A/C Compressor Clutch Relay
2. Radiator Fan Motor Relay (Low-2)
3. Radiator Fan Motor Relay (High)
4. Radiator Fan Motor Relay (Low-1)
5. Condenser Fan Motor Relay (Low)
6. Condenser Fan Motor Relay (High)
93F19310
Courtesy of Mitsubishi Motor Sales of America.

Fig. 8: Identifying A/C-Heater Relays

Diamante (Cont.)

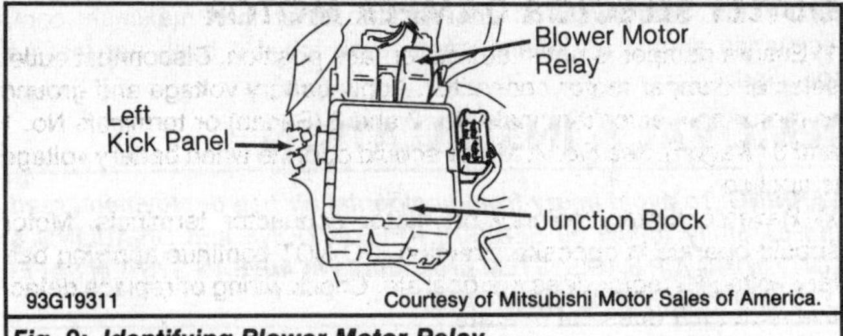

Blower Motor
Relay
Left
Kick Panel
Junction Block
93G19311
Courtesy of Mitsubishi Motor Sales of America.

Fig. 9: Identifying Blower Motor Relay

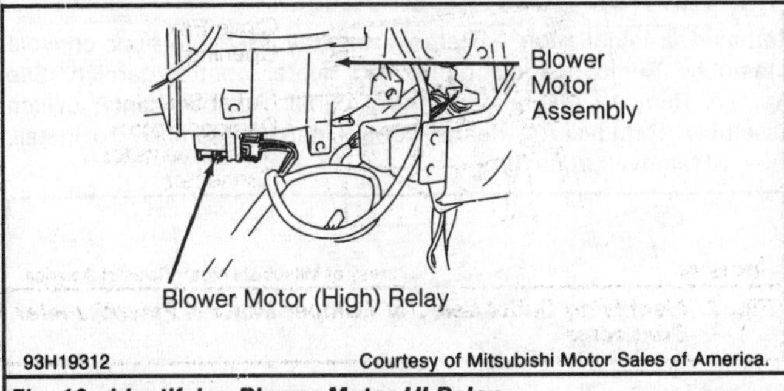

Blower
Motor
Assembly
Blower Motor (High) Relay
93H19312
Courtesy of Mitsubishi Motor Sales of America.

Fig. 10: Identifying Blower Motor HI Relay

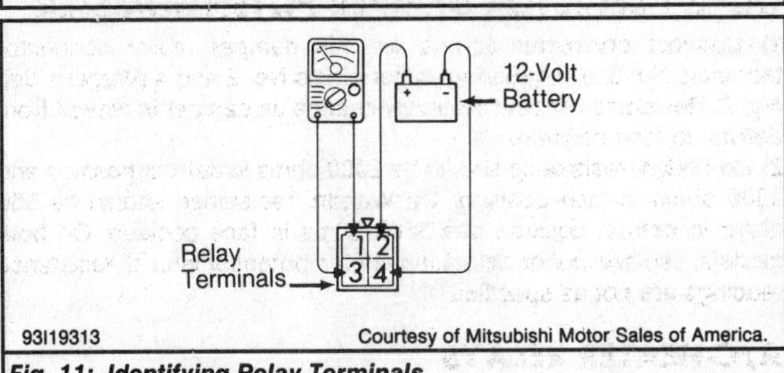

12-Volt
Battery
Relay
Terminals
1 2
3 4
93I19313
Courtesy of Mitsubishi Motor Sales of America.

Fig. 11: Identifying Relay Terminals

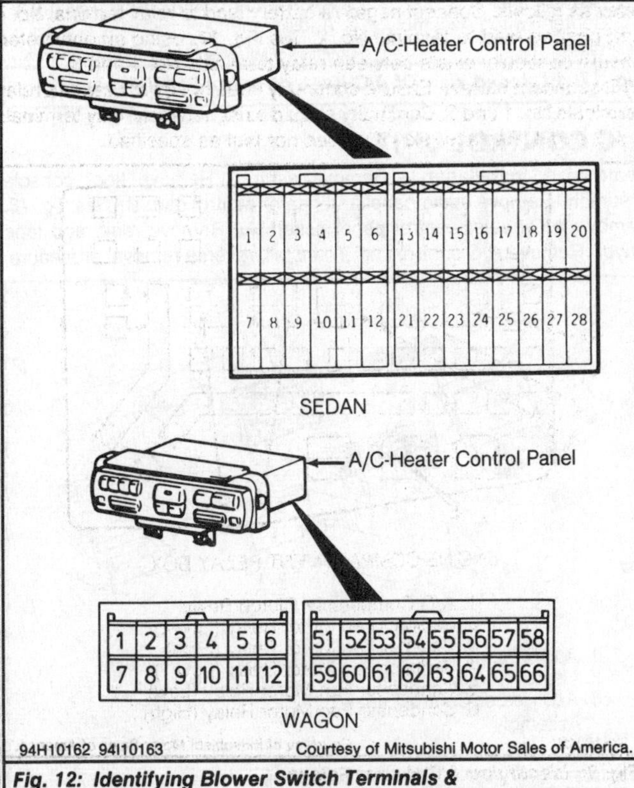

A/C-Heater Control Panel
1 2 3 4 5 6 13 14 15 16 17 18 19 20
7 8 9 10 11 12 21 22 23 24 25 26 27 28
SEDAN
A/C-Heater Control Panel
1 2 3 4 5 6 51 52 53 54 55 56 57 58
7 8 9 10 11 12 59 60 61 62 63 64 65 66
WAGON
94H10162 94I10163
Courtesy of Mitsubishi Motor Sales of America.

Fig. 12: Identifying Blower Switch Terminals & Temperature Control Switch Terminals

BLOWER SWITCH

1) Disconnect blower switch connector. With blower switch in AUTO position, continuity should exist between blower switch terminals No. 1 and 25 (Sedan) or terminals No. 8 and 63 (Wagon). *See Fig. 12*.
2) On Sedan, with blower switch in maximum speed position, continuity should exist between blower switch terminals No. 3 and 25. With blower switch in any position (except maximum), continuity should exist between blower switch terminals No. 2 and 25.
3) On both models, operate blower switch. Measure resistance between blower switch terminals No. 8 and 20 (Sedan) or terminals No. 8 and 63 (Wagon). With blower switch in minimum speed position, resistance should be 250 ohms. With blower switch in maximum speed position, resistance should be 1800-2200 ohms. Replace blower switch if it does not test as specified.

PHOTO SENSOR

Photo sensor is located on top center of dash. Connect voltmeter and battery to photo sensor terminals. *See Fig. 13*. Measure voltage with photo sensor covered and uncovered. Compare voltage readings. Voltage should be greater when sensor is not covered.

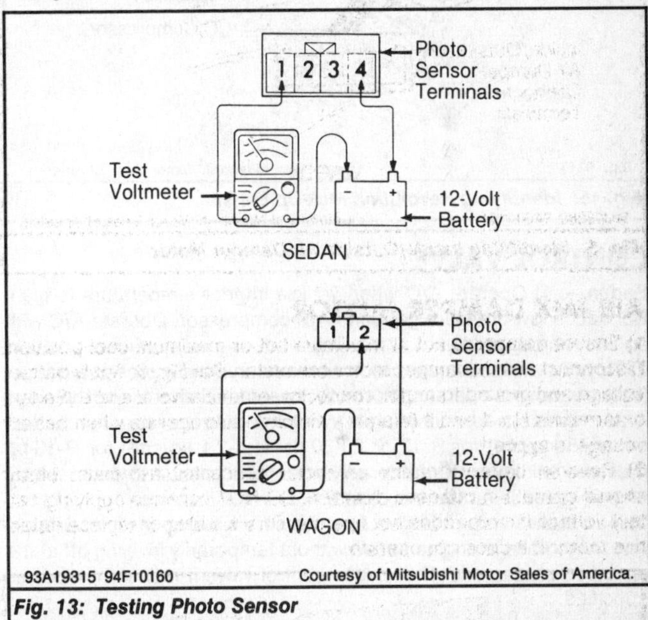

1 2 3 4
Photo
Sensor
Terminals
Test
Voltmeter
12-Volt
Battery
SEDAN
1 2
Photo
Sensor
Terminals
Test
Voltmeter
12-Volt
Battery
WAGON
93A19315 94F10160
Courtesy of Mitsubishi Motor Sales of America.

Fig. 13: Testing Photo Sensor

BLOWER MOTOR

Disconnect blower motor connector. Connect a 12-volt battery to blower motor terminals. Blower motor should operate smoothly. Reverse battery leads. Blower motor should operate smoothly in reverse direction. Replace blower motor if it does not function as described.

REFRIGERANT TEMPERATURE SENSOR

Sedan – Submerge refrigerant temperature sensor tip in engine oil. Using an ohmmeter, check continuity between refrigerant sensor terminals No. 1 and 2 (SOHC) or terminals No. 3 and 6 (DOHC). *See Fig. 14*. When engine oil is heated to 230°F (110°C), continuity should exist. When engine oil is heated to 311°F (155°C), no continuity should exist.

REVOLUTION PICK-UP SENSOR

Sedan – Using an ohmmeter, measure resistance between revolution pick-up sensor terminals No. 2 and 5. *See Fig. 15*. Resistance should be 370-440 ohms at 68°F (20°C). Replace revolution pick-up sensor if it does not test as specified.

1993 AUTOMATIC A/C-HEATER SYSTEMS
Diamante (Cont.)

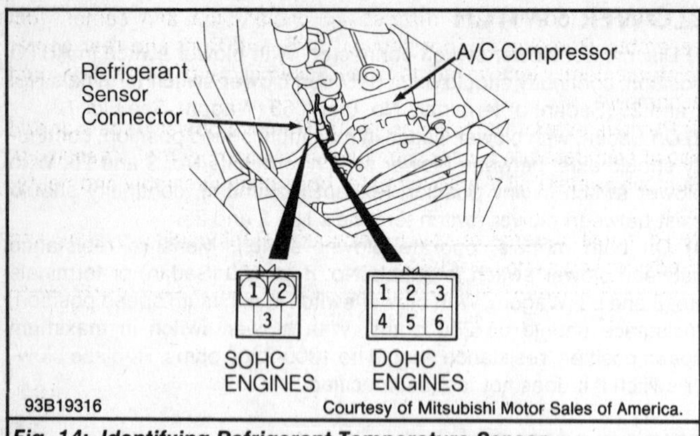
A/C Compressor
Refrigerant Sensor Connector
1 2
3
1 2 3
4 5 6
SOHC ENGINES
DOHC ENGINES
93B19316
Courtesy of Mitsubishi Motor Sales of America.

Fig. 14: Identifying Refrigerant Temperature Sensor

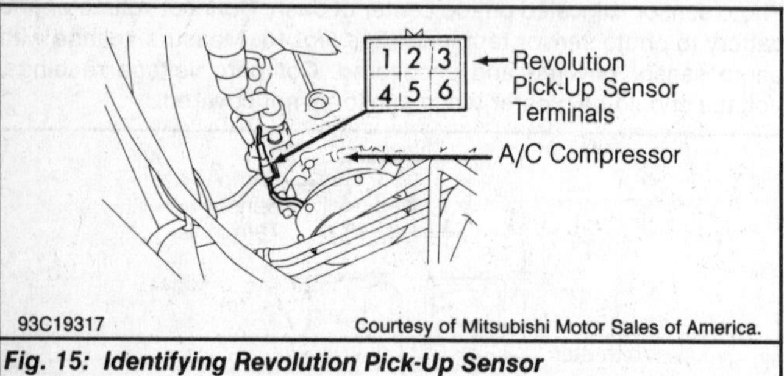
1 2 3
4 5 6
Revolution Pick-Up Sensor Terminals
A/C Compressor
93C19317
Courtesy of Mitsubishi Motor Sales of America.

Fig. 15: Identifying Revolution Pick-Up Sensor

CONTROL VALVE

Sedan - 1) Operate A/C when vehicle interior temperature is high. Connect a low pressure gauge to A/C compressor. Operate A/C with engine running at idle.

2) Slowly increase engine speed while observing low pressure gauge. If control valve is operating normally, low-side pressure will drop slowly as engine speed is increased. When low-side pressure reaches 25 psi (1.75 kg/cm²) for R-12 or 20-30 psi (1.4-2.1 kg/cm²) for R-134a, pressure will level off temporarily and then continue to decrease as engine speed is further increased.

3) If control valve is defective, low pressure will drop in direct proportion to increase in engine speed without temporarily leveling off at the specified pressure level. Replace control valve if it does not test as specified.

CONDENSER FAN MOTOR

Voltage Check - Apply battery voltage to condenser fan motor terminal No. 3. Ensure condenser fan motor turns when terminal No. 4 is grounded. *See Fig. 16.* Replace condenser fan motor if it does not operate with battery voltage applied.

Resistance Check - Using an ohmmeter, check resistance between condenser fan motor terminals No. 1 and 2. *See Fig. 16.* Resistance should be 290 ohms. Replace condenser fan motor if resistance is not as specified.

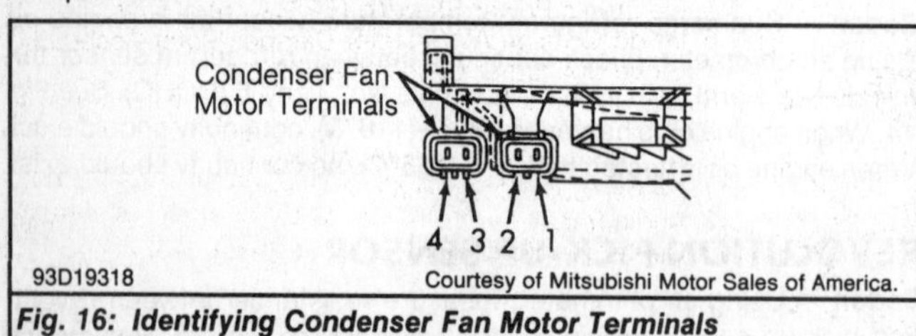
Condenser Fan Motor Terminals
4 3 2 1
93D19318
Courtesy of Mitsubishi Motor Sales of America.

Fig. 16: Identifying Condenser Fan Motor Terminals

TEMPERATURE CONTROL SWITCH

Sedan - Disconnect temperature control switch connector. *See Fig. 12.* Measure resistance between switch connector terminals No. 4 and 20. With switch at maximum cool position, resistance should be zero ohms. With switch at any position other than maximum cool, resistance should be infinite. replace switch if it does not test as specified.

REMOVAL & INSTALLATION

WARNING: To avoid injury from accidental air bag deployment, read and carefully follow all SERVICE PRECAUTIONS and DISABLING & ACTIVATING AIR BAG SYSTEM procedures in AIR BAG SYSTEM SAFETY article in GENERAL SERVICING.

A/C-HEATER CONTROL PANEL

Removal & Installation - Remove ashtray. Remove floor console assembly. Remove audio panel and heater control garnish. *See Fig. 17.* Remove A/C-heater control panel. Remove center switch assembly. Remove A/C-heater control panel assembly. To install, reverse removal procedure.

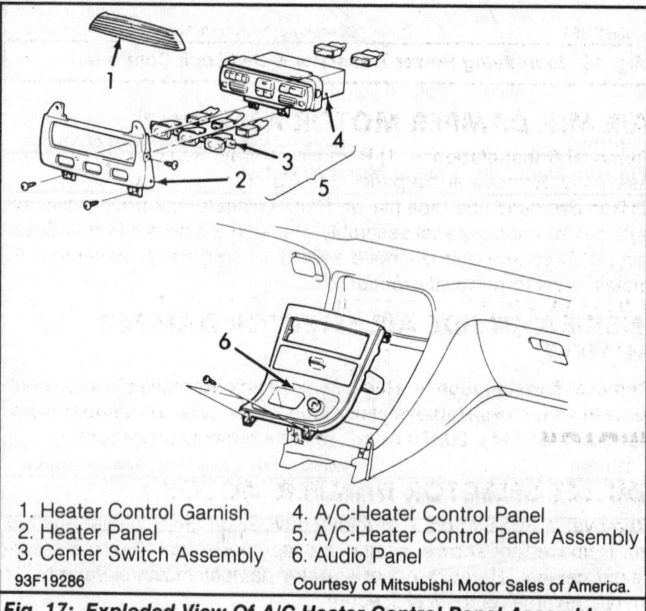
1
2
3
4
5
6
1. Heater Control Garnish
2. Heater Panel
3. Center Switch Assembly
4. A/C-Heater Control Panel
5. A/C-Heater Control Panel Assembly
6. Audio Panel
93F19286
Courtesy of Mitsubishi Motor Sales of America.

Fig. 17: Exploded View Of A/C-Heater Control Panel Assembly

A/C CONTROL UNIT

Removal & Installation - Remove ashtray. Remove floor console assembly. Remove audio panel and heater control garnish. *See Fig. 18.* Remove A/C-heater control panel assembly. Remove radio and tape player. Remove A/C control unit. To install, reverse removal procedure.

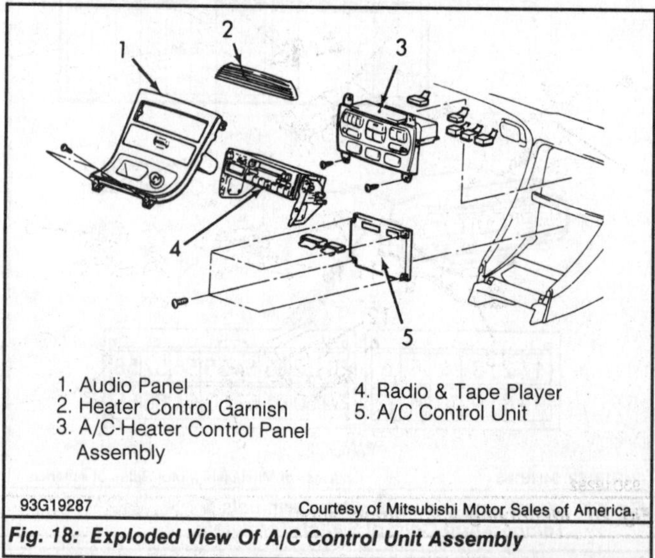
1
2
3
4
5
1. Audio Panel
2. Heater Control Garnish
3. A/C-Heater Control Panel Assembly
4. Radio & Tape Player
5. A/C Control Unit
93G19287
Courtesy of Mitsubishi Motor Sales of America.

Fig. 18: Exploded View Of A/C Control Unit Assembly

POWER TRANSISTOR & BELT LOCK CONTROLLER

Removal & Installation – Remove glove box. Remove power transistor and/or belt lock controller (DOHC engines). *See Fig. 19.* To install, reverse removal procedure.

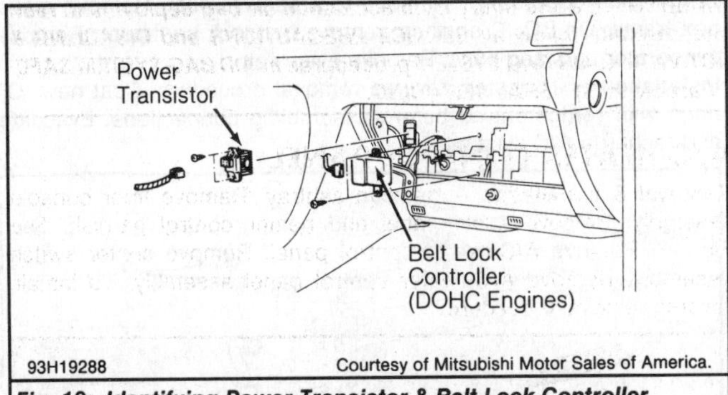
Power
Transistor
Belt Lock
Controller
(DOHC Engines)
93H19288
Courtesy of Mitsubishi Motor Sales of America.

Fig. 19: Identifying Power Transistor & Belt Lock Controller

AIR MIX DAMPER MOTOR ASSEMBLY

Removal & Installation – **1)** Remove ashtray. Remove floor console assembly. Remove audio panel. *See Fig. 20.*

2) Remove radio and tape player. Remove heater control garnish and A/C-heater control panel assembly. Remove Electronic Power Steering (EPS) control unit. Remove air mix damper motor assembly. To install, reverse removal procedure.

INSIDE/OUTSIDE AIR SELECTOR DAMPER MOTOR

Removal & Installation – Remove glove box. Remove glove box outer case assembly. Remove inside/outside air selector damper motor assembly. *See Fig. 20.* To install, reverse removal procedure.

OUTLET SELECTOR DAMPER MOTOR

Removal & Installation – Remove driver-side lower panel. *See Fig. 20.* Remove foot shower nozzle and lap cooler duct. Remove center reinforcement. Remove outlet selector damper motor assembly. To install, reverse removal procedure.

HEATER CORE

Removal & Installation – **1)** Drain coolant. Disconnect heater hoses. Remove passenger-side undercover. *See Fig. 21.* Remove right foot shower duct. Remove instrument panel. See INSTRUMENT PANEL under REMOVAL & INSTALLATION.

2) Remove foot shower nozzle, lap cooler duct and center duct assembly. Remove left foot shower duct, and front and rear center reinforcement. Remove center stay assembly and distribution duct assembly.

3) Remove evaporator bolts and nuts. Remove power transistor and coolant temperature sensor. Remove air mix damper motor assembly. Remove heater unit. Remove heater hose plate assembly and heater core.

4) To install, reverse removal procedure. Refill cooling system and check cooling system for leaks.

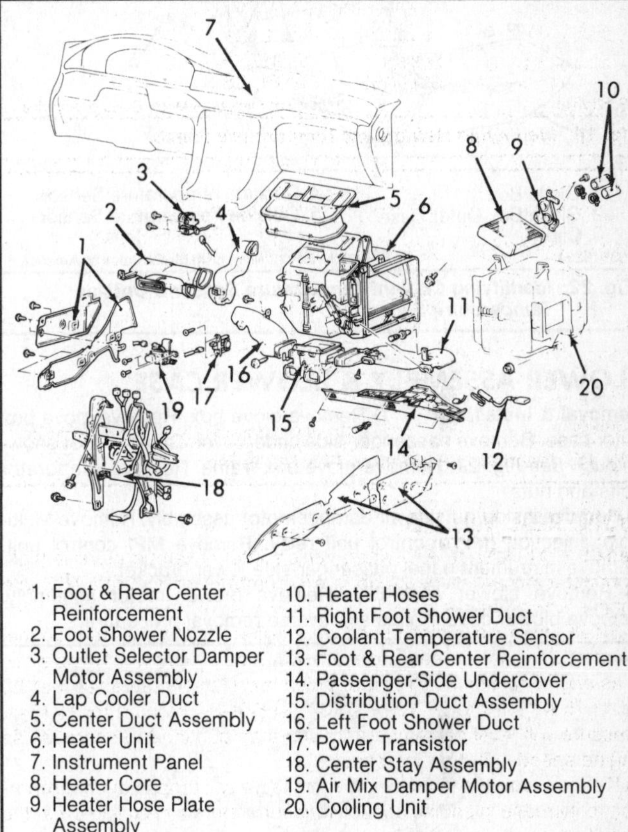
1. Foot & Rear Center Reinforcement
2. Foot Shower Nozzle
3. Outlet Selector Damper Motor Assembly
4. Lap Cooler Duct
5. Center Duct Assembly
6. Heater Unit
7. Instrument Panel
8. Heater Core
9. Heater Hose Plate Assembly
10. Heater Hoses
11. Right Foot Shower Duct
12. Coolant Temperature Sensor
13. Foot & Rear Center Reinforcement
14. Passenger-Side Undercover
15. Distribution Duct Assembly
16. Left Foot Shower Duct
17. Power Transistor
18. Center Stay Assembly
19. Air Mix Damper Motor Assembly
20. Cooling Unit
93C19291
Courtesy of Mitsubishi Motor Sales of America.

Fig. 21: Exploded View Of Heater Core Assembly

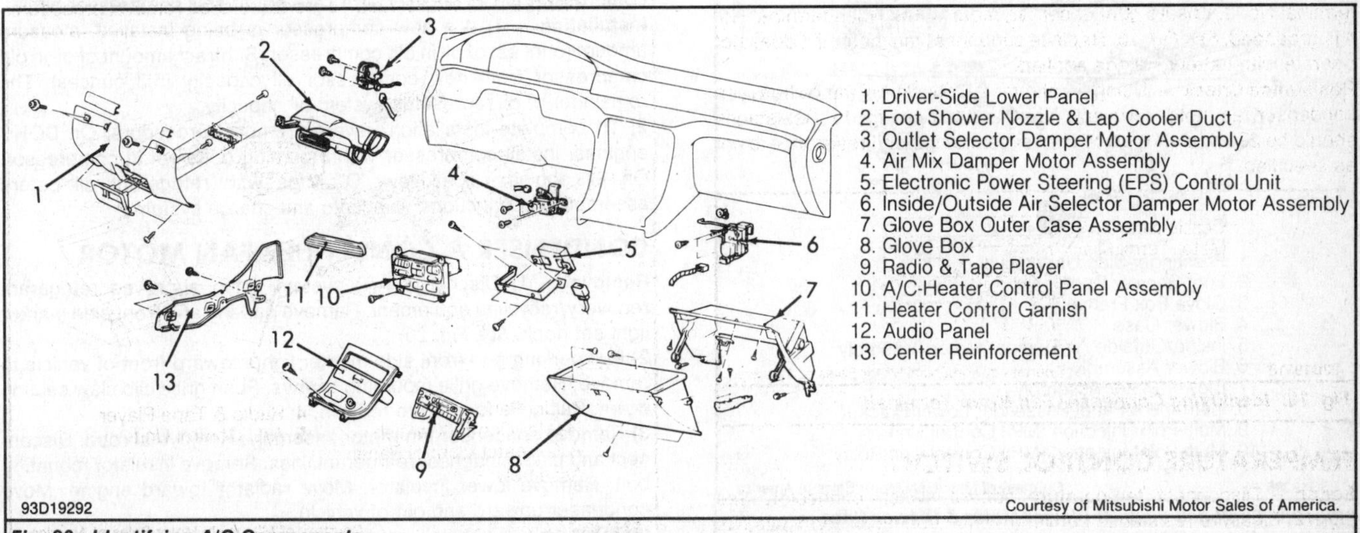
1. Driver-Side Lower Panel
2. Foot Shower Nozzle & Lap Cooler Duct
3. Outlet Selector Damper Motor Assembly
4. Air Mix Damper Motor Assembly
5. Electronic Power Steering (EPS) Control Unit
6. Inside/Outside Air Selector Damper Motor Assembly
7. Glove Box Outer Case Assembly
8. Glove Box
9. Radio & Tape Player
10. A/C-Heater Control Panel Assembly
11. Heater Control Garnish
12. Audio Panel
13. Center Reinforcement
93D19292
Courtesy of Mitsubishi Motor Sales of America.

Fig. 20: Identifying A/C Components

COOLANT TEMPERATURE SENSOR

Removal & Installation - Remove glove box. Remove glove box outer case. Remove clip holding sensor. *See Fig. 22.* Remove coolant temperature sensor. To install, reverse removal procedure.

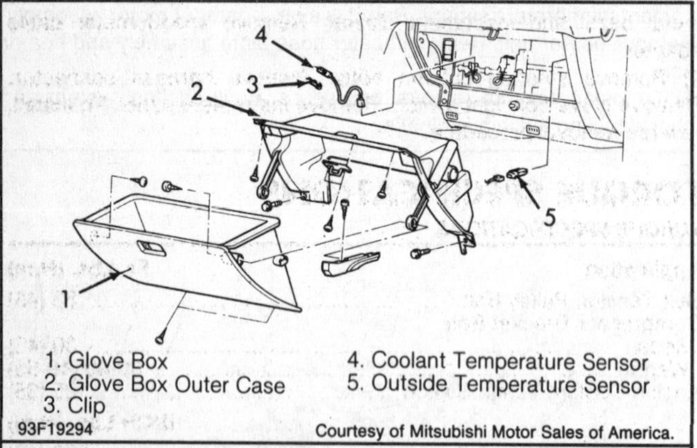
1. Glove Box
2. Glove Box Outer Case
3. Clip
4. Coolant Temperature Sensor
5. Outside Temperature Sensor
93F19294
Courtesy of Mitsubishi Motor Sales of America.

Fig. 22: Identifying Coolant Temperature Sensor & Outside Temperature Sensor

BLOWER ASSEMBLY & BLOWER CASE

Removal & Installation - **1)** Remove glove box. Remove glove box outer case. Remove passenger-side undercover. Remove foot shower duct. *See Fig. 23.* Remove glove box frame. Remove evaporator bolts and nuts.

2) Remove inside/outside air damper motor assembly. Remove Multi-Point Injection (MPI) control unit relay. Remove MPI control unit. Remove instrument panel passenger-side lower bracket.

3) Remove blower assembly. Remove blower motor assembly. Remove blower case. To install, reverse removal procedure.

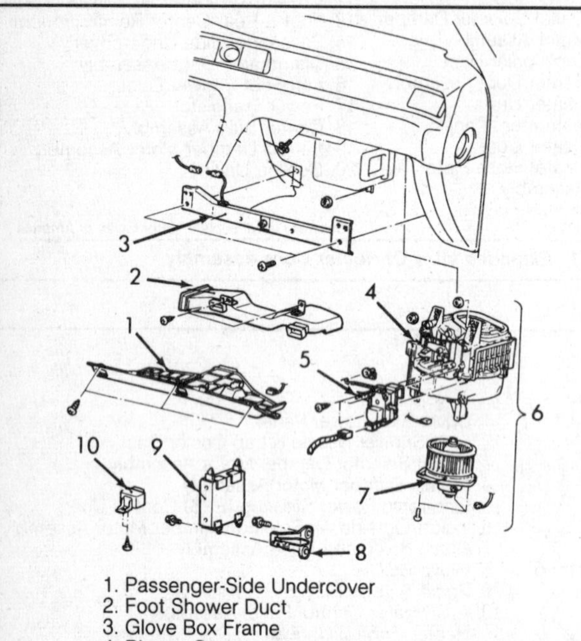
1. Passenger-Side Undercover
2. Foot Shower Duct
3. Glove Box Frame
4. Blower Case
5. Inside/Outside Air Damper Motor Assembly
6. Blower Assembly
7. Blower Motor Assembly
8. Instrument Panel Passenger Lower Bracket
9. Multi-Point Injection (MPI) Control Unit
10. Multi-Point Injection (MPI) Control Unit Relay
93G19295
Courtesy of Mitsubishi Motor Sales of America.

Fig. 23: Exploded View Of Blower Motor & Blower Case Assemblies

EVAPORATOR

Removal - **1)** Discharge A/C system using approved refrigerant recovery/recycling equipment. Remove glove box and glove box outer case. Disconnect and plug suction and discharge hoses.

2) Disconnect evaporator case drain hose. *See Fig. 24.* Remove passenger-side undercover. Remove foot shower duct. Remove glove box frame. On DOHC engines, remove belt lock controller. Remove evaporator nuts and bolts. Remove evaporator.

Installation - To install, reverse removal procedure. Coat new "O" rings with refrigerant oil before assembling connections. Evacuate and recharge A/C system.

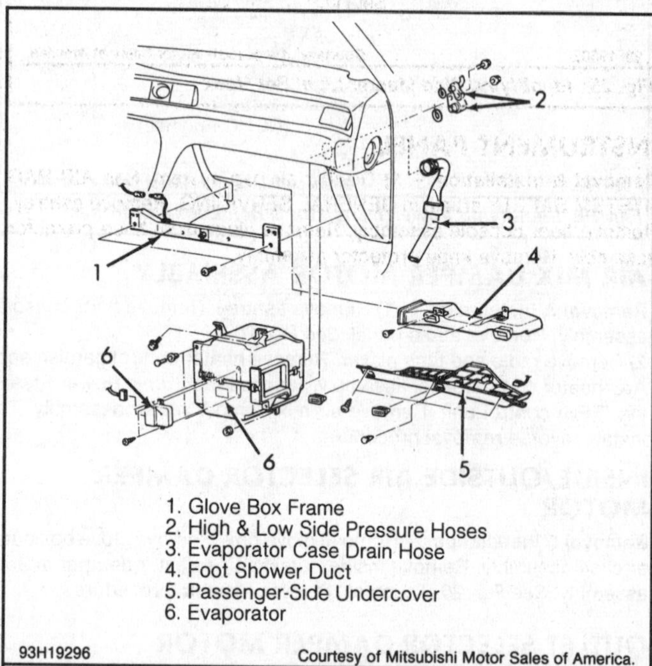
1. Glove Box Frame
2. High & Low Side Pressure Hoses
3. Evaporator Case Drain Hose
4. Foot Shower Duct
5. Passenger-Side Undercover
6. Evaporator
93H19296
Courtesy of Mitsubishi Motor Sales of America.

Fig. 24: Exploded View Of Evaporator Assembly

COMPRESSOR

Removal - **1)** Discharge A/C system using approved refrigerant recovery/recycling equipment. Remove compressor belt. Disconnect and plug discharge and suction hoses at compressor.

2) Remove "O" rings and discard. On DOHC engines, remove condenser fan assembly and alternator. Remove compressor with mounting bolts set in compressor. On SOHC engines, remove compressor. On all engines, use care not to spill compressor oil.

Installation - **1)** If a new compressor is being installed, measure amount (ounces) of oil in old compressor. Subtract amount of oil in old compressor from new compressor oil capacity (5.3 ounces). The remainder of oil represents system oil capacity.

2) To complete installation, reverse removal procedure. On DOHC engines, install compressor with mounting bolts set in compressor. On all engines, coat new "O" rings with refrigerant oil before assembling connections. Evacuate and charge system.

CONDENSER & CONDENSER FAN MOTOR

Removal - **1)** Discharge A/C system using approved refrigerant recovery/recycling equipment. Remove parking and front side marker light set hook. *See Fig. 25.*

2) Pull parking and front side marker lights toward front of vehicle to remove. Remove grille mounting screws. Push grille clip claw section down. Pull grille forward to remove.

3) Remove condenser fan motor assembly. Remove shroud. Disconnect and plug condenser refrigerant lines. Remove insulator mounting bolt. Remove lower insulator. Move radiator toward engine. Move condenser upward and out of vehicle.

Installation - To install, reverse removal procedure. Coat new "O" rings with refrigerant oil before assembling connections. Evacuate and charge system.

1993 AUTOMATIC A/C-HEATER SYSTEMS
Diamante (Cont.)

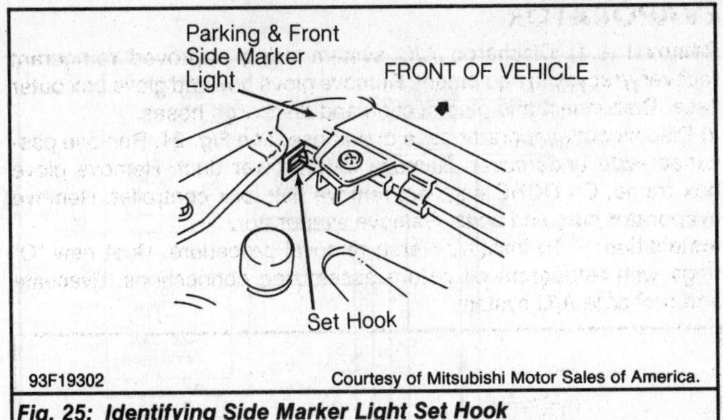
Parking & Front
Side Marker
Light
FRONT OF VEHICLE
Set Hook
93F19302
Courtesy of Mitsubishi Motor Sales of America.

Fig. 25: Identifying Side Marker Light Set Hook

INSTRUMENT PANEL

Removal & Installation – 1) Disable air bag system. See AIR BAG SYSTEM SAFETY article in GENERAL SERVICING. Remove ashtray. Remove floor console assembly. Remove plugs from knee protector assembly. Remove knee protector assembly.

2) Remove knee protector support bracket. Remove steering column cover. Remove glove box striker. Remove glove box and glove box outer case. Remove undercover insulation screw.

3) Remove radio cover panel, radio and tape player. Remove A/C-heater control panel. Remove cup holder. Remove speaker. Remove metal bezel and instrument cluster. Remove speedometer cable adapter.

4) Remove steering column bolts. Remove harness connector. Remove glove box light switch. Remove instrument panel. To install, reverse removal procedure.

TORQUE SPECIFICATIONS

TORQUE SPECIFICATIONS

Application	Ft. Lbs. (N.m)
Belt Tension Pulley Bolt	33 (45)
Compressor Bracket Bolt	
Sedan	30 (42)
Wagon	30-40 (40-55)
Engine Coolant Temp. Switch	25 (35)
	INCH Lbs. (N.m)
Condenser Insulator Bolt	108 (12)

1993 AUTOMATIC A/C-HEATER SYSTEMS
Diamante (Cont.)

WIRING DIAGRAMS

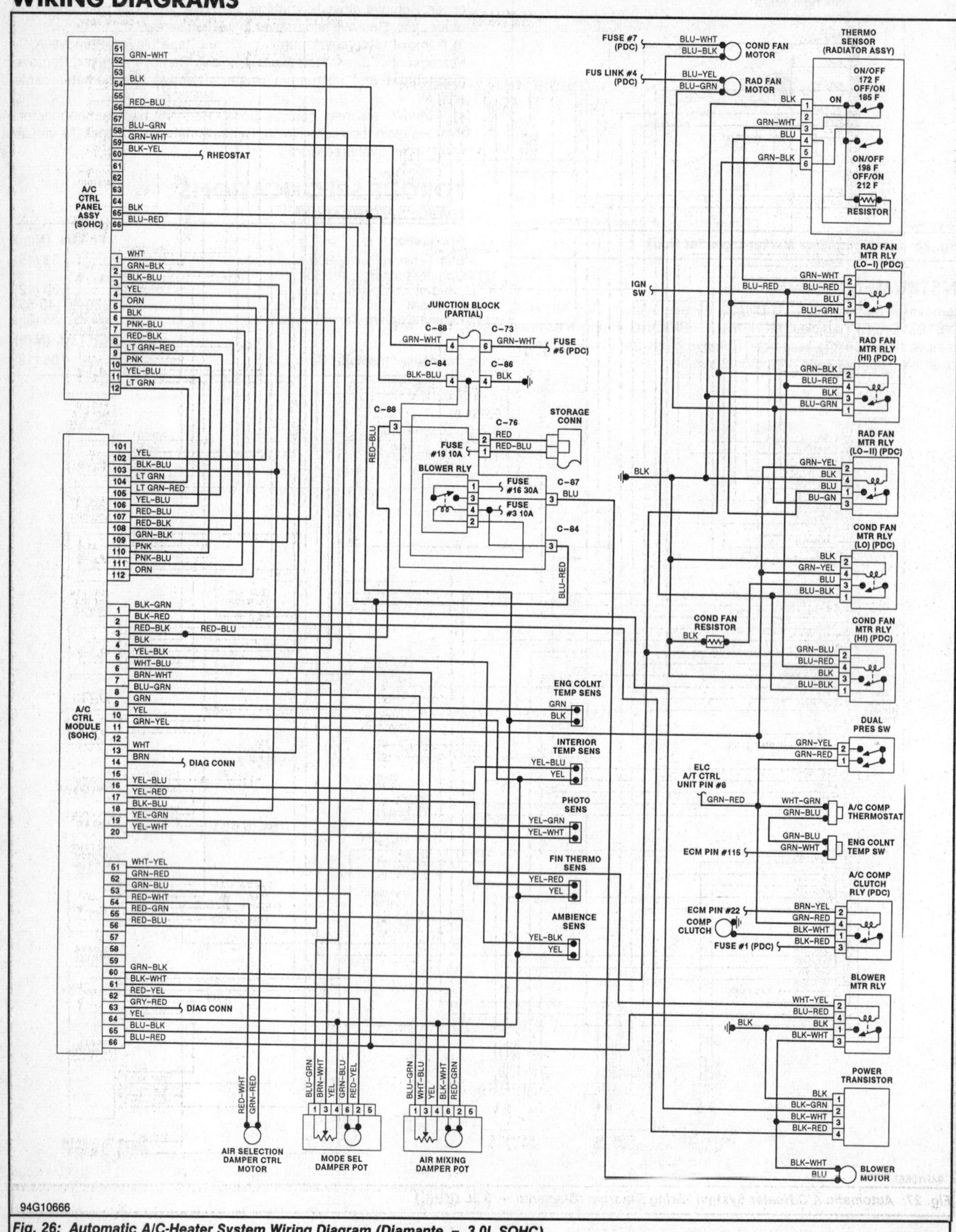
A/C CTRL PANEL ASSY (SOHC)
RHEOSTAT
A/C CTRL MODULE (SOHC)
DIAG CONN
JUNCTION BLOCK (PARTIAL)
FUSE #5 (PDC)
STORAGE CONN
FUSE #19 10A
BLOWER RLY
FUSE #16 30A
FUSE #3 10A
FUSE #7 (PDC)
COND FAN MOTOR
FUS LINK #4 (PDC)
RAD FAN MOTOR
THERMO SENSOR (RADIATOR ASSY)
ON/OFF 172 F OFF/ON 185 F
ON/OFF 198 F OFF/ON 212 F
RESISTOR
IGN SW
RAD FAN MTR RLY (LO-I) (PDC)
RAD FAN MTR RLY (HI) (PDC)
RAD FAN MTR RLY (LO-II) (PDC)
COND FAN MTR RLY (LO) (PDC)
COND FAN RESISTOR
COND FAN MTR RLY (HI) (PDC)
ENG COLNT TEMP SENS
INTERIOR TEMP SENS
PHOTO SENS
FIN THERMO SENS
AMBIENCE SENS
DUAL PRES SW
ELC A/T CTRL UNIT PIN #8
A/C COMP THERMOSTAT
ENG COLNT TEMP SW
ECM PIN #115
A/C COMP CLUTCH RLY (PDC)
ECM PIN #22
COMP CLUTCH
FUSE #1 (PDC)
BLOWER MTR RLY
POWER TRANSISTOR
BLOWER MOTOR
AIR SELECTION DAMPER CTRL MOTOR
MODE SEL DAMPER POT
AIR MIXING DAMPER POT
94G10666

Fig. 26: Automatic A/C-Heater System Wiring Diagram (Diamante – 3.0L SOHC)

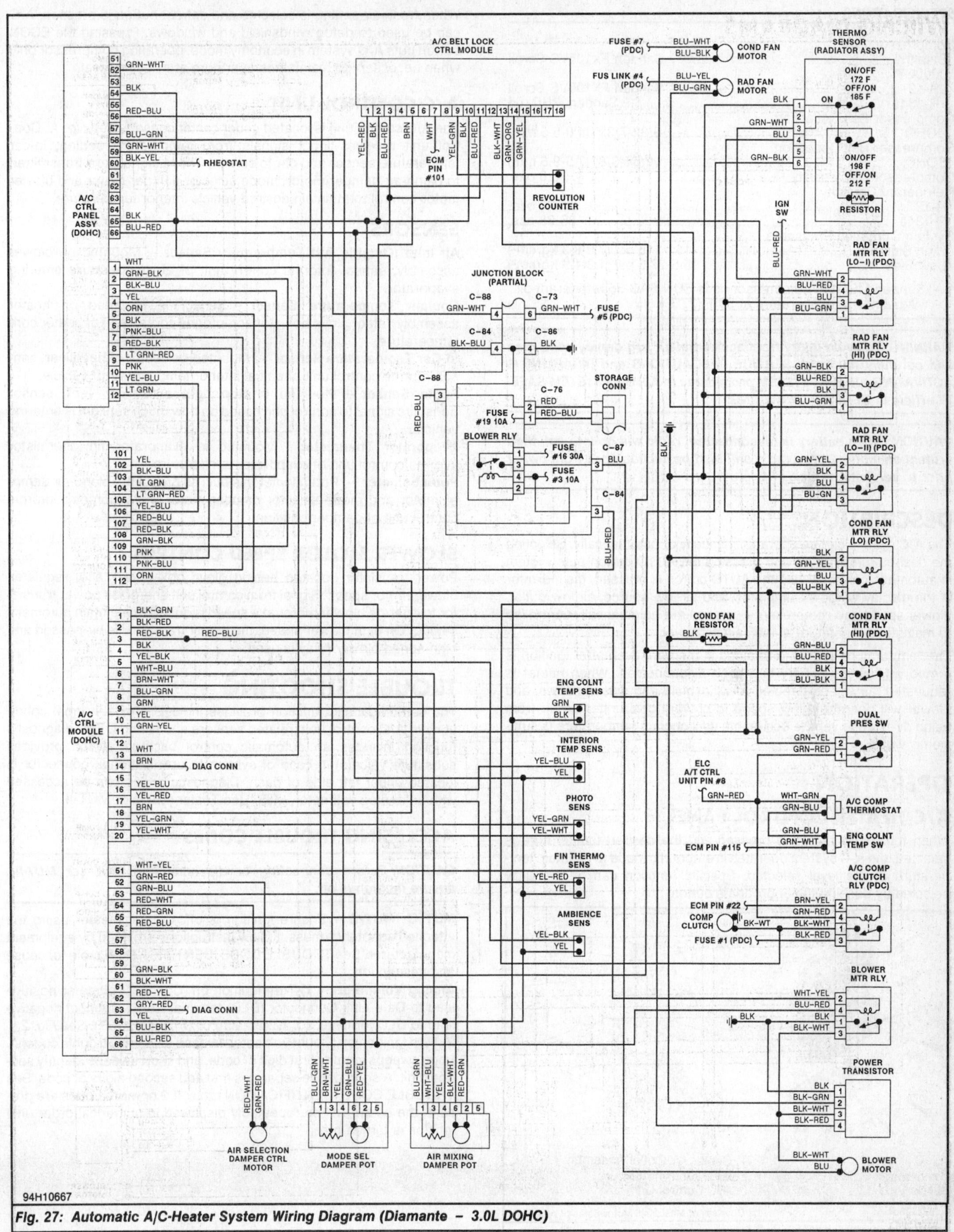
A/C BELT LOCK CTRL MODULE
ECM PIN #101
REVOLUTION COUNTER
FUSE #7 (PDC)
COND FAN MOTOR
FUS LINK #4 (PDC)
RAD FAN MOTOR
THERMO SENSOR (RADIATOR ASSY)
ON/OFF 172 F OFF/ON 185 F
ON/OFF 198 F OFF/ON 212 F
RESISTOR
IGN SW
RAD FAN MTR RLY (LO-I) (PDC)
RAD FAN MTR RLY (HI) (PDC)
RAD FAN MTR RLY (LO-II) (PDC)
COND FAN MTR RLY (LO) (PDC)
COND FAN MTR RLY (HI) (PDC)
COND FAN RESISTOR
DUAL PRES SW
A/C COMP THERMOSTAT
ENG COLNT TEMP SW
A/C COMP CLUTCH RLY (PDC)
BLOWER MTR RLY
POWER TRANSISTOR
BLOWER MOTOR
RHEOSTAT
A/C CTRL PANEL ASSY (DOHC)
JUNCTION BLOCK (PARTIAL)
FUSE #5 (PDC)
STORAGE CONN
FUSE #19 10A
BLOWER RLY
FUSE #16 30A
FUSE #3 10A
A/C CTRL MODULE (DOHC)
DIAG CONN
ENG COLNT TEMP SENS
INTERIOR TEMP SENS
PHOTO SENS
FIN THERMO SENS
AMBIENCE SENS
ELC A/T CTRL UNIT PIN #8
ECM PIN #115
ECM PIN #22
COMP CLUTCH
FUSE #1 (PDC)
AIR SELECTION DAMPER CTRL MOTOR
MODE SEL DAMPER POT
AIR MIXING DAMPER POT
94H10667

Fig. 27: Automatic A/C-Heater System Wiring Diagram (Diamante – 3.0L DOHC)

1993 AUTOMATIC A/C-HEATER SYSTEMS Stealth & 3000GT

SPECIFICATIONS

Compressor Type
Stealth ..... Sanden FX105VS Scroll
3000GT
R-12 ..... Sanden FX105VS Scroll
R-134a ..... Sanden MSC105
Compressor Belt Deflection
DOHC ..... 5/32-7/32" (4.0-5.5 mm)
Compressor Belt Deflection
SOHC ..... 19/64-3/8" (7.5-9.5 mm)
Compressor Oil Capacity [1] ..... 4.7-6.0 ozs.
Refrigerant Capacity
R-12 ..... 29 ozs.
R-134a ..... 26-28 ozs.
System Operating Pressures [2]
High Side ..... 111-118 psi (7.8-8.3 kg/cm²)
Low Side ..... 18.5-27.5 psi (1.3-1.9 kg/cm²)

[1] – Sanden MSC105 compressor uses SUN PAG 56 refrigerant oil.
[2] – With ambient temperature at 80°F (27°C).

WARNING: To avoid injury from accidental air bag deployment, read and carefully follow all SERVICE PRECAUTIONS and DISABLING & ACTIVATING AIR BAG SYSTEM procedures in AIR BAG SYSTEM SAFETY article in GENERAL SERVICING.

CAUTION: When battery is disconnected, radio will go into anti-theft protection mode. Obtain radio anti-theft protection code from owner prior to servicing vehicle.

DESCRIPTION

The A/C system can be operated manually or automatically. Selecting the desired temperature and pressing the AUTO button puts system in automatic control. When the AUTO button is pressed, the indicator in the display window illuminates, and airflow source, airflow outlet, blower speed and compressor operation are automatically controlled to maintain temperature at the selected level.

The temperature setting is retained in memory even after ignition is turned off, unless battery has been disconnected. When heater is requested, air will be directed to windshield and side windows, and blower will operate in low speed to prevent cold/unheated air from being directed to vehicle occupants until coolant temperature is sufficiently warm.

OPERATION

A/C-HEATER CONTROL PANEL

When the AUTO button is pressed and the desired temperature is selected, the A/C system operates in automatic mode to maintain temperature at the level selected. Specific function can be manually selected by pushing the appropriate button.

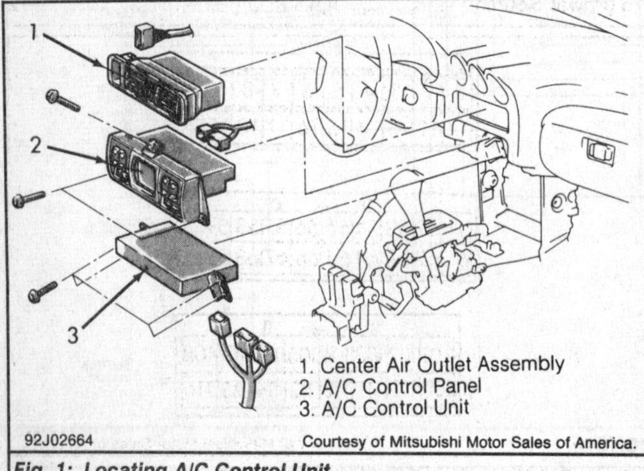
1
2
3
1. Center Air Outlet Assembly
2. A/C Control Panel
3. A/C Control Unit
92J02664
Courtesy of Mitsubishi Motor Sales of America.

Fig. 1: Locating A/C Control Unit

When fresh air setting is selected and defrost button is pressed, A/C can be used to defog windshield and windows. Pressing the ECON button puts A/C system in economy mode, operating compressor only when necessary to maintain temperature at selected level.

A/C CONTROL UNIT

The A/C control unit is located under center console. *See Fig. 1.*. Control unit receives input signals from temperature setting, in-car temperature sensor and photo sensor. These signals are transmitted to blend-air damper motor, mode selector damper motor and blower motor control to maintain desired vehicle interior temperature.

SENSORS

Air Inlet (Outside Air) Temperature Sensor – Mounted on blower assembly, sensor informs control unit of air temperature entering evaporator.

Coolant Temperature Sensor – Sensor is mounted on heater assembly, left of glove box. Sensor informs control unit of heater core temperature.

In-Car Temperature Sensor – Mounted on center of headliner, sensor informs control unit of actual interior temperature of vehicle.

Photo Sensor – Mounted on top right of airflow vent, sensor transmits signal to control unit based on how much sunlight is entering vehicle.

Evaporator Thermistor – Mounted in evaporator fin, thermistor informs control unit of evaporator temperature.

Potentiometer – Potentiometer is built as part of the blend-air damper motor and mode selector damper motor. Potentiometer informs control unit of damper position.

BLOWER MOTOR SPEED CONTROL

Power transistor, located behind glove box outer case, regulates blower motor speed. Signal from control unit energizes power transistor to operate blower motor at a speed required to maintain automatic setting. On high blower speed, the power transistor is by-passed and high-speed blower relay is used.

TROUBLE SHOOTING

The self-diagnostic function provides indication of abnormal conditions in A/C control unit, related sensors and wirings. Self-diagnostic function includes an automatic control back-up, which provides substitute value(s) in case of system failure. Data link connector is located under left side of dash. Diagnostic codes can be accessed with an analog voltmeter, Multi-Use Tester (MUT) or MUT-II.

ACCESSING TROUBLE CODES

CAUTION: Before connecting or disconnecting MUT (or MUT-II), ensure ignition is off.

MUT Or MUT-II – Ensure ignition is off. Connect tester using the attached adapter harness. Follow instructions provided by equipment manufacturer. See TROUBLE CODE IDENTIFICATION table for cause and description.

Analog Voltmeter – **1)** Turn ignition off. Connect voltmeter positive lead to Data Link Connector (DLC) terminal No. 7. Connect negative lead to DLC terminal No. 12 (Stealth) or No. 6 (3000GT). *See Fig. 2.*

2) Turn ignition on. Count voltmeter sweeps to identify trouble code(s). Long sweeps identify first digit of code, and short sweeps identify second digit. A short pause separates first and second digits of code. See TROUBLE CODE IDENTIFICATION table. If 2 or more codes are present, the codes will be repeatedly displayed in numerical order until ignition is turned off.

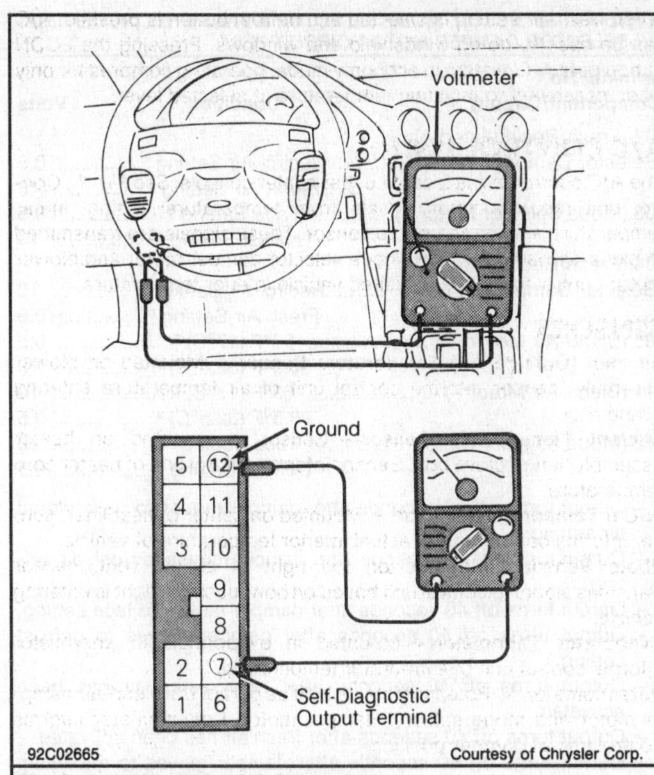
Voltmeter
Ground
5
12
4
11
3
10
9
8
2
7
1
6
Self-Diagnostic
Output Terminal
92C02665
Courtesy of Chrysler Corp.

Fig. 2: Locating Data Link Connector

TROUBLE CODE IDENTIFICATION

Code	Cause
0	Normal
11	In-Car Temp. Sensor Open Circuit
12	In-Car Temp. Sensor Short Circuit
13	Air Inlet (Outside Air) Temp. Sensor Open Circuit
14	Air Inlet (Outside Air) Temp. Sensor Short Circuit
21	Evaporator Thermistor Open Circuit
22	Evaporator Thermistor Short Circuit
31	Blend-Air Damper Potentiometer Short/Open Circuit
32	Mode Selector Damper Potentiometer Short/Open Circuit
41	Defective Blend-Air Damper Motor
42	Defective Mode Selector Damper Motor

CLEARING TROUBLE CODES

Turn ignition off. Disconnect battery cable for at least 10 seconds. Reconnect battery cable, and check voltmeter. Ensure a normal code (Code 0) is displayed. When using an analog voltmeter, normal code is indicated by continuous voltmeter needle sweep pattern.

TESTING

WARNING: To avoid injury from accidental air bag deployment, read and carefully follow all SERVICE PRECAUTIONS and DISABLING & ACTIVATING AIR BAG SYSTEM procedures in AIR BAG SYSTEM SAFETY article in GENERAL SERVICING.

A/C SYSTEM PERFORMANCE

R-12 – 1) Park vehicle out of direct sunlight. Turn adapter valve all the way back, and install adapter valves to high-pressure and low-pressure service valves. Connect manifold gauge to service valves. Tighten adapter valve handle, and open service valves.

2) Start engine. Set mode selector lever at face position, and temperature control lever at maximum cool setting. Move air selector lever to recirculated air setting. Turn A/C on. Operate blower fan in high speed. Adjust engine speed to 1000 RPM with compressor clutch engaged. Close all doors and windows. Ensure hood is open.

NOTE: If clutch cycles, take temperature reading before clutch disengages.

3) Insert thermometer in center vent. Run engine for 20 minutes, and note discharge air temperature on thermometer. Ensure discharge temperature and system low-side and high-side pressures are within specification. See A/C SYSTEM PERFORMANCE SPECIFICATIONS table.

R-134a – 1) Park vehicle away from direct sunlight. Close high-pressure and low-pressure valves of manifold gauge. Connect manifold gauge to A/C system. Start engine.

2) Set mode selector lever at face position. Set temperature control lever at maximum cool setting, and air selector lever at recirculated air setting. Turn A/C on. Operate blower fan in high speed. Adjust engine speed to 1000 RPM with compressor clutch engaged. Close all doors and windows. Ensure hood is open.

NOTE: If clutch cycles, take temperature reading before clutch disengages.

3) Insert thermometer in center vent. Run engine for 20 minutes, and note discharge air temperature on thermometer. Ensure discharge temperature and system low-side and high-side pressures are within specification. See A/C SYSTEM PERFORMANCE SPECIFICATIONS table.

A/C SYSTEM PERFORMANCE SPECIFICATIONS

Application	[1] Specification
Discharge Air Temperature	33.8-39.2°F (1.0-4.0°C)
Low-Side Pressure	18.5-27.5 psi (1.30-1.93 kg/cm²)
High-Side Pressure	110.9-118.1 psi (7.80-8.30 kg/cm²)

[1] – Specification listed with ambient temperature at 80°F (27°C).

A/C CONTROL UNIT CIRCUIT TEST

Check voltage between ground and indicated A/C control unit terminals. See A/C CONTROL UNIT CIRCUIT TEST table. *See Fig. 3.*

A/C CONTROL UNIT CIRCUIT TEST

Terminal No. (Component/Circuit)	Condition	Volts
53 (Back-Up Power)	At All Times	12
107 (Ground)	At All Times	0
108 (Power Source)	Ignition On	12
115 (Ground)	At All Times	0
116 (Power Source)	Ignition On	12

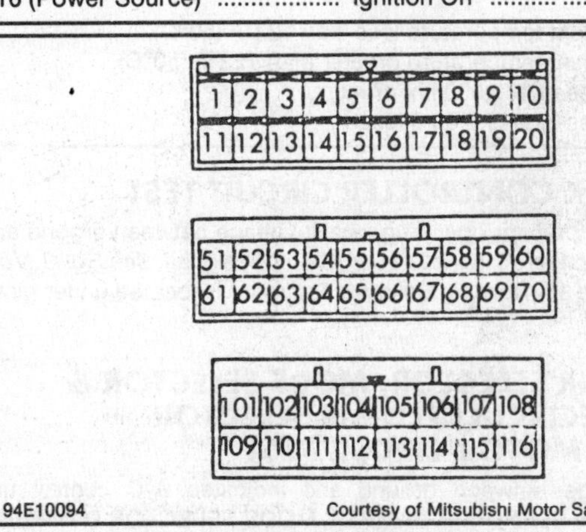
1 2 3 4 5 6 7 8 9 10
11 12 13 14 15 16 17 18 19 20
51 52 53 54 55 56 57 58 59 60
61 62 63 64 65 66 67 68 69 70
101 102 103 104 105 106 107 108
109 110 111 112 113 114 115 116
94E10094
Courtesy of Mitsubishi Motor Sales of America.

Fig. 3: Identifying A/C Control Unit Terminals

1993 AUTOMATIC A/C-HEATER SYSTEMS
Stealth & 3000GT (Cont.)

POTENTIOMETER CIRCUIT TEST

Check voltage between ground and indicated A/C control unit terminals. See POTENTIOMETER CIRCUIT TEST table. *See Fig. 3.*

POTENTIOMETER CIRCUIT TEST

Terminal No. (Component/Circuit)	Condition	Volts
56 (Blend-Air Damper)	Max. Cool Setting [1]	0.1-0.3
	Max. Hot Setting [1]	4.7-5.0
57 (Mode Selector Damper)	Face Setting [1]	0.1-0.3
	Defrost Setting [1]	4.7-5.0
58 (Damper Ground)	At All Times	0
60 (Power Source)	At All Times	4.8-5.2

[1] – Damper position

IN-CAR TEMPERATURE SENSOR, AIR INLET TEMPERATURE SENSOR & EVAPORATOR THERMISTOR CIRCUIT TEST

Check voltage between ground and indicated A/C control unit terminals. See IN-CAR TEMPERATURE SENSOR, AIR INLET TEMPERATURE SENSOR & EVAPORATOR THERMISTOR CIRCUIT TEST table. *See Fig. 3.*

IN-CAR TEMPERATURE SENSOR, AIR INLET TEMPERATURE SENSOR & EVAPORATOR THERMISTOR CIRCUIT TEST

Terminal No. (Component/Circuit)	Condition	Volts
55 (Air Inlet Temp. Sensor)	77°C (25°C) [1]	2.2-2.8
60 (Sensor Power Source)	At All Times	4.8-5.2
66 (In-Car Temp. Sensor)	77°C (25°C) [1]	2.3-2.9
67 (Evaporator Thermistor)	77°C (25°C) [1 2]	2.3-2.9

[1] – Sensor resistance should be 4000 ohms.
[2] – Measure voltage with A/C off.

COOLANT TEMPERATURE SENSOR & PHOTO SENSOR CIRCUIT TEST

Check voltage between ground and indicated A/C control unit terminals. See COOLANT TEMPERATURE SENSOR & PHOTO SENSOR CIRCUIT TEST table. *See Fig. 3.*

COOLANT TEMPERATURE SENSOR & PHOTO SENSOR CIRCUIT TEST

Terminal No. (Component/Circuit)	Condition	Volts
59 (Coolant Temp. Sensor)	Ignition Off [1]	12
	Ignition On [2]	0
69 (Photo Sensor –)	In Sunlight [3]	–0.1 To –0.2
	In Darkness [4]	0
70 (Photo Sensor +)	At All Times	0

[1] – With coolant temperature less than 122°F (50°C).
[2] – With coolant temperature greater than 122°F (50°C).
[3] – Brightness at 100,000 lux or more.
[4] – Brightness at less than 0 lux.

BELT LOCK CONTROLLER CIRCUIT TEST

With A/C compressor operating, check voltage between ground and A/C control unit terminal No. 116 (A/C output signal). *See Fig. 3.* Voltage should be 10-12 volts. Belt lock controller is located under glove box.

BLEND-AIR SELECTOR, MODE SELECTOR & FRESH/RECIRCULATED AIR SELECTOR DAMPER MOTOR CIRCUIT TEST

Check voltage between ground and indicated A/C control unit terminals. See BLEND-AIR DAMPER, MODE SELECTOR DAMPER & FRESH/RECIRCULATED AIR SELECTOR DAMPER MOTOR CIRCUIT TEST table. *See Fig. 3.*

BLEND-AIR SELECTOR, MODE SELECTOR & FRESH/RECIRCULATED AIR SELECTOR DAMPER MOTOR CIRCUIT TEST

Terminal No. (Component/Circuit)	Condition	Volts
102 (Fresh/Recirculated Air Selector Damper Motor –)	Recirc. Air Setting [1]	0.5
	Fresh Air Setting [2]	10
103 (Mode Selector Motor –)	Face Setting [3]	0.5
	Defrost Setting [4]	10
104 (Fresh/Recirculated Air Selector Damper Motor +)	Recirc. Air Setting [5]	10
	Fresh Air Setting [6]	0.5
105 (Blend-Air Motor +)	63°F (17°C) [7]	0.5
	90.5°F (32.5°C) [8]	10
111 (Blend-Air Motor –)	63°F (17°C) [7]	10
	90.5°F (32.5°C) [8]	0.5
112 (Mode Selector Motor +)	Face Setting [3]	10
	Defrost Setting [4]	0.5

[1] – Output turns off 40 seconds after damper moves to recirculated air setting.
[2] – Output turns off 40 seconds after damper moves to fresh air setting.
[3] – Output turns off 40 seconds after damper moves to face setting.
[4] – Output turns off 40 seconds after damper moves to defrost setting.
[5] – Output turns off 40 seconds after recirculated air has been activated.
[6] – Output turns off 40 seconds after fresh air has been activated.
[7] – Output turns off 40 seconds after damper moves to maximum cool setting.
[8] – Output turns off 40 seconds after damper moves to maximum hot setting.

POWER TRANSISTOR & BLOWER MOTOR RELAY CIRCUIT TEST

Check voltage between ground and indicated A/C control unit terminals. See POWER TRANSISTOR & BLOWER MOTOR RELAY CIRCUIT TEST table. *See Fig. 3.*

POWER TRANSISTOR & BLOWER MOTOR RELAY CIRCUIT TEST

Terminal No. (Component/Circuit)	Condition	Volts
51 (Power Transistor Collector)	OFF	12
	Low	7
	High	0
52 (Power Transistor Base)	OFF	0
	Low	Approx. 1.3
	High	Approx. 1.2
101 (High-Speed Relay)	High	1.5 Or Less
	Medium	12
	Low	12
	OFF	12

IN-CAR TEMPERATURE SENSOR

1) Connect ohmmeter to in-car temperature sensor terminals. Measure resistance value of sensor at room temperature of 77°F (25°C). Resistance should be approximately 4000 ohms. Replace sensor if resistance is not as specified.

2) To check in-car temperature sensor circuit, measure voltage between A/C control unit terminal No. 66 and ground, at room temperature of 77°F (25°C). *See Fig. 3.* Voltage should be 2.3-2.9 volts.

3) If voltage is not as specified, check circuit on harness between sensor and A/C control unit. Check for poor connection at A/C control unit connector, or check for a defective A/C control unit. Repair or replace as necessary.

1993 AUTOMATIC A/C-HEATER SYSTEMS
Stealth & 3000GT (Cont.)

AIR INLET TEMPERATURE SENSOR

1) Connect ohmmeter to air inlet temperature sensor terminals. Measure sensor resistance at room temperature of 77°F (25°C). Resistance should be approximately 4000 ohms. Replace sensor if resistance is not as specified.
2) To check sensor circuit, measure voltage between A/C control unit terminal No. 55 and ground, at room temperature of 77°F (25°C). *See Fig. 3*. Voltage should be 2.2-2.8 volts.
3) If voltage is not as specified, check circuit on harness between sensor and A/C control unit. Check for poor connection at A/C control unit connector, or check for a defective A/C control unit. Repair or replace as necessary.

COOLANT TEMPERATURE SENSOR

1) Disconnect coolant temperature sensor connector. Connect ohmmeter to coolant temperature sensor terminals. Check sensor continuity with coolant temperature at 73-87°F (23-31°C). Continuity should be present. If continuity does not exist, replace coolant temperature sensor.
2) To check sensor circuit, measure voltage between A/C control unit terminal No. 59 and ground, with temperature less than 122°F (50°C). Voltage should be 12 volts with ignition off. Measure voltage between control unit terminal No. 59 and ground, with temperature greater than 122°F (50°C). Ensure voltage is zero volts with ignition on.
3) If voltage is not as specified, check harness circuit between coolant temperature sensor and A/C control unit. Check for poor connection at A/C control unit connector, or check for a defective A/C control unit. Repair or replace as necessary.

EVAPORATOR THERMISTOR

1) Using ohmmeter, check resistance of thermistor at indicated temperatures. See EVAPORATOR THERMISTOR RESISTANCE table. Replace evaporator thermistor if resistance largely deviates from specified value.
2) To check thermistor circuit, measure voltage between A/C control unit terminal No. 67 and ground, with temperature at 77°F (25°C). *See Fig. 3*. Voltage should be 2.3-2.9 volts.
3) If voltage is not as specified, check harness circuit between evaporator thermistor and A/C control unit. Check for poor connection at A/C control unit connector, or check for a defective A/C control unit. Repair or replace as necessary.

EVAPORATOR THERMISTOR RESISTANCE [1]

Water Temperature °F (°C)	Ohms
77 (25)	3980-4120
104 (40)	2210-2350

[1] – With thermistor submerged in warm water at specified temperatures for minimum of one minute.

FRESH/RECIRCULATED AIR DAMPER MOTOR

CAUTION: DO NOT continue to apply battery voltage when damper has completed its travel or if motor fails to rotate.

1) Ensure damper is not in recirculated or fresh air position. Disconnect fresh/recirculated air damper motor connector. Apply battery voltage to motor connector. *See Fig. 4*. Ensure motor rotates when battery voltage is applied.
2) Reverse battery polarity on motor connector. Ensure motor rotates in the opposite direction. If motor does not function as specified, check wiring or replace defective motor.

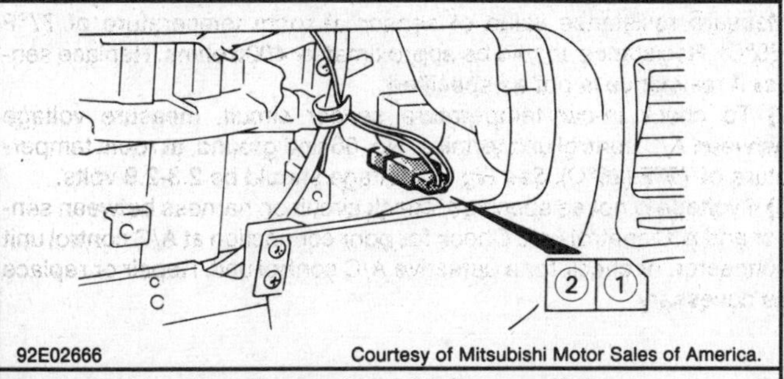
2
1
92E02666
Courtesy of Mitsubishi Motor Sales of America.

Fig. 4: Testing Fresh/Recirculated Air Damper Motor

BLEND-AIR DAMPER MOTOR

CAUTION: DO NOT continue to apply battery voltage when damper has completed its travel or if motor fails to rotate.

1) Ensure damper is not in maximum hot or maximum cool position. Disconnect blend-air damper motor connector. Apply battery voltage to motor connector Red/Green wire and Black/White wire terminals. Ensure motor rotates when battery voltage is applied.
2) Reverse battery polarity on motor connector. Ensure motor rotates in the opposite direction. If motor does not function as specified, check wiring or replace defective motor.

BLEND-AIR DAMPER POTENTIOMETER

1) Connect ohmmeter between motor connector Blue/Green wire and Blue/White wire terminals. Resistance should gradually change as damper is moved from maximum hot to maximum cool position.
2) Resistance should be 200 ohms at maximum hot position, and 4800 ohms at maximum cool position. Replace blend-air damper motor if resistance is not as specified.
3) To check potentiometer circuit, set damper to maximum cool position. Measure voltage between A/C control unit connector terminal No. 56 and ground. *See Fig. 3*. Voltage should be 0.1-0.3 volt. Measure voltage between control unit terminal No. 56 and ground with damper at maximum hot position. Voltage should be 4.7-5.0 volts.
4) If voltage is not as specified, check harness circuit between air mix damper potentiometer and A/C control unit. Check for poor connection at A/C control unit connector, or check for a defective A/C control unit. Repair or replace as necessary.

MODE SELECTOR DAMPER MOTOR

CAUTION: DO NOT continue to apply battery voltage when damper has completed its travel, or if motor does not rotate.

1) Ensure damper is not in defrost or face position. Disconnect mode selector damper motor connector. Apply battery voltage to motor connector Red/Yellow wire and Green/Blue wire terminals. Ensure motor rotates when battery voltage is applied.
2) Reverse battery polarity on motor connector. Motor should rotate in the opposite direction. If motor does not function as specified, check wiring or replace defective motor.

MODE SELECTOR DAMPER POTENTIOMETER

1) Connect ohmmeter between damper motor connector Blue/Green wire and Blue/White wire terminals. Resistance should gradually change as damper is moved from defrost to face position.
2) Resistance should be 200 ohms at defrost position, and 4800 ohms at face position. Replace mode selector damper motor if resistance is not as specified.
3) To check potentiometer circuit, set damper to face position. Measure voltage between A/C control unit connector terminal No. 57 and ground. *See Fig. 3*. Voltage should be 0.1-0.3 volt. Measure voltage between control unit terminal No. 57 and ground with damper at defrost position. Voltage should be 4.7-5.0 volts.
4) If voltage is not as specified, check harness circuit between outlet selector damper potentiometer and A/C control unit. Check for poor connection at A/C control unit connector, or check for a defective A/C control unit. Repair or replace as necessary.

1993 AUTOMATIC A/C-HEATER SYSTEMS
Stealth & 3000GT (Cont.)

REMOVAL & INSTALLATION

WARNING: To avoid injury from accidental air bag deployment, read and carefully follow all SERVICE PRECAUTIONS and DISABLING & ACTIVATING AIR BAG SYSTEM procedures in AIR BAG SYSTEM SAFETY article in GENERAL SERVICING.

CAUTION: When battery is disconnected, radio will go into anti-theft protection mode. Obtain radio anti-theft protection code from owner prior to servicing vehicle.

NOTE: For removal of basic A/C-heater system components, see appropriate HEATER SYSTEMS and/or MANUAL A/C-HEATER SYSTEMS article.

A/C-HEATER CONTROL PANEL

Removal & Installation – 1) Disconnect battery ground cable. Drain coolant. Remove cup holder and plug from rear floor console. Remove rear console. Remove radio panel, radio and switch panel from front floor console. Remove front console side covers and trim plates. Remove shift lever knob (M/T models) and front floor console.

2) Using flat-tip screwdriver, remove clips from center air outlet panel. Remove center air outlet assembly using plastic trim stick. Remove A/C-heater control panel. Remove A/C control unit from panel. To install, reverse removal procedure.

POWER TRANSISTOR & BELT LOCK CONTROLLER

Removal & Installation – Remove glove box door stops and outer case. Remove power transistor. Remove glove box under cover and belt lock controller. To install, reverse removal procedure.

FRESH/RECIRCULATED AIR DAMPER MOTOR

Removal & Installation – Remove glove box door stops and outer case. Remove fresh/recirculated air selector damper motor. To install, reverse removal procedure.

BLEND-AIR DAMPER MOTOR

Removal & Installation – 1) Disconnect battery ground cable. Drain coolant. Remove cup holder and plug from rear floor console. Remove rear console. Remove radio panel, radio and switch panel from front floor console. Remove front console side covers and trim plates. Remove shift lever knob (M/T models) and front floor console.

2) Using flat-tip screwdriver, remove clips from center air outlet panel. Remove center air outlet assembly using plastic trim stick. Remove A/C-heater control panel and A/C control unit. Remove blend-air damper motor. To install, reverse removal procedure.

MODE SELECTOR DAMPER MOTOR

Removal & Installation – Remove left knee protector. Remove left console cover, left shower duct and lap cooler duct. Remove mode selector damper motor assembly. To install, reverse removal procedure.

PHOTO SENSOR

Removal & Installation – Remove glove box door stops and outer case. Disconnect photo sensor connector. Using a trim stick, pry out photo sensor from top of left defroster outlet. To install, reverse removal procedure.

COOLANT TEMPERATURE SENSOR

Removal & Installation – Drain coolant. Remove glove box door stops and outer case. Reach behind glove box opening and remove coolant temperature sensor. To install, reverse removal procedure. Refill coolant and check for leaks.

AIR INLET TEMPERATURE SENSOR

Removal & Installation – Remove glove box door stops and outer case. Remove air inlet temperature sensor mounted near evaporator case. To install, reverse removal procedure.

IN-CAR TEMPERATURE SENSOR

Removal & Installation – Use trim stick to pry out in-car temperature sensor from headliner. Disconnect electrical connector, and remove sensor. To install, reverse removal procedure.

WIRING DIAGRAM

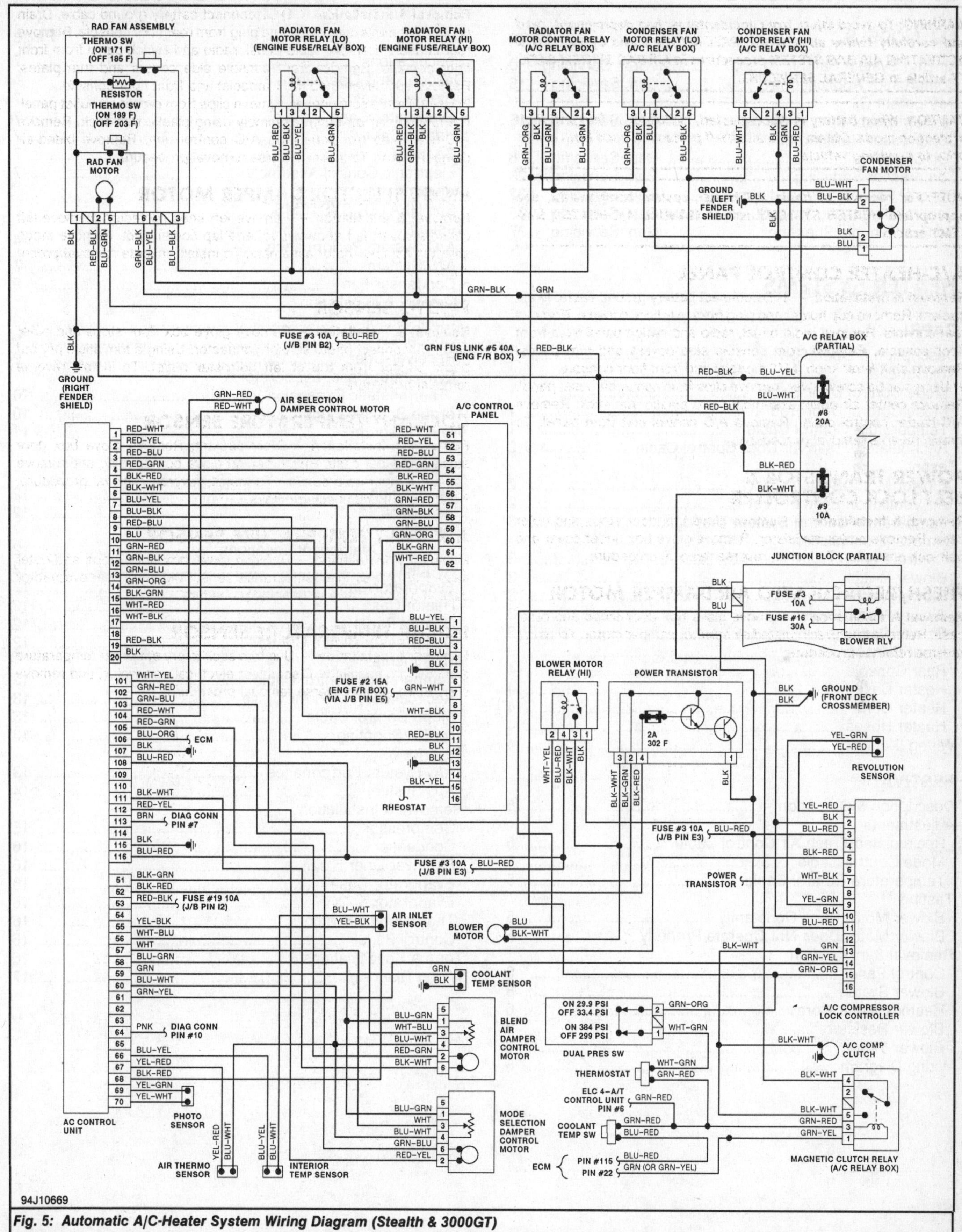
RAD FAN ASSEMBLY
THERMO SW (ON 171 F) (OFF 185 F)
RESISTOR
THERMO SW (ON 189 F) (OFF 203 F)
RAD FAN MOTOR
RADIATOR FAN MOTOR RELAY (LO) (ENGINE FUSE/RELAY BOX)
RADIATOR FAN MOTOR RELAY (HI) (ENGINE FUSE/RELAY BOX)
RADIATOR FAN MOTOR CONTROL RELAY (A/C RELAY BOX)
CONDENSER FAN MOTOR RELAY (LO) (A/C RELAY BOX)
CONDENSER FAN MOTOR RELAY (HI) (A/C RELAY BOX)
CONDENSER FAN MOTOR
GROUND (LEFT FENDER SHIELD)
GROUND (RIGHT FENDER SHIELD)
FUSE #3 10A (J/B PIN B2)
GRN FUS LINK #5 40A (ENG F/R BOX)
A/C RELAY BOX (PARTIAL)
#8 20A
#9 10A
AIR SELECTION DAMPER CONTROL MOTOR
A/C CONTROL PANEL
JUNCTION BLOCK (PARTIAL)
FUSE #3 10A
FUSE #16 30A
BLOWER RLY
FUSE #2 15A (ENG F/R BOX) (VIA J/B PIN E5)
BLOWER MOTOR RELAY (HI)
POWER TRANSISTOR
2A 302 F
GROUND (FRONT DECK CROSSMEMBER)
REVOLUTION SENSOR
RHEOSTAT
ECM
DIAG CONN PIN #7
FUSE #3 10A (J/B PIN E3)
POWER TRANSISTOR
FUSE #19 10A (J/B PIN I2)
AIR INLET SENSOR
BLOWER MOTOR
COOLANT TEMP SENSOR
A/C COMPRESSOR LOCK CONTROLLER
ON 29.9 PSI OFF 33.4 PSI
ON 384 PSI OFF 299 PSI
DUAL PRES SW
BLEND AIR DAMPER CONTROL MOTOR
DIAG CONN PIN #10
A/C COMP CLUTCH
THERMOSTAT
ELC 4-A/T CONTROL UNIT PIN #6
COOLANT TEMP SW
MODE SELECTION DAMPER CONTROL MOTOR
AC CONTROL UNIT
PHOTO SENSOR
AIR THERMO SENSOR
INTERIOR TEMP SENSOR
ECM PIN #115 PIN #22
MAGNETIC CLUTCH RELAY (A/C RELAY BOX)
94J10669

Fig. 5: Automatic A/C-Heater System Wiring Diagram (Stealth & 3000GT)

1993 FORD MOTOR CO. CONTENTS

GENERAL SERVICING

HEATER SYSTEMS

MANUAL A/C-HEATER SYSTEMS

1993 HEATER SYSTEMS
Capri

DESCRIPTION & OPERATION

Heater case is located behind center of instrument panel. Heater case contains heater core, temperature (air mix) door and mode doors. *See Fig. 1.* Temperature lever operates temperature door in heater case. Temperature door controls amount of air directed through the heater core.

Control panel contains blower switch and control levers. Levers are attached to control cables that operate air control doors. Recirculated/fresh control lever operates recirculated/fresh air door on top of blower case. When recirculated/fresh air door is open, outside air enters heating system. When recirculated/fresh air door is closed, recirculated (passenger compartment) air enters heating system.

Mode control lever cable operates mode control doors (one cable operates 2 doors). Mode control door levers are connected together by a rod. *See Fig. 3.* Depending on mode control lever position, mode control doors direct air to floor outlets, instrument panel vents and/or defroster registers.

Blower case is located behind far right end of instrument panel. Blower case contains blower motor and blower resistor assembly mounted on bottom half of case. Recirculated/fresh air door is located inside blower case.

WARNING: To avoid injury from accidental air bag deployment, read and carefully follow all SERVICE PRECAUTIONS and DISABLING & ACTIVATING AIR BAG SYSTEM procedures in AIR BAG SYSTEM SAFETY article in GENERAL SERVICING.

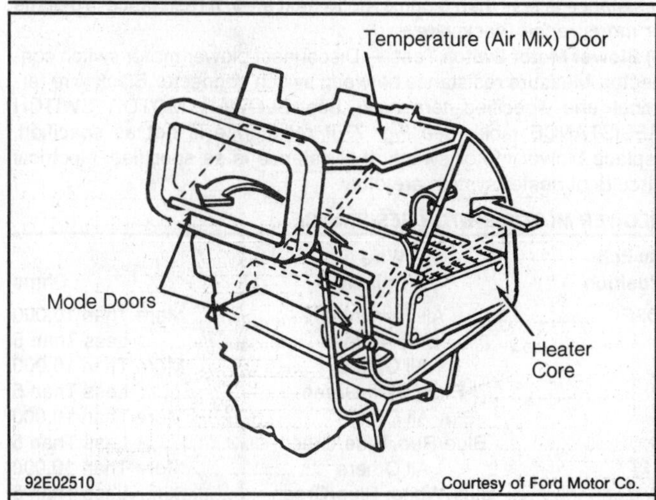
Temperature (Air Mix) Door
Mode Doors
Heater
Core
92E02510
Courtesy of Ford Motor Co.

Fig. 1: Cut-Away View Of Heater Case

ADJUSTMENTS

MODE CONTROL DOOR CABLE

Remove right carpet panel from console bracket. *See Fig. 10.* Move mode door lever to defrost position. Release cable from housing brace on side of heater case. *See Fig. 2.* With cable end connected to door lever pin, push door lever down to its stop. Secure cable into cable housing brace. Adjust mode control door rod.

MODE CONTROL DOOR ROD

Remove right carpet panel from console bracket. *See Fig. 10.* Separate rod and threaded adjuster from upper mode control door lever on heater case. Retaining clip secures rod to lever. *See Fig. 3.* Push upper mode control door lever down to its extreme stop. Turn threaded adjuster until it aligns with hole in lever. Secure rod into retaining clip. Check lever for correct operation. Install right carpet panel.

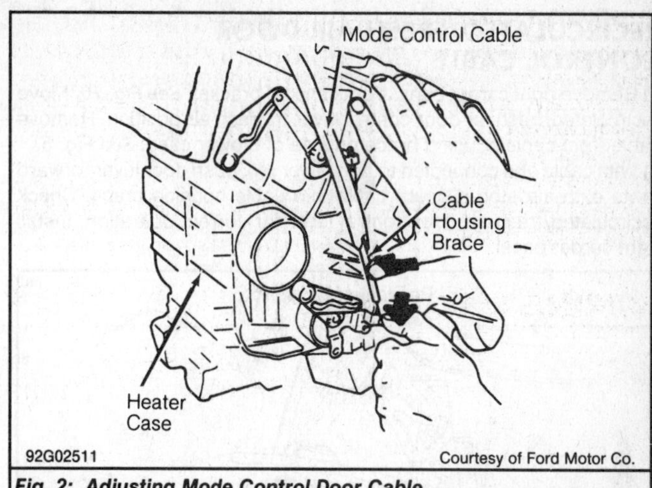
Mode Control Cable
Cable
Housing
Brace
Heater
Case
92G02511
Courtesy of Ford Motor Co.

Fig. 2: Adjusting Mode Control Door Cable

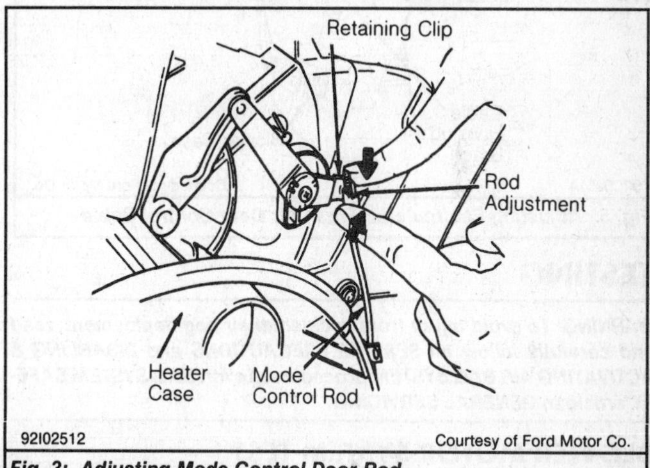
Retaining Clip
Rod
Adjustment
Heater
Case
Mode
Control Rod
92I02512
Courtesy of Ford Motor Co.

Fig. 3: Adjusting Mode Control Door Rod

TEMPERATURE CONTROL CABLE

1) Remove left carpet panel from console bracket. *See Fig. 10.* Move temperature control lever to maximum cold position. Remove cable from cable housing brace on side of heater case. *See Fig. 4.*

2) With cable end connected to door lever pin, push door lever down to its extreme stop. Secure cable into cable housing brace. Check temperature control lever for correct operation. Install left carpet panel.

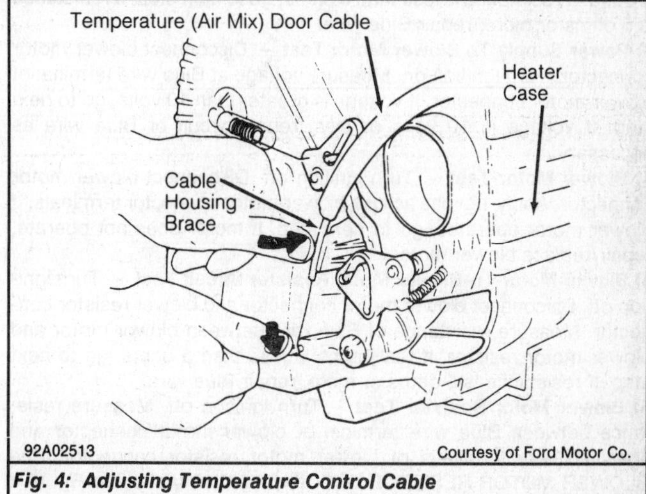
Temperature (Air Mix) Door Cable
Heater
Case
Cable
Housing
Brace
92A02513
Courtesy of Ford Motor Co.

Fig. 4: Adjusting Temperature Control Cable

1993 HEATER SYSTEMS
Capri (Cont.)

RECIRCULATED/FRESH AIR DOOR CONTROL CABLE

1) Remove right carpet panel from console bracket. *See Fig. 10.* Move recirculated/fresh air door control lever to fresh air position. Remove cable from cable housing brace on side of blower case. *See Fig. 5.*

2) With cable end connected to door lever pin, push door lever forward to its extreme stop. Secure cable into cable housing brace. Check recirculated/fresh air door control lever for correct operation. Install right carpet panel.

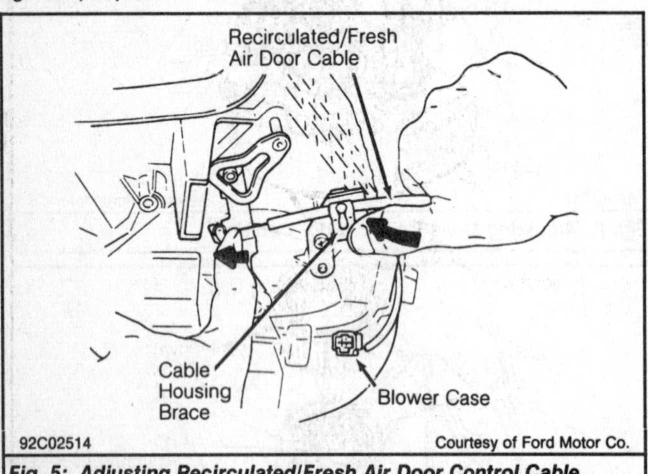
Recirculated/Fresh Air Door Cable
Cable Housing Brace
Blower Case
92C02514
Courtesy of Ford Motor Co.

Fig. 5: Adjusting Recirculated/Fresh Air Door Control Cable

TESTING

WARNING: To avoid injury from accidental air bag deployment, read and carefully follow all SERVICE PRECAUTIONS and DISABLING & ACTIVATING AIR BAG SYSTEM procedures in AIR BAG SYSTEM SAFETY article in GENERAL SERVICING.

BLOWER MOTOR SYSTEM TEST

1) Heater Circuit Breaker Test – Turn ignition off. Check 30-amp heater circuit breaker located behind left end of instrument panel, in fuse block. If reset button on circuit breaker is sticking out, press button down to reset circuit breaker. Turn on ignition and blower motor. If reset button pops up, go to next step. If reset button does not pop up, go to step **3)**.

2) Short Circuit To Ground Test – Turn ignition off. Disconnect fuse block connector. Disconnect blower motor connector. Measure resistance between Blue wire terminal of fuse block connector and chassis ground. If resistance is less than 5 ohms, go to next step. If resistance is 5 ohms or more, repair Blue wire.

3) Power Supply To Blower Motor Test – Disconnect blower motor connector. Turn ignition on. Measure voltage at Blue wire terminal of blower motor connector. If voltage is greater than 10 volts, go to next step. If voltage is 10 volts or less, repair circuit or Blue wire as necessary.

4) Blower Motor Test – Turn ignition off. Disconnect blower motor connector. Apply 12 volts across blower motor connector terminals. If blower motor operates, go to next step. If motor does not operate, repair/replace blower motor.

5) Blower Motor-To-Blower Motor Resistor Circuit Test – Turn ignition off. Disconnect blower motor connector and blower resistor connector. Measure resistance of Blue wire between blower motor and blower motor resistor. If resistance is less than 5 ohms, go to next step. If resistance is 5 ohms or more, repair Blue wire.

6) Blower Motor Resistor Test – Turn ignition off. Measure resistance between Blue wire terminal of blower motor connector and specified wire terminals of blower motor resistor connector. See BLOWER MOTOR RESISTOR SPECIFICATIONS table. *See Fig. 6.* If resistance is as specified, go to next step. If resistance is not as specified, replace blower motor resistor.

BLOWER MOTOR RESISTOR SPECIFICATIONS

Wire Terminal	Resistance (Ohms)
Blue/Yellow	2.6
Blue	1.2
Blue/Red	0.6
Blue/White	0.1

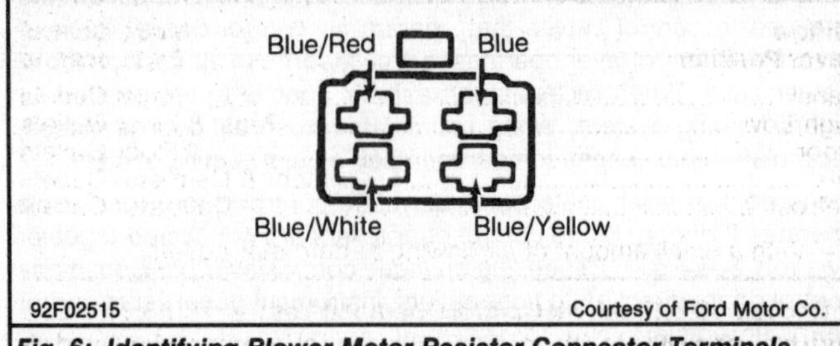
Blue/Red
Blue
Blue/White
Blue/Yellow
92F02515
Courtesy of Ford Motor Co.

Fig. 6: Identifying Blower Motor Resistor Connector Terminals

7) Blower Motor Resistor-To-Blower Motor Switch Circuit Test – Measure resistance of Blue/Yellow, Blue, Blue/Red and Blue/White wires between blower motor resistor connector and blower motor switch connector. *See Figs. 6 and 7.* If resistance of each wire is less than 5 ohms, go to next step. If resistance of any wire is 5 ohms or more, inspect and repair wire(s).

8) Blower Motor Switch Ground Circuit Test – Measure resistance of Black wire between blower motor switch and ground. *See Fig. 7.* If resistance is less than 5 ohms, go to next step. If resistance is 5 ohms or more, repair Black wire.

9) Blower Motor Switch Test – Disconnect blower motor switch connector. Measure resistance between switch connector Black wire terminal and specified terminals. See BLOWER MOTOR SWITCH RESISTANCE table. *See Fig. 7.* If resistance is not as specified, replace blower motor switch. If resistance is as specified, electrical circuits of heater system are okay.

BLOWER MOTOR SWITCH RESISTANCE

Switch Position	Wire Terminals	Ohms
OFF	All Terminals	More Than 10,000
1	Blue/Yellow	Less Than 5
	All Others	More Than 10,000
2	Blue, Blue/Green	Less Than 5
	All Others	More Than 10,000
3	Blue/Red, Blue/Green	Less Than 5
	All Others	More Than 10,000
4	Blue/White, Blue/Green	Less Than 5
	All Others	More Than 10,000

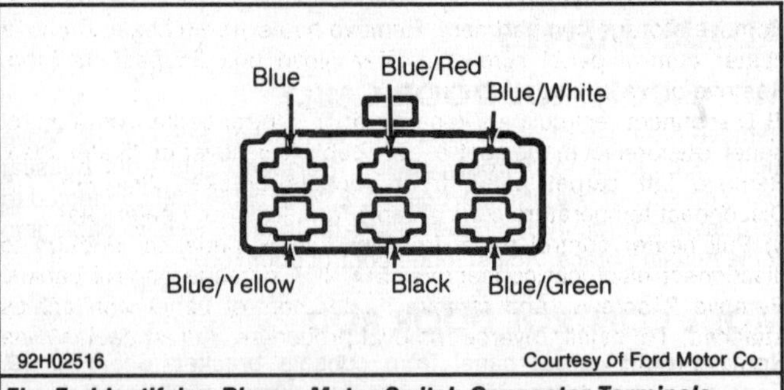
Blue
Blue/Red
Blue/White
Blue/Yellow
Black
Blue/Green
92H02516
Courtesy of Ford Motor Co.

Fig. 7: Identifying Blower Motor Switch Connector Terminals

AIR VENTILATION SYSTEM TEST

1) Cable Test – Slide control levers back and forth. If levers slide smoothly, go to next step. If levers do not slide smoothly, check control panel and cables for damage. Repair or replace panel and/or cables as necessary.

2) Mode Control Test – Turn ignition on. Turn blower switch to 4th position. Ensure airflow from outlets matches position of mode control lever. See MODE CONTROL TEST table. If air flows from appropriate outlets, go to next step. If air does not flow from appropriate outlets, adjust mode control cable. See ADJUSTMENTS. If mode control cable is adjusted, repair or replace heater case or ducting as necessary.

MODE CONTROL TEST

Airflow Lever Position	Mode Control Exit Location
Panel	Panel Outlets
High/Low	Panel & Floor Outlets
Floor	[1] Floor Outlets
Mix	Floor & Defroster Outlets
Defrost	Defroster Outlets

[1] – With a small amount of air flowing to defroster outlets.

3) Recirculated/Fresh Air Control Operation Test – Turn ignition on. Turn blower switch to 4th position. With control lever in recirculated air position, airflow should be felt coming into recirculated air inlet openings of blower case. With control lever in fresh air position, no airflow should be felt at recirculated air inlet openings of blower case.
4) If airflow is as specified, air ventilation system is okay. If airflow is not as specified, adjust recirculated/fresh air control cable. See ADJUSTMENTS. If cable is adjusted, repair or replace blower case as necessary.

TEMPERATURE CONTROL SYSTEM TEST

1) Start and warm engine to normal operating temperature. Turn blower motor switch to 4th position. Move mode control lever to vent position. Gradually move temperature control lever from extreme left to extreme right. If output air temperature does not gradually increase from cold to hot, check coolant level. Ensure engine thermostat is opening.
2) If coolant level and thermostat are okay, check for blocked heater core. If heater core is not blocked, check for blocked air passages in blower case and heater case. If air passage are okay, adjust temperature control cable. See ADJUSTMENTS. If cable is adjusted, repair or replace heater case.

REMOVAL & INSTALLATION

WARNING: To avoid injury from accidental air bag deployment, read and carefully follow all SERVICE PRECAUTIONS and DISABLING & ACTIVATING AIR BAG SYSTEM procedures in AIR BAG SYSTEM SAFETY article in GENERAL SERVICING.

CONTROL PANEL

Removal & Installation – 1) Disconnect negative battery cable. Remove storage compartment. Remove heater/radio bezel. Remove heater control panel screws. Lower glove box lid past its stop. Remove glove box upper support.
2) Disconnect recirculated/fresh air door control cable from control panel. Disconnect mode control door cable from lever on heater case. Remove left carpet panel from console bracket. *See Fig. 10.* Disconnect temperature control cable from lever on heater case.
3) Pull heater control panel from instrument panel far enough to disconnect electrical connectors. DO NOT damage control cables. Remove 2 screws, and remove heater control panel with cables attached. To install, reverse removal procedure. Adjust cables. See ADJUSTMENTS.

BLOWER SWITCH

Removal & Installation – Partially remove heater control panel to access blower switch. Cables do not need to be disconnected from control panel. Remove blower switch knob. Remove blower switch screws and blower switch. To install, reverse removal procedure.

BLOWER MOTOR

Removal & Installation – Disconnect negative battery cable. Disconnect blower motor connector. Remove 3 screws retaining motor and cover to blower case. *See Fig. 8.* Remove cover, cooling tube and blower motor. Remove nut, blower wheel and gasket from blower motor. To install, reverse removal procedure.

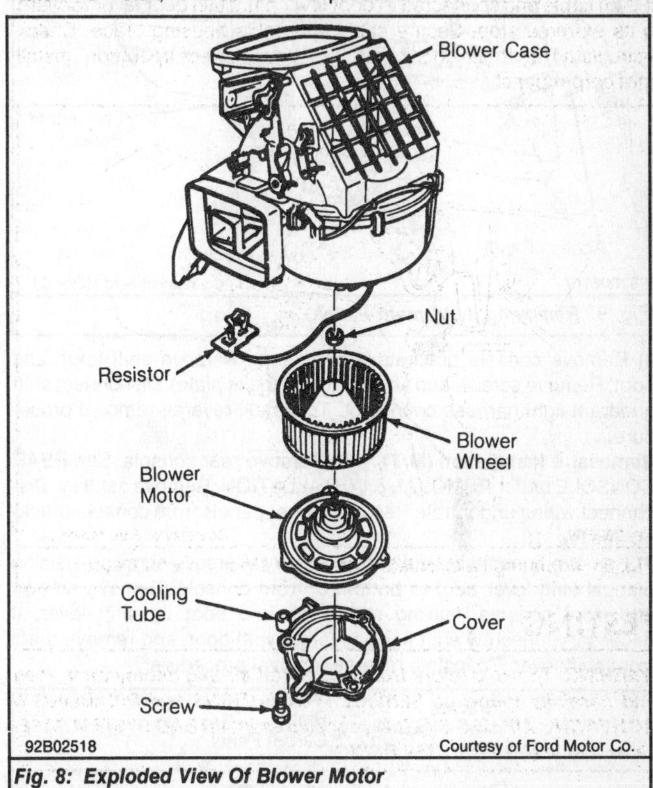
Blower Case
Nut
Resistor
Blower Wheel
Blower Motor
Cooling Tube
Cover
Screw
92B02518
Courtesy of Ford Motor Co.
Fig. 8: Exploded View Of Blower Motor

BLOWER MOTOR RESISTOR

Removal & Installation – Disconnect negative battery cable. Disconnect resistor and blower motor connectors. Remove 2 screws and resistor from blower case. Lower glove box past its stops. Disconnect blower feed connector. To install, reverse removal procedure.

BLOWER CASE

Removal – 1) Disconnect negative battery cable. Disconnect recirculated/fresh air door cable from lever on blower case. Disconnect resistor and blower motor connectors. Remove wiring harness from blower case and set aside. Disconnect ducting from blower case.
2) If necessary, loosen instrument panel bolts and slightly raise instrument panel to provide clearance for blower case removal. To loosen instrument panel, remove 3 screws, lock washers and plain washers located near base of windshield. *See Fig. 9.*
3) Remove 2 bolts and washers from each side of instrument panel. An access panel is provided for upper bolts. Remove 2 screws and lock washers retaining instrument panel to center floor bracket. Remove 2 screws retaining instrument panel to steering column support. Slightly raise instrument panel with help of an assistant. Remove 3 nuts securing blower case to firewall. Remove blower case.
Installation – Install components in reverse order of removal procedure. Adjust control cables. See ADJUSTMENTS.

FRONT CONSOLE

Removal & Installation (A/T) – 1) Remove rear console. See REAR CONSOLE under REMOVAL & INSTALLATION. Loosen shift handle jam nut. Unscrew shift handle. Remove ashtray. Disconnect wiring under tray. Remove carpet panels from console bracket. *See Fig. 10.*

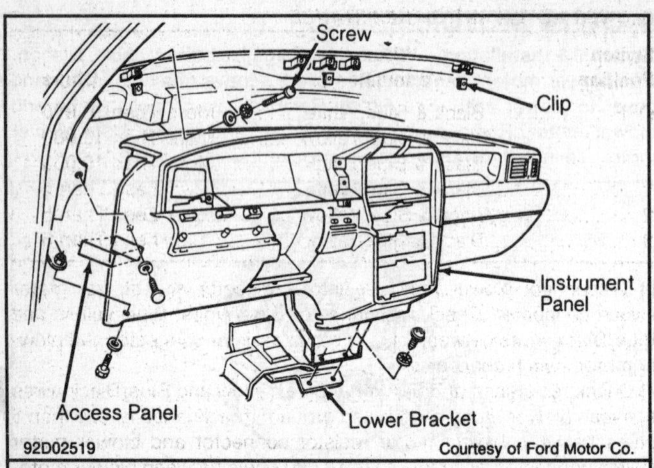
Screw
Clip
Instrument Panel
Access Panel
Lower Bracket
92D02519
Courtesy of Ford Motor Co.

Fig. 9: Removing Instrument Panel

2) Remove console brackets if necessary. Remove shift knob and boot. Remove screws and shift quadrant (base plate). Disconnect shift quadrant light harness connector. To install, reverse removal procedure.

Removal & Installation (M/T) – 1) Remove rear console. See REAR CONSOLE under REMOVAL & INSTALLATION. Remove ashtray. Disconnect wiring under tray. Remove carpet panels from console bracket. *See Fig. 10.*

2) Remove console brackets if necessary. Remove screws retaining manual shift lever boot to bottom of front console. Remove screws and front console, leaving shift knob and boot on shift lever. If necessary, unscrew shift knob together with boot, and remove them from shift lever. To install, reverse removal procedure.

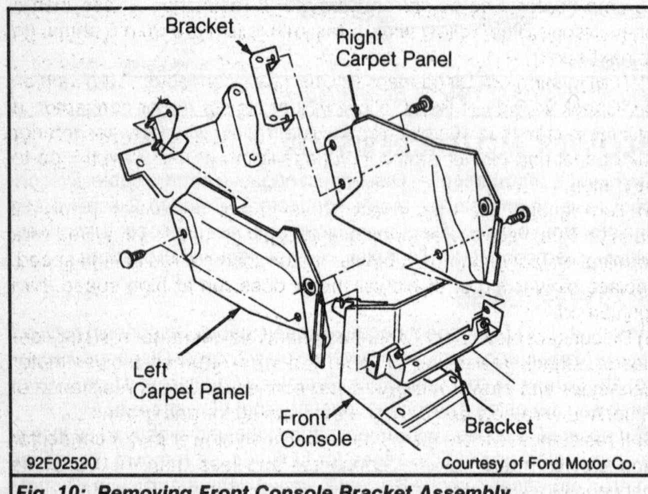
Bracket
Right Carpet Panel
Left Carpet Panel
Front Console
Bracket
92F02520
Courtesy of Ford Motor Co.

Fig. 10: Removing Front Console Bracket Assembly

REAR CONSOLE

Removal & Installation – 1) Slide front seats completely forward. Remove screws retaining rear of console. Slide front seats completely rearward. Remove screws retaining rear console to front console.

2) Raise parking brake lever as far as possible. Raise rear of console, and pull it backward to remove. Disconnect wiring harness from rear console switches.

HEATER CASE

Removal – 1) Disconnect negative battery cable. Remove rear and front floor console assemblies. See REAR CONSOLE and FRONT CONSOLE under REMOVAL & INSTALLATION.

2) Remove heater/radio bezel, trim covers, instrument cluster bezel and storage compartment. Disconnect speedometer cable from transaxle. Remove screws, and slide instrument cluster outward. Press lock tab, and release speedometer cable from instrument cluster. Disconnect connectors from rear of cluster. Remove cluster.

3) Drain cooling system. Disconnect heater hoses from heater core extension tubes. Plug heater tubes to prevent spilling coolant into passenger compartment. Remove plastic rivets securing defroster hoses to heater case. Remove defroster hoses.

4) Remove main air duct connecting heater case to blower case. Roll carpet back to gain access to lower duct and heater case lower bolts. If necessary, remove carpet fasteners. Disconnect lower duct (rear seat supply) from heater case.

5) Disconnect control cables from heater case. Disconnect wiring harness from heater case. Remove 2 lower bolts, 2 upper nuts and one center nut securing heater case to firewall. Remove heater case.

Installation – Install components in reverse order of removal procedure. Adjust control cables. See ADJUSTMENTS.

HEATER CORE

Removal & Installation – 1) Drain cooling system. Remove heater case. See HEATER CASE under REMOVAL & INSTALLATION. Disconnect heater hoses from heater core extension tubes. Cap tubes to prevent coolant from spilling into passenger compartment.

2) Remove heater core cover from left side of heater case. Remove screws securing extension tube braces. Loosen clamps. Separate extension tubes from heater core. Remove "O" ring from outlet tube. Pull heater core straight out of heater case. Remove extension tubes and firewall grommets if necessary. To install, reverse removal procedure. Use NEW "O" ring on extension tube.

HEATER HOSES

Removal & Installation – 1) Drain cooling system. Loosen clamps. Disconnect heater hose(s) from heater core extension tubes.

2) To install, ensure grommets are in place and seated against firewall. Place clamps on hose or fitting. Colored dot identifies engine end of original equipment hose. Ensure dot faces upward when installed to provide proper twist in hose.

3) Install hose. Slide hose all the way up fitting until it reaches ferrule. Install and tighten clamps. Fill cooling system.

WIRING DIAGRAM

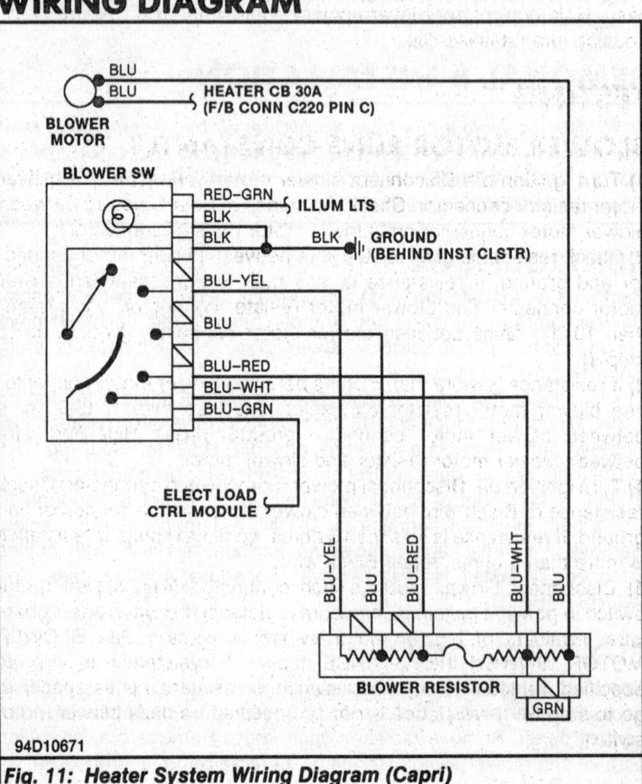
BLU
BLU
HEATER CB 30A
(F/B CONN C220 PIN C)
BLOWER MOTOR
BLOWER SW
RED-GRN
ILLUM LTS
BLK
BLK
BLK
GROUND
(BEHIND INST CLSTR)
BLU-YEL
BLU
BLU-RED
BLU-WHT
BLU-GRN
ELECT LOAD
CTRL MODULE
BLU-YEL
BLU
BLU-RED
BLU-WHT
BLU
BLOWER RESISTOR
GRN
94D10671

Fig. 11: Heater System Wiring Diagram (Capri)

DESCRIPTION & OPERATION

Heater case (heater unit), located behind center of instrument panel, contains blower motor, blower resistor, temperature control door and mode control door. *See Fig. 1*. Levers on control panel are connected to cables that operate control doors.

Intake plenum, behind far right end of instrument panel, contains recirculated/fresh air control door. Door position determines whether fresh (outside) air or recirculated (passenger compartment) air enters heater case.

Blower motor forces air through or around heater core depending on position of temperature control door. Mode control door directs airflow to floor registers, instrument panel registers and/or defroster registers depending on position of mode control door.

When blower switch on control panel is turned on, blower switch completes path to ground through blower resistor (except high speed) or by-passes blower resistor (high speed). Blower resistor is located on left half of heater case, above blower motor.

ADJUSTMENTS

RECIRCULATED/FRESH AIR CONTROL CABLE

Remove glove box. Release recirculated/fresh air control cable housing from retaining clip on heater case. Move control panel lever to recirculated position. Hold door lever in recirculated position. Secure cable housing into retaining clip.

MODE CONTROL CABLE

Release mode control cable housing from retaining clip on right side of heater case. Move control panel lever to vent position. Hold door lever downward against its stop. Secure cable housing into retaining clip.

TEMPERATURE CONTROL CABLE

Set temperature control lever to maximum cold position. Release temperature control cable housing from retaining clip on left side of heater case. Hold control door lever upward against its stop. Secure cable housing into retaining clip.

TESTING

BLOWER MOTOR RUNS CONSTANTLY

1) Turn ignition off. Disconnect blower motor connector and blower motor resistor connector. Check resistance of Blue/Red wire between blower motor connector and blower motor resistor connector.

2) Check resistance of Blue/Red wire between blower motor connector and ground. If resistance is less than 5 ohms between blower motor connector and blower motor resistor connector, and greater than 10,000 ohms between blower motor connector ground, go to step **4)**.

3) If resistance is more than 5 ohms between blower motor connector and blower motor resistor connector, and less than 10,000 ohms between blower motor connector ground, repair Blue/Red wire between blower motor resistor and blower motor.

4) Turn ignition off. Disconnect blower motor switch connector. Check resistance of Black wire between blower motor switch connector and ground. If resistance is less than 5 ohms, go to next step. If resistance is more than 5 ohms, repair Black wire.

5) Disconnect blower motor switch connector. With blower motor switch in position indicated, measure resistance between appropriate wire terminals of blower motor switch connector. See BLOWER MOTOR SWITCH RESISTANCE table. If resistance is not as specified, replace blower motor switch. If resistance is as specified, go to step **6)**. If resistance is not as specified, replace blower motor switch.

BLOWER MOTOR SWITCH RESISTANCE

Switch Position	Wire Terminals	Ohms
OFF	Black & Blue/White	More Than 10,000
	Black & Blue/Yellow	More Than 10,000
	Black & Blue/Black	More Than 10,000
1	Black & Blue/White	Less Than 5
2	Black & Blue/Yellow	Less Than 5
3	Black & Blue/Black	Less Than 5

6) Disconnect blower motor resistor connector and blower motor switch connector. Check resistance of Blue/White, Blue/Yellow and Blue/Black wires between blower motor resistor connector and blower motor switch connector.

7) Check resistance of Blue/White, Blue/Yellow and Blue/Black wires between blower motor switch and ground. If resistance is less than 5 ohms between blower motor resistor connector and blower motor switch connector, and more than 10,000 ohms between blower motor switch connector and ground, replace blower motor resistor.

8) If resistance is more than 5 ohms between blower motor resistor connector and blower motor switch connector, and less than 10,000 ohms between blower motor switch connector and ground, repair appropriate wires between blower motor resistor and blower motor switch.

BLOWER MOTOR DOES NOT OPERATE PROPERLY

1) Turn ignition off. Check 15-amp heater fuse. If fuse is okay, go to step **3)**. If fuse is not okay, replace fuse and turn ignition on. If fuse does not fail, go to step **3)**. If fuse fails again, turn ignition off and remove fuse. Disconnect blower motor connector.

2) Check resistance of Blue/Yellow wire between bottom terminal of 15-amp heater fuse holder and ground. If resistance is less than 5 ohms, repair Blue/Yellow wire. If resistance is more than 5 ohms, go to next step.

3) Turn ignition off. Disconnect blower motor connector. Turn ignition on. Check voltage of Blue/Yellow wire at blower motor connector. If voltage is less than 10 volts, repair Blue/Yellow wire between interior fuse panel and blower motor. If voltage is more than 10 volts, go to next step.

4) Turn ignition off. Disconnect blower motor connector. Apply 12 volts to Blue/Yellow wire terminal and apply ground to Blue/Red wire terminal on blower motor. If blower motor does not run at high speed, replace blower motor. If blower motor does run at high speed, turn ignition off.

5) Disconnect blower motor connector and blower motor resistor connector. Check resistance of Blue/Red wire between blower motor connector and blower motor resistor connector. Check resistance of Blue/Red wire between blower motor connector and ground.

6) If resistance is more than 5 ohms between blower motor connector and blower motor resistor connector and less than 10,000 ohms between blower motor connector and ground, repair Blue/Red.

7) If resistance is less than 5 ohms between blower motor connector and blower motor resistor connector, and more than 10,000 ohms between blower motor connector and ground, turn ignition off and disconnect blower motor switch connector.

8) Check resistance of Black wire between blower motor switch connector and ground. If resistance is more than 5 ohms, repair Black wire. If resistance is less than 5 ohms, turn ignition off. With blower motor switch in position indicated, measure resistance between appropriate wire terminals of blower motor switch connector. See BLOWER MOTOR SWITCH RESISTANCE table.

9) If resistance is not as specified, replace blower motor switch. If resistance is as specified, check resistance of Blue/White, Blue/Yellow and Blue/Black wires between blower motor switch connector and ground. If resistance is less than 5 ohms between blower motor resistor connector and the blower motor switch connector, and more than 10,000 ohms between blower motor switch connector and ground, replace blower motor resistor.

10) If resistance is more than 5 ohms between blower motor resistor connector and blower motor switch connector, and less than 10,000 ohms between blower motor switch connector and ground, repair appropriate wires.

REMOVAL & INSTALLATION

CONTROL PANEL

Removal & Installation – **1)** Remove accessory bezel screws and accessory bezel. Remove radio. Remove 4 screws securing control panel to instrument panel. Remove glove box screws and glove box. Disconnect recirculated/fresh air door cable from door lever on blower case.

2) Disconnect mode control cable and temperature control cable from door levers on heater case. Pull control panel away from instrument panel. Disconnect blower motor switch connector. Disconnect A/C switch and illumination light electrical connectors. Remove control panel. To install, reverse removal procedure. Adjust control cables. See ADJUSTMENTS.

BLOWER SWITCH

Removal & Installation – Partially remove control panel without disconnecting control cables. See CONTROL PANEL under REMOVAL & INSTALLATION. Remove blower switch knob. Remove nut and blower switch. To install, reverse removal procedure.

HEATER CASE & CORE

Removal & Installation – **1)** Drain cooling system. Disconnect negative battery cable. Remove 2 steering wheel cover screws from back of steering wheel. Remove steering wheel cover. Remove steering wheel nut. Using steering wheel puller, remove steering wheel.

2) Remove steering column covers. Disconnect combination switch electrical connectors. Loosen band clamp securing combination switch to steering column jacket. Remove combination switch. Remove 5 screws securing instrument cluster hood to instrument panel. Pull hood rearward. Disconnect electrical connectors. Remove hood.

3) Remove left and right heater ducts. Disconnect speedometer cable from transaxle. Remove 4 instrument cluster screws. Pull instrument cluster rearward. Disconnect electrical connectors and speedometer cable (lock tabs secure connectors and cable). Remove instrument cluster.

4) Remove shield and shield bracket mounted under steering column. Remove glove box. Open fuse panel cover. Remove 2 fuse panel screws. Push fuse panel forward. DO NOT remove fuse panel.

5) Remove shift lever knob. Remove shift console. Remove shift console support bracket. Remove radio/heater control panel bezel screws. Remove bezel. Remove 4 radio mounting screws. Pull radio out. Disconnect antenna lead and electrical connectors. Disconnect radio ground wire. Remove radio.

6) Remove control panel. See CONTROL PANEL under REMOVAL & INSTALLATION. Pry out bolt covers (3 on top of instrument panel, near windshield; one on each end of instrument panel, near door openings). Remove bolts under covers. Remove 2 nuts (one below each speaker). Pull instrument panel rearward. Disconnect electrical connectors. Remove instrument panel.

7) Disconnect heater hoses from firewall in engine compartment. Disconnect blower motor and blower resistor connectors. Disconnect wiring harness and antenna cable from routing brackets on heater case. Loosen band clamp securing air inlet housing to heater case. Remove nuts securing heater case to firewall. Disconnect defroster ducts. Remove heater case.

8) Disconnect link connecting 2 defroster doors. Remove clips and screws securing case halves together. Separate case halves. Remove heater core.

9) To install, reverse removal procedure. Adjust control cables. See ADJUSTMENTS. Fill cooling system. Check for leaks.

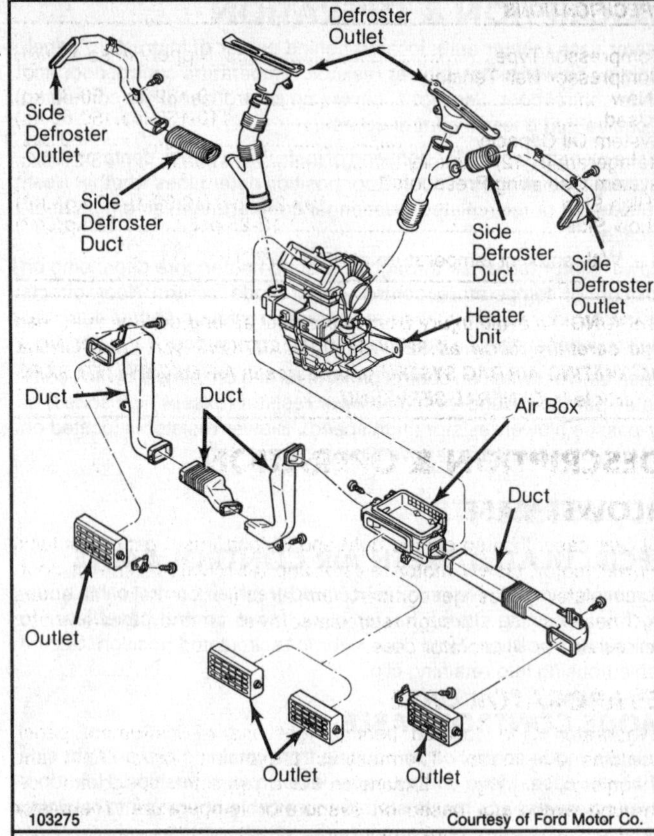
Defroster
Outlet
Side
Defroster
Outlet
Side
Defroster
Duct
Side
Defroster
Duct
Side
Defroster
Outlet
Heater
Unit
Duct
Duct
Air Box
Duct
Outlet
Outlet
Outlet
103275
Courtesy of Ford Motor Co.

Fig. 1: Exploded View Of Heater Ducting Components

BLOWER RESISTOR

CAUTION: DO NOT remove screw forward of blower resistor (above blower motor upper mounting screw). If screw is removed, blower resistor mounting plate will fall into heater case. Plate can only be retrieved by disassembling heater case.

Removal & Installation – Disconnect negative battery cable. Remove airflow duct below steering column. Disconnect blower resistor connector. Remove blower resistor screws. Remove blower resistor. To install, reverse removal procedure.

BLOWER MOTOR

Removal & Installation – Disconnect negative battery cable. Remove airflow duct below steering column. Disconnect blower motor connector. Remove blower motor screws and blower motor. Remove blower wheel nut. To install, reverse removal procedure.

WIRING DIAGRAM

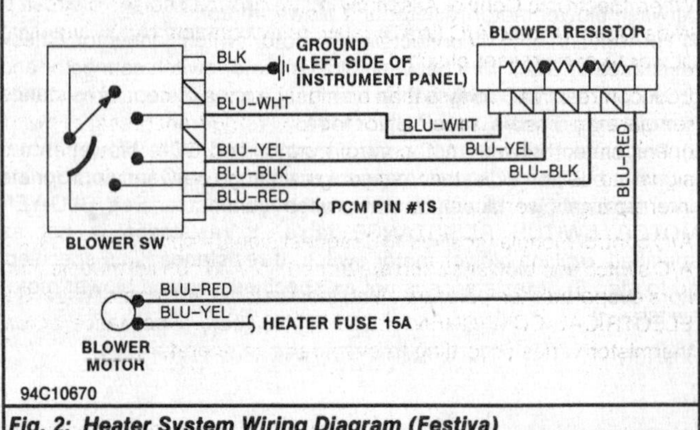
BLOWER RESISTOR
BLK
GROUND
(LEFT SIDE OF
INSTRUMENT PANEL)
BLU-WHT
BLU-WHT
BLU-YEL
BLU-YEL
BLU-BLK
BLU-BLK
BLU-RED
BLU-RED
PCM PIN #1S
BLOWER SW
BLU-RED
BLU-YEL
HEATER FUSE 15A
BLOWER
MOTOR
94C10670

Fig. 2: Heater System Wiring Diagram (Festiva)

SPECIFICATIONS

Compressor Type	Nippondenso 10-Cyl.
Compressor Belt Tension	
New	110-132 lbs. (50-60 kg)
Used	110-132 lbs. (50-60 kg)
System Oil Capacity	10 ozs.
Refrigerant (R-12) Capacity	23-27 ozs.
System Operating Pressures [1]	
High Side	199-220 psi (13.99-15.47 kg/cm²)
Low Side	19-25 psi (1.34-1.76 kg/cm²)

[1] – With ambient temperature of 80°F (27°C).

WARNING: To avoid injury from accidental air bag deployment, read and carefully follow all SERVICE PRECAUTIONS and DISABLING & ACTIVATING AIR BAG SYSTEM procedures in AIR BAG SYSTEM SAFETY article in GENERAL SERVICING.

DESCRIPTION & OPERATION

BLOWER CASE

Blower case, located behind right end of instrument panel, contains blower motor, blower motor resistor and recirculated/fresh air door. Recirculated (passenger compartment) air or fresh (outside) air enters A/C-heater system through recirculated/fresh air door. Blower motor forces air into evaporator case.

EVAPORATOR CASE

Evaporator case, located behind right end of instrument panel, contains evaporator, Thermostatic Expansion Valve (TXV) and thermistor. *See Fig. 1.* Expansion valve regulates refrigerant flow through evaporator based on evaporator temperature. Thermistor provides evaporator core temperature signal for A/C control module. See ELECTRICAL COMPONENT LOCATIONS table.

HEATER CASE

From evaporator case, air enters heater case where it passes through or by-passes heater core depending on position of temperature control door. Two mode control doors in heater case direct air to floor registers, instrument panel registers and/or defroster registers depending on position of mode control doors. Airflow modes include: vent, bi-level, heat, heat/defrost and defrost.

CONTROL PANEL

Control panel at center of instrument panel contains blower switch, door control levers and A/C switch. Door control levers are attached to cables that operate air control doors.

Blower switch, located in lower right corner of control panel, controls blower motor speed. Blower switch completes path to ground through blower resistor coils (except high speed) or by-passes blower resistor coils (high speed).

ELECTRONIC CONTROL ASSEMBLY

When Electronic Control Assembly (ECA) grounds solenoid circuit of Wide Open Throttle A/C (WAC) relay, relay contacts close, supplying power to compressor clutch.

ECA controls WAC relay based on signal from A/C control module. If refrigerant pressure is too high or too low, refrigerant pressure switch opens circuit between A/C control module and ECA. This interrupts signal to ECA. ECA then stops grounding WAC relay solenoid, interrupting power supply to compressor clutch.

A/C control module receives A/C request signal from A/C switch when A/C switch and blower switch are turned on. A/C control module monitors evaporator temperature using thermistor in evaporator case. See ELECTRICAL COMPONENT LOCATIONS table. Resistance across thermistor varies according to evaporator temperature.

ELECTRICAL COMPONENT LOCATIONS

Component	Location
A/C Control Module	Right Side Of Evaporator Case
Condenser Fan Relay	Left Rear Corner Of Engine Compartment
Blower Motor Resistor	Bottom Of Blower Case
Electronic Control Assy. (ECA)	Behind Lower Center Of Instrument Panel
Ignition Relay	Behind Left End Of Instrument Panel, On Fuse/Relay Block
In-Line Fuse (15-Amp)	Next To WAC Relay
Refrigerant Pressure Switch	Right Rear Corner Of Engine Compartment, On Liquid Line
Thermistor	Inside Evaporator Case
WAC Relay	Left Rear Corner Of Engine Compartment

ADJUSTMENTS

NOTE: See HEATER SYSTEMS – CAPRI article.

TESTING

WARNING: To avoid injury from accidental air bag deployment, read and carefully follow all SERVICE PRECAUTIONS and DISABLING & ACTIVATING AIR BAG SYSTEM procedures in AIR BAG SYSTEM SAFETY article in GENERAL SERVICING.

A/C SYSTEM PERFORMANCE

1) System Integrity – Inspect system hoses and plumbing for signs of damage and loose connectors. Inspect compressor clutch for signs of leaks. Inspect drive belt for tension and signs of wear. If system does not appear to be in good condition, repair or replace damaged components as necessary. If system is okay, go to next step.

2) System Pressures – Connect manifold set to A/C system. Allow engine to idle at 2000 RPM. Turn blower on high. Turn A/C on. Move lever to extreme left (cool setting). Wait 5 minutes for system to stabilize. Check gauges, and feel temperatures of suction and pressure lines near compressor. Check for build up of condensation on A/C plumbing near compressor and receiver-drier. Ensure A/C system operating pressures are within specifications. See SPECIFICATIONS.

A/C SYSTEM

1) System Integrity – Ensure battery is fully charged. Check for blown fuses and poor electrical connections. Check for signs of opens, shorts or damage to wiring harness. Start engine. With engine idling turn A/C and blower on. Check wiring harness and look for signs of opens or shorts. Check for bad connectors. If there is a problem with system, repair or replace damaged components as necessary. If system is in good condition, go to next step.

2) Clutch Voltage – With engine running, turn A/C and blower on. Check voltage on Black/White wire at compressor clutch connector. If voltage is more than 10 volts, go to next step. If voltage is less than 10 volts, go to step **4)**.

3) Clutch Resistance – Turn ignition off. With A/C in OFF position, allow engine to cool. Disconnect compressor clutch connector. Check resistance between compressor clutch connector (clutch side) and compressor clutch case. If resistance is between 2.7 and 3.5 ohms, check condition of drive belt, clutch material and compressor. Repair as necessary. If resistance is not between 2.7 and 3.5 ohms, repair compressor clutch ground. If okay, replace compressor clutch.

4) Short In Clutch Wire – Turn ignition off. Disconnect compressor clutch and Wide Open Throttle Cut-Off (WAC) relay. Check resistance between Black/White wire at WAC relay connector and ground. If resistance is less than 5 ohms, repair Black/White wire. If resistance is more than 5 ohms, go to next step.

1993 MANUAL A/C-HEATER SYSTEMS
Capri (Cont.)

5) Compressor Clutch Wire – Turn ignition off. Disconnect compressor clutch and WAC relay. Check resistance of Black/White wire between WAC relay and compressor clutch. If resistance is more than 5 ohms, repair Black/White wire. If resistance is less than 5 ohms, go to next step.

6) Voltage From Wide Open Throttle Cut-Off (WAC) Relay – With engine idling, A/C and blower on, check voltage on Black/White wire at WAC relay. If voltage is more than 10 volts, go to step **11)**. If voltage is less than 10 volts, go to next step.

7) Heater Circuit Breaker – Check 30-amp heater circuit breaker in interior fuse panel. If reset button on circuit breaker is sticking out, go to step **9)**. If reset button is not sticking out, go to next step.

8) System Check – Push in reset button on heater circuit breaker. Turn ignition on. If reset button popped out again, repair Blue wire at interior fuse panel for a short to ground. If reset button did not pop out, go to next step.

9) In-line Cooler Fuse – Check 15-amp in-line cooler fuse. If fuse fails, repair Blue wire between in-line fuse and WAC relay for a short to ground. If fuse does not fail, go to next step.

10) Voltage To Wide Open Throttle Cut-Off (WAC) Relay – Turn ignition on. Check voltage on Blue wire at WAC relay connector. If voltage is less than 10 volts, repair Blue wire. If voltage is more than 10 volts, go to next step.

11) A/C Fuse – Check 15-amp A/C fuse. If fuse is okay, go to step **13)**. If fuse is not okay, replace fuse. Turn ignition on. If fuse fails again, go to next step. If fuse does not fail again, go to step **13)**.

12) Short To Ground – Turn ignition off. Disconnect interior fuse panel connector. Disconnect A/C switch, WAC relay, condenser fan motor and relay. Check resistance between Blue wire at interior fuse panel connector and ground. If resistance is less than 5 ohms, repair Blue wire(s) for short(s) to ground. If resistance is more than 5 ohms, go to next step.

13) Power Supply To Wide Open Throttle Cut-Off (WAC) Relay – Turn ignition on. Check voltage on Blue/Black wire at connector. If voltage is less than 10 volts, repair Blue/Black wire between interior fuse panel and WAC relay. If voltage is more than 10 volts, go to next step.

NOTE: Blue/Black wire changes to a Blue wire at splice before interior fuse panel.

14) Wide Open Throttle Cut-Off (WAC) Relay Operation – Turn ignition on. Ground White wire at WAC relay with a jumper wire. Check voltage on Black/White wire at WAC relay. If voltage is less than 10 volts with White wire grounded and more than one volt with White wire open, replace WAC relay. If voltage is more than 10 volts with White wire grounded and less than one volt with White wire open, go to next step.

15) Voltage To Power Control Module (PCM) – Disconnect PCM connector located at center of instrument panel. Turn ignition on. Check voltage on White wire at PCM connector. If voltage is less than 10 volts, repair White wire between WAC relay and PCM. If voltage is more than 10 volts, go to next step.

16) Cooling Fan Fuse – Check 20-amp fuse. If fuse is okay, go to step **18)**. If fuse is not okay, replace fuse. Turn ignition on. If fuse fails again, go to next step. If fuse does not fail again, go to step **18)**.

17) Short To Ground – Turn ignition off. Disconnect interior fuse panel connector. Disconnect cooling fan motor and A/C control module located behind lower right side of instrument panel. Check resistance between Yellow wire at interior fuse panel connector and ground. If resistance is less than 5 ohms, repair Yellow wire. If resistance is more than 5 ohms, go to next step.

18) Power Supply To A/C Control Module – Disconnect A/C control module connector located behind lower right side of instrument panel. Turn ignition on and A/C to OFF position. Check voltage on Yellow wire at A/C control module connector. If voltage is less than 10 volts, repair Yellow wire between interior fuse panel and A/C control module. If voltage is more than 10 volts, go to next step.

19) A/C Control Module Operation – Checks are made at harness side of A/C control module connector with module connected. See A/C CONTROL MODULE VOLTAGE TEST table for correct voltage. If voltage is not correct, replace A/C control module. If voltage is correct go to next step.

A/C CONTROL MODULE VOLTAGE TEST

Test Conditions & Wire Color	Volts
Key On, A/C Off	
Blower Off	
Red	More Than 10
Yellow	More Than 10
Green	More Than 10
White/Blue	More Than 10
White/Blue	More Than 10
Yellow/Green	More Than 10
Key On, A/C Off	
Blower On	
Red	2.2
Yellow	More Than 10
Green	1.5
White/Blue	3.3
White/Blue	3.3
Yellow/Green	1.5

20) A/C Switch & Condenser Fan Relay Wire – Turn ignition off. Disconnect A/C switch. Disconnect A/C control module located behind lower right side of instrument panel. Disconnect condenser fan relay located in left right corner of engine compartment at bulkhead. Check resistance between Green wire at A/C control module to A/C switch and condenser fan relay. If resistance is more than 5 ohms, repair Green wire. If resistance is less than 5 ohms, go to next step.

21) Thermistor Circuit – Turn ignition off. Disconnect A/C control module and thermistor. Check resistance of Yellow/Green wire and White/Blue wires between A/C control module and thermistor. If resistance is more than 5 ohms on wires, repair wires. If resistance is less than 5 ohms, go to next step.

22) Thermistor – Remove thermistor located behind right side of instrument panel. Check resistance between White/Blue and Yellow/Green wire terminals on thermistor. Cool sensing bulb on switch to bring temperature of sensing bulb below 32°F. If resistance is more than 1,500 ohms with sensing bulb warm (above 77°F) and less than 4,500 ohms with sensing bulb cold (32°F or below), replace thermistor. If resistance is less than 1,500 ohms with sensing bulb warm (above 77°F) and more than 4,500 ohms with sensing bulb cold (32°F or below), go to next step.

23) Power Supply To A/C Switch – Disconnect A/C switch. Turn ignition on. Check voltage on Blue/Black wire at A/C switch connector. If voltage is less than 10 volts, repair Blue/Black wire. If voltage is more than 10 volts, go to next step.

24) A/C Switch Operation – Turn ignition on. Place A/C in ON position. Check A/C switch voltages at harness side of connector. See A/C SWITCH VOLTAGE TEST table. If voltages are not correct, replace A/C switch. If voltages are correct, go to next step.

A/C SWITCH VOLTAGE TEST

Test Conditions & Wire Color	Voltage
Key On, A/C Off	
Blower On	
Green	Less Than 2
Blue/Black	More Than 10
Blue/Yellow	Less Than 1
Blower Off	
Green	More Than 10
Blue/Black	More Than 10
Blue/Yellow	More Than 10

25) Blower Motor Control Switch & Blower Motor Resistor Wire – Turn ignition off. Check resistance of Blue/Yellow wire(s) between A/C switch, blower motor control switch and blower motor resistor located behind right side of instrument panel, behind glove box. If resistance is more than 5 ohms, repair Blue/Yellow wire(s). If resistance is less than 5 ohms, go to next step.

26) A/C Control Module & Clutch Cycling Pressure Switch Wire – Turn ignition off. Disconnect clutch cycling pressure switch and A/C control module connectors. Check resistance of Red wire between clutch cycling pressure switch connector and A/C control module connector. If resistance is more than 5 ohms, repair Red wire. If resistance is less than 5 ohms, go to step **28)**.
27) Clutch Cycling Pressure Switch – Connect manifold set to service gauge port valves. Disconnect clutch cycling pressure switch connector. Check resistance between Red wire terminals of clutch cycling pressure switch. If resistance is more than 5 ohms, when system high side pressure is above 27-33 psi, replace clutch cycling pressure switch. If resistance is less than 5 ohms when system high side pressure is above 27-33 psi, go to next step.
28) Clutch Cycling Pressure Switch & PCM Wire – Turn ignition off. Disconnect Power Control Module (PCM) located below center of instrument panel. Disconnect clutch cycling pressure switch. Check resistance of Red wire between clutch cycling pressure switch and PCM. If resistance is more than 5 ohms, repair Red wire. If resistance is less than 5 ohms, check PCM. See appropriate ENGINE PERFORMANCE article in appropriate MITCHELL® manual.

CONDENSER FAN

1) System Integrity – Ensure battery is fully charged. Check for blown fuses and poor electrical connections. Check for signs of opens, shorts or damage to wiring harness. Start engine. With engine idling turn A/C and blower on. Check wiring harness from condenser fan motor to condenser fan relay and refrigerant pressure switch. Look for signs of opens or shorts. Check for bad connectors. If there is a problem with system, repair or replace damaged components as necessary. If system is in good condition, go to next step.
2) Fuse Check – Check 15-amp A/C fuse. If fuse is okay, go to step **4)**. If fuse is not okay, replace fuse. Turn ignition on. If fuse fails again, go to step **4)**. If fuse does not fail again, go to next step.
3) Short To Ground – Disconnect interior fuse panel connector. Disconnect condenser fan motor, condenser fan relay, Wide Open Throttle (WAC) relay located at left right corner or engine compartment at bulkhead. Disconnect A/C switch connectors. Check resistance between Blue wire at interior fuse panel connector and ground. If resistance is less than 5 ohms, repair Blue wire. If resistance is more than 5 ohms, go to next step.
4) Fuse Check – Check cooling fuse. If fuse is okay, go to step **6)**. If fuse is not okay, replace fuse. Turn ignition on. If fuse fails again, go to next step. If fuse is okay, go to step **6)**.
5) Short To Ground – Disconnect interior fuse panel connector. Disconnect A/C control module and cooling fan motor connectors. Check resistance between Yellow wire at interior fuse panel connector and ground. If resistance is less than 5 ohms, repair Yellow wire. If resistance is more than 5 ohms, go to next step.
6) Power Supply To Condenser Fan Motor – Turn ignition on. Check voltage on Blue wire at condenser fan motor. If voltage is less than 10 volts, repair Blue wire between condenser fan motor and interior fuse panel. If voltage is more than 10 volts, go to next step.
7) Power Supply To Condenser Fan Relay – Turn ignition on. Check voltage on Blue/Black wire at condenser fan relay connector. If voltage is less than 10 volts, repair Blue/Black wire. If voltage is more than 10 volts, go to next step.
8) Condenser Fan Relay Control Circuit – Turn ignition off. Disconnect A/C control module, condenser fan relay and A/C switch. Check resistance of Green wire between each components. If resistance is more than 5 ohms, repair Green wire. If resistance is less than 5 ohms, go to next step.
9) Condenser Fan Motor Operation – Turn ignition off. Disconnect condenser fan motor. Apply 12 volts to Blue wire terminal at condenser fan motor. Ground Green/Red wire terminal at condenser fan motor. If condenser fan motor does not run, replace motor. If motor does run, go to next step.
10) Condenser Fan Relay Wire – Turn ignition on. Disconnect condenser fan relay. Check resistance of Green/Red wire between condenser fan relay and condenser fan motor. If resistance is more than 5 ohms, repair Green/Red wire. If resistance is less than 5 ohms, go to next step.
11) Condenser Fan Relay Ground (Condenser Fan Motor) – Disconnect condenser fan relay connector. Check resistance between Black wire at the condenser fan relay connector and ground. If resistance is more than 5 ohms, repair Black wire. If resistance is less than 5 ohms, go to next step.
12) Condenser Fan Relay – Disconnect condenser fan relay. Check resistance between Green/Red wire terminal and Black wire terminal of relay. If resistance is less than 10,000 ohms, replace condenser fan relay. Resistance should be more than 10,000 ohms. If not, replace relay. If resistance is as specified, apply 12 volts to Blue/Black wire terminal and ground Green wire terminal. If resistance is more than 5 ohms, replace condenser fan relay. If resistance is less than 5 ohms, condenser fan circuit is working properly at this time.

REMOVAL & INSTALLATION

WARNING: To avoid injury from accidental air bag deployment, read and carefully follow all SERVICE PRECAUTIONS and DISABLING & ACTIVATING AIR BAG SYSTEM procedures in AIR BAG SYSTEM SAFETY article in GENERAL SERVICING.

NOTE: For removal and installation procedures not covered in this article, see HEATER SYSTEMS – CAPRI article.

COMPRESSOR

Removal – Run engine at fast idle for 10 minutes with A/C on. Turn engine off. Disconnect negative battery cable. Remove compressor drive belt. Discharge A/C system using approved refrigerant recovery/recycling equipment. Raise and support vehicle. Remove engine undercovers. Disconnect compressor clutch connector. Disconnect refrigerant hoses from compressor. Remove compressor bolts. Remove compressor.
Installation – To install, reverse removal procedure. Tighten compressor bolts to specification. See TORQUE SPECIFICATIONS. Evacuate and charge A/C system.

CONDENSER

Removal – **1)** Disconnect negative battery cable. Discharge A/C system using approved refrigerant recovery/recycling equipment. Drain cooling system. Disconnect upper and lower radiator hoses from radiator. Remove upper radiator mounts.
2) Disconnect cooling fan connector. Release cooling fan harness retainer. Disconnect coolant overflow hose. Remove radiator and fan assembly. Disconnect A/C lines from condenser. Position wiring harness aside. Remove condenser bolts. Carefully remove condenser.
Installation – If condenser is replaced, add one ounce of refrigerant oil to condenser. Carefully install condenser. Connect A/C lines. Install radiator and fan assembly. Connect electrical connector. Engage cooling fan harness into retainer. Connect radiator hoses. Fill cooling system. Connect negative battery cable. Evacuate and charge A/C system.

RECEIVER-DRIER

Removal – Disconnect negative battery cable. Discharge A/C system using approved refrigerant recovery/recycling equipment. Remove air cleaner assembly and front mounting bracket. Disconnect A/C lines from receiver-drier. Loosen receiver-drier bracket. Remove receiver-drier.
Installation – If replacing receiver-drier, add 1/2 ounce of compressor oil to receiver-drier. Install receiver-drier into bracket. Connect A/C lines, ensuring line from condenser is connected to port marked "IN". Install air cleaner assembly and mounting bracket. Connect negative battery cable. Evacuate and charge A/C system.

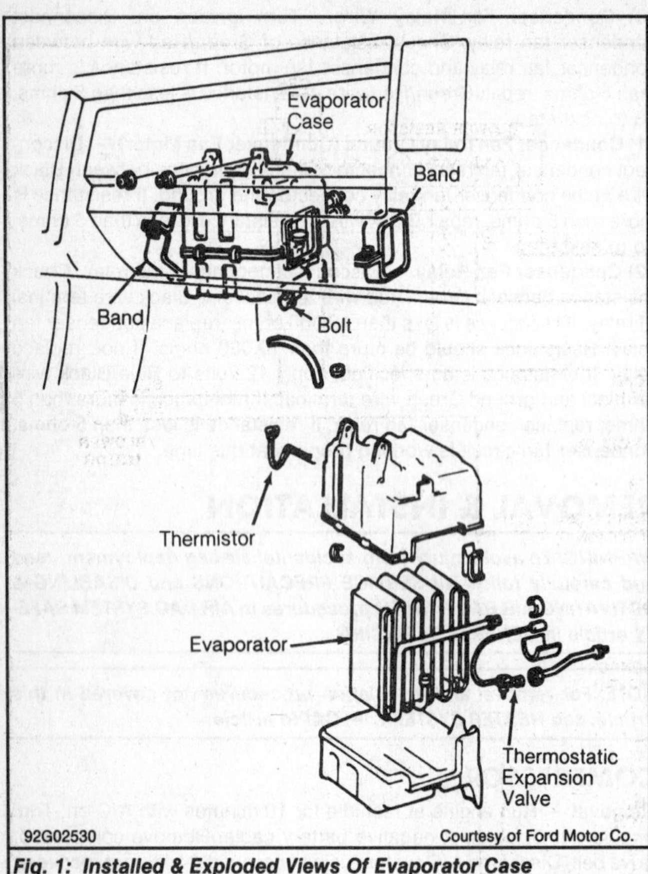
Evaporator
Case
Band
Band
Bolt
Thermistor
Evaporator
Thermostatic
Expansion
Valve
92G02530
Courtesy of Ford Motor Co.
Fig. 1: Installed & Exploded Views Of Evaporator Case

EVAPORATOR CASE, EVAPORATOR & THERMOSTATIC EXPANSION VALVE

Removal – **1)** Disconnect negative battery cable. Discharge A/C system using approved refrigerant recovery/recycling equipment. Disconnect A/C lines from evaporator in engine compartment.

2) Remove glove box, glove box upper panel and bracket. Disconnect wiring harness connectors, and release harness retainers. Remove defroster tube, air duct bands and drain hose. Remove nuts and bolts securing evaporator case to firewall. Carefully remove evaporator case. Disassemble case to remove evaporator and Thermostatic Expansion Valve (TXV). *See Fig. 1*.

Installation – Add one ounce of compressor oil to evaporator. Reassemble evaporator case if disassembled. Carefully install evaporator case. Ensure evaporator grommet in firewall is in proper position. Tighten nuts and bolts to specification. See TORQUE SPECIFICATIONS. To complete installation, reverse removal procedure. Evacuate and charge A/C system.

TORQUE SPECIFICATIONS

TORQUE SPECIFICATIONS

Application	Ft. Lbs. (N.m)
Compressor Bolt	29-39 (39-53)
	INCH Lbs. (N.m)
Evaporator Case Bolt/Nut	80-115 (9-13)

WIRING DIAGRAM

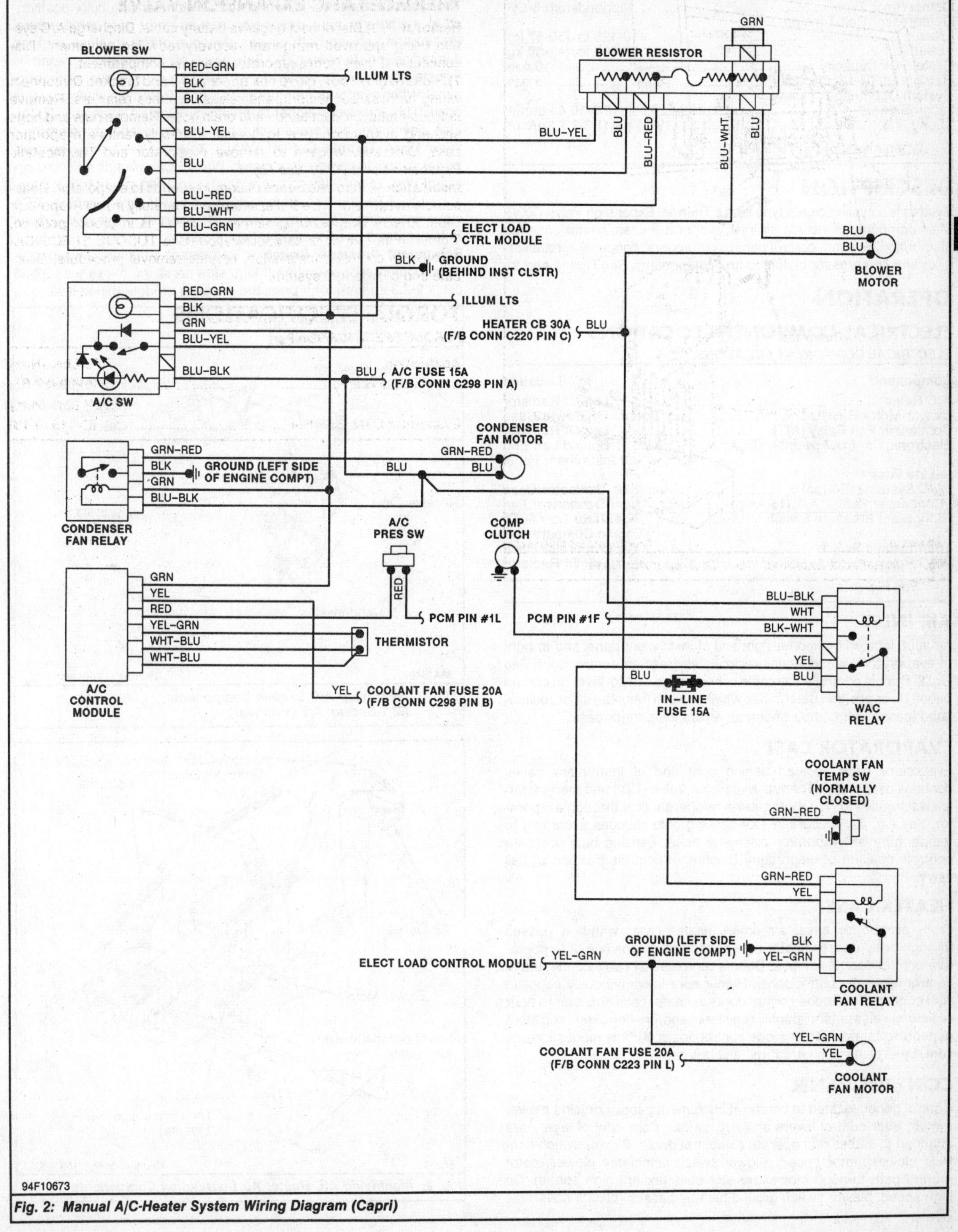
BLOWER SW
RED-GRN
BLK
BLK
BLU-YEL
BLU
BLU-RED
BLU-WHT
BLU-GRN
ILLUM LTS
BLOWER RESISTOR
GRN
BLU-YEL
BLU
BLU-RED
BLU-WHT
BLU
ELECT LOAD CTRL MODULE
BLU
BLU
BLOWER MOTOR
BLK
GROUND (BEHIND INST CLSTR)
RED-GRN
BLK
GRN
BLU-YEL
BLU-BLK
ILLUM LTS
HEATER CB 30A (F/B CONN C220 PIN C)
BLU
A/C SW
BLU
A/C FUSE 15A (F/B CONN C298 PIN A)
CONDENSER FAN MOTOR
GRN-RED
BLK
GRN
BLU-BLK
GROUND (LEFT SIDE OF ENGINE COMPT)
GRN-RED
BLU
BLU
CONDENSER FAN RELAY
A/C PRES SW
COMP CLUTCH
GRN
YEL
RED
YEL-GRN
WHT-BLU
WHT-BLU
RED
PCM PIN #1L
PCM PIN #1F
THERMISTOR
A/C CONTROL MODULE
YEL
COOLANT FAN FUSE 20A (F/B CONN C298 PIN B)
BLU-BLK
WHT
BLK-WHT
YEL
BLU
BLU
IN-LINE FUSE 15A
WAC RELAY
COOLANT FAN TEMP SW (NORMALLY CLOSED)
GRN-RED
GRN-RED
YEL
GROUND (LEFT SIDE OF ENGINE COMPT)
BLK
YEL-GRN
YEL-GRN
ELECT LOAD CONTROL MODULE
COOLANT FAN RELAY
YEL-GRN
YEL
COOLANT FAN FUSE 20A (F/B CONN C223 PIN L)
COOLANT FAN MOTOR
94F10673

Fig. 2: Manual A/C-Heater System Wiring Diagram (Capri)

1993 MANUAL A/C-HEATER SYSTEMS
Festiva

SPECIFICATIONS

Compressor Type	Nippondenso 6-Cyl.
Compressor Belt Tension	
New	110-125 lb. (50-57 kg)
Used	92-110 lb. (42-50 kg)
System Oil Capacity	10 ozs.
Refrigerant (R-12) Capacity	25 ozs.
System Operating Pressure [1]	
High Side	199-220 psi (13.9-15.4 kg/cm²)
Low Side	19-25 psi (1.3-1.7 kg/cm²)

[1] - When measured at 79°F (26°C).

DESCRIPTION

System is a cycling clutch type with a Thermal Expansion Valve (TXV). Main components include air inlet, evaporator case, heater case (air distribution plenum), control panel, compressor, condenser, receiver-drier and compressor clutch control components. *See Figs. 1 and 2.*

OPERATION

ELECTRICAL COMPONENT LOCATIONS

ELECTRICAL COMPONENT LOCATIONS

Component	Location
A/C Relay	Left Of Radiator
Blower Motor Resistor	Bottom Of Blower Case
Condenser Fan Relay (A/T)	Left Of Radiator
Electronic Control Assembly (ECA)	Behind Left End Of Instrument Panel
In-Line Fuse	
A/C System (10-Amp)	Left Side Of Heater Case
Condenser Fan - A/T (15-Amp)	Near Condenser Fan
Refrigerant Pressure Switch	[1] Right Rear Corner Of Engine Compartment
Thermostatic Switch	On Evaporator Case
WAC Relay	Left Of Radiator

[1] - *See Fig. 1.*

AIR INLET

Air inlet, located behind far right end of instrument panel and to right of evaporator case, contains recirculated/fresh air control door. *See Fig. 2.* Door is controlled by cable connected to control lever on control panel. Door position determines whether fresh (outside) air or recirculated (passenger compartment) air enters evaporator case.

EVAPORATOR CASE

Evaporator case, located behind right end of instrument panel, contains evaporator, Thermal Expansion Valve (TXV) and thermostatic switch. *See Fig. 1.* TXV regulates refrigerant flow through evaporator. *See Fig. 3.* Pressure in TXV sensing bulb changes according to temperature at evaporator discharge hose. Sensing bulb pressure controls position of diaphragm. Diaphragm controls position of ball valve.

HEATER CASE

From evaporator case, air enters heater case, where it passes through or by-passes heater core depending on position of temperature control door. *See Fig. 2.* Door is controlled by cable connected to control lever on control panel. Heater core is continuously supplied with coolant. Two mode control doors in heater case direct air to floor registers, instrument panel registers and/or defroster registers depending on position of mode control doors. Airflow modes include vent, bi-level, heat, heat/defrost and defrost.

CONTROL PANEL

Control panel, located at center of instrument panel, contains blower switch, door control levers and A/C switch. Door control levers are attached to cables that operate air control doors. Blower switch controls blower motor speed. Blower switch completes blower motor ground path through blower resistor coils (except high speed). On high speed, blower switch ground path by-passes resistor coils.

COMPRESSOR CLUTCH CONTROL

Thermostatic Switch - Thermostatic switch sensing bulb, positioned in evaporator core, responds to evaporator core temperature. Pressure in sensing bulb causes switch contacts to close or open depending on temperature. Sensitivity of thermostatic switch is adjusted by cable connected to temperature control lever on control panel. When evaporator temperature is near freezing, switch contacts open. This interrupts signal to Electronic Control Assembly (ECA). ECA disengages compressor clutch to prevent evaporator freezing.

Wide Open Throttle Cut-Off (WAC) Relay - WAC relay controls power supply to compressor clutch. When ECA grounds solenoid circuit of WAC relay, relay contacts close, supplying power to compressor clutch. To improve driveability during wide open throttle, ECA stops grounding WAC relay solenoid, de-energizing solenoid in relay. Relay contacts open, turning off compressor.

Refrigerant Pressure Switch - Refrigerant pressure switch prevents compressor operation if high side pressure is less than 27-33 psi (1.9-2.3 kg/cm²), or if pressure exceeds predetermined level.

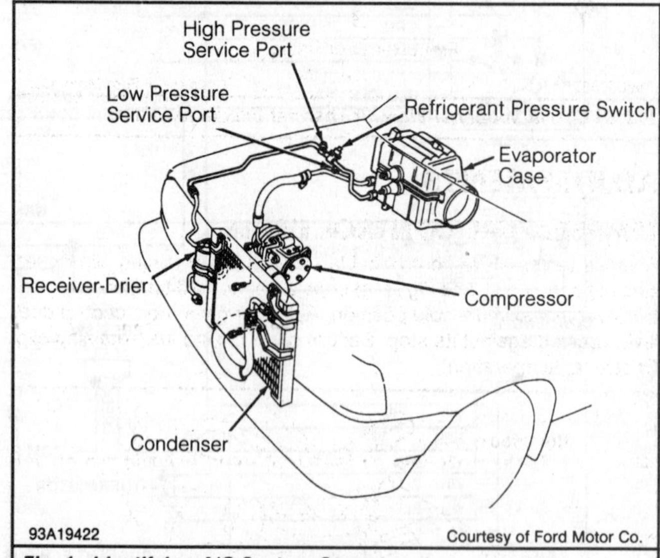
High Pressure Service Port
Low Pressure Service Port
Refrigerant Pressure Switch
Evaporator Case
Receiver-Drier
Compressor
Condenser
93A19422
Courtesy of Ford Motor Co.

Fig. 1: Identifying A/C System Components (M/T Shown; A/T Is Similar)

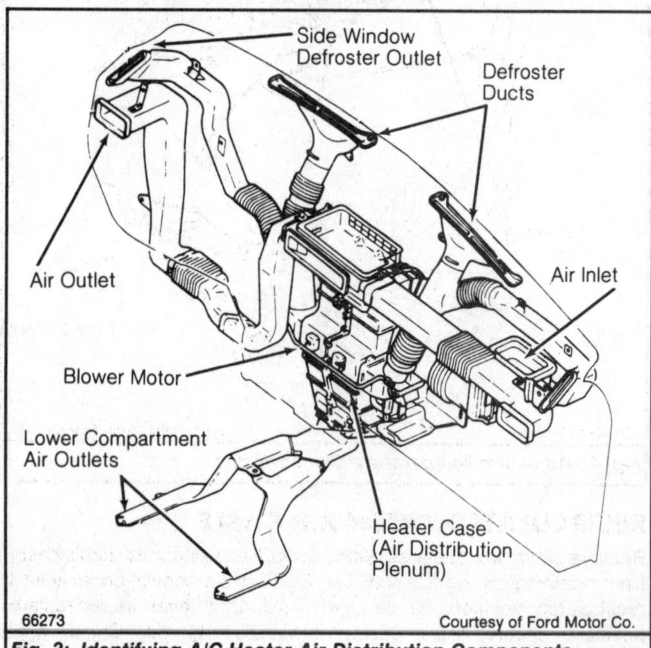
Side Window Defroster Outlet
Defroster Ducts
Air Outlet
Air Inlet
Blower Motor
Lower Compartment Air Outlets
Heater Case (Air Distribution Plenum)
66273
Courtesy of Ford Motor Co.

Fig. 2: Identifying A/C-Heater Air Distribution Components

1993 MANUAL A/C-HEATER SYSTEMS
Festiva (Cont.)

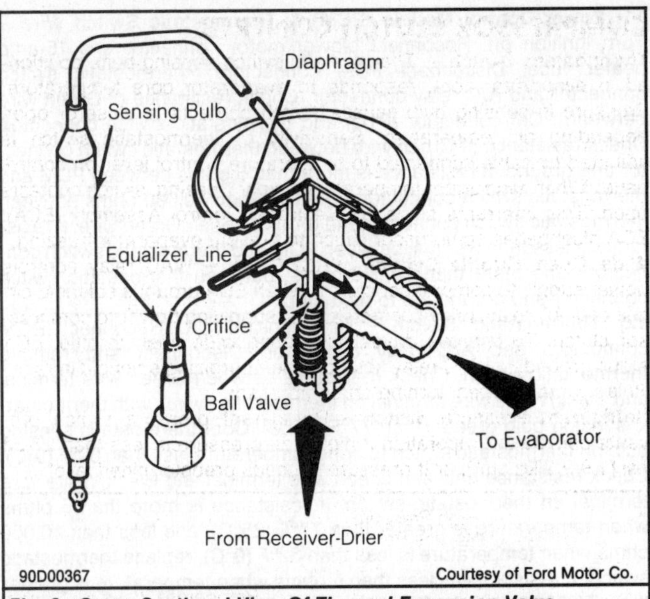
Diaphragm
Sensing Bulb
Equalizer Line
Orifice
Ball Valve
To Evaporator
From Receiver-Drier
90D00367
Courtesy of Ford Motor Co.

Fig. 3: Cross-Sectional View Of Thermal Expansion Valve

ADJUSTMENTS

TEMPERATURE CONTROL CABLE

Release temperature control cable casing from retaining clip on left side of heater case. *See Fig. 4*. At control panel, hold temperature control lever in maximum cold position. At heater case, hold control door lever upward against its stop. Secure cable casing into retaining clip. Check cable operation.

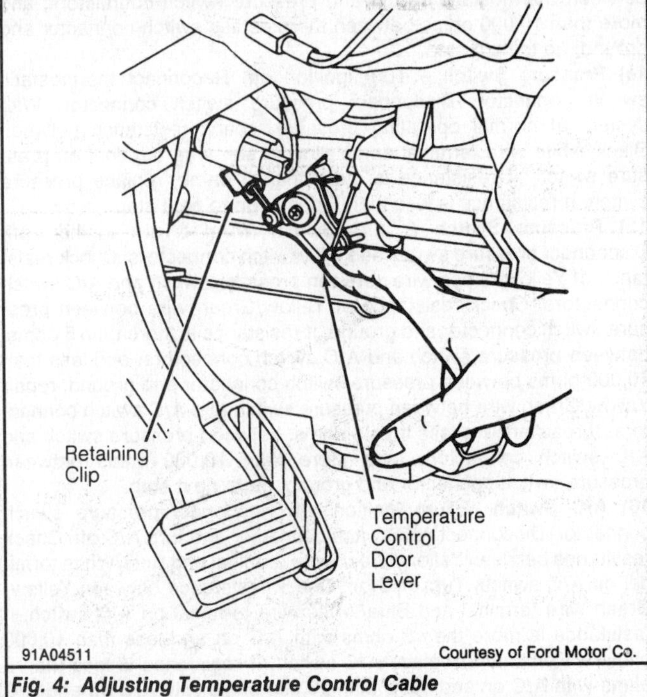
Retaining Clip
Temperature Control Door Lever
91A04511
Courtesy of Ford Motor Co.

Fig. 4: Adjusting Temperature Control Cable

RECIRCULATED/FRESH AIR CABLE

Remove glove box. Release recirculated/fresh air control cable casing from retaining clip on air inlet. *See Fig. 5*. Hold control panel lever in recirculated position. At air inlet, hold door lever in recirculated position. Secure cable casing into retaining clip. Check cable operation.

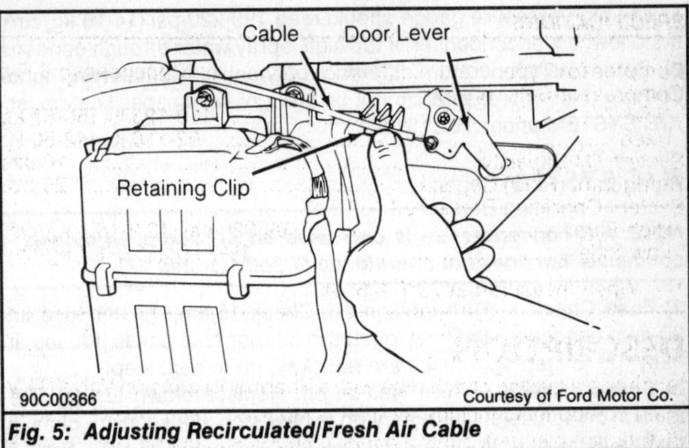
Cable
Door Lever
Retaining Clip
90C00366
Courtesy of Ford Motor Co.

Fig. 5: Adjusting Recirculated/Fresh Air Cable

MODE CONTROL CABLE

Release mode control cable casing from retaining clip on right side of heater case. *See Fig. 6*. Hold control panel lever in vent position. At heater case, hold door lever downward against its stop. Secure cable casing into retaining clip. Check cable operation.

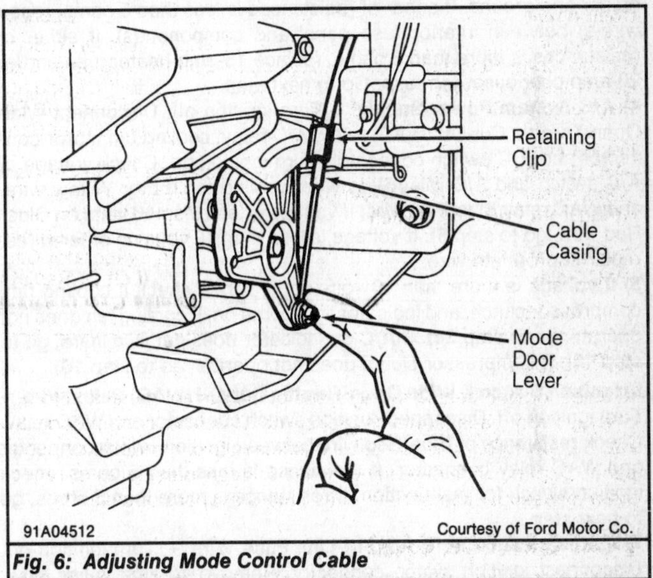
Retaining Clip
Cable Casing
Mode Door Lever
91A04512
Courtesy of Ford Motor Co.

Fig. 6: Adjusting Mode Control Cable

TROUBLE SHOOTING

TROUBLE SHOOTING SYMPTOM CHART

Symptom	Go To A/C SYSTEM Test Step
A/C Compressor Clutch Does Not Engage	1)
A/C Compressor Clutch Constantly Engaged	10)
Frost Blows Out Of Vents	12)
Cooling Fan Does Not Operate With A/C On	1)
A/C Condenser Fan Does Not Operate [1]	22)
A/C Condenser Fan Operates Continuously	29)
A/C On Indicator Does Not Come On	4)
A/C On Indicator Constantly On	10)

[1] – A/C condenser fan is only used on A/T models.

TESTING

A/C SYSTEM PERFORMANCE

1) Start engine and allow it to idle at 2000 RPM. Set A/C controls to outside air, panel (vent) mode, full cold, and A/C button on.

2) Set blower/fan on 3 position and open windows. Operate system for 5-10 minutes to allow system to stabilize. Insert thermometer in center console duct and insert thermometer in blower inlet under right hand side of dash. Measure relative humidity at blower inlet.

1993 MANUAL A/C-HEATER SYSTEMS
Festiva (Cont.)

3) The high-pressure gauge should read 199-220 psi (14-16 kg/cm²). If too low, cover condenser; if too high, spray water through condenser. Determine temperature difference between blower inlet and center console duct. If pressure cannot be brought within specification, see A/C SYSTEM under TESTING.

A/C SYSTEM

NOTE: A/C condenser fan is only used on A/T equipped models. If condenser fan does not operate, go directly to step 22).

1) Fuse Check – Turn ignition off. Check 15-amp heater fuse and 20-amp condenser fan fuse located in interior fuse panel. If fuses are okay, go to step **4)**. If fuses are not okay, go to next step.

2) System Check – Turn ignition off. Replace blown fuse(s). Turn ignition on. If fuse(s) fails again, go to next step. If fuse(s) are okay, go to step **4)**.

3) Short To Ground – Turn ignition off. Remove 15-amp heater fuse and 20-amp condenser fan fuse. Disconnect A/C switch connector, A/C relay, cooling fan motor connector and Wide Open Throttle Cut-Off (WAC). Check resistance of Yellow wire between bottom terminal of 20-amp condenser fan fuse holder and ground. Check resistance of Blue/Yellow wire between bottom terminal of 15-amp heater fuse holder and ground. If either of resistances is less than 5 ohms, repair wire(s) between interior fuse panel and component(s). If either of resistances is more than 5 ohms, replace 15-amp heater fuse and/or 20-amp condenser fan fuse. Go to next step.

4) A/C System Power Supply – Turn ignition off. Disconnect Wide Open Throttle Cut-Off (WAC) relay, A/C relay, cooling fan motor connector and A/C switch connector. Turn ignition on. Check voltage at A/C switch and A/C relay Blue wire, cooling fan motor Yellow wire, and WAC relay Blue/Red wire. If voltage is less than 10 volts on Blue/Red wire, go to step **6)**. If voltage is less than 10 volts on other wires, repair appropriate wire.

5) If voltage is more than 10 volts on all wires, check if cooling fan, compressor clutch, and indicator light come on. If cooling fan does not operate, go to step **34)**. If A/C on indicator does not illuminate, go to step **16)**. If compressor clutch does not operate, go to step **10)**.

6) Ignition Switch & Wide Open Throttle Cut-Off (WAC) Relay Wire – Turn ignition off. Disconnect ignition switch connector and WAC relay. Check resistance of Blue/Red wire between ignition switch connector and WAC relay connector. If resistance is less than 5 ohms, check ignition switch for malfunction. If resistance is more than 5 ohms, go to next step.

7) Ignition Switch & 10-Amp In-Line Fuse Wire – Turn ignition off. Disconnect ignition switch connector. Remove 10-amp in-line fuse. Check resistance of Blue/Red wire between ignition switch connector and 10-amp in-line fuse connector. If resistance is more than 5 ohms, repair Blue/Red wire. If resistance is less than 5 ohms, go to next step.

8) 10-Amp In-Line Fuse – Turn ignition off. Remove 10-amp in-line fuse and check if fuse is okay. If fuse is okay, repair open in Blue/Red wire between 10-amp in-line fuse and WAC relay connector. If fuse is not okay, go to next step.

9) 10-Amp In-Line Fuse & Wide Open Throttle Cut-Off (WAC) Relay Wire – Turn ignition off. Disconnect WAC relay connector. Remove 10-amp in-line fuse. Check resistance of Blue/Red wire between 10-amp in-line fuse connector (WAC relay side) and ground. If resistance is less than 5 ohms, repair short in Blue/Red wire. If resistance is more than 5 ohms, replace 10-amp fuse and go to step **21)**.

10) A/C Control Circuit To Power Control Module (PCM) – Turn ignition off. Reconnect WAC relay, A/C relay, cooling fan motor and A/C switch connectors. Disconnect blower motor connector and PCM connectors. Remove 15-amp heater fuse. Place blower switch in 1, 2 or 3 position and turn A/C switch on. Check resistance of Green wire between PCM connector (Pin 1Q) and ground with A/C switch on and then with it off. If resistance is less than 5 ohms, with A/C switch on and more than 10,000 ohms with A/C switch off, go to step **20)**. If resistance is more than 5 ohms, with A/C switch on, and less than 10,000 ohms with A/C switch off, go to next step.

11) Power Control Module (PCM) & Thermostatic Switch Wire – Turn ignition off. Reconnect blower motor connector and 15-amp heater fuse. Disconnect PCM connectors, thermostatic switch connector and A/C relay connector. Check resistance of Green wire between PCM connector (P1Q) and thermostatic switch connector. Check resistance of Green wire between thermostatic switch connector and ground. If resistance is more than 5 ohms between PCM and thermostatic switch connectors and less than 10,000 ohms between thermostatic switch connector and ground, repair Green wire. If resistance is less than 5 ohms, between PCM and thermostatic switch connectors and more than 10,000 ohms, between thermostatic switch connector and ground, go to next step.

12) Thermostatic Switch – Turn ignition off. Reconnect PCM connectors and A/C relay connector. Disconnect and remove thermostatic switch. Check resistance between Green wire terminal and Black/White wire terminal on thermostatic switch with thermostatic sensing bulb greater than 77°F (25°C). Cool thermostatic sensing bulb on thermostatic switch to bring temperature less than 32°F (0°C). Check resistance between Green wire terminal and Black/White wire terminal on thermostatic switch. If resistance is more than 5 ohms when temperature is greater than 77°F (25°C), and less than 10,000 ohms when temperature is less than 32°F (0°C), replace thermostatic switch. If resistance is less than 5 ohms when temperature is greater than 77°F (32°C) and more than 10,000 ohms when temperature is less than 32°F (0°C), go to next step.

13) If compressor clutch operates continuously, go to step **20)**. If compressor clutch does not engage, turn ignition off. Disconnect thermostatic switch and pressure switch connectors. Check resistance of Black/White wire between thermostatic switch and pressure switch connectors. Check resistance of Black/White wire between thermostatic switch connector and ground. If resistance is more than 5 ohms, between thermostatic switch and pressure switch connectors, and less than 10,000 ohms between thermostatic switch connector and ground, repair Black/White wire. If resistance is less than 5 ohms between thermostatic switch and pressure switch connectors, and more than 10,000 ohms between thermostatic switch connector and ground, go to next step.

14) Pressure Switch – Turn ignition off. Reconnect thermostatic switch connector. Disconnect pressure switch connector. With system at normal operating pressure, check resistance between Black/White wire terminal and Yellow/Green wire terminal on pressure switch. If resistance is more than 5 ohms, replace pressure switch. If resistance is less than 5 ohms, go to next step.

15) Pressure Switch & A/C Switch Wire – Turn ignition off. Disconnect pressure switch and A/C switch connectors. Check resistance of Yellow/Green wire between pressure switch and A/C switch connectors. Check resistance of Yellow/Green wire between pressure switch connector and ground. If resistance is more than 5 ohms, between pressure switch and A/C switch connectors, and less than 10,000 ohms between pressure switch connector and ground, repair Yellow/Green wire between pressure switch and A/C switch connectors. If resistance is less than 5 ohms, between pressure switch and A/C switch connectors, and more than 10,000 ohms between pressure switch connector and ground, go to next step.

16) A/C Switch – Turn ignition off. Reconnect pressure switch connector. Disconnect A/C switch connector and turn A/C off. Check resistance between Yellow/Green wire terminal and Blue/White terminal on A/C switch. Turn A/C on. Check resistance between Yellow/Green wire terminal and Blue/White wire terminal on A/C switch. If resistance is more than 5 ohms with A/C on and less than 10,000 ohms with A/C off, replace A/C switch. If resistance is less than 5 ohms with A/C on and more than 10,000 ohms with A/C off and A/C light does not come on, go to next step. If compressor clutch does not operate, go to step **19)**.

17) Power Supply To A/C Switch Bulb – Turn ignition off. Reconnect A/C switch connector and remove A/C switch bulb. Turn ignition on. Check voltage at A/C switch bulb connector. If voltage is less than 10 volts, replace A/C switch. If voltage is more than 10 volts, go to next step.

18) A/C Switch Bulb Control Circuit – Turn ignition off. Disconnect A/C switch connector and remove A/C switch bulb. Check resistance between Yellow/Green wire terminal on A/C switch and A/C switch bulb connectors. If resistance is less than 5 ohms, replace A/C switch bulb. If resistance is more than 5 ohms, replace A/C switch.

19) Blower Motor Switch & A/C Switch Wire – Turn ignition off. Disconnect blower motor switch and A/C switch connectors. Check resistance of Blue/White wire between blower motor switch and A/C switch connectors. If resistance is less than 5 ohms, check for malfunction of blower motor system. If resistance is more than 5 ohms, repair Blue/White wire.

20) Wide Open Throttle Cut-Off (WAC) Relay – Turn ignition off. Reconnect A/C relay, cooling fan motor and A/C switch connectors. Reconnect Power Control Module (PCM) and blower motor connectors. Install 15-amp heater fuse. Disconnect WAC relay. Apply 12 volts to Blue/Red wire terminal and Yellow wire terminal on WAC relay. Check resistance of Black/White wire terminal on WAC relay. Apply ground to Green/Yellow wire terminal on WAC relay. Check voltage of Black/Wire wire terminal on WAC relay. If voltage is more than one volt with ground not applied, and less than 10 volts with ground applied, replace WAC relay. If voltage is less than one volt with ground not applied and more than 10 volts with ground applied, go to next step.

21) Wide Open Throttle Cut-Off (WAC) Relay & Compressor Clutch Wire – Turn ignition off. Disconnect WAC relay, compressor clutch and pressure switch (A/T) connectors. Check resistance of Black wire (A/T) or Black/White wire (M/T) between WAC relay and compressor clutch connectors. Check resistance of Black wire (A/T) or Black/White wire (M/T) between WAC relay connector and ground. If resistance is less than 5 ohms between WAC relay and compressor clutch connectors, and more than 10,000 ohms between WAC relay connector and ground, replace compressor clutch. If resistance is more than 5 ohms, between WAC relay and compressor clutch connectors, and less than 10,000 ohms between WAC relay connector and ground, repair Black wire (A/T) or Black/White wire (M/T) between WAC relay and compressor clutch connectors.

22) Power Supply To Condenser Fan Motor – Turn ignition off. Disconnect condenser fan motor connector. Check voltage of Yellow wire at condenser fan motor connector. If voltage is more than 10 volts, go to step **28)**. If voltage is less than 10 volts, go to next step.

23) Fuse Check – Turn ignition off. Check 25-amp main fuse link. If fuse link is okay, go to step **26)**. If fuse link is not okay, go to next step.

24) System Check – Turn ignition off. Replace 25-amp main fuse link. If fuse link is okay, go to step **26)**. If fuse link fails again, go to next step.

25) Short To Ground – Turn ignition off. Remove 25-amp main fuse link. Remove 15-amp in-line fuse connector. Check resistance of White wire between rear terminal of 25-amp main fuse link holder and ground. If resistance is less than 5 ohms, repair White wire. If resistance is more than 5 ohms, replace 25-amp main fuse link and go to next step.

26) Power Supply To 15-Amp In-Line Fuse – Turn ignition off. Remove 15-amp in-line fuse. Check voltage of White wire at 15-amp in-line fuse connector. If voltage is less than 10 volts, repair White wire. If voltage is more than 10 volts, go to next step.

27) 15-Amp In-Line Fuse – Turn ignition off. Remove and inspect 15-amp in-line fuse. If fuse is okay, repair open in Yellow wire between 15-amp in-line fuse and cooling fan motor. If fuse is not okay, repair short to ground in Yellow wire and replace 15-amp in-line fuse.

28) Condenser Fan Motor – Turn ignition off. Disconnect condenser fan motor connector. Apply 12 volts to Yellow wire terminal of condenser fan motor. Apply ground to Green/Red wire terminal of condenser fan motor. If condenser fan motor does not operate, replace condenser fan motor. If condenser fan motor operates, go to next step.

29) Condenser Fan Motor & Condenser Fan Relay Wire – Turn ignition off. Disconnect condenser fan motor and condenser fan relay connectors. Check resistance of Green/Red wire between connectors. Check resistance of Green/Red wire between condenser fan motor connector and ground. If resistance is more than 5 ohms between connectors and less than 10,000 ohms between condenser fan motor connector and ground, repair Green/Red wire between condenser fan motor and condenser fan relay connectors. If resistance is less than 5 ohms between connectors and more than 10,000 ohms between condenser fan motor connector and ground, go to next step.

30) Condenser Fan Relay – Turn ignition off. Disconnect condenser fan relay connector. Apply ground to Black wire terminals on relay. Check resistance between Green/Red wire terminal on relay and ground. Apply 12 volts to White wire terminal on relay. Check resistance between Green/Red wire terminal on relay and ground. If resistance is more than 5 ohms with 12 volts applied and less than 10,000 ohms with no voltage applied, replace condenser fan relay. If resistance is less than 5 ohms with 12 volts applied, and more than 10,000 ohms with no voltage applied, go to next step.

31) Condenser Fan Relay Ground – Turn ignition off. Disconnect condenser fan relay connector. Check resistance of Black wires between relay connector and ground. If resistance is more than 5 ohms, repair Black wire(s). If resistance is less than 5 ohms, go to next step.

32) Condenser Fan Relay & Pressure Switch Wire – Turn ignition off. Disconnect condenser fan relay and pressure switch connectors. Check resistance of White wire between connectors. Check resistance of White wire between pressure switch connector and ground. If resistance is more than 5 ohms between connectors and less than 10,000 ohms between pressure switch connector and ground, repair White wire between pressure switch and condenser fan relay connectors. If resistance is less than 5 ohms between connectors and more than 10,000 ohms between pressure switch connector and ground, go to next step.

33) Pressure Switch & Compressor Clutch Wire – Turn ignition off. Reconnect condenser fan relay connector. Disconnect pressure switch and compressor clutch connectors. Check resistance of Black wire between connectors. If resistance is less than 5 ohms, replace pressure switch. If resistance is more than 5 ohms, repair Black wire between pressure switch and compressor clutch connectors.

34) A/C Relay & Thermostatic Switch Wire – Turn ignition off. Disconnect A/C relay and thermostatic switch connectors. Check resistance of Green wire between connectors. If resistance is more than 5 ohms, repair Green wire. If resistance is less than 5 ohms, go to next step.

35) Cooling Fan Motor & A/C Relay Wire – Turn ignition off. Disconnect cooling fan motor and A/C relay connectors. Check resistance of Yellow/Red wire between connectors. If resistance is more than 5 ohms, repair Yellow/Red wire. If resistance is less than 5 ohms, go to next step.

36) A/C Relay – Turn ignition off. Disconnect A/C relay connector. Apply 12 volts to Yellow/Red wire terminal and Blue wire terminal on relay. Check voltage of Black wire terminal on relay. Apply ground to Green wire terminal on A/C relay. Check voltage of Black wire terminal on A/C relay. If voltage is less then one volt with ground not applied and more than 10 volts with ground applied, repair open on Black wire between A/C relay and ground. If voltage is more than one volt with ground not applied and less 10 volts with ground applied, replace A/C relay.

REMOVAL & INSTALLATION

CAUTION: When battery is disconnected, vehicle computer and memory systems may lose memory data. Driveability problems may exist until computer systems have completed a relearn cycle.

NOTE: After disconnecting refrigerant lines, plug opening at end of line. Install NEW "O" rings on refrigerant line fittings before reconnecting lines.

COMPRESSOR

Removal – Discharge A/C system using approved refrigerant recovery/recycling equipment. Disconnect negative battery cable. Remove compressor drive belt. Disconnect compressor clutch connector. Disconnect refrigerant lines from compressor. Remove compressor bolts and compressor.

Installation - If installing a new compressor, drain 1.2 ounces of refrigerant oil from compressor before installation. To install, reverse removal procedure. Tighten nuts and bolts to specification. See TORQUE SPECIFICATIONS. Evacuate and charge A/C system.

CONDENSER

Removal - **1)** Discharge A/C system using approved refrigerant recovery/recycling equipment. Remove radiator grille. Remove sight glass cover from receiver-drier. Disconnect refrigerant line from receiver-drier.

2) Remove refrigerant line clamp from condenser bracket. Remove hood latch and center brace. Remove condenser fan (A/T). Remove condenser bolts. Lift out condenser and grommets.

Installation - To install, reverse removal procedure. Ensure grommets are properly positioned. Evacuate and charge A/C system.

RECEIVER-DRIER

Removal & Installation - Discharge A/C system using approved refrigerant recovery/recycling equipment. Remove condenser. See CONDENSER. Disconnect refrigerant lines from receiver-drier. Remove receiver-drier bolts and receiver-drier. To install, reverse removal procedure. Evacuate and charge A/C system.

EVAPORATOR CASE

Removal & Installation - **1)** Disconnect negative battery cable. Discharge A/C system using approved refrigerant recovery/recycling equipment. Disconnect evaporator inlet and outlet tubes at firewall in engine compartment. Remove glove box. Disconnect thermostatic switch electrical connector.

2) Disconnect control cable from thermostatic switch. Disengage wiring harness from clamps on evaporator housing. Loosen band clamp screw. Band clamp secures evaporator housing to heater case. Disconnect drain hose from evaporator case. Remove bolt from right end of air inlet.

3) Remove bolt and 2 nuts securing evaporator case to firewall. Remove evaporator case. To install, reverse removal procedure. Evacuate and charge A/C system.

EVAPORATOR & TXV

Removal & Installation - **1)** Remove evaporator case. See EVAPORATOR CASE. Remove clips securing upper and lower case halves. Remove upper case. Remove thermostatic switch screws. Carefully pull sensing tube from evaporator core fins while removing thermostatic switch. Remove evaporator from lower housing.

2) Remove brace positioned between inlet and outlet tubes. Remove insulator from capillary tube and TXV. Remove clamp securing capillary tube to suction tube. Disconnect evaporator tube fitting and TXV. To install, reverse removal procedure. Evacuate and charge A/C system.

THERMOSTATIC SWITCH

Removal & Installation - Remove evaporator case. See EVAPORATOR CASE. Remove clips securing upper and lower evaporator case halves. Remove upper case. Remove thermostatic switch screws. Carefully pull sensing tube from evaporator core fins while removing thermostatic switch. To install, reverse removal procedure. Evacuate and charge A/C system.

CONTROL PANEL

Removal & Installation - **1)** Remove accessory bezel. Remove radio (if necessary). Remove glove box. Disconnect recirculated/fresh air cable from door lever. *See Fig. 5.* Disconnect mode control cable from door lever. *See Fig. 6.*

2) Disconnect temperature control cable from door lever. *See Fig. 4.* Pull control panel away from instrument panel. Disconnect control panel connectors. Remove control panel.

3) To install, reverse removal procedure. Check and adjust control cables. See ADJUSTMENTS. Check control panel operation.

TORQUE SPECIFICATIONS

TORQUE SPECIFICATIONS

Application	Ft. Lbs. (N.m)
A/C Idler Pulley Nut	23-34 (31-46)
Compressor Bracket-To-Engine Bolt	30-40 (41-54)
Compressor-To-Compressor Bracket Bolt	30-40 (41-54)
Hose Manifold-To-Compressor Bolt	13-17 (18-23)

1993 MANUAL A/C-HEATER SYSTEMS
Festiva (Cont.)

WIRING DIAGRAM

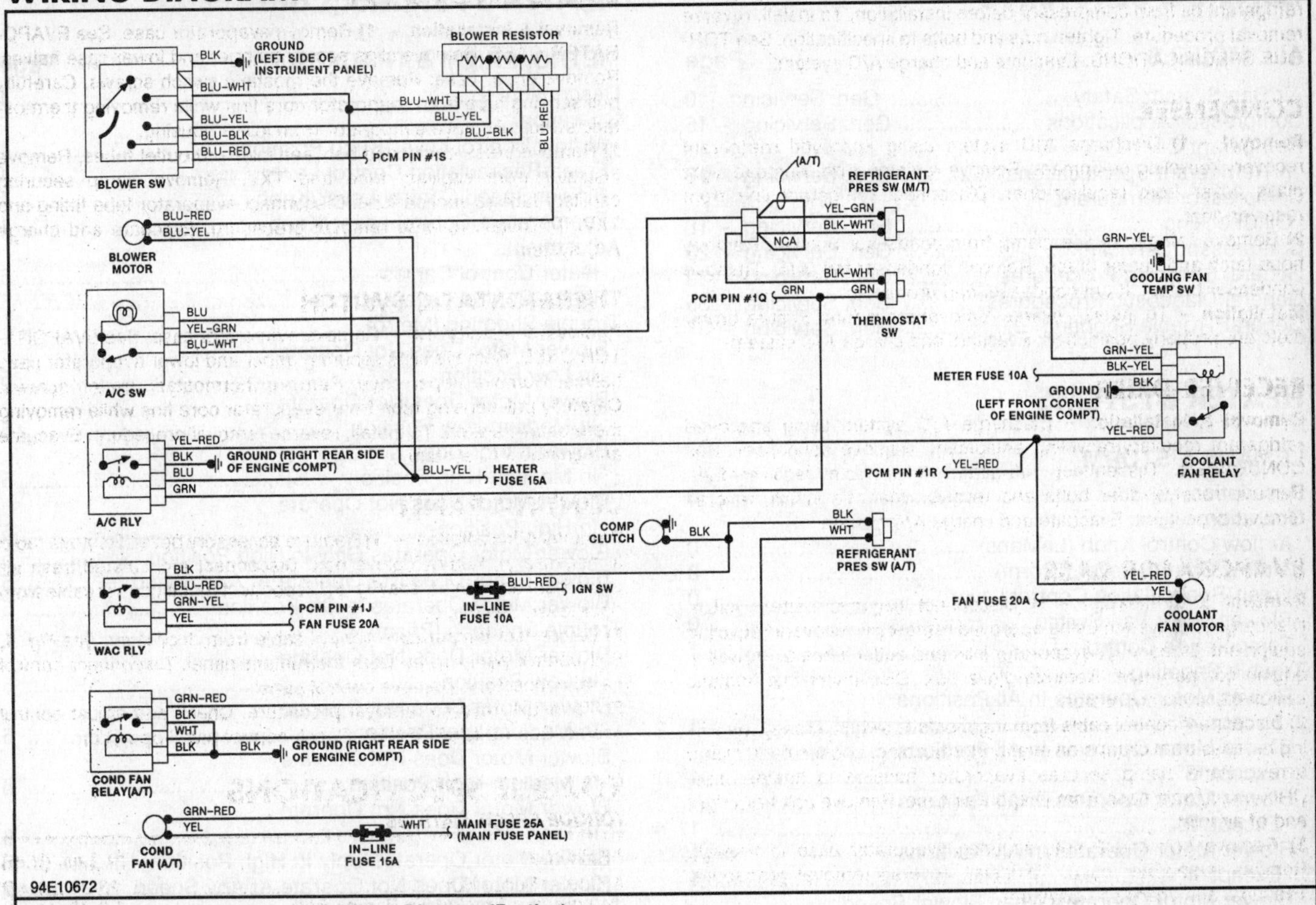

BLOWER SW
BLK
GROUND (LEFT SIDE OF INSTRUMENT PANEL)
BLU-WHT
BLU-YEL
BLU-BLK
BLU-RED
PCM PIN #1S
BLOWER RESISTOR
BLOWER MOTOR
A/C SW
BLU
YEL-GRN
A/C RLY
YEL-RED
GROUND (RIGHT REAR SIDE OF ENGINE COMPT)
GRN
HEATER FUSE 15A
WAC RLY
GRN-YEL
YEL
PCM PIN #1J
FAN FUSE 20A
IN-LINE FUSE 10A
IGN SW
COND FAN RELAY(A/T)
GRN-RED
WHT
COND FAN (A/T)
IN-LINE FUSE 15A
MAIN FUSE 25A (MAIN FUSE PANEL)
(A/T)
REFRIGERANT PRES SW (M/T)
YEL-GRN
BLK-WHT
NCA
PCM PIN #1Q
THERMOSTAT SW
COOLING FAN TEMP SW
METER FUSE 10A
GROUND (LEFT FRONT CORNER OF ENGINE COMPT)
BLK-YEL
COOLANT FAN RELAY
PCM PIN #1R
COMP CLUTCH
REFRIGERANT PRES SW (A/T)
COOLANT FAN MOTOR
94E10672

Fig. 7: Manual A/C-Heater System Wiring Diagram (Festiva)

1993 GENERAL MOTORS/GEO CONTENTS

GENERAL SERVICING

ALL MODELS — Page

HEATER SYSTEMS

LEMANS & STORM

HEATER SYSTEMS (Cont.)

METRO, PRIZM & TRACKER — Page

1993 GENERAL MOTORS/GEO CONTENTS (Cont.)

MANUAL A/C-HEATER SYSTEMS

MANUAL A/C-HEATER SYSTEMS (Cont.)

1993 HEATER SYSTEMS LeMans & Storm

DESCRIPTION

Heater system delivers fresh (outside) air or recirculated (compartment) air to passenger compartment. *See Figs. 1 and 2.* Air passes through heater unit, where it is warmed before distribution to selected passenger compartment outlets. Outlets are chosen with airflow control knob (LeMans) or lever (Storm). Temperature of delivered air is regulated by temperature control knob (LeMans) or lever (Storm). Blower motor is controlled by a 4-speed rotary knob (LeMans) or 4-speed sliding fan lever (Storm). *See Fig. 3 or 5.*

WARNING: To avoid injury from accidental air bag deployment, read and carefully follow all SERVICE PRECAUTIONS and DISABLING & ACTIVATING AIR BAG SYSTEM procedures in AIR BAG SYSTEM SAFETY article in GENERAL SERVICING.

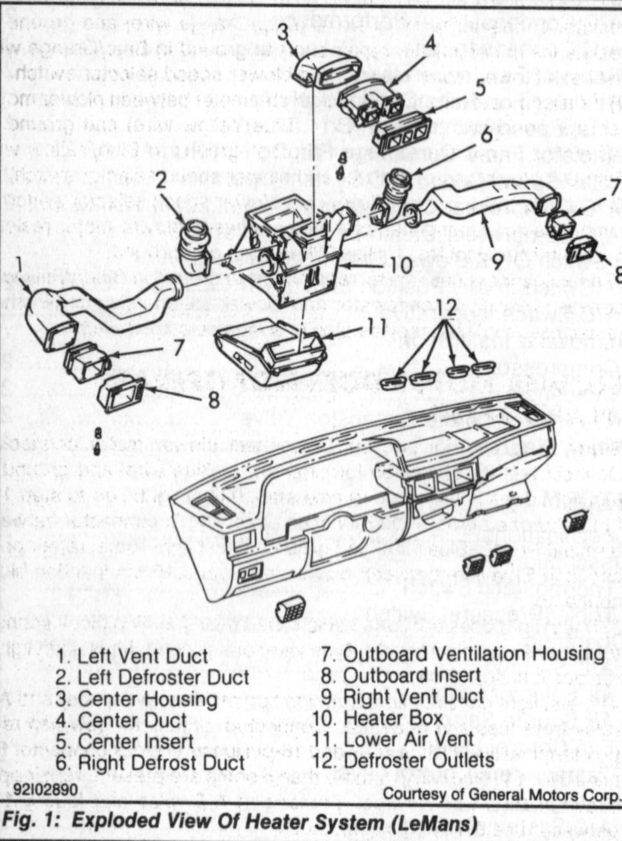
1. Left Vent Duct
2. Left Defroster Duct
3. Center Housing
4. Center Duct
5. Center Insert
6. Right Defrost Duct
7. Outboard Ventilation Housing
8. Outboard Insert
9. Right Vent Duct
10. Heater Box
11. Lower Air Vent
12. Defroster Outlets
92I02890
Courtesy of General Motors Corp.

Fig. 1: Exploded View Of Heater System (LeMans)

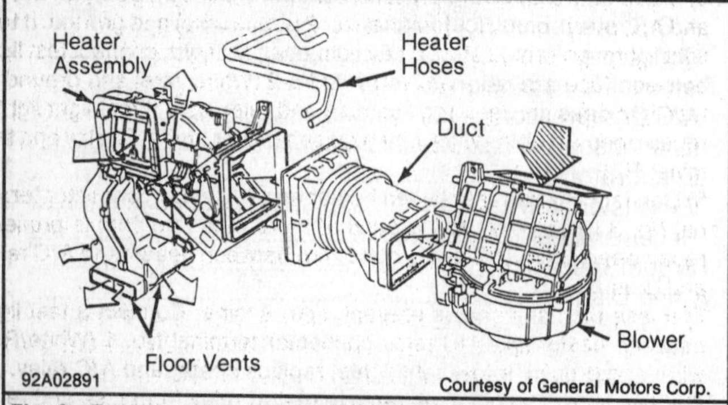
Heater Assembly
Heater Hoses
Duct
Blower
Floor Vents
92A02891
Courtesy of General Motors Corp.

Fig. 2: Exploded View Of Heater System (Storm)

OPERATION

AIRFLOW CONTROL KNOB (LEMANS)

The airflow control knob regulates airflow from heater, defroster and center instrument panel outlets. *See Fig. 3.* Outside air flows continually into passenger compartment. Turning knob to first position (max/recirculate) provides recirculated air. Turning knob to next position (bi-level) directs air flow from panel and floor vents.

Turning knob to third position (vent) directs airflow from panel vents. Fourth position (heater) provides airflow from floor vents with a small amount of air directed to defroster vents. Fifth position (defrost) directs airflow to defroster outlets.

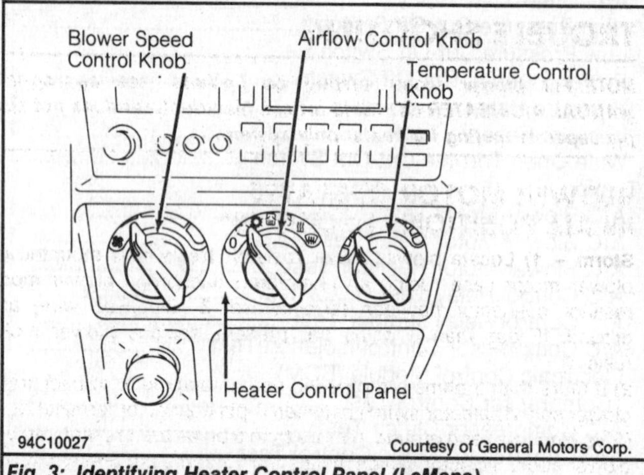
Blower Speed Control Knob
Airflow Control Knob
Temperature Control Knob
Heater Control Panel
94C10027
Courtesy of General Motors Corp.

Fig. 3: Identifying Heater Control Panel (LeMans)

AIRFLOW CONTROL LEVER (STORM)

NOTE: Refer to heater control panel illustration to identify airflow control lever positions. See Fig. 4.

Face - Air is discharged to upper instrument panel outlets.
Bi-Level - Air flows between upper instrument panel outlets and floor outlets. Air from floor outlets is warmer than air from the upper instrument panel outlets.
Defrost - Most air is discharged to defroster outlets; a small amount of air is delivered to side windows.
Floor - Air is discharged to floor outlets.
Floor/Defrost - Air is discharged to both floor and defrost outlets.

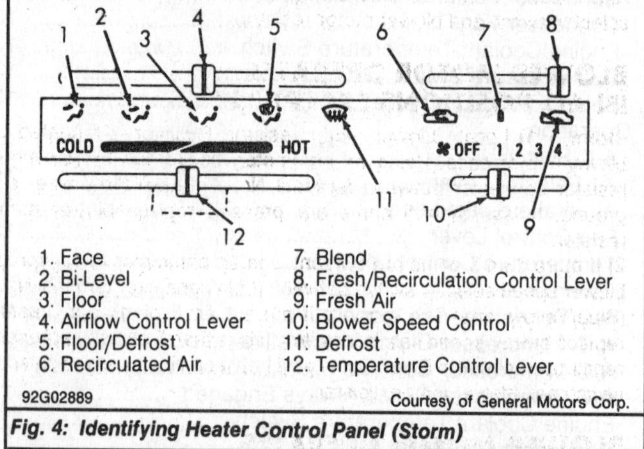
COLD
HOT
OFF 1 2 3 4
1. Face
2. Bi-Level
3. Floor
4. Airflow Control Lever
5. Floor/Defrost
6. Recirculated Air
7. Blend
8. Fresh/Recirculation Control Lever
9. Fresh Air
10. Blower Speed Control
11. Defrost
12. Temperature Control Lever
92G02889
Courtesy of General Motors Corp.

Fig. 4: Identifying Heater Control Panel (Storm)

FRESH/RECIRCULATION CONTROL LEVER

Storm - The fresh/recirculation lever mechanically operates a cable that opens or closes the fresh/recirculation mode door to fresh (outside) air. When in recirculation position, outside air is shut off and air from inside passenger compartment is recirculated through the blower motor to selected air outlets. *See Fig. 4.*

BLOWER MOTOR FAN SWITCH

The blower motor fan switch lever operates the blower motor through a 4-speed rotary knob (LeMans) or a 4-speed lever (Storm).

1993 HEATER SYSTEMS
LeMans & Storm (Cont.)

TEMPERATURE CONTROL

When the temperature control knob (LeMans) or lever (Storm) is moved to full HOT position, the air mix door is fully opened. Fresh/recirculated air is mixed with air flowing through the heater core and distributed to selected outlets. In the full COLD position, the air mix door closes, by-passing the heater core. Adjusting the air temperature control allows more or less unheated air to mix with heated air.

TROUBLE SHOOTING

NOTE: For blower motor testing on LeMans, see appropriate MANUAL A/C-HEATER SYSTEMS article. Manufacturer does not supply separate testing for heater-only system.

BLOWER MOTOR OPERATES IN ALL POSITIONS EXCEPT "4"

Storm - 1) Locate blower motor resistor. Resistor is mounted on blower motor case. Using an ohmmeter, backprobe blower motor resistor connector between terminal No. 3 (Blue/Red wire) and ground. If less than 5 ohms are present, replace blower motor resistor.

2) If more than 5 ohms are present, use an ohmmeter to backprobe blower speed selector switch between 6-pin connector terminal No. 1 (Blue/Red wire) and ground. If more than 5 ohms are present, replace blower speed selector switch. If less than 5 ohms are present, repair open circuit in Blue/Red wire between blower speed selector switch and blower motor resistor.

BLOWER MOTOR OPERATES IN ALL POSITIONS EXCEPT "3"

Storm - 1) Locate blower motor resistor. Resistor is mounted on blower motor case. Using an ohmmeter, backprobe blower motor resistor connector between terminal No. 6 (Blue/Orange wire) and ground. If less than 5 ohms are present, replace blower motor resistor.

2) If more than 5 ohms are present, use an ohmmeter to backprobe blower speed selector switch between 6-pin connector terminal No. 2 (Blue/Orange wire) and ground. If more than 5 ohms are present, replace blower speed selector switch. If less than 5 ohms are present, repair open circuit in Blue/Orange wire between blower speed selector switch and blower motor resistor.

BLOWER MOTOR OPERATES IN ALL POSITIONS EXCEPT "2"

Storm - 1) Locate blower motor resistor. Resistor is mounted on blower motor case. Using an ohmmeter, backprobe blower motor resistor connector between terminal No. 4 (Blue/Yellow wire) and ground. If less than 5 ohms are present, replace blower motor resistor.

2) If more than 5 ohms are present, use an ohmmeter to backprobe blower speed selector switch between 6-pin connector terminal No. 3 (Blue/Yellow wire) and ground. If more than 5 ohms are present, replace blower speed selector switch. If less than 5 ohms are present, repair open circuit in Blue/Yellow wire between blower speed selector switch and blower motor resistor.

BLOWER MOTOR OPERATES IN ALL POSITIONS EXCEPT "1"

Storm - 1) Locate blower motor resistor. Resistor is mounted on blower motor case. Using an ohmmeter, backprobe blower motor resistor connector between terminal No. 1 (Blue/White wire) and ground. If less than 5 ohms are present, replace blower motor resistor.

2) If more than 5 ohms are present, use an ohmmeter to backprobe blower speed selector switch between 2-pin connector terminal No. 1 (Blue/White wire) and ground. If more than 5 ohms are present, replace blower speed selector switch. If less than 5 ohms are present, repair open circuit in Blue/White wire between blower speed selector switch and blower motor resistor.

BLOWER MOTOR OPERATES WHEN BLOWER SPEED SELECTOR SWITCH IS IN OFF POSITION

Storm - 1) Locate blower motor resistor. Resistor is mounted on blower motor case. Disconnect blower motor resistor connector. If blower motor continues to operate, repair short to ground in Blue/Black wire between blower motor and blower motor resistor.

2) If blower motor stops, disconnect blower speed selector switch 6-pin and 2-pin connectors. Connect an ohmmeter between blower motor resistor connector terminal No. 3 (Blue/Red wire) and ground. If resistance is not infinite, repair short to ground in Blue/Red wire between blower motor resistor and blower speed selector switch.

3) If resistance is infinite, connect an ohmmeter between blower motor resistor connector terminal No. 6 (Blue/Orange wire) and ground. If resistance is not infinite, repair short to ground in Blue/Orange wire between blower motor resistor and blower speed selector switch.

4) If resistance is infinite, connect an ohmmeter between blower motor resistor connector terminal No. 4 (Blue/Yellow wire) and ground. If resistance is not infinite, repair short to ground in Blue/Yellow wire between blower motor resistor and blower speed selector switch.

5) If resistance is infinite, disconnect blower speed selector switch 2-pin connector. Connect an ohmmeter between blower motor resistor connector terminal No. 1 (Blue/White wire) and ground.

6) If resistance is not infinite, repair short to ground in Blue/White wire between blower motor resistor and blower speed selector switch. If resistance is infinite, replace blower speed selector switch.

BLOWER MOTOR DOES NOT OPERATE IN ANY SPEED

Storm - 1) Turn ignition on. Disconnect blower motor connector. Connect test light between terminal No. 1 (Blue wire) and ground. If test light does not light, go to next step. If light lights, go to step **11)**.

2) Backprobe blower motor junction block 16-pin connector between terminal No. 11 (Blue wire) and ground. If test light lights, repair open circuit in Blue wire between blower motor and 16-pin junction block connector.

3) If test light does not light, backprobe 16-pin junction block connector between terminal No. 14 (Blue wire) and ground. If test light lights, replace junction block.

4) If test light does not light, turn ignition off. Remove heater and A/C relay from fuse and relay box. Connect an ohmmeter between relay box terminal No. 4 (Blue wire) and 16-pin junction block connector terminal No. 14 (Blue wire). If more than 5 ohms are present, repair open circuit in Blue wire between heater and A/C relay and fuse E-1 or between fuse E-1 and junction block.

5) If less than 5 ohms are present, connect a test light between heater and A/C relay connector terminal No. 2 (White wire) and ground. If test light lights, go to next step. If test light does not light, connect test light between fuse and relay box terminal FL-2 (White wire) and ground. If test light does not light, replace fuse and relay box. If test light lights, repair open circuit in White wire between heater and A/C relay and terminal FL-2.

6) Connect ohmmeter between heater and A/C relay connector terminal No. 3 (Black wire) and ground. If more than one ohm is present, repair open circuit in Black ground wire between heater and A/C relay and ground.

7) If less than one ohm is present, start engine. Connect a test light between heater and A/C relay connector terminal No. 1 (White/Red wire) and ground. If test light lights, replace heater and A/C relay.

8) If test light does not light, remove restart relay from fuse and relay box. Connect an ohmmeter between connector terminal No. 5 (White/Red wire) and A/C relay connector terminal No. 1 (White/Red wire). If more than one ohm is present, repair open circuit in White/Red wire between heater and A/C relay and restart relay.

9) If less than one ohm is present, connect a test light between restart relay connector terminal No. 4 (White/Blue wire) and ground. Start engine. If test light lights, replace restart relay. If test light does not

1993 HEATER SYSTEMS
LeMans & Storm (Cont.)

light, use a test light to backprobe alternator connector between terminal No. 1 (White/Blue wire) and ground.

10) If test light lights, repair open circuit in White/Blue wire between restart relay and alternator. If test light does not light, alternator or related components are defective.

11) Move blower speed selector switch to position "4". Connect an ohmmeter between blower motor connector terminal No. 2 (Blue/Black wire) and ground. If less than 5 ohms are present, replace blower motor.

12) If more than 5 ohms are present, use an ohmmeter to backprobe blower motor resistor connector between terminal No. 2 (Blue/Black wire) and ground. Blower motor resistor is mounted on blower motor case. If less than 5 ohms are present, repair open circuit in Blue/Black wire between blower motor resistor and blower motor.

13) If more than 5 ohms are present, use an ohmmeter to backprobe blower motor resistor connector between terminal No. 3 (Blue/Red wire) and ground. If less than 5 ohms are present, replace blower motor resistor.

14) If more than 5 ohms are present, use an ohmmeter to backprobe blower speed selector switch 2-pin connector between terminal No. 2 (Black wire) and ground. If less than 5 ohms are present, replace blower speed selector switch. If more than 5 ohms are present, repair Black ground wire between blower speed selector switch and ground.

TESTING

WARNING: To avoid injury from accidental air bag deployment, read and carefully follow all SERVICE PRECAUTIONS and DISABLING & ACTIVATING AIR BAG SYSTEM procedures in AIR BAG SYSTEM SAFETY article in GENERAL SERVICING.

BLOWER MOTOR RESISTOR

Locate blower motor resistor. Resistor is mounted on blower motor case. Disconnect blower motor resistor connector. Using an ohmmeter, check resistance across all resistor terminals. If continuity exists between all terminals, heater blower motor resistor is okay. If continuity does not exist between all terminals, replace blower motor resistor.

REMOVAL & INSTALLATION

WARNING: To avoid injury from accidental air bag deployment, read and carefully follow all SERVICE PRECAUTIONS and DISABLING & ACTIVATING AIR BAG SYSTEM procedures in AIR BAG SYSTEM SAFETY article in GENERAL SERVICING.

BLOWER MOTOR

Removal & Installation (LeMans) – Disconnect negative battery cable. Disconnect blower motor connector. Remove air hose from blower housing. Remove blower motor-to-case screws. Remove blower motor and fan assembly. To install, reverse removal procedure.

Removal & Installation (Storm) – Disconnect negative battery cable. Disconnect blower motor connector. Remove 4 screws and blower motor from blower motor case. To install, reverse removal procedure.

BLOWER RESISTOR

Removal & Installation – Disconnect negative battery cable. Disconnect blower resistor connector. Resistor is mounted on blower motor case. Remove 2 blower resistor screws and resistor assembly. To install, reverse removal procedure.

HEATER CONTROL PANEL

Removal & Installation (LeMans) – 1) Disconnect negative battery cable. Remove shift lever boot (M/T models). Remove package tray. Remove front console shift plate and front center console.

2) Remove right and left lower knee panels. Disconnect temperature control cable from control panel. Remove screw from under heater control panel. Remove blower fan switch electrical connector. Remove heater control panel. To install, reverse removal procedure.

Removal & Installation (Storm) – 1) Disconnect negative battery cable. Remove lever knobs from heater control panel. Remove ashtray from console. Remove 4 screws in ashtray cavity and one screw on each side of console trim bezel, and remove bezel.

2) Remove 4 heater control panel screws, and remove control panel. Remove control cables from heater control panel. Disconnect heater control panel connector. Remove control panel. To install, reverse removal procedure.

HEATER CORE

Removal & Installation (LeMans) – 1) Disconnect negative battery cable. Drain cooling system. Disconnect heater hoses at heater connections. Disconnect temperature control cable. Remove package panel tray.

2) Remove temperature control linkage from heater assembly. Pull back carpet and remove screw on lower right of heater box. Remove 4 heater outlet case screws, and remove outlet case.

3) Position temperature mode door to access 2 upper heater core screws, and remove screws. Remove 3 remaining heater core retaining screws. Remove heater core bracket and heater core.

4) To install, reverse removal procedure. Fill cooling system, and check for leaks. Check heater operation.

Removal (Storm) – 1) Disable air bag system. Remove air bag module. Drain radiator, and remove heater hoses at heater connections. Remove steering wheel nut and washer. Mark position of steering wheel on shaft, and remove steering wheel using puller. Remove instrument panel and center console. See INSTRUMENT PANEL.

2) Remove 3 duct mounting screws and pull out duct between blower assembly and heater unit. Remove 5 screws retaining mode control case to heater case. Move mode case away from heater case, leaving control cables attached. Remove 5 screws attaching heater case halves, and separate cases. Remove heater core assembly.

Installation – To install, reverse removal procedure. Activate air bag system and ensure air bag system is functioning properly. See SYSTEM OPERATION CHECK in AIR BAG SYSTEM SAFETY article in GENERAL SERVICING.

INSTRUMENT PANEL

Removal & Installation (Storm) – 1) Disconnect negative battery cable. Pull out all instrument panel switch bezels. Disconnect electrical connectors from all switches. Remove cigarette lighter and trim. Remove 2 screws retaining engine hood release cable handle. Remove shift trim bezel and center console retaining screws. Remove center console.

2) Remove 2 upper hole covers and meter hood retaining screws. Remove 4 lower instrument cluster hood retaining screws. Pull out and up on instrument cluster hood. Disconnect front wiper switch and lighting switch electrical connectors on instrument cluster hood. Remove instrument cluster hood with wiper and lighting switches attached.

3) Remove speedometer cable from instrument cluster. Remove 4 screws retaining instrument cluster. Disconnect electrical connectors, and remove instrument cluster. Remove 5 screws attaching knee pad assembly. Remove knee pad assembly. Remove glove box. Remove front console bracket.

4) Remove front instrument panel trim retaining screw covers and screws. Remove front instrument panel trim cover. Remove 4 bolts and 2 screws retaining instrument panel. Remove wiring harness clips on instrument panel. Remove instrument panel assembly. To install, reverse removal procedure.

TORQUE SPECIFICATIONS

TORQUE SPECIFICATIONS

Application	Ft. Lbs. (N.m)
Steering Wheel Hub Nut	25 (34)
	INCH Lbs. (N.m)
Blower Motor Fan Nut	89 (10)
Blower Motor Case Bolts	89 (10)

1993 HEATER SYSTEMS
LeMans & Storm (Cont.)

WIRING DIAGRAMS

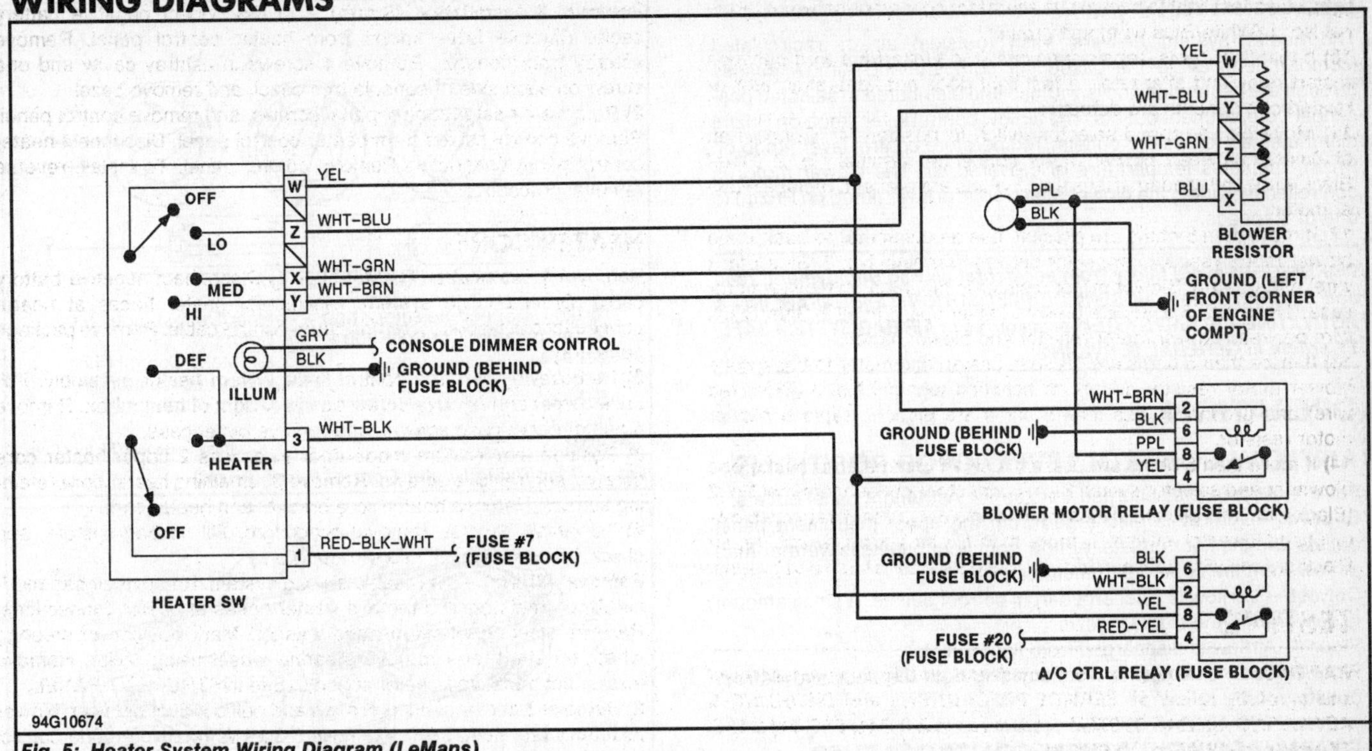
YEL
W
WHT-BLU
Y
WHT-GRN
Z
BLU
X
PPL
BLK
BLOWER
RESISTOR
GROUND (LEFT
FRONT CORNER
OF ENGINE
COMPT)
OFF
LO
MED
HI
YEL
WHT-BLU
WHT-GRN
WHT-BRN
GRY
BLK
CONSOLE DIMMER CONTROL
GROUND (BEHIND
FUSE BLOCK)
DEF
ILLUM
WHT-BLK
HEATER
OFF
RED-BLK-WHT
FUSE #7
(FUSE BLOCK)
HEATER SW
WHT-BRN
BLK
PPL
YEL
GROUND (BEHIND
FUSE BLOCK)
BLOWER MOTOR RELAY (FUSE BLOCK)
GROUND (BEHIND
FUSE BLOCK)
BLK
WHT-BLK
YEL
RED-YEL
FUSE #20
(FUSE BLOCK)
A/C CTRL RELAY (FUSE BLOCK)
94G10674

Fig. 5: Heater System Wiring Diagram (LeMans)

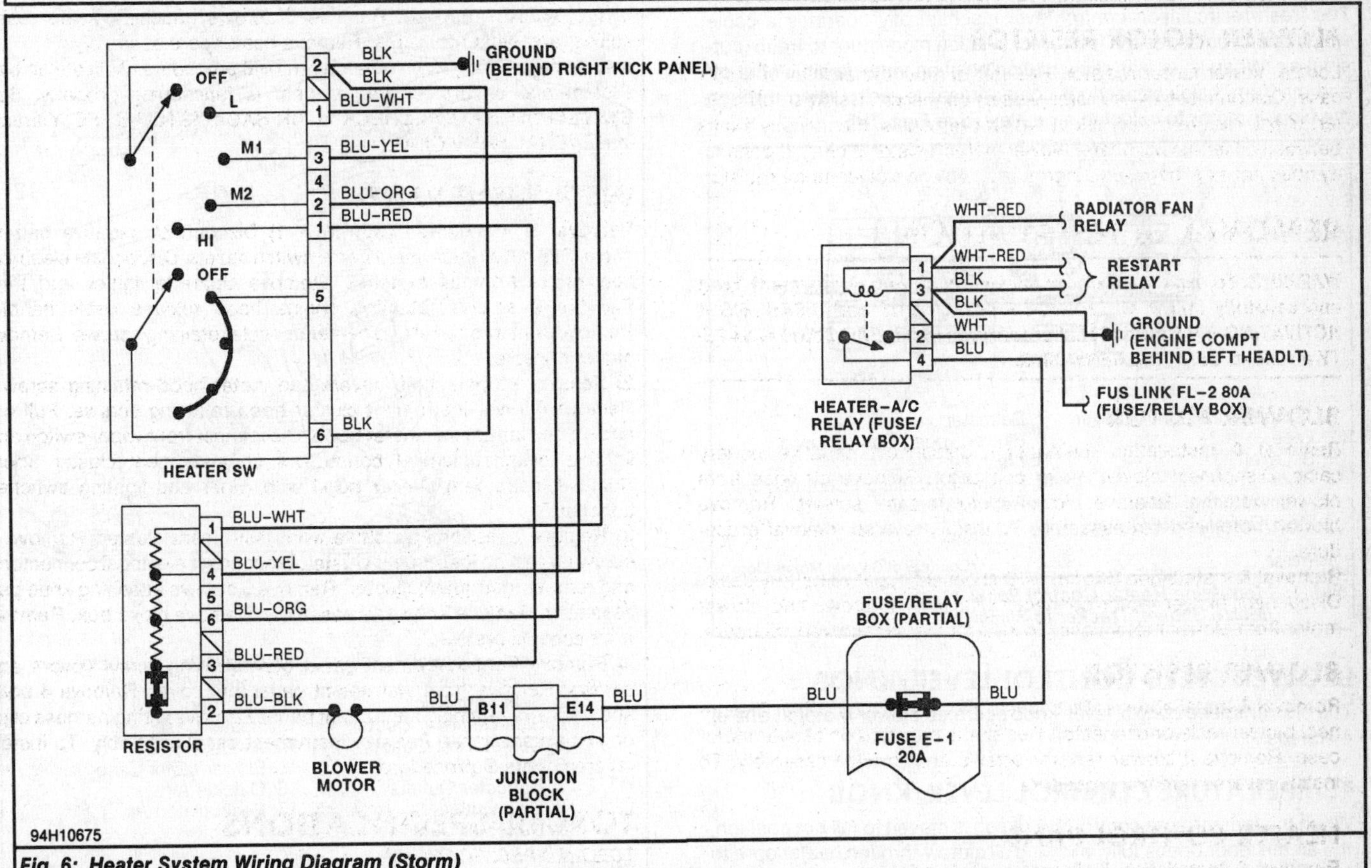

BLK
BLK
GROUND
(BEHIND RIGHT KICK PANEL)
OFF
L
BLU-WHT
M1
BLU-YEL
M2
BLU-ORG
BLU-RED
HI
OFF
BLK
HEATER SW
WHT-RED
RADIATOR FAN
RELAY
WHT-RED
RESTART
RELAY
BLK
BLK
WHT
GROUND
(ENGINE COMPT
BEHIND LEFT HEADLT)
BLU
FUS LINK FL-2 80A
(FUSE/RELAY BOX)
HEATER-A/C
RELAY (FUSE/
RELAY BOX)
BLU-WHT
BLU-YEL
BLU-ORG
BLU-RED
BLU-BLK
RESISTOR
BLU
B11
E14
BLU
BLOWER
MOTOR
JUNCTION
BLOCK
(PARTIAL)
FUSE/RELAY
BOX (PARTIAL)
BLU
BLU
FUSE E-1
20A
94H10675

Fig. 6: Heater System Wiring Diagram (Storm)

1993 HEATER SYSTEMS
Metro, Prizm & Tracker

DESCRIPTION

The heater system delivers fresh (outside) air or recirculated (compartment) air to the passenger compartment. Airflow passes through the heater unit and is warmed and distributed to selected passenger compartment outlets. The airflow control lever (knob on Prizm) distributes air to desired outlets. Temperature control lever (knob on Prizm) regulates temperature of delivered air. The blower motor is controlled by sliding the blower speed control lever (knob on Prizm) to one of 4 speeds.

WARNING: To avoid injury from accidental air bag deployment, read and carefully follow all SERVICE PRECAUTIONS and DISABLING & ACTIVATING AIR BAG SYSTEM procedures in AIR BAG SYSTEM SAFETY article in GENERAL SERVICING.

OPERATION

AIRFLOW CONTROL LEVER/KNOB POSITIONS

Face - Airflow is discharged from upper instrument panel outlets.
Bi-Level - Airflow is discharged from the upper instrument panel outlets and the floor outlets. Airflow from floor outlets is warmer than airflow from the upper instrument panel outlets.
Defrost - Airflow is discharged from defrost outlets. A small amount is delivered to the side windows.
Floor - Airflow is discharged from floor outlets.
Floor/Defrost - Airflow is discharged to both the floor and defrost outlets.

FRESH/RECIRCULATION CONTROL LEVER

The fresh/recirculation control lever mechanically operates a cable which opens or closes the fresh/recirculation mode door to fresh (outside) air. When lever is in recirculation position, outside air is shut off and air from inside passenger compartment is recirculated through the blower motor to selected air outlets. *See Figs. 1-4.*

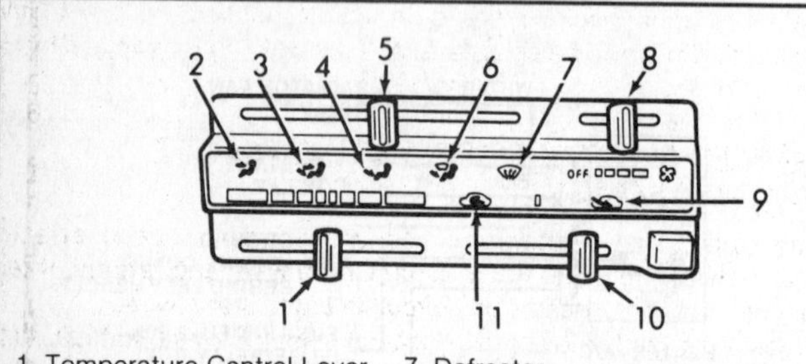
2
3
4
5
6
7
8
9
1
11
10
OFF

1. Temperature Control Lever
2. Face
3. Bi-Level
4. Floor
5. Airflow Control Lever
6. Floor/Defrost Side Outlet
7. Defroster
8. Blower Speed Control Lever
9. Fresh Air
10. Fresh/Recirculation Control Lever
11. Recirculated Air

94H10030 Courtesy of General Motors Corp.

Fig. 1: Identifying Heater Control Panel (Metro Shown; Tracker Is Similar)

BLOWER SPEED CONTROL LEVER/KNOB

The blower speed control lever/knob operates blower motor at one of 4 speeds.

TEMPERATURE CONTROL LEVER/KNOB

When the temperature control lever/knob is moved to full hot position, the air mix door opens fully, allowing all airflow through heater core to selected outlets. *See Fig. 3.* In full cold position, the air mix door closes off airflow through the heater core. Adjusting the air temperature control lever allows more or less air to by-pass heater core.

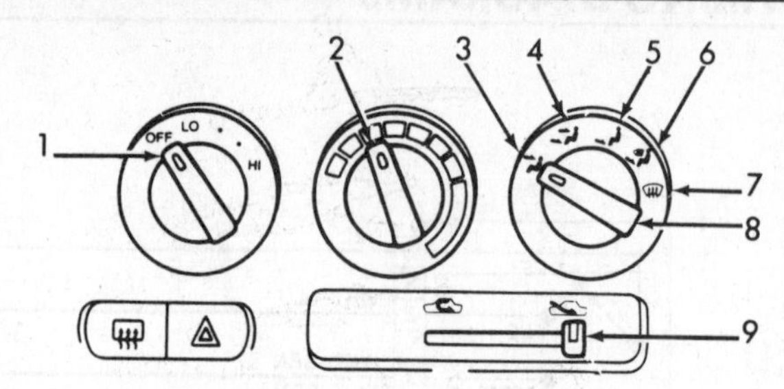
1
2
3
4
5
6
7
8
9
OFF
LO
HI

1. Blower Speed Selector Knob
2. Temperature Control Knob
3. Face
4. Bi-Level
5. Floor
6. Floor/Defrost Side Outlet
7. Defroster
8. Air Intake Control Knob
9. Fresh/Recirculated Air Control Knob

94E10037 Courtesy of General Motors Corp.

Fig. 2: Identifying Heater Control Panel (Prizm)

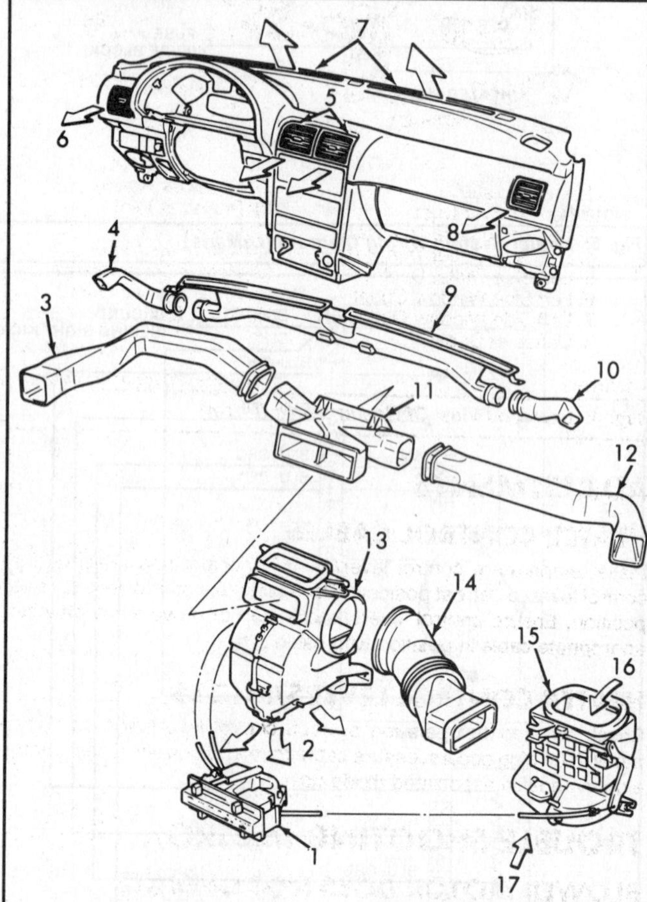
1
2
3
4
5
6
7
8
9
10
11
12
13
14
15
16
17

1. Heater Control Panel
2. Floor Outlet
3. Side Vent Duct
4. Side Demister Ducts
5. Center Vent Outlets
6. Side Outlet
7. Defroster Outlets
8. Side Outlet
9. Defroster Duct
10. Side Demister Ducts
11. Center Vent Duct
12. Side Vent Duct
13. Heater Case
14. Air Duct
15. Blower Motor Case
16. Outside Air
17. Recirculated Air

94I10031 Courtesy of General Motors Corp.

Fig. 3: Exploded View Of Heater System (Metro Shown; Tracker Is Similar)

1993 HEATER SYSTEMS
Metro, Prizm & Tracker (Cont.)

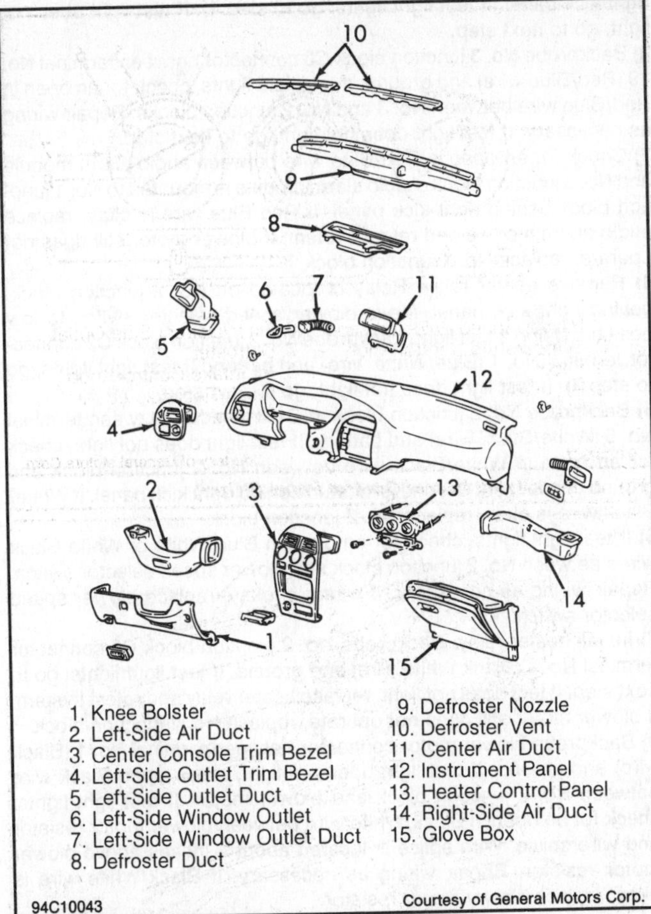
1. Knee Bolster
2. Left-Side Air Duct
3. Center Console Trim Bezel
4. Left-Side Outlet Trim Bezel
5. Left-Side Outlet Duct
6. Left-Side Window Outlet
7. Left-Side Window Outlet Duct
8. Defroster Duct
9. Defroster Nozzle
10. Defroster Vent
11. Center Air Duct
12. Instrument Panel
13. Heater Control Panel
14. Right-Side Air Duct
15. Glove Box
94C10043
Courtesy of General Motors Corp.

Fig. 4: Exploded View Of Heater Ducts (Prizm)

ADJUSTMENTS

HEATER CONTROL CABLES

Place temperature control lever/knob in hot position. Place airflow control lever to defrost position. Place air intake control lever to fresh position. Ensure control levers/knobs do not move while attaching appropriate cable in position with cable clip.

HEATER CONTROL LEVERS/KNOBS

Check for smooth operation of each control lever/knob on control panel. If binding occurs, ensure cable routing is correct. Check for foreign material in associated mode door.

TROUBLE SHOOTING (METRO)

BLOWER MOTOR DOES NOT OPERATE IN LOW POSITION

Metro – 1) Move blower speed selector switch to low position. Using a test light, backprobe blower speed selector switch connector between terminal No. 4 (Pink/Black wire) and ground. If test light does not light, replace blower speed selector switch.

2) If test light lights, use a test light to backprobe blower motor resistor connector between terminal No. 4 (Pink/Black wire) and ground. If test light lights, replace blower motor resistor. If test light does not light, repair open circuit in Pink/Black wire between blower speed selector switch and blower motor resistor.

BLOWER MOTOR DOES NOT OPERATE IN MEDIUM-LOW POSITION

Metro – 1) Move blower speed selector switch to medium-low position. Using a test light, backprobe blower speed selector switch connector between terminal No. 5 (Pink/Blue wire) and ground. If test light does not light, replace blower speed selector switch.

2) If test light lights, use a test light to backprobe blower motor resistor connector between terminal No. 3 (Pink/Blue wire) and ground. If test light does not light, repair open circuit in Pink/Blue wire. If test light lights, replace blower motor resistor.

BLOWER MOTOR DOES NOT OPERATE IN MEDIUM-HIGH POSITION

Metro – 1) Move blower speed selector switch to medium-high position. Using a test light, backprobe blower speed selector switch connector between terminal No. 6 (Pink/Green wire) and ground. If test light does not light, replace blower speed selector switch.

2) If test light lights, use a test light to backprobe blower motor resistor connector between terminal No. 1 (Pink/Green wire) and ground. If test light does not light, repair open circuit in Pink/Green wire. If test light lights, replace blower motor resistor.

BLOWER MOTOR DOES NOT OPERATE IN HIGH POSITION

Metro – Move blower speed selector switch to high position. Using a test light, backprobe blower speed selector switch connector between terminal No. 3 (Red wire) and ground. If test light does not light, replace blower speed selector switch. If test light lights, repair open circuit in blower speed selector switch Red wire.

BLOWER MOTOR OPERATES ONLY IN HIGH POSITION

Metro – 1) Turn ignition switch to ON position. Slide blower speed selector switch to high position. Using a test light, backprobe blower motor resistor connector between terminal No. 2 (Red wire) and ground. If test light does not light, repair open circuit in blower motor resistor Red wire.

2) Move blower speed selector switch to low position. Using a test light, backprobe blower speed selector switch connector between terminal No. 4 (Pink/Black wire) and ground. If test light does not light, replace blower speed selector switch. If test light lights, replace blower motor resistor.

BLOWER MOTOR DOES NOT OPERATE AT ANY SPEED

Metro – 1) Using a test light, backprobe blower speed selector switch between terminal No. 1 (Light Green wire) and ground. If test light does not light, repair open circuit in Light Green wire.

2) If test light lights, move blower speed selector switch to high position. Using a test light, backprobe blower speed selector switch between terminal No. 3 (Red wire) and ground. If test light does not light, replace blower speed selector switch.

3) If test light lights, backprobe blower motor connector between terminal No. 2 (Red wire) and ground. If test light does not light, repair open circuit in Red wire between blower motor and blower speed selector switch.

4) If test light lights, turn ignition switch to OFF position. Disconnect blower motor connector. Using an ohmmeter, backprobe blower motor between terminal No. 1 (Black wire) and ground. If more than 5 ohms are present, repair blower motor Black wire. If less than 5 ohms are present, replace blower motor.

BLOWER MOTOR OPERATES IN OFF POSITION

Metro – 1) Disconnect blower speed selector switch connector. If blower motor stops, replace blower speed selector switch. If blower motor does not stop, use a test light to backprobe blower motor connector between terminal No. 2 (Red wire) and ground.

2) If test light lights, repair short to voltage in Red wire between blower motor and blower speed selector switch. If test light does not light, connect a test light between blower speed selector switch connector terminal No. 6 (Pink/Green wire) and ground. If test light lights, repair short to voltage in Pink/Green wire.

1993 HEATER SYSTEMS
Metro, Prizm & Tracker (Cont.)

3) If test light does not light, connect a test light between blower speed selector switch connector terminal No. 5 (Pink/Blue wire) and ground. If test light lights, repair short to voltage in Pink/Blue wire. If test light does not light, repair short to voltage in Pink/Black wire.

TROUBLE SHOOTING (PRIZM)

BLOWER MOTOR DOES NOT OPERATE IN LOW POSITION

Prizm – 1) Turn ignition switch to ON position. Move blower speed selector switch to low position. Using a test light, backprobe blower speed selector switch connector between terminal No. 3 (Blue/White wire) and battery. If test light lights, go to next step. If test light does not light, replace blower speed selector switch.
2) Backprobe blower motor resistor connector between terminal No. 1 (White/Black wire) and battery. If test light lights, replace blower motor resistor. If test light does not light, check for an open in White/Black wire between junction block 2 and blower motor resistor. Junction block 2 is located is behind right kick panel. If White/Black wire is okay, replace junction block 2.

BLOWER MOTOR DOES NOT OPERATE IN MEDIUM-LOW POSITION

Prizm – 1) Turn ignition switch to OFF position. Move blower speed selector switch to medium-low position. Disconnect blower motor resistor connector. Connect a test light between blower motor resistor connector terminal No. 3 (Red wire) and battery.
2) If test light lights, replace blower motor resistor. If test light does not light, check for an open in Red wire between blower speed selector switch and blower motor resistor. Repair as necessary. If Red wire is okay, replace blower speed selector switch.

BLOWER MOTOR DOES NOT OPERATE IN MEDIUM-HIGH POSITION

Prizm – 1) Turn ignition switch to OFF position. Move blower speed selector switch to medium-high position. Disconnect blower motor resistor connector. Connect a test light between blower motor resistor connector terminal No. 2 (Blue/Black wire) and battery.
2) If test light lights, replace blower motor resistor. If test light does not light, check for an open in Blue/Black wire between blower speed selector switch and blower motor resistor. Repair wiring as necessary. If Blue/Black wire is okay, replace blower speed selector switch.

BLOWER MOTOR DOES NOT OPERATE IN HIGH POSITION

Prizm – Check for an open in Black/White wire between wire splice and blower speed selector switch. Wire splice is located about 4 inches above blower motor resistor. If Black/White wire is okay, replace blower speed selector switch.

BLOWER MOTOR OPERATES ONLY IN HIGH POSITION

Prizm – 1) Turn ignition switch to ON position. Move blower speed selector switch to low position. Using a test light, backprobe blower speed selector switch connector between terminal No. 3 (Blue/White wire) and battery.
2) If test light does not light, replace blower speed selector switch. If test light lights, check for an open in Black/White wire between wire splice and blower motor resistor. Wire splice is located about 4 inches above blower motor resistor. If Black/White wire is okay, replace blower motor resistor.

BLOWER MOTOR DOES NOT OPERATE AT ANY SPEED

Prizm – 1) Turn ignition switch to ON position. Using a test light, backprobe No. 2 junction block C2 connector between terminal No. 6 (Red/Blue wire) and ground. No. 2 junction block is located behind right kick panel. If test light lights, go to step **4)**. If test light does not light, go to next step.
2) Backprobe No. 3 junction block C3 connector between terminal No. 19 (Red/Blue wire) and ground. If test light lights, check for an open in Red/Blue wire between No. 3 and No. 2 junction blocks. Repair wiring as necessary. If test light does not light, go to next step.
3) Check for an open in Red/Blue wire between audio alarm module and No. 3 junction block. Audio alarm module is mounted to No. 1 junction block behind right kick panel. If Red/Blue wire is okay, replace audio alarm module and retest system. If blower motor still does not operate, replace No. 1 junction block.
4) Remove heater relay. Relay is located on No. 2 junction block, behind right kick panel. Move blower speed selector switch to low position. Using a test light, backprobe No. 2 junction block C2 connector terminal No. 1 (Blue/White wire) and battery. If test light lights, go to step **7)**. If test light does not light, go to next step.
5) Backprobe No. 2 junction block at C1 connector between terminal No. 6 (White/Black wire) and battery. If test light does not light, check for an open in White/Black wire between No. 2 junction block and ground connection. Ground is located behind right kick panel. If White/Black wire is okay, replace No. 2 junction block.
6) If test light lights, check for an open in Blue/White or White/Black wires between No. 2 junction block and blower speed selector switch. Repair wiring as necessary. If wiring is okay, replace blower speed selector switch.
7) Install heater relay. Backprobe No. 2 junction block C2 connector terminal No. 7 (Black White wire) and ground. If test light lights, go to next step. If test does not light, replace heater relay and retest system. If blower motor still does not operate, replace No. 2 junction block.
8) Backprobe blower motor connector between terminal No. 1 (Black wire) and ground. If test light does not light, repair open Black wire between No. 2 junction block and blower motor. If test light lights, check for an open in Black/White wire between blower motor resistor and wire splice. Wire splice is located about 4 inches above blower motor resistor. Repair wiring as necessary. If Black/White wire is okay, replace blower motor resistor.

TROUBLE SHOOTING (TRACKER)

BLOWER MOTOR DOES NOT OPERATE IN LOW POSITION

Tracker – 1) Move blower speed selector switch to low position. Using a test light, backprobe blower speed selector switch connector between terminal No. 4 (Pink/Black wire) and ground. If test light does not light, replace blower speed selector switch.
2) If test light lights, use a test light to backprobe blower motor resistor connector between terminal No. 4 (Pink/Black wire) and ground. If test light does not light, repair open circuit in Pink/Black wire between blower speed selector switch and blower motor resistor. If test light lights, replace blower motor resistor.

BLOWER MOTOR DOES NOT OPERATE IN MEDIUM-LOW POSITION

Tracker – 1) Move blower speed selector switch to medium-low position. Using a test light, backprobe blower speed selector switch connector between terminal No. 5 (Pink/Blue wire) and ground. If test light does not light, replace blower speed selector switch.
2) If test light lights, use a test light to backprobe blower motor resistor connector between terminal No. 3 (Pink/Blue wire) and ground. If test light does not light, repair open circuit in Pink/Blue wire between blower speed selector switch and blower motor resistor. If test light lights, replace blower motor resistor.

BLOWER MOTOR DOES NOT OPERATE IN MEDIUM-HIGH POSITION

Tracker – 1) Move blower speed selector switch to medium-high position. Using a test light, backprobe blower speed selector switch connector between terminal No. 6 (Pink/Green wire) and ground. If test light does not light, replace blower speed selector switch.

1993 HEATER SYSTEMS
Metro, Prizm & Tracker (Cont.)

2) If test light lights, use a test light to backprobe blower motor resistor connector between terminal No. 1 (Pink/Green wire) and ground. If test light does not light, repair open circuit in Pink/Green wire between blower speed selector switch and blower motor resistor. If test light lights, replace blower motor resistor.

BLOWER MOTOR DOES NOT OPERATE IN HIGH POSITION

Tracker – Move blower speed selector switch to high position. Using a test light, backprobe blower speed selector switch connector between terminal No. 3 (Pink wire) and ground. If test light lights, repair open circuit in blower speed selector Pink wire. If test light does not light, replace blower speed selector switch.

BLOWER MOTOR OPERATES ONLY IN HIGH POSITION

Tracker – 1) Move blower speed selector switch to high position. Using a test light, backprobe blower motor resistor connector between terminal No. 2 (Pink wire) and ground. If test light does not light, repair open circuit in blower motor resistor Pink wire.

2) If test light lights, move blower speed selector switch to low position. Using a test light, backprobe blower speed selector switch connector between terminal No. 4 (Pink/Black wire) and ground. If test light does not light, replace blower speed selector switch. If test light lights, replace blower motor resistor.

BLOWER MOTOR DOES NOT OPERATE AT ANY SPEED

Tracker – 1) Turn ignition on. Using a test light, backprobe blower speed selector switch connector between terminal No. 1 (Light Green wire) and ground. If test light does not light, repair open circuit in Light Green wire between fuse block and blower speed selector switch.

2) If test light lights, move blower speed selector switch to high position. Use a test light to backprobe blower speed selector switch between terminal No. 3 (Pink wire) and ground. If test light does not light, replace blower speed selector switch.

3) If test light lights, use a test light to backprobe blower motor connector between terminal No. 2 (Pink wire) and ground. If test light does not light, repair open circuit in Pink wire between blower motor and blower speed selector switch.

4) If test light lights, turn ignition switch to OFF position. Using an ohmmeter, backprobe blower motor connector between terminal No. 1 (Black wire) and ground. If resistance is more than 3 ohms, repair open circuit in blower motor Black ground wire. If resistance is less than 3 ohms, replace blower motor.

BLOWER MOTOR OPERATES IN OFF POSITION

Tracker – 1) Disconnect blower speed selector switch connector. If blower motor stops, replace blower speed selector switch. If blower motor does not stop, disconnect blower motor resistor connector.

2) If blower motor stops, repair short to voltage in Pink/Black wire, Pink/Blue wire or Pink/Green wire between blower speed selector switch and blower motor resistor.

3) If blower motor does not stop, repair short to voltage in Pink wire between blower speed selector switch, blower motor resistor and blower motor.

REMOVAL & INSTALLATION

WARNING: To avoid injury from accidental air bag deployment, read and carefully follow all SERVICE PRECAUTIONS and DISABLING & ACTIVATING AIR BAG SYSTEM procedures in AIR BAG SYSTEM SAFETY article in GENERAL SERVICING.

BLOWER MOTOR

Removal & Installation (Metro) – 1) Disconnect negative battery cable. Remove screw and upper glove box liner. Disconnect blower motor and blower motor resistor wiring harness connectors. Disconnect fresh/recirculate air control cable from blower motor case.

2) Remove 3 screws and blower motor case from vehicle. Disconnect air hose from blower case. Remove blower motor from blower case. Remove nut attaching fan to blower motor. Remove fan from blower motor. To install, reverse removal procedure.

Removal & Installation (Prizm) – Disconnect negative battery cable. Remove glove box. Disconnect blower motor connector. Remove screws and blower motor from blower case. To install, reverse removal procedure.

Removal & Installation (Tracker) – 1) Disconnect negative battery cable. Remove 2 hinge pins and glove box door. Disconnect blower motor and blower motor resistor wiring harness connectors. Disconnect fresh/recirculate air control cable from blower motor case.

2) Disconnect wiring harness from guide brackets on blower motor case. Remove blower motor case from vehicle. Remove blower motor from blower case. Remove nut attaching fan to blower motor. Remove fan from blower motor. To install, reverse removal procedure.

BLOWER MOTOR RESISTOR

Removal & Installation – Disconnect negative battery cable. On Prizm, remove glove box. On Tracker, remove 2 hinged pins and glove box door by removing 2 hinged pins. On all models, disconnect blower resistor connector. Remove screw and resistor. To install, reverse removal procedure.

BLOWER SPEED SELECTOR SWITCH

Removal & Installation (Metro) – Remove instrument panel. See INSTRUMENT PANEL. Remove heater control panel from instrument panel. Remove blower speed selector switch from heater control panel. To install, reverse removal procedure.

Removal & Installation (Prizm) – Disconnect negative battery cable. Remove center trim bezel from instrument panel. Remove cigarette lighter and ashtray bulb sockets from center trim bezel. Remove heater control panel from instrument panel. Remove blower speed selector switch knob. Remove clip, harness connector, screws and blower speed selector switch from control panel. To install, reverse removal procedure.

Removal & Installation (Tracker) – Disconnect negative battery cable. Remove heater control panel knobs. Remove heater control panel front plate and illumination bulb from instrument panel. Remove center console bezel. Remove 2 hinged pins and glove box door. Disconnect blower switch connector. Remove blower speed selector switch from heater control panel. To install, reverse removal procedure.

CENTER CONSOLE

Removal & Installation (Prizm) – 1) Disconnect negative battery cable. Remove ashtray. Remove center console trim bezel. Disconnect cigarette lighter, rear defogger switch and hazard switch connectors from bezel. Remove both kick panels.

2) Remove glove box. Remove driver-side knee bolster. On M/T models, remove shift boot. On A/T models, remove center console lower tray by gently prying up tray with screwdriver. On all models, remove screws and center console. To install, reverse removal procedure.

INSTRUMENT PANEL

Removal (Metro) – 1) Disable air bag system. See DISABLING & ACTIVATING AIR BAG SYSTEM in AIR BAG SYSTEM SAFETY article in GENERAL SERVICING. Remove air bag module from steering wheel. Remove steering wheel nut and washer. Mark position of steering wheel on shaft, and remove steering wheel using puller. Remove 2 screws and lower steering column trim panel.

2) Remove combination switch from steering column. Remove left and right kick panels from center console. Remove left and right speaker grills from instrument panel. Remove clip securing instrument panel to each door jamb (convertible models).

3) Remove left and right front speakers from instrument panel. Remove glove box. Disconnect A/C switch connector (if equipped), access connector through glove box opening. Remove heater control lever knobs. Remove 3 screws and instrument panel center trim bezel.

1993 HEATER SYSTEMS
Metro, Prizm & Tracker (Cont.)

4) Remove 2 screws and heater control panel. Disconnect heater control panel illumination connector from center trim bezel. Remove shift boot (manual transaxle). Remove 4 screws and center console. Remove ashtray. Remove 4 screws and center console trim bezel. Remove radio.
5) Remove 4 screws and instrument panel cluster trim bezel. Disconnect connectors from cluster trim bezel mounted switches (if equipped). To aid removal of instrument cluster, disconnect speedometer cable from transaxle. Remove 4 screws and pull instrument cluster assembly away from instrument panel.
6) Disconnect speedometer cable and all wiring harness connectors from back of instrument cluster. Remove instrument cluster. Disconnect illumination connectors from ashtray and cigarette lighter. Remove cigarette lighter assembly.
7) Remove 2 instrument panel screws from instrument cluster opening (convertible). Remove 3 lower instrument panel screws, one screw is located below steering column and remaining screws are located below glove box. Remove 3 upper instrument panel screw covers and screws.
8) Remove screw attaching instrument panel to floor pan (hardtop models). Disconnect illumination controller connector. Remove screw attaching hood latch release lever to instrument panel, disconnect cable from lever and remove lever. Unwind 4 retainers attaching wiring harnesses to instrument panel. Remove instrument panel.
Installation – To install, reverse removal procedure. Tighten air bag module screws and steering wheel hub nut to specification. See TORQUE SPECIFICATIONS. Activate air bag system and ensure air bag system is functioning properly. See SYSTEM OPERATION CHECK in AIR BAG SYSTEM SAFETY article in GENERAL SERVICING.
Removal (Prizm) – 1) Disable air bag system. See DISABLING & ACTIVATING AIR BAG SYSTEM in AIR BAG SYSTEM SAFETY article in GENERAL SERVICING. Remove air bag module. Remove steering wheel nut and washer. Mark position of steering wheel on shaft, and remove steering wheel using puller. Remove left and right lower trim panels from A-pillars and B-pillars.
2) Remove upper and lower steering column covers. Remove center console. See CENTER CONSOLE. Remove instrument cluster trim panel and instrument cluster. Remove left and right air ducts from instrument panel. Disconnect wiring harness connectors from instrument panel as necessary.
3) Remove fuse blocks from instrument panel. Disconnect ground wires from left and right kick panel area. Remove heater control panel. Remove cruise control module (if equipped). Disconnect ground wires from instrument panel support bracket.
4) Disconnect left and right rear door lock connectors (if equipped). Remove remote control mirror switch (if equipped). Disconnect steering column from instrument panel. Remove instrument panel.
Installation – To install, reverse removal procedure. Tighten air bag module screws and steering wheel hub nut to specification. See TORQUE SPECIFICATIONS. Activate air bag system and ensure air bag system is functioning properly. See SYSTEM OPERATION CHECK in AIR BAG SYSTEM SAFETY article in GENERAL SERVICING.
Removal & Installation (Tracker) – 1) Disconnect negative battery cable. Remove lower steering column cover panel. Remove steering wheel nut and washer. Mark position of steering wheel on shaft, and remove steering wheel using puller. Remove 2 screws and lower steering column trim panel.
2) Remove upper and lower steering column covers. Disconnect combination switch connector. Remove combination switch. Remove instrument cluster bezel and cluster from instrument panel. Disconnect all connectors and speedometer from instrument cluster.
3) Disconnect A/C switch connector (if equipped). Remove heater control lever knobs. Remove instrument panel center trim bezel. Remove heater control panel.
Remove ashtray and ashtray guide. Remove 4 screws and instrument panel center trim bezel. Remove instrument panel handle from passenger-side of instrument panel. Disconnect antenna lead from radio.
4) Ensure all wiring harness connectors that are necessary to remove instrument panel are disconnected. Pull instrument panel from support member. Detach defroster ducts, and remove instrument panel. To install, reverse removal procedure.

HEATER CONTROL PANEL

Removal & Installation (Metro & Prizm) – See BLOWER SPEED SELECTOR SWITCH.
Removal & Installation (Tracker) – Information is not available from manufacturer.

HEATER CORE

Removal & Installation – Remove instrument panel. See INSTRUMENT PANEL. Drain coolant from cooling system. Disconnect all cables and ducts from heater case. Remove heater case from vehicle. Remove screws and clips from heater case. Separate heater case into halves (if necessary). Remove heater core from case. To install, reverse removal procedure.

TORQUE SPECIFICATIONS

TORQUE SPECIFICATIONS

Application	Ft. Lbs. (N.m)
Steering Wheel Hub Nut	25 (34)
	INCH Lbs. (N.m)
Air Bag Module Screw	
Metro & Storm	44 (5)
Prizm	78 (9)
Blower Motor Case Bolts	89 (10)
Heater Case Bolts & Nuts	89 (10)

WIRING DIAGRAMS

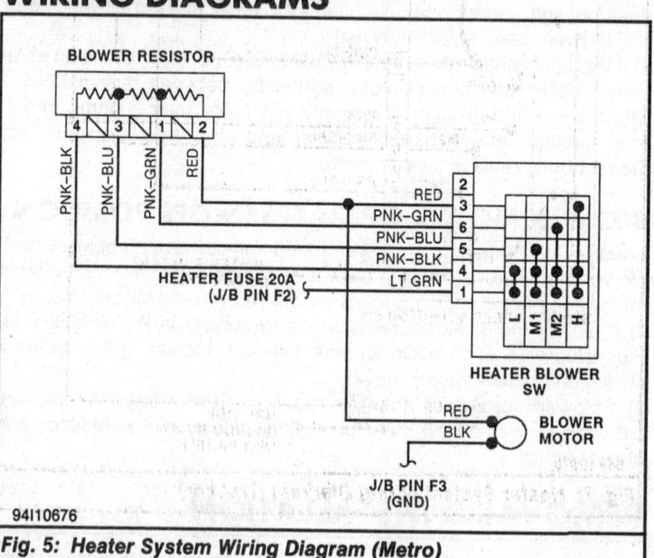
BLOWER RESISTOR
4
3
1
2
PNK-BLK
PNK-BLU
PNK-GRN
RED
RED
PNK-GRN
PNK-BLU
PNK-BLK
LT GRN
HEATER FUSE 20A
(J/B PIN F2)
2
3
6
5
4
1
L
M1
M2
H
HEATER BLOWER
SW
RED
BLK
BLOWER
MOTOR
J/B PIN F3
(GND)
94I10676

Fig. 5: Heater System Wiring Diagram (Metro)

1993 HEATER SYSTEMS
Metro, Prizm & Tracker (Cont.)

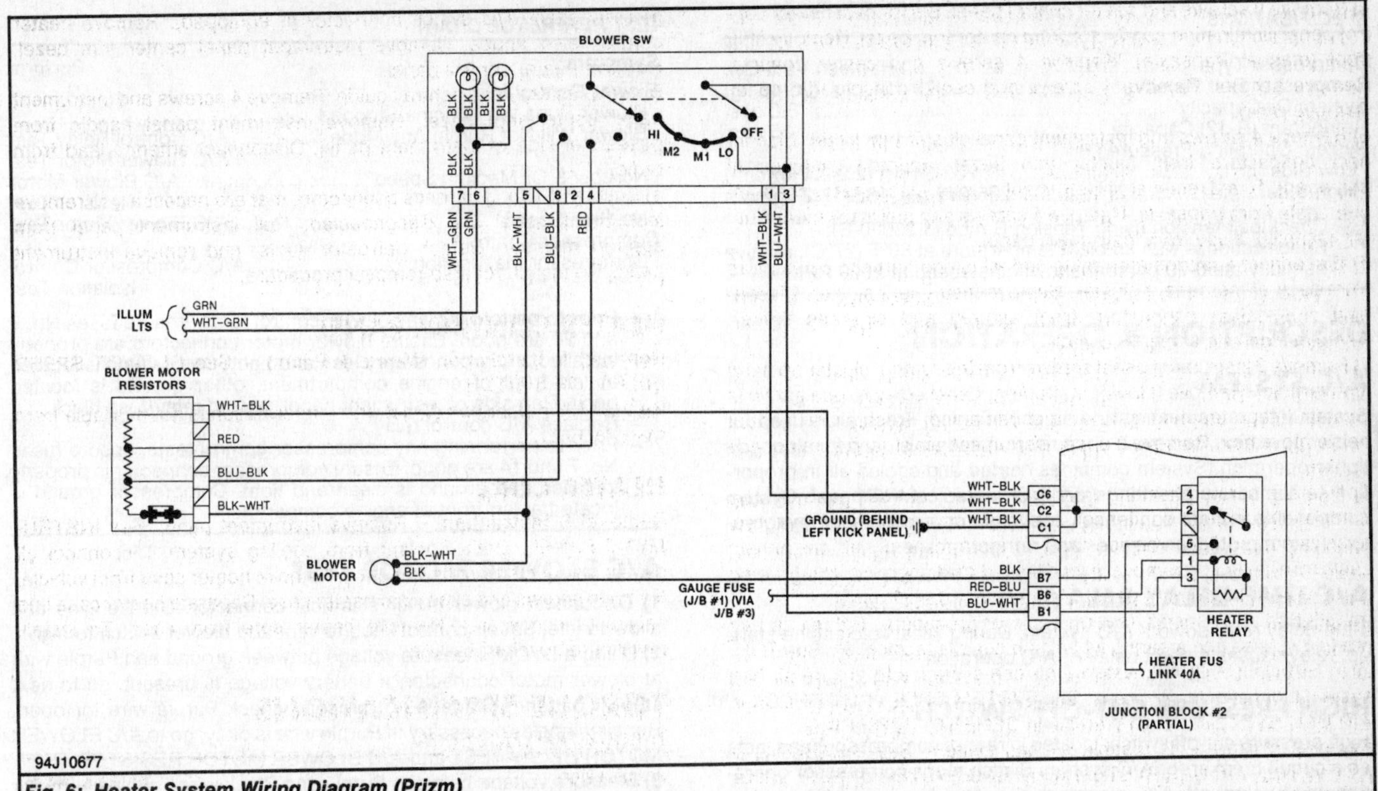
BLOWER SW
BLK
BLK
BLK
BLK
BLK
BLK
HI
M2
M1
LO
OFF
7
6
5
8
2
4
1
3
WHT-GRN
GRN
BLK-WHT
BLU-BLK
RED
WHT-BLK
BLU-WHT
ILLUM LTS
GRN
WHT-GRN
BLOWER MOTOR RESISTORS
WHT-BLK
RED
BLU-BLK
BLK-WHT
BLOWER MOTOR
BLK-WHT
BLK
GROUND (BEHIND LEFT KICK PANEL)
WHT-BLK
WHT-BLK
WHT-BLK
C6
C2
C1
GAUGE FUSE (J/B #1) (VIA J/B #3)
BLK
RED-BLU
BLU-WHT
B7
B6
B1
HEATER RELAY
HEATER FUS LINK 40A
JUNCTION BLOCK #2 (PARTIAL)
94J10677

Fig. 6: Heater System Wiring Diagram (Prizm)

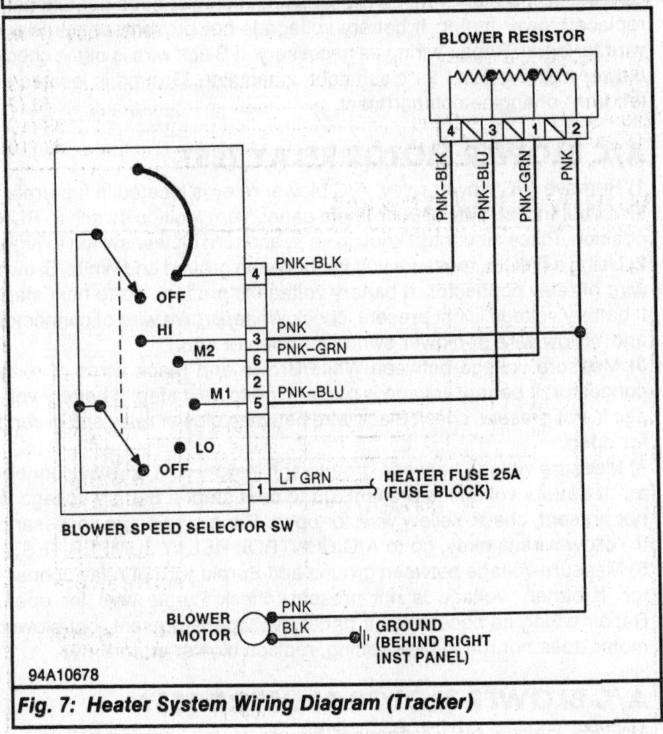
BLOWER RESISTOR
4
3
1
2
PNK-BLK
PNK-BLU
PNK-GRN
PNK
PNK-BLK
OFF
HI
PNK
M2
PNK-GRN
M1
PNK-BLU
LO
OFF
LT GRN
HEATER FUSE 25A (FUSE BLOCK)
BLOWER SPEED SELECTOR SW
BLOWER MOTOR
PNK
BLK
GROUND (BEHIND RIGHT INST PANEL)
94A10678

Fig. 7: Heater System Wiring Diagram (Tracker)

1993 MANUAL A/C-HEATER SYSTEMS
LeMans

SPECIFICATIONS

Compressor Type	Harrison V5 5-Cyl.
Compressor Belt Tension [1]	79-101 Lbs. (36-46 kg)
System Oil Capacity	8.0 ozs.
Refrigerant (R-12) Capacity	35 ozs.
System Operating Pressures [2]	
Low Side	32-34 psi (2.2-2.4 kg/cm²)
High Side	235-245 psi (16.5-17.2 kg/cm²)

[1] – Check belt tension using Tension Gauge (J 23600-B).
[2] – Specification is with ambient temperature at 80°F (27°C), relative humidity at 50-70 percent and engine speed at 2000 RPM.

DESCRIPTION & OPERATION

A/C SYSTEM

System integrates heating and air conditioning. Fresh air is used for heater operation, and fresh air or recirculated air is used for air conditioner operation. System combines heated and cooled air in proportion to temperature settings on A/C-heater control panel. System components include condenser, accumulator, compressor, evaporator, system protection devices and refrigerant lines.

A/C TIME-DELAY RELAY

Time-delay relay powers A/C system. During initial cold engine start-up, relay causes a short delay of A/C operation.

HIGH PRESSURE CUT-OFF SWITCH

High pressure cut-off switch, located in rear of compressor head, acts as a circuit breaker for A/C system. Switch stops compressor operation by turning off A/C electrical circuits when system pressure exceeds 410-450 psi (28.8-31.6 kg/cm²) and closes when system pressure drops to 150-250 psi (10.5-15.6 kg/cm²).

LOW PRESSURE CUT-OFF SWITCH

Low pressure cut-off switch, located in liquid line, acts as a circuit breaker for A/C system. Switch stops compressor operation by turning off A/C electrical circuits when refrigerant pressure drops below a specified range. Switch also prevents compressor engagement in cold weather.

POWER STEERING CUT-OFF SWITCH

Switch prevents compressor operation during engine idle, when high power steering demand exists. Compressor operation is restored when power steering demand is reduced or vehicle engine speed is increased.

PRESSURE RELIEF VALVE

Pressure relief valve, located on compressor, opens when system pressure exceeds approximately 440 psi (30.4 kg/cm²).

VACUUM RESERVE TANK

Vacuum reserve tank is used to operate door-positioning mode. Door positioning is determined by vacuum signals delivered through hoses. To maintain signal strength during acceleration, a check valve is used to maintain vacuum tank pressure.

WIDE OPEN THROTTLE CUT-OUT SWITCH

Wide open throttle cut-out switch, located on throttle body, opens compressor clutch circuit during full throttle acceleration. Compressor disengagement is performed by Electronic Control Module (ECM) after receiving a full throttle signal from Throttle Position Sensor (TPS).

TESTING

To ald in determining which test to perform first, see TEST REFERENCE CHART table.

TEST REFERENCE CHART

Symptom	Perform
Blower Control [1]	
Blower Runs With Engine Stopped	[2]
Blower Will Not Run In Any Mode	A/C Control Relay Test A/C Blower Motor Test
No Low & Or Medium Speed	A/C Blower Motor Resistor Test
No High Speed	A/C Blower Motor Test
Compressor Control [3]	
Compressor Malfunction	A/C Compressor Control Isolation Test

[1] – Prior to performing any blower control tests, ensure fuses No. 7 and 20 are good. Ensure blower motor connectors are properly installed and grounds are clean and tight. One ground is located at left front of engine compartment, other ground is located behind left side of instrument panel, behind relay/fuse block.
[2] – Replace A/C control relay.
[3] – Prior to performing any compressor control tests, ensure fuses No. 7 and 14 are good. Ensure compressor connector is properly installed and ground is clean and tight. Compressor ground is located at left front of engine compartment.

A/C BLOWER MOTOR TEST

1) Disconnect blower motor electrical connector. Start engine and allow to idle. Set air control knob to vent and blower switch to high.
2) Using a DVOM, measure voltage between ground and Purple wire at blower motor connector. If battery voltage is present, go to next step. If battery voltage is not present, check Purple wire for open. Repair wiring as necessary. If Purple wire is okay, go to A/C BLOWER MOTOR RELAY TEST and A/C BLOWER MOTOR RESISTOR TEST.
3) Measure voltage between Purple and Black wires at blower motor connector. If battery voltage is present, but blower does not function, replace blower motor. If battery voltage is not present, check Black wire for open. Repair wiring as necessary. If Black wire is okay, check blower motor ground for clean tight connection. Ground is located at left front of engine compartment.

A/C BLOWER MOTOR RELAY TEST

1) Remove A/C blower relay. A/C blower relay is located in fuse/relay block behind left side of instrument panel. Turn ignition switch to RUN position. Place air control knob in vent, and turn blower switch to high.
2) Using a DVOM, measure voltage between ground and White/Brown wire of relay connector. If battery voltage is present, go to next step. If battery voltage is not present, check White/Brown wire of connector and Yellow wire of blower switch for open or short .
3) Measure voltage between White/Brown and Black wires of relay connector. If battery voltage is present, go to next step. If battery voltage is not present, check Black wire between blower relay and ground for open.
4) Measure voltage between ground and Yellow wire of relay connector. If battery voltage is present, go to next step. If battery voltage is not present, check Yellow wire for open. Repair wiring as necessary. If Yellow wire is okay, go to A/C CONTROL RELAY JUMPER TEST.
5) Measure voltage between ground and Purple wire of relay connector. If battery voltage is not present, check Purple wire for open. Repair wiring as necessary. If battery voltage is present, but blower motor does not run in high setting, replace blower motor.

A/C BLOWER MOTOR RESISTOR TEST

1) Turn ignition off. Disconnect blower motor resistor connector. Resistor is mounted on blower motor case. Using a DVOM, measure resistance between Yellow wire of A/C control relay and Purple wire terminal of blower motor relay. Resistance should be 1.9-2.9 ohms.
2) If resistance is as specified, check Yellow, White/Blue, White/Green and Blue wires for open or short. If resistance is not as specified, measure resistance between Yellow and Blue wire terminals of blower motor resistor. Resistance should be 1.9-2.9 ohms.
3) If resistance is as specified, check Blue and Yellow wires for an open or short. If resistance is not as specified, replace blower motor resistor.

A/C CONTROL RELAY TEST

1) Remove A/C control relay from connector. A/C control relay is located in fuse/relay block behind left side of instrument panel. Start engine and allow to idle. Set air control knob to vent, and turn blower switch to medium position.
2) Using a DVOM, measure voltage between ground and White/Black wire of relay connector. If battery voltage is present, go to next step. If battery voltage is not present, check Brown, Red/White/Black and White/Black wires for open or short. Repair wiring as necessary.
3) Measure voltage between ground and Red/Yellow wire of relay connector. If battery voltage is present, go to next step. If battery voltage is not present, check Red/Yellow wire for open. Repair wiring as necessary.
4) Measure voltage between White/Black and Black wires of relay connector. If battery voltage is present, go to A/C CONTROL RELAY JUMPER TEST. If battery voltage is not present, check Black wire for open. Repair wiring as necessary.

A/C CONTROL RELAY JUMPER TEST

Remove A/C control relay. Connect a fused jumper wire between Red/Yellow and Yellow wires of relay connector. If blower motor operates, go to A/C CONTROL RELAY TEST. If blower motor does not operate, go to A/C BLOWER MOTOR TEST.

A/C COMPRESSOR CONTROL ISOLATION TEST

1) Remove A/C compressor relay. A/C compressor relay is located in fuse/relay block behind left side of instrument panel. Start engine and allow to idle. Set air control knob to bi-level. For proper test results, temperature outside of vehicle must be 60°F (16°C) or more.
2) Using a DVOM, measure voltage between ground and Brown wire (terminal No. 6) at A/C compressor relay connector. If battery voltage is present, go to next step. If battery voltage is not present, check fuse No. 7 and Brown wire for open. Repair wiring as necessary.
3) Measure voltage between ground and Brown wire (terminal No. 4) at A/C compressor relay connector. If battery voltage is present, go to next step. If battery voltage is not present, check Brown wire for open. Repair wiring as necessary. If Brown wire is okay, go to A/C COMPRESSOR MODE CONTROL TEST.
4) With engine running and air control knob in bi-level position, connect a fused jumper wire between Brown wire (terminal No. 4) and Red/Yellow wire of A/C compressor relay connector. A/C compressor clutch should engage. If A/C compressor clutch engages, go to A/C COMPRESSOR CLUTCH TEST. If A/C compressor clutch engages, but A/C system does not operate, go to ELECTRONIC CONTROL MODULE (ECM) COMPRESSOR CONTROL TEST.

ELECTRONIC CONTROL MODULE (ECM) COMPRESSOR CONTROL TEST

1) Ensure ignition is off. Disconnect ECM 24-pin connector. ECM is located behind right kick panel. Ensure A/C compressor is connected. Turn ignition switch to RUN (engine off) position.
2) Set air control knob to bi-level. For proper test results, temperature outside of vehicle must be 60°F (16°C) or more. Using a DVOM, measure voltage between ground and Brown wire (terminal B8) of ECM connector. If battery voltage is present, go to next step. If battery voltage is not present, check Brown wire for open. Repair wiring as necessary.
3) Measure voltage between ground and Blue wire of ECM connector. If battery voltage is present, go to next step. If battery voltage is not present, check Blue wire for open. Repair wiring as necessary. If Blue wire is okay, replace A/C compressor relay.
4) Connect a fused jumper wire between ground and Blue wire of ECM connector. With fused jumper wire connected, A/C compressor relay should operate and A/C compressor clutch should engage.
5) If relay does not operate and compressor clutch does not engage, replace A/C compressor relay. If relay and compressor clutch operate properly, but A/C system still malfunctions, problem may be caused by faulty ECM.

A/C COMPRESSOR CLUTCH TEST

1) Disconnect A/C compressor clutch connector. Turn ignition switch to RUN (engine off) position. Set air control knob to normal. For proper test results, temperature outside of vehicle must be 60°F (16°C) or more.
2) Disconnect A/C compressor relay connector. A/C control relay is located in fuse/relay block behind left side of instrument panel. Connect a jumper wire between Brown wire (terminal No. 4) and Red/Yellow wire of A/C compressor relay.
3) Using a DVOM, measure voltage between ground and Red/Yellow wire at A/C compressor clutch connector. If battery voltage is present, go to next step. If battery voltage is not present, check Red/Yellow wire for open. Repair wiring as necessary.
4) Measure voltage between Black and Red/Yellow wires of A/C compressor clutch connector. If battery voltage is not present, check Black wire for open between ground connection and A/C compressor clutch connector. Ground connection is located at left front of engine compartment. If battery voltage is present, but A/C compressor clutch does not operate, replace A/C compressor clutch.

A/C COMPRESSOR MODE CONTROL TEST

1) Start engine and allow to idle. Turn air control knob to off position. For proper test results, temperature outside of vehicle must be 60°F (16°C) or more.
2) With A/C-heater control panel connected, measure voltage between ground and Red/Black/White wire (backprobe wire) of A/C-heater control panel connector. If battery voltage is present, go to next step. If battery voltage is not present, check Red/Black/White and Brown wires for open. Repair wiring as necessary.
3) Measure voltage between ground and Black/White wire (backprobe wire) of A/C-heater control panel connector. No voltage should be present. If no voltage is present, go to next step. If voltage is present, check Black/White wire for short to voltage. Repair wiring as necessary. If Black/White wire is okay, replace A/C-heater control panel.
4) Turn ignition off. Ensure air control knob is in off position. Disconnect A/C-heater control panel 3-pin connector. Using a DVOM, measure resistance between Red/Black/White and Black/White wires of A/C-heater control panel connector. Resistance should be infinite. If resistance is infinite, go to next step. If resistance is not infinite, replace A/C-heater control panel.
5) Set air control knob, in succession, to maximum, normal, bi-level and defrost. Using a DVOM, measure resistance between Red/Black/White and Black/White wires of A/C-heater control panel connector at each knob position. Resistance should be zero ohms. If resistance is zero ohms, go to next step. If resistance is not zero ohms, replace A/C-heater control panel.
6) Disconnect A/C low pressure cut-out switch. Connect a fused jumper wire between switch terminals on harness side. Measure voltage between ground and Blue wire (backprobe connector) of A/C compressor relay connector. If battery voltage is not present, go to next step. If battery voltage is present, check A/C system refrigerant charge. If A/C system refrigerant charge is okay, replace low pressure cut-out switch.
7) Disconnect A/C high pressure cut-out switch. Connect a fused jumper wire between switch terminals on harness side. Measure voltage between ground and Blue wire (backprobe connector) of A/C compressor relay connector. If battery voltage is present, replace high pressure cut-out switch. If battery voltage is not present, check Blue wire for open or short.

REMOVAL & INSTALLATION

NOTE: For removal and installation procedures not covered in this article, see appropriate HEATER SYSTEMS article.

ACCUMULATOR

Removal & Installation – 1) Disconnect negative battery cable. Discharge A/C system using approved refrigerant recovery/recycling equipment. Disconnect refrigerant lines at accumulator. Cap open fittings to prevent moisture and dust from entering system. Remove accumulator mounting screws. Remove accumulator.

2) To install, reverse removal procedure. If new accumulator is being installed, add 3.5 ounces of clean refrigerant oil to new accumulator. Use NEW seals on refrigerant lines. Evacuate and recharge system.

A/C COMPRESSOR

Removal & Installation – 1) Disconnect negative battery cable. Discharge A/C system using approved refrigerant recovery/recycling equipment. Remove heat shield and compressor strut from back of compressor. Disconnect compressor wiring.

2) Remove refrigerant lines at compressor, and plug fittings. Loosen compressor mounting bolts, and remove drive belt. Remove compressor mounting bolts and A/C compressor. To install, reverse removal procedure. Replace all seals. Evacuate and recharge system. Adjust drive belt.

CONDENSER

Removal & Installation – 1) Disconnect negative battery cable. Discharge A/C system using approved refrigerant recovery/recycling equipment. Raise and support vehicle. Drain cooling system. Remove radiator and power steering reservoir.

2) Remove compressor discharge line at condenser. Remove connectors from low pressure cut-off switch and condenser fan. Disconnect A/C hoses at condenser. Remove condenser-to-evaporator line at orifice tube. Remove condenser.

3) Cap open fittings to prevent moisture and dust from entering system. To install, reverse removal procedure. Replace all seals. Evacuate and recharge system. Check for leaks.

EVAPORATOR CORE

Removal & Installation – 1) Disconnect negative battery cable. Discharge A/C system using approved refrigerant recovery/recycling equipment. Remove heater core. See appropriate HEATER SYSTEMS article.

2) Disconnect accumulator-to-evaporator pipe and orifice tube-to-evaporator at dash panel. Remove evaporator cover, bracket screws and clamps. Remove evaporator.

3) To install, reverse removal procedure. Evacuate and recharge system. Check system for leaks.

ORIFICE TUBE

Removal & Installation – 1) Orifice tube is located in liquid line between evaporator and condenser. Disconnect negative battery cable. Discharge A/C system using approved refrigerant recovery/recycling equipment.

2) Disconnect tube connection at orifice. Raise and support vehicle. From underneath vehicle, disconnect tube connection at evaporator. Remove orifice tube. To install, reverse removal procedure. Evacuate and recharge system. Check for leaks.

TORQUE SPECIFICATIONS

TORQUE SPECIFICATIONS

Application	Ft. Lbs. (N.m)
Compressor Strut Bolt	33 (45)
Compressor Bracket Bolts	
Left Bolt	20 (27)
Right Bolt	37 (50)
Compressor Front Bracket Bolt	26 (35)
Compressor Rear Bracket Bolt	18 (25)
Heat Shield Nut	26 (35)
Pulley & Bracket Bolts	24 (32)

WIRING DIAGRAM

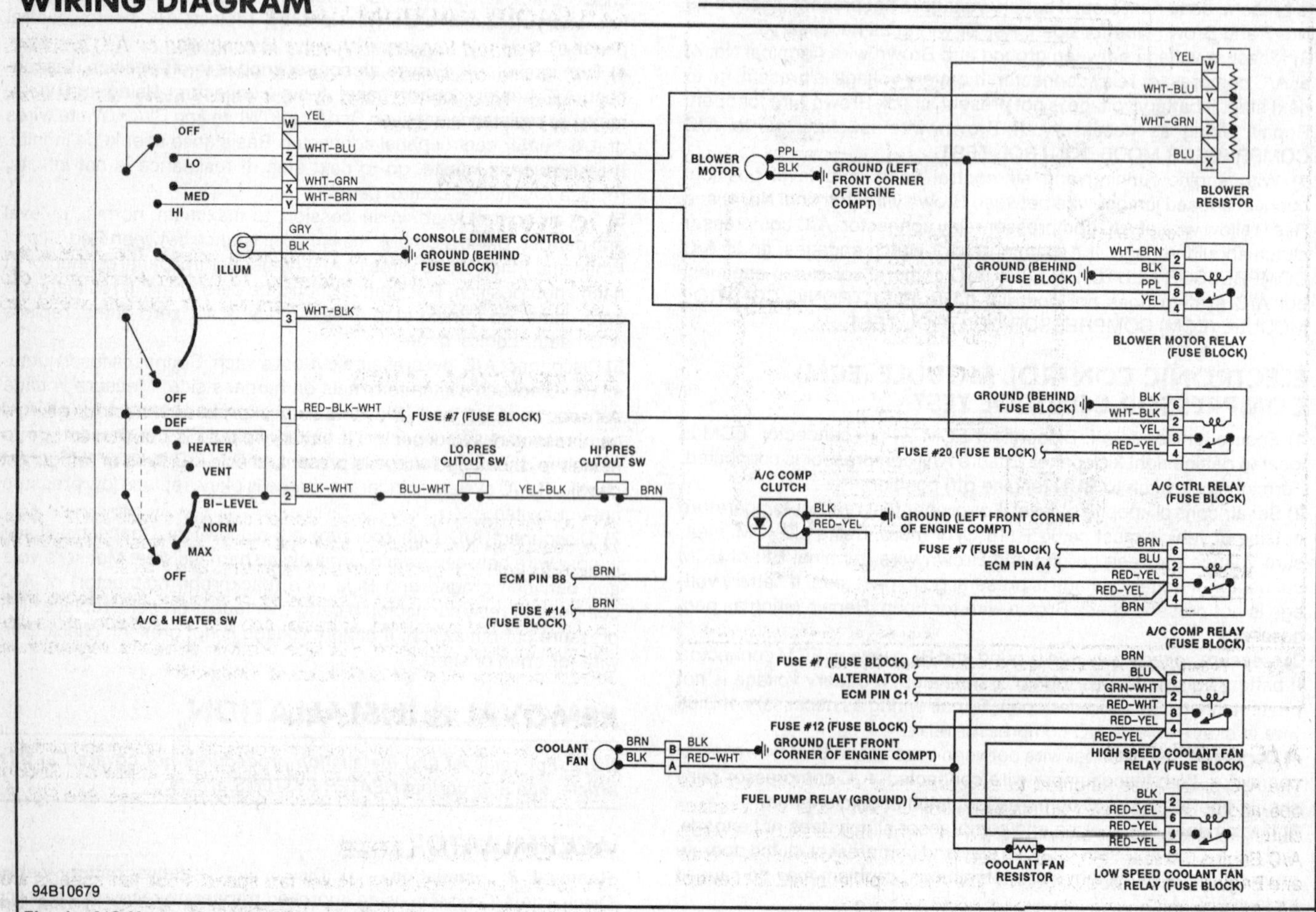
OFF
LO
MED
HI
ILLUM
DEF
HEATER
VENT
BI-LEVEL
NORM
MAX
A/C & HEATER SW
YEL
WHT-BLU
WHT-GRN
WHT-BRN
GRY
BLK
WHT-BLK
RED-BLK-WHT
BLK-WHT
BLU-WHT
YEL-BLK
BRN
CONSOLE DIMMER CONTROL
GROUND (BEHIND FUSE BLOCK)
FUSE #7 (FUSE BLOCK)
LO PRES CUTOUT SW
HI PRES CUTOUT SW
ECM PIN B8
FUSE #14 (FUSE BLOCK)
BLOWER MOTOR
PPL
GROUND (LEFT FRONT CORNER OF ENGINE COMPT)
BLOWER RESISTOR
WHT-BRN
BLOWER MOTOR RELAY (FUSE BLOCK)
FUSE #20 (FUSE BLOCK)
RED-YEL
A/C CTRL RELAY (FUSE BLOCK)
A/C COMP CLUTCH
GROUND (LEFT FRONT CORNER OF ENGINE COMPT)
FUSE #7 (FUSE BLOCK)
ECM PIN A4
A/C COMP RELAY (FUSE BLOCK)
FUSE #7 (FUSE BLOCK)
ALTERNATOR
ECM PIN C1
GRN-WHT
RED-WHT
FUSE #12 (FUSE BLOCK)
HIGH SPEED COOLANT FAN RELAY (FUSE BLOCK)
COOLANT FAN
GROUND (LEFT FRONT CORNER OF ENGINE COMPT)
FUEL PUMP RELAY (GROUND)
COOLANT FAN RESISTOR
LOW SPEED COOLANT FAN RELAY (FUSE BLOCK)
94B10679

Fig. 1: A/C-Heater System Wiring Diagram (LeMans)

1993 MANUAL A/C-HEATER SYSTEMS
Metro & Tracker

SPECIFICATIONS

Compressor Type
Metro & Tracker .... Nippondenso 10-Cyl.
Compressor Belt Deflection [1] .... 13/64-1/4" (2.0-6.4 mm)
System Oil Capacity .... 2.7 ozs.
Refrigerant (R-12) Capacity
Metro .... 18 ozs.
Tracker .... 21 ozs.
System Operating Pressure [2]
Low Side .... 32-34 psi (2.2-2.4 kg/cm²)
High Side .... 235-245 psi (16.5-17.2 kg/cm²)

[1] – Specification is with 22 lbs. (100 N.m) force applied midway on longest span of belt.
[2] – Specification is with ambient temperature at 80°F (27°C), relative humidity at 50-70 percent and engine speed at 2000 RPM.

WARNING: To avoid injury from accidental air bag deployment, read and carefully follow all SERVICE PRECAUTIONS and DISABLING & ACTIVATING AIR BAG SYSTEM procedures in AIR BAG SYSTEM SAFETY article in GENERAL SERVICING.

DESCRIPTION

System integrates heating and air conditioning. Fresh air is used for heater operation, and fresh air or recirculated air is used for air conditioner operation. System combines heated and cooled air in proportion to temperature settings on A/C-heater control panel. System components include condenser, receiver-drier, compressor, evaporator, system protection devices and refrigerant lines. *See Figs. 1 and 2.*

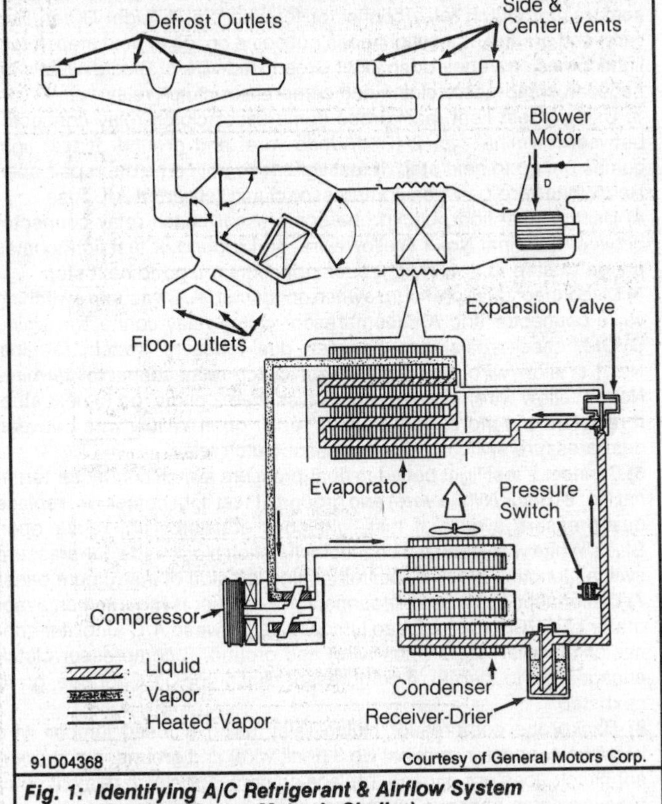
Defrost Outlets
Side & Center Vents
Blower Motor
Floor Outlets
Expansion Valve
Evaporator
Pressure Switch
Compressor
Liquid
Vapor
Heated Vapor
Condenser
Receiver-Drier
91D04368
Courtesy of General Motors Corp.

Fig. 1: Identifying A/C Refrigerant & Airflow System (Tracker Shown; Metro Is Similar)

A/C AMPLIFIER

The A/C amplifier is mounted to evaporator case. Amplifier controls operations of A/C Solenoid Vacuum Valve (SVV) and compressor clutch in response to signals received from dual-pressure switch, A/C Engine Coolant Temperature (ECT) switch, evaporator thermistor and Engine Control Module (ECM). The A/C amplifier and ECM control A/C system and engine idle speed when A/C is on.

COMPRESSOR

The compressor compresses low pressure refrigerant vapor into a high pressure, high temperature vapor. When activated, the compressor continuously pumps R-12 refrigerant and refrigerant oil through the A/C system.

CONDENSER

The condenser assembly is located in front of radiator. The assembly is made up of coils carrying refrigerant. Fins provide cooling for rapid transfer of heat. Air passing through the condenser cools high pressure refrigerant vapor, condensing it into a liquid.

CONDENSER FAN

The condenser fan provides airflow across the condenser to dissipate heat generated by refrigerant system pressure. Air passing through the condenser cools high pressure refrigerant vapor to a liquid. Failure of condenser fan circuit may cause excessive high side pressure.

ENGINE COOLANT TEMPERATURE SWITCH

The A/C Engine Coolant Temperature (ECT) switch is located on intake manifold. The Electronic Control Module (ECM) uses signals from the ECT switch to monitor engine coolant temperature. If engine coolant temperature exceeds 226°F (108°C), ECM will interrupt A/C operation.

DUAL-PRESSURE SWITCH

The dual-pressure switch is mounted in top of receiver-drier and acts as an A/C system circuit breaker. The switch stops compressor operation by turning off the A/C compressor circuit when refrigerant pressure drops below or exceeds a specified range.

SOLENOID VACUUM VALVE

The A/C Solenoid Vacuum (SV) valve is controlled by A/C amplifier. During engine idle speeds, compressor exerts an excessive load on the engine. To prevent stalling or poor engine idling, the SV valve increases engine idle speed.

OPERATION

A/C SWITCH

Push A/C switch to operate air conditioning system. The diode in the switch lights when system is operating. To turn air conditioning off, push the switch again. The A/C system will not operate unless fan lever is in one of the on positions.

AIR SELECTOR LEVER

Air selector lever has 5 positions. Each position controls where air will be discharged. With lever in the ventilation position, cooled air or normal air is discharged from the center and side registers of instrument panel.

With air selector lever in bi-level position and A/C switch in OFF position, heated air is discharged from floor vents and fresh unheated air is discharged from center and side registers. *See Fig. 2.*

In the heater position, most of heated air or dehumidified heated air is discharged from floor vents. In heater and defrost position, air is discharged to floor, defroster and side window defroster registers. In defrost position, most air is directed to windshield.

AIR INTAKE SELECT LEVER

A sliding air intake select lever controls outside air intake and circulation of inside air. Sliding lever to right recirculates inside air. Sliding lever to left brings fresh air into passenger compartment. *See Fig. 2.*

FAN CONTROL LEVER

Fan control lever regulates blower fan speed. Four fan speeds are available. *See Fig. 2.* In order for A/C system to operate, blower fan must be in one of 4 speeds.

1993 MANUAL A/C-HEATER SYSTEMS
Metro & Tracker (Cont.)

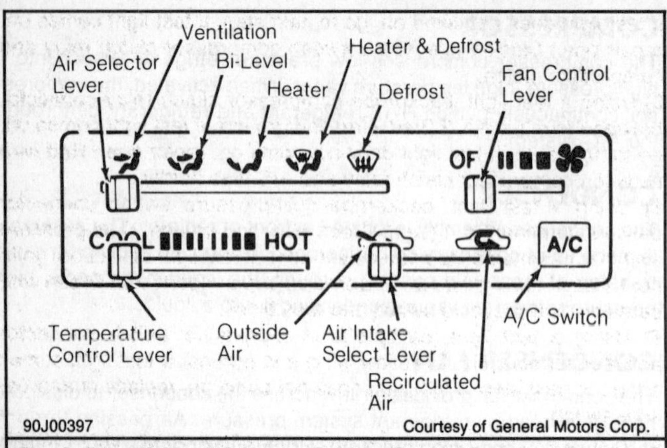
Ventilation
Air Selector Lever
Bi-Level
Heater & Defrost
Heater
Defrost
Fan Control Lever
OF
COOL
HOT
A/C
A/C Switch
Temperature Control Lever
Outside Air
Air Intake Select Lever
Recirculated Air
90J00397
Courtesy of General Motors Corp.

Fig. 2: Identifying A/C-Heater System Control Panel (Metro Shown; Tracker Is Similar)

TEMPERATURE CONTROL LEVER

Temperature control lever controls amount of airflow through and/or around heater core. Depending upon system control positions, mixture of warm and cold air regulates temperature and humidity of air inside of vehicle. *See Fig. 2.*

TESTING

WARNING: To avoid injury from accidental air bag deployment, read and carefully follow all SERVICE PRECAUTIONS and DISABLING & ACTIVATING AIR BAG SYSTEM procedures in AIR BAG SYSTEM SAFETY article in GENERAL SERVICING.

A/C CONDENSER FAN INOPERATIVE

Metro – 1) Start engine. Press A/C switch to on position. If compressor clutch engages, go to next step. If compressor clutch does not engage, go to A/C COMPRESSOR CLUTCH INOPERATIVE.

2) Using a test light, backprobe fan motor connector between terminal No. 2 (Blue/Black wire) and ground. If test light does not come on, go to next step. If test light comes on, check for an open Black wire between wire splice and condenser fan motor. Repair wiring as necessary. If Black wire is okay, replace condenser fan motor.

3) Remove fuse/relay box. Fuse/relay box is located in engine compartment, near battery. Using a test light, backprobe condenser fan relay connector between terminal No. 4 (Blue/Black wire) and ground. If test light does not come on, go to next step. If test light comes on, repair open Blue/Black wire between condenser fan relay and condenser fan motor.

4) Using a test light, backprobe condenser fan relay connector between terminal No. 2 (Red/White wire) and ground. If test light comes on, go to next step. If test light does not come on, repair open Red/White wire between wire splice and condenser fan relay.

5) Using a test light, backprobe condenser fan relay connector between terminal No. 3 (Black wire) and battery voltage. If test light comes on, check for open Light Green/Red wire between wire splice and condenser fan relay. If Light Green/Red wire is okay, replace condenser fan relay. If test light does not come on, check for poor ground connection at right front inner fender. If ground connection is okay, repair open Black wire between ground connection at right front inner fender and condenser fan relay.

Tracker – 1) Turn ignition on. Press A/C switch. Move blower speed selector switch to any position but OFF. If condenser fan operates, system is okay. If condenser fan does not operate, go to next step.

2) Disconnect A/C condenser fan connector. Connect a test light between connector terminals No. 1 (Blue/Black wire) and No. 2 (Black wire). If test light does not comes on, go to next step. If test light comes on, replace condenser fan.

3) Connect a test light between A/C condenser fan connector terminal No. 1 (Blue/Black wire) and ground. If test light does not come on, go to next step. If test light comes on, repair open Black wire between ground connection and condenser fan. Ground connection for condenser fan is located at right front of engine compartment, near battery.

4) Using a test light, backprobe A/C condenser fan relay connector between terminal No. 4 (Blue/Black wire) and ground. A/C condenser fan relay is located in right side of engine compartment, near fusible link box. If test light does not come on, go to next step. If test light comes on, repair open Blue/Black wire.

5) Disconnect A/C condenser fan relay connector. Connect a test light between connector terminal No. 3 (Blue/Red wire) and battery voltage. If test light does not come on, go to next step. If test light comes on, check for an open Yellow or Red wire to condenser fan relay. If wires are okay, replace A/C condenser fan relay.

6) Using a test light, backprobe A/C amplifier between terminal No. 6 (Blue/Red wire) and battery voltage. A/C amplifier is located behind right side of instrument panel, on evaporator case. If test light does not come on, replace A/C amplifier. If test light comes on, repair open Blue/Red wire between A/C amplifier and condenser fan relay.

A/C COMPRESSOR CLUTCH INOPERATIVE

Metro – 1) Start engine. Press A/C switch to on position. Move blower speed selector switch to any position but OFF. Using a test light, backprobe between compressor clutch connector terminal (Black wire) and ground. If test light does not come on, go to next step. If test light comes on, replace compressor clutch.

2) Remove fuse/relay box. Fuse/Relay box is located in engine compartment, near battery. Using a test light, backprobe between compressor clutch relay connector terminal No. 4 (Light Green/Red wire) and ground. If test light does not come on, go to next step. If test light comes on, repair open Light Green/Red wire or Black/White wire between compressor clutch and compressor clutch relay.

3) Using a test light, backprobe compressor clutch relay connector between terminal No. 2 (Red/White wire) and ground. If test light comes on, go to next step. If test light does not come on, repair open Red/White wire between compressor clutch relay and A/C fuse.

4) Using a test light, backprobe compressor clutch relay connector between terminal No. 1 (Yellow wire) and ground. If test light comes on, go to step **7)**. If test light does not come on, go to next step.

5) Disconnect dual-pressure switch connector, A/C vacuum switching valve connector and A/C compressor clutch relay connector. Using DVOM, check resistance between dual-pressure switch, terminal No. 1 (Yellow wire) and compressor clutch relay connector terminal No. 1 (Yellow wire). If resistance is less than 2 ohms, go to next step. If resistance is more than 2 ohms, repair open Yellow wire between dual-pressure switch and compressor clutch relay.

6) Connect a test light between dual-pressure switch connector terminal No. 2 (Black/White wire) and ground. If test light comes on, replace dual-pressure switch. If test light does not come on, repair open Black/White wire between connector junction block and dual-pressure switch. Junction block is located behind left side of instrument panel

7) Disconnect A/C amplifier connector. Amplifier is mounted on evaporator case. Connect a fused jumper wire between A/C amplifier connector terminal No. 7 (Pink wire) and ground. If compressor clutch engages, go to step **9)**. If compressor clutch does not engage, go to next step.

8) Backprobe compressor clutch relay using a fused jumper wire between connector terminal No.3 (Pink wire) and ground. If compressor clutch does not engage, replace compressor clutch relay. If compressor clutch engages, repair open Pink wire between compressor clutch relay and A/C amplifier.

9) Connect a test light between A/C amplifier connector terminal No. 8 (Black/White wire) and ground. If test light comes on, go to next step. If test light does not come on, repair open Black/White wire between A/C amplifier and wire splice.

10) Connect test light between A/C amplifier connector terminal No. 9 (Black wire) and battery voltage. If test light comes on, go to next step. If test light does not come on, check for bad ground connection behind right kick panel. If ground is okay, repair open Black wire between ground connection and A/C amplifier.

1993 MANUAL A/C-HEATER SYSTEMS
Metro & Tracker (Cont.)

11) Connect a test light between A/C amplifier connector terminal No. 11 (Blue/White wire) and ground. If test light does not come on, go to next step. If test light comes on, go to step **14)**.

12) Using a test light, backprobe between A/C switch connector terminal No. 2 (Blue/White wire) and ground. If test light does not come on, go to next step. If test light comes on, repair open Blue/White wire between A/C switch and A/C amplifier.

13) Using a test light, backprobe between A/C switch connector terminal No. 1 (Red/Black wire) and ground. If test light comes on, replace A/C switch. If test light does not come on, repair open Pink/Black or Red/Black wires between A/C switch and wire splice.

14) Connect a test light between A/C amplifier connector terminal No. 12 (Yellow/Black wire) and battery voltage. If test light comes on, go to step **16)**. If test light does not come on, go to next step.

15) Using a test light, backprobe between A/C Engine Coolant Temperature (ECT) switch connector terminal (Yellow/Black wire) and battery voltage. If test light does not come on, replace A/C ECT switch. If test comes on, repair open Yellow/Black wire between A/C amplifier and A/C ECT switch.

16) Disconnect evaporator thermistor connector at evaporator case. Using a DVOM, check resistance between thermistor connector terminals. Resistance check must be made at room temperature. If resistance is 2000 ohms or less, go to next step. If resistance is more than 2000 ohms, replace evaporator thermistor.

17) Reconnect evaporator thermistor. Using a DVOM, check resistance between A/C amplifier connector terminals No. 4 (White/Blue wire) and No. 10 (Yellow/Green wire). If resistance is more than 2000 ohms, repair open White/Blue or Yellow/Green wires between A/C amplifier and evaporator thermistor. If resistance is 2000 ohms or less on A/T models, go to next step. If resistance is 2000 ohms or less on M/T models, go to step **20)**.

18) On A/T models, disconnect Transaxle Control Module (TCM) 14-pin connector. TCM is located behind left side of instrument panel, near steering column. Using a DVOM, check resistance between A/C amplifier connector terminal No. 5 (Light Green/Red wire) and ground. If resistance is infinite, go to next step. If resistance is not infinite, repair short to ground in Light Green/Red wire between A/C amplifier and TCM.

19) Reconnect A/C amplifier. Using a test light, backprobe between A/C compressor clutch connector terminal and ground. If test light comes on, check for transaxle trouble codes and repair as necessary. If no codes are present, replace TCM. If test light does not come on, replace A/C amplifier.

20) On M/T models, disconnect A/C accelerator cut-off switch connector. Switch is located above accelerator pedal. Using a DVOM, between A/C amplifier connector terminal No. 5 (Light Green/Red wire) and ground. If resistance is infinite, go to next step. If resistance is not infinite, repair short to ground in Light Green/Red wire between A/C amplifier and A/C accelerator cut-off switch.

21) Using a DVOM, check resistance between A/C accelerator cut-off switch terminals (switch side). Ensure accelerator pedal is released. If resistance is more than 5 ohms, replace A/C amplifier. If resistance is 5 ohms or less, replace accelerator cut-off switch.

A/C COMPRESSOR CONTROLS

Tracker – 1) Start engine. Ensure A/C switch is in OFF position. Turn blower switch to any position but OFF. Compressor clutch should not be engaged. If compressor clutch is not engaged, go to next step. If compressor clutch is engaged, go to step **27)**.

2) Press A/C switch to on position. If compressor clutch engages but blower motor does not operate, go to TROUBLE SHOOTING (TRACKER) in appropriate HEATER SYSTEMS article. If blower motor operates but compressor clutch does not engage, go to next step.

3) Turn ignition switch to LOCK and then ON position. Using a test light, backprobe compressor clutch connector between connector terminal and ground. If test light does not come on, go to next step. If test light comes on, replace compressor clutch.

4) Using a test light, backprobe compressor clutch relay between terminal No. 4 (Black/White wire) and ground. Compressor clutch relay is located on right side of engine compartment, near fusible link box. If test light does not come on, go to next step. If test light comes on, repair open Black/White wire between compressor clutch relay and compressor clutch.

5) Using a test light, backprobe compressor clutch relay connector between terminal No. 2 (Red wire) and ground. If test light comes on, go to next step. If test light does not come on, repair open Red wire between compressor clutch relay and A/C fuse holder.

6) Using a test light, backprobe dual-pressure switch connector between terminal No. 1 (Light Green wire) and ground. Dual-pressure switch is mounted on top of receiver-drier. If test light comes on, go to next step. If test light does not come on, repair open Light Green wire between dual-pressure switch and fuse block.

7) Using a test light, backprobe dual-pressure switch connector between terminal No. 2 (Yellow wire) and ground. If test light comes on, go to next step. If test light does not come on, replace dual-pressure switch.

8) Using a test light, backprobe A/C compressor clutch relay connector between terminal No. 1 (Yellow wire) and ground. If test light comes on, go to next step. If test light does not come on, repair open Yellow wire between dual-pressure switch and compressor clutch relay.

9) Disconnect compressor clutch relay connector. Connect a test light between compressor clutch relay connector terminal No. 3 (Pink wire) and battery voltage. If test light does not come on, go to next step. If test light comes on, replace compressor clutch relay.

10) Disconnect A/C amplifier. A/C amplifier is located behind right side of instrument panel, on evaporator case. Connect DVOM between A/C compressor clutch relay connector terminal No. 3 (Pink wire) and A/C amplifier connector terminal No. 7 (Pink wire). If resistance is less than .5 ohm, go to next step. If resistance is .5 ohm or more, repair open Pink wire.

11) Using a DVOM, check resistance between terminal No. 9 (Black wire) and ground. If resistance is less than 3 ohms, go to next step. If resistance is 3 ohms or more, check for good ground connection behind right side on instrument panel, near blower case. If ground connection is okay, repair open in Black wire between ground connection and A/C amplifier.

12) Using a test light, backprobe blower speed selector switch between terminal No. 1 (Light Green wire) and ground. If test light comes on, go to next step. If test light does not come on, repair open Light Green wire between blower speed selector switch and wire splice.

13) Using a test light, backprobe blower speed selector switch connector between terminal No. 4 (Pink/Black wire) and ground. If test light comes on, go to next step. If test light does not come on, replace blower speed selector switch.

14) Using a test light, backprobe A/C switch connector between terminal No. 1 (Pink/Black wire) and ground. If test light comes on, go to next step. If test light does not come on, repair open in A/C switch fuse or Pink/Black wire between blower speed selector switch and A/C switch.

15) Using a test light, backprobe A/C switch connector between terminal No. 2 (Blue wire) and ground. If test light comes on, go to next step. If test light does not come on, replace A/C switch.

16) Connect a test light between A/C amplifier connector terminal No. 11 (Blue wire) and ground. If test light comes on, go to next step. If test light does not come on, repair open Blue wire between A/C amplifier and A/C switch.

17) Using a DVOM, check resistance between A/C amplifier connector terminal No. 12 (Yellow/Blue wire) and ground. If resistance is less than 5 ohms, go to next step. If resistance is 5 ohms or more, go to step **19)**.

18) Using a DVOM, backprobe Engine Coolant Temperature (ECT) switch between connector terminal and ground. ECT switch is located right side of engine compartment, on intake manifold. If resistance is less than 5 ohms, replace ECT switch. If resistance is 5 ohms or more, repair open Yellow/Blue wire between ECT switch and A/C amplifier.

19) Turn ignition switch to LOCK position. Connect a test light between A/C amplifier connector terminal No. 2 (Black/Yellow wire) and ground. If test light does not come on, go to step **24)**. On A/T models, if test light comes on, go to next step. On M/T models, if test light comes on, go to step **22)**.

1993 MANUAL A/C-HEATER SYSTEMS
Metro & Tracker (Cont.)

20) On A/T models, disconnect park/neutral switch connector. Switch is located on right side of transmission. Connect a test light, between A/C amplifier connector terminal No. 2 (Black/Yellow wire) and ground. If test light does not come on, go to next step. If test light comes on, repair short to voltage in Black/Yellow wire between park/neutral position switch and A/C amplifier.
21) Disconnect ignition switch connector. Connect a test light between park/neutral position switch connector terminal No. 1 (Black/Red wire) and ground. If test light does not come on, replace ignition switch. If test light comes on, repair short to voltage in Black/Red wire between park/neutral position switch and ignition switch.
22) On M/T models, if test light comes on in step **19)**, disconnect Clutch Pedal Position (CPP) switch. CPP switch is located behind left side of instrument panel, above clutch pedal. Connect a test light between A/C amplifier connector terminal No. 2 (Black/Yellow wire) and ground. If test light does not come on, go to next step. If test light comes on, repair short to voltage in Black/Yellow wire between CPP switch and A/C amplifier.
23) Disconnect ignition switch connector. Connect a test light between CPP switch connector Black/Red wire and ground. If test light comes on, repair short to voltage in Black/Red wire between CPP switch and ignition switch. If test light does not come on, replace ignition switch.
24) If test light does not come on in step **19)**, check resistance between A/C amplifier connectors No. 10 (Yellow/Green wire) and No. 4 (White/Blue wire) using a DVOM. If resistance is 2000 ohms or more, go to next step. If resistance is less than 2000 ohms, replace A/C amplifier.
25) Disconnect evaporator thermistor connector. Evaporator thermistor connector is located behind right side of instrument panel in evaporator case. Using a DVOM, check resistance between evaporator thermistor connector terminal No. 2 (Yellow/Green wire) and A/C amplifier connector terminal No. 10 (Yellow/Green wire). If resistance is less than 5 ohms, go to next step. If resistance is 5 ohms or more, repair open Yellow/Green wire between amplifier and evaporator thermistor.
26) Using a DVOM, check resistance between A/C amplifier connector terminal No. 4 (White/Blue wire) and evaporator thermistor connector terminal No. 1 (White/Blue wire). If resistance is 5 ohms or more, repair open White/Blue wire. If resistance is less than 5 ohms, replace evaporator thermistor.
27) If compressor clutch is engaged in step **1)**, disconnect A/C amplifier. A/C amplifier is located behind right side of instrument panel, on evaporator case. If compressor clutch is not engaged, go to next step. If compressor clutch is engaged, check for short to ground in Pink wire between compressor clutch relay and A/C amplifier. If Pink wire is okay, check for a short in Black/White wire between compressor clutch relay and compressor clutch. If Black/White wire is okay, replace compressor clutch relay.
28) Ensure A/C switch is off. Connect a test light between A/C amplifier connector terminal No. 11 (Blue wire) and ground. If test light does not come on, replace A/C amplifier. If test light comes on, check for short to voltage in Blue wire between A/C switch and A/C amplifier. If Blue wire is okay, replace A/C switch.

A/C COMPRESSOR CLUTCH ALWAYS ENGAGED

Metro – 1) Start engine. Disconnect A/C switch connector. If compressor is still engaged, go to next step. If compressor is not engaged, replace A/C switch.
2) Disconnect A/C amplifier connector. A/C amplifier is mounted to evaporator case. Connect a test light between A/C switch connector terminal No. 2 (Blue/White wire) and ground. If test light does not come on, go to next step. If test light comes on, repair short to voltage in Blue/White wire between A/C switch and A/C amplifier.
3) Remove fuse/relay box. Fuse/Relay box is located in engine compartment, near battery. Disconnect compressor clutch relay connector and condenser fan relay connector. If compressor clutch is not engaged, go to next step. If compressor clutch is engaged, repair short to voltage in Light Green wire between compressor clutch relay and condenser fan relay or Black/White wire between wire splice and compressor clutch.
4) Reconnect condenser fan relay connector. If compressor clutch is not engaged, go to next step. If compressor clutch is engaged, replace condenser fan relay.
5) Using a DVOM, check resistance between compressor clutch relay connector terminal No. 3 (Pink wire) and ground. If resistance is infinite, go to next step. If resistance is not infinite, repair short to ground in Pink wire between condenser fan relay and A/C amplifier.
6) Reconnect compressor clutch relay connector. If compressor clutch is not engaged, replace A/C amplifier. If compressor clutch is engaged, replace compressor clutch relay.

ENGINE COOLANT TEMPERATURE SWITCH

Metro – 1) Remove Engine Coolant Temperature (ECT) switch. Switch is located on intake manifold. Place ECT switch into container of water. Heat container. Using an ohmmeter, check switch continuity between switch terminal and switch body.
2) Continuity should exist with water temperature at 226°F (108°C) or less. With water temperature at more than 226° (108°C), continuity should not exist. If ECT switch does not test as specified, replace ECT switch.

CONDENSER FAN RELAY & COMPRESSOR CLUTCH RELAY

Remove relay from fuse/relay box. Fuse/relay box is located in engine compartment, near battery. Connect battery voltage between relay terminals No. 1 and 3. *See Fig. 3.* Using a DVOM, check for continuity between relay terminals No. 2 and 4. Continuity should exist. If continuity does not exist, replace relay.

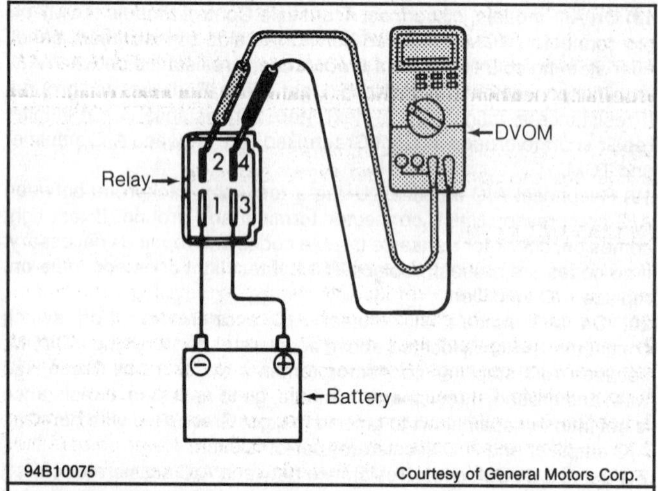
DVOM
Relay
2
4
1
3
Battery
94B10075
Courtesy of General Motors Corp.

Fig. 3: Testing Condenser Fan Relay Or Compressor Clutch Relay

EXPANSION VALVE

1) Remove expansion valve. See EVAPORATOR CORE, EXPANSION VALVE & THERMISTOR under REMOVAL & INSTALLATION. Connect A/C manifold gauge set to expansion valve. Connect gauge set charging hose to R-12 refrigerant bottle. *See Fig. 4.* Soak expansion valve's sensing bulb in water.
2) Close both high and low pressure valves. Open valve to refrigerant bottle. Open high pressure valve to approximately 70 psi (5.0 kg/cm²). Read and record low pressure gauge reading. Measure temperature of water.
3) Pressure/temperature relationship should be within specifications. See EXPANSION VALVE SPECIFICATIONS table. If pressure/temperature relationship is not within specifications, replace expansion valve.

EXPANSION VALVE SPECIFICATIONS

Water Temperature °F (C°)	Low Side Pressure psi (kg/cm²)
33 (1)	20-30 (1.4-2.1)
40 (5)	28-35 (2.0-2.5)
50 (10)	33-43 (2.3-3.0)
60 (15)	41-55 (2.9-3.9)
70 (20)	52-65 (3.7-4.6)

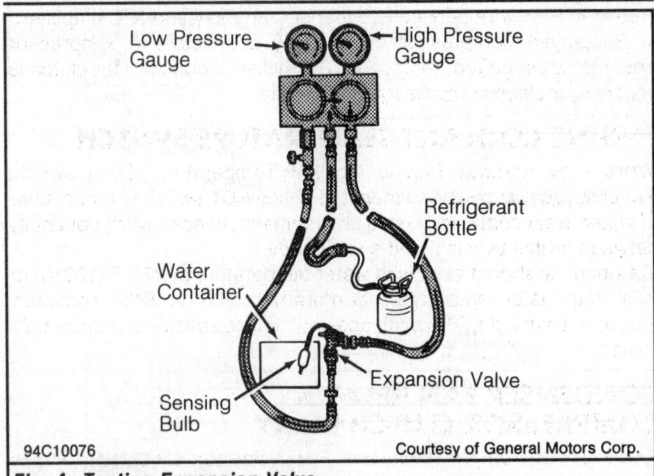
Low Pressure Gauge
High Pressure Gauge
Refrigerant Bottle
Water Container
Expansion Valve
Sensing Bulb
94C10076
Courtesy of General Motors Corp.

Fig. 4: Testing Expansion Valve

REMOVAL & INSTALLATION

WARNING: To avoid injury from accidental air bag deployment, read and carefully follow all SERVICE PRECAUTIONS and DISABLING & ACTIVATING AIR BAG SYSTEM procedures in AIR BAG SYSTEM SAFETY article in GENERAL SERVICING.

NOTE: For removal and installation procedures not covered in this article, see appropriate HEATER SYSTEMS article.

COMPRESSOR

Removal - 1) Disconnect negative battery cable. Discharge A/C system using approved refrigerant recovery/recycling equipment. Remove compressor clutch wiring harness connector.

2) Remove refrigerant lines and "O" rings at compressor. Cap all refrigerant line openings. Remove upper compressor bolt. Raise and support vehicle. On Metro, remove right lower splash shield.

3) Loosen idler pulley bolt and remove compressor drive belt. Remove 2 lower compressor bolts. On Tracker, loosen 2 lower compressor bolts and remove drive belt. On all models, remove compressor from bottom of vehicle.

Installation - 1) To install, reverse removal procedure. Use new "O" rings. If new compressor is being installed, drain 1.4 ounces of refrigerant oil from new compressor. New compressor is filled from factory with refrigerant oil for total A/C system.

2) The 1.4 ounces drained from compressor represents amount of refrigerant oil remaining in other A/C system components. Adjust drive belt. Evacuate and recharge system. Check for leaks.

CONDENSER & CONDENSER FAN

Removal - 1) Discharge A/C system using approved refrigerant recovery/recycling equipment. Disconnect high pressure line from condenser. On Metro, remove hood latch assembly. Remove center brace. On Tracker, remove front grille and grille net. Disconnect horn connector. On all models, disconnect outlet line from bottom of condenser. Cap all refrigerant line openings.

2) Disconnect condenser fan wiring harness connector. Disconnect receiver-drier outlet line and mount from front of condenser. Remove receiver-drier from mounting bracket. Remove condenser bolts. Remove condenser and condenser fan as an assembly.

Installation - To install, reverse removal procedure. If installing new condenser, add .7-1.0 ounce of refrigerant oil to suction side fitting of compressor. Evacuate and recharge system. Check for leaks.

EVAPORATOR CORE, EXPANSION VALVE & THERMISTOR

Removal (Metro) - 1) Discharge A/C system using approved refrigerant recovery/recycling equipment. Disconnect negative battery cable. Remove blower motor case. Disconnect A/C amplifier and evaporator thermistor connectors. Disconnect refrigerant lines from evaporator case.

2) Cap all refrigerant line openings. Remove drain hose from evaporator case. Remove bolts and evaporator case from vehicle. Release 2 lock tabs and slide A/C amplifier upward and remove amplifier from case. *See Fig. 5.* Separate evaporator assembly halves. Remove evaporator core from case. Remove expansion valve. Remove thermistor.

Installation - To install, reverse removal procedure. If installing new evaporator, add .7-1.0 ounce of refrigerant oil to suction side fitting of compressor. Evacuate and recharge system. Check for leaks.

Removal (Tracker) - 1) Discharge A/C system using approved refrigerant recovery/recycling equipment. Disconnect negative battery cable. Disconnect refrigerant lines from evaporator case. Cap all refrigerant line openings. Remove evaporator vase nut one engine side of bulkhead. Remove glove box.

2) Loosen 2 blower motor housing support bolts. Loosen evaporator-to-heater clamp. Slide clamp on to heater case. Remove evaporator case drain hose. Disconnect A/C amplifier and evaporator thermistor connectors. Remove 2 upper evaporator case bolts. Remove evaporator case from vehicle.

3) Release 2 lock tabs and slide A/C amplifier upward and remove amplifier from case. *See Fig. 5.* Separate evaporator assembly halves. Remove evaporator core from case. Remove expansion valve. Remove thermistor.

Installation - To install, reverse removal procedure. If installing new evaporator, add .7-1.0 ounce of refrigerant oil to suction side fitting of compressor. Evacuate and recharge system. Check for leaks.

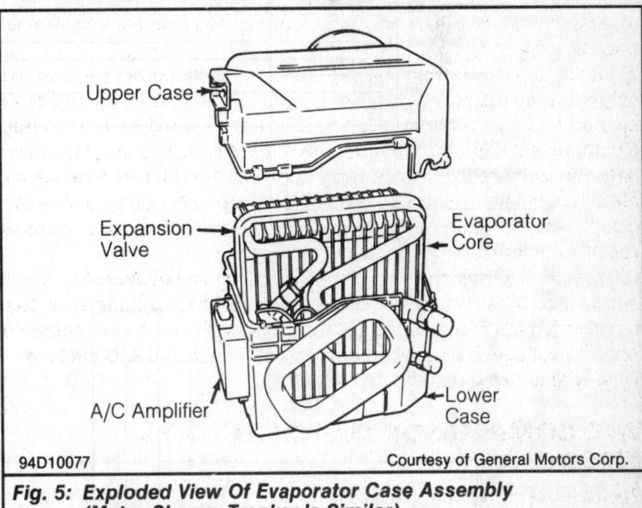
Upper Case
Expansion Valve
Evaporator Core
A/C Amplifier
Lower Case
94D10077
Courtesy of General Motors Corp.

Fig. 5: Exploded View Of Evaporator Case Assembly (Metro Shown; Tracker Is Similar)

RECEIVER-DRIER

Removal & Installation - 1) Discharge A/C system using approved refrigerant recovery/recycling equipment. Remove grille (if necessary). Disconnect receiver-drier electrical leads and refrigerant lines. Remove receiver-drier.

2) To install, reverse removal procedure. If installing new receiver-drier, add .3 ounce of refrigerant oil to suction side fitting of compressor. Evacuate and recharge system. Check for leaks.

1993 MANUAL A/C-HEATER SYSTEMS
Metro & Tracker (Cont.)

WIRING DIAGRAMS

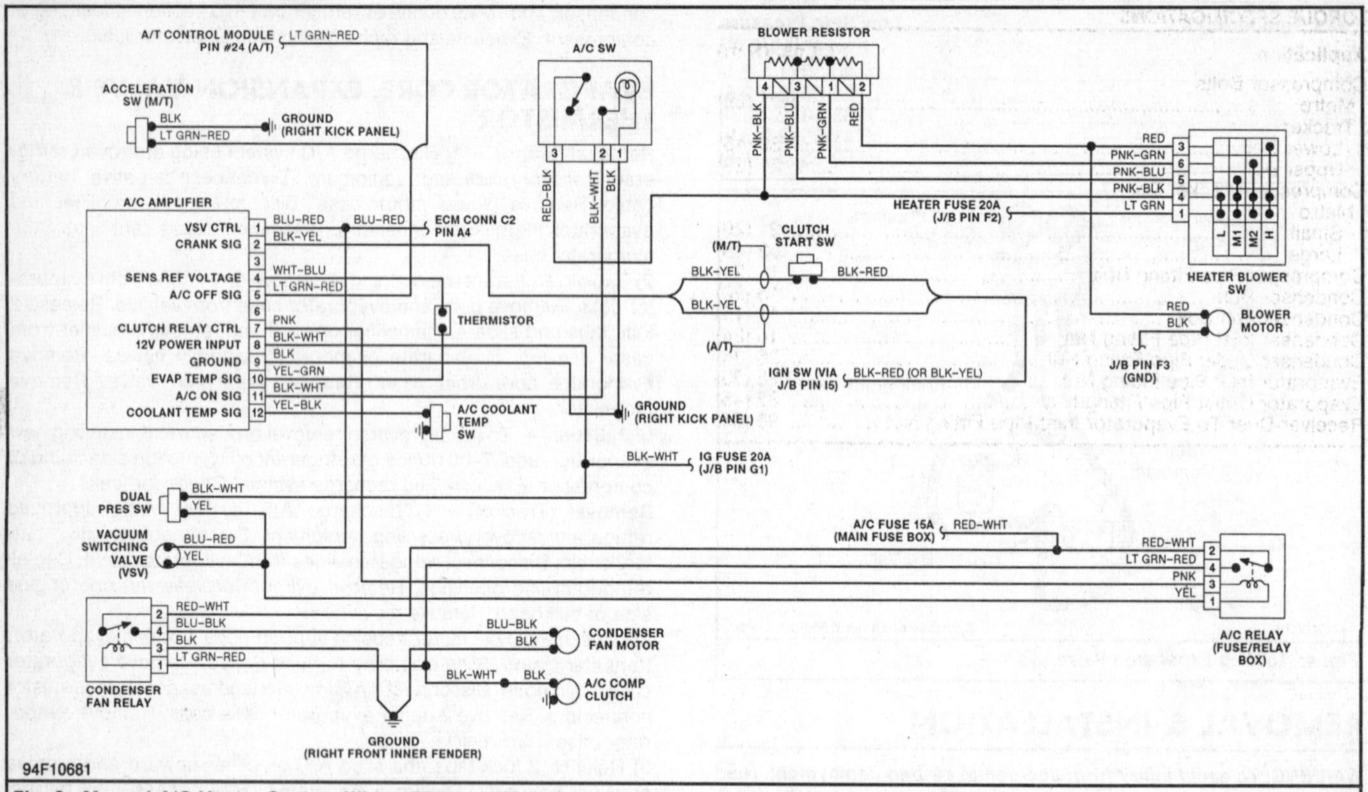

A/T CONTROL MODULE PIN #24 (A/T)
ACCELERATION SW (M/T)
GROUND (RIGHT KICK PANEL)
A/C AMPLIFIER
VSV CTRL
CRANK SIG
SENS REF VOLTAGE
A/C OFF SIG
CLUTCH RELAY CTRL
12V POWER INPUT
GROUND
EVAP TEMP SIG
A/C ON SIG
COOLANT TEMP SIG
ECM CONN C2 PIN A4
THERMISTOR
A/C COOLANT TEMP SW
A/C SW
BLOWER RESISTOR
HEATER FUSE 20A (J/B PIN F2)
CLUTCH START SW
HEATER BLOWER SW
BLOWER MOTOR
J/B PIN F3 (GND)
IGN SW (VIA J/B PIN I5)
GROUND (RIGHT KICK PANEL)
IG FUSE 20A (J/B PIN G1)
DUAL PRES SW
VACUUM SWITCHING VALVE (VSV)
A/C FUSE 15A (MAIN FUSE BOX)
A/C RELAY (FUSE/RELAY BOX)
CONDENSER FAN MOTOR
A/C COMP CLUTCH
CONDENSER FAN RELAY
GROUND (RIGHT FRONT INNER FENDER)
94F10681

Fig. 6: Manual A/C-Heater System Wiring Diagram (Metro)

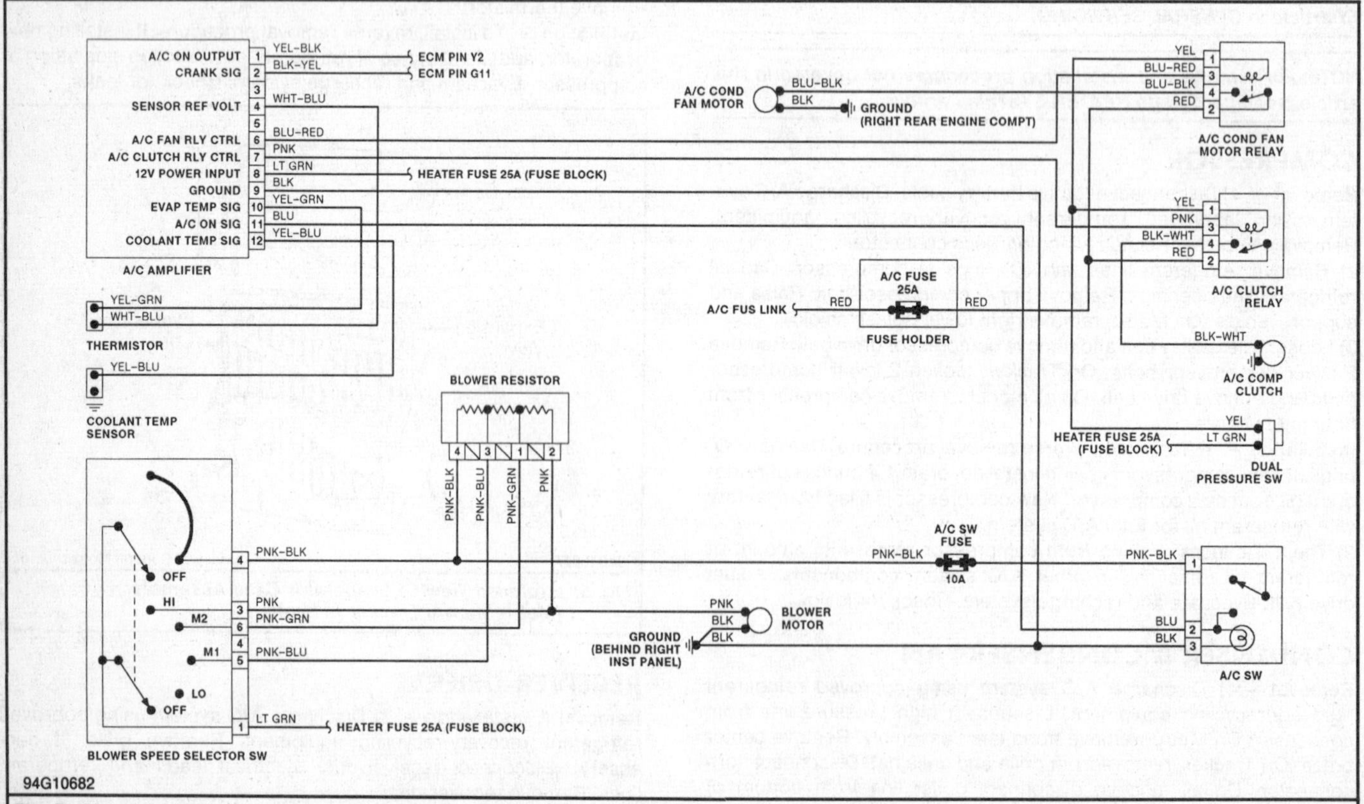

A/C ON OUTPUT
CRANK SIG
SENSOR REF VOLT
A/C FAN RLY CTRL
A/C CLUTCH RLY CTRL
12V POWER INPUT
GROUND
EVAP TEMP SIG
A/C ON SIG
COOLANT TEMP SIG
ECM PIN Y2
ECM PIN G11
HEATER FUSE 25A (FUSE BLOCK)
A/C AMPLIFIER
THERMISTOR
COOLANT TEMP SENSOR
A/C COND FAN MOTOR
GROUND (RIGHT REAR ENGINE COMPT)
A/C COND FAN MOTOR RELAY
A/C CLUTCH RELAY
A/C FUSE 25A
A/C FUS LINK
FUSE HOLDER
A/C COMP CLUTCH
HEATER FUSE 25A (FUSE BLOCK)
DUAL PRESSURE SW
BLOWER RESISTOR
A/C SW FUSE 10A
BLOWER MOTOR
GROUND (BEHIND RIGHT INST PANEL)
A/C SW
OFF
HI
M2
M1
LO
OFF
BLOWER SPEED SELECTOR SW
94G10682

Fig. 7: Manual A/C-Heater System Wiring Diagram (Tracker)

1993 MANUAL A/C-HEATER SYSTEMS
Metro & Tracker (Cont.)

TORQUE SPECIFICATIONS

TORQUE SPECIFICATIONS

Application	Ft. Lbs. (N.m)
Compressor Bolts	
Metro	21 (29)
Tracker	
Lower Bolt	33 (45)
Upper Bolt	21 (29)
Compressor Bracket Bolt	
Metro	
Small	21 (29)
Large	33 (45)
Compressor Pipe Fitting Bolt	18 (24)
Condenser Bolt	15 (20)
Condenser Fan Bolt	11 (15)
Condenser Inlet Pipe Fitting Nut	18 (24)
Condenser Outlet Pipe Fitting Nut	26 (35)
Evaporator Inlet Pipe Fitting Nut	26 (35)
Evaporator Outlet Pipe Fitting Nut	33 (45)
Receiver-Drier To Evaporator Inlet Pipe Fitting Nut	26 (35)

1993 MANUAL A/C-HEATER SYSTEMS
Prizm

SPECIFICATIONS

Compressor Type .... Nippondenso 10PA15 10-Cyl.
Compressor Belt Deflection [1]
New .... 1/4-3/32" (6-7 mm)
Used .... 11/32-3/8" (8.5-9.5 mm)
System Oil Capacity .... 6.0 ozs.
Refrigerant (R-12) Capacity .... 25 ozs.
System Operating Pressure [2]
Low Side .... 32-34 psi (2.2-2.4 kg/cm²)
High Side .... 235-245 psi (16.5-17.2 kg/cm²)

[1] – Specification is with 22 lbs. (100 N.m) force applied midway on longest span of belt.
[2] – Specification is with ambient temperature at 80°F (27°C), relative humidity at 50-70 percent and engine speed at 2000 RPM.

WARNING: To avoid injury from accidental air bag deployment, read and carefully follow all SERVICE PRECAUTIONS and DISABLING & ACTIVATING AIR BAG SYSTEM procedures in AIR BAG SYSTEM SAFETY article in GENERAL SERVICING.

DESCRIPTION

System integrates heating and air conditioning. Fresh air is used for heater operation, and fresh air or recirculated air is used for air conditioner operation. System combines heated and cooled air in proportion to temperature settings on A/C-heater control panel. System components include condenser, receiver-drier, compressor, evaporator, system protection devices and refrigerant lines.

A/C AMPLIFIER

The A/C amplifier is mounted to evaporator case. Amplifier controls operations of A/C solenoid vacuum valve and compressor clutch in response to signals received from triple-pressure switch, Engine Coolant Temperature (ECT) switch, evaporator thermistor and Engine Control Module (ECM). The A/C amplifier and ECM control A/C system and engine idle speed when A/C is on.

COMPRESSOR

The compressor compresses low pressure refrigerant vapor into a high pressure, high temperature vapor. When activated, the compressor continuously pumps R-12 refrigerant and refrigerant oil through the A/C system.

CONDENSER

The condenser assembly is located in front of radiator. The assembly is made up of coils carrying refrigerant. Fins provide cooling for rapid transfer of heat. Air passing through the condenser cools high pressure refrigerant vapor, condensing it into a liquid.

CONDENSER FAN

The condenser fan provides airflow across the condenser to dissipate heat generated by refrigerant system pressure. Air passing through the condenser cools high pressure refrigerant vapor to a liquid. Failure of condenser fan circuit may cause excessive high side pressure.

SOLENOID VACUUM VALVE

The A/C solenoid vacuum valve is controlled by A/C amplifier. During engine idle speeds, compressor exerts an excessive load on the engine. To prevent stalling or poor engine idling, the solenoid vacuum valve increases engine idle speed.

TRIPLE-PRESSURE SWITCH

The triple-pressure switch is located at right front inner fender, in the liquid line, between the receiver-drier and evaporator. Switch consists of 2 separate switches, a dual-pressure switch and a high pressure switch. The dual-pressure switch stops compressor operation by turning off the A/C compressor circuit when refrigerant pressure drops to less than 33 psi (2.3 kg/cm²) or more than 384 psi (29.9 kg/cm²). The high pressure switch opens when refrigerant pressure exceeds 192 psi (13.5 kg/cm²), allowing both cooling fans to operate at high speed. When refrigerant pressure returns to normal, fan speed is reduced to low speed.

TROUBLE SHOOTING

A/C CONDENSER FAN

1) Check A/C condenser fan operation. See A/C CONDENSER FAN PERFORMANCE under TESTING. Before performing any A/C condenser fan testing procedures, ensure all related A/C condenser fan circuit fuses and fusible links are good. Ensure audio alarm module is mounted securely in No. 1 junction block.
2) No. 1 junction block is located behind left kick panel. Ensure heater relay is mounted securely in No. 2 junction block. No. 2 junction block is located behind right kick panel. Ensure all other relays are mounted securely in A/C fuse/relay box.
3) A/C fuse/relay box is located in engine compartment, near battery. *See Fig. 1.* Ensure ground connections are clean and tight. Condenser fan grounds are located behind right kick panel and, at left front inner fender, behind headlight.
4) If A/C condenser fan still does not operate properly after performing steps **1) - 3)**, go to A/C CONDENSER FAN under TESTING.

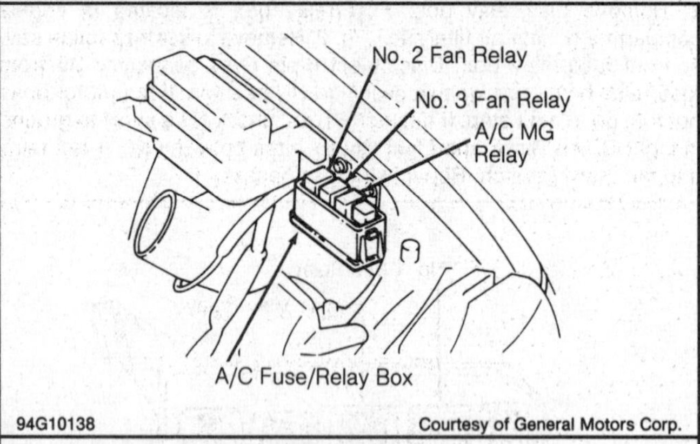
No. 2 Fan Relay
No. 3 Fan Relay
A/C MG
Relay
A/C Fuse/Relay Box
94G10138
Courtesy of General Motors Corp.

Fig. 1: Identifying A/C Fuse/Relay Box

TESTING

WARNING: To avoid injury from accidental air bag deployment, read and carefully follow all SERVICE PRECAUTIONS and DISABLING & ACTIVATING AIR BAG SYSTEM procedures in AIR BAG SYSTEM SAFETY article in GENERAL SERVICING.

NOTE: Before performing any A/C condenser fan testing procedures, perform A/C CONDENSER FAN under TROUBLE SHOOTING.

A/C CONDENSER FAN PERFORMANCE

1) Start and run engine until engine coolant temperature reaches 194°F (90°C). Radiator fan motor should run at high speed. When engine coolant temperature drops to less than 181°F (83°C), radiator fan should stop running.
2) Turn blower speed selector knob to any position other than off. Press A/C switch to on position. Start and run engine until engine coolant temperature reaches 194°F (90°C). Radiator fan and condenser fan should run at half speed. If A/C system pressure exceeds 192 psi (13.5 kg/cm²), both radiator and condenser fans will operate at high speed. A/C condenser fan will cycle on and off in conjunction with the A/C compressor clutch.
3) Press A/C switch to off position. A/C condenser fan should stop. Radiator fan will stay on until engine coolant temperature drops to less than 181°F (83°C). If condenser fan does not operate as specified, go to A/C CONDENSER FAN.

A/C CONDENSER FAN

1) Before proceeding, perform A/C CONDENSER FAN PERFORMANCE. If radiator fan does not operate, go to RADIATOR FAN INOPERATIVE. If radiator fan runs continuously at full speed with ignition switch on, go to RADIATOR FAN RUNS CONTINUOUSLY AT FULL SPEED WITH IGNITION ON.

2) If the radiator fan and condenser fan do not run at half speed during A/C system operation, go to RADIATOR FAN & CONDENSER FAN DO NOT RUN AT HALF SPEED DURING A/C SYSTEM OPERATION. If radiator fan runs continuously with ignition switch in lock position, replace engine main relay. *See Fig. 2.*

3) If condenser fan runs during A/C system operation when engine coolant temperature exceeds 194°F (90°C), but A/C system provides insufficient cooling and A/C system operation checks out okay, replace triple-pressure switch.

4) If condenser fan does not run at full speed during A/C operation when engine coolant temperature exceeds 194°F (90°C), check for open White/Black wire between ground connection and No. 2 fan relay. *See Fig. 1.* Ground is located at left front inner fender, behind headlight. If ground is okay, replace No. 2 fan relay.

RADIATOR FAN INOPERATIVE

1) Remove fuse/relay box. Fuse/relay box is located in engine compartment, near air filter. *See Fig. 2.* Remove lower inspection cover from fuse/relay box. Disconnect 6-pin Gray connector C6 from fuse/relay box. Turn ignition switch to ON position. If fan motor does not run, go to next step. If fan motor runs, check for a short to ground in Light Green/Black and Light Green wires between No. 1 fan relay and fan thermoswitch. Repair wiring as necessary.

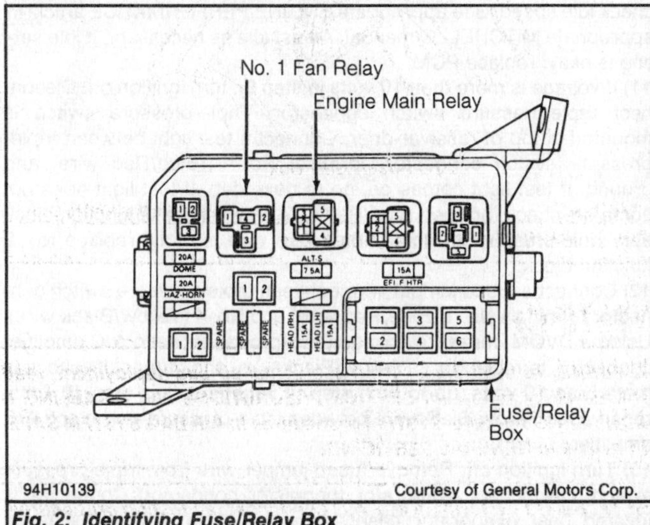
No. 1 Fan Relay
Engine Main Relay
Fuse/Relay Box
94H10139
Courtesy of General Motors Corp.

Fig. 2: Identifying Fuse/Relay Box

2) Using a test light, backprobe fuse/relay box 10-pin White connector C1 between terminal No. 4 (Blue/Black wire) and battery voltage. If test light does not come on, go to next step. If test light comes on, repair short to ground in Blue/Black wire between No. 2 fan relay connector and fuse/relay box. *See Figs. 1 and 2.*

3) Using a test light, backprobe fuse/relay box 6-pin White connector C3 between terminal No. 6 (Black/Yellow wire) and ground. If test light comes on, go to step **5)**. If test light does not come on, go to next step.

4) Using a test light, backprobe No. 3 junction block (behind center of instrument panel) 22-pin White connector C3 between terminal No. 17 (Black/Yellow wire) and ground. If test light comes on, check for open Black/Yellow wire between fuse/relay box and No. 3 junction block. Repair wiring as necessary. If test light does not come on, check for open Black/Yellow wire between No. 1 junction block and No. 3 junction block. If Black/Yellow wire is okay, replace No. 1 junction block.

5) Using a test light, backprobe fuse/relay box 10-pin White connector C1 between terminal No. 3 (White/Black wire) and battery voltage. If test light comes on, go to next step. If test light does not come on, repair open or poor connection in White/Black wire between fuse/relay box and chassis ground connection. Ground is located at left front inner fender, behind headlight.

6) Turn ignition off. Remove engine main relay from fuse/relay box. *See Fig. 2.* Connect a fused jumper between engine main relay connector terminals No. 4 and 5. See WIRING DIAGRAM. Turn ignition on. If fan motor does not run, go to next step. If fan motor runs, remove fused jumper wire from main relay connector. Replace engine main relay. If radiator fan motor is still inoperative, replace fuse/relay box.

7) Turn ignition off. Remove fused jumper from engine main relay connector and reinstall relay. Remove No. 1 fan relay. *See Fig. 2.* Connect a fused jumper between No. 1 fan relay connector terminals No. 3 and 4. See WIRING DIAGRAM. Turn ignition on. If fan motor does not run, go to next step. If fan motor runs, remove fused jumper wire from No. 1 fan relay connector. Replace No. 1 fan relay. If radiator fan motor is still inoperative, replace fuse/relay box.

8) Turn ignition off. Remove fused jumper from fan relay connector. Reinstall No. 1 fan relay. Using a test light, backprobe radiator fan motor connector between terminal No. 1 (White/Black wire) and battery voltage. If test light comes on, go to next step. If test light does not come on, check for open White/Black wire between radiator fan motor and fuse/relay box. If White/Black wire is okay, replace fuse/relay box.

9) Using a fused jumper wire, backprobe radiator fan motor connector between terminal No. 2 (Blue wire) and battery voltage. If radiator fan motor does not run, replace fan motor. If radiator fan motor runs, check for open Black/Red wire between radiator fan motor and fuse/relay box. If Black/Red wire is okay, replace fuse/relay box.

RADIATOR FAN RUNS CONTINUOUSLY AT FULL SPEED WITH IGNITION ON

1) Ensure engine coolant is less than 194°F (90°C). Remove No. 1 fan relay from fuse/relay box. *See Fig. 2.* Fuse/relay box is located in engine compartment, near air filter. Turn ignition on. If fan motor does not run, go to next step. If fan motor runs, check for a short to voltage in Black/Red wire between fuse/relay box, radiator fan motor and No. 2 fan relay. *See Figs. 1 and 2.* If Black/Red wire is okay, replace fuse/relay box.

2) Connect a test light to No. 1 fan relay connector between terminal No. 1 (Light Green/Black wire) and battery voltage. If test light does not come on, go to next step. If test light comes on, replace No. 1 fan relay and recheck system operation. If fan motor continues to run at high speed with ignition switch on, replace fuse/relay box.

3) Using a test light, backprobe triple pressure switch connector between terminal No. 2 (Light Green wire) and battery voltage. If test light comes on, go to next step. If test light does not come on, check for open Light Green wire between triple pressure switch connector and fan thermoswitch. If Light Green wire is okay, replace fan thermoswitch.

4) Check for open Light Green/Black wire between fuse/relay box and triple pressure switch connector. Repair wiring as necessary. If Light Green/Black wire is okay, replace triple-pressure switch.

RADIATOR FAN & CONDENSER FAN DO NOT RUN AT HALF SPEED DURING A/C SYSTEM OPERATION

1) Turn ignition on. Set blower speed to any position except off. If blower motor runs, go to next step. If bower motor does not run, go to TROUBLE SHOOTING (PRIZM) in appropriate HEATER SYSTEMS article.

2) Start engine. Press A/C switch to on position. If A/C clutch cycles off and on, go to next step. If A/C clutch does not cycle off and on, go to A/C COMPRESSOR CLUTCH INOPERATIVE.

3) Turn ignition off. Remove A/C fuse/relay box. A/C fuse/relay box is located in engine compartment, near battery. *See Fig. 1.* Remove A/C fuse/relay box inspection cover. Disconnect A/C amplifier connector. A/C amplifier is mounted to evaporator case. Connect a fused jumper wire between A/C amplifier connector, terminal No. 9 (Blue/Black wire) and ground. If test light comes on, go to

1993 MANUAL A/C-HEATER SYSTEMS
Prizm (Cont.)

next step. If test light does not come on, repair open Black/White wire between A/C MG relay and No. 3 fan relay. *See Fig. 1.*

4) Using a test light, backprobe No. 3 fan relay between connector No. 1 (White/Black wire) and battery voltage. If test light comes on, go to next step. If test light does not come on, repair open White/Black wire between ground connection and No. 3 fan relay. Ground is located at left front inner fender, behind headlight.

5) Using a test light, backprobe condenser fan motor connector between terminal No. 2 (Blue wire) and ground. If test light comes on, go to next step. If test light does not come on, check for open Blue/Red wire between condenser fan motor and A/C fuse/relay box. If Blue/Red wire is okay, check for open Blue wire between A/C fuse/relay box and fuse/relay box. Repair wiring as necessary. if Blue wire is okay, replace fuse/relay box.

6) Using a test light, backprobe No. 2 fan relay connector between terminal No. 1 (Blue/Black wire) and battery voltage. If test light comes on, go to next step. If test light does not come on, check for open Blue/Black wire between No. 2 fan relay and fuse/relay box. Repair wiring as necessary. If Blue/Black wire is okay, replace fuse/relay box.

7) Using a test light, backprobe No. 2 fan relay connector between terminal No. 2 (Black/Yellow wire) and ground. If test light comes on, go to next step. If test light does not come on, repair open Black/Yellow wire.

8) Using a DVOM, measure voltage (backprobe) between No. 3 fan relay connector, terminal No. 3 (White wire) and ground. If voltage is more than 10 volts, go to next step. If voltage is less than 10 volts, check for open White wire between No. 3 fan relay and condenser fan motor. Repair wiring as necessary. If White wire is okay, replace condenser fan motor.

9) Using a DVOM, measure voltage (backprobe) between No. 2 fan relay connector, terminal No. 3 (White/Red wire) and ground. If voltage is more than 10 volts, check for open Black/Red wire between wire splice and No. 2 fan relay. Repair wiring as necessary. If Black/Red wire is okay, replace No. 2 fan relay.

10) If voltage is less than 10 volts, check for open White/Red wire between No. 2 and 3 fan relays. Repair wiring as necessary. If White/Red wire is okay, replace No. 3 fan relay.

A/C COMPRESSOR CLUTCH INOPERATIVE

1) Start engine. Press A/C switch to on position. Move blower speed selector switch to any position except off. Using a test light, backprobe between compressor clutch connector terminal (Black wire) and ground. If test light does not come on, go to next step. If test light comes on, replace compressor clutch.

2) Remove A/C fuse/relay box. A/C fuse/relay box is located in engine compartment, near battery. *See Fig. 1.* Remove inspection cover from bottom of A/C fuse/relay box. Using a test light, backprobe between A/C MG relay connector terminal No. 5 (Black/White wire) and ground. If test light does not come on, go to next step. If test light comes on, repair open Black/White wire between A/C MG relay and compressor clutch.

3) Using a test light, backprobe A/C MG relay connector between terminal No. 3 (Blue/Red wire) and ground. If test light comes on, go to next step. If test light does not come on, check blower motor operation. If blower motor runs, check for open Blue/Red wire between No. 2 junction block and A/C MG relay. If Blue/Red wire is okay, replace No. 2 junction block. No. 2 junction block is located behind right kick panel. If blower motor does not run, go to step **15)**.

4) Using a test light, backprobe A/C MG relay between terminal No. 2 (Blue/Red wire) and ground. If test light comes on, go to next step. If test light does not come on, repair open Blue/Red wire between A/C MG relay connector terminals No. 2 and 3.

5) Turn ignition off. Disconnect A/C amplifier connector. A/C amplifier is mounted to evaporator case. Connect a fused jumper wire between A/C amplifier connector terminal No. 9 (Blue/Black wire) and ground. Start engine. If compressor clutch engages, go to next step. If compressor clutch does not engage, check for open Blue/Black wire between A/C MG relay and A/C amplifier. If Blue/Black wire is okay, replace A/C MG relay.

6) Remove fused jumper wire from A/C amplifier connector. Connect a test light between A/C amplifier connector terminal No. 4 (White/Black wire) and battery voltage. If test light comes on, go to next step. If test light does not come on, check for open White/Black wire between No. 2 junction block and A/C amplifier. If White/Black wire is okay, replace A/C MG relay.

7) Using a test light, backprobe A/C amplifier between terminal No. 5 (Yellow/White wire) and ground. If test light comes on, go to step **9)**. If test light does not come on, go to next step.

8) Using a test light, backprobe A/C switch connector between terminal No. 6 (Blue/Black wire) and ground. If test light comes on, check for open Yellow or Yellow/White wire between A/C switch and A/C amplifier. If wires are okay, replace A/C switch. If test light does not come on, check for open Blue/Black wire between A/C switch and No. 2 junction block. If Blue/Back wire is okay, replace No. 2 junction block.

9) If test light comes on in step **7)**, turn ignition off. Reconnect A/C amplifier connector. Press A/C switch to off position. Turn ignition on. Using a DVOM, measure voltage at Yellow/Red wire between ground and Powertrain Control Module (PCM) terminal No. 6 on M/T models or terminal No. 21 on A/T models. On all models, if voltage is more than 10 volts, go to step **11)**. If voltage is less than 10 volts, go to next step.

10) Turn ignition off. Disconnect PCM connector C1 (Gray 12-pin connector on M/T models or Gray 22-pin connector on A/T models). Using a DVOM, measure voltage at Yellow/Red wire between ground and PCM terminal No. 6 on M/T models or terminal No. 21 on A/T models. On all models, if voltage is less than 10 volts, check for short to ground in Red/Yellow wire between PCM and A/C amplifier. If Red/Yellow wire is okay, replace A/C amplifier. If voltage is more than 10 volts, check idle speed. See appropriate ENGINE PERFORMANCE article in appropriate MITCHELL® manual. Adjust idle as necessary. If idle setting is okay, replace PCM.

11) If voltage is more than 10 volts in step **9)**, turn ignition off. Disconnect triple-pressure switch connector. Triple-pressure switch is mounted in top of receiver-drier. Connect a test light between triple-pressure switch connector, terminal No. 1 (Blue/Red wire) and ground. If test light comes on, go to next step. If test light does not come on, check for open Blue/Red wire between No. 2 junction block and triple-pressure switch. If Blue/Red wire is okay, replace No. 2 junction block.

12) Connect a fused jumper wire between triple-pressure switch connector terminals No. 1 (Blue/Red wire) and No. 4 (Yellow/Black wire). Using a DVOM, measure voltage (backprobe) between A/C amplifier connector, terminal No. 1 (Yellow/Black wire) and ground. If voltage is more than 10 volts, go to next step. If voltage is less than 10 volts, repair open Yellow/Black wire between triple-pressure switch and A/C amplifier.

13) Turn ignition off. Remove fused jumper wire from triple-pressure switch. Disconnect evaporator thermistor connector. Connector is located near evaporator case. Using a DVOM, check resistance between evaporator thermistor connector terminals No. 3 (Black wire) and No. 4 (Black wire). Resistance check should be made with temperature at 77°F (25°C). If resistance is 1400-1600 ohms, go to next step. If resistance is not 1400-1600 ohms, replace evaporator thermistor.

14) Check for open Black/White wire between A/C amplifier connector terminals No. 2 and 6. If Black/White wire is okay, check for open Black/White or Black/Red wire between A/C amplifier and evaporator thermistor. If wires are okay, replace A/C amplifier.

15) If blower motor does not run in step **3)**, turn ignition off. Disconnect A/C amplifier connector. A/C amplifier is mounted to evaporator case. Start engine. Using a test light, backprobe No. 2 junction block, C1 10-pin White connector between terminal No. 6 (White/Black wire) and battery voltage. If test light comes on, go to next step. If test light does not come on, check for open White/Black wire between No. 2 junction block and ground connection. Ground connection is located behind right kick panel. If White/Black wire is okay, replace No. 2 junction block.

16) Using a test light, backprobe blower speed selector switch connector between terminal No. 3 (Blue/White wire) and battery voltage. If test light comes on, go to next step. If test light does not come on, check for open White/Black wire between No. 2 junction block and blower speed selector switch. If White/Black wire is okay, replace blower speed selector switch.

17) Using a test light, backprobe No. 2 junction block C2 9-pin White connector between terminal No. 1 (Blue/Black wire) and battery voltage. If test light comes on, go to next step. If test light does not come on, repair open Blue/White wire between No. 2 junction block and blower speed selector switch.

18) Using a test light, backprobe No. 2 junction block, C2 9-pin connector between terminal No. 6 (Red/Blue wire) and ground. If test light does not come on, go to next step. If test light comes on, replace heater relay and retest system. Heater relay is located in No. 2 junction block, behind right kick panel. If system is still inoperative, replace No. 2 junction block.

19) Using a test light, backprobe No. 3 junction block, C3 White 22-pin connector between terminal No. 19 (Red/Blue wire) and ground. If test light does not come on, go to next step. If test light comes on, check for open Red/Blue wire between No. 3 and No. 2 junction blocks. If Red/Blue wire is okay, replace No. 3 junction block.

20) Check for open Red/Blue wire between No. 3 junction block and audio alarm module. Audio alarm module is located behind left kick panel and is mounted to No. 1 junction block. If Red/Blue wire is okay, replace audio alarm module and retest system. If system is still inoperative, replace No. 1 junction block.

A/C COMPRESSOR CLUTCH ENGAGES WITH A/C SWITCH OFF & BLOWER SPEED SELECTOR SWITCH IN ANY POSITION EXCEPT OFF

Disconnect A/C amplifier connector. A/C amplifier is mounted to evaporator case. Start engine. Move blower speed selector switch to any position except off. If compressor clutch does not engage, replace compressor clutch. If compressor clutch engages, check for short to ground in Blue/Black wire between A/C MG relay and A/C amplifier. If Blue/Black wire is okay, replace A/C MG relay.

A/C SWITCH INOPERATIVE

Disconnect A/C amplifier connector. A/C amplifier is mounted to evaporator case. Move blower speed selector switch to any position except off. Press A/C switch to on position. Turn ignition on. Connect a fused jumper wire between A/C amplifier connector, terminal No. 7 (Green/White wire) and ground. If A/C switch indicator light is on, replace A/C amplifier. If A/C switch indicator light is off, check for open Green/White wire between A/C switch and A/C amplifier. If Green/White wire is okay, replace A/C switch.

REMOVAL & INSTALLATION

WARNING: To avoid injury from accidental air bag deployment, read and carefully follow all SERVICE PRECAUTIONS and DISABLING & ACTIVATING AIR BAG SYSTEM procedures in AIR BAG SYSTEM SAFETY article in GENERAL SERVICING.

NOTE: For removal and installation procedures not covered in this article, see appropriate HEATER SYSTEMS article.

COMPRESSOR

Removal – 1) Discharge A/C system using approved refrigerant recovery/recycling equipment. Disconnect negative battery cable. Remove windshield washer reservoir.

2) Disconnect compressor connector. Remove refrigerant lines at compressor, and plug fittings. Loosen idler pulley, and remove drive belt. Remove compressor mounting bolts and compressor.

Installation – To install, reverse removal procedure. Replace all seals. Fill compressor with correct amount of oil. See COMPRESSOR REFRIGERANT OIL CHECKING article in GENERAL SERVICING. Adjust drive belt. Evacuate and recharge system. Check for leaks.

CONDENSER

Removal – 1) Discharge A/C system using approved refrigerant recovery/recycling equipment. Disconnect battery cables. Remove battery. Remove front grille and horn. Remove hood latch. Remove center core support brace. Remove cooling system recovery tank and bracket.

2) Disconnect receiver-drier refrigerant lines. Remove receiver-drier. Disconnect condenser fan motor connector. Remove condenser fan motor. Disconnect oxygen sensor connector. Remove oxygen sensor.

3) Disconnect compressor discharge line at condenser. Remove bolts from radiator support bracket and remove brackets. Remove condenser bolts. Lean radiator back and remove condenser.

Installation – To install, reverse removal procedure. Replace all seals. Fill compressor with correct amount of oil. See COMPRESSOR REFRIGERANT OIL CHECKING article in GENERAL SERVICING. Evacuate and recharge system. Check for leaks.

EVAPORATOR CORE & EXPANSION VALVE

Removal – 1) Discharge A/C system using approved refrigerant recovery/recycling equipment. Disconnect negative battery. Remove right kick panel. Remove glove box. Disconnect evaporator refrigerant lines from evaporator. Remove hold-down bracket for evaporator refrigerant lines.

2) Disconnect A/C amplifier connector and remove A/C amplifier. Disconnect evaporator thermistor connector. Disconnect nuts and screws, and remove evaporator case from vehicle. Separate evaporator assembly halves.

3) Remove evaporator thermistor from evaporator. Remove evaporator core from case. Disconnect expansion valve inlet line from expansion valve. Remove expansion valve.

Installation – To install, reverse removal procedure. Use new seals on refrigerant lines. Fill compressor with correct amount of oil. See COMPRESSOR REFRIGERANT OIL CHECKING article in GENERAL SERVICING. Evacuate and recharge system. Check for leaks.

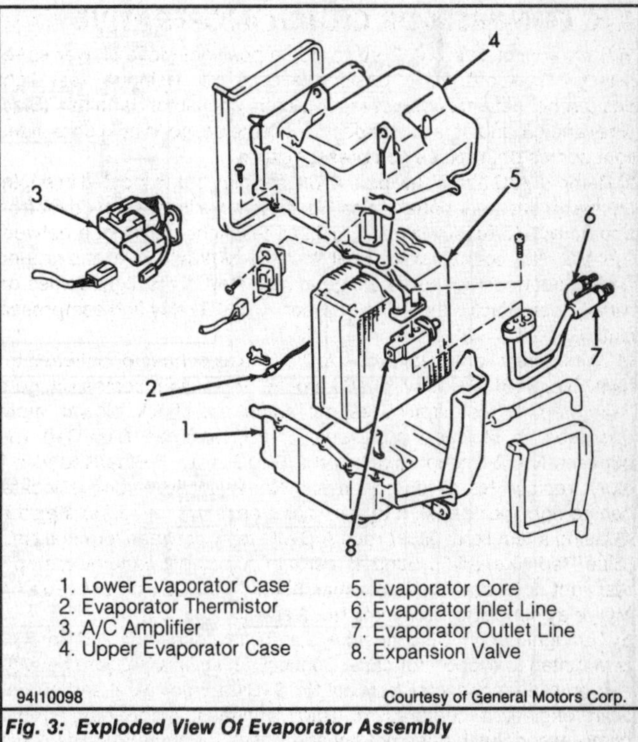
1
2
3
4
5
6
7
8
1. Lower Evaporator Case
2. Evaporator Thermistor
3. A/C Amplifier
4. Upper Evaporator Case
5. Evaporator Core
6. Evaporator Inlet Line
7. Evaporator Outlet Line
8. Expansion Valve
94I10098
Courtesy of General Motors Corp.

Fig. 3: Exploded View Of Evaporator Assembly

1993 MANUAL A/C-HEATER SYSTEMS
Prizm (Cont.)

WIRING DIAGRAM

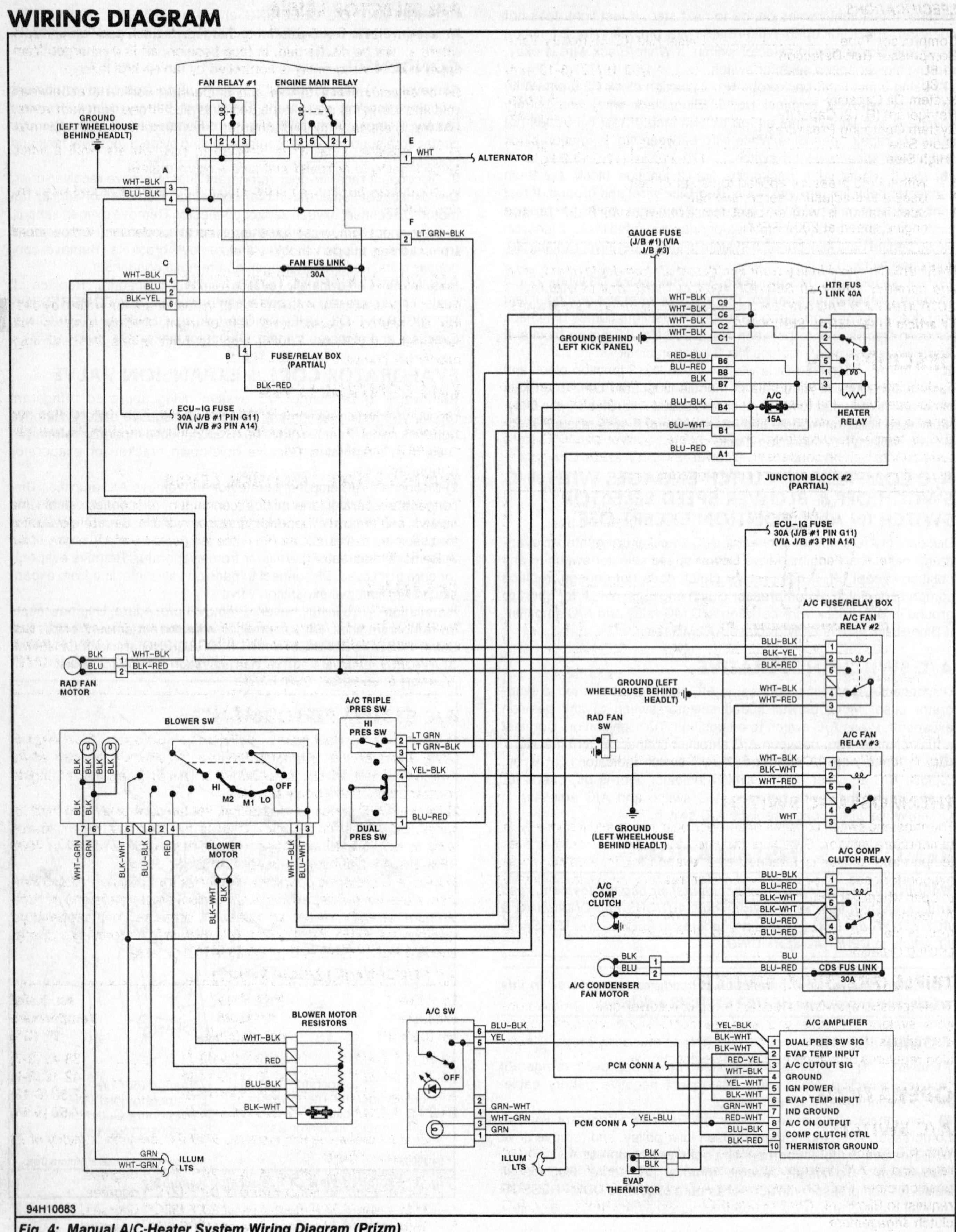

FAN RELAY #1
ENGINE MAIN RELAY
GROUND (LEFT WHEELHOUSE BEHIND HEADLT)
ALTERNATOR
FAN FUS LINK 30A
FUSE/RELAY BOX (PARTIAL)
ECU-IG FUSE 30A (J/B #1 PIN G11) (VIA J/B #3 PIN A14)
GAUGE FUSE (J/B #1) (VIA J/B #3)
HTR FUS LINK 40A
GROUND (BEHIND LEFT KICK PANEL)
A/C 15A
HEATER RELAY
JUNCTION BLOCK #2 (PARTIAL)
A/C FUSE/RELAY BOX
A/C FAN RELAY #2
A/C FAN RELAY #3
A/C COMP CLUTCH RELAY
RAD FAN MOTOR
A/C TRIPLE PRES SW
HI PRES SW
DUAL PRES SW
BLOWER SW
BLOWER MOTOR
GROUND (LEFT WHEELHOUSE BEHIND HEADLT)
RAD FAN SW
A/C COMP CLUTCH
A/C CONDENSER FAN MOTOR
CDS FUS LINK 30A
BLOWER MOTOR RESISTORS
A/C SW
A/C AMPLIFIER
DUAL PRES SW SIG
EVAP TEMP INPUT
A/C CUTOUT SIG
GROUND
IGN POWER
EVAP TEMP INPUT
IND GROUND
A/C ON OUTPUT
COMP CLUTCH CTRL
THERMISTOR GROUND
PCM CONN A
ILLUM LTS
EVAP THERMISTOR
94H10683

Fig. 4: Manual A/C-Heater System Wiring Diagram (Prizm)

1993 MANUAL A/C-HEATER SYSTEMS
Storm

SPECIFICATIONS

Compressor Type .... Diesel Kiki KC-50 Rotary Vane
Compressor Belt Defection
 1.6L .... [1] 1/32-15/32" (8-12 mm)
 1.8L .... [2]
System Oil Capacity .... 5.1 ozs.
Refrigerant (R-12) Capacity .... 21 ozs.
System Operating Pressures [3]
 Low Side .... 18-23 psi (1.3-1.6 kg/cm²)
 High Side .... 170-210 psi (12.0-14.8 kg/cm²)

[1] – With thumb pressure applied to center of belt.
[2] – Uses a self-adjusting serpentine belt.
[3] – Specification is with ambient temperature at 80°F (27°C), and engine speed at 2000 RPM.

WARNING: To avoid injury from accidental air bag deployment, read and carefully follow all SERVICE PRECAUTIONS and DISABLING & ACTIVATING AIR BAG SYSTEM procedures in AIR BAG SYSTEM SAFETY article in GENERAL SERVICING.

DESCRIPTION

System integrates heating and air conditioning. Fresh air is used for heater operation, and fresh air or recirculated air is used for air conditioner operation. System combines heated and cooled air in proportion to temperature settings on A/C-heater control panel. System components include condenser, receiver-drier, compressor, evaporator, system protection devices and refrigerant lines.

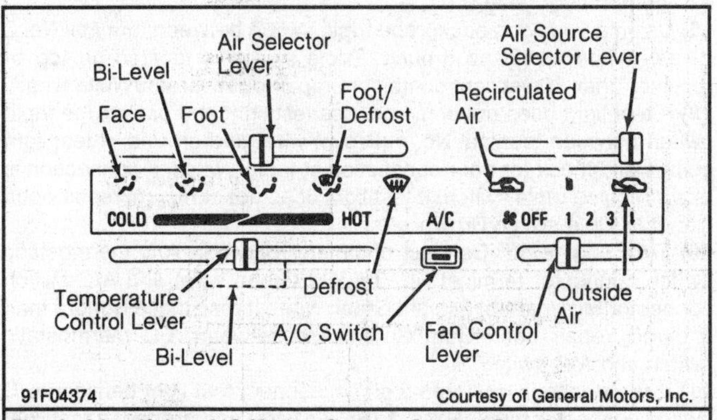
Air Selector Lever
Bi-Level
Face
Foot
Foot/ Defrost
Recirculated Air
Air Source Selector Lever
COLD
HOT
A/C
OFF 1 2 3 4
Temperature Control Lever
Bi-Level
Defrost
A/C Switch
Fan Control Lever
Outside Air
91F04374
Courtesy of General Motors, Inc.

Fig. 1: Identifying A/C-Heater System Control Panel

THERMOSTATIC SWITCH

Thermostatic switch consists of an electronic switch and a probe-type temperature sensor. Switch is fastened to evaporator case and its temperature sensor is attached to a evaporator fin located inside evaporator case. To prevent evaporator freezing, switch is calibrated to open whenever evaporator temperature drops to 37°F (3°C) or less. At temperatures less than 37°F (3°C), evaporator fins will develop frost or ice. This reduces airflow through evaporator core and lowers cooling capacity.

TRIPLE (PRESSURE) SWITCH

Triple (pressure) switch is located in top of receiver-drier. Switch monitors system pressure and ensures compressor magnetic clutch disengages if pressure is not within proper operating range. Switch also regulates operation of condenser cooling fan.

OPERATION

A/C SWITCH

With A/C switch depressed, voltage is supplied to coil of A/C thermo relay and to A/C thermostatic switch. With fan control lever in any position other than off, depressing A/C switch will provide an A/C request to Electronic Control Unit (ECM), and if conditions allow, A/C clutch engagement.

AIR SELECTOR LEVER

Air selector lever has 5 positions. *See Fig. 1.* Each position controls where air will be discharged. In face position, air is discharged from upper outlets. Air quantity is controlled by fan control lever.

Set air selector lever to bi-level and temperature control lever between cold and hot. In this position, heated air is discharged from floor vents, and fresh, unheated air is discharged from center and side registers.

In foot position, most air is directed to floor outlets, with a small amount going to defroster and side window outlets.

In foot/defrost position, air is directed to floor, defroster and side window outlets.

In defrost position, most air is directed to windshield, with a small amount going to side window outlets.

AIR SOURCE SELECTOR LEVER

Intake of outside air and circulation of inside air are controlled by sliding air source selector lever left or right. Sliding lever to left recirculates inside air. Sliding lever to right brings fresh air into passenger compartment. *See Fig. 1.*

FAN CONTROL LEVER

Fan control lever regulates blower fan speed. Four fan speeds are available. *See Fig. 1.* In order for A/C system to operate, blower fan must be in one of 4 speeds.

TEMPERATURE CONTROL LEVER

Temperature control lever controls amount of airflow through and/or around heater core. Depending upon system control positions, mixture of warm and cold air regulates temperature and humidity of air inside of vehicle. *See Fig. 1.*

TESTING

WARNING: To avoid injury from accidental air bag deployment, read and carefully follow all SERVICE PRECAUTIONS and DISABLING & ACTIVATING AIR BAG SYSTEM procedures in AIR BAG SYSTEM SAFETY article in GENERAL SERVICING.

A/C SYSTEM PERFORMANCE

1) Install A/C manifold gauge set. Open vehicle doors. Start engine. Using a jumper wire, ground condenser fan check connector White wire. Condenser fan check connector is located in left rear of engine compartment, above brake booster.

2) Depress A/C switch to on position, set fan control lever to third (3) speed, set temperature control lever to full cold and set air source lever to recirculated air. Raise and maintain engine speed at 2000 RPM. Place a thermometer in right center air outlet.

3) Allow A/C system to operate and stabilize for 5 minutes. After 5 minutes, measure and record ambient (outside) temperature and air temperature at right center air outlet. If pressure and temperature readings are within specification, A/C system is performing properly. See A/C PERFORMANCE SPECIFICATIONS table.

A/C PERFORMANCE SPECIFICATIONS

Low Side [1] Pressure psi (kg/cm²)	High Side [1] Pressure psi (kg/cm²)	Air Outlet Temperature F° (C°)
15-20 (1.1-1.4) [2]	150-180 (10.5-12.7)	38-45 (3-7)
18-23 (1.3-1.6) [3]	170-210 (11.9-14.8)	42-48 (6-9)
22-27 (1.5-1.9) [4]	190-230 (13.4-16.2)	42-53 (6-12)
24-30 (1.7-2.1) [5]	220-270 (15.5-18.9)	47-58 (8-14)

[1] – System pressures can increase 5-10 percent with humidity of 70 percent or more.
[2] – With ambient air temperature of 70°F (21C°) degrees.
[3] – With ambient air temperature of 80°F (27C°) degrees.
[4] – With ambient air temperature of 90°F (32C°) degrees.
[5] – With ambient air temperature of 100°F (38C°) degrees.

1993 MANUAL A/C-HEATER SYSTEMS
Storm (Cont.)

PRELIMINARY INSPECTION

1) Ensure fuses C-11, C-21 and E-2 are good. Fuses are located in fuse block, behind left kick panel. Ensure fusible link FL-2 is good. Fusible link is located in engine compartment fuse/relay box, near battery.

2) Ensure all A/C related relays are securely mounted in fuse/relay box or relay box. Relay box is located in engine compartment, near right strut. Fuse/relay box is located on left side of engine compartment, near battery. Ensure A/C system is fully charged.

3) If compressor clutch is always engaged, check for a short to voltage in Green/Orange wire between compressor relay, compressor clutch and Electronic Control Unit (ECM). Also, check for short to voltage in Green and Black wires between compressor relay and compressor clutch.

4) If compressor clutch engages every time fan control switch is turned on, check for short to voltage in Light Green wire between A/C switch, thermo relay and thermostatic switch. If wire is okay, replace A/C switch.

A/C SYSTEM ELECTRICAL CIRCUIT

1) Start and run engine. Turn on A/C. Move fan control lever to first (1) speed. If A/C clutch engages, system is operating properly.

2) If clutch does not engage, turn engine off. Disconnect A/C compressor temperature switch from clutch switch, located near A/C compressor. Connect a test light between switch connector terminal and ground. Start engine. If test light comes on, replace A/C compressor clutch.

3) If test light does not come on, turn engine off. Disconnect A/C compressor switch located behind radiator. Connect a test light between A/C compressor switch connector terminal and ground. Start engine. If test light comes on, replace A/C compressor temperature switch.

4) If test light does not come on, turn engine off. Remove A/C compressor relay from fuse/relay box located on left side of engine compartment, near battery. Connect an ohmmeter between A/C compressor relay connector terminal No. 4 (Green wire) and A/C compressor clutch connector terminal. If resistance is more than 5 ohms, repair open Green wire between A/C compressor relay and A/C compressor clutch.

5) If resistance is less than 5 ohms, connect a test light between A/C compressor relay connector terminal No. 2 (Green/Orange wire) and ground. Start engine. If test light does not come on, go to step **8)**.

6) If test light comes on, connect a test light between A/C compressor relay connector terminal No. 3 (Gray/Red wire) and voltage source. If test light does not come on, go to step **14)**.

7) If test light comes on, connect a test light between A/C compressor relay connector terminal No. 1 (Brown wire) and ground. If test light comes on, replace A/C compressor relay. If test light does not come on, repair open Brown wire in A/C compressor relay circuit.

8) Turn engine off. Remove A/C thermo relay from relay box. Connect a test light between A/C thermo relay connector terminal No. 3 (Pink/Green wire) and voltage source. Start engine. If test light comes on, go to step **16)**. If test light does not come on, go to next step.

9) Disconnect A/C thermostatic switch connector, located on evaporator assembly. Connect ohmmeter between A/C thermo relay connector terminal No. 3 (Pink/Green wire) and A/C thermostatic switch connector terminal No. 1 (Pink/Green wire), located on evaporator assembly. If resistance is more than 5 ohms, repair open Pink/Green wire between A/C thermo relay and A/C thermostatic switch. If resistance is 5 ohms or less, go to next step.

10) Connect a test light between A/C thermostatic switch connector terminal No. 3 (Light Green wire) and ground. Restart engine. If test light does not come on, go to step **20)**.

11) If test light comes on, connect test light between fan control lever switch connector terminal No. 2 (Black wire) and voltage source. If test light does not come on, repair fan control lever switch Black wire.

12) If test light comes on, connect test light between fan control lever switch connector terminal No. 5 (Green/Yellow wire) and ground. If test light does not come on, replace fan control lever switch.

13) If test light comes on, connect test light between A/C thermostatic switch connector terminal No. 2 (Green/Yellow wire) and voltage source. If test light comes on, replace A/C thermostatic switch. If test light does not come on, repair open Green/Yellow wire between A/C thermostatic switch and fan control lever switch.

14) Using a DVOM, backprobe Engine Control Module (ECM) connector between terminal B8 (Green/Orange wire) and ground. ECM is located behind instrument panel, left of steering column. If voltage is less than 10 volts, repair open Green/Orange wire between ECM and A/C thermo relay.

15) If voltage is 10 volts or more, use a test light and backprobe ECM connector between terminal A2 (Gray/Red wire) and voltage source. If test light comes on, repair open Gray/Red wire between ECM and A/C compressor relay. If test light does not come on, ECM is not providing proper ground. If inputs to ECM are normal and no diagnostic codes are set, replace ECM.

16) Connect test light between A/C thermo relay connector terminal No. 2 (Green/White wire) and ground. If test light does not come on, go to step **18)**. If test light comes on, connect test light between A/C thermo relay connector terminal No. 1 (Light Green wire) and ground. If test light does not come on, repair open Light Green wire between A/C thermo relay and A/C switch.

17) If test light comes on, connect an ohmmeter between A/C thermo relay connector terminal No. 4 (Green/Orange wire) and compressor relay connector terminal No. 2 (Green/Orange wire). If resistance is less than 5 ohms, replace A/C thermo relay. If resistance is 5 ohms or more, repair open Green/Orange wire between A/C thermo relay and A/C compressor relay.

18) Using a test light, backprobe triple switch between terminal No. 2 (Green/White wire) and ground. Triple switch is located on top of receiver-drier. If test light comes on, repair open Green/White wire.

19) If test light does not come on, use test light and backprobe triple switch between terminal No. 4 (Brown wire) and ground. If test light comes on, check for poor connection at triple switch. If connection is okay, replace triple switch. If test light does not come on, repair open circuit in triple switch Brown wire.

20) Turn engine off. Connect ohmmeter between A/C thermostatic switch connector terminal No. 3 (Light Green wire) and A/C switch connector terminal No. 2 (Light Green wire). If resistance is more than 5 ohms, repair open Light Green wire between A/C thermostatic switch and A/C switch.

21) If resistance is less than 5 ohms, connect test light between A/C switch connector terminal No. 1 (Brown wire) and ground. If test light comes on, replace A/C switch.

22) If test light does not come on, turn engine off. Remove A/C-heater relay from fuse/relay box. Connect test light between A/C-heater relay connector terminal No. 2 (White wire) and ground. Start engine. If test light does not come on, repair open circuit in A/C-heater relay White wire. If test light comes on, go to next step.

23) Turn engine off. Connect an ohmmeter between A/C-heater relay connector terminal No. 4 (Blue wire) and A/C switch connector terminal No. 1 (Brown wire). If resistance is less than 5 ohms, go to next step. If resistance is more than 5 ohms, repair open Blue wire between A/C-heater relay and fuse E-2, or Brown wire between fuse E-2 and A/C switch.

24) Connect ohmmeter between A/C-heater relay connector terminal No. 3 (Black wire) and ground. If resistance is 5 ohms or more, repair A/C-heater relay Black ground wire. If resistance is less than 5 ohms, go to next step.

25) Connect a test light between A/C-heater relay terminal No. 1 (White/Red wire) and ground. Start engine. If test light comes on, replace A/C-heater relay. If test light does not come on, go to next step.

26) Turn engine off. Remove restart relay from fuse/relay box. Connect ohmmeter between restart relay connector terminal No. 5 (White/Red wire) and A/C-heater relay connector terminal No. 1 (White/Red wire). If resistance is 5 ohms or more, repair open White/Red wire between restart relay and A/C-heater relay. If resistance is less than 5 ohms, go to next step.

27) Disconnect alternator. Connect DVOM between restart relay connector terminal No. 4 (White/Blue wire) and alternator connector terminal No. 1 (White/Blue wire). If resistance is less than 5 ohms, replace restart relay. If resistance is 5 ohms or more, repair open White/Blue wire between restart relay and alternator.

CONDENSER FAN

1) Start and run engine until coolant temperature reaches 179°F (82°C). Turn engine off. Remove condenser fan relay and radiator fan relay from fuse/relay box, located on left side of engine compartment next to battery. Using a DVOM, measure resistance between condenser fan relay connector terminal No. 3 (White wire) and radiator fan relay connector terminal No. 3 (White wire). If resistance is less than 2 ohms, go to next step. If resistance is 2 ohms or more, repair open White wire between radiator fan relay and condenser fan relay.
2) Connect test light between condenser fan relay connector terminal No. 1 (White/Red wire) and ground. Start engine. If test light comes on, go to next step. If test light does not come on, repair open in White/Red wire between condenser fan relay and radiator fan relay.
3) Turn engine off. Connect test light between condenser fan relay connector terminal No. 2 (Blue/Orange wire) and ground. If test light comes on, go to next step. If test light does not come on, repair open in Blue/Orange wire between fuse E-4 and condenser fan relay.
4) Disconnect condenser fan motor connector. Using a DVOM, measure resistance between condenser fan relay connector terminal No. 4 (Blue wire) and condenser fan motor connector terminal No. 1 (Blue wire). If resistance is less than 2 ohms, go to next step. If resistance is 2 ohms or more, repair open in Blue wire between condenser fan motor and fuse/relay box.
5) Reinstall condenser fan motor relay. Start engine. Using a test light, backprobe between condenser fan motor connector terminal No. 1 (Blue wire) and ground. If test light comes on, go to next step. If test light does not come on, replace condenser fan motor.
6) Turn engine off. Disconnect condenser fan motor connector. Using a DVOM, measure resistance between condenser fan motor connector terminal No. 2 (Black wire) and ground. If resistance is less than 3 ohms, replace condenser fan motor. If resistance is 3 ohms or more, repair Black wire between ground connection and condenser fan motor. Ground connection is located at right front of engine compartment, behind headlight.

REMOVAL & INSTALLATION

WARNING: To avoid injury from accidental air bag deployment, read and carefully follow all SERVICE PRECAUTIONS and DISABLING & ACTIVATING AIR BAG SYSTEM procedures in AIR BAG SYSTEM SAFETY article in GENERAL SERVICING.

NOTE: For removal and installation procedures not covered in this article, see appropriate HEATER SYSTEMS article.

A/C COMPRESSOR

Removal & Installation – 1) Disconnect negative battery cable. Discharge A/C system using approved refrigerant recovery/recycling equipment. Disconnect wiring harness connector.
2) Remove refrigerant lines at compressor, and plug fittings. Loosen compressor mounting bolts, and remove drive belt or serpentine belt. Remove engine undercover (if installed).
3) Remove compressor mounting bolts and A/C compressor. To install, reverse removal procedure. Replace all seals. Evacuate and recharge system. Check for leaks. Adjust drive belt (1.6L).

CONDENSER

Removal & Installation – 1) Disconnect negative battery cable. Discharge A/C system using approved refrigerant recovery/recycling equipment. Remove support bracket. Disconnect triple (pressure) switch and condenser fan connectors. Remove compressor discharge line at condenser.
2) Remove receiver-drier outlet line at receiver-drier. Cap open fittings to prevent contamination from entering system. Remove 2 condenser bolts. Remove condenser, condenser fan and receiver-drier as an assembly.
3) To install, reverse removal procedure. Replace all seals. Fill condenser with one ounce of refrigerant oil. Evacuate and recharge system. Check for leaks.

EVAPORATOR CORE

Removal & Installation – 1) Disconnect negative battery cable. Discharge A/C system using approved refrigerant recovery/recycling equipment. Remove refrigerant lines from expansion valve. Remove expansion valve. Remove evaporator case nut from bulkhead in engine compartment.
2) Remove glove box assembly and lower dash support bracket. Disconnect air inlet cable. Remove electrical connectors from A/C thermostatic switch and blower motor resistor. Remove 2 evaporator case nuts.
3) Remove evaporator case. *See Fig. 2.* Remove evaporator case clips and screws. Separate evaporator case into 2 halves. Remove evaporator core from lower case.
4) To install, reverse removal procedure. Use NEW seals on refrigerant lines. Evacuate and recharge system.

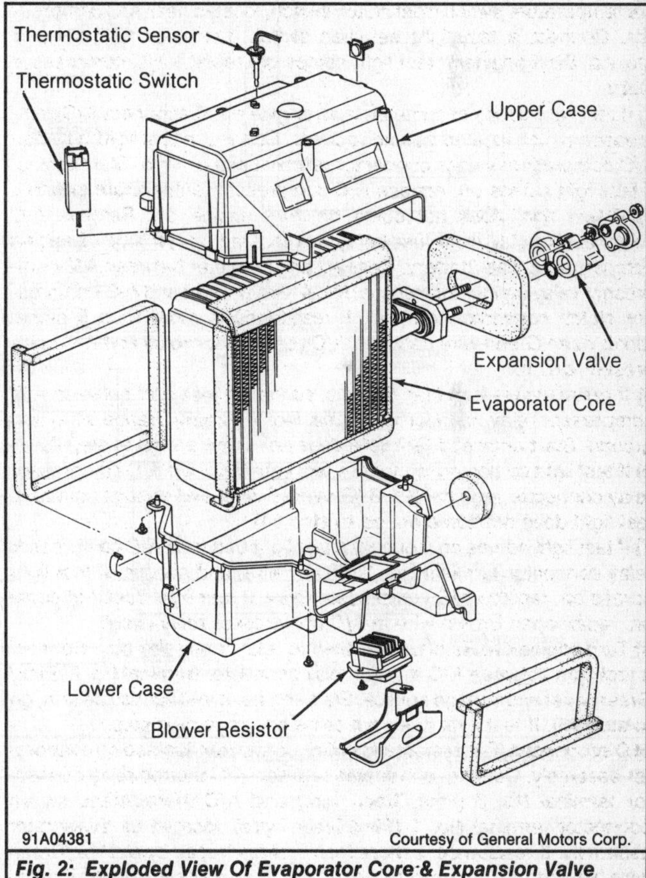
Thermostatic Sensor
Thermostatic Switch
Upper Case
Expansion Valve
Evaporator Core
Lower Case
Blower Resistor
91A04381
Courtesy of General Motors Corp.

Fig. 2: Exploded View Of Evaporator Core & Expansion Valve Assembly

EXPANSION VALVE

Removal & Installation – Discharge A/C system using approved refrigerant recovery/recycling equipment. Remove refrigerant line clamps. Remove expansion valve refrigerant lines and retaining clamp. Remove expansion valve. To install, reverse removal procedure. *See Fig. 2.*

1993 MANUAL A/C-HEATER SYSTEMS
Storm (Cont.)

RECEIVER-DRIER

Removal & Installation – 1) Remove condenser. See CONDENSER. Remove refrigerant line at receiver-drier. Cap open fittings to prevent moisture and dust from entering system. Remove triple (pressure) switch connector. Remove receiver-drier mounting screws. Remove receiver-drier.

2) To install, reverse removal procedure. Add one ounce of clean refrigerant oil to system. Use NEW seals on refrigerant lines. Evacuate and recharge system. Check for leaks.

TORQUE SPECIFICATIONS

TORQUE SPECIFICATIONS

Application	Ft. Lbs. (N.m)
Compressor Lower & Upper Bolts	30 (40)
Compressor Bracket Bolts	30 (40)
Evaporator Case Nuts	11 (15)
	INCH Lbs. (N.m)
Condenser Fan Bolts	89 (10)
Condenser Retaining Bolts	62 (7)
Receiver-Dryer Mounting Bolts	89 (10)

WIRING DIAGRAM

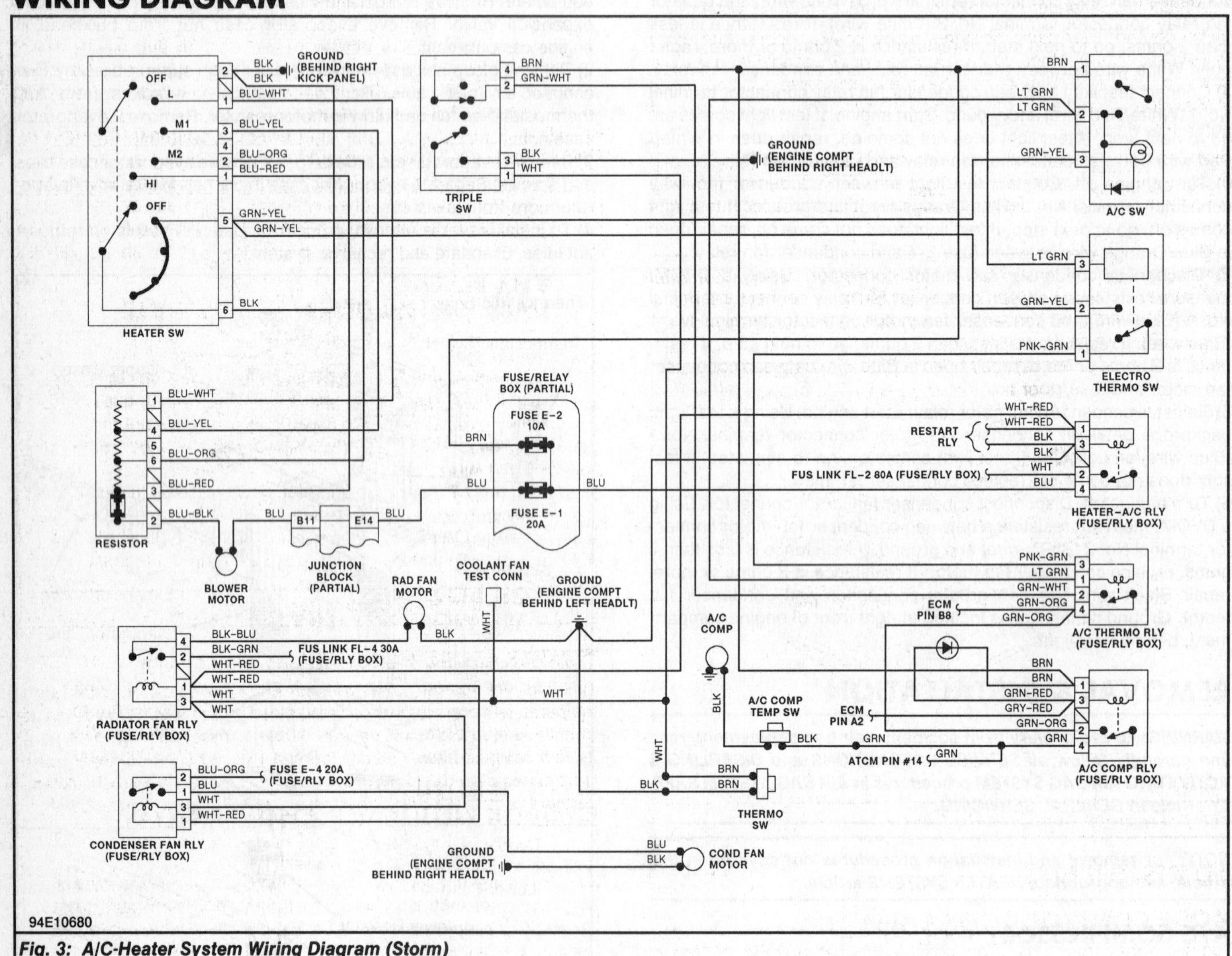
HEATER SW
OFF
L
M1
M2
HI
GROUND (BEHIND RIGHT KICK PANEL)
TRIPLE SW
A/C SW
GROUND (ENGINE COMPT BEHIND RIGHT HEADLT)
ELECTRO THERMO SW
RESISTOR
BLOWER MOTOR
JUNCTION BLOCK (PARTIAL)
FUSE/RELAY BOX (PARTIAL)
FUSE E-2 10A
FUSE E-1 20A
RESTART RLY
FUS LINK FL-2 80A (FUSE/RLY BOX)
HEATER-A/C RLY (FUSE/RLY BOX)
RAD FAN MOTOR
COOLANT FAN TEST CONN
GROUND (ENGINE COMPT BEHIND LEFT HEADLT)
A/C COMP
ECM PIN B8
A/C THERMO RLY (FUSE/RLY BOX)
FUS LINK FL-4 30A (FUSE/RLY BOX)
RADIATOR FAN RLY (FUSE/RLY BOX)
A/C COMP TEMP SW
ECM PIN A2
ATCM PIN #14
A/C COMP RLY (FUSE/RLY BOX)
FUSE E-4 20A (FUSE/RLY BOX)
CONDENSER FAN RLY (FUSE/RLY BOX)
THERMO SW
GROUND (ENGINE COMPT BEHIND RIGHT HEADLT)
COND FAN MOTOR
94E10680

Fig. 3: A/C-Heater System Wiring Diagram (Storm)

1993 HONDA CONTENTS

GENERAL SERVICING

HEATER SYSTEMS

HEATER SYSTEMS (Cont.)

MANUAL A/C-HEATER SYSTEMS

1993 HONDA CONTENTS (Cont.)

MANUAL A/C-HEATER SYSTEMS (Cont.)

CIVIC & CIVIC DEL SOL **Page**

MANUAL A/C-HEATER SYSTEMS (Cont.)

PRELUDE **Page**

1993 HEATER SYSTEMS
Accord & Prelude

DESCRIPTION

The heating and ventilating system consists of heater control panel, heater assembly, blower assembly, heater ducts and hoses. *See Fig. 1, 2 or 3.* On lever-type heater control panels, air source selection and air outlet distributions are controlled by sliding levers. Blower on-off speed and temperature are controlled by lever or rotating dial. On push button heater control panels, functions are controlled by various push buttons, levers or rotating dials.

WARNING: To avoid injury from accidental air bag deployment, read and carefully follow all SERVICE PRECAUTIONS and DISABLING & ACTIVATING AIR BAG SYSTEM procedures in AIR BAG SYSTEM SAFETY article in GENERAL SERVICING.

CAUTION: Radio is equipped with anti-theft circuitry. Obtain code number from owner before disconnecting battery, removing fuse No. 24 on Accord (No. 43 Prelude) or removing radio. After service, turn on radio. When CODE appears, enter 5-digit code to restore operation.

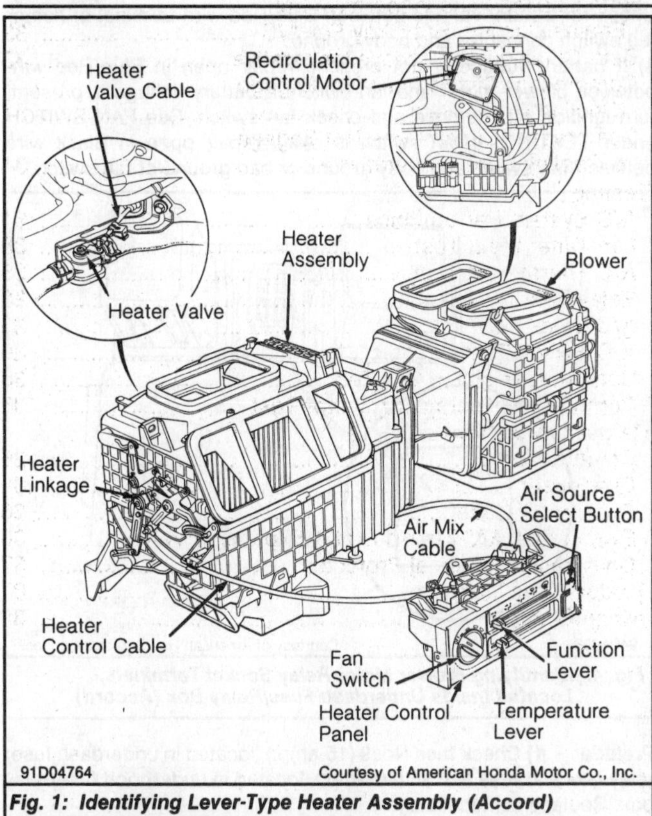
Heater Valve Cable
Recirculation Control Motor
Heater Assembly
Blower
Heater Valve
Heater Linkage
Air Source Select Button
Air Mix Cable
Heater Control Cable
Function Lever
Fan Switch
Heater Control Panel
Temperature Lever
91D04764
Courtesy of American Honda Motor Co., Inc.

Fig. 1: Identifying Lever-Type Heater Assembly (Accord)

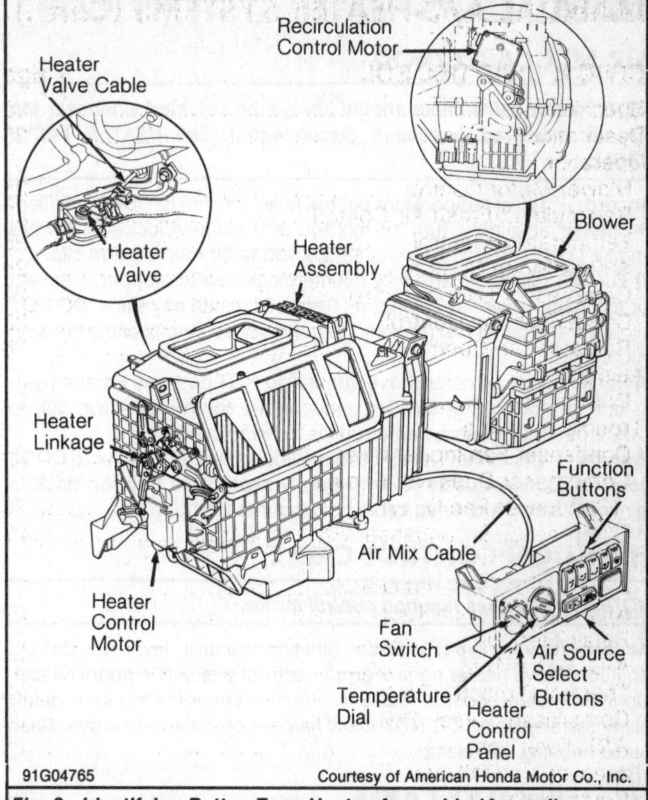
Recirculation Control Motor
Heater Valve Cable
Heater Valve
Heater Assembly
Blower
Heater Linkage
Function Buttons
Air Mix Cable
Heater Control Motor
Fan Switch
Air Source Select Buttons
Temperature Dial
Heater Control Panel
91G04765
Courtesy of American Honda Motor Co., Inc.

Fig. 2: Identifying Button-Type Heater Assembly (Accord)

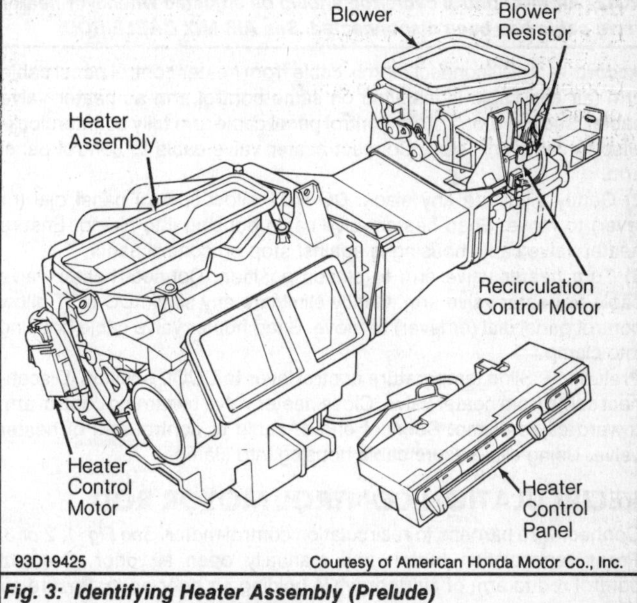
Blower
Blower Resistor
Heater Assembly
Recirculation Control Motor
Heater Control Motor
Heater Control Panel
93D19425
Courtesy of American Honda Motor Co., Inc.

Fig. 3: Identifying Heater Assembly (Prelude)

OPERATION

HEATER CONTROL PANEL

Air Source Select (Fresh Air & Recirculation) Lever/Buttons – To recirculate air inside vehicle, slide air select lever to recirculation position or press recirculation button, depending on control assembly type. Indicator light will come on, and outside air will be shut off.

Select the fresh air position with appropriate button or lever to circulate fresh air from outside vehicle; indicator light should come on. If equipped, ensure recirculation button is off.

Fan Switch – When fan switch is set to low, medium-low, medium-high or high position, fan will circulate warm, cool or outside air, depending on selected temperature and functions.

Temperature Control Lever/Dial – Depending on control assembly type, either slide appropriate lever from left to right or rotate dial clockwise for warmer air.

Function Control Lever/Buttons – Slide lever or push appropriate button to direct fresh or recirculated air to and from heater, defrosters and vents. Set function lever or button in vent (face) position. Outside air will now flow through side and center vents.

To ventilate, set temperature dial or lever to cold position. If equipped, ensure recirculation button is in OFF position. On all, select fresh air position with air select button or lever.

To defrost windshield or windows, set temperature lever or dial in hot position. Select defrost position with appropriate function button or lever, and switch on fan. Warmed (outside) air will flow from windshield and side defroster vents.

1993 HEATER SYSTEMS
Accord & Prelude (Cont.)

ADJUSTMENTS

AIR MIX CABLE/ROD

NOTE: Heater valve cable should always be adjusted whenever the air mix cable/rod has been disconnected. See HEATER VALVE CABLE.

Accord – **1)** Set temperature control lever (or dial) to COOL position. On heater assembly, turn air mix rod arm counterclockwise toward engine compartment. Connect air mix rod to air mix rod arm clip.
2) Turn air mix cable arm fully counterclockwise to stopper. Connect air mix cable to air mix cable arm. Gently eliminate any slack. DO NOT allow control panel dial (or lever) to move. Snap air mix cable housing into clamp.
3) Set temperature control lever (or dial) to HOT position. Ensure heater unit is blowing hot air. Set temperature control lever (or dial) to COOL position. Ensure heater unit is blowing cool air.
Prelude – Disconnect air mix cable. Slide temperature lever to COOL position. Connect cable to arm. Gently slide cable housing back to eliminate slack, and snap cable housing into clamp.

FUNCTION CONTROL CABLE

NOTE: Prelude uses function control motor.

Accord (Lever Type) – Slide function control lever to defrost position. Move heater control arm to defrost position in door link slot. Connect heater control cable to heater control arm, and gently eliminate any slack. DO NOT allow heater control arm to move. Snap cable housing into clamp.

HEATER VALVE CABLE

NOTE: Air mix control cable/rod should be adjusted whenever heater valve cable has been disconnected. See AIR MIX CABLE/ROD.

Accord – **1)** Disconnect air mix cable from heater control panel cable arm (air mix cable is installed on same control arm as heater valve cable). *See Fig. 1 or 2*. Turn control panel cable arm fully counterclockwise to cable arm stop. Connect heater valve cable to control panel arm.
2) Gently eliminate any slack. DO NOT allow control panel dial (or lever) to move. Snap heater valve cable housing into clamp. Ensure heater valve cable housing is against stop on control panel.
3) Turn heater valve arm to closed position. Connect heater valve cable to heater valve arm. Gently eliminate any slack. DO NOT allow control panel dial (or lever) to move. Snap heater valve cable housing into clamp.
Prelude – Slide temperature control lever to COOL position. Disconnect cable from heater valve. Close heater valve by turning control arm toward cable clamp. Connect end of cable to control arm of heater valve. Using clip, secure cable housing into clamp.

RECIRCULATION CONTROL MOTOR ROD

Connect wire harness to recirculation control motor. *See Fig. 1, 2 or 3*. Press recirculation button and manually open air door. Connect control rod to arm of air door while holding air door open. Ensure air door and linkage move smoothly.

TROUBLE SHOOTING

BLOWER MOTOR DOES NOT RUN

Accord – **1)** Check heater blower fuse No. 8 (7.5-amp) and No. 18 (30-amp.) in underhood relay/fuse box. If fuses are okay, disconnect 2-pin connector at blower motor. Turn ignition on. Using a voltmeter, check for battery voltage between Yellow/Black wire and body ground. If battery voltage is present, go to step **6)**.
2) If battery voltage is not present, turn ignition off. Remove blower relay from underdash fuse/relay box, and check relay. See BLOWER MOTOR RELAY under TESTING. Replace blower motor relay if faulty.
3) If blower motor relay is okay, turn ignition on. Check for battery voltage at blower motor relay socket in fuse/relay box terminal No. 1 of blower relay connector and ground. *See Fig. 4*. If battery voltage is not present, replace underdash fuse/relay box.
4) If battery voltage is present, check for battery voltage between relay socket No. 4 and ground. If battery voltage is present, go to next step. If battery voltage is not present, check for open in White wire between underhood fuse/relay box and underdash fuse/relay box.
5) Turn ignition off. Using an ohmmeter, check continuity between relay socket terminal No. 3 and ground. *See Fig. 4*. If continuity is not present, check for open in Black wire between underdash fuse/relay box and ground. If wire is okay, check for poor ground connections. If continuity is present, check for open in Yellow/Black wire between underdash fuse/relay box and blower motor.
6) Turn ignition off. Connect battery power to blower motor connector terminal No. 1 (positive) and terminal No. 2 (ground). If blower motor runs, go to next step. If blower motor does not run, replace blower motor.
7) Reconnect blower motor 2-pin connector. Disconnect 8-pin connector at heater fan switch (behind control panel). Turn ignition on. Check for battery voltage between Blue/Red wire terminal of heater fan switch connector and body ground.
8) If battery voltage is not present, repair open in Blue/Red wire between blower motor and fan switch. If battery voltage is present, turn ignition off. Remove and check fan switch. See FAN SWITCH under TESTING. If fan switch is okay, repair open in Black wire between fan switch and body ground or bad ground at fan switch.

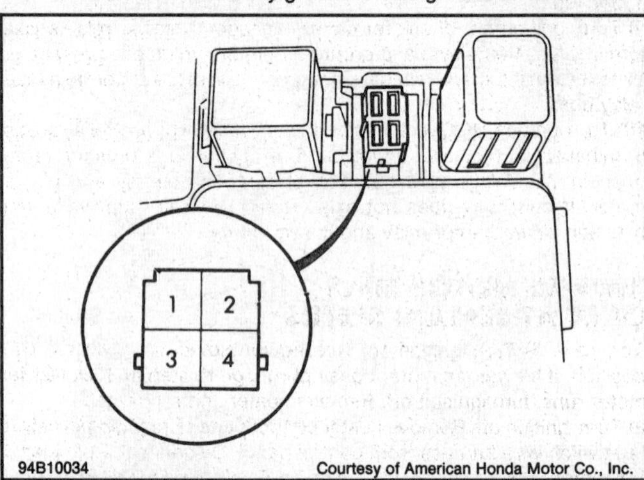
1
2
3
4
94B10034
Courtesy of American Honda Motor Co., Inc.

Fig. 4: Identifying Blower Motor Relay Socket Terminals, Located Inside Underdash Fuse/Relay Box (Accord)

Prelude – **1)** Check fuse No. 9 (15-amp.), located in underdash fuse/relay box and fuse No. 35 (40-amp.), located in underhood fuse/relay box. Replace as necessary.
2) If fuses are okay, turn ignition on. Using a jumper wire, jumper Blue/Red at 2-pin blower motor connector to ground. If blower motor runs, go to next step. If blower motor does not run, go to step **6)**.
3) Turn ignition off. Remove radio/cassette player. Disconnect 7-pin blower fan switch connector. Turn ignition on. Check for battery voltage between Blue/Red wire terminal and body ground.
4) If battery voltage is present, go to next step. If battery voltage is not present, repair open in Blue/Red wire between blower motor and blower fan switch.
5) Turn ignition off. Check for continuity in Black wire between blower fan switch and body ground. If continuity is present, replace blower fan switch. If there is no continuity, repair open in Black wire between blower fan switch and body ground. If wire is okay, check for a bad ground at switch.
6) Disconnect 2-pin connector at blower motor. Turn ignition on. Check for battery voltage between Blue/White wire terminal and body ground. If battery voltage is not present, go to next step. If battery voltage is present, replace blower motor.

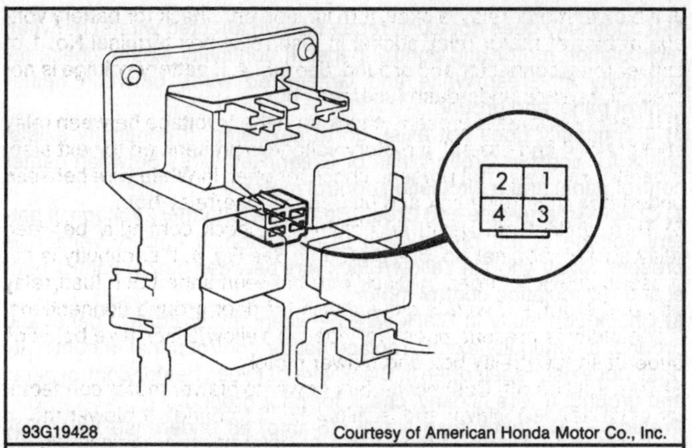
2
1
4
3
93G19428
Courtesy of American Honda Motor Co., Inc.

Fig. 5: Identifying Blower Relay Socket Terminals, Located Inside Underdash Fuse/Relay Box (Prelude)

7) Turn ignition off. Remove blower relay and test. See BLOWER MOTOR RELAY under TESTING. Replace blower motor relay if faulty. If blower relay is okay, go to next step.

8) Check for battery voltage at blower relay socket terminal No. 4 (positive). If battery voltage is present, go to next step. If battery voltage is not present, repair open in White wire between heater blower 40-amp fuse in underhood relay/fuse box and blower relay socket terminal No. 4. *See Fig. 5*.

9) Turn ignition on. Check for battery voltage at blower relay socket terminal No. 1 (positive) and ground. If battery voltage is present, go to next step. If battery voltage is not present, replace underdash fuse/relay box.

10) Turn ignition off. Check for continuity between blower relay socket terminal No. 3 (positive) and ground. If continuity is present, repair open in Blue/White wire between blower motor relay and blower motor. If continuity does not exist, repair open in Blue/White wire between blower motor relay and blower motor.

BLOWER MOTOR RUNS ONLY AT CERTAIN SPEEDS

Accord – 1) Turn ignition on. Turn heater blower fan switch to OFF position. If blower fan motor does not run, go to step **4)**. If blower fan motor runs, turn ignition off. Remove heater control panel.

2) Turn ignition off. Remove heater control panel. Unplug 8-pin blower fan switch wire harness from control panel. Disconnect 5-pin blower fan motor resistor connector. Using an ohmmeter, check Blue, Blue/White, Blue/Yellow, Blue/Black and Blue/Red wires for continuity to ground.

3) If continuity to ground does not exist, replace blower fan switch. If continuity exists in any wire, repair short between blower fan switch and blower fan motor resistor.

4) Turn ignition off. Disconnect 5-pin blower fan motor resistor connector. Check resistance between all resistor terminals No. 1 (Blue/Red wire) and No. 5 (Blue wire). Resistance should be about 2.7 ohms. If resistance is not as specified, replace blower fan motor resistor. If resistance is as specified, go to next step.

5) Reconnect 5-pin resistor connector. Remove heater control panel. Disconnect 8-pin connector from blower fan motor switch. Turn ignition on. At blower fan motor 8-pin connector, ground each wire individually in the following order: Blue, Blue/White, Blue/Yellow, Blue/Black and Blue/Red wire terminals.

6) If blower fan motor operates at progressively higher speeds, replace blower fan motor switch. If blower fan motor does not operate at progressively higher speeds, repair open or cause of excessive resistance in wires between blower fan motor switch and blower fan motor resistor.

Prelude – 1) Turn ignition on. Turn heater blower fan switch to OFF position. If blower fan motor does not run, go to step **4)**. If blower fan motor does run, turn ignition off. Remove radio/cassette player.

2) Disconnect 7-pin blower fan switch connector. Disconnect wire harness from heater resistor at blower case. Using an ohmmeter, check Blue/Black, Blue/Red, Blue/White and Blue/Yellow wires for continuity to ground.

3) If any wire has continuity to ground, repair short in wire(s) between heater fan switch and blower motor resistor. If there is no continuity to ground, replace fan switch.

4) Turn ignition off. Disconnect 5-pin connector from blower resistor at blower case. Measure resistance between blower motor resistor terminals No. 1 and 5. *See Fig. 6*. Resistance should be about 2.5 ohms. If resistance is not as specified, replace blower motor resistor. If resistance is as specified, go to next step.

5) Reconnect blower motor resistor connector. Remove radio/cassette player. Disconnect 7-pin connector from blower fan switch. Turn ignition on. At the heater fan switch 7-pin connector, ground each wire individually in the following order: Blue/White, Blue/Yellow, Blue/Black and Blue/Red wire terminals.

6) If blower motor operates at progressively higher speeds, replace heater fan switch. If blower motor does not operate at progressively higher speeds, repair open or cause of excessive resistance in appropriate wire(s) between heater fan switch and blower motor resistor.

1
2
4
5
94C10035
Courtesy of American Honda Motor Co., Inc.

Fig. 6: Identifying Blower Motor Resistor Terminals (Prelude)

FUNCTION CONTROL MOTOR MALFUNCTION

NOTE: On all models, before beginning trouble shooting procedures, check function motor links and doors for binding or sticking.

Accord – 1) Check fuse No. 13 (7.5-amp) in underdash fuse/relay box. Replace fuse if faulty. If fuse is okay, disconnect 8-pin connector from function control motor. Turn ignition on.

2) Using a voltmeter, check for voltage between Yellow/Black wire between underdash fuse/relay box and function control motor. If battery voltage exists, go to next step. If battery voltage does not exist, repair open in wiring harness between function control motor and fuse block. See WIRING DIAGRAMS.

3) Turn ignition off. Using an ohmmeter, check for continuity in Black wire between function control motor and ground. If continuity exists, go to next step. If continuity does not exist, repair open circuit in Black wire between function control motor and ground. If wire is okay, check for poor ground connection.

4) Test function control motor. See FUNCTION CONTROL MOTOR under TESTING. If motor is okay, go to next step. If motor is faulty, replace motor. Ensure function control linkage and doors are operating smoothly. Repair as necessary.

1993 HEATER SYSTEMS
Accord & Prelude (Cont.)

5) Remove heater control panel. Disconnect 14-pin connector from heater control panel. Using an ohmmeter, check for continuity in wire harness between heater control panel harness connector and function control motor harness connector Yellow/Green, Blue/Red, Blue, Light Green/Black, Light Green/White and Blue wires.
6) If continuity does not exist, go to next step. If continuity exists, repair short in wire(s) between heater control panel and function control motor.
7) Check for voltage in Yellow/Green, Blue/Red, Light Green/Black, Light Green/White and Blue wires. If voltage is not present in any of the wires, replace heater control panel. If voltage is present in any of the wires, repair short to power in Yellow/Black wire between heater control panel and function control motor.
Prelude - 1) Check fuse No. 9 (15-amp) in underdash fuse/relay box. Replace fuse if faulty. If fuse is okay, disconnect 8-pin connector from function control motor. Turn ignition on.
2) Switch control panel function control back and forth several times from fresh to recirculation modes. If recirculation control motor runs, go to step **5)**. If recirculation control motor does not run, turn ignition off. Disconnect function control motor 8-pin connector.
3) Turn ignition on. Check voltage between Black/Yellow wire terminal and ground. If battery voltage is present, go to next step. If battery voltage is not present, repair open in Black/Yellow wire between underdash fuse/relay box and function control motor.
4) Turn ignition off. Remove radio/cassette player. Disconnect 16-pin heater control panel. Check continuity in Black wire between heater control panel and ground. If continuity exists, replace heater control panel. If continuity does not exist, check for open in Black wire between heater control panel and ground. If wire is okay, check for poor ground connection.
5) Turn ignition off. Disconnect function control motor 8-pin connector. Turn ignition on. Check for battery voltage at Black/Yellow wire terminal of function control motor harness connector and ground. If battery voltage exists, go to next step. If battery voltage does not exist, repair open in Black/Yellow wire between function control motor and underdash fuse/relay box. See WIRING DIAGRAMS.
6) Turn ignition off. Perform test on function control motor. See FUNCTION CONTROL MOTOR under TESTING. Replace motor if faulty. If motor is okay, remove radio/cassette player. Disconnect 16-pin heater control panel.
7) Using an ohmmeter, check for continuity between Brown/White, Blue, Blue/Red, Yellow/Green, Light Green/White and Light Green/Red wires between function control motor harness connector and body ground. If continuity does not exist, go to next step. If continuity exists, repair short in affected wire(s).
8) Check for continuity in Brown/White, Blue, Blue/Red, Yellow/Green and Light Green/White wires in harness from control panel connector to function control motor harness connector. If continuity does not exist, repair open in affected wire. If continuity does exist, replace heater control panel.

RECIRCULATION CONTROL MOTOR MALFUNCTION

Accord - 1) Check fuse No. 8 (7.5-amp) in underdash fuse/relay box. If fuse is okay, turn ignition off. Disconnect recirculation motor 3-pin connector at blower case. Turn ignition on. Check for battery voltage between Yellow/Black wire and body ground.
2) If voltage does not exist, repair open in Yellow/Black wire between underdash fuse/relay box and recirculation control motor. If voltage exists, go to next step.
3) Test recirculation control motor. See RECIRCULATION CONTROL MOTOR under TESTING. Ensure that recirculation control linkage and doors operate smoothly. If linkage and door are okay, replace motor. If motor operates properly, go to next step.
4) Turn ignition off. Remove heater control panel. Disconnect 14-pin connector (button type) or 10-pin connector (lever type). Using ohmmeter, check continuity in Green/White and Green/Red wires between heater control panel and recirculation control motor.
5) If continuity does not exist, repair open in affected wire(s) between recirculation motor and control panel. If continuity exists, check for continuity in Green/White and Green/Red wires between heater control panel and ground.
6) If continuity does not exist, go to next step. If continuity exists, check for short in Green/White or Green/Red wires between heater control panel and recirculation control motor.
7) Check Green/White and Green/Red wires for battery voltage. If battery voltage is not present, go to next step. If battery voltage is present, repair short in Yellow/Black wire between heater control panel and recirculation control motor.
8) Check continuity in Black wire between heater control panel and ground. If continuity exists, replace heater control panel. If continuity does not exist, repair open in Black wire between heater control panel and ground. If wire is okay, check for poor ground.
Prelude - 1) Check fuse No. 9 (15-amp), in underdash fuse/relay box. If fuse is okay, turn ignition on. Switch controls between the different ventilation modes (VENT, HEAT, etc.). Observe if recirculation control motor operates. If motor operates, go to step **4)**. If motor does not operate, go to next step.
2) Turn ignition off. disconnect 4-pin recirculation motor connector. Turn ignition on. Check for battery voltage between Black/Yellow wire and body ground. If battery voltage is present, go to next step. If battery voltage is not present, repair open in Black/Yellow wire between motor and fuse box.
3) Turn ignition off. Remove radio/cassette player. Disconnect 16-pin heater control panel harness connector. Check continuity in Black wire between heater control panel and ground. If continuity exists, replace heater control panel. If continuity does not exist, repair open in Black wire between heater control and ground.
4) Turn ignition off. Disconnect 4-pin recirculation control motor connector. Turn ignition on. Measure voltage between Black/Yellow wire terminal and ground. If voltage exists, go to next step. If voltage does not exist, check open in Black/Yellow wire between underdash fuse/relay box and recirculation control motor.
5) Turn ignition off. Test recirculation control motor. See RECIRCULATION CONTROL MOTOR under TESTING. Ensure recirculation control linkage and doors operate smoothly. Replace motor if faulty. If motor is okay, go to next step.
6) Remove radio/cassette player. Disconnect 16-pin heater control panel connector. Check continuity in Green/White and Green/Red wires between recirculation control motor and ground. If continuity does not exist, go to next step. If continuity exists, check for short in Green/White or Green/Red wires between recirculation control motor and heater control panel.
7) Check Green/White and Green/Red wires for battery voltage. If battery voltage is not present, go to next step. If battery voltage is present, check for short in Black/Yellow wire between recirculation control motor and heater control panel.
8) Check continuity in Green/White and Green/Red wires between recirculation control motor and heater control panel. If continuity exists, replace heater control panel. If continuity does not exist, check for open circuit in Green/White or Green/Red wires between recirculation control motor and heater control panel.

TESTING

WARNING: To avoid injury from accidental air bag deployment, read and carefully follow all SERVICE PRECAUTIONS and DISABLING & ACTIVATING AIR BAG SYSTEM procedures in AIR BAG SYSTEM SAFETY article in GENERAL SERVICING.

BLOWER MOTOR RELAY

Remove relay from underdash fuse/relay box. Connect 12-volt battery to terminals No. 3 and 4. *See Fig. 7.* Using ohmmeter, ensure continuity is present between terminals No. 1 and 2. Disconnect battery, and ensure continuity is no longer present between terminals No. 1 and 2.

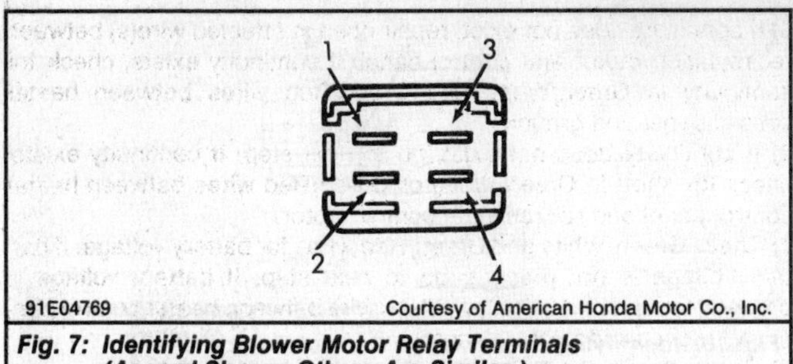
1
3
2
4
91E04769
Courtesy of American Honda Motor Co., Inc.

Fig. 7: Identifying Blower Motor Relay Terminals (Accord Shown; Others Are Similar)

FAN SWITCH

Check for continuity between specified terminals of fan switch. See FAN SWITCH CONTINUITY table. *See Fig. 8 or 9.* If continuity is not present, replace fan switch.

FAN SWITCH CONTINUITY

Switch Position	Continuity Between Terminal No.
Accord	
"A"	1 & 2; 2 & 3
"B"	1 & 2; 2 & 4
"C"	1 & 2; 2 & 5
"D"	1 & 2; 2 & 6
"E"	1 & 2; 2 & 7
Prelude	
Low	1 & 3; 3 & 4
Medium-Low	1 & 3; 3 & 5
Medium-High	1 & 3; 3 & 6
High	1 & 2; 2 & 3

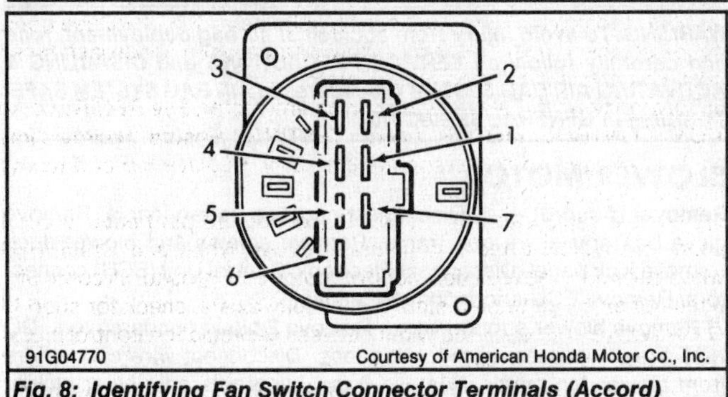
3
2
4
1
5
7
6
91G04770
Courtesy of American Honda Motor Co., Inc.

Fig. 8: Identifying Fan Switch Connector Terminals (Accord)

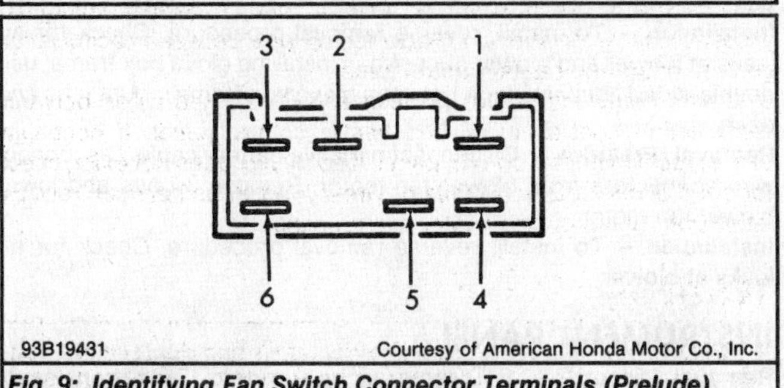
3
2
1
6
5
4
93B19431
Courtesy of American Honda Motor Co., Inc.

Fig. 9: Identifying Fan Switch Connector Terminals (Prelude)

AIR SOURCE SELECT SWITCH (FRESH & RECIRCULATED AIR)

Check for continuity between specified terminals. See AIR SOURCE SELECT SWITCH CONTINUITY table. *See Fig. 10 or 11.* If continuity is not present, replace switch.

AIR SOURCE SELECT SWITCH CONTINUITY

Switch Position	Continuity Between Terminals
Accord	
Fresh Air	"A" & "B"
Recirculation	"A" & "C"
Prelude	
Fresh Air	"B" & "C"
Recirculation	"A" & "C"

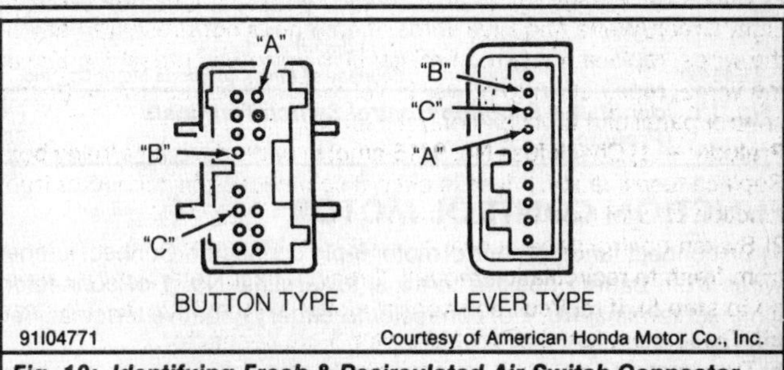
"A"
"B"
"C"
"A"
"B"
"C"
BUTTON TYPE
LEVER TYPE
91I04771
Courtesy of American Honda Motor Co., Inc.

Fig. 10: Identifying Fresh & Recirculated Air Switch Connector Terminals (Accord)

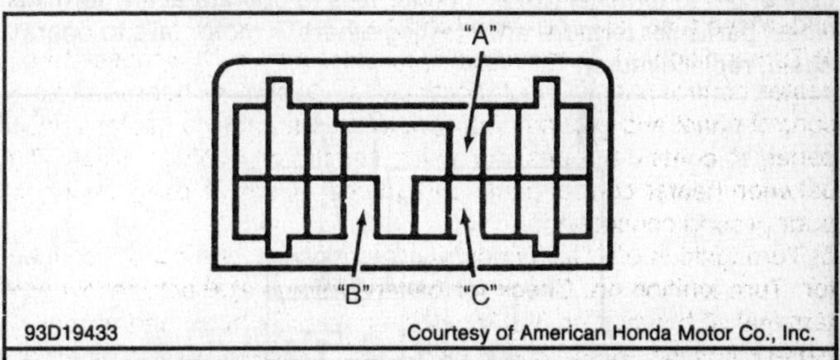
"A"
"B"
"C"
93D19433
Courtesy of American Honda Motor Co., Inc.

Fig. 11: Identifying Fresh & Recirculated Air Switch Connector Terminals (Prelude)

FUNCTION CONTROL SWITCH

Check for continuity between specified terminals of function control switch. See FUNCTION CONTROL SWITCH CONTINUITY table. *See Fig. 12 or 13.* If continuity is not present, replace switch.

FUNCTION CONTROL SWITCH CONTINUITY

Switch Position	Continuity Between Terminal No.
Accord	
Vent (Face)	1 & 6
Bi-Level (Face-Foot)	2 & 6
Heat (Foot)	3 & 6
Heat/Defrost	4 & 6
Defrost	5 & 6
Prelude	
Vent	13 & 7
Heat	13 & 15
Heat/Defrost	13 & 14
Defrost	13 & 3
Heat/Vent	13 & 16

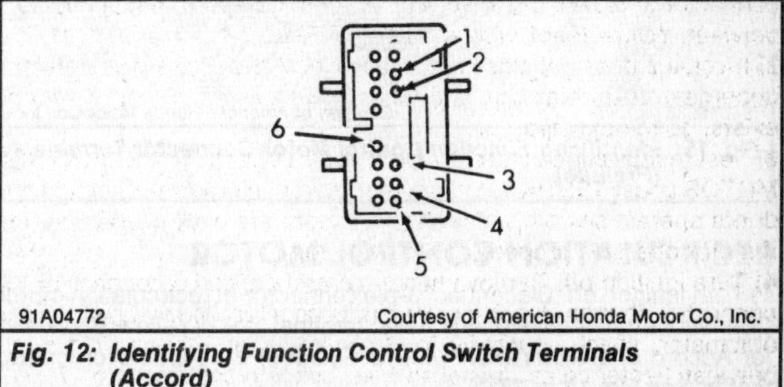
1
2
6
3
4
5
91A04772
Courtesy of American Honda Motor Co., Inc.

Fig. 12: Identifying Function Control Switch Terminals (Accord)

1993 HEATER SYSTEMS
Accord & Prelude (Cont.)

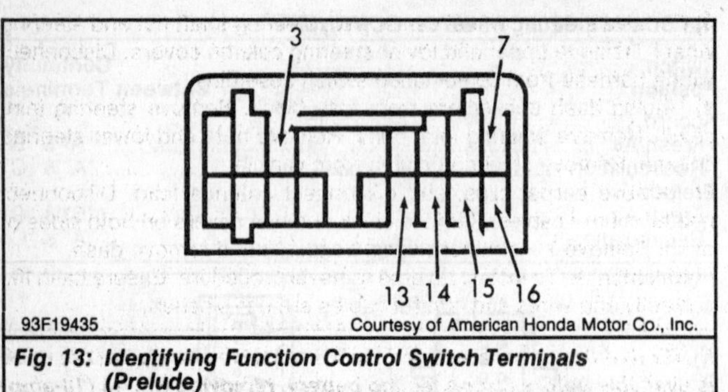
3
7
13 14 15 16

93F19435 Courtesy of American Honda Motor Co., Inc.

Fig. 13: Identifying Function Control Switch Terminals (Prelude)

FUNCTION CONTROL MOTOR

1) Disconnect function control motor 8-pin connector. Connect jumper wires from battery positive terminal to terminal No. 1 of connector. Connect terminal No. 2 of connector to battery negative terminal. *See Fig. 14 or 15.*

2) Using a jumper wire, connect terminal No. 2 to terminals No. 3, 4, 5, 6 and 7 in order. Motor should operate as each terminal is connected to terminal No. 2. If motor fails to operate at any terminal, retest particular terminal after testing others. If motor fails to operate again, replace motor.

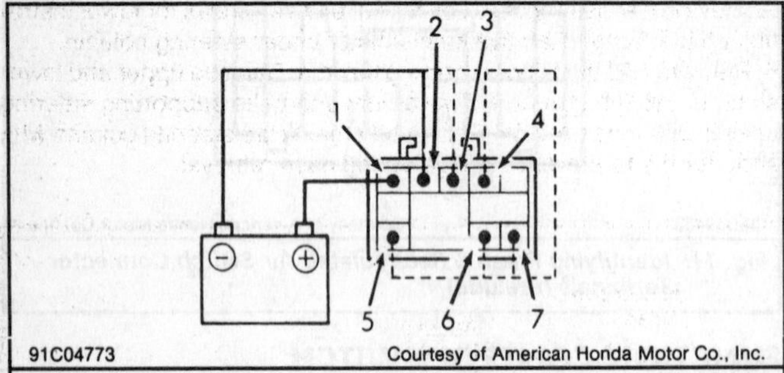
2 3
1
4
5 6 7

91C04773 Courtesy of American Honda Motor Co., Inc.

Fig. 14: Identifying Function Control Motor Connector Terminals (Accord)

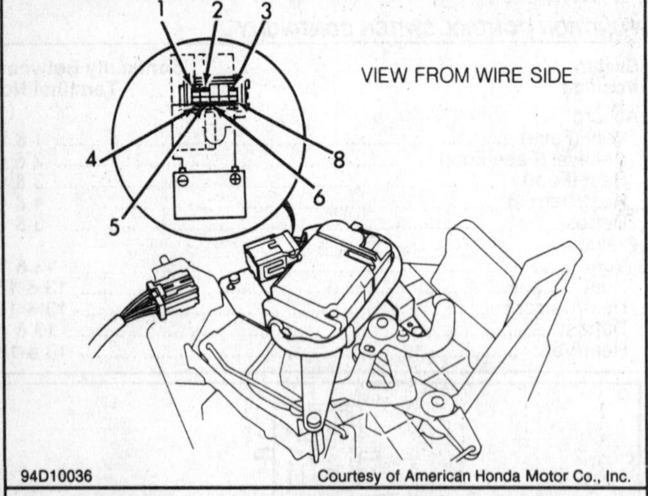
1 2 3
VIEW FROM WIRE SIDE
4
8
6
5

94D10036 Courtesy of American Honda Motor Co., Inc.

Fig. 15: Identifying Function Control Motor Connector Terminals (Prelude)

RECIRCULATION CONTROL MOTOR

1) Turn ignition off. Disconnect 3-pin connector at recirculation motor. Connect battery positive terminal to terminal No. 1 (Yellow/Black wire for Accord or Black/Yellow wire for Prelude) of recirculation control motor. *See Fig. 16 or 17.*

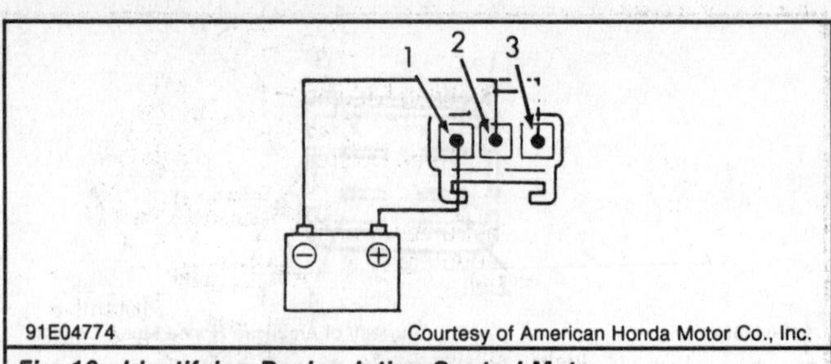
1 2 3

91E04774 Courtesy of American Honda Motor Co., Inc.

Fig. 16: Identifying Recirculation Control Motor Connector Terminals (Accord)

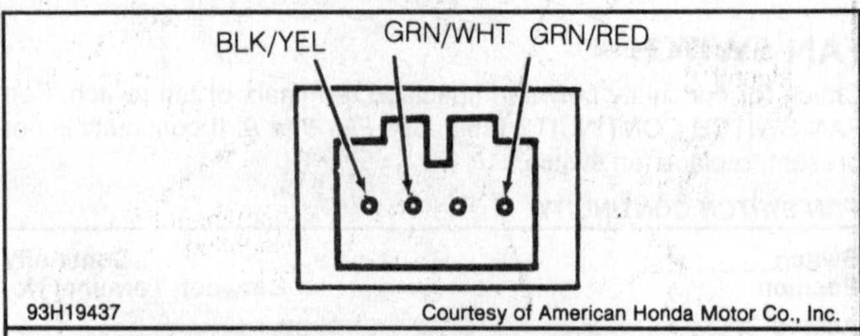
BLK/YEL
GRN/WHT GRN/RED

93H19437 Courtesy of American Honda Motor Co., Inc.

Fig. 17: Identifying Recirculation Control Motor Connector Terminals (Prelude)

2) Alternately connect terminals No. 2 and 3 (Green/White and Green/Red wires) to battery negative terminal. Motor should move to fresh air position and then to recirculation position. If motor does not operate as indicated, replace recirculation control motor.

REMOVAL & INSTALLATION

WARNING: To avoid injury from accidental air bag deployment, read and carefully follow all SERVICE PRECAUTIONS and DISABLING & ACTIVATING AIR BAG SYSTEM procedures in AIR BAG SYSTEM SAFETY article in GENERAL SERVICING.

BLOWER MOTOR

Removal (Accord) – 1) Disconnect negative battery cable. Remove glove box and glove box frame. Remove screws and blower duct. Remove kick panel. Disconnect Electronic Control Unit (ECU) connectors. Remove ECU and mounting bracket.

2) Remove blower support band. Remove 2 blower undercovers. DO NOT break undercover mounting tabs. Disconnect wire connectors from blower fan motor. Remove 3 mounting nuts and lower blower unit.

Installation – To install, reverse removal procedure. Check for air leaks at blower and blower duct. When installing glove box frame, use double-sided adhesive tape between glove box frame mount tabs and dash.

Removal (Prelude) – Disconnect negative battery cable. Disconnect wire connectors from blower fan motor. Remove 3 bolts and lower blower fan motor.

Installation – To install, reverse removal procedure. Check for air leaks at blower.

INSTRUMENT PANEL

Removal (Accord) – 1) Disable air bag system. Slide front seats toward rear of vehicle. Remove screws from front and rear consoles. Remove rear ashtray from rear console.

2) Remove 2 screws from rear of rear console. Remove gearshift knob (M/T models). Remove front and rear console. Remove knee bolster. *See Fig. 18.* Remove lower panel under steering column.

1993 HEATER SYSTEMS
Accord & Prelude (Cont.)

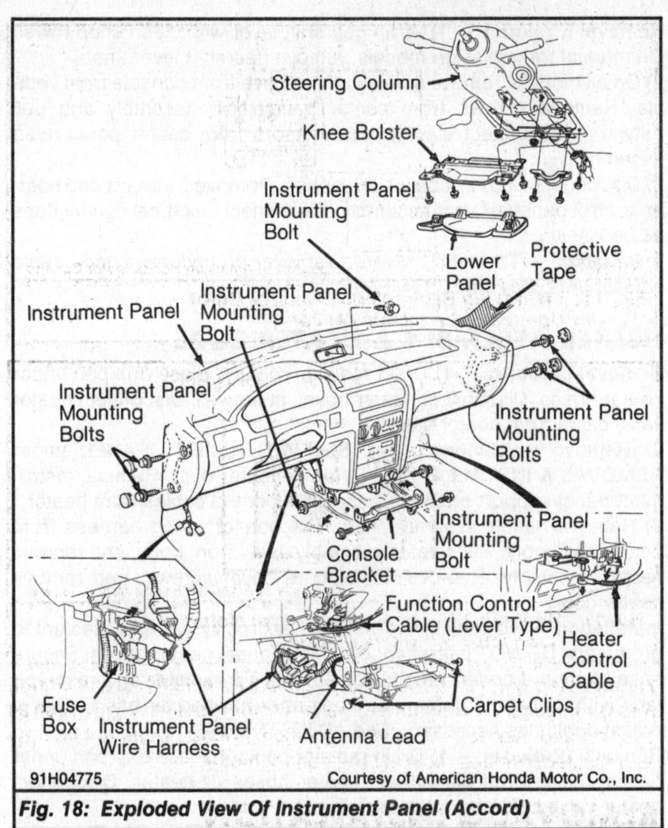
Steering Column
Knee Bolster
Instrument Panel Mounting Bolt
Lower Panel
Protective Tape
Instrument Panel
Instrument Panel Mounting Bolt
Instrument Panel Mounting Bolts
Instrument Panel Mounting Bolts
Instrument Panel Mounting Bolt
Console Bracket
Function Control Cable (Lever Type)
Heater Control Cable
Carpet Clips
Fuse Box
Instrument Panel Wire Harness
Antenna Lead
91H04775
Courtesy of American Honda Motor Co., Inc.

Fig. 18: Exploded View Of Instrument Panel (Accord)

3) Remove steering wheel center pad, steering shaft nut and steering wheel. Remove upper and lower steering column covers. Disconnect wiring harness from combination switch assembly.

4) Unplug dash connectors from fuse block. Remove steering joint cover. Remove steering joint bolts. Remove nuts and lower steering column. Remove steering column from vehicle.

5) Remove carpet clips, and disconnect antenna lead. Disconnect heater control cables. Remove clock and bolt covers on both sides of dash. Remove 7 instrument panel bolts. Lift and remove dash.

Installation – To install, reverse removal procedure. Ensure dash fits correctly and wires and control cables are not pinched.

NOTE: Radio may have a coded theft protection circuit. Ensure code is available before disconnecting battery, removing No. 43 (10-amp) fuse or removing radio.

Removal (Prelude) – **1)** Disable air bag system. Disconnect negative battery cable. Remove seat track covers and remove 4 track bolts from each seat. Disconnect electrical connectors and remove seats.

2) Wrap gearshift lever with clean shop towel. On manual transmission models, remove gearshift lever knob. On all models, remove screws and remove front console from vehicle.

3) Remove screws from center panel/radio assembly and pull outward. Disconnect electrical connectors from center panel/radio assembly.

4) Open glove box, and remove glove box screws and glove box. Remove lower dash access cover and remove screws for lower instrument panel cover. Remove knee bolster under steering column.

5) Remove A/C duct under steering column. Remove upper and lower steering column covers. Remove nuts and bolts supporting steering column and lower column from dash area. Wrap steering column with shop towels to prevent damage during dash removal.

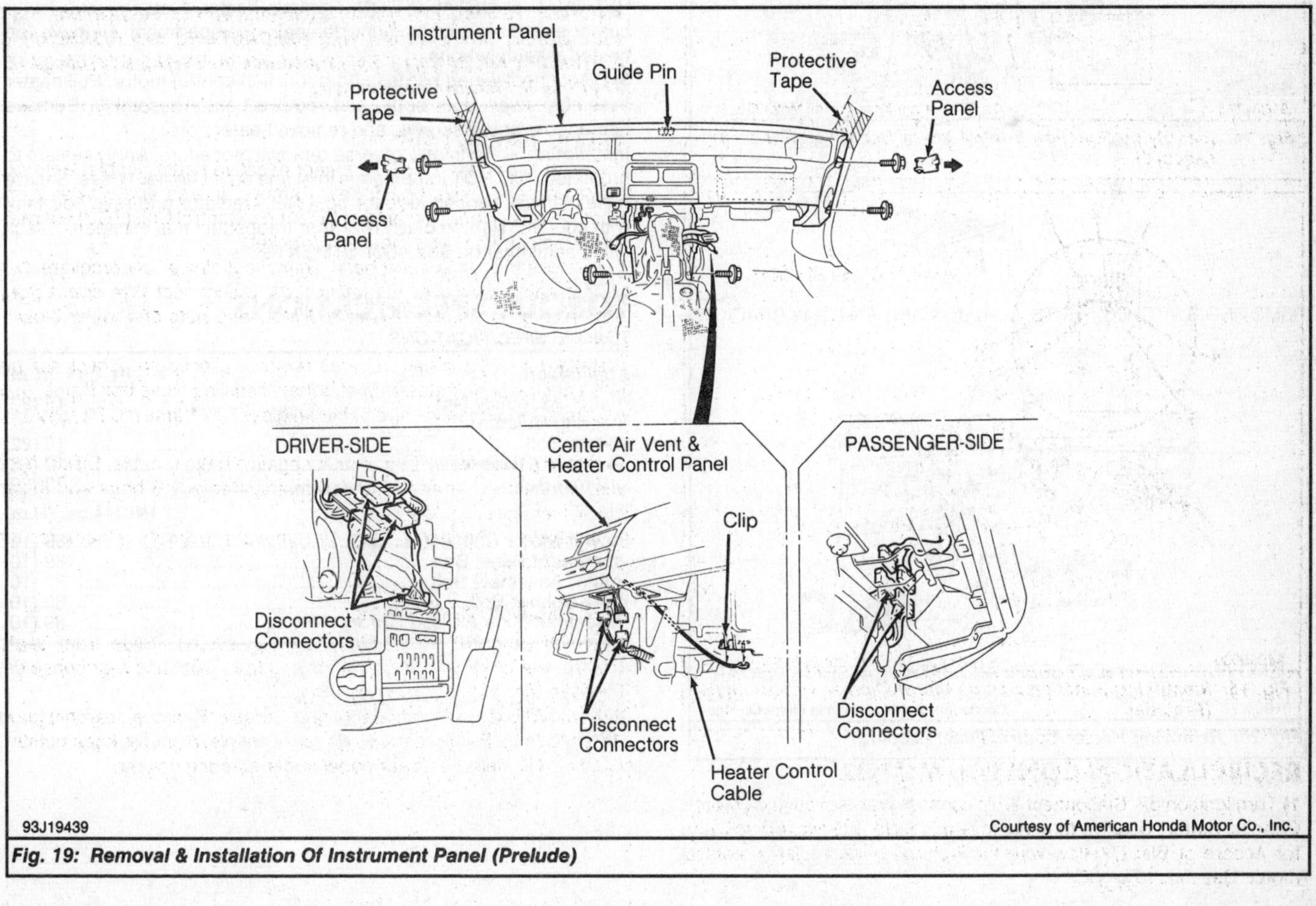

Instrument Panel
Guide Pin
Protective Tape
Protective Tape
Access Panel
Access Panel
DRIVER-SIDE
Disconnect Connectors
Center Air Vent & Heater Control Panel
Clip
Disconnect Connectors
Heater Control Cable
PASSENGER-SIDE
Disconnect Connectors
93J19439
Courtesy of American Honda Motor Co., Inc.

Fig. 19: Removal & Installation Of Instrument Panel (Prelude)

1993 HEATER SYSTEMS
Accord & Prelude (Cont.)

6) On 4-wheel steering models, ensure Supplemental Restraint short connector is installed on passenger-side air bag inflator connector before disconnecting air bag wire harness. Remove passenger-side air bag.
7) Remove bolt access panels on both side of dash. Disconnect electrical connectors and heater control cable. *See Fig. 19.* Use protective tape on front pillars to protect dash during removal and installation. Remove 6 dash bolts. Lift and remove dash. Use care not to scratch or damage dash during removal.
Installation – To install, reverse removal procedure. Ensure electrical harness and heater control cable are not pinched when installing instrument panel.

HEATER CONTROL PANEL

***NOTE:** Radio may have a coded theft protection circuit. Ensure code is available before disconnecting battery, removing fuse No. 24 (Accord) or fuse No. 43 (Prelude), or removing radio.*

Removal & Installation (Accord) – **1)** Disconnect battery negative cable. Remove ashtray and console. Remove switches, coin box, air vents and ashtray bracket. *See Fig. 20.* Remove radio/cassette player.
2) Tilt steering wheel down and remove instrument bezel. Disconnect control cables at heater assembly. Remove heater control panel screws. Disconnect electrical connectors. Remove heater control panel from vehicle. To install, reverse removal procedure.

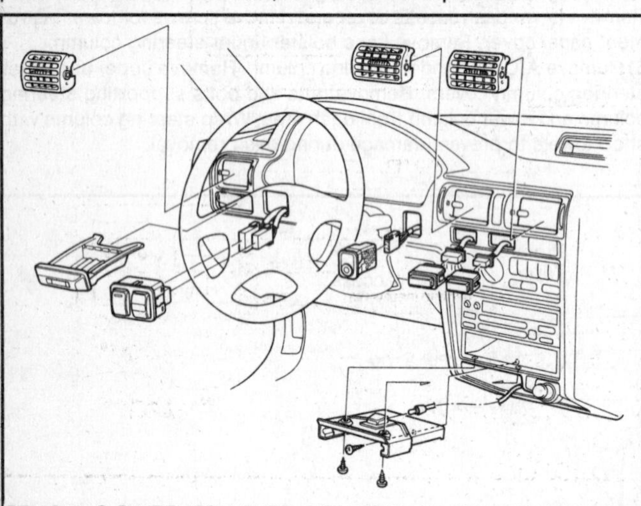

REMOVING SWITCHES, VENTS, COIN BOX AND ASHTRAY BRACKET

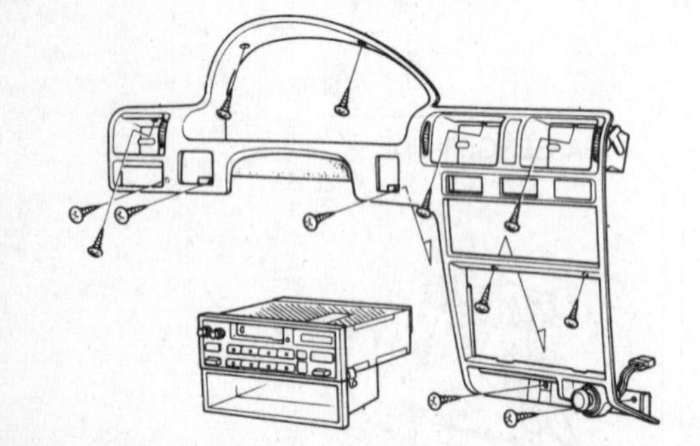

REMOVING INSTRUMENT BEZEL AND RADIO/CASSETTE PLAYER

91B04777 Courtesy of American Honda Motor Co., Inc.

Fig. 20: Removing Heater Control Panel (Accord)

Removal (Prelude) – **1)** Wrap gearshift lever with clean shop towel. On manual transmission models, remove gearshift lever knob.
2) On all models, remove screws and remove front console from vehicle. Remove screws from center panel/radio assembly and pull outward. Disconnect electrical connectors from center panel/radio assembly.
3) Disconnect air mix cable at heater box. Remove 3 screws and heater control panel/air vent assembly. Disconnect electrical connections as necessary.
Installation – To install, reverse removal procedure. Check cable adjustments. See ADJUSTMENTS.

HEATER ASSEMBLY & HEATER CORE

Removal (Accord) – **1)** Drain radiator coolant. Place drip pan under heater hoses. Disconnect heater hoses at firewall. Disconnect heater valve cable from heater valve.
2) Remove instrument panel. See INSTRUMENT PANEL under REMOVAL & INSTALLATION. Remove heater duct. Remove instrument panel support bracket. Disconnect control cables from heater.
3) Remove heater assembly nuts. Disconnect wiring harness from heater assembly. Pull heater assembly away from body, and remove heater assembly. Remove heater core cover screws, and remove heater core.
Installation – To install, reverse removal procedure. Apply sealant to grommets. DO NOT interchange inlet and outlet heater hoses. Secure hose clamps. Loosen radiator bleed bolt. Fill radiator and reservoir tank with coolant. Tighten bleed bolt after trapped air has escaped. Adjust cables as necessary. See ADJUSTMENTS.
Removal (Prelude) – **1)** Drain radiator coolant. Place drip pan under heater hoses, and disconnect heater hoses at heater. Disconnect heater valve cable from heater valve.
2) Remove instrument panel. See INSTRUMENT PANEL under REMOVAL & INSTALLATION. Remove heater duct. Remove lower heater assembly nuts from inside engine compartment. Remove top heater assembly bolts.
3) Disconnect wiring harness from function control motor. Pull heater assembly away from body, and remove heater assembly. Remove heater core cover screws, and remove heater core.
Installation – To install, reverse removal procedure. Apply sealant to grommets. DO NOT interchange inlet and outlet heater hoses. Secure hose clamps. Loosen radiator bolt. Refill radiator and reservoir tank with coolant. Tighten bleed bolt after trapped air has escaped. Check cable adjustments. See ADJUSTMENTS.

TORQUE SPECIFICATIONS

TORQUE SPECIFICATIONS

Application	Ft. Lbs. (N.m)
Heater Assembly Nut	16 (22)
Steering Column	
8-mm Bolt	16 (22)
8-mm Nut (Use New)	12 (16)
10-mm Bolt	29 (39)
	INCH Lbs. (N.m)
Blower Motor Bolt/Nut	89 (10)
Instrument Panel Bolt	89 (10)
Heater Assembly Bolt	89 (10)
Knee Bolster Bolt	89 (10)
Passenger-Side Air Bag Bracket Nut	89 (10)

1993 HEATER SYSTEMS
Accord & Prelude (Cont.)

WIRING DIAGRAMS

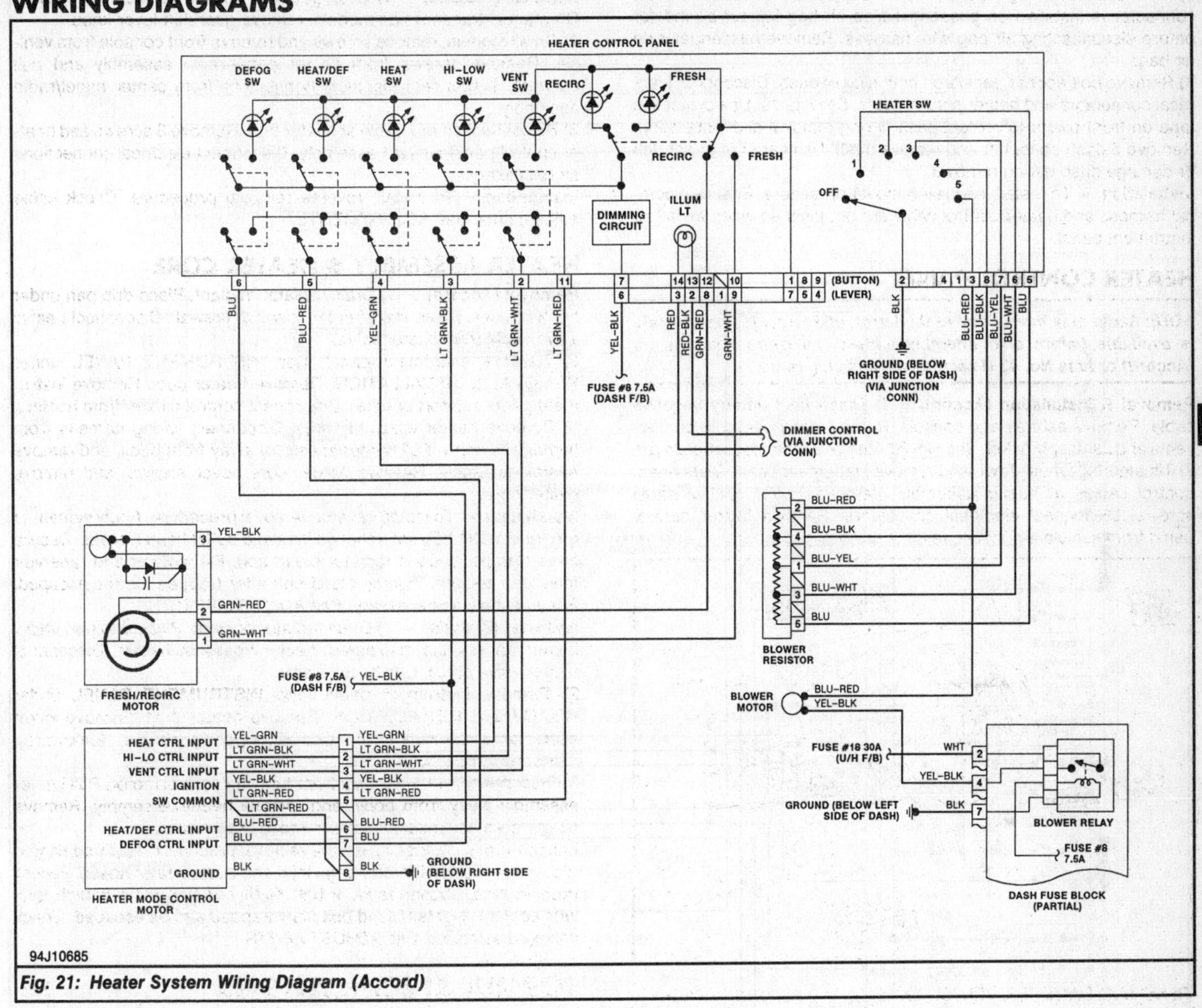
HEATER CONTROL PANEL
DEFOG SW
HEAT/DEF SW
HEAT SW
HI-LOW SW
VENT SW
RECIRC
FRESH
RECIRC
FRESH
HEATER SW
OFF
DIMMING CIRCUIT
ILLUM LT
(BUTTON)
(LEVER)
BLU
BLU-RED
YEL-GRN
LT GRN-BLK
LT GRN-WHT
LT GRN-RED
YEL-BLK
RED
RED-BLK
GRN-RED
GRN-WHT
BLK
BLU-RED
BLU-BLK
BLU-YEL
BLU-WHT
BLU
FUSE #8 7.5A (DASH F/B)
GROUND (BELOW RIGHT SIDE OF DASH) (VIA JUNCTION CONN)
DIMMER CONTROL (VIA JUNCTION CONN)
YEL-BLK
GRN-RED
GRN-WHT
FRESH/RECIRC MOTOR
BLOWER RESISTOR
BLOWER MOTOR
FUSE #8 7.5A (DASH F/B)
HEAT CTRL INPUT
HI-LO CTRL INPUT
VENT CTRL INPUT
IGNITION
SW COMMON
HEAT/DEF CTRL INPUT
DEFOG CTRL INPUT
GROUND
HEATER MODE CONTROL MOTOR
GROUND (BELOW RIGHT SIDE OF DASH)
FUSE #18 30A (U/H F/B)
GROUND (BELOW LEFT SIDE OF DASH)
WHT
YEL-BLK
BLK
BLOWER RELAY
FUSE #8 7.5A
DASH FUSE BLOCK (PARTIAL)
94J10685

Fig. 21: Heater System Wiring Diagram (Accord)

1993 HEATER SYSTEMS
Accord & Prelude (Cont.)

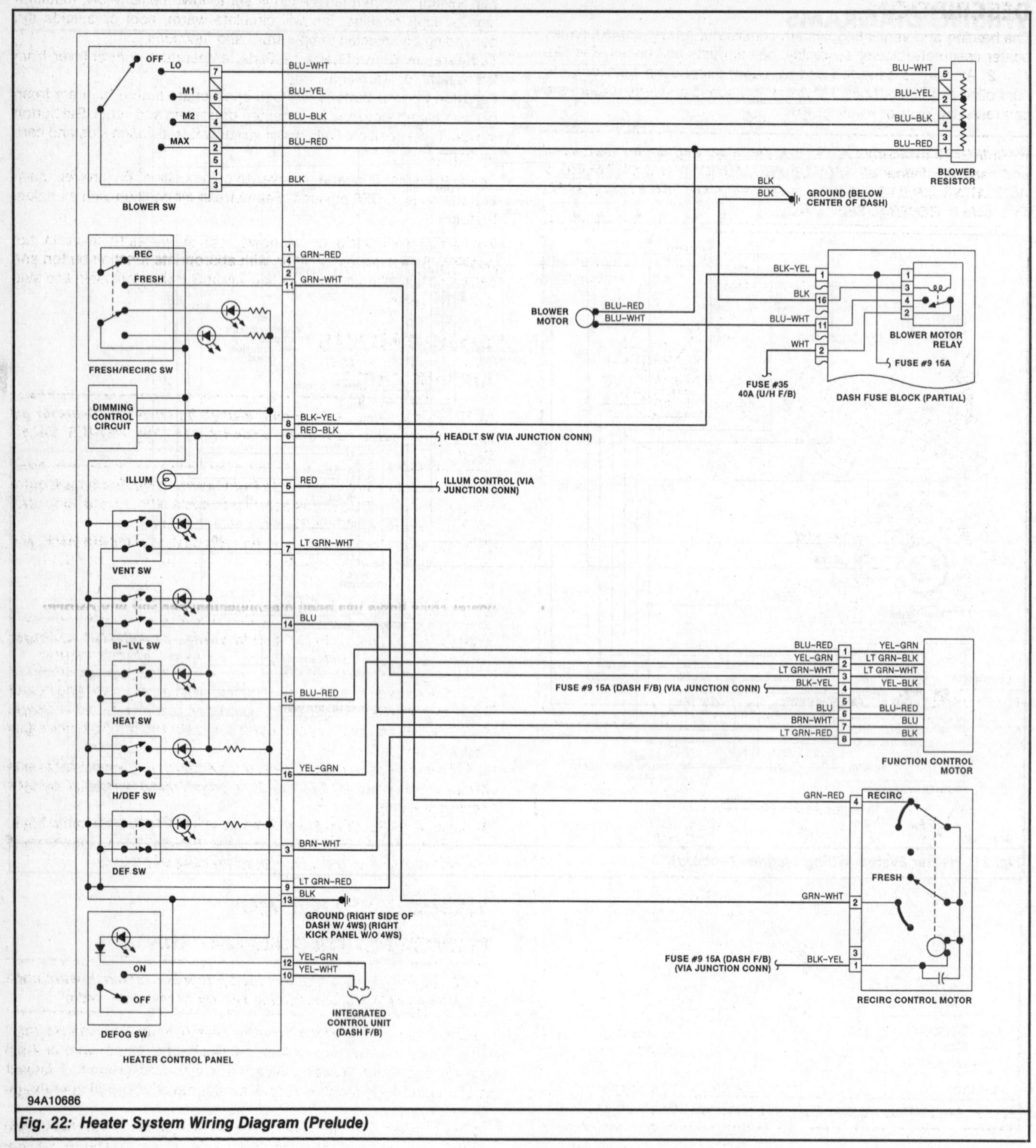
OFF
LO
M1
M2
MAX
BLU-WHT
BLU-YEL
BLU-BLK
BLU-RED
BLK
BLOWER SW
BLOWER RESISTOR
BLK
BLK
GROUND (BELOW CENTER OF DASH)
REC
FRESH
GRN-RED
GRN-WHT
FRESH/RECIRC SW
BLK-YEL
BLK
BLU-WHT
WHT
BLOWER MOTOR
BLU-RED
BLU-WHT
BLOWER MOTOR RELAY
FUSE #9 15A
FUSE #35 40A (U/H F/B)
DASH FUSE BLOCK (PARTIAL)
DIMMING CONTROL CIRCUIT
BLK-YEL
RED-BLK
HEADLT SW (VIA JUNCTION CONN)
ILLUM
RED
ILLUM CONTROL (VIA JUNCTION CONN)
VENT SW
LT GRN-WHT
BI-LVL SW
BLU
HEAT SW
BLU-RED
H/DEF SW
YEL-GRN
DEF SW
BRN-WHT
LT GRN-RED
BLK
GROUND (RIGHT SIDE OF DASH W/ 4WS) (RIGHT KICK PANEL W/O 4WS)
DEFOG SW
ON
OFF
YEL-GRN
YEL-WHT
INTEGRATED CONTROL UNIT (DASH F/B)
HEATER CONTROL PANEL
BLU-RED
YEL-GRN
LT GRN-WHT
BLK-YEL
BLU
BRN-WHT
LT GRN-RED
YEL-GRN
LT GRN-BLK
LT GRN-WHT
YEL-BLK
BLU-RED
BLU
BLK
FUSE #9 15A (DASH F/B) (VIA JUNCTION CONN)
FUNCTION CONTROL MOTOR
GRN-RED
RECIRC
FRESH
GRN-WHT
FUSE #9 15A (DASH F/B) (VIA JUNCTION CONN)
BLK-YEL
RECIRC CONTROL MOTOR
94A10686

Fig. 22: Heater System Wiring Diagram (Prelude)

1993 HEATER SYSTEMS
Civic & Civic Del Sol

DESCRIPTION

The heating and ventilating system consists of heater control panel, heater assembly, blower assembly, heater ducts and hoses. *See Fig. 1 or 2.* Air source selection and air outlet distribution functions are controlled by push buttons. Blower on-off speed and temperature are controlled by lever or rotating dial.

WARNING: To avoid injury from accidental air bag deployment, read and carefully follow all SERVICE PRECAUTIONS and DISABLING & ACTIVATING AIR BAG SYSTEM procedures in AIR BAG SYSTEM SAFETY article in GENERAL SERVICING.

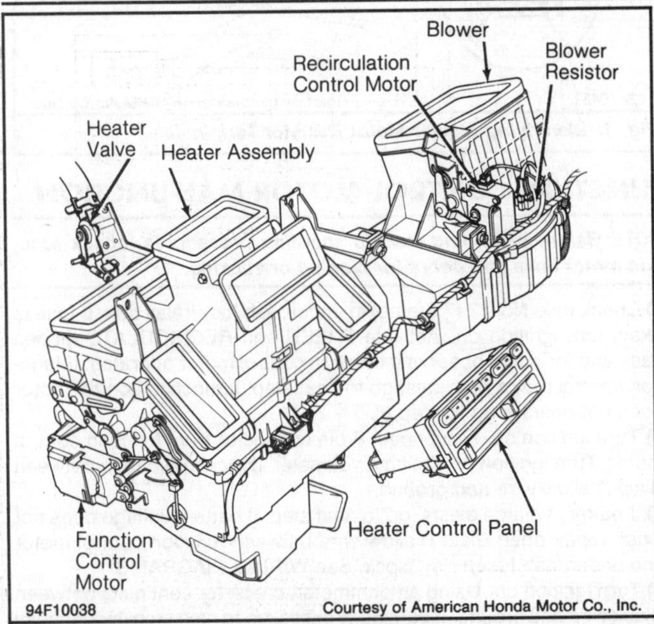
Blower
Recirculation Control Motor
Blower Resistor
Heater Valve
Heater Assembly
Function Control Motor
Heater Control Panel
94F10038
Courtesy of American Honda Motor Co., Inc.

Fig. 1: Identifying Heater Assembly (Civic)

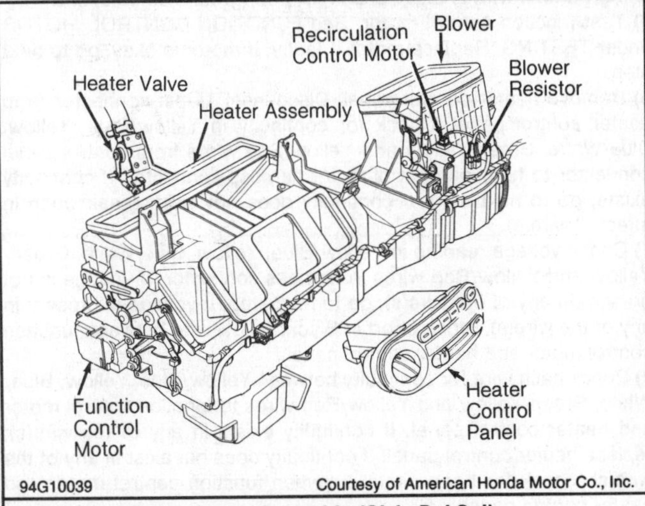
Recirculation Control Motor
Blower
Blower Resistor
Heater Valve
Heater Assembly
Function Control Motor
Heater Control Panel
94G10039
Courtesy of American Honda Motor Co., Inc.

Fig. 2: Identifying Heater Assembly (Civic Del Sol)

OPERATION

HEATER CONTROL PANEL

Air Source Select (Fresh Air & Recirculation) Buttons – To recirculate air inside vehicle, press recirculation button. On Civic Del Sol models, indicator light will come on, and outside air will be shut off.

Select the fresh air position with appropriate button to circulate fresh air from outside vehicle. If equipped, ensure recirculation button is off.

Fan Switch – When fan switch is set to low, medium-low, medium-high or high position, fan will circulate warm, cool or outside air, depending on selected temperature and functions.

Temperature Control Lever – Slide temperature control lever from left to right for warmer air.

Function Control Buttons – Push appropriate button to direct fresh or recirculated air to and from heater, defrosters and vents. Set button in vent (face) position. Outside air will now flow through side and center vents.

To ventilate, set temperature lever to cold position. Ensure recirculation button is in OFF position. Select fresh air position with air select button.

To defrost windshield or windows, set temperature lever in hot position. Select defrost position with appropriate function button and switch on fan. Warmed (outside) air will flow from windshield and side defroster vents.

ADJUSTMENTS

AIR MIX CABLE

NOTE: Heater valve cable should always be adjusted whenever air mix control cable has been disconnected. See HEATER VALVE CABLE.

1) Disconnect heater valve cable from heater valve. Set temperature control lever to COOL position. Turn cable arm to the stop and connect the end of air mix control cable to cable arm.
2) Gently slide air mix cable outer housing back to eliminate slack, and snap cable housing into clamp.

HEATER VALVE CABLE

NOTE: Air mix control cable should always be adjusted whenever heater valve cable has been disconnected. See AIR MIX CABLE.

1) With both ends of cable disconnected from air mix door and heater valve, close heater valve by turning control arm toward cable clamp. Connect one end of cable to heater valve control arm. Secure cable using clamp.
2) Slide temperature control lever to cold position. Connect other end of cable to control arm of air mix door (air mix cable is installed on connecting linkage).
3) Close air mix door and heater water valve. Gently slide cable housing back to eliminate any slack in cable without moving temperature control lever and air mix door. Snap housing into clamp.

TROUBLE SHOOTING

BLOWER MOTOR DOES NOT RUN

NOTE: Radio may have a coded theft protection circuit. Ensure code is available before disconnecting battery or removing radio.

1) Check blower relay fuse No. 13 (7.5-amp) in underdash fuse/relay box. If fuse is okay, turn ignition on. Connect a jumper wire at 2-pin blower connector between Blue/Black wire and ground. If blower motor operates, go to next step. If blower motor does not operate, go to step **4)**.
2) Turn ignition off. Remove heater control panel. Disconnect 6-pin heater fan switch connector. Turn ignition on. Measure voltage between Blue/Black wire terminal and ground. If battery voltage is present, go to next step. If battery voltage is not present, check for open in Blue/Black wire between blower motor and heater fan switch.
3) Turn ignition off. Check for continuity in Black wire between blower fan switch and body ground. If continuity exists, replace blower fan switch. If continuity does not exist, repair open in Black wire between blower fan switch and body ground. If wire is okay, check for a bad ground at switch.

1993 HEATER SYSTEMS
Civic & Civic Del Sol (Cont.)

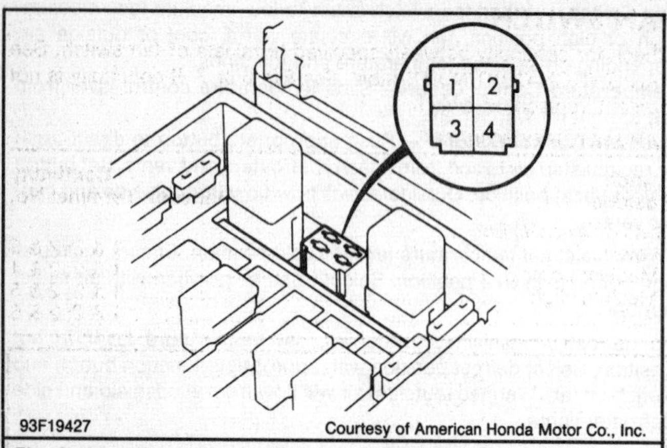
1
2
3
4
93F19427
Courtesy of American Honda Motor Co., Inc.

Fig. 3: Identifying Blower Relay Socket Terminals, Located Inside Underhood Fuse/Relay Box

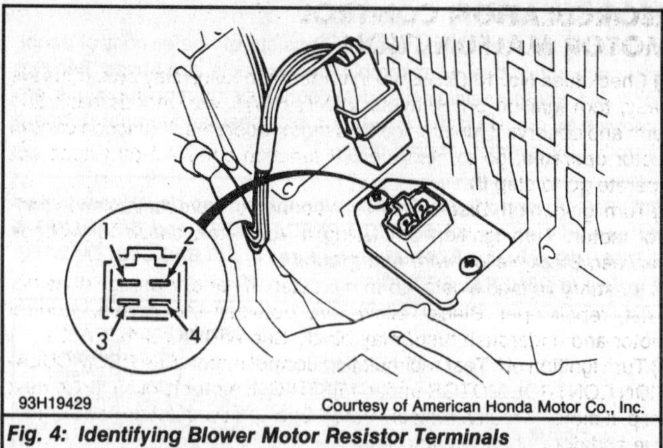
1
2
3
4
93H19429
Courtesy of American Honda Motor Co., Inc.

Fig. 4: Identifying Blower Motor Resistor Terminals

4) Disconnect 2-pin connector at blower motor. Turn ignition on. Using a voltmeter, check for battery voltage between Blue/White wire and body ground. If battery voltage is present, replace blower motor. If battery voltage is not present, go to next step.
5) Turn ignition off. Remove blower relay (located in underhood fuse/relay box) and test. See BLOWER MOTOR RELAY under TESTING. Replace relay if faulty. If relay is okay, go to next step.
6) Check for battery voltage at blower relay socket terminal No. 3. and ground. *See Fig. 3*. If battery voltage is present, go to next step. If battery voltage is not present, replace underhood fuse/relay box and retest.
7) Turn ignition on. Check for battery voltage at blower relay socket terminal No. 2. *See Fig. 3*. If battery voltage is not present, repair open in Black/Yellow wire between blower motor relay fuse No. 13 (7.5-amp) and relay socket terminal No. 2. If battery voltage is present, go to next step.
8) Turn ignition off. Check for continuity to ground at blower relay socket terminal No. 4. If continuity exists, repair open in Blue/White wire between blower motor relay and blower motor. If continuity does not exist, repair open in Black wire between terminal No. 4 and body ground. If wire is okay, check for bad ground at blower fan switch.

BLOWER MOTOR RUNS ONLY AT CERTAIN SPEEDS

1) Turn ignition on. Turn heater blower fan switch to OFF position. If blower motor does not run, go to step **4)**. If blower motor does run, turn ignition off. Remove heater control panel.
2) Disconnect blower fan switch wire harness from control panel. Disconnect wire harness from heater resistor at blower case. Using an ohmmeter, check Blue, Blue/White, Blue/Yellow and Blue/Black wires for continuity.
3) If any wire has continuity to ground, repair or replace wire harness between blower fan switch and blower resistor as necessary. If there is no continuity to ground, replace fan switch.
4) Turn ignition off. Disconnect 4-pin connector from blower resistor at blower case. Measure resistance between resistor terminals No. 2 and 4. *See Fig. 4*. Resistance should be about 2.15 ohms. If resistance is not as specified, replace resistor. If resistance is okay, go to next step.
5) Reconnect blower motor resistor connector. Remove heater control panel. Disconnect 6-pin connector from blower fan switch. Turn ignition on. At the 6-pin blower fan switch connector, ground each of following wires individually in the following order: Blue, Blue/White, Blue/Yellow and Blue/Black.
6) Blower motor should run at progressively higher speeds. If motor runs at progressively higher speed, replace blower fan switch. If motor did not operate at progressively higher speed, repair open in circuit or cause of excessive resistance in appropriate wire(s) between blower motor and blower motor resistor.

FUNCTION CONTROL MOTOR MALFUNCTION

NOTE: Before beginning trouble shooting procedures, check function motor links and doors for binding or sticking.

1) Check fuse No. 13 (7.5-amp) in underdash fuse/relay box. If fuse is okay, turn ignition on. Activate FRESH and RECIRCULATE modes back and forth and observe if function control motor operates. If function control motor operates, go to next step. If function control motor does not operate go to step **8)**.
2) Turn ignition off. Disconnect 8-pin connector from function control motor. Turn ignition on. Using a voltmeter, check for voltage between Black/Yellow wire and ground.
3) If battery voltage exists, go to next step. If battery voltage does not exist, repair open Black/Yellow wire between function control motor and underdash fuse/relay block. See WIRING DIAGRAMS.
4) Turn ignition off. Using an ohmmeter, check for continuity between Black wire and ground. If continuity exists, go to next step. If continuity does not exist, repair open Black wire between function control motor and ground. If wire is okay, check for poor ground connections.
5) Test function control motor. See FUNCTION CONTROL MOTOR under TESTING. Replace motor if faulty. If motor is okay, go to next step.
6) Remove heater control panel. Disconnect 14-pin connector from heater control panel. Check for continuity in Yellow/Blue, Yellow, Blue/White, Green/Yellow and Yellow/Red wires from control panel connector to function control motor harness connector. If continuity exists, go to next step. If continuity does not exist, repair open in affected wire(s).
7) Check voltage reading in Yellow/Blue, Yellow, Blue/White, Green/Yellow and Yellow/Red wires in harness connector. If voltage is not present in any of the wire(s), go to next step. If voltage is present in any of the wire(s), repair short in Black/Yellow wire between function control motor and heater control panel.
8) Check each wire for continuity between Yellow/Blue, Yellow, Blue/White, Green/Yellow and Yellow/Red wires to function control motor and heater control panel. If continuity exists in any of the wire(s), replace heater control panel. If continuity does not exist in any of the wire(s), check for open circuit between function control motor and heater control panel.
9) Turn ignition off. Disconnect 8-pin function control motor connector. Turn ignition on. Check battery voltage between Yellow/Black wire terminal and ground. If battery voltage is present, go to next step. If battery voltage is not present, repair open in Yellow/Black wire between underdash fuse/relay box and function control motor.
10) Turn ignition off. Remove heater control panel. Disconnect 14-pin heater control panel connector. Check continuity between Black wire between heater control panel and ground. If continuity exists, replace heater control panel. If continuity does not exist, check for open in Black wire between heater control panel and ground. If wire is okay, check for poor ground connection.

RECIRCULATION CONTROL MOTOR MALFUNCTION

1) Check fuse No. 13 (7.5-amp) in underdash fuse/relay box. If fuse is okay, turn ignition on. Activate VENT, HEAT, etc. modes back and forth and observe if function control motor operates. If function control motor operates, go to next step. If function control motor does not operate go to step **8)**.

2) Turn ignition off. Disconnect 4-pin connector from recirculation control motor. Turn ignition on. Using a voltmeter, check for voltage between Black/Yellow wire and ground.

3) If battery voltage exists, go to next step. If battery voltage does not exist, repair open Black/Yellow wire between recirculation control motor and underdash fuse/relay block. See WIRING DIAGRAMS.

4) Turn ignition off. Test recirculation control motor. See RECIRCULATION CONTROL MOTOR under TESTING. If motor is okay, go to next step. If motor is faulty, replace motor. Ensure recirculation control linkage and door operates smoothly.

5) Remove heater control panel. Disconnect 14-pin connector from heater control panel. Check for continuity in Green/White and Green/Red wires between recirculation control motor and ground. If continuity exists, go to next step. If continuity does not exist, repair short in affected wire(s).

6) Check voltage reading in Green/White and Green/Red wires between recirculation control motor and heater control panel. If voltage is not present in any of the wire(s), go to next step. If voltage is present in any of the wires, repair short to power in affected wire(s) between recirculation control motor and heater control panel.

7) Check each wire for continuity in Green/White and Green/Red wires between recirculation control motor and heater control panel. If continuity exists in any of the wire(s), replace heater control panel. If continuity does not exist in any of the wire(s), check for open Green/White and Green/Red wires between recirculation control motor and heater control panel.

8) Turn ignition off. Disconnect 4-pin recirculation control motor connector. Turn ignition on. Check battery voltage between Black/Yellow wire terminal and ground. If battery voltage is present, go to next step. If battery voltage is not present, repair open in Black/Yellow wire between underdash fuse/relay box and recirculation control motor.

9) Turn ignition off. Remove heater control panel. Disconnect 14-pin heater control panel connector. Check for continuity in Black wire between heater control panel and ground. If continuity exists, replace heater control panel. If continuity does not exist, check for open in Black wire between heater control panel and ground. If wire is okay, check for poor ground connection.

TESTING

WARNING: To avoid injury from accidental air bag deployment, read and carefully follow all SERVICE PRECAUTIONS and DISABLING & ACTIVATING AIR BAG SYSTEM procedures in AIR BAG SYSTEM SAFETY article in GENERAL SERVICING.

BLOWER MOTOR RELAY

Remove relay from dash fuse box. Connect 12-volt battery to terminals No. 3 and 4. *See Fig. 5.* Using ohmmeter, ensure continuity is present between terminals No. 1 and 2. Disconnect battery, and ensure continuity is no longer present between terminals No. 1 and 2.

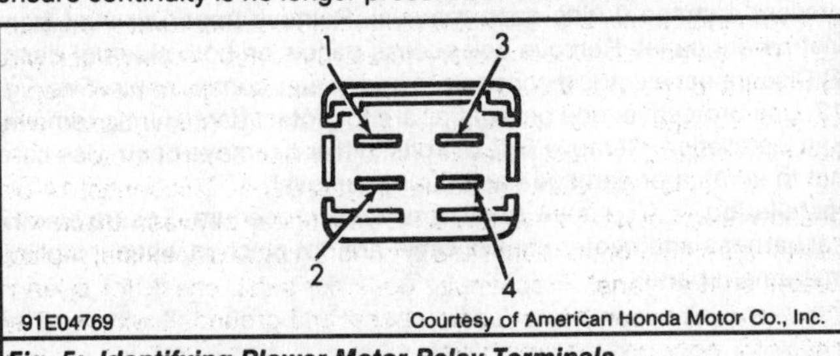
1
3
2
4
91E04769
Courtesy of American Honda Motor Co., Inc.

Fig. 5: Identifying Blower Motor Relay Terminals

FAN SWITCH

Check for continuity between specified terminals of fan switch. See FAN SWITCH CONTINUITY table. *See Fig. 6 or 7.* If continuity is not present, replace fan switch.

FAN SWITCH CONTINUITY

Switch Position	Continuity Between Terminal No.
Civic & Civic Del Sol	
Low	1 & 2; 2 & 3
Medium-Low	1 & 2; 2 & 4
Medium-High	1 & 2; 2 & 5
High	1 & 2; 2 & 6

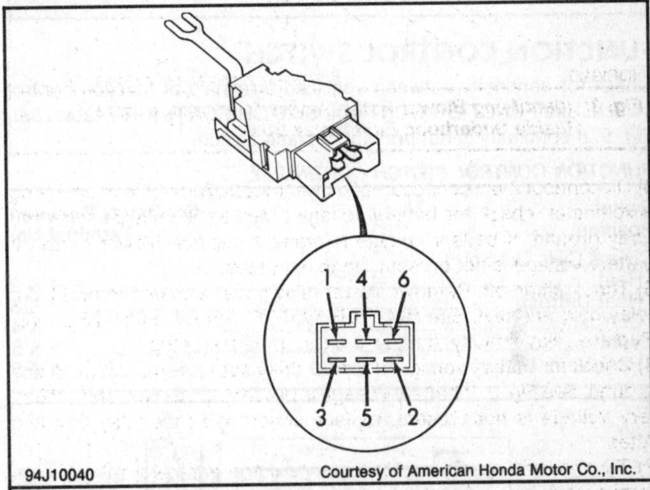
1
4
6
3
5
2
94J10040
Courtesy of American Honda Motor Co., Inc.

Fig. 6: Identifying Fan Switch Connector Terminals (Civic)

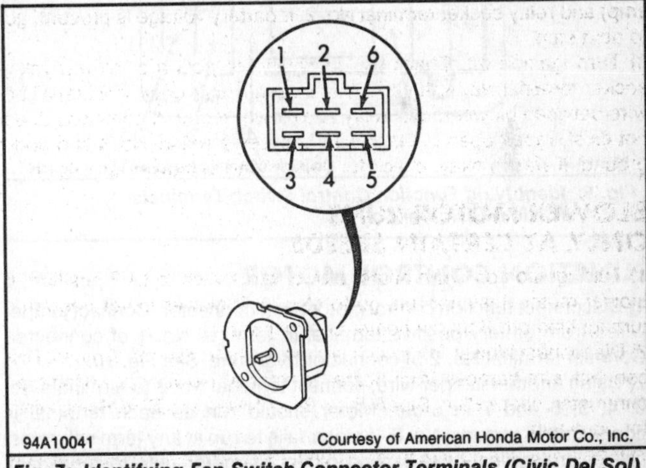
1
2
6
3
4
5
94A10041
Courtesy of American Honda Motor Co., Inc.

Fig. 7: Identifying Fan Switch Connector Terminals (Civic Del Sol)

AIR SOURCE SELECT SWITCH (FRESH & RECIRCULATED AIR)

Check for continuity between specified terminals. See AIR SOURCE SELECT SWITCH CONTINUITY table. *See Fig. 8.* If continuity is not present, replace switch.

AIR SOURCE SELECT SWITCH CONTINUITY

Switch Position	Continuity Between Terminals
Civic	
Fresh Air	"A" & "C"
Recirculation	"B" & "C"
Civic Del Sol	
Fresh Air	"B" & "C"
Recirculation	"A" & "C"

1993 HEATER SYSTEMS
Civic & Civic Del Sol (Cont.)

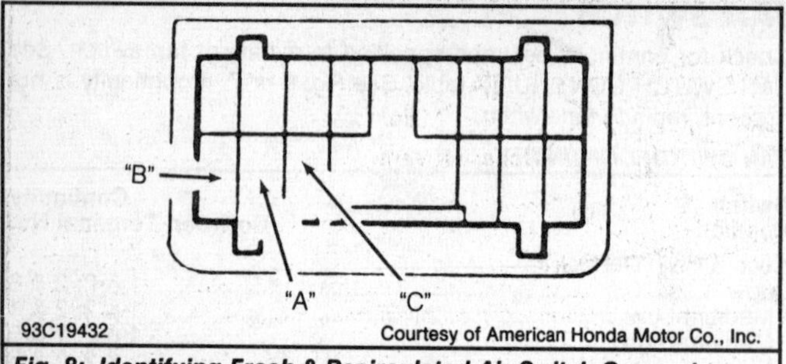
"B"
"A"
"C"
93C19432
Courtesy of American Honda Motor Co., Inc.

***Fig. 8:* Identifying Fresh & Recirculated Air Switch Connector Terminals (Civic & Civic Del Sol)**

FUNCTION CONTROL SWITCH

Check for continuity between specified terminals of function control switch. See FUNCTION CONTROL SWITCH CONTINUITY table. *See Fig. 9.* If continuity is not present, replace switch.

FUNCTION CONTROL SWITCH CONTINUITY

Switch Position	Continuity Between Terminal No.
Civic & Civic Del Sol	
Heat	1 & 2
Heat/Defrost	1 & 3
Defrost	1 & 4
Vent	1 & 5
Heat/Vent	1 & 6

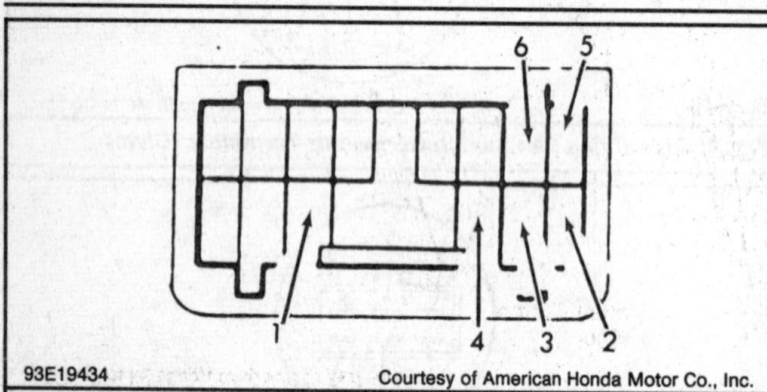
6
5
1
4
3
2
93E19434
Courtesy of American Honda Motor Co., Inc.

***Fig. 9:* Identifying Function Control Switch Terminals (Civic & Civic Del Sol)**

FUNCTION CONTROL MOTOR

1) Disconnect function control motor 8-pin connector. Connect jumper wires from battery positive terminal to terminal No. 1 of connector. Connect terminal No. 2 of connector to ground. *See Fig. 10.*

2) Using another jumper wire, connect terminal No. 2 to terminals No. 3, 4, 5, 6 and 7 in order. Motor should run as each terminal is connected to terminal No. 2. If motor fails to run at any terminal, retest particular terminal after testing others. If motor fails to run again, replace motor.

RECIRCULATION CONTROL MOTOR

1) Turn ignition off. Disconnect 3-pin connector at recirculation motor. Connect battery positive terminal to terminal No. 1 of recirculation motor. *See Fig. 11.*

2) Alternately connect terminals No. 2 and 3 to battery negative terminal. *See Fig. 11.* Motor should move to fresh air position and then to recirculation position. If motor does not function as indicated, replace motor.

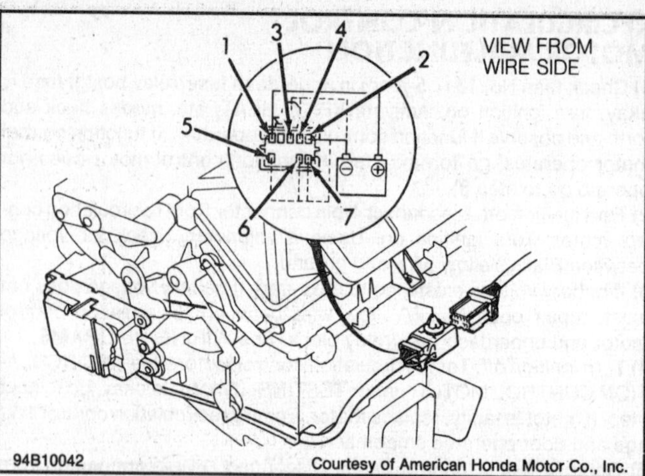
VIEW FROM
WIRE SIDE
1
3
4
2
5
6
7
94B10042
Courtesy of American Honda Motor Co., Inc.

***Fig. 10:* Identifying Function Control Motor Connector Terminals (Civic & Civic Del Sol)**

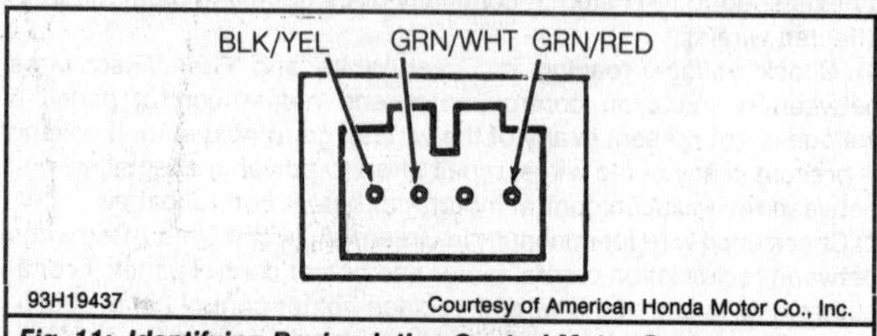
BLK/YEL
GRN/WHT
GRN/RED
93H19437
Courtesy of American Honda Motor Co., Inc.

***Fig. 11:* Identifying Recirculation Control Motor Connector Terminals (Civic & Civic Del Sol)**

REMOVAL & INSTALLATION

WARNING: To avoid injury from accidental air bag deployment, read and carefully follow all SERVICE PRECAUTIONS and DISABLING & ACTIVATING AIR BAG SYSTEM procedures in AIR BAG SYSTEM SAFETY article in GENERAL SERVICING.

BLOWER MOTOR

Removal – Disconnect negative battery cable. Remove glove box and glove box frame. Remove blower duct. Disconnect wiring and pull wiring harness from clamps. Remove bolts and nut and lower blower unit.

Installation – To install, reverse removal procedure. Apply sealant to grommets. Check for air leaks at receiver, blower and blower duct.

INSTRUMENT PANEL

Removal – **1)** Disable air bag system. Disconnect negative battery cable. Remove seat track covers and remove 4 track bolts from each seat. Disconnect electrical connectors and remove seats. Remove screws and access cover from middle of center console.

2) Remove lower instrument panel cover and knee bolster under steering column. Remove glove box bolts and glove box.

3) Remove nuts and bolts supporting steering column and lower column from dash area. Wrap steering column with shop towels to prevent damage during dash removal. Remove upper air vent from instrument panel. Remove bolt access panels on both sides of dash.

4) Disconnect electrical connectors and heater control cable. *See Fig. 12.* Use protective tape on front pillars to protect dash during removal and installation. Remove 6 dash bolts. Lift and remove dash. Use care not to scratch or damage dash during removal.

Installation – To install, reverse removal procedure. Ensure electrical harness and heater control cable are not pinched when installing instrument panel.

1993 HEATER SYSTEMS
Civic & Civic Del Sol (Cont.)

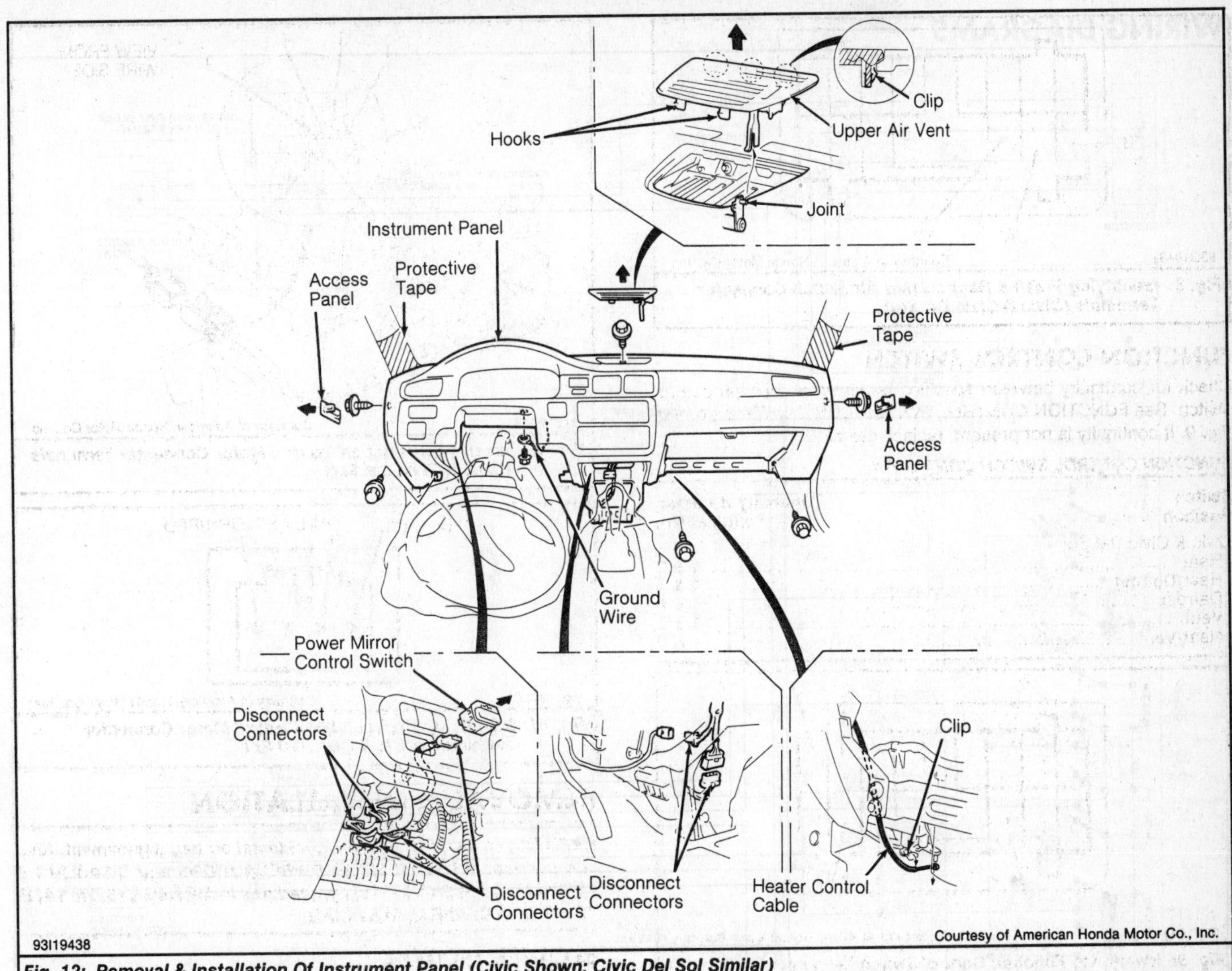
Clip
Upper Air Vent
Hooks
Joint
Instrument Panel
Access Panel
Protective Tape
Protective Tape
Access Panel
Ground Wire
Power Mirror Control Switch
Disconnect Connectors
Disconnect Connectors
Disconnect Connectors
Clip
Heater Control Cable
93I19438
Courtesy of American Honda Motor Co., Inc.

Fig. 12: Removal & Installation Of Instrument Panel (Civic Shown; Civic Del Sol Similar)

HEATER CONTROL PANEL

NOTE: Radio may have a coded theft protection circuit. Ensure code is available before disconnecting battery or removing radio or No. 43 (10-amp) fuse.

Removal – 1) Remove 4 screws, and remove center lower panel. Disconnect radio electrical connectors. Remove 2 screws, and remove radio/cassette player.

2) Disconnect heater control cable at heater assembly. Remove 3 screws and pull out heater control panel. Disconnect electrical connections, and remove heater control panel.

Installation – To install, reverse removal procedure. Check cable adjustments. See ADJUSTMENTS.

HEATER ASSEMBLY & HEATER CORE

Removal – 1) Drain radiator coolant. Place drip pan under heater hoses, and disconnect heater hoses at heater. Disconnect heater valve cable from heater valve.

2) Remove instrument panel. See INSTRUMENT PANEL under REMOVAL & INSTALLATION. Remove heater duct. Remove steering column bracket.

3) Remove heater nut from inside engine compartment. Remove top heater assembly bolts and clip. Pull heater assembly away from body, and remove heater assembly. Remove heater core cover screws, and remove heater core.

Installation – To install, reverse removal procedure. Apply sealant to grommets. DO NOT interchange inlet and outlet heater hoses. Secure hose clamps. Loosen coolant bleed bolt. Fill radiator and reservoir tank with coolant. Tighten bleed bolt after trapped air has escaped. Check cable adjustments. See ADJUSTMENTS.

TORQUE SPECIFICATIONS

TORQUE SPECIFICATIONS

Application	Ft. Lbs. (N.m)
Heater Assembly Nut	16 (22)
Steering Column	
8-mm Bolt	16 (22)
8-mm Nut (Use New)	12 (16)
10-mm Bolt	29 (39)
	INCH Lbs. (N.m)
Blower Motor Bolt/Nut	89 (10)
Instrument Panel Bolt	89 (10)
Heater Assembly Bolt	89 (10)
Knee Bolster Bolt	89 (10)
Passenger-Side Air Bag Bracket Nut	89 (10)

1993 HEATER SYSTEMS
Civic & Civic Del Sol (Cont.)

WIRING DIAGRAMS

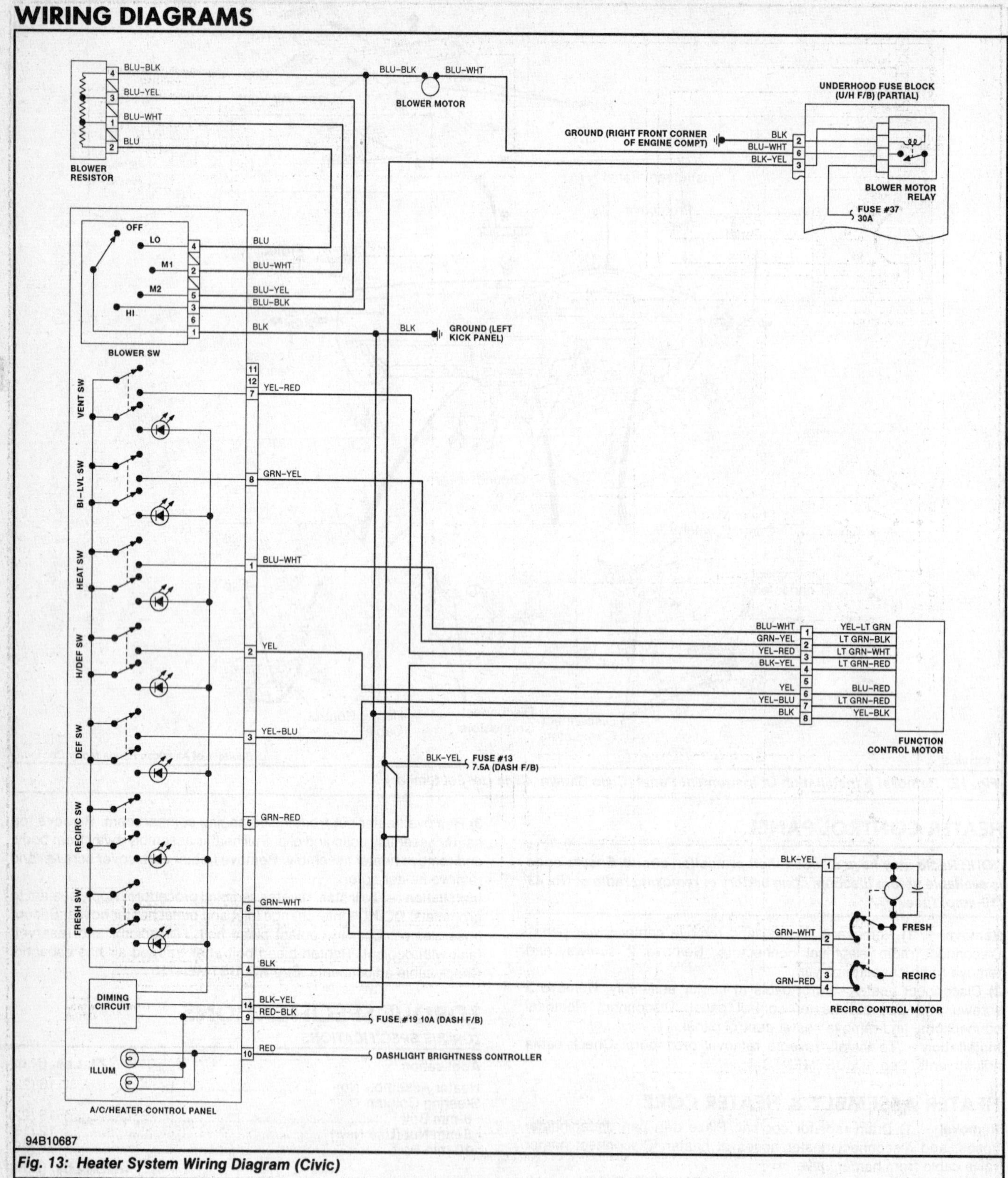
BLU-BLK
BLU-YEL
BLU-WHT
BLU
BLOWER RESISTOR
BLU-BLK
BLU-WHT
BLOWER MOTOR
UNDERHOOD FUSE BLOCK (U/H F/B) (PARTIAL)
GROUND (RIGHT FRONT CORNER OF ENGINE COMPT)
BLK
BLU-WHT
BLK-YEL
BLOWER MOTOR RELAY
FUSE #37 30A
OFF
LO
M1
M2
HI
BLU
BLU-WHT
BLU-YEL
BLU-BLK
BLK
GROUND (LEFT KICK PANEL)
BLOWER SW
VENT SW
BI-LVL SW
HEAT SW
H/DEF SW
DEF SW
RECIRC SW
FRESH SW
YEL-RED
GRN-YEL
BLU-WHT
YEL
YEL-BLU
GRN-RED
GRN-WHT
BLK
BLK-YEL
RED-BLK
RED
BLK-YEL
FUSE #13 7.5A (DASH F/B)
BLU-WHT
GRN-YEL
YEL-RED
BLK-YEL
YEL
YEL-BLU
BLK
YEL-LT GRN
LT GRN-BLK
LT GRN-WHT
LT GRN-RED
BLU-RED
LT GRN-RED
YEL-BLK
FUNCTION CONTROL MOTOR
BLK-YEL
GRN-WHT
GRN-RED
FRESH
RECIRC
RECIRC CONTROL MOTOR
DIMING CIRCUIT
FUSE #19 10A (DASH F/B)
DASHLIGHT BRIGHTNESS CONTROLLER
ILLUM
A/C/HEATER CONTROL PANEL
94B10687

Fig. 13: Heater System Wiring Diagram (Civic)

1993 HEATER SYSTEMS
Civic & Civic Del Sol (Cont.)

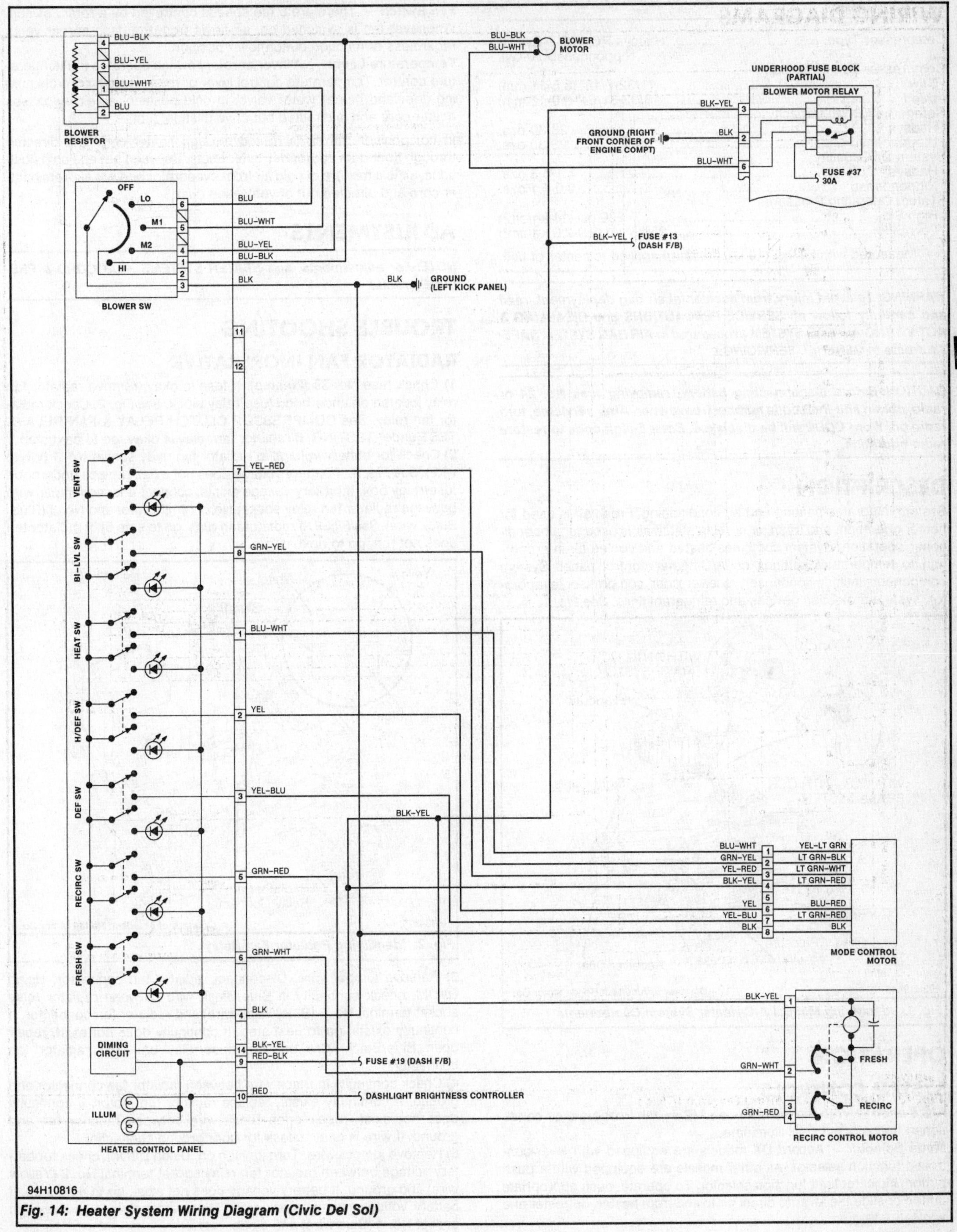
BLU-BLK
BLU-YEL
BLU-WHT
BLU
BLOWER RESISTOR
BLU-BLK
BLU-WHT
BLOWER MOTOR
UNDERHOOD FUSE BLOCK (PARTIAL)
BLOWER MOTOR RELAY
BLK-YEL
GROUND (RIGHT FRONT CORNER OF ENGINE COMPT)
BLK
BLU-WHT
FUSE #37 30A
OFF
LO
M1
M2
HI
BLOWER SW
BLU
BLU-WHT
BLU-YEL
BLU-BLK
BLK
BLK-YEL
FUSE #13 (DASH F/B)
BLK
GROUND (LEFT KICK PANEL)
VENT SW
YEL-RED
BI-LVL SW
GRN-YEL
HEAT SW
BLU-WHT
H/DEF SW
YEL
DEF SW
YEL-BLU
BLK-YEL
RECIRC SW
GRN-RED
FRESH SW
GRN-WHT
BLK
DIMING CIRCUIT
BLK-YEL
RED-BLK
FUSE #19 (DASH F/B)
RED
DASHLIGHT BRIGHTNESS CONTROLLER
ILLUM
HEATER CONTROL PANEL
BLU-WHT
GRN-YEL
YEL-RED
BLK-YEL
YEL
YEL-BLU
BLK
YEL-LT GRN
LT GRN-BLK
LT GRN-WHT
LT GRN-RED
BLU-RED
LT GRN-RED
BLK
MODE CONTROL MOTOR
BLK-YEL
GRN-WHT
GRN-RED
FRESH
RECIRC
RECIRC CONTROL MOTOR
94H10816

Fig. 14: Heater System Wiring Diagram (Civic Del Sol)

1993 MANUAL A/C-HEATER SYSTEMS
Accord

SPECIFICATIONS

Compressor Type .... Hadsys RC-17S 7-Cyl. Or Nippondenso 10-Cyl.
Compressor Belt Deflection [1]
  New .... 11/32-7/16" (8.5-11 mm)
  Used .... 13/32-31/64" (10-12 mm)
Refrigerant (R-12) Capacity
  Hadsys .... 28-30 ozs.
  Nippondenso .... 28-30 ozs.
System Oil Capacity
  Hadsys .... 4.1-4.3 ozs.
  Nippondenso .... 3.0-4.1 ozs.
System Operating Pressures
  High Side .... 200 psi (14 kg/cm²)
  Low Side .... 25-35 psi (2.0-2.5 kg/cm²)

[1] – Measured with 22 lbs. (10 kg) pressure applied to center of belt.

WARNING: To avoid injury from accidental air bag deployment, read and carefully follow all SERVICE PRECAUTIONS and DISABLING & ACTIVATING AIR BAG SYSTEM procedures in AIR BAG SYSTEM SAFETY article in GENERAL SERVICING.

CAUTION: Before disconnecting battery, removing fuse No. 24 or radio, obtain anti-theft code number from owner. After servicing, turn radio on. Word CODE will be displayed. Enter 5-digit code to restore radio operation.

DESCRIPTION

System integrates heating and air conditioning. Fresh air is used for heater operation, and fresh air or recirculated air is used for air conditioner operation. System combines heated and cooled air in proportion to temperature settings on A/C-heater control panel. System components include condenser, receiver-drier, compressor, evaporator, system protection devices and refrigerant lines. *See Fig. 1.*

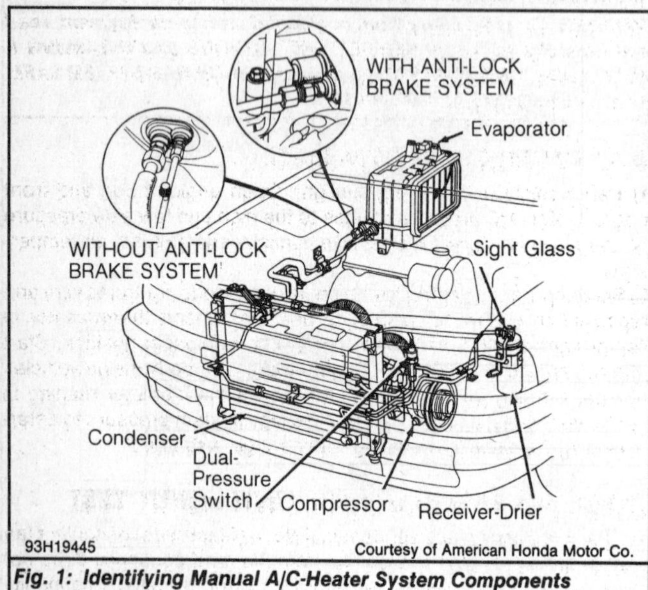
WITH ANTI-LOCK BRAKE SYSTEM
Evaporator
WITHOUT ANTI-LOCK BRAKE SYSTEM
Sight Glass
Condenser
Dual-Pressure Switch
Compressor
Receiver-Drier
93H19445
Courtesy of American Honda Motor Co.

Fig. 1: Identifying Manual A/C-Heater System Components

OPERATION

SYSTEM CONTROLS

A/C Switch – With the fan on, push A/C switch to operate air conditioner. Indicator light will illuminate.

Mode Selector – Accord DX models are equipped with lever-controlled function selector. All other models are equipped with a push button, indicator light function selector. To operate, push appropriate button or slide the lever to direct air to and from heater, defroster and vents.

Fan Switch – There are 5 fan speeds controlled by a rotary switch. Whenever fan is switched on, air flows from the dash corner vents regardless of function button/lever position.

Temperature Lever – A lever or rotary switch operates the temperature control. Temperature control lever or rotary switch controls mixing door and heater water valve. In cold position, all air by-passes heater core and is directed out of ventilation duct.

In hot position, all air is routed through heater core and directed through floor duct and/or defroster ducts. Between hot and cold positions, air is a mixture of cold air from evaporator and hot air from heater core and directed out of ventilation duct.

ADJUSTMENTS

NOTE: For adjustments, see HEATER SYSTEMS – ACCORD & PRELUDE article.

TROUBLE SHOOTING

RADIATOR FAN INOPERATIVE

1) Check fuse No. 39 (20-amp). If fuse is okay, remove radiator fan relay located on underhood fuse/relay block. *See Fig. 2.* Check radiator fan relay. See COMPRESSOR CLUTCH RELAY & FAN RELAYS TEST under TESTING. If radiator fan relay is okay, go to next step.

2) Check for battery voltage in radiator fan relay socket No. 1 (White wire). *See Fig. 2.* If battery voltage does not exist, replace underhood fuse/relay box. If battery voltage exists, connect a fused jumper wire between radiator fan relay socket No. 1 (White wire) and No. 3 (Blue/Black wire). *See Fig. 2.* If radiator fan runs, go to step **5)**. If radiator fan does not run, go to next step.

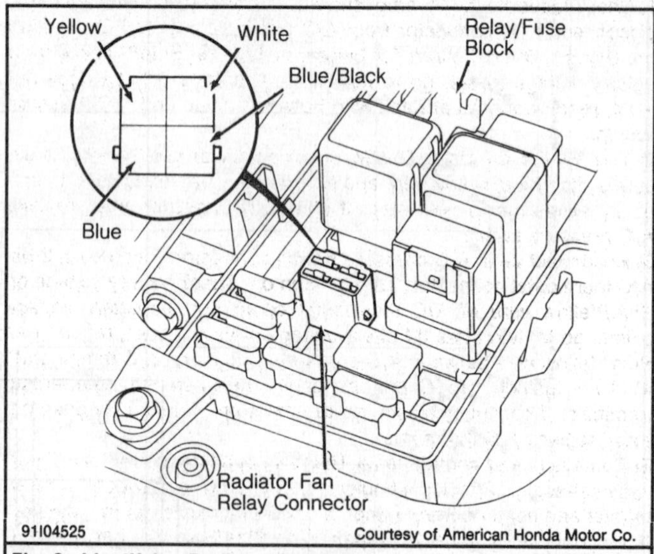
Yellow
White
Relay/Fuse Block
Blue/Black
Blue
Radiator Fan Relay Connector
91I04525
Courtesy of American Honda Motor Co.

Fig. 2: Identifying Radiator Fan Relay

3) Remove jumper wire. Disconnect radiator fan connector. Using DVOM, check continuity in Blue/Black wire between radiator relay socket terminal No. 3 (Blue/Black wire) and radiator fan connector. If continuity exists, go to next step. If continuity does not exist, repair open Blue/Black wire between fuse/relay box and radiator fan connector.

4) Check continuity in Black wire between radiator fan connector and ground. If continuity exists, replace radiator fan motor. If continuity does not exist, repair open Black wire between radiator fan and ground. If wire is okay, check for poor ground connection.

5) Remove jumper wire. Turn ignition on. Using DVOM, check for battery voltage between radiator fan relay socket terminal No. 2 (Yellow wire) and ground. If battery voltage does not exist, go to next step. If battery voltage exists, repair open Blue wire between radiator fan socket No. 4 (Blue wire) and diode.

6) Check for battery voltage between Yellow wire terminal of radiator fan control module and ground. If battery voltage does not exist, repair open Yellow wire between radiator fan control module and fuse/relay box. If battery voltage exists, go to COOLING FAN CONTROL UNIT INPUT TEST under TESTING.

CONDENSER FAN INOPERATIVE

1) Check fuse No. 29 (15-amp). If fuse is okay, remove and test condenser fan relay (located on left fender panel, near headlight). See COMPRESSOR CLUTCH RELAY & FAN RELAYS TEST under TESTING. If condenser fan relay is okay, go to next step.
2) Using a DVOM, check battery voltage between condenser fan relay White wire terminal and ground. If battery voltage is present, go to next step. If battery voltage is not present, repair open White wire between underhood fuse/relay box and condenser fan relay.
3) Connect a fused jumper wire between condenser fan relay White wire and Blue/Yellow wire terminals. If condenser fan runs, go to step 5). If condenser fan does not run, go to next step.
4) Remove jumper wire. Disconnect condenser fan motor connector. Using a DVOM, check continuity in Blue/Yellow wire between condenser fan relay and condenser fan. If continuity exists, replace condenser fan motor. If continuity does not exist, repair open Blue/Yellow wire between condenser fan relay and condenser fan.
5) Remove jumper wire. Turn ignition on. Check battery voltage between radiator fan control module Yellow/White wire terminal and ground. If battery voltage is present, repair open Yellow/White wire between condenser fan relay and radiator fan control module. If battery voltage is not present, go to COOLING FAN CONTROL UNIT INPUT TEST under TESTING.

A/C SYSTEM INOPERATIVE

1) Check fuses No. 8 (7.5-amp) and No. 7 (7.5-amp). If fuses are okay, disconnect 2-pin connector from A/C pressure switch. Turn ignition on. Using a DVOM, check for battery voltage on Blue/Black wire. If battery voltage exists, go to next step. If battery voltage does not exist, repair open Blue/Black wire between diode and A/C pressure switch.
2) Turn ignition off. Using DVOM, check continuity between A/C pressure switch Blue/Yellow wire and Blue/Black wire connectors. If continuity exists, go to next step. If continuity does not exist, replace A/C pressure switch.
3) Reconnect 2-pin A/C pressure switch connector. Disconnect 2-pin A/C thermostat connector. Turn ignition on. Check battery voltage on Blue/Yellow wire of A/C thermostat connector. If battery voltage exists, go to next step. If battery voltage does not exist, repair open Blue/Yellow wire between A/C pressure switch and A/C thermostat.
4) Turn ignition off. Check continuity between A/C thermostat terminals. If continuity exists, go to next step. If continuity does not exist, replace A/C thermostat.
5) Remove heater control panel. Disconnect heater control panel harness connector. Check continuity in Blue/Red wire between A/C thermostat and heater control panel. If continuity exists, go to next step. If continuity does not exist, repair open Blue/Red wire between A/C thermostat and heater control panel.
6) Test A/C switch. See A/C SWITCH TEST under TESTING. If A/C switch is okay, disconnect 8-pin heater fan switch connector. Check continuity in Green wire between heater control panel and heater fan switch. If continuity exists, go to next step. If continuity does not exist, repair open Green wire between heater control panel and heater fan switch.
7) Check continuity in Black wire between heater fan switch and ground. If continuity exists, replace heater switch. If continuity does not exist, repair open Black wire between heater fan switch and ground. If wire is okay, check for poor ground connection.

A/C COMPRESSOR INOPERATIVE

1) Disconnect 4-pin connector from compressor clutch relay. Compressor clutch relay is located on left fender panel, near condenser fan relay. Turn ignition on and measure voltage between Black/Yellow wire and ground. If battery voltage does not exist, repair open Black/Yellow wire between fuse No. 7 (7.5-amp) and compressor clutch relay.
2) If battery voltage exists, measure voltage between Black/Yellow wire terminal and ground. If battery voltage does not exist, repair open Black/Yellow wire between fuse No. 7 (7.5-amp) and compressor clutch relay.
3) If battery voltage exists, start engine. Connect jumper wire between Black/Yellow wire and Red wire terminals. If compressor clutch engages, go to step 5). If compressor clutch does not engage, turn ignition off. Disconnect Red wire from compressor clutch and turn ignition on.
4) Measure voltage between Red wire terminal and ground. If battery voltage exists, replace compressor clutch. If battery voltage does not exist, repair open Red wire between compressor clutch relay and clutch connector.
5) Turn ignition off. Reconnect compressor clutch relay. Restart engine and connect jumper wire between Red/Blue wire terminal and ground. If compressor clutch does not engage, replace compressor clutch relay. If compressor clutch engages, turn ignition off. Disconnect PGM-FI (fuel injection) ECM connector.
6) Install ECM Test Harness (07LAJ-PT3010A). Restart engine. Connect jumper wire between test harness terminal No. A15 (Red/Blue wire) and ground. If compressor clutch does not engage, repair open Red/Blue wire between compressor clutch relay and ECM. If compressor clutch engages, install jumper wire between test harness terminal No. B5 (Blue/Black wire) and ground.
7) If compressor clutch engages, repair open Blue/Black wire between ECM and A/C pressure switch. If compressor clutch does not engage, substitute a known good ECM and recheck. If compressor clutch engages, replace defective ECM.

TESTING

WARNING: To avoid injury from accidental air bag deployment, read and carefully follow all SERVICE PRECAUTIONS and DISABLING & ACTIVATING AIR BAG SYSTEM procedures in AIR BAG SYSTEM SAFETY article in GENERAL SERVICING.

A/C SYSTEM PERFORMANCE

1) Park vehicle out of direct sunlight. Open engine hood and front doors. Install A/C pressure gauges to the high and low side pressure ports of system. Determine relative humidity and ambient air temperature.
2) Set temperature control to maximum cool, mode control to vent and recirculation control to recirculate positions. Insert thermometer in center vent outlet. Turn blower fan switch to highest position. Start and run engine at 1500 RPM. Ensure there is nobody inside vehicle.
3) After running A/C for 10 minutes, check thermometer reading in center vent outlet and the high and low side system pressure to determine if A/C system is operating within range. *See Fig. 3.*

COOLING FAN CONTROL UNIT INPUT TEST

1) Check continuity between terminal No. 4 (Black wire) of cooling fan control unit connector and ground. *See Fig. 4.* If continuity does not exist, repair open between terminal No. 4 and ground. If continuity exists, go to next step.
2) Check for battery voltage at terminal No. 6 (White wire). If battery voltage exists, go to next step. If battery voltage does not exist, check fuse No. 29. If fuse is okay, repair open White wire.
3) With ignition on, check for battery voltage on terminal No. 7 (Black/Yellow wire). If battery voltage exists, go to next step. If battery voltage does not exist, check fuse No. 2. If fuse is okay, repair open Black/Yellow wire.

1993 MANUAL A/C-HEATER SYSTEMS
Accord (Cont.)

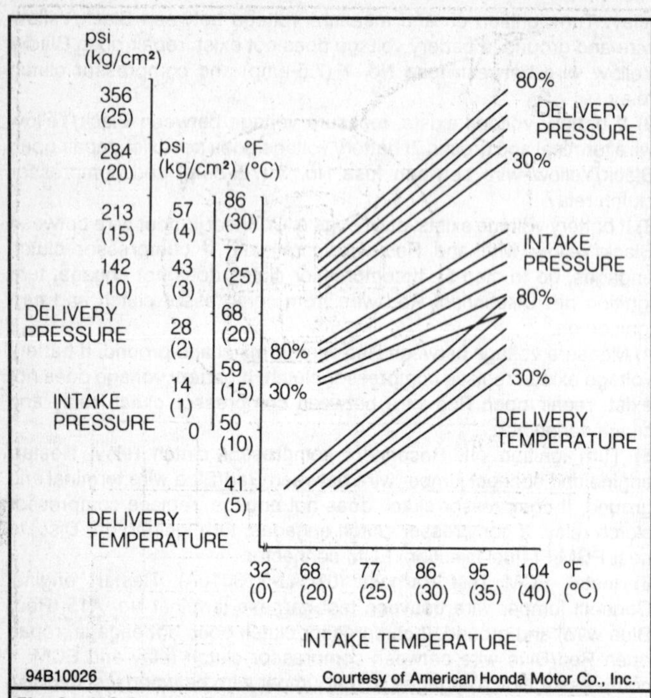
psi
(kg/cm²)
356
(25)
284
(20)
213
(15)
142
(10)
DELIVERY
PRESSURE
psi
(kg/cm²)
57
(4)
43
(3)
28
(2)
14
(1)
0
INTAKE
PRESSURE
°F
(°C)
86
(30)
77
(25)
68
(20)
59
(15)
50
(10)
41
(5)
DELIVERY
TEMPERATURE
80%
DELIVERY
PRESSURE
30%
INTAKE
PRESSURE
80%
80%
30%
30%
DELIVERY
TEMPERATURE
32 (0)
68 (20)
77 (25)
86 (30)
95 (35)
104 (40)
°F (°C)
INTAKE TEMPERATURE
94B10026
Courtesy of American Honda Motor Co., Inc.

Fig. 3: A/C System Performance Test Chart

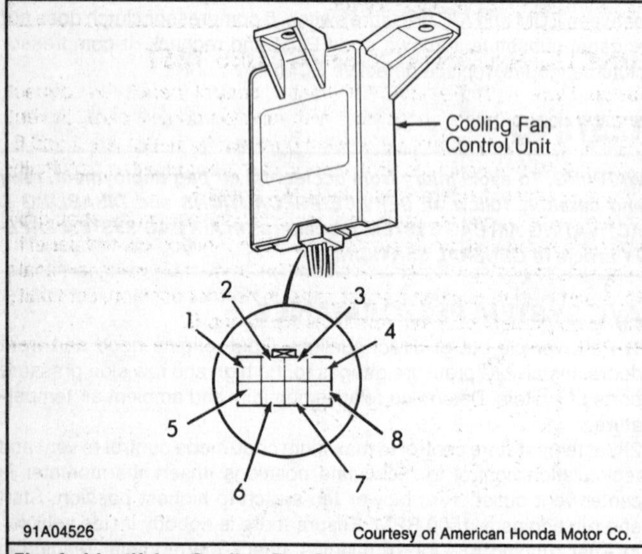
Cooling Fan
Control Unit
1
2
3
4
5
6
7
8
91A04526
Courtesy of American Honda Motor Co.

Fig. 4: Identifying Cooling Fan Control Unit Terminals

4) With ignition on, check for battery voltage on terminal No. 2 (Yellow/Black wire). If battery voltage exists, go to next step. If battery voltage does not exist, check fuse No. 8. If fuse is okay, repair open Yellow/Black wire.

5) Check for battery voltage on terminals No. 1 (Yellow/White wire) and No. 3 (Yellow wire). If battery voltage does not exist at either terminal, replace cooling fan control unit. If battery voltage exists, go to next step.

CAUTION: Before connecting new cooling fan control unit, check Yellow and Yellow/White wires for continuity to ground. There should not be continuity. Repair wire(s) as necessary before connecting new control unit.

6) Connect body ground to terminal No. 8 (Blue wire). If radiator and condenser fans come on, go to step **8)**. If both fans do not come on, check for open Blue wire between cooling fan control unit and radiator fan relay or condenser fan relay.

7) If Blue wire is okay, check for open Yellow/White wire between cooling fan control unit and condenser fan relay. Check for open Yellow wire between cooling fan control unit and radiator fan relay. If no open circuits are found, test radiator fan or condenser fan relays. See COMPRESSOR CLUTCH RELAY & FAN RELAYS TEST under TESTING.

8) Check for 11 volts on terminal No. 5 (White/Green wire) with coolant temperature less than 223°F (106°C). If 11 volts do not exist, check for bad coolant temperature switch, short to ground or bad cooling fan control unit. If 11 volts exist, cooling fan control unit input test is complete.

COMPRESSOR CLUTCH COIL TEST

1) Inspect pressure plate surface and rotor for wear or for oil-soaked condition. Check clutch bearing for wear, noise and grease leakage. Replace components as necessary. Disconnect clutch wires at connector.

2) Connect one ohmmeter lead to clutch wire and other to ground. Resistance should be 3.85-4.15 ohms at 68°F (20°C). If resistance is not as specified, replace clutch coil.

COMPRESSOR CLUTCH RELAY & FAN RELAYS TEST

Disconnect relay connector. Connect positive side of battery to relay terminal No. 1 and negative side to terminal No. 2. *See Fig. 5.* Connect ohmmeter leads to relay terminals No. 3 and 4 and check for continuity. If continuity exists, relay is good. If continuity does not exist, replace relay.

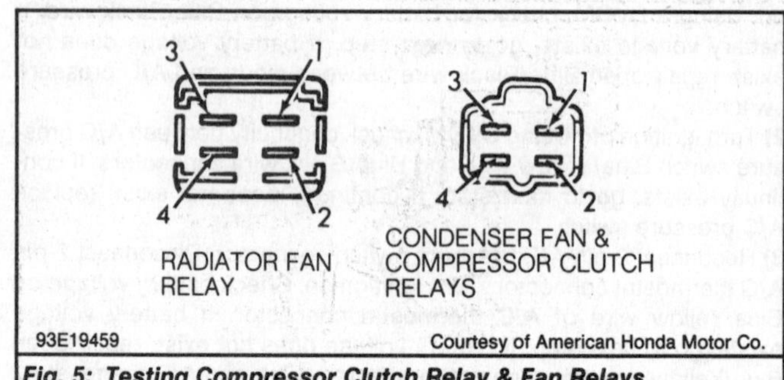
3
1
4
2
RADIATOR FAN
RELAY
3
1
4
2
CONDENSER FAN &
COMPRESSOR CLUTCH
RELAYS
93E19459
Courtesy of American Honda Motor Co.

Fig. 5: Testing Compressor Clutch Relay & Fan Relays

A/C SWITCH TEST

Check for continuity between A/C switch terminals No. 1 and 2. *See Fig. 6.* With A/C switch on, continuity should be present between terminals.

A/C THERMOSTAT TEST

1) Remove evaporator assembly. With evaporator removed, remove A/C thermostat from evaporator case. Connect ohmmeter leads to thermostat connectors. Dip capillary tube of thermostat into ice cold water. *See Fig. 7.*

2) As ohmmeter reading (suddenly, not gradually) changes, note cut-off and cut-in temperature of thermostat. Cut-off temperature should be 32-35°F (0.5-1.5°C). Cut-in temperature should be 37-41°F (2.5-5.0°C). If cut-in and cut-off temperatures are not within specifications, replace thermostat.

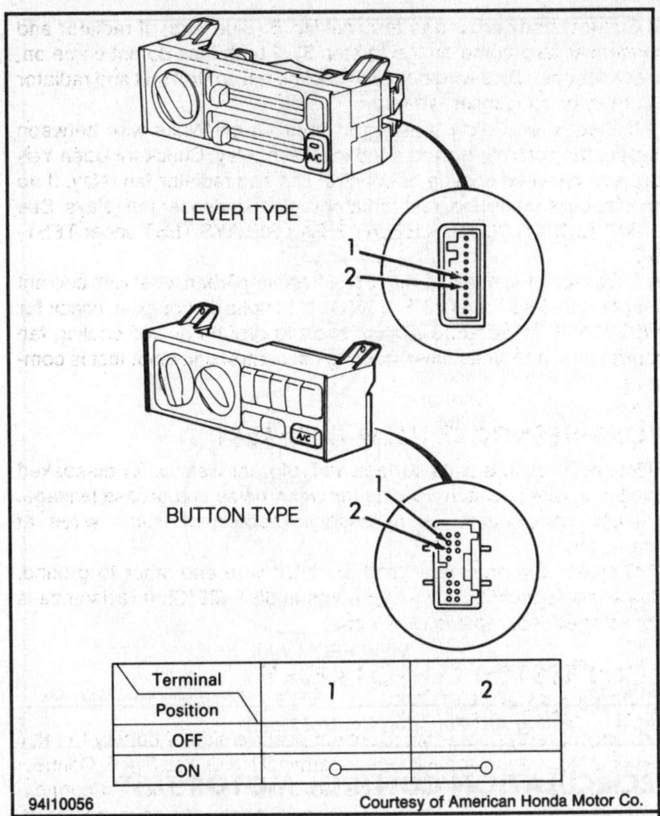
LEVER TYPE
1
2
BUTTON TYPE
1
2
A/C
94I10056
Courtesy of American Honda Motor Co.

Terminal / Position	1	2
OFF		
ON	O	O

Fig. 6: Testing A/C Switches

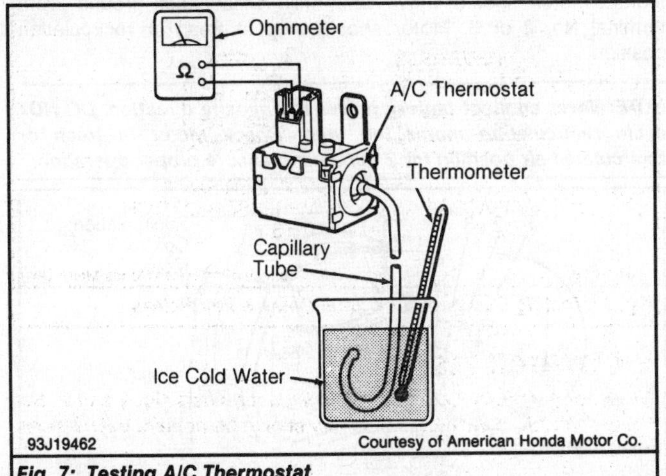
Ohmmeter
Ω
A/C Thermostat
Thermometer
Capillary Tube
Ice Cold Water
93J19462
Courtesy of American Honda Motor Co.

Fig. 7: Testing A/C Thermostat

A/C DIODE TEST

Check continuity between diode terminals in both directions. Continuity should be present in one direction only. If continuity is not as specified, replace diode.

BLOWER SWITCH TEST

1) Remove A/C-heater control panel. Disconnect blower switch connector. With blower switch off, continuity should not be present between any terminals. With blower switch in position "A", continuity should be present between terminals No. 1, 2 and 3. *See Fig. 8.*

2) With blower switch in position "B", continuity should be present between terminals No. 1, 2 and 4. With blower switch in position "C", continuity should be present between terminals No. 1, 2 and 5.

3) With blower switch in position "D", continuity should be present between terminals No. 1, 2 and 6. With blower switch in position "E", continuity should be present between terminals No. 1, 2 and 7.

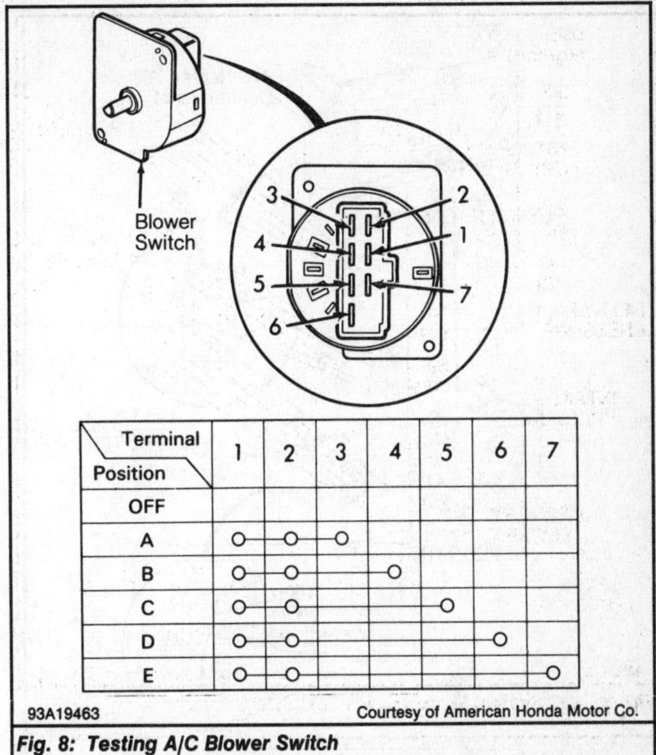
Blower Switch
3
2
4
1
5
7
6
93A19463
Courtesy of American Honda Motor Co.

Terminal / Position	1	2	3	4	5	6	7
OFF							
A	O	O	O				
B	O	O		O			
C	O	O			O		
D	O	O				O	
E	O	O					O

Fig. 8: Testing A/C Blower Switch

FUNCTION CONTROL SWITCHES TEST

Button Type – 1) Remove A/C-heater control panel. Disconnect function control panel connector. With function control panel in vent position, continuity should be present between terminals No. 1 and 6. *See Fig. 9.* With function control panel in vent/floor position, continuity should be present between terminals No. 2 and 6.

2) With function control panel in floor position, continuity should be present between terminals No. 3 and 6. With function control panel in defrost/floor position, continuity should be present between terminals No. 4 and 6. With function control panel in defrost position, continuity should be present between terminals No. 5 and 6.

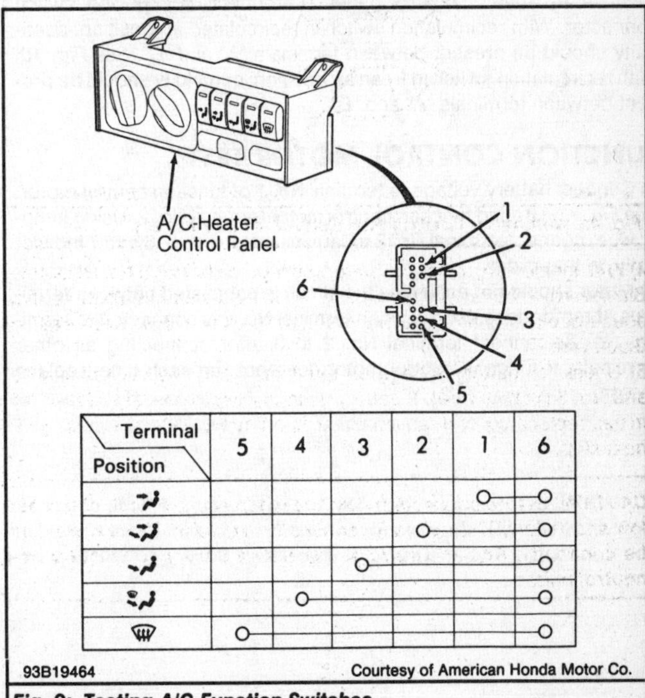
A/C-Heater Control Panel
1
2
6
3
4
5
93B19464
Courtesy of American Honda Motor Co.

Terminal / Position	5	4	3	2	1	6
					O	O
				O		O
			O			O
		O				O
	O					O

Fig. 9: Testing A/C Function Switches

1993 MANUAL A/C-HEATER SYSTEMS
Accord (Cont.)

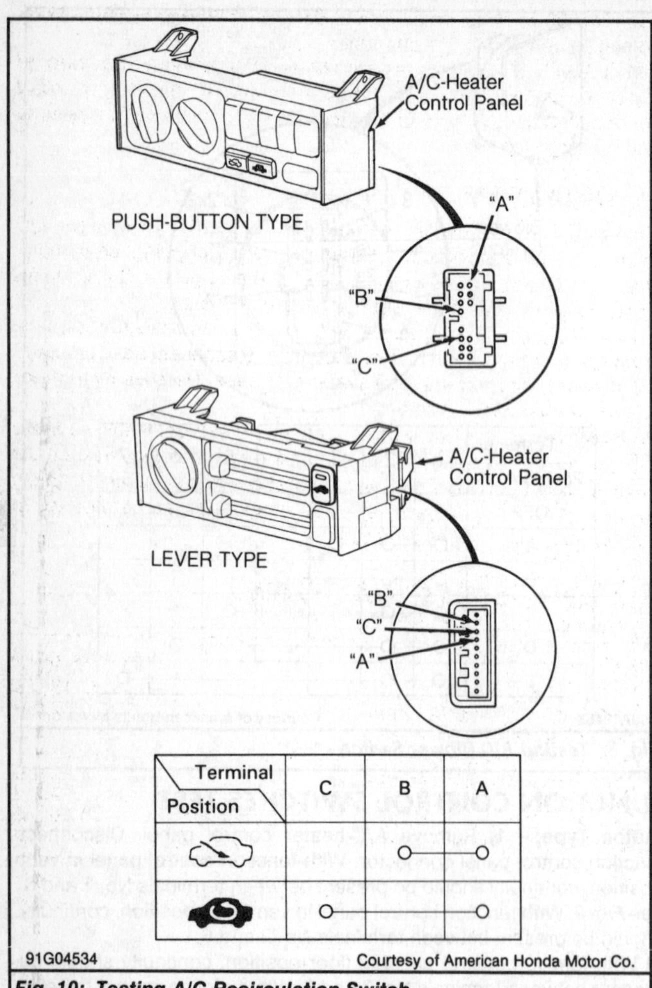
A/C-Heater
Control Panel
PUSH-BUTTON TYPE
"A"
"B"
"C"
A/C-Heater
Control Panel
LEVER TYPE
"B"
"C"
"A"

Terminal / Position	C	B	A
(fresh air)		o	o
(recirculated air)	o		o

91G04534 Courtesy of American Honda Motor Co.

Fig. 10: Testing A/C Recirculation Switch

RECIRCULATION SWITCH TEST

Remove A/C-heater control panel. Disconnect recirculation switch connector. With recirculation switch in recirculated air position, continuity should be present between terminals "A" and "C". *See Fig. 10.* With recirculation switch in fresh air position, continuity should be present between terminals "A" and "B".

FUNCTION CONTROL MOTOR TEST

1) Connect battery voltage to terminal No. 1 of function control motor. *See Fig. 11*. Ground function control motor terminal No. 2. Using jumper wire, connect terminal No. 2 to terminals No. 3, 4, 5, 6 and 7 individually, in that order.

2) Motor should run each time the circuit is completed between terminals. If motor does not run when terminal No. 2 is connected to terminal No. 3, connect terminal No. 2 to 3 after connecting all other terminals. If function control motor does not run each time, replace motor.

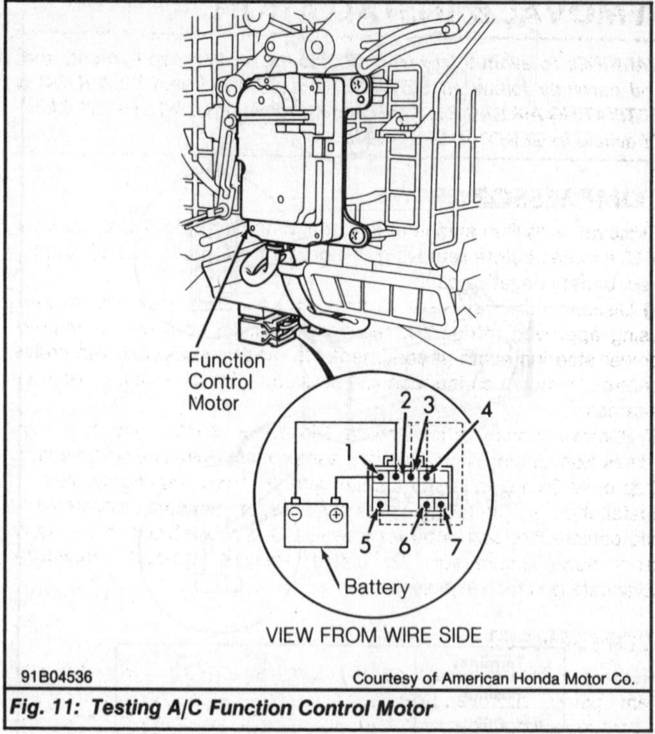
Function
Control
Motor
1
2
3
4
5
6
7
Battery
VIEW FROM WIRE SIDE

91B04536 Courtesy of American Honda Motor Co.

Fig. 11: Testing A/C Function Control Motor

RECIRCULATION CONTROL MOTOR TEST

Connect battery voltage to terminal No. 1 of recirculation control motor. *See Fig. 12*. Ground terminal No. 2 or 3 of recirculation control motor. Motor should move smoothly. Disconnect ground from terminal No. 2 or 3. Motor should stop at fresh or recirculation position.

NOTE: Never connect battery power in opposite direction. DO NOT cycle recirculation motor too long. Check motor in fresh or recirculated air position for 2 minutes to ensure proper operation.

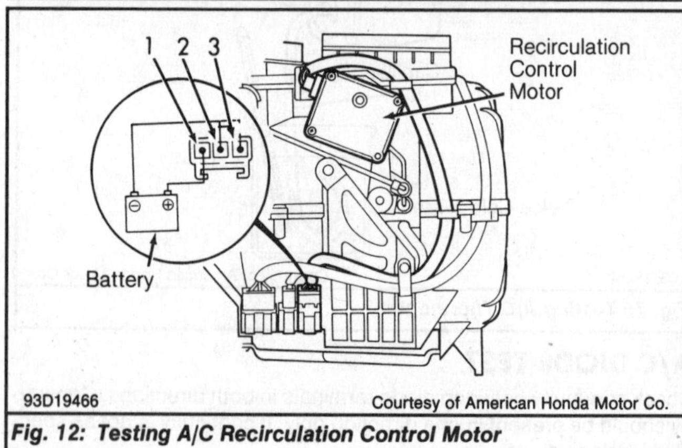
1
2
3
Recirculation
Control
Motor
Battery

93D19466 Courtesy of American Honda Motor Co.

Fig. 12: Testing A/C Recirculation Control Motor

1993 MANUAL A/C-HEATER SYSTEMS
Accord (Cont.)

REMOVAL & INSTALLATION

WARNING: To avoid injury from accidental air bag deployment, read and carefully follow all SERVICE PRECAUTIONS and DISABLING & ACTIVATING AIR BAG SYSTEM procedures in AIR BAG SYSTEM SAFETY article in GENERAL SERVICING.

COMPRESSOR

Removal – 1) Run engine at idle speed and operate A/C system for 5-10 minutes before removing compressor. Stop engine and disconnect battery negative cable.

2) Disconnect compressor clutch coil lead. Discharge A/C system using approved refrigerant recovery/recycling equipment. Remove power steering pump (if equipped). On models equipped with cruise control, remove cruise control actuator. On all models, remove alternator.

3) Remove condenser fan shroud. Disconnect suction and discharge hoses from compressor. Remove compressor bolts and compressor. Cap open fittings to keep moisture and dirt from entering system.

Installation – If installing a new compressor, measure oil contents of old compressor and subtract from 3 1/3 ounces. Drain this amount from new compressor. To install, reverse removal procedure. Evacuate and recharge system.

CONDENSER

Removal – 1) Disconnect battery negative cable. Discharge A/C system using approved refrigerant recovery/recycling equipment. Remove radiator reservoir and air intake tube. Remove front grille. Remove radiator fan and shroud. Remove condenser fan and shroud. Remove upper radiator brackets.

2) Disconnect discharge hose and condenser line from condenser inlet and outlet fittings. Remove condenser nuts and condenser. Cap open fittings to keep moisture and dirt from entering system. Avoid damaging condenser fins and tubes.

Installation – To install, reverse removal procedure. Be sure to install condenser legs into rubber mounts. If installing a NEW condenser add 1/3 ounce of refrigeration oil to condenser. Evacuate and recharge system.

EVAPORATOR

Removal – 1) Disconnect battery ground cable. Discharge A/C system using approved refrigerant recovery/recycling equipment. Disconnect suction hose and liquid line from evaporator. Cap open fittings to keep moisture and dirt from entering system.

2) Remove glove box and glove box frame. Disconnect wiring harness from A/C thermostat and blower assembly. Disconnect band connecting blower motor assembly to evaporator case. Remove evaporator assembly bolts and evaporator.

Installation – To install, reverse removal procedure. Install capillary tube in its original position. Ensure no gaps exist between evaporator case. Ensure evaporator and blower sealing bands are secured tightly to prevent air leaks. If installing a new evaporator, add 5/6 ounce of refrigerant oil before charging system.

TORQUE SPECIFICATIONS

TORQUE SPECIFICATIONS

Application	Ft. Lbs. (N.m)
A/C Compressor Bolts	18 (25)
A/C Compressor Bracket Bolt/Nut	37 (50)
Refrigerant Hoses	
Suction Line (At Evaporator)	
With Anti-Lock Brake System	22 (30)
Without Anti-Lock Brake System	24 (32)
Discharge Hose & Condenser Line (At Condenser)	16 (22)
Receiver-Drier Lines	13 (17)

1993 MANUAL A/C-HEATER SYSTEMS
Accord (Cont.)

WIRING DIAGRAM

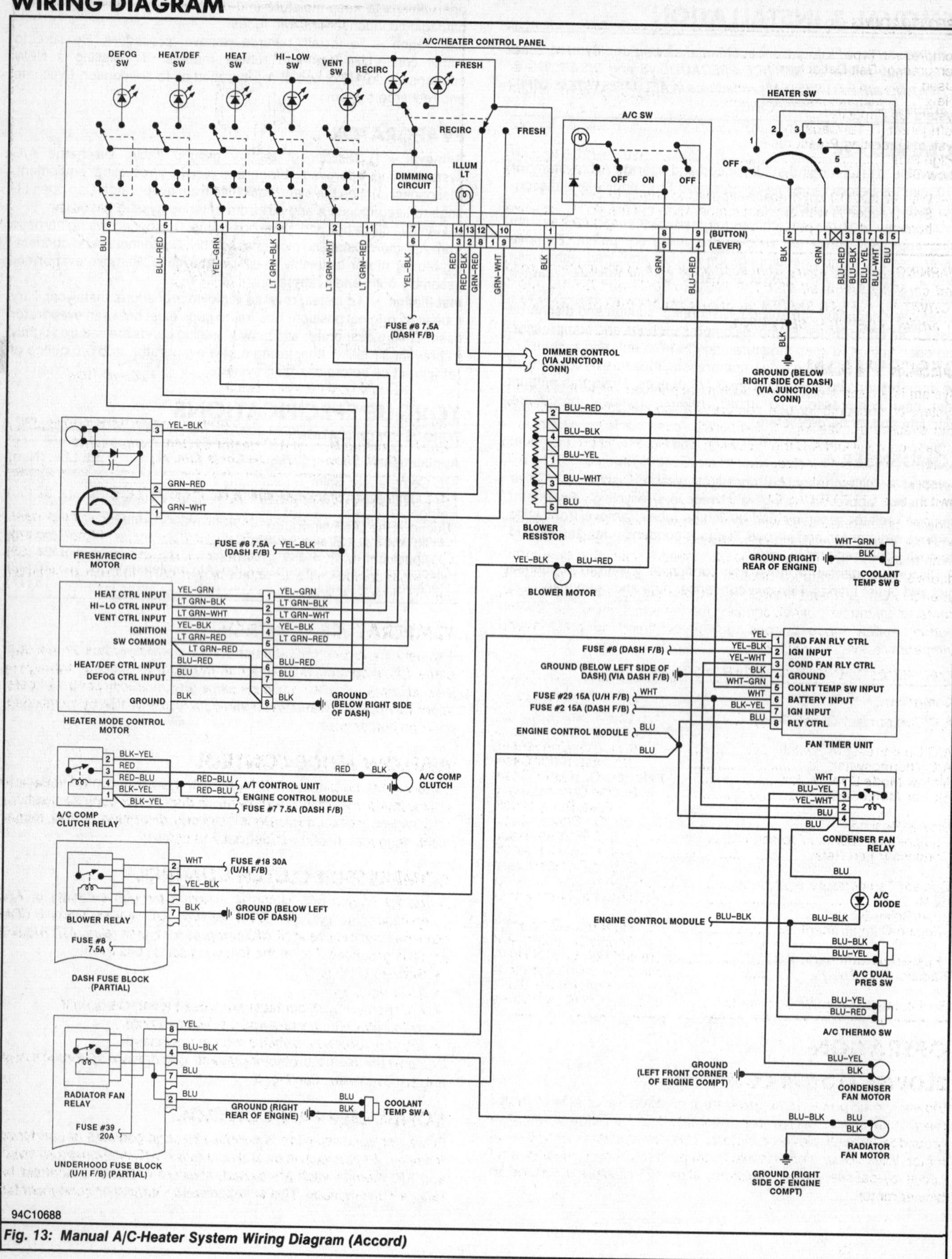
A/C/HEATER CONTROL PANEL
DEFOG SW
HEAT/DEF SW
HEAT SW
HI-LOW SW
VENT SW
RECIRC
FRESH
DIMMING CIRCUIT
ILLUM LT
A/C SW
OFF
ON
HEATER SW
(BUTTON)
(LEVER)
FUSE #8 7.5A (DASH F/B)
DIMMER CONTROL (VIA JUNCTION CONN)
GROUND (BELOW RIGHT SIDE OF DASH) (VIA JUNCTION CONN)
FRESH/RECIRC MOTOR
BLOWER RESISTOR
BLOWER MOTOR
GROUND (RIGHT REAR OF ENGINE)
COOLANT TEMP SW B
HEAT CTRL INPUT
HI-LO CTRL INPUT
VENT CTRL INPUT
IGNITION
SW COMMON
HEAT/DEF CTRL INPUT
DEFOG CTRL INPUT
GROUND
HEATER MODE CONTROL MOTOR
GROUND (BELOW RIGHT SIDE OF DASH)
FUSE #8 (DASH F/B)
GROUND (BELOW LEFT SIDE OF DASH) (VIA DASH F/B)
FUSE #29 15A (U/H F/B)
FUSE #2 15A (DASH F/B)
ENGINE CONTROL MODULE
RAD FAN RLY CTRL
IGN INPUT
COND FAN RLY CTRL
GROUND
COLNT TEMP SW INPUT
BATTERY INPUT
IGN INPUT
RLY CTRL
FAN TIMER UNIT
A/C COMP CLUTCH RELAY
A/C COMP CLUTCH
A/T CONTROL UNIT
ENGINE CONTROL MODULE
FUSE #7 7.5A (DASH F/B)
CONDENSER FAN RELAY
FUSE #18 30A (U/H F/B)
GROUND (BELOW LEFT SIDE OF DASH)
BLOWER RELAY
FUSE #8 7.5A
DASH FUSE BLOCK (PARTIAL)
A/C DIODE
ENGINE CONTROL MODULE
A/C DUAL PRES SW
A/C THERMO SW
RADIATOR FAN RELAY
GROUND (RIGHT REAR OF ENGINE)
COOLANT TEMP SW A
FUSE #39 20A
UNDERHOOD FUSE BLOCK (U/H F/B) (PARTIAL)
GROUND (LEFT FRONT CORNER OF ENGINE COMPT)
CONDENSER FAN MOTOR
RADIATOR FAN MOTOR
GROUND (RIGHT SIDE OF ENGINE COMPT)
94C10688

Fig. 13: Manual A/C-Heater System Wiring Diagram (Accord)

1993 MANUAL A/C-HEATER SYSTEMS
Civic & Civic Del Sol

SPECIFICATIONS

Compressor Type	Sanden Scroll
Compressor Belt Deflection [1]	
Used	1/4-13/32" (6.5-10.5 mm)
New	13/64-9/32" (5.0-7.0 mm)
System Oil Capacity	4.0-4.7 ozs.
Refrigerant (R-12) Capacity	21-23 ozs.
System Operating Pressures [2]	
High Side	320 psi (22.5 kg/cm²)
Low Side	36 psi (2.5 kg/cm²)

1 – With 22 lbs. (10 kg) pressure applied to center of belt.
2 – Specification is with ambient temperature at 80°F (27°C), relative humidity at 50-70 percent and engine speed at 1500 RPM.

WARNING: To avoid injury from accidental air bag deployment, read and carefully follow all SERVICE PRECAUTIONS and DISABLING & ACTIVATING AIR BAG SYSTEM procedures in AIR BAG SYSTEM SAFETY article in GENERAL SERVICING.

DESCRIPTION

System is a cycling-clutch type with an expansion valve. Refrigerant system components include compressor, condenser, receiver-drier and evaporator. *See Fig. 1.* Evaporator case contains evaporator, expansion valve and A/C thermoswitch. *See Fig. 7.* Compressor clutch control components include Electronic Control Module (ECM), A/C compressor clutch relay, A/C dual-pressure switch and A/C thermoswitch. See ELECTRICAL COMPONENT LOCATIONS table.

Blower case contains blower motor, blower resistor, recirculated/fresh air door and recirculated/fresh air door motor. Heater case contains heater core, air mix (temperature blend) door, 3 airflow mode doors and an airflow mode door motor. Heater water valve is located at engine compartment firewall. A/C-heater control panel, located in center of instrument panel, contains blower switch lever, A/C switch button, airflow mode buttons, recirculated/fresh air buttons and temperature lever. *See Fig. 6.*

ELECTRICAL COMPONENT LOCATIONS

Component	Location
A/C Compressor Clutch Relay	Left Front Corner Of Engine Compartment
A/C Dual-Pressure Switch	Left Side Of Condenser
A/C Thermoswitch	On Evaporator Case
Airflow Mode Door Motor	Left Side Of Heater Case
Blower Motor Relay	In Engine Compartment Fuse/Relay Block
Blower Resistor	On Blower Case
Compressor Thermal Protector	On Compressor
Condenser Fan Relay	Left Front Corner Of Engine Compartment
Coolant Temperature Switch	On Thermostat Housing
ECM	Behind Right Kick Panel
Fuse/Relay Block	
Engine Compartment	Right Rear Corner Of Engine Compartment
Passenger Compartment	Behind Left End Of Dash
Radiator Fan Relay	In Engine Compartment Fuse/Relay Block
Recirculated/Fresh Air Door Motor	On Blower Case

OPERATION

BLOWER MOTOR CONTROL

Blower motor power is supplied through contacts of blower motor relay. With blower switch in positions I, II and III, blower motor is grounded through blower resistors. This reduces voltage to blower motor. With blower switch in maximum position, blower motor ground circuit by-passes blower resistors, allowing full battery voltage to blower motor.

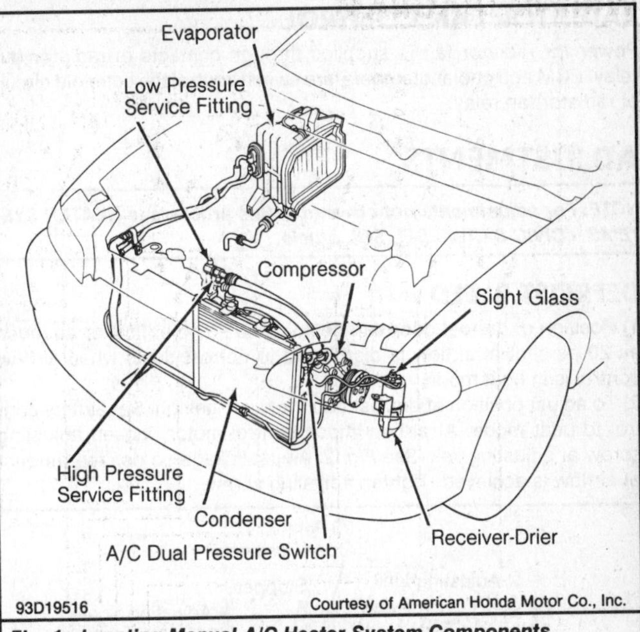
Evaporator
Low Pressure Service Fitting
Compressor
Sight Glass
High Pressure Service Fitting
Condenser
A/C Dual Pressure Switch
Receiver-Drier
93D19516
Courtesy of American Honda Motor Co., Inc.

Fig. 1: Locating Manual A/C-Heater System Components (Civic Shown; Civic Del Sol Is Similar)

RECIRCULATED/FRESH AIR CONTROL

Recirculated/fresh air control buttons on A/C-heater control panel control voltage to recirculated/fresh air door motor. Motor controls door position. In recirculated air position, outside air is shut off, and passenger compartment air enters blower case. In fresh air position, outside air enters blower case.

TEMPERATURE CONTROL

Temperature lever on A/C-heater control panel operates air mix door cable. Cable controls position of air mix door to direct air through or around heater core. Air mix door cable also indirectly controls heater water valve cable. Heater water valve cable is operated by air mix door lever on heater case.

AIRFLOW MODE CONTROL

Airflow mode buttons on A/C-heater control panel control voltage to airflow mode door motor. Airflow mode door motor controls positions of 3 airflow mode doors. Door positions determine airflow modes (vent, heat/vent, heat, heat/defrost and defrost).

COMPRESSOR CLUTCH CONTROL

Power for compressor clutch is supplied through contacts of A/C compressor clutch relay. If ECM receives A/C request signals, ECM grounds solenoid circuit of A/C compressor clutch relay. A/C request circuit is grounded if all of the following conditions exist:

- Blower switch is on.
- A/C switch is on.
- A/C thermoswitch contacts are closed (contacts open if evaporator temperature approaches freezing).
- A/C dual-pressure switch contacts are closed.

Compressor thermal protector prevents compressor operation if compressor overheats. *See Fig. 8.*

CONDENSER FAN CONTROL

Power for condenser fan is supplied through contacts of condenser fan relay. If A/C switch is on and contacts in A/C dual-pressure switch and A/C thermoswitch are closed, solenoid circuit of condenser fan relay will be grounded. This energizes relay, turning on condenser fan.

1993 MANUAL A/C-HEATER SYSTEMS
Civic & Civic Del Sol (Cont.)

RADIATOR FAN CONTROL

Power for radiator fan is supplied through contacts of radiator fan relay. ECM and coolant temperature switch control the solenoid circuit of radiator fan relay.

ADJUSTMENTS

NOTE: For adjustments not covered in this article, see HEATER SYSTEMS – CIVIC & CIVIC DEL SOL article.

DEFROST BLEED

1) Position of defrost door can be adjusted so no airflow or as much as 20 percent of airflow is distributed to defrost ducts when airflow control is in heat mode.
2) To adjust position of defrost door, turn on ignition. Set airflow control to heat mode. At airflow mode control motor, loosen adjusting screw at adjusting link. *See Fig. 2.* Adjust linkage so desired amount of airflow is achieved. Tighten adjusting screw.

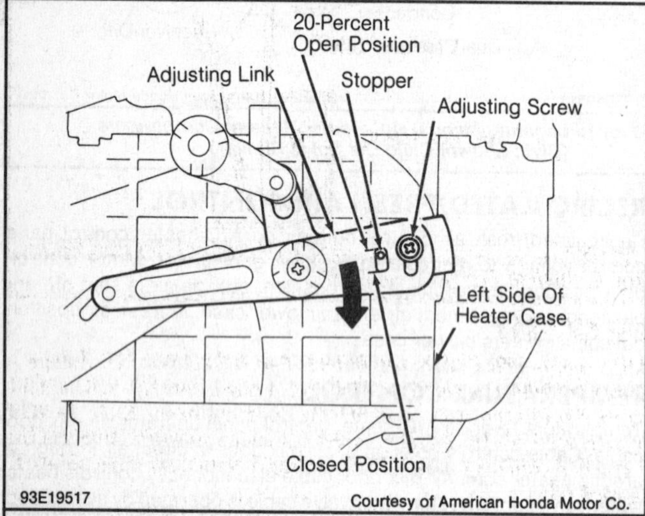
20-Percent
Open Position
Adjusting Link
Stopper
Adjusting Screw
Left Side Of
Heater Case
Closed Position
93E19517
Courtesy of American Honda Motor Co.

Fig. 2: Adjusting Defrost Bleed

TROUBLE SHOOTING

NOTE: For trouble shooting procedures not covered in this article, see HEATER SYSTEMS – CIVIC & CIVIC DEL SOL article.

CONDENSER FAN INOPERATIVE

1) Check fuses No. 13 (7.5-amp) and No. 35 (20-amp). If fuses are okay, disconnect condenser fan relay connector. Connect jumper wire between White and Blue/Black wire terminals of condenser fan relay connector. If condenser fan does not run, disconnect jumper wire and go to step **4)**. If condenser fan runs, go to next step.
2) Disconnect jumper wire. Turn ignition on. Check battery voltage at Yellow wire terminal of condenser fan relay connector. If battery voltage does not exist, go to next step. If battery voltage exists, repair open Yellow/White wire between condenser fan relay and A/C thermostat.
3) Remove and test A/C diode. See A/C DIODE TEST under TESTING. If diode is okay, check battery voltage at Black/Yellow wire terminal of diode connector. If battery voltage exists, repair open Yellow wire between diode and condenser fan relay. If battery voltage does not exist, repair open Black/Yellow wire between passenger compartment fuse/relay block and condenser fan relay.
4) Disconnect jumper wire. Check voltage at White wire terminal of condenser fan relay connector. If battery voltage does not exist, repair open White wire between condenser fan relay and engine compartment fuse/relay block. If battery voltage exists, go to next step.
5) Disconnect 2-pin condenser fan connector. Check continuity of Blue/Black wire between condenser fan relay and condenser fan. If continuity exists, go to next step. If continuity does not exist, repair open Blue/Black wire between condenser fan relay and condenser fan.
6) Check continuity in Black wire between condenser fan motor and ground. If continuity exists, replace condenser fan motor. If continuity does not exist, repair open Black wire between condenser fan and ground. If wire is okay, check for poor connection.

COMPRESSOR DOES NOT ENGAGE (CONDENSER FAN OKAY)

NOTE: Check A/C refrigerant pressure before proceeding with this test.

1) Check fuses No. 13 (7.5-amp) and No. 35 (20-amp). If fuses are okay, Remove and test compressor clutch relay. See RELAY TEST under TESTING. If compressor clutch relay is okay, go to next step.
2) Connect a jumper wire between White and Red wire compressor clutch relay terminals. Start engine. If compressor clutch engages, go to step **6)**. If compressor clutch does not engage, turn ignition off and disconnect jumper wire.
3) Check battery voltage at White wire compressor clutch relay terminal connector. If battery voltage exists, go to next step. If battery voltage does not exist, repair open White wire between engine compartment fuse/relay block and compressor clutch relay.
4) Disconnect compressor clutch connector. Check continuity in Red wire between compressor clutch relay and compressor clutch. If continuity does not exist, repair open Red wire. If continuity exists, go to next step.
5) Check compressor clutch clearance. Compressor clutch clearance should be .014-.026" (.35-.65 mm). Check thermal protector or compressor clutch coil. See COMPRESSOR CLUTCH COIL TEST or THERMAL PROTECTOR TEST under TESTING.
6) Turn ignition off. Disconnect jumper wire. Turn ignition on. Check battery voltage in Black/Yellow wire terminal of compressor clutch relay connector. If battery voltage exists, go to next step. If battery voltage does not exist, repair open Black/Yellow wire between passenger compartment fuse/relay block and compressor clutch relay.
7) Turn ignition off. Reinstall compressor clutch relay. Disconnect 2-pin A/C pressure switch connector. Using jumper wire, jumper Blue/Red and Yellow/White wires of A/C pressure switch connector. Start engine and turn on A/C and A/C-heater fan switch. If compressor clutch engages, replace A/C pressure switch. If compressor clutch does not engage, go to next step.
8) Turn ignition off. Disconnect jumper wire. Connect Blue/Red wire terminal to ground. Start engine and turn on A/C and A/C-heater fan switch. If compressor clutch does not engage, go to next step. If compressor clutch engages, repair open Yellow/White wire between A/C pressure switch and A/C thermoswitch.

CAUTION: To prevent terminal damage, backprobe ECM terminal connectors or use ECM Test Harness (07LAJ-PT3010A).

9) Turn off ignition, A/C and A/C-heater fan switch. Reconnect A/C pressure switch connector. Connect ECM Test Harness (07LAJ-PT3010A) on ECM wire harness. Turn ignition on. Check battery voltage between ECM terminal A15 (Black/Red wire) and ground. If battery voltage exists, go to next step. If battery voltage does not exist, repair open Black/Red wire between compressor clutch relay and ECM.
10) Check battery voltage between ECM terminal B5 (Blue/Red wire) and ground. If battery voltage does not exist, repair open Blue/Red wire between A/C pressure switch and ECM. If battery voltage exists, substitute a known good ECM and retest.

1993 MANUAL A/C-HEATER SYSTEMS
Civic & Civic Del Sol (Cont.)

COMPRESSOR & CONDENSER FAN INOPERATIVE

1) Check fuses No. 13 (7.5-amp) and No. 35 (20-amp). If fuses are okay, disconnect 2-pin A/C thermoswitch connector. Turn ignition on. Check voltage at Yellow/White wire of A/C thermoswitch connector. If battery voltage exists, go to next step. If battery voltage does not exist, repair open Yellow/White wire between condenser fan relay and A/C thermoswitch.
2) Turn ignition off. Test A/C thermoswitch. See A/C THERMOSWITCH TEST under TESTING. If A/C thermoswitch is okay, remove heater control panel. Disconnect 14-pin heater control panel harness connector. Using a DVOM, check continuity in Blue/Red wire between A/C thermoswitch and heater control panel.
3) If continuity exists, disconnect 6-pin A/C-heater fan switch connector and go to next step. If continuity does not exist, repair open Blue/Red wire between A/C thermoswitch and heater control panel.
4) Check continuity in Black wire between A/C-heater fan switch and ground. If continuity exists, replace heater control panel. If continuity does not exist, repair open Black wire between A/C-heater fan switch and ground. If wire is okay, check for poor ground connection.

TESTING

WARNING: To avoid injury from accidental air bag deployment, read and carefully follow all SERVICE PRECAUTIONS and DISABLING & ACTIVATING AIR BAG SYSTEM procedures in AIR BAG SYSTEM SAFETY article in GENERAL SERVICING.

A/C SYSTEM PERFORMANCE

1) Park vehicle out of direct sunlight. Open engine hood and front doors. Install A/C pressure gauges to the high and low side pressure ports of system. Determine relative humidity and ambient air temperature.
2) Set temperature control to cool, mode control to vent and recirculation control to recirculate positions. Insert thermometer in center vent outlet. Turn blower fan switch to highest position. Start and run engine at 1500 RPM. Ensure there is nobody inside vehicle.
3) After running A/C for 10 minutes, check thermometer reading in center vent outlet and the high and low side system pressure to determine if A/C system is operating within range. *See Fig. 3.*

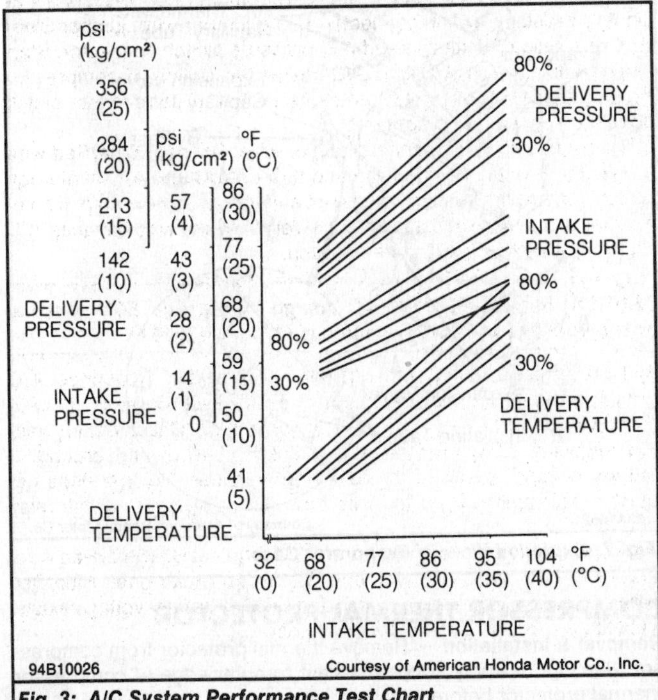
psi
(kg/cm²)
356
(25)
284
(20)
213
(15)
142
(10)
DELIVERY PRESSURE
psi
(kg/cm²)
57
(4)
43
(3)
28
(2)
14
(1)
0
INTAKE PRESSURE
°F
(°C)
86
(30)
77
(25)
68
(20)
59
(15)
50
(10)
41
(5)
DELIVERY TEMPERATURE
80%
DELIVERY PRESSURE
30%
INTAKE PRESSURE
80%
30%
80%
30%
DELIVERY TEMPERATURE
32 (0)
68 (20)
77 (25)
86 (30)
95 (35)
104 (40)
°F (°C)
INTAKE TEMPERATURE
94B10026
Courtesy of American Honda Motor Co., Inc.

Fig. 3: A/C System Performance Test Chart

A/C THERMOSWITCH TEST

1) Remove A/C thermoswitch. See EVAPORATOR, A/C THERMOSWITCH & EXPANSION VALVE under REMOVAL & INSTALLATION. Submerge A/C thermoswitch capillary tube into ice cold water. *See Fig. 4.* Check continuity across A/C thermoswitch connector terminals.
2) There should be no continuity (cut-off) when water temperature is 33-35°F (0.5-1.5°C). There should be continuity (cut-in) when water temperature is 36-41°F (2.5-5°C). If cut-off or cut-in temperature is not as specified, replace A/C thermoswitch.

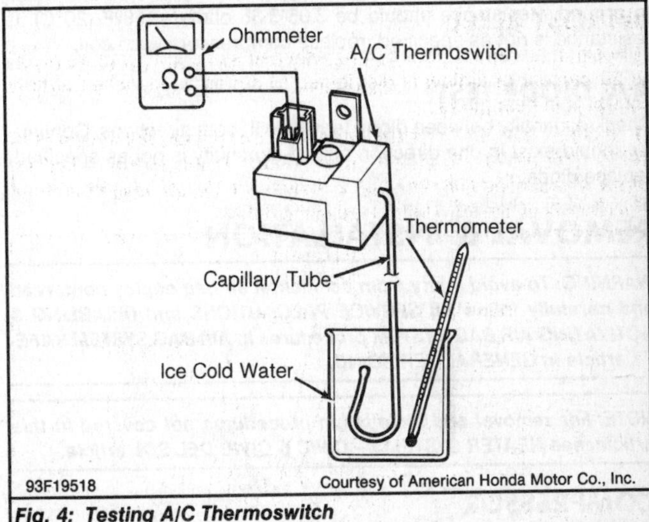
Ohmmeter
Ω
A/C Thermoswitch
Thermometer
Capillary Tube
Ice Cold Water
93F19518
Courtesy of American Honda Motor Co., Inc.

Fig. 4: Testing A/C Thermoswitch

RELAY TEST

A/C Compressor Clutch, Condenser Fan & Radiator Fan Relays – Check continuity between terminals No. 1 and 3. *See Fig. 5.* If continuity exists, replace relay. If continuity does not exist, apply 12 volts across terminals No. 2 and 4. Check continuity between terminals No. 1 and 3. If continuity exists, relay is okay. If continuity does not exist, replace relay.

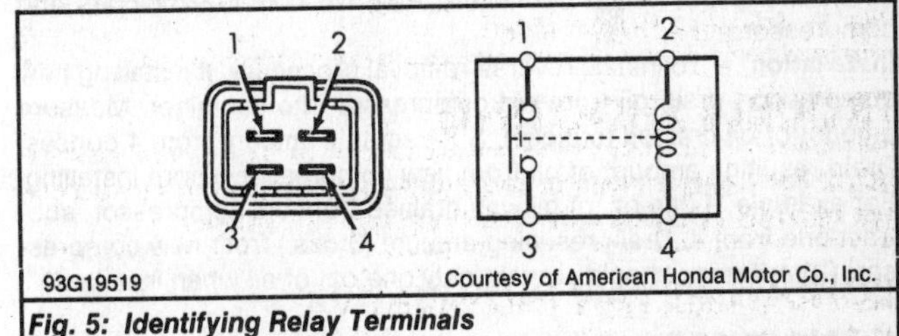
1
2
3
4
1
2
3
4
93G19519
Courtesy of American Honda Motor Co., Inc.

Fig. 5: Identifying Relay Terminals

A/C SWITCH TEST

Remove A/C-heater control panel. With A/C off, there should be no continuity between terminals No. 1 and 2. *See Fig. 6.* With A/C on, there should be continuity between terminals No. 1 and 2. If continuity is not as specified, replace A/C switch.

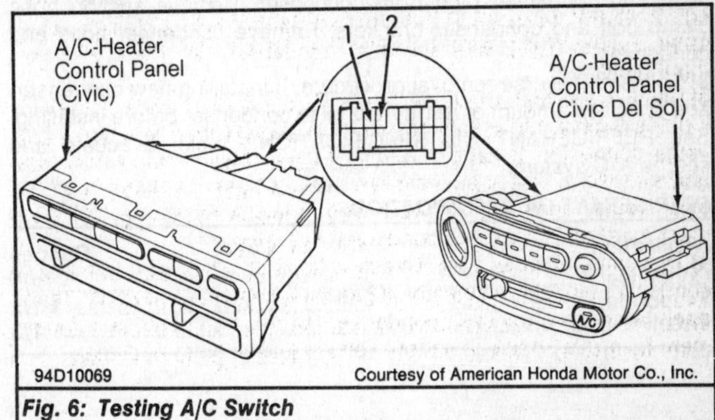
A/C-Heater Control Panel (Civic)
1
2
A/C-Heater Control Panel (Civic Del Sol)
94D10069
Courtesy of American Honda Motor Co., Inc.

Fig. 6: Testing A/C Switch

1993 MANUAL A/C-HEATER SYSTEMS
Civic & Civic Del Sol (Cont.)

THERMAL PROTECTOR TEST

Check continuity between thermal protector terminals. *See Fig. 8.* If continuity does not exist, replace thermal protector.

COMPRESSOR CLUTCH COIL TEST

1) Inspect pressure plate surface and rotor for wear or for oil-soaked condition. Check clutch bearing for wear, noise and grease leakage. Replace components as necessary. Disconnect compressor clutch wires at connector.

2) Connect one ohmmeter lead to compressor clutch wire and other to ground. Resistance should be 3.05-3.35 ohms at 68°F (20°C). If resistance is not as specified, replace compressor clutch coil.

A/C DIODE TEST

Check continuity between diode terminals in both directions. Continuity should exist in one direction only. If continuity is not as specified, replace diode.

REMOVAL & INSTALLATION

WARNING: To avoid injury from accidental air bag deployment, read and carefully follow all SERVICE PRECAUTIONS and DISABLING & ACTIVATING AIR BAG SYSTEM procedures in AIR BAG SYSTEM SAFETY article in GENERAL SERVICING.

NOTE: For removal and installation procedures not covered in this article, see HEATER SYSTEMS - CIVIC & CIVIC DEL SOL article.

COMPRESSOR

Removal - 1) Run engine at idle with A/C on for several minutes. Turn engine off. Disconnect negative battery cable. Discharge A/C system using approved refrigerant recovery/recycling equipment. Remove power steering pump. Disconnect refrigerant lines from compressor.

2) Loosen compressor drive belt adjuster. To remove compressor drive belt, remove 2 bolts from left engine mount bracket, then pass belt through gap between body and left engine mount bracket. Disconnect compressor clutch connector. Remove compressor bolts and compressor.

Installation - To install, reverse removal procedure. If installing new compressor, drain oil from old compressor into container. Measure amount of oil drained (ounces). Subtract this amount from 4 ounces. Drain resulting amount of oil from new compressor before installing. For example, if one oz. of oil was drained from old compressor, subtract one from 4. Drain resulting amount (3 ozs.) from new compressor. Compressor should contain only one oz. of oil when installed.

CONDENSER

Removal & Installation - 1) Disconnect negative battery cable. Discharge A/C system using approved refrigerant recovery/recycling equipment. Disconnect A/C dual-pressure switch connector and condenser fan connector.

2) Remove hood latch and grille as necessary. Disconnect discharge hose and condenser pipe from condenser. Remove suction hose clamp bolt and condenser brackets. Remove condenser bolts and condenser.

3) To install, reverse removal procedure. If installing new condenser, add specified amount of refrigerant oil to condenser before installing. See REFRIGERANT OIL SPECIFICATIONS table. Evacuate and charge A/C system.

REFRIGERANT OIL SPECIFICATIONS

Application	Ounces
Condenser	2/3
Evaporator	1 1/2
Receiver-Drier	1/3

EVAPORATOR CASE

Removal & Installation - 1) Disconnect battery cables. Remove battery. Discharge A/C system using approved refrigerant recovery/recycling equipment. Disconnect refrigerant hoses from evaporator core at engine compartment firewall.

2) Remove glove box and frame. Disconnect A/C thermoswitch connector. Remove bands from each side of evaporator case. Remove evaporator screws, bolt and nut. Disconnect drain hose. Remove evaporator case.

3) To install, reverse removal procedure. Evacuate and charge A/C system.

EVAPORATOR, A/C THERMOSWITCH & EXPANSION VALVE

Removal - Remove evaporator case. See EVAPORATOR CASE under REMOVAL & INSTALLATION. Pull A/C thermoswitch capillary tube from evaporator fins, noting location of tube for installation reference. *See Fig. 7.* Remove screws and clips securing upper and lower case halves. Separate case halves. Remove evaporator covers. Remove evaporator, expansion valve and A/C thermoswitch.

Installation - 1) To install, reverse removal procedure. If installing new evaporator, add specified amount of refrigerant oil to evaporator before installing. See REFRIGERANT OIL SPECIFICATIONS table. Correctly position A/C thermoswitch capillary tube in evaporator fins. *See Fig. 7.*

2) Position expansion valve capillary tube against suction tube. Wrap capillary tube with insulating tape. Ensure air gaps do not exist between case halves. Evacuate and charge A/C system.

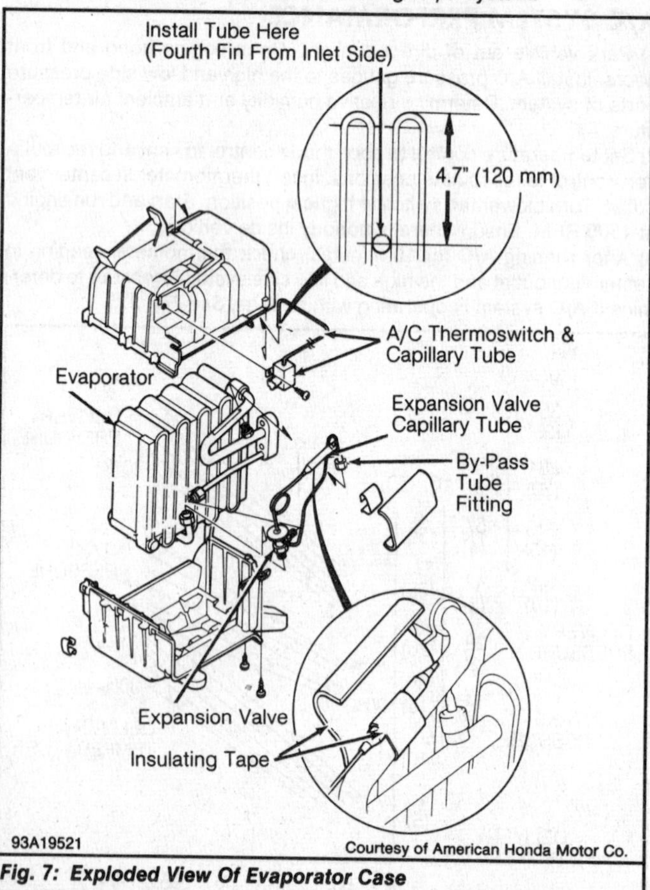
Install Tube Here
(Fourth Fin From Inlet Side)
4.7" (120 mm)
A/C Thermoswitch &
Capillary Tube
Evaporator
Expansion Valve
Capillary Tube
By-Pass
Tube
Fitting
Expansion Valve
Insulating Tape
93A19521
Courtesy of American Honda Motor Co.

Fig. 7: Exploded View Of Evaporator Case

COMPRESSOR THERMAL PROTECTOR

Removal & Installation - Remove thermal protector from compressor. *See Fig. 8.* Apply silicone sealant to outer edge of compressor thermal protector before installing.

1993 MANUAL A/C-HEATER SYSTEMS
Civic & Civic Del Sol (Cont.)

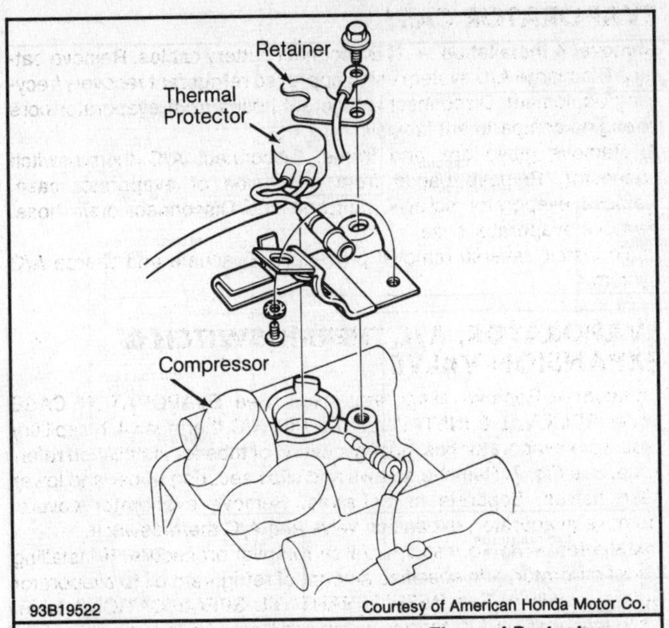
Retainer
Thermal
Protector
Compressor
93B19522
Courtesy of American Honda Motor Co.

Fig. 8: Removing & Installing Compressor Thermal Protector

TORQUE SPECIFICATIONS

TORQUE SPECIFICATIONS

Application	Ft. Lbs. (N.m)
Compressor Bracket-To-Engine Bolt	35 (47)
Compressor-To-Compressor Bracket Bolt	18 (24)
Refrigerant Pipe-To-Compressor Bolt	16 (22)
Refrigerant Pipe-To-Evaporator Bolt (Suction Pipe)	16 (22)
	INCH Lbs. (N.m)
Refrigerant Pipe-To-Evaporator Bolt (Discharge Pipe)	89 (10)

1993 MANUAL A/C-HEATER SYSTEMS
Civic & Civic Del Sol (Cont.)

WIRING DIAGRAMS

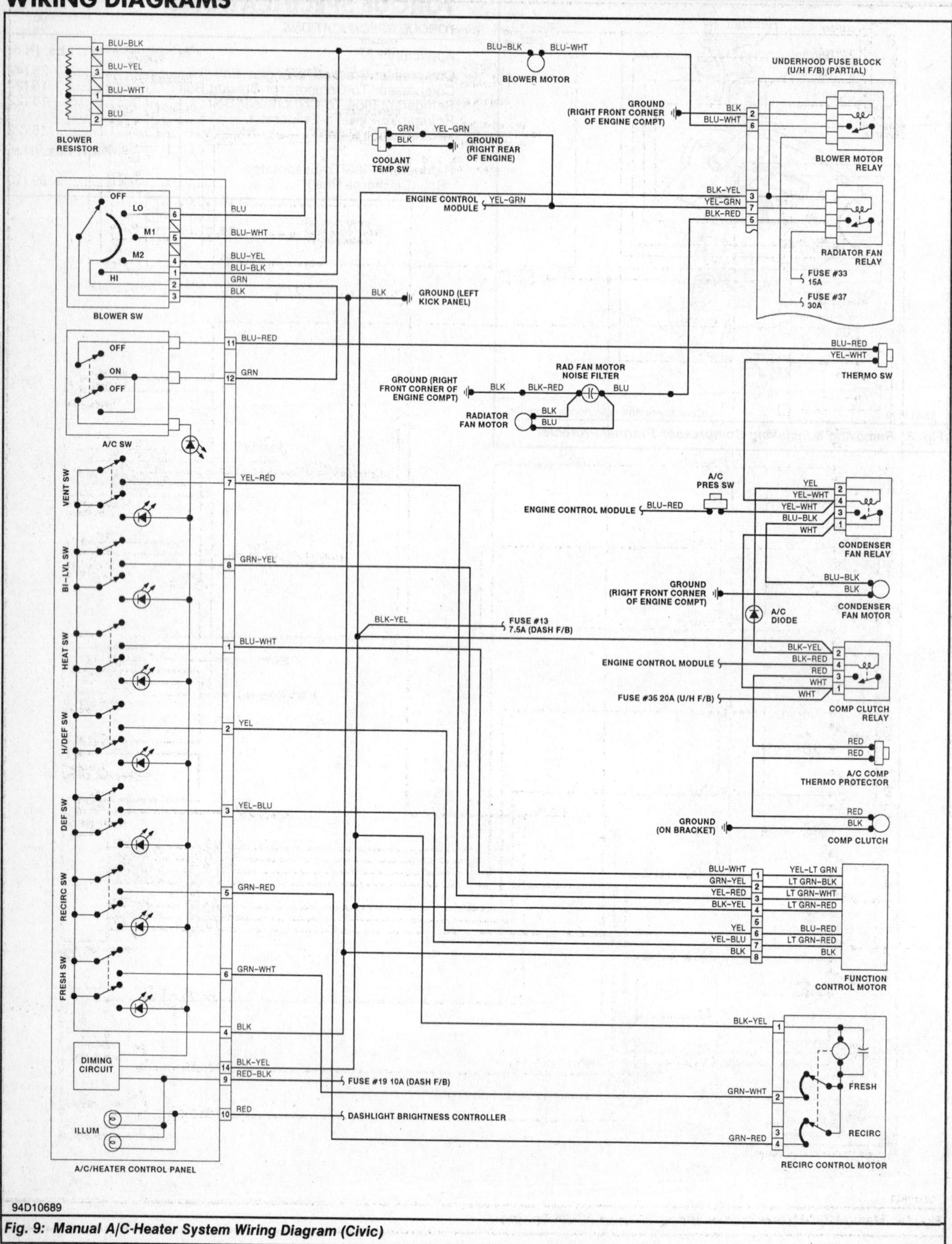
BLOWER RESISTOR
BLU-BLK
BLU-YEL
BLU-WHT
BLU
BLOWER MOTOR
BLU-WHT
GROUND (RIGHT FRONT CORNER OF ENGINE COMPT)
UNDERHOOD FUSE BLOCK (U/H F/B) (PARTIAL)
BLOWER MOTOR RELAY
COOLANT TEMP SW
GRN
YEL-GRN
BLK
GROUND (RIGHT REAR OF ENGINE)
ENGINE CONTROL MODULE
BLK-YEL
BLK-RED
RADIATOR FAN RELAY
FUSE #33 15A
FUSE #37 30A
OFF
LO
M1
M2
HI
BLOWER SW
GROUND (LEFT KICK PANEL)
ON
A/C SW
BLU-RED
YEL-WHT
THERMO SW
GROUND (RIGHT FRONT CORNER OF ENGINE COMPT)
RAD FAN MOTOR NOISE FILTER
RADIATOR FAN MOTOR
VENT SW
BI-LVL SW
HEAT SW
H/DEF SW
DEF SW
RECIRC SW
FRESH SW
YEL-RED
GRN-YEL
A/C PRES SW
YEL
WHT
CONDENSER FAN RELAY
CONDENSER FAN MOTOR
GROUND (RIGHT FRONT CORNER OF ENGINE COMPT)
A/C DIODE
FUSE #13 7.5A (DASH F/B)
RED
FUSE #35 20A (U/H F/B)
COMP CLUTCH RELAY
A/C COMP THERMO PROTECTOR
GROUND (ON BRACKET)
COMP CLUTCH
YEL-BLU
GRN-RED
GRN-WHT
YEL-LT GRN
LT GRN-BLK
LT GRN-WHT
LT GRN-RED
FUNCTION CONTROL MOTOR
DIMING CIRCUIT
RED-BLK
FUSE #19 10A (DASH F/B)
DASHLIGHT BRIGHTNESS CONTROLLER
ILLUM
A/C/HEATER CONTROL PANEL
FRESH
RECIRC
RECIRC CONTROL MOTOR
94D10689

Fig. 9: Manual A/C-Heater System Wiring Diagram (Civic)

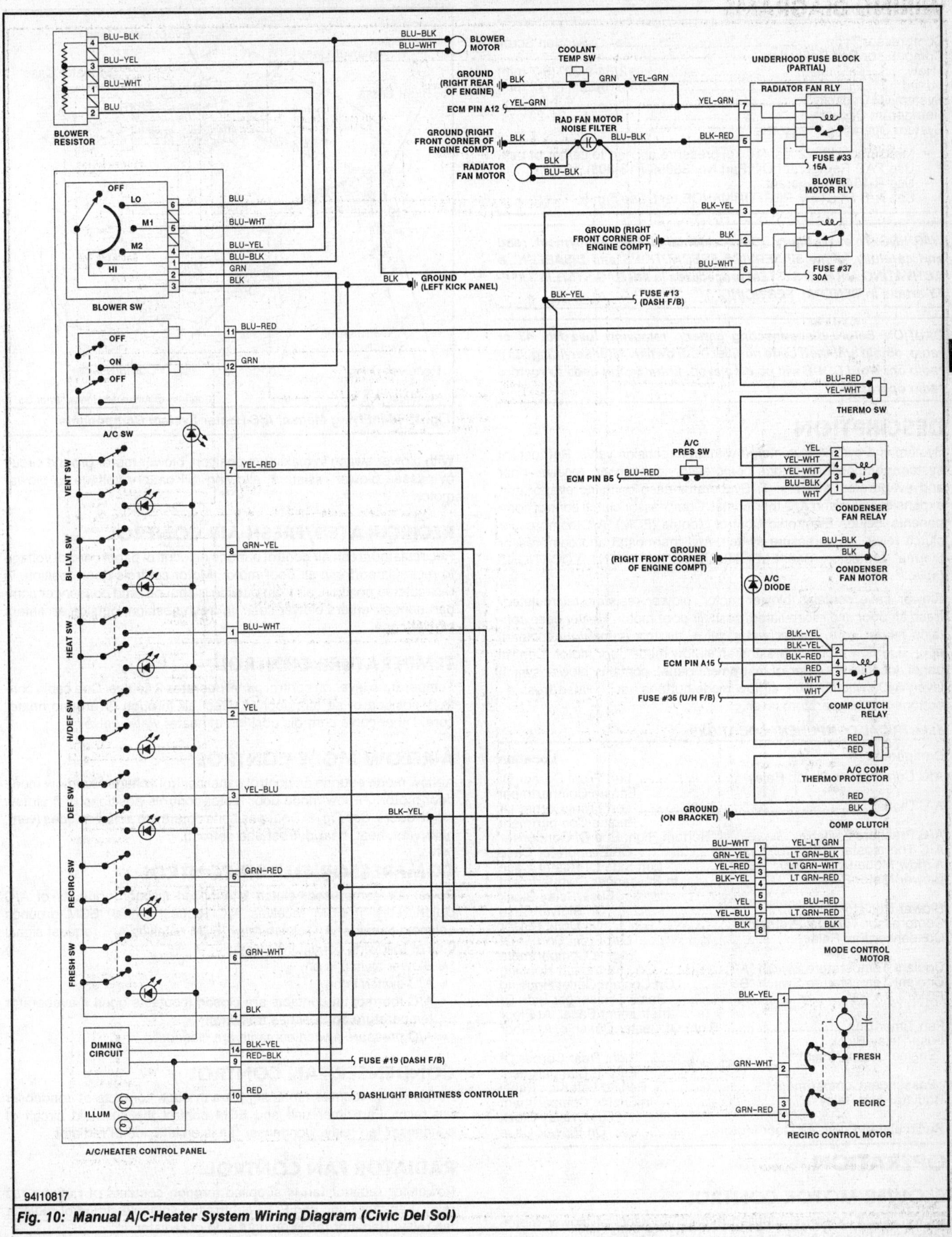
BLOWER RESISTOR
BLU-BLK
BLU-YEL
BLU-WHT
BLU
BLOWER MOTOR
COOLANT TEMP SW
GROUND (RIGHT REAR OF ENGINE)
BLK
GRN
YEL-GRN
ECM PIN A12
RAD FAN MOTOR NOISE FILTER
GROUND (RIGHT FRONT CORNER OF ENGINE COMPT)
BLK-RED
RADIATOR FAN MOTOR
UNDERHOOD FUSE BLOCK (PARTIAL)
RADIATOR FAN RLY
FUSE #33 15A
BLOWER MOTOR RLY
BLK-YEL
GROUND (RIGHT FRONT CORNER OF ENGINE COMPT)
FUSE #37 30A
OFF
LO
M1
M2
HI
BLOWER SW
GROUND (LEFT KICK PANEL)
FUSE #13 (DASH F/B)
BLU-RED
ON
A/C SW
YEL-WHT
THERMO SW
A/C PRES SW
ECM PIN B5
YEL
WHT
CONDENSER FAN RELAY
GROUND (RIGHT FRONT CORNER OF ENGINE COMPT)
CONDENSER FAN MOTOR
A/C DIODE
VENT SW
YEL-RED
BI-LVL SW
GRN-YEL
HEAT SW
H/DEF SW
DEF SW
YEL-BLU
RECIRC SW
GRN-RED
FRESH SW
GRN-WHT
ECM PIN A15
FUSE #35 (U/H F/B)
RED
COMP CLUTCH RELAY
A/C COMP THERMO PROTECTOR
GROUND (ON BRACKET)
COMP CLUTCH
YEL-LT GRN
LT GRN-BLK
LT GRN-WHT
LT GRN-RED
MODE CONTROL MOTOR
DIMING CIRCUIT
RED-BLK
FUSE #19 (DASH F/B)
DASHLIGHT BRIGHTNESS CONTROLLER
ILLUM
A/C/HEATER CONTROL PANEL
FRESH
RECIRC
RECIRC CONTROL MOTOR
94I10817

Fig. 10: Manual A/C-Heater System Wiring Diagram (Civic Del Sol)

1993 MANUAL A/C-HEATER SYSTEMS
Prelude

SPECIFICATIONS

Compressor Type	Sanden Scroll
Compressor Belt Deflection [1]	
New	13/64-9/32" (5-7 mm)
Used	25/64-15/32" (10-12 mm)
System Oil Capacity [2]	4.3-5.0 ozs.
Refrigerant Capacity [3]	21-23 ozs.
System Operating Pressures [4]	

[1] – Measured with 22 lbs. (10 kg) pressure applied to center of belt.
[2] – Use PAG Refrigerant Oil (Part No. 38899-P13-003).
[3] – Use R-134a refrigerant.
[4] – See A/C SYSTEM PERFORMANCE test. *See Fig. 5.*

WARNING: To avoid injury from accidental air bag deployment, read and carefully follow all SERVICE PRECAUTIONS and DISABLING & ACTIVATING AIR BAG SYSTEM procedures in AIR BAG SYSTEM SAFETY article in GENERAL SERVICING.

CAUTION: Before disconnecting battery, removing fuse No. 43 or radio, obtain anti-theft code number from owner. After servicing, turn radio on. Word CODE will be displayed. Enter 5-digit code to restore radio operation.

DESCRIPTION

System is a cycling-clutch type with an expansion valve. Refrigerant system components include compressor, condenser, receiver-drier and evaporator. *See Fig. 1.* Evaporator case contains evaporator, expansion valve and A/C thermostat. Compressor clutch control components include Electronic Control Module (ECM), A/C compressor clutch relay, A/C pressure switch, A/C thermostat and compressor thermal protector. See ELECTRICAL COMPONENT LOCATIONS table.

Blower case contains blower motor, blower resistor, recirculated/fresh air door and recirculated/fresh air door motor. Heater case contains heater core, heater water valve, air mix (temperature blend) door, 3 airflow mode doors and an airflow mode door motor. Control panel, located in center of instrument panel, contains blower switch lever, A/C switch button, airflow mode buttons, recirculated/fresh air buttons and temperature lever.

ELECTRICAL COMPONENT LOCATIONS

Component	Location
A/C Compressor Clutch Relay	Left Front Corner Of Engine Compartment
A/C Diode	Left Front Corner Of Engine Compartment
A/C Pressure Switch	Bottom Right End Of Condenser
A/C Thermostat	On Evaporator Case
Airflow Mode Door Motor	Left Side Of Heater Case
Blower Motor Relay	In Passenger Compartment Fuse/Relay Block
Blower Resistor	On Blower Case
Compressor Thermal Protector	On Compressor
Condenser Fan Relay	Left Front Corner Of Engine Compartment
Coolant Temperature Switch "A"	On Thermostat Housing
Coolant Temperature Switch "B"	On Coolant Outlet Housing
ECM	Below Passenger Side Of Instrument Panel, At Floor
Fan Timer Unit	Right Of Center Console, At Floor
Fuse/Relay Block	
Engine Compartment	Right Rear Corner Of Engine Compartment
Passenger Compartment	Behind Left Kick Panel
Radiator Fan Relay	In Engine Compartment Fuse/Relay Block
Recirculated/Fresh Air Door Motor	On Blower Case

OPERATION

BLOWER MOTOR CONTROL

Blower motor power is supplied through contacts of blower motor relay. With blower switch in positions No. 1, 2 and 3, blower motor is grounded through blower resistors, reducing voltage to blower motor.

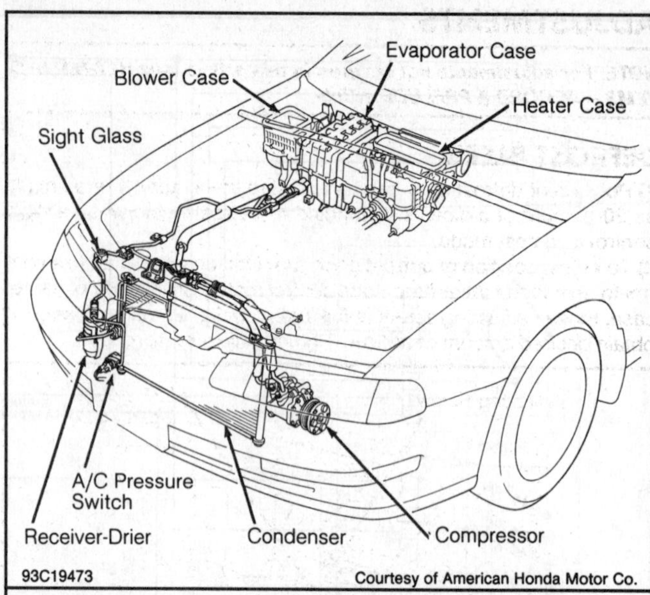
Evaporator Case
Blower Case
Heater Case
Sight Glass
A/C Pressure Switch
Receiver-Drier
Condenser
Compressor
93C19473
Courtesy of American Honda Motor Co.

Fig. 1: Identifying Manual A/C-Heater System Components

With blower switch in maximum position, blower motor ground circuit by-passes blower resistors, allowing full battery voltage to blower motor.

RECIRCULATED/FRESH AIR CONTROL

Recirculated/fresh air control buttons on control panel control voltage to recirculated/fresh air door motor. Motor controls door position. In recirculated position, air from outside is shut off, and passenger compartment air enters blower case. In fresh position, outside air enters blower case.

TEMPERATURE CONTROL

Temperature lever on control panel operates 2 cables. One cable controls position of air mix door to direct air through or around heater core. Other cable controls position of heater water valve.

AIRFLOW MODE CONTROL

Airflow mode buttons on control panel control voltage to airflow mode door motor. Airflow mode door motor controls positions of 3 airflow mode doors. *See Fig. 2.* Door positions determine airflow modes (vent, heat/vent, heat, heat/defrost and defrost).

COMPRESSOR CLUTCH CONTROL

Power for compressor clutch is supplied through contacts of A/C clutch relay. If ECM receives A/C request signal, ECM grounds solenoid circuit of A/C clutch relay. ECM receives A/C request signal if all of following conditions exists:

- Blower switch is on.
- A/C switch is on.
- A/C thermostat contacts are closed (contacts open if evaporator temperature approaches freezing).
- A/C pressure switch contacts are closed.

CONDENSER FAN CONTROL

Power for condenser fan is supplied through contacts of condenser fan relay. Fan timer unit and ECM control the solenoid circuit of condenser fan relay. Condenser fan is on left side of radiator.

RADIATOR FAN CONTROL

Power for radiator fan is supplied through contacts of radiator fan relay. Fan timer unit and ECM control the solenoid circuit of radiator fan relay. Radiator fan is on right side of radiator.

1993 MANUAL A/C-HEATER SYSTEMS
Prelude (Cont.)

ADJUSTMENTS

NOTE: For adjustments not covered in this article, see HEATER SYSTEMS – ACCORD & PRELUDE article.

DEFROST BLEED

1) Position of defrost door can be adjusted so no airflow or as much as 20 percent of airflow is distributed to defrost ducts when airflow control is in heat mode.

2) To adjust position of defrost door, turn ignition on. Set airflow control to heat mode. At airflow mode control motor, on left side of heater case, loosen adjusting screw at linkage. *See Fig. 2.* Adjust linkage to obtain desired amount of airflow. Tighten adjusting screw.

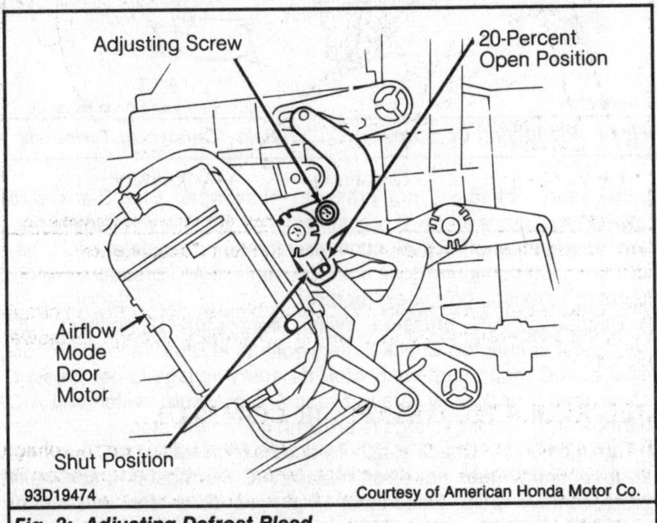
Adjusting Screw
20-Percent Open Position
Airflow Mode Door Motor
Shut Position
93D19474
Courtesy of American Honda Motor Co.

Fig. 2: Adjusting Defrost Bleed

TROUBLE SHOOTING

NOTE: For problems concerning blower motor, airflow mode (function) control and recirculated/fresh air control, see HEATER SYSTEMS – ACCORD & PRELUDE article.

RADIATOR FAN INOPERATIVE

1) Check fuse No. 47 (15-amp) in engine compartment fuse/relay block. If fuse is okay, test radiator fan relay. See RELAY TEST under TESTING. If relay is okay, check voltage at terminal No. 4 of radiator fan relay socket. *See Fig. 3.*

2) If battery voltage is not present, replace engine compartment fuse/relay block. If battery voltage is present, connect jumper wire between terminals No. 2 and 4 of radiator fan relay socket. If radiator fan runs, go to step **5)**. If radiator fan does not run, go to next step.

3) Disconnect jumper wire. Disconnect radiator fan connector. Check continuity of Blue/Black wire between radiator fan relay terminal No. 2 socket and radiator fan. If continuity is not present, repair wire. If continuity is present, go to next step.

4) Check continuity of Black wire between radiator fan motor and chassis ground. If continuity is present, replace radiator fan motor. If continuity is not present, repair open Black wire between radiator fan and ground. If wire is okay, check for poor ground.

5) Disconnect jumper wire. Turn ignition on. Check voltage at terminal No. 3 of radiator fan relay socket. *See Fig. 3.* If battery voltage is present, repair open Blue/Red wire between radiator fan relay connector terminal No. 1 and A/C diode.

6) If battery voltage is not present, check voltage at Yellow wire terminal of fan timer connector. *See Fig. 6.* If battery voltage is not present, go to FAN TIMER INPUT TEST under TESTING. If battery voltage is present, repair open Yellow wire between fan timer unit and radiator fan relay connector terminal No. 3.

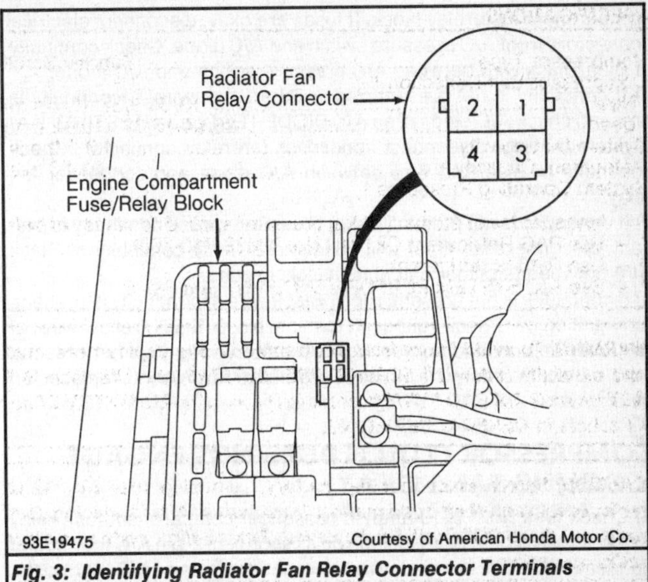
Radiator Fan Relay Connector
2
1
4
3
Engine Compartment Fuse/Relay Block
93E19475
Courtesy of American Honda Motor Co.

Fig. 3: Identifying Radiator Fan Relay Connector Terminals

CONDENSER FAN INOPERATIVE

1) Check fuse No. 45 (15-amp) in engine compartment fuse/relay block. If fuse is okay, test condenser fan relay. See RELAY TEST under TESTING. If relay is okay, check voltage at White/Green (or White) wire terminal of condenser fan relay connector.

2) If battery voltage is not present, repair open White/Green (or White) wire between engine compartment fuse/relay block and condenser fan relay. If battery voltage is present, connect jumper wire between White/Green (or White) wire terminal and Blue/Yellow wire terminal of condenser fan relay connector. If condenser fan runs, go to step **5)**.

3) If condenser fan does not run, disconnect jumper wire. Disconnect condenser fan connector. Check continuity of Blue/Yellow wire between condenser fan relay and condenser fan.

4) If continuity is not present, repair Blue/Yellow wire. If continuity is present, check continuity of Black wire between condenser fan motor and chassis ground. If continuity is not present, repair Black wire. If continuity is present, replace condenser fan motor.

5) Disconnect jumper wire. Turn ignition on. Check voltage at Yellow/White wire terminal of condenser fan relay connector. If battery voltage is present, repair open Blue/Red (or Blue) wire between condenser fan relay and A/C diode.

6) If battery voltage is not present, check voltage at Yellow/White wire terminal of fan timer unit connector. *See Fig. 6.* If battery voltage is not present, see FAN TIMER INPUT TEST under TESTING. If battery voltage is present, repair open Yellow/White wire between fan timer and condenser fan relay.

BOTH COOLING FANS INOPERATIVE FOR ENGINE COOLING, BUT OKAY FOR A/C

1) Disconnect coolant temperature switch "A" 2-pin connector. Turn on ignition. Check voltage at Blue/Red wire terminal of coolant temperature switch "A" connector. If battery voltage is not present, repair open Blue/Red wire between coolant temperature switch "A" and radiator or condenser fan relays.

2) If battery voltage is present, turn ignition off. Check continuity of Black wire between coolant temperature switch "A" and chassis ground. If continuity is not present, repair Black wire. If continuity is present, feel lower radiator hose. If hose is hot, replace coolant temperature switch "A". If hose is not hot, repair restriction in cooling system.

BOTH COOLING FANS ALWAYS INOPERATIVE

1) Check fuse No. 9 (15-amp) in passenger compartment fuse/relay block. Check fuses No. 45 (15-amp) and No. 47 (15-amp) in engine

1993 MANUAL A/C-HEATER SYSTEMS
Prelude (Cont.)

compartment fuse/relay block. If fuses are okay, disconnect electrical connectors from A/C pressure switch and A/C diode. Check continuity of Blue/Black wire between A/C pressure switch and A/C diode.

2) If continuity is not present, repair Blue/Black wire. If continuity is present, check A/C diode. See A/C DIODE TEST under TESTING. If A/C diode is okay, disconnect condenser fan relay connector. Check continuity of Blue/Red wire between A/C diode and condenser fan relay.

3) If continuity is not present, repair Blue/Red wire. If continuity is present, disconnect fan timer unit connector. Check continuity of Black wire between fan timer unit and chassis ground.

4) If continuity is not present, repair Black wire. If continuity is present, turn ignition on. Check voltage at terminal No. 3 (Black/Yellow wire) of fan timer unit connector. *See Fig. 6*. If battery voltage is not present, repair Black/Yellow wire. If battery voltage is present, replace fan timer.

COMPRESSOR CLUTCH DOES NOT ENGAGE (COOLING FANS OKAY)

1) Check fuse No. 11 (10-amp) in passenger compartment fuse/relay block. If fuse is okay, turn ignition on. Disconnect 2-pin A/C thermostat connector. Connect jumper wire between terminals of A/C thermostat harness connector. Start engine and turn on A/C and heater fan switch.

2) If compressor clutch engages, replace A/C thermostat. If compressor clutch does not engage, turn engine off. Remove and test A/C compressor clutch relay. See RELAY TEST under TESTING. If relay is okay, go to next step.

3) Check battery voltage at Yellow/Black (or Black/Yellow) wire of A/C compressor clutch relay connector. *See Fig. 4*. If battery voltage is not present, repair Black/Yellow (or Yellow/Black) wire between fuse/relay block and relay. If battery voltage is present, go to next step.

4) Using a jumper wire, jumper between Yellow/Black (or Black/Yellow) and Red wire terminals of A/C compressor clutch relay connector. Start engine. If compressor clutch engages, go to step **6)**. If compressor clutch does not engage, disconnect jumper wire. Turn ignition off.

5) Disconnect compressor clutch connector. Check continuity of Red wire between A/C compressor clutch relay and compressor clutch. If continuity does not exist, repair open Red wire. If continuity exists, check compressor clutch clearance. See COMPRESSOR SERVICING article in GENERAL SERVICING. If clearance is okay, check compressor clutch coil. See COMPRESSOR CLUTCH COIL TEST under TESTING.

6) Disconnect jumper wire. Check battery voltage at Yellow/Black (or Black/Yellow) wire terminal of A/C compressor clutch relay. *See Fig. 4*. If battery voltage is not present, repair Yellow/Black (or Black/Yellow) wire between fuse/relay block and relay. If battery voltage is present, turn off ignition. Reconnect A/C compressor clutch relay connector.

7) Turn ignition on. Check voltage at Red/Blue wire terminal (A15) of ECM 26-pin connector. If battery voltage is not present, repair open Red/Blue wire between A/C compressor clutch relay and ECM. If battery voltage is present, go to next step.

8) Turn off A/C switch and blower switch. Check voltage at Blue/Black wire terminal (B5) of ECM 22-pin connector. If battery voltage is not present, repair open Blue/Black wire between A/C diode and ECM. If battery voltage is present, substitute a known good ECM and retest.

COMPRESSOR CLUTCH DOES NOT ENGAGE & COOLING FANS INOPERATIVE

NOTE: Check A/C refrigerant pressure before proceeding with this test.

1) Check fuses No. 9 (15-amp) and No. 11 (10-amp) in passenger compartment fuse/relay block. If fuses are okay, disconnect A/C pressure switch connector. Turn ignition on. Check voltage at Blue/Black wire terminal of A/C pressure switch connector.

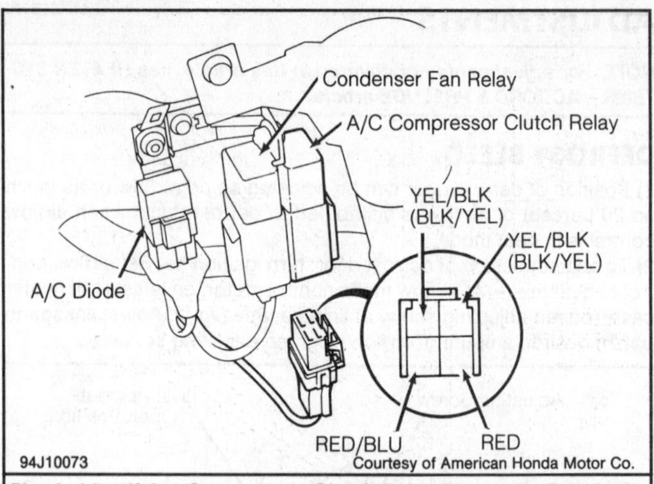
Condenser Fan Relay
A/C Compressor Clutch Relay
YEL/BLK
(BLK/YEL)
YEL/BLK
(BLK/YEL)
A/C Diode
RED/BLU
RED
94J10073
Courtesy of American Honda Motor Co.

Fig. 4: Identifying Compressor Clutch Relay Connector Terminals

2) If battery voltage is not present, repair open Blue/Black wire between A/C diode and A/C pressure switch. If battery voltage is present, turn ignition off. Check continuity across terminals of A/C pressure switch. If continuity does not exist, replace A/C pressure switch. If continuity exists, go to next step.

3) Reconnect A/C pressure switch connector. Disconnect A/C thermostat connector. Check battery voltage at Blue/Yellow wire terminal of A/C thermostat connector. If battery voltage is not present, repair open Blue/Yellow wire between A/C pressure switch and A/C thermostat. If battery voltage is present, go to next step.

4) Turn ignition off. Check continuity across terminals of A/C thermostat. If continuity does not exist, replace A/C thermostat. If continuity exists, remove radio. Disconnect 16-pin connector from A/C-heater control panel.

5) Check continuity in Blue/Red wire between A/C thermostat and A/C-heater control panel 16-pin connector. If continuity does not exist, repair open Blue/Red wire. If continuity exists, test A/C switch. See A/C SWITCH TEST under TESTING. If A/C switch is okay, go to next step.

6) Disconnect A/C-heater control panel 7-pin connector. Check continuity of Green wire between A/C-heater control panel 7-pin and 16-pin connectors. If continuity does not exist, repair open Green wire. If continuity exists, go to next step.

7) Check continuity of Black wire between 7-pin connector and chassis ground. If continuity exists, replace blower switch. If continuity does not exist, repair open Black wire between heater fan switch and ground. If wire is okay, check for poor ground connection.

TESTING

WARNING: To avoid injury from accidental air bag deployment, read and carefully follow all SERVICE PRECAUTIONS and DISABLING & ACTIVATING AIR BAG SYSTEM procedures in AIR BAG SYSTEM SAFETY article in GENERAL SERVICING.

A/C SYSTEM PERFORMANCE

1) Park vehicle out of direct sunlight. Open engine hood and front doors. Install A/C pressure gauges to the high and low side pressure ports of system. Determine relative humidity and ambient air temperature.

2) Set temperature control to maximum cool, mode control to vent and recirculation control to recirculate positions. Insert thermometer in center vent outlet. Turn blower fan switch to highest position. Start and run engine at 1500 RPM. Ensure there is nobody inside vehicle.

3) After running A/C for 10 minutes, check thermometer reading in center vent outlet and the high and low side system pressure to determine if A/C system is operating within range. *See Fig. 5*.

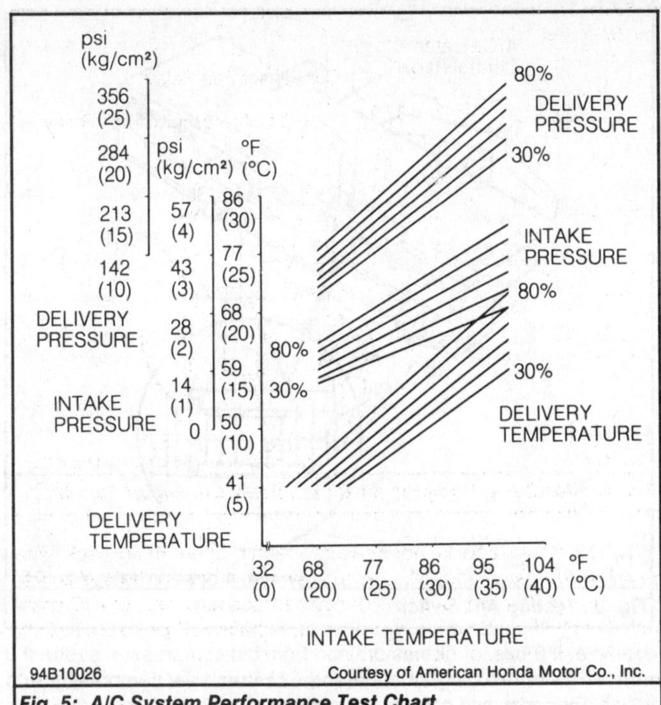
psi
(kg/cm²)
356
(25)
284
(20)
213
(15)
142
(10)
DELIVERY
PRESSURE
INTAKE
PRESSURE
DELIVERY
TEMPERATURE
psi
(kg/cm²)
57
(4)
43
(3)
28
(2)
14
(1)
0
°F
(°C)
86
(30)
77
(25)
68
(20)
59
(15)
50
(10)
41
(5)
80%
DELIVERY
PRESSURE
30%
INTAKE
PRESSURE
80%
30%
80%
30%
DELIVERY
TEMPERATURE
32
(0)
68
(20)
77
(25)
86
(30)
95
(35)
104
(40)
°F
(°C)
INTAKE TEMPERATURE
94B10026
Courtesy of American Honda Motor Co., Inc.
Fig. 5: A/C System Performance Test Chart

FAN TIMER INPUT TEST

1) Turn ignition on. With fan timer connector attached to unit, test each wire at fan timer connector as follows.
2) Check voltage at terminal No. 1 (Black wire). *See Fig. 6*. If less than one volt is present, go to next step. If one or more volts are present, repair open Black wire.
3) Check voltage at terminal No. 7 (White/Green wire). If battery voltage is present, go to next step. If battery voltage is not present, check fuse No. 45 in engine compartment fuse/relay block. If fuse is okay, repair open White/Green wire.
4) Check voltage at terminal No. 6 (Black/Yellow wire). If battery voltage is present, go to next step. If battery voltage is not present, check fuse No. 19 (No. 23 on vehicles with air bag) in passenger compartment fuse/relay block. If fuse is okay, repair open Black/Yellow wire.
5) Check voltage at terminal No. 3 (Black/Yellow wire). If battery voltage is present, go to next step. If battery voltage is not present, check fuse No. 9 in passenger compartment fuse/relay block. If fuse is okay, repair open Black/Yellow wire.
6) Check voltage at terminal No. 2 (Yellow/White wire). If battery voltage is present, go to next step. If battery voltage is not present, replace fan timer.

CAUTION: Before replacing fan unit, check for a short to ground in Yellow/White wire between fan timer and condenser fan relay, and in Yellow wire between fan timer and radiator fan relay. If a short to ground exists in these circuits, fan timer will be damaged.

7) Check voltage at terminal No. 4 (Yellow wire). If battery voltage is present, go to next step. If battery voltage is not present, replace fan timer.
8) Connect jumper wire between terminal No. 5 (Blue/Red wire) and ground. If condenser and radiator fans come on, go to next step. If condenser and radiator fans do not come on, check for open Blue/Red wire between fan timer and condenser and radiator fan relays. If Blue/Red wire is okay, check for open Yellow/White wire between fan timer and condenser fan relay, and in Yellow wire between fan timer and radiator fan relay. If wires are okay, replace condenser fan relay or radiator fan relay as necessary.
9) Ensure coolant temperature is less than 223°F (106°C). Check voltage at terminal No. 8 (White/Yellow wire). If 11 volts is present, fan

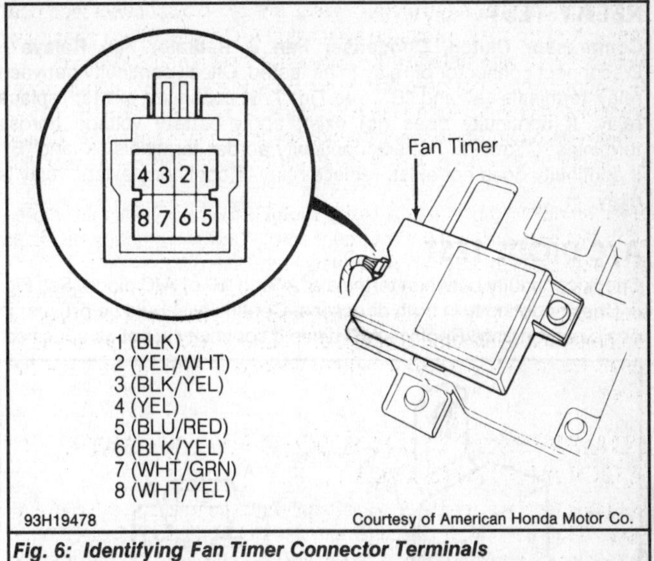
4 3 2 1
8 7 6 5
Fan Timer
1 (BLK)
2 (YEL/WHT)
3 (BLK/YEL)
4 (YEL)
5 (BLU/RED)
6 (BLK/YEL)
7 (WHT/GRN)
8 (WHT/YEL)
93H19478
Courtesy of American Honda Motor Co.
Fig. 6: Identifying Fan Timer Connector Terminals

timer inputs are okay. If 11 volts is not present, check continuity across connector terminals of coolant temperature switch "B". If there is no continuity, replace switch. If continuity exists, check for short to ground in White/Yellow wire between fan timer and coolant temperature switch "B". If White/Yellow wire is okay, replace fan timer.

A/C THERMOSTAT TEST

1) Remove A/C thermostat. See EVAPORATOR, A/C THERMOSTAT & EXPANSION VALVE under REMOVAL & INSTALLATION. Connect ohmmeter across switch connector terminals. Dip capillary tube of thermostat into ice cold water.
2) As ohmmeter reading suddenly (not gradually) changes, note temperatures at which switch contacts open (cut-off) and close (cut-in). Cut-off temperature should be 31-35°F (0.5-1.5°C). Cut-in temperature should be 36-41°F (2.5-5.0°C). If cut-off and cut-in temperatures are not as specified, replace switch.

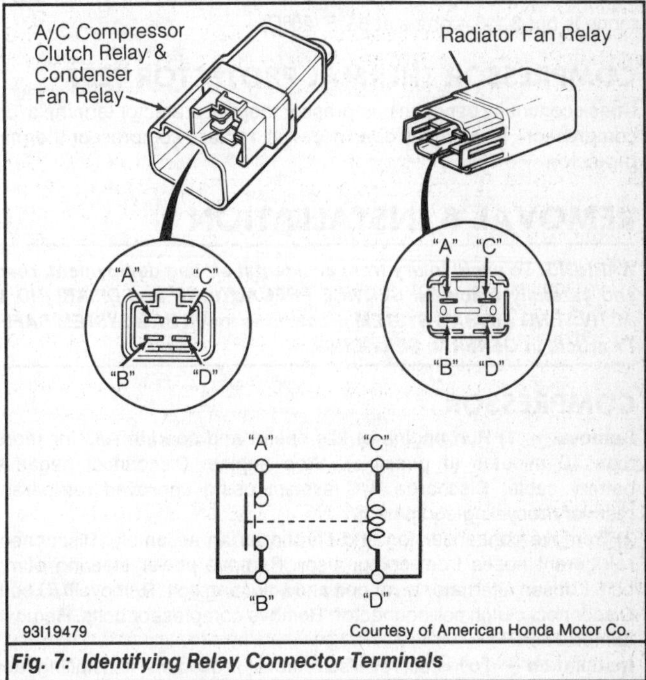
A/C Compressor
Clutch Relay &
Condenser
Fan Relay
Radiator Fan Relay
"A"
"C"
"B"
"D"
"A"
"C"
"B"
"D"
"A"
"C"
"B"
"D"
93I19479
Courtesy of American Honda Motor Co.
Fig. 7: Identifying Relay Connector Terminals

1993 MANUAL A/C-HEATER SYSTEMS
Prelude (Cont.)

RELAY TEST

Compressor Clutch, Condenser Fan & Radiator Fan Relays – Disconnect connector of relay to be tested. Check continuity between relay terminals "A" and "B". *See Fig. 7*. If continuity exists, replace relay. If continuity does not exist, apply battery voltage across terminals "C" and "D". Check continuity across terminals "A" and "B". If continuity does not exist, replace relay. If continuity exists, relay is okay.

A/C DIODE TEST

Check continuity between terminals "A" and "B" of A/C diode. *See Fig. 8*. Check continuity in both directions. Continuity should be present in one direction only. Replace A/C diode if continuity is not as specified.

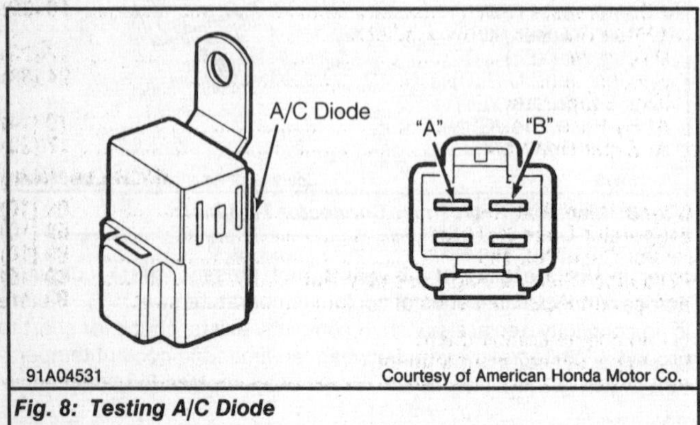
A/C Diode
"A"
"B"
91A04531
Courtesy of American Honda Motor Co.

Fig. 8: Testing A/C Diode

A/C SWITCH TEST

Remove A/C switch from control panel. With A/C switch off, continuity should not exist between A/C switch connector terminals No. 1 and 2. *See Fig. 9*. With A/C switch on, continuity should exist between terminals No. 1 and 2. If continuity is not as specified, replace switch.

COMPRESSOR CLUTCH COIL TEST

Ensure compressor thermal protector is okay. See COMPRESSOR THERMAL PROTECTOR TEST. Check resistance between clutch connector and compressor body (ground). Replace clutch coil if resistance is not 3.1-3.4 ohms at 68°F (20°C).

COMPRESSOR THERMAL PROTECTOR TEST

Check continuity between compressor thermal protector terminals (on compressor). If continuity does not exist, replace compressor thermal protector.

REMOVAL & INSTALLATION

WARNING: To avoid injury from accidental air bag deployment, read and carefully follow all SERVICE PRECAUTIONS and DISABLING & ACTIVATING AIR BAG SYSTEM procedures in AIR BAG SYSTEM SAFETY article in GENERAL SERVICING.

COMPRESSOR

Removal – **1)** Run engine at idle speed and operate A/C for more than 10 minutes (if possible). Stop engine. Disconnect negative battery cable. Discharge A/C system using approved refrigerant recovery/recycling equipment.

2) Remove condenser fan and shroud as an assembly. Disconnect refrigerant hoses from compressor. Remove power steering pump belt. Loosen alternator pivot bolt and adjusting bolt. Remove A/C belt. Disconnect clutch coil connector. Remove compressor bolts. Remove compressor.

Installation – To install, reverse removal procedure. If installing new compressor, drain oil from old compressor into a metered container. Note quantity of oil drained. Subtract this quantity from 4.0 ounces. Drain resulting quantity from new compressor before installing. For example, if 3 ozs. of oil was drained from old compressor, subtract 3 from 4. Drain resulting amount (one oz.) from new compressor and install. Evacuate and charge A/C system.

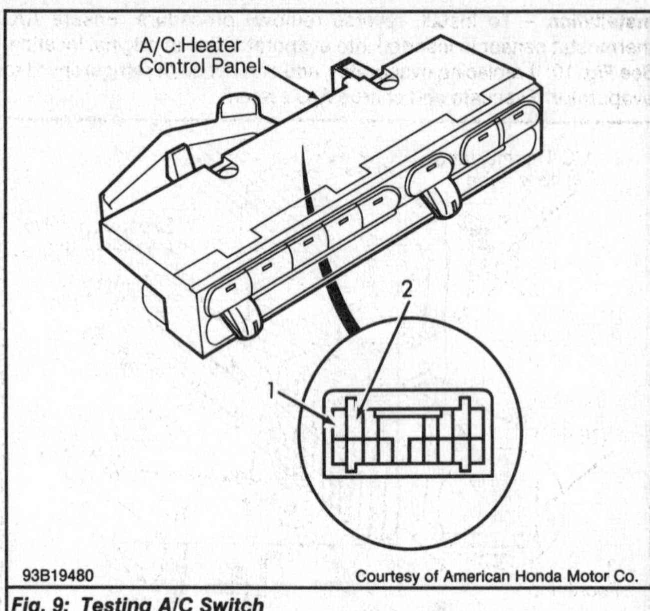
A/C-Heater
Control Panel
2
1
93B19480
Courtesy of American Honda Motor Co.

Fig. 9: Testing A/C Switch

CONDENSER

Removal – **1)** Disconnect negative battery cable. Discharge A/C system using approved refrigerant recovery/recycling equipment. If necessary, remove front bumper, engine hood lock, front grille, fans and shrouds. Disconnect A/C pressure switch connector.

2) Remove A/C pressure switch and pipe. Disconnect discharge pipe fitting from condenser. Remove A/C hose bracket and upper radiator mount brackets. Remove condenser bolts. Remove condenser.

Installation – To install, reverse removal procedure. Ensure rubber mounts on bottom of condenser are in holes. Add 1/3 ounce of refrigerant oil to condenser. Evacuate and charge A/C system.

EVAPORATOR CASE

Removal – **1)** Disconnect both battery cables. Discharge A/C system using approved refrigerant recovery/recycling equipment. In engine compartment, disconnect refrigerant lines from evaporator. Remove small speaker from right side of instrument panel.

WARNING: To avoid injury from accidental air bag deployment, read and carefully follow all SERVICE PRECAUTIONS and DISABLING & ACTIVATING AIR BAG SYSTEM procedures in AIR BAG SYSTEM SAFETY article in GENERAL SERVICING.

2) Remove visor and Black face panel from instrument panel. Remove glove box. Remove passenger-side air bag assembly. Store assembly with pad facing upward. Remove air bag assembly stay and bracket. Disconnect A/C thermostat connector. Remove evaporator case bolts and evaporator case.

Installation – To install, reverse removal procedure. Evacuate and charge A/C system.

EVAPORATOR, A/C THERMOSTAT & EXPANSION VALVE

Removal – Remove evaporator case. See EVAPORATOR CASE. Note where A/C thermostat sensor is inserted into evaporator fins. *See Fig. 10*. Pull A/C thermostat sensor out of evaporator fins. Remove screws and clips securing case halves together. Carefully separate case halves. Remove evaporator and A/C thermostat. Remove expansion valve, backing up fittings with wrench to prevent tube breakage.

Installation – To install, reverse removal procedure. Ensure A/C thermostat sensor is inserted into evaporator fins in original location. *See Fig. 10.* If replacing evaporator, add one ounce of refrigerant oil to evaporator. Evacuate and charge A/C system.

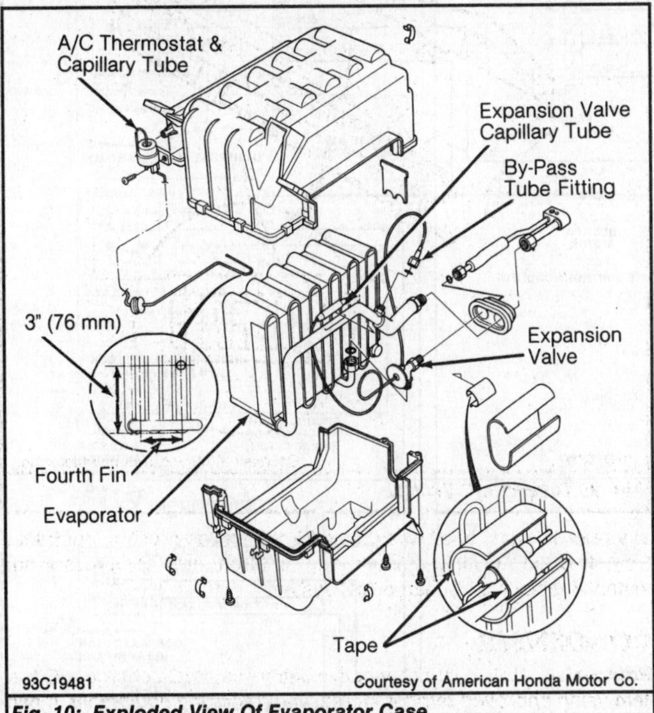
A/C Thermostat &
Capillary Tube
Expansion Valve
Capillary Tube
By-Pass
Tube Fitting
3" (76 mm)
Expansion
Valve
Fourth Fin
Evaporator
Tape
93C19481
Courtesy of American Honda Motor Co.

Fig. 10: Exploded View Of Evaporator Case

COMPRESSOR THERMAL PROTECTOR

Removal & Installation – Remove thermal protector from compressor. It is not necessary to discharge refrigerant to remove compressor thermal protector. Apply silicone sealant to outer edge of compressor thermal protector before installing.

TORQUE SPECIFICATIONS

TORQUE SPECIFICATIONS

Application	Ft. Lbs. (N.m)
Compressor Bracket-To-Engine Bolt/Nut	36 (49)
Compressor-To-Compressor Bracket Bolt	16 (22)
Heater Case-To-Firewall Nut [1]	16 (22)
Refrigerant Pipe Connections	
At Compressor	16 (22)
At Hose Bracket (Above Radiator)	
Discharge	17 (23)
Suction	24 (33)
Inside Evaporator	
At By-Pass Tube	10 (14)
At Expansion Valve	17 (23)
	INCH Lbs. (N.m)
Blower Case Bolt/Nut	89 (10)
Evaporator Case Bolt/Nut	89 (10)
Heater Case Bolt/Nut [2]	89 (10)
Passenger-Side Air Bag Assembly Nut	89 (10)
Refrigerant Pipe Connections	89 (10)

[1] – In engine compartment.
[2] – In passenger compartment.

1993 MANUAL A/C-HEATER SYSTEMS
Prelude (Cont.)

WIRING DIAGRAM

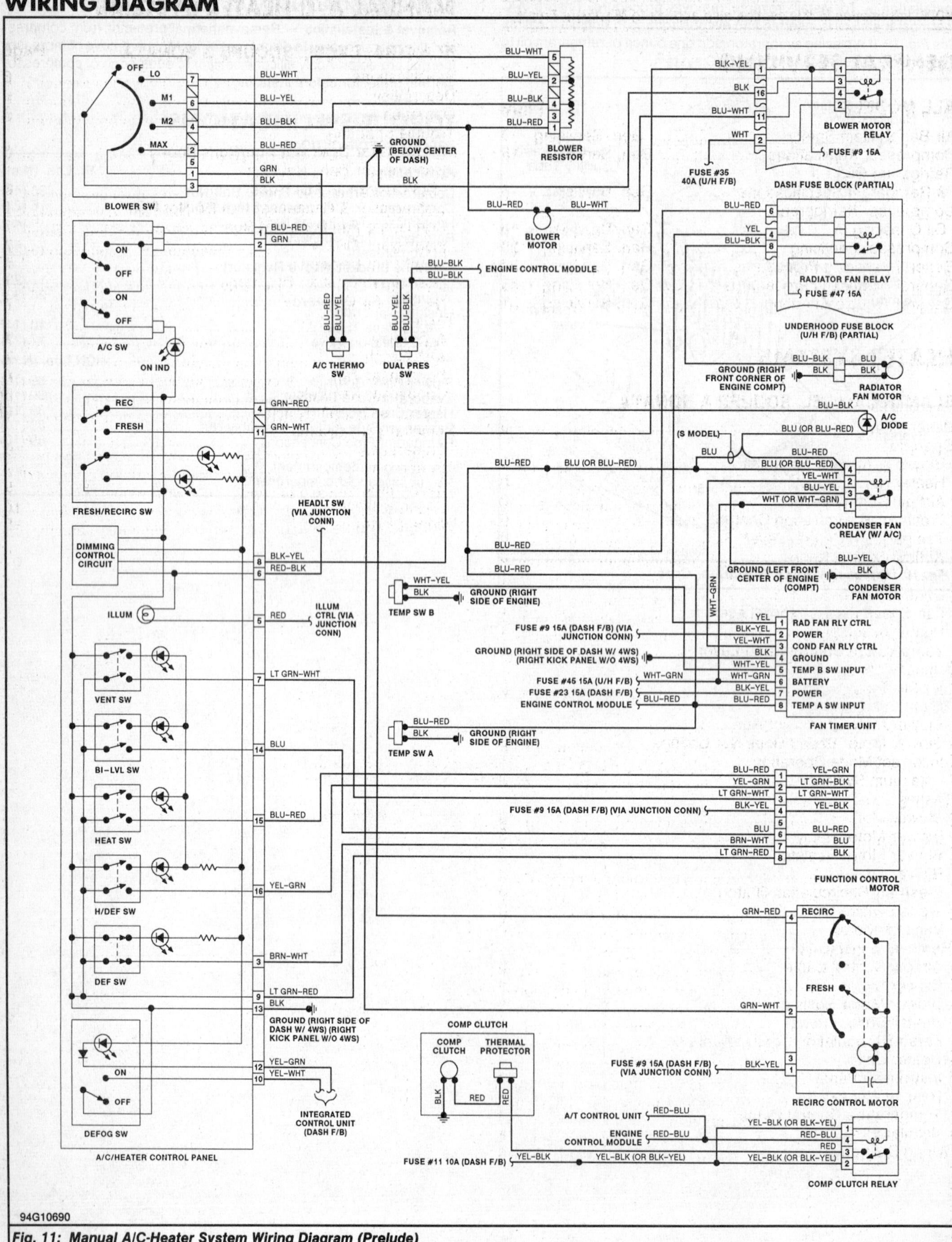
BLOWER SW
OFF
LO
M1
M2
MAX
BLU-WHT
BLU-YEL
BLU-BLK
BLU-RED
GRN
BLK
GROUND (BELOW CENTER OF DASH)
BLOWER RESISTOR
BLOWER MOTOR
A/C SW
ON
OFF
ON IND
FRESH/RECIRC SW
REC
FRESH
DIMMING CONTROL CIRCUIT
ILLUM
VENT SW
BI-LVL SW
HEAT SW
H/DEF SW
DEF SW
DEFOG SW
A/C/HEATER CONTROL PANEL
ENGINE CONTROL MODULE
A/C THERMO SW
DUAL PRES SW
HEADLT SW (VIA JUNCTION CONN)
ILLUM CTRL (VIA JUNCTION CONN)
TEMP SW B
TEMP SW A
GROUND (RIGHT SIDE OF ENGINE)
GROUND (RIGHT SIDE OF DASH W/ 4WS) (RIGHT KICK PANEL W/O 4WS)
INTEGRATED CONTROL UNIT (DASH F/B)
COMP CLUTCH
THERMAL PROTECTOR
DASH FUSE BLOCK (PARTIAL)
BLOWER MOTOR RELAY
FUSE #9 15A
FUSE #35 40A (U/H F/B)
RADIATOR FAN RELAY
FUSE #47 15A
UNDERHOOD FUSE BLOCK (U/H F/B) (PARTIAL)
GROUND (RIGHT FRONT CORNER OF ENGINE COMPT)
RADIATOR FAN MOTOR
A/C DIODE
(S MODEL)
CONDENSER FAN RELAY (W/ A/C)
GROUND (LEFT FRONT CENTER OF ENGINE (COMPT)
CONDENSER FAN MOTOR
FUSE #9 15A (DASH F/B) (VIA JUNCTION CONN)
FUSE #45 15A (U/H F/B)
FUSE #23 15A (DASH F/B)
RAD FAN RLY CTRL
POWER
COND FAN RLY CTRL
GROUND
TEMP B SW INPUT
BATTERY
TEMP A SW INPUT
FAN TIMER UNIT
FUNCTION CONTROL MOTOR
RECIRC
RECIRC CONTROL MOTOR
A/T CONTROL UNIT
FUSE #11 10A (DASH F/B)
COMP CLUTCH RELAY
94G10690

Fig. 11: Manual A/C-Heater System Wiring Diagram (Prelude)

1993 HYUNDAI CONTENTS

NOTE: Information in this section also applies to Misubishi Precis.

GENERAL SERVICING

ALL MODELS

HEATER SYSTEMS

ELANTRA, EXCEL, SCOUPE & SONATA

MANUAL A/C-HEATER SYSTEMS

ELANTRA, EXCEL, SCOUPE & SONATA — Page

1993 HEATER SYSTEMS
Elantra, Excel, Scoupe & Sonata

NOTE: This article also applies to Mitsubishi Precis.

DESCRIPTION

The heater system consists of blower, air inlet assembly, heater unit, heater control panel and heater valve. Excel and Precis use a lever type or rotary knob (vacuum type) control panel. Elantra, Scoupe and Sonata use rotary knob (vacuum type) controls.

OPERATION

BLOWER & AIR INLET ASSEMBLY

Excel & Precis (Lever Type) – The fresh air inlet door is used to select outside (fresh) air or inside (recirculated) air. Setting fresh air/recirculation control lever to fresh position allows outside air to enter. Setting fresh air/recirculation control lever to recirculation position recirculates inside air. The air blend door is always open and admits recirculated air regardless of position of fresh air inlet door.

HEATER UNIT

Excel & Precis (Lever Type) – The heater unit houses heater core, temperature door and vent/defrost door. *See Fig. 1.*

AIRFLOW CONTROL LEVER

Excel & Precis (Lever Type) – Airflow control lever controls flow of air to selected vents by mechanically opening mode doors. Air can be directed to floor, dashboard or defroster outlets. Airflow lever can be set to face, bi-level, floor, floor/defrost or defrost position.

Setting lever to face position directs air to dashboard vents. Selecting bi-level position allows cooler airflow to dashboard vents and warmer air to floor outlets. Selecting floor position directs airflow to floor outlets. Selecting floor/defrost position allows airflow to floor and defroster outlets. Selecting defrost position directs airflow to defroster outlets. *See Fig. 4.*

FRESH AIR/RECIRCULATION CONTROL LEVER

Excel & Precis (Lever System) – Move fresh air/recirculation control lever to recirculation position. The vent/fresh mode door closes off outside vent to heater blower motor housing. Move fresh air/recirculation control lever to fresh air position. The vent/fresh mode door opens to let outside air into heater blower housing to be vented through outlets selected by mode lever. *See Fig. 4.*

TEMPERATURE CONTROL LEVER

Excel & Precis (Lever System) – To regulate temperature of air entering passenger compartment, temperature control lever mechanically controls flow of engine coolant entering heater core. *See Fig. 4.*

AIRFLOW CONTROL KNOB

Vacuum Type – The airflow control knob controls airflow to selected vents by directing source vacuum to vacuum motors. *See Fig. 2 or 3.* On all models, airflow can be directed to floor, dashboard or defroster outlets. The airflow knob can be set to panel, panel/floor, floor, defrost/floor or defrost. Setting lever to panel position directs airflow to dashboard vents.

Selecting panel/floor position allows cooler airflow to dashboard vents and warmer air to floor outlets. Selecting floor position directs airflow to floor outlets. Selecting defrost/floor position allows airflow to floor and defroster outlets. Selecting defrost position directs airflow to defroster outlets.

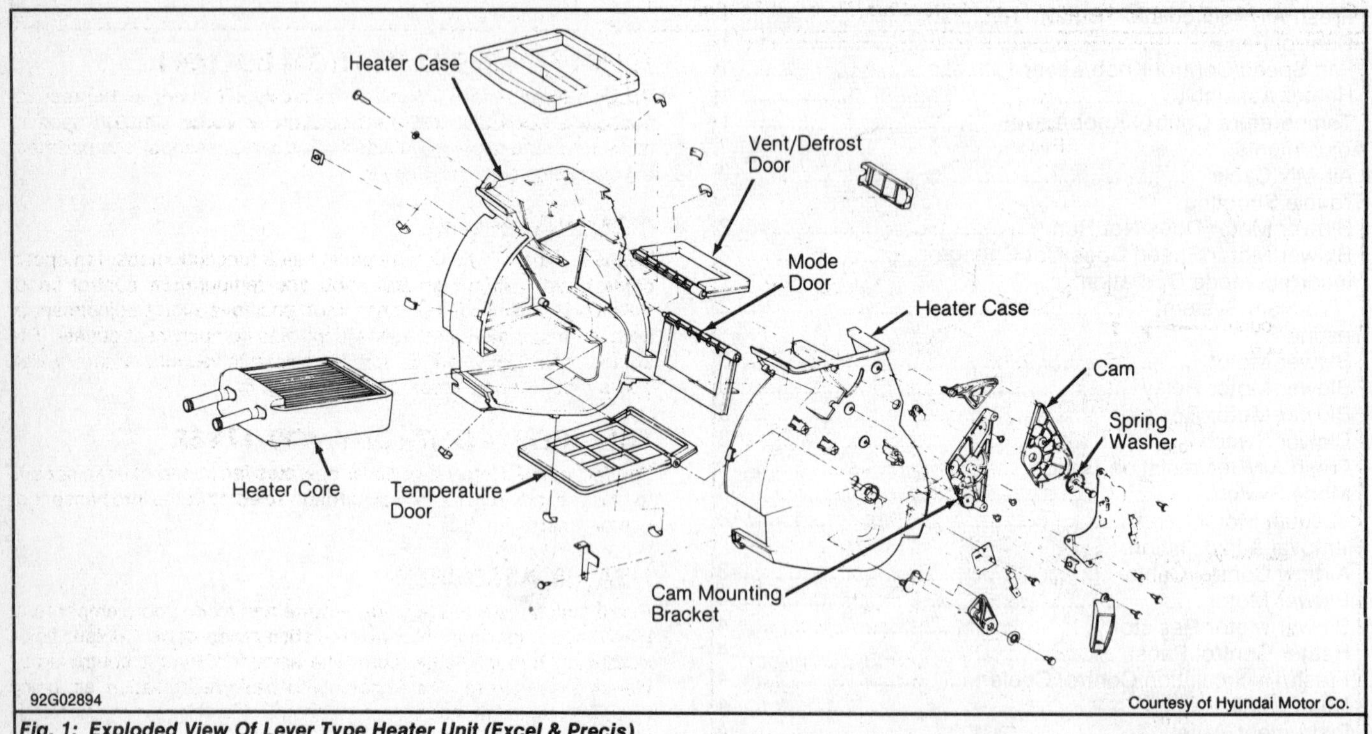
Heater Case
Vent/Defrost Door
Mode Door
Heater Case
Cam
Spring Washer
Heater Core
Temperature Door
Cam Mounting Bracket
92G02894
Courtesy of Hyundai Motor Co.

Fig. 1: Exploded View Of Lever Type Heater Unit (Excel & Precis)

1993 HEATER SYSTEMS
Elantra, Excel, Scoupe & Sonata (Cont.)

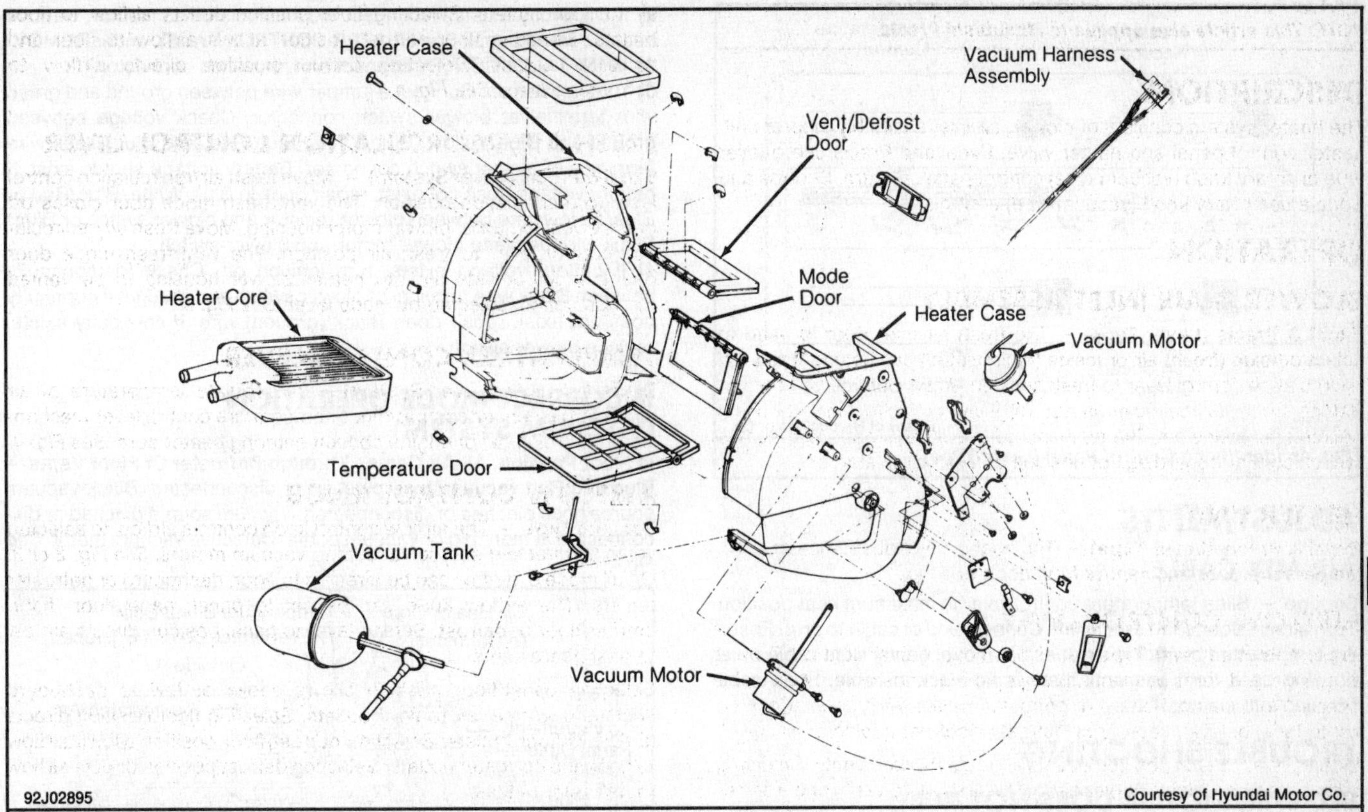

Heater Case
Vacuum Harness Assembly
Vent/Defrost Door
Mode Door
Heater Case
Vacuum Motor
Heater Core
Temperature Door
Vacuum Tank
Vacuum Motor
92J02895
Courtesy of Hyundai Motor Co.

Fig. 2: Exploded View Of Vacuum Type Heater Unit (Elantra & Scoupe)

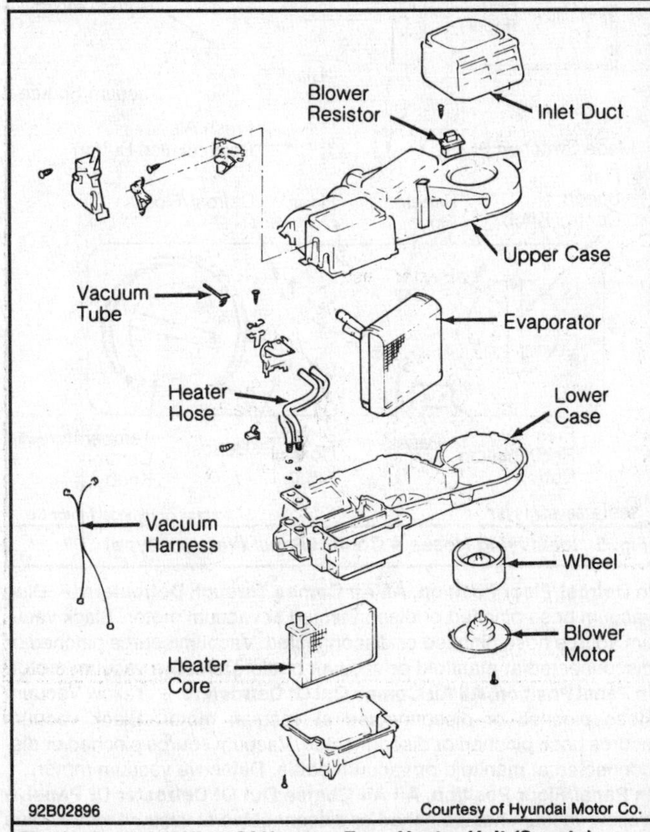
Blower Resistor
Inlet Duct
Upper Case
Vacuum Tube
Evaporator
Heater Hose
Lower Case
Vacuum Harness
Wheel
Blower Motor
Heater Core
92B02896
Courtesy of Hyundai Motor Co.

Fig. 3: Exploded View Of Vacuum Type Heater Unit (Sonata)

FRESH AIR/RECIRCULATION BUTTON

Vacuum Type - When fresh air/recirculation button is depressed, vacuum is applied to fresh/recirculation air vacuum motor, opening mode door and allowing outside airflow into passenger compartment through selected vents. *See Fig. 5.*

CONTROL PANEL

Vacuum Type - The control panel has 3 function knobs: fan speed control knob, airflow control knob and temperature control knob. Selecting combinations of these knob positions allows adjustment of both air temperature and airflow control to compartment outlets. The airflow control knob directs source vacuum to vacuum motors, which operate appropriate mode doors. *See Fig. 5.*

FAN SPEED CONTROL KNOB/LEVER

The fan speed control knob/lever operates fan in one of 4 fan speeds to blow fresh or recirculated air through selected vents into passenger compartment. *See Fig. 4 or 5.*

HEATER ASSEMBLY

Heater unit houses heater core, vent/defrost mode door, temperature blend mode door and fresh/recirculation mode door. Coolant flows continually through heater core. The amount of heat is controlled by blending air across heater core with fresh/recirculation air being vented to selected outlets.

TEMPERATURE CONTROL KNOB/LEVER

Temperature control knob/lever mechanically adjusts blend door opening, controlling airflow volume across heater core. Airflow from heater core is blended with fresh or recirculated air and vented into passenger compartment through selected outlets. *See Fig. 4 or 5.*

1993 HEATER SYSTEMS
Elantra, Excel, Scoupe & Sonata (Cont.)

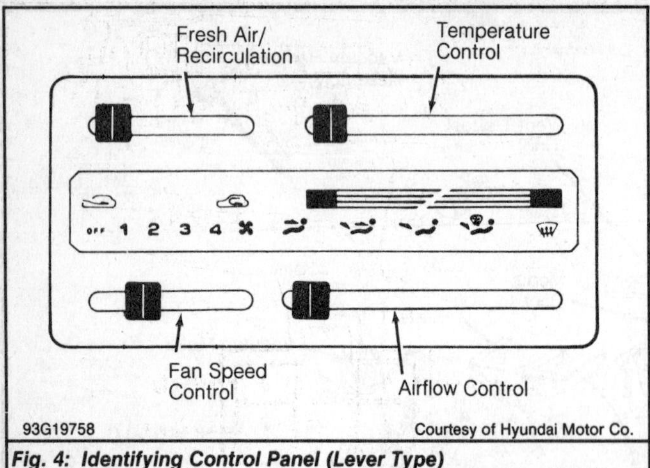
Fresh Air/
Recirculation
Temperature
Control
OFF 1 2 3 4
Fan Speed
Control
Airflow Control
93G19758
Courtesy of Hyundai Motor Co.

Fig. 4: Identifying Control Panel (Lever Type)

ADJUSTMENTS

AIR MIX CABLE

Scoupe – Slide temperature control lever to maximum heat position. Turn air mix door shaft arm to left. Connect end of cable to arm. Ensuring temperature control lever does not move, gently slide cable outer housing back from end until there is no slack in cable. Snap cable housing into clamp.

TROUBLE SHOOTING

BLOWER MOTOR DOES NOT RUN

Scoupe – **1)** Check fuses No. 1 (30-amp) and No. 11 (20-amp) in dash fuse box. If fuse(s) are blown, replace as necessary. If fuses are okay, disconnect blower motor. With ignition and blower switches turned to ON position, measure voltage between ground and Red/White wire at blower motor. Battery voltage should exist. If battery voltage does not exist, go to next step. If battery voltage does exist, go to step **3)**.

2) Remove blower relay from passenger compartment relay box. Measure voltage between ground and Light Green and Blue/Red wires at blower relay. Battery voltage should exist. If battery voltage does not exist, repair open in appropriate wire. If battery voltage exists, check blower relay operation. See BLOWER MOTOR RELAY under TESTING. If blower relay is okay, repair open Green wire between blower relay and blower switch.

3) Turn ignition off. Reconnect blower motor. Connect a jumper wire to ground. Using jumper wire, backprobe Blue/Black wire terminal at blower motor. Turn ignition on. Blower motor should run. If blower motor runs, go to next step. If blower motor does not run, replace blower motor.

4) Turn ignition off. Disconnect jumper wire. Remove heater control panel. See HEATER CONTROL PANEL under REMOVAL & INSTALLATION. Disconnect blower switch connector. Connect a jumper wire between ground and blower switch Blue/Black and Green wire terminals. Turn ignition switch on. Blower motor should run. If blower motor runs, go to next step. If blower motor does not run, repair open Green wire between blower relay and blower switch or Blue/Black wire between blower motor and blower switch.

5) Turn ignition off. Remove jumper wire. Check blower switch, and repair as necessary. See BLOWER SWITCH under TESTING. If blower switch is okay, repair open Black wire between blower switch and ground or poor ground.

BLOWER MOTOR SPEED DOES NOT CHANGE

Scoupe – **1)** Turn ignition off. Remove glove box cover. Disconnect blower resistor connector. Check for continuity between Blue/Black and Blue/White wire terminals. If continuity does not exist, replace blower resistor.

2) If continuity exists, reconnect blower resistor connector. remove heater control panel. See HEATER CONTROL PANEL under REMOVAL & INSTALLATION. Disconnect blower switch connector.

3) Turn ignition on. Connect a jumper wire between ground and green wire terminal at blower switch connector. Check voltage between ground and Blue/Yellow, Blue/White, Blue/Red, and Blue/Black wire terminals of blower switch connector. Battery voltage should exist. If battery voltage does not exist, repair open in Blue/White, Blue/Red or Blue/Yellow wire between blower resistor and blower switch or Blue/Black wire between blower motor and blower switch.

4) If battery voltage exists, turn ignition off. Check for continuity between Black wire terminal of blower switch and ground. If continuity does not exist, repair open Black (ground) wire. If continuity exists, replace blower switch.

INCORRECT MODE OPERATION (VACUUM SYSTEM)

In Floor Position, All Air Comes Through Defroster Or Floor Vents – Blue and Red vacuum hose pinched or disconnected. Black vacuum source hose pinched or disconnected. Vacuum source pinched or disconnected at manifold or vacuum bottle. Defective vacuum motor. *See Fig. 5.*

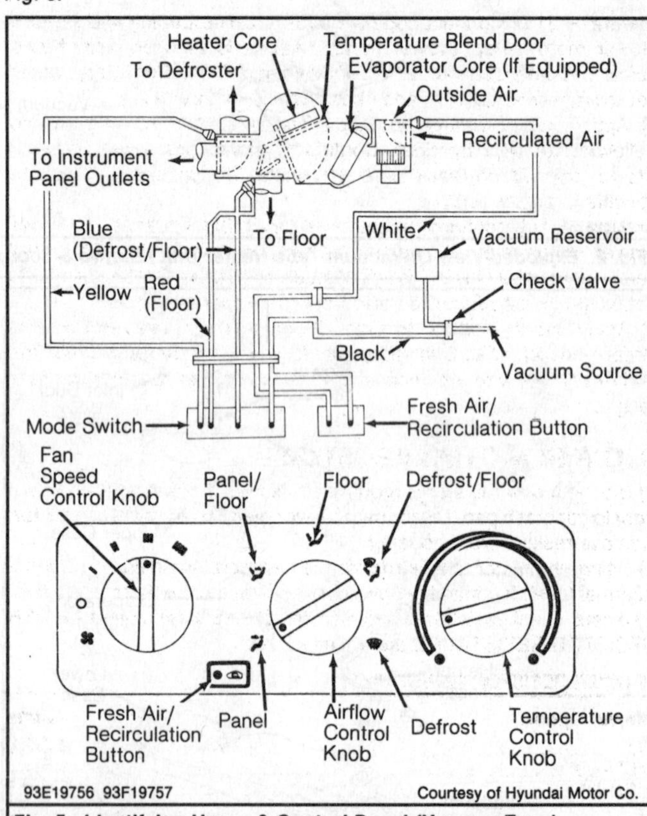
Heater Core
Temperature Blend Door
To Defroster
Evaporator Core (If Equipped)
Outside Air
Recirculated Air
To Instrument
Panel Outlets
Blue
(Defrost/Floor)
To Floor
White
Vacuum Reservoir
Check Valve
Yellow
Red
(Floor)
Black
Vacuum Source
Fresh Air/
Recirculation Button
Mode Switch
Fan
Speed
Control Knob
Panel/
Floor
Floor
Defrost/Floor
Fresh Air/
Recirculation
Button
Panel
Airflow
Control
Knob
Defrost
Temperature
Control
Knob
93E19756 93F19757
Courtesy of Hyundai Motor Co.

Fig. 5: Identifying Hoses & Control Panel (Vacuum Type)

In Defrost/Floor Position, All Air Comes Through Defrosters – Blue vacuum hose pinched or disconnected at vacuum motor. Black vacuum source hose pinched or disconnected. Vacuum source pinched or disconnected at manifold or vacuum bottle. Defective vacuum motor.

In Panel Position, All Air Comes Out Of Defrosters – Yellow Vacuum Hose pinched or disconnected at vacuum motor. Black vacuum source hose pinched or disconnected. Vacuum source pinched or disconnected at manifold or vacuum bottle. Defective vacuum motor.

In Panel/Floor Position, All Air Comes Out Of Defroster Or Panel – Yellow vacuum hose pinched or disconnected at vacuum motor. Blue hose pinched or disconnected at vacuum motor. Black vacuum source hose pinched or disconnected. Vacuum source pinched or disconnected at manifold or vacuum bottle. Defective vacuum motor.

1993 HEATER SYSTEMS
Elantra, Excel, Scoupe & Sonata (Cont.)

In Defrost Position, No Vacuum To Recirculation Vacuum Motor; In Recirculation Position, All Air Comes Out Fresh – White vacuum hose disconnected at recirculation vacuum motor. Black vacuum source hose pinched or disconnected. Vacuum source pinched or disconnected at manifold or vacuum bottle. Defective vacuum motor.

TESTING

BLOWER MOTOR

1) Blower motor is located in blower motor housing, behind right lower crash pad. Disconnect blower motor electrical connector. Remove blower motor from case.
2) Holding blower motor securely, check for abnormal noise, bent fan shaft and cracked or damaged blower fan. If blower motor shaft or fan are damaged, replace defective part as needed.
3) Carefully connect jumper leads from battery negative and positive posts directly to blower motor terminals. Ensure motor operates smoothly. Reverse jumper leads. Ensure motor operates smoothly in reverse direction. If blower motor is inoperative or makes abnormal noise, replace blower motor.

BLOWER MOTOR RELAY

Elantra – 1) Disconnect negative battery cable. Locate and remove blower motor relay. Blower motor relay is located on relay board below instrument cluster, to left of steering column. Continuity should not exist between Brown and Green/Black wire terminals.
2) Apply battery voltage to Black/Red wire terminal, and ground Yellow/White wire terminal. Continuity should now exist between Brown and Green/Black wire terminals. If continuity is not as specified, replace relay.
Scoupe – 1) Disconnect negative battery cable. Locate and remove blower motor relay. Blower motor relay is located on relay board below instrument cluster, to left of steering column. Continuity should not exist between Blue/Red and Red/White wire terminals.
2) Apply battery voltage to Light Green wire terminal, and ground Green wire terminal. Continuity should now exist between Blue/Red and Red/White wire terminals. If continuity is not as specified, replace relay.

BLOWER MOTOR RESISTOR

1) Blower motor resistor is mounted in blower motor housing, behind right lower crash pad. Disconnect blower resistor electrical connector. Remove resistor from housing.
2) Using ohmmeter, check resistance between terminals No. 1 and 2 (thermal fuse). If continuity does not exist, replace resistor. If continuity exists, check resistance between resistor terminals. See BLOWER RESISTOR RESISTANCE table. *See Fig. 6.*

BLOWER RESISTOR RESISTANCE

Blower Speed	Ohms
LO	2.2-2.6
MED-LO	1.1-1.3
MED-HI	0.4-0.5
HI	0

BLOWER SWITCH

Scoupe – Ensure continuity exists between specified terminals in indicated switch positions. See BLOWER SWITCH CONTINUITY table. If continuity is not as specified, replace blower switch.
Elantra – 1) Remove heater control panel, leaving connector connected. Connect a jumper wire between blower switch Yellow/White wire terminal and ground. Turning blower switch on and off, measure voltage between blower switch Blue/Black wire terminal and ground.
2) When blower switch is off, there should be zero volts. When blower switch is on, battery voltage should exist. If voltage is as specified, go to next step. If voltage is not as specified, check fuse No. 12 and blower relay.

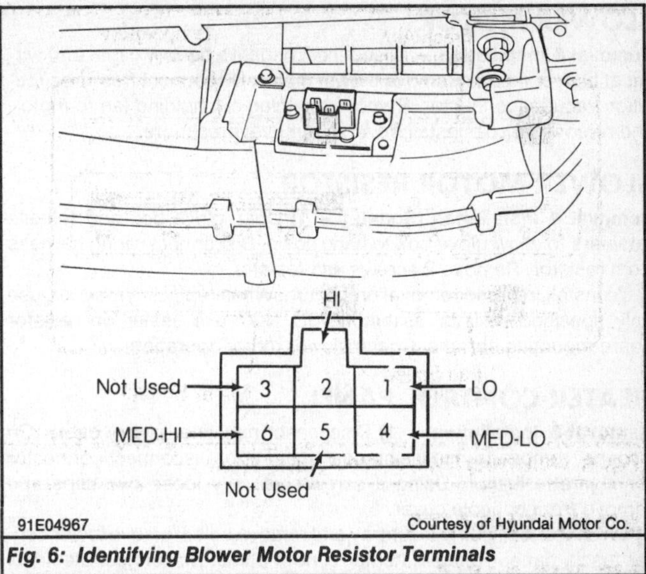
HI
Not Used
3
2
1
LO
MED-HI
6
5
4
MED-LO
Not Used
91E04967
Courtesy of Hyundai Motor Co.

Fig. 6: Identifying Blower Motor Resistor Terminals

3) Disconnect blower switch connector. Ensure continuity exists between specified terminals in indicated switch positions. See BLOWER SWITCH CONTINUITY table. If continuity is not as specified, replace blower switch.

BLOWER SWITCH CONTINUITY

Switch Position	Terminal No.
Off	No Continuity
1	1, 2 & 4
2	1, 2 & 5
3	1, 2 & 3
4	1, 2 & 6

FRESH AIR/RECIRCULATION BUTTON

Scoupe – Connect vacuum tester to Black hose of fresh air/recirculation control button. With button in fresh air position, vacuum should exist at Black hose. With button in recirculation position, vacuum should exist at Black and White hoses. Repair as necessary.

MODE SWITCH

Scoupe – Connect vacuum tester to Black hose of vacuum connector. Plug vacuum port at fresh/recirculation button. Vacuum is present at Black hose in all mode positions. In panel position, vacuum should exist at Black and Yellow hoses. In panel/floor position, vacuum should exist at Black, Blue and Yellow hoses. In floor position, vacuum should exist at Black, Blue, Red and Yellow hoses. In floor/defrost position, vacuum should exist at Black and Blue hoses. In defrost position, vacuum should exist only at Black hose.

VACUUM MOTOR

Scoupe – Using vacuum tester, apply 26 in. Hg. pressure to vacuum motor. Ensure hiss is heard from vacuum motor and that shaft returns to initial position smoothly. If motor does not operate as specified, replace vacuum motor.

REMOVAL & INSTALLATION

AIRFLOW CONTROL CABLE

Removal & Installation (Excel & Precis) – Disconnect negative battery cable. Remove control panel screws, and pull out control panel. Remove cable retaining clip from heater box. Remove cable at mode door arm. Remove cable retaining clip at control panel. Disconnect airflow control cable from control panel. To install, reverse removal procedure. Inspect cable and mode cam to ensure good working condition.

1993 HEATER SYSTEMS
Elantra, Excel, Scoupe & Sonata (Cont.)

BLOWER MOTOR

Removal & Installation – Disconnect negative battery cable and wiring at blower motor. Remove blower motor. Disconnect fresh/recirculation vacuum connector. Remove retaining clip holding fan to motor, and remove fan. To install, reverse removal procedure.

BLOWER MOTOR RESISTOR

Removal & Installation (Sonata) – **1)** Open glove box and release retainers to allow glove box to hang down. Disconnect wiring harness from resistor. Remove 2 screws and resistor.

2) To install, reverse removal procedure. When replacing resistor, use only specified resistor assembly. DO NOT use sealer on resistor board mounting surface. Check blower motor operation.

HEATER CONTROL PANEL

Removal & Installation – **1)** Disconnect negative battery cable. On Scoupe, remove transmission gear shift knob. Disconnect connector for cigarette lighter. Using a screwdriver, pry loose two clips and remove front console cover.

2) On all models, pull out ashtray and remove bolt. Remove lower center fascia panel. Remove heater control panel. Disconnect electrical connections and cable clips. Remove cables from control panel.

3) On rotary knob control panels, disconnect vacuum connector. On all models, to install, reverse removal procedure. On Scoupe, adjust air mix cable. See AIR MIX CABLE under ADJUSTMENTS.

FRESH/RECIRCULATION CONTROL CABLE

Removal & Installation (Excel & Precis) – Disconnect negative battery cable. Remove heater control panel. Remove fresh/recirculation cable from heater control panel. Remove cable retaining clip from fresh/recirculation air mode door. Remove fresh/recirculation air cable. To install, reverse removal procedure. Inspect cable, fresh/recirculation mode pin and fresh/recirculation control arm.

HEATER UNIT

Removal – **1)** Disconnect negative battery cable. On lever type control panels, set temperature control knob/lever to maximum heat position. Drain coolant. Remove heater hoses.

2) On A/C equipped models, remove evaporator drain hose. Using Line Separator (09977-33600 A/B), remove suction and liquid lines. On all models, remove center console, ECU (Electronic Control Unit) and mounting bracket.

3) Remove center fascia panel. Remove glove box and main lower crash pad. Remove heater control panel. Remove left lower crash pad and center support bracket. Remove evaporator unit (if equipped).

4) Loosen rear heating duct mounting screw. Push on rear of heating joint duct and pull duct out. Remove blower heater duct. Loosen heater mounting bolts. Remove heater unit.

Installation – Check link mechanism for operation. Check heater core for clogging and coolant leakage. To install, reverse removal procedure.

INSTRUMENT PANEL

Removal & Installation – **1)** Disconnect negative battery cable. Remove steering wheel and steering column upper and lower shrouds. Remove cassette player and radio. Remove lower center fascia assembly. Remove driver-side lower crash pad. Remove hood release handle screws.

2) Remove left side lower instrument panel. Remove right side main lower crash pad. Remove glove box. Disconnect speedometer cable and electrical connectors from instrument cluster. Remove instrument cluster. Remove heater control panel. Remove right and left front speaker grilles. Remove instrument panel. To install, reverse removal procedure.

REAR HEATER DUCTS

Removal & Installation – Remove front seat. Remove supplement and main console (if equipped). Remove rear heating joint duct and rear heating duct. To install, reverse removal procedure.

TEMPERATURE CONTROL CABLE

Removal & Installation – **1)** Disconnect negative battery cable. Remove heater control panel retaining screws. Remove cable from heater control panel. Remove heater control panel. Remove temperature control cover plate at heater housing.

2) Remove temperature control cable retaining clip from heater box. Remove temperature control cable from mode door arm. To install, reverse removal procedure. Inspect cable, temperature control arm pin and temperature control arm.

VENTILATORS

Removal & Installation – Remove instrument panel. See INSTRUMENT PANEL. Remove side defroster hose. Disconnect vent hose. Remove side register louver. Remove side defroster nozzle and side register louver nozzle. Remove instrument panel upper cover. Remove defroster nozzle. Remove heater connection. Remove center register louver duct. To install, reverse removal procedure.

WIRING DIAGRAMS

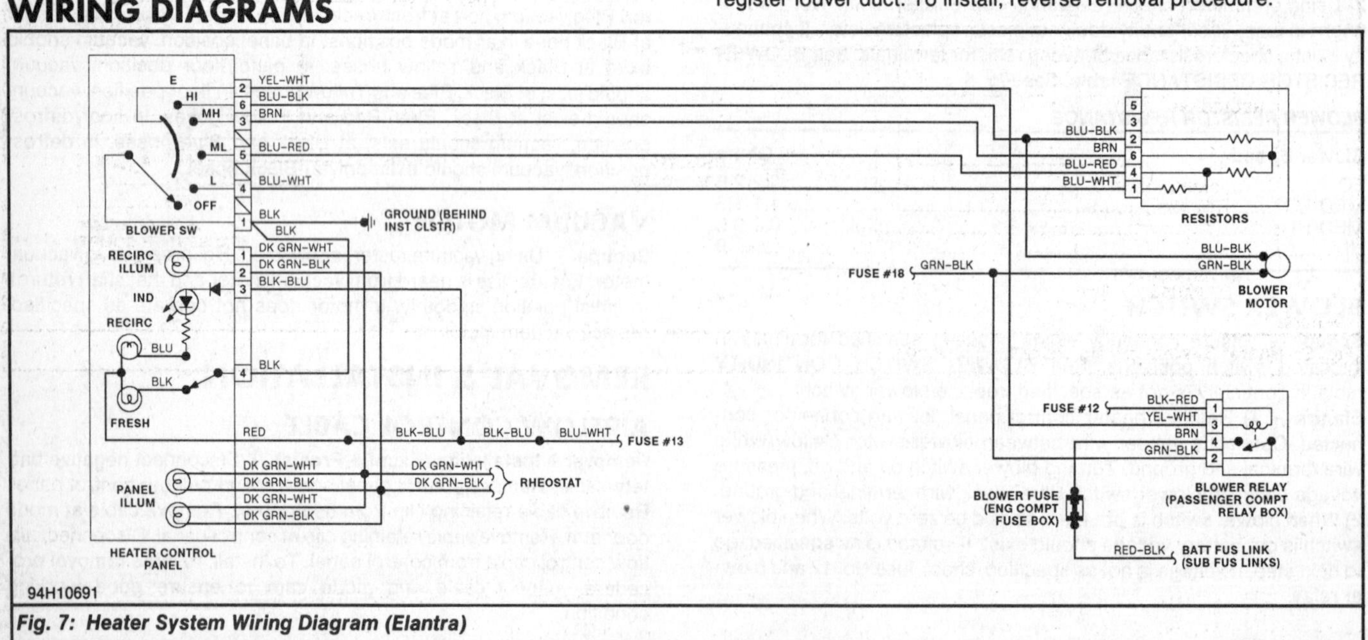
E
HI
MH
ML
L
OFF
BLOWER SW
YEL-WHT
BLU-BLK
BRN
BLU-RED
BLU-WHT
BLK
GROUND (BEHIND INST CLSTR)
RECIRC ILLUM
DK GRN-WHT
DK GRN-BLK
BLK-BLU
IND
RECIRC
BLU
FRESH
RED
BLK-BLU
BLU-WHT
FUSE #13
RHEOSTAT
PANEL ILLUM
HEATER CONTROL PANEL
94H10691
RESISTORS
FUSE #18
GRN-BLK
BLOWER MOTOR
FUSE #12
BLK-RED
BLOWER FUSE (ENG COMPT FUSE BOX)
BLOWER RELAY (PASSENGER COMPT RELAY BOX)
RED-BLK
BATT FUS LINK (SUB FUS LINKS)

Fig. 7: Heater System Wiring Diagram (Elantra)

1993 HEATER SYSTEMS
Elantra, Excel, Scoupe & Sonata (Cont.)

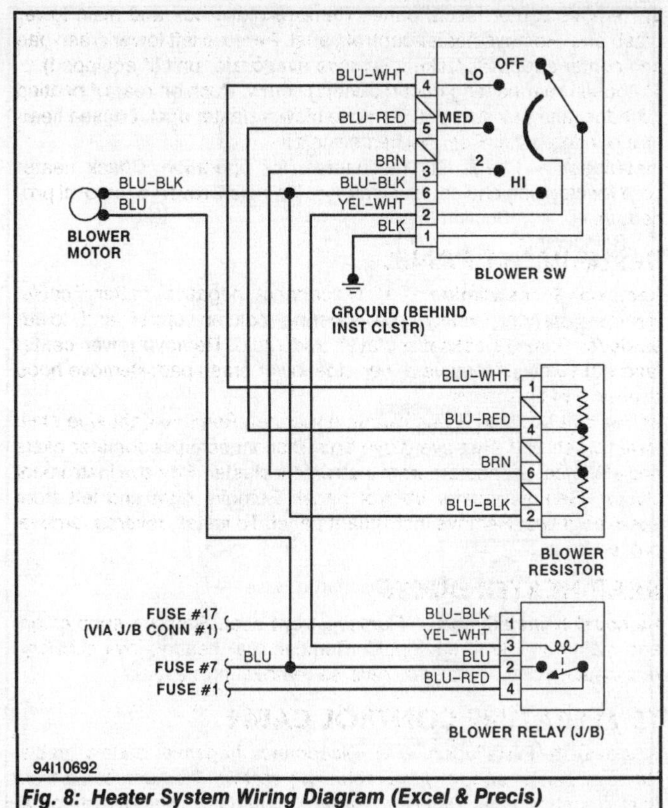
OFF
LO
BLU-WHT
4
BLU-RED
5
MED
BRN
3
2
HI
BLU-BLK
BLU
BLU-BLK
6
YEL-WHT
2
BLK
1
BLOWER MOTOR
BLOWER SW
GROUND (BEHIND INST CLSTR)
BLU-WHT
1
BLU-RED
4
BRN
6
BLU-BLK
2
BLOWER RESISTOR
FUSE #17 (VIA J/B CONN #1)
BLU-BLK
YEL-WHT
BLU
FUSE #7
BLU
BLU-RED
FUSE #1
3
BLOWER RELAY (J/B)
94I10692

Fig. 8: Heater System Wiring Diagram (Excel & Precis)

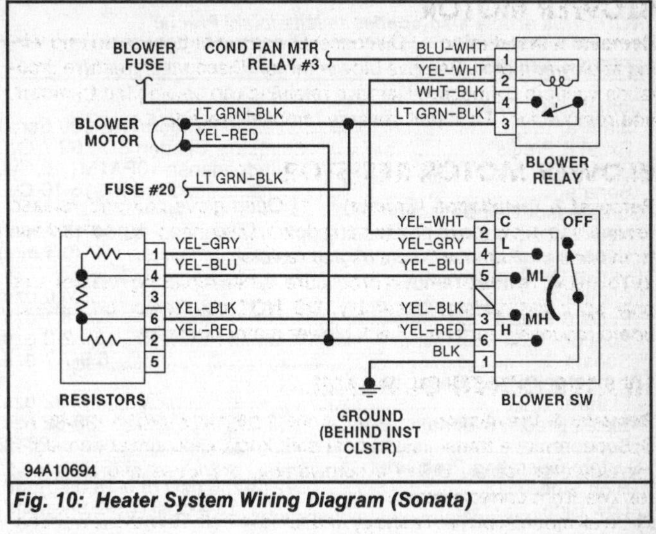
BLOWER FUSE
COND FAN MTR RELAY #3
BLU-WHT
YEL-WHT
WHT-BLK
LT GRN-BLK
BLOWER MOTOR
LT GRN-BLK
YEL-RED
BLOWER RELAY
FUSE #20
LT GRN-BLK
YEL-WHT
C
OFF
YEL-GRY
YEL-GRY
L
YEL-BLU
YEL-BLU
ML
YEL-BLK
YEL-BLK
MH
YEL-RED
YEL-RED
H
BLK
RESISTORS
GROUND (BEHIND INST CLSTR)
BLOWER SW
94A10694

Fig. 10: Heater System Wiring Diagram (Sonata)

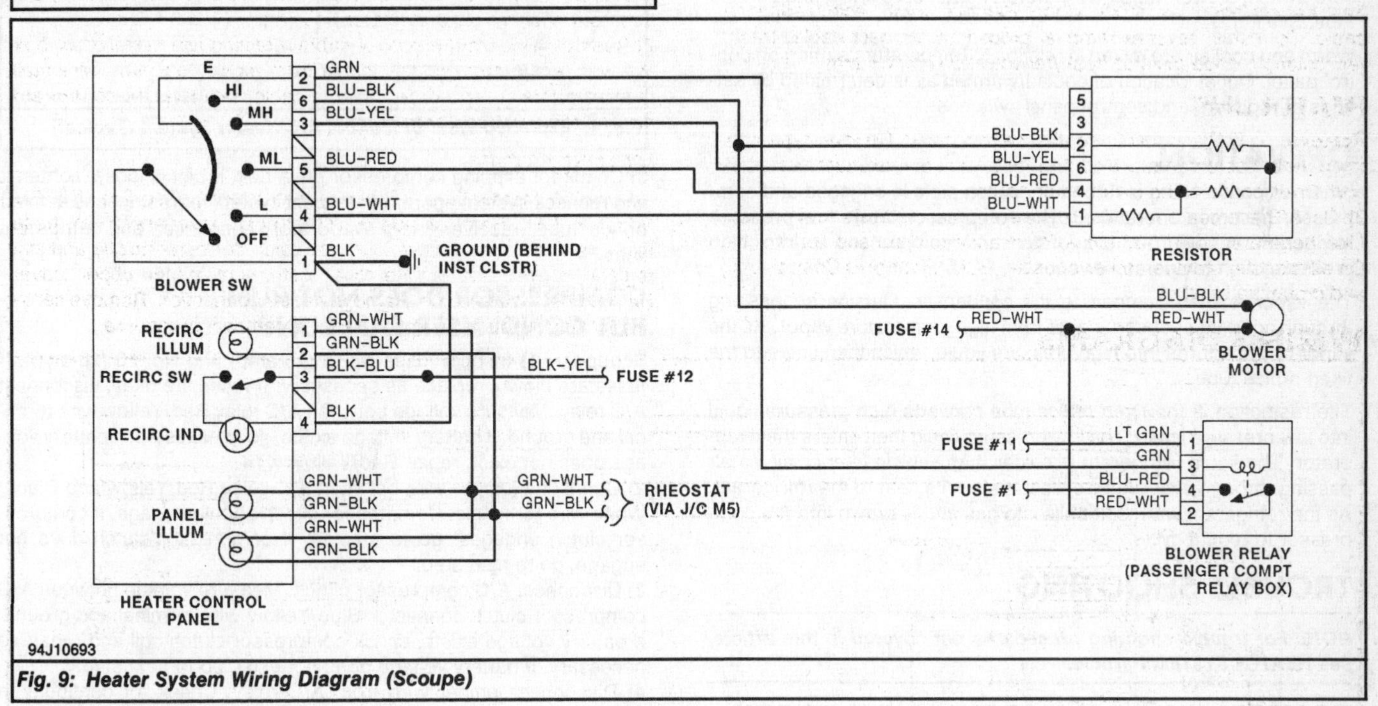
E
HI
MH
ML
L
OFF
GRN
BLU-BLK
BLU-YEL
BLU-RED
BLU-WHT
BLK
GROUND (BEHIND INST CLSTR)
BLOWER SW
RESISTOR
BLU-BLK
BLU-YEL
BLU-RED
BLU-WHT
RECIRC ILLUM
RECIRC SW
RECIRC IND
GRN-WHT
GRN-BLK
BLK-BLU
BLK
BLK-YEL
FUSE #12
FUSE #14
RED-WHT
BLU-BLK
RED-WHT
BLOWER MOTOR
PANEL ILLUM
GRN-WHT
GRN-BLK
GRN-WHT
GRN-BLK
GRN-WHT
GRN-BLK
RHEOSTAT (VIA J/C M5)
FUSE #11
LT GRN
GRN
FUSE #1
BLU-RED
RED-WHT
BLOWER RELAY (PASSENGER COMPT RELAY BOX)
HEATER CONTROL PANEL
94J10693

Fig. 9: Heater System Wiring Diagram (Scoupe)

1993 MANUAL A/C-HEATER SYSTEMS
Elantra, Excel, Scoupe & Sonata

NOTE: This article also applies to Mitsubishi Precis.

SPECIFICATIONS

Compressor Type	
Elantra	Sanden TRF-090 Scroll
Excel & Precis	Sanden SD-709 7-Cyl.
Scoupe	Nippondenso 10PA15C 10-Cyl.
Sonata	Ford FX-15 10-Cyl.
Compressor Belt Deflection [1]	
New	13/64" (5.2 mm)
Used	1/4" (6.4 mm)
System Oil Capacity	
Elantra	4.0 ozs.
Excel & Precis	8.1 ozs.
Scoupe	2-3 ozs.
Sonata	6.9-7.7 ozs.
Refrigerant (R-12) Capacity	
Elantra	32 ozs.
Excel, Precis, & Sonata	30-32 ozs.
Scoupe	28-32
System Operating Pressures	
High Side	213-256 psi (15.0-18.0 kg/cm²)
Low Side	28-42 psi (1.9-2.9 kg/cm²)

[1] - Measured mid-span of longest run of belt.

CAUTION: When battery is disconnected, radio will go into anti-theft protection mode. Obtain radio anti-theft protection code from owner prior to servicing vehicle.

DESCRIPTION

Integrated heating/air conditioning system, a blend-air type system, consists of compressor, cooling fan, condenser, receiver-drier, pressure switch, blower motor, evaporator, heater core and a fixed orifice tube. *See Fig. 1.*

Warm and cool air are mixed in relation to temperature setting on control panel. Outlet location of cooled/warmed air is determined by settings of registers and control panel switches.

OPERATION

When air conditioning is turned on, clutch plate is engaged and compressor becomes operational. The compressor draws low pressure refrigerant vapor from evaporator and compresses it into high pressure, high temperature vapor.

The vapor is then pumped to the condenser. Outside air passing through condenser absorbs heat from high temperature vapor. As the vapor cools, it turns into high pressure liquid, which then flows to the fixed orifice tube.

The restriction in the fixed orifice tube converts high pressure liquid into low pressure liquid. The low pressure liquid then enters the evaporator. The liquid refrigerant is colder than vehicle interior air so air passing through evaporator coils transfers its heat to the refrigerant. As the refrigerant warms, it boils into gas and is drawn into the compressor to repeat cycle.

TROUBLE SHOOTING

NOTE: For trouble shooting procedures not covered in this article, see HEATER SYSTEMS article.

COMPRESSOR DOES NOT RUN/RUNS POORLY

Excel & Precis - 1) Check A/C fuse and relay. Replace components if defective. Check wiring for short if A/C fuse blows again. Check voltage at compressor clutch field coil. If voltage does not exist, check fuse No. 5 (10-amp). If voltage exists, check battery and fuse No. 5.

2) Check A/C switch operation. Replace switch if necessary. Check pressure switch. Replace switch if necessary. Check battery voltage. Charge or replace battery if necessary. Check A/C system charge. If charge is low, recharge system and check for leaks.

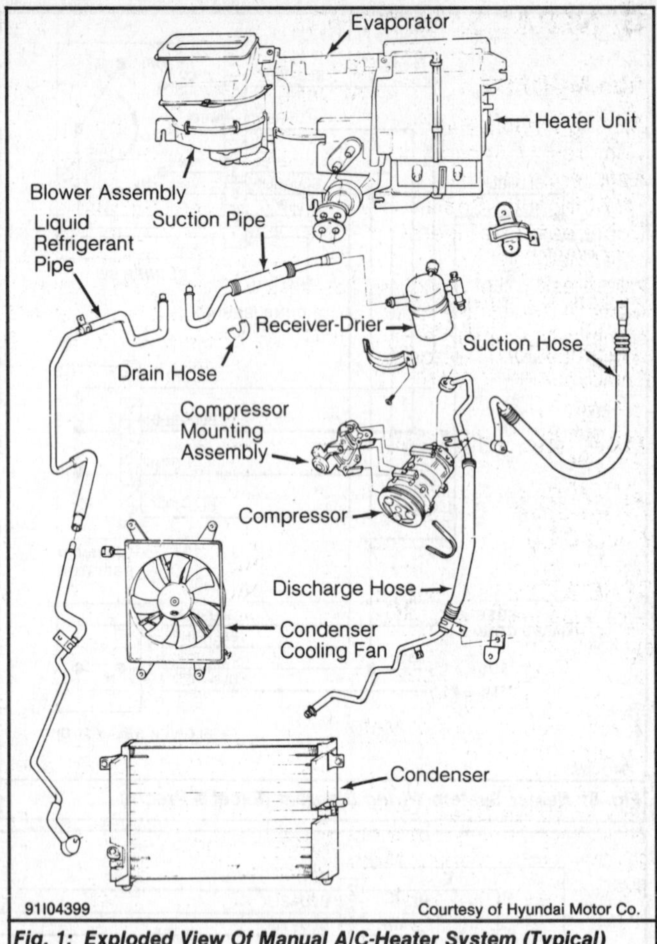
Evaporator
Heater Unit
Blower Assembly
Liquid
Refrigerant
Pipe
Suction Pipe
Receiver-Drier
Suction Hose
Drain Hose
Compressor
Mounting
Assembly
Compressor
Discharge Hose
Condenser
Cooling Fan
Condenser
91I04399
Courtesy of Hyundai Motor Co.

Fig. 1: Exploded View Of Manual A/C-Heater System (Typical)

3) Check for slipping compressor drive belt. If belt is loose, tighten it and recheck system operation. Inspect system for restrictions at fixed orifice tube, receiver-drier, evaporator, condenser and refrigerant lines.

COMPRESSOR DOES NOT RUN BUT CONDENSER FAN RUNS

Scoupe - 1) Inspect fuses No. 5 (10-amp) and No. 13 (10-amp). If fuses are blown, replace as necessary. If fuses are okay, disconnect A/C relay. Measure voltage between A/C relay Red/Yellow wire terminal and ground. If battery voltage exists, go to next step. If battery voltage does not exist, repair Red/Yellow wire.

2) Connect a jumper wire between A/C relay Red/Yellow and Black/White wire terminals. Compressor clutch should engage. If compressor clutch engages, go to step **5)**. If compressor clutch does not engage, go to next step.

3) Disconnect A/C compressor clutch. Measure voltage between A/C compressor clutch connector Blue/Yellow wire terminal and ground. If battery voltage exists, check compressor clutch coil and repair as necessary. If battery voltage does not exist, go to next step.

4) Disconnect jumper wire from A/C relay. Check for continuity in Black/White and Blue/Yellow wires between A/C relay and A/C compressor clutch. If continuity exists, check compressor clutch coil and repair as necessary. If continuity does not exist, repair open Black/White or Blue/Yellow wire.

5) Turn ignition on. Measure voltage between A/C relay Blue/Black wire terminal and ground. If battery voltage exists, go to next step. If battery voltage does not exist, repair Blue/Black wire.

6) Check A/C relay operation. See A/C RELAY under TESTING. If A/C relay operates as specified, go to next step. If A/C relay does not operate as specified, replace relay.

7) Turn ignition off. Reinstall A/C relay. Disconnect Electronic Control Unit (ECU) connector. Connect a jumper wire from ECU connector Black/Red wire terminal to ground. Turn ignition on. Compressor clutch should engage. If compressor clutch engages, go to next step. If compressor clutch does not engage, repair open Black/Red wire.
8) Turn blower and A/C switches on. Measure voltage between ECU connector Black/White wire terminal and ground. If battery voltage does not exist, go to next step. If battery voltage exists, substitute a known good ECU and recheck. Replace ECU if necessary.
9) Turn ignition off. Reconnect ECU connector. Disconnect low pressure switch connector. Turn ignition, blower and A/C on. Measure voltage between ground and terminal No. 2 (Black/Blue wire) of low pressure switch connector. If battery voltage exists, go to step **11)**. If battery voltage does not exist, go to next step.
10) Turn ignition off. Reconnect low pressure switch. Disconnect thermo switch connector. Connect a jumper wire between thermo switch terminals. Turn blower and A/C switches on. Start engine. Compressor clutch should engage. If compressor clutch engages, replace thermo switch. If compressor clutch does not engage, go to next step.
11) Turn ignition off. Connect a jumper wire between low pressure switch terminals. Start engine. Turn blower and A/C switches on. Compressor should run. If compressor runs, go to next step. If compressor does not run, repair Black/Blue or Black/White wire between low pressure switch and ECU.
12) Disconnect jumper wire. Using manifold gauge set, check A/C system pressure. If pressure is okay, replace low pressure switch. If pressure is not okay, recharge and test system.

COMPRESSOR & CONDENSER FAN DO NOT RUN

Scoupe - **1)** Check blower motor operation. If blower motor is okay, go to next step. If blower motor is not okay, see BLOWER MOTOR DOES NOT RUN in HEATER SYSTEMS article.
2) Check fuse No. 14 (10-amp) in dash fuse box. Check fusible link "B" (20-amp) and fusible link "C" (30-amp) in the main fusible link box. If fuse(s) is blown, replace as necessary. If fuses are okay, turn ignition off. Remove heater control panel. See REMOVAL & INSTALLATION in HEATER SYSTEMS article. Disconnect A/C switch connector.
3) Turn ignition and blower switches on. Measure voltage between A/C switch connector Black/Yellow wire terminal and ground. If battery voltage exists, go to next step. If battery voltage does not exist, repair open Black/Yellow wire.
4) Turn ignition off. Connect a jumper wire between Black/Yellow and Black/Light Green wire terminals. Start engine. Turn blower switch on. Compressor clutch and condenser fan should operate. If clutch and fan operate, replace A/C switch. If clutch and fan do not operate, go to next step.
5) Turn ignition off. Reconnect A/C switch. Remove glove box and disconnect thermo switch connector. Turn ignition, blower and A/C switches on. Measure voltage between Black/Light Green wire terminal and ground. If battery voltage exists, see COMPRESSOR DOES NOT RUN BUT CONDENSER FAN RUNS. If battery voltage does not exist, go to next step.
6) Turn ignition off. Disconnect Electronic Control Unit (ECU) connector. Turn ignition on. Measure voltage between ECU Black/White wire terminal and ground. If battery voltage exists, turn ignition off. Repair open Black/Light Green wire between A/C switch and thermo switch. If battery voltage does not exist, go to next step.
7) Turn ignition off. Disconnect A/C wiring harness connector located above brake pedal. Turn ignition on. Measure voltage between wiring harness male Black/Light Green wire terminal and ground. If battery voltage exists, circuit is okay. If battery voltage does not exist, repair short between A/C switch and ECU or open Black/Light Green wire.

CONDENSER FAN DOES NOT RUN

Scoupe - **1)** Check fusible link "B" (20-amp) and fusible link "C" (30-amp) in main fusible link box, and replace if necessary. If fuses are okay, turn ignition off. Disconnect condenser fan motor relay (located in engine compartment relay box). Turn ignition, blower and A/C switches on.
2) Measure voltage between condenser fan motor relay Blue wire terminal and ground. If battery voltage exists, go to next step. If battery voltage does not exist, turn ignition off. Repair open in Blue or Black/Light Green wires between relay and thermo switch.
3) Measure voltage between condenser fan motor relay Green/Yellow wire terminal and ground. If battery voltage exists, go to step **6)**. If battery voltage does not exist, go to next step.
4) Disconnect condenser fan motor. Measure voltage between Blue wire terminal and ground. If battery voltage exists, go to next step. If battery voltage does not exist, repair open in Blue wire between condenser fan motor and fusible link "B".
5) Reconnect condenser fan motor. Connect a jumper wire between condenser fan motor Black wire terminal and ground. Condenser fan should run. If condenser fan runs, repair poor connection or open between condenser fan motor Black wire terminal and ground. If condenser fan does not run, replace condenser fan motor.
6) Connect a jumper wire between condenser fan motor relay Green/Yellow wire terminal and ground. Condenser fan should run. If condenser fan runs, replace condenser fan relay. If condenser fan does not run, go to next step.
7) Turn ignition off. Measure continuity between condenser fan motor relay Black wire terminal and ground. Continuity should exist. If continuity exists, circuit is okay. If continuity does not exist, repair poor connection or open Black wire between condenser fan motor relay and ground.

INSUFFICIENT AIRFLOW

Elantra - Check for leakage at duct joint. Check for evaporator frost. Replace thermostat if necessary. Check for faulty blower motor. Repair or replace as necessary.

INSUFFICIENT COOLING

Elantra - Check for insufficient or excessive refrigerant. Check for clogged receiver-drier or condenser. Check for loose drive belt. Check for faulty compressor, thermostat, expansion valve or magnetic clutch. Check for air in system. Repair or replace as necessary.

INTERMITTENT COOL AIR DISCHARGE

Elantra - Check for air in refrigerant. Check for faulty expansion valve. Repair or replace as necessary.

NO COOL AIR DISCHARGE

Elantra - Check for faulty magnetic clutch. Check fuses No. 1 (10-amp), 12 (10-amp) and No. 18 (10-amp). Check A/C, blower and low pressure switches. Check blower relay. Check thermostat. Check for clogged expansion valve or receiver-drier. Check for insufficient refrigerant. Check for faulty compressor. Repair or replace as necessary.

TESTING

A/C RELAY

Locate A/C relay. *See Figs. 2, 4, 6 and 7.* Remove relay. Continuity should not exist between terminals No. 2 and 4. Apply battery voltage to terminal No. 1, and ground terminal No. 3. Continuity should now exist between terminals No. 2 and 4. If continuity is not as specified, replace relay.

A/C SWITCH

Elantra - **1)** Remove A/C switch, leaving connector connected. Turning blower switch on and off, measure voltage between Brown/Black wire terminal and ground. When blower switch is off, there should be zero volts. When blower switch is on, battery voltage should exist. If voltage is as specified, go to next step. If voltage is not as specified, check fuse No. 18 (10-amp) and blower circuit.
2) Disconnect A/C switch connector. Turning A/C switch on and off, check for continuity between Brown/Black and Blue/Red wire terminals. When A/C switch is off, there should be no continuity. When A/C switch is on, continuity should exist. If continuity is not as specified, replace A/C switch.

1993 MANUAL A/C-HEATER SYSTEMS
Elantra, Excel, Scoupe & Sonata (Cont.)

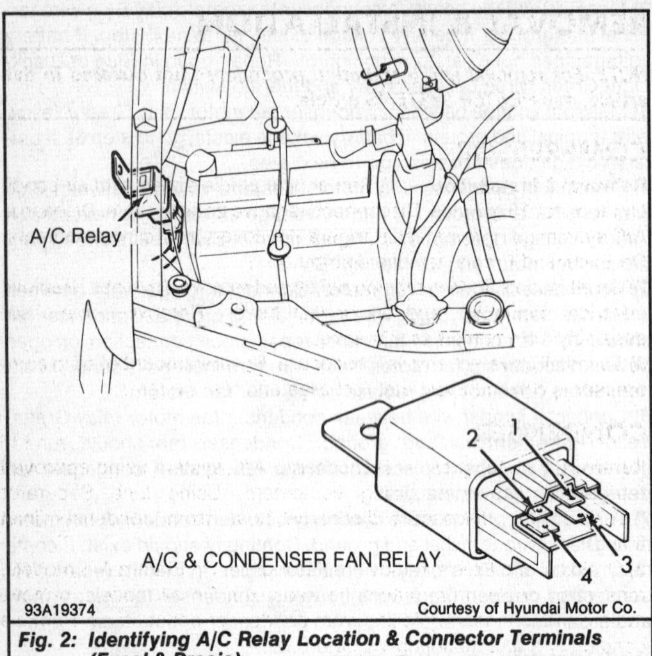
A/C Relay
A/C & CONDENSER FAN RELAY
1
2
3
4
93A19374
Courtesy of Hyundai Motor Co.

Fig. 2: Identifying A/C Relay Location & Connector Terminals (Excel & Precis)

Scoupe – 1) Disconnect A/C switch connector. Turn A/C switch off. Ensure continuity exists between A/C switch Green/White and Green/Black wire terminals.

2) Turn A/C switch on. Ensure continuity exists between Green/White and Green/Black wire terminals, and between Black, Black/Yellow and Black/Light Green wire terminals. If continuity is not as specified, replace A/C switch.

CONDENSER FAN

Except Sonata – Check condenser fan for restriction and damage. If fan is okay, disconnect wiring harness connector. Using an ohmmeter, check for continuity between connector terminals. Continuity should be present. If continuity is not present, replace condenser fan motor.

Sonata – Disconnect wiring harness connector. Using an ohmmeter, check for continuity between terminals "B" and "LW" and between terminals "B" and "LR". *See Fig. 3.* Continuity should exist. If continuity is not as specified, replace condenser fan motor.

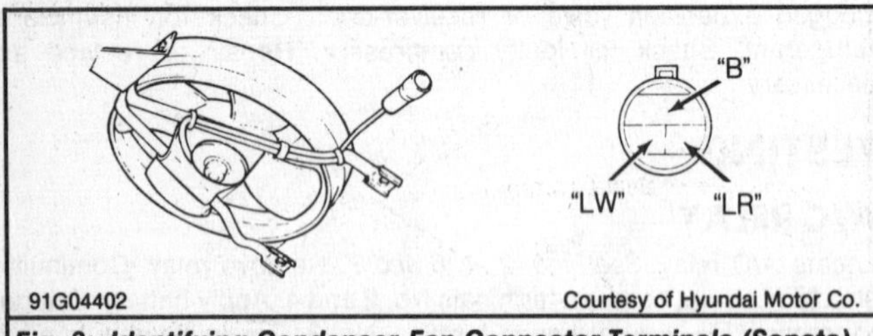
"B"
"LW"
"LR"
91G04402
Courtesy of Hyundai Motor Co.

Fig. 3: Identifying Condenser Fan Connector Terminals (Sonata)

CONDENSER FAN RELAY

Except Scoupe – 1) Locate condenser fan relay in relay box in engine compartment. *See Fig. 4, 5 or 7.* Unplug relay, and check for continuity between terminals No. 2 and 4. *See Fig. 2, 4 or 7.* If continuity exists, replace relay.

2) If continuity is not present, apply battery voltage to terminals No. 1 and 3. Continuity should be present between terminals No. 2 and 4. If continuity is not present, replace relay.

Scoupe – Locate condenser fan relay in relay box in right side of engine compartment. *See Fig. 6.* Unplug relay. Apply battery voltage to terminals No. 1 and 2. If continuity does not exist between terminals No. 2 and 3, replace relay.

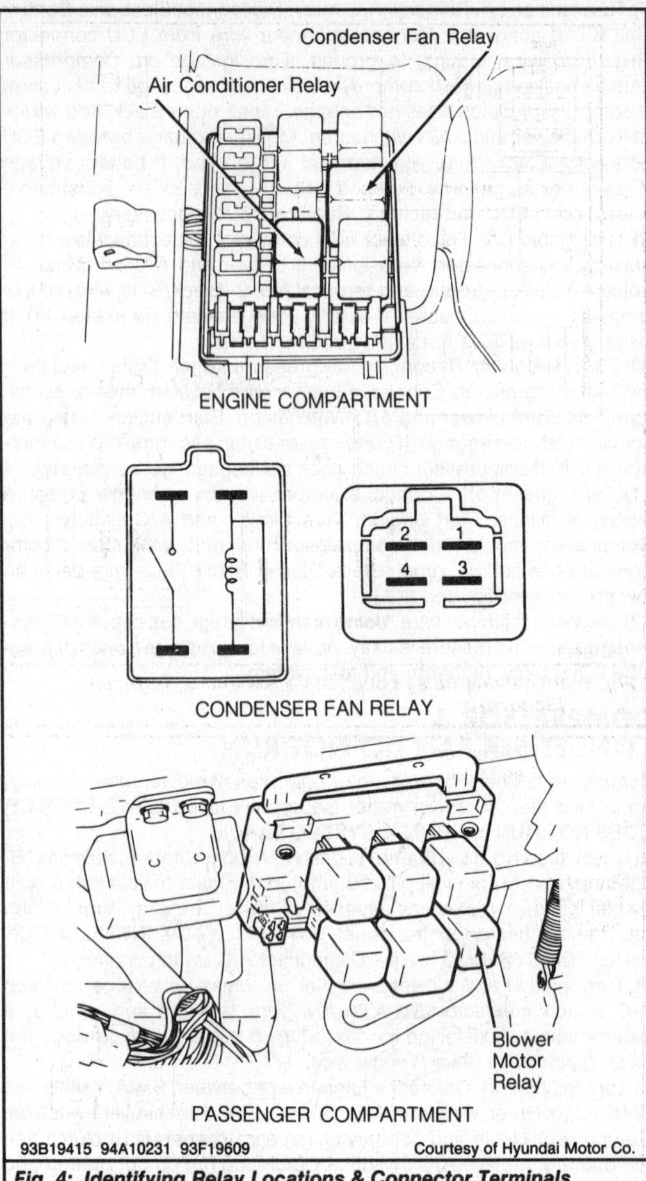
Condenser Fan Relay
Air Conditioner Relay
ENGINE COMPARTMENT
2
1
4
3
CONDENSER FAN RELAY
Blower Motor Relay
PASSENGER COMPARTMENT
93B19415 94A10231 93F19609
Courtesy of Hyundai Motor Co.

Fig. 4: Identifying Relay Locations & Connector Terminals (Elantra)

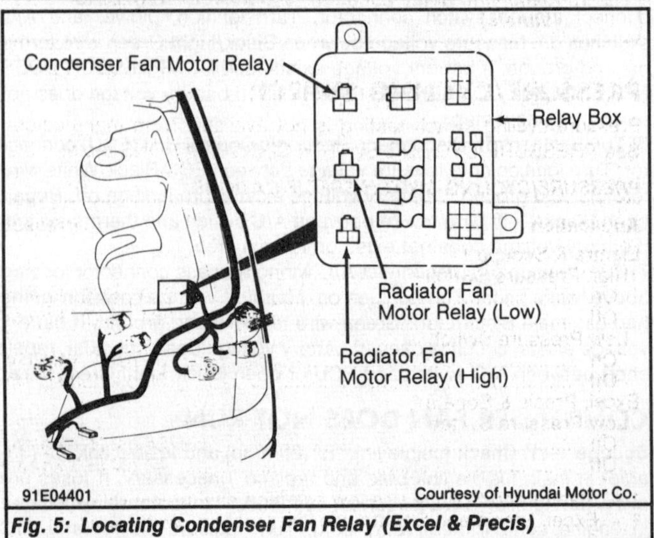
Condenser Fan Motor Relay
Relay Box
Radiator Fan Motor Relay (Low)
Radiator Fan Motor Relay (High)
91E04401
Courtesy of Hyundai Motor Co.

Fig. 5: Locating Condenser Fan Relay (Excel & Precis)

1993 MANUAL A/C-HEATER SYSTEMS
Elantra, Excel, Scoupe & Sonata (Cont.)

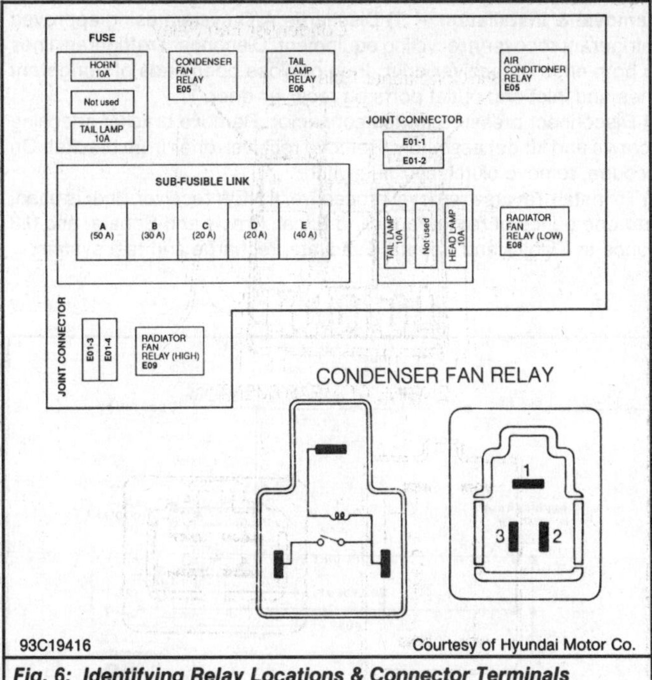
FUSE
HORN 10A
Not used
TAIL LAMP 10A
CONDENSER FAN RELAY E05
TAIL LAMP RELAY E06
AIR CONDITIONER RELAY E05
JOINT CONNECTOR
E01-1
E01-2
SUB-FUSIBLE LINK
A (50 A)
B (30 A)
C (20 A)
D (20 A)
E (40 A)
TAIL LAMP 10A
Not used
HEAD LAMP 10A
RADIATOR FAN RELAY (LOW) E08
JOINT CONNECTOR
E01-3
E01-4
RADIATOR FAN RELAY (HIGH) E09
CONDENSER FAN RELAY
1
3
2
93C19416
Courtesy of Hyundai Motor Co.

Fig. 6: Identifying Relay Locations & Connector Terminals (Scoupe)

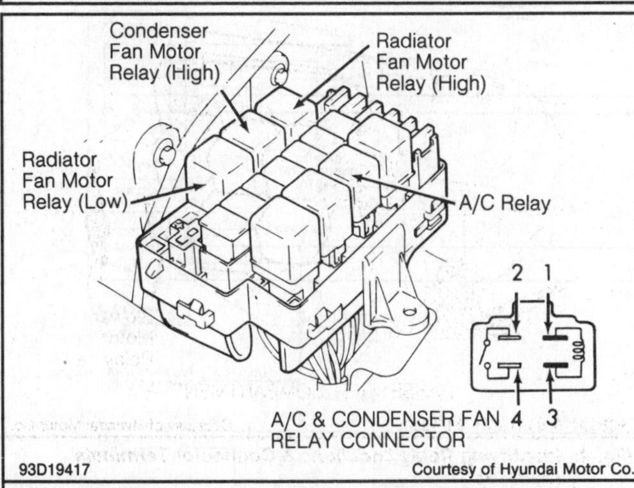
Condenser Fan Motor Relay (High)
Radiator Fan Motor Relay (High)
Radiator Fan Motor Relay (Low)
A/C Relay
2 1
4 3
A/C & CONDENSER FAN RELAY CONNECTOR
93D19417
Courtesy of Hyundai Motor Co.

Fig. 7: Identifying Relay Locations & Connector Terminals (Sonata)

PRESSURE/CYCLING SWITCH

Pressure/cycling switch testing is not available from manufacturer. See PRESSURE/CYCLING SWITCH SPECIFICATIONS table.

PRESSURE/CYCLING SWITCH SPECIFICATIONS

Application	Pressure
Elantra & Scoupe [1]	
High Pressure Switch	
On	299 psi (21 kg/cm²)
Off	384 psi (27 kg/cm²)
Low Pressure Switch	
On	30 psi (2.1 kg/cm²)
Off	28 psi (2.0 kg/cm²)
Excel, Precis & Sonata [2]	
Low Pressure Switch	
On	24 psi (1.7 kg/cm²)
Off	47 psi (3.3 kg/cm²)

[1] – Elantra and Scoupe use low and high dual pressure switch.
[2] – Excel, Precis and Sonata use low pressure switch only.

REMOVAL & INSTALLATION

NOTE: For removal and installation procedures not covered in this article, see HEATER SYSTEMS article.

COMPRESSOR

Removal & Installation – 1) Run engine at idle speed with air conditioner on for 10 minutes. Disconnect negative battery cable. Discharge A/C system using approved refrigerant recovery/recycling equipment. On Excel and Precis, remove distributor.

2) On all models, loosen tension pulley and remove drive belt. Remove electrical connector, and disconnect hoses. Remove compressor assembly from compressor bracket.

3) To install, reverse removal procedure. Ensure amount of oil in compressor is correct. Evacuate, recharge and test system.

CONDENSER

Removal & Installation – 1) Discharge A/C system using approved refrigerant recovery/recycling equipment. Using Line Separator (09977-33600), disconnect discharge hose from condenser inlet fitting.

2) On Excel and Precis, remove radiator grille. On Elantra A/T models, remove oil cooler from automatic transaxle. On all models, remove radiator. Disconnect liquid line from condenser outlet fitting. Remove condenser and 2 mounting insulators.

3) To install, reverse removal procedure. If NEW condenser is installed, add one ounce of refrigerant oil. Evacuate, recharge and test system.

EVAPORATOR

Removal & Installation – 1) Disconnect negative battery cable. Discharge A/C system using approved refrigerant recovery/recycling equipment. Disconnect outlet and inlet pipes from evaporator, and plug openings. Remove grommets from inlet and outlet tubes. Remove center console. Remove instrument panel lower covers and glove box.

2) Remove blower motor, if necessary. Remove drain hose. Disconnect electrical connectors, if necessary. Remove mounting bolts and nuts. Carefully lift out evaporator unit.

3) To disassemble evaporator unit, remove clamps holding upper case to lower case. *See Fig. 8*. Remove evaporator from lower case.

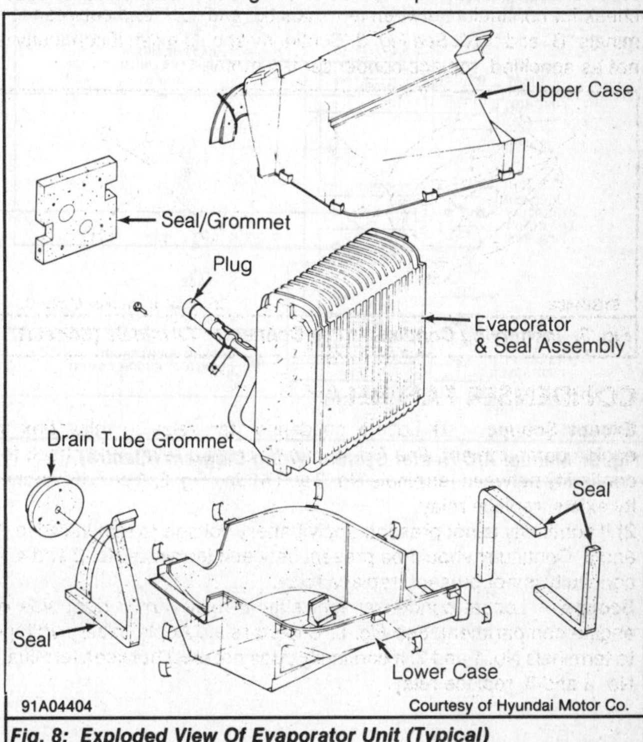
Upper Case
Seal/Grommet
Plug
Evaporator & Seal Assembly
Drain Tube Grommet
Seal
Seal
Lower Case
91A04404
Courtesy of Hyundai Motor Co.

Fig. 8: Exploded View Of Evaporator Unit (Typical)

1993 MANUAL A/C-HEATER SYSTEMS
Elantra, Excel, Scoupe & Sonata (Cont.)

4) To install, reverse removal procedure. If NEW evaporator is installed, add 3 ounces of refrigerant oil to Excel, Precis and Sonata, and 0.3 ounce to Elantra and Scoupe. Evacuate, recharge and test system.

RECEIVER-DRIER

***NOTE:** Receiver-drier should be replaced if it has been exposed to atmosphere for more than 24 hours.*

Removal & Installation – 1) Discharge A/C system using approved refrigerant recovery/recycling equipment. Disconnect refrigerant lines to both ends of receiver-drier. Plug or close open ends of refrigerant lines and inlet and outlet ports on receiver-drier.

2) Disconnect pressure switch connector. Remove bracket attaching screws and lift out assembly. Remove receiver-drier from bracket. On Scoupe, remove clutch cycling switch.

3) To install, reverse removal procedure. If NEW receiver-drier is used, add one ounce of refrigerant oil to Excel, Precis and Sonata, and 0.3 ounce to Elantra and Sonata. Evacuate, recharge and test system.

WIRING DIAGRAMS

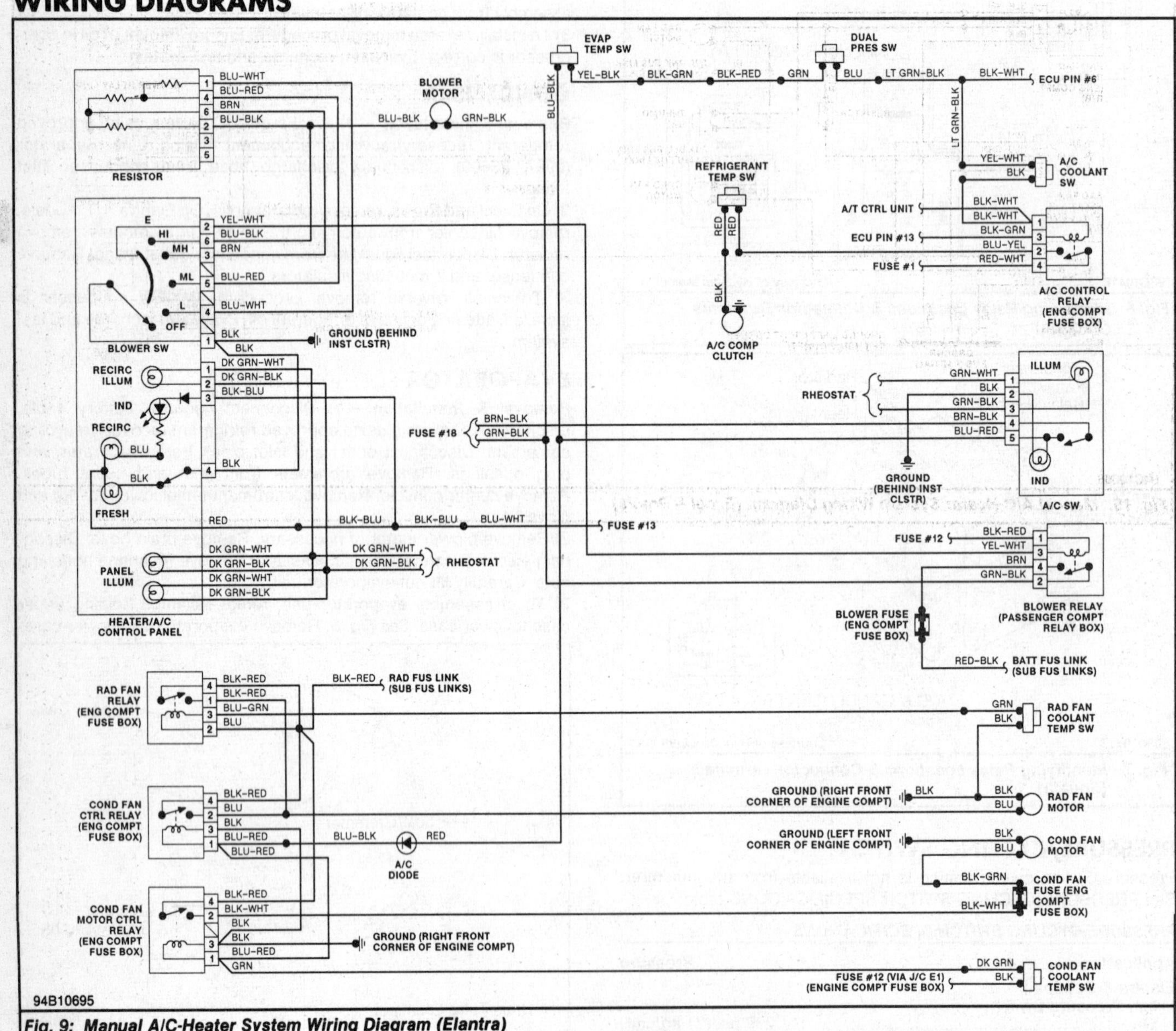
EVAP TEMP SW
DUAL PRES SW
ECU PIN #6
BLOWER MOTOR
RESISTOR
REFRIGERANT TEMP SW
A/C COOLANT SW
A/T CTRL UNIT
ECU PIN #13
FUSE #1
A/C CONTROL RELAY (ENG COMPT FUSE BOX)
BLOWER SW
GROUND (BEHIND INST CLSTR)
A/C COMP CLUTCH
RECIRC ILLUM
IND
RECIRC
FRESH
ILLUM
RHEOSTAT
FUSE #18
A/C SW
FUSE #13
FUSE #12
PANEL ILLUM
HEATER/A/C CONTROL PANEL
BLOWER RELAY (PASSENGER COMPT RELAY BOX)
BLOWER FUSE (ENG COMPT FUSE BOX)
BATT FUS LINK (SUB FUS LINKS)
RAD FAN RELAY (ENG COMPT FUSE BOX)
RAD FUS LINK (SUB FUS LINKS)
RAD FAN COOLANT TEMP SW
GROUND (RIGHT FRONT CORNER OF ENGINE COMPT)
RAD FAN MOTOR
COND FAN CTRL RELAY (ENG COMPT FUSE BOX)
A/C DIODE
GROUND (LEFT FRONT CORNER OF ENGINE COMPT)
COND FAN MOTOR
COND FAN FUSE (ENG COMPT FUSE BOX)
COND FAN MOTOR CTRL RELAY (ENG COMPT FUSE BOX)
GROUND (RIGHT FRONT CORNER OF ENGINE COMPT)
FUSE #12 (VIA J/C E1) (ENGINE COMPT FUSE BOX)
COND FAN COOLANT TEMP SW
94B10695

Fig. 9: Manual A/C-Heater System Wiring Diagram (Elantra)

1993 MANUAL A/C-HEATER SYSTEMS
Elantra, Excel, Scoupe & Sonata (Cont.)

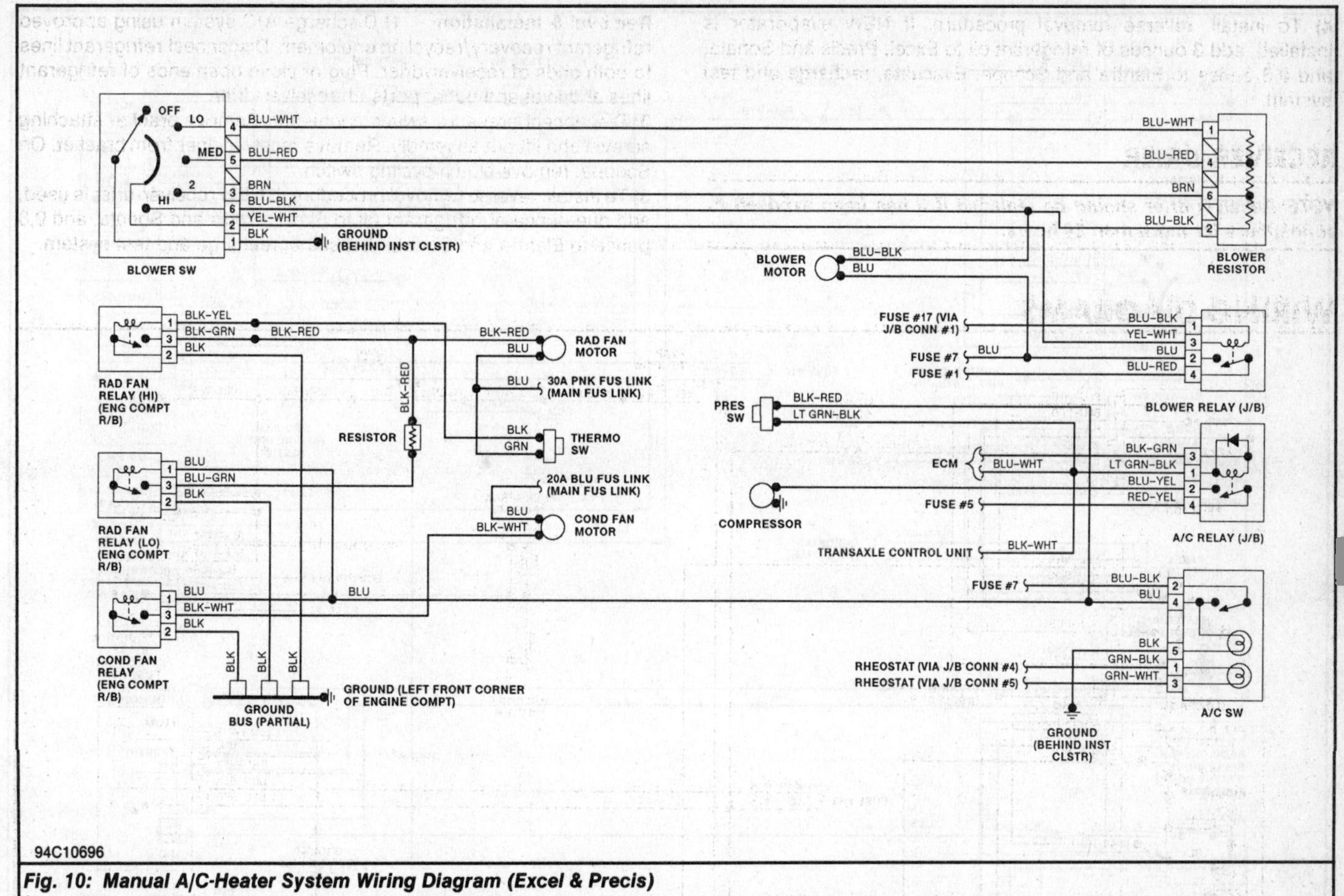
OFF
LO
MED
2
HI
BLU-WHT
BLU-RED
BRN
BLU-BLK
YEL-WHT
BLK
GROUND (BEHIND INST CLSTR)
BLOWER SW
BLOWER MOTOR
BLOWER RESISTOR
RAD FAN RELAY (HI) (ENG COMPT R/B)
BLK-YEL
BLK-GRN
BLK-RED
RAD FAN MOTOR
30A PNK FUS LINK (MAIN FUS LINK)
RESISTOR
THERMO SW
GRN
RAD FAN RELAY (LO) (ENG COMPT R/B)
BLU-GRN
20A BLU FUS LINK (MAIN FUS LINK)
BLK-WHT
COND FAN MOTOR
COND FAN RELAY (ENG COMPT R/B)
GROUND BUS (PARTIAL)
GROUND (LEFT FRONT CORNER OF ENGINE COMPT)
FUSE #17 (VIA J/B CONN #1)
FUSE #7
FUSE #1
BLOWER RELAY (J/B)
PRES SW
LT GRN-BLK
ECM
COMPRESSOR
FUSE #5
BLU-YEL
RED-YEL
A/C RELAY (J/B)
TRANSAXLE CONTROL UNIT
RHEOSTAT (VIA J/B CONN #4)
RHEOSTAT (VIA J/B CONN #5)
GRN-BLK
GRN-WHT
A/C SW
GROUND (BEHIND INST CLSTR)
94C10696

Fig. 10: Manual A/C-Heater System Wiring Diagram (Excel & Precis)

1993 MANUAL A/C-HEATER SYSTEMS
Elantra, Excel, Scoupe & Sonata (Cont.)

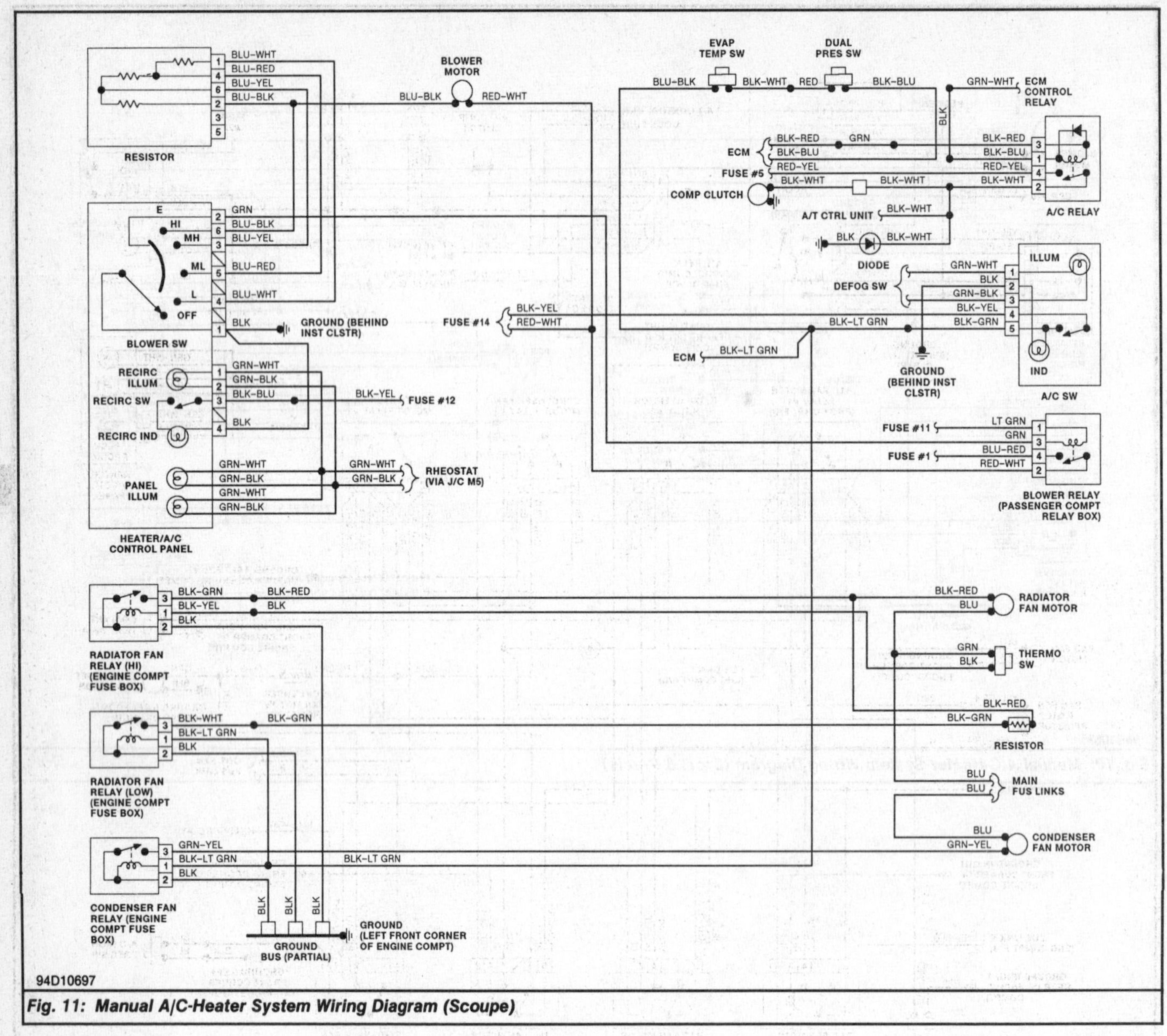
BLU-WHT
BLU-RED
BLU-YEL
BLU-BLK
RESISTOR
BLOWER MOTOR
BLU-BLK
RED-WHT
EVAP TEMP SW
DUAL PRES SW
BLU-BLK
BLK-WHT
RED
BLK-BLU
GRN-WHT
ECM CONTROL RELAY
BLK
BLK-RED
GRN
BLK-BLU
RED-YEL
BLK-WHT
ECM
FUSE #5
COMP CLUTCH
A/C RELAY
A/T CTRL UNIT
DIODE
DEFOG SW
GRN-WHT
GRN-BLK
BLK-YEL
BLK-GRN
ILLUM
IND
A/C SW
BLK-LT GRN
GROUND (BEHIND INST CLSTR)
E
HI
MH
ML
L
OFF
BLOWER SW
GROUND (BEHIND INST CLSTR)
FUSE #14
RED-WHT
ECM
RECIRC ILLUM
RECIRC SW
RECIRC IND
FUSE #12
PANEL ILLUM
RHEOSTAT (VIA J/C M5)
HEATER/A/C CONTROL PANEL
FUSE #11
FUSE #1
LT GRN
BLOWER RELAY (PASSENGER COMPT RELAY BOX)
RADIATOR FAN RELAY (HI) (ENGINE COMPT FUSE BOX)
RADIATOR FAN MOTOR
THERMO SW
RESISTOR
RADIATOR FAN RELAY (LOW) (ENGINE COMPT FUSE BOX)
MAIN FUS LINKS
CONDENSER FAN MOTOR
GRN-YEL
BLU
CONDENSER FAN RELAY (ENGINE COMPT FUSE BOX)
GROUND BUS (PARTIAL)
GROUND (LEFT FRONT CORNER OF ENGINE COMPT)
94D10697

Fig. 11: Manual A/C-Heater System Wiring Diagram (Scoupe)

1993 MANUAL A/C-HEATER SYSTEMS
Elantra, Excel, Scoupe & Sonata (Cont.)

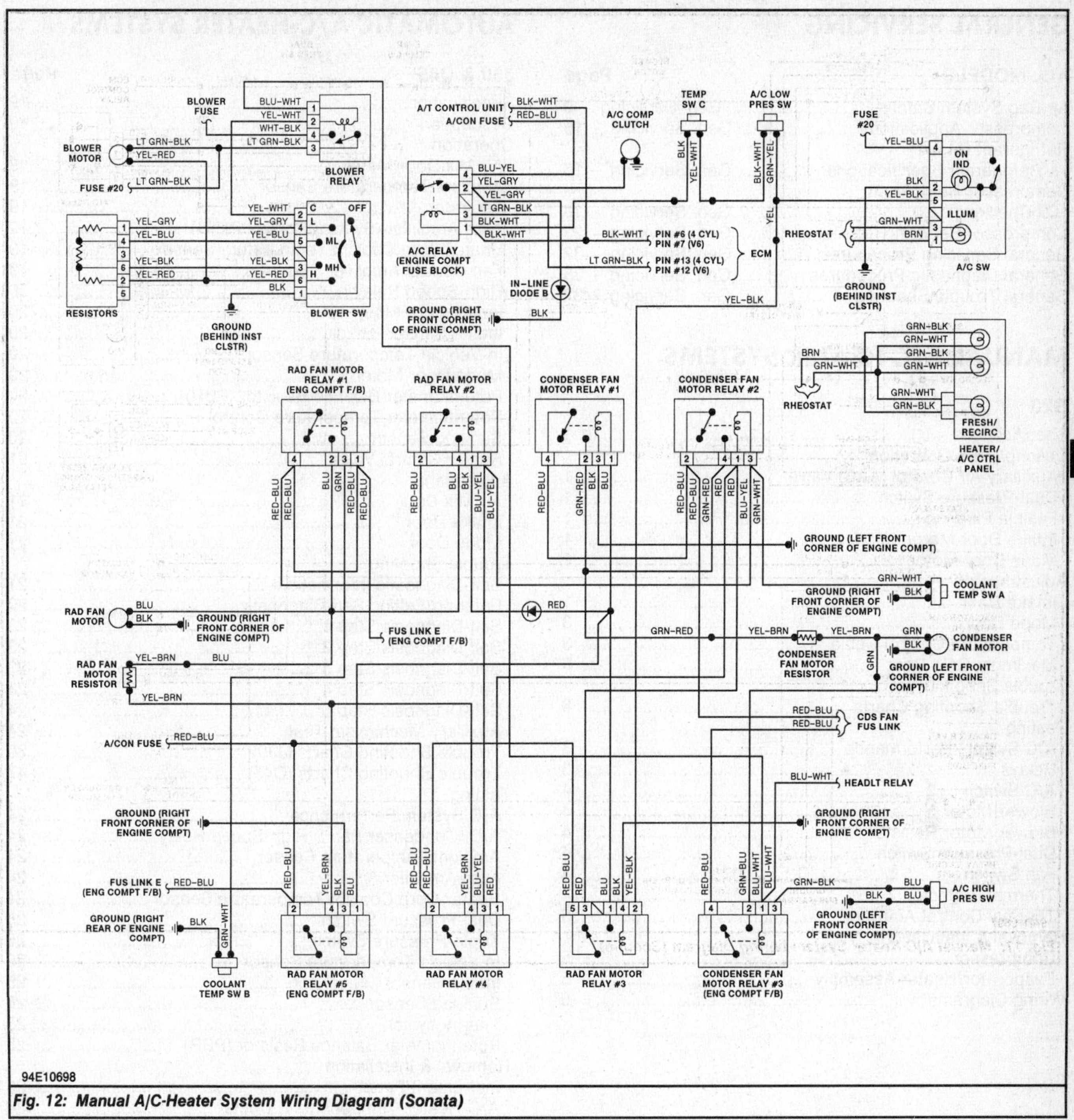
BLOWER FUSE
BLOWER MOTOR
FUSE #20
BLOWER RELAY
RESISTORS
GROUND (BEHIND INST CLSTR)
BLOWER SW
A/T CONTROL UNIT
A/CON FUSE
A/C RELAY (ENGINE COMPT FUSE BLOCK)
A/C COMP CLUTCH
TEMP SW C
A/C LOW PRES SW
IN-LINE DIODE B
GROUND (RIGHT FRONT CORNER OF ENGINE COMPT)
PIN #6 (4 CYL) PIN #7 (V6)
PIN #13 (4 CYL) PIN #12 (V6)
ECM
RHEOSTAT
GROUND (BEHIND INST CLSTR)
A/C SW
ON IND
ILLUM
FRESH/ RECIRC
HEATER/ A/C CTRL PANEL
RAD FAN MOTOR RELAY #1 (ENG COMPT F/B)
RAD FAN MOTOR RELAY #2
CONDENSER FAN MOTOR RELAY #1
CONDENSER FAN MOTOR RELAY #2
GROUND (LEFT FRONT CORNER OF ENGINE COMPT)
COOLANT TEMP SW A
RAD FAN MOTOR
RAD FAN MOTOR RESISTOR
FUS LINK E (ENG COMPT F/B)
CONDENSER FAN MOTOR RESISTOR
CONDENSER FAN MOTOR
CDS FAN FUS LINK
HEADLT RELAY
GROUND (RIGHT FRONT CORNER OF ENGINE COMPT)
GROUND (RIGHT REAR OF ENGINE COMPT)
COOLANT TEMP SW B
RAD FAN MOTOR RELAY #5 (ENG COMPT F/B)
RAD FAN MOTOR RELAY #4
RAD FAN MOTOR RELAY #3
CONDENSER FAN MOTOR RELAY #3 (ENG COMPT F/B)
A/C HIGH PRES SW
GROUND (LEFT FRONT CORNER OF ENGINE COMPT)
94E10698

Fig. 12: Manual A/C-Heater System Wiring Diagram (Sonata)

1993 INFINITI CONTENTS

GENERAL SERVICING

MANUAL A/C-HEATER SYSTEMS

AUTOMATIC A/C-HEATER SYSTEMS

1993 MANUAL A/C-HEATER SYSTEMS G20

SPECIFICATIONS

Compressor Type	Atsugi NVR 140S Rotary Vane
Compressor Belt Defection [1]	9/32-5/16" (7-8 mm)
Refrigerant (R-12) Capacity	24-29 ozs.
System Oil Capacity	6.8 ozs.
System Operating Pressures [2]	
High Side	162-210 psi (11.4-14.8 kg/cm²)
Low Side	14-26 psi (1.0-1.8 kg/cm²)

[1] – With 22 lbs. (10 kg) applied midway on longest belt run.
[2] – With ambient temperature of 86°F (30°C). Engine speed 1500 RPM. Let system operate for at least 10 minutes before checking.

WARNING: To avoid injury from accidental air bag deployment, read and carefully follow all SERVICE PRECAUTIONS and DISABLING & ACTIVATING AIR BAG SYSTEM procedures in AIR BAG SYSTEM SAFETY article in GENERAL SERVICING.

DESCRIPTION & OPERATION

A separate evaporator housing assembly is combined with a standard heater assembly to create an integrated A/C-heating unit. Evaporator is in the center with blower motor directing airflow through evaporator and then through the heater.

Push button control panel (auto amplifier) operates the mode door motors to position doors according to selection. *See Fig. 1*. Temperature control lever controls temperature level. A dial switch controls fan speed. The A/C button controls air conditioner operation. Pressing the air recirculation button will stop fresh air intake and recirculate inside air.

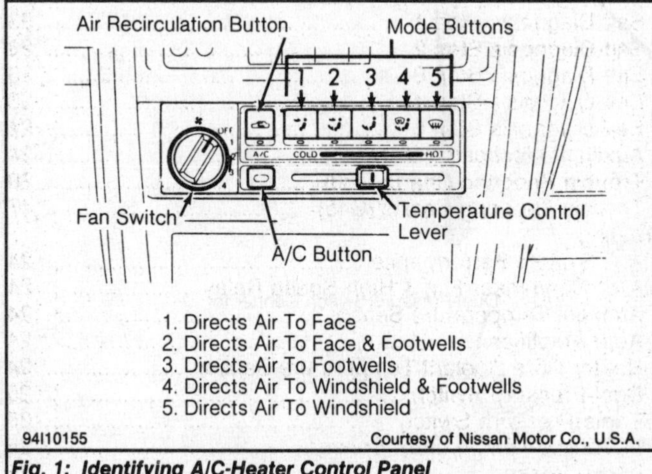
Air Recirculation Button
Mode Buttons
1 2 3 4 5
OFF
A/C
COLD
HOT
Fan Switch
Temperature Control Lever
A/C Button
1. Directs Air To Face
2. Directs Air To Face & Footwells
3. Directs Air To Footwells
4. Directs Air To Windshield & Footwells
5. Directs Air To Windshield
94I10155
Courtesy of Nissan Motor Co., U.S.A.

Fig. 1: Identifying A/C-Heater Control Panel

AUXILIARY AIR CONTROL (AAC) VALVE

When A/C system is operating, vacuum flows through AAC valve (located on right rear of engine compartment) and engine idle speed is increased. Additional air results in higher engine idle. This higher idle speed allows engine to idle smoothly during compressor operation.

DUAL-PRESSURE SWITCH

The dual-pressure switch is mounted on receiver-drier to protect A/C system from high pressure build-up (due to restriction, overcharge or compressor malfunction). *See Fig. 3*. If excessively low or high pressure is sensed within system, dual-pressure switch electrically stops compressor clutch operation.

FUSIBLE PLUG

Fusible plug, mounted on receiver-drier, is a high temperature relief. When temperature of 221°F (105°C) is sensed, plug melts to vent refrigerant to atmosphere, thereby protecting the system.

INTAKE DOOR MOTOR

The intake door motor, attached to heater unit, rotates so air is drawn from inlets set by push button control panel. Motor rotation is transferred to a lever which moves intake door.

MODE DOOR MOTOR

The mode door motor, attached to heater unit, rotates so air is discharged from outlet(s) set by push button control panel. Motor rotation is transferred to a link which moves mode door.

ADJUSTMENTS

INTAKE DOOR

1) Turn ignition switch to ACC position. Ensure air recirculation button is off. Install intake door motor on intake unit (connect harness before installing motor). Install intake door lever.

2) Set intake door rod in fresh position, and secure door rod to holder on intake door lever. *See Fig. 2*. Ensure intake door operates properly when air recirculation button is pressed on and off.

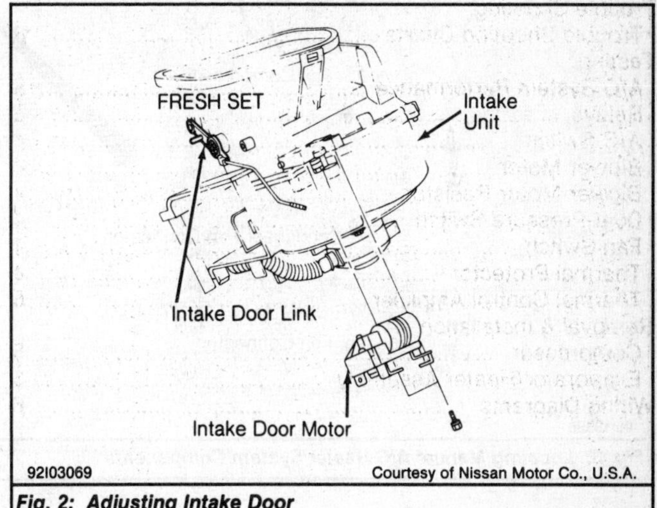
FRESH SET
Intake Unit
Intake Door Link
Intake Door Motor
92I03069
Courtesy of Nissan Motor Co., U.S.A.

Fig. 2: Adjusting Intake Door

1993 MANUAL A/C-HEATER SYSTEMS
G20 (Cont.)

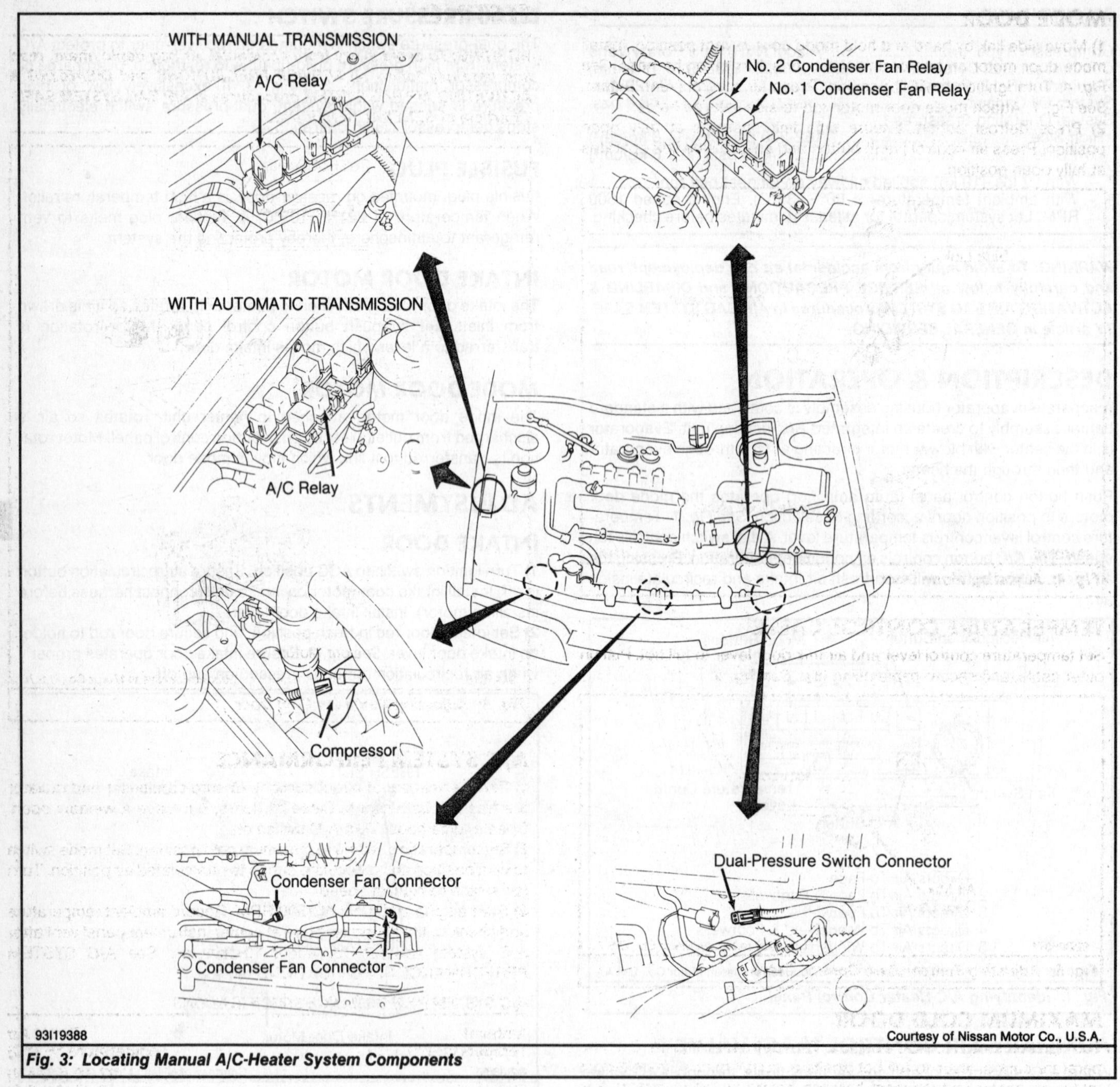
WITH MANUAL TRANSMISSION
A/C Relay
WITH AUTOMATIC TRANSMISSION
A/C Relay
Compressor
Condenser Fan Connector
Condenser Fan Connector
No. 2 Condenser Fan Relay
No. 1 Condenser Fan Relay
Dual-Pressure Switch Connector
93I19388
Courtesy of Nissan Motor Co., U.S.A.

Fig. 3: Locating Manual A/C-Heater System Components

MODE DOOR

1) Move side link by hand and hold mode door in vent position. Install mode door motor on heater unit and connect to wiring harness. *See Fig. 4*. Turn ignition to ACC position. Press air control (vent) button. *See Fig. 1*. Attach mode door motor rod to side link rod holder.
2) Press defrost button. Ensure side link operates at fully open position. Press air control (vent) button and ensure side link operates at fully open position.

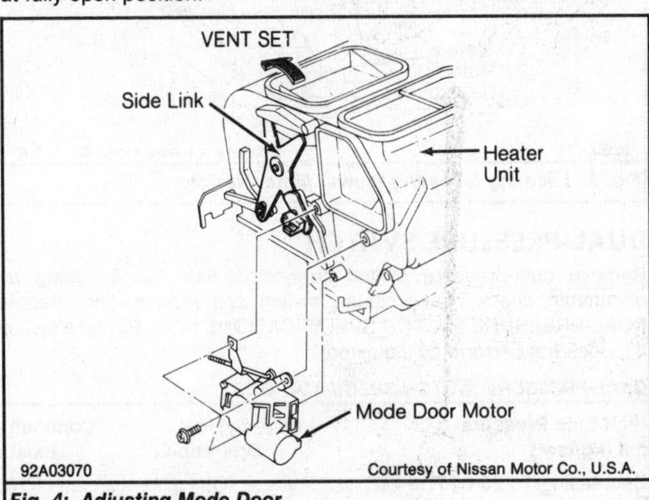
VENT SET
Side Link
Heater Unit
Mode Door Motor
92A03070
Courtesy of Nissan Motor Co., U.S.A.

Fig. 4: Adjusting Mode Door

TEMPERATURE CONTROL CABLE

Set temperature control lever and air mix door lever to full hot. Pull on outer cable, and secure cable using clip. *See Fig. 5*.

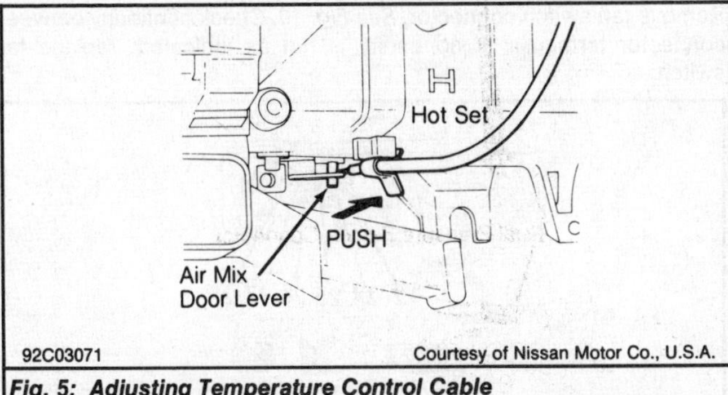
Hot Set
PUSH
Air Mix Door Lever
92C03071
Courtesy of Nissan Motor Co., U.S.A.

Fig. 5: Adjusting Temperature Control Cable

MAXIMUM COLD DOOR

Turn ignition switch to ACC position. Turn defrost switch on. Set temperature control lever to full hot position. Install maximum cold door motor on heater unit (connect harness before installing motor). *See Fig. 6*. Attach maximum cold door lever to rod holder. Check that maximum cold door operates properly when mode switch is turned to vent and defrost position.

TROUBLE SHOOTING

NOTE: See TROUBLE SHOOTING – G20 charts following this article.

TESTING

WARNING: To avoid injury from accidental air bag deployment, read and carefully follow all SERVICE PRECAUTIONS and DISABLING & ACTIVATING AIR BAG SYSTEM procedures in AIR BAG SYSTEM SAFETY article in GENERAL SERVICING.

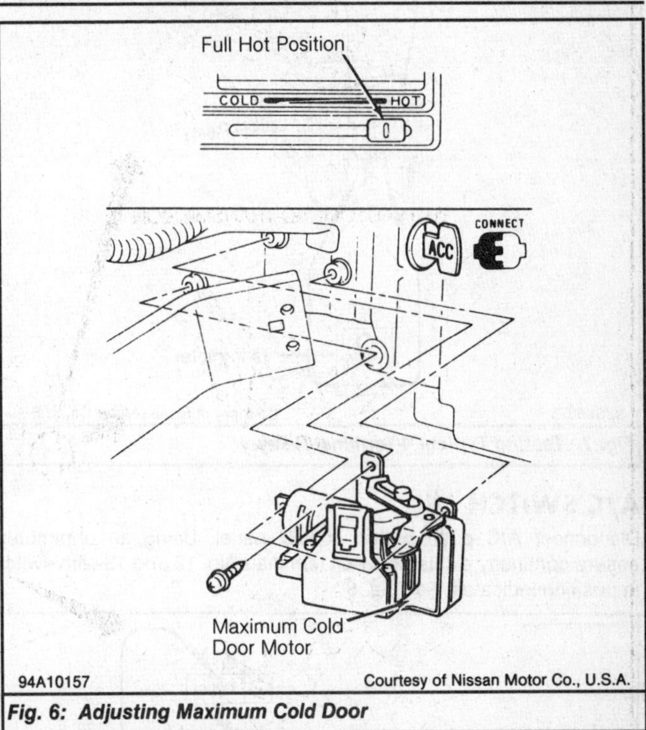
Full Hot Position
COLD
HOT
CONNECT
ACC
Maximum Cold Door Motor
94A10157
Courtesy of Nissan Motor Co., U.S.A.

Fig. 6: Adjusting Maximum Cold Door

A/C SYSTEM PERFORMANCE

1) Park vehicle out of direct sunlight. Ensure condenser and radiator are free of obstructions. Close all doors, but leave a window open. Open engine hood. Turn A/C switch on.
2) Set temperature setting to maximum cold position. Set mode switch to vent position and recirculate button to recirculated air position. Turn fan switch to highest speed.
3) Start engine and run it at 1500 RPM. Record ambient temperature and check outlet air temperature at center instrument panel vent after A/C system has run for about 10 minutes. See A/C SYSTEM PERFORMANCE SPECIFICATIONS table.

A/C SYSTEM PERFORMANCE SPECIFICATIONS [1]

Ambient Temperature °F (°C)	Outlet Air Temperature °F (°C)
68 (20)	37-40 (2.8-4.4)
77 (25)	43-48 (6.1-9.0)
86 (30)	51-57 (10.6-14.0)
95 (35)	62-69 (16.7-20.6)
104 (40)	73-82 (22.7-27.8)

[1] – Based on a relative humidity of 40-60 percent.

RELAYS

Remove appropriate relay from vehicle. *See Fig. 3*. Apply 12 volts to coil side of relay. *See Fig. 7*. Check for continuity between remaining terminals of relay. If no continuity exists, replace relay.

1993 MANUAL A/C-HEATER SYSTEMS G20 (Cont.)

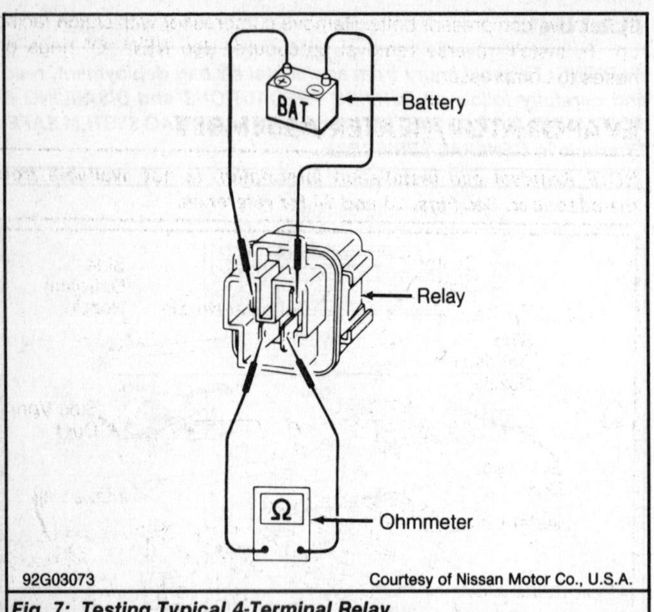
BAT
Battery
Relay
Ω
Ohmmeter
92G03073
Courtesy of Nissan Motor Co., U.S.A.

Fig. 7: Testing Typical 4-Terminal Relay

A/C SWITCH

Disconnect A/C push button control panel. Using an ohmmeter, ensure continuity exists between terminals No. 12 and 13 with switch in position indicated. *See Fig. 8.*

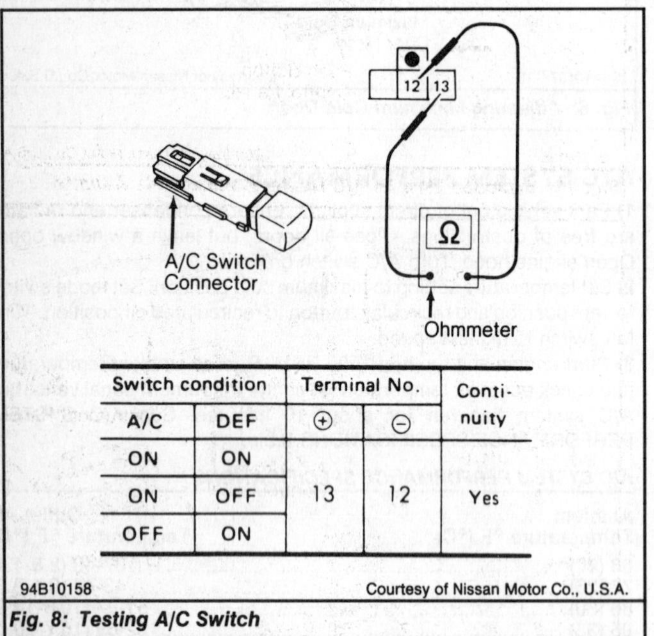
12 13
A/C Switch Connector
Ω
Ohmmeter
94B10158
Courtesy of Nissan Motor Co., U.S.A.

Switch condition		Terminal No.		Continuity
A/C	DEF	⊕	⊖	
ON	ON			
ON	OFF	13	12	Yes
OFF	ON			

Fig. 8: Testing A/C Switch

BLOWER MOTOR

Disconnect wiring harness at blower motor. Apply battery voltage to blower motor terminals. Ensure blower motor operation is smooth. If blower motor operation is rough or not up to speed, replace blower motor.

BLOWER MOTOR RESISTOR

Disconnect blower motor resistor connector. *See Fig. 9.* Using an ohmmeter, check for continuity between resistor terminals. If continuity does not exist, replace blower motor resistor.

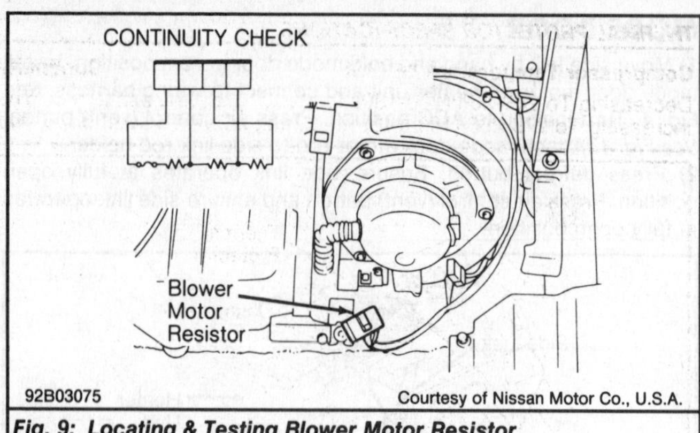
CONTINUITY CHECK
Blower Motor Resistor
92B03075
Courtesy of Nissan Motor Co., U.S.A.

Fig. 9: Locating & Testing Blower Motor Resistor

DUAL-PRESSURE SWITCH

Remove dual-pressure switch connector. *See Fig. 3.* Using an ohmmeter, check dual-pressure switch operation as indicated in DUAL-PRESSURE SWITCH SPECIFICATIONS table. Replace switch if it does not perform as indicated.

DUAL-PRESSURE SWITCH SPECIFICATIONS

High Side Pressure psi (kg/cm²)	System Operation	Continuity Exists
Decreasing To 26-31 (1.8-2.2)	Off	No
Increasing To 356-412 (25-29)	Off	No
Increasing To 26-34 (1.8-2.4)	On	Yes
Decreasing To 270-341 (19-24)	On	Yes

FAN SWITCH

Remove fan switch connector. *See Fig. 10.* Check continuity between connector terminals. If continuity is not as indicated, replace fan switch.

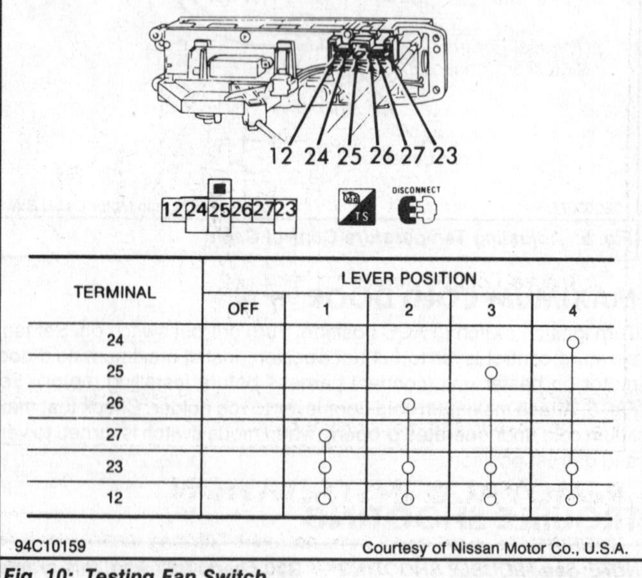
12 24 25 26 27 23
12 24 25 26 27 23
TS
DISCONNECT
94C10159
Courtesy of Nissan Motor Co., U.S.A.

TERMINAL	LEVER POSITION				
	OFF	1	2	3	4
24					O
25				O	
26			O		
27		O			
23		O	O	O	O
12		O	O	O	O

Fig. 10: Testing Fan Switch

THERMAL PROTECTOR

Remove thermal protector connector. *See Fig. 11.* Using an ohmmeter, check for continuity as indicated in THERMAL PROTECTOR SPECIFICATIONS table. Replace thermal protector if it does not perform as indicated.

THERMAL PROTECTOR SPECIFICATIONS

Compressor Temperature °F (°C)	Continuity
Decreasing To 248-266 (120-130)	Yes
Increasing To 275-293 (135-145)	No

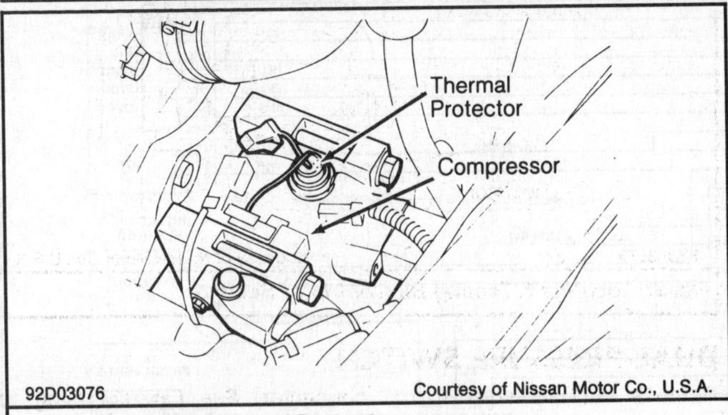
Thermal
Protector
Compressor
92D03076
Courtesy of Nissan Motor Co., U.S.A.

Fig. 11: Locating Thermal Protector

THERMAL CONTROL AMPLIFIER

With engine running, operate A/C system. Using a DVOM, measure voltage between terminal No. 59 of thermal control amplifier connector and ground. *See Fig. 12*. Check thermal control amplifier operation as indicated in THERMAL CONTROL AMPLIFIER SPECIFICATIONS table. Replace amplifier if it does not perform as indicated.

THERMAL CONTROL AMPLIFIER SPECIFICATIONS

Evaporator Outlet Air Temperature °F (°C)	Thermo Amplifier Operation	Measured Voltage
Decreasing To 37-38 (2.5-3.5)	Off	12
Increasing To 39-41 (4-5)	On	0

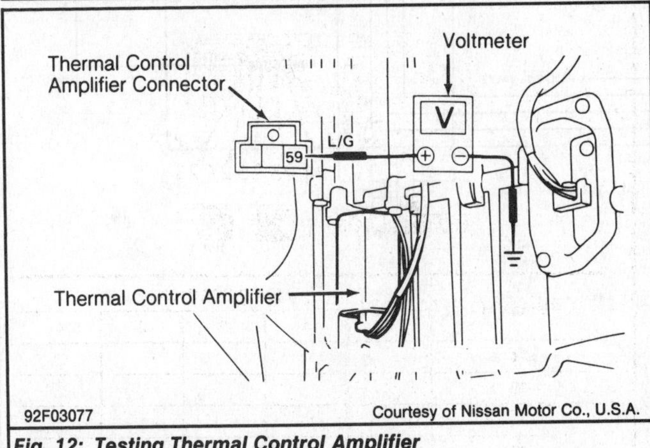
Voltmeter
Thermal Control
Amplifier Connector
V
L/G
59
Thermal Control Amplifier
92F03077
Courtesy of Nissan Motor Co., U.S.A.

Fig. 12: Testing Thermal Control Amplifier

REMOVAL & INSTALLATION

WARNING: To avoid injury from accidental air bag deployment, read and carefully follow all SERVICE PRECAUTIONS and DISABLING & ACTIVATING AIR BAG SYSTEM procedures in AIR BAG SYSTEM SAFETY article in GENERAL SERVICING.

COMPRESSOR

Removal & Installation – 1) If possible, operate compressor while engine idles for at least 10-15 minutes to stabilize system and allow oil to return to compressor. Turn A/C system off, and turn ignition off. Loosen idler pulley bolt, and remove compressor belt.

2) Discharge A/C system using approved refrigerant recovery/recycling equipment. Disconnect compressor clutch lead. Disconnect discharge and suction hoses from compressor and plug openings.

3) Remove compressor bolts. Remove compressor with clutch facing up. To install, reverse removal procedure. Use NEW "O" rings on hoses to compressor.

EVAPORATOR/HEATER ASSEMBLY

NOTE: Removal and installation information is not available from manufacturer. See Figs. 13 and 14 for reference.

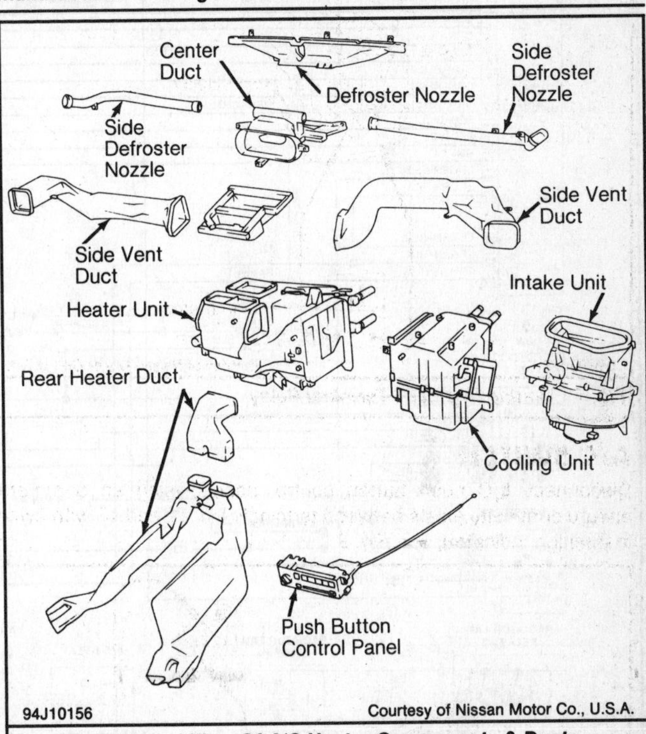
Center
Duct
Defroster Nozzle
Side
Defroster
Nozzle
Side
Defroster
Nozzle
Side Vent
Duct
Side Vent
Duct
Intake Unit
Heater Unit
Rear Heater Duct
Cooling Unit
Push Button
Control Panel
94J10156
Courtesy of Nissan Motor Co., U.S.A.

Fig. 13: Exploded View Of A/C-Heater Components & Ducts

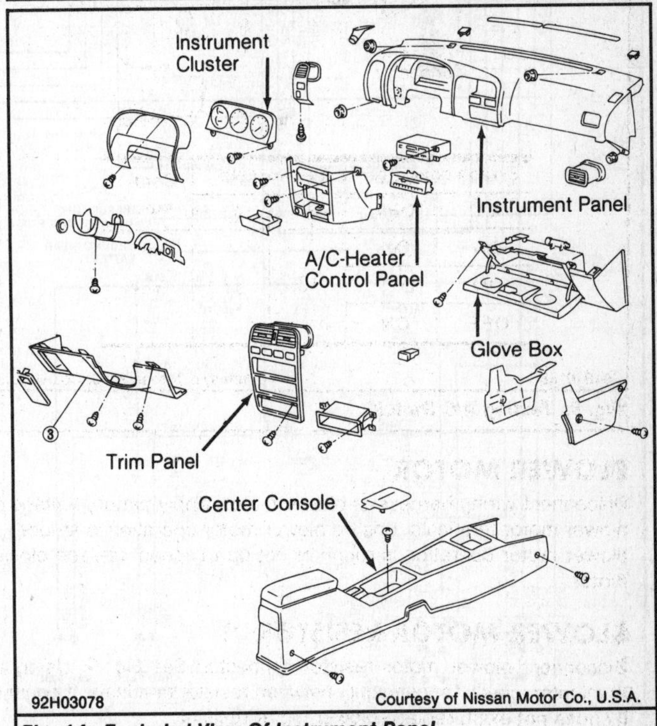
Instrument
Cluster
Instrument Panel
A/C-Heater
Control Panel
Glove Box
Trim Panel
Center Console
92H03078
Courtesy of Nissan Motor Co., U.S.A.

Fig. 14: Exploded View Of Instrument Panel

1993 MANUAL A/C-HEATER SYSTEMS G20 (Cont.)

WIRING DIAGRAMS

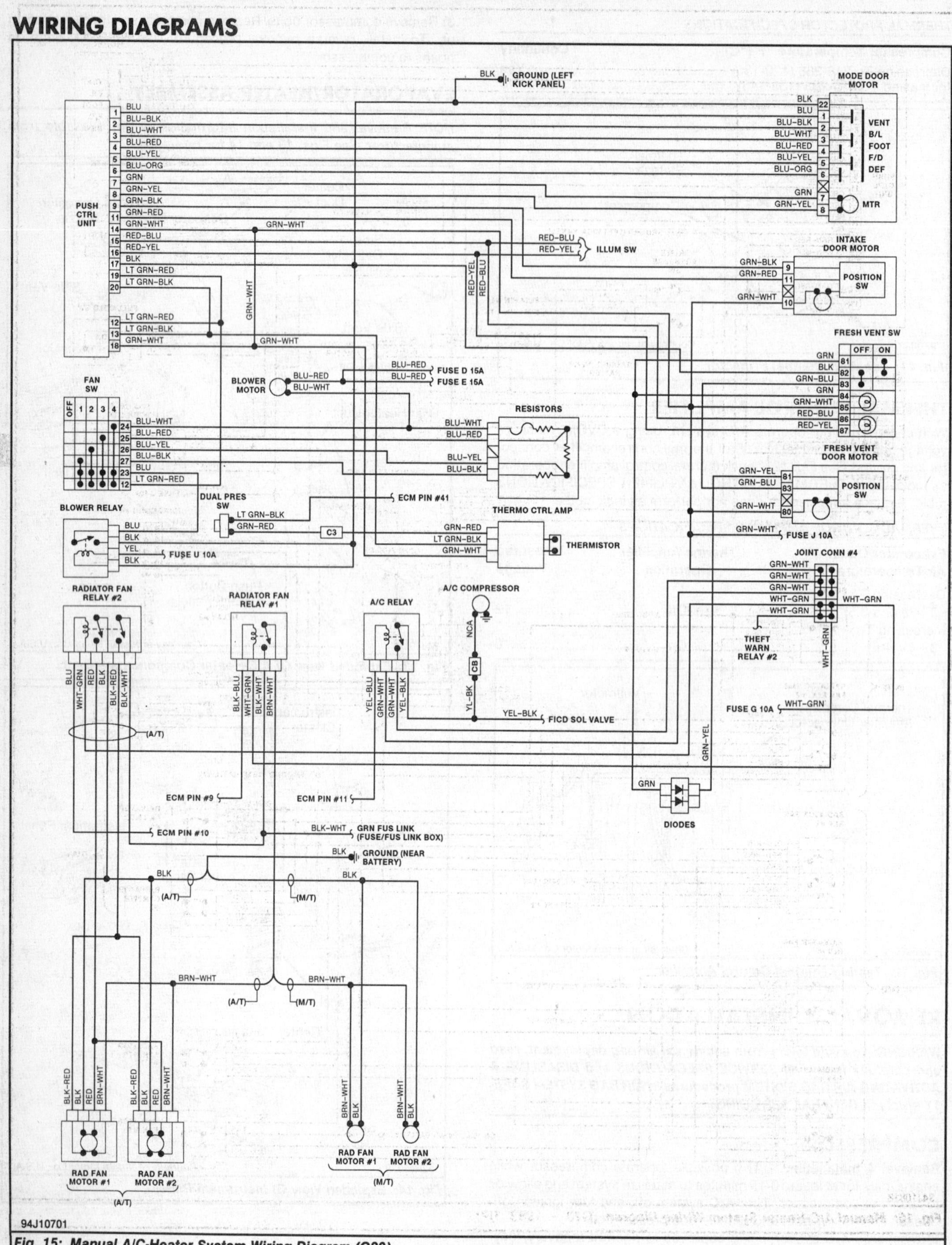
GROUND (LEFT KICK PANEL)
MODE DOOR MOTOR
VENT
B/L
FOOT
F/D
DEF
MTR
PUSH CTRL UNIT
ILLUM SW
INTAKE DOOR MOTOR
POSITION SW
FRESH VENT SW
OFF
ON
FAN SW
BLOWER MOTOR
FUSE D 15A
FUSE E 15A
RESISTORS
FRESH VENT DOOR MOTOR
ECM PIN #41
BLOWER RELAY
DUAL PRES SW
C3
THERMO CTRL AMP
THERMISTOR
FUSE U 10A
FUSE J 10A
JOINT CONN #4
RADIATOR FAN RELAY #2
RADIATOR FAN RELAY #1
A/C RELAY
A/C COMPRESSOR
THEFT WARN RELAY #2
FICD SOL VALVE
FUSE G 10A
(A/T)
ECM PIN #9
ECM PIN #11
DIODES
ECM PIN #10
GRN FUS LINK (FUSE/FUS LINK BOX)
GROUND (NEAR BATTERY)
(M/T)
RAD FAN MOTOR #1
RAD FAN MOTOR #2
94J10701

Fig. 15: Manual A/C-Heater System Wiring Diagram (G20)

1993 MANUAL A/C-HEATER SYSTEMS
G20 (Cont.)

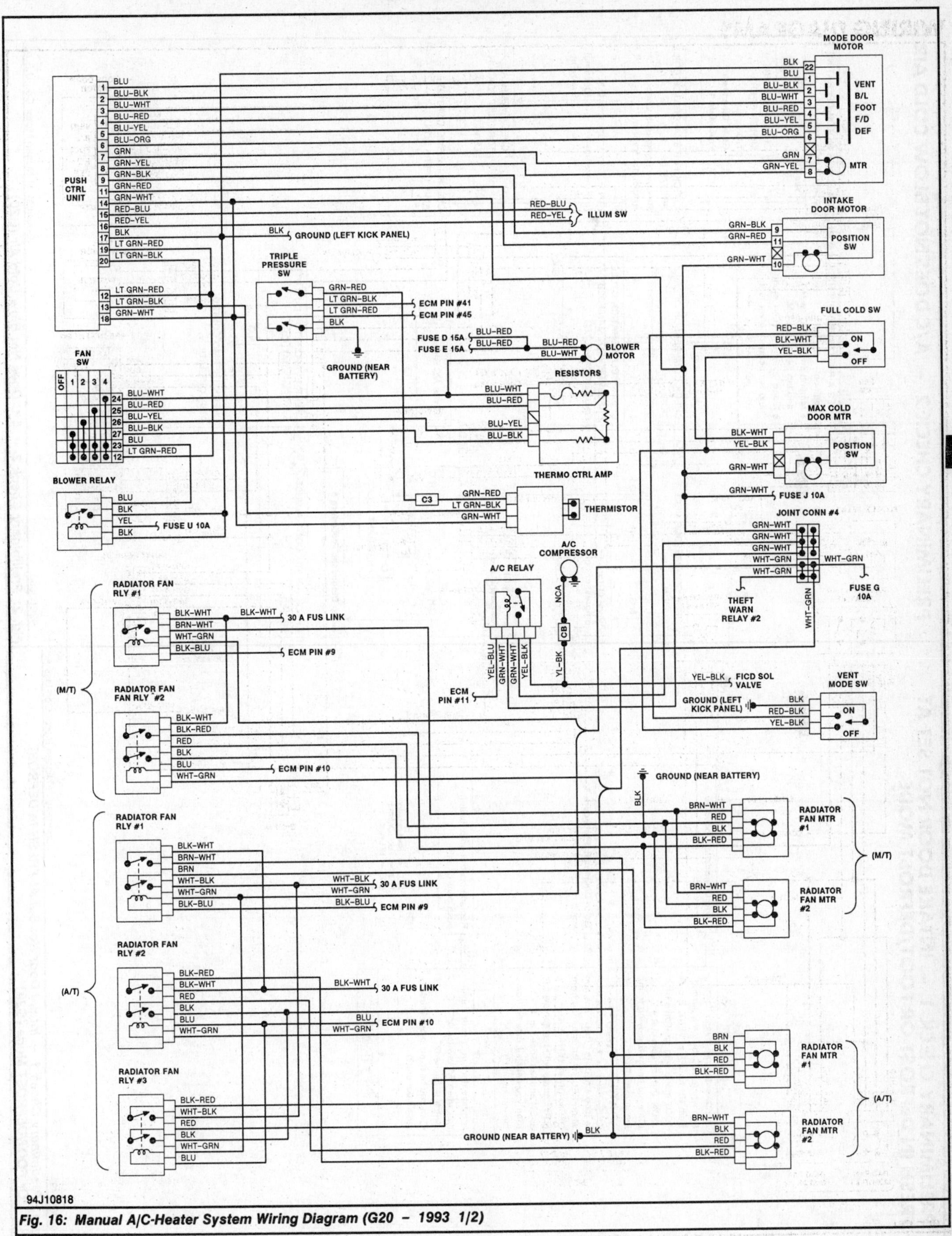
MODE DOOR MOTOR
VENT
B/L
FOOT
F/D
DEF
MTR
PUSH CTRL UNIT
ILLUM SW
GROUND (LEFT KICK PANEL)
INTAKE DOOR MOTOR
POSITION SW
TRIPLE PRESSURE SW
ECM PIN #41
ECM PIN #45
GROUND (NEAR BATTERY)
FUSE D 15A
FUSE E 15A
BLOWER MOTOR
FULL COLD SW
ON
OFF
FAN SW
RESISTORS
MAX COLD DOOR MTR
POSITION SW
THERMO CTRL AMP
FUSE J 10A
BLOWER RELAY
THERMISTOR
FUSE U 10A
JOINT CONN #4
A/C COMPRESSOR
A/C RELAY
FUSE G 10A
THEFT WARN RELAY #2
RADIATOR FAN RLY #1
30 A FUS LINK
ECM PIN #9
FICD SOL VALVE
ECM PIN #11
VENT MODE SW
(M/T)
RADIATOR FAN FAN RLY #2
GROUND (LEFT KICK PANEL)
ECM PIN #10
GROUND (NEAR BATTERY)
RADIATOR FAN RLY #1
RADIATOR FAN MTR #1
(M/T)
RADIATOR FAN MTR #2
30 A FUS LINK
ECM PIN #9
RADIATOR FAN RLY #2
(A/T)
30 A FUS LINK
ECM PIN #10
RADIATOR FAN MTR #1
(A/T)
RADIATOR FAN RLY #3
GROUND (NEAR BATTERY)
RADIATOR FAN MTR #2
94J10818

Fig. 16: Manual A/C-Heater System Wiring Diagram (G20 – 1993 1/2)

1993 MANUAL A/C-HEATER SYSTEMS
Trouble Shooting – G20

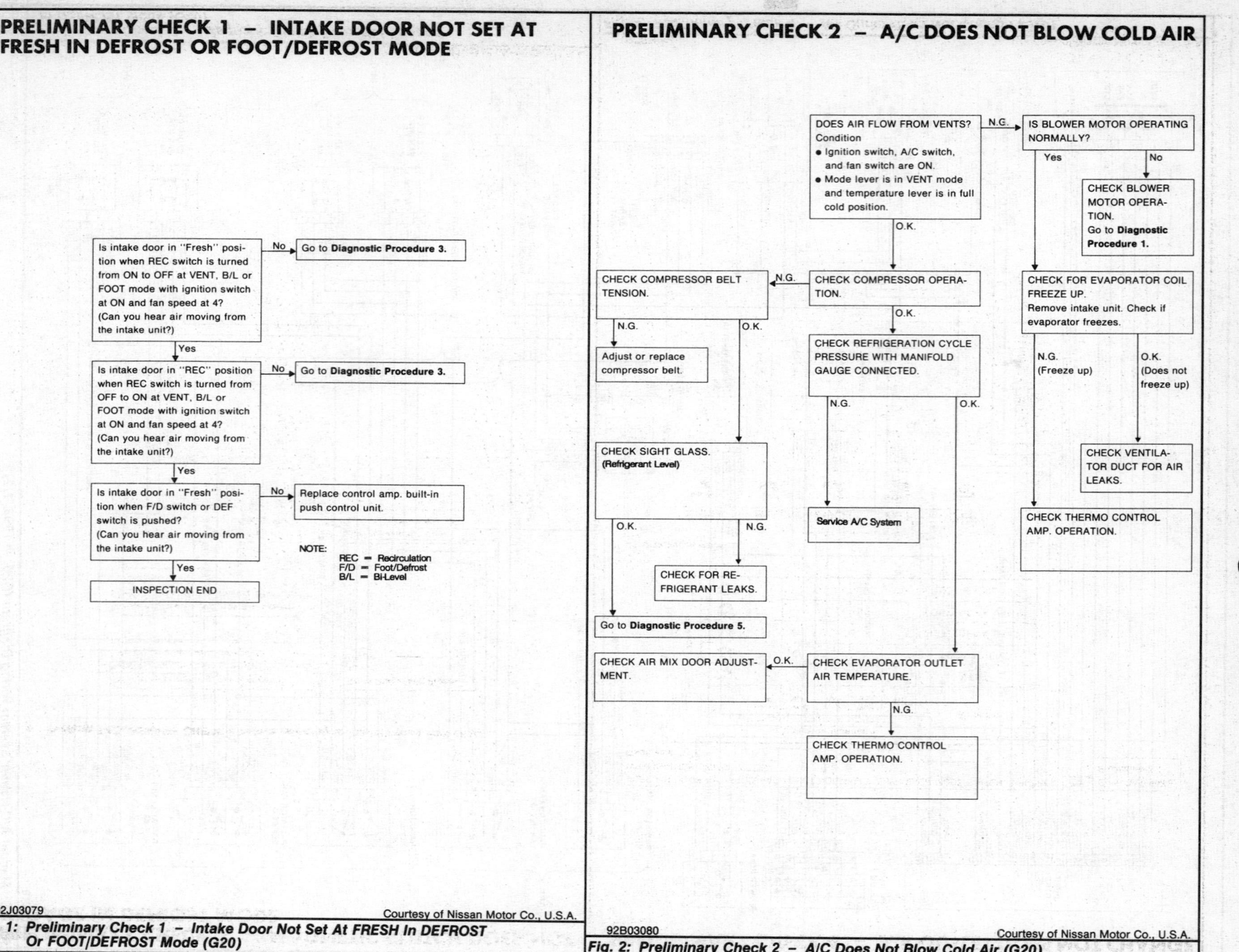
PRELIMINARY CHECK 1 – INTAKE DOOR NOT SET AT FRESH IN DEFROST OR FOOT/DEFROST MODE
Is intake door in "Fresh" position when REC switch is turned from ON to OFF at VENT, B/L or FOOT mode with ignition switch at ON and fan speed at 4? (Can you hear air moving from the intake unit?)
No
Go to Diagnostic Procedure 3.
Yes
Is intake door in "REC" position when REC switch is turned from OFF to ON at VENT, B/L or FOOT mode with ignition switch at ON and fan speed at 4? (Can you hear air moving from the intake unit?)
No
Go to Diagnostic Procedure 3.
Yes
Is intake door in "Fresh" position when F/D switch or DEF switch is pushed? (Can you hear air moving from the intake unit?)
No
Replace control amp. built-in push control unit.
Yes
INSPECTION END
NOTE:
REC = Recirculation
F/D = Foot/Defrost
B/L = Bi-Level
92J03079
Courtesy of Nissan Motor Co., U.S.A.
PRELIMINARY CHECK 2 – A/C DOES NOT BLOW COLD AIR
DOES AIR FLOW FROM VENTS? Condition
• Ignition switch, A/C switch, and fan switch are ON.
• Mode lever is in VENT mode and temperature lever is in full cold position.
N.G.
IS BLOWER MOTOR OPERATING NORMALLY?
Yes
No
CHECK BLOWER MOTOR OPERATION. Go to Diagnostic Procedure 1.
O.K.
CHECK COMPRESSOR OPERATION.
N.G.
CHECK COMPRESSOR BELT TENSION.
N.G.
Adjust or replace compressor belt.
O.K.
CHECK SIGHT GLASS. (Refrigerant Level)
O.K.
N.G.
CHECK FOR REFRIGERANT LEAKS.
Go to Diagnostic Procedure 5.
CHECK REFRIGERATION CYCLE PRESSURE WITH MANIFOLD GAUGE CONNECTED.
N.G.
Service A/C System
O.K.
CHECK EVAPORATOR OUTLET AIR TEMPERATURE.
O.K.
CHECK AIR MIX DOOR ADJUSTMENT.
N.G.
CHECK THERMO CONTROL AMP. OPERATION.
CHECK FOR EVAPORATOR COIL FREEZE UP. Remove intake unit. Check if evaporator freezes.
N.G. (Freeze up)
O.K. (Does not freeze up)
CHECK VENTILATOR DUCT FOR AIR LEAKS.
CHECK THERMO CONTROL AMP. OPERATION.
92B03080
Courtesy of Nissan Motor Co., U.S.A.

Fig. 1: Preliminary Check 1 – Intake Door Not Set At FRESH In DEFROST Or FOOT/DEFROST Mode (G20)

Fig. 2: Preliminary Check 2 – A/C Does Not Blow Cold Air (G20)

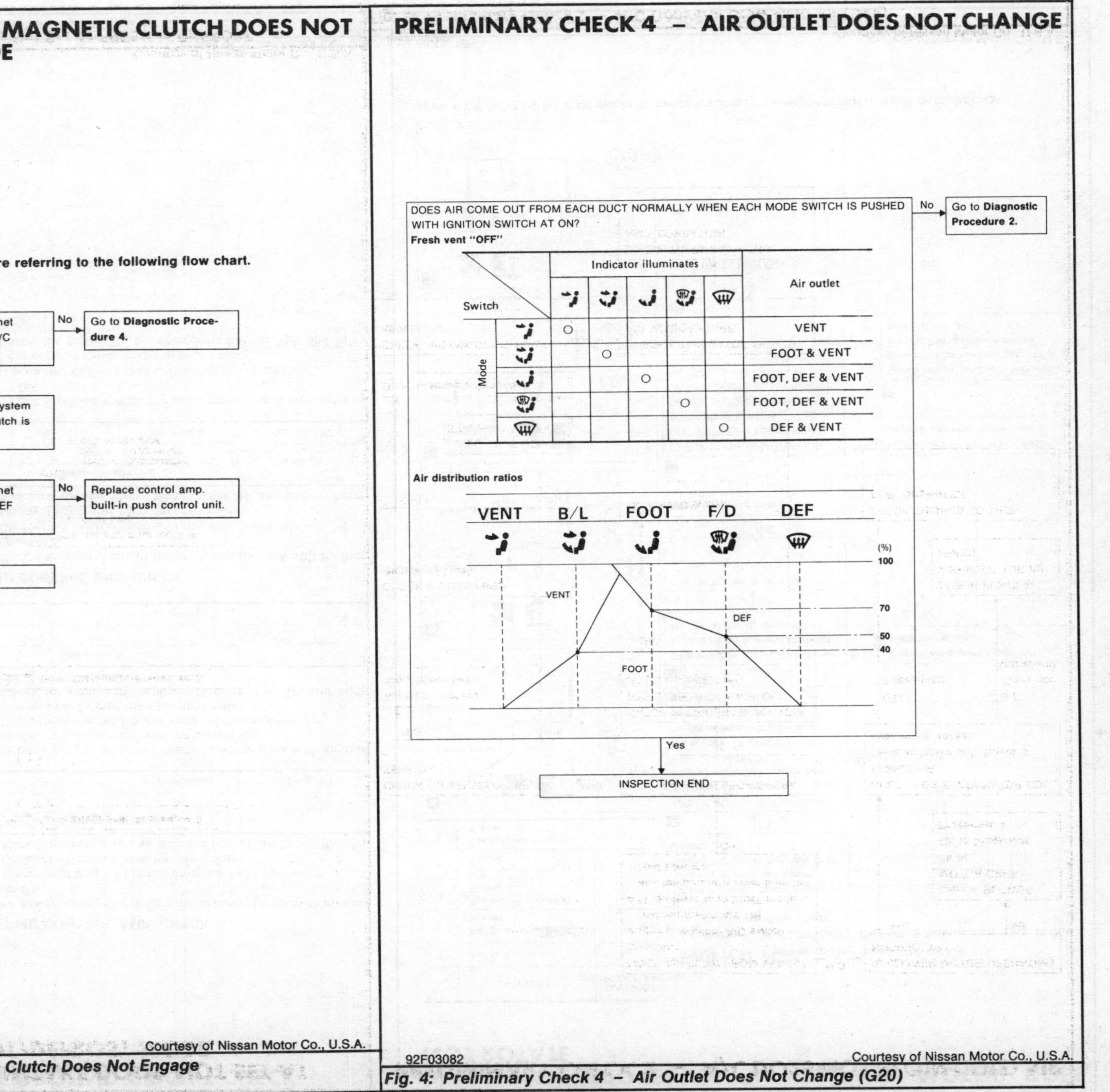

PRELIMINARY CHECK 3 – MAGNETIC CLUTCH DOES NOT ENGAGE IN DEFROST MODE
• Perform PRELIMINARY CHECK 2 before referring to the following flow chart.
With engine running, does magnet clutch engage normally when A/C switch and fan switch are ON?
No
Go to Diagnostic Procedure 4.
Yes
Push A/C switch and turn A/C system OFF. Make sure that magnet clutch is disengaged.
With engine running, does magnet clutch engage normally when DEF switch and fan switch are ON?
No
Replace control amp. built-in push control unit.
Yes
INSPECTION END
94J10164
Courtesy of Nissan Motor Co., U.S.A.
PRELIMINARY CHECK 4 – AIR OUTLET DOES NOT CHANGE
DOES AIR COME OUT FROM EACH DUCT NORMALLY WHEN EACH MODE SWITCH IS PUSHED WITH IGNITION SWITCH AT ON?
Fresh vent "OFF"
No
Go to Diagnostic Procedure 2.
Switch
Mode
Indicator illuminates
Air outlet
VENT
FOOT & VENT
FOOT, DEF & VENT
FOOT, DEF & VENT
DEF & VENT
Air distribution ratios
VENT
B/L
FOOT
F/D
DEF
(%)
100
70
50
40
VENT
FOOT
DEF
Yes
INSPECTION END
92F03082
Courtesy of Nissan Motor Co., U.S.A.

Fig. 3: Preliminary Check 3 – Magnetic Clutch Does Not Engage In DEFROST Mode (G20)

Fig. 4: Preliminary Check 4 – Air Outlet Does Not Change (G20)

1993 MANUAL A/C-HEATER SYSTEMS
Trouble Shooting – G20 (Cont.)

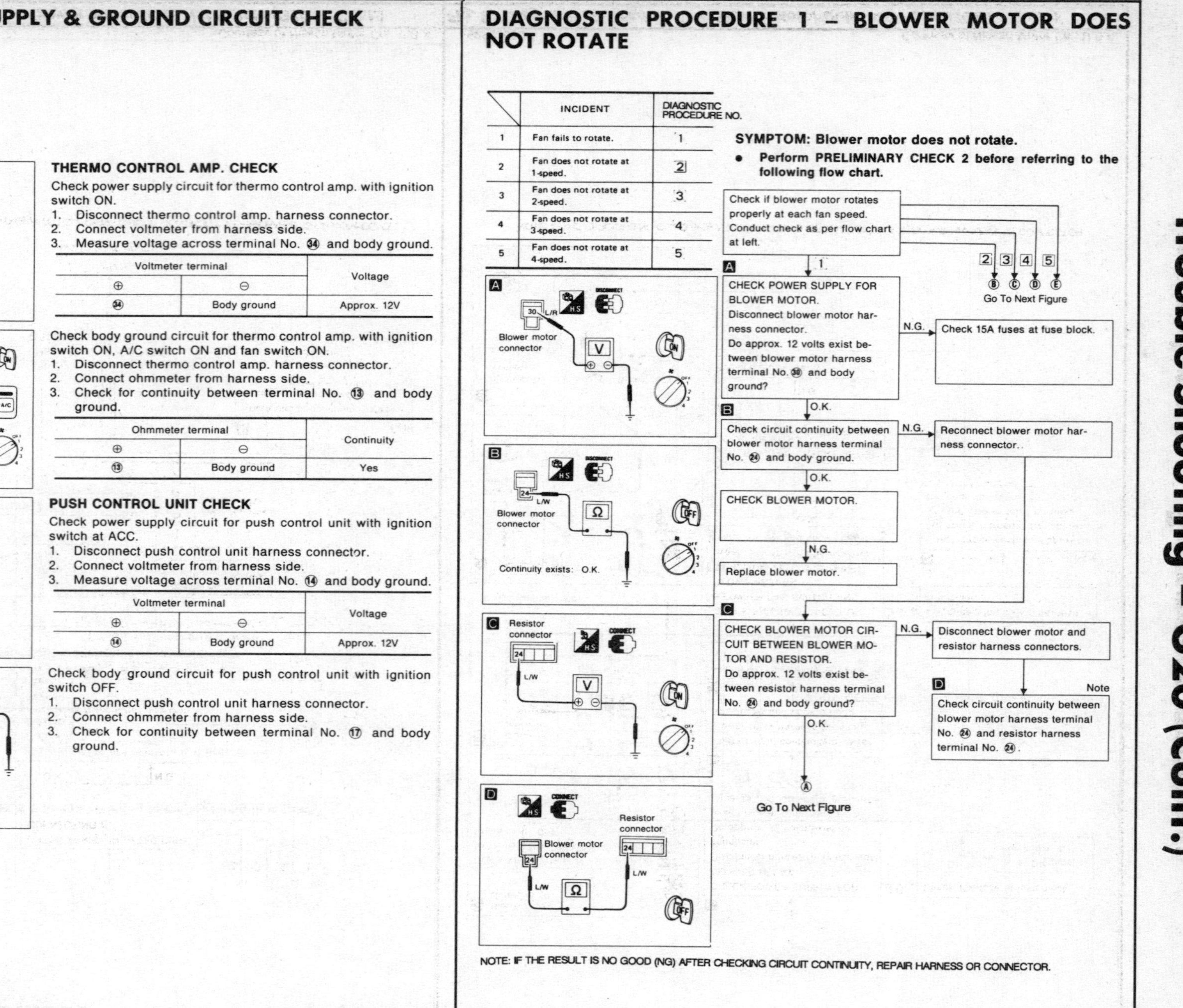

MAIN POWER SUPPLY & GROUND CIRCUIT CHECK

Thermo control amp. connector
34
G/W
V
Thermo control amp. connector
13
LG/B
Ω
Continuity exists: O.K.
Push control unit connector
14
G/W
V
Push control unit connector
17
B
Ω

THERMO CONTROL AMP. CHECK

Check power supply circuit for thermo control amp. with ignition switch ON.

1. Disconnect thermo control amp. harness connector.
2. Connect voltmeter from harness side.
3. Measure voltage across terminal No. ㉞ and body ground.

Voltmeter terminal		Voltage
⊕	⊖	
㉞	Body ground	Approx. 12V

Check body ground circuit for thermo control amp. with ignition switch ON, A/C switch ON and fan switch ON.

1. Disconnect thermo control amp. harness connector.
2. Connect ohmmeter from harness side.
3. Check for continuity between terminal No. ⑬ and body ground.

Ohmmeter terminal		Continuity
⊕	⊖	
⑬	Body ground	Yes

PUSH CONTROL UNIT CHECK

Check power supply circuit for push control unit with ignition switch at ACC.

1. Disconnect push control unit harness connector.
2. Connect voltmeter from harness side.
3. Measure voltage across terminal No. ⑭ and body ground.

Voltmeter terminal		Voltage
⊕	⊖	
⑭	Body ground	Approx. 12V

Check body ground circuit for push control unit with ignition switch OFF.

1. Disconnect push control unit harness connector.
2. Connect ohmmeter from harness side.
3. Check for continuity between terminal No. ⑰ and body ground.

92H03083 Courtesy of Nissan Motor Co., U.S.A.

Fig. 5: Main Power Supply & Ground Circuit Check (G20)

DIAGNOSTIC PROCEDURE 1 – BLOWER MOTOR DOES NOT ROTATE

	INCIDENT	DIAGNOSTIC PROCEDURE NO.
1	Fan fails to rotate.	1
2	Fan does not rotate at 1-speed.	2
3	Fan does not rotate at 2-speed.	3
4	Fan does not rotate at 3-speed.	4
5	Fan does not rotate at 4-speed.	5

SYMPTOM: Blower motor does not rotate.

- **Perform PRELIMINARY CHECK 2 before referring to the following flow chart.**

Check if blower motor rotates properly at each fan speed. Conduct check as per flow chart at left.
1
2 3 4 5
Ⓑ Ⓒ Ⓓ Ⓔ
Go To Next Figure
A
CHECK POWER SUPPLY FOR BLOWER MOTOR.
Disconnect blower motor harness connector.
Do approx. 12 volts exist between blower motor harness terminal No. ㉚ and body ground?
N.G.
Check 15A fuses at fuse block.
O.K.
B
Check circuit continuity between blower motor harness terminal No. ㉔ and body ground.
N.G.
Reconnect blower motor harness connector..
O.K.
CHECK BLOWER MOTOR.
N.G.
Replace blower motor.
C
CHECK BLOWER MOTOR CIRCUIT BETWEEN BLOWER MOTOR AND RESISTOR.
Do approx. 12 volts exist between resistor harness terminal No. ㉔ and body ground?
N.G.
Disconnect blower motor and resistor harness connectors.
D
Note
Check circuit continuity between blower motor harness terminal No. ㉔ and resistor harness terminal No. ㉔.
O.K.
Ⓐ
Go To Next Figure
A
30
L/R
Blower motor connector
V
B
24
L/W
Blower motor connector
Ω
Continuity exists: O.K.
C
Resistor connector
24
L/W
V
D
Blower motor connector
24
L/W
Resistor connector
24
L/W
Ω

NOTE: IF THE RESULT IS NO GOOD (NG) AFTER CHECKING CIRCUIT CONTINUITY, REPAIR HARNESS OR CONNECTOR.

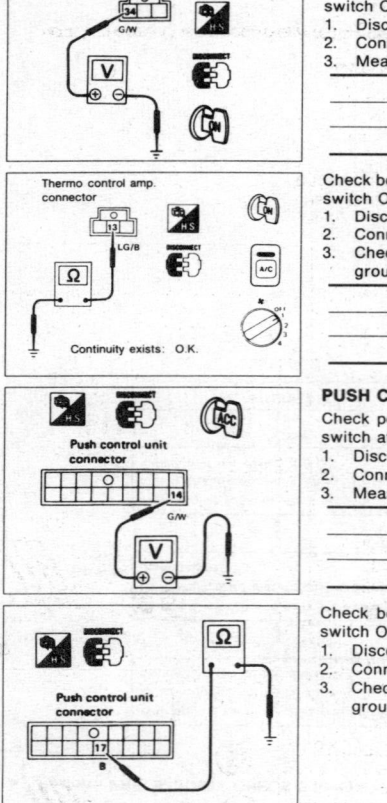

94A10165 Courtesy of Nissan Motor Co., U.S.A.

Fig. 6: Diagnostic Procedure 1 – Blower Motor Does Not Rotate (G20)

1993 MANUAL A/C-HEATER SYSTEMS
Trouble Shooting – G20 (Cont.)

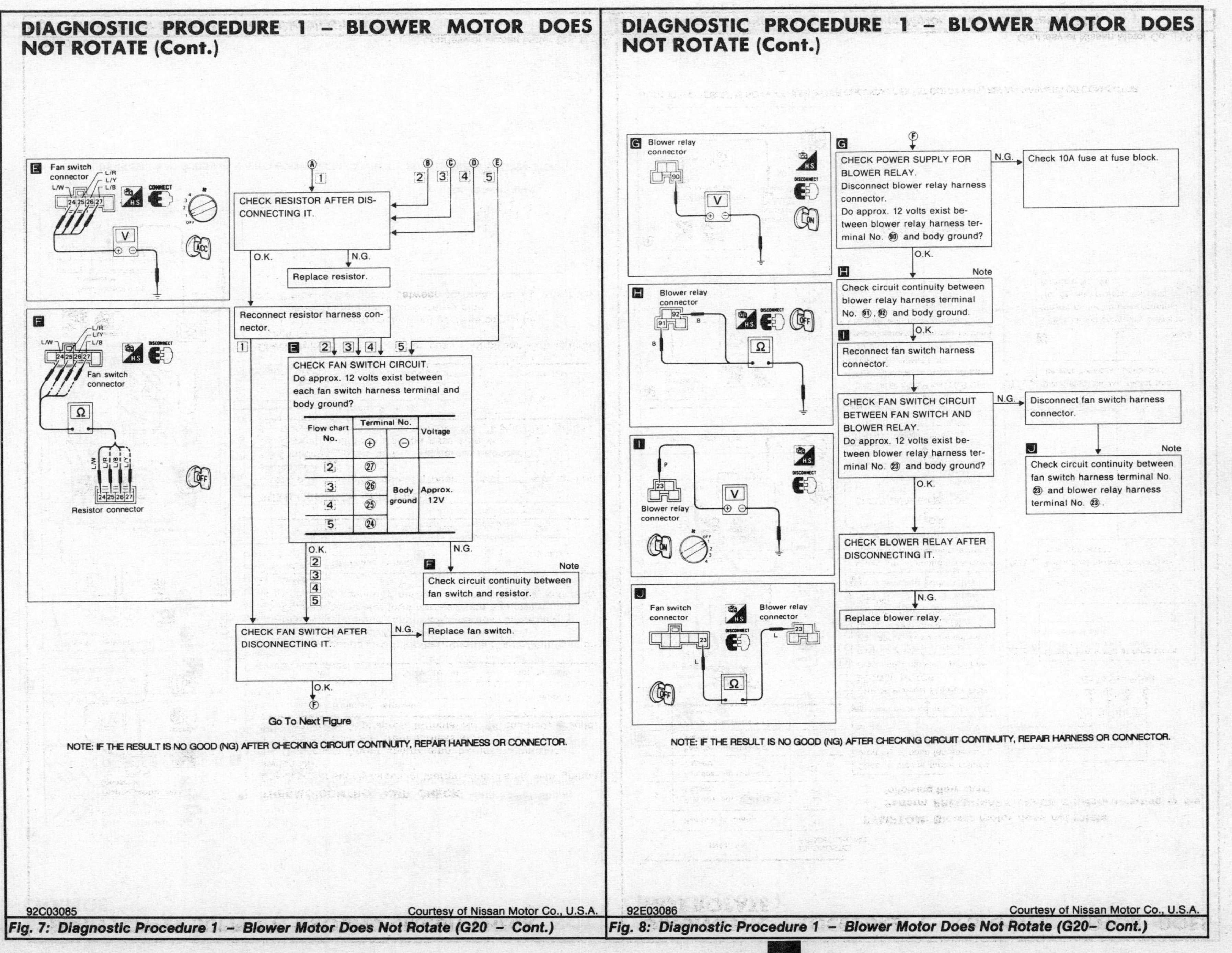
DIAGNOSTIC PROCEDURE 1 – BLOWER MOTOR DOES NOT ROTATE (Cont.)
E
Fan switch connector
L/W
L/R
L/Y
L/B
24 25 26 27
CONNECT
H.S
ACC
OFF
F
Fan switch connector
Resistor connector
DISCONNECT
A 1
CHECK RESISTOR AFTER DISCONNECTING IT.
N.G.
Replace resistor.
O.K.
Reconnect resistor harness connector.
B C D E
2 3 4 5
E CHECK FAN SWITCH CIRCUIT.
Do approx. 12 volts exist between each fan switch harness terminal and body ground?
Flow chart No.
Terminal No.
⊕
⊖
Voltage
2 27
3 26
4 25
5 24
Body ground
Approx. 12V
N.G.
F Check circuit continuity between fan switch and resistor.
Note
O.K.
CHECK FAN SWITCH AFTER DISCONNECTING IT.
N.G.
Replace fan switch.
O.K.
Go To Next Figure
NOTE: IF THE RESULT IS NO GOOD (NG) AFTER CHECKING CIRCUIT CONTINUITY, REPAIR HARNESS OR CONNECTOR.
92C03085
Courtesy of Nissan Motor Co., U.S.A.
DIAGNOSTIC PROCEDURE 1 – BLOWER MOTOR DOES NOT ROTATE (Cont.)
G Blower relay connector
90
H Blower relay connector
91 92
I Blower relay connector
23
J Fan switch connector
Blower relay connector
DISCONNECT
H.S
ON
OFF
G CHECK POWER SUPPLY FOR BLOWER RELAY.
Disconnect blower relay harness connector.
Do approx. 12 volts exist between blower relay harness terminal No. 90 and body ground?
N.G.
Check 10A fuse at fuse block.
O.K.
H Check circuit continuity between blower relay harness terminal No. 91, 92 and body ground.
Note
O.K.
I Reconnect fan switch harness connector.
CHECK FAN SWITCH CIRCUIT BETWEEN FAN SWITCH AND BLOWER RELAY.
Do approx. 12 volts exist between blower relay harness terminal No. 23 and body ground?
N.G.
Disconnect fan switch harness connector.
J Check circuit continuity between fan switch harness terminal No. 23 and blower relay harness terminal No. 23.
Note
O.K.
CHECK BLOWER RELAY AFTER DISCONNECTING IT.
N.G.
Replace blower relay.
NOTE: IF THE RESULT IS NO GOOD (NG) AFTER CHECKING CIRCUIT CONTINUITY, REPAIR HARNESS OR CONNECTOR.
92E03086
Courtesy of Nissan Motor Co., U.S.A.

Fig. 7: Diagnostic Procedure 1 – Blower Motor Does Not Rotate (G20 – Cont.)

Fig. 8: Diagnostic Procedure 1 – Blower Motor Does Not Rotate (G20– Cont.)

1993 MANUAL A/C-HEATER SYSTEMS
Trouble Shooting – G20 (Cont.)

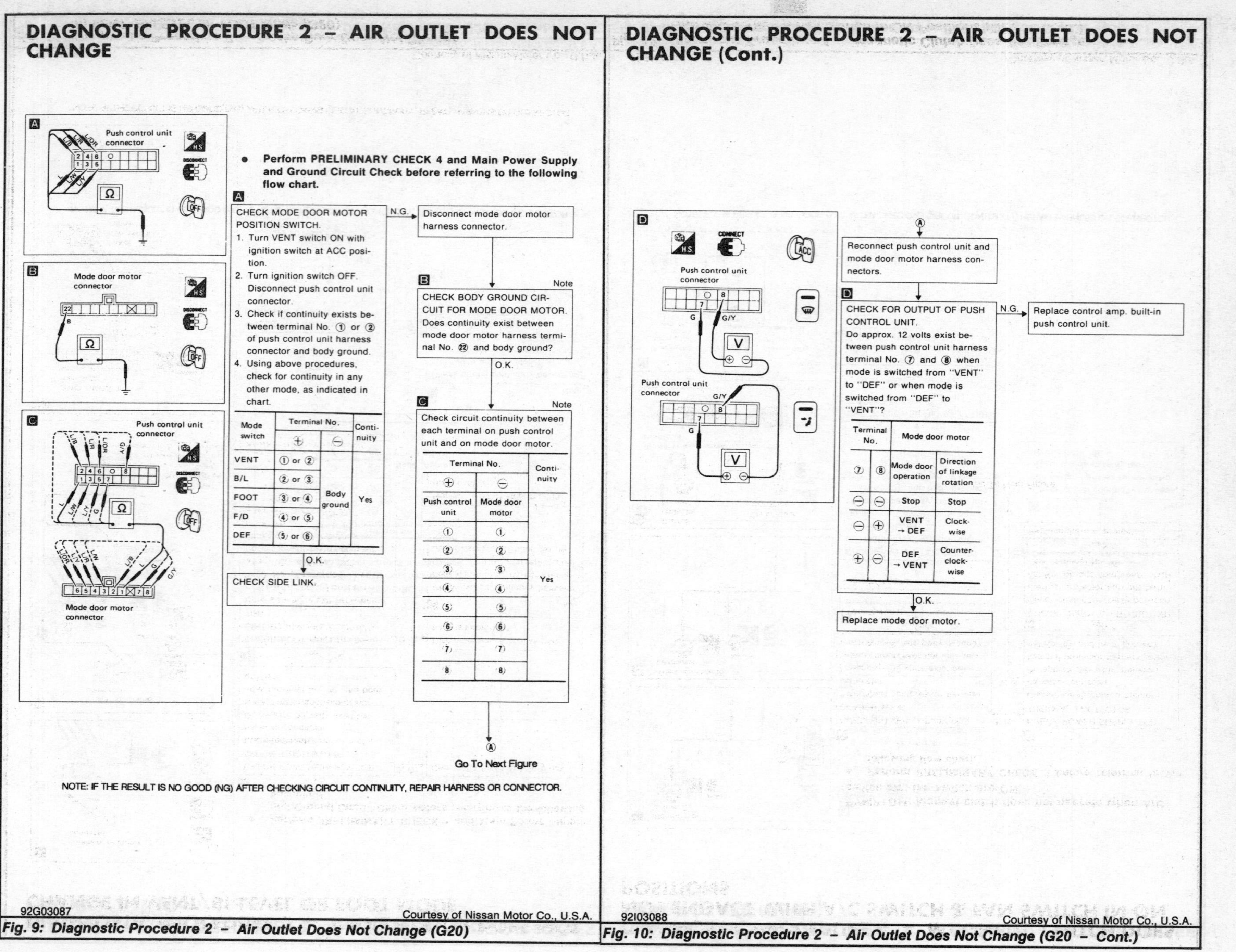
DIAGNOSTIC PROCEDURE 2 – AIR OUTLET DOES NOT CHANGE
A
Push control unit connector
L/OR
L/R
L/B
L/W
L/Y
L
B
Mode door motor connector
22
C
Push control unit connector
G/Y
Mode door motor connector
• Perform PRELIMINARY CHECK 4 and Main Power Supply and Ground Circuit Check before referring to the following flow chart.
A CHECK MODE DOOR MOTOR POSITION SWITCH.
1. Turn VENT switch ON with ignition switch at ACC position.
2. Turn ignition switch OFF. Disconnect push control unit connector.
3. Check if continuity exists between terminal No. ① or ② of push control unit harness connector and body ground.
4. Using above procedures, check for continuity in any other mode, as indicated in chart.
N.G.
O.K.
CHECK SIDE LINK.
Disconnect mode door motor harness connector.
B CHECK BODY GROUND CIRCUIT FOR MODE DOOR MOTOR. Does continuity exist between mode door motor harness terminal No. ㉒ and body ground?
Note
O.K.
C Check circuit continuity between each terminal on push control unit and on mode door motor.
Note
Ⓐ
Go To Next Figure
NOTE: IF THE RESULT IS NO GOOD (NG) AFTER CHECKING CIRCUIT CONTINUITY, REPAIR HARNESS OR CONNECTOR.
DIAGNOSTIC PROCEDURE 2 – AIR OUTLET DOES NOT CHANGE (Cont.)
D
Push control unit connector
G
G/Y
7
8
Ⓐ
Reconnect push control unit and mode door motor harness connectors.
D CHECK FOR OUTPUT OF PUSH CONTROL UNIT. Do approx. 12 volts exist between push control unit harness terminal No. ⑦ and ⑧ when mode is switched from "VENT" to "DEF" or when mode is switched from "DEF" to "VENT"?
N.G.
Replace control amp. built-in push control unit.
O.K.
Replace mode door motor.

Mode switch	Terminal No. ⊕	Terminal No. ⊖	Continuity
VENT	① or ②	Body ground	Yes
B/L	② or ③		
FOOT	③ or ④		
F/D	④ or ⑤		
DEF	⑤ or ⑥		

Terminal No. ⊕ Push control unit	Terminal No. ⊖ Mode door motor	Continuity
①	①	Yes
②	②	
③	③	
④	④	
⑤	⑤	
⑥	⑥	
⑦	⑦	
⑧	⑧	

Terminal No. ⑦	Terminal No. ⑧	Mode door operation	Direction of linkage rotation
⊖	⊖	Stop	Stop
⊖	⊕	VENT → DEF	Clockwise
⊕	⊖	DEF → VENT	Counterclockwise

92G03087 Courtesy of Nissan Motor Co., U.S.A.

Fig. 9: Diagnostic Procedure 2 – Air Outlet Does Not Change (G20)

92I03088 Courtesy of Nissan Motor Co., U.S.A.

Fig. 10: Diagnostic Procedure 2 – Air Outlet Does Not Change (G20 – Cont.)

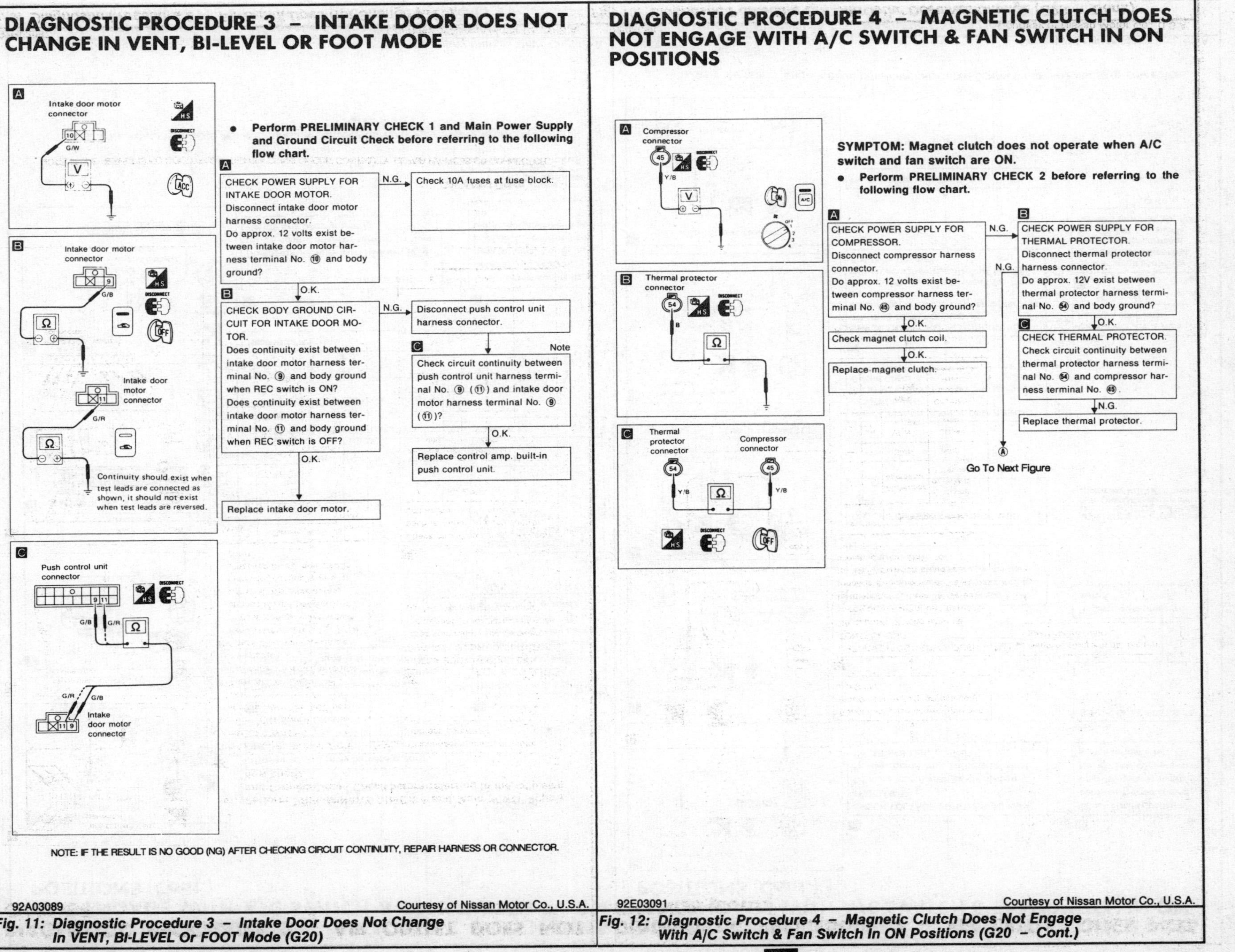
DIAGNOSTIC PROCEDURE 3 – INTAKE DOOR DOES NOT CHANGE IN VENT, BI-LEVEL OR FOOT MODE
A
Intake door motor connector
G/W
B
Intake door motor connector
G/B
Intake door motor connector
G/R
Continuity should exist when test leads are connected as shown, it should not exist when test leads are reversed.
C
Push control unit connector
G/B
G/R
G/R
G/B
Intake door motor connector
• Perform PRELIMINARY CHECK 1 and Main Power Supply and Ground Circuit Check before referring to the following flow chart.
A
CHECK POWER SUPPLY FOR INTAKE DOOR MOTOR.
Disconnect intake door motor harness connector.
Do approx. 12 volts exist between intake door motor harness terminal No. ⑩ and body ground?
N.G.
Check 10A fuses at fuse block.
O.K.
B
CHECK BODY GROUND CIRCUIT FOR INTAKE DOOR MOTOR.
Does continuity exist between intake door motor harness terminal No. ⑨ and body ground when REC switch is ON?
Does continuity exist between intake door motor harness terminal No. ⑪ and body ground when REC switch is OFF?
N.G.
Disconnect push control unit harness connector.
C
Note
Check circuit continuity between push control unit harness terminal No. ⑨ (⑪) and intake door motor harness terminal No. ⑨ (⑪)?
O.K.
Replace control amp. built-in push control unit.
O.K.
Replace intake door motor.
NOTE: IF THE RESULT IS NO GOOD (NG) AFTER CHECKING CIRCUIT CONTINUITY, REPAIR HARNESS OR CONNECTOR.
92A03089
Courtesy of Nissan Motor Co., U.S.A.
DIAGNOSTIC PROCEDURE 4 – MAGNETIC CLUTCH DOES NOT ENGAGE WITH A/C SWITCH & FAN SWITCH IN ON POSITIONS
A
Compressor connector
Y/B
B
Thermal protector connector
B
C
Thermal protector connector
Compressor connector
Y/B
Y/B
SYMPTOM: Magnet clutch does not operate when A/C switch and fan switch are ON.
• Perform PRELIMINARY CHECK 2 before referring to the following flow chart.
A
CHECK POWER SUPPLY FOR COMPRESSOR.
Disconnect compressor harness connector.
Do approx. 12 volts exist between compressor harness terminal No. ㊺ and body ground?
O.K.
Check magnet clutch coil.
O.K.
Replace magnet clutch.
N.G.
B
CHECK POWER SUPPLY FOR THERMAL PROTECTOR.
Disconnect thermal protector harness connector.
Do approx. 12V exist between thermal protector harness terminal No. ㊹ and body ground?
N.G.
O.K.
C
CHECK THERMAL PROTECTOR.
Check circuit continuity between thermal protector harness terminal No. ㊹ and compressor harness terminal No. ㊺.
N.G.
Replace thermal protector.
Ⓐ
Go To Next Figure
92E03091
Courtesy of Nissan Motor Co., U.S.A.

Fig. 11: Diagnostic Procedure 3 – Intake Door Does Not Change In VENT, BI-LEVEL Or FOOT Mode (G20)

Fig. 12: Diagnostic Procedure 4 – Magnetic Clutch Does Not Engage With A/C Switch & Fan Switch In ON Positions (G20 – Cont.)

1993 MANUAL A/C-HEATER SYSTEMS
Trouble Shooting – G20 (Cont.)

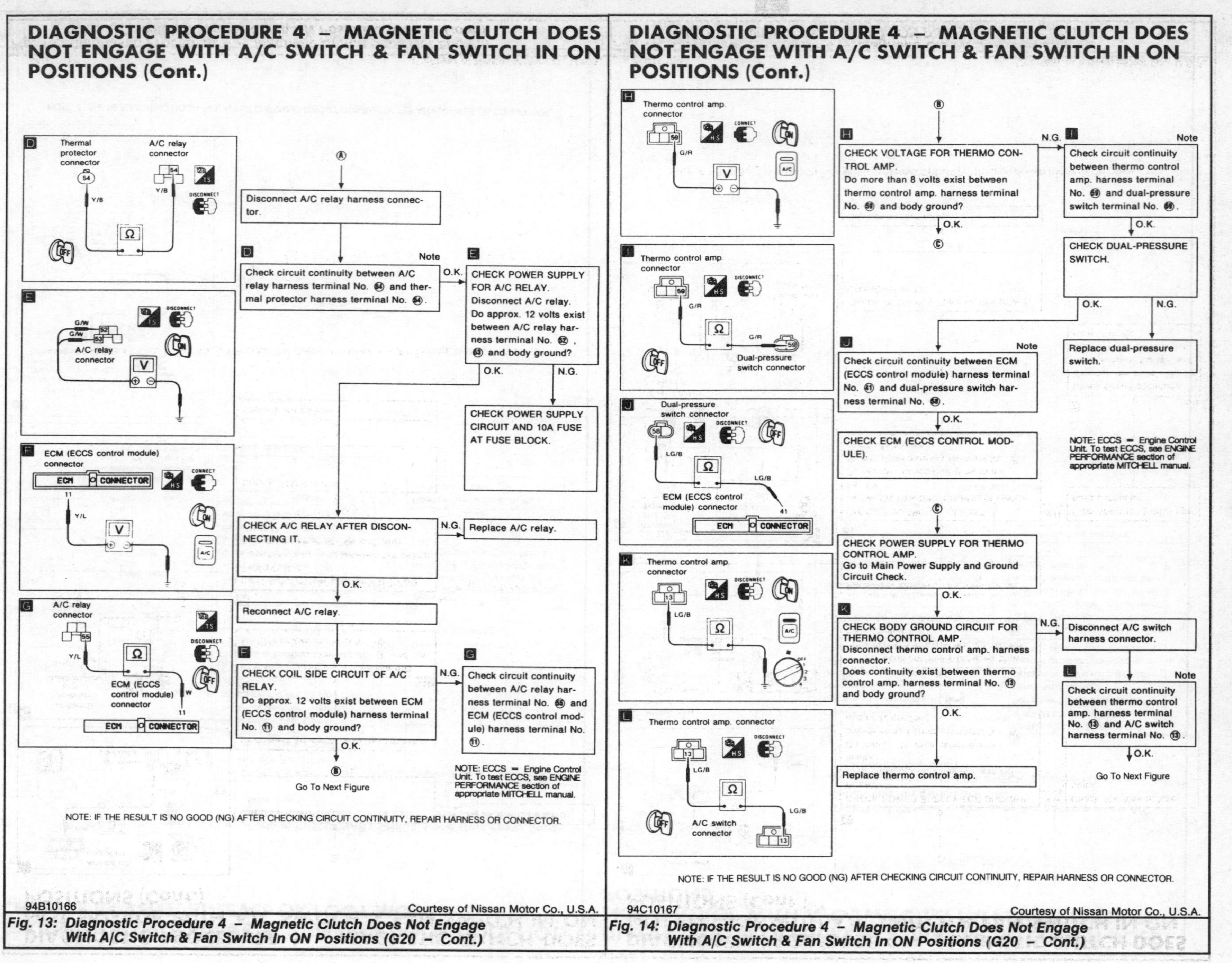
DIAGNOSTIC PROCEDURE 4 – MAGNETIC CLUTCH DOES NOT ENGAGE WITH A/C SWITCH & FAN SWITCH IN ON POSITIONS (Cont.)
D
Thermal protector connector
A/C relay connector
Y/B
DISCONNECT
E
G/W
A/C relay connector
DISCONNECT
F
ECM (ECCS control module) connector
ECM
CONNECTOR
CONNECT
Y/L
G
A/C relay connector
ECM (ECCS control module) connector
DISCONNECT
W
A
Disconnect A/C relay harness connector.
D
Note
Check circuit continuity between A/C relay harness terminal No. 54 and thermal protector harness terminal No. 54.
O.K.
E
CHECK POWER SUPPLY FOR A/C RELAY.
Disconnect A/C relay.
Do approx. 12 volts exist between A/C relay harness terminal No. 52, 53 and body ground?
O.K.
N.G.
CHECK POWER SUPPLY CIRCUIT AND 10A FUSE AT FUSE BLOCK.
CHECK A/C RELAY AFTER DISCONNECTING IT.
N.G.
Replace A/C relay.
O.K.
Reconnect A/C relay.
F
CHECK COIL SIDE CIRCUIT OF A/C RELAY.
Do approx. 12 volts exist between ECM (ECCS control module) harness terminal No. 11 and body ground?
N.G.
G
Check circuit continuity between A/C relay harness terminal No. 55 and ECM (ECCS control module) harness terminal No. 11.
O.K.
B
Go To Next Figure
NOTE: ECCS – Engine Control Unit. To test ECCS, see ENGINE PERFORMANCE section of appropriate MITCHELL manual.
NOTE: IF THE RESULT IS NO GOOD (NG) AFTER CHECKING CIRCUIT CONTINUITY, REPAIR HARNESS OR CONNECTOR.
94B10166
Courtesy of Nissan Motor Co., U.S.A.
DIAGNOSTIC PROCEDURE 4 – MAGNETIC CLUTCH DOES NOT ENGAGE WITH A/C SWITCH & FAN SWITCH IN ON POSITIONS (Cont.)
H
Thermo control amp. connector
CONNECT
G/R
I
Thermo control amp. connector
DISCONNECT
G/R
Dual-pressure switch connector
J
Dual-pressure switch connector
DISCONNECT
LG/B
ECM (ECCS control module) connector
ECM
CONNECTOR
K
Thermo control amp. connector
DISCONNECT
LG/B
L
Thermo control amp. connector
DISCONNECT
LG/B
A/C switch connector
B
H
CHECK VOLTAGE FOR THERMO CONTROL AMP.
Do more than 8 volts exist between thermo control amp. harness terminal No. 59 and body ground?
N.G.
I
Note
Check circuit continuity between thermo control amp. harness terminal No. 59 and dual-pressure switch terminal No. 59.
O.K.
C
CHECK DUAL-PRESSURE SWITCH.
O.K.
N.G.
Replace dual-pressure switch.
J
Note
Check circuit continuity between ECM (ECCS control module) harness terminal No. 41 and dual-pressure switch harness terminal No. 58.
O.K.
CHECK ECM (ECCS CONTROL MODULE).
NOTE: ECCS – Engine Control Unit. To test ECCS, see ENGINE PERFORMANCE section of appropriate MITCHELL manual.
C
CHECK POWER SUPPLY FOR THERMO CONTROL AMP.
Go to Main Power Supply and Ground Circuit Check.
O.K.
K
CHECK BODY GROUND CIRCUIT FOR THERMO CONTROL AMP.
Disconnect thermo control amp. harness connector.
Does continuity exist between thermo control amp. harness terminal No. 13 and body ground?
N.G.
Disconnect A/C switch harness connector.
L
Note
Check circuit continuity between thermo control amp. harness terminal No. 13 and A/C switch harness terminal No. 13.
O.K.
Go To Next Figure
O.K.
Replace thermo control amp.
NOTE: IF THE RESULT IS NO GOOD (NG) AFTER CHECKING CIRCUIT CONTINUITY, REPAIR HARNESS OR CONNECTOR.
94C10167
Courtesy of Nissan Motor Co., U.S.A.

Fig. 13: Diagnostic Procedure 4 – Magnetic Clutch Does Not Engage With A/C Switch & Fan Switch In ON Positions (G20 – Cont.)

Fig. 14: Diagnostic Procedure 4 – Magnetic Clutch Does Not Engage With A/C Switch & Fan Switch In ON Positions (G20 – Cont.)

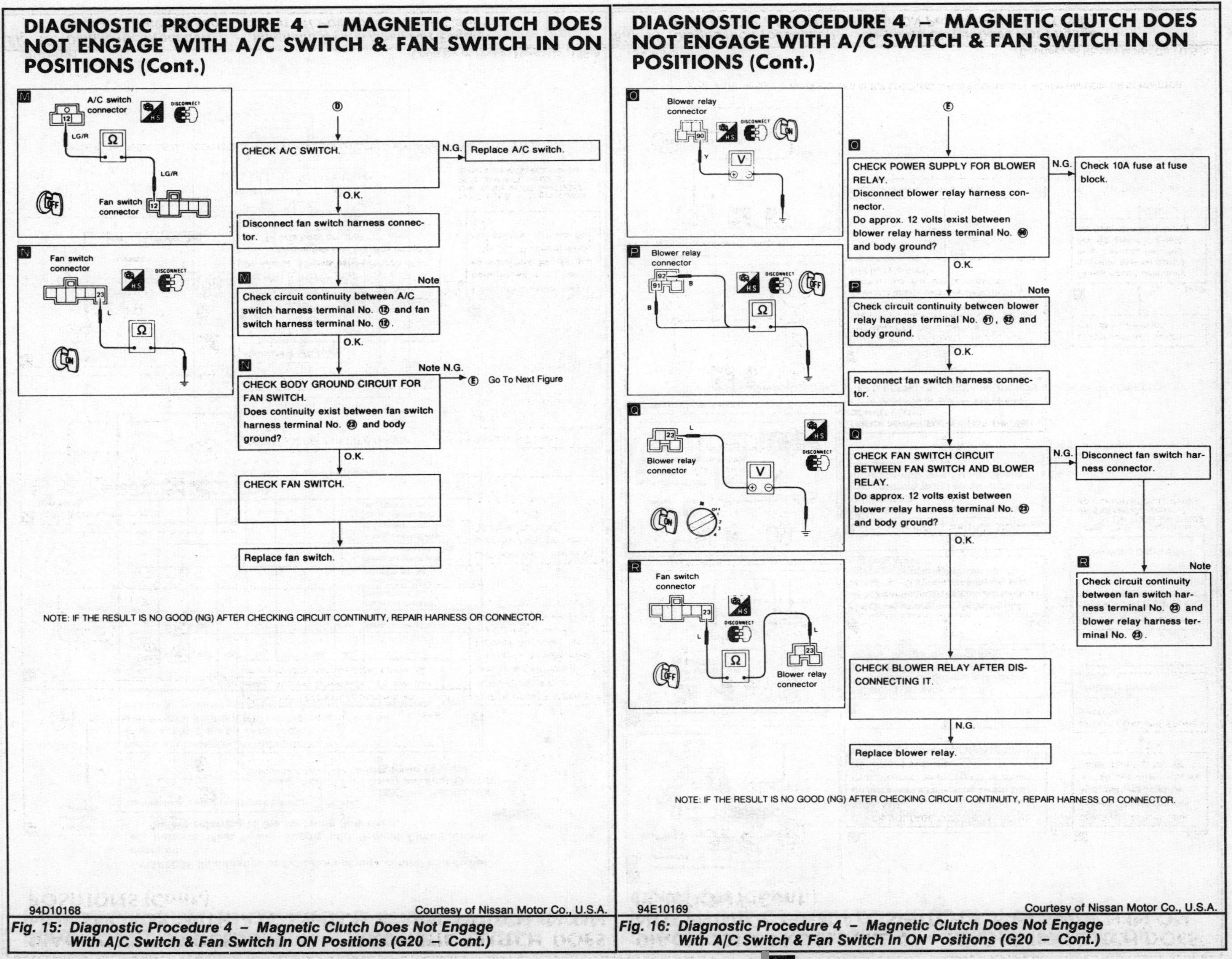
DIAGNOSTIC PROCEDURE 4 – MAGNETIC CLUTCH DOES NOT ENGAGE WITH A/C SWITCH & FAN SWITCH IN ON POSITIONS (Cont.)
M
A/C switch connector
12
LG/R
Ω
LG/R
Fan switch connector
12
DISCONNECT
H.S.
OFF
N
Fan switch connector
23
L
Ω
DISCONNECT
H.S.
ON
D
CHECK A/C SWITCH.
N.G.
Replace A/C switch.
O.K.
Disconnect fan switch harness connector.
M
Note
Check circuit continuity between A/C switch harness terminal No. 12 and fan switch harness terminal No. 12.
O.K.
N
Note N.G.
E Go To Next Figure
CHECK BODY GROUND CIRCUIT FOR FAN SWITCH.
Does continuity exist between fan switch harness terminal No. 23 and body ground?
O.K.
CHECK FAN SWITCH.
Replace fan switch.
NOTE: IF THE RESULT IS NO GOOD (NG) AFTER CHECKING CIRCUIT CONTINUITY, REPAIR HARNESS OR CONNECTOR.
94D10168
Courtesy of Nissan Motor Co., U.S.A.
DIAGNOSTIC PROCEDURE 4 – MAGNETIC CLUTCH DOES NOT ENGAGE WITH A/C SWITCH & FAN SWITCH IN ON POSITIONS (Cont.)
O
Blower relay connector
90
Y
V
DISCONNECT
H.S.
ON
P
Blower relay connector
92
91
B
B
Ω
DISCONNECT
H.S.
OFF
Q
23
L
Blower relay connector
V
DISCONNECT
H.S.
ON
OFF
1
2
3
4
R
Fan switch connector
23
L
Ω
L
23
Blower relay connector
DISCONNECT
H.S.
OFF
E
O
CHECK POWER SUPPLY FOR BLOWER RELAY.
Disconnect blower relay harness connector.
Do approx. 12 volts exist between blower relay harness terminal No. 90 and body ground?
N.G.
Check 10A fuse at fuse block.
O.K.
P
Note
Check circuit continuity between blower relay harness terminal No. 91, 92 and body ground.
O.K.
Reconnect fan switch harness connector.
Q
CHECK FAN SWITCH CIRCUIT BETWEEN FAN SWITCH AND BLOWER RELAY.
Do approx. 12 volts exist between blower relay harness terminal No. 23 and body ground?
N.G.
Disconnect fan switch harness connector.
R
Note
Check circuit continuity between fan switch harness terminal No. 23 and blower relay harness terminal No. 23.
O.K.
CHECK BLOWER RELAY AFTER DISCONNECTING IT.
N.G.
Replace blower relay.
NOTE: IF THE RESULT IS NO GOOD (NG) AFTER CHECKING CIRCUIT CONTINUITY, REPAIR HARNESS OR CONNECTOR.
94E10169
Courtesy of Nissan Motor Co., U.S.A.

Fig. 15: Diagnostic Procedure 4 – Magnetic Clutch Does Not Engage With A/C Switch & Fan Switch In ON Positions (G20 – Cont.)

Fig. 16: Diagnostic Procedure 4 – Magnetic Clutch Does Not Engage With A/C Switch & Fan Switch In ON Positions (G20 – Cont.)

1993 MANUAL A/C-HEATER SYSTEMS
Trouble Shooting – G20 (Cont.)

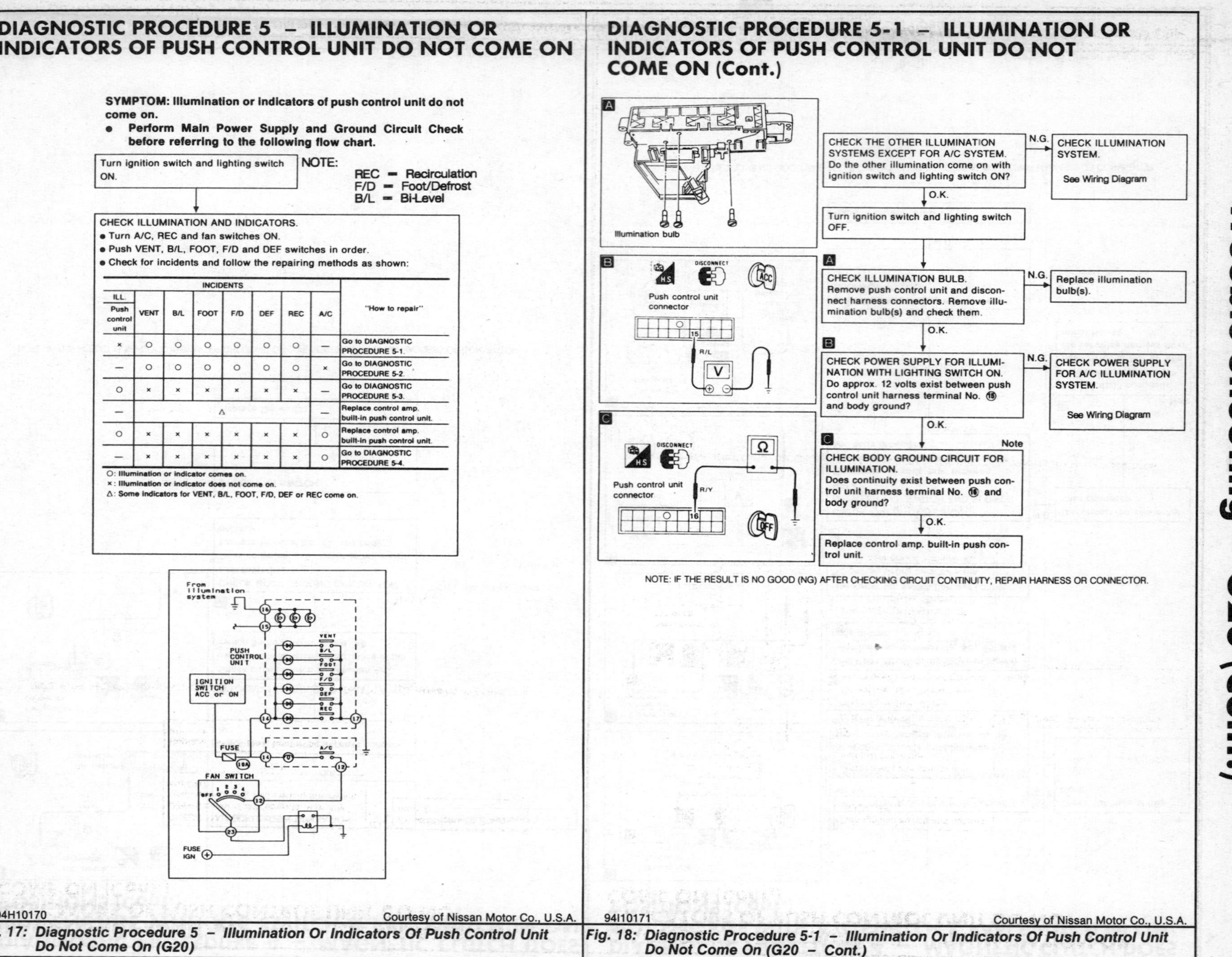

DIAGNOSTIC PROCEDURE 5 – ILLUMINATION OR INDICATORS OF PUSH CONTROL UNIT DO NOT COME ON

SYMPTOM: Illumination or indicators of push control unit do not come on.

- **Perform Main Power Supply and Ground Circuit Check before referring to the following flow chart.**

Turn ignition switch and lighting switch ON.

NOTE:
REC = Recirculation
F/D = Foot/Defrost
B/L = Bi-Level

CHECK ILLUMINATION AND INDICATORS.
- Turn A/C, REC and fan switches ON.
- Push VENT, B/L, FOOT, F/D and DEF switches in order.
- Check for incidents and follow the repairing methods as shown:

INCIDENTS: ILL. Push control unit	VENT	B/L	FOOT	F/D	DEF	REC	A/C	"How to repair"
×	○	○	○	○	○	○	—	Go to DIAGNOSTIC PROCEDURE 5-1.
—	○	○	○	○	○	○	×	Go to DIAGNOSTIC PROCEDURE 5-2.
○	×	×	×	×	×	×	—	Go to DIAGNOSTIC PROCEDURE 5-3.
—			Δ				—	Replace control amp. built-in push control unit.
○	×	×	×	×	×	×	○	Replace control amp. built-in push control unit.
—	×	×	×	×	×	×	○	Go to DIAGNOSTIC PROCEDURE 5-4.

○: Illumination or indicator comes on.
×: Illumination or indicator does not come on.
Δ: Some indicators for VENT, B/L, FOOT, F/D, DEF or REC come on.

From illumination system
PUSH CONTROL UNIT
IGNITION SWITCH ACC or ON
VENT
B/L
FOOT
F/D
DEF
REC
A/C
FUSE
FAN SWITCH
OFF 1 2 3 4
FUSE IGN

94H10170 Courtesy of Nissan Motor Co., U.S.A.

Fig. 17: Diagnostic Procedure 5 – Illumination Or Indicators Of Push Control Unit Do Not Come On (G20)

DIAGNOSTIC PROCEDURE 5-1 – ILLUMINATION OR INDICATORS OF PUSH CONTROL UNIT DO NOT COME ON (Cont.)

A
Illumination bulb
B
DISCONNECT
ACC
Push control unit connector
15
R/L
V
C
DISCONNECT
Push control unit connector
16
R/Y
Ω
OFF

CHECK THE OTHER ILLUMINATION SYSTEMS EXCEPT FOR A/C SYSTEM. Do the other illumination come on with ignition switch and lighting switch ON?
- N.G. → CHECK ILLUMINATION SYSTEM. See Wiring Diagram
- O.K. ↓

Turn ignition switch and lighting switch OFF.

A — CHECK ILLUMINATION BULB. Remove push control unit and disconnect harness connectors. Remove illumination bulb(s) and check them.
- N.G. → Replace illumination bulb(s).
- O.K. ↓

B — CHECK POWER SUPPLY FOR ILLUMINATION WITH LIGHTING SWITCH ON. Do approx. 12 volts exist between push control unit harness terminal No. ⑮ and body ground?
- N.G. → CHECK POWER SUPPLY FOR A/C ILLUMINATION SYSTEM. See Wiring Diagram
- O.K. ↓

C — CHECK BODY GROUND CIRCUIT FOR ILLUMINATION. (Note) Does continuity exist between push control unit harness terminal No. ⑯ and body ground?
- O.K. ↓

Replace control amp. built-in push control unit.

NOTE: IF THE RESULT IS NO GOOD (NG) AFTER CHECKING CIRCUIT CONTINUITY, REPAIR HARNESS OR CONNECTOR.

94I10171 Courtesy of Nissan Motor Co., U.S.A.

Fig. 18: Diagnostic Procedure 5-1 – Illumination Or Indicators Of Push Control Unit Do Not Come On (G20 – Cont.)

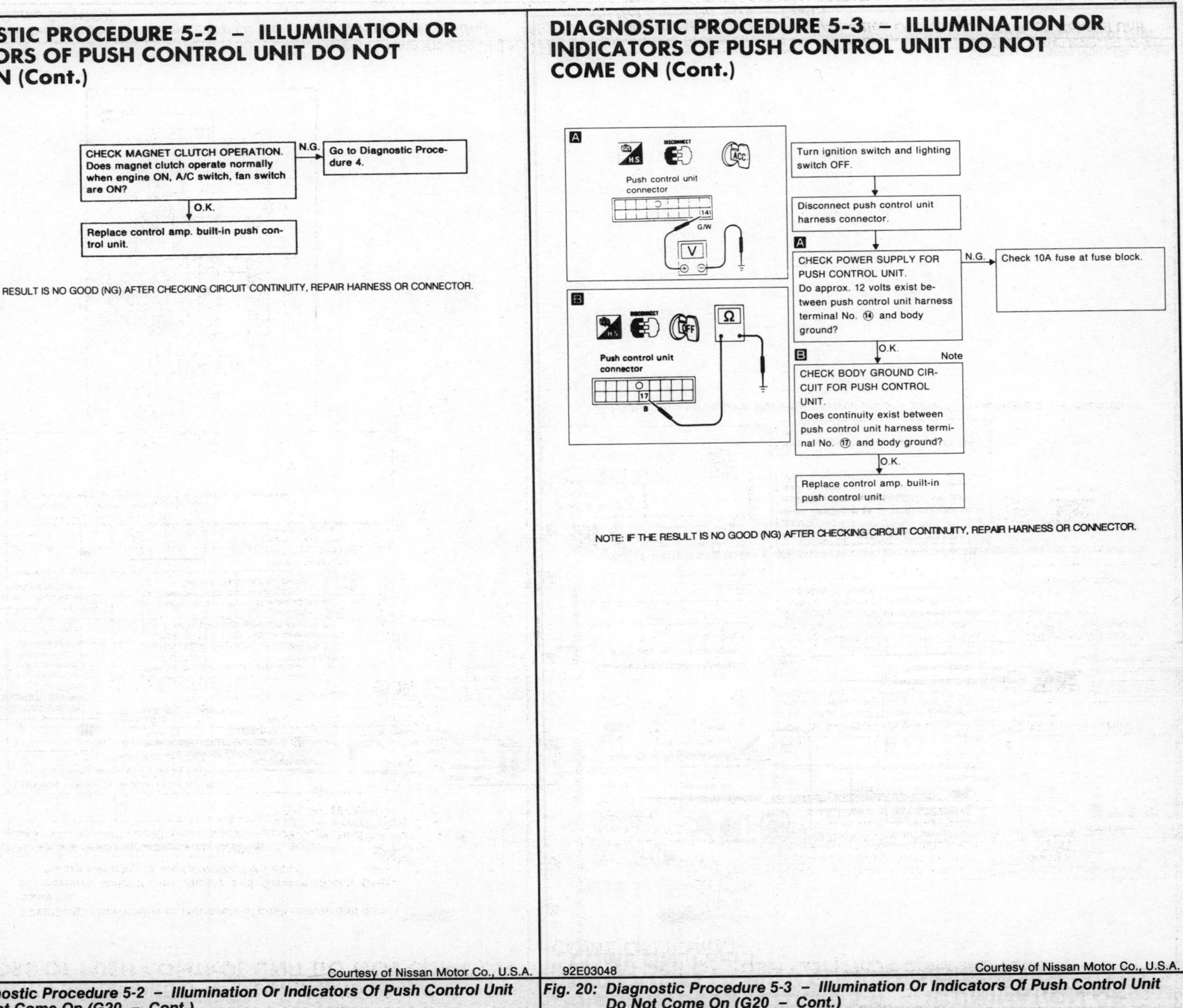
DIAGNOSTIC PROCEDURE 5-2 – ILLUMINATION OR INDICATORS OF PUSH CONTROL UNIT DO NOT COME ON (Cont.)
CHECK MAGNET CLUTCH OPERATION. Does magnet clutch operate normally when engine ON, A/C switch, fan switch are ON?
N.G.
Go to Diagnostic Procedure 4.
O.K.
Replace control amp. built-in push control unit.
NOTE: IF THE RESULT IS NO GOOD (NG) AFTER CHECKING CIRCUIT CONTINUITY, REPAIR HARNESS OR CONNECTOR.
92C03047
Courtesy of Nissan Motor Co., U.S.A.
DIAGNOSTIC PROCEDURE 5-3 – ILLUMINATION OR INDICATORS OF PUSH CONTROL UNIT DO NOT COME ON (Cont.)
A
H.S
DISCONNECT
ACC
Push control unit connector
14
G/W
V
B
H.S
DISCONNECT
OFF
Ω
Push control unit connector
17
B
Turn ignition switch and lighting switch OFF.
Disconnect push control unit harness connector.
A
CHECK POWER SUPPLY FOR PUSH CONTROL UNIT. Do approx. 12 volts exist between push control unit harness terminal No. ⑭ and body ground?
N.G.
Check 10A fuse at fuse block.
O.K.
B
Note
CHECK BODY GROUND CIRCUIT FOR PUSH CONTROL UNIT. Does continuity exist between push control unit harness terminal No. ⑰ and body ground?
O.K.
Replace control amp. built-in push control unit.
NOTE: IF THE RESULT IS NO GOOD (NG) AFTER CHECKING CIRCUIT CONTINUITY, REPAIR HARNESS OR CONNECTOR.
92E03048
Courtesy of Nissan Motor Co., U.S.A.

Fig. 19: Diagnostic Procedure 5-2 – Illumination Or Indicators Of Push Control Unit Do Not Come On (G20 – Cont.)

Fig. 20: Diagnostic Procedure 5-3 – Illumination Or Indicators Of Push Control Unit Do Not Come On (G20 – Cont.)

1993 MANUAL A/C-HEATER SYSTEMS
Trouble Shooting – G20 (Cont.)

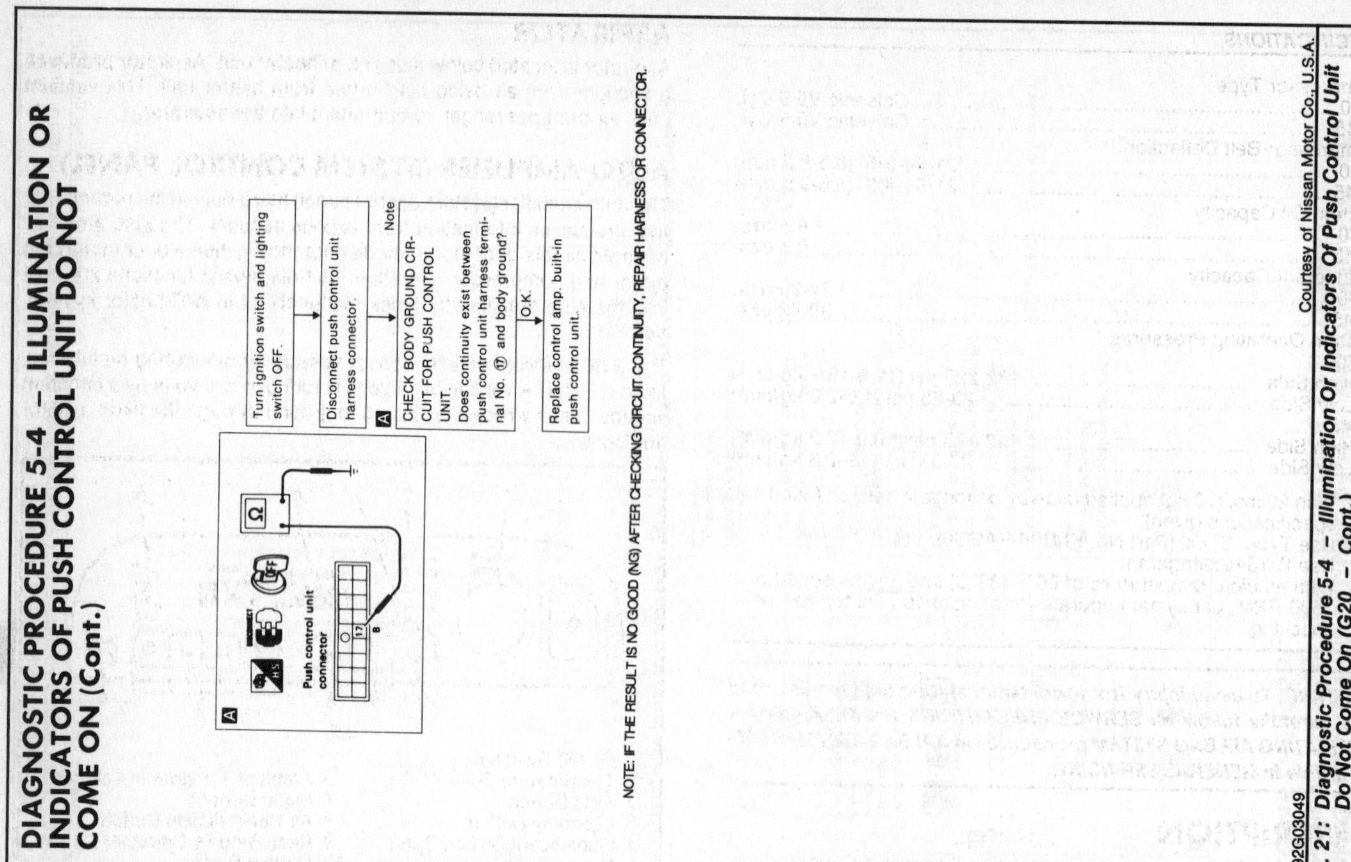
DIAGNOSTIC PROCEDURE 5-4 – ILLUMINATION OR INDICATORS OF PUSH CONTROL UNIT DO NOT COME ON (Cont.)
A
DISCONNECT
H.S.
OFF
Ω
Push control unit connector
17
B
Turn ignition switch and lighting switch OFF.
Disconnect push control unit harness connector.
A
Note
CHECK BODY GROUND CIRCUIT FOR PUSH CONTROL UNIT.
Does continuity exist between push control unit harness terminal No. ⑰ and body ground?
O.K.
Replace control amp. built-in push control unit.
NOTE: IF THE RESULT IS NO GOOD (NG) AFTER CHECKING CIRCUIT CONTINUITY, REPAIR HARNESS OR CONNECTOR.
92G03049
Courtesy of Nissan Motor Co., U.S.A.

Fig. 21: Diagnostic Procedure 5-4 – Illumination Or Indicators Of Push Control Unit Do Not Come On (G20 – Cont.)

1993 AUTOMATIC A/C-HEATER SYSTEMS J30 & Q45

SPECIFICATIONS

Application	Specification
Compressor Type	
J30	Calsonic V6 6-Cyl.
Q45	Calsonic V5 5-Cyl.
Compressor Belt Deflection [1]	
J30	21/64-3/8" (8.5-9.5 mm)
Q45	21/64-3/8" (8.5-9.5 mm)
System Oil Capacity	
J30	[2] 8.5 ozs.
Q45	9.7 ozs.
Refrigerant Capacity	
J30	[3] 24-26 ozs.
Q45	38-42 ozs.
System Operating Pressures [4]	
J30	
High Side	182-223 psi (12.8-15.7 kg/cm²)
Low Side	23-28 psi (1.6-2.0 kg/cm²)
Q45	
High Side	142-173 psi (10.0-12.2 kg/cm²)
Low Side	27-33 psi (1.9-2.3 kg/cm²)

1 – With 22 lbs. (10 kg) applied midway on longest belt run (used belt specifications given).
2 – Use Type "S" Oil (Part No. KLH00-PAGS0).
3 – Use R-134a refrigerant.
4 – With ambient temperature of 86°F (30°C) and engine speed of 1500 RPM. Let system operate for at least 10 minutes before checking.

WARNING: To avoid injury from accidental air bag deployment, read and carefully follow all SERVICE PRECAUTIONS and DISABLING & ACTIVATING AIR BAG SYSTEM procedures in AIR BAG SYSTEM SAFETY article in GENERAL SERVICING.

DESCRIPTION

Automatic A/C-heater system consists of a standard A/C-heater system and added electronically controlled components. The A/C-heater system is controlled by air mix door control, fan speed control, outlet door control, intake door control, A/C compressor clutch and memory function. Coolant temperature in heater core is monitored by heater core coolant temperature sensor.

OPERATION

Automatic A/C-heater system automatically selects optimum airflow, outlet air temperature and outlet vent to maintain vehicle interior temperature at desired setting.

AIR MIX DOOR MOTOR

Air mix door motor is attached to heater unit. Door motor rotates into position by commands received from the auto amplifier (system control panel). Motor rotation is transferred through a shaft. Door position (angle) is fed back to auto amplifier by the Potentiometer Balance Resistor (PBR). The PBR is located inside air mix door motor.

AMBIENT TEMPERATURE SENSOR

Ambient temperature sensor is located below hood latch. This sensor senses ambient temperature and converts temperature reading into a resistance value. Resistance value is sent to auto amplifier (system control panel).

If auto amplifier detects an abrupt ambient temperature change, it will gradually adjust temperature until desired setting is reached. If, for example, the vehicle is stopped in traffic after traveling at highway speeds, ambient temperature sensor will detect high ambient temperature from heat radiating from radiator. To prevent an unpleasant change in A/C operation from this sudden change in ambient temperature, ambient temperature input process will gradually adjust the temperature.

ASPIRATOR

Aspirator is located below side link of heater unit. Aspirator produces a vacuum from air being discharged from heater unit. This vacuum pulls air from passenger compartment into the aspirator.

AUTO AMPLIFIER (SYSTEM CONTROL PANEL)

The auto amplifier (system control panel) has a built-in microcomputer that processes information from various sensors. The auto amplifier controls air mix door motor, mode door motor, intake door motor, fan motor and compressor operation. Self-diagnostic functions are built into the auto amplifier to check malfunctions in A/C-heater system. *See Fig. 1.*

The auto amplifier detects sensor voltage by monitoring an internal, fixed resistor. A voltage of 12 volts is reduced to 5 volts by a constant voltage circuit where it is applied to ground through the fixed resistor and sensor.

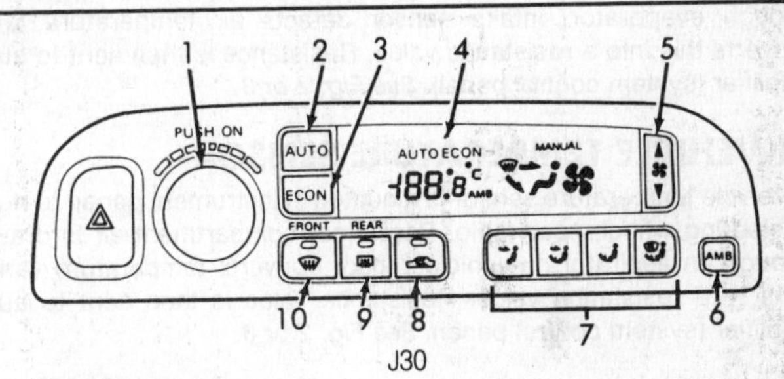
1
2
3
4
5
PUSH ON
AUTO
ECON
AUTO ECON
MANUAL
FRONT
REAR
AMB
10
9
8
7
6
J30

1. On-Off Switch & Temperature Control
2. Auto Button
3. Economy Button
4. Fluorescent Display Tube
5. Manual Fan Control Button
6. Ambient Temperature Switch
7. Mode Buttons
8. Air Recirculation Button
9. Rear Window Defroster Button
10. Defrost Button

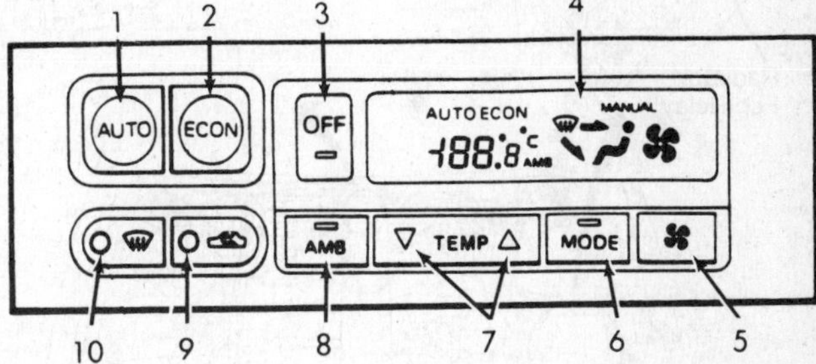
1
2
3
4
AUTO
ECON
OFF
AUTO ECON
MANUAL
AMB
TEMP
MODE
10
9
8
7
6
5

Q45

1. Auto Button
2. Economy Button
3. Off Button
4. Fluorescent Display Tube
5. Manual Fan Control Button
6. Manual Airflow Control Button
7. Temperature Set Button
8. Ambient Temperature Button
9. Air Recirculation Button
10. Defrost Button

94C10084 93I19628

Courtesy of Nissan Motor Co., U.S.A.

Fig. 1: Identifying Auto Amplifier (System Control Panel)

HEATER CORE COOLANT TEMPERATURE SENSOR

Q45 – Heater core coolant temperature sensor is mounted on heater control unit inlet pipe. *See Fig. 3.* Sensor converts heater core coolant temperatures into a resistance value, which is sent to auto amplifier.

FAN CONTROL AMPLIFIER

Located in evaporator housing, fan control amplifier amplifies base current flowing from auto amplifier (system control panel). This change in base current changes blower speed. Voltage range is 5-10.5 volts. At voltage greater than 10.5 volts, high-speed relay applies a direct ground to blower motor.

1993 AUTOMATIC A/C-HEATER SYSTEMS J30 & Q45 (Cont.)

HIGH-SPEED RELAY

NOTE: The high-speed relay may be referred to as a "hi" relay in diagnostic charts.

High-speed relay is located in air intake unit. This relay receives a signal from auto amplifier (system control panel) to operate blower motor at high speed. *See Fig. 2 or 3.*

INTAKE DOOR MOTOR

Intake door motor is attached to heater unit. This door rotates so air is drawn from inlets set by the auto amplifier (system control panel). Motor rotation is transferred to a lever that moves intake door. *See Fig. 2 or 3.*

INTAKE SENSOR

Intake sensor is located in evaporator housing. After air passes through evaporator, intake sensor detects air temperature, and converts this into a resistance value. Resistance is then sent to auto amplifier (system control panel). *See Fig. 2 or 3.*

IN-VEHICLE TEMPERATURE SENSOR

In-vehicle temperature sensor is mounted in instrument panel, to right of steering wheel, near radio. Passenger compartment air is drawn through an aspirator. In-vehicle sensor converts temperature variations to a resistance value. Resistance value is then sent to auto amplifier (system control panel). *See Fig. 2 or 3.*

MODE DOOR MOTOR

Mode door motor is attached to heater unit. This motor rotates so air is discharged from outlet(s) according to auto amplifier (system control panel) setting. Motor rotation is transferred to a link that moves the mode door. *See Fig. 2 or 3.*

POTENTIOMETER BALANCE RESISTOR (PBR)

NOTE: The potentiometer balance resistor may be referred to as a "potentio" balance resistor in diagnostic charts.

This variable resistor converts power servo value (air mix door position) into a resistance value. PBR inputs voltage that varies according to change in resistance value into auto amplifier (system control panel).

POTENTIOMETER TEMPERATURE CONTROL

NOTE: Potentiometer temperature control may be referred to as a "potentio" temperature control in diagnostic charts.

Potentiometer Temperature Control (PTC) is built into auto amplifier (system control panel). Temperature can be set in 1°F increments. Temperature is digitally displayed.

SUNLOAD SENSOR

Sunload sensor is located on right defroster grille. *See Fig. 2 or 3.* It detects sunload using a photo diode. This sunload is converted into a

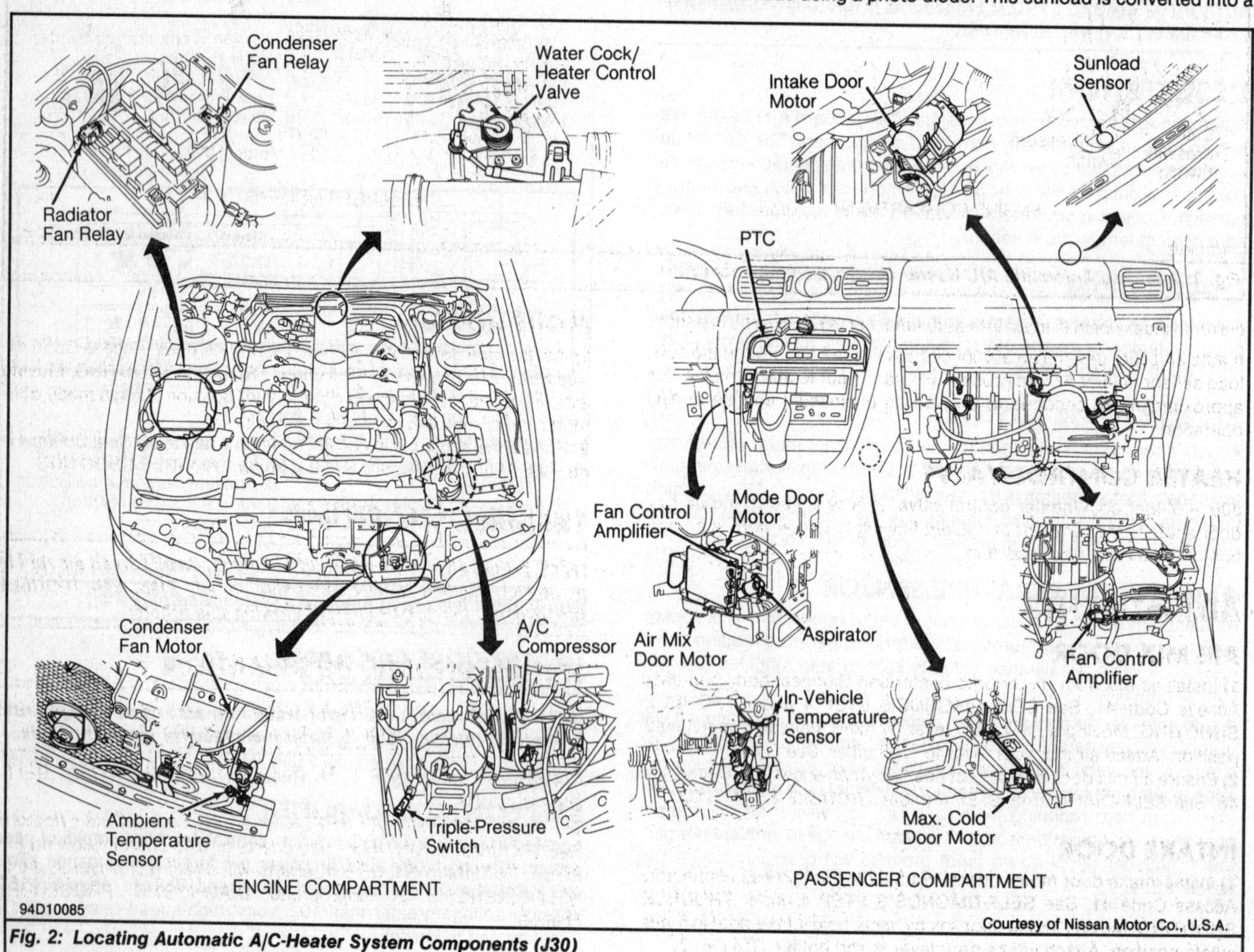
Condenser Fan Relay
Water Cock/ Heater Control Valve
Radiator Fan Relay
Intake Door Motor
Sunload Sensor
PTC
Fan Control Amplifier
Mode Door Motor
Air Mix Door Motor
Aspirator
Fan Control Amplifier
Condenser Fan Motor
A/C Compressor
In-Vehicle Temperature Sensor
Ambient Temperature Sensor
Triple-Pressure Switch
Max. Cold Door Motor
ENGINE COMPARTMENT
PASSENGER COMPARTMENT
94D10085
Courtesy of Nissan Motor Co., U.S.A.

Fig. 2: Locating Automatic A/C-Heater System Components (J30)

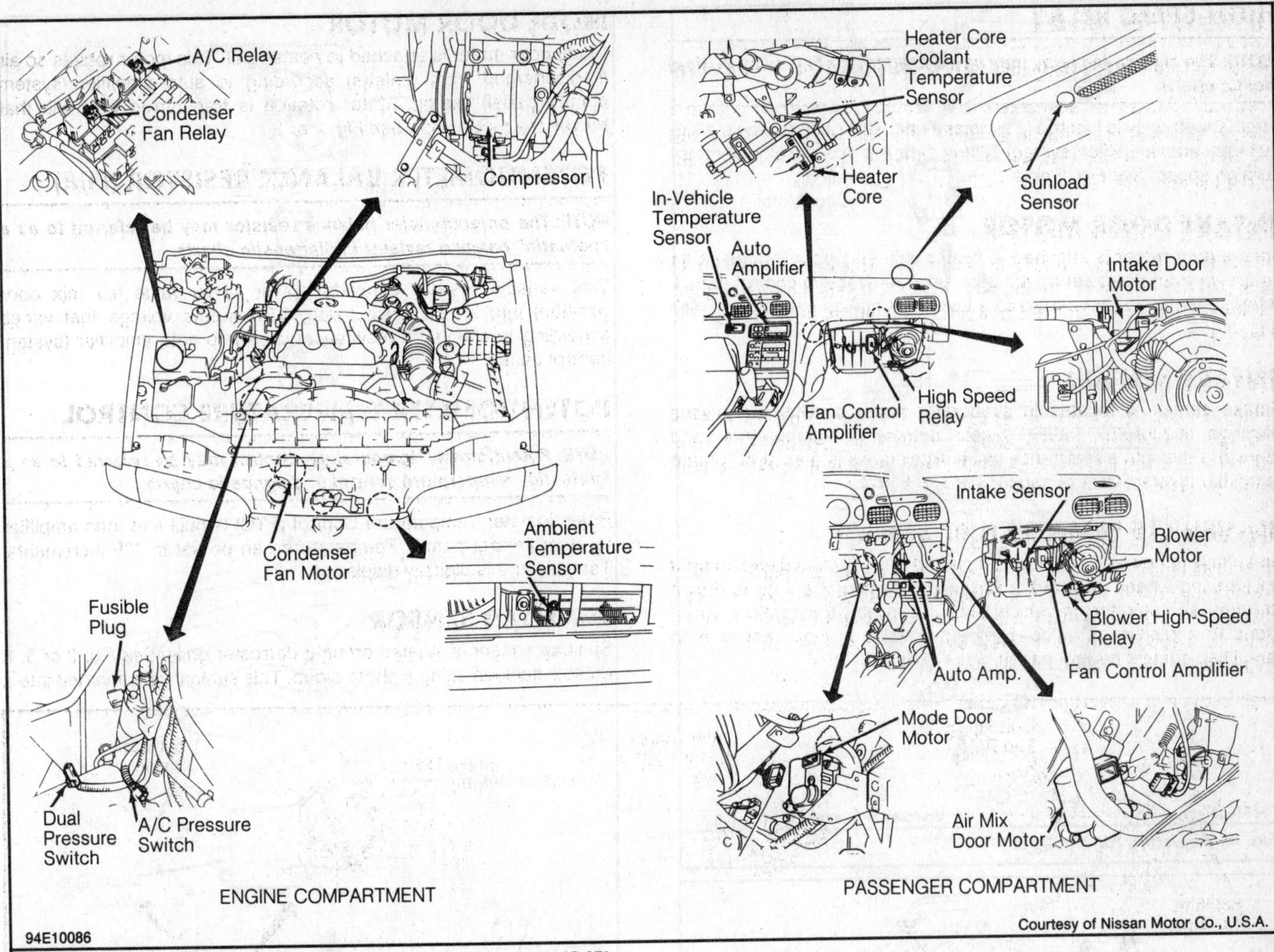
A/C Relay
Condenser Fan Relay
Compressor
Condenser Fan Motor
Ambient Temperature Sensor
Fusible Plug
Dual Pressure Switch
A/C Pressure Switch
ENGINE COMPARTMENT
Heater Core Coolant Temperature Sensor
Heater Core
Sunload Sensor
In-Vehicle Temperature Sensor
Auto Amplifier
Intake Door Motor
Fan Control Amplifier
High Speed Relay
Intake Sensor
Blower Motor
Blower High-Speed Relay
Auto Amp.
Fan Control Amplifier
Mode Door Motor
Air Mix Door Motor
PASSENGER COMPARTMENT
94E10086
Courtesy of Nissan Motor Co., U.S.A.

Fig. 3: Locating Automatic A/C-Heater System Components (Q45)

current value, which is input into auto amplifier (system control panel).

If auto amplifier detects an abrupt change in sunload through the sunload sensor, sunload input process will vary input to auto amplifier for approximately 38 seconds to prevent an unpleasant change in A/C operation.

HEATER CONTROL VALVE

J30 - Water cock/heater control valve lever is linked to the air mix door shaft so that amount of coolant flowing to heater core is a function of the air mix door aperture.

ADJUSTMENTS

AIR MIX DOOR

1) Install air mix door motor onto heater unit. Connect body harness. Access Code 41. See SELF-DIAGNOSIS STEP 4 under TROUBLE SHOOTING. Moving air mix door lever by hand, hold door in full cold position. Attach air mix door lever to rod holder. *See Fig. 4.*
2) Ensure air mix door is in correct position when accessing Codes 41-46. See SELF-DIAGNOSIS STEP 4 under TROUBLE SHOOTING.

INTAKE DOOR

1) Install intake door motor on intake unit. Plug in harness connector. Access Code 41. See SELF-DIAGNOSIS STEP 4 under TROUBLE SHOOTING. Moving intake door link by hand, hold intake door in recirculate position. Attach intake door lever to rod holder. *See Fig. 5.*
2) Ensure intake door is in correct position when accessing Codes 41-46. See SELF-DIAGNOSIS STEP 4 under TROUBLE SHOOTING.

MODE DOOR

1) Install mode door motor. Connect wiring harness. Access Code 41. See SELF-DIAGNOSIS STEP 4 under TROUBLE SHOOTING. Moving side link by hand, hold mode door in vent position. Attach mode door motor rod to side link rod holder. *See Fig. 6.*
2) Ensure mode door is in correct position when accessing Codes 41-46. See SELF-DIAGNOSIS STEP 4 under TROUBLE SHOOTING.

TROUBLE SHOOTING

NOTE: During all trouble shooting functions, ensure fresh air vent is in closed position unless otherwise noted. Also, see TROUBLE SHOOTING - J30 or Q45 charts following this article.

SELF-DIAGNOSTIC INFORMATION

NOTE: On J30 models, CONSULT tester may also be used to perform preliminary checks. Refer to tester manufacturer for instructions.

Preliminary Information - 1) Read ENTERING/EXITING SELF-DIAGNOSTICS.
2) Perform PRELIMINARY CHECK for appropriate vehicle symptom. See TROUBLE SHOOTING - J30 charts or Q45 charts following this article. PRELIMINARY CHECK charts will direct technician to either SELF-DIAGNOSIS or appropriate DIAGNOSTIC PROCEDURE chart(s).

1993 AUTOMATIC A/C-HEATER SYSTEMS J30 & Q45 (Cont.)

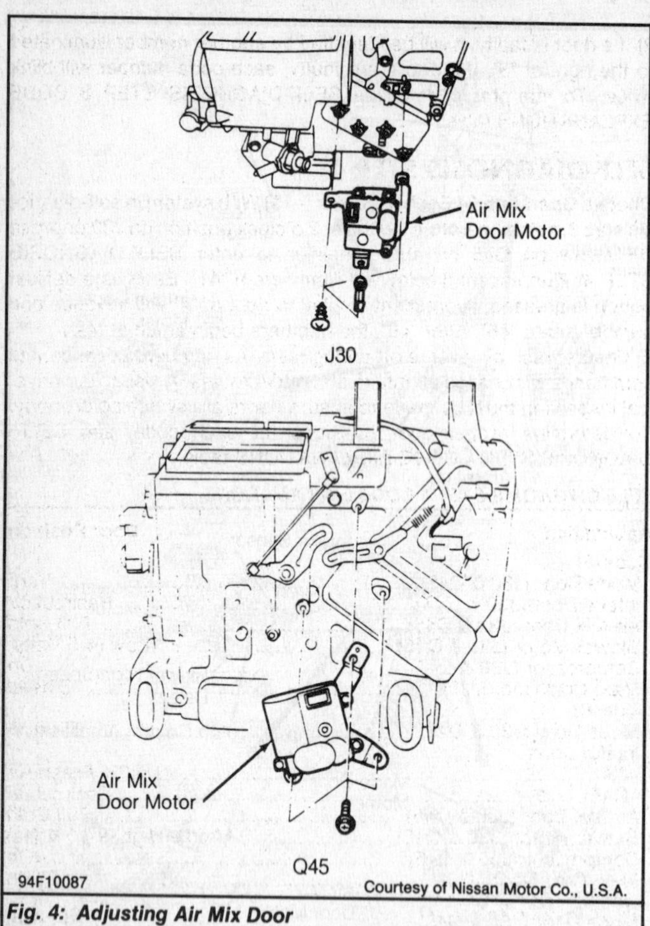
Air Mix
Door Motor
J30
Air Mix
Door Motor
Q45
94F10087
Courtesy of Nissan Motor Co., U.S.A.

Fig. 4: Adjusting Air Mix Door

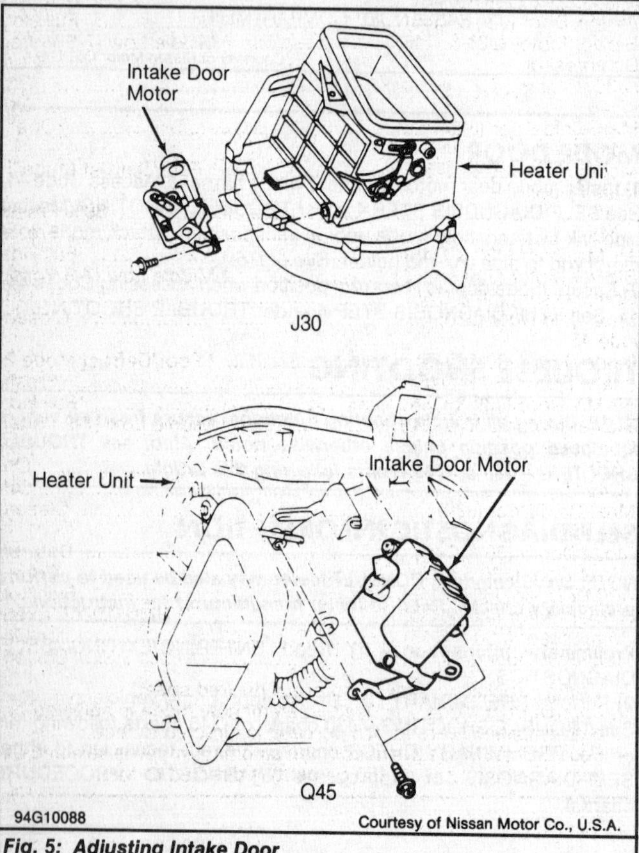
Intake Door
Motor
Heater Uni
J30
Heater Unit
Intake Door Motor
Q45
94G10088
Courtesy of Nissan Motor Co., U.S.A.

Fig. 5: Adjusting Intake Door

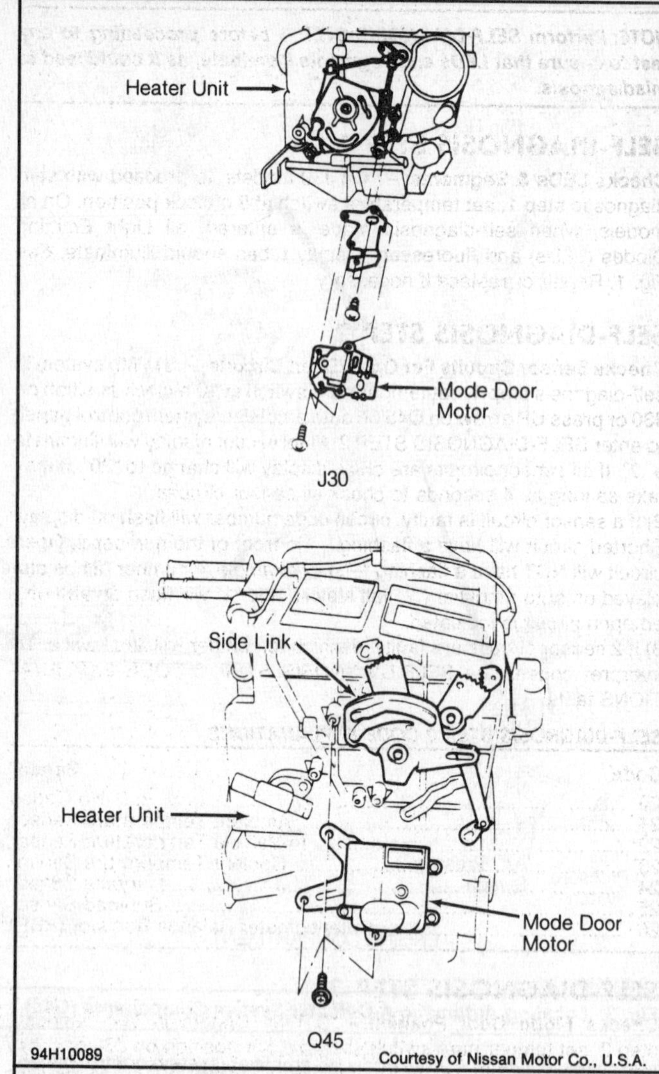
Heater Unit
Mode Door
Motor
J30
Side Link
Heater Unit
Mode Door
Motor
Q45
94H10089
Courtesy of Nissan Motor Co., U.S.A.

Fig. 6: Adjusting Mode Door Motor

3) Perform appropriate SELF-DIAGNOSIS step under TROUBLE SHOOTING or perform appropriate DIAGNOSTIC PROCEDURE. See TROUBLE SHOOTING – J30 charts or TROUBLE SHOOTING – Q45 charts following this article.

ENTERING/EXITING SELF-DIAGNOSTICS

1) To enter self-diagnostic mode, turn ignition off. Without starting engine, turn ignition on. Press vent button on J30 or OFF button on Q45 on auto amplifier (system control panel) for at least 5 seconds.
2) If engine is started, vent button on J30 or OFF button on Q45 must be pressed within 10 seconds after engine has started. The vent button on J30 or OFF button on Q45 must be pressed for at least 5 seconds to enter self-diagnostic mode with engine running.
3) There are 5 SELF-DIAGNOSIS STEPS and one AUXILIARY MECHANISM TEST. The AUXILIARY MECHANISM TEST checks the temperature setting trimmer. If diagnostics are entered without engine running, SELF-DIAGNOSIS STEPS 4 and 5 cannot be completed.
4) To move from one diagnostic step to another, press AUTO switch on J30 or UP or DOWN arrow (temperature control switch) on Q45 on auto amplifier. To move from SELF-DIAGNOSIS STEP 5 to AUXILIARY MECHANISM TEST, press fan switch. On all models, to end self-diagnostics, press AUTO button or turn ignition off.

1993 AUTOMATIC A/C-HEATER SYSTEMS J30 & Q45 (Cont.)

NOTE: Perform SELF-DIAGNOSIS STEP 1 before proceeding to any test to ensure that LEDs and segments illuminate, as it could lead to misdiagnosis.

SELF-DIAGNOSIS STEP 1

Checks LEDs & Segments – On J30 models, to proceed with self-diagnostic step 1, set temperature switch at 9 o'clock position. On all models, when self-diagnosis mode is entered, all Light Emitting Diodes (LEDs) and fluorescent display tubes should illuminate. *See Fig. 1.* Repair or replace if necessary.

SELF-DIAGNOSIS STEP 2

Checks Sensor Circuits For Open/Short Circuits – **1)** With system in self-diagnosis step 1, set temperature switch at 10 o'clock position on J30 or press UP arrow on Q45 on auto amplifier (system control panel) to enter SELF-DIAGNOSIS STEP 2. Fluorescent display will illuminate a "2". If all sensor circuits are okay, display will change to "20". It may take as long as 4 seconds to check all sensor circuits.

2) If a sensor circuit is faulty, circuit code number will flash on display. Shorted circuit will have a flashing "–" in front of the number 2. Open circuit will NOT have a flashing "–". For example, if number "21" is displayed on auto amplifier ("2" will stay lit, and "1" will flash on and off), an open circuit is indicated.

3) If 2 sensor circuits are faulty, each code number will flash twice. To interpret codes, see SELF-DIAGNOSIS STEP 2 CODE EXPLANATIONS table.

SELF-DIAGNOSIS STEP 2 CODE EXPLANATIONS

Code	Sensor
20	No Codes
21	Ambient Temperature Sensor
22	In-Vehicle Temperature Sensor
23	Coolant Temperature Sensor
24	Intake Sensor
25	Sunload Sensor
26	Potentiometer Balance Resistor (PBR)

SELF-DIAGNOSIS STEP 3

Checks Mode Door Position – **1)** With system in self-diagnosis step 2, set temperature switch at 12 o'clock position on J30 or press UP arrow on Q45 on auto amplifier to enter SELF-DIAGNOSIS STEP 3. Fluorescent display will illuminate a "3". If all doors are in good order, display will change to "30". It may take as long as 16-20 seconds to check all doors.

NOTE: If any mode door motor position switch is malfunctioning, mode door motor also will malfunction.

SELF-DIAGNOSIS STEP 3 CODE EXPLANATIONS

Code	Door
30 (J30 & Q45)	No Codes
31 (J30 & Q45)	Vent
32 (J30 & Q45)	Bi-Level (B/L)
33 (J30 & Q45)	Bi-Level (B/L)
34 (J30 & Q45)	[1] Foot/Defrost Mode 1 (F/D 1)
35 (J30 & Q45)	[2] Foot/Defrost Mode 2 (F/D 2)
36 (J30)	Fresh Air
36 (Q45)	Defrost
37 (J30)	80% Fresh Air
38 (J30)	20% Fresh Air
39 (J30)	Recirculated

[1] – Foot/Defrost Mode 1 is used when manual mode is selected on auto amplifier. More air (75 percent) is directed to feet.

[2] – Foot/Defrost Mode 2 is used when automatic mode is selected on auto amplifier. Less air (50 percent) is directed to feet.

2) If a door is faulty, it will be identified by another number illuminated to the right of "3". If 2 doors are faulty, each code number will blink twice. To interpret codes, see SELF-DIAGNOSIS STEP 3 CODE EXPLANATIONS table.

SELF-DIAGNOSIS STEP 4

Checks Operation Of Each Actuator – **1)** With system in self-diagnosis step 3, set temperature switch at 2 o'clock position on J30 or press UP arrow on Q45 on auto amplifier to enter SELF-DIAGNOSIS STEP 4. Fluorescent display will illuminate a "41". Each time defrost button is pressed, fluorescent display to right of "4" will advance one number, up to "46". After "46", the numbers begin again at "41".

2) Ensure fresh air lever is off during tests. As numbers advance, the commands will change air intake and outlet routes. A visual and physical inspection must be made to ensure doors are switching properly. To determine proper door positions for each code, see SELF-DIAGNOSIS STEP 4 CODE EXPLANATIONS table.

SELF-DIAGNOSIS STEP 4 CODE EXPLANATIONS

Application	Door Position
Code 41	
Mode Door (J30 & Q45)	Vent
Intake Door (J30 & Q45)	Recirculate
Air Mix Door (J30 & Q45)	Full Cold
Blower Motor (J30 & Q45)	[1] Low (4-5 Volts)
Compressor (J30 & Q45)	On
Max. Cold Door (J30)	Closed
Code 42	
Mode Door (J30 & Q45)	Bi-Level
Intake Door	
J30	20% Fresh Air
Q45	Recirculate
Air Mix Door (J30 & Q45)	Full Cold
Blower Motor (J30 & Q45)	[1] Middle High (9-11 Volts)
Compressor (J30 & Q45)	On
Max. Cold Door (J30)	Open
Code 43	
Mode Door (J30 & Q45)	Bi-Level
Intake Door (J30 & Q45)	20% Fresh Air
Air Mix Door (J30 & Q45)	Full Hot
Blower Motor (J30 & Q45)	[1] Middle Low (7-9 Volts)
Compressor	
J30	Off
Q45	On
Max. Cold Door (J30)	Open
Code 44	
Mode Door (J30 & Q45)	[2] Foot/Defrost Mode 1
Intake Door	
J30	80% Fresh
Q45	Fresh
Air Mix Door (J30 & Q45)	Full Hot
Blower Motor (J30 & Q45)	[1] Middle Low (7-9 Volts)
Compressor (J30 & Q45)	Off
Max. Cold Door (J30)	Closed
Code 45	
Mode Door (J30 & Q45)	[3] Foot/Defrost Mode 2
Intake Door (J30 & Q45)	Fresh
Air Mix Door (J30 & Q45)	Full Hot
Blower Motor (J30 & Q45)	[1] Middle Low (7-9 Volts)
Compressor	
J30	On
Q45	Off
Max. Cold Door (J30)	Closed
Code 46	
Mode Door (J30 & Q45)	Defrost
Intake Door (J30 & Q45)	Fresh
Air Mix Door (J30 & Q45)	Full Hot
Blower Motor (J30 & Q45)	[1] High (10-12 Volts)
Compressor (J30 & Q45)	On
Max. Cold Door (J30)	Closed

[1] – Voltage applied to blower motor for desired speed.

[2] – Foot/Defrost Mode 1 is used when manual mode is selected on auto amplifier. More air (75 percent) is directed to feet.

[3] – Foot/Defrost Mode 2 is used when automatic mode is selected on auto amplifier. Less air (50 percent) is directed to feet.

SELF-DIAGNOSIS STEP 5

Checks Temperature Detected By Sensors – **1)** With system in self-diagnosis step 4, set temperature switch at 3 o'clock position on J30 or press UP arrow on Q45 on auto amplifier to enter SELF-DIAGNOSIS STEP 5. Fluorescent display will illuminate a "5". When defrost button is pressed once, fluorescent display will show temperature detected by intake sensor.

2) Press defrost button again; fluorescent display will show temperature detected by in-vehicle sensor. Press defrost button again; fluorescent display will show temperature detected by intake sensor.

3) Press defrost button again; fluorescent display again will illuminate "5". If temperature shown on fluorescent display differs greatly from actual temperature, inspect sensor circuit. If sensor circuit is okay, go to TESTING.

AUXILIARY MECHANISM TEST

Temperature Setting Trimmer – **1)** Temperature setting trimmer compensates for small differences between temperature setting (fluorescent display) and temperature felt by passengers in a range of plus or minus 6°F.

2) With system in SELF-DIAGNOSIS STEP 5, press fan button to enter auxiliary mode. Press UP or DOWN arrow buttons as desired. Each time an arrow button is pressed, temperature will change 1°F on fluorescent display. If vehicle battery is disconnected, temperature setting goes to 0°F.

TESTING

WARNING: To avoid injury from accidental air bag deployment, read and carefully follow all SERVICE PRECAUTIONS and DISABLING & ACTIVATING AIR BAG SYSTEM procedures in AIR BAG SYSTEM SAFETY article in GENERAL SERVICING.

A/C SYSTEM PERFORMANCE

1) Park vehicle out of direct sunlight. Ensure condenser and radiator are free of obstructions. Close all doors, but leave a window open. Open engine hood. Turn A/C switch to AUTO position. Set temperature setting to maximum cold position, mode switch to vent position and fan switch to highest speed.

2) Start engine and run it at 1500 RPM. Record ambient temperature and check outlet air temperature at center instrument panel vent after A/C system has run for about 10 minutes. See A/C SYSTEM PERFORMANCE SPECIFICATIONS table.

A/C SYSTEM PERFORMANCE SPECIFICATIONS [1]

Ambient Temperature °F (°C)	Outlet Air Temperature °F (°C)
68 (20)	35-37 (1.7-2.8)
77 (25)	46-50 (7.8-10.0)
86 (30)	51-55 (10.6-12.8)
95 (35)	56-61 (13.3-16.1)
104 (40)	62-66 (16.7-19.0)

[1] – Based on a relative humidity of 50-60 percent.

A/C, CONDENSER FAN & HIGH-SPEED RELAY

Remove relay from vehicle. Apply 12 volts to coil side of relay. Check for continuity between 2 remaining relay terminals. *See Fig. 7.* If continuity is not present, replace relay.

AMBIENT TEMPERATURE SENSOR

Turn ignition off. Disconnect underhood ambient temperature sensor connector. *See Fig. 2 or 3.* Using an ohmmeter, measure resistance between harness terminals. See AMBIENT TEMPERATURE, IN-VEHICLE & INTAKE SENSORS RESISTANCE table.

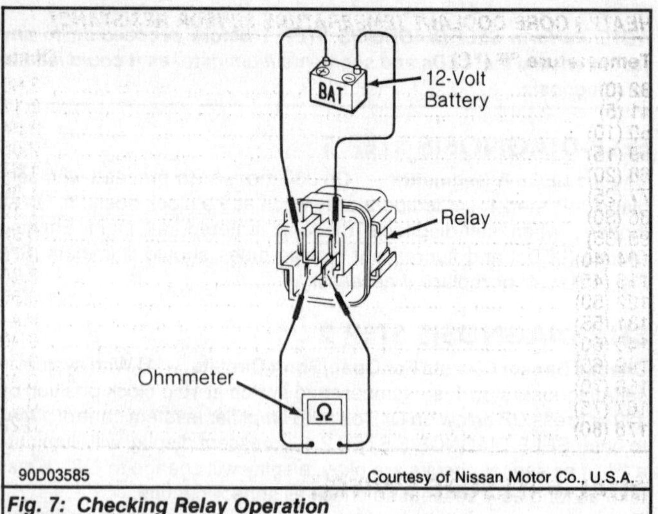
BAT
12-Volt Battery
Relay
Ohmmeter
Ω
90D03585
Courtesy of Nissan Motor Co., U.S.A.
Fig. 7: Checking Relay Operation

AMBIENT TEMPERATURE, IN-VEHICLE & INTAKE SENSORS RESISTANCE

Temperature °F (°C)	Ohms
-31 (-35)	38,350
-22 (-30)	28,620
-13 (-25)	21,610
-4 (-20)	16,500
5 (-15)	12,730
14 (-10)	9920
23 (-5)	7800
32 (0)	6190
41 (5)	4950
50 (10)	3990
59 (15)	3240
68 (20)	2650
77 (25)	2190
86 (30)	1810
95 (35)	1510
104 (40)	1270
113 (45)	1070
122 (50)	910
131 (55)	77
140 (60)	660
149 (65)	570

AUTO AMPLIFIER

Power Supply Check – Ensure ignition is off. Disconnect auto amplifier (system control panel) connector. Turn ignition on. Connect voltmeter, in turn, between ground and following auto amplifier terminals: No. 1, No. 2 and No. 3. For terminal identification, see WIRING DIAGRAMS. Voltage should be 12 volts at each terminal. Repair if necessary. If malfunction still exists after performing proper trouble shooting procedures and ensuring voltage readings are okay, replace auto amplifier.

Ground Circuit Check – Ensure ignition is off. Disconnect auto amplifier connector. Connect an ohmmeter between auto amplifier connector terminal No. 8 and ground. For terminal identification, see WIRING DIAGRAMS. Continuity should exist. Repair if necessary. If voltage readings are okay but malfunction still exists, replace auto amplifier.

HEATER CORE COOLANT TEMPERATURE SENSOR

Q45 – Turn ignition off. Disconnect heater core coolant temperature sensor connector. *See Fig. 3.* Using an ohmmeter, measure resistance between harness terminals. See HEATER CORE COOLANT TEMPERATURE SENSOR RESISTANCE table.

HEATER CORE COOLANT TEMPERATURE SENSOR RESISTANCE

Temperature °F (°C)	Ohms
32 (0)	3.99
41 (5)	3.17
50 (10)	2.54
59 (15)	2.05
68 (20)	1.67
77 (25)	1.36
86 (30)	1.12
95 (35)	0.93
104 (40)	0.78
113 (45)	0.65
122 (50)	0.55
131 (55)	0.47
140 (60)	0.40
149 (65)	0.34
158 (70)	0.29
167 (75)	0.25
176 (80)	0.22

DUAL-PRESSURE SWITCH

Q45 – Using an ohmmeter, check dual-pressure switch operation. See DUAL-PRESSURE SWITCH SPECIFICATIONS table.

DUAL-PRESSURE SWITCH SPECIFICATIONS

High-Side Line Pressure psi (kg/cm²)	System Operation	Continuity Exists
Decreasing To 26-31 (1.8-2.2)	Off	No
Increasing To 356-412 (25-29)	Off	No
Increasing To 26-34 (1.8-2.4)	On	Yes
Decreasing To 270-327 (19-23)	On	Yes

TRIPLE-PRESSURE SWITCH

J30 – Using an ohmmeter, check triple-pressure switch operation. See TRIPLE-PRESSURE SWITCH SPECIFICATIONS table.

TRIPLE-PRESSURE SWITCH SPECIFICATIONS

High-Side Line Pressure psi (kg/cm²)	System Operation	Continuity Exists
Decreasing To 22-29 (1.6-2.1)	Off	No
Increasing To 356-412 (25-29)	Off	No
Increasing To 23-33 (1.6-2.3)	On	Yes
Decreasing To 270-327 (19-23)	On	Yes

IN-VEHICLE TEMPERATURE SENSOR

Turn ignition off. Disconnect underdash in-vehicle sensor connector. *See Fig. 2 or 3*. Using an ohmmeter, measure resistance between harness terminals. See AMBIENT TEMPERATURE, IN-VEHICLE & INTAKE SENSORS RESISTANCE table under AMBIENT TEMPERATURE SENSOR.

INTAKE SENSOR

Turn ignition off. Disconnect underdash intake sensor connector. *See Fig. 2 or 3*. Using an ohmmeter, measure resistance between harness terminals. See AMBIENT TEMPERATURE, IN-VEHICLE & INTAKE SENSORS RESISTANCE table under AMBIENT TEMPERATURE SENSOR.

SUNLOAD SENSOR

1) Turn ignition off. Using a voltmeter, measure voltage between auto amplifier connector terminal No. 46 and ground on J30 or terminals No. 16 and 35 on Q45. *See Fig. 8*. This will measure output voltage. To vary voltage reading, apply direct sunlight to sensor, and then shield sensor.

2) To measure input of sunload sensor to auto amplifier (system control panel), disconnect sensor from vehicle harness. Connect an ammeter between sensor connector terminals. To vary current reading, apply direct sunlight to sensor, and then shield sensor. See SUNLOAD SENSOR SPECIFICATIONS table.

SUNLOAD SENSOR SPECIFICATIONS

Input Current (Milliamps)	Output Voltage (Volts)
0	5.0
.1	4.1
.2	3.1
.3	2.2
.4	1.3
.5	.4

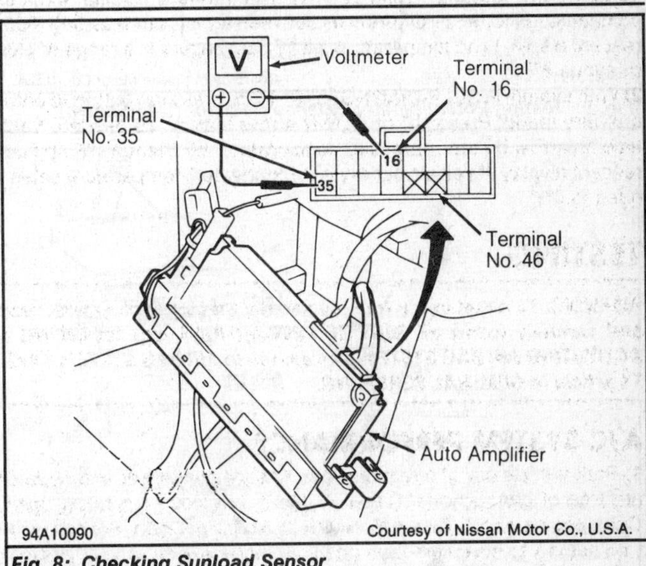
V
Voltmeter
Terminal No. 16
Terminal No. 35
16
35
Terminal No. 46
Auto Amplifier
94A10090
Courtesy of Nissan Motor Co., U.S.A.

Fig. 8: Checking Sunload Sensor

THERMOSWITCH

Using an ohmmeter, check thermoswitch operation. See THERMOSWITCH SPECIFICATIONS table.

THERMOSWITCH SPECIFICATIONS

Coolant Temperature °F (°C)	System Operation	Continuity Exists
Decreasing To 176-187 (80-86)	Off	No
Increasing To 189-199 (87-93)	On	Yes

POTENTIOMETER BALANCE RESISTOR (PBR)

1) Turn ignition on. On J30, with air mix door motor connected, measure voltage between terminals No. 34 and 48. See WIRING DIAGRAMS. On Q45, with air mix door connected, measure voltage between terminals No. 16 and 27. *See Fig. 9*. With air mix door in full cold position, voltmeter should indicate zero volt.

2) As air mix door motor moves from full cold to full hot position, voltmeter should indicate voltage slowly rising to 5 volts. PBR is located inside air mix door motor.

1993 AUTOMATIC A/C-HEATER SYSTEMS J30 & Q45 (Cont.)

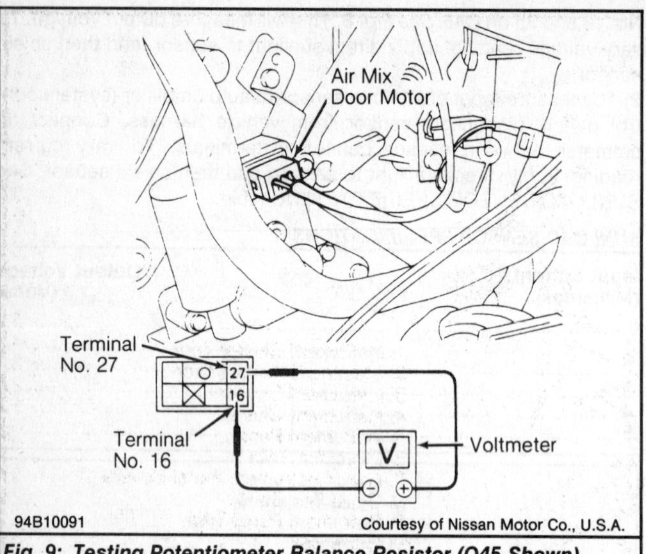
Air Mix
Door Motor
Terminal
No. 27
27
16
Terminal
No. 16
V
Voltmeter
94B10091
Courtesy of Nissan Motor Co., U.S.A.

Fig. 9: Testing Potentiometer Balance Resistor (Q45 Shown)

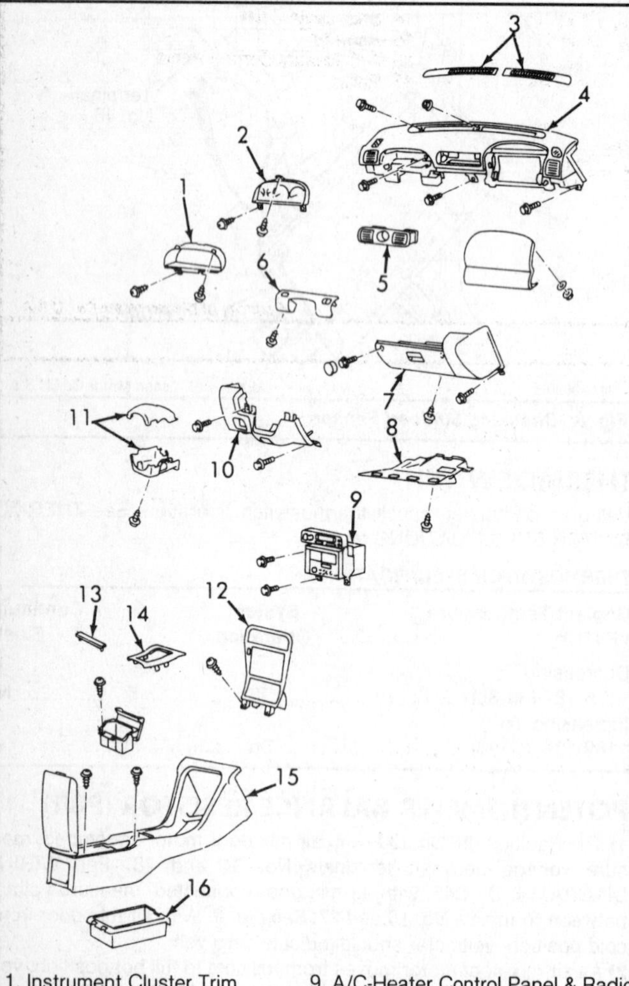
1. Instrument Cluster Trim
2. Instrument Cluster
3. Defroster Grille
4. Instrument Panel
5. Center Vent
6. Cluster Trim
7. Glove Box
8. Lower Instrument Panel Cover
9. A/C-Heater Control Panel & Radio
10. Lower Instrument Panel Cover
11. Steering Column Cover
12. Center Console Trim
13. Center Console Mask
14. Shift Console Trim
15. Center Console Assembly
16. Center Console Pocket
94C10092
Courtesy of Nissan Motor Co., U.S.A.

Fig. 10: Exploded View Of Instrument Panel (J30)

REMOVAL & INSTALLATION

WARNING: To avoid injury from accidental air bag deployment, read and carefully follow all SERVICE PRECAUTIONS and DISABLING & ACTIVATING AIR BAG SYSTEM procedures in AIR BAG SYSTEM SAFETY article in GENERAL SERVICING.

INSTRUMENT PANEL

Removal & Installation (J30) – 1) Disable air bag system. See AIR BAG SYSTEM SAFETY article in GENERAL SERVICING. Remove steering wheel. Remove steering column cover and lower instrument panel on driver's side. *See Fig. 10.*

2) Remove instrument cluster trim panels and instrument cluster assembly. Remove lower instrument cover on passenger's side. Remove glove box assembly. Remove shift console cover and center console cover. Remove A/C-heater control panel and radio assembly.

3) Remove center vent, center console trim and cup holder. Remove console pocket and lower instrument center panel. Remove defroster grille and front pillar garnish. Remove instrument panel and pads. *See Fig. 10.* To install, reverse removal procedure.

Removal & Installation (Q45) – 1) Disable air bag system. See AIR BAG SYSTEM SAFETY article in GENERAL SERVICING. Remove steering wheel. Remove steering column cover. Remove shift console cover. *See Fig. 12.*

2) Remove ashtray, center console panel trim and lower instrument panel trim on driver's side. Remove front floor console and rear floor console assembly. Remove instrument cluster panel. Remove glove box and lower instrument panel cover on passenger side. *See Fig. 12.*

3) Remove instrument panel finisher, defroster grille, radio and A/C-heater control panel. Remove instrument cluster assembly. Remove instrument panel assembly and pads. *See Fig. 12.* To install, reverse removal procedure.

A/C-HEATER COMPONENTS & DUCTS

NOTE: Removal and installation information is not available from manufacturer. On J30, use Figs. 2, 10 and 12 as guides. On Q45, use Figs. 3, 11 and 13 as guides.

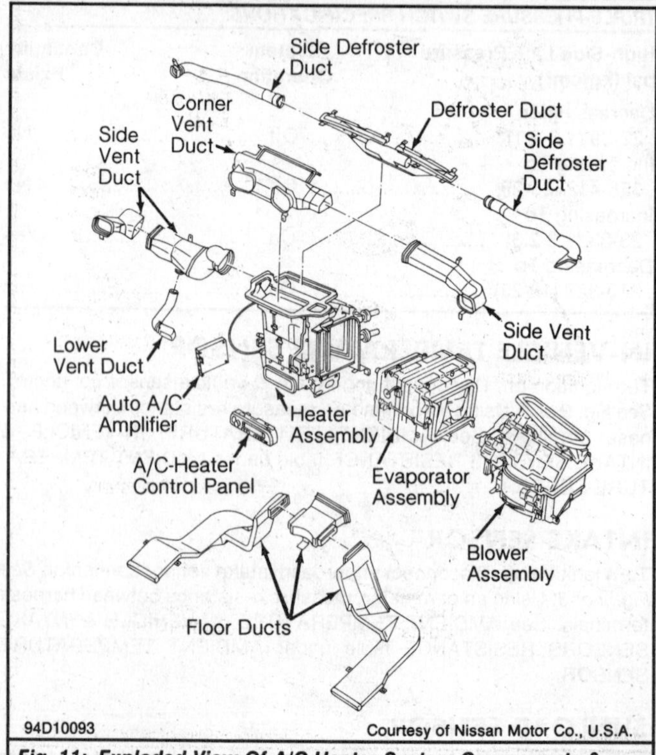
Side Defroster
Duct
Corner
Vent
Duct
Defroster Duct
Side
Vent
Duct
Side
Defroster
Duct
Side Vent
Duct
Lower
Vent Duct
Auto A/C
Amplifier
Heater
Assembly
A/C-Heater
Control Panel
Evaporator
Assembly
Blower
Assembly
Floor Ducts
94D10093
Courtesy of Nissan Motor Co., U.S.A.

Fig. 11: Exploded View Of A/C-Heater System Components & Ducts (J30)

1. Instrument Cluster Trim
2. Steering Column Cover
3. Instrument Cluster Lid
4. Instrument Cluster
5. Instrument Panel
6. Defroster Grille
7. Lower Instrument Panel Covers
8. Glove Box Covers
9. Instrument Panel Trim
10. Glove Box
12. Center Console Trim
13. Center Console Assembly
14. Shift Lever Trim
15. Ashtray
16. A/C-Heater Control Panel
17. Radio

92J02541

Courtesy of Nissan Motor Co., U.S.A.

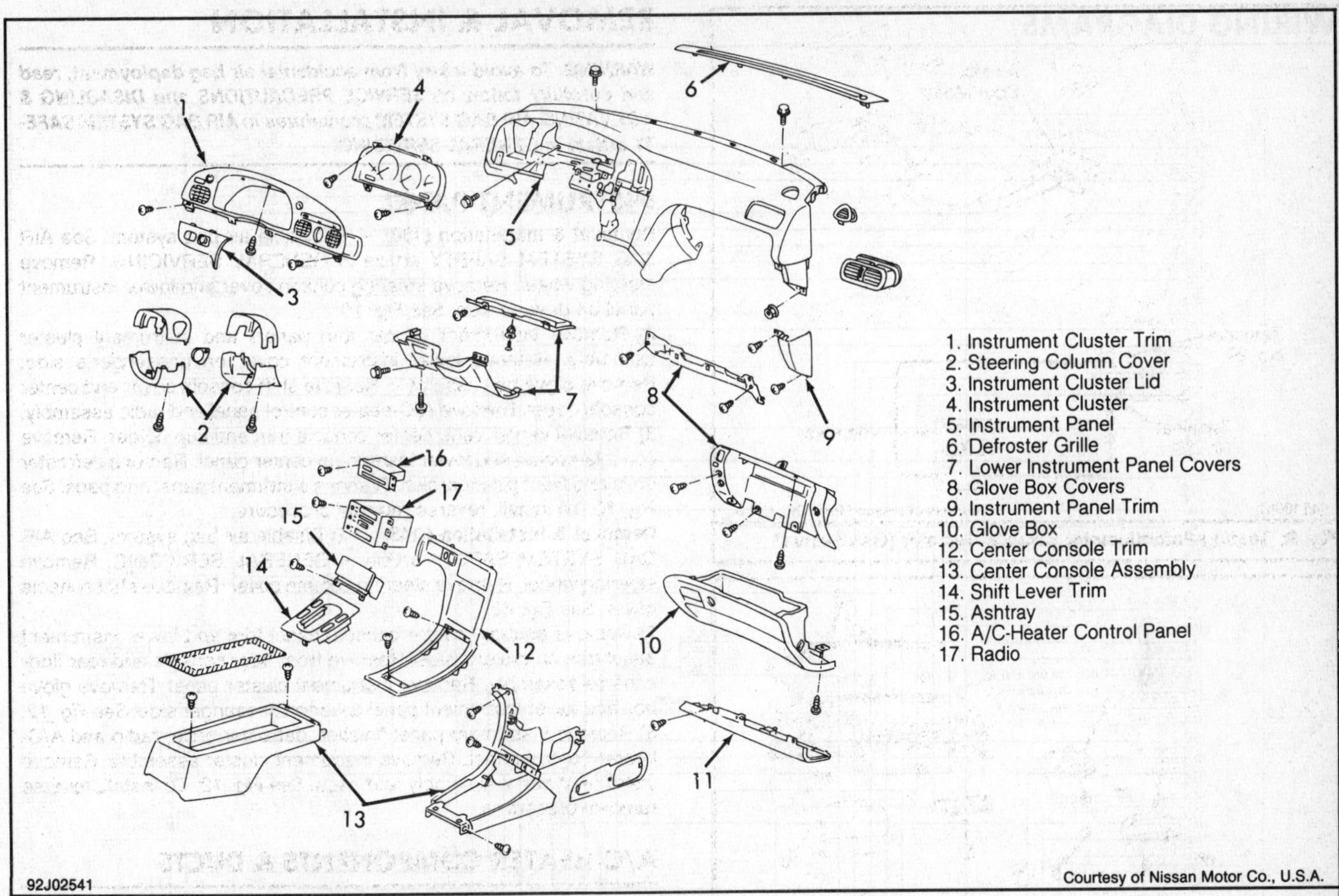

Fig. 12: Exploded View Of Instrument Panel (Q45)

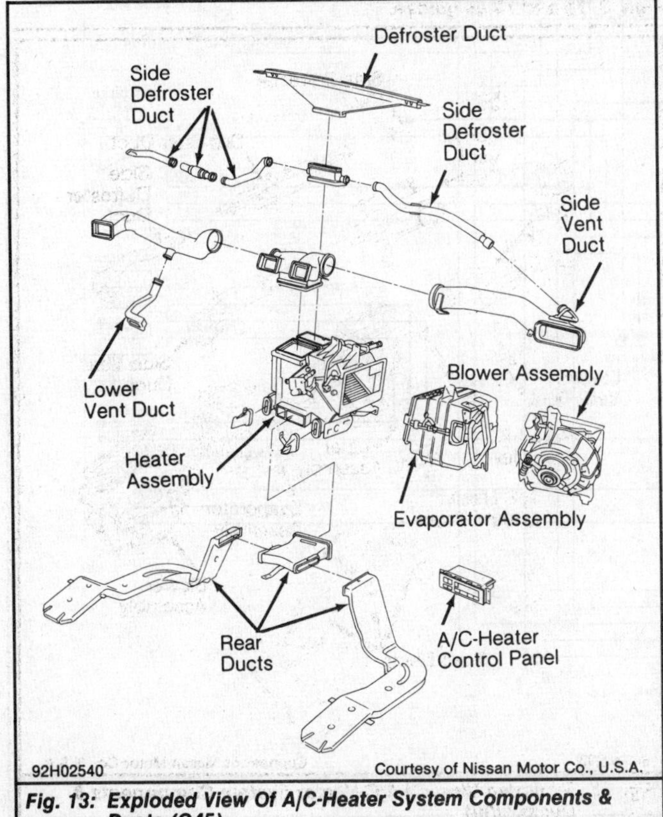
Defroster Duct
Side Defroster Duct
Side Defroster Duct
Side Vent Duct
Lower Vent Duct
Blower Assembly
Heater Assembly
Evaporator Assembly
Rear Ducts
A/C-Heater Control Panel
92H02540
Courtesy of Nissan Motor Co., U.S.A.

Fig. 13: Exploded View Of A/C-Heater System Components & Ducts (Q45)

1993 AUTOMATIC A/C-HEATER SYSTEMS J30 & Q45 (Cont.)

WIRING DIAGRAMS

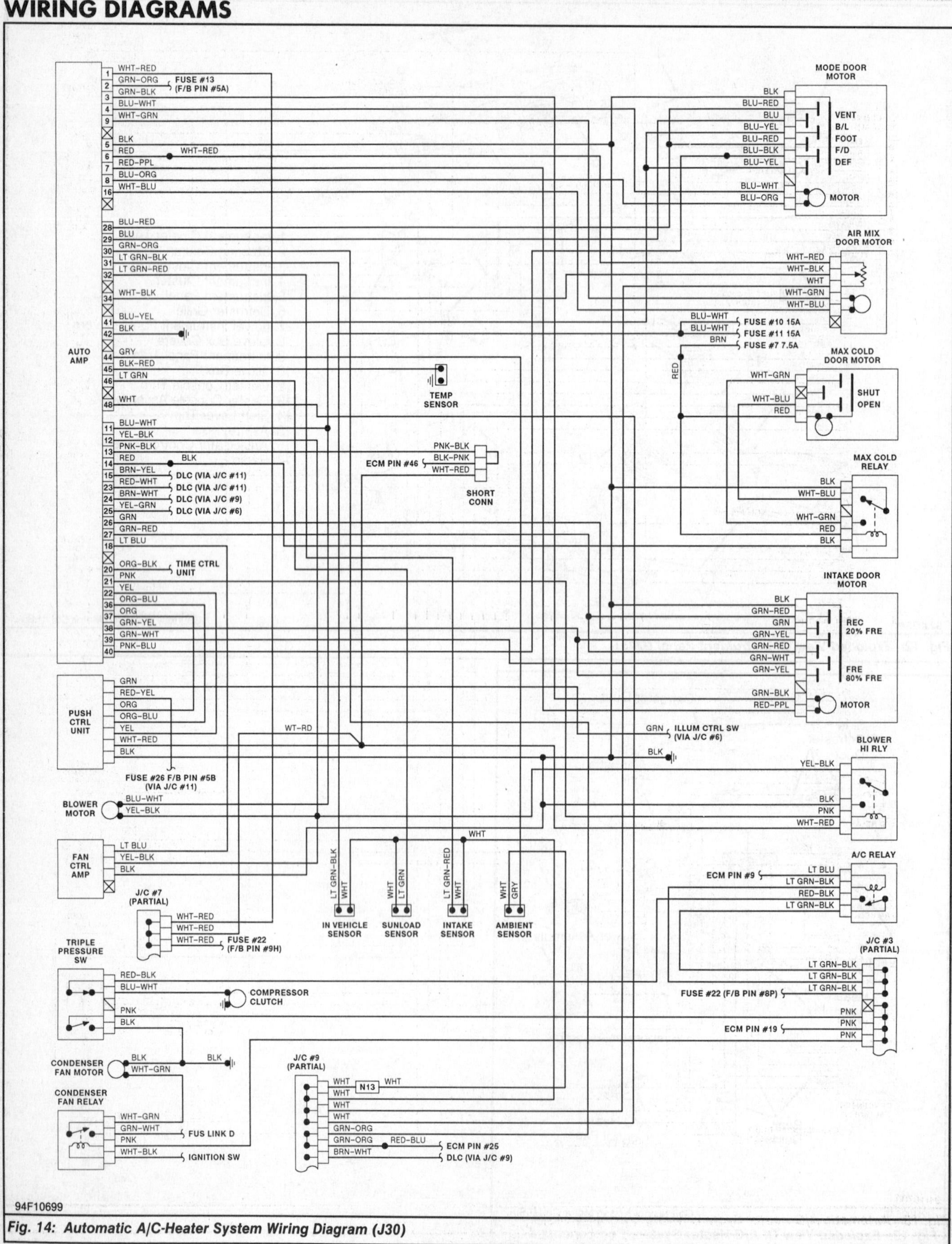
AUTO AMP
WHT-RED
GRN-ORG
GRN-BLK
BLU-WHT
WHT-GRN
BLK
RED
RED-PPL
BLU-ORG
WHT-BLU
FUSE #13 (F/B PIN #5A)
WHT-RED
BLU-RED
BLU
GRN-ORG
LT GRN-BLK
LT GRN-RED
WHT-BLK
BLU-YEL
BLK
GRY
BLK-RED
LT GRN
WHT
BLU-WHT
YEL-BLK
PNK-BLK
RED
BLK
BRN-YEL
RED-WHT
BRN-WHT
YEL-GRN
GRN
GRN-RED
LT BLU
DLC (VIA J/C #11)
DLC (VIA J/C #11)
DLC (VIA J/C #9)
DLC (VIA J/C #6)
ORG-BLK
PNK
TIME CTRL UNIT
YEL
ORG-BLU
ORG
GRN-YEL
GRN-WHT
PNK-BLU
PUSH CTRL UNIT
GRN
RED-YEL
ORG
ORG-BLU
YEL
WHT-RED
BLK
WT-RD
FUSE #26 F/B PIN #5B (VIA J/C #11)
BLOWER MOTOR
BLU-WHT
YEL-BLK
FAN CTRL AMP
LT BLU
YEL-BLK
BLK
J/C #7 (PARTIAL)
WHT-RED
WHT-RED
WHT-RED
FUSE #22 (F/B PIN #9H)
TRIPLE PRESSURE SW
RED-BLK
BLU-WHT
PNK
BLK
COMPRESSOR CLUTCH
CONDENSER FAN MOTOR
BLK
WHT-GRN
BLK
CONDENSER FAN RELAY
WHT-GRN
GRN-WHT
PNK
WHT-BLK
FUS LINK D
IGNITION SW
TEMP SENSOR
ECM PIN #46
PNK-BLK
BLK-PNK
WHT-RED
SHORT CONN
LT GRN-BLK
WHT
IN VEHICLE SENSOR
WHT
LT GRN
SUNLOAD SENSOR
LT GRN-RED
WHT
INTAKE SENSOR
WHT
GRY
AMBIENT SENSOR
J/C #9 (PARTIAL)
WHT
N13
WHT
WHT
WHT
WHT
GRN-ORG
GRN-ORG
RED-BLU
BRN-WHT
ECM PIN #25
DLC (VIA J/C #9)
MODE DOOR MOTOR
BLK
BLU-RED
BLU
BLU-YEL
BLU-RED
BLU-BLK
BLU-YEL
BLU-WHT
BLU-ORG
VENT
B/L
FOOT
F/D
DEF
MOTOR
AIR MIX DOOR MOTOR
WHT-RED
WHT-BLK
WHT
WHT-GRN
WHT-BLU
BLU-WHT
BLU-WHT
BRN
FUSE #10 15A
FUSE #11 15A
FUSE #7 7.5A
RED
MAX COLD DOOR MOTOR
WHT-GRN
WHT-BLU
RED
SHUT
OPEN
MAX COLD RELAY
BLK
WHT-BLU
WHT-GRN
RED
BLK
INTAKE DOOR MOTOR
BLK
GRN-RED
GRN
GRN-YEL
GRN-RED
GRN-WHT
GRN-YEL
GRN-BLK
RED-PPL
REC
20% FRE
FRE
80% FRE
MOTOR
GRN
ILLUM CTRL SW (VIA J/C #6)
BLK
BLOWER HI RLY
YEL-BLK
BLK
PNK
WHT-RED
A/C RELAY
ECM PIN #9
LT BLU
LT GRN-BLK
RED-BLK
LT GRN-BLK
J/C #3 (PARTIAL)
LT GRN-BLK
LT GRN-BLK
LT GRN-BLK
FUSE #22 (F/B PIN #8P)
PNK
PNK
PNK
ECM PIN #19
94F10699

Fig. 14: Automatic A/C-Heater System Wiring Diagram (J30)

1993 AUTOMATIC A/C-HEATER SYSTEMS J30 & Q45 (Cont.)

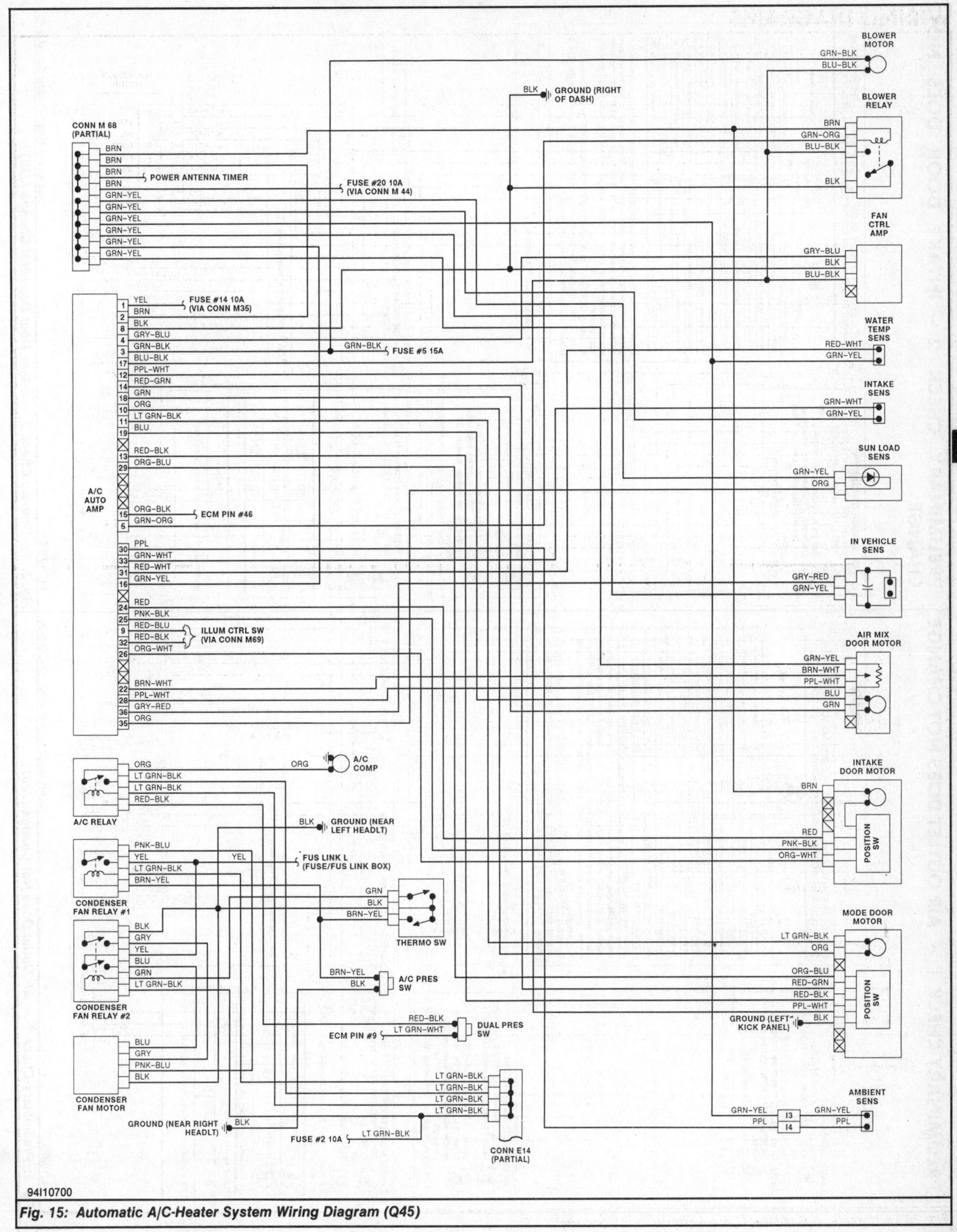

BLOWER MOTOR
GRN-BLK
BLU-BLK
GROUND (RIGHT OF DASH)
BLOWER RELAY
BRN
GRN-ORG
BLU-BLK
BLK
CONN M 68 (PARTIAL)
BRN
POWER ANTENNA TIMER
GRN-YEL
FUSE #20 10A (VIA CONN M 44)
FAN CTRL AMP
GRY-BLU
BLK
BLU-BLK
YEL
FUSE #14 10A (VIA CONN M35)
GRY-BLU
GRN-BLK
FUSE #5 15A
BLU-BLK
PPL-WHT
RED-GRN
GRN
ORG
LT GRN-BLK
BLU
RED-BLK
ORG-BLU
WATER TEMP SENS
RED-WHT
GRN-YEL
INTAKE SENS
GRN-WHT
SUN LOAD SENS
A/C AUTO AMP
ORG-BLK
GRN-ORG
ECM PIN #46
PPL
GRN-WHT
RED-WHT
IN VEHICLE SENS
GRY-RED
RED
PNK-BLK
RED-BLU
ILLUM CTRL SW (VIA CONN M69)
ORG-WHT
AIR MIX DOOR MOTOR
BRN-WHT
PPL-WHT
GRY-RED
A/C COMP
A/C RELAY
GROUND (NEAR LEFT HEADLT)
INTAKE DOOR MOTOR
POSITION SW
PNK-BLU
FUS LINK L (FUSE/FUS LINK BOX)
BRN-YEL
CONDENSER FAN RELAY #1
THERMO SW
MODE DOOR MOTOR
GRY
CONDENSER FAN RELAY #2
A/C PRES SW
GROUND (LEFT KICK PANEL)
DUAL PRES SW
ECM PIN #9
LT GRN-WHT
CONDENSER FAN MOTOR
AMBIENT SENS
GROUND (NEAR RIGHT HEADLT)
FUSE #2 10A
CONN E14 (PARTIAL)
I3
I4
94I10700

Fig. 15: Automatic A/C-Heater System Wiring Diagram (Q45)

1993 AUTOMATIC A/C-HEATER SYSTEMS
Trouble Shooting – J30

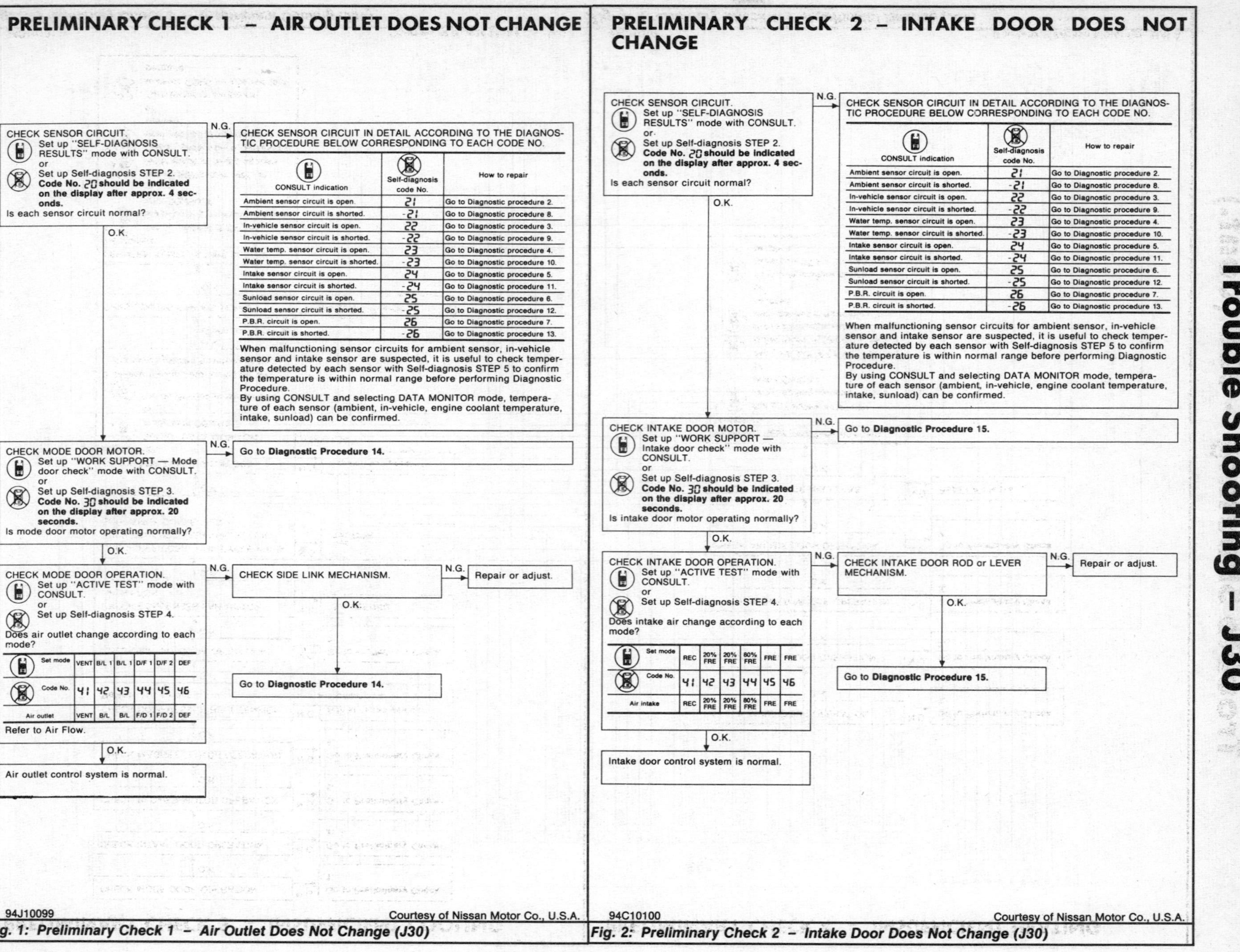
PRELIMINARY CHECK 1 – AIR OUTLET DOES NOT CHANGE
CHECK SENSOR CIRCUIT.
Set up "SELF-DIAGNOSIS RESULTS" mode with CONSULT.
or
Set up Self-diagnosis STEP 2.
Code No. 20 should be indicated on the display after approx. 4 seconds.
Is each sensor circuit normal?
N.G.
CHECK SENSOR CIRCUIT IN DETAIL ACCORDING TO THE DIAGNOSTIC PROCEDURE BELOW CORRESPONDING TO EACH CODE NO.
CONSULT indication | Self-diagnosis code No. | How to repair
Ambient sensor circuit is open. | 21 | Go to Diagnostic procedure 2.
Ambient sensor circuit is shorted. | -21 | Go to Diagnostic procedure 8.
In-vehicle sensor circuit is open. | 22 | Go to Diagnostic procedure 3.
In-vehicle sensor circuit is shorted. | -22 | Go to Diagnostic procedure 9.
Water temp. sensor circuit is open. | 23 | Go to Diagnostic procedure 4.
Water temp. sensor circuit is shorted. | -23 | Go to Diagnostic procedure 10.
Intake sensor circuit is open. | 24 | Go to Diagnostic procedure 5.
Intake sensor circuit is shorted. | -24 | Go to Diagnostic procedure 11.
Sunload sensor circuit is open. | 25 | Go to Diagnostic procedure 6.
Sunload sensor circuit is shorted. | -25 | Go to Diagnostic procedure 12.
P.B.R. circuit is open. | 26 | Go to Diagnostic procedure 7.
P.B.R. circuit is shorted. | -26 | Go to Diagnostic procedure 13.
When malfunctioning sensor circuits for ambient sensor, in-vehicle sensor and intake sensor are suspected, it is useful to check temperature detected by each sensor with Self-diagnosis STEP 5 to confirm the temperature is within normal range before performing Diagnostic Procedure.
By using CONSULT and selecting DATA MONITOR mode, temperature of each sensor (ambient, in-vehicle, engine coolant temperature, intake, sunload) can be confirmed.
O.K.
CHECK MODE DOOR MOTOR.
Set up "WORK SUPPORT — Mode door check" mode with CONSULT.
or
Set up Self-diagnosis STEP 3.
Code No. 30 should be indicated on the display after approx. 20 seconds.
Is mode door motor operating normally?
N.G.
Go to Diagnostic Procedure 14.
O.K.
CHECK MODE DOOR OPERATION.
Set up "ACTIVE TEST" mode with CONSULT.
or
Set up Self-diagnosis STEP 4.
Does air outlet change according to each mode?
Set mode | VENT | B/L 1 | B/L 1 | D/F 1 | D/F 2 | DEF
Code No. | 41 | 42 | 43 | 44 | 45 | 46
Air outlet | VENT | B/L | B/L | F/D 1 | F/D 2 | DEF
Refer to Air Flow.
N.G.
CHECK SIDE LINK MECHANISM.
N.G.
Repair or adjust.
O.K.
Go to Diagnostic Procedure 14.
O.K.
Air outlet control system is normal.
94J10099
Courtesy of Nissan Motor Co., U.S.A.
PRELIMINARY CHECK 2 – INTAKE DOOR DOES NOT CHANGE
CHECK SENSOR CIRCUIT.
Set up "SELF-DIAGNOSIS RESULTS" mode with CONSULT.
or.
Set up Self-diagnosis STEP 2.
Code No. 20 should be indicated on the display after approx. 4 seconds.
Is each sensor circuit normal?
N.G.
CHECK SENSOR CIRCUIT IN DETAIL ACCORDING TO THE DIAGNOSTIC PROCEDURE BELOW CORRESPONDING TO EACH CODE NO.
CONSULT indication | Self-diagnosis code No. | How to repair
Ambient sensor circuit is open. | 21 | Go to Diagnostic procedure 2.
Ambient sensor circuit is shorted. | -21 | Go to Diagnostic procedure 8.
In-vehicle sensor circuit is open. | 22 | Go to Diagnostic procedure 3.
In-vehicle sensor circuit is shorted. | -22 | Go to Diagnostic procedure 9.
Water temp. sensor circuit is open. | 23 | Go to Diagnostic procedure 4.
Water temp. sensor circuit is shorted. | -23 | Go to Diagnostic procedure 10.
Intake sensor circuit is open. | 24 | Go to Diagnostic procedure 5.
Intake sensor circuit is shorted. | -24 | Go to Diagnostic procedure 11.
Sunload sensor circuit is open. | 25 | Go to Diagnostic procedure 6.
Sunload sensor circuit is shorted. | -25 | Go to Diagnostic procedure 12.
P.B.R. circuit is open. | 26 | Go to Diagnostic procedure 7.
P.B.R. circuit is shorted. | -26 | Go to Diagnostic procedure 13.
When malfunctioning sensor circuits for ambient sensor, in-vehicle sensor and intake sensor are suspected, it is useful to check temperature detected by each sensor with Self-diagnosis STEP 5 to confirm the temperature is within normal range before performing Diagnostic Procedure.
By using CONSULT and selecting DATA MONITOR mode, temperature of each sensor (ambient, in-vehicle, engine coolant temperature, intake, sunload) can be confirmed.
O.K.
CHECK INTAKE DOOR MOTOR.
Set up "WORK SUPPORT — Intake door check" mode with CONSULT.
or
Set up Self-diagnosis STEP 3.
Code No. 30 should be indicated on the display after approx. 20 seconds.
Is intake door motor operating normally?
N.G.
Go to Diagnostic Procedure 15.
O.K.
CHECK INTAKE DOOR OPERATION.
Set up "ACTIVE TEST" mode with CONSULT.
or
Set up Self-diagnosis STEP 4.
Does intake air change according to each mode?
Set mode | REC | 20% FRE | 20% FRE | 80% FRE | FRE | FRE
Code No. | 41 | 42 | 43 | 44 | 45 | 46
Air intake | REC | 20% FRE | 20% FRE | 80% FRE | FRE | FRE
N.G.
CHECK INTAKE DOOR ROD or LEVER MECHANISM.
N.G.
Repair or adjust.
O.K.
Go to Diagnostic Procedure 15.
O.K.
Intake door control system is normal.
94C10100
Courtesy of Nissan Motor Co., U.S.A.

Fig. 1: Preliminary Check 1 – Air Outlet Does Not Change (J30)

Fig. 2: Preliminary Check 2 – Intake Door Does Not Change (J30)

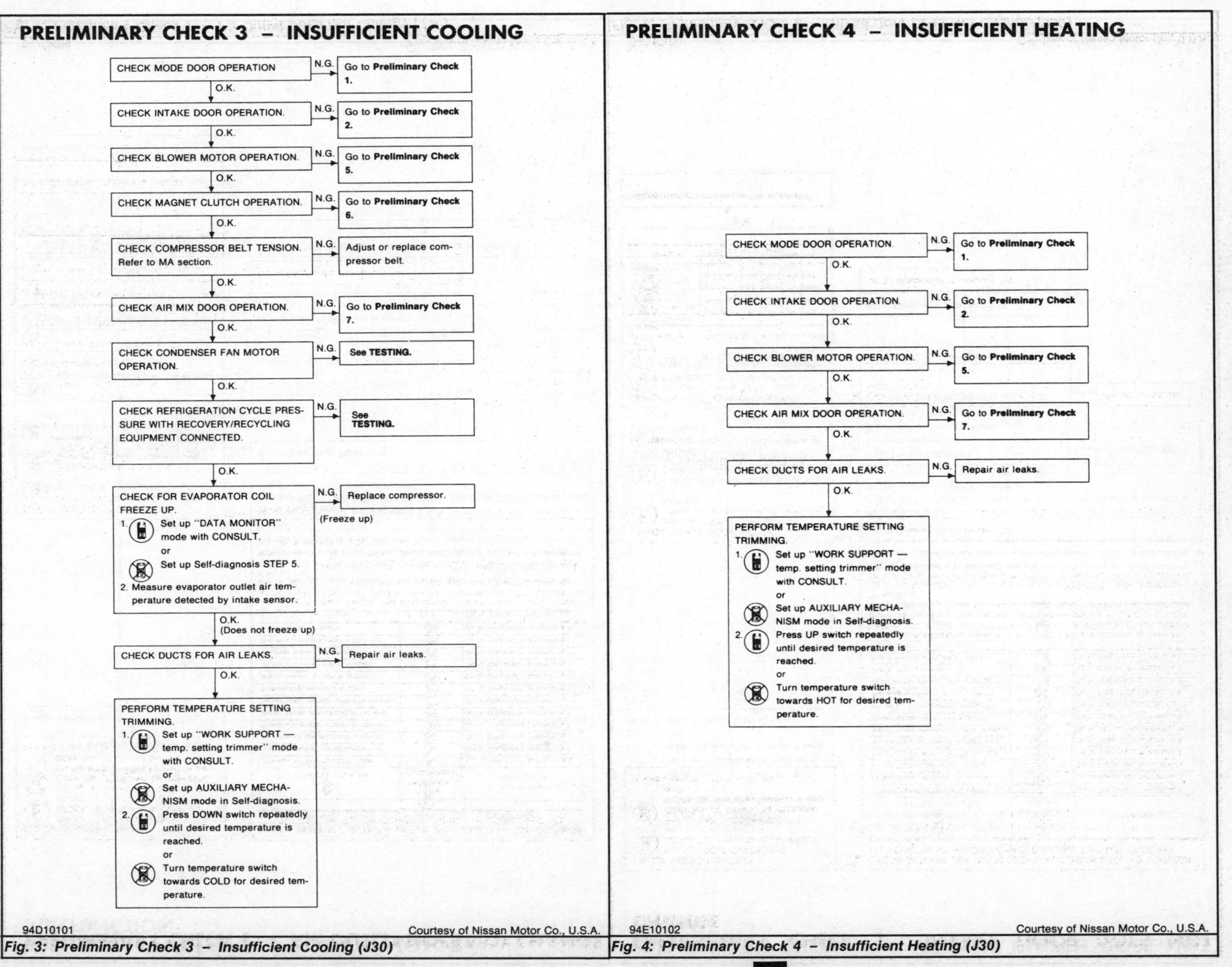
PRELIMINARY CHECK 3 – INSUFFICIENT COOLING
CHECK MODE DOOR OPERATION
N.G.
Go to Preliminary Check 1.
O.K.
CHECK INTAKE DOOR OPERATION.
N.G.
Go to Preliminary Check 2.
O.K.
CHECK BLOWER MOTOR OPERATION.
N.G.
Go to Preliminary Check 5.
O.K.
CHECK MAGNET CLUTCH OPERATION.
N.G.
Go to Preliminary Check 6.
O.K.
CHECK COMPRESSOR BELT TENSION. Refer to MA section.
N.G.
Adjust or replace compressor belt.
O.K.
CHECK AIR MIX DOOR OPERATION.
N.G.
Go to Preliminary Check 7.
O.K.
CHECK CONDENSER FAN MOTOR OPERATION.
N.G.
See TESTING.
O.K.
CHECK REFRIGERATION CYCLE PRESSURE WITH RECOVERY/RECYCLING EQUIPMENT CONNECTED.
N.G.
See TESTING.
O.K.
CHECK FOR EVAPORATOR COIL FREEZE UP.
1. Set up "DATA MONITOR" mode with CONSULT.
or
Set up Self-diagnosis STEP 5.
2. Measure evaporator outlet air temperature detected by intake sensor.
N.G.
(Freeze up)
Replace compressor.
O.K.
(Does not freeze up)
CHECK DUCTS FOR AIR LEAKS.
N.G.
Repair air leaks.
O.K.
PERFORM TEMPERATURE SETTING TRIMMING.
1. Set up "WORK SUPPORT — temp. setting trimmer" mode with CONSULT.
or
Set up AUXILIARY MECHANISM mode in Self-diagnosis.
2. Press DOWN switch repeatedly until desired temperature is reached.
or
Turn temperature switch towards COLD for desired temperature.
94D10101
Courtesy of Nissan Motor Co., U.S.A.
PRELIMINARY CHECK 4 – INSUFFICIENT HEATING
CHECK MODE DOOR OPERATION.
N.G.
Go to Preliminary Check 1.
O.K.
CHECK INTAKE DOOR OPERATION.
N.G.
Go to Preliminary Check 2.
O.K.
CHECK BLOWER MOTOR OPERATION.
N.G.
Go to Preliminary Check 5.
O.K.
CHECK AIR MIX DOOR OPERATION.
N.G.
Go to Preliminary Check 7.
O.K.
CHECK DUCTS FOR AIR LEAKS.
N.G.
Repair air leaks.
O.K.
PERFORM TEMPERATURE SETTING TRIMMING.
1. Set up "WORK SUPPORT — temp. setting trimmer" mode with CONSULT.
or
Set up AUXILIARY MECHANISM mode in Self-diagnosis.
2. Press UP switch repeatedly until desired temperature is reached.
or
Turn temperature switch towards HOT for desired temperature.
94E10102
Courtesy of Nissan Motor Co., U.S.A.

Fig. 3: Preliminary Check 3 – Insufficient Cooling (J30)

Fig. 4: Preliminary Check 4 – Insufficient Heating (J30)

1993 AUTOMATIC A/C-HEATER SYSTEMS
Trouble Shooting – J30 (Cont.)

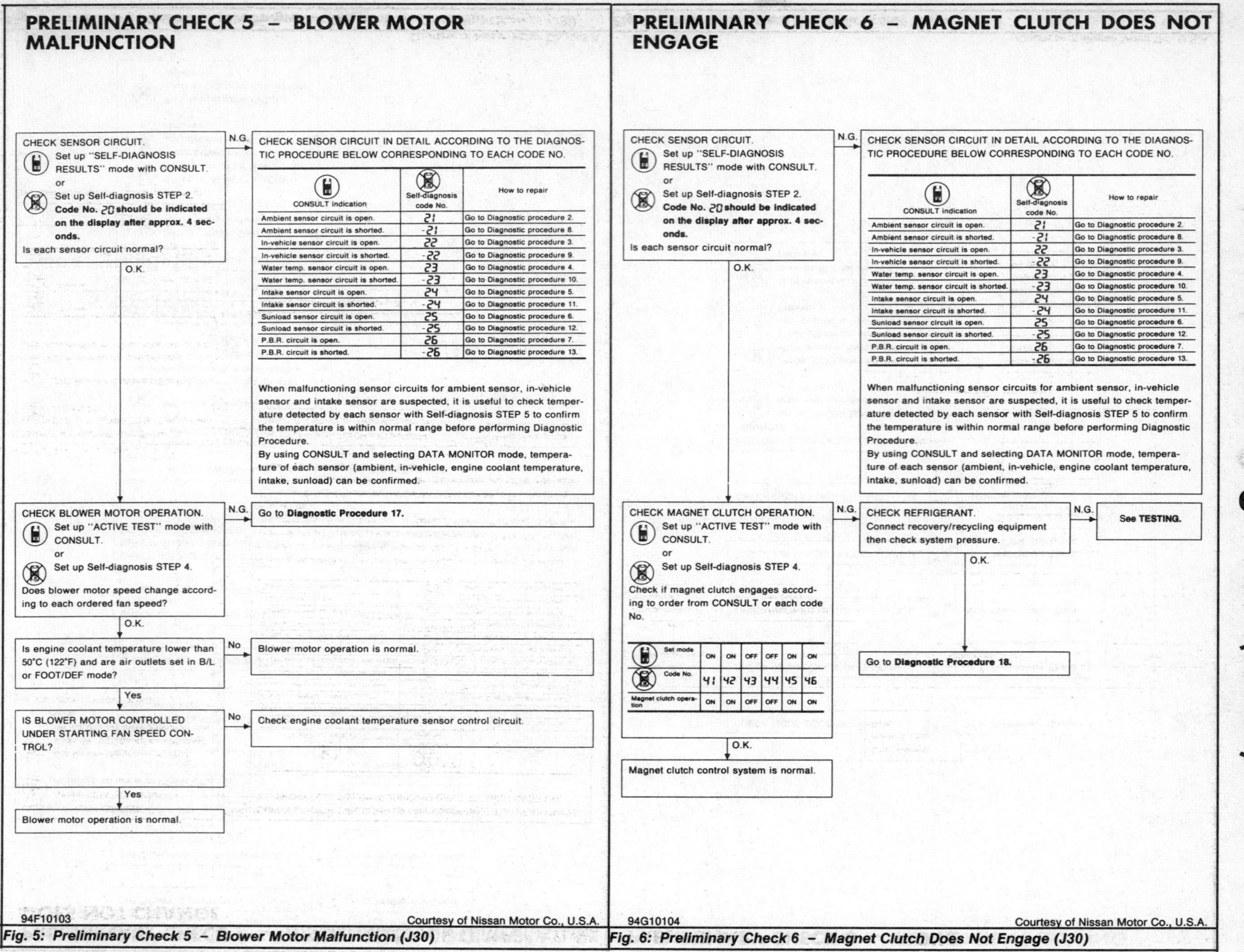
PRELIMINARY CHECK 5 – BLOWER MOTOR MALFUNCTION
CHECK SENSOR CIRCUIT.
Set up "SELF-DIAGNOSIS RESULTS" mode with CONSULT.
or
Set up Self-diagnosis STEP 2.
Code No. 20 should be indicated on the display after approx. 4 seconds.
Is each sensor circuit normal?
N.G.
O.K.
CHECK SENSOR CIRCUIT IN DETAIL ACCORDING TO THE DIAGNOSTIC PROCEDURE BELOW CORRESPONDING TO EACH CODE NO.
CONSULT indication
Self-diagnosis code No.
How to repair
Ambient sensor circuit is open. | 21 | Go to Diagnostic procedure 2.
Ambient sensor circuit is shorted. | -21 | Go to Diagnostic procedure 8.
In-vehicle sensor circuit is open. | 22 | Go to Diagnostic procedure 3.
In-vehicle sensor circuit is shorted. | -22 | Go to Diagnostic procedure 9.
Water temp. sensor circuit is open. | 23 | Go to Diagnostic procedure 4.
Water temp. sensor circuit is shorted. | -23 | Go to Diagnostic procedure 10.
Intake sensor circuit is open. | 24 | Go to Diagnostic procedure 5.
Intake sensor circuit is shorted. | -24 | Go to Diagnostic procedure 11.
Sunload sensor circuit is open. | 25 | Go to Diagnostic procedure 6.
Sunload sensor circuit is shorted. | -25 | Go to Diagnostic procedure 12.
P.B.R. circuit is open. | 26 | Go to Diagnostic procedure 7.
P.B.R. circuit is shorted. | -26 | Go to Diagnostic procedure 13.
When malfunctioning sensor circuits for ambient sensor, in-vehicle sensor and intake sensor are suspected, it is useful to check temperature detected by each sensor with Self-diagnosis STEP 5 to confirm the temperature is within normal range before performing Diagnostic Procedure.
By using CONSULT and selecting DATA MONITOR mode, temperature of each sensor (ambient, in-vehicle, engine coolant temperature, intake, sunload) can be confirmed.
CHECK BLOWER MOTOR OPERATION.
Set up "ACTIVE TEST" mode with CONSULT.
or
Set up Self-diagnosis STEP 4.
Does blower motor speed change according to each ordered fan speed?
N.G.
Go to Diagnostic Procedure 17.
O.K.
Is engine coolant temperature lower than 50°C (122°F) and are air outlets set in B/L or FOOT/DEF mode?
No
Blower motor operation is normal.
Yes
IS BLOWER MOTOR CONTROLLED UNDER STARTING FAN SPEED CONTROL?
No
Check engine coolant temperature sensor control circuit.
Yes
Blower motor operation is normal.
94F10103
Courtesy of Nissan Motor Co., U.S.A.
PRELIMINARY CHECK 6 – MAGNET CLUTCH DOES NOT ENGAGE
CHECK SENSOR CIRCUIT.
Set up "SELF-DIAGNOSIS RESULTS" mode with CONSULT.
or
Set up Self-diagnosis STEP 2.
Code No. 20 should be indicated on the display after approx. 4 seconds.
Is each sensor circuit normal?
N.G.
O.K.
CHECK SENSOR CIRCUIT IN DETAIL ACCORDING TO THE DIAGNOSTIC PROCEDURE BELOW CORRESPONDING TO EACH CODE NO.
CONSULT indication
Self-diagnosis code No.
How to repair
Ambient sensor circuit is open. | 21 | Go to Diagnostic procedure 2.
Ambient sensor circuit is shorted. | -21 | Go to Diagnostic procedure 8.
In-vehicle sensor circuit is open. | 22 | Go to Diagnostic procedure 3.
In-vehicle sensor circuit is shorted. | -22 | Go to Diagnostic procedure 9.
Water temp. sensor circuit is open. | 23 | Go to Diagnostic procedure 4.
Water temp. sensor circuit is shorted. | -23 | Go to Diagnostic procedure 10.
Intake sensor circuit is open. | 24 | Go to Diagnostic procedure 5.
Intake sensor circuit is shorted. | -24 | Go to Diagnostic procedure 11.
Sunload sensor circuit is open. | 25 | Go to Diagnostic procedure 6.
Sunload sensor circuit is shorted. | -25 | Go to Diagnostic procedure 12.
P.B.R. circuit is open. | 26 | Go to Diagnostic procedure 7.
P.B.R. circuit is shorted. | -26 | Go to Diagnostic procedure 13.
When malfunctioning sensor circuits for ambient sensor, in-vehicle sensor and intake sensor are suspected, it is useful to check temperature detected by each sensor with Self-diagnosis STEP 5 to confirm the temperature is within normal range before performing Diagnostic Procedure.
By using CONSULT and selecting DATA MONITOR mode, temperature of each sensor (ambient, in-vehicle, engine coolant temperature, intake, sunload) can be confirmed.
CHECK MAGNET CLUTCH OPERATION.
Set up "ACTIVE TEST" mode with CONSULT.
or
Set up Self-diagnosis STEP 4.
Check if magnet clutch engages according to order from CONSULT or each code No.
Set mode | ON | ON | OFF | OFF | ON | ON
Code No. | 41 | 42 | 43 | 44 | 45 | 46
Magnet clutch operation | ON | ON | OFF | OFF | ON | ON
N.G.
CHECK REFRIGERANT.
Connect recovery/recycling equipment then check system pressure.
N.G.
See TESTING.
O.K.
Go to Diagnostic Procedure 18.
O.K.
Magnet clutch control system is normal.
94G10104
Courtesy of Nissan Motor Co., U.S.A.

Fig. 5: Preliminary Check 5 – Blower Motor Malfunction (J30)

Fig. 6: Preliminary Check 6 – Magnet Clutch Does Not Engage (J30)

PRELIMINARY CHECK 7 – DISCHARGED AIR TEMPERATURE DOES NOT CHANGE

PRELIMINARY CHECK 8 – NOISE

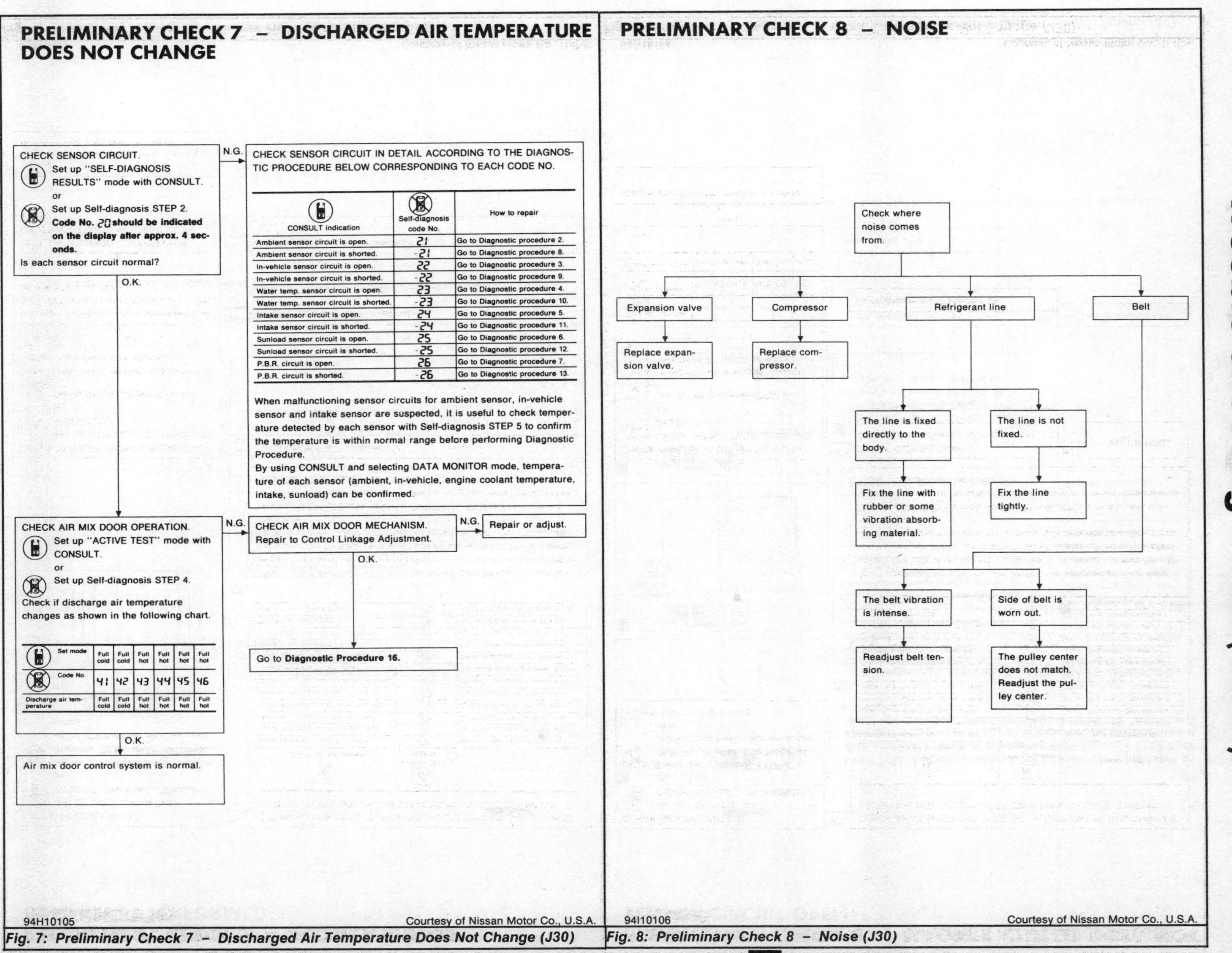

CHECK SENSOR CIRCUIT.
Set up "SELF-DIAGNOSIS RESULTS" mode with CONSULT.
or
Set up Self-diagnosis STEP 2.
Code No. 20 should be indicated on the display after approx. 4 seconds.
Is each sensor circuit normal?
N.G.
O.K.
CHECK SENSOR CIRCUIT IN DETAIL ACCORDING TO THE DIAGNOSTIC PROCEDURE BELOW CORRESPONDING TO EACH CODE NO.
When malfunctioning sensor circuits for ambient sensor, in-vehicle sensor and intake sensor are suspected, it is useful to check temperature detected by each sensor with Self-diagnosis STEP 5 to confirm the temperature is within normal range before performing Diagnostic Procedure.
By using CONSULT and selecting DATA MONITOR mode, temperature of each sensor (ambient, in-vehicle, engine coolant temperature, intake, sunload) can be confirmed.
CHECK AIR MIX DOOR OPERATION.
Set up "ACTIVE TEST" mode with CONSULT.
or
Set up Self-diagnosis STEP 4.
Check if discharge air temperature changes as shown in the following chart.
N.G.
CHECK AIR MIX DOOR MECHANISM.
Repair to Control Linkage Adjustment.
N.G.
Repair or adjust.
O.K.
Go to Diagnostic Procedure 16.
O.K.
Air mix door control system is normal.
94H10105
Courtesy of Nissan Motor Co., U.S.A.
Check where noise comes from.
Expansion valve
Compressor
Refrigerant line
Belt
Replace expansion valve.
Replace compressor.
The line is fixed directly to the body.
The line is not fixed.
Fix the line with rubber or some vibration absorbing material.
Fix the line tightly.
The belt vibration is intense.
Side of belt is worn out.
Readjust belt tension.
The pulley center does not match. Readjust the pulley center.
94I10106
Courtesy of Nissan Motor Co., U.S.A.

CONSULT indication	Self-diagnosis code No.	How to repair
Ambient sensor circuit is open.	21	Go to Diagnostic procedure 2.
Ambient sensor circuit is shorted.	-21	Go to Diagnostic procedure 8.
In-vehicle sensor circuit is open.	22	Go to Diagnostic procedure 3.
In-vehicle sensor circuit is shorted.	-22	Go to Diagnostic procedure 9.
Water temp. sensor circuit is open.	23	Go to Diagnostic procedure 4.
Water temp. sensor circuit is shorted.	-23	Go to Diagnostic procedure 10.
Intake sensor circuit is open.	24	Go to Diagnostic procedure 5.
Intake sensor circuit is shorted.	-24	Go to Diagnostic procedure 11.
Sunload sensor circuit is open.	25	Go to Diagnostic procedure 6.
Sunload sensor circuit is shorted.	-25	Go to Diagnostic procedure 12.
P.B.R. circuit is open.	26	Go to Diagnostic procedure 7.
P.B.R. circuit is shorted.	-26	Go to Diagnostic procedure 13.

Set mode	Full cold	Full cold	Full hot	Full hot	Full hot	Full hot
Code No.	41	42	43	44	45	46
Discharge air temperature	Full cold	Full cold	Full hot	Full hot	Full hot	Full hot

Fig. 7: Preliminary Check 7 – Discharged Air Temperature Does Not Change (J30)

Fig. 8: Preliminary Check 8 – Noise (J30)

1993 AUTOMATIC A/C-HEATER SYSTEMS
Trouble Shooting – J30 (Cont.)

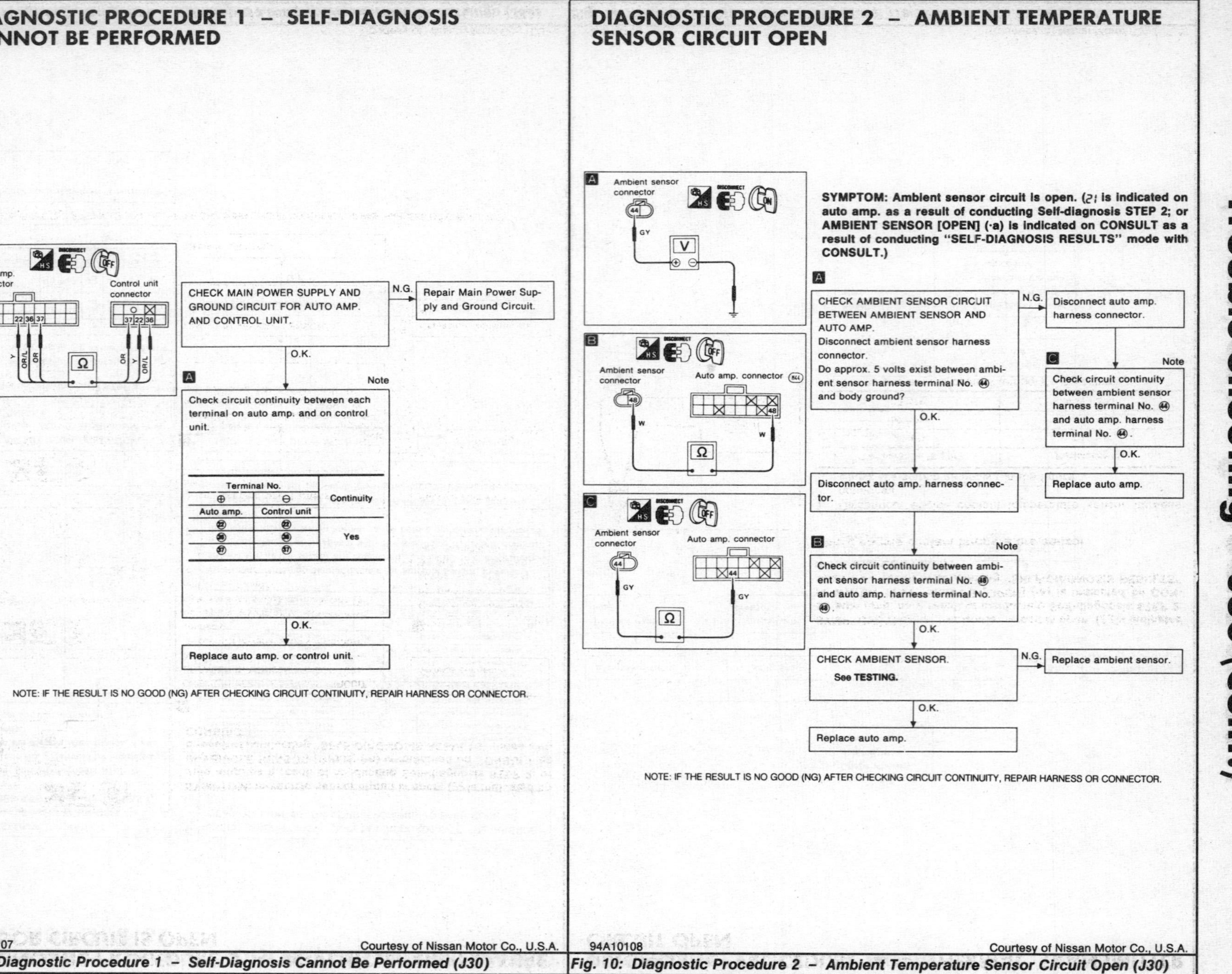
DIAGNOSTIC PROCEDURE 1 – SELF-DIAGNOSIS CANNOT BE PERFORMED
A
Auto amp. connector
Control unit connector
22 36 37
37 22 36
Y OR/L OR
OR Y OR/L
Ω
CHECK MAIN POWER SUPPLY AND GROUND CIRCUIT FOR AUTO AMP. AND CONTROL UNIT.
N.G.
Repair Main Power Supply and Ground Circuit.
O.K.
A
Note
Check circuit continuity between each terminal on auto amp. and on control unit.
Terminal No.
⊕ Auto amp.
⊖ Control unit
Continuity
22 22
36 36
37 37
Yes
O.K.
Replace auto amp. or control unit.
NOTE: IF THE RESULT IS NO GOOD (NG) AFTER CHECKING CIRCUIT CONTINUITY, REPAIR HARNESS OR CONNECTOR.
94J10107
Courtesy of Nissan Motor Co., U.S.A.
DIAGNOSTIC PROCEDURE 2 – AMBIENT TEMPERATURE SENSOR CIRCUIT OPEN
A
Ambient sensor connector
44
GY
V
B
Ambient sensor connector
48
Auto amp. connector
48
W
Ω
C
Ambient sensor connector
44
Auto amp. connector
44
GY
Ω
SYMPTOM: Ambient sensor circuit is open. (21 is indicated on auto amp. as a result of conducting Self-diagnosis STEP 2; or AMBIENT SENSOR [OPEN] (·a) is indicated on CONSULT as a result of conducting "SELF-DIAGNOSIS RESULTS" mode with CONSULT.)
A
CHECK AMBIENT SENSOR CIRCUIT BETWEEN AMBIENT SENSOR AND AUTO AMP.
Disconnect ambient sensor harness connector.
Do approx. 5 volts exist between ambient sensor harness terminal No. 44 and body ground?
N.G.
Disconnect auto amp. harness connector.
C
Note
Check circuit continuity between ambient sensor harness terminal No. 44 and auto amp. harness terminal No. 44.
O.K.
Replace auto amp.
O.K.
Disconnect auto amp. harness connector.
B
Note
Check circuit continuity between ambient sensor harness terminal No. 48 and auto amp. harness terminal No. 48.
O.K.
CHECK AMBIENT SENSOR.
See TESTING.
N.G.
Replace ambient sensor.
O.K.
Replace auto amp.
NOTE: IF THE RESULT IS NO GOOD (NG) AFTER CHECKING CIRCUIT CONTINUITY, REPAIR HARNESS OR CONNECTOR.
94A10108
Courtesy of Nissan Motor Co., U.S.A.

Fig. 9: Diagnostic Procedure 1 – Self-Diagnosis Cannot Be Performed (J30)

Fig. 10: Diagnostic Procedure 2 – Ambient Temperature Sensor Circuit Open (J30)

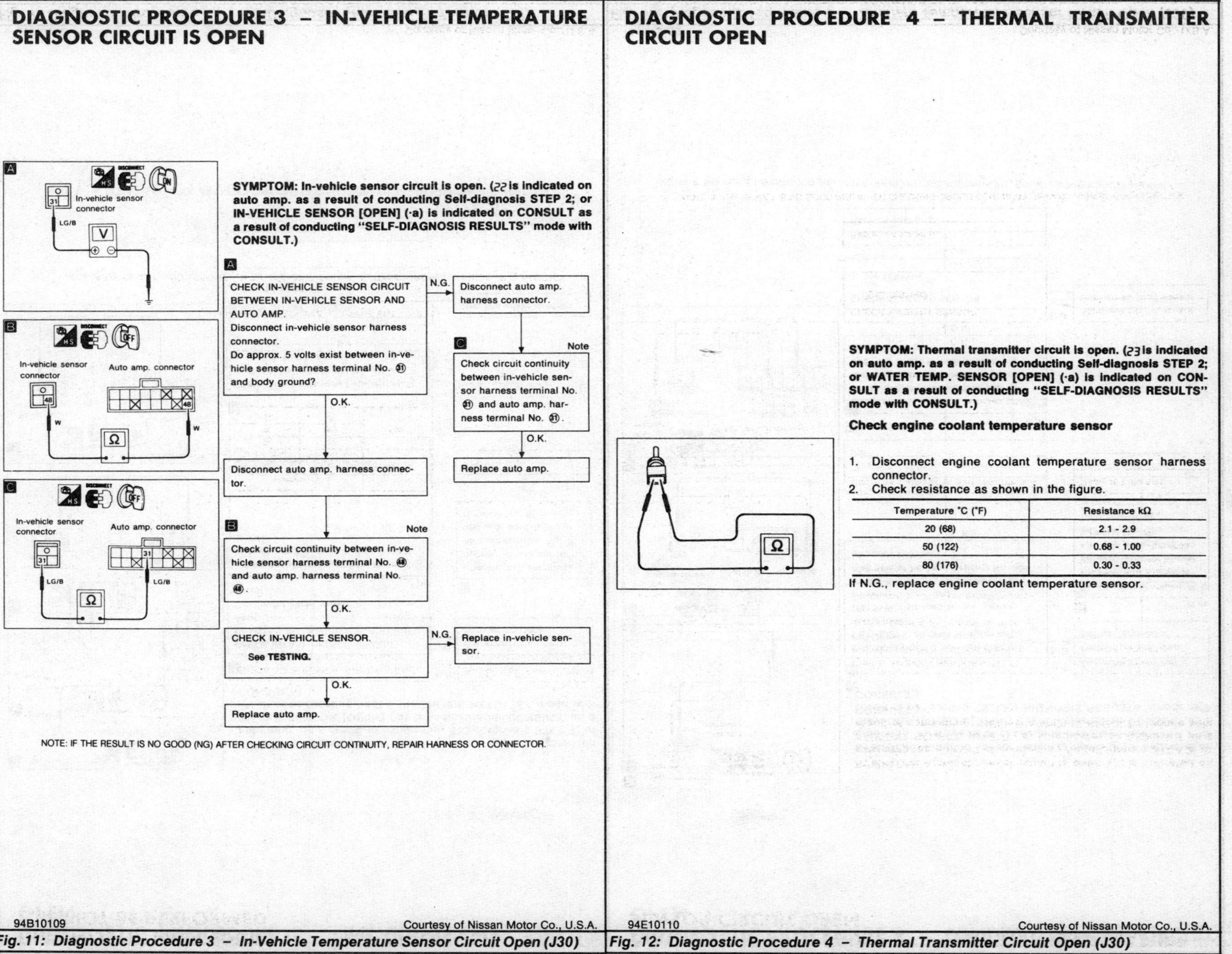
DIAGNOSTIC PROCEDURE 3 – IN-VEHICLE TEMPERATURE SENSOR CIRCUIT IS OPEN
A
In-vehicle sensor connector
31
LG/B
V
B
In-vehicle sensor connector
Auto amp. connector
48
W
Ω
C
In-vehicle sensor connector
Auto amp. connector
31
LG/B
Ω
SYMPTOM: In-vehicle sensor circuit is open. (22 is indicated on auto amp. as a result of conducting Self-diagnosis STEP 2; or IN-VEHICLE SENSOR [OPEN] (-a) is indicated on CONSULT as a result of conducting "SELF-DIAGNOSIS RESULTS" mode with CONSULT.)
A
CHECK IN-VEHICLE SENSOR CIRCUIT BETWEEN IN-VEHICLE SENSOR AND AUTO AMP.
Disconnect in-vehicle sensor harness connector.
Do approx. 5 volts exist between in-vehicle sensor harness terminal No. 31 and body ground?
N.G.
Disconnect auto amp. harness connector.
C
Note
Check circuit continuity between in-vehicle sensor harness terminal No. 31 and auto amp. harness terminal No. 31.
O.K.
Replace auto amp.
O.K.
Disconnect auto amp. harness connector.
B
Note
Check circuit continuity between in-vehicle sensor harness terminal No. 48 and auto amp. harness terminal No. 48.
O.K.
CHECK IN-VEHICLE SENSOR.
See TESTING.
N.G.
Replace in-vehicle sensor.
O.K.
Replace auto amp.
NOTE: IF THE RESULT IS NO GOOD (NG) AFTER CHECKING CIRCUIT CONTINUITY, REPAIR HARNESS OR CONNECTOR.
94B10109
Courtesy of Nissan Motor Co., U.S.A.
DIAGNOSTIC PROCEDURE 4 – THERMAL TRANSMITTER CIRCUIT OPEN
Ω
SYMPTOM: Thermal transmitter circuit is open. (23 is indicated on auto amp. as a result of conducting Self-diagnosis STEP 2; or WATER TEMP. SENSOR [OPEN] (-a) is indicated on CONSULT as a result of conducting "SELF-DIAGNOSIS RESULTS" mode with CONSULT.)
Check engine coolant temperature sensor
1. Disconnect engine coolant temperature sensor harness connector.
2. Check resistance as shown in the figure.

Temperature °C (°F)	Resistance kΩ
20 (68)	2.1 - 2.9
50 (122)	0.68 - 1.00
80 (176)	0.30 - 0.33

If N.G., replace engine coolant temperature sensor.
94E10110
Courtesy of Nissan Motor Co., U.S.A.

Fig. 11: Diagnostic Procedure 3 – In-Vehicle Temperature Sensor Circuit Open (J30)

Fig. 12: Diagnostic Procedure 4 – Thermal Transmitter Circuit Open (J30)

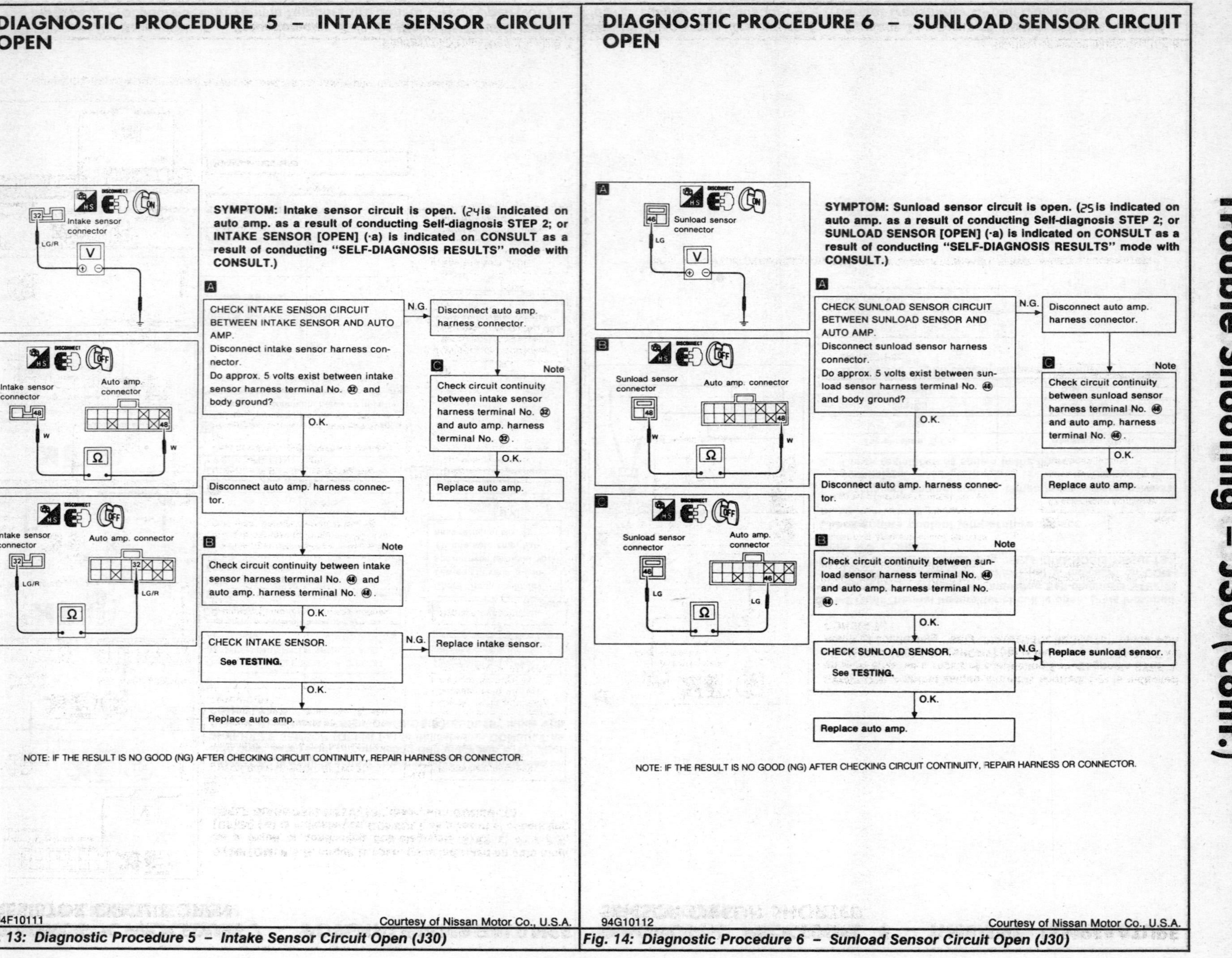
DIAGNOSTIC PROCEDURE 5 – INTAKE SENSOR CIRCUIT OPEN
A
Intake sensor connector
LG/R
V
B
Intake sensor connector
Auto amp. connector
48
W
Ω
C
Intake sensor connector
Auto amp. connector
32
LG/R
Ω
SYMPTOM: Intake sensor circuit is open. (24 is indicated on auto amp. as a result of conducting Self-diagnosis STEP 2; or INTAKE SENSOR [OPEN] (·a) is indicated on CONSULT as a result of conducting "SELF-DIAGNOSIS RESULTS" mode with CONSULT.)
A
CHECK INTAKE SENSOR CIRCUIT BETWEEN INTAKE SENSOR AND AUTO AMP.
Disconnect intake sensor harness connector.
Do approx. 5 volts exist between intake sensor harness terminal No. 32 and body ground?
N.G.
Disconnect auto amp. harness connector.
C
Note
Check circuit continuity between intake sensor harness terminal No. 32 and auto amp. harness terminal No. 32.
O.K.
Replace auto amp.
O.K.
Disconnect auto amp. harness connector.
B
Note
Check circuit continuity between intake sensor harness terminal No. 48 and auto amp. harness terminal No. 48.
O.K.
CHECK INTAKE SENSOR.
See TESTING.
N.G.
Replace intake sensor.
O.K.
Replace auto amp.
NOTE: IF THE RESULT IS NO GOOD (NG) AFTER CHECKING CIRCUIT CONTINUITY, REPAIR HARNESS OR CONNECTOR.
94F10111
Courtesy of Nissan Motor Co., U.S.A.
DIAGNOSTIC PROCEDURE 6 – SUNLOAD SENSOR CIRCUIT OPEN
A
Sunload sensor connector
46
LG
V
B
Sunload sensor connector
Auto amp. connector
48
W
Ω
C
Sunload sensor connector
Auto amp. connector
46
LG
Ω
SYMPTOM: Sunload sensor circuit is open. (25 is indicated on auto amp. as a result of conducting Self-diagnosis STEP 2; or SUNLOAD SENSOR [OPEN] (·a) is indicated on CONSULT as a result of conducting "SELF-DIAGNOSIS RESULTS" mode with CONSULT.)
A
CHECK SUNLOAD SENSOR CIRCUIT BETWEEN SUNLOAD SENSOR AND AUTO AMP.
Disconnect sunload sensor harness connector.
Do approx. 5 volts exist between sunload sensor harness terminal No. 46 and body ground?
N.G.
Disconnect auto amp. harness connector.
C
Note
Check circuit continuity between sunload sensor harness terminal No. 46 and auto amp. harness terminal No. 46.
O.K.
Replace auto amp.
O.K.
Disconnect auto amp. harness connector.
B
Note
Check circuit continuity between sunload sensor harness terminal No. 48 and auto amp. harness terminal No. 48.
O.K.
CHECK SUNLOAD SENSOR.
See TESTING.
N.G.
Replace sunload sensor.
O.K.
Replace auto amp.
NOTE: IF THE RESULT IS NO GOOD (NG) AFTER CHECKING CIRCUIT CONTINUITY, REPAIR HARNESS OR CONNECTOR.
94G10112
Courtesy of Nissan Motor Co., U.S.A.

Fig. 13: Diagnostic Procedure 5 – Intake Sensor Circuit Open (J30)

Fig. 14: Diagnostic Procedure 6 – Sunload Sensor Circuit Open (J30)

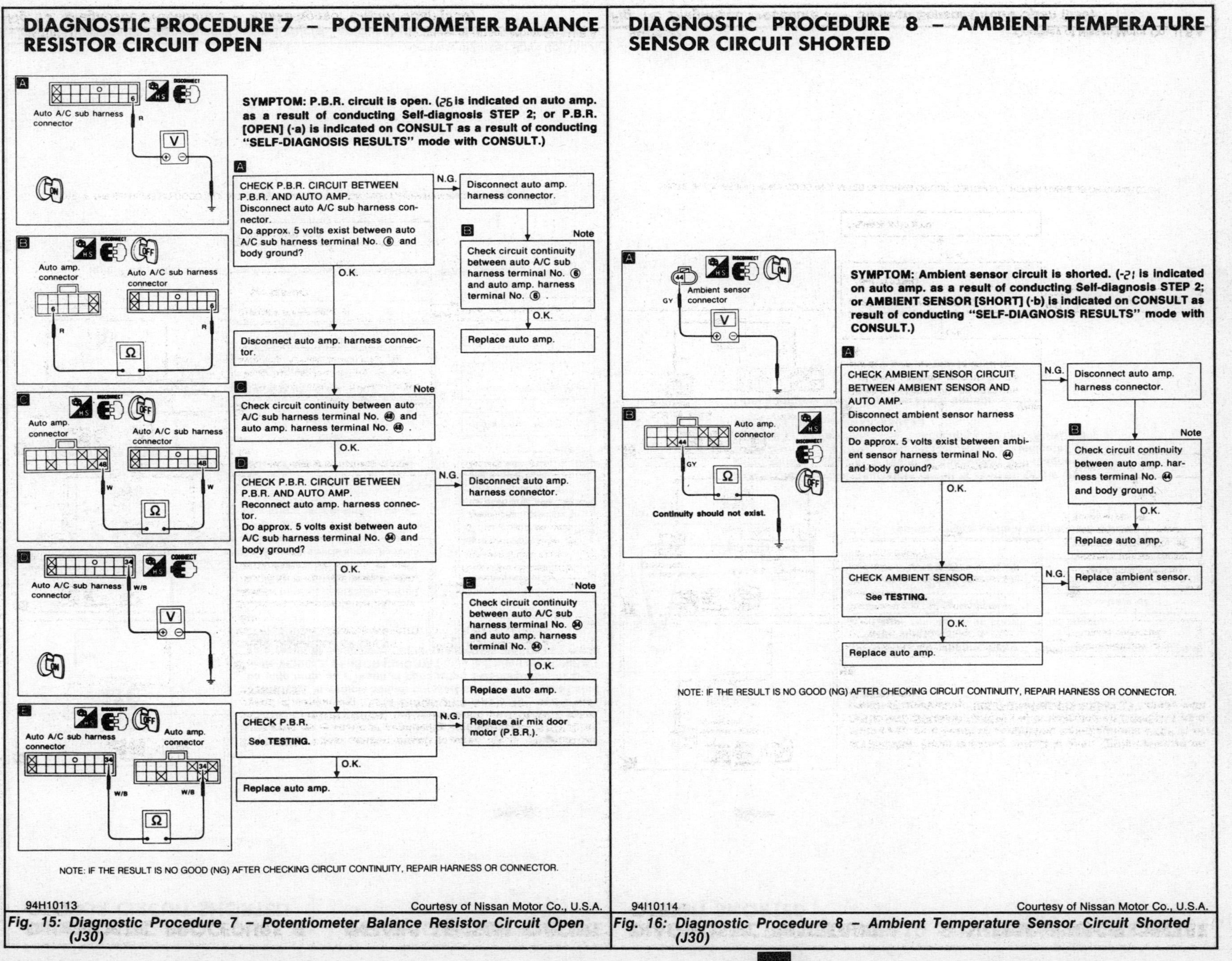

DIAGNOSTIC PROCEDURE 7 – POTENTIOMETER BALANCE RESISTOR CIRCUIT OPEN
SYMPTOM: P.B.R. circuit is open. (25 is indicated on auto amp. as a result of conducting Self-diagnosis STEP 2; or P.B.R. [OPEN] (-a) is indicated on CONSULT as a result of conducting "SELF-DIAGNOSIS RESULTS" mode with CONSULT.)
A
Auto A/C sub harness connector
R
V
A
CHECK P.B.R. CIRCUIT BETWEEN P.B.R. AND AUTO AMP.
Disconnect auto A/C sub harness connector.
Do approx. 5 volts exist between auto A/C sub harness terminal No. 6 and body ground?
N.G.
Disconnect auto amp. harness connector.
B
Check circuit continuity between auto A/C sub harness terminal No. 6 and auto amp. harness terminal No. 6.
Note
O.K.
Replace auto amp.
B
Auto amp. connector
Auto A/C sub harness connector
R
Ω
O.K.
Disconnect auto amp. harness connector.
C
Check circuit continuity between auto A/C sub harness terminal No. 48 and auto amp. harness terminal No. 48.
Note
C
Auto amp. connector
Auto A/C sub harness connector
W
Ω
O.K.
D
CHECK P.B.R. CIRCUIT BETWEEN P.B.R. AND AUTO AMP.
Reconnect auto amp. harness connector.
Do approx. 5 volts exist between auto A/C sub harness terminal No. 34 and body ground?
N.G.
Disconnect auto amp. harness connector.
E
Check circuit continuity between auto A/C sub harness terminal No. 34 and auto amp. harness terminal No. 34.
Note
O.K.
Replace auto amp.
D
Auto A/C sub harness connector
W/B
V
O.K.
CHECK P.B.R.
See TESTING.
N.G.
Replace air mix door motor (P.B.R.).
O.K.
Replace auto amp.
E
Auto A/C sub harness connector
Auto amp. connector
W/B
Ω
NOTE: IF THE RESULT IS NO GOOD (NG) AFTER CHECKING CIRCUIT CONTINUITY, REPAIR HARNESS OR CONNECTOR.
94H10113
Courtesy of Nissan Motor Co., U.S.A.
DIAGNOSTIC PROCEDURE 8 – AMBIENT TEMPERATURE SENSOR CIRCUIT SHORTED
SYMPTOM: Ambient sensor circuit is shorted. (-21 is indicated on auto amp. as a result of conducting Self-diagnosis STEP 2; or AMBIENT SENSOR [SHORT] (-b) is indicated on CONSULT as result of conducting "SELF-DIAGNOSIS RESULTS" mode with CONSULT.)
A
Ambient sensor connector
GY
V
A
CHECK AMBIENT SENSOR CIRCUIT BETWEEN AMBIENT SENSOR AND AUTO AMP.
Disconnect ambient sensor harness connector.
Do approx. 5 volts exist between ambient sensor harness terminal No. 44 and body ground?
N.G.
Disconnect auto amp. harness connector.
B
Check circuit continuity between auto amp. harness terminal No. 44 and body ground.
Note
O.K.
Replace auto amp.
B
Auto amp. connector
GY
Ω
Continuity should not exist.
O.K.
CHECK AMBIENT SENSOR.
See TESTING.
N.G.
Replace ambient sensor.
O.K.
Replace auto amp.
NOTE: IF THE RESULT IS NO GOOD (NG) AFTER CHECKING CIRCUIT CONTINUITY, REPAIR HARNESS OR CONNECTOR.
94I10114
Courtesy of Nissan Motor Co., U.S.A.

Fig. 15: Diagnostic Procedure 7 – Potentiometer Balance Resistor Circuit Open (J30)

Fig. 16: Diagnostic Procedure 8 – Ambient Temperature Sensor Circuit Shorted (J30)

1993 AUTOMATIC A/C-HEATER SYSTEMS
Trouble Shooting – J30 (Cont.)

DIAGNOSTIC PROCEDURE 9 – IN-VEHICLE TEMPERATURE SENSOR CIRCUIT SHORTED

A — In-vehicle sensor connector; 31; LG/B; V; DISCONNECT; H.S.; ON

B — Auto amp. connector; 31; LG/B; Ω; DISCONNECT; H.S.; OFF; Continuity should not exist.

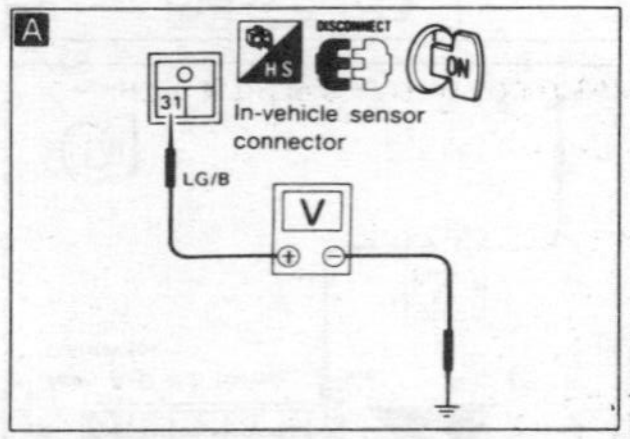

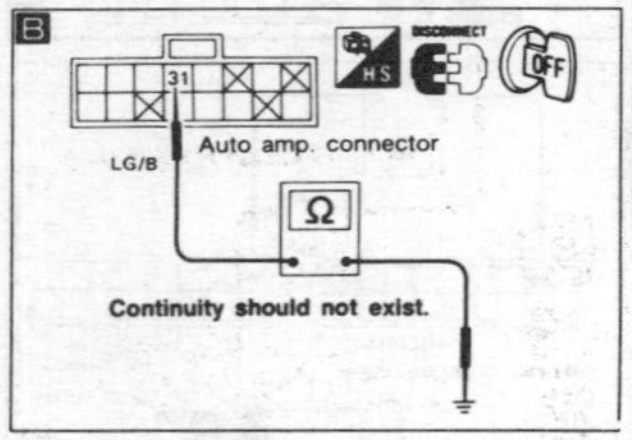

SYMPTOM: In-vehicle sensor circuit is shorted. (-22 is indicated on auto amp. as a result of conducting Self-diagnosis STEP 2; or IN-VEHICLE SENSOR [SHORT] (·b) is indicated on CONSULT as a result of conducting "SELF-DIAGNOSIS RESULTS" mode with CONSULT.)

A — CHECK IN-VEHICLE SENSOR CIRCUIT BETWEEN IN-VEHICLE SENSOR AND AUTO AMP. Disconnect in-vehicle sensor harness connector. Do approx. 5 volts exist between in-vehicle sensor harness terminal No. 31 and body ground?

- N.G. → Disconnect auto amp. harness connector. → B — Check circuit continuity between auto amp. harness terminal No. 31 and body ground. (Note) → O.K. → Replace auto amp.
- O.K. → CHECK IN-VEHICLE SENSOR. See **TESTING.**
  - N.G. → Replace in-vehicle sensor.
  - O.K. → Replace auto amp.

NOTE: IF THE RESULT IS NO GOOD (NG) AFTER CHECKING CIRCUIT CONTINUITY, REPAIR HARNESS OR CONNECTOR.

94J10115 Courtesy of Nissan Motor Co., U.S.A.

Fig. 17: Diagnostic Procedure 9 – In-Vehicle Temperature Sensor Circuit Shorted (J30)

DIAGNOSTIC PROCEDURE 10 – THERMAL TRANSMITTER CIRCUIT SHORTED

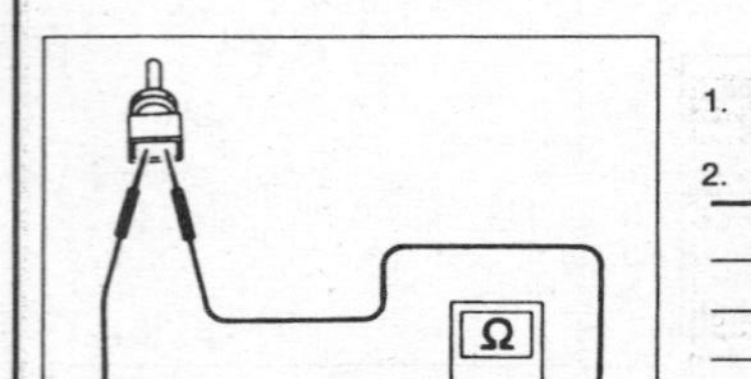
Ω

1. Disconnect engine coolant temperature sensor harness connector.
2. Check resistance as shown in the figure.

Temperature °C (°F)	Resistance kΩ
20 (68)	2.1 - 2.9
50 (122)	0.68 - 1.00
80 (176)	0.30 - 0.33

If N.G., replace engine coolant temperature sensor.

SYMPTOM: Thermal transmitter circuit is shorted. (-23 is indicated on auto amp. as a result of conducting Self-diagnosis STEP 2; or WATER TEMP. SENSOR [SHORT] (·b) is indicated on CONSULT as a result of conducting "SELF-DIAGNOSIS RESULTS" mode with CONSULT.)

Check engine coolant temperature sensor

94E10110 Courtesy of Nissan Motor Co., U.S.A.

Fig. 18: Diagnostic Procedure 10 – Thermal Transmitter Circuit Shorted (J30)

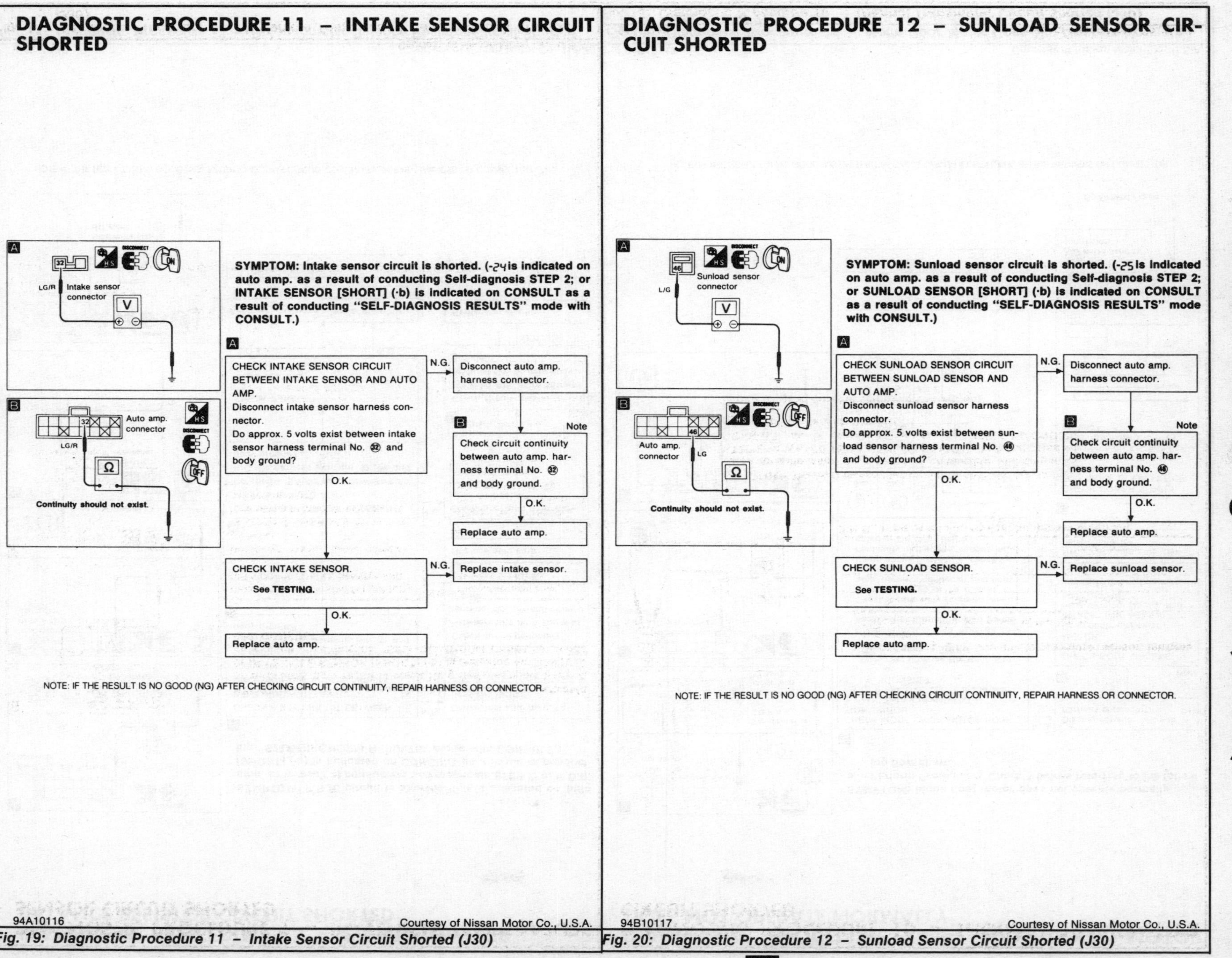
DIAGNOSTIC PROCEDURE 11 – INTAKE SENSOR CIRCUIT SHORTED
A
32
LG/R
Intake sensor connector
V
B
Auto amp. connector
32
LG/R
Ω
Continuity should not exist.
SYMPTOM: Intake sensor circuit is shorted. (-24 is indicated on auto amp. as a result of conducting Self-diagnosis STEP 2; or INTAKE SENSOR [SHORT] (·b) is indicated on CONSULT as a result of conducting "SELF-DIAGNOSIS RESULTS" mode with CONSULT.)
A
CHECK INTAKE SENSOR CIRCUIT BETWEEN INTAKE SENSOR AND AUTO AMP.
Disconnect intake sensor harness connector.
Do approx. 5 volts exist between intake sensor harness terminal No. 32 and body ground?
N.G.
Disconnect auto amp. harness connector.
B
Note
Check circuit continuity between auto amp. harness terminal No. 32 and body ground.
O.K.
Replace auto amp.
O.K.
CHECK INTAKE SENSOR.
See TESTING.
N.G.
Replace intake sensor.
O.K.
Replace auto amp.
NOTE: IF THE RESULT IS NO GOOD (NG) AFTER CHECKING CIRCUIT CONTINUITY, REPAIR HARNESS OR CONNECTOR.
94A10116
Courtesy of Nissan Motor Co., U.S.A.
DIAGNOSTIC PROCEDURE 12 – SUNLOAD SENSOR CIRCUIT SHORTED
A
46
L/G
Sunload sensor connector
V
B
Auto amp. connector
46
LG
Ω
Continuity should not exist.
SYMPTOM: Sunload sensor circuit is shorted. (-25 is indicated on auto amp. as a result of conducting Self-diagnosis STEP 2; or SUNLOAD SENSOR [SHORT] (·b) is indicated on CONSULT as a result of conducting "SELF-DIAGNOSIS RESULTS" mode with CONSULT.)
A
CHECK SUNLOAD SENSOR CIRCUIT BETWEEN SUNLOAD SENSOR AND AUTO AMP.
Disconnect sunload sensor harness connector.
Do approx. 5 volts exist between sunload sensor harness terminal No. 46 and body ground?
N.G.
Disconnect auto amp. harness connector.
B
Note
Check circuit continuity between auto amp. harness terminal No. 46 and body ground.
O.K.
Replace auto amp.
O.K.
CHECK SUNLOAD SENSOR.
See TESTING.
N.G.
Replace sunload sensor.
O.K.
Replace auto amp.
NOTE: IF THE RESULT IS NO GOOD (NG) AFTER CHECKING CIRCUIT CONTINUITY, REPAIR HARNESS OR CONNECTOR.
94B10117
Courtesy of Nissan Motor Co., U.S.A.

Fig. 19: Diagnostic Procedure 11 – Intake Sensor Circuit Shorted (J30)

Fig. 20: Diagnostic Procedure 12 – Sunload Sensor Circuit Shorted (J30)

1993 AUTOMATIC A/C-HEATER SYSTEMS
Trouble Shooting – J30 (Cont.)

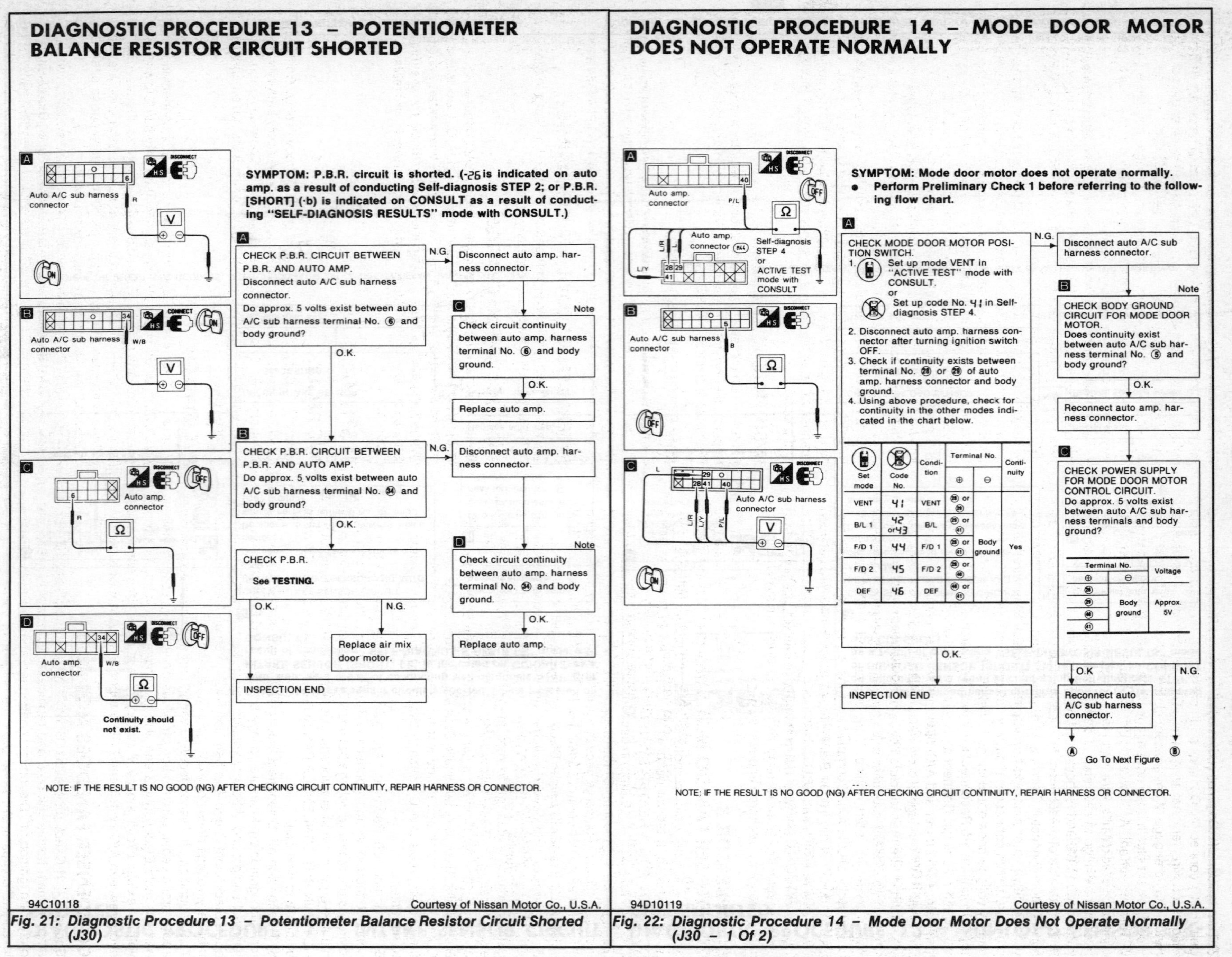
DIAGNOSTIC PROCEDURE 13 – POTENTIOMETER BALANCE RESISTOR CIRCUIT SHORTED
SYMPTOM: P.B.R. circuit is shorted. (-26 is indicated on auto amp. as a result of conducting Self-diagnosis STEP 2; or P.B.R. [SHORT] (-b) is indicated on CONSULT as a result of conducting "SELF-DIAGNOSIS RESULTS" mode with CONSULT.)
A CHECK P.B.R. CIRCUIT BETWEEN P.B.R. AND AUTO AMP. Disconnect auto A/C sub harness connector. Do approx. 5 volts exist between auto A/C sub harness terminal No. 6 and body ground?
N.G. Disconnect auto amp. harness connector.
C Check circuit continuity between auto amp. harness terminal No. 6 and body ground.
O.K. Replace auto amp.
O.K.
B CHECK P.B.R. CIRCUIT BETWEEN P.B.R. AND AUTO AMP. Do approx. 5 volts exist between auto A/C sub harness terminal No. 34 and body ground?
N.G. Disconnect auto amp. harness connector.
D Check circuit continuity between auto amp. harness terminal No. 34 and body ground.
O.K. Replace auto amp.
O.K.
CHECK P.B.R. See TESTING.
O.K. INSPECTION END
N.G. Replace air mix door motor.
Note
Auto A/C sub harness connector
Auto amp. connector
Continuity should not exist.
NOTE: IF THE RESULT IS NO GOOD (NG) AFTER CHECKING CIRCUIT CONTINUITY, REPAIR HARNESS OR CONNECTOR.
94C10118
Courtesy of Nissan Motor Co., U.S.A.
DIAGNOSTIC PROCEDURE 14 – MODE DOOR MOTOR DOES NOT OPERATE NORMALLY
SYMPTOM: Mode door motor does not operate normally.
Perform Preliminary Check 1 before referring to the following flow chart.
A CHECK MODE DOOR MOTOR POSITION SWITCH.
1. Set up mode VENT in "ACTIVE TEST" mode with CONSULT. or Set up code No. 41 in Self-diagnosis STEP 4.
2. Disconnect auto amp. harness connector after turning ignition switch OFF.
3. Check if continuity exists between terminal No. 28 or 29 of auto amp. harness connector and body ground.
4. Using above procedure, check for continuity in the other modes indicated in the chart below.
N.G. Disconnect auto A/C sub harness connector.
B CHECK BODY GROUND CIRCUIT FOR MODE DOOR MOTOR. Does continuity exist between auto A/C sub harness terminal No. 5 and body ground?
O.K. Reconnect auto amp. harness connector.
C CHECK POWER SUPPLY FOR MODE DOOR MOTOR CONTROL CIRCUIT. Do approx. 5 volts exist between auto A/C sub harness terminals and body ground?
O.K Reconnect auto A/C sub harness connector.
N.G.
Go To Next Figure
O.K. INSPECTION END
Self-diagnosis STEP 4 or ACTIVE TEST mode with CONSULT
NOTE: IF THE RESULT IS NO GOOD (NG) AFTER CHECKING CIRCUIT CONTINUITY, REPAIR HARNESS OR CONNECTOR.
94D10119
Courtesy of Nissan Motor Co., U.S.A.

Set mode	Code No.	Condition	Terminal No. ⊕	Terminal No. ⊖	Continuity
VENT	41	VENT	28 or 29	Body ground	Yes
B/L 1	42 or 43	B/L	29 or 41		
F/D 1	44	F/D 1	28 or 41		
F/D 2	45	F/D 2	29 or 40		
DEF	46	DEF	40 or 41		

Terminal No. ⊕	Terminal No. ⊖	Voltage
28	Body ground	Approx. 5V
29		
40		
41		

Fig. 21: Diagnostic Procedure 13 – Potentiometer Balance Resistor Circuit Shorted (J30)

Fig. 22: Diagnostic Procedure 14 – Mode Door Motor Does Not Operate Normally (J30 – 1 Of 2)

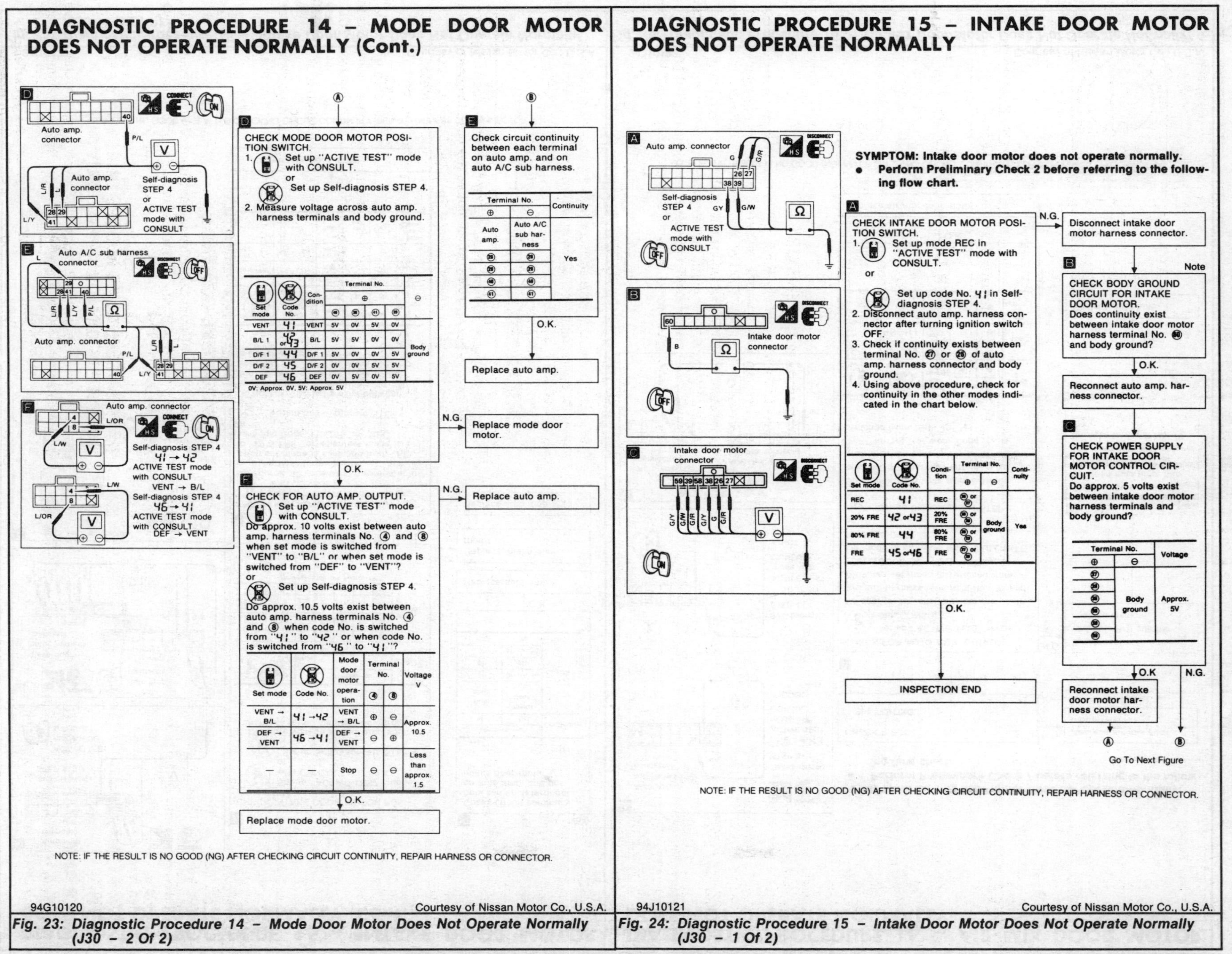

DIAGNOSTIC PROCEDURE 14 – MODE DOOR MOTOR DOES NOT OPERATE NORMALLY (Cont.)

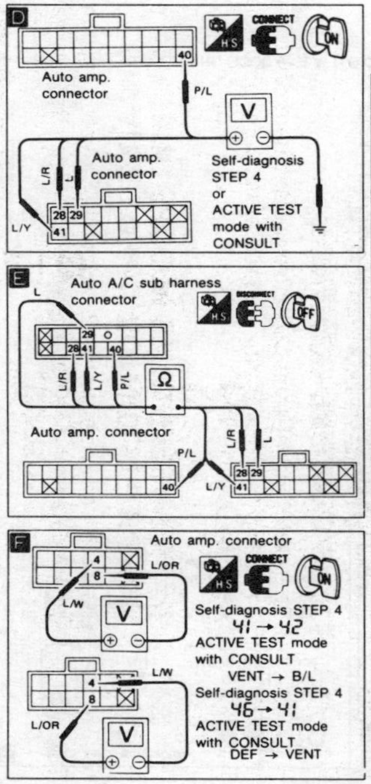
D
Auto amp. connector
40
P/L
V
Auto amp. connector
L/R
L
28 29
41
L/Y
Self-diagnosis STEP 4 or ACTIVE TEST mode with CONSULT
CONNECT
E
Auto A/C sub harness connector
L
29
28 41
40
L/R
L/Y
P/L
Auto amp. connector
L/Y
DISCONNECT
F
Auto amp. connector
4
8
L/OR
L/W
V
Self-diagnosis STEP 4 41 → 42
ACTIVE TEST mode with CONSULT VENT → B/L
L/W
L/OR
Self-diagnosis STEP 4 46 → 41
ACTIVE TEST mode with CONSULT DEF → VENT

(A) ↓

D CHECK MODE DOOR MOTOR POSITION SWITCH.
1. Set up "ACTIVE TEST" mode with CONSULT.
or
Set up Self-diagnosis STEP 4.
2. Measure voltage across auto amp. harness terminals and body ground.

Set mode	Code No.	Condition	Terminal No. ⊕ (40)	⊕ (28)	⊕ (41)	⊕ (29)	⊖
VENT	41	VENT	5V	0V	5V	0V	Body ground
B/L 1	42 or 43	B/L	5V	5V	0V	0V	
D/F 1	44	D/F 1	5V	0V	0V	5V	
D/F 2	45	D/F 2	0V	0V	5V	5V	
DEF	46	DEF	0V	5V	0V	5V	

0V: Approx. 0V, 5V: Approx. 5V

N.G. → Replace mode door motor.

O.K. ↓

F CHECK FOR AUTO AMP. OUTPUT.
Set up "ACTIVE TEST" mode with CONSULT.
Do approx. 10 volts exist between auto amp. harness terminals No. (4) and (8) when set mode is switched from "VENT" to "B/L" or when set mode is switched from "DEF" to "VENT"?
or
Set up Self-diagnosis STEP 4.
Do approx. 10.5 volts exist between auto amp. harness terminals No. (4) and (8) when code No. is switched from "41" to "42" or when code No. is switched from "46" to "41"?

Set mode	Code No.	Mode door motor operation	Terminal No. (4)	Terminal No. (8)	Voltage V
VENT → B/L	41 → 42	VENT → B/L	⊕	⊖	Approx. 10.5
DEF → VENT	46 → 41	DEF → VENT	⊖	⊕	
—	—	Stop	⊖	⊖	Less than approx. 1.5

N.G. → Replace auto amp.

O.K. ↓

Replace mode door motor.

(B) ↓

E Check circuit continuity between each terminal on auto amp. and on auto A/C sub harness.

Terminal No. ⊕ Auto amp.	Terminal No. ⊖ Auto A/C sub harness	Continuity
(28)	(28)	Yes
(29)	(29)	
(40)	(40)	
(41)	(41)	

O.K. ↓

Replace auto amp.

NOTE: IF THE RESULT IS NO GOOD (NG) AFTER CHECKING CIRCUIT CONTINUITY, REPAIR HARNESS OR CONNECTOR.

94G10120 Courtesy of Nissan Motor Co., U.S.A.

Fig. 23: Diagnostic Procedure 14 – Mode Door Motor Does Not Operate Normally (J30 – 2 Of 2)

DIAGNOSTIC PROCEDURE 15 – INTAKE DOOR MOTOR DOES NOT OPERATE NORMALLY

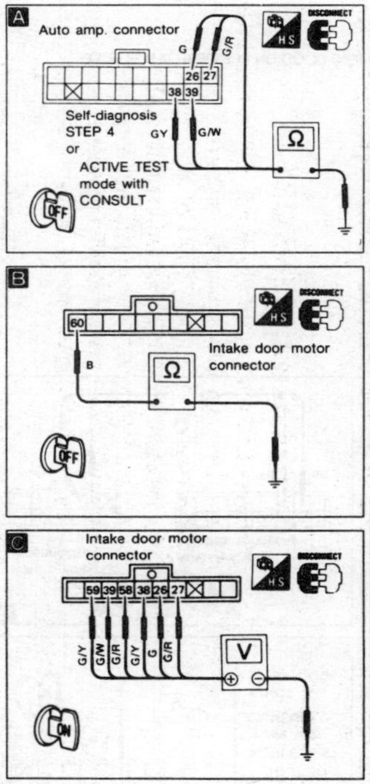
A
Auto amp. connector
G
G/R
26 27
38 39
Self-diagnosis STEP 4 or ACTIVE TEST mode with CONSULT
GY
G/W
Ω
DISCONNECT
B
60
B
Intake door motor connector
Ω
DISCONNECT
C
Intake door motor connector
59 39 58 38 26 27
G/Y
G/W
G/R
G/Y
G
G/R
V
DISCONNECT

SYMPTOM: Intake door motor does not operate normally.
- **Perform Preliminary Check 2 before referring to the following flow chart.**

A CHECK INTAKE DOOR MOTOR POSITION SWITCH.
1. Set up mode REC in "ACTIVE TEST" mode with CONSULT.
or
Set up code No. 41 in Self-diagnosis STEP 4.
2. Disconnect auto amp. harness connector after turning ignition switch OFF.
3. Check if continuity exists between terminal No. (27) or (28) of auto amp. harness connector and body ground.
4. Using above procedure, check for continuity in the other modes indicated in the chart below.

Set mode	Code No.	Condition	Terminal No. ⊕	Terminal No. ⊖	Continuity
REC	41	REC	(38) or (27)	Body ground	Yes
20% FRE	42 or 43	20% FRE	(38) or (39)		
80% FRE	44	80% FRE	(38) or (39)		
FRE	45 or 46	FRE	(27) or (38)		

O.K. ↓

INSPECTION END

N.G. → Disconnect intake door motor harness connector.

↓ **B** Note

CHECK BODY GROUND CIRCUIT FOR INTAKE DOOR MOTOR.
Does continuity exist between intake door motor harness terminal No. (60) and body ground?

O.K. ↓

Reconnect auto amp. harness connector.

↓ **C**

CHECK POWER SUPPLY FOR INTAKE DOOR MOTOR CONTROL CIRCUIT.
Do approx. 5 volts exist between intake door motor harness terminals and body ground?

Terminal No. ⊕	Terminal No. ⊖	Voltage
(27)	Body ground	Approx. 5V
(26)		
(38)		
(58)		
(39)		
(59)		

O.K. ↓ Reconnect intake door motor harness connector. → (A)

N.G. → (B)

Go To Next Figure

NOTE: IF THE RESULT IS NO GOOD (NG) AFTER CHECKING CIRCUIT CONTINUITY, REPAIR HARNESS OR CONNECTOR.

94J10121 Courtesy of Nissan Motor Co., U.S.A.

Fig. 24: Diagnostic Procedure 15 – Intake Door Motor Does Not Operate Normally (J30 – 1 Of 2)

1993 AUTOMATIC A/C-HEATER SYSTEMS
Trouble Shooting – J30 (Cont.)

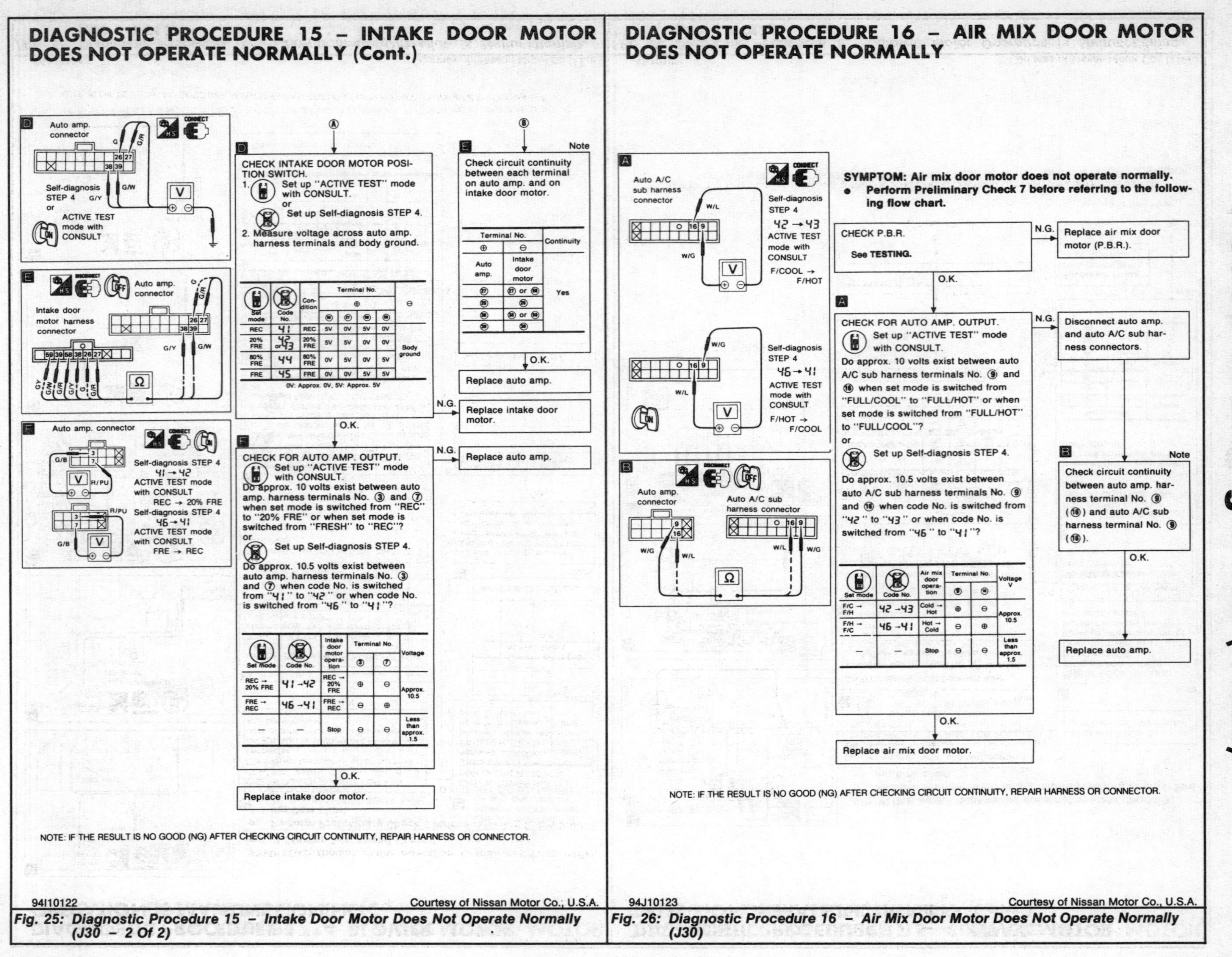
DIAGNOSTIC PROCEDURE 15 – INTAKE DOOR MOTOR DOES NOT OPERATE NORMALLY (Cont.)
D
Auto amp. connector
Self-diagnosis STEP 4 or ACTIVE TEST mode with CONSULT
E
Intake door motor harness connector
Auto amp. connector
F
Auto amp. connector
Self-diagnosis STEP 4 41 → 42 ACTIVE TEST mode with CONSULT REC → 20% FRE
Self-diagnosis STEP 4 46 → 41 ACTIVE TEST mode with CONSULT FRE → REC
D CHECK INTAKE DOOR MOTOR POSITION SWITCH.
1. Set up "ACTIVE TEST" mode with CONSULT. or Set up Self-diagnosis STEP 4.
2. Measure voltage across auto amp. harness terminals and body ground.

Set mode	Code No.	Condition	⊕ 38	⊕ 27	⊕ 26	⊕ 39	⊖
REC	41	REC	5V	0V	5V	0V	Body ground
20% FRE	42 or 43	20% FRE	5V	5V	0V	0V	
80% FRE	44	80% FRE	0V	5V	0V	5V	
FRE	45	FRE	0V	0V	5V	5V	

0V: Approx. 0V, 5V: Approx. 5V
E Check circuit continuity between each terminal on auto amp. and on intake door motor.

Terminal No. ⊕ Auto amp.	⊖ Intake door motor	Continuity
27	27 or 58	Yes
26	26	
38	38 or 59	
39	39	

F CHECK FOR AUTO AMP. OUTPUT.
Set up "ACTIVE TEST" mode with CONSULT.
Do approx. 10 volts exist between auto amp. harness terminals No. 3 and 7 when set mode is switched from "REC" to "20% FRE" or when set mode is switched from "FRESH" to "REC"?
or
Set up Self-diagnosis STEP 4.
Do approx. 10.5 volts exist between auto amp. harness terminals No. 3 and 7 when code No. is switched from "41" to "42" or when code No. is switched from "46" to "41"?

Set mode	Code No.	Intake door motor operation	Terminal No. 3	Terminal No. 7	Voltage
REC → 20% FRE	41 → 42	REC → 20% FRE	⊕	⊖	Approx. 10.5
FRE → REC	46 → 41	FRE → REC	⊖	⊕	
—	—	Stop	⊖	⊖	Less than approx. 1.5

O.K. → Replace intake door motor.
N.G. → Replace intake door motor.
N.G. → Replace auto amp.
O.K. → Replace auto amp.
Note
NOTE: IF THE RESULT IS NO GOOD (NG) AFTER CHECKING CIRCUIT CONTINUITY, REPAIR HARNESS OR CONNECTOR.
DIAGNOSTIC PROCEDURE 16 – AIR MIX DOOR MOTOR DOES NOT OPERATE NORMALLY
A
Auto A/C sub harness connector
Self-diagnosis STEP 4 42 → 43 ACTIVE TEST mode with CONSULT F/COOL → F/HOT
Self-diagnosis STEP 4 46 → 41 ACTIVE TEST mode with CONSULT F/HOT → F/COOL
B
Auto amp. connector
Auto A/C sub harness connector
SYMPTOM: Air mix door motor does not operate normally.
• Perform Preliminary Check 7 before referring to the following flow chart.
CHECK P.B.R. See TESTING.
N.G. → Replace air mix door motor (P.B.R.).
A CHECK FOR AUTO AMP. OUTPUT.
Set up "ACTIVE TEST" mode with CONSULT.
Do approx. 10 volts exist between auto A/C sub harness terminals No. 9 and 16 when set mode is switched from "FULL/COOL" to "FULL/HOT" or when set mode is switched from "FULL/HOT" to "FULL/COOL"?
or
Set up Self-diagnosis STEP 4.
Do approx. 10.5 volts exist between auto A/C sub harness terminals No. 9 and 16 when code No. is switched from "42" to "43" or when code No. is switched from "46" to "41"?

Set mode	Code No.	Air mix door operation	Terminal No. 9	Terminal No. 16	Voltage V
F/C → F/H	42 → 43	Cold → Hot	⊕	⊖	Approx. 10.5
F/H → F/C	46 → 41	Hot → Cold	⊖	⊕	
—	—	Stop	⊖	⊖	Less than approx. 1.5

O.K. → Replace air mix door motor.
N.G. → Disconnect auto amp. and auto A/C sub harness connectors.
B Check circuit continuity between auto amp. harness terminal No. 9 (16) and auto A/C sub harness terminal No. 9 (16).
Note
O.K. → Replace auto amp.
NOTE: IF THE RESULT IS NO GOOD (NG) AFTER CHECKING CIRCUIT CONTINUITY, REPAIR HARNESS OR CONNECTOR.

94I10122 Courtesy of Nissan Motor Co., U.S.A.

Fig. 25: Diagnostic Procedure 15 – Intake Door Motor Does Not Operate Normally (J30 – 2 Of 2)

94J10123 Courtesy of Nissan Motor Co., U.S.A.

Fig. 26: Diagnostic Procedure 16 – Air Mix Door Motor Does Not Operate Normally (J30)

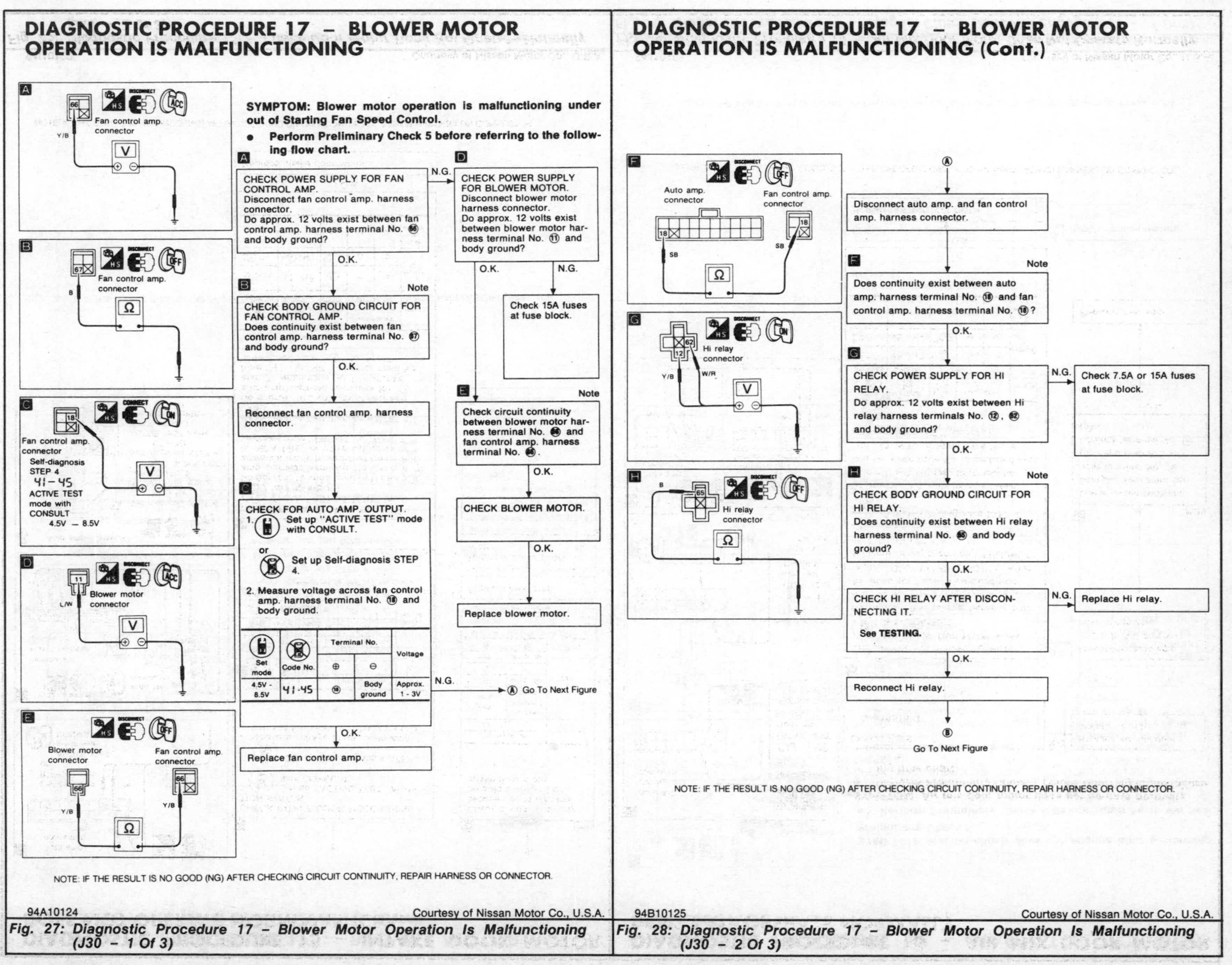
DIAGNOSTIC PROCEDURE 17 – BLOWER MOTOR OPERATION IS MALFUNCTIONING
A
66
Fan control amp. connector
Y/B
V
B
67
Fan control amp. connector
B
Ω
C
18
Fan control amp. connector
Self-diagnosis STEP 4
41-45
ACTIVE TEST mode with CONSULT
4.5V – 8.5V
V
D
11
Blower motor connector
L/W
V
E
Blower motor connector
Fan control amp. connector
66
66
Y/B
Y/B
Ω
SYMPTOM: Blower motor operation is malfunctioning under out of Starting Fan Speed Control.
• Perform Preliminary Check 5 before referring to the following flow chart.
A
CHECK POWER SUPPLY FOR FAN CONTROL AMP.
Disconnect fan control amp. harness connector.
Do approx. 12 volts exist between fan control amp. harness terminal No. 66 and body ground?
N.G.
O.K.
B
Note
CHECK BODY GROUND CIRCUIT FOR FAN CONTROL AMP.
Does continuity exist between fan control amp. harness terminal No. 67 and body ground?
O.K.
Reconnect fan control amp. harness connector.
C
CHECK FOR AUTO AMP. OUTPUT.
1. Set up "ACTIVE TEST" mode with CONSULT.
or
Set up Self-diagnosis STEP 4.
2. Measure voltage across fan control amp. harness terminal No. 18 and body ground.
Set mode
Code No.
Terminal No.
⊕
⊖
Voltage
4.5V - 8.5V
41-45
18
Body ground
Approx. 1 - 3V
N.G.
A Go To Next Figure
O.K.
Replace fan control amp.
D
CHECK POWER SUPPLY FOR BLOWER MOTOR.
Disconnect blower motor harness connector.
Do approx. 12 volts exist between blower motor harness terminal No. 11 and body ground?
O.K.
N.G.
Check 15A fuses at fuse block.
E
Note
Check circuit continuity between blower motor harness terminal No. 66 and fan control amp. harness terminal No. 66.
O.K.
CHECK BLOWER MOTOR.
O.K.
Replace blower motor.
NOTE: IF THE RESULT IS NO GOOD (NG) AFTER CHECKING CIRCUIT CONTINUITY, REPAIR HARNESS OR CONNECTOR.
94A10124
Courtesy of Nissan Motor Co., U.S.A.
DIAGNOSTIC PROCEDURE 17 – BLOWER MOTOR OPERATION IS MALFUNCTIONING (Cont.)
F
Auto amp. connector
Fan control amp. connector
18
18
SB
SB
Ω
G
62
12
Hi relay connector
Y/B
W/R
V
H
65
B
Hi relay connector
Ω
A
Disconnect auto amp. and fan control amp. harness connector.
F
Note
Does continuity exist between auto amp. harness terminal No. 18 and fan control amp. harness terminal No. 18?
O.K.
G
CHECK POWER SUPPLY FOR HI RELAY.
Do approx. 12 volts exist between Hi relay harness terminals No. 12, 62 and body ground?
N.G.
Check 7.5A or 15A fuses at fuse block.
O.K.
H
Note
CHECK BODY GROUND CIRCUIT FOR HI RELAY.
Does continuity exist between Hi relay harness terminal No. 65 and body ground?
O.K.
CHECK HI RELAY AFTER DISCONNECTING IT.
See TESTING.
N.G.
Replace Hi relay.
O.K.
Reconnect Hi relay.
B
Go To Next Figure
NOTE: IF THE RESULT IS NO GOOD (NG) AFTER CHECKING CIRCUIT CONTINUITY, REPAIR HARNESS OR CONNECTOR.
94B10125
Courtesy of Nissan Motor Co., U.S.A.

Fig. 27: Diagnostic Procedure 17 – Blower Motor Operation Is Malfunctioning (J30 – 1 Of 3)

Fig. 28: Diagnostic Procedure 17 – Blower Motor Operation Is Malfunctioning (J30 – 2 Of 3)

1993 AUTOMATIC A/C-HEATER SYSTEMS
Trouble Shooting – J30 (Cont.)

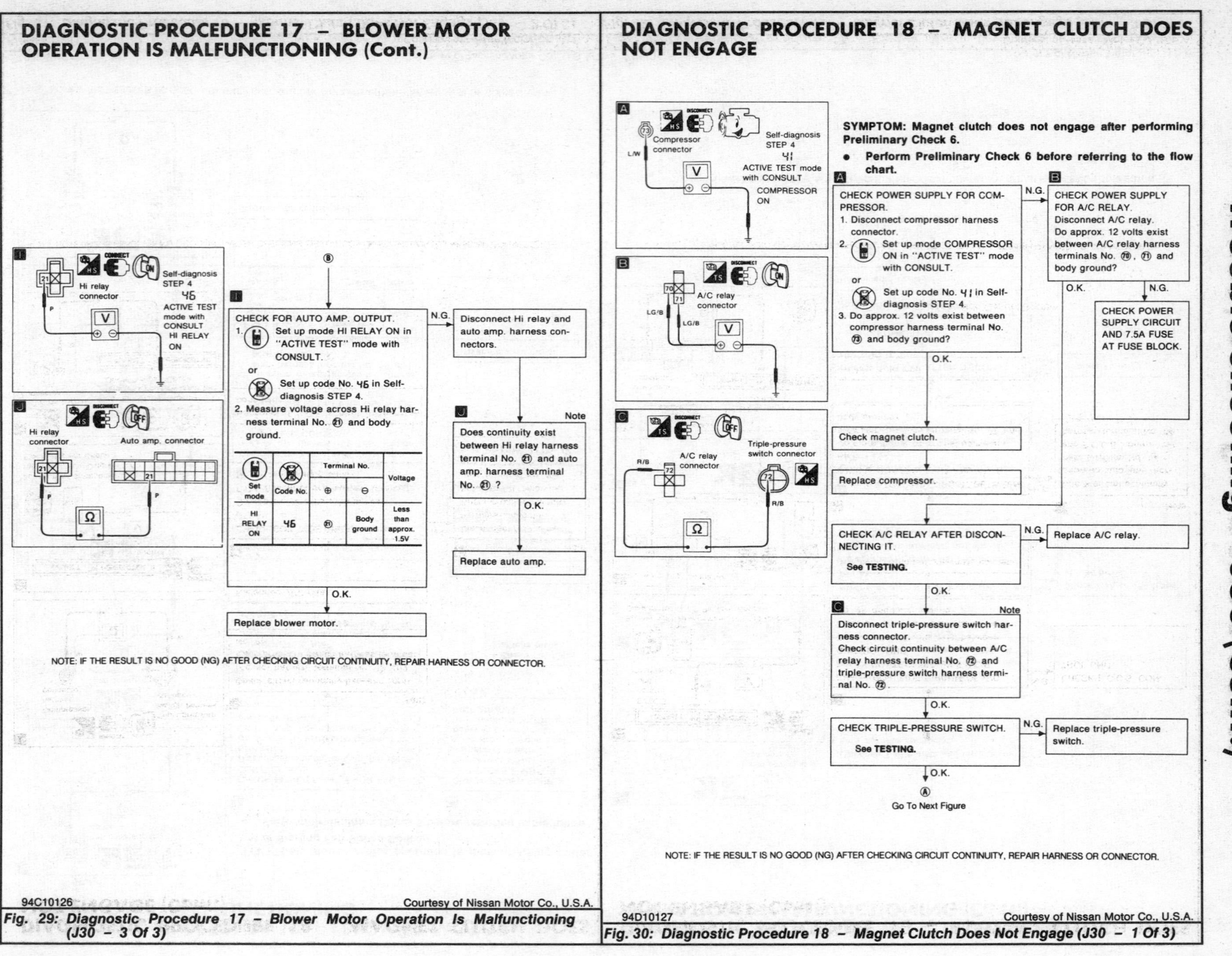
DIAGNOSTIC PROCEDURE 17 – BLOWER MOTOR OPERATION IS MALFUNCTIONING (Cont.)
I
Hi relay connector
21
P
V
Self-diagnosis STEP 4
46
ACTIVE TEST mode with CONSULT HI RELAY ON
J
Hi relay connector
Auto amp. connector
21
P
Ω
B
I
CHECK FOR AUTO AMP. OUTPUT.
1. Set up mode HI RELAY ON in "ACTIVE TEST" mode with CONSULT.
or
Set up code No. 46 in Self-diagnosis STEP 4.
2. Measure voltage across Hi relay harness terminal No. 21 and body ground.
Set mode | Code No. | Terminal No. ⊕ | Terminal No. ⊖ | Voltage
HI RELAY ON | 46 | 21 | Body ground | Less than approx. 1.5V
N.G.
Disconnect Hi relay and auto amp. harness connectors.
J
Note
Does continuity exist between Hi relay harness terminal No. 21 and auto amp. harness terminal No. 21 ?
O.K.
Replace auto amp.
O.K.
Replace blower motor.
NOTE: IF THE RESULT IS NO GOOD (NG) AFTER CHECKING CIRCUIT CONTINUITY, REPAIR HARNESS OR CONNECTOR.
94C10126
Courtesy of Nissan Motor Co., U.S.A.
DIAGNOSTIC PROCEDURE 18 – MAGNET CLUTCH DOES NOT ENGAGE
A
Compressor connector
73
L/W
V
Self-diagnosis STEP 4
41
ACTIVE TEST mode with CONSULT
COMPRESSOR ON
B
70
71
A/C relay connector
LG/B
V
C
A/C relay connector
R/B
72
Triple-pressure switch connector
Ω
SYMPTOM: Magnet clutch does not engage after performing Preliminary Check 6.
• Perform Preliminary Check 6 before referring to the flow chart.
A
CHECK POWER SUPPLY FOR COMPRESSOR.
1. Disconnect compressor harness connector.
2. Set up mode COMPRESSOR ON in "ACTIVE TEST" mode with CONSULT.
or
Set up code No. 41 in Self-diagnosis STEP 4.
3. Do approx. 12 volts exist between compressor harness terminal No. 73 and body ground?
N.G.
B
CHECK POWER SUPPLY FOR A/C RELAY.
Disconnect A/C relay.
Do approx. 12 volts exist between A/C relay harness terminals No. 70, 71 and body ground?
N.G.
CHECK POWER SUPPLY CIRCUIT AND 7.5A FUSE AT FUSE BLOCK.
O.K.
O.K.
Check magnet clutch.
Replace compressor.
CHECK A/C RELAY AFTER DISCONNECTING IT.
See TESTING.
N.G.
Replace A/C relay.
O.K.
C
Note
Disconnect triple-pressure switch harness connector.
Check circuit continuity between A/C relay harness terminal No. 72 and triple-pressure switch harness terminal No. 72.
O.K.
CHECK TRIPLE-PRESSURE SWITCH.
See TESTING.
N.G.
Replace triple-pressure switch.
O.K.
A
Go To Next Figure
NOTE: IF THE RESULT IS NO GOOD (NG) AFTER CHECKING CIRCUIT CONTINUITY, REPAIR HARNESS OR CONNECTOR.
94D10127
Courtesy of Nissan Motor Co., U.S.A.

Fig. 29: Diagnostic Procedure 17 – Blower Motor Operation Is Malfunctioning (J30 – 3 Of 3)

Fig. 30: Diagnostic Procedure 18 – Magnet Clutch Does Not Engage (J30 – 1 Of 3)

1993 AUTOMATIC A/C-HEATER SYSTEMS
Trouble Shooting – J30 (Cont.)

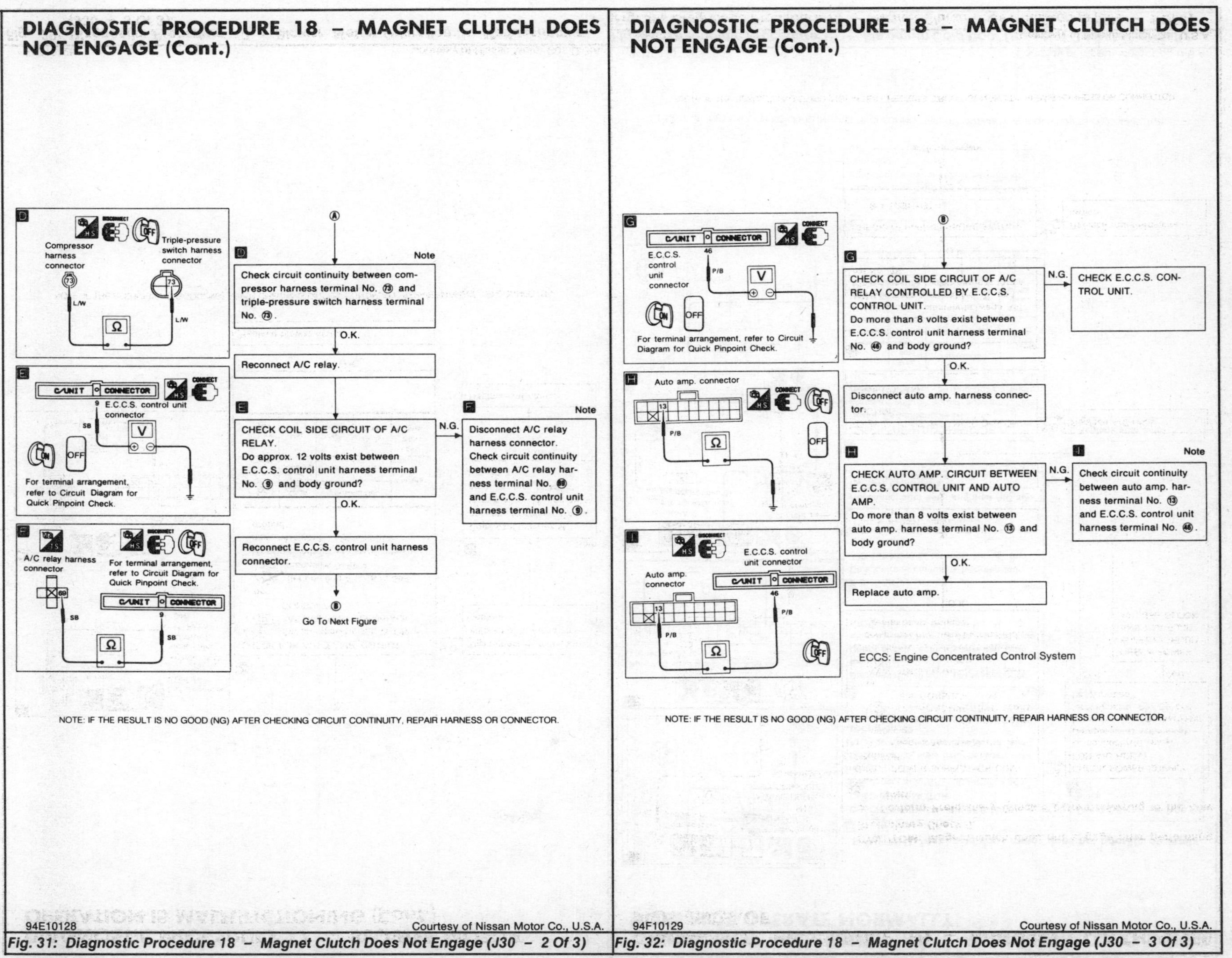
DIAGNOSTIC PROCEDURE 18 – MAGNET CLUTCH DOES NOT ENGAGE (Cont.)
D
Compressor harness connector
Triple-pressure switch harness connector
DISCONNECT
OFF
73
L/W
Ω
A
Note
Check circuit continuity between compressor harness terminal No. 73 and triple-pressure switch harness terminal No. 73.
O.K.
Reconnect A/C relay.
E
C/UNIT CONNECTOR
CONNECT
9
E.C.C.S. control unit connector
SB
V
ON
OFF
For terminal arrangement, refer to Circuit Diagram for Quick Pinpoint Check.
CHECK COIL SIDE CIRCUIT OF A/C RELAY.
Do approx. 12 volts exist between E.C.C.S. control unit harness terminal No. 9 and body ground?
N.G.
F
Note
Disconnect A/C relay harness connector.
Check circuit continuity between A/C relay harness terminal No. 69 and E.C.C.S. control unit harness terminal No. 9.
O.K.
Reconnect E.C.C.S. control unit harness connector.
F
A/C relay harness connector
For terminal arrangement, refer to Circuit Diagram for Quick Pinpoint Check.
69
SB
B
Go To Next Figure
NOTE: IF THE RESULT IS NO GOOD (NG) AFTER CHECKING CIRCUIT CONTINUITY, REPAIR HARNESS OR CONNECTOR.
94E10128
Courtesy of Nissan Motor Co., U.S.A.
DIAGNOSTIC PROCEDURE 18 – MAGNET CLUTCH DOES NOT ENGAGE (Cont.)
G
C/UNIT CONNECTOR
CONNECT
E.C.C.S. control unit connector
46
P/B
V
ON
OFF
For terminal arrangement, refer to Circuit Diagram for Quick Pinpoint Check.
B
CHECK COIL SIDE CIRCUIT OF A/C RELAY CONTROLLED BY E.C.C.S. CONTROL UNIT.
Do more than 8 volts exist between E.C.C.S. control unit harness terminal No. 46 and body ground?
N.G.
CHECK E.C.C.S. CONTROL UNIT.
O.K.
H
Auto amp. connector
13
P/B
Ω
Disconnect auto amp. harness connector.
CHECK AUTO AMP. CIRCUIT BETWEEN E.C.C.S. CONTROL UNIT AND AUTO AMP.
Do more than 8 volts exist between auto amp. harness terminal No. 13 and body ground?
N.G.
I
Note
Check circuit continuity between auto amp. harness terminal No. 13 and E.C.C.S. control unit harness terminal No. 46.
O.K.
Replace auto amp.
I
DISCONNECT
E.C.C.S. control unit connector
Auto amp. connector
ECCS: Engine Concentrated Control System
NOTE: IF THE RESULT IS NO GOOD (NG) AFTER CHECKING CIRCUIT CONTINUITY, REPAIR HARNESS OR CONNECTOR.
94F10129
Courtesy of Nissan Motor Co., U.S.A.

Fig. 31: Diagnostic Procedure 18 – Magnet Clutch Does Not Engage (J30 – 2 Of 3)

Fig. 32: Diagnostic Procedure 18 – Magnet Clutch Does Not Engage (J30 – 3 Of 3)

1993 AUTOMATIC A/C-HEATER SYSTEMS
Trouble Shooting – J30 (Cont.)

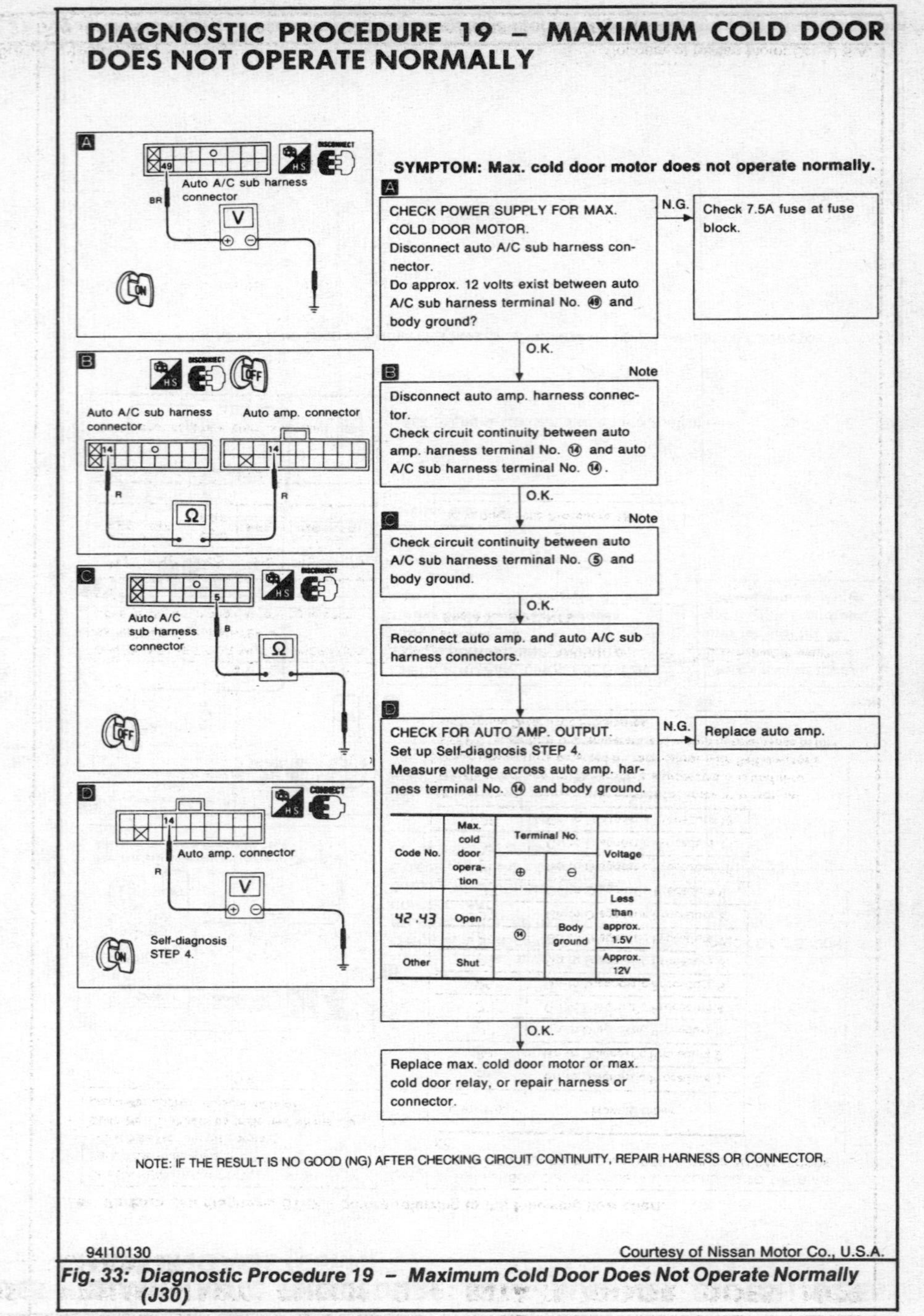
DIAGNOSTIC PROCEDURE 19 – MAXIMUM COLD DOOR DOES NOT OPERATE NORMALLY
A
49
Auto A/C sub harness connector
BR
V
B
Auto A/C sub harness connector
Auto amp. connector
14
R
Ω
C
5
Auto A/C sub harness connector
B
Ω
D
14
Auto amp. connector
R
V
Self-diagnosis STEP 4.
SYMPTOM: Max. cold door motor does not operate normally.
A
CHECK POWER SUPPLY FOR MAX. COLD DOOR MOTOR.
Disconnect auto A/C sub harness connector.
Do approx. 12 volts exist between auto A/C sub harness terminal No. ㊾ and body ground?
N.G.
Check 7.5A fuse at fuse block.
O.K.
B
Note
Disconnect auto amp. harness connector.
Check circuit continuity between auto amp. harness terminal No. ⑭ and auto A/C sub harness terminal No. ⑭.
O.K.
C
Note
Check circuit continuity between auto A/C sub harness terminal No. ⑤ and body ground.
O.K.
Reconnect auto amp. and auto A/C sub harness connectors.
D
CHECK FOR AUTO AMP. OUTPUT.
Set up Self-diagnosis STEP 4.
Measure voltage across auto amp. harness terminal No. ⑭ and body ground.
N.G.
Replace auto amp.
O.K.
Replace max. cold door motor or max. cold door relay, or repair harness or connector.
NOTE: IF THE RESULT IS NO GOOD (NG) AFTER CHECKING CIRCUIT CONTINUITY, REPAIR HARNESS OR CONNECTOR.
94I10130
Courtesy of Nissan Motor Co., U.S.A.

Code No.	Max. cold door operation	Terminal No. ⊕	Terminal No. ⊖	Voltage
42 . 43	Open	⑭	Body ground	Less than approx. 1.5V
Other	Shut			Approx. 12V

Fig. 33: Diagnostic Procedure 19 – Maximum Cold Door Does Not Operate Normally (J30)

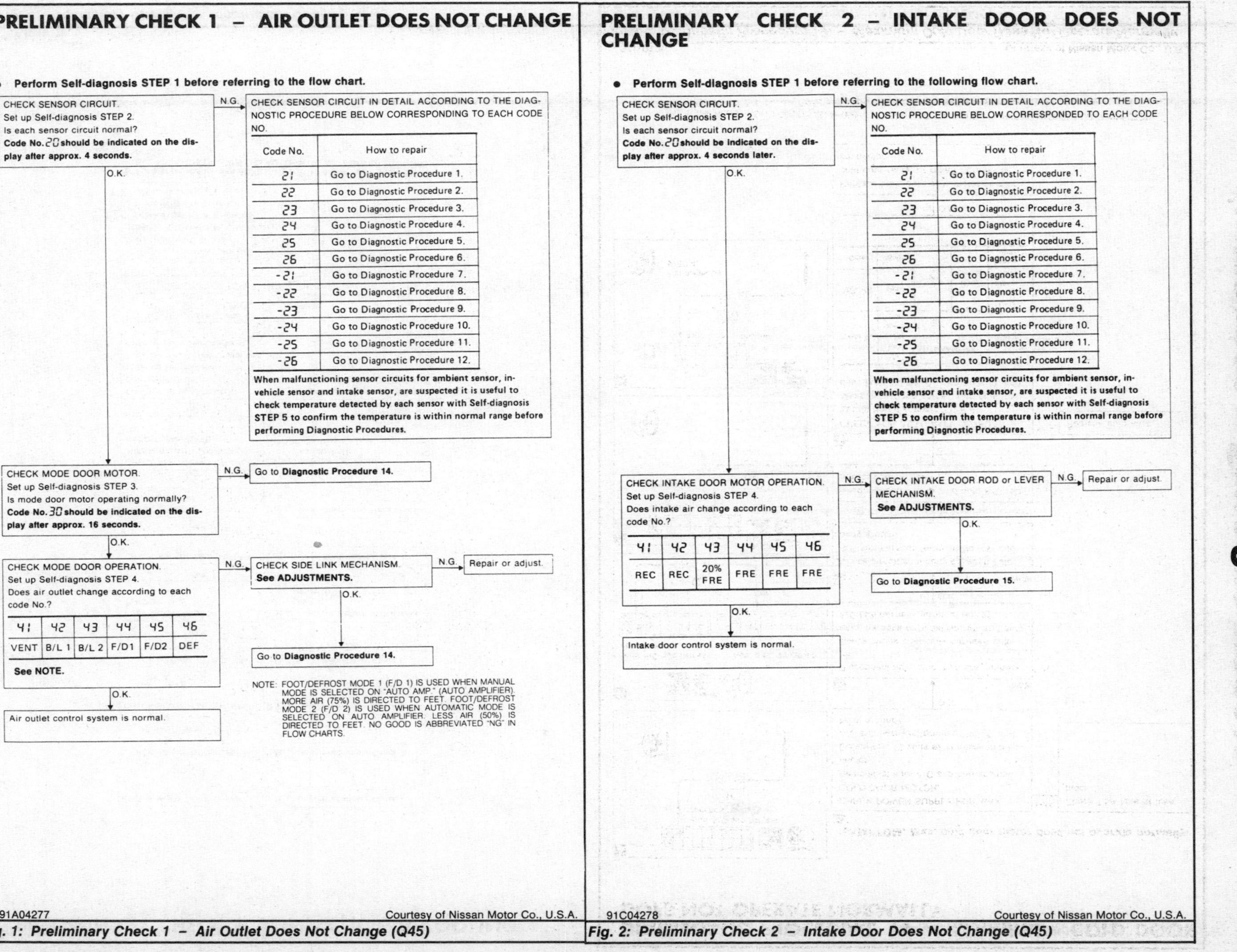

PRELIMINARY CHECK 1 – AIR OUTLET DOES NOT CHANGE

- **Perform Self-diagnosis STEP 1 before referring to the flow chart.**

CHECK SENSOR CIRCUIT.
Set up Self-diagnosis STEP 2.
Is each sensor circuit normal?
Code No. 20 should be indicated on the display after approx. 4 seconds.

N.G. → CHECK SENSOR CIRCUIT IN DETAIL ACCORDING TO THE DIAGNOSTIC PROCEDURE BELOW CORRESPONDING TO EACH CODE NO.

Code No.	How to repair
21	Go to Diagnostic Procedure 1.
22	Go to Diagnostic Procedure 2.
23	Go to Diagnostic Procedure 3.
24	Go to Diagnostic Procedure 4.
25	Go to Diagnostic Procedure 5.
26	Go to Diagnostic Procedure 6.
-21	Go to Diagnostic Procedure 7.
-22	Go to Diagnostic Procedure 8.
-23	Go to Diagnostic Procedure 9.
-24	Go to Diagnostic Procedure 10.
-25	Go to Diagnostic Procedure 11.
-26	Go to Diagnostic Procedure 12.

When malfunctioning sensor circuits for ambient sensor, in-vehicle sensor and intake sensor, are suspected it is useful to check temperature detected by each sensor with Self-diagnosis STEP 5 to confirm the temperature is within normal range before performing Diagnostic Procedures.

O.K. ↓

CHECK MODE DOOR MOTOR.
Set up Self-diagnosis STEP 3.
Is mode door motor operating normally?
Code No. 30 should be indicated on the display after approx. 16 seconds.

N.G. → Go to **Diagnostic Procedure 14.**

O.K. ↓

CHECK MODE DOOR OPERATION.
Set up Self-diagnosis STEP 4.
Does air outlet change according to each code No.?

41	42	43	44	45	46
VENT	B/L 1	B/L 2	F/D1	F/D2	DEF

See NOTE.

N.G. → CHECK SIDE LINK MECHANISM. **See ADJUSTMENTS.**
- N.G. → Repair or adjust.
- O.K. → Go to **Diagnostic Procedure 14.**

O.K. ↓

Air outlet control system is normal.

NOTE: FOOT/DEFROST MODE 1 (F/D 1) IS USED WHEN MANUAL MODE IS SELECTED ON "AUTO AMP." (AUTO AMPLIFIER). MORE AIR (75%) IS DIRECTED TO FEET. FOOT/DEFROST MODE 2 (F/D 2) IS USED WHEN AUTOMATIC MODE IS SELECTED ON AUTO AMPLIFIER. LESS AIR (50%) IS DIRECTED TO FEET. NO GOOD IS ABBREVIATED "NG" IN FLOW CHARTS.

91A04277 Courtesy of Nissan Motor Co., U.S.A.

Fig. 1: Preliminary Check 1 – Air Outlet Does Not Change (Q45)

PRELIMINARY CHECK 2 – INTAKE DOOR DOES NOT CHANGE

- **Perform Self-diagnosis STEP 1 before referring to the following flow chart.**

CHECK SENSOR CIRCUIT.
Set up Self-diagnosis STEP 2.
Is each sensor circuit normal?
Code No. 20 should be indicated on the display after approx. 4 seconds later.

N.G. → CHECK SENSOR CIRCUIT IN DETAIL ACCORDING TO THE DIAGNOSTIC PROCEDURE BELOW CORRESPONDED TO EACH CODE NO.

Code No.	How to repair
21	Go to Diagnostic Procedure 1.
22	Go to Diagnostic Procedure 2.
23	Go to Diagnostic Procedure 3.
24	Go to Diagnostic Procedure 4.
25	Go to Diagnostic Procedure 5.
26	Go to Diagnostic Procedure 6.
-21	Go to Diagnostic Procedure 7.
-22	Go to Diagnostic Procedure 8.
-23	Go to Diagnostic Procedure 9.
-24	Go to Diagnostic Procedure 10.
-25	Go to Diagnostic Procedure 11.
-26	Go to Diagnostic Procedure 12.

When malfunctioning sensor circuits for ambient sensor, in-vehicle sensor and intake sensor, are suspected it is useful to check temperature detected by each sensor with Self-diagnosis STEP 5 to confirm the temperature is within normal range before performing Diagnostic Procedures.

O.K. ↓

CHECK INTAKE DOOR MOTOR OPERATION.
Set up Self-diagnosis STEP 4.
Does intake air change according to each code No.?

41	42	43	44	45	46
REC	REC	20% FRE	FRE	FRE	FRE

N.G. → CHECK INTAKE DOOR ROD or LEVER MECHANISM. **See ADJUSTMENTS.**
- N.G. → Repair or adjust.
- O.K. → Go to **Diagnostic Procedure 15.**

O.K. ↓

Intake door control system is normal.

91C04278 Courtesy of Nissan Motor Co., U.S.A.

Fig. 2: Preliminary Check 2 – Intake Door Does Not Change (Q45)

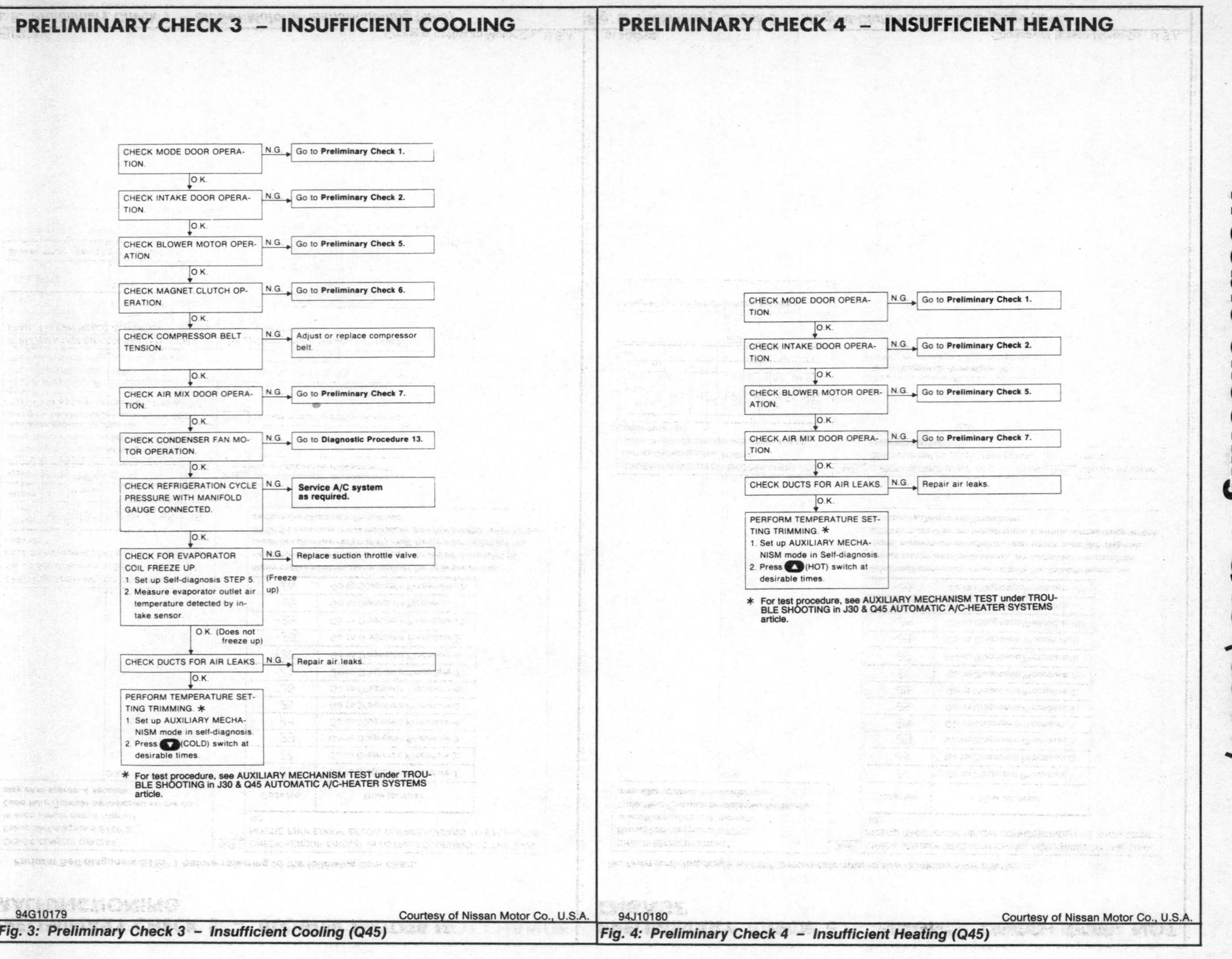
PRELIMINARY CHECK 3 – INSUFFICIENT COOLING
CHECK MODE DOOR OPERATION.
N.G.
Go to Preliminary Check 1.
O.K.
CHECK INTAKE DOOR OPERATION.
N.G.
Go to Preliminary Check 2.
O.K.
CHECK BLOWER MOTOR OPERATION.
N.G.
Go to Preliminary Check 5.
O.K.
CHECK MAGNET CLUTCH OPERATION.
N.G.
Go to Preliminary Check 6.
O.K.
CHECK COMPRESSOR BELT TENSION.
N.G.
Adjust or replace compressor belt.
O.K.
CHECK AIR MIX DOOR OPERATION.
N.G.
Go to Preliminary Check 7.
O.K.
CHECK CONDENSER FAN MOTOR OPERATION.
N.G.
Go to Diagnostic Procedure 13.
O.K.
CHECK REFRIGERATION CYCLE PRESSURE WITH MANIFOLD GAUGE CONNECTED.
N.G.
Service A/C system as required.
O.K.
CHECK FOR EVAPORATOR COIL FREEZE UP.
1. Set up Self-diagnosis STEP 5.
2. Measure evaporator outlet air temperature detected by intake sensor.
N.G. (Freeze up)
Replace suction throttle valve.
O.K. (Does not freeze up)
CHECK DUCTS FOR AIR LEAKS.
N.G.
Repair air leaks.
O.K.
PERFORM TEMPERATURE SETTING TRIMMING. *
1. Set up AUXILIARY MECHANISM mode in self-diagnosis.
2. Press (COLD) switch at desirable times.
* For test procedure, see AUXILIARY MECHANISM TEST under TROUBLE SHOOTING in J30 & Q45 AUTOMATIC A/C-HEATER SYSTEMS article.
94G10179
Courtesy of Nissan Motor Co., U.S.A.
PRELIMINARY CHECK 4 – INSUFFICIENT HEATING
CHECK MODE DOOR OPERATION.
N.G.
Go to Preliminary Check 1.
O.K.
CHECK INTAKE DOOR OPERATION.
N.G.
Go to Preliminary Check 2.
O.K.
CHECK BLOWER MOTOR OPERATION.
N.G.
Go to Preliminary Check 5.
O.K.
CHECK AIR MIX DOOR OPERATION.
N.G.
Go to Preliminary Check 7.
O.K.
CHECK DUCTS FOR AIR LEAKS.
N.G.
Repair air leaks.
O.K.
PERFORM TEMPERATURE SETTING TRIMMING. *
1. Set up AUXILIARY MECHANISM mode in Self-diagnosis.
2. Press (HOT) switch at desirable times.
* For test procedure, see AUXILIARY MECHANISM TEST under TROUBLE SHOOTING in J30 & Q45 AUTOMATIC A/C-HEATER SYSTEMS article.
94J10180
Courtesy of Nissan Motor Co., U.S.A.

Fig. 3: Preliminary Check 3 – Insufficient Cooling (Q45)

Fig. 4: Preliminary Check 4 – Insufficient Heating (Q45)

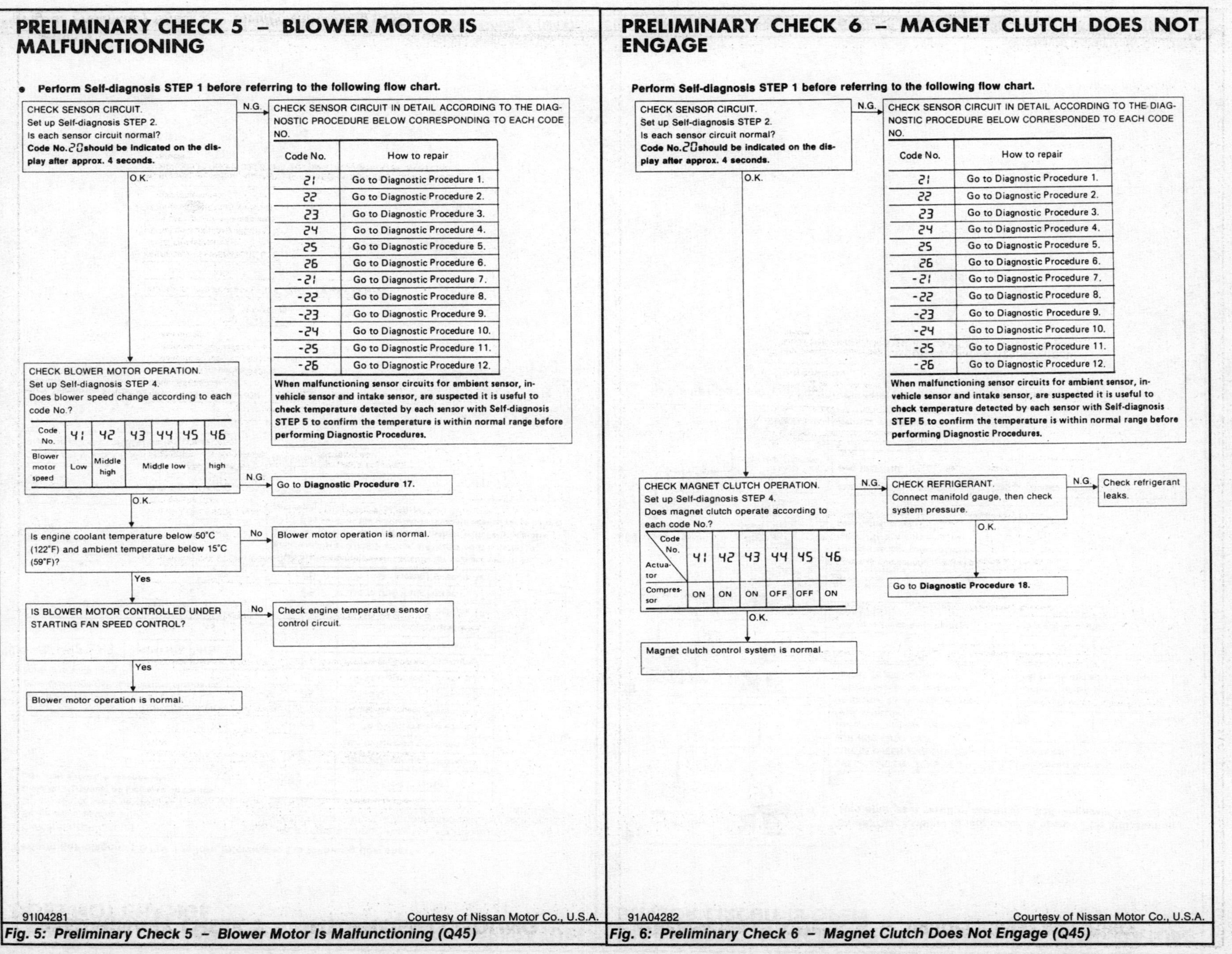

PRELIMINARY CHECK 5 – BLOWER MOTOR IS MALFUNCTIONING
• Perform Self-diagnosis STEP 1 before referring to the following flow chart.
CHECK SENSOR CIRCUIT.
Set up Self-diagnosis STEP 2.
Is each sensor circuit normal?
Code No. 20 should be indicated on the display after approx. 4 seconds.
N.G.
CHECK SENSOR CIRCUIT IN DETAIL ACCORDING TO THE DIAGNOSTIC PROCEDURE BELOW CORRESPONDING TO EACH CODE NO.
Code No.
How to repair
21 Go to Diagnostic Procedure 1.
22 Go to Diagnostic Procedure 2.
23 Go to Diagnostic Procedure 3.
24 Go to Diagnostic Procedure 4.
25 Go to Diagnostic Procedure 5.
26 Go to Diagnostic Procedure 6.
-21 Go to Diagnostic Procedure 7.
-22 Go to Diagnostic Procedure 8.
-23 Go to Diagnostic Procedure 9.
-24 Go to Diagnostic Procedure 10.
-25 Go to Diagnostic Procedure 11.
-26 Go to Diagnostic Procedure 12.
When malfunctioning sensor circuits for ambient sensor, in-vehicle sensor and intake sensor, are suspected it is useful to check temperature detected by each sensor with Self-diagnosis STEP 5 to confirm the temperature is within normal range before performing Diagnostic Procedures.
O.K.
CHECK BLOWER MOTOR OPERATION.
Set up Self-diagnosis STEP 4.
Does blower speed change according to each code No.?
Code No.
41 42 43 44 45 46
Blower motor speed
Low
Middle high
Middle low
high
N.G.
Go to Diagnostic Procedure 17.
O.K.
Is engine coolant temperature below 50°C (122°F) and ambient temperature below 15°C (59°F)?
No
Blower motor operation is normal.
Yes
IS BLOWER MOTOR CONTROLLED UNDER STARTING FAN SPEED CONTROL?
No
Check engine temperature sensor control circuit.
Yes
Blower motor operation is normal.
91I04281
Courtesy of Nissan Motor Co., U.S.A.
PRELIMINARY CHECK 6 – MAGNET CLUTCH DOES NOT ENGAGE
Perform Self-diagnosis STEP 1 before referring to the following flow chart.
CHECK SENSOR CIRCUIT.
Set up Self-diagnosis STEP 2.
Is each sensor circuit normal?
Code No. 20 should be indicated on the display after approx. 4 seconds.
N.G.
CHECK SENSOR CIRCUIT IN DETAIL ACCORDING TO THE DIAGNOSTIC PROCEDURE BELOW CORRESPONDED TO EACH CODE NO.
Code No.
How to repair
21 Go to Diagnostic Procedure 1.
22 Go to Diagnostic Procedure 2.
23 Go to Diagnostic Procedure 3.
24 Go to Diagnostic Procedure 4.
25 Go to Diagnostic Procedure 5.
26 Go to Diagnostic Procedure 6.
-21 Go to Diagnostic Procedure 7.
-22 Go to Diagnostic Procedure 8.
-23 Go to Diagnostic Procedure 9.
-24 Go to Diagnostic Procedure 10.
-25 Go to Diagnostic Procedure 11.
-26 Go to Diagnostic Procedure 12.
When malfunctioning sensor circuits for ambient sensor, in-vehicle sensor and intake sensor, are suspected it is useful to check temperature detected by each sensor with Self-diagnosis STEP 5 to confirm the temperature is within normal range before performing Diagnostic Procedures.
O.K.
CHECK MAGNET CLUTCH OPERATION.
Set up Self-diagnosis STEP 4.
Does magnet clutch operate according to each code No.?
Code No.
Actuator
41 42 43 44 45 46
Compressor
ON ON ON OFF OFF ON
N.G.
CHECK REFRIGERANT.
Connect manifold gauge, then check system pressure.
N.G.
Check refrigerant leaks.
O.K.
Go to Diagnostic Procedure 18.
O.K.
Magnet clutch control system is normal.
91A04282
Courtesy of Nissan Motor Co., U.S.A.

Fig. 5: Preliminary Check 5 – Blower Motor Is Malfunctioning (Q45)

Fig. 6: Preliminary Check 6 – Magnet Clutch Does Not Engage (Q45)

1993 AUTOMATIC A/C-HEATER SYSTEMS
Trouble Shooting – Q45 (Cont.)

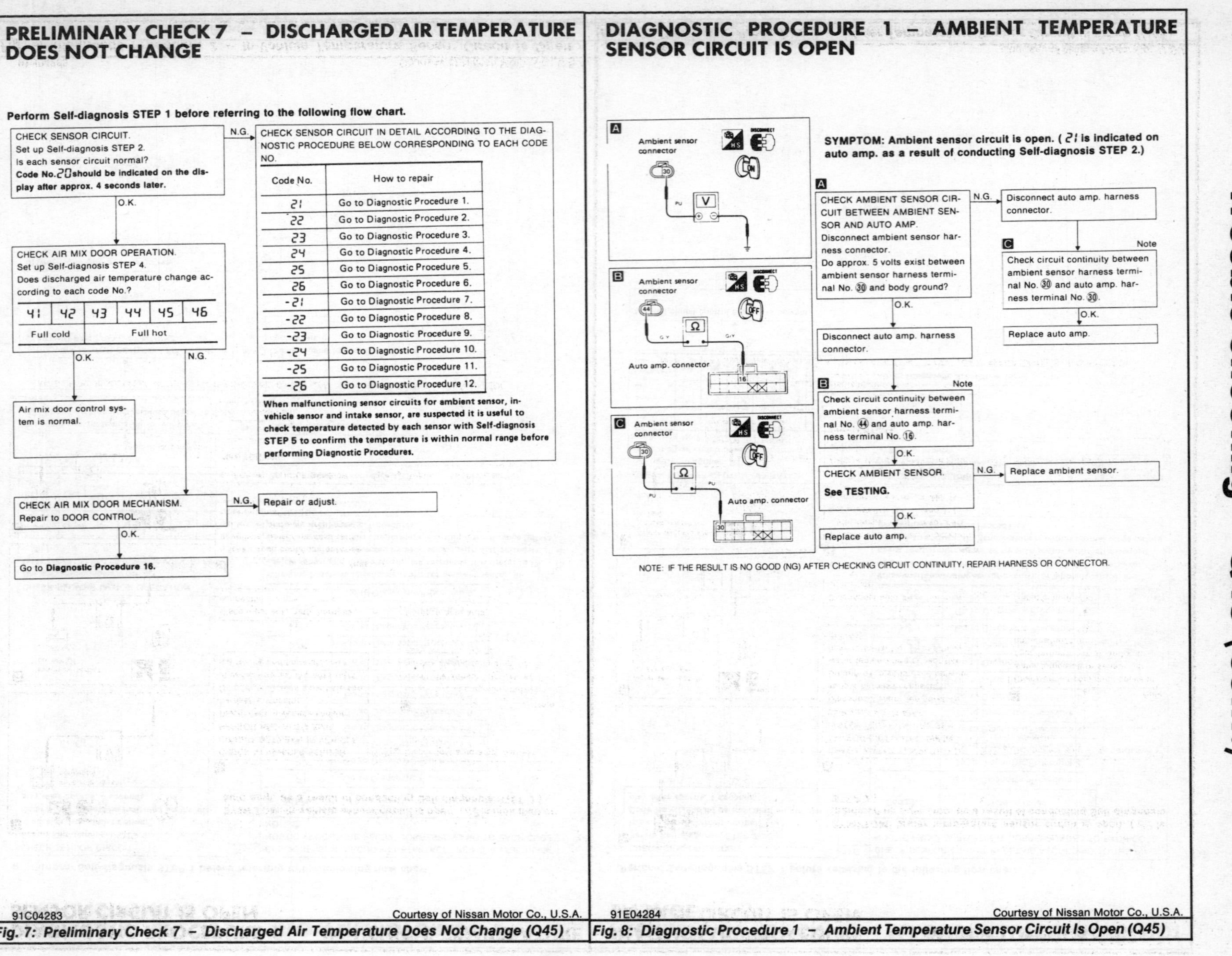
PRELIMINARY CHECK 7 – DISCHARGED AIR TEMPERATURE DOES NOT CHANGE
Perform Self-diagnosis STEP 1 before referring to the following flow chart.
CHECK SENSOR CIRCUIT. Set up Self-diagnosis STEP 2. Is each sensor circuit normal? Code No. 20 should be indicated on the display after approx. 4 seconds later.
N.G.
CHECK SENSOR CIRCUIT IN DETAIL ACCORDING TO THE DIAGNOSTIC PROCEDURE BELOW CORRESPONDING TO EACH CODE NO.
When malfunctioning sensor circuits for ambient sensor, in-vehicle sensor and intake sensor, are suspected it is useful to check temperature detected by each sensor with Self-diagnosis STEP 5 to confirm the temperature is within normal range before performing Diagnostic Procedures.
O.K.
CHECK AIR MIX DOOR OPERATION. Set up Self-diagnosis STEP 4. Does discharged air temperature change according to each code No.?
41 42 43 44 45 46
Full cold
Full hot
O.K.
Air mix door control system is normal.
N.G.
CHECK AIR MIX DOOR MECHANISM. Repair to DOOR CONTROL.
N.G.
Repair or adjust.
O.K.
Go to Diagnostic Procedure 16.
91C04283
Courtesy of Nissan Motor Co., U.S.A.
DIAGNOSTIC PROCEDURE 1 – AMBIENT TEMPERATURE SENSOR CIRCUIT IS OPEN
A
Ambient sensor connector
30
PU
V
B
Ambient sensor connector
44
G/Y
Auto amp. connector
16
C
Ambient sensor connector
30
PU
Auto amp. connector
30
SYMPTOM: Ambient sensor circuit is open. (21 is indicated on auto amp. as a result of conducting Self-diagnosis STEP 2.)
A
CHECK AMBIENT SENSOR CIRCUIT BETWEEN AMBIENT SENSOR AND AUTO AMP. Disconnect ambient sensor harness connector. Do approx. 5 volts exist between ambient sensor harness terminal No. 30 and body ground?
N.G.
Disconnect auto amp. harness connector.
C
Note
Check circuit continuity between ambient sensor harness terminal No. 30 and auto amp. harness terminal No. 30.
O.K.
Replace auto amp.
O.K.
Disconnect auto amp. harness connector.
B
Note
Check circuit continuity between ambient sensor harness terminal No. 44 and auto amp. harness terminal No. 16.
O.K.
CHECK AMBIENT SENSOR. See TESTING.
N.G.
Replace ambient sensor.
O.K.
Replace auto amp.
NOTE: IF THE RESULT IS NO GOOD (NG) AFTER CHECKING CIRCUIT CONTINUITY, REPAIR HARNESS OR CONNECTOR.
91E04284
Courtesy of Nissan Motor Co., U.S.A.

Code No.	How to repair
21	Go to Diagnostic Procedure 1.
22	Go to Diagnostic Procedure 2.
23	Go to Diagnostic Procedure 3.
24	Go to Diagnostic Procedure 4.
25	Go to Diagnostic Procedure 5.
26	Go to Diagnostic Procedure 6.
-21	Go to Diagnostic Procedure 7.
-22	Go to Diagnostic Procedure 8.
-23	Go to Diagnostic Procedure 9.
-24	Go to Diagnostic Procedure 10.
-25	Go to Diagnostic Procedure 11.
-26	Go to Diagnostic Procedure 12.

Fig. 7: Preliminary Check 7 – Discharged Air Temperature Does Not Change (Q45)

Fig. 8: Diagnostic Procedure 1 – Ambient Temperature Sensor Circuit Is Open (Q45)

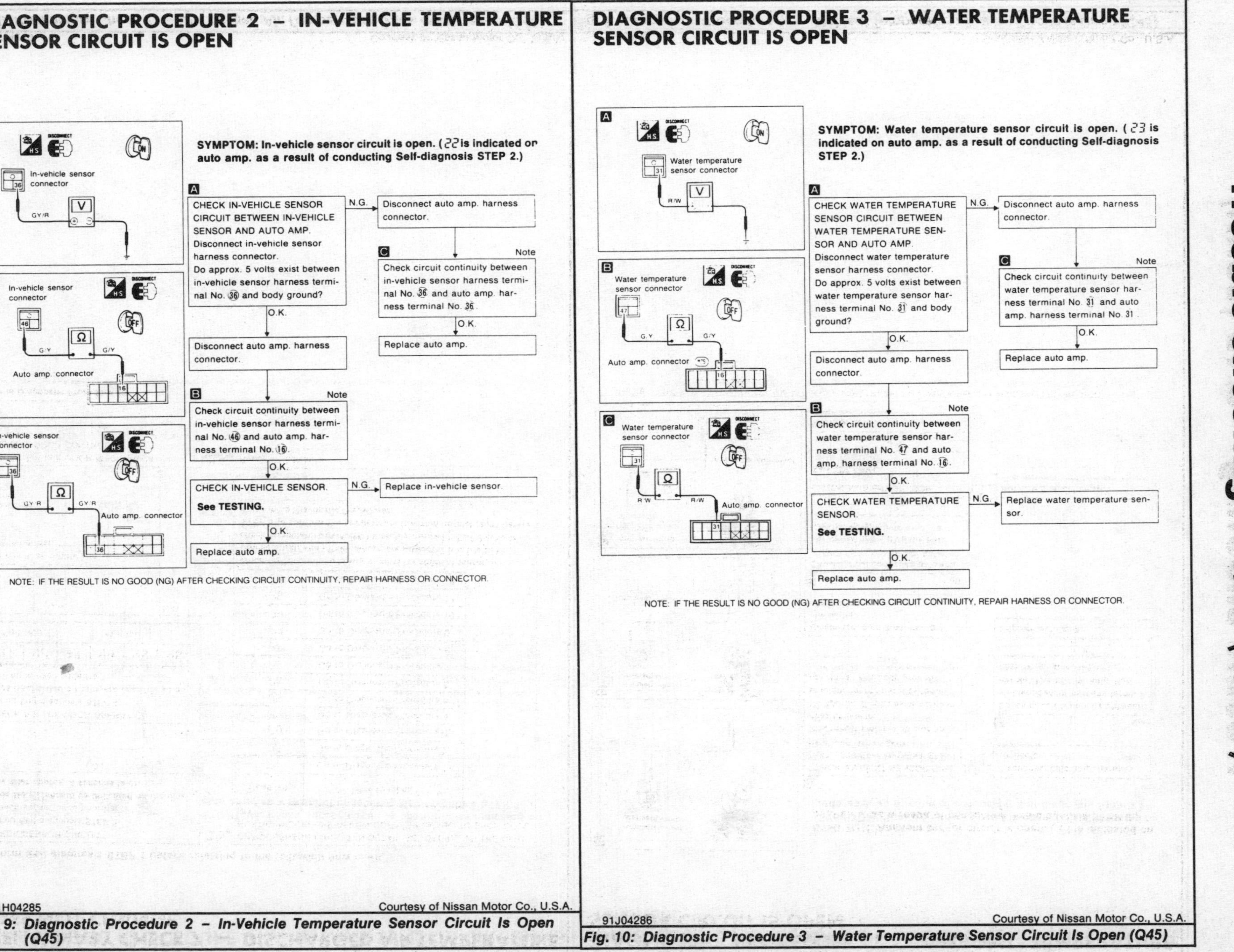
DIAGNOSTIC PROCEDURE 2 – IN-VEHICLE TEMPERATURE SENSOR CIRCUIT IS OPEN
A
In-vehicle sensor connector
36
GY/R
V
B
In-vehicle sensor connector
46
G/Y
Ω
G/Y
Auto amp. connector
16
C
In-vehicle sensor connector
36
GY/R
Ω
GY/R
Auto amp. connector
36
SYMPTOM: In-vehicle sensor circuit is open. (22 is indicated on auto amp. as a result of conducting Self-diagnosis STEP 2.)
A
CHECK IN-VEHICLE SENSOR CIRCUIT BETWEEN IN-VEHICLE SENSOR AND AUTO AMP.
Disconnect in-vehicle sensor harness connector.
Do approx. 5 volts exist between in-vehicle sensor harness terminal No. 36 and body ground?
N.G.
Disconnect auto amp. harness connector.
C
Note
Check circuit continuity between in-vehicle sensor harness terminal No. 36 and auto amp. harness terminal No. 36.
O.K.
Replace auto amp.
O.K.
Disconnect auto amp. harness connector.
B
Note
Check circuit continuity between in-vehicle sensor harness terminal No. 46 and auto amp. harness terminal No. 16.
O.K.
CHECK IN-VEHICLE SENSOR.
See TESTING.
N.G.
Replace in-vehicle sensor.
O.K.
Replace auto amp.
NOTE: IF THE RESULT IS NO GOOD (NG) AFTER CHECKING CIRCUIT CONTINUITY, REPAIR HARNESS OR CONNECTOR.
91H04285
Courtesy of Nissan Motor Co., U.S.A.
DIAGNOSTIC PROCEDURE 3 – WATER TEMPERATURE SENSOR CIRCUIT IS OPEN
A
Water temperature sensor connector
31
R/W
V
B
Water temperature sensor connector
47
G/Y
Ω
G/Y
Auto amp. connector
16
C
Water temperature sensor connector
31
R/W
Ω
R/W
Auto amp. connector
31
SYMPTOM: Water temperature sensor circuit is open. (23 is indicated on auto amp. as a result of conducting Self-diagnosis STEP 2.)
A
CHECK WATER TEMPERATURE SENSOR CIRCUIT BETWEEN WATER TEMPERATURE SENSOR AND AUTO AMP.
Disconnect water temperature sensor harness connector.
Do approx. 5 volts exist between water temperature sensor harness terminal No. 31 and body ground?
N.G.
Disconnect auto amp. harness connector.
C
Note
Check circuit continuity between water temperature sensor harness terminal No. 31 and auto amp. harness terminal No. 31.
O.K.
Replace auto amp.
O.K.
Disconnect auto amp. harness connector.
B
Note
Check circuit continuity between water temperature sensor harness terminal No. 47 and auto amp. harness terminal No. 16.
O.K.
CHECK WATER TEMPERATURE SENSOR.
See TESTING.
N.G.
Replace water temperature sensor.
O.K.
Replace auto amp.
NOTE: IF THE RESULT IS NO GOOD (NG) AFTER CHECKING CIRCUIT CONTINUITY, REPAIR HARNESS OR CONNECTOR.
91J04286
Courtesy of Nissan Motor Co., U.S.A.

Fig. 9: Diagnostic Procedure 2 – In-Vehicle Temperature Sensor Circuit Is Open (Q45)

Fig. 10: Diagnostic Procedure 3 – Water Temperature Sensor Circuit Is Open (Q45)

1993 AUTOMATIC A/C-HEATER SYSTEMS
Trouble Shooting – Q45 (Cont.)

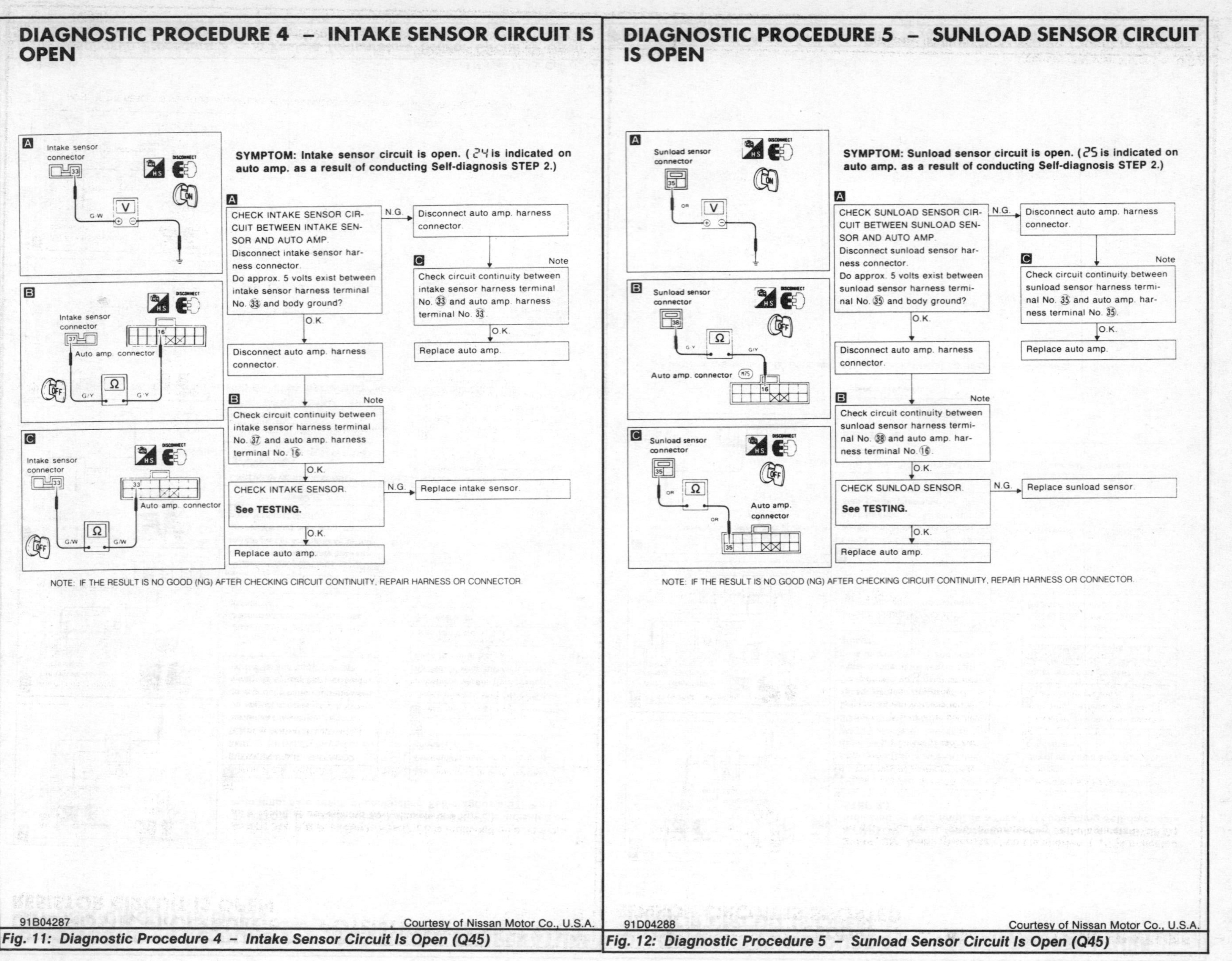
DIAGNOSTIC PROCEDURE 4 – INTAKE SENSOR CIRCUIT IS OPEN
A
Intake sensor connector
33
G/W
V
DISCONNECT
HS
ON
B
Intake sensor connector
37
16
Auto amp. connector
G/Y
G/Y
OFF
C
Intake sensor connector
33
33
Auto amp. connector
G/W
G/W
OFF
SYMPTOM: Intake sensor circuit is open. (24 is indicated on auto amp. as a result of conducting Self-diagnosis STEP 2.)
A
CHECK INTAKE SENSOR CIRCUIT BETWEEN INTAKE SENSOR AND AUTO AMP.
Disconnect intake sensor harness connector.
Do approx. 5 volts exist between intake sensor harness terminal No. 33 and body ground?
N.G.
Disconnect auto amp. harness connector.
C
Note
Check circuit continuity between intake sensor harness terminal No. 33 and auto amp. harness terminal No. 33.
O.K.
Replace auto amp.
O.K.
Disconnect auto amp. harness connector.
B
Note
Check circuit continuity between intake sensor harness terminal No. 37 and auto amp. harness terminal No. 16.
O.K.
CHECK INTAKE SENSOR.
See TESTING.
N.G.
Replace intake sensor.
O.K.
Replace auto amp.
NOTE: IF THE RESULT IS NO GOOD (NG) AFTER CHECKING CIRCUIT CONTINUITY, REPAIR HARNESS OR CONNECTOR.
91B04287
Courtesy of Nissan Motor Co., U.S.A.
DIAGNOSTIC PROCEDURE 5 – SUNLOAD SENSOR CIRCUIT IS OPEN
A
Sunload sensor connector
35
OR
V
DISCONNECT
HS
ON
B
Sunload sensor connector
38
G/Y
G/Y
Auto amp. connector
16
OFF
C
Sunload sensor connector
35
OR
OR
Auto amp. connector
35
OFF
SYMPTOM: Sunload sensor circuit is open. (25 is indicated on auto amp. as a result of conducting Self-diagnosis STEP 2.)
A
CHECK SUNLOAD SENSOR CIRCUIT BETWEEN SUNLOAD SENSOR AND AUTO AMP.
Disconnect sunload sensor harness connector.
Do approx. 5 volts exist between sunload sensor harness terminal No. 35 and body ground?
N.G.
Disconnect auto amp. harness connector.
C
Note
Check circuit continuity between sunload sensor harness terminal No. 35 and auto amp. harness terminal No. 35.
O.K.
Replace auto amp.
O.K.
Disconnect auto amp. harness connector.
B
Note
Check circuit continuity between sunload sensor harness terminal No. 38 and auto amp. harness terminal No. 16.
O.K.
CHECK SUNLOAD SENSOR.
See TESTING.
N.G.
Replace sunload sensor.
O.K.
Replace auto amp.
NOTE: IF THE RESULT IS NO GOOD (NG) AFTER CHECKING CIRCUIT CONTINUITY, REPAIR HARNESS OR CONNECTOR.
91D04288
Courtesy of Nissan Motor Co., U.S.A.

Fig. 11: Diagnostic Procedure 4 – Intake Sensor Circuit Is Open (Q45)

Fig. 12: Diagnostic Procedure 5 – Sunload Sensor Circuit Is Open (Q45)

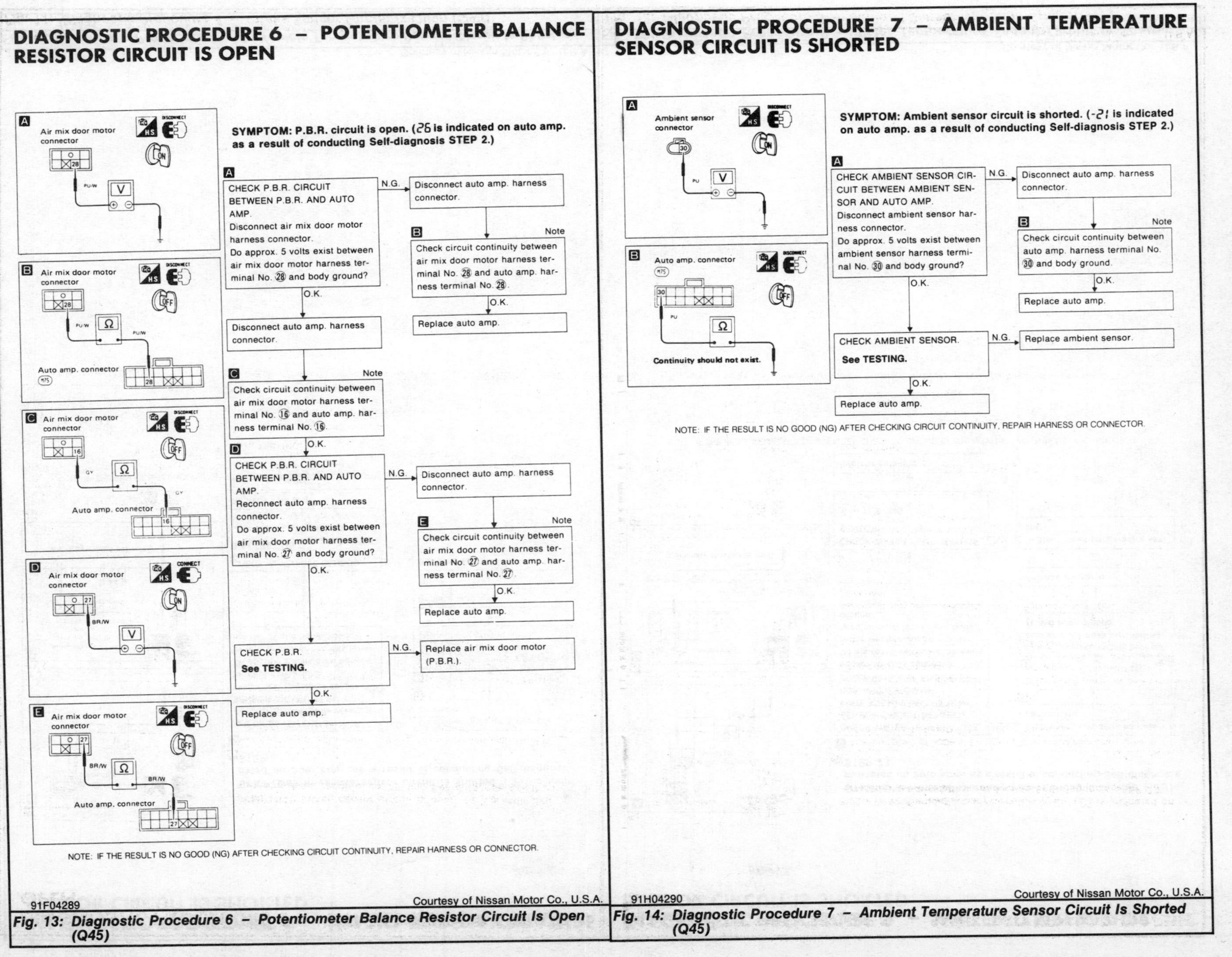

DIAGNOSTIC PROCEDURE 6 – POTENTIOMETER BALANCE RESISTOR CIRCUIT IS OPEN
A
Air mix door motor connector
28
PU/W
V
DISCONNECT
ON
B
Air mix door motor connector
28
PU/W
Ω
OFF
Auto amp. connector
M75
C
Air mix door motor connector
16
GY
Ω
Auto amp. connector
D
Air mix door motor connector
27
BR/W
V
CONNECT
E
Air mix door motor connector
27
BR/W
Ω
Auto amp. connector
SYMPTOM: P.B.R. circuit is open. (26 is indicated on auto amp. as a result of conducting Self-diagnosis STEP 2.)
A
CHECK P.B.R. CIRCUIT BETWEEN P.B.R. AND AUTO AMP.
Disconnect air mix door motor harness connector.
Do approx. 5 volts exist between air mix door motor harness terminal No. 28 and body ground?
N.G.
Disconnect auto amp. harness connector.
B
Note
Check circuit continuity between air mix door motor harness terminal No. 28 and auto amp. harness terminal No. 28.
O.K.
Replace auto amp.
O.K.
Disconnect auto amp. harness connector.
C
Note
Check circuit continuity between air mix door motor harness terminal No. 16 and auto amp. harness terminal No. 16.
O.K.
D
CHECK P.B.R. CIRCUIT BETWEEN P.B.R. AND AUTO AMP.
Reconnect auto amp. harness connector.
Do approx. 5 volts exist between air mix door motor harness terminal No. 27 and body ground?
N.G.
Disconnect auto amp. harness connector.
E
Note
Check circuit continuity between air mix door motor harness terminal No. 27 and auto amp. harness terminal No. 27.
O.K.
Replace auto amp.
O.K.
CHECK P.B.R.
See TESTING.
N.G.
Replace air mix door motor (P.B.R.).
O.K.
Replace auto amp.
NOTE: IF THE RESULT IS NO GOOD (NG) AFTER CHECKING CIRCUIT CONTINUITY, REPAIR HARNESS OR CONNECTOR.
91F04289
Courtesy of Nissan Motor Co., U.S.A.
DIAGNOSTIC PROCEDURE 7 – AMBIENT TEMPERATURE SENSOR CIRCUIT IS SHORTED
A
Ambient sensor connector
30
PU
V
DISCONNECT
ON
B
Auto amp. connector
M75
30
PU
Ω
OFF
Continuity should not exist.
SYMPTOM: Ambient sensor circuit is shorted. (-21 is indicated on auto amp. as a result of conducting Self-diagnosis STEP 2.)
A
CHECK AMBIENT SENSOR CIRCUIT BETWEEN AMBIENT SENSOR AND AUTO AMP.
Disconnect ambient sensor harness connector.
Do approx. 5 volts exist between ambient sensor harness terminal No. 30 and body ground?
N.G.
Disconnect auto amp. harness connector.
B
Note
Check circuit continuity between auto amp. harness terminal No. 30 and body ground.
O.K.
Replace auto amp.
O.K.
CHECK AMBIENT SENSOR.
See TESTING.
N.G.
Replace ambient sensor.
O.K.
Replace auto amp.
NOTE: IF THE RESULT IS NO GOOD (NG) AFTER CHECKING CIRCUIT CONTINUITY, REPAIR HARNESS OR CONNECTOR.
91H04290
Courtesy of Nissan Motor Co., U.S.A.

Fig. 13: Diagnostic Procedure 6 – Potentiometer Balance Resistor Circuit Is Open (Q45)

Fig. 14: Diagnostic Procedure 7 – Ambient Temperature Sensor Circuit Is Shorted (Q45)

1993 AUTOMATIC A/C-HEATER SYSTEMS
Trouble Shooting – Q45 (Cont.)

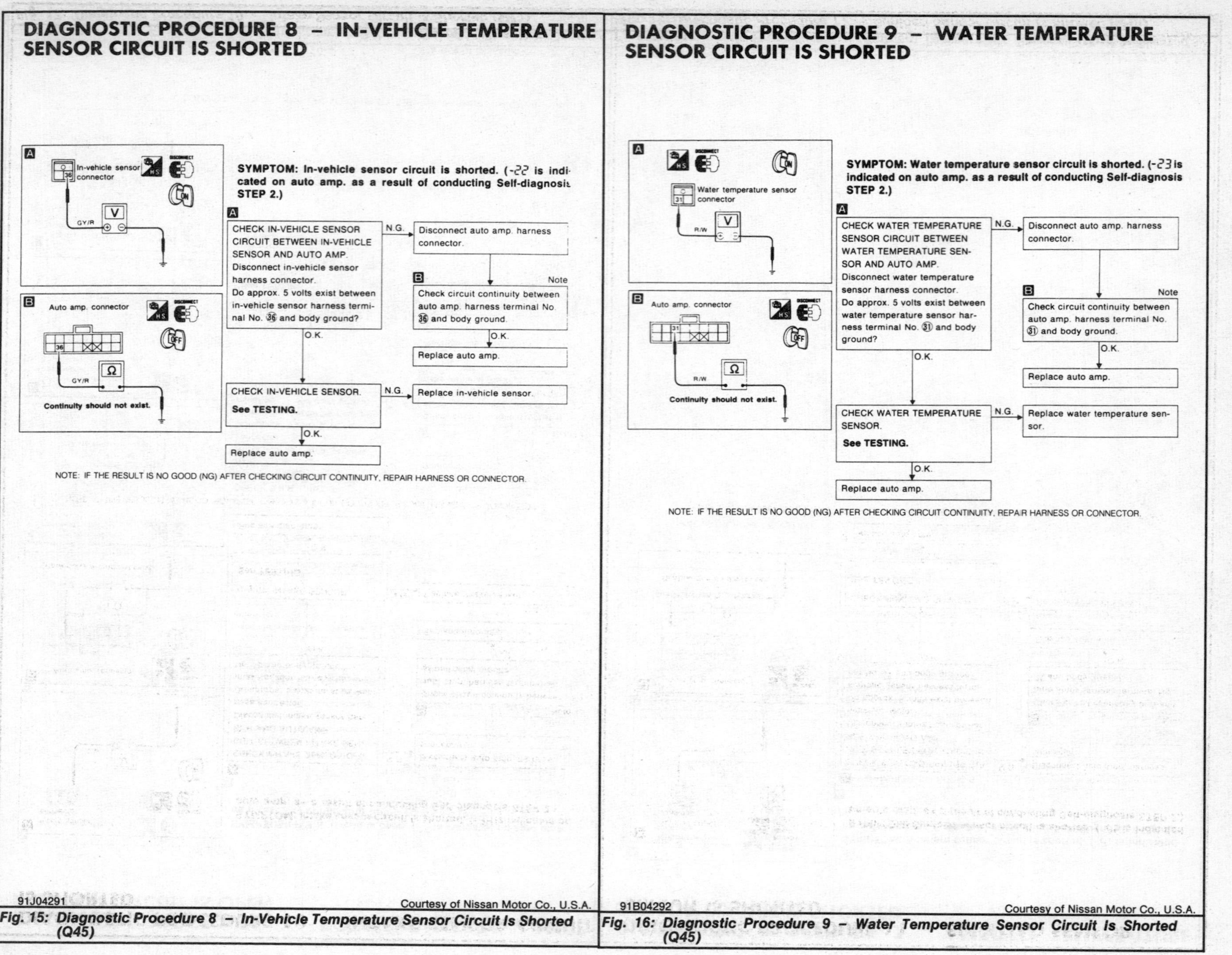
DIAGNOSTIC PROCEDURE 8 – IN-VEHICLE TEMPERATURE SENSOR CIRCUIT IS SHORTED
A
In-vehicle sensor connector
36
GY/R
V
DISCONNECT
HS
ON
B
Auto amp. connector
36
GY/R
Ω
OFF
Continuity should not exist.
SYMPTOM: In-vehicle sensor circuit is shorted. (-22 is indicated on auto amp. as a result of conducting Self-diagnosis STEP 2.)
A
CHECK IN-VEHICLE SENSOR CIRCUIT BETWEEN IN-VEHICLE SENSOR AND AUTO AMP. Disconnect in-vehicle sensor harness connector. Do approx. 5 volts exist between in-vehicle sensor harness terminal No. 36 and body ground?
N.G.
Disconnect auto amp. harness connector.
B
Note
Check circuit continuity between auto amp. harness terminal No. 36 and body ground.
O.K.
Replace auto amp.
O.K.
CHECK IN-VEHICLE SENSOR. See TESTING.
N.G.
Replace in-vehicle sensor.
O.K.
Replace auto amp.
NOTE: IF THE RESULT IS NO GOOD (NG) AFTER CHECKING CIRCUIT CONTINUITY, REPAIR HARNESS OR CONNECTOR.
91J04291
Courtesy of Nissan Motor Co., U.S.A.
DIAGNOSTIC PROCEDURE 9 – WATER TEMPERATURE SENSOR CIRCUIT IS SHORTED
A
DISCONNECT
HS
ON
Water temperature sensor connector
31
R/W
V
B
Auto amp. connector
31
R/W
Ω
OFF
Continuity should not exist.
SYMPTOM: Water temperature sensor circuit is shorted. (-23 is indicated on auto amp. as a result of conducting Self-diagnosis STEP 2.)
A
CHECK WATER TEMPERATURE SENSOR CIRCUIT BETWEEN WATER TEMPERATURE SENSOR AND AUTO AMP. Disconnect water temperature sensor harness connector. Do approx. 5 volts exist between water temperature sensor harness terminal No. 31 and body ground?
N.G.
Disconnect auto amp. harness connector.
B
Note
Check circuit continuity between auto amp. harness terminal No. 31 and body ground.
O.K.
Replace auto amp.
O.K.
CHECK WATER TEMPERATURE SENSOR. See TESTING.
N.G.
Replace water temperature sensor.
O.K.
Replace auto amp.
NOTE: IF THE RESULT IS NO GOOD (NG) AFTER CHECKING CIRCUIT CONTINUITY, REPAIR HARNESS OR CONNECTOR.
91B04292
Courtesy of Nissan Motor Co., U.S.A.

Fig. 15: Diagnostic Procedure 8 – In-Vehicle Temperature Sensor Circuit Is Shorted (Q45)

Fig. 16: Diagnostic Procedure 9 – Water Temperature Sensor Circuit Is Shorted (Q45)

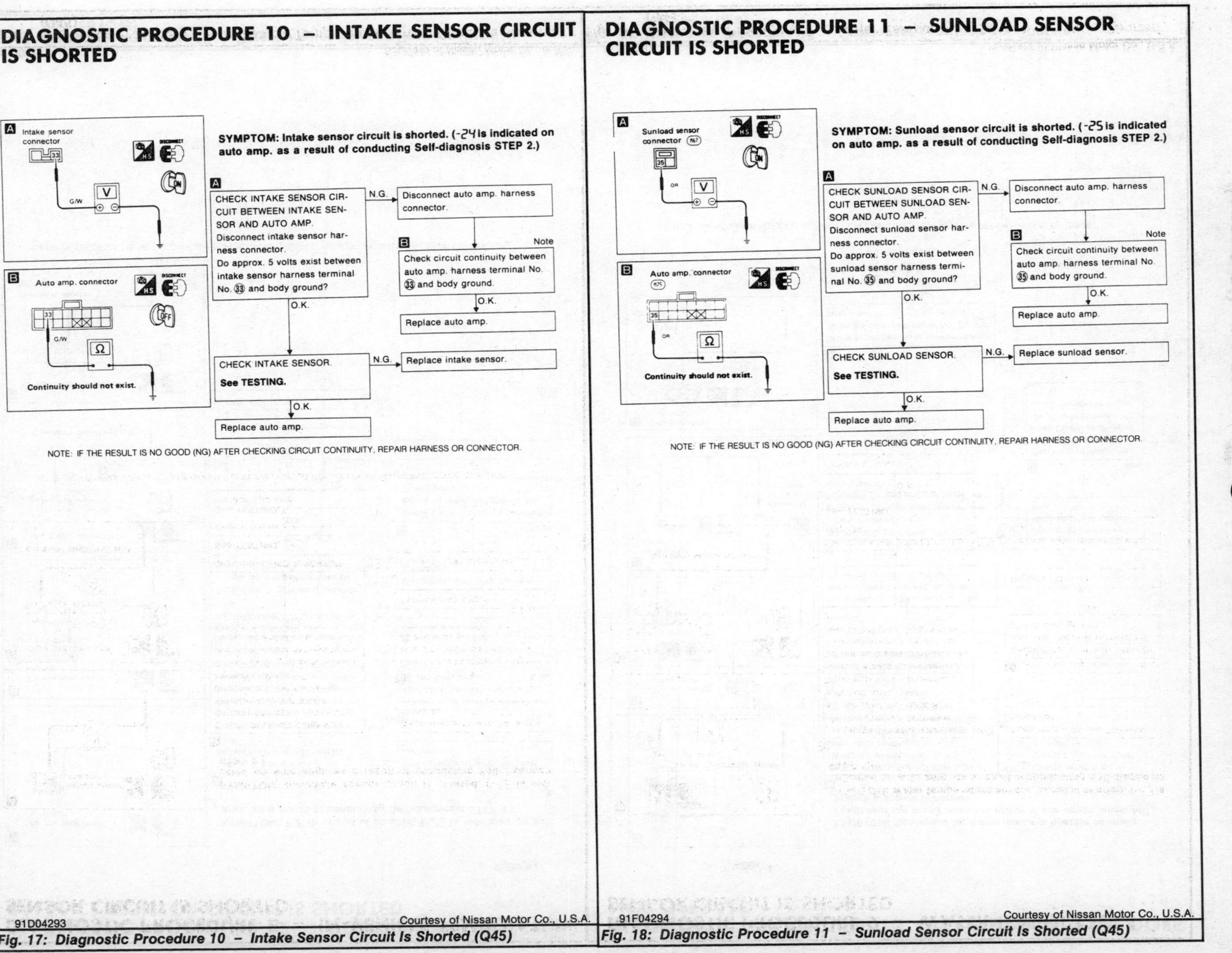
DIAGNOSTIC PROCEDURE 10 – INTAKE SENSOR CIRCUIT IS SHORTED
A Intake sensor connector
G/W
V
B Auto amp. connector
G/W
Ω
Continuity should not exist.
SYMPTOM: Intake sensor circuit is shorted. (-24 is indicated on auto amp. as a result of conducting Self-diagnosis STEP 2.)
A CHECK INTAKE SENSOR CIRCUIT BETWEEN INTAKE SENSOR AND AUTO AMP. Disconnect intake sensor harness connector. Do approx. 5 volts exist between intake sensor harness terminal No. 33 and body ground?
N.G.
Disconnect auto amp. harness connector.
B Check circuit continuity between auto amp. harness terminal No. 33 and body ground.
Note
O.K.
Replace auto amp.
O.K.
CHECK INTAKE SENSOR. See TESTING.
N.G.
Replace intake sensor.
O.K.
Replace auto amp.
NOTE: IF THE RESULT IS NO GOOD (NG) AFTER CHECKING CIRCUIT CONTINUITY, REPAIR HARNESS OR CONNECTOR.
91D04293
Courtesy of Nissan Motor Co., U.S.A.
DIAGNOSTIC PROCEDURE 11 – SUNLOAD SENSOR CIRCUIT IS SHORTED
A Sunload sensor connector (M67)
OR
V
B Auto amp. connector (M75)
OR
Ω
Continuity should not exist.
SYMPTOM: Sunload sensor circuit is shorted. (-25 is indicated on auto amp. as a result of conducting Self-diagnosis STEP 2.)
A CHECK SUNLOAD SENSOR CIRCUIT BETWEEN SUNLOAD SENSOR AND AUTO AMP. Disconnect sunload sensor harness connector. Do approx. 5 volts exist between sunload sensor harness terminal No. 35 and body ground?
N.G.
Disconnect auto amp. harness connector.
B Check circuit continuity between auto amp. harness terminal No. 35 and body ground.
Note
O.K.
Replace auto amp.
O.K.
CHECK SUNLOAD SENSOR. See TESTING.
N.G.
Replace sunload sensor.
O.K.
Replace auto amp.
NOTE: IF THE RESULT IS NO GOOD (NG) AFTER CHECKING CIRCUIT CONTINUITY, REPAIR HARNESS OR CONNECTOR.
91F04294
Courtesy of Nissan Motor Co., U.S.A.

Fig. 17: Diagnostic Procedure 10 – Intake Sensor Circuit Is Shorted (Q45)

Fig. 18: Diagnostic Procedure 11 – Sunload Sensor Circuit Is Shorted (Q45)

1993 AUTOMATIC A/C-HEATER SYSTEMS
Trouble Shooting – Q45 (Cont.)

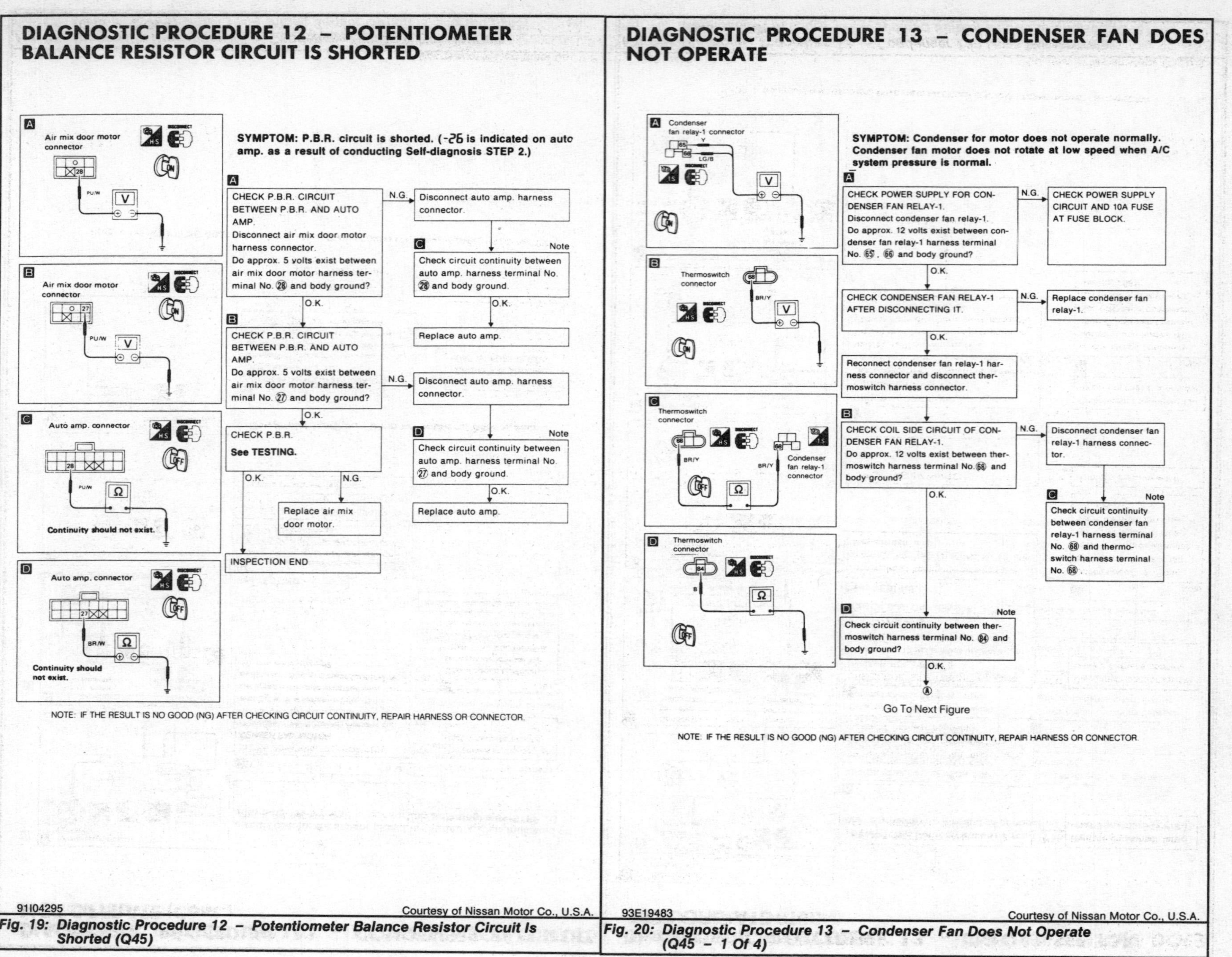
DIAGNOSTIC PROCEDURE 12 – POTENTIOMETER BALANCE RESISTOR CIRCUIT IS SHORTED
A Air mix door motor connector
B Air mix door motor connector
C Auto amp. connector
Continuity should not exist.
D Auto amp. connector
Continuity should not exist.
SYMPTOM: P.B.R. circuit is shorted. (-26 is indicated on auto amp. as a result of conducting Self-diagnosis STEP 2.)
A CHECK P.B.R. CIRCUIT BETWEEN P.B.R. AND AUTO AMP. Disconnect air mix door motor harness connector. Do approx. 5 volts exist between air mix door motor harness terminal No. 28 and body ground?
N.G. Disconnect auto amp. harness connector.
C Check circuit continuity between auto amp. harness terminal No. 28 and body ground.
O.K. Replace auto amp.
B CHECK P.B.R. CIRCUIT BETWEEN P.B.R. AND AUTO AMP. Do approx. 5 volts exist between air mix door motor harness terminal No. 27 and body ground?
N.G. Disconnect auto amp. harness connector.
D Check circuit continuity between auto amp. harness terminal No. 27 and body ground.
O.K. Replace auto amp.
CHECK P.B.R. See TESTING.
N.G. Replace air mix door motor.
O.K. INSPECTION END
NOTE: IF THE RESULT IS NO GOOD (NG) AFTER CHECKING CIRCUIT CONTINUITY, REPAIR HARNESS OR CONNECTOR.
DIAGNOSTIC PROCEDURE 13 – CONDENSER FAN DOES NOT OPERATE
A Condenser fan relay-1 connector
B Thermoswitch connector
C Thermoswitch connector
Condenser fan relay-1 connector
D Thermoswitch connector
SYMPTOM: Condenser for motor does not operate normally. Condenser fan motor does not rotate at low speed when A/C system pressure is normal.
A CHECK POWER SUPPLY FOR CONDENSER FAN RELAY-1. Disconnect condenser fan relay-1. Do approx. 12 volts exist between condenser fan relay-1 harness terminal No. 65, 66 and body ground?
N.G. CHECK POWER SUPPLY CIRCUIT AND 10A FUSE AT FUSE BLOCK.
O.K. CHECK CONDENSER FAN RELAY-1 AFTER DISCONNECTING IT.
N.G. Replace condenser fan relay-1.
O.K. Reconnect condenser fan relay-1 harness connector and disconnect thermoswitch harness connector.
B CHECK COIL SIDE CIRCUIT OF CONDENSER FAN RELAY-1. Do approx. 12 volts exist between thermoswitch harness terminal No. 68 and body ground?
N.G. Disconnect condenser fan relay-1 harness connector.
C Check circuit continuity between condenser fan relay-1 harness terminal No. 68 and thermoswitch harness terminal No. 68.
O.K.
D Check circuit continuity between thermoswitch harness terminal No. 84 and body ground?
O.K. A
Go To Next Figure
NOTE: IF THE RESULT IS NO GOOD (NG) AFTER CHECKING CIRCUIT CONTINUITY, REPAIR HARNESS OR CONNECTOR.

91I04295 Courtesy of Nissan Motor Co., U.S.A.

Fig. 19: Diagnostic Procedure 12 – Potentiometer Balance Resistor Circuit Is Shorted (Q45)

93E19483 Courtesy of Nissan Motor Co., U.S.A.

Fig. 20: Diagnostic Procedure 13 – Condenser Fan Does Not Operate (Q45 – 1 Of 4)

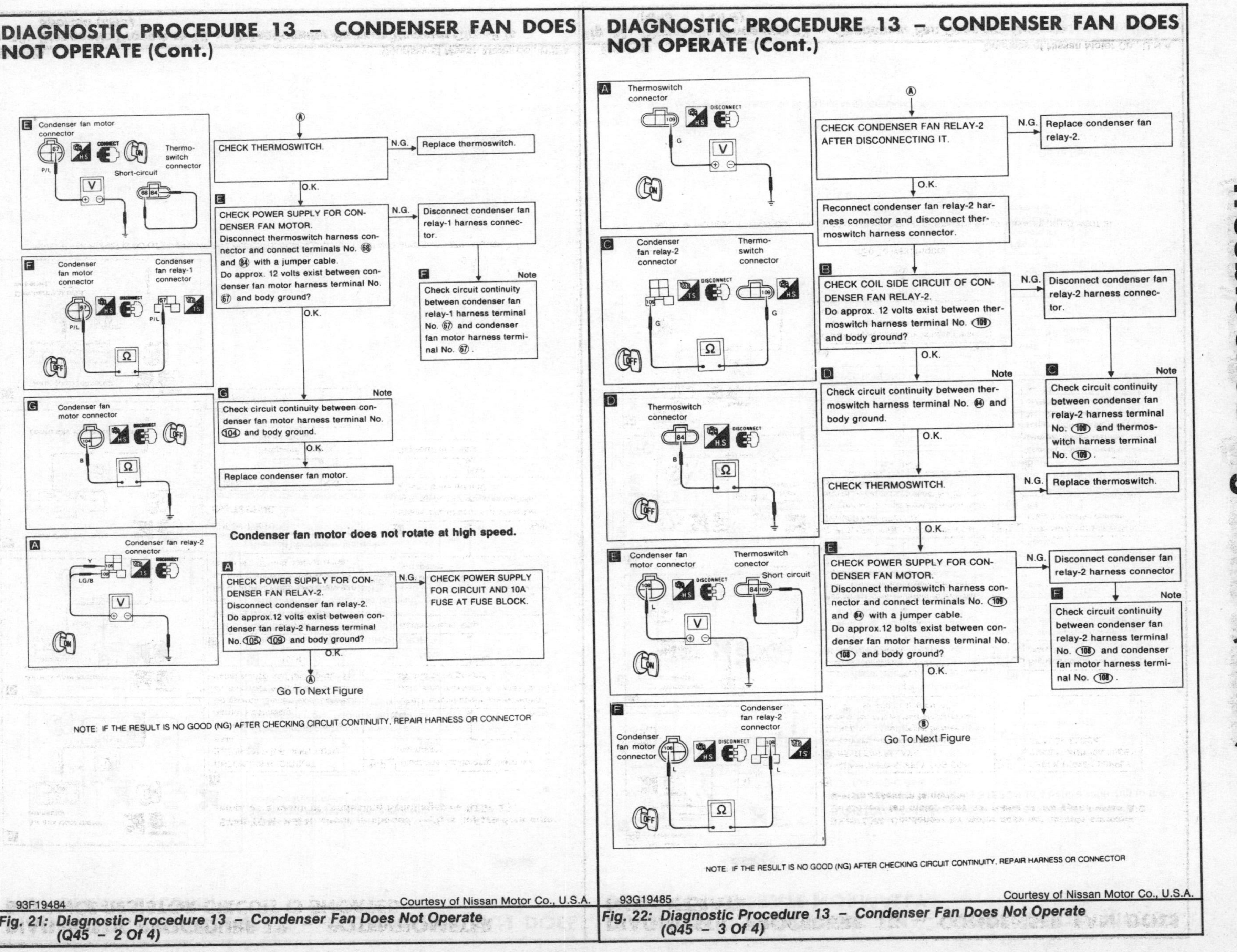
DIAGNOSTIC PROCEDURE 13 – CONDENSER FAN DOES NOT OPERATE (Cont.)
Condenser fan motor connector
Thermo-switch connector
Short-circuit
CHECK THERMOSWITCH.
N.G.
Replace thermoswitch.
O.K.
CHECK POWER SUPPLY FOR CONDENSER FAN MOTOR.
Disconnect thermoswitch harness connector and connect terminals No. 68 and 84 with a jumper cable.
Do approx. 12 volts exist between condenser fan motor harness terminal No. 67 and body ground?
Disconnect condenser fan relay-1 harness connector.
Condenser fan relay-1 connector
Check circuit continuity between condenser fan relay-1 harness terminal No. 67 and condenser fan motor harness terminal No. 67.
Note
Check circuit continuity between condenser fan motor harness terminal No. 104 and body ground.
Replace condenser fan motor.
Condenser fan motor does not rotate at high speed.
Condenser fan relay-2 connector
CHECK POWER SUPPLY FOR CONDENSER FAN RELAY-2.
Disconnect condenser fan relay-2.
Do approx.12 volts exist between condenser fan relay-2 harness terminal No. 105 109 and body ground?
CHECK POWER SUPPLY FOR CIRCUIT AND 10A FUSE AT FUSE BLOCK.
Go To Next Figure
NOTE: IF THE RESULT IS NO GOOD (NG) AFTER CHECKING CIRCUIT CONTINUITY, REPAIR HARNESS OR CONNECTOR
93F19484
Courtesy of Nissan Motor Co., U.S.A.
DIAGNOSTIC PROCEDURE 13 – CONDENSER FAN DOES NOT OPERATE (Cont.)
Thermoswitch connector
CHECK CONDENSER FAN RELAY-2 AFTER DISCONNECTING IT.
Replace condenser fan relay-2.
Reconnect condenser fan relay-2 harness connector and disconnect thermoswitch harness connector.
Condenser fan relay-2 connector
CHECK COIL SIDE CIRCUIT OF CONDENSER FAN RELAY-2.
Do approx. 12 volts exist between thermoswitch harness terminal No. 109 and body ground?
Disconnect condenser fan relay-2 harness connector.
Check circuit continuity between thermoswitch harness terminal No. 84 and body ground.
Check circuit continuity between condenser fan relay-2 harness terminal No. 109 and thermoswitch harness terminal No. 109.
Condenser fan motor connector
Thermoswitch conector
Short circuit
CHECK POWER SUPPLY FOR CONDENSER FAN MOTOR.
Disconnect thermoswitch harness connector and connect terminals No. 109 and 84 with a jumper cable.
Do approx.12 bolts exist between condenser fan motor harness terminal No. 108 and body ground?
Disconnect condenser fan relay-2 harness connector
Check circuit continuity between condenser fan relay-2 harness terminal No. 108 and condenser fan motor harness terminal No. 108.
93G19485

Fig. 21: Diagnostic Procedure 13 – Condenser Fan Does Not Operate (Q45 – 2 Of 4)

Fig. 22: Diagnostic Procedure 13 – Condenser Fan Does Not Operate (Q45 – 3 Of 4)

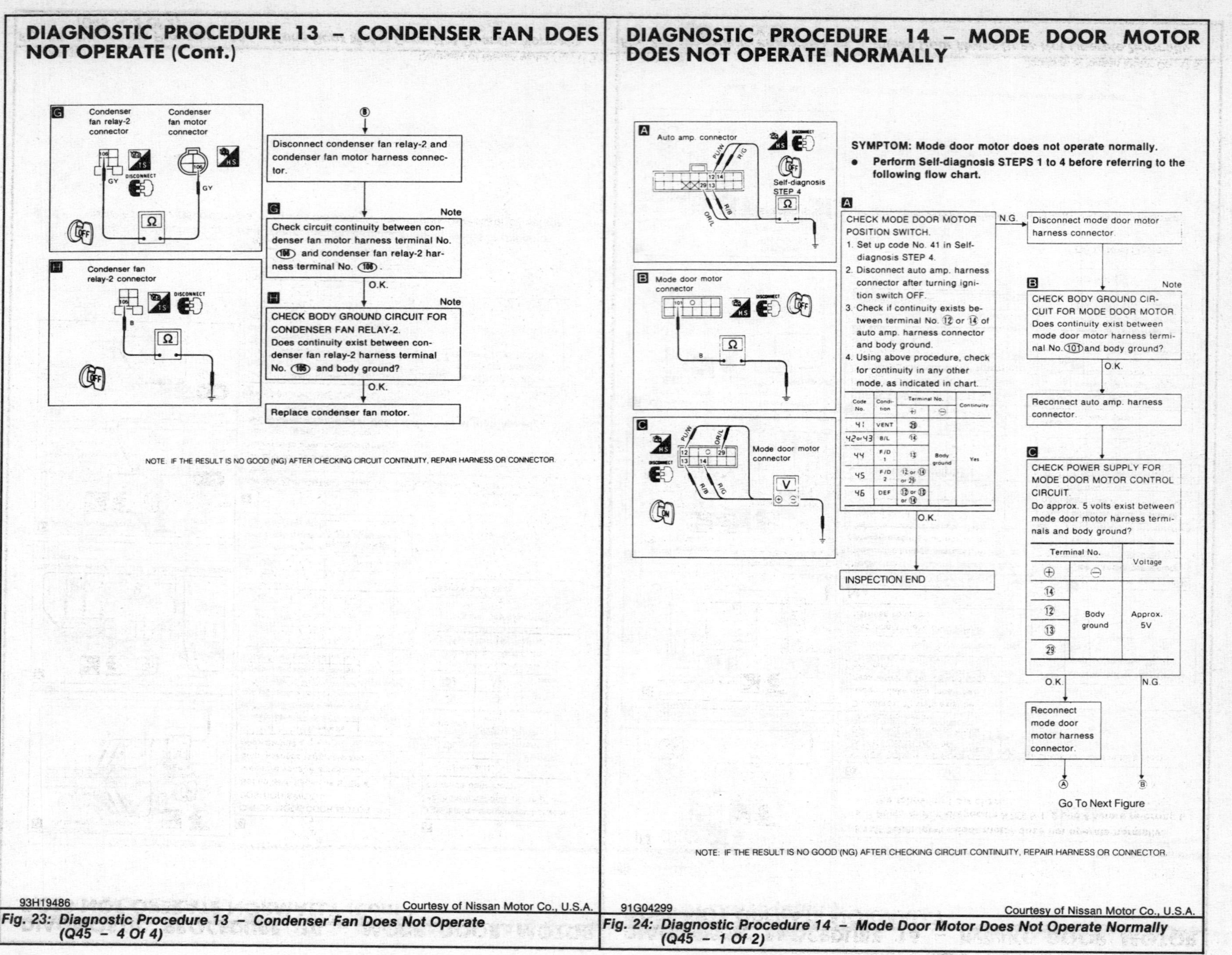
DIAGNOSTIC PROCEDURE 13 – CONDENSER FAN DOES NOT OPERATE (Cont.)
G
Condenser fan relay-2 connector
Condenser fan motor connector
GY
GY
DISCONNECT
H
Condenser fan relay-2 connector
B
DISCONNECT
B
Disconnect condenser fan relay-2 and condenser fan motor harness connector.
G
Note
Check circuit continuity between condenser fan motor harness terminal No. 106 and condenser fan relay-2 harness terminal No. 106.
O.K.
H
Note
CHECK BODY GROUND CIRCUIT FOR CONDENSER FAN RELAY-2.
Does continuity exist between condenser fan relay-2 harness terminal No. 105 and body ground?
O.K.
Replace condenser fan motor.
NOTE: IF THE RESULT IS NO GOOD (NG) AFTER CHECKING CIRCUIT CONTINUITY, REPAIR HARNESS OR CONNECTOR.
93H19486
Courtesy of Nissan Motor Co., U.S.A.
DIAGNOSTIC PROCEDURE 14 – MODE DOOR MOTOR DOES NOT OPERATE NORMALLY
A
Auto amp. connector
PU/W
R/G
R/B
OR/L
DISCONNECT
Self-diagnosis STEP 4
B
Mode door motor connector
B
DISCONNECT
C
PU/W
OR/L
R/B
R/G
Mode door motor connector
DISCONNECT
SYMPTOM: Mode door motor does not operate normally.
• Perform Self-diagnosis STEPS 1 to 4 before referring to the following flow chart.
A
CHECK MODE DOOR MOTOR POSITION SWITCH.
1. Set up code No. 41 in Self-diagnosis STEP 4.
2. Disconnect auto amp. harness connector after turning ignition switch OFF.
3. Check if continuity exists between terminal No. 12 or 14 of auto amp. harness connector and body ground.
4. Using above procedure, check for continuity in any other mode, as indicated in chart.
Code No. | Condition | Terminal No. ⊕ | Terminal No. ⊖ | Continuity
41 | VENT | 29 | Body ground | Yes
42 or 43 | B/L | 14
44 | F/D 1 | 13
45 | F/D 2 | 12 or 14 or 29
46 | DEF | 13 or 13 or 14
N.G.
Disconnect mode door motor harness connector.
B
Note
CHECK BODY GROUND CIRCUIT FOR MODE DOOR MOTOR
Does continuity exist between mode door motor harness terminal No. 101 and body ground?
O.K.
Reconnect auto amp. harness connector.
C
CHECK POWER SUPPLY FOR MODE DOOR MOTOR CONTROL CIRCUIT.
Do approx. 5 volts exist between mode door motor harness terminals and body ground?
Terminal No. ⊕ | ⊖ | Voltage
14 | Body ground | Approx. 5V
12
13
29
O.K.
N.G.
Reconnect mode door motor harness connector.
A
B
Go To Next Figure
O.K.
INSPECTION END
NOTE: IF THE RESULT IS NO GOOD (NG) AFTER CHECKING CIRCUIT CONTINUITY, REPAIR HARNESS OR CONNECTOR.
91G04299
Courtesy of Nissan Motor Co., U.S.A.

Fig. 23: Diagnostic Procedure 13 – Condenser Fan Does Not Operate (Q45 – 4 Of 4)

Fig. 24: Diagnostic Procedure 14 – Mode Door Motor Does Not Operate Normally (Q45 – 1 Of 2)

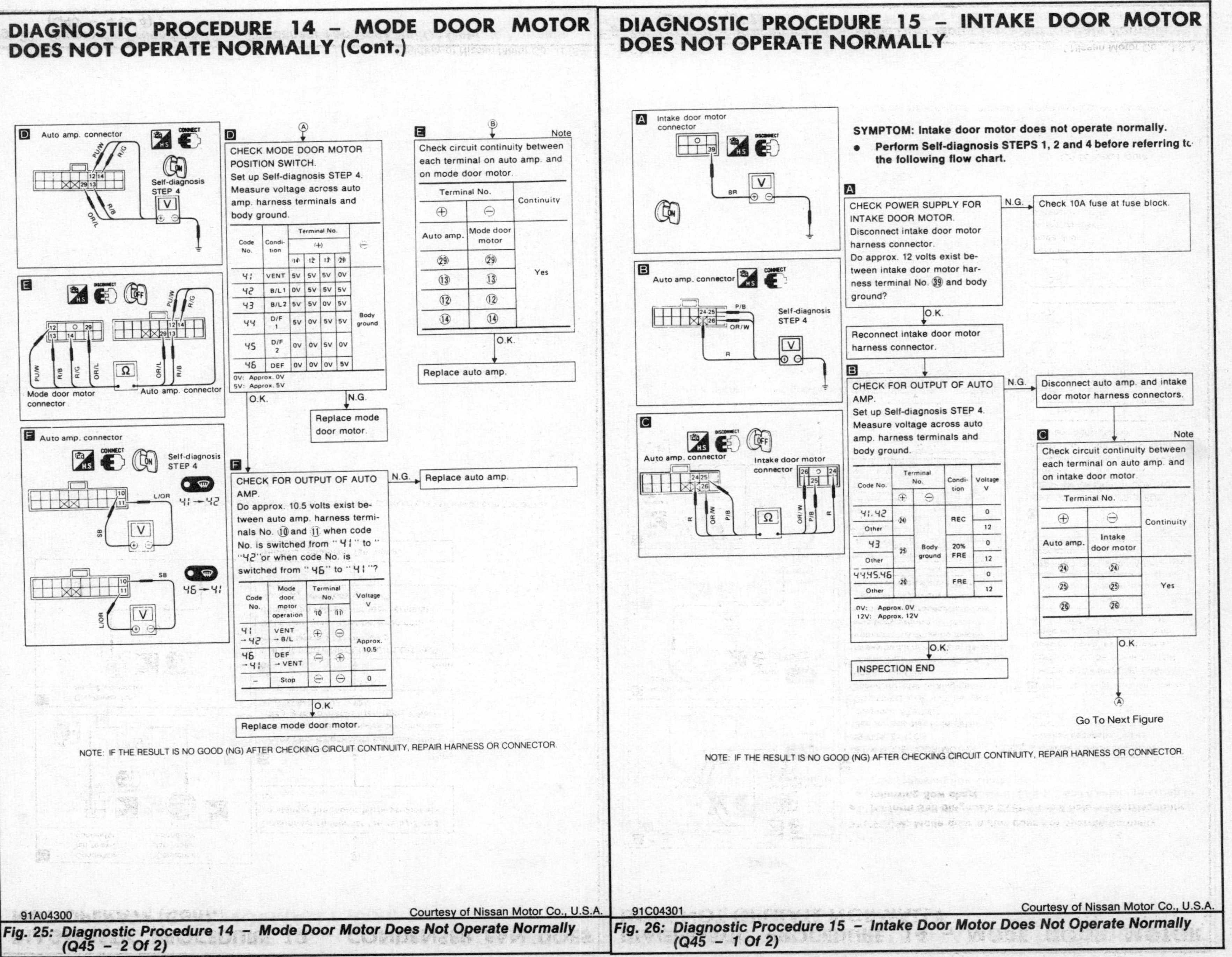
DIAGNOSTIC PROCEDURE 14 – MODE DOOR MOTOR DOES NOT OPERATE NORMALLY (Cont.)
D Auto amp. connector
Self-diagnosis STEP 4
E Mode door motor connector
Auto amp. connector
F Auto amp. connector
Self-diagnosis STEP 4
D CHECK MODE DOOR MOTOR POSITION SWITCH.
Set up Self-diagnosis STEP 4.
Measure voltage across auto amp. harness terminals and body ground.
Code No. | Condition | Terminal No. (+) 10 12 13 29 | (−) Body ground
41 | VENT | 5V 5V 5V 0V
42 | B/L1 | 0V 5V 5V 5V
43 | B/L2 | 5V 5V 0V 5V
44 | D/F 1 | 5V 0V 5V 5V
45 | D/F 2 | 0V 0V 5V 0V
46 | DEF | 0V 0V 0V 5V
0V: Approx. 0V
5V: Approx. 5V
O.K.
N.G.
Replace mode door motor.
E Check circuit continuity between each terminal on auto amp. and on mode door motor.
Terminal No. (+) Auto amp. | (−) Mode door motor | Continuity
29 | 29 | Yes
13 | 13
12 | 12
14 | 14
Note
O.K.
Replace auto amp.
F CHECK FOR OUTPUT OF AUTO AMP.
Do approx. 10.5 volts exist between auto amp. harness terminals No. 10 and 11 when code No. is switched from "41" to "42" or when code No. is switched from "46" to "41"?
Code No. | Mode door motor operation | Terminal No. 10 | 11 | Voltage V
41 → 42 | VENT → B/L | + | − | Approx. 10.5
46 → 41 | DEF → VENT | − | +
– | Stop | − | − | 0
N.G.
Replace auto amp.
O.K.
Replace mode door motor.
NOTE: IF THE RESULT IS NO GOOD (NG) AFTER CHECKING CIRCUIT CONTINUITY, REPAIR HARNESS OR CONNECTOR.
91A04300
Courtesy of Nissan Motor Co., U.S.A.
DIAGNOSTIC PROCEDURE 15 – INTAKE DOOR MOTOR DOES NOT OPERATE NORMALLY
A Intake door motor connector
B Auto amp. connector
Self-diagnosis STEP 4
C Auto amp. connector
Intake door motor connector
SYMPTOM: Intake door motor does not operate normally.
• Perform Self-diagnosis STEPS 1, 2 and 4 before referring to the following flow chart.
A CHECK POWER SUPPLY FOR INTAKE DOOR MOTOR.
Disconnect intake door motor harness connector.
Do approx. 12 volts exist between intake door motor harness terminal No. 39 and body ground?
N.G.
Check 10A fuse at fuse block.
O.K.
Reconnect intake door motor harness connector.
B CHECK FOR OUTPUT OF AUTO AMP.
Set up Self-diagnosis STEP 4.
Measure voltage across auto amp. harness terminals and body ground.
Code No. | Terminal No. (+) | (−) | Condition | Voltage V
41, 42 | 26 | Body ground | REC | 0
Other | | | | 12
43 | 25 | | 20% FRE | 0
Other | | | | 12
44, 45, 46 | 26 | | FRE | 0
Other | | | | 12
0V: Approx. 0V
12V: Approx. 12V
O.K.
INSPECTION END
N.G.
Disconnect auto amp. and intake door motor harness connectors.
C Check circuit continuity between each terminal on auto amp. and on intake door motor.
Terminal No. (+) Auto amp. | (−) Intake door motor | Continuity
24 | 24 | Yes
25 | 25
26 | 26
Note
O.K.
Go To Next Figure
NOTE: IF THE RESULT IS NO GOOD (NG) AFTER CHECKING CIRCUIT CONTINUITY, REPAIR HARNESS OR CONNECTOR.
91C04301
Courtesy of Nissan Motor Co., U.S.A.

Fig. 25: Diagnostic Procedure 14 – Mode Door Motor Does Not Operate Normally (Q45 – 2 Of 2)

Fig. 26: Diagnostic Procedure 15 – Intake Door Motor Does Not Operate Normally (Q45 – 1 Of 2)

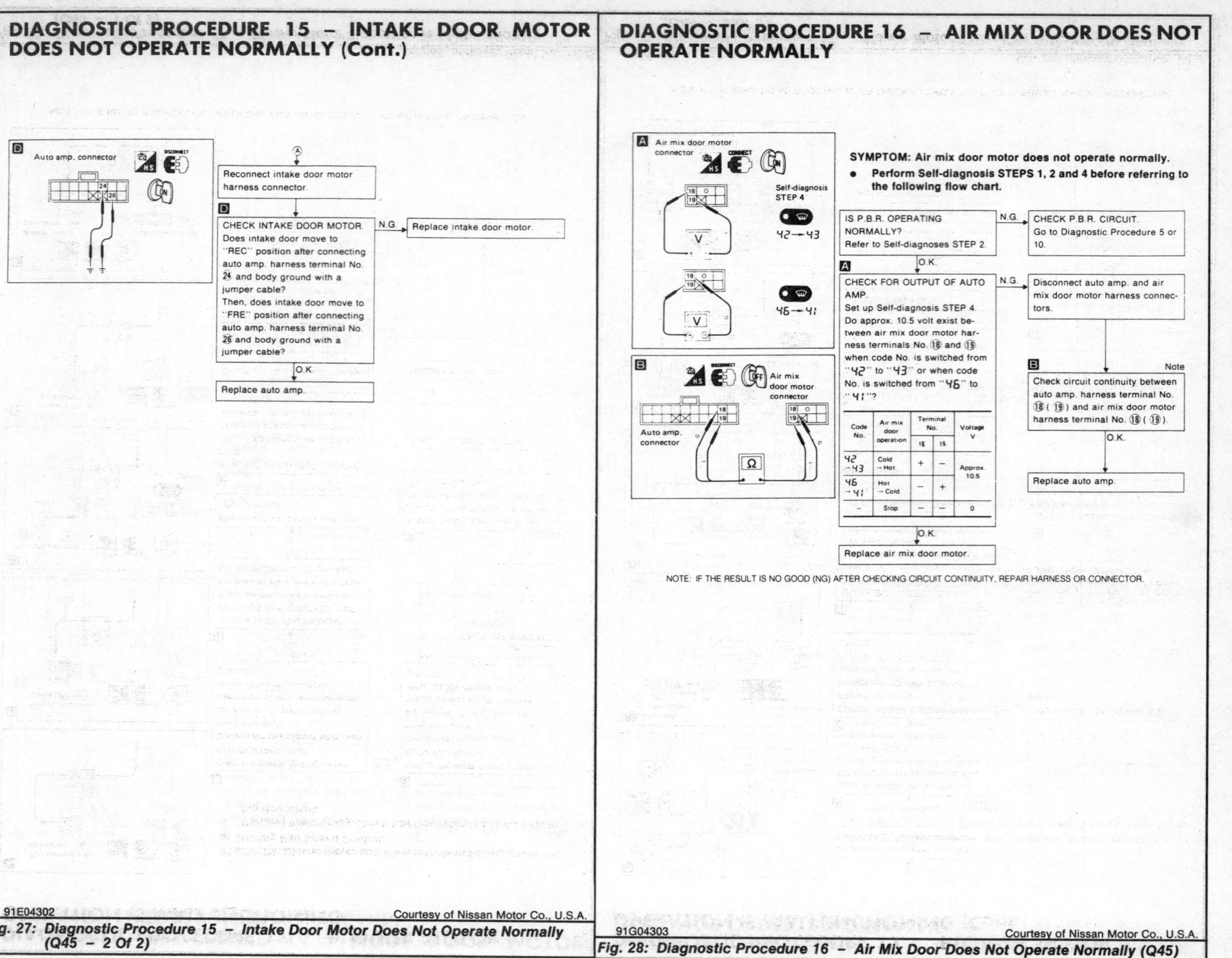
DIAGNOSTIC PROCEDURE 15 - INTAKE DOOR MOTOR DOES NOT OPERATE NORMALLY (Cont.)
D Auto amp. connector
DISCONNECT
ON
24
26
A
Reconnect intake door motor harness connector.
D
CHECK INTAKE DOOR MOTOR. Does intake door move to "REC" position after connecting auto amp. harness terminal No. 24 and body ground with a jumper cable? Then, does intake door move to "FRE" position after connecting auto amp. harness terminal No. 26 and body ground with a jumper cable?
N.G.
Replace intake door motor.
O.K.
Replace auto amp.
91E04302
DIAGNOSTIC PROCEDURE 16 - AIR MIX DOOR DOES NOT OPERATE NORMALLY
A Air mix door motor connector
CONNECT
ON
Self-diagnosis STEP 4
42→43
46→41
B
DISCONNECT
OFF
Air mix door motor connector
Auto amp. connector
18
19
SYMPTOM: Air mix door motor does not operate normally.
• Perform Self-diagnosis STEPS 1, 2 and 4 before referring to the following flow chart.
IS P.B.R. OPERATING NORMALLY? Refer to Self-diagnoses STEP 2.
N.G.
CHECK P.B.R. CIRCUIT. Go to Diagnostic Procedure 5 or 10.
O.K.
A
CHECK FOR OUTPUT OF AUTO AMP. Set up Self-diagnosis STEP 4. Do approx. 10.5 volt exist between air mix door motor harness terminals No. 18 and 19 when code No. is switched from "42" to "43" or when code No. is switched from "46" to "41"?
N.G.
Disconnect auto amp. and air mix door motor harness connectors.
B
Note
Check circuit continuity between auto amp. harness terminal No. 18 (19) and air mix door motor harness terminal No. 18 (19).
O.K.
Replace auto amp.
O.K.
Replace air mix door motor.
NOTE: IF THE RESULT IS NO GOOD (NG) AFTER CHECKING CIRCUIT CONTINUITY, REPAIR HARNESS OR CONNECTOR.
91G04303

Code No.	Air mix door operation	Terminal No. 18	Terminal No. 19	Voltage V
42 → 43	Cold → Hot	+	−	Approx. 10.5
46 → 41	Hot → Cold	−	+	
−	Stop	−	−	0

Courtesy of Nissan Motor Co., U.S.A.

Fig. 27: Diagnostic Procedure 15 - Intake Door Motor Does Not Operate Normally (Q45 - 2 Of 2)

Courtesy of Nissan Motor Co., U.S.A.

Fig. 28: Diagnostic Procedure 16 - Air Mix Door Does Not Operate Normally (Q45)

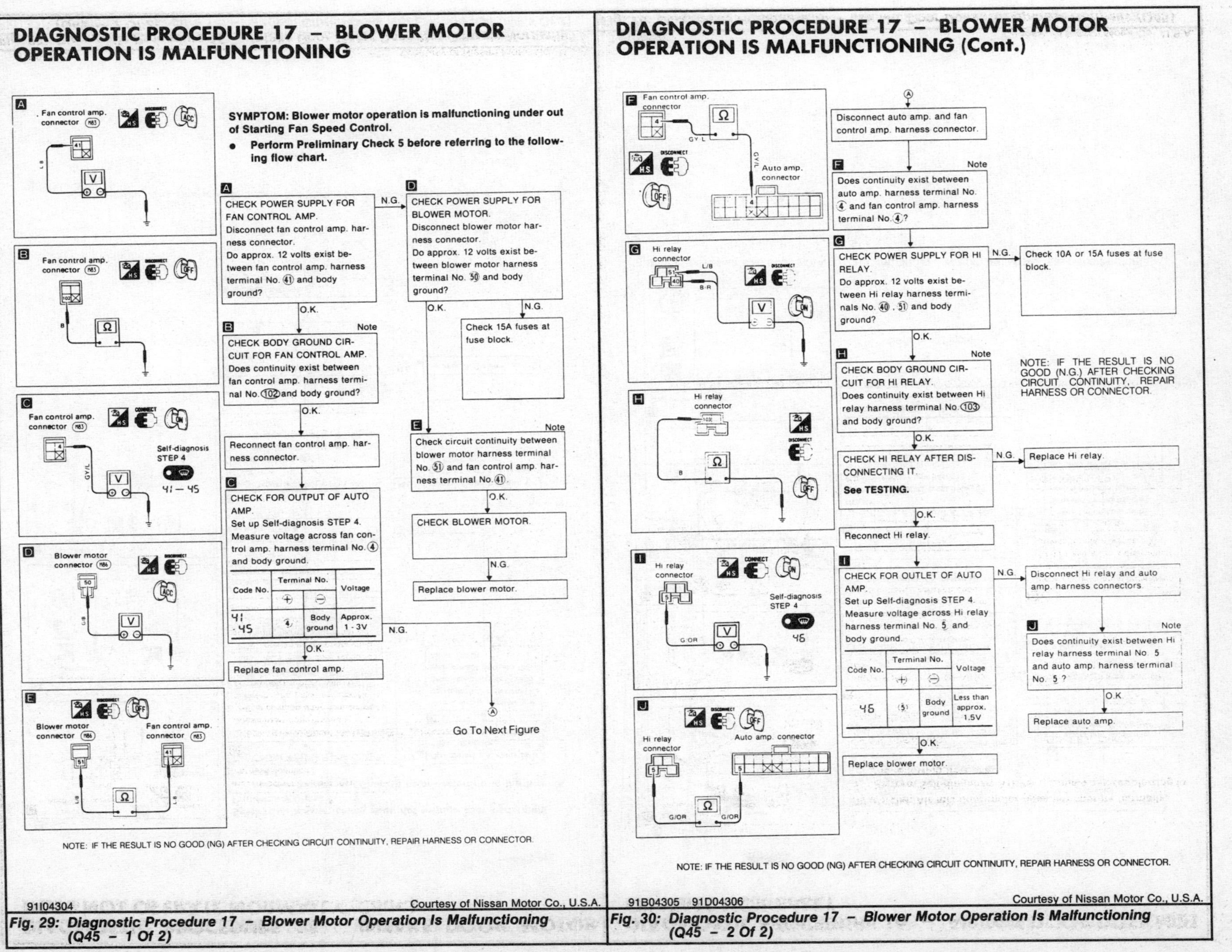
DIAGNOSTIC PROCEDURE 17 – BLOWER MOTOR OPERATION IS MALFUNCTIONING
SYMPTOM: Blower motor operation is malfunctioning under out of Starting Fan Speed Control.
• Perform Preliminary Check 5 before referring to the following flow chart.
A
CHECK POWER SUPPLY FOR FAN CONTROL AMP.
Disconnect fan control amp. harness connector.
Do approx. 12 volts exist between fan control amp. harness terminal No. 41 and body ground?
N.G.
D
CHECK POWER SUPPLY FOR BLOWER MOTOR.
Disconnect blower motor harness connector.
Do approx. 12 volts exist between blower motor harness terminal No. 50 and body ground?
N.G.
Check 15A fuses at fuse block.
O.K.
B
Note
CHECK BODY GROUND CIRCUIT FOR FAN CONTROL AMP.
Does continuity exist between fan control amp. harness terminal No. 102 and body ground?
O.K.
Reconnect fan control amp. harness connector.
C
CHECK FOR OUTPUT OF AUTO AMP.
Set up Self-diagnosis STEP 4.
Measure voltage across fan control amp. harness terminal No. 4 and body ground.
Code No.
Terminal No.
+
−
Voltage
41 - 45
4
Body ground
Approx. 1 - 3V
O.K.
Replace fan control amp.
N.G.
Go To Next Figure
E
Note
Check circuit continuity between blower motor harness terminal No. 51 and fan control amp. harness terminal No. 41.
O.K.
CHECK BLOWER MOTOR.
N.G.
Replace blower motor.
A
Fan control amp. connector
L/B
V
ACC
B
Fan control amp. connector
102
B
Ω
OFF
C
Fan control amp. connector
4
GY/L
V
CONNECT
ON
Self-diagnosis STEP 4
41 – 45
D
Blower motor connector
50
L/B
V
DISCONNECT
ACC
E
Blower motor connector
Fan control amp. connector
51
41
L/B
Ω
OFF
NOTE: IF THE RESULT IS NO GOOD (NG) AFTER CHECKING CIRCUIT CONTINUITY, REPAIR HARNESS OR CONNECTOR.
91I04304
Courtesy of Nissan Motor Co., U.S.A.
DIAGNOSTIC PROCEDURE 17 – BLOWER MOTOR OPERATION IS MALFUNCTIONING (Cont.)
A
Disconnect auto amp. and fan control amp. harness connector.
F
Note
Does continuity exist between auto amp. harness terminal No. 4 and fan control amp. harness terminal No. 4?
G
CHECK POWER SUPPLY FOR HI RELAY.
Do approx. 12 volts exist between Hi relay harness terminals No. 40, 51 and body ground?
N.G.
Check 10A or 15A fuses at fuse block.
O.K.
H
Note
CHECK BODY GROUND CIRCUIT FOR HI RELAY.
Does continuity exist between Hi relay harness terminal No. 103 and body ground?
NOTE: IF THE RESULT IS NO GOOD (N.G.) AFTER CHECKING CIRCUIT CONTINUITY, REPAIR HARNESS OR CONNECTOR.
O.K.
CHECK HI RELAY AFTER DISCONNECTING IT.
See TESTING.
N.G.
Replace Hi relay.
O.K.
Reconnect Hi relay.
I
CHECK FOR OUTLET OF AUTO AMP.
Set up Self-diagnosis STEP 4.
Measure voltage across Hi relay harness terminal No. 5 and body ground.
Code No.
Terminal No.
+
−
Voltage
46
5
Body ground
Less than approx. 1.5V
O.K.
Replace blower motor.
N.G.
Disconnect Hi relay and auto amp. harness connectors.
J
Note
Does continuity exist between Hi relay harness terminal No. 5 and auto amp. harness terminal No. 5?
O.K.
Replace auto amp.
F
Fan control amp. connector
4
GY/L
Ω
Auto amp. connector
OFF
G
Hi relay connector
51
40
L/B
B/R
V
ON
H
Hi relay connector
103
B
Ω
DISCONNECT
OFF
I
Hi relay connector
5
G/OR
V
CONNECT
ON
Self-diagnosis STEP 4
46
J
Hi relay connector
Auto amp. connector
5
G/OR
Ω
OFF
NOTE: IF THE RESULT IS NO GOOD (NG) AFTER CHECKING CIRCUIT CONTINUITY, REPAIR HARNESS OR CONNECTOR.
91B04305 91D04306
Courtesy of Nissan Motor Co., U.S.A.

Fig. 29: Diagnostic Procedure 17 – Blower Motor Operation Is Malfunctioning (Q45 – 1 Of 2)

Fig. 30: Diagnostic Procedure 17 – Blower Motor Operation Is Malfunctioning (Q45 – 2 Of 2)

1993 AUTOMATIC A/C-HEATER SYSTEMS
Trouble Shooting – Q45 (Cont.)

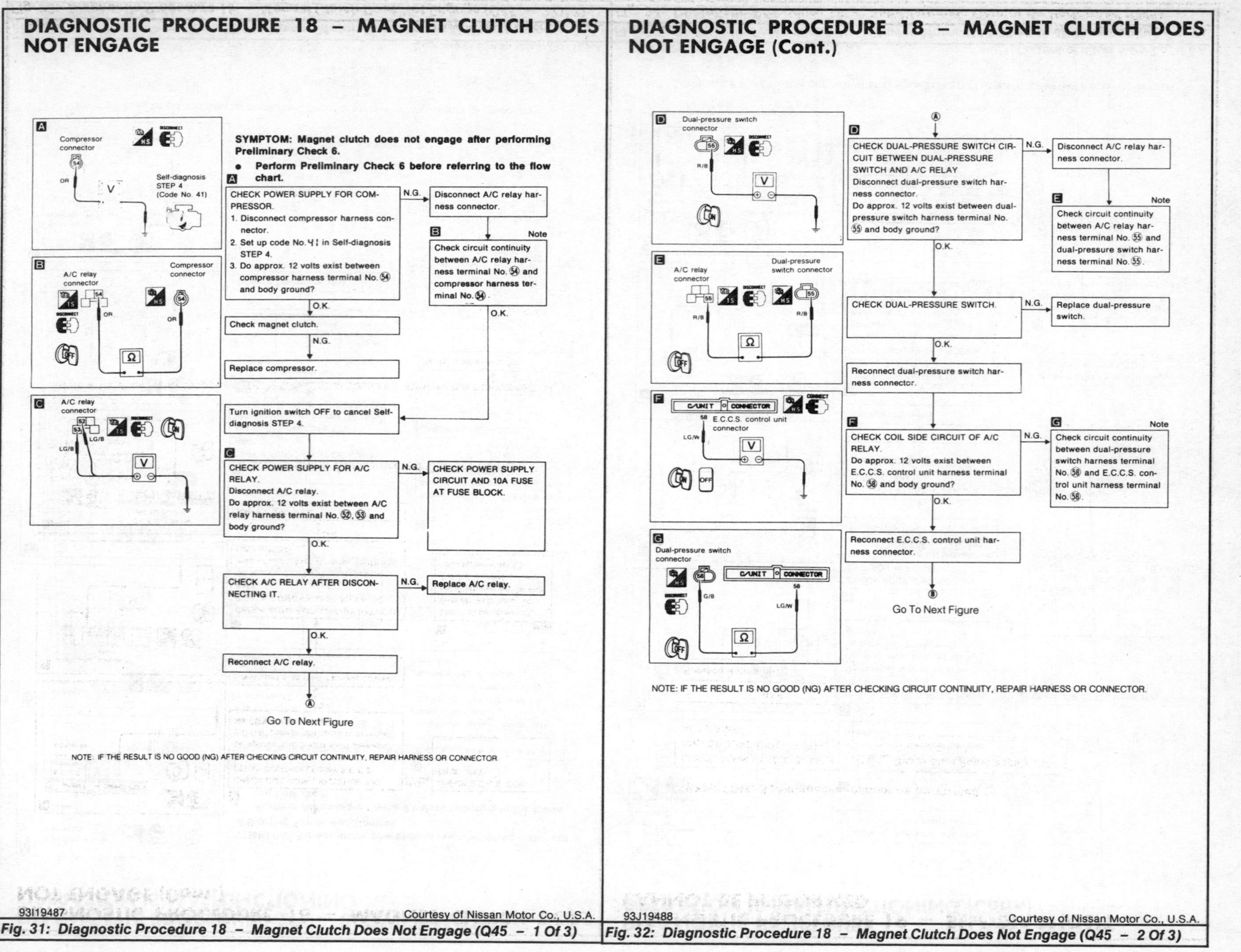
DIAGNOSTIC PROCEDURE 18 – MAGNET CLUTCH DOES NOT ENGAGE
A Compressor connector
54
OR
V
Self-diagnosis STEP 4 (Code No. 41)
H.S.
DISCONNECT
B A/C relay connector
54
OR
Compressor connector
T.S.
Ω
OFF
C A/C relay connector
52
53
LG/B
V
ON
SYMPTOM: Magnet clutch does not engage after performing Preliminary Check 6.
• Perform Preliminary Check 6 before referring to the flow chart.
A CHECK POWER SUPPLY FOR COMPRESSOR.
1. Disconnect compressor harness connector.
2. Set up code No. 41 in Self-diagnosis STEP 4.
3. Do approx. 12 volts exist between compressor harness terminal No. 54 and body ground?
N.G.
Disconnect A/C relay harness connector.
B Note
Check circuit continuity between A/C relay harness terminal No. 54 and compressor harness terminal No. 54.
O.K.
Check magnet clutch.
N.G.
Replace compressor.
Turn ignition switch OFF to cancel Self-diagnosis STEP 4.
C CHECK POWER SUPPLY FOR A/C RELAY.
Disconnect A/C relay.
Do approx. 12 volts exist between A/C relay harness terminal No. 52, 53 and body ground?
CHECK POWER SUPPLY CIRCUIT AND 10A FUSE AT FUSE BLOCK.
CHECK A/C RELAY AFTER DISCONNECTING IT.
Replace A/C relay.
Reconnect A/C relay.
A
Go To Next Figure
NOTE: IF THE RESULT IS NO GOOD (NG) AFTER CHECKING CIRCUIT CONTINUITY, REPAIR HARNESS OR CONNECTOR
93I19487
Courtesy of Nissan Motor Co., U.S.A.
DIAGNOSTIC PROCEDURE 18 – MAGNET CLUTCH DOES NOT ENGAGE (Cont.)
D Dual-pressure switch connector
55
R/B
V
ON
E A/C relay connector
Dual-pressure switch connector
55
R/B
Ω
OFF
F C/UNIT CONNECTOR
58
E.C.C.S. control unit connector
LG/W
V
ON
OFF
G Dual-pressure switch connector
C/UNIT CONNECTOR
58
G/B
LG/W
Ω
OFF
A
D CHECK DUAL-PRESSURE SWITCH CIRCUIT BETWEEN DUAL-PRESSURE SWITCH AND A/C RELAY
Disconnect dual-pressure switch harness connector.
Do approx. 12 volts exist between dual-pressure switch harness terminal No. 55 and body ground?
N.G.
Disconnect A/C relay harness connector.
E Note
Check circuit continuity between A/C relay harness terminal No. 55 and dual-pressure switch harness terminal No. 55.
O.K.
CHECK DUAL-PRESSURE SWITCH.
Replace dual-pressure switch.
Reconnect dual-pressure switch harness connector.
F CHECK COIL SIDE CIRCUIT OF A/C RELAY.
Do approx. 12 volts exist between E.C.C.S. control unit harness terminal No. 58 and body ground?
G Note
Check circuit continuity between dual-pressure switch harness terminal No. 58 and E.C.C.S. control unit harness terminal No. 58.
Reconnect E.C.C.S. control unit harness connector.
B
Go To Next Figure
NOTE: IF THE RESULT IS NO GOOD (NG) AFTER CHECKING CIRCUIT CONTINUITY, REPAIR HARNESS OR CONNECTOR.
93J19488
Courtesy of Nissan Motor Co., U.S.A.

Fig. 31: Diagnostic Procedure 18 – Magnet Clutch Does Not Engage (Q45 – 1 Of 3)

Fig. 32: Diagnostic Procedure 18 – Magnet Clutch Does Not Engage (Q45 – 2 Of 3)

1993 AUTOMATIC A/C-HEATER SYSTEMS
Trouble Shooting – Q45 (Cont.)

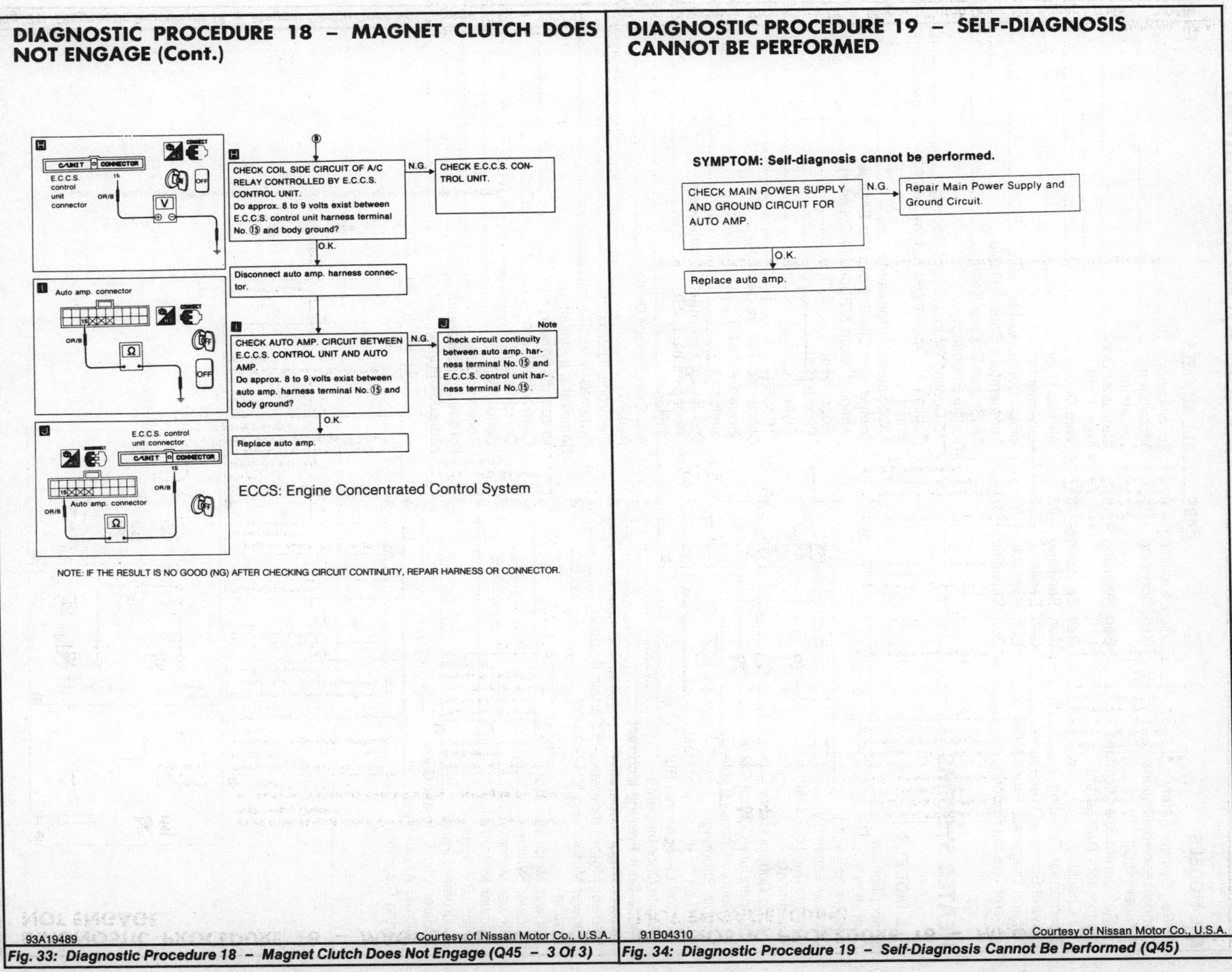
DIAGNOSTIC PROCEDURE 18 – MAGNET CLUTCH DOES NOT ENGAGE (Cont.)
H
E.C.C.S. control unit connector
15
OR/B
OFF
V
CHECK COIL SIDE CIRCUIT OF A/C RELAY CONTROLLED BY E.C.C.S. CONTROL UNIT.
Do approx. 8 to 9 volts exist between E.C.C.S. control unit harness terminal No. 15 and body ground?
N.G.
CHECK E.C.C.S. CONTROL UNIT.
O.K.
Disconnect auto amp. harness connector.
I
Auto amp. connector
CHECK AUTO AMP. CIRCUIT BETWEEN E.C.C.S. CONTROL UNIT AND AUTO AMP.
Do approx. 8 to 9 volts exist between auto amp. harness terminal No. 15 and body ground?
N.G.
J
Note
Check circuit continuity between auto amp. harness terminal No. 15 and E.C.C.S. control unit harness terminal No. 15.
O.K.
Replace auto amp.
E.C.C.S. control unit connector
Auto amp. connector
ECCS: Engine Concentrated Control System
NOTE: IF THE RESULT IS NO GOOD (NG) AFTER CHECKING CIRCUIT CONTINUITY, REPAIR HARNESS OR CONNECTOR.
DIAGNOSTIC PROCEDURE 19 – SELF-DIAGNOSIS CANNOT BE PERFORMED
SYMPTOM: Self-diagnosis cannot be performed.
CHECK MAIN POWER SUPPLY AND GROUND CIRCUIT FOR AUTO AMP.
N.G.
Repair Main Power Supply and Ground Circuit.
O.K.
Replace auto amp.
93A19489
Courtesy of Nissan Motor Co., U.S.A.
91B04310
Courtesy of Nissan Motor Co., U.S.A.

Fig. 33: Diagnostic Procedure 18 – Magnet Clutch Does Not Engage (Q45 – 3 Of 3)

Fig. 34: Diagnostic Procedure 19 – Self-Diagnosis Cannot Be Performed (Q45)

1993 ISUZU CONTENTS

GENERAL SERVICING

HEATER SYSTEMS

MANUAL A/C-HEATER SYSTEMS

1993 HEATER SYSTEMS
All Models

Amigo, Pickup, Rodeo, Stylus, Trooper

DESCRIPTION

The heater system delivers warm air to passenger compartment after engine warms up. The system draws in outside air, passes it through heater core and distributes it to various outlet vents. The system consists of circulation ducts, heater unit, blower assembly and control lever assembly. *See Fig. 1, 2 or 3.*

WARNING: To avoid injury from accidental air bag deployment, read and carefully follow all SERVICE PRECAUTIONS and DISABLING & ACTIVATING AIR BAG SYSTEM procedures in AIR BAG SYSTEM SAFETY article in GENERAL SERVICING.

CAUTION: When battery is disconnected, radio will go into anti-theft protection mode. Obtain radio anti-theft protection code from owner prior to servicing vehicle.

OPERATION

HEATER ASSEMBLY

The heater assembly houses the heater core and mode doors. Coolant flowing into the heater core is controlled by a heater valve mounted on side of heater assembly.

BLOWER ASSEMBLY

The blower motor forces outside air through the heater assembly and into the interior of the vehicle. Operation of blower motor is controlled by fan control lever.

HEATER CONTROL PANEL

Fan Speed Select Lever/Knob – Lever/knob controls fan speeds to regulate amount of airflow. Fan can be operated at 4 different speeds.
Mode Select Lever/Knob – Depending on position selected, airflow can be directed to different areas of passenger compartment. Airflow selection capabilities include individual areas or a combination of windshield, upper body, knee and/or foot area.
Air Source Select Lever – Lever controls the intake of outside air or recirculation of inside air.
Temperature Select Lever/Knob – Lever controls blend-air door position. Depending of lever position, airflow is directed through the heater core (hot setting), around the heater core (cold setting) or through and around the heater core, resulting in modulated temperatures between full hot and full cold.

ADJUSTMENTS

NOTE: Perform adjustment after installation of control lever/knob assembly.

MODE CONTROL CABLE

Amigo, Pickup, Rodeo & Stylus – Slide mode select lever to the right. Connect cable with control lever at defrost position. Secure cable using clip. Check mode select lever operation.
Trooper – Turn select knob to defrost setting. Connect damper cable with mode control link of heater unit at defrost position. Secure cable using clip. Check mode select knob operation.

TEMPERATURE CONTROL CABLE

Amigo, Pickup, Rodeo & Stylus – Slide select lever to the left. Connect cable with control lever at cold setting. Secure cable using clip. Check temperature select lever operation.
Trooper – Turn select knob to maximum cold setting. Connect cable with temperature control link of heater unit at cold setting. Secure cable using clip. Check temperature select knob operation.

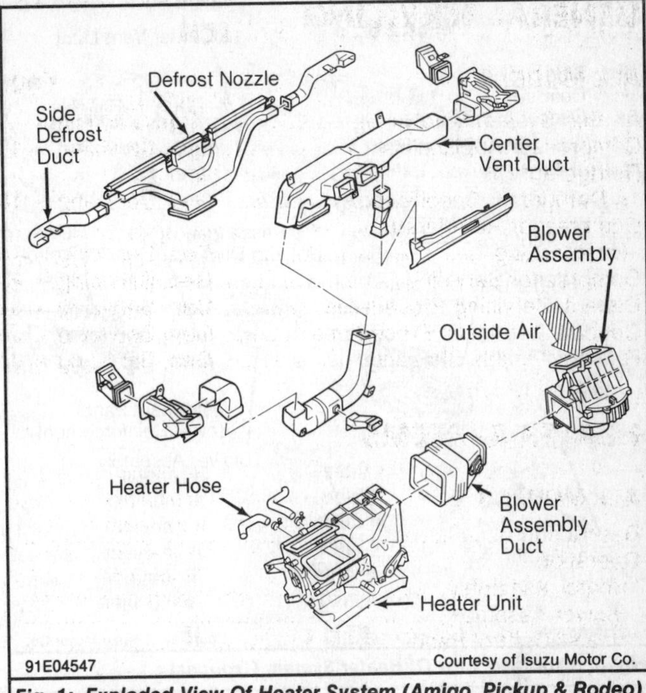
Defrost Nozzle
Side
Defrost
Duct
Center
Vent Duct
Blower
Assembly
Outside Air
Heater Hose
Blower
Assembly
Duct
Heater Unit
91E04547
Courtesy of Isuzu Motor Co.

Fig. 1: Exploded View Of Heater System (Amigo, Pickup & Rodeo)

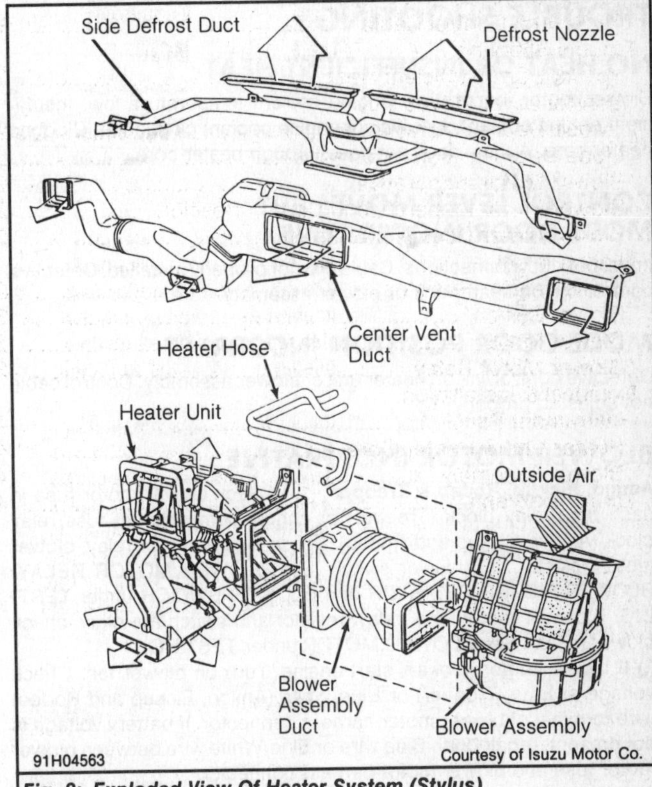
Side Defrost Duct
Defrost Nozzle
Center Vent
Duct
Heater Hose
Heater Unit
Outside Air
Blower
Assembly
Duct
Blower Assembly
91H04563
Courtesy of Isuzu Motor Co.

Fig. 2: Exploded View Of Heater System (Stylus)

AIR SOURCE CONTROL CABLE

Slide select lever to the left. Connect control cable to blower assembly control link. Secure cable using clip. Check air source select lever operation.

1993 HEATER SYSTEMS
All Models (Cont.)

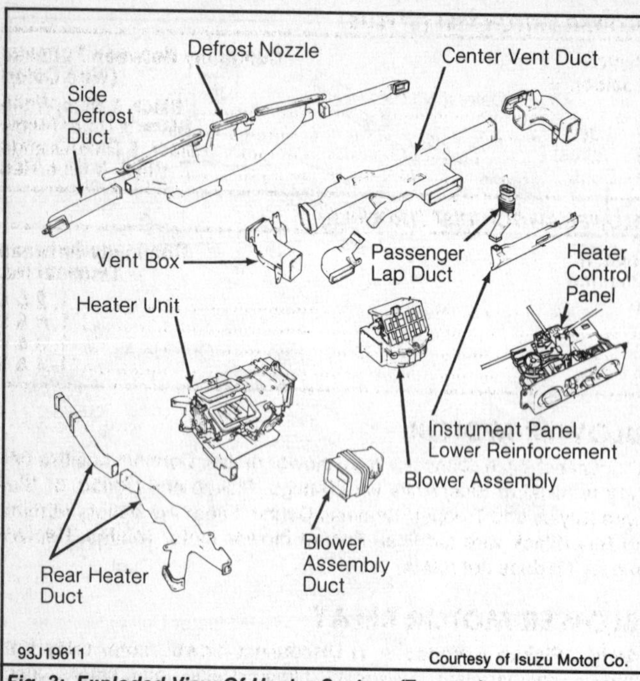
Defrost Nozzle
Center Vent Duct
Side
Defrost
Duct
Vent Box
Passenger
Lap Duct
Heater
Control
Panel
Heater Unit
Instrument Panel
Lower Reinforcement
Blower Assembly
Blower
Assembly
Duct
Rear Heater
Duct
93J19611
Courtesy of Isuzu Motor Co.

Fig. 3: Exploded View Of Heater System (Trooper)

TROUBLE SHOOTING

NO HEAT OR INSUFFICIENT HEAT

Blower motor inoperative. Engine coolant temperature low. Insufficient engine coolant. Insufficient engine coolant circulation. Clogged heater core. Airflow does not pass through heater core.

CONTROL LEVER MOVES BUT MODE DOOR INOPERATIVE

Improper duct connections. Cable clip not properly installed. Defective control link on heater unit or blower assembly.

MODE DOOR POSITION INCORRECT

Defective control link on heater unit or blower assembly. Control cable not adjusted properly.

BLOWER MOTOR INOPERATIVE

Amigo, Pickup, Rodeo & Trooper – 1) Check blower motor fuse in dash fuse/relay block (Trooper) or engine compartment fuse/relay block (Amigo, Pickup and Rodeo). Check blower motor relay, blower motor resistor and blower switch. See BLOWER MOTOR RELAY, BLOWER MOTOR RESISTOR and BLOWER SWITCH under TESTING. If blower motor fuse, relay, resistor and switch are okay, check blower motor. See BLOWER MOTOR under TESTING.

2) If blower motor is okay, start engine. Turn on blower fan. Check voltage at Blue (Trooper) or Blue/White (Amigo, Pickup and Rodeo) wire terminal of blower motor harness connector. If battery voltage is not present, repair open Blue wire or Blue/White wire between blower motor fuse and blower motor harness connector.

3) If battery voltage exists, check for poor ground or open circuit in Blue/Black wire between blower motor and blower resistor harness connectors. Also check Black wire between blower switch harness connector and body ground.

Stylus – 1) Disconnect blower motor 2-pin connector. Turn ignition on, and set fan speed select lever at high-speed setting. Check voltage between blower motor harness connector terminals. If battery voltage is present, replace defective blower motor. If battery voltage is not present, go to next step.

2) Check voltage between harness connector Blue wire terminal (power) and ground. If battery voltage is present, go to next step. If battery voltage is not present, check blower motor fuse in engine compartment fuse/relay block. If fuse is okay, check for open Blue wire.

3) Check blower motor resistor. See BLOWER MOTOR RESISTOR under TESTING. If resistor is okay, check blower switch. See BLOWER SWITCH under TESTING. If blower switch is okay, check for open Blue/Black wire between blower motor and resistor harness connectors. Also check Black wire between blower switch 2-pin harness connector and body ground.

BLOWER MOTOR INOPERATIVE IN CERTAIN POSITION

1) Check blower motor resistor. See BLOWER MOTOR RESISTOR under TESTING. If resistor is okay, check blower switch. See BLOWER SWITCH under TESTING. If blower switch is okay, go to next step. If blower switch does not test as specified, replace heater control panel.

2) If blower does not operate in low speed, check for open Blue/White wire between blower motor resistor and blower switch harness connectors. If blower motor does not operate in medium-low speed, check for open Blue/Yellow wire (Stylus and Trooper) or Light Green/Black wire (Amigo, Pickup and Rodeo) between blower motor resistor and blower switch harness connectors.

3) If blower does not operate in medium-high speed, check for open Blue/Orange wire between blower motor resistor and blower switch harness connectors. If blower motor does not operate in high speed, check for open Blue/Red wire between blower motor resistor and blower switch harness connectors.

BLOWER MOTOR DOES NOT SHUT OFF

1) Check blower switch. See BLOWER SWITCH under TESTING. If blower switch is not okay, replace heater control panel. If blower switch is okay, check following wiring harness for short circuits.

2) Check Blue/Black wire between blower motor resistor and blower motor harness connectors. Check Blue/Red wire between blower motor resistor and blower switch harness connectors. Check Blue/Orange wire between blower motor resistor and blower switch harness connectors.

3) Check Blue/Yellow wire (Stylus and Trooper) or Light Green/Black wire (Amigo, Pickup and Rodeo) between blower motor resistor and blower switch harness connectors. Check Blue/White wire between blower motor resistor and blower switch harness connectors.

TESTING

WARNING: To avoid injury from accidental air bag deployment, read and carefully follow all SERVICE PRECAUTIONS and DISABLING & ACTIVATING AIR BAG SYSTEM procedures in AIR BAG SYSTEM SAFETY article in GENERAL SERVICING.

BLOWER MOTOR RESISTOR

Disconnect resistor. Check resistance between indicated terminals. See appropriate BLOWER MOTOR RESISTOR TEST table. *See Fig. 4.* If resistance is not as specified, replace resistor.

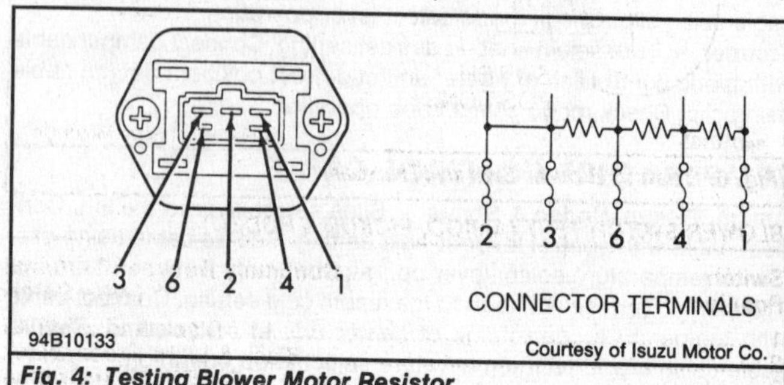
3
6
2
4
1
2
3
6
4
1
CONNECTOR TERMINALS
94B10133
Courtesy of Isuzu Motor Co.

Fig. 4: Testing Blower Motor Resistor (Amigo, Pickup, Rodeo & Trooper Shown; Stylus Similar)

BLOWER MOTOR RESISTOR TEST (AMIGO, PICKUP, RODEO & TROOPER)

Terminal No.	Ohms
1 & 2	2.4
2 & 4	0.9
2 & 6	0.28
2 & 3	0

BLOWER MOTOR RESISTOR TEST (STYLUS)

Terminal No.	Ohms
1 & 4	1.60
4 & 6	0.65
3 & 6	0.35
2 & 3	0

BLOWER SWITCH

Disconnect blower switch connector. Check continuity between indicated switch terminals. See appropriate BLOWER SWITCH TEST table. *See Fig. 5 or 6.*

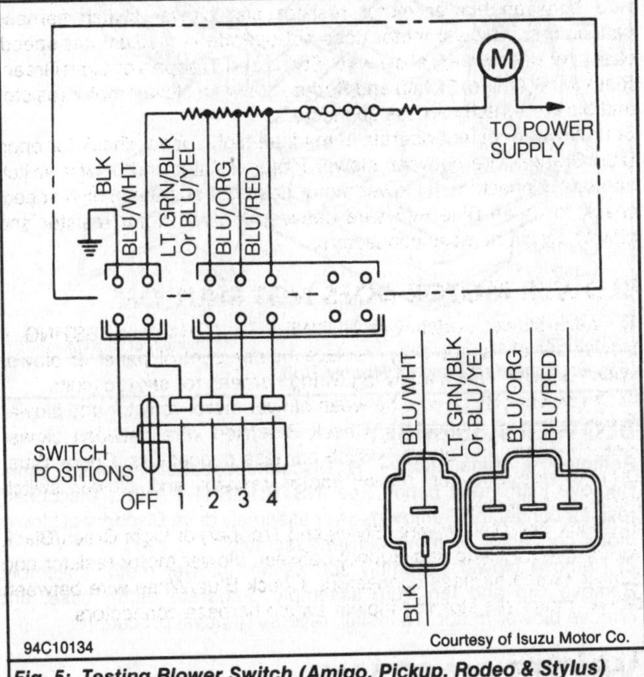

M
TO POWER SUPPLY
BLK
BLU/WHT
LT GRN/BLK Or BLU/YEL
BLU/ORG
BLU/RED
SWITCH POSITIONS
OFF 1 2 3 4
BLU/WHT
LT GRN/BLK Or BLU/YEL
BLU/ORG
BLU/RED
BLK
94C10134
Courtesy of Isuzu Motor Co.

Fig. 5: Testing Blower Switch (Amigo, Pickup, Rodeo & Stylus)

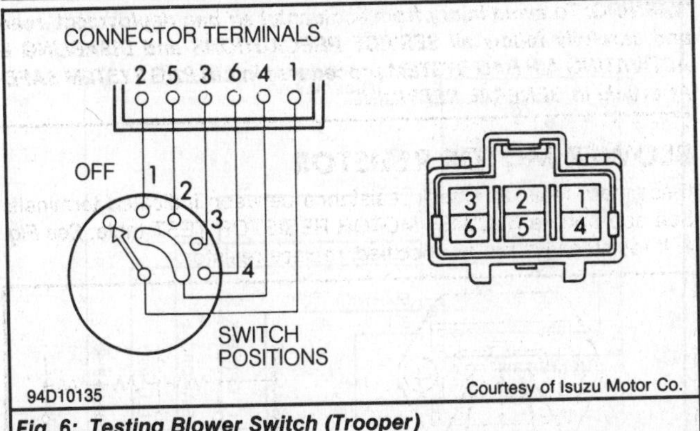

CONNECTOR TERMINALS
2 5 3 6 4 1
OFF
1
2
3
4
SWITCH POSITIONS
3 2 1
6 5 4
94D10135
Courtesy of Isuzu Motor Co.

Fig. 6: Testing Blower Switch (Trooper)

BLOWER SWITCH TEST (AMIGO, PICKUP & RODEO)

Switch Position	Continuity Between Terminal (Wire Color)
1	Black & Blue/White
2	Black & Light Green/Black
3	Black & Blue/Orange
4	Black & Blue/Red

BLOWER SWITCH TEST (STYLUS)

Switch Position	Continuity Between Terminal (Wire Color)
1	Black & Blue/White
2	Black & Blue/Yellow
3	Black & Blue/Orange
4	Black & Blue/Red

BLOWER SWITCH TEST (TROOPER)

Switch Position	Continuity Between Terminal No.
1	1, 2 & 4
2	1, 4 & 5
3	1, 3 & 4
4	1, 4 & 6

BLOWER MOTOR

Disconnect 2-pin connector from blower motor. Connect positive battery terminal to Blue/White wire (Amigo, Pickup and Rodeo) or Blue wire (Stylus and Trooper) terminal. Connect negative battery terminal to Blue/Black wire terminal. Ensure blower motor rotates. Replace motor if it does not rotate.

BLOWER MOTOR RELAY

Amigo, Pickup & Rodeo – 1) Disconnect blower motor relay from engine compartment fuse/relay block. Using ohmmeter, check continuity between terminals No. 1 and 2. *See Fig. 7.* Ensure continuity exists. Check continuity between terminals No. 1 and 3. Continuity should not exist.

2) Apply battery voltage between terminals No. 4 and 5. Ensure continuity now exists between terminals No. 1 and 3. There should be no continuity between terminals No. 1 and 2 with voltage applied. Replace relay if continuity is not as specified.

Stylus & Trooper – 1) Disconnect blower motor relay from engine compartment fuse/relay block (Stylus) or dash fuse/relay block (Trooper). Using voltmeter, check continuity between relay terminals No. 1 and 3. *See Fig. 8.* Continuity should exist.

2) Check continuity between terminals No. 2 and 4. Continuity should not exist. Apply battery voltage between terminals No. 1 and 3. Ensure continuity exists between terminals No. 2 and 4 with voltage applied. Replace relay if continuity is not as specified.

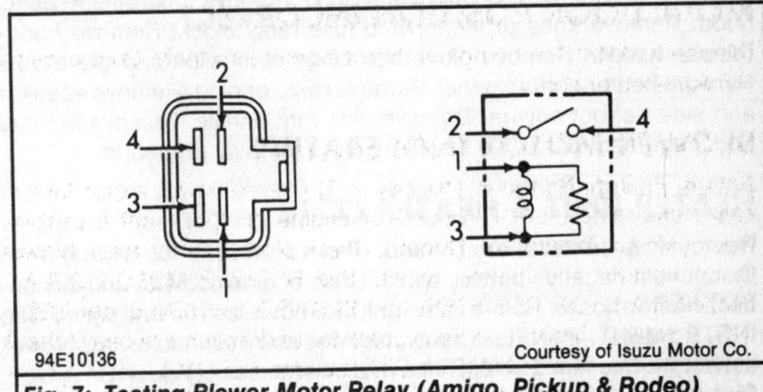

2
4
3
1
5
2
4
1
3
94E10136
Courtesy of Isuzu Motor Co.

Fig. 7: Testing Blower Motor Relay (Amigo, Pickup & Rodeo)

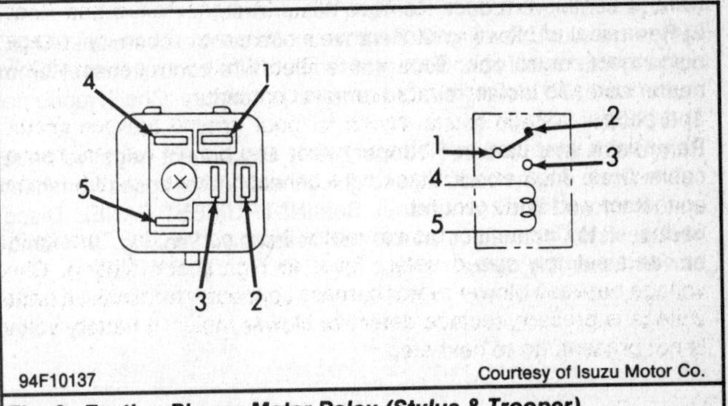

4
1
5
3
2
2
1
3
4
5
94F10137
Courtesy of Isuzu Motor Co.

Fig. 8: Testing Blower Motor Relay (Stylus & Trooper)

1993 HEATER SYSTEMS
All Models (Cont.)

REMOVAL & INSTALLATION

WARNING: To avoid injury from accidental air bag deployment, read and carefully follow all SERVICE PRECAUTIONS and DISABLING & ACTIVATING AIR BAG SYSTEM procedures in AIR BAG SYSTEM SAFETY article in GENERAL SERVICING.

INSTRUMENT PANEL

CAUTION: Do not hammer steering shaft/column assembly to remove or install steering wheel.

Removal (Amigo, Pickup & Rodeo) – 1) Disable air bag system. Disconnect negative battery cable. Scribe mating marks on steering wheel and shaft for installation reference. Using Steering Remover (J-29752), remove steering wheel. Remove steering cowl. Remove instrument panel grilles and plug, or driving pattern indicator panel (A/T models). Disconnect electrical connections. Remove instrument cluster hood, instrument cluster bezel and instrument cluster. Remove hood release handle. Remove knee protector.

2) Remove dash fuse/relay block and side trim. Remove engine control module box. Remove radio console and glove box lower reinforcement. Remove speaker covers and glove box. Remove heater control panel knobs and cover. Disconnect heater control cables, and remove heater control panel. Remove illumination control knob. Remove instrument panel.

Installation – Install instrument panel. Install and adjust heater control cables. To complete installation, reverse removal procedure. Ensure mating marks on steering wheel and shaft align. Apply grease to contact ring, and tighten steering wheel nut to 26 ft. lbs. (35 N.m).

Removal & Installation (Stylus) – Disconnect battery ground cable. Remove switch bezel and cigarette lighter bezel. Remove hood release cable and knee protector. Remove hinge pins located inside glove box, and remove glove box. Remove radio console. Disconnect electrical connectors. Remove instrument cluster hood and instrument cluster. Remove plugs from defrost vent cover. Remove defrost vent cover and instrument panel. To install, reverse removal procedure.

Removal & Installation (Trooper) – Disconnect negative battery cable. Remove steering cowl. Disconnect electrical connectors, and remove instrument panel console. Remove instrument cluster. Remove engine control module cover. Remove instrument panel hood. Remove knee protector and fuse/relay block. Remove hood-release handle. Remove glove box hinge pins, clips and glove box. Remove heater control panel. Remove radio or plug. Remove speaker and side defrost covers. Remove side trim panels. Remove ashtray and instrument panel. To install, reverse removal procedure.

HEATER UNIT & HEATER CORE

Removal & Installation (Amigo, Pickup, Rodeo & Stylus) – 1) Disconnect negative battery cable. Drain engine coolant, and disconnect heater hoses from heater unit. Remove instrument panel. See INSTRUMENT PANEL. Disconnect resistor connector at blower assembly. *See Fig. 1 or 2.* Remove blower assembly duct. On Amigo, Pickup and Rodeo, remove instrument panel support. On Stylus, remove center vent duct. Remove heater unit.

2) Remove duct. *See Fig. 9.* Remove mode control case, but DO NOT disconnect control link. Separate temperature control case. Remove heater core. To install, reverse removal procedure. Check mode door operation.

Removal & Installation (Trooper) – 1) Disconnect negative battery cable. Drain engine coolant, and disconnect heater hoses from heater unit. Remove instrument panel. See INSTRUMENT PANEL. Disconnect resistor connector at blower assembly. *See Fig. 3.* Remove blower assembly duct.

2) Remove Electronic Control Module (ECM). Remove instrument panel support. Remove front console. Remove rear heater duct and heater unit. Remove duct. *See Fig. 9.* Remove mode control case, but DO NOT disconnect control link. Separate temperature control case, and remove heater core. To install, reverse removal procedure. Check mode door operation.

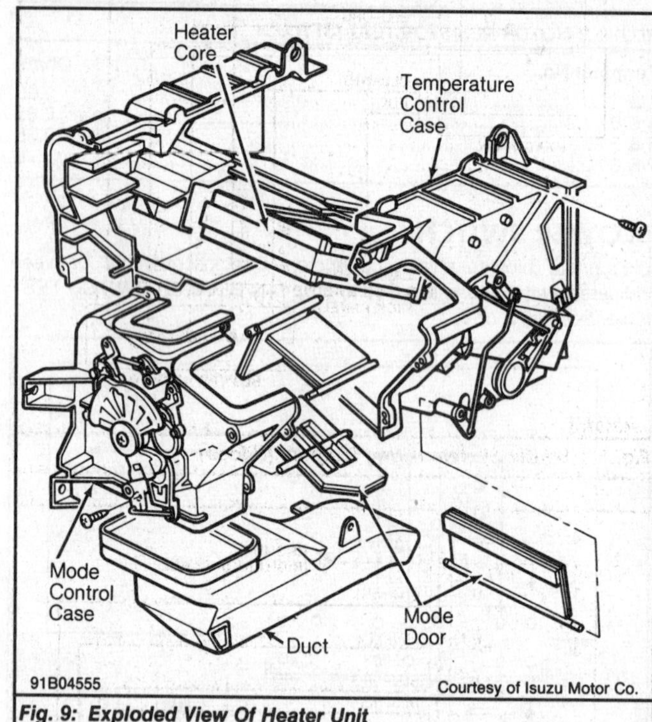
Heater
Core
Temperature
Control
Case
Mode
Control
Case
Duct
Mode
Door
91B04555
Courtesy of Isuzu Motor Co.

Fig. 9: Exploded View Of Heater Unit

BLOWER ASSEMBLY

Removal & Installation – 1) Disconnect battery ground cable. Remove instrument panel. See INSTRUMENT PANEL. Disconnect resistor connector. Remove blower assembly duct. Disconnect blower motor connector. Remove blower assembly.

2) Remove blower assembly screws and blower motor assembly. Remove clip and fan from assembly. Separate motor case, and remove blower motor. To install, reverse removal procedure.

WIRING DIAGRAMS

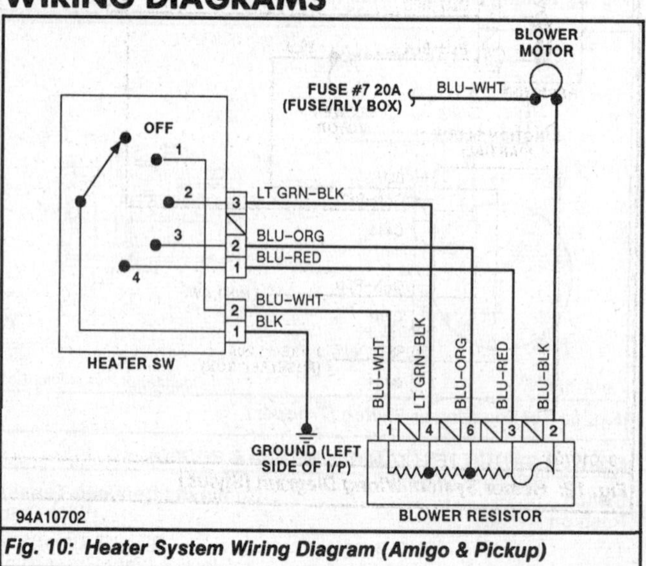
BLOWER
MOTOR
FUSE #7 20A
(FUSE/RLY BOX)
BLU-WHT
OFF
1
2
3
4
LT GRN-BLK
BLU-ORG
BLU-RED
BLU-WHT
BLK
HEATER SW
BLU-WHT
LT GRN-BLK
BLU-ORG
BLU-RED
BLU-BLK
GROUND (LEFT
SIDE OF I/P)
BLOWER RESISTOR
94A10702

Fig. 10: Heater System Wiring Diagram (Amigo & Pickup)

1993 HEATER SYSTEMS
All Models (Cont.)

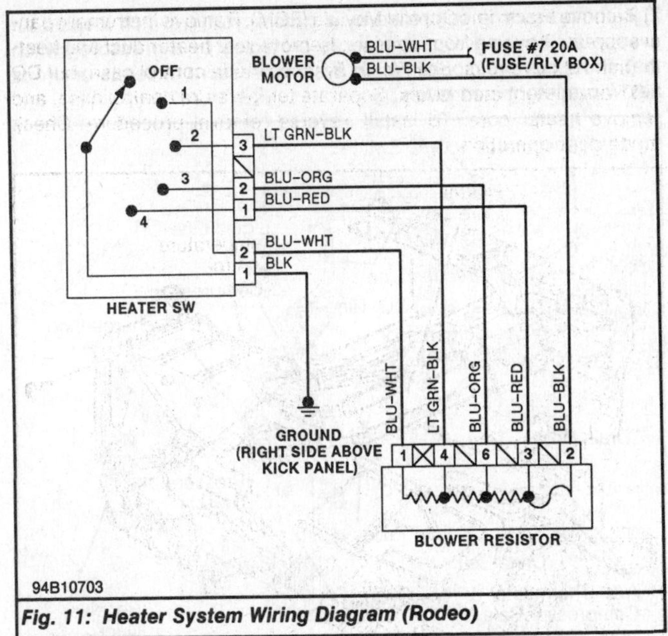
HEATER SW
OFF
1
2
3
4
BLOWER MOTOR
BLU-WHT
BLU-BLK
FUSE #7 20A (FUSE/RLY BOX)
LT GRN-BLK
BLU-ORG
BLU-RED
BLU-WHT
BLK
GROUND (RIGHT SIDE ABOVE KICK PANEL)
LT GRN-BLK
BLU-ORG
BLU-RED
BLU-BLK
BLOWER RESISTOR
94B10703

Fig. 11: Heater System Wiring Diagram (Rodeo)

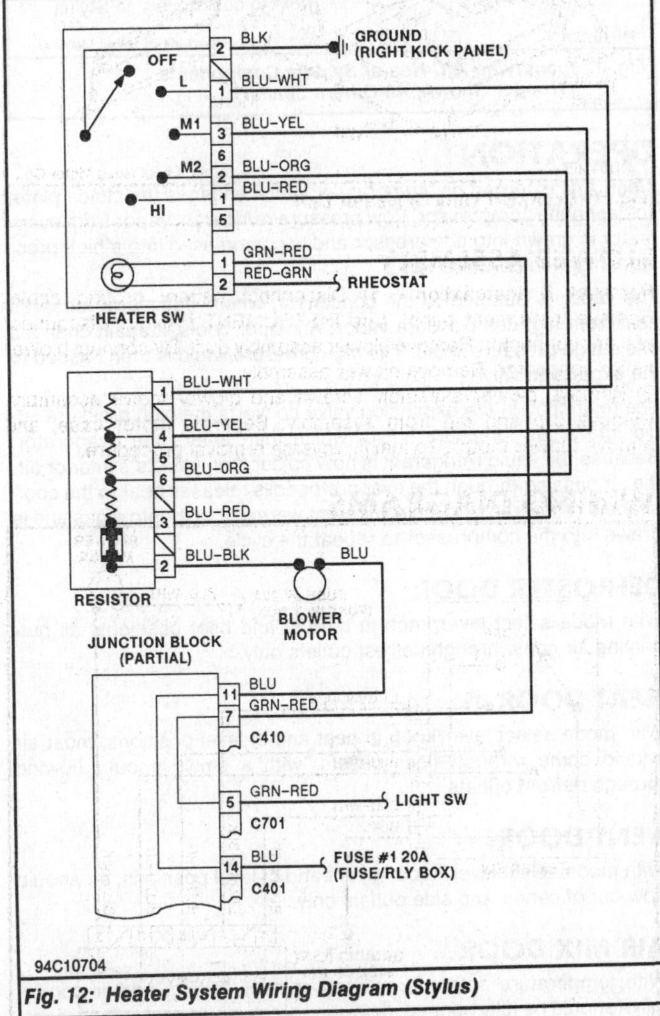
BLK
GROUND (RIGHT KICK PANEL)
OFF
L
BLU-WHT
M1
BLU-YEL
M2
BLU-ORG
BLU-RED
HI
GRN-RED
RED-GRN
RHEOSTAT
HEATER SW
BLU-WHT
BLU-YEL
BLU-ORG
BLU-RED
BLU-BLK
BLU
RESISTOR
BLOWER MOTOR
JUNCTION BLOCK (PARTIAL)
BLU
GRN-RED
C410
GRN-RED
LIGHT SW
C701
BLU
FUSE #1 20A (FUSE/RLY BOX)
C401
94C10704

Fig. 12: Heater System Wiring Diagram (Stylus)

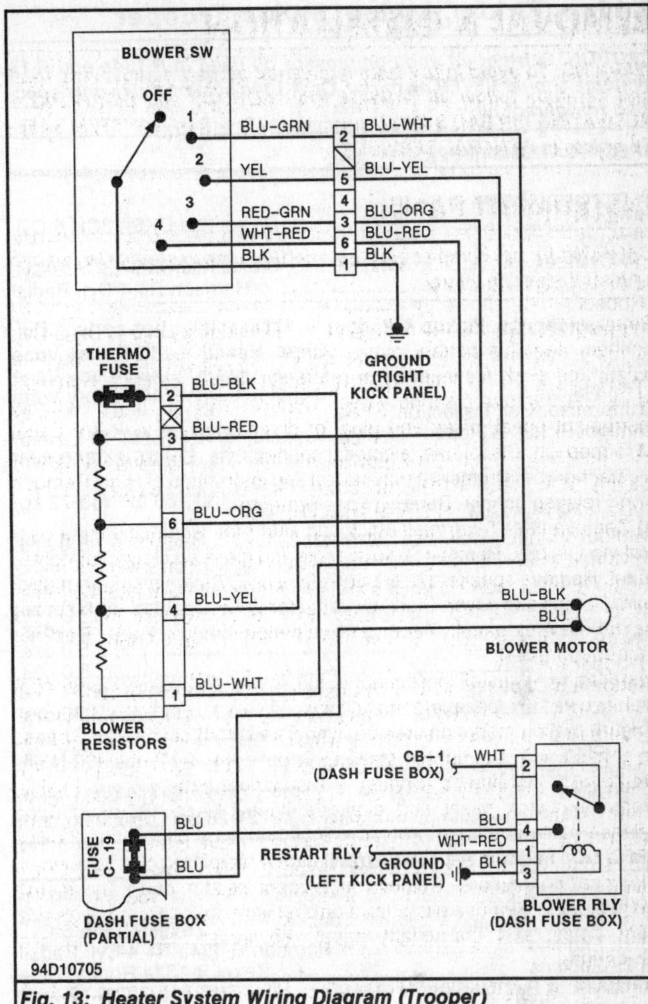
BLOWER SW
OFF
1
2
3
4
BLU-GRN
YEL
RED-GRN
WHT-RED
BLK
BLU-WHT
BLU-YEL
BLU-ORG
BLU-RED
BLK
GROUND (RIGHT KICK PANEL)
THERMO FUSE
BLU-BLK
BLU-RED
BLU-ORG
BLU-YEL
BLU-WHT
BLOWER RESISTORS
BLU-BLK
BLU
BLOWER MOTOR
CB-1 (DASH FUSE BOX)
WHT
BLU
FUSE C-19
BLU
BLU
WHT-RED
RESTART RLY
GROUND (LEFT KICK PANEL)
BLK
BLOWER RLY (DASH FUSE BOX)
DASH FUSE BOX (PARTIAL)
94D10705

Fig. 13: Heater System Wiring Diagram (Trooper)

1993 MANUAL A/C-HEATER SYSTEMS
All Models

Amigo, Pickup, Rodeo, Stylus, Trooper

CAUTION: Refrigerant and compressor oil used in R-134a and R-12 systems should NEVER be mixed. On R-134a systems, use only specified refrigerant oil.

SPECIFICATIONS (R-12)

Application	Specification
Compressor Type	
Amigo	Diesel Kiki DKS-13CH 6-Cyl.
Pickup	
4-Cylinder	Diesel Kiki DKS-13CH 6-Cyl.
V6	Harrison R4 4-Cyl. Radial
Rodeo	
4-Cylinder	Diesel Kiki DKS-17CH 6-Cyl.
V6	Diesel Kiki DKV-14D Rotary Vane
Stylus	Diesel Kiki DKV-14D Rotary Vane
Trooper	Diesel Kiki DKV-14D Rotary Vane
Compressor Belt Deflection	
Amigo, Pickup & Rodeo	5/16 - 15/32" (8-12 mm)
Trooper	25/64" (10 mm)
Compressor Belt Tension	
Stylus	130-160 lbs. (59-72 kg)
System Oil Capacity	
Amigo	5.0 ozs.
Pickup	
4-Cylinder	5.0 ozs.
V6	6.0 ozs.
Rodeo	5.0 ozs.
Stylus	5.0 ozs.
Trooper	5.0 ozs.
Refrigerant Capacity	
Amigo, Pickup & Rodeo	26 ozs.
Stylus	21 ozs.
Trooper	30 ozs.
System Operating Pressures	
High Side	199-213 psi (14.0-15.0 kg/cm²)
Low Side	21-28 psi (1.5-2.0 kg/cm²)

SPECIFICATIONS ([1] R-134a OPTION)

Application	Specification
Compressor Type	
2.3L & 2.6L Engines	Zexel R-134a 6-Cyl.
3.1L Engines	Harrison R-134a R4 4-Cyl. Radial
3.2L Engines	Zexel R-134a Rotary Vane
Compressor Belt Deflection	5/16 - 15/32" (8-12 mm)
System Oil Capacity	
2.3L & 2.6L Engines [2]	5ozs.
3.1L Engines [3]	7.5-8.5 ozs.
3.2L Engines [4]	5 ozs.
Refrigerant Capacity	
2.3L, 2.6L & 3.1L Engines	23 ozs.
Trooper	26 ozs.
System Operating Pressures	
High Side	213-242 psi (14.0-17.0 kg/cm²)
Low Side	18-28 psi (1.3-2.0 kg/cm²)

[1] - R-134a system is standard equipment on some models built after 5/1/93.
[2] - Use R-134a Swash Plate Compressor Oil (Part No. 2-90188-300-0).
[3] - Use R-134a R4 Compressor Oil (Part No. 2-90222-320-0).
[4] - Use R-134a Rotary Vane Compressor Oil (Part No. 2-90188-301-0).

WARNING: To avoid injury from accidental air bag deployment, read and carefully follow all SERVICE PRECAUTIONS and DISABLING & ACTIVATING AIR BAG SYSTEM procedures in AIR BAG SYSTEM SAFETY article in GENERAL SERVICING.

CAUTION: When battery is disconnected, radio will go into anti-theft protection mode. Obtain radio anti-theft protection code from owner prior to servicing vehicle.

DESCRIPTION

The A/C-heating system blends cool and warm air in correct proportions to meet cooling/heating requirements. System components include evaporator, compressor, condenser, receiver-drier and expansion valve. *See Fig. 1 or 2.*

The compressor is controlled by a clutch cycling switch located on evaporator housing. Compressor is protected by a pressure switch that shuts compressor off when system pressure exceeds or drops below predetermined levels.

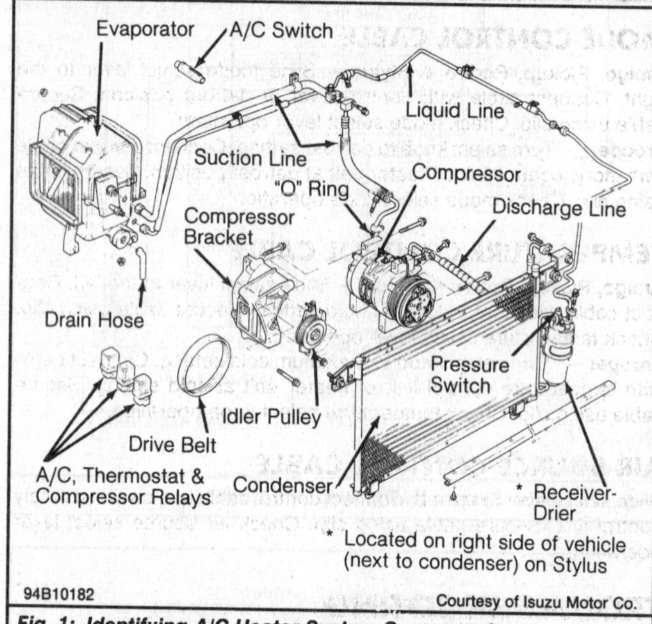
Evaporator
A/C Switch
Liquid Line
Suction Line
Compressor
"O" Ring
Compressor
Bracket
Discharge Line
Drain Hose
Pressure
Switch
Idler Pulley
Drive Belt
A/C, Thermostat &
Compressor Relays
Condenser
* Receiver-
Drier
* Located on right side of vehicle
(next to condenser) on Stylus
94B10182
Courtesy of Isuzu Motor Co.

Fig. 1: Identifying A/C-Heater System Components (Trooper Shown; All Others Similar)

OPERATION

When A/C is turned on, compressor clutch engages the clutch plate, actuating the compressor. Low pressure refrigerant vapor from evaporator is drawn into compressor and is compressed into a high pressure, high temperature vapor.

The vapor is pumped to the condenser, where outside air absorbs heat from high temperature vapor. As vapor cools, it again changes into a high pressure liquid. The high pressure liquid is then passed to the expansion valve.

The restriction in the expansion valve converts the high pressure liquid into a low pressure liquid, which then enters the evaporator. Because the liquid refrigerant is now colder than vehicle's interior air, the air passing through the evaporator coils releases heat to the cooler liquid refrigerant. As the refrigerant warms, it boils into a gas and is drawn into the compressor to repeat the cycle.

DEFROSTER DOOR

With mode select lever/knob in defrost and heat positions, all outcoming air goes through defrost outlets only.

HEAT DOOR

With mode select lever/knob in heat and bi-level positions, most air should come through floor outlets, with a small amount flowing through defrost outlets.

VENT DOOR

With mode select lever/knob in vent and bi-level positions, air should flow out of center and side outlets only.

AIR MIX DOOR

With temperature select lever/knob at heat setting, heater control valve should be fully opened, delivering warm air. At cool setting, heater valve should be closed, and non-heated air is delivered.

ADJUSTMENTS

NOTE: Perform adjustment after installation of control lever/knob assembly.

MODE CONTROL CABLE

Amigo, Pickup, Rodeo & Stylus – Slide mode select lever to the right. Connect cable with control lever at defrost position. Secure cable using clip. Check mode select lever operation.

Trooper – Turn select knob to defrost setting. Connect damper cable with mode control link of heater unit at defrost position. Secure cable using clip. Check mode select knob operation.

TEMPERATURE CONTROL CABLE

Amigo, Pickup, Rodeo & Stylus – Slide select lever to the left. Connect cable with control lever at cold setting. Secure cable using clip. Check temperature select lever operation.

Trooper – Turn select knob to maximum cold setting. Connect cable with temperature control link of heater unit at cold setting. Secure cable using clip. Check temperature select knob operation.

AIR SOURCE CONTROL CABLE

Slide select lever to the left. Connect control cable to blower assembly control link. Secure cable using clip. Check air source select lever operation.

TROUBLE SHOOTING

NO COOLING OR INSUFFICIENT COOLING

Compressor clutch does not engage. Compressor not rotating properly. Incorrect refrigerant level. Refrigerant system leakage. Condenser clogged. Defective temperature control link of heater unit. Contaminated expansion valve. Defective electronic thermostat.

COOLING AIR DISCHARGED AT LOW VELOCITY

Evaporator clogged or frosted. Air leaking from cooling unit or air duct. Blower motor inoperative.

TESTING

WARNING: To avoid injury from accidental air bag deployment, read and carefully follow all SERVICE PRECAUTIONS and DISABLING & ACTIVATING AIR BAG SYSTEM procedures in AIR BAG SYSTEM SAFETY article in GENERAL SERVICING.

NOTE: For heater component test procedures, see HEATER SYSTEMS article.

A/C SYSTEM PERFORMANCE

1) Ensure ambient temperature is 86-95°F (30-35°C). Connect manifold gauge set. Run engine at 1500 RPM. Turn A/C on. Operate blower in high speed. Set temperature select lever/knob at maximum cool setting. Open all doors and engine compartment hood. Check low- and high-side pressures.

2) On R-12 systems, low pressure should be 21-28 psi (1.5-2.0 kg/cm²), and high pressure should be 199-213 psi (14.0-15.0 kg/cm²). On R-134a systems, low pressure should be 18-28 psi (1.3-2.0 kg/cm²), and high pressure should be 213-242 psi (14.0-17.0 kg/cm²).

COMPRESSOR CLUTCH DOES NOT ENGAGE

Amigo, Pickup & Rodeo (4-Cylinder) – **1)** Check blower motor operation. If blower motor is okay, go to next step. If blower motor does not function properly, go to TROUBLE SHOOTING in HEATER SYSTEMS article.

2) Check A/C fuse (10-amp) in engine compartment fuse/relay block. If fuse is okay, check thermostat relay. See RELAYS. If relay is okay, check A/C switch and blower switch. See SWITCHES. If switches are okay, go to next step.

3) Check continuity between dual-pressure switch terminals. Dual-pressure switch is located on receiver-drier. If continuity is present, go to next step. If continuity is not present, check refrigerant level. If refrigerant level is correct, replace dual-pressure switch.

4) Check body ground connection. If ground connection is okay, disconnect compressor clutch connector. Apply battery voltage to compressor clutch terminal. If compressor clutch comes on, go to next step. If clutch does not engage, compressor clutch is defective.

5) Turn ignition and A/C on. Check voltage at Brown wire terminal of A/C switch and dual-pressure switch harness connector. If battery voltage exists, go to next step. If battery voltage is not present, repair open Brown wire.

6) Check voltage at Light Green/Yellow wire terminal of thermostat relay harness connector and electronic thermostat. If battery voltage exists, go to next step. If battery voltage is not present, repair open Light Green/Yellow wire.

7) Measure voltage at Green/Blue wire terminal of thermostat relay harness connector. If battery voltage is present, go to next step. If battery voltage is not present, repair open Green/Blue wire.

8) Measure voltage at White wire terminal of blower switch harness connector. If voltage is present, go to next step. If voltage is not present, repair open White wire.

9) Check A/C switch indicator light. If indicator light is on, go to next step. If light is not on, repair open Black wire between blower switch harness connector and body ground.

10) Ensure ignition is off. Check continuity between Green/Black wire terminal of thermostat relay and compressor clutch harness connector. If continuity exists, go to next step. If continuity is not present, repair open Green/Black wire.

11) Check continuity between Green/Red wire terminal of electronic thermostat harness connector and thermostat relay. If continuity exists, go to next step. If continuity is not present, repair open Green/Red wire.

12) Check continuity between White wire terminal of electronic thermostat harness connector and blower switch. If continuity exists, electronic thermostat is defective. If continuity is not present, repair open White wire.

Rodeo (V6) – **1)** Check blower motor operation. If blower motor is okay, go to next step. If blower motor does not function properly, go to TROUBLE SHOOTING in HEATER SYSTEMS article.

2) Check A/C fuse (10-amp) in engine compartment fuse/relay block. If fuse is okay, check thermostat and A/C compressor relays. See RELAYS. If relays are okay, go to next step.

3) Check continuity between Brown wire and Green/Blue wire terminal of triple-pressure (A/T) or dual-pressure (M/T) switch harness connector. If continuity exists, go to next step. If continuity is not present, check refrigerant level. If refrigerant level is correct, replace defective pressure switch.

4) Check A/C switch and blower switch. See SWITCHES. If switches are okay, start engine. Turn A/C on. Measure voltage at Green wire terminal of compressor clutch harness connector. If battery voltage is not present, go to next step. If battery voltage exists, check compressor clutch coil for open or short circuit. Replace if necessary. If coil is okay, compressor clutch circuit is okay.

5) Measure voltage at Brown wire terminal of pressure switch harness connector. If battery voltage exists, go to next step. If battery voltage is not present, repair open Brown wire between A/C fuse (10-amp) and pressure switch.

6) Disconnect thermostat relay. Measure voltage at Green/Blue wire terminal of thermostat relay harness connector. If battery voltage exists, go to next step. If battery voltage is not present, repair open Green/Blue wire between pressure switch and thermostat relay.

7) Measure voltage between Light Green/Yellow wire and Green/Red wire terminals of thermostat relay harness connector. If battery voltage is not present, go to step **12)**. If voltage exists, reconnect thermostat relay, and go to next step.

8) Disconnect A/C compressor relay. Measure voltage at Green/Black wire terminal of A/C compressor relay harness connector. If battery

1993 MANUAL A/C-HEATER SYSTEMS
All Models (Cont.)

voltage exists, go to next step. If battery voltage is not present, repair open Green/Black wire between thermostat relay and A/C compressor relay.

9) Ensure ignition is off. Check continuity between Green wire terminal of A/C compressor relay and compressor clutch harness connector. If continuity exists, go to next step. If continuity is not present, repair open circuit.

10) Measure voltage at Green/Blue wire terminal of thermostat relay harness connector. If battery voltage exists, go to next step. If battery voltage is not present, repair open Green/Blue wire circuit between A/C compressor relay and pressure switch.

11) Measure voltage at Yellow/Black wire and Gray/Red wire terminal of ECM harness connector. If battery voltage exists at each terminal, ECM is defective. If battery voltage is not present at any terminal, repair appropriate open circuit.

12) Measure voltage at Light Green/Yellow wire terminal of thermostat relay harness connector. If voltage exists, go to step **14)**. If battery voltage is not present, go to next step.

13) Measure voltage at Brown wire terminal of A/C switch harness connector. If battery voltage exists, repair open Light Green/Yellow wire between A/C switch and thermostat relay. If battery voltage is not present, repair open Brown wire between A/C fuse (10-amp) and A/C switch.

14) Check A/C indicator light. If light is on, go to next step. If light is off, measure voltage at White wire terminal of blower switch harness connector. If battery voltage exists, check for poor ground or open Black wire between blower switch and body ground. If battery voltage is not present, repair open White wire between blower switch and A/C switch.

15) Reconnect thermostat relay. Measure voltage at Light Green/Yellow wire terminal of electronic thermostat harness connector. If battery voltage exists, go to next step. If battery voltage is not present, repair open Light Green/Yellow wire between electronic thermostat and A/C switch.

16) Check continuity between Green/Red wire terminal of electronic thermostat and thermostat relay harness connector. If continuity is present, electronic thermostat is defective. If continuity is not present, repair open circuit.

Pickup (V6) – 1) Check blower motor operation. If blower motor is okay, go to next step. If blower motor does not function properly, go to TROUBLE SHOOTING in HEATER SYSTEMS article.

2) Start engine. Apply battery voltage to Black/Red wire terminal of A/C-cut relay Data Link Connector (DLC). Check if compressor clutch engages. If clutch engages, go to step **6)**. If clutch does not engage, go to next step.

3) Connect positive battery cable to Brown wire terminal of compressor clutch. Connect negative battery cable to Black wire terminal of clutch terminal. If compressor clutch engages, go to next step. Compressor clutch is defective if it does not engage.

4) Check continuity between Black/Red wire terminal of A/C-cut relay DLC and A/C-cut relay harness connector. Check continuity between Brown wire terminal of A/C-cut relay and compressor clutch harness connector. If continuity exists, go to next step. If continuity is not present, repair appropriate open circuit.

5) Check continuity between Black wire terminal of compressor clutch harness connector and engine ground. If continuity exists, A/C-cut relay is defective. If continuity does not exists, repair open circuit or poor ground.

6) Turn ignition off. Check A/C fuse in engine compartment fuse/relay block. If fuse is okay, check thermostat and A/C-cut relays. See RELAYS. If relays are okay, check continuity between dual-pressure switch terminals. If continuity is not present, replace dual-pressure switch. If continuity exists, go to next step.

7) Check A/C switch and blower switch. See SWITCHES. If switches are okay, start engine. Turn A/C on. Measure voltage at Brown wire terminal of dual-pressure switch and A/C switch harness connector. If battery voltage exists, go to next step. If battery voltage is not present, repair open circuit.

8) Measure voltage at Green/Blue wire terminal of thermostat relay harness connector. If battery voltage exists, go to next step. If battery voltage is not present, repair open circuit between dual-pressure switch and thermostat relay.

9) Measure voltage at Light Green/Yellow wire terminal of thermostat relay and electronic thermostat harness connector. If battery voltage exists, go to next step. If battery voltage is not present, repair open Light Green/Yellow wire between A/C switch and thermostat relay or electronic thermostat.

10) Ensure ignition is off. Check continuity between Green/Red wire terminal of thermostat relay and electronic thermostat harness connector. If continuity exists, go to next step. If continuity is not present, repair open circuit.

NOTE: Voltage to A/C-cut relay terminal No. 5 (Green/Yellow wire) is provided via terminal No. 3 (Green/Black wire).

11) Check continuity between Green/Black wire terminal of thermostat relay and A/C-cut relay harness connector. Check continuity between Green/Black wire terminal of thermostat relay harness connector and Green/Yellow wire terminal of A/C-cut relay harness connector. If continuity exists, go to next step. If continuity does not exist, repair appropriate open circuit.

12) Check A/C switch indicator light. If light is off, go to next step. If light is on, measure voltage at Green/Black wire and Blue/Yellow wire terminals of ECM harness connector. If battery voltage exists at each terminal, ECM is defective. If battery voltage is not present at any terminal, repair appropriate open circuit.

13) Ensure ignition is off. Check continuity between White wire terminal of A/C switch and blower switch harness connector. If continuity exists, go to next step. If continuity does not exist, repair open circuit.

14) Check continuity between Black wire terminal of blower switch and body ground. If continuity exists, go to next step. If continuity is not present, repair open circuit.

15) Check continuity between White wire terminal of electronic thermostat and blower switch harness connector. If continuity exists, electronic thermostat is defective. If continuity does not exist, repair open circuit.

Stylus – 1) Turn ignition on. Turn A/C and blower on. Measure voltage at Black wire terminal of compressor clutch harness connector. If battery voltage does not exist, go to next step. If battery voltage exists, check compressor clutch coil for open or short circuit. Replace compressor clutch if necessary. If clutch coil is okay, replace temperature sensor.

2) Disconnect triple-pressure switch 4-pin connector from receiver-drier. Measure voltage at Brown wire terminal of triple-pressure switch harness connector. If battery voltage exists, go to next step. If battery voltage is not present, repair open Brown wire between A/C-heater fuse (10-amp) and triple-pressure switch.

3) Check continuity between Brown wire and Green/White wire terminal of triple-pressure switch harness connector. If continuity exists, go to next step. If continuity does not exist, check refrigerant level. If refrigerant level is correct, replace defective triple-pressure switch.

4) Reconnect triple-pressure switch connector. Disconnect thermoswitch relay from engine compartment relay block. Measure voltage at Green/White wire terminal of thermoswitch relay harness connector. If battery voltage is present, go to next step. If battery voltage is not present, repair open Green/White wire between thermoswitch relay and triple-pressure switch.

5) Test thermoswitch relay. See RELAYS. If relay is okay, measure voltage between Light Green wire and Pink/Green wire terminal of thermoswitch relay harness connector. If voltage is about 10 volts, go to next step. If voltage is not about 10 volts, go to step **12)**.

6) Reconnect thermoswitch relay. Disconnect A/C compressor relay from engine compartment relay block. Measure voltage at Green/Orange wire terminal of compressor relay harness connector. If battery voltage exists, go to next step. If battery voltage is not present, repair open Green/Orange wire between compressor relay and thermoswitch relay.

7) Measure voltage between Brown wire and Gray/Red wire terminals of compressor relay harness connector. If battery voltage exists, go to next step. If battery voltage does not exist, go to step **9)**.

1993 MANUAL A/C-HEATER SYSTEMS
All Models (Cont.)

8) Turn ignition off. Check continuity between Green wire terminal of compressor relay harness connector and Black wire terminal of compressor clutch harness connector. If continuity exists, replace compressor relay. If continuity does not exist, repair open circuit.
9) Measure voltage at Brown wire terminal of compressor relay harness connector. If battery voltage is not present, repair open Brown wire between A/C-heater fuse and compressor relay. If battery voltage exists, go to next step on M/T models or step **17)** on A/T models.
10) Reconnect compressor relay. Measure voltage at Gray/Red wire terminal of ECM harness connector. If battery voltage exists, go to next step. If battery voltage is not present, repair open Gray/Red wire between ECM and compressor relay.
11) Measure voltage at Green/Orange wire of ECM harness connector. If battery voltage exists, replace defective ECM. If battery voltage is not present, repair open Green/Orange wire between ECM and thermoswitch relay.
12) Check A/C switch indicator light. If light is on, go to next step. If light is off, disconnect A/C switch 3-pin connector from A/C-heater control panel. Measure voltage at Brown wire terminal of A/C switch harness connector. If battery voltage exists, replace defective A/C switch. If battery voltage is not present, repair open Brown wire between A/C-heater fuse (10-amp) and A/C switch.
13) Measure voltage at Light Green wire terminal of thermoswitch relay harness connector. If battery voltage exists, go to next step. If battery voltage is not present, repair open Light Green wire between thermoswitch relay and A/C switch.
14) Measure voltage at Light Green wire of electronic thermostat harness connector. If battery voltage exists, go to next step. If battery voltage is not present, repair open Light Green wire between electronic thermostat and A/C switch.
15) Reconnect thermoswitch relay. Measure voltage at Pink/Green wire terminal of electronic thermostat harness connector. If battery voltage is present, go to next step. If battery voltage is not present, repair open Pink/Green wire between electronic thermostat and thermoswitch relay.
16) Turn ignition off. Check continuity between Green/Yellow wire terminal of electronic thermostat and blower switch harness connector. Check continuity between Green/Yellow wire terminal of electronic thermostat and A/C switch harness connector. If continuity exists, replace defective electronic thermostat. If continuity is not present, repair appropriate open circuit.
17) Measure voltage between Green/Orange wire and Black wire (ground) terminals of A/C-cut control unit. If battery voltage exists, go to step **19)**. If battery voltage does not exist, go to next step.
18) Measure voltage at Green/Orange wire terminal of A/C-cut control unit harness connector. If battery voltage exists, repair poor ground connection or open Black wire between A/C-cut control unit and body ground.
19) Measure voltage at Orange/Blue wire terminal of A/C-cut control unit harness connector. If battery voltage exists, go to next step. If battery voltage is not present, repair open Orange/Blue wire between A/C-cut control unit and ECM.
20) Reconnect compressor relay. Measure voltage at Gray/Red wire terminal of ECM harness connector. If battery voltage is not present, repair open Gray/Red wire between compressor relay and ECM. If battery voltage exists, replace defective ECM, and check A/C compressor diode for short or open circuit. See A/C DIODE.
Trooper – 1) Check A/C fuse (7.5-amp) in engine compartment fuse/relay block and blower fuse (25-amp) in dash fuse block. Replace fuses if blown and check for short circuits. Check blower motor, thermostat and A/C compressor relays. See RELAYS. Replace relays as necessary.
2) If relays are okay, disconnect dual-pressure switch from receiver-drier. Check continuity between dual-pressure switch terminals. If continuity is not present, check refrigerant level. If refrigerant level is correct, replace dual-pressure switch. If continuity is present, check A/C switch and blower switch. See SWITCHES. Replace switch(es) as necessary.
3) If switches are okay, start engine. Turn A/C and blower on. Check voltage at Black wire terminal of compressor clutch harness connector. If battery voltage is not present, go to next step. If battery voltage is present, check compressor clutch coil for open or short circuit. Replace compressor clutch if necessary. If coil is okay, compressor clutch circuit is okay.
4) Check voltage at Brown wire terminal of dual-pressure switch harness connector. If battery voltage exists, go to next step. If battery voltage does not exist, repair open Brown wire between A/C fuse and dual-pressure switch.
5) Disconnect thermostat relay. Check voltage at Green/White wire terminal of thermostat relay connector. If battery voltage exists, go to next step. If battery voltage does not exist. repair open Green/White wire between dual-pressure switch and thermostat relay.
6) Check voltage between Light Green wire and Pink/Green wire terminals of thermostat relay harness connector. If voltage is not about 10 volts, go to step **13)**. If voltage is about 10 volts, go to next step.
7) Reconnect thermostat relay. Disconnect A/C compressor relay. Check voltage at Green/Orange wire terminal of A/C compressor clutch harness connector. If battery voltage exists, go to next step. If battery voltage is not present, repair open Green/Orange wire between thermostat relay and A/C compressor relay.
8) Ensure ignition is off. Check continuity between Green wire terminal of A/C compressor relay harness connector and Black wire terminal of compressor clutch harness connector. If continuity exists, go to next step. If continuity is not present, repair open circuit.
9) Turn ignition on. Check voltage between Brown wire terminal and Gray/Yellow wire terminal of compressor relay harness connector. If battery voltage is not present, go to step **11)**. If battery voltage exists, go to next step.
10) Check voltage at Gray/Yellow wire terminal of ECM harness connector. If battery voltage exists, ECM is defective. If battery voltage is not present, repair open Gray/Yellow wire between A/C compressor relay and ECM.
11) Check voltage at Brown wire terminal of compressor relay harness connector. If battery voltage exists, go to next step. If battery voltage is not present, repair open Brown wire between A/C fuse and compressor relay.
12) Check continuity between Green/Orange wire terminal of thermostat relay and ECM harness connector. If continuity exists, ECM is defective. If continuity is not present, repair open circuit.
13) Check voltage at Light Green wire terminal of thermostat relay connector. If battery voltage exists, go to step **15)**. If battery voltage does not exist, go to next step.
14) Check voltage at Brown wire terminal of A/C switch. If battery voltage exists, repair open Light Green wire between A/C switch and thermostat relay. If battery voltage does not exist, repair open Brown wire between A/C fuse and A/C switch.
15) Reconnect thermostat relay. Check voltage at Light Green wire terminal of electronic thermostat harness connector. If battery voltage exists, go to next step. If battery voltage does not exist, repair open Light Green wire between A/C switch and electronic thermostat.
16) Check voltage at Pink/Green wire terminal of electronic thermostat harness connector. If voltage is about 10 volts, go to next step. If voltage is not about 10 volts, repair open Pink/Green wire between thermostat relay and electronic thermostat.
17) Check continuity between Green/Yellow wire terminal of electronic thermostat and blower switch harness connector. If continuity exists, electronic thermostat is defective. If continuity is not present, repair poor ground in blower switch or open Green/Yellow wire electronic thermostat and blower switch.

CONDENSER FAN INOPERATIVE

Rodeo V6 (A/T) – 1) Check A/C system operation. Service A/C system if necessary. Check condenser fan fuse (30-amp) in engine compartment fuse/relay block. Replace if necessary. Check condenser fan relay. See RELAYS. Replace relay if necessary.

1993 MANUAL A/C-HEATER SYSTEMS
All Models (Cont.)

2) If relay is okay, connect positive battery terminal to Blue wire terminal of condenser fan motor. Connect negative battery terminal to Black wire terminal of condenser fan motor. If condenser fan operates, go to next step. If condenser fan does not operate, replace defective motor.
3) Test triple-pressure switch. See SWITCHES. Replace if necessary. If pressure switch is okay, disconnect condenser fan relay. Measure voltage at Blue/Orange wire terminal of condenser fan relay harness connector. If battery voltage exists, go to next step. If battery voltage does not exist, repair open Blue/Orange wire between condenser fan fuse and condenser fan relay.
4) Turn A/C on. Measure voltage at Light Green/Yellow wire terminal of triple-pressure switch harness connector. If battery voltage exists, go to next step. If battery voltage is not present, repair open Light Green/Yellow wire between A/C switch and triple-pressure switch.
5) Turn A/C off. Check continuity between Pink/White wire terminal of triple-pressure switch and condenser fan relay harness connector. If continuity exists, go to next step. If continuity does not exist, repair open Pink/White wire.
6) Check continuity between Blue wire terminal of condenser fan relay and condenser fan motor harness connector. If continuity is not present, repair open Blue wire. If continuity exists, repair open Black wire between body ground and condenser fan relay or condenser fan motor.
Stylus – **1)** Remove condenser fan relay from engine compartment fuse/relay block. Test condenser fan relay. See RELAYS. Replace if necessary. If relay is okay, disconnect condenser fan motor 2-pin connector.
2) Check continuity between Blue wire terminal of condenser fan motor and condenser fan relay harness connector. If continuity exists, go to next step. If continuity does not exist, repair open Blue wire.
3) Check continuity of Blue/Black wire between condenser fan motor harness connector and ground. If continuity exists, go to next step. If continuity does not exist, repair open Blue/Black wire or poor ground connection.
4) Reconnect condenser fan motor connector. Disconnect Engine Coolant Temperature (ECT) switch 2-pin connector, located at lower left rear of radiator. Disconnect triple-pressure switch connector, located on receiver-drier.
5) Check continuity of White wire between condenser fan relay and triple-pressure switch harness connectors. Check continuity of White wire between condenser fan relay and ECT switch harness connectors. If continuity exists, go to next step. If continuity is not present, repair appropriate open White wire.
6) Check continuity of Black wire between triple-pressure switch harness connector and ground. Check continuity of Black wire between ECT switch harness connector and ground. If continuity exists in each test, go to next step. If continuity is not present in any test, repair open circuit or poor ground connection.
7) Turn ignition on. Measure voltage at Blue/Orange wire terminal of condenser fan relay harness connector. If battery voltage exists, go to next step. If battery voltage is not present, replace blown A/C condenser fan fuse, or repair open Blue/Orange wire between condenser fan relay and condenser fan fuse.
8) Measure voltage at White/Red wire terminal of condenser fan relay harness connector. If battery voltage exists, go to next step. If battery voltage is not present, replace defective restart relay, or repair open White/Red wire between restart relay and condenser fan relay.
9) Connect jumper wire between Blue/Orange wire and Blue wire terminals of condenser fan relay harness connector. If condenser fan does not run, replace defective condenser fan motor. If condenser fan runs, check triple-pressure switch and ECT switch. See SWITCHES. Replace if necessary.

CONDENSER FAN RUNS CONTINUOUSLY

Rodeo – Check triple pressure switch and condenser fan relay. See SWITCHES and RELAYS. Replace if necessary.
Stylus – **1)** Remove condenser fan relay from engine compartment fuse/relay block. Test condenser fan relay. See RELAYS. Replace if necessary. If relay is okay, disconnect triple-pressure switch 4-pin connector on receiver-drier.
2) Check continuity between White wire and Black wire terminals of triple-pressure switch harness connector. If continuity does not exist, go to next step. If continuity exists, replace defective triple-pressure switch.
3) Disconnect Engine Coolant Temperature (ECT) switch connector from radiator. Check continuity between ECT switch harness connector terminals. If continuity exists, replace defective ECT switch. If continuity does not exist, go to next step.
4) Check White wire between condenser fan relay and triple-pressure switch, and White wire between condenser fan relay and ECT switch for short circuit. Repair appropriate wire as necessary.

A/C COMPRESSOR DIODE

Stylus – Remove A/C compressor diode from engine compartment relay block. Set analog volt-ohmmeter in ohms mode. Connect positive ohmmeter lead to diode terminal No. 4 and negative ohmmeter lead to terminal No. 3. *See Fig. 2.* Ohmmeter should indicate continuity. Reverse ohmmeter leads, and ensure continuity does not exist. Replace diode if continuity is not as specified.
Trooper – Remove diode from engine compartment fuse/relay block. Using ohmmeter, connect test leads to diode terminals, and check continuity. Reverse leads on diode terminals, and check continuity. Continuity should exist in only one direction. If continuity is not as specified, replace diode.

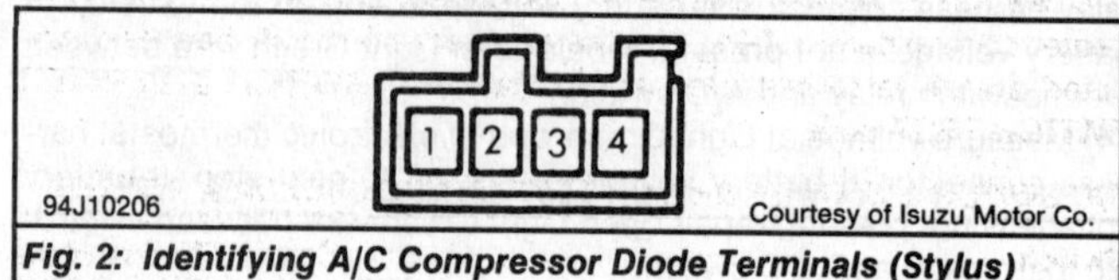
1
2
3
4
94J10206
Courtesy of Isuzu Motor Co.

Fig. 2: Identifying A/C Compressor Diode Terminals (Stylus)

RELAYS

5-Pin Relay – **1)** Remove relay from engine compartment fuse/relay block. Check continuity between terminals No. 1 and 2. *See Fig. 3.* Continuity should exist. Check continuity between terminals No. 1 and 3. Continuity should not exist.
2) Apply battery voltage between terminals No. 4 and 5. Ensure continuity does not exist between terminals No. 1 and 2 with voltage applied. Continuity should exist between terminals No. 1 and 3 with voltage applied. Replace relay if continuity is not as specified.
4-Pin Relay – **1)** Disconnect relay to be tested. Using ohmmeter, check continuity between relay terminals No. 3 and 4 (Amigo, Pickup and Rodeo), or 2 and 4 (Stylus and Trooper). *See Fig. 4.* Continuity should not exist.
2) Check continuity between terminals No. 1 and 2 (Amigo, Pickup and Rodeo), or 1 and 3 (Stylus and Trooper). Ensure continuity exists. Apply battery voltage between terminals No. 1 and 2 (Amigo, Pickup and Rodeo), or 1 and 3 (Stylus and Trooper). With voltage applied ensure continuity exists between terminals No. 3 and 4 (Amigo, Pickup and Rodeo), or 2 and 4 (Stylus and Trooper). Replace relay if continuity is not as specified.

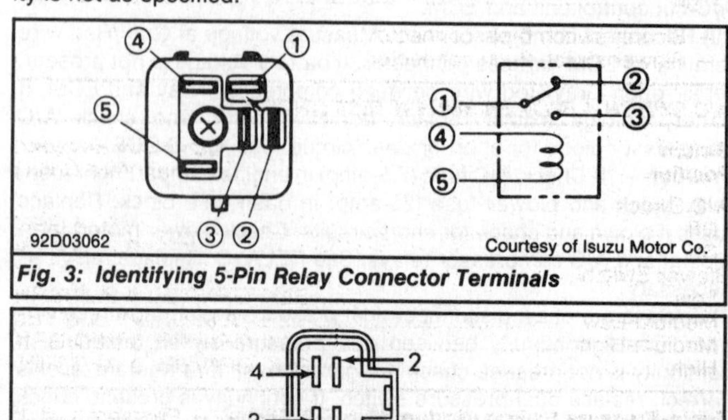
④
①
⑤
③
②
②
①
③
④
⑤
92D03062
Courtesy of Isuzu Motor Co.

Fig. 3: Identifying 5-Pin Relay Connector Terminals

4
2
3
1
94A10215
Courtesy of Isuzu Motor Co.

Fig. 4: Identifying 4-Pin Connector Terminals

1993 MANUAL A/C-HEATER SYSTEMS
All Models (Cont.)

ELECTRONIC THERMOSTAT

Amigo, Pickup, Rodeo & Trooper – Remove thermosensor from evaporator. Start engine. Turn A/C and blower on. Check continuity between indicated thermostat relay harness connector terminals. See ELECTRONIC THERMOSTAT CONTINUITY TEST table. Replace electronic thermostat if it does not test as specified.

ELECTRONIC THERMOSTAT CONTINUITY TEST

Application & Temperature °F (°C)	Terminal No. [1]	Continuity
4-Pin Relay		
Less Than 37-39 (3-4)	3 & 4 [2]	[3] No
Greater Than 40-42 (4.5-5.5)	3 & 4 [2]	[4] Yes
5-Pin Relay		
Less Than 37-39 (3-4)	1 & 3	[3] No
Greater Than 40-42 (4.5-5.5)	1 & 3	[4] Yes

[1] – *See Fig. 3 or 4* for terminal identification.
[2] – On Trooper, check between terminals No. 2 and 4.
[3] – Relay off.
[4] – Relay on.

SWITCHES

A/C Switch & Blower Switch – Disconnect connectors from A/C-heater control panel. Using ohmmeter, check continuity between indicated switch terminals. See appropriate A/C SWITCH & BLOWER SWITCH TEST table.

A/C SWITCH & BLOWER SWITCH TEST (AMIGO, PICKUP & RODEO)

Switch Position	Continuity Between Terminal (Wire Color)
A/C Switch	
Off	[1] LT GRN/YEL & WHT
On	BRN, [1] LT GRN/YEL & WHT
Blower Switch	
Low	[2] BLK & WHT; [3] BLK & BLU/WHT
Medium-Low	[2] BLK & WHT; [3] BLK & LT GRN/BLK
Medium-High	[2] BLK & WHT; [3] BLK & BLU/ORG
High	[2] BLK & WHT; [3] BLK & BLU/RED

[1] – LT GRN/RED on Rodeo V6.
[2] – Blower switch 6-pin connector.
[3] – Blower switch 2-pin connector.

A/C SWITCH & BLOWER SWITCH TEST (STYLUS)

Switch Position	Continuity Between Terminal (Wire Color)
A/C Switch	
Off	LT GRN & GRN/YEL
On	BRN, LT GRN & GRN/YEL
Blower Switch	
Low	[1] BLK & GRN/YEL; [2] BLK & BLU/WHT
Medium-Low	[1] BLK & GRN/YEL; [2] BLK & BLU/YEL
Medium-High	[1] BLK & GRN/YEL; [2] BLK & BLU/ORG
High	[1] BLK & GRN/YEL; [2] BLK & BLU/RED

[1] – Blower switch 6-pin connector.
[2] – Blower switch 2-pin connector.

A/C SWITCH & BLOWER SWITCH TEST (TROOPER)

Switch Position	Continuity Between Terminal (Wire Color)
A/C Switch	
Off	YEL & GRN
On	YEL, BLU & GRN
Blower Switch	
Low	BLK, GRN/YEL & BLU/GRN
Medium-Low	BLK, GRN/YEL & YEL
Medium-High	BLK, GRN/YEL & RED/GRN
High	BLK, GRN/YEL & WHT/RED

Triple-Pressure Switch (Rodeo V6 A/T & Stylus) – Pressure switch controls condenser fan and compressor relays. Check continuity between indicated switch terminals. See appropriate TRIPLE-PRESSURE SWITCH TEST table. Replace switch if it does not test as specified.

TRIPLE-PRESSURE SWITCH TEST (RODEO V6 A/T)

Test Condition	Terminal No. [1]	Continuity
A/C Off [2]	1 & 2	Yes
	3 & 4	No
A/C On [3]		
199-227 psi (14.0-16.0 kg/cm²)	3 & 4	[4] Yes
142-170 psi (10.0-12.0 kg/cm²)	3 & 4	[5] No

[1] – *See Fig. 5* for terminal identification.
[2] – With triple-pressure switch disconnected.
[3] – With triple-pressure switch connected.
[4] – Condenser fan on.
[5] – Condenser fan off.

TRIPLE-PRESSURE SWITCH TEST (STYLUS)

Test Condition	Terminal No. [1]	Continuity
A/C Off [2]	1 & 2	Yes
	3 & 4	No
A/C On [3]		
199-227 psi (14.0-16.0 kg/cm²)	3 & 4	[4] Yes

[1] – *See Fig. 5* for terminal identification.
[2] – With triple-pressure switch disconnected.
[3] – With triple-pressure switch connected.
[4] – Condenser fan on.

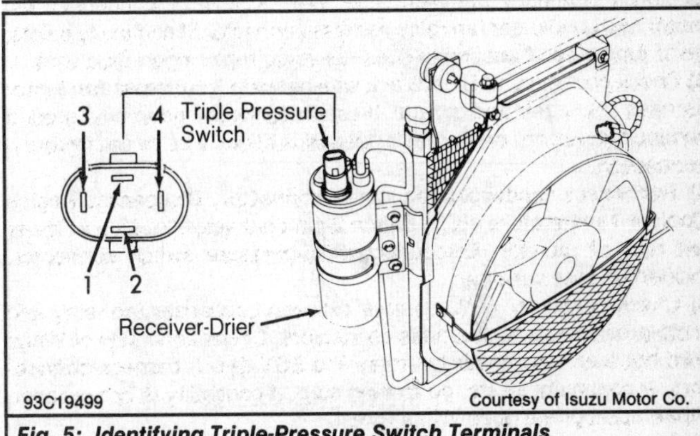
3
4
Triple Pressure Switch
1
2
Receiver-Drier
93C19499
Courtesy of Isuzu Motor Co.
Fig. 5: Identifying Triple-Pressure Switch Terminals (Stylus Shown; Rodeo Similar)

REMOVAL & INSTALLATION

WARNING: To avoid injury from accidental air bag deployment, read and carefully follow all SERVICE PRECAUTIONS and DISABLING & ACTIVATING AIR BAG SYSTEM procedures in AIR BAG SYSTEM SAFETY article in GENERAL SERVICING.

NOTE: For heater system component removal and installation procedures, refer to HEATER SYSTEM article.

EVAPORATOR ASSEMBLY

Removal (Amigo, Pickup, Rodeo & Trooper) – **1)** Obtain radio anti-theft protection code from owner before disconnecting battery cable. Disconnect negative battery cable.

2) Discharge A/C system using approved refrigerant recovery/recycling equipment. Remove glove box. On Amigo, Pickup and Rodeo, remove center console. On Trooper, remove ECM cover.

3) On all models, remove speaker cover. Remove air duct/instrument panel reinforcement. Mark and remove wiring harness connectors as necessary. Remove drain hose from evaporator case. Disconnect and plug refrigerant lines at evaporator core. Carefully remove evaporator assembly.

1993 MANUAL A/C-HEATER SYSTEMS
All Models (Cont.)

Installation – If installing a new evaporator, add 1.7 ounces of compressor oil. On Amigo, Pickup and Rodeo, ensure White mark on drain hose is facing up. DO NOT reuse "O" rings. Coat "O" rings with new compressor oil before installing. To complete installation, reverse removal procedure.

Removal (Stylus) – **1)** Disconnect negative battery cable. Discharge A/C system using approved refrigerant recovery/recycling equipment. Drain cooling system. Remove drain hose from evaporator case. Remove glove box.

2) Remove A/C-cut control unit connector (A/T). Remove instrument panel reinforcement bracket. Disconnect evaporator thermosensor and resistor connectors. Remove refrigerant line clamp. Disconnect and plug refrigerant lines at evaporator core. Carefully remove evaporator assembly.

Installation – To install, reverse removal procedure. If installing a new evaporator, add 1.7 ounces of compressor oil. Ensure White mark on drain hose is facing up.

EVAPORATOR CORE

Removal & Installation (Amigo, Pickup, Rodeo & Trooper) – **1)** Remove evaporator assembly. See EVAPORATOR ASSEMBLY. Remove clips and screws from evaporator housing. Separate upper and lower evaporator housing. *See Fig. 6.*

2) Remove evaporator core. To install, reverse removal procedure. DO NOT reuse "O" rings. Coat "O" rings with compressor oil before installing. Apply adhesive to evaporator lining. If installing new evaporator core, add 1.7 ounces of refrigerant oil to new core.

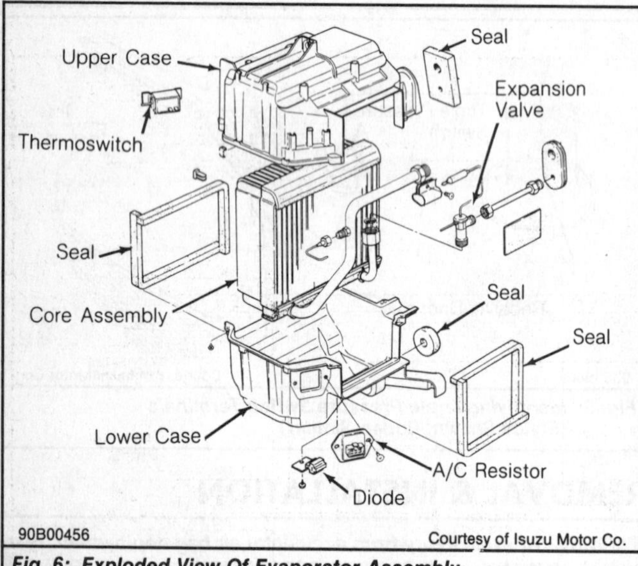
Upper Case
Seal
Expansion Valve
Thermoswitch
Seal
Seal
Core Assembly
Seal
Lower Case
A/C Resistor
Diode
90B00456
Courtesy of Isuzu Motor Co.

Fig. 6: Exploded View Of Evaporator Assembly (Amigo, Pickup, Rodeo & Trooper)

Removal & Installation (Stylus) – **1)** Remove evaporator assembly. See EVAPORATOR ASSEMBLY. Disconnect clips and screws. Separate upper and lower evaporator housing (case). *See Fig. 7.* Remove evaporator core.

2) To install, reverse removal procedure. Apply adhesive to evaporator lining. If installing new evaporator core, add 1.7 ounces of refrigerant oil to new core.

COMPRESSOR

Removal (Except Pickup V6 & Stylus) – **1)** Disconnect negative battery cable. Discharge A/C system using approved refrigerant recovery/recycling equipment. On 4-cylinder Amigo, Pickup and Rodeo, remove power steering pump with hoses attached. Remove power steering pump bracket. On Rodeo V6 and Trooper, remove radiator fan shroud and radiator fan. Temporarily tighten fan nuts to original positions.

2) On all models, remove compressor clutch harness connector. Loosen idler pulley center nut and tension adjustment bolt. Remove

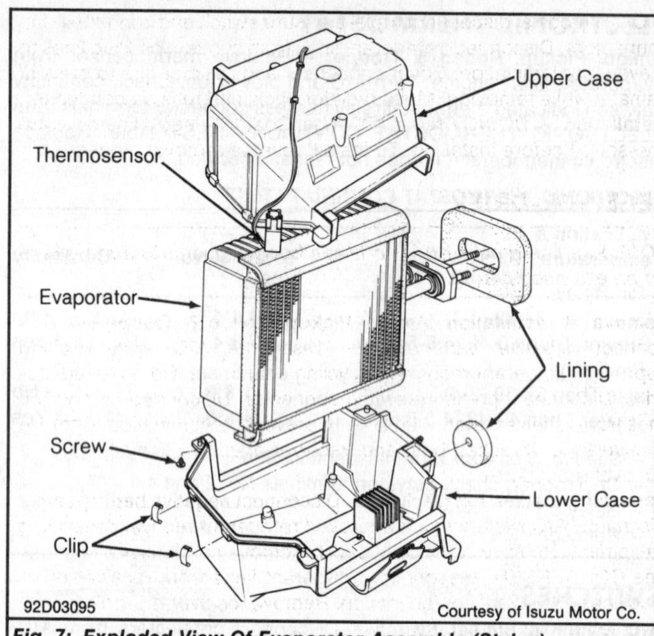
Upper Case
Thermosensor
Evaporator
Lining
Screw
Lower Case
Clip
92D03095
Courtesy of Isuzu Motor Co.

Fig. 7: Exploded View Of Evaporator Assembly (Stylus)

drive belt. Remove refrigerant line connector and plug lines to prevent contamination. Remove compressor.

Installation – Install compressor. Install refrigerant line connector and new "O" rings. Coat "O" rings with new compressor oil before installing. Install drive belt. Apply 22 lbs. (9.98 kg) to drive belt, and tighten tension adjustment bolt until drive belt deflection is .4 inch (10 mm). To complete installation, reverse removal procedure.

Removal (Pickup V6) – Disconnect negative battery cable. Discharge A/C system using approved refrigerant recovery/recycling equipment. Remove compressor clutch harness connector. Remove drive belt and dynamic damper. Remove refrigerant line connector and plug lines to prevent contamination. Remove compressor bracket with compressor.

Installation – DO NOT reuse seal washers. Coat seal washers with new compressor oil before installing. To install, reverse removal procedure.

Removal (Stylus) – **1)** Disconnect negative battery cable. Discharge A/C system using approved refrigerant recovery/recycling equipment. On models with power steering, remove engine undercover.

2) On all models, remove compressor clutch harness connector. Remove refrigerant line connector and plug lines to prevent contamination. Remove drive belt and compressor.

Installation – DO NOT reuse "O" rings. Coat "O" rings with NEW compressor oil before installing. To install, reverse removal procedure. Adjust drive belt tension to 130-160 lbs (59-72).

CONDENSER

Removal (Amigo, Pickup, Rodeo & Trooper) – **1)** Disconnect negative battery cable. Discharge A/C system using approved refrigerant recovery/recycling equipment. Remove radiator grille. On Trooper, remove front bumper. On all models, remove hood stay bracket. On Amigo and Pickup, scribe mating marks and remove engine hood lock.

2) On all models, remove pressure switch connector. Disconnect refrigerant lines from condenser. Plug lines to prevent contamination. Carefully remove condenser to prevent damage. To install, reverse removal procedure.

Installation – If installing a new condenser, add one ounce of compressor oil. DO NOT reuse "O" rings. Coat "O" rings with compressor oil before installing. To complete installation, reverse removal procedure.

Removal (Stylus) – **1)** Disconnect negative battery cable. Discharge A/C system using approved refrigerant recovery/recycling equipment. Remove radiator support. On 1.8L engines, remove engine hood lock.

1993 MANUAL A/C-HEATER SYSTEMS
All Models (Cont.)

2) On all models, disconnect triple-pressure switch and condenser fan connectors. Disconnect refrigerant lines from condenser. Plug lines to prevent contamination. Cover condenser and radiator fins to prevent damage while removing. Move radiator back, and remove condenser.
Installation – DO NOT reuse "O" rings. Coat "O" rings with new compressor oil before installing. To install, reverse removal procedure.

RECEIVER-DRIER

NOTE: Replace receiver-drier if it has been exposed to atmosphere for an extended period.

Removal & Installation (Amigo, Pickup, Rodeo & Trooper) – Disconnect negative battery cable. Discharge A/C system using approved refrigerant recovery/recycling equipment. Remove radiator grille. Disconnect pressure switch connector. Disconnect refrigerant lines from receiver-drier. Plug lines to prevent contamination. Remove receiver-drier bracket bolt and receiver-drier. To install, reverse removal procedure.
Removal & Installation (Stylus) – Disconnect negative battery cable. Discharge A/C system using approved refrigerant recovery/recycling equipment. Remove radiator support. Remove condenser assembly. See CONDENSER. Disconnect refrigerant lines from receiver-drier. Plug lines to prevent contamination. Remove receiver-drier. To install, reverse removal procedure.

TORQUE SPECIFICATIONS

TORQUE SPECIFICATIONS

Application	Ft. Lbs. (N.m)
Compressor Bolt	
Pickup V6	35 (47)
Rodeo V6 & Trooper	14 (19)
All Others	29 (40)
Compressor Bracket Bolt	35 (47)
Compressor Refrigerant Line	
Connector Bolt	
Rodeo V6, Stylus & Trooper	11 (15)
All Others	20 (28)
Condenser Bolt	52 (6)
Evaporator Refrigerant Line Nut	
Stylus	13 (18)
Idler Pulley Center Nut	
Rodeo V6 & Trooper	31 (42)
Refrigerant Inlet Line	
Condenser (Except Stylus)	11 (15)
Evaporator (Except Stylus)	11 (15)
Refrigerant Outlet Line	
Evaporator (Except Stylus)	18 (25)
	INCH Lbs. (N.m)
Condenser Bolts	52 (6)
Receiver-Drier Refrigerant Line	
Connector Bolt	52 (6)
Refrigerant Inlet Line	
Condenser (Stylus)	(104) 12
Refrigerant Outlet Line	
Condenser (All Models)	52 (6)

WIRING DIAGRAMS

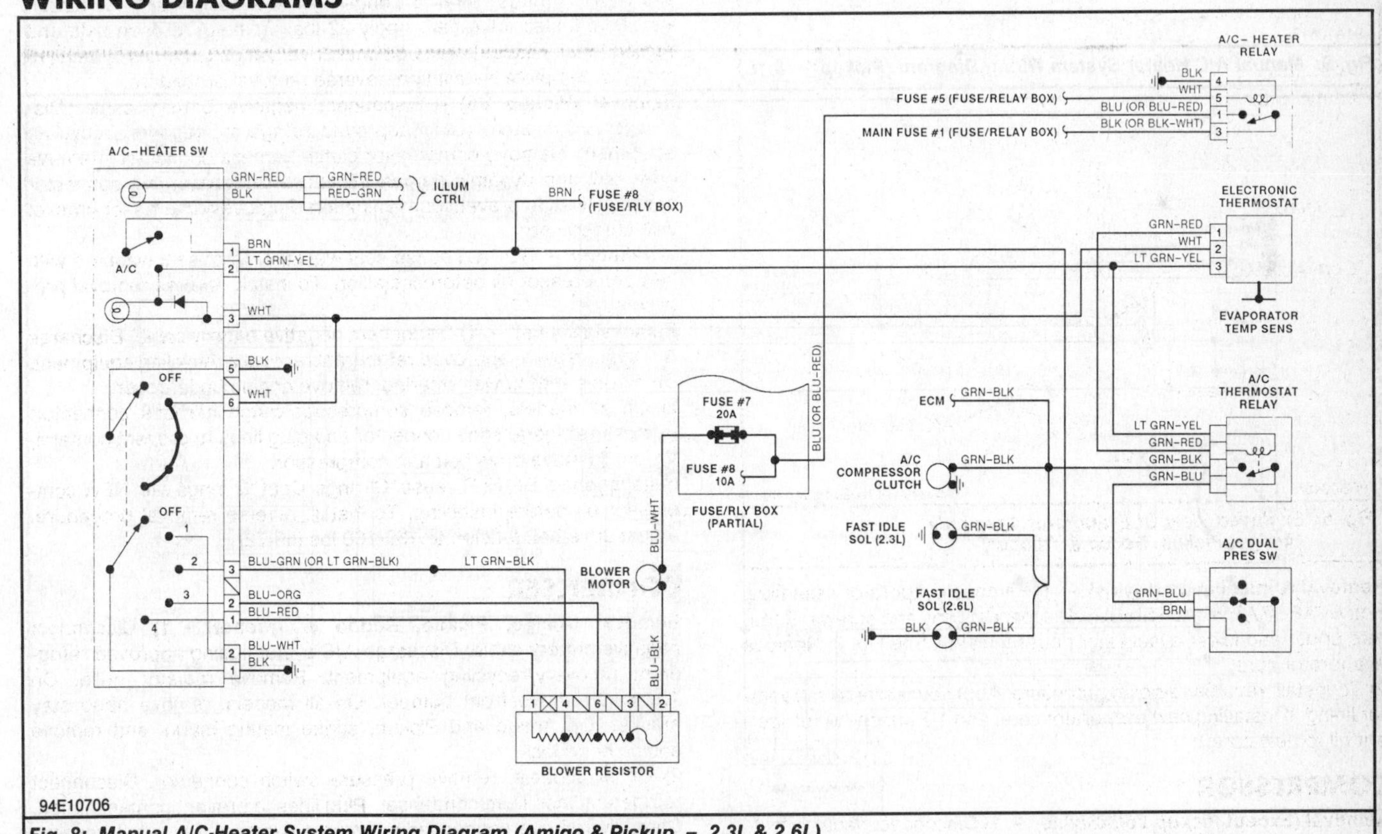
A/C- HEATER RELAY
BLK
WHT
FUSE #5 (FUSE/RELAY BOX)
BLU (OR BLU-RED)
MAIN FUSE #1 (FUSE/RELAY BOX)
BLK (OR BLK-WHT)
A/C-HEATER SW
GRN-RED
BLK
RED-GRN
ILLUM CTRL
BRN
FUSE #8 (FUSE/RLY BOX)
ELECTRONIC THERMOSTAT
LT GRN-YEL
A/C
WHT
EVAPORATOR TEMP SENS
OFF
BLU (OR BLU-RED)
FUSE #7 20A
FUSE #8 10A
FUSE/RLY BOX (PARTIAL)
ECM
GRN-BLK
A/C THERMOSTAT RELAY
A/C COMPRESSOR CLUTCH
GRN-BLU
FAST IDLE SOL (2.3L)
A/C DUAL PRES SW
BLU-WHT
BLU-GRN (OR LT GRN-BLK)
LT GRN-BLK
BLOWER MOTOR
BLU-ORG
BLU-RED
FAST IDLE SOL (2.6L)
BLU-BLK
BLOWER RESISTOR
94E10706

Fig. 8: Manual A/C-Heater System Wiring Diagram (Amigo & Pickup – 2.3L & 2.6L)

1993 MANUAL A/C-HEATER SYSTEMS
All Models (Cont.)

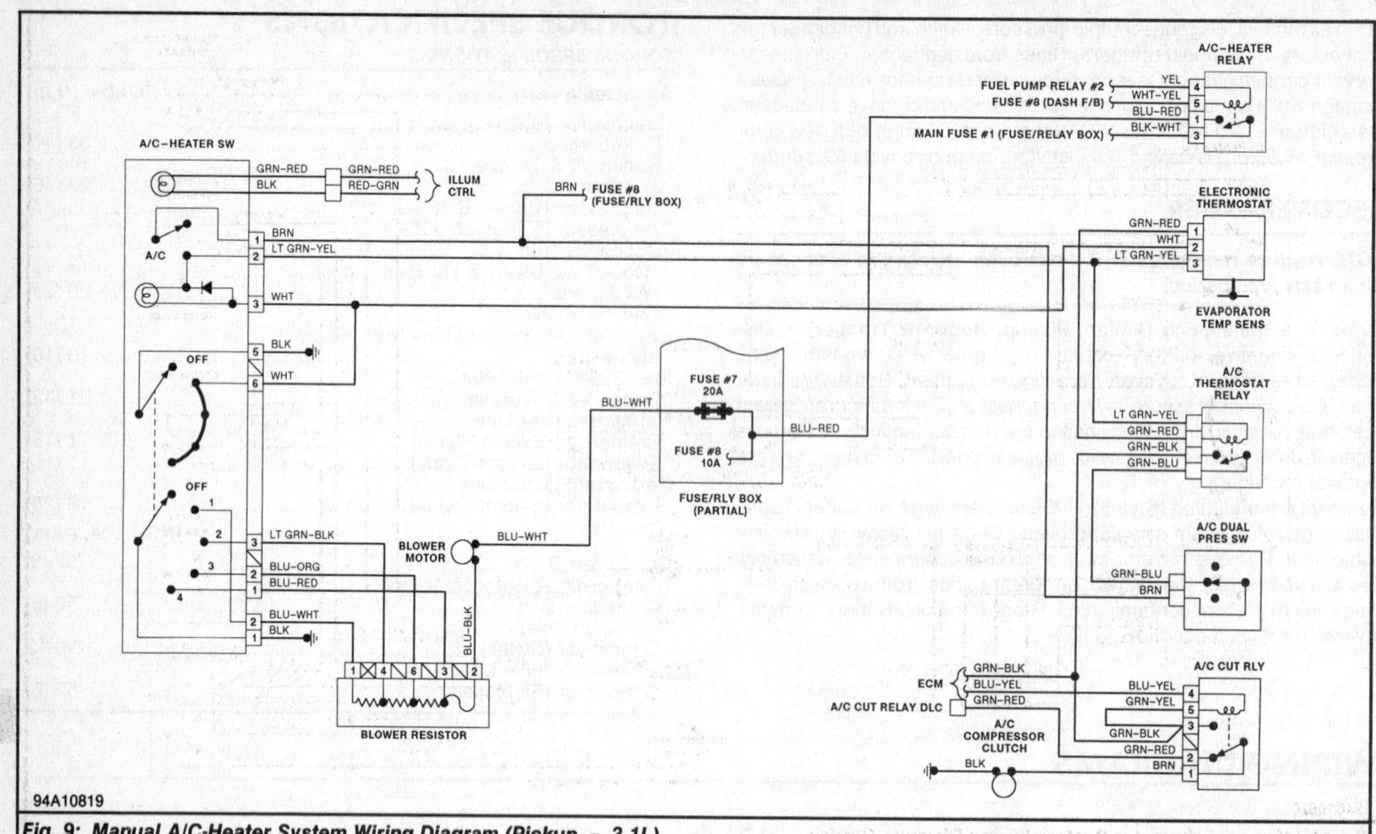
A/C-HEATER SW
GRN-RED
BLK
GRN-RED
RED-GRN
ILLUM CTRL
BRN
FUSE #8 (FUSE/RLY BOX)
A/C
BRN
LT GRN-YEL
WHT
BLK
OFF
WHT
FUSE #7 20A
BLU-WHT
BLU-RED
FUSE #8 10A
FUSE/RLY BOX (PARTIAL)
OFF
LT GRN-BLK
BLU-ORG
BLU-RED
BLU-WHT
BLK
BLOWER MOTOR
BLU-WHT
BLU-BLK
BLOWER RESISTOR
A/C-HEATER RELAY
FUEL PUMP RELAY #2
FUSE #8 (DASH F/B)
MAIN FUSE #1 (FUSE/RELAY BOX)
YEL
WHT-YEL
BLU-RED
BLK-WHT
ELECTRONIC THERMOSTAT
GRN-RED
WHT
LT GRN-YEL
EVAPORATOR TEMP SENS
A/C THERMOSTAT RELAY
LT GRN-YEL
GRN-RED
GRN-BLK
GRN-BLU
A/C DUAL PRES SW
GRN-BLU
BRN
ECM
GRN-BLK
BLU-YEL
GRN-RED
A/C CUT RELAY DLC
A/C COMPRESSOR CLUTCH
BLK
A/C CUT RLY
BLU-YEL
GRN-YEL
GRN-BLK
GRN-RED
BRN
94A10819

Fig. 9: Manual A/C-Heater System Wiring Diagram (Pickup - 3.1L)

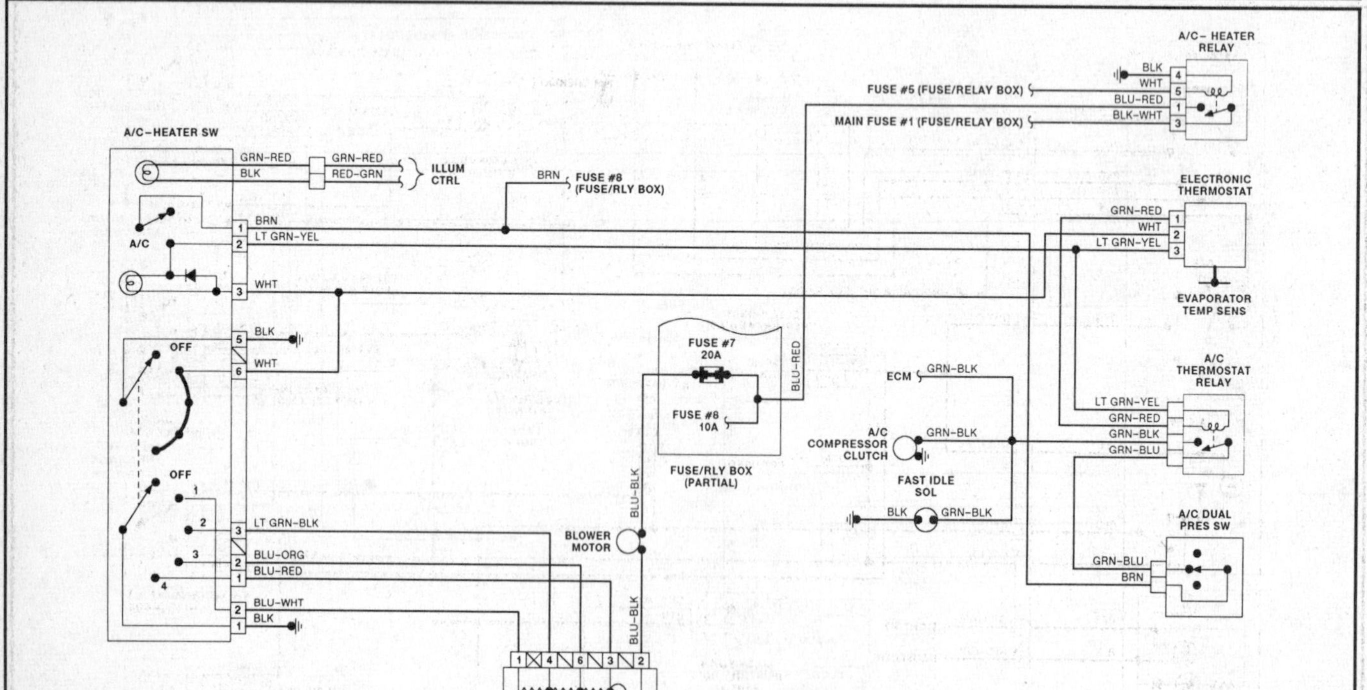

94F10707

Fig. 10: Manual A/C-Heater System Wiring Diagram (Rodeo - 2.6L)

1993 MANUAL A/C-HEATER SYSTEMS
All Models (Cont.)

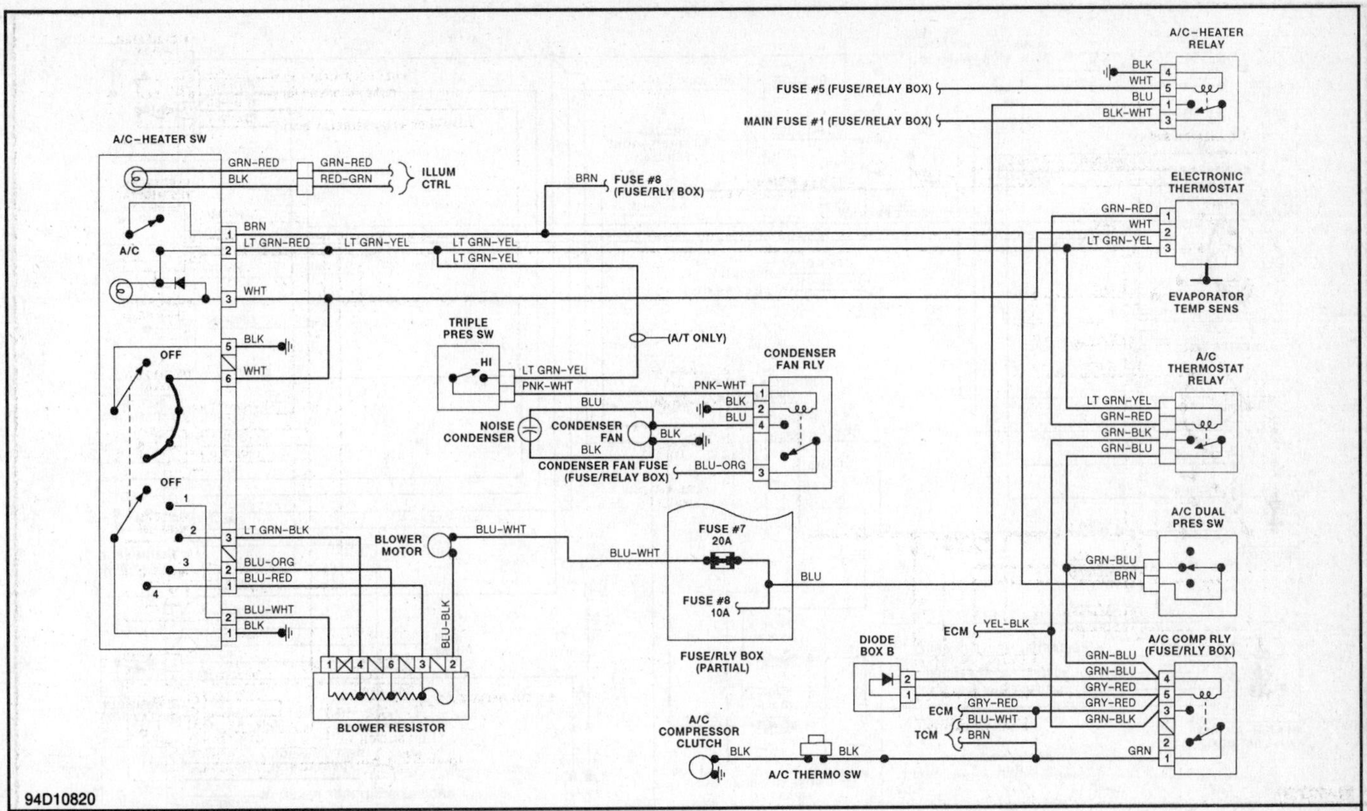

94D10820

Fig. 11: Manual A/C-Heater System Wiring Diagram (Rodeo – 3.2L)

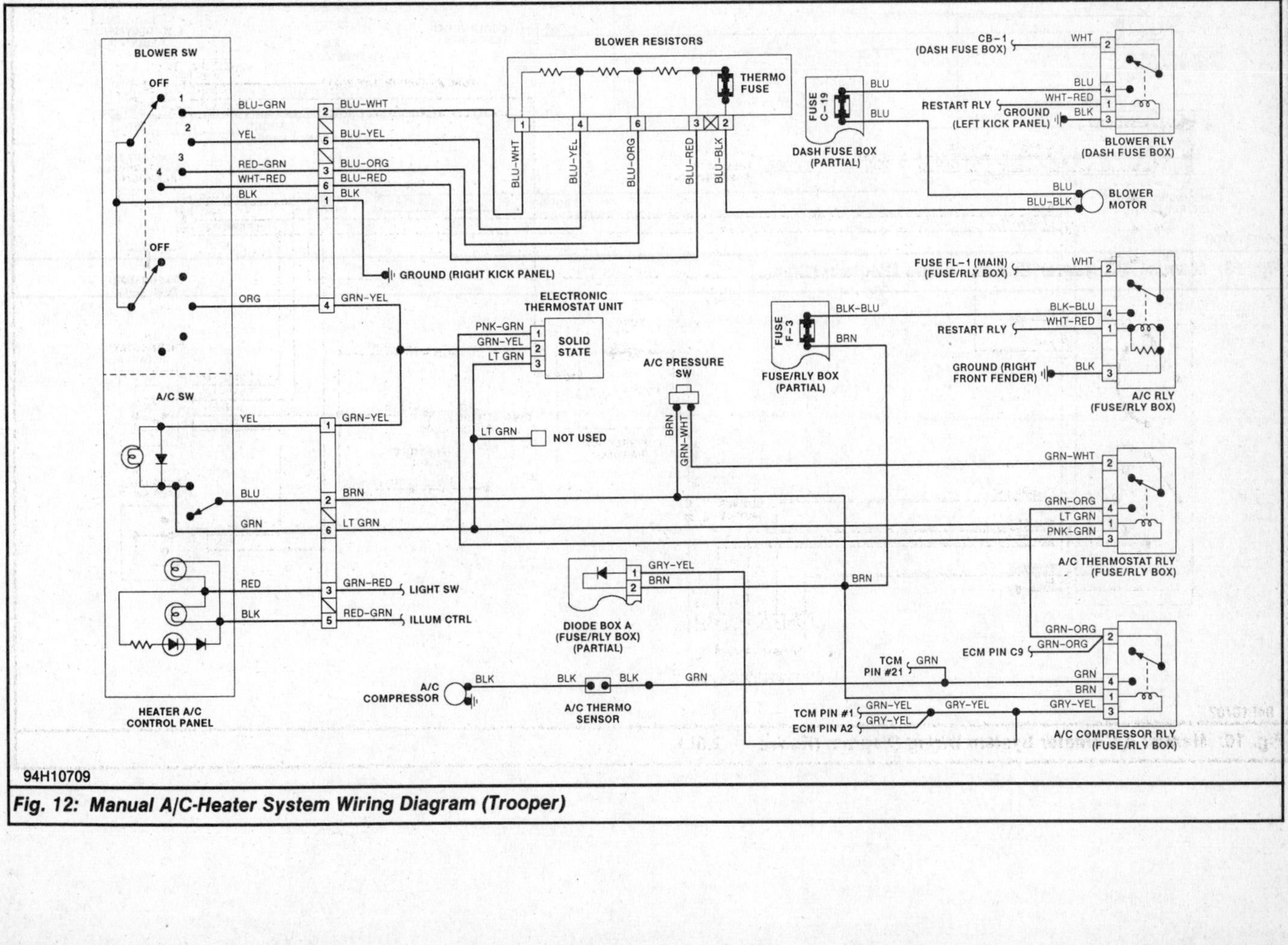

94H10709

Fig. 12: Manual A/C-Heater System Wiring Diagram (Trooper)

1993 MANUAL A/C-HEATER SYSTEMS
All Models (Cont.)

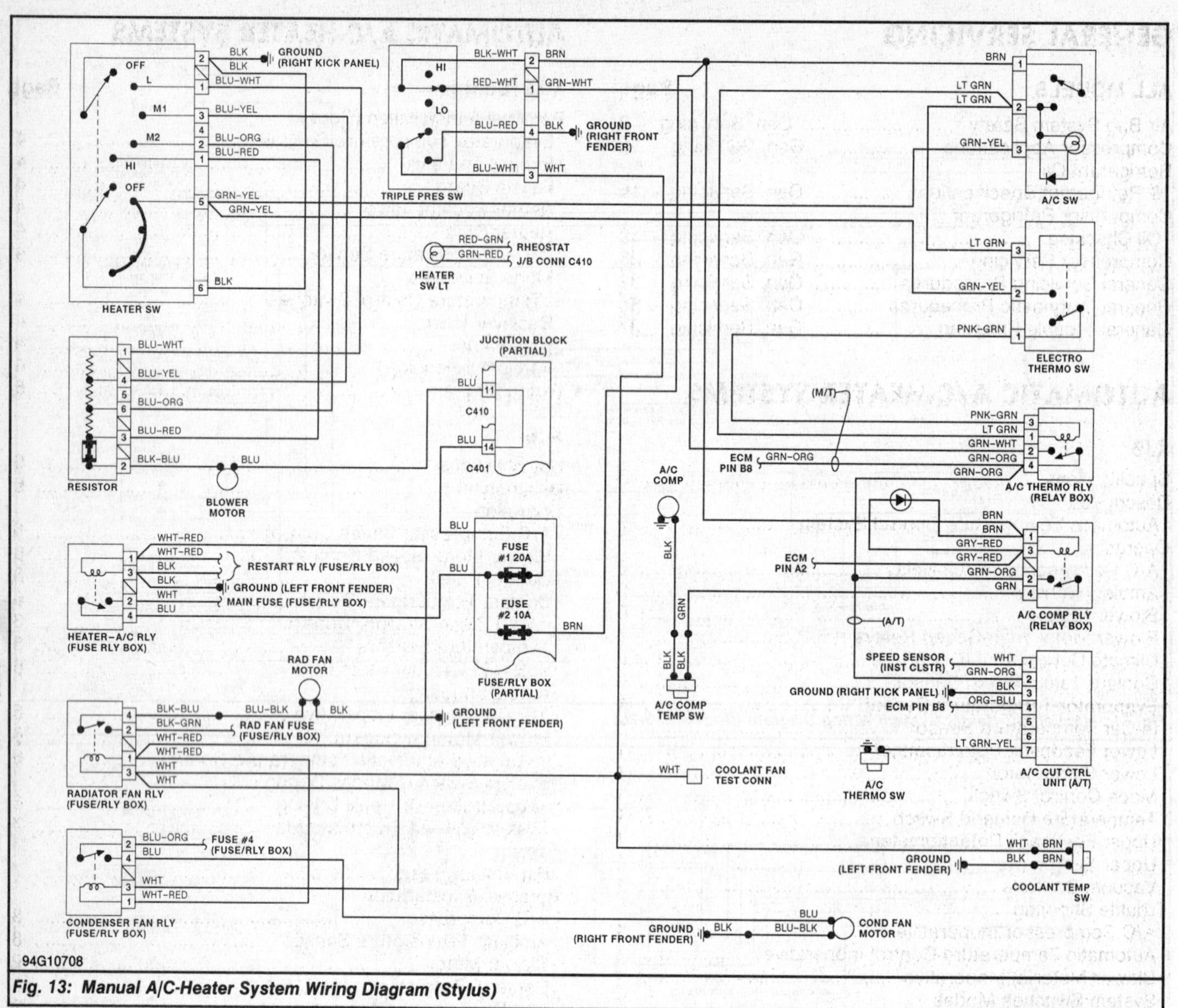
HEATER SW
OFF
L
M1
M2
HI
OFF
GROUND (RIGHT KICK PANEL)
BLK
BLU-WHT
BLU-YEL
BLU-ORG
BLU-RED
GRN-YEL
TRIPLE PRES SW
HI
LO
BLK-WHT
BRN
RED-WHT
GRN-WHT
BLU-RED
GROUND (RIGHT FRONT FENDER)
BLU-WHT
WHT
RED-GRN
GRN-RED
RHEOSTAT
J/B CONN C410
HEATER SW LT
JUCTION BLOCK (PARTIAL)
C410
C401
RESISTOR
BLK-BLU
BLU
BLOWER MOTOR
HEATER-A/C RLY (FUSE RLY BOX)
WHT-RED
RESTART RLY (FUSE/RLY BOX)
GROUND (LEFT FRONT FENDER)
MAIN FUSE (FUSE/RLY BOX)
FUSE #1 20A
FUSE #2 10A
FUSE/RLY BOX (PARTIAL)
RAD FAN MOTOR
BLU-BLK
BLK-GRN
RAD FAN FUSE (FUSE/RLY BOX)
GROUND (LEFT FRONT FENDER)
RADIATOR FAN RLY (FUSE/RLY BOX)
COOLANT FAN TEST CONN
BLU-ORG
FUSE #4 (FUSE/RLY BOX)
CONDENSER FAN RLY (FUSE/RLY BOX)
A/C SW
LT GRN
GRN-YEL
ELECTRO THERMO SW
PNK-GRN
(M/T)
ECM PIN B8
GRN-ORG
A/C COMP
A/C THERMO RLY (RELAY BOX)
GRN-WHT
ECM PIN A2
GRY-RED
GRN
A/C COMP RLY (RELAY BOX)
(A/T)
A/C COMP TEMP SW
SPEED SENSOR (INST CLSTR)
GROUND (RIGHT KICK PANEL)
ECM PIN B8
ORG-BLU
LT GRN-YEL
A/C THERMO SW
A/C CUT CTRL UNIT (A/T)
GROUND (LEFT FRONT FENDER)
COOLANT TEMP SW
GROUND (RIGHT FRONT FENDER)
COND FAN MOTOR
94G10708

Fig. 13: Manual A/C-Heater System Wiring Diagram (Stylus)

1993 JAGUAR CONTENTS

GENERAL SERVICING

AUTOMATIC A/C-HEATER SYSTEMS

AUTOMATIC A/C-HEATER SYSTEMS

1993 AUTOMATIC A/C-HEATER SYSTEMS XJS

SPECIFICATIONS

Compressor Type	Sanden SD-709 7-Cyl.
Compressor Belt Deflection (New) [1]	7/32" (5.6 mm)
Compressor Oil Capacity	4.6 ozs.
Refrigerant (R-12) Capacity	40 ozs.
System Operating Pressures [2]	
High Side	228 psi (16.0 kg/cm²)
Low Side	34 psi (2.4 kg/cm²)

[1] – With thumb pressure at belt center.
[2] – Pressure readings will vary depending on ambient temperature and humidity.

WARNING: To avoid injury from accidental air bag deployment, read and carefully follow all SERVICE PRECAUTIONS and DISABLING & ACTIVATING AIR BAG SYSTEM procedures in AIR BAG SYSTEM SAFETY article in GENERAL SERVICING.

DESCRIPTION

AUTOMATIC TEMPERATURE CONTROL SYSTEM

Temperature selection knob on automatic temperature control panel allows selection of temperature between 65°F (18°C) and 85°F (29°C). The mode control switch has 5 positions: off, LOW, "M" (normal), HIGH and defrost. Blower fan operates at a variable speed on any of the other settings except in HIGH & defrost positions. A slide lever controls air temperature delivered through face level vents without affecting automatic temperature setting.

The automatic temperature control uses in-car temperature sensors to compare vehicle interior temperature to temperature set on control panel. This comparison provides an electrical signal (negative or positive) to Climate Control Unit (CCU). The CCU sends electrical signals to a servomotor and blower speed relays mounted on heater box, changing heater box air door position and blower speed to maintain interior temperature.

OPERATION

A/C COMPRESSOR CLUTCH RELAY

A/C compressor clutch is engaged or disengaged through compressor clutch relay. A/C compressor clutch is energized by battery voltage when compressor clutch relay is closed (energized) by a voltage signal from CCU center connector pin No. 5 (Green/White wire).

AMBIENT SENSOR

Ambient sensor, located in right side blower motor air inlet, provides amplifier with incoming air temperature. Colder outside air causes system to increase heated air to car interior.

BLOWER MOTORS

A/C system has 2 blower motors which operate together to maintain desired airflow. Motors are powered by transistorized control circuits fitted in motor outlets. Circuits allow variable motor speed in LOW or "M" setting of mode control switch.

When mode switch is in HIGH, high-speed relays are energized from CCU center connector pin No. 1 (Orange wire), opening a path to ground, allowing full battery voltage to be applied to motor. In LOW and "M" positions, CCU provides ground, and power transistor supplies a continuously variable voltage to motor. A feedback diode enables CCU to sense voltage at negative terminal of blower motor.

BLOWER MOTOR HIGH-SPEED RELAYS

When mode switch is set to HIGH, high-speed relays are energized from CCU center connector pin No. 1 (Orange wire), opening a path to ground, allowing full battery voltage to be applied to motor. High-speed relays are located in blower motor assemblies.

CLIMATE CONTROL UNIT (CCU)

CCU uses input and feedback signals to control A/C system functions, providing desired in-car temperatures for each selected mode. CCU is energized from ignition switch (auxiliary position 1). CCU has its own power unit, which supplies 5 volts for temperature sensors, feedback potentiometers and high-speed relays. A safety circuit is incorporated in CCU to protect it against reversed polarity and voltage surges.

COOLANT TEMPERATURE SENSOR

A coolant temperature sensor is fitted to lower side of heater core inlet. *See Fig. 1.* Sensor contacts are open to prevent blower motors from operating until coolant temperature in heater core reaches 86°F (30°C). The coolant temperature sensor is overridden when cold air is demanded.

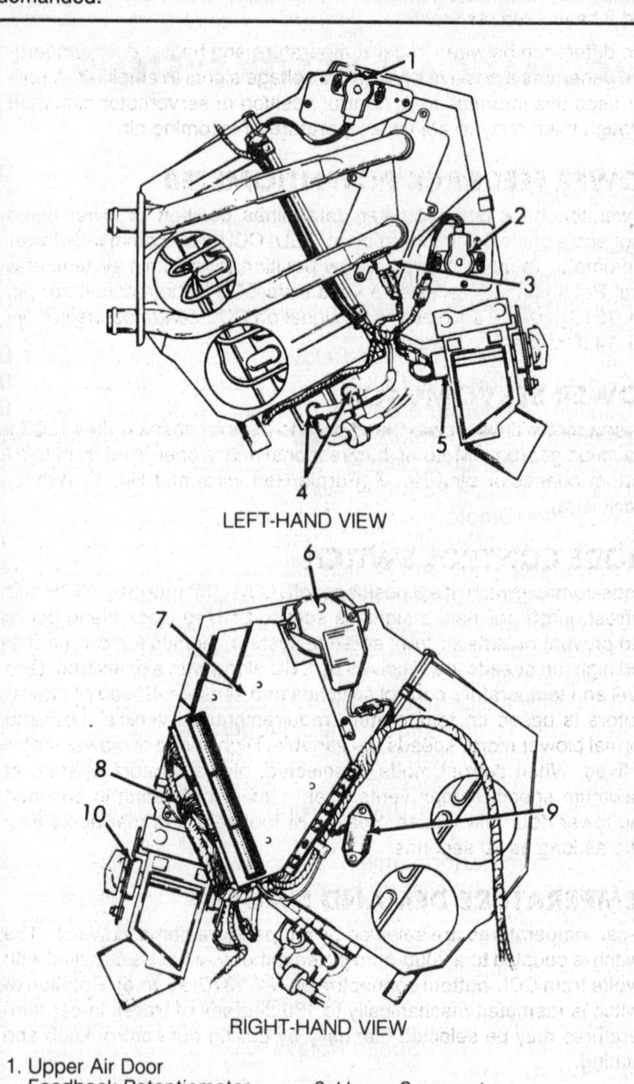
1
2
3
4
5
LEFT-HAND VIEW
6
7
8
9
10
RIGHT-HAND VIEW
1. Upper Air Door Feedback Potentiometer
2. Lower Air Door Feedback Potentiometer
3. Coolant Temperature Sensor
4. Vacuum Solenoids
5. Temperature Demand Potentiometer
6. Upper Servomotor
7. Climate Control Unit
8. Lower Servomotor
9. Evaporator Temperature Sensor
10. Mode Control Switch
93C19440
Courtesy of Jaguar Cars, Inc.

Fig. 1: Identifying Automatic A/C System Components

EVAPORATOR TEMPERATURE SENSOR

Sensor, mounted on heater assembly, measures evaporator temperature and controls A/C compressor clutch operation. *See Fig. 1.* A capillary tube senses evaporator temperature and interrupts electrical feed to compressor clutch if evaporator temperature is less than 36°F (2°C). When evaporator temperature is greater than 36°F (2°C), thermostat contacts close, supplying current to compressor clutch.

IN-CAR TEMPERATURE SENSOR

In-car temperature sensor (thermistor), located in center-dash vent duct, has an aspirator tube leading from left side fan ducting. Air is drawn through aspirator tube across a Wheatstone bridge circuit in sensor. Wheatstone bridge circuit has 4 arms. One arm is for in-car temperature thermistor, one for control panel temperature selected, and 2 have fixed resistance.

The difference between in-car temperature and heater duct temperature generates a positive or negative voltage signal to amplifier. Amplifier uses this information to control position of servomotor camshaft through main relay to adjust temperature of incoming air.

LOWER FEEDBACK POTENTIOMETER

Lower feedback potentiometer determines position of lower blend door and signals this information to CCU. CCU then commands lower servomotor to move door to a new position to maintain air temperature. Potentiometer receives 5 volts from CCU bottom connector pin No. 13 (Gray wire) and returns its signal on CCU center connector pin No. 14 (Orange/Black wire).

LOWER SERVOMOTOR

A servomotor drives lower blend door to desired position via a 1500:1 reduction gearbox. Motor is bi-directional and is energized from CCU bottom connector pins No. 7 (Purple/Red wire) and No. 11 (White/Black wire).

MODE CONTROL SWITCH

Mode control switch has 5 positions: off, LOW, "M" (normal), HIGH and defrost. In off position, a signal is sent to CCU to close blend doors and prevent outside air from entering system. Signals for low, normal and high fan speeds are received by CCU along with signals from face level and temperature control switches and sensors. Speed of blower motors is based on temperature requirements of vehicle. Low and normal blower motor speeds are variable. High speed of blower motor is fixed. When defrost mode is selected, blower motors operate at maximum speed, screen vents open, maximum heating is obtained and lower door fully closes. Sealing of footwells and rear ducts may take as long as 30 seconds.

TEMPERATURE DEMAND SWITCH

In-car temperatures are selected by temperature demand switch. The switch is coupled to a 2000-ohm potentiometer, which is supplied with 5 volts from CCU bottom connector pin No. 13 (Gray wire). Rotation of switch is restricted mechanically to 180 degrees of travel. In-car temperatures may be selected manually by pulling out control knob and rotating.

UPPER FEEDBACK POTENTIOMETER

Upper feedback potentiometer determines position of upper blend door and sends this information to CCU. CCU then commands upper door servomotor to move door to a new position and maintain temperature of air at dashboard, center, screen and side demist vents. Potentiometer receives 5 volts from CCU bottom connector pin No. 13 (Gray wire) and returns its signal on CCU center connector pin No. 15 (Yellow/Green wire).

UPPER SERVOMOTOR

Upper servomotor drives upper blend flap to desired position via a 1500:1 reduction gearbox. Motor is bi-directional and is energized from CCU bottom connector pins No. 10 (Gray/Black wire) and No. 12 (Yellow/Red wire).

VACUUM CONTROLS

System uses 5 solenoid-controlled vacuum actuators to control air delivery. One is for defrost/demist, one for dash-center vent, one for heater coolant valve, and 2 for recirculation mode. *See Fig. 2.* Each solenoid vacuum circuit is color coded. Defrost solenoid vacuum circuit is identified by Green vacuum hoses. Recirculation circuit uses Blue vacuum hoses. Heater coolant valve vacuum circuit uses Red vacuum hoses, and center vent circuit uses Black vacuum hoses.

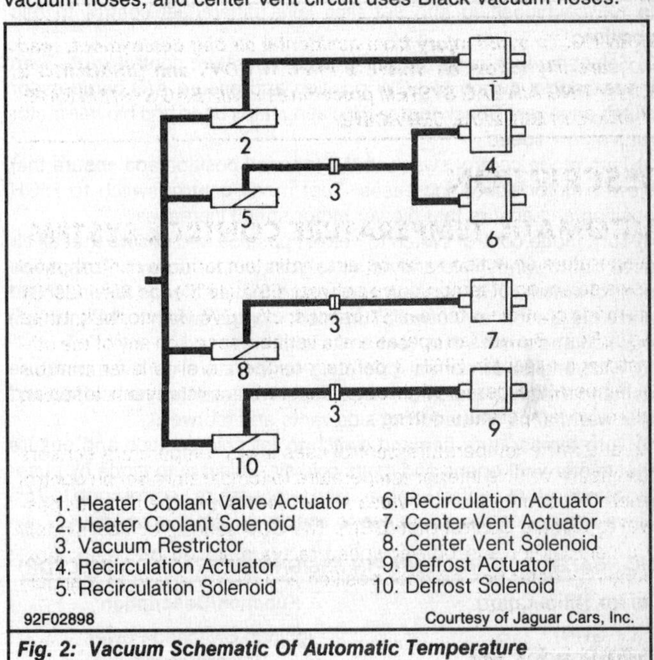
1
2
3
4
5
6
3
7
8
3
9
10
1. Heater Coolant Valve Actuator
2. Heater Coolant Solenoid
3. Vacuum Restrictor
4. Recirculation Actuator
5. Recirculation Solenoid
6. Recirculation Actuator
7. Center Vent Actuator
8. Center Vent Solenoid
9. Defrost Actuator
10. Defrost Solenoid
92F02898
Courtesy of Jaguar Cars, Inc.

Fig. 2: Vacuum Schematic Of Automatic Temperature Control System

TROUBLE SHOOTING

NOTE: Verify proper coolant level, refrigerant charge and engine performance before trouble shooting system.

A/C COMPRESSOR INOPERATIVE

Defective CCU. Defective compressor clutch. Defective superheat switch/thermal fuse. Defective heater coolant temperature switch. Defective evaporator temperature sensor. Defective main relay or no electrical power to main relay.

AUTOMATIC TEMPERATURE CONTROL INOPERATIVE

Defective in-car sensor. Defective coolant temperature switch. Defective servomotor. Defective vacuum actuators. Defective temperature control switch.

BLOWER MOTOR(S) INOPERATIVE

Blown fuse. Defective high-speed relay(s). Defective blower resistor. Defective coolant thermostat.

SYSTEM SWITCHES MODES ON ACCELERATION OR UPHILL DRIVING

Vacuum leak in vacuum reservoir tank. Defective vacuum check valve (located near engine, in vacuum supply line). Leaking vacuum hoses. Leaking mode switch.

1993 AUTOMATIC A/C-HEATER SYSTEMS
XJS (Cont.)

TESTING

WARNING: To avoid injury from accidental air bag deployment, read and carefully follow all SERVICE PRECAUTIONS and DISABLING & ACTIVATING AIR BAG SYSTEM procedures in AIR BAG SYSTEM SAFETY article in GENERAL SERVICING.

A/C SYSTEM PERFORMANCE

1) Park car in shade. Start and warm engine to normal operating temperature. Ensure dash side vents are open. Turn temperature switch to full cold position and set face level differential control to mid position.

2) Select manual mode by pulling out temperature control knob. Turn mode control switch to LOW position and ensure A/C compressor clutch engages. Check that recirculating flaps open and blower motor runs at low speed.

3) Turn mode control switch to "M" (normal) position and ensure that blower motor speed increases. Turn mode control switch to HIGH position and ensure that blower motor speed increases.

4) Turn mode control switch to defrost position and ensure that all air goes out to windshield and no air to goes out to footwell. Turn mode control switch HIGH position and ensure that air bleeds to windshield and air is present at footwell. Turn mode control switch to "M" (normal) position and ensure that vent emits cold air.

5) With engine at normal operating temperature, turn temperature demand switch to maximum heat. Ensure that center vent closes and that warm air is emitted from side vents and footwell.

6) Turn temperature demand switch to full cold position and ensure that center vent opens and emits cold air. Select auto mode by pushing temperature control knob in. Turn temperature control knob to 75°. Drive vehicle for short distance to enable system to stabilize.

7) Apply heat to in-car temperature sensor, located in center-dash vent duct. Ensure air temperature drops at side vents and that center vents open.

EVAPORATOR TEMPERATURE SENSOR

1) Using an ohmmeter, check continuity across sensor terminals. Continuity should exist until evaporator temperature is less than 36°F (2°C). Ensure electrical power is supplied to thermostat through Yellow/Brown wire.

2) If electrical power is not present with engine running and system on, check in-line 10-amp fuse and wire harness. If 10-amp fuse is blown, disconnect A/C compressor clutch. Replace fuse. If fuse remains okay, fault is in compressor clutch. If fuse blows with compressor clutch disconnected, replace sensor.

SERVOMOTOR

Rotate temperature control from full warm to full cool. CCU should signal servomotor to turn fully left and fully right as temperature control is rotated. Observe servomotor. If servomotor does not perform as indicated, check power supply to amplifier. Replace amplifier if necessary.

PIN VOLTAGE TESTS

NOTE: Perform all voltage tests using Digital Volt-Ohmmeter (DVOM) with a minimum 10-megohm input impedance.

Pin voltage charts are supplied to reduce diagnostic time. Checking pin voltages at the A/C-heater control unit determines whether it is receiving and transmitting proper voltage signals. Charts may also help determine if control unit wiring harness has short or open circuit.

A/C-HEATER CONTROL UNIT PIN ASSIGNMENTS (TOP CONNECTOR) [1]

Pin No. (Wire Color)	Function/Description	Signal Type Or Voltage Value
1 (LT GRN)	Ignition Switched Power	13.5-14.2 Volts (On); Zero Volts (Off)
2 (GRN/RED)	Power Ground	Ground Circuit
3 (RED/BLU)	Recirculation Vacuum Solenoid	12 Volts (On); Zero Volts (Off)
4 (BLU)	Inside Temperature Sensor	2.73 Volts At 0°C (On); Zero Volts (Off)
5 (PNK)	Evaporator Temperature Sensor	2.73 Volts At 0°C (On); Zero Volts (Off)
6 (GRN)	Power Ground	Ground Circuit
9 (WHT/RED)	Mode Control Switch	Zero Volts (On); 4 Volts (Off)
10 (GRN)	Inside Temperature Sensor	Ground Circuit
11 (ORG/RED)	Defrost Temperature Solenoid	12 Volts
12 (GRY/BLU)	Defrost Solenoid Mode Switch	12 Volts (On); 4 Volts (Off)
13 (PNK/BLK)	Mode Switch/LOW	Zero Volts (On); 4 Volts (Off)
14 (GRY/BLK)	Mode Switch/"M"	Zero Volts (On); 4 Volts (Off)
15 (RED/BLK)	Mode Switch/HIGH	Zero Volts (On); 4 Volts (Off)

[1] – Pin assignments not listed are not used.

A/C-HEATER CONTROL UNIT PIN ASSIGNMENTS (CENTER CONNECTOR) [1]

Pin No. (Wire Color)	Function/Description	Signal Type Or Voltage Value
1 (ORG)	High Speed Blower Motor Relays	12 Volts (On); Zero Volts (Off)
2 (RED)	Coolant Valve Vacuum Solenoid	12 Volts (Closed); Zero Volts (Open)
3 (BLK)	Center Vent Vacuum Solenoid	12 Volts (Open); Zero Volts (Closed)
4 (BLU)	Manual Mode Switch	Zero Volts (On); 4 Volts (Off)
5 (GRN/WHT)	Compressor Clutch Relay	12 Volts (On); Zero Volts (Off)
6 (BLK)	Coolant Temperature Switch	5 Volts (More Than 40°C); Zero Volts (Less Than 40°C)
7 (PPL)	Left Blower Motor Feedback	5 Volts (Low); 2 Volts (Medium); 1 Volt (High)
9 (PPL/RED)	Power Ground	Ground Circuit
12 (WHT/BLK)	Mode Switch/Defrost	Zero Volts (On); 4 Volts (Off)
13 (ORG)	Temperature Potentiometer	2.89 Volts (Cool); Zero Volts (Warm)
14 (RED)	Lower Feedback Potentiometer	0.1 Volt (Full Cold); 1.2 Volts (Full Hot); 2.9 Volts (Defrost)
15 (YEL)	Upper Feedback Potentiometer	0.2 Volt (Full Cold); 1.9 Volts (Full Hot); 1.9 Volts (Defrost)

[1] – Pin assignments not listed are not used.

A/C-HEATER CONTROL UNIT PIN ASSIGNMENTS (BOTTOM CONNECTOR) [1]

Pin No. (Wire Color)	Function/Description	Signal Type Or Voltage Value
1 (BLU)	Left Blower Motor Power Transistor	1.2 Volts (Low); 1 Volt (High)
2 (PNK)	Right Blower Motor Power Transistor	1.2 Volts (Low); 1 Volt (High)
3 (PNK/BLU)	Right Blower Motor Feedback	5 Volts (Low); 2 Volts (Medium); 1 Volt (High)
4 (YEL/RED)	Ambient Temperature Sensor	2.93 Volts At 0°C (On); Zero Volts (Off)
5 (BRN)	Temperature Demand Potentiometer	Zero Volts (Full Cool); 2.89 Volts (Full Hot)
7 (PPL/RED)	Lower Servo	7 Volts (On); Zero Volts (Off)
8 (GRN/RED)	Power Ground	Ground Circuit
10 (GRY/BLK)	Upper Servo	7 Volts (On); Zero Volts (Off)
11 (WHT/BLK)	Lower Servo	7 Volts (On); Zero Volts (Off)
12 (YEL/RED)	Upper Servo	7 Volts (On); Zero Volts (Off)
13 (GRY)	Sensor Reference Voltage	5 Volts (On); Zero Volts (Off)
14 (ORG/BLK)	Mode Control Switch	12 Volts (On); Zero Volts (Off)
15 (YEL/GRN)	Power Ground	Ground Circuit

[1] – Pin assignments not listed are not used.

REMOVAL & INSTALLATION

WARNING: To avoid injury from accidental air bag deployment, read and carefully follow all SERVICE PRECAUTIONS and DISABLING & ACTIVATING AIR BAG SYSTEM procedures in AIR BAG SYSTEM SAFETY article in GENERAL SERVICING.

A/C UNIT

Removal & Installation – 1) Discharge A/C system using approved refrigerant/recycling equipment. Disconnect negative battery cable. Remove center console assembly and front seats for better accessibility. Remove fascia board. See FASCIA BOARD. Disconnect electrical and optical fiber connectors, as necessary.

2) Remove A/C switch panel. Remove face level differential control assembly screws and move panel out of the way. Disconnect differential potentiometer block connector and remove plate. Remove radio.

3) Move tunnel carpet out of the way. Remove lower bolts securing A/C unit brackets and remove brackets. Remove heater hoses from heater core. Remove refrigerant hose to evaporator and expansion valve. Remove and discard "O" rings. Plug all open A/C connections.

4) Remove A/C unit-to-firewall nuts. From inside vehicle, disconnect pliable ducts from A/C unit. Remove A/C unit stub pipes. Remove defroster duct assembly from firewall. Disconnect blower assembly vacuum lines. Disconnect heater control valve.

5) Remove left hand ventilator outlet duct and blower motor connector. Remove steering column bracket nuts and bolts and reposition bracket out of the way. Remove right hand ventilator outlet duct. Remove drain hoses. Disconnect A/C unit main harness connector and move out of the way.

6) Remove A/C unit assembly from vehicle. To install, reverse removal procedure. Ensure NEW "O" rings are used on all A/C fittings.

BLOWER MOTOR

Removal & Installation (Left Side) – 1) Disconnect negative battery cable. Remove left side footwell trim pad, dash liner and console side cover. Remove bulb failure unit from component panel. Remove component panel-to-blower assembly nuts, and move panel aside.

2) Disconnect blower motor harness connector. Disconnect flexible ducting at blower housing. Disconnect ambient temperature sensor. Remove footwell vent control nuts and remove control.

3) Disconnect vacuum hose at actuator. Manually open recirculation flap and wedge in open position with block of wood. Remove blower assembly bolts and nuts. Remove blower assembly. To install, reverse removal procedure.

Removal & Installation (Right Side) – 1) Remove right side footwell trim pad, dash liner, console trim pad and glove box. Remove component panel-to-blower housing nuts, and remove panel.

2) Disconnect blower wire harness connector. Remove in-car sensor pipe from flexible ducting. Disconnect flexible ducting from blower housing.

3) Disconnect vacuum hose at actuator. Manually open recirculation flap and wedge in open position with block of wood. Remove blower assembly bolts and nuts. Remove blower assembly. To install, reverse removal procedure.

BLOWER MOTOR HIGH-SPEED RELAYS

Removal & Installation – 1) Disconnect negative battery cable. Remove driver- and/or passenger-side dash liner. Disconnect vacuum hose from blower motor assembly. Fit a dummy hose to vacuum servo, and apply vacuum to open lower door.

2) Seal off vacuum. Disconnect lower door connecting rod clips, and disconnect rods from lower door. Open door for access, and remove relay from blower assembly. To install, reverse removal procedure.

BLOWER RESISTOR

Removal & Installation – Disconnect negative battery cable. Remove left side dash liner. Note position of wire connectors on resistor, and disconnect wiring. Remove retaining screws and remove resistor. To install, reverse removal procedure.

CLIMATE CONTROL UNIT

Removal & Installation – Disconnect negative battery cable. Remove right dash liner. Remove console side casing. Disconnect CCU harness connector. Remove CCU screws, and remove CCU. To install, reverse removal procedure.

COMPRESSOR

Removal – 1) Discharge A/C system using approved refrigerant recovery/recycling equipment. Disconnect negative battery cable. Remove compressor thermal fuse. Remove link arm-to-compressor bolts. Loosen pivot bolt, and remove belt.

2) Remove bolts securing freon cooler and clamp plate to compressor. Remove bolt securing compressor discharge and suction lines. Disconnect discharge and suction lines. Plug compressor and line openings. Remove remaining compressor bolts. Remove compressor.

Installation – To install, reverse removal procedure. Ensure NEW "O" rings are in place when installing discharge and suction lines. Ensure proper refrigerant oil level. Evacuate and recharge A/C system.

CONDENSER

Removal – 1) Discharge A/C system using approved refrigerant recovery/recycling equipment. Disconnect A/C lines from receiver-drier and condenser. Plug condenser and line openings.

2) Move headlight wiring harness and hood rubber buffer to one side. Remove top brace and engine fan shroud bolts. Remove fan shroud.

1993 AUTOMATIC A/C-HEATER SYSTEMS XJS (Cont.)

Remove condenser bolts and A/C line clips. Move receiver-drier and mounting bracket clear of radiator. Carefully push radiator toward engine, and lift condenser from brackets.

Installation – To install, reverse removal procedure. Install refrigerant lines to condenser before tightening condenser bolts. Ensure proper refrigerant oil level. Evacuate and recharge A/C system.

COOLANT TEMPERATURE SWITCH

Removal & Installation – Disconnect negative battery cable. Remove left side dash liner. Disconnect electrical connectors at switch. Remove 2 switch screws and remove switch. To install, reverse removal procedure.

EVAPORATOR

Removal & Installation – **1)** Discharge A/C system using approved refrigerant recovery/recycling equipment. Disconnect negative battery cable. Drain engine cooling system. Remove fascia board. See FASCIA BOARD.

2) Remove A/C unit assembly. See A/C UNIT removal and installation. Remove heater pipe guide plate. Remove evaporator sensor from evaporator. Remove solenoid mounting plate. *See Fig. 1.* Remove electrical connectors and vacuum hoses as needed.

3) Split A/C unit casing and remove evaporator from unit. Remove expansion valve guide plate from evaporator. To install, reverse removal procedure. Replace receiver-drier when replacing evaporator. Check for proper refrigerant oil level. Evacuate and recharge A/C system.

EVAPORATOR TEMPERATURE SENSOR

Removal & Installation – Disconnect negative battery cable. Remove right side console pad and dash liner. Remove sensor-to-heater unit screws. Disconnect cables, and carefully remove sensor by pulling capillary tube from A/C unit. To install, reverse removal procedure. Ensure capillary tube is properly positioned in A/C unit with tube touching evaporator fins.

EXPANSION VALVE

Removal & Installation – **1)** Discharge A/C system using approved refrigerant recovery/recycling equipment. Loosen capillary tube clamp screws. Disconnect A/C hoses at expansion valve, and plug openings.

2) Support expansion valve to avoid pressure on evaporator. Remove expansion valve by carefully unscrewing union nut and pulling capillary tube from clamps. To install, reverse removal procedure. Ensure proper refrigerant oil level, and recharge A/C system.

FASCIA BOARD

Removal & Installation – **1)** Disconnect negative battery cable. Loosen steering wheel adjuster and pull steering wheel to its full extent. Remove steering column lower shroud and plate. Remove steering column upper shroud. Remove steering column pinch bolt and remove steering wheel.

2) Remove fascia side trims. Remove driver's dash liner. Disconnect light rheostat wires, trip cable (if equipped), and remove dash liner. Remove light switch knob. Remove trim panel around instrument cluster, ignition switch and light switch.

3) Disconnect fiber optics harness and speedometer cable (if equipped). Disconnect harness connectors to instrument panel. Remove instrument panel. Remove passenger side dash liner and glove box. To install, reverse removal procedure.

HEATER COOLANT VALVE

Removal & Installation – Drain engine coolant. Disconnect vacuum hose, and move air vent to one side. Remove coolant valve-to-firewall bolts. Pull valve out to access coolant hoses. Disconnect coolant hoses, and remove coolant valve. To install, reverse removal procedure. Refill cooling system.

HEATER CORE

Removal & Installation – **1)** Disconnect negative battery cable. Drain engine cooling system. Remove left hand console side casing and dash liner. Remove glove box. Remove heater box cover screws. Remove rear heater box panel and move front panel and foam seal out of the way for access.

2) Disconnect heater pipe from heater box. Remove and discard gasket. Disconnect wire from coolant temperature switch. Remove foam pad from pipes and move vacuum hoses out of the way. Remove front heater panel. Disconnect heater hoses from heater core and remove heater core. To install, reverse removal procedure. Ensure new gaskets are used.

IN-CAR TEMPERATURE SENSOR

Removal & Installation – Remove 2 outer retaining screws, and remove upper dash panel. Disconnect and remove temperature sensor from air pick-up tube. Remove plastic strap, and remove sensor from elbow in hose. To install, reverse removal procedure.

MODE SELECTOR & TEMPERATURE CONTROL SWITCHES

Removal & Installation – **1)** Disconnect negative battery cable. Remove 2 lower shroud-to-parking brake assembly screws, noting position of vents. Remove 2 vent and side trim panel screws. Remove vent. Carefully pull side vent away from upper dash pad, and remove upper dash pad. Remove opposite side trim in same manner.

2) Remove center console screws. Move console slightly, and disconnect electrical connectors at power window and cigarette lighter switches. Remove center console. Remove switch panel-to-A/C unit nuts.

3) Carefully pull switch panel out, and mark vacuum hoses for installation reference. Remove selector cover screws and remove cover. Disconnect switches, noting position of connectors. To install, reverse removal procedure.

RECEIVER-DRIER

Removal & Installation – Discharge A/C system using approved refrigerant recovery/recycling equipment. Disconnect refrigerant lines from receiver-drier, and plug openings. Remove receiver-drier bolts. Remove receiver-drier. To install, reverse removal procedure. Install NEW "O" rings. Ensure proper refrigerant oil level, and recharge A/C system.

SERVOMOTOR

Removal & Installation – **1)** Disconnect negative battery cable. Remove right console cover. Remove 4 screws, and remove right footwell vent. Note air door operating rod position, and disconnect at servomotor.

2) Mark vacuum hoses for installation reference, and remove hoses. Disconnect electrical connector at servomotor. Remove servomotor cap nut and servomotor. To install, reverse removal procedure.

VACUUM SOLENOID(S)

Removal & Installation – **1)** Disconnect negative battery cable. Remove console side trim. Remove footwell duct screws. and remove duct assembly.

2) Remove solenoid bracket bolts and move plate for access. Disconnect White vacuum hose from vacuum "T". Mark hoses for installation reference, and disconnect hoses from solenoid. Disconnect solenoid harness connector. Remove solenoid from plate. To install, reverse removal procedure.

WIRING DIAGRAM

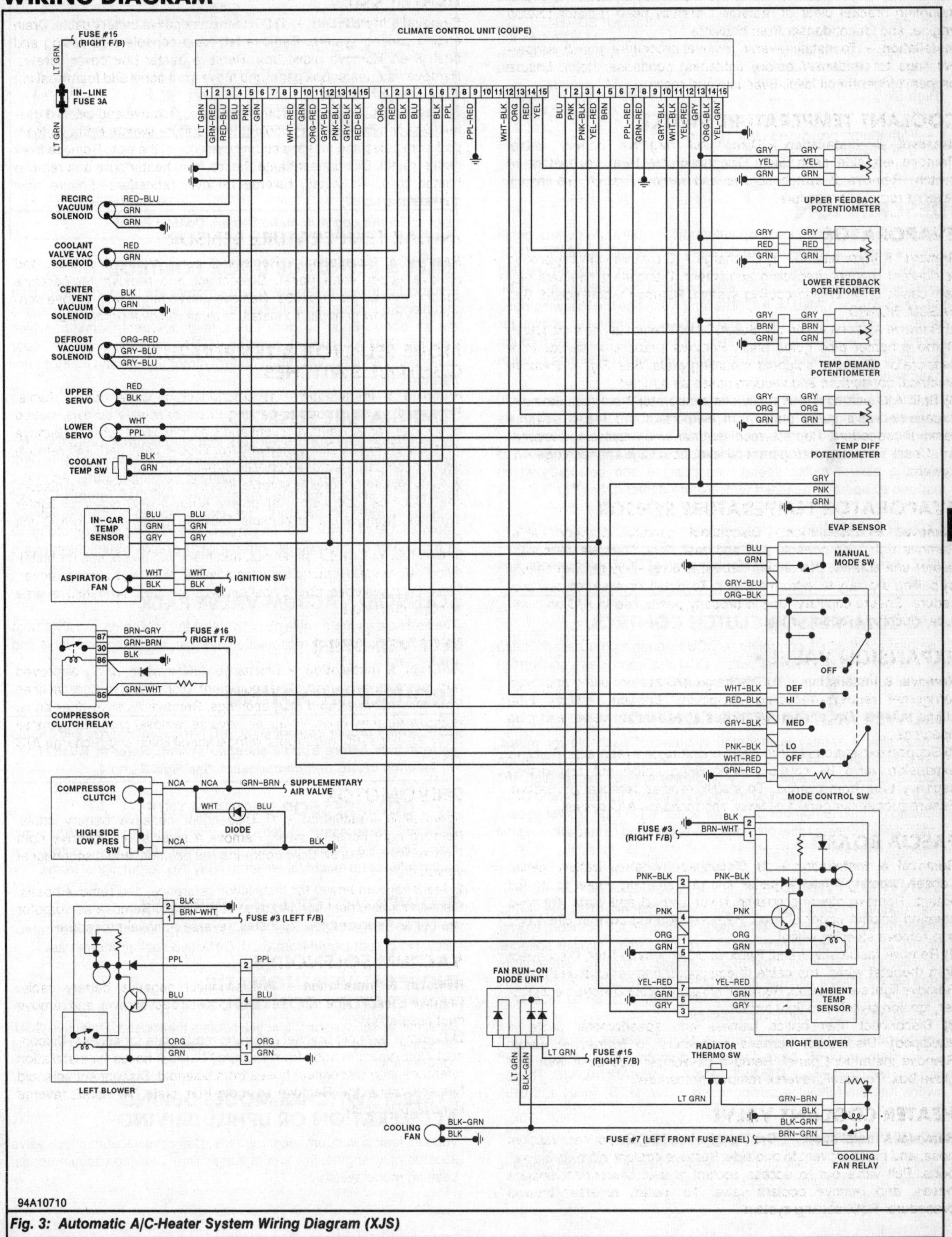
CLIMATE CONTROL UNIT (COUPE)
FUSE #15 (RIGHT F/B)
IN-LINE FUSE 3A
LT GRN
RECIRC VACUUM SOLENOID
COOLANT VALVE VAC SOLENOID
CENTER VENT VACUUM SOLENOID
DEFROST VACUUM SOLENOID
UPPER SERVO
LOWER SERVO
COOLANT TEMP SW
IN-CAR TEMP SENSOR
ASPIRATOR FAN
IGNITION SW
FUSE #16 (RIGHT F/B)
COMPRESSOR CLUTCH RELAY
COMPRESSOR CLUTCH
SUPPLEMENTARY AIR VALVE
DIODE
HIGH SIDE LOW PRES SW
FUSE #3 (LEFT F/B)
LEFT BLOWER
FAN RUN-ON DIODE UNIT
FUSE #15 (RIGHT F/B)
RADIATOR THERMO SW
COOLING FAN
FUSE #7 (LEFT FRONT FUSE PANEL)
COOLING FAN RELAY
UPPER FEEDBACK POTENTIOMETER
LOWER FEEDBACK POTENTIOMETER
TEMP DEMAND POTENTIOMETER
TEMP DIFF POTENTIOMETER
EVAP SENSOR
MANUAL MODE SW
OFF
DEF
HI
MED
LO
OFF
MODE CONTROL SW
FUSE #3 (RIGHT F/B)
AMBIENT TEMP SENSOR
RIGHT BLOWER
94A10710

Fig. 3: Automatic A/C-Heater System Wiring Diagram (XJS)

1993 AUTOMATIC A/C-HEATER SYSTEMS
XJ6

SPECIFICATIONS

Compressor Type .... Sanden SD-7H15 7-Cyl.
Compressor Belt Tension [1] .... 11/64" (4.4 mm)
Compressor Oil Capacity .... [2] 4.5 ozs.
Refrigerant (R-134a) Capacity .... 40 ozs.
System Operating Pressures [3]
High Side .... 145-180 psi (10-13 kg/cm²)
Low Side .... 70 psi (5.0 kg/cm²)

[1] – With thumb pressure at belt center.
[2] – Use PAG SP20 refrigerant oil.
[3] – Pressure readings based on ambient temperature of 70°F (21°C).

DESCRIPTION

Temperature selection knob on automatic temperature control panel allows selection of temperature between 65°F (18°C) and 86°F (30°C). The MODE buttons are used to turn A/C system on or off, heated windshield control (if equipped), select defrost, recirculated air, DEMIST, MAX A/C or MANUAL A/C. The fan switch has the following positions: off, LOW, MED, HIGH and DEF. A sliding lever allows for increase or decrease in temperature of air being delivered through face level vents without affecting interior temperature setting of automatic setting. *See Fig. 1.*

The Climate Control Unit (CCU), located on right side of heater unit, receives data signals from control panel and compares these signals with those returned from system temperature sensors and feedback devices. This comparison provides output voltage changes needed to vary the blower motor speed, flap position and solenoids which respond to operator selected temperature demand. *See Fig. 1.*

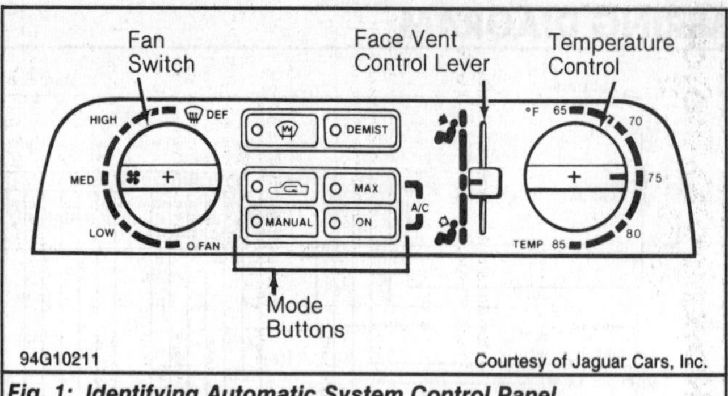
Fan
Switch
Face Vent
Control Lever
Temperature
Control
HIGH
DEF
DEMIST
MED
MAX
A/C
MANUAL
ON
LOW
O FAN
°F 65
70
75
80
TEMP 85
Mode
Buttons
94G10211
Courtesy of Jaguar Cars, Inc.

Fig. 1: Identifying Automatic System Control Panel

OPERATION

NOTE: Refer to illustration for identification of CCU components. See Fig. 2.

A/C COMPRESSOR CLUTCH CONTROL

Compressor clutch is controlled by CCU through a compressor clutch relay, superheat and thermal switch. CCU also energizes a cooling fan relay when A/C compressor clutch is turned on.

BLOWER MOTOR SPEED CONTROL

A heat sink assembly is mounted in outlet of each blower motor. These heat sinks contain a suppressor diode, a feedback isolation diode and a power transistor. On all blower speeds except high, the ground circuit for each blower motor is via power transistor and CCU, allowing an infinite number of blower speeds. On high blower speed, a high-speed blower relay provides a direct ground circuit, allowing full speed of blowers.

CONTROL PANEL

The rotating mode switch has following positions: off, LOW, MED, HIGH and DEF. *See Fig. 1.* With mode switch in DEF position, blower motors are operated at high speed through a relay. Blower speed is controlled by CCU in all other mode settings. A rotating temperature knob allows selection of interior temperature between 65°F (18°C) and 85°F (29°C). A sliding lever allows temperature of air at face level vents to be varied from automatic setting.

Control panel also has 6 push buttons. MODE buttons are used to turn A/C system on or off, heated windshield control (if equipped), select defrost, recirculated air, DEMIST, MAX A/C or MANUAL A/C. The fan switch has the following positions: off, LOW, MED, HIGH and DEF. *See Fig. 1.*

COOLANT TEMPERATURE SWITCH

Coolant temperature switch is mounted on heater core inlet pipe and informs CCU of engine coolant temperature.

INLET & BLEND-AIR DOOR CONTROL

Electrically driven, reversible control motors are used to control inlet and blend-air doors. An amplified electrical signal from CCU positions the air doors. Each air door has a feedback potentiometer, which informs CCU of current position. CCU, depending on air door movement required, will rotate control motor to maintain interior temperature.

TEMPERATURE SENSORS

System has 4 temperature sensors that feed information to CCU for system control. An ambient temperature sensor, mounted in right blower air duct, informs CCU of incoming air temperature. An in-car temperature sensor, mounted in right lower A/C duct, informs CCU of vehicle interior temperature. An evaporator temperature sensor informs CCU of evaporator fin temperature. A solar sensor, mounted in top center of dash panel, informs CCU of direct sunlight entering vehicle.

SOLENOID VACUUM VALVE PACK

The solenoid vacuum valve pack contains the solenoids and 4 vacuum valves for operation of recirculation, defrost, heater control valve and center vent.

TROUBLE SHOOTING

NOTE: Verify proper coolant level, A/C refrigerant charge and engine performance before trouble shooting system. Refer to illustrations for location of A/C unit components. See Figs. 3 and 4.

A/C COMPRESSOR INOPERATIVE

Defective compressor clutch. Defective superheat switch/thermal fuse. Defective heater coolant thermostat. Defective compressor clutch relay or no electrical power to relay. No output signal from CCU.

BLOWER MOTOR(S) INOPERATIVE

Defective blower motor heat sink assembly. Defective blower motor relay. No output signal from CCU. Defective coolant thermostat.

INOPERATIVE AUTOMATIC TEMPERATURE CONTROL

Defective in-car sensor. Defective coolant thermostat. Defective CCU. Defective servo control. Defective vacuum actuators. Defective control panel.

SYSTEM SWITCHES MODES DURING ACCELERATION OR UPHILL DRIVING

Vacuum leak in vacuum reservoir tank. Defective vacuum check valve (located near engine, in vacuum supply line). Leaking vacuum hoses. Leaking mode switch.

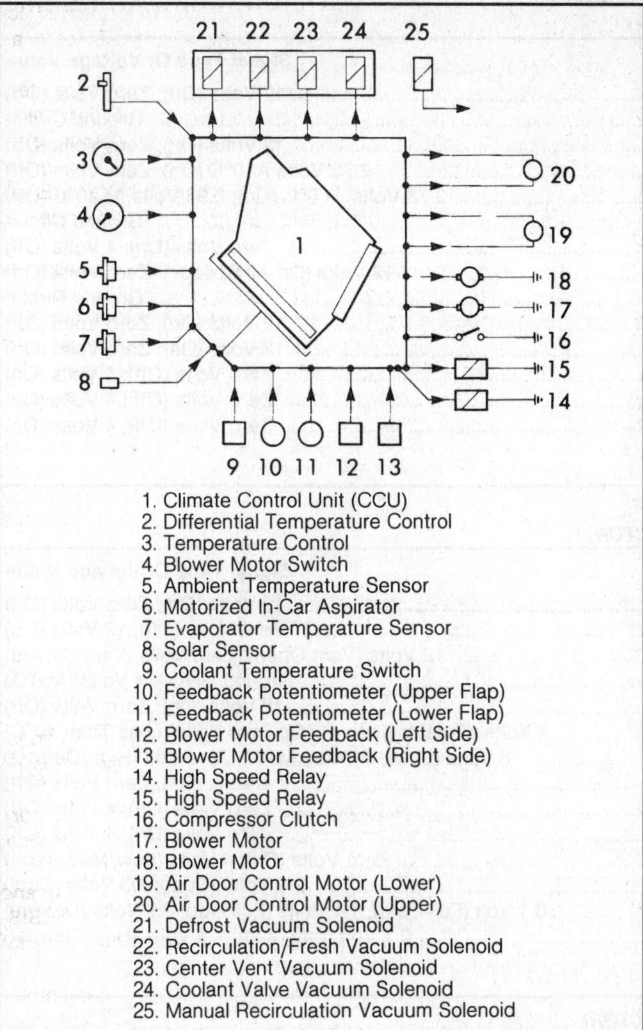

1. Climate Control Unit (CCU)
2. Differential Temperature Control
3. Temperature Control
4. Blower Motor Switch
5. Ambient Temperature Sensor
6. Motorized In-Car Aspirator
7. Evaporator Temperature Sensor
8. Solar Sensor
9. Coolant Temperature Switch
10. Feedback Potentiometer (Upper Flap)
11. Feedback Potentiometer (Lower Flap)
12. Blower Motor Feedback (Left Side)
13. Blower Motor Feedback (Right Side)
14. High Speed Relay
15. High Speed Relay
16. Compressor Clutch
17. Blower Motor
18. Blower Motor
19. Air Door Control Motor (Lower)
20. Air Door Control Motor (Upper)
21. Defrost Vacuum Solenoid
22. Recirculation/Fresh Vacuum Solenoid
23. Center Vent Vacuum Solenoid
24. Coolant Valve Vacuum Solenoid
25. Manual Recirculation Vacuum Solenoid
94H10212
Courtesy of Jaguar Cars, Inc.

Fig. 2: Identifying CCU Components

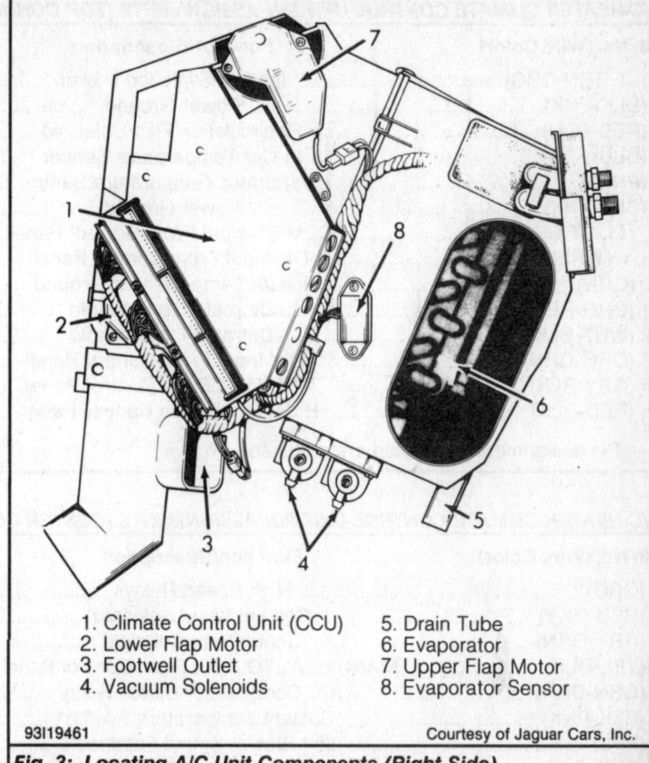

1. Climate Control Unit (CCU)
2. Lower Flap Motor
3. Footwell Outlet
4. Vacuum Solenoids
5. Drain Tube
6. Evaporator
7. Upper Flap Motor
8. Evaporator Sensor
93I19461
Courtesy of Jaguar Cars, Inc.

Fig. 3: Locating A/C Unit Components (Right Side)

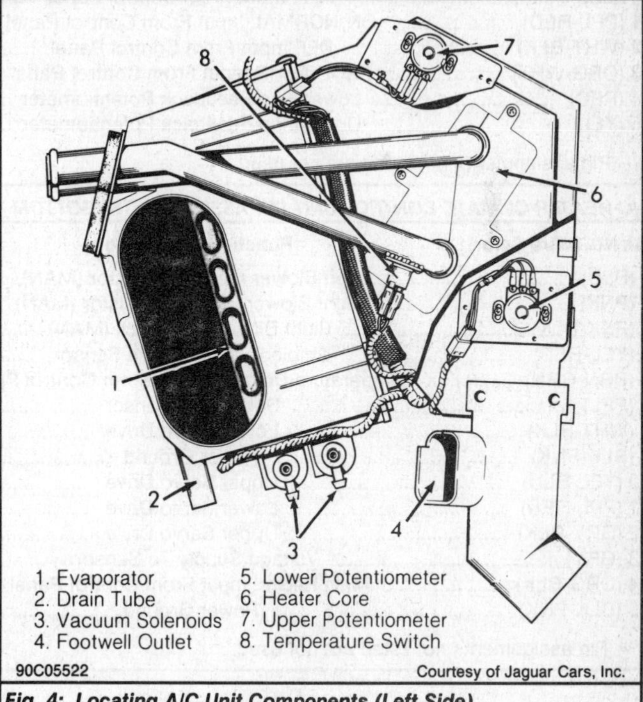

1. Evaporator
2. Drain Tube
3. Vacuum Solenoids
4. Footwell Outlet
5. Lower Potentiometer
6. Heater Core
7. Upper Potentiometer
8. Temperature Switch
90C05522
Courtesy of Jaguar Cars, Inc.

Fig. 4: Locating A/C Unit Components (Left Side)

SYSTEM WILL NOT SWITCH MODES

Vacuum supply loss from engine to firewall connector. Vacuum supply loss from firewall connector to control panel mode switch. Defective CCU. Defective vacuum solenoid. Defective mode switch. Binding linkage or stuck air doors.

TESTING

PIN VOLTAGE TESTS

NOTE: Perform all voltage tests using Digital Volt-Ohmmeter (DVOM) with a minimum 10-megohm input impedance.

Pin voltage charts are supplied to reduce diagnostic time. Checking pin voltages at A/C-heater Climate Control Unit (CCU) determines whether it is receiving and transmitting proper voltage signals. Charts may also help determine if control unit wiring harness has short or open circuit.

1993 AUTOMATIC A/C-HEATER SYSTEMS
XJ6 (Cont.)

A/C-HEATER CLIMATE CONTROL UNIT PIN ASSIGNMENTS (TOP CONNECTOR) [1]

Pin No. (Wire Color)	Function/Description	Signal Type Or Voltage Value
1 (LT GRN-ORG)	Ignition Switched Power	12 Volts (On); Zero Volts (Off)
2 (BLK-PNK)	Power Ground	Ground Circuit
3 (RED-BLU)	Recirculation Flap Solenoid	12 Volts (On); Zero Volts (Off)
4 (BLU)	In-Car Temperature Sensor	2.73 Volts At 0°C (On); Zero Volts (Off)
5 (PNK)	Evaporator Temperature Sensor	2.73 Volts At 0°C (On); 2.93 Volts At 20°C (Off)
6 (BLK-PNK)	Power Ground	Ground Circuit
8 (YEL-LT GRN)	DEMIST Input From Control Panel	Zero Volts (On); 4 Volts (Off)
9 (WHT-RED)	ON Input From Control Panel	12 Volts (On-All Speeds); Zero Volts (Off)
10 (GRN)	In-Car Temp. Sensor Ground	Ground Circuit
11 (ORG-RED)	Defrost Flap Solenoid	12 Volts (On); Zero Volts (Off)
12 (WHT-BLK)	Defrost Flap Solenoid	12 Volts (On); Zero Volts (Off)
13 (ORG-GRN)	LOW Input From Control Panel	Zero Volts (Off); 4 Volts (On)
14 (GRY-BLK)	MED Input From Control Panel	Zero Volts (Off); 4 Volts (On)
15 (RED-BLK)	HIGH Input From Control Panel	Zero Volts (Off); 4 Volts (On)

[1] – Pin assignments not listed are not used.

A/C-HEATER CLIMATE CONTROL UNIT PIN ASSIGNMENTS (CENTER CONNECTOR) [1]

Pin No. (Wire Color)	Function/Description	Signal Type Or Voltage Value
1 (ORG)	High Speed Relays	12 Volts (On); Zero Volts (Off)
2 (RED-GRY)	Coolant Valve Solenoid	Zero Volts (Off); 12 Volts (On)
3 (GRY-GRN)	Center Vent Solenoid	12 Volts (Vent Open); Zero Volts (Vent Closed)
4 (YEL-BLK)	MANUAL/AUTO Input From Control Panel	Ground (MAN); 4 Volts (AUTO)
5 (GRN-BRN)	A/C Compressor Clutch Relay	12 Volts (On); Zero Volts (Off)
6 (BLK-PNK)	Coolant Temperature Switch	5 Volts (Greater Than 40°C); Zero Volts (Less Than 40°C)
7 (PPL)	Left Blower Speed Feedback	8 Volts (Low); 5 Volts (Med.); Zero Volt (High/Defrost)
8 (RED-ORG)	ECON Input From Control Panel	4 Volts (On); Zero Volts (Off)
9 (BLU)	MAX Input From Control Panel	Zero Volts (On); 4 Volts (Off)
11 (PPL-RED)	ON/NORMAL Input From Control Panel	Zero Volts (On); 4 Volts (Off)
12 (WHT-BLK)	DEF Input From Control Panel	Zero Volts (On); 4 Volts (Low/Med./High)
13 (ORG-WHT)	FACE TEMP Input From Control Panel	2.9 Volts (Cool); .03 Volts (Cool)
14 (RED)	Lower Flap Feedback Potentiometer	0.1 Volt (Full Cold); 1.1 Volts (Full Hot); 2.9 Volts (Defrost)
15 (YEL)	Upper Flap Feedback Potentiometer	0.1 Volt (Full Cold); 1.9 Volts (High/Defrost)

[1] – Pin assignments not listed are not used.

A/C-HEATER CLIMATE CONTROL UNIT PIN ASSIGNMENTS (BOTTOM CONNECTOR) [1]

Pin No. (Wire Color)	Function/Description	Signal Type Or Voltage Value
1 (BLU)	Left Blower Motor Transistor (MAN)	1.27 Volts (Low); 1.46 Volts (Med); 0.9 Volt (High/Defrost)
2 (PNK)	Right Blower Motor Transistor (MAN)	1.27 Volts (Low); 1.46 Volts (Med); 0.9 Volt (High/Defrost)
3 (PNK-BLK)	Right Blower Feedback (MAN)	8 Volts (Low); 5 Volts (Med); One Volt (High/Defrost)
4 (YEL-RED)	Ambient Temperature Sensor	2.93 Volts At 20°C (On); Zero Volts (Off)
5 (BRN-GRN)	Temperature Demand Input From Control Panel	.06 Volt (Full Cold); 2.9 Volts (Full Hot)
6 (PPL)	Solar Load Sensor	2.88 Volts (Max. Light); .02 Volt (Dark)
7 (WHT-BLK)	Lower Servo Drive	7 Volts (On); Zero Volts (Off)
8 (BLK-PNK)	Power Ground	Ground Circuit
10 (YEL-BLU)	Upper Servo Drive	7 Volts (On); Zero Volts (Off)
11 (PPL-RED)	Lower Servo Drive	7 Volts (On); Zero Volts (Off)
12 (GRY-BLK)	Upper Servo Drive	7 Volts (On); Zero Volts (Off)
13 (GRY)	Voltage Supply To Sensors	5 Volts
14 (ORG-BLK)	Main Recirc. Input From Control Panel	12 Volts (On); Zero Volts (Off)
15 (BLK-PNK)	Power Ground	Ground Circuit

[1] – Pin assignments not listed are not used.

REMOVAL & INSTALLATION

A/C COMPRESSOR

Removal – 1) Disconnect negative battery cable. Discharge A/C system using approved refrigerant recovery/recycling equipment. Remove compressor muffler and refrigerant lines. Plug compressor and refrigerant line ports.

2) Remove and discard compressor port "O" ring seals and plug or seal openings. Disconnect electrical connectors to compressor. Remove upper compressor pivot bolt nut.

3) Raise and support vehicle. From underneath, remove lower pivot bolt and drive belt adjuster assembly. Remove compressor belt. Support compressor and remove upper pivot bolt. Remove compressor from under vehicle.

Installation – To install, reverse removal procedure. Ensure NEW "O" rings are in place when installing discharge and suction pipes. Ensure proper refrigerant oil level, and recharge A/C system.

AMBIENT TEMPERATURE SENSOR

Removal & Installation – 1) Disconnect negative battery cable. Remove right side dash liner. Remove flexible ducting from A/C unit. Remove right blower motor housing bolts.

2) Disconnect electrical connector. Disconnect vacuum hose from blower motor actuator. Remove blower motor assembly. Remove 2 sensor screws. Remove sensor. To install, reverse removal procedure.

BLOWER MOTOR

Removal & Installation (Left Side) - 1) Disconnect negative battery cable. Remove left side dash liner. Remove CCU lower screw. Disconnect ground wire, and remove spacers. Loosen CCU upper screw, and move CCU aside. Remove screws and CCU bracket.

2) Disconnect flexible ducting at blower motor housing. Remove blower motor housing bolts. Remove in-car sensor pipe from flexible ducting. Disconnect electrical connector at blower motor. Disconnect vacuum hose at vacuum actuator. Remove blower motor housing.

3) Disconnect ambient temperature sensor. Remove rubber gasket from housing, and remove blower motor. To install reverse removal procedure.

Removal & Installation (Right Side) - 1) Remove right side dash liner and glove box door. Remove CCU lower screw. Disconnect ground wire, and remove spacers. Loosen CCU upper screw, and move CCU aside. Remove screws and CCU bracket.

2) Disconnect flexible ducting at blower motor housing. Remove blower motor housing bolts. Remove in-car sensor pipe from flexible ducting. Disconnect electrical connector at blower motor. Disconnect vacuum hose at vacuum actuator. Remove blower motor housing.

3) Disconnect ambient temperature sensor. Remove rubber gasket from housing, and remove blower motor. *See Fig. 5*. To install reverse removal procedure.

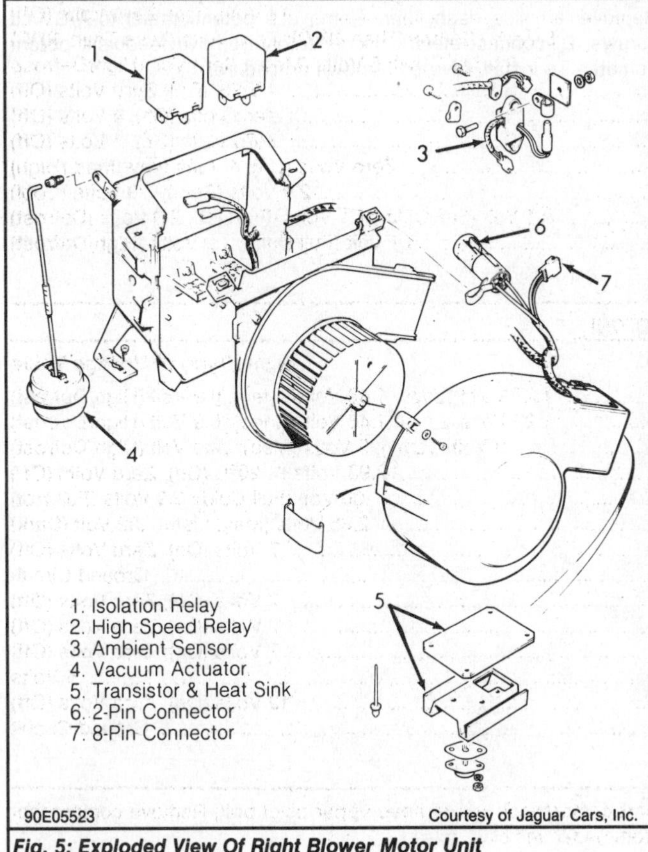
1
2
3
4
5
6
7
1. Isolation Relay
2. High Speed Relay
3. Ambient Sensor
4. Vacuum Actuator
5. Transistor & Heat Sink
6. 2-Pin Connector
7. 8-Pin Connector
90E05523
Courtesy of Jaguar Cars, Inc.

Fig. 5: Exploded View Of Right Blower Motor Unit

CENTER & DEFROSTER AIR DOOR VACUUM ACTUATOR

Removal & Installation - Disconnect negative battery cable. Remove glove box. Remove dash center vent trim and vent grille. Remove upper dash panel. Disconnect and remove solar sensor. Disconnect vacuum hose from actuator, and lift center air door out of dash. Remove clips, and remove vacuum actuator. To install, reverse removal procedure.

CENTER & DEFROSTER AIR DOOR VACUUM SOLENOID

Removal & Installation - Disconnect negative battery cable. Remove right side dash liner and footwell duct. Remove 2 solenoid panel screws, and pull panel back for access. Note position of vacuum hose and electrical connectors, and remove vacuum solenoid. To install, reverse removal procedure.

CLIMATE CONTROL UNIT (CCU)

Removal & Installation - Disconnect negative battery cable. Remove right side dash liner. Remove glove box. Remove CCU screws. Disconnect ground lead and connector. Remove CCU. To install, reverse removal procedure.

CONDENSER

Removal - 1) Discharge A/C system using approved refrigerant recovery/recycling equipment. Disconnect A/C lines from receiver-drier and condenser. Remove receiver-drier bracket bolt, and move receiver-drier aside. Remove and discard "O" rings. Plug condenser and line openings.

2) Remove top brace and engine fan shroud bolts. Remove condenser bolts and A/C line clips. Carefully push radiator toward engine, and lift condenser out of brackets.

Installation - To install, reverse removal procedure. Install NEW "O" rings on refrigerant lines. Ensure proper refrigerant oil level, and recharge A/C system.

CONTROL PANEL

Removal & Installation - 1) Disconnect negative battery cable. Remove center console ashtray. Remove center console trim plate. Remove screws and remove radio console.

2) Loosen control panel top and side screws. Pull control panel out, disconnecting connector as control module is removed. To install, reverse removal procedure.

COOLANT TEMPERATURE SENSOR

Removal & Installation - Disconnect negative battery cable. Remove left side dash panel. Note electrical connector location and disconnect. Remove sensor screws, and remove sensor. To install, reverse removal procedure.

EVAPORATOR/HEATER CORE

Removal - 1) Discharge A/C system using approved refrigerant recovery/recycling equipment. Disconnect negative battery cable. Drain engine cooling system. Remove right and left dash liners. Remove left and right dash end panels.

2) Remove steering wheel. Remove instrument module and control panel. Remove glove box door. Remove center dash panel and vent grille. Remove center console trim, ashtray, radio, rear vent outlet and glove box. Remove center console.

3) Remove battery. Disconnect evaporator line from expansion valve. Remove and discard "O" rings. Plug refrigerant line openings. Disconnect heater hoses at firewall. Remove sponge collars from heater pipes, and retain for installation.

4) From engine compartment side, remove heater assembly-to-firewall nuts. Loosen CCU upper screw. Remove lower screw and remove unit. Remove defrost flexible ducting. Remove left and right blower motor flexible ducting.

5) Disconnect electrical connections at main harness, left and right blower motors and in-car sensor. Note position of vacuum hoses, and disconnect from vacuum solenoids and vacuum actuators. Remove heater unit-to-dash bolts. Carefully move assembly, and disconnect evaporator drain tubes from floor pan tunnel. Carefully remove assembly from vehicle. *See Fig. 3 or 4*.

Installation - To install, reverse removal procedure. Replace receiver-drier when replacing evaporator. Install NEW "O" rings. Ensure proper refrigerant oil level, and recharge A/C system.

1993 AUTOMATIC A/C-HEATER SYSTEMS XJ6 (Cont.)

EXPANSION VALVE

Removal & Installation – **1)** Discharge A/C system using approved refrigerant recovery/recycling equipment. Remove battery. Remove clamp securing receiver-drier to expansion valve pipe. Disconnect A/C hoses at expansion valve, and plug openings.

2) Support expansion valve to avoid pressure on evaporator. Carefully unscrew top union nut, and cap hose. Remove lower union nut, and cap hose. Unscrew union nuts on evaporator stub pipes. Remove expansion valve. To install, reverse removal procedure. Ensure proper refrigerant oil level, and recharge A/C system.

IN-CAR TEMPERATURE SENSOR

Removal & Installation – Disconnect negative battery cable. Open glove box, and remove sensor cover plate. Disconnect sensor electrical connector. Disconnect rubber tube from sensor assembly. Remove screws and remove sensor. To install, reverse removal procedure.

RECEIVER-DRIER

Removal & Installation – Discharge A/C system using approved refrigerant recovery/recycling equipment. Disconnect refrigerant lines from receiver-drier, and plug openings. Remove and discard "O" rings. Remove receiver-drier bolts. Remove receiver-drier. To install, reverse removal procedure. Install NEW "O" rings. Ensure proper refrigerant oil level, and recharge A/C system.

RECIRCULATION/FRESH AIR DOOR & COOLANT VALVE VACUUM SOLENOID

Removal & Installation – Disconnect negative battery cable. Remove left side dash liner and footwell duct. Remove 2 solenoid panel screws, and pull panel back for access. Note position of vacuum hose and electrical connectors, and remove vacuum solenoid. To install, reverse removal procedure.

SOLAR SENSOR

Removal & Installation – Disconnect negative battery cable. Carefully pry solar sensor panel from top of dash center. Disconnect multi-pin electrical connector. Remove sensor assembly. Pry clips from assembly, and remove sensor. To install, reverse removal procedure.

UPPER & LOWER AIR DOOR MOTOR

Removal & Installation – **1)** Disconnect negative battery cable. Remove glove box. Move relay bracket aside. Remove right side dash liner.

2) Remove CCU-to-A/C assembly screws, and move assembly aside. Remove motor screws, and disconnect electrical connector. Remove air door motor. To install, reverse removal procedure.

UPPER & LOWER AIR DOOR FEEDBACK POTENTIOMETER

Removal & Installation – Disconnect negative battery cable. Remove left side dash liner. Remove 3 potentiometer-to-A/C unit screws. Disconnect electrical connector. Remove feedback potentiometer. To install, reverse removal procedure.

WIRING DIAGRAM

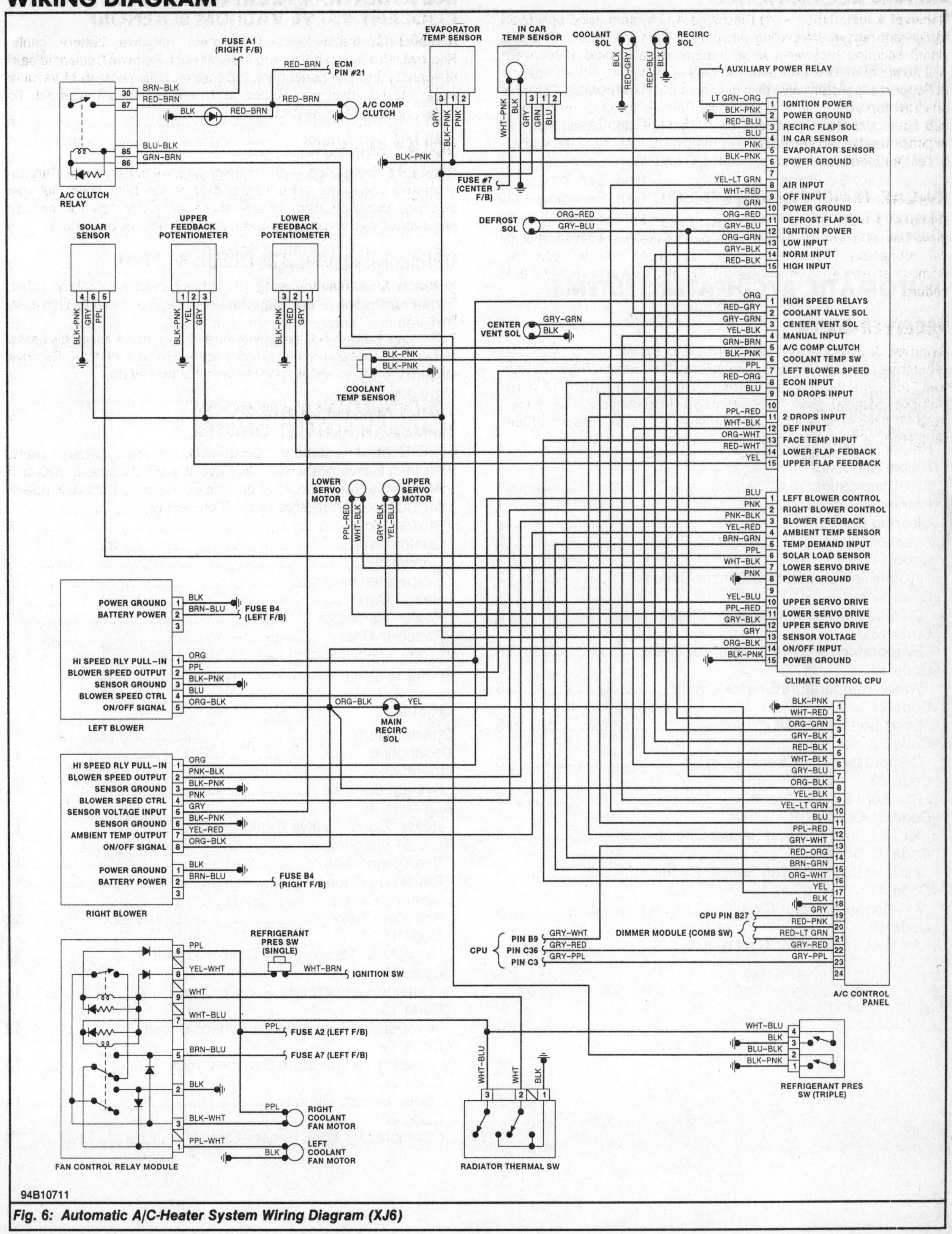
FUSE A1
(RIGHT F/B)
RED-BRN
ECM
PIN #21
A/C COMP
CLUTCH
A/C CLUTCH
RELAY
EVAPORATOR
TEMP SENSOR
IN CAR
TEMP SENSOR
COOLANT
SOL
RECIRC
SOL
AUXILIARY POWER RELAY
FUSE #7
(CENTER
F/B)
DEFROST
SOL
SOLAR
SENSOR
UPPER
FEEDBACK
POTENTIOMETER
LOWER
FEEDBACK
POTENTIOMETER
CENTER
VENT SOL
COOLANT
TEMP SENSOR
LOWER
SERVO
MOTOR
UPPER
SERVO
MOTOR
1 IGNITION POWER
2 POWER GROUND
3 RECIRC FLAP SOL
4 IN CAR SENSOR
5 EVAPORATOR SENSOR
6 POWER GROUND
8 AIR INPUT
9 OFF INPUT
10 POWER GROUND
11 DEFROST FLAP SOL
12 IGNITION POWER
13 LOW INPUT
14 NORM INPUT
15 HIGH INPUT
1 HIGH SPEED RELAYS
2 COOLANT VALVE SOL
3 CENTER VENT SOL
4 MANUAL INPUT
5 A/C COMP CLUTCH
6 COOLANT TEMP SW
7 LEFT BLOWER SPEED
8 ECON INPUT
9 NO DROPS INPUT
11 2 DROPS INPUT
12 DEF INPUT
13 FACE TEMP INPUT
14 LOWER FLAP FEDBACK
15 UPPER FLAP FEEDBACK
1 LEFT BLOWER CONTROL
2 RIGHT BLOWER CONTROL
3 BLOWER FEEDBACK
4 AMBIENT TEMP SENSOR
5 TEMP DEMAND INPUT
6 SOLAR LOAD SENSOR
7 LOWER SERVO DRIVE
8 POWER GROUND
10 UPPER SERVO DRIVE
11 LOWER SERVO DRIVE
12 UPPER SERVO DRIVE
13 SENSOR VOLTAGE
14 ON/OFF INPUT
15 POWER GROUND
CLIMATE CONTROL CPU
POWER GROUND
BATTERY POWER
FUSE B4
(LEFT F/B)
HI SPEED RLY PULL-IN
BLOWER SPEED OUTPUT
SENSOR GROUND
BLOWER SPEED CTRL
ON/OFF SIGNAL
LEFT BLOWER
MAIN
RECIRC
SOL
HI SPEED RLY PULL-IN
BLOWER SPEED OUTPUT
SENSOR GROUND
BLOWER SPEED CTRL
SENSOR VOLTAGE INPUT
SENSOR GROUND
AMBIENT TEMP OUTPUT
ON/OFF SIGNAL
POWER GROUND
BATTERY POWER
FUSE B4
(RIGHT F/B)
RIGHT BLOWER
CPU PIN B27
DIMMER MODULE (COMB SW)
CPU
PIN B9
PIN C36
PIN C3
A/C CONTROL
PANEL
REFRIGERANT
PRES SW
(SINGLE)
IGNITION SW
FUSE A2 (LEFT F/B)
FUSE A7 (LEFT F/B)
RIGHT
COOLANT
FAN MOTOR
LEFT
COOLANT
FAN MOTOR
FAN CONTROL RELAY MODULE
RADIATOR THERMAL SW
REFRIGERANT PRES
SW (TRIPLE)
94B10711

Fig. 6: Automatic A/C-Heater System Wiring Diagram (XJ6)

1993 LEXUS CONTENTS

GENERAL SERVICING

ALL MODELS

AUTOMATIC A/C-HEATER SYSTEMS

ES300

AUTOMATIC A/C-HEATER SYSTEMS (Cont.)

ES300 (Cont.)

GS300

AUTOMATIC A/C-HEATER SYSTEMS (Cont.)

AUTOMATIC A/C-HEATER SYSTEMS (Cont.)

1993 LEXUS CONTENTS (Cont.)

AUTOMATIC A/C-HEATER SYSTEMS (Cont.)

AUTOMATIC A/C-HEATER SYSTEMS (Cont.)

1993 AUTOMATIC A/C-HEATER SYSTEMS ES300

SPECIFICATIONS

Compressor Type .... Nippondenso 10PA20 10-Cyl.
Compressor Belt Tension [1]
New .... 139-191 lbs. (63-87 kg)
Used .... 66-110 lbs. (20-50 kg)
Compressor Oil Capacity .... 3.5 ozs.
Refrigerant (R-12) Capacity .... 32-35 ozs.
System Operating Pressures
High Side .... 206-213 psi (14.5-15.0 kg/cm²)
Low Side .... 21-28 psi (1.5-2.0 kg/cm²)

[1] – Check belt tension using tension gauge.

WARNING: To avoid injury from accidental air bag deployment, read and carefully follow all SERVICE PRECAUTIONS and DISABLING & ACTIVATING AIR BAG SYSTEM procedures in AIR BAG SYSTEM SAFETY article in GENERAL SERVICING.

NOTE: When battery is disconnected, radio will go into anti-theft protection mode. Obtain radio anti-theft protection code from owner prior to servicing vehicle.

DESCRIPTION

An Electronic Control Unit (ECU), located within A/C control assembly, automatically controls all A/C and heating functions. Manual controls allow the driver to select air distribution mode and desired temperature. In addition to normal A/C system components, automatic A/C-heater system includes various motors, controls and sensors. *See Fig. 1.* The system has self-diagnostic capabilities.

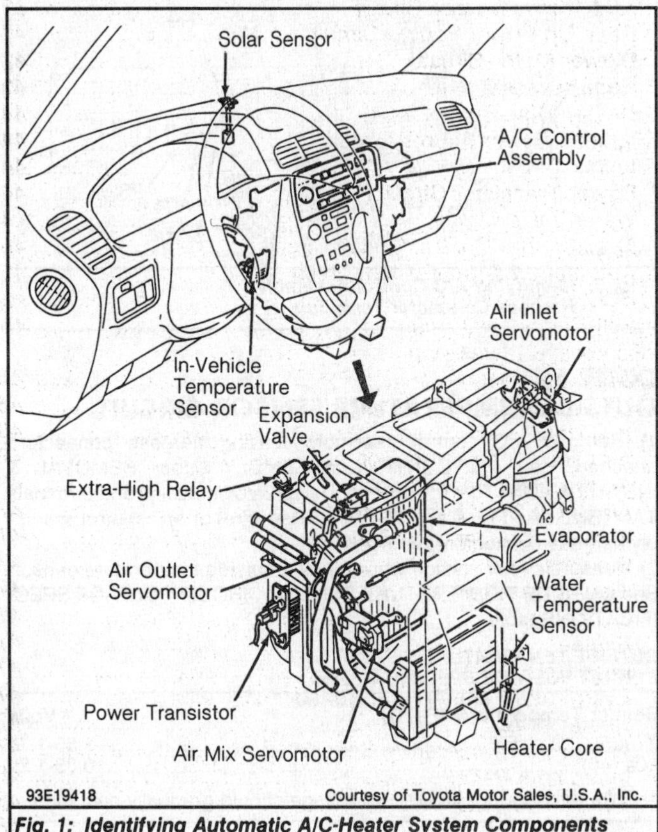
Solar Sensor
A/C Control Assembly
Air Inlet Servomotor
In-Vehicle Temperature Sensor
Expansion Valve
Extra-High Relay
Evaporator
Air Outlet Servomotor
Water Temperature Sensor
Power Transistor
Air Mix Servomotor
Heater Core
93E19418
Courtesy of Toyota Motor Sales, U.S.A., Inc.

Fig. 1: Identifying Automatic A/C-Heater System Components

OPERATION

SYSTEM CONTROLS

The A/C-heater control assembly consists of a liquid crystal display, a temperature control knob and various push buttons which activate A/C-heater system, set desired temperature, direct discharged air to desired outlets, activate rear defogger and control blower fan speed. *See Fig. 2.*

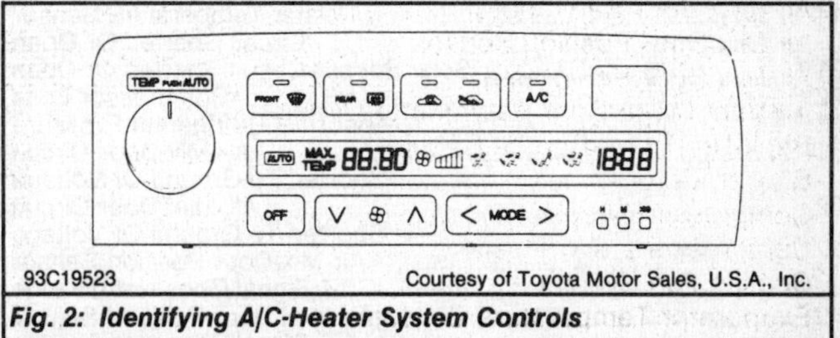
TEMP PUSH AUTO
FRONT
REAR
A/C
AUTO
MAX TEMP
88.80
1888
OFF
MODE
93C19523
Courtesy of Toyota Motor Sales, U.S.A., Inc.

Fig. 2: Identifying A/C-Heater System Controls

ADJUSTMENTS

HEATER WATER CONTROL VALVE

Disconnect heater water control valve cable, located in heater inlet line near firewall. Turn ignition on. Press A/C button. Set temperature control knob to maximum cool position (counterclockwise). Set heater water control valve to cool position. Install control cable, and secure it using clamp. *See Fig. 3.*

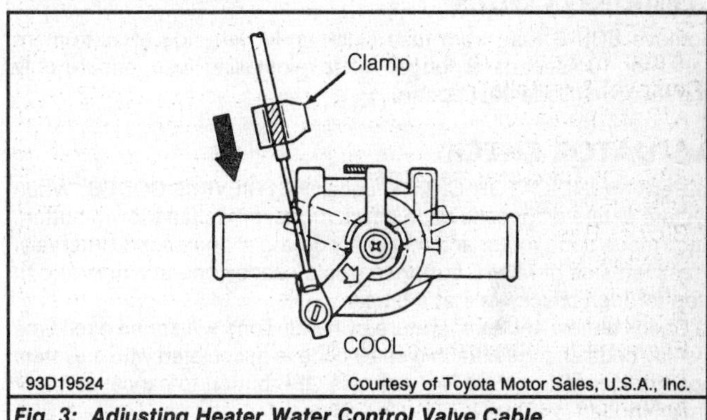
Clamp
COOL
93D19524
Courtesy of Toyota Motor Sales, U.S.A., Inc.

Fig. 3: Adjusting Heater Water Control Valve Cable

TROUBLE SHOOTING

SELF-DIAGNOSTICS

A/C control assembly monitors system circuits and stores a code in memory if a problem is detected. All codes are stored in memory except Codes 22 and 23. Malfunction is current if Code 22 or 23 is displayed. To retrieve stored codes, see RETRIEVING CODES. Codes are displayed at A/C control assembly temperature display.

RETRIEVING CODES

Indicator Check – 1) While pressing and holding temperature control knob and left side of fan (down) button, turn ignition on. Indicators will flash and tone will sound as a check. Press OFF button to cancel indicator check. After indicator check is complete, system will enter self-diagnostic mode. Stored trouble codes will appear in sequence on temperature display panel. See AUTOMATIC A/C-HEATER SYSTEM TROUBLE CODES table.

2) Press left side of MODE button to display codes one at a time. If tone sounds when code is displayed, problem causing code currently exists. If tone does not sound when code is displayed, associated problem is past history and does not currently exist. Press OFF button to exit self-diagnostics.

1993 AUTOMATIC A/C-HEATER SYSTEMS ES300 (Cont.)

AUTOMATIC A/C-HEATER SYSTEM TROUBLE CODES

Code Number	Condition/Affected Circuit
00	Normal
11 [1]	In-Vehicle Temperature Sensor Circuit Shorted Or Open
12 [2]	Outside Temperature Sensor Circuit Shorted Or Open
13	Evaporator Temperature Sensor Circuit Shorted Or Open
14	Water Temperature Sensor Circuit Shorted Or Open
21 [3]	Solar Sensor Circuit Shorted Or Open
22 [4]	Compressor Lock
23 [4]	Abnormal Refrigerant Pressure
31	Air Mix Door Circuit Shorted To Ground Or Voltage
32	Air Inlet Door Circuit Shorted To Ground Or Voltage
41	Air Mix Door Position Sensor Signal Does Not Change
42	Air Inlet Door Position Sensor Signal Does Not Change

[1] – If in-vehicle temperature is -4°F (-20C°) or less, Code 11 may occur even though system is normal.
[2] – If outside air temperature is -58°F (-50C°) or less, Code 12 may occur even though system is normal.
[3] – If testing is done in a dark area, Code 21 may occur even though system is normal. Shine a light at solar sensor and recheck codes.
[4] – Malfunction is current. Code is not stored in memory.

CLEARING CODES

Remove ECU-B fuse from fuse block under left side of instrument panel for 10 seconds or longer. After reinstalling fuse, ensure only normal code (Code 00) appears.

ACTUATOR CHECK

1) Perform INDICATOR CHECK under RETRIEVING CODES. When system enters diagnostic code check mode, press fan (down) button. Each mode door, motor and relay will operate at one-second intervals. Press left side of MODE button to display codes one at a time and to step through checks one at a time.

2) Check airflow and temperature by hand. Tone will sound each time display code changes. Each display code is associated with a system operating condition. *See Fig. 4.* Press OFF button to cancel actuator check mode.

Step No.	Display code	Conditions				
		Blower motor	Air flow vent	Air inlet dampar	Magnet clutch	Air mix damper
1	20	OFF ( )	FACE ( )	FRESH ( )	OFF	Cool side (0% open)
2	21	( )	↑	↑	↑	↑
3	22	( )	↑	↑	ON	↑
4	23	↑	↑	F/R ( )	↑	↑
5	24	↑	↑	RECIRC ( )	↑	Cool/Hot (50% open)
6	25	↑	BI-LEVEL ( )	↑	↑	↑
7	26	↑	FOOT ( )	↑	↑	Hot side (100% open)
8	27	↑	↑	↑	↑	↑
9	28	↑	F/D ( )	↑	↑	↑
10	29	( )	DEF ( )	↑	↑	↑

93G19444 Courtesy of Toyota Motor Sales, U.S.A., Inc.

Fig. 4: Identifying Actuator Check Display Codes

CODE 11
IN-VEHICLE TEMPERATURE SENSOR CIRCUIT

1) Remove A/C control assembly, leaving harness connectors attached. See A/C CONTROL ASSEMBLY under REMOVAL & INSTALLATION. Turn ignition on. Using DVOM, backprobe terminals TR (Green/Yellow wire) and SG (White/Red wire) of A/C control assembly harness connector. *See Fig. 5.*

2) Measure circuit voltage while heating sensor. See IN-VEHICLE TEMPERATURE SENSOR CIRCUIT VOLTAGE SPECIFICATIONS table.

IN-VEHICLE TEMPERATURE SENSOR CIRCUIT VOLTAGE SPECIFICATIONS

Sensor Temperature °F (°C)	[1] Volts
77 (25)	1.8-2.2
104 (40)	1.2-1.6

[1] – As temperature increases, voltage should gradually decrease.

3) If circuit voltage is not as specified, test in-vehicle sensor. See IN-VEHICLE TEMPERATURE SENSOR under TESTING. Replace sensor if it is defective. If sensor is okay, go to next step.

4) Check wiring harness and connectors between sensor and A/C control assembly. Repair harness and connectors as necessary. If wiring harness and connectors are okay, temporarily substitute a known good A/C control assembly. Retest system.

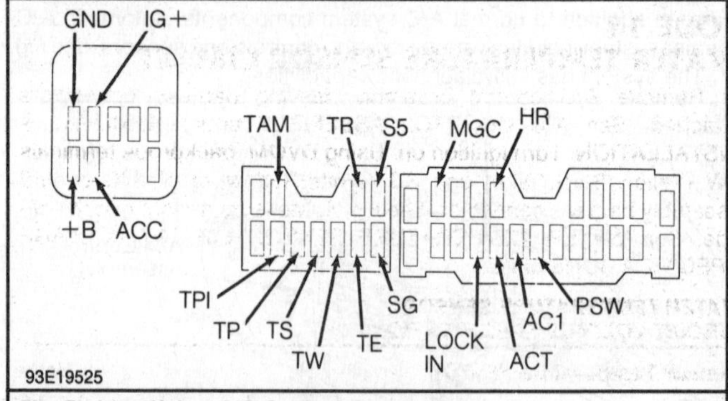
GND
IG+
+B
ACC
TAM
TR
S5
MGC
HR
TPI
TP
TS
TW
TE
SG
LOCK IN
AC1
ACT
PSW
93E19525

Fig. 5: Identifying A/C Control Assembly Harness Connector Terminals

CODE 12
OUTSIDE TEMPERATURE SENSOR CIRCUIT

1) Remove A/C control assembly, leaving harness connectors attached. See A/C CONTROL ASSEMBLY under REMOVAL & INSTALLATION. Turn ignition on. Using DVOM, backprobe terminals TAM (Black/Red wire) and SG (White/Red wire) of A/C control assembly harness connector. *See Fig. 5.*

2) Measure circuit voltage while heating outside temperature sensor. See OUTSIDE TEMPERATURE SENSOR CIRCUIT VOLTAGE SPECIFICATIONS table.

OUTSIDE TEMPERATURE SENSOR CIRCUIT VOLTAGE SPECIFICATIONS

Sensor Temperature °F (°C)	[1] Volts
77 (25)	1.35-1.75
104 (40)	0.85-1.25

[1] – As temperature increases, voltage should gradually decrease.

3) If circuit voltage is not as specified, test sensor. See OUTSIDE TEMPERATURE SENSOR under TESTING. Replace sensor if it is defective. If sensor is okay, go to next step.

4) Check wiring harness and connectors between sensor and A/C control assembly. Repair harness and connectors as necessary. If wiring harness and connectors are okay, temporarily substitute a known good A/C control assembly. Retest system.

CODE 13
EVAPORATOR TEMPERATURE SENSOR CIRCUIT

1) Remove A/C control assembly, leaving harness connectors attached. See A/C CONTROL ASSEMBLY under REMOVAL & INSTALLATION. Turn ignition on. Using DVOM, backprobe terminals TE (Blue/White wire) and SG (White/Red wire) of A/C control assembly harness connector. *See Fig. 5.*
2) Measure evaporator temperature sensor circuit voltage. See EVAPORATOR TEMPERATURE SENSOR CIRCUIT VOLTAGE SPECIFICATIONS table.

EVAPORATOR TEMPERATURE SENSOR CIRCUIT VOLTAGE SPECIFICATIONS

Sensor Temperature °F (°C)	[1] Volts
32 (0)	2.0-2.4
59 (15)	1.4-1.8

[1] – As temperature increases, voltage should gradually decrease.

3) If circuit voltage is not as specified, test evaporator temperature sensor. See EVAPORATOR TEMPERATURE SENSOR under TESTING. Replace sensor if it is defective. If sensor is okay, go to next step.
4) Check wiring harness and connectors between sensor and A/C control assembly. Repair harness and connectors as necessary. If wiring harness and connectors are okay, temporarily substitute a known good A/C control assembly. Retest system.

CODE 14
WATER TEMPERATURE SENSOR CIRCUIT

1) Remove A/C control assembly, leaving harness connectors attached. See A/C CONTROL ASSEMBLY under REMOVAL & INSTALLATION. Turn ignition on. Using DVOM, backprobe terminals TW (Yellow/Black wire) and SG (White/Red wire) of A/C control assembly harness connector. *See Fig. 5.* Measure sensor circuit voltage. See WATER TEMPERATURE SENSOR CIRCUIT VOLTAGE SPECIFICATIONS table.

WATER TEMPERATURE SENSOR CIRCUIT VOLTAGE SPECIFICATIONS

Sensor Temperature °F (°C)	[1] Volts
32 (0)	2.8-3.2
104 (40)	1.8-2.2
158 (70)	0.9-1.3

[1] – As temperature increases, voltage should gradually decrease.

2) If circuit voltage is not as specified, test water temperature sensor. See WATER TEMPERATURE SENSOR under TESTING. Replace sensor if it is defective. If sensor is okay, go to next step.
3) Check wiring harness and connectors between sensor and A/C control assembly. Repair harness and connectors as necessary. If wiring harness and connectors are okay, temporarily substitute a known good A/C control assembly. Retest system.

CODE 21
SOLAR SENSOR CIRCUIT

NOTE:* *If testing is done in a dark area, Code 21 may occur even though system is normal. Shine a light at solar sensor and recheck for Code 21.

1) Remove A/C control assembly, leaving harness connectors attached. See A/C CONTROL ASSEMBLY under REMOVAL & INSTALLATION. Turn ignition on. Using DVOM, backprobe terminals S5 (Blue wire) and TS (White wire) of A/C control assembly harness connector. *See Fig. 5.* Measure sensor circuit voltage. See SOLAR SENSOR CIRCUIT VOLTAGE SPECIFICATIONS table.

SOLAR SENSOR CIRCUIT VOLTAGE SPECIFICATIONS

Condition	[1] Volts
Sensor Subjected To Bright Light	Less Than 4.0
Sensor Covered By Cloth	4.0-4.5

[1] – As light intensity decreases, voltage should increase.

2) If circuit voltage is not as specified, test solar sensor. See SOLAR SENSOR under TESTING. Replace sensor if it is defective. If sensor is okay, go to next step.
3) Check wiring harness and connectors between sensor and A/C control assembly. Repair harness and connectors as necessary. If wiring harness and connectors are okay, temporarily substitute a known good A/C control assembly. Retest system.

CODE 22
COMPRESSOR LOCK SENSOR CIRCUIT

1) Ensure drive belt is installed properly, and belt tension is correct. Start engine. Turn blower and A/C on. Observe compressor. If compressor locks during operation, repair compressor. If compressor does not lock during operation, test compressor lock sensor. See COMPRESSOR LOCK SENSOR under TESTING.
2) Replace compressor lock sensor if it is defective. If sensor is okay, check wiring harness and connectors between sensor and A/C control assembly. Repair harness and connectors as necessary. If wiring harness and connectors are okay, temporarily substitute a known good A/C control assembly. Retest system.

CODE 23
PRESSURE SWITCH CIRCUIT

1) Remove A/C control assembly, leaving harness connectors attached. See A/C CONTROL ASSEMBLY under REMOVAL & INSTALLATION. Install manifold gauge set. Turn ignition on. Using DVOM, backprobe terminal PSW (Red/Blue wire) of A/C control assembly harness connector and ground. *See Fig. 5*
2) Start engine. Turn A/C on. Pressure switch operation should be as shown. *See Fig. 6.* If pressure switch operation is not as specified, go to next step. If pressure switch operation is as specified, circuit is okay.
3) Unplug pressure switch connector, located below battery. Check for continuity between switch terminals at refrigerant pressures shown. *See Fig. 7.* Replace pressure switch if operation is not as specified. If switch is okay, check wiring harness and connectors between switch and A/C control assembly. If wiring harness and connectors are okay, substitute a known good A/C control assembly. Retest system.

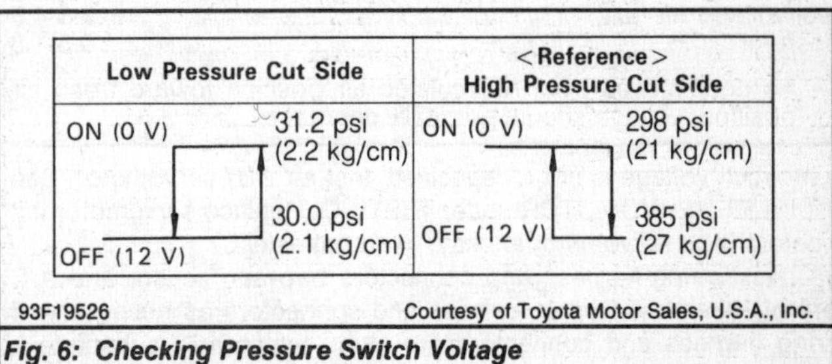

Low Pressure Cut Side
<Reference>
High Pressure Cut Side
ON (0 V)
31.2 psi
(2.2 kg/cm)
30.0 psi
(2.1 kg/cm)
OFF (12 V)
ON (0 V)
298 psi
(21 kg/cm)
385 psi
(27 kg/cm)
OFF (12 V)
93F19526
Courtesy of Toyota Motor Sales, U.S.A., Inc.

Fig. 6: Checking Pressure Switch Voltage

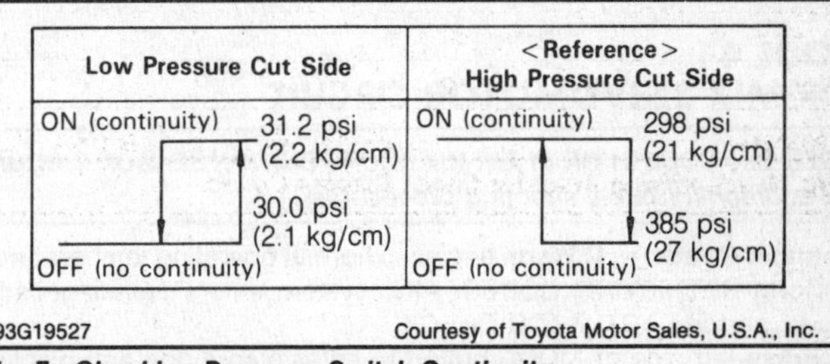

Low Pressure Cut Side
<Reference>
High Pressure Cut Side
ON (continuity)
31.2 psi
(2.2 kg/cm)
30.0 psi
(2.1 kg/cm)
OFF (no continuity)
ON (continuity)
298 psi
(21 kg/cm)
385 psi
(27 kg/cm)
OFF (no continuity)
93G19527
Courtesy of Toyota Motor Sales, U.S.A., Inc.

Fig. 7: Checking Pressure Switch Continuity

1993 AUTOMATIC A/C-HEATER SYSTEMS ES300 (Cont.)

CODE 31 OR 41 AIR MIX DOOR POSITION SENSOR CIRCUIT

***NOTE:** For Code 41, see CODE 41 AIR MIX SERVOMOTOR CIRCUIT for additional trouble shooting procedures.*

1) Remove A/C control assembly, leaving harness connectors attached. See A/C CONTROL ASSEMBLY under REMOVAL & INSTALLATION. Turn ignition on. Using DVOM, backprobe terminals TP (Black/Yellow wire) and SG (White/Red wire) of A/C control assembly harness connector. *See Fig. 5.*

2) Measure sensor circuit voltage while changing set temperature to activate air mix door. See AIR MIX DOOR POSITION SENSOR CIRCUIT VOLTAGE table.

AIR MIX DOOR POSITION SENSOR CIRCUIT VOLTAGE

Set Temperature	[1] Volts
Maximum Cool	3.5-4.5
Maximum Hot	0.5-1.8

[1] – As set temperature increases, voltage should gradually decrease.

3) If circuit voltage is not as specified, test air mix servomotor. See AIR MIX SERVOMOTOR under TESTING. Replace servomotor if it is defective. If servomotor is okay, go to next step.

4) Check wiring harness and connectors between sensor and A/C control assembly. Repair harness and connectors as necessary. If wiring harness and connectors are okay, temporarily substitute a known good A/C control assembly. Retest system.

CODE 32 OR 42 AIR INLET DOOR POSITION SENSOR CIRCUIT

***NOTE:** For Code 42, see CODE 42 AIR INLET SERVOMOTOR CIRCUIT for additional trouble shooting procedures.*

1) Remove A/C control assembly, leaving harness connectors attached. See A/C CONTROL ASSEMBLY under REMOVAL & INSTALLATION. Turn ignition on. Using DVOM, backprobe terminals TPI (Blue/Yellow wire) and SG (White/Red wire) of A/C control assembly harness connector. *See Fig. 5.*

2) Measure sensor circuit voltage while alternately pressing fresh air and recirculated air buttons to activate air inlet door. See AIR INLET DOOR POSITION CIRCUIT VOLTAGE SPECIFICATIONS table.

AIR INLET DOOR POSITION CIRCUIT VOLTAGE SPECIFICATIONS

Switch Pressed	[1] Volts
Recirculated Air	3.5-4.5
Fresh Air	0.5-1.8

[1] – As door moves from recirculated air position toward fresh air position, voltage should gradually decrease.

3) If circuit voltage is not as specified, test air inlet servomotor. See AIR INLET SERVOMOTOR under TESTING. Replace servomotor if it is defective. If servomotor is okay, go to next step.

4) Check wiring harness and connectors between sensor and A/C control assembly. Repair harness and connectors as necessary. If wiring harness and connectors are okay, temporarily substitute a known good A/C control assembly. Retest system.

CODE 41 AIR MIX SERVOMOTOR CIRCUIT

***NOTE:** See CODE 31 OR 41 AIR MIX DOOR POSITION SENSOR CIRCUIT for additional trouble shooting procedures.*

Actuator Check – 1) Warm engine to normal operating temperature. Perform RETRIEVING CODES. After system enters self-diagnostic mode, perform ACTUATOR CHECK.

2) Press left side of MODE button to enter step mode and display codes. See AIR MIX DOOR AIRFLOW table. Air mix door operation should be as specified.

3) If air mix door functions as specified, circuit is okay. If air mix door does not function as specified, see AIR MIX SERVOMOTOR FUNCTIONAL CHECK.

AIR MIX DOOR AIRFLOW

Code	Air Mix Door	Expected Result
20-23	Fully Closed	Cool Air Comes Out
24-25	Half Open	Blend (Cool/Hot) Air Comes Out
26-29	Fully Open	Hot Air Comes Out

Air Mix Servomotor Functional Check – 1) Remove air mix servomotor. See AIR MIX SERVOMOTOR under REMOVAL & INSTALLATION. Unplug air mix servomotor connector.

2) Apply battery voltage to servomotor connector terminal No. 2 (Pink wire). *See Fig. 8.* Connect terminal No. 6 (Orange wire) to ground. Air mix servomotor lever should move to cool position. Reverse battery and ground leads. Servomotor lever should move to hot position.

3) If air mix servomotor does not function as described, replace air mix servomotor. If servomotor functions correctly, check wiring harness and connectors between servomotor and A/C control assembly. Repair or replace harness and connectors as necessary. If wiring harness and connectors are okay, substitute a known good A/C control assembly. Retest system.

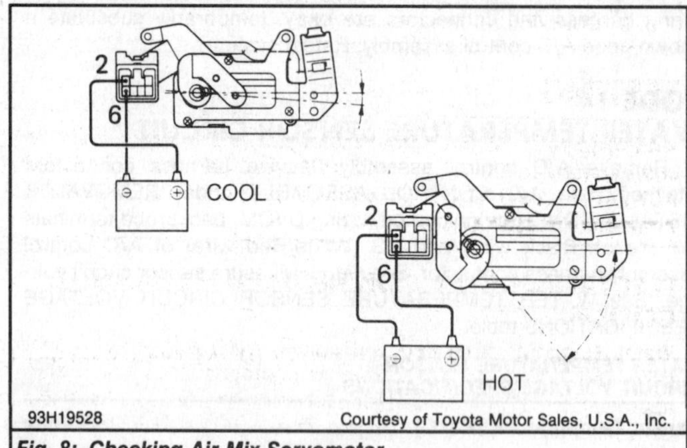
2
6
COOL
2
6
HOT
93H19528
Courtesy of Toyota Motor Sales, U.S.A., Inc.

Fig. 8: Checking Air Mix Servomotor

CODE 42 AIR INLET SERVOMOTOR CIRCUIT

***NOTE:** See CODE 32 OR 42 AIR INLET DOOR POSITION SENSOR CIRCUIT for additional trouble shooting procedures.*

Actuator Check – 1) Warm engine to normal operating temperature. Perform RETRIEVING CODES. After system enters self-diagnostic mode, perform ACTUATOR CHECK.

2) Press left side of MODE button to enter step mode and display codes. See AIR INLET DOOR AIRFLOW table. Air inlet door operation should be as specified.

AIR INLET DOOR AIRFLOW

Code	Door Position
20-22	Fresh Air
23	Fresh/Recirculated Air
24-29	Recirculated Air

3) If air inlet door functions as specified, circuit is okay. If air inlet door does not function as specified, test air inlet servomotor. See AIR INLET SERVOMOTOR under TESTING.

Air Inlet Servomotor Functional Check – 1) Remove air inlet servomotor. See AIR INLET SERVOMOTOR under REMOVAL & INSTALLATION. Unplug air inlet servomotor connector.

2) Connect battery voltage to air inlet servomotor connector terminal No. 2 (Red wire). *See Fig. 9.* Connect terminal No. 1 (Red/Blue wire) to ground. Air inlet servomotor lever should move to recirculated air position. Reverse battery and ground leads. Air inlet servomotor lever should move to fresh air position.

3) If air inlet servomotor does not operate as specified, replace air inlet servomotor assembly. If servomotor operates correctly, check wiring harness and connectors between servomotor and A/C control assembly. Repair or replace harness and connectors as necessary. If wiring harness and connectors are okay, substitute a known good A/C control assembly. Retest system.

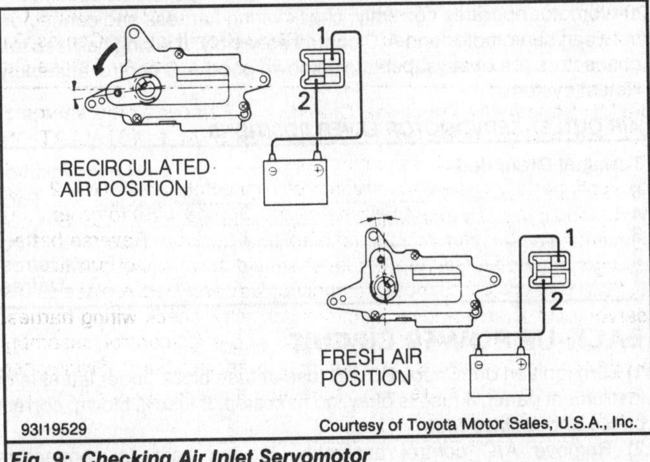

1
2
RECIRCULATED
AIR POSITION
1
2
FRESH AIR
POSITION
93I19529
Courtesy of Toyota Motor Sales, U.S.A., Inc.

Fig. 9: Checking Air Inlet Servomotor

TESTING

WARNING: To avoid injury from accidental air bag deployment, read and carefully follow all SERVICE PRECAUTIONS and DISABLING & ACTIVATING AIR BAG SYSTEM procedures in AIR BAG SYSTEM SAFETY article in GENERAL SERVICING.

ELECTRONICALLY CONTROLLED HYDRAULIC COOLING FAN

Water Temperature Sensor – Remove water temperature sensor from front of engine block. Heat temperature sensor in water to approximately 176°F (80°C). Using an ohmmeter, measure resistance between sensor terminals. If resistance is not 1480-1580 ohms, replace sensor.

Cooling Fan Electronic Control Unit – 1) Disconnect Cooling Fan Electronic Control Unit (ECU) connector. Using a voltmeter, measure voltage between ECU connector terminal No. 1 and ground. *See Fig. 10.* Battery voltage should be present.

2) Turn ignition off. Using an ohmmeter, measure resistance between remaining connector terminals. See ECU CIRCUIT RESISTANCE SPECIFICATIONS table. Repair or replace as necessary.

ECU CIRCUIT RESISTANCE SPECIFICATIONS

ECU Terminals	Condition	Specifications
2 & 3	Solenoid Valve 77°F (25°C)	7.6-8.0 Ohms
4 & GND		Continuity
5 & GND	Throttle Valve Open	No Continuity
5 & GND	Throttle Valve Closed	Continuity
8 & GND	A/C Pressure Switch Disconnected	No Continuity
8 & GND	A/C Pressure Switch Connected	Continuity
9 & 10	Coolant Temp. 176°F (80°C)	1480-1580 Ohms

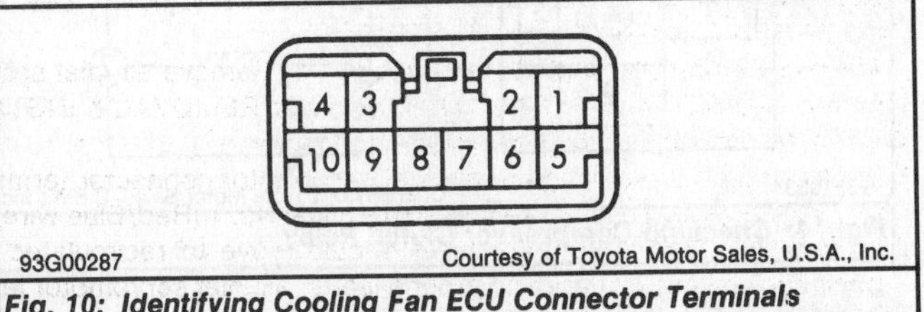

4
3
2
1
10
9
8
7
6
5
93G00287
Courtesy of Toyota Motor Sales, U.S.A., Inc.

Fig. 10: Identifying Cooling Fan ECU Connector Terminals

Pressure Switch – For pressure switch testing procedures, see CODE 23 PRESSURE SWITCH CIRCUIT under TROUBLE SHOOTING.

Solenoid Valve – Disconnect solenoid valve connector, located at right rear of engine compartment. Using an ohmmeter, measure resistance between connector terminals. If resistance is not 7.6-8.0 ohms at 77°F (80°C), replace solenoid valve.

ACCESSORY POWER CIRCUIT

1) Turn ignition on. Check CIG/RADIO fuse at fuse block under left side of instrument panel. If fuse is okay, go next step. If fuse is blown, correct cause and replace fuse.

2) Turn ignition off. Remove console upper panel. Remove A/C control assembly, leaving harness connectors attached. Turn ignition on. Using DVOM, backprobe A/C control assembly 8-pin connector between terminal ACC (Blue/Red wire) and body ground. *See Fig. 5.* If battery voltage does not exist, repair Blue/Red wire between connector and CIG/RADIO fuse.

AIR INLET SERVOMOTOR

1) Unplug air inlet servomotor connector. See AIR INLET SERVOMOTOR under REMOVAL & INSTALLATION. Measure resistance between servomotor connector terminals No. 4 and 5. *See Fig. 11.* If resistance is not 4700-7200 ohms, replace air inlet servomotor. If resistance is 4700-7200 ohms, go to next step.

2) Connect ohmmeter between terminals No. 3 and 5. Connect battery voltage to terminal No. 2. *See Fig. 9.* Connect terminal No. 1 to ground. Reverse battery and ground leads. Resistance should be as specified for each door position. See AIR INLET DOOR POSITION RESISTANCE SPECIFICATIONS table.

AIR INLET DOOR POSITION RESISTANCE SPECIFICATIONS

Position	[1] Ohms
Recirculated Air	3800-5800
Fresh Air	950-1450

[1] – Resistance should gradually decrease as air inlet door moves from recirculated air position toward fresh air position.

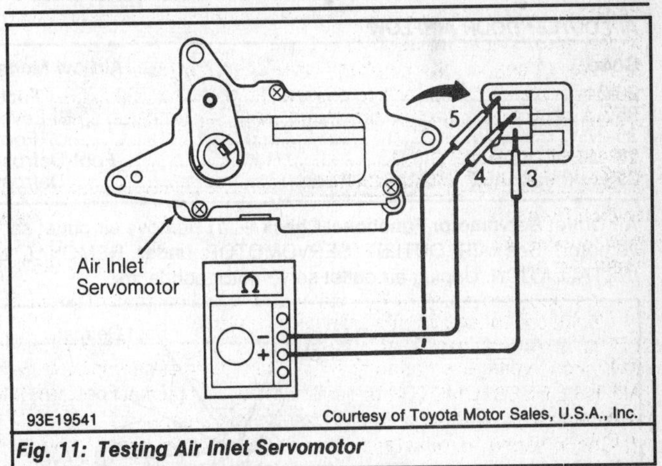

5
4
3
Air Inlet
Servomotor
Ω
93E19541
Courtesy of Toyota Motor Sales, U.S.A., Inc.

Fig. 11: Testing Air Inlet Servomotor

AIR MIX SERVOMOTOR

1) Remove air mix servomotor. See AIR MIX SERVOMOTOR under REMOVAL & INSTALLATION. Unplug air mix servomotor connector. Measure resistance between servomotor connector terminals No. 1 and 3. *See Fig. 12.* If resistance is not 4700-7200 ohms, replace air mix servomotor. If resistance is as 4700-7200 ohms, go to next step.

2) Connect ohmmeter between servomotor terminals No. 1 and 4. Apply battery voltage to air mix servomotor connector terminal No. 2. *See Fig. 8.* Connect terminal No. 6 to ground. Measure resistance between terminals No. 1 and 4. Reverse battery and ground leads. Resistance should be as specified for each door position. See AIR MIX DOOR POSITION RESISTANCE SPECIFICATIONS table.

1993 AUTOMATIC A/C-HEATER SYSTEMS
ES300 (Cont.)

AIR MIX DOOR POSITION RESISTANCE SPECIFICATIONS

Position	[1] Ohms
Cold	3800-5800
Hot	950-1450

[1] - Resistance should decrease gradually as air mix door moves from cold position toward hot position.

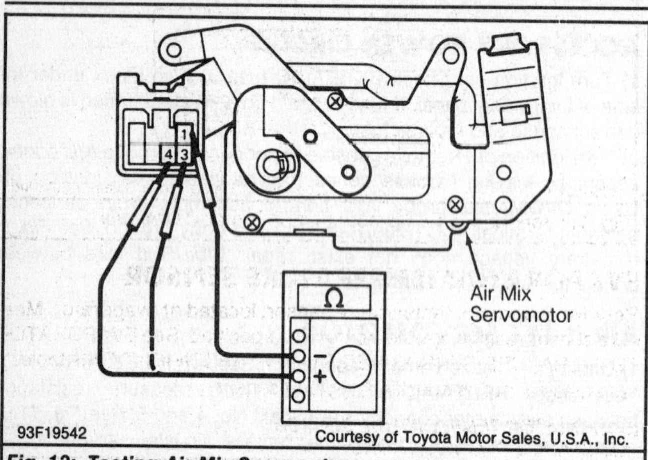
1
4 3
Ω
Air Mix
Servomotor
93F19542
Courtesy of Toyota Motor Sales, U.S.A., Inc.

Fig. 12: Testing Air Mix Servomotor

AIR OUTLET SERVOMOTOR CIRCUIT

1) Warm engine to normal operating temperature. Perform RETRIEVING CODES under TROUBLE SHOOTING. After system enters self-diagnostic mode, perform ACTUATOR CHECK under TROUBLE SHOOTING.
2) Press left side of MODE button to enter step mode and display codes. See AIR OUTLET DOOR AIRFLOW table. Air outlet door operation should be as specified.
3) If air outlet door servomotor functions as specified, circuit is okay. If air outlet door does not function as specified, check air outlet servomotor. See AIR OUTLET SERVOMOTOR FUNCTIONAL CHECK.

AIR OUTLET DOOR AIRFLOW

Code	Airflow Mode
20-24	Face
25	Bi-Level
26-27	Foot
28	Foot-Defrost
29	Defrost

Air Outlet Servomotor Functional Check - 1) Remove air outlet servomotor. See AIR OUTLET SERVOMOTOR under REMOVAL & INSTALLATION. Unplug air outlet servomotor connector.

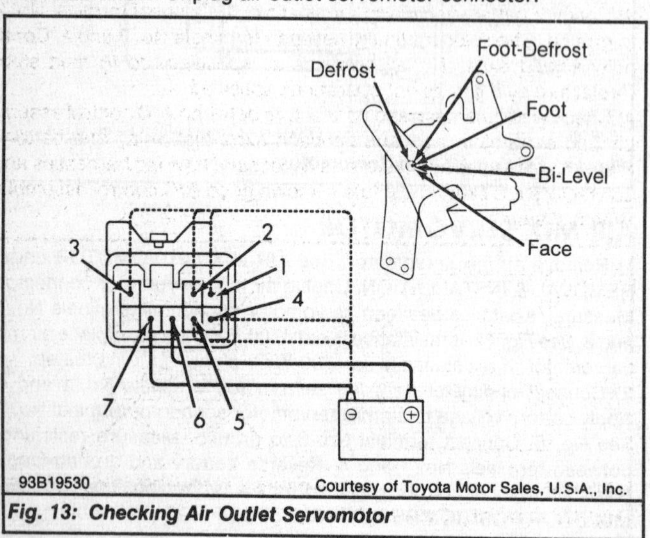
Foot-Defrost
Defrost
Foot
Bi-Level
Face
3
2
1
4
7
6
5
93B19530
Courtesy of Toyota Motor Sales, U.S.A., Inc.

Fig. 13: Checking Air Outlet Servomotor

2) Apply battery voltage to air outlet servomotor connector terminal No. 6. *See Fig. 13.* Connect terminal No. 7 to ground. Air outlet servomotor lever should move to specified position when the appropriate terminal is grounded. See AIR OUTLET SERVOMOTOR LEVER POSITIONS table.
3) Replace air outlet servomotor if it does not operate as specified. If servomotor operates correctly, check wiring harness and connectors between servomotor and A/C control assembly. If wiring harness and connectors are okay, substitute a known good A/C control assembly. Retest system.

AIR OUTLET SERVOMOTOR LEVER POSITIONS

Terminal Grounded	Lever Position
5	Face
4	Bi-Level
3	Foot
2	Foot-Defrost
1	Defrost

BACK-UP POWER CIRCUIT

1) Turn ignition off. Check ECU-B fuse at fuse block under left side of instrument panel. If fuse is okay, go next step. If fuse is blown, correct cause and replace fuse.
2) Remove A/C control assembly, leaving harness connectors attached. Turn ignition on. Using DVOM, backprobe between A/C control assembly 8-pin connector terminal +B (Blue/Yellow wire) and body ground. *See Fig. 5.* If battery voltage does not exist, repair Blue/Yellow wire between connector and ECU-B fuse.

BLOWER MOTOR CIRCUIT

1) Turn ignition off. Remove blower motor. See BLOWER MOTOR under REMOVAL & INSTALLATION. Connect battery voltage to terminal No. 2 (Black wire) of blower motor. Connect terminal No. 1 (Black/White wire) to ground. If blower motor runs smoothly, go to next step. Replace blower motor if it does not run smoothly.
2) Check wiring between blower motor and battery and between blower motor and ground. Repair wiring as necessary.

COMPRESSOR CIRCUIT

1) Turn ignition on. Check GAUGE fuse at fuse block under left side of instrument panel. If fuse is okay, go next step. If fuse is blown, correct cause and replace fuse.
2) Turn ignition off. Remove A/C control assembly, leaving harness connectors attached. See A/C CONTROL ASSEMBLY under REMOVAL & INSTALLATION. Start engine. Using DVOM, backprobe A/C control assembly connector terminal MGC (Blue/Yellow wire) and body ground. *See Fig. 5.*
3) Press A/C button. Voltmeter should indicate less than one volt. Press OFF button. Voltmeter should indicate battery voltage. If operation is as specified, go to next step. If operation is as not as specified, go to step **8)**.
4) Remove compressor clutch relay from relay box No. 5, located at left side of engine compartment, toward rear. Measure resistance between terminals No. 1 and 2. *See Fig. 14.* Resistance should be 62.5-90.9 ohms. Check for continuity between terminals No. 3 and 5. Continuity should not exist.

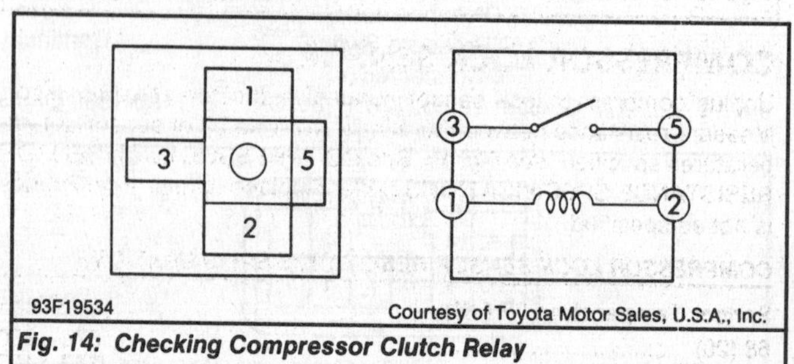
1
3
5
2
3
5
1
2
93F19534
Courtesy of Toyota Motor Sales, U.S.A., Inc.

Fig. 14: Checking Compressor Clutch Relay

5) Connect battery voltage to terminal No. 1 of relay. Connect terminal No. 2 to ground. Check for continuity between terminals No. 3 and 5. Continuity should exist. If relay operates as specified, go to next step. Replace relay if it does not operate as specified.
6) Unplug connector from compressor clutch. Apply battery voltage to compressor clutch connector terminal No. 4 (Black/White wire). If clutch engages, go to next step. If clutch does not engage, repair or replace compressor clutch.
7) Check wiring and connectors associated with compressor relay and compressor. Repair or replace wiring and connectors as necessary. If wiring and connectors are okay, go to next step.
8) Turn ignition off. Unplug 23-pin connector from A/C control assembly. Turn ignition on. Check for voltage at harness connector terminal AC1 (Black/Yellow wire). If battery voltage exists, go to next step. If battery voltage does not exist, substitute a known good Engine Control Module (ECM). Retest system.
9) Connect wiring to A/C control assembly. Backprobe terminal AC1 (Black/Yellow wire) of 23-pin connector and ground. *See Fig. 5.* Start engine. Press AUTO button. Cycle A/C system on and off by pressing A/C button. With compressor clutch engaged, meter should indicate less than one volt. With compressor clutch disengaged, meter should indicate battery voltage. If readings are as specified, go to next step. If readings are not as specified, substitute a known good A/C control assembly. Retest system.
10) Start engine. Press AUTO button. Cycle A/C system on and off by pressing A/C button. With A/C system off, meter should indicate less than 1.5 volts. With A/C system on, meter should indicate battery voltage. If readings are not as specified, go to next step. If readings are as specified, substitute a known good A/C control assembly. Retest system.
11) Check wiring and connectors associated with A/C control assembly and ECM. Repair or replace wiring and connectors as necessary. If wiring harnesses and connectors are okay, go to next step.
12) Turn ignition off. Remove glove box. Unplug connectors from ECM. Turn ignition on. Press A/C button to turn system on. Measure voltage between terminal ACT (Light Green/Red wire) on engine/electronically controlled transmission ECU and ground. *See Fig. 15.* If battery voltage exists, substitute a known good ECM. Retest system.

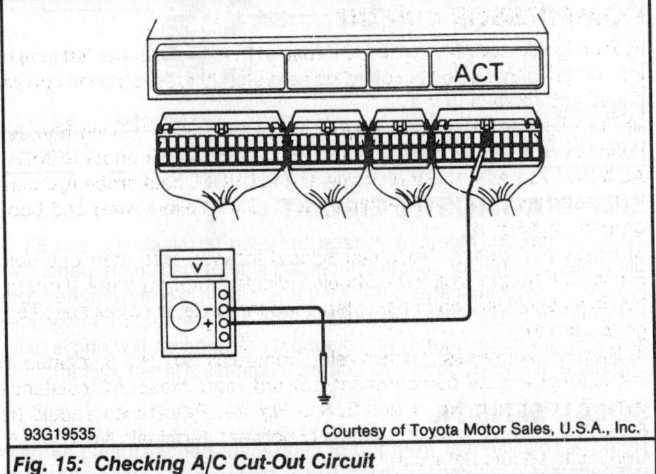
ACT
V
93G19535
Courtesy of Toyota Motor Sales, U.S.A., Inc.

Fig. 15: Checking A/C Cut-Out Circuit

COMPRESSOR LOCK SENSOR

Unplug compressor lock sensor connector, located at compressor. Measure resistance between terminals No. 1 and 2 of sensor at temperatures specified. *See Fig. 16.* See COMPRESSOR LOCK SENSOR RESISTANCE SPECIFICATIONS table. Replace sensor if resistance is not as specified.

COMPRESSOR LOCK SENSOR RESISTANCE SPECIFICATIONS

Sensor Temperature °F (°C)	Ohms
68 (20)	570-1050
212 (100)	740-1400

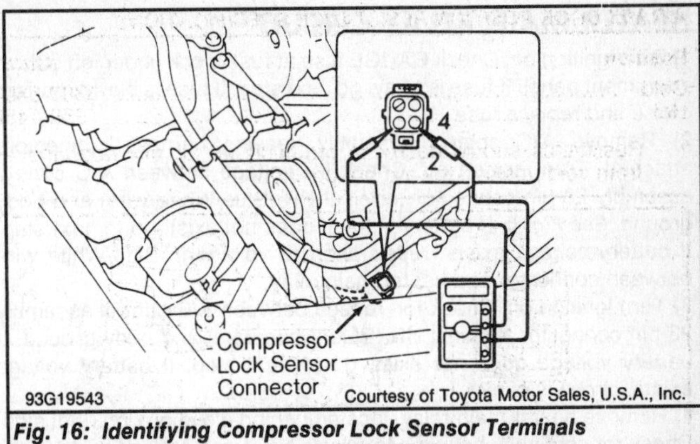
4
1
2
Compressor
Lock Sensor
Connector
93G19543
Courtesy of Toyota Motor Sales, U.S.A., Inc.

Fig. 16: Identifying Compressor Lock Sensor Terminals

EVAPORATOR TEMPERATURE SENSOR

Remove evaporator temperature sensor, located at evaporator. Measure sensor resistance at temperatures specified. See EVAPORATOR TEMPERATURE SENSOR RESISTANCE SPECIFICATIONS table. If resistance is not as specified, replace sensor.

EVAPORATOR TEMPERATURE SENSOR RESISTANCE SPECIFICATIONS

Sensor Temperature °F (°C)	[1] Ohms
32 (0)	4600-5200
59 (15)	2100-2600

[1] – As temperature increases, resistance should gradually decrease.

EXTRA-HIGH RELAY CIRCUIT

1) Perform RETRIEVING CODES under TROUBLE SHOOTING. After system enters self-diagnostic mode, perform ACTUATOR CHECK under TROUBLE SHOOTING. Press left side of MODE button to enter step mode and display codes. See BLOWER SPEED table. If blower speed does not change as specified, go to next step. If blower motor speed is as specified, circuit is okay.

BLOWER SPEED

Code	Blower Speed
21	Low
22-28	Medium
29	High

2) Remove extra-high relay, located on evaporator assembly. Measure resistance between relay terminals No. 1 and 2. *See Fig. 17.* Resistance should be 55.8-88.9 ohms. Check for continuity between terminals No. 3 and 4. Continuity should not exist.
3) Connect battery voltage to terminal No. 1. Connect terminal No. 2 to ground. Check for continuity between terminals No. 3 and 4. Continuity should exist. If relay operates as specified, go to next step. Replace relay if it does not operate as specified.
4) Check wiring harness and connectors between A/C control assembly and extra-high relay and between extra-high relay and battery. Repair harness and connectors as necessary. If wiring harnesses and connectors are okay, substitute a known good A/C control assembly. Retest system.

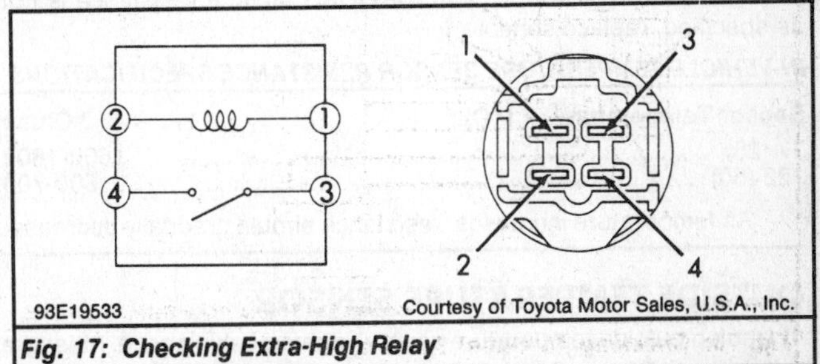
2
1
4
3
1
3
2
4
93E19533
Courtesy of Toyota Motor Sales, U.S.A., Inc.

Fig. 17: Checking Extra-High Relay

HEATER MAIN RELAY CIRCUIT

1) Turn ignition on. Check GAUGE fuse at fuse block under left side of instrument panel. If fuse is okay, go next step. If fuse is blown, correct cause and replace fuse.
2) Remove A/C control assembly, leaving harness connectors attached. Turn ignition off. Check for voltage between A/C control assembly 23-pin connector terminal HR (Blue/White wire) and body ground. *See Fig. 5.* If battery voltage does not exist, go to next step. If battery voltage exists, repair short to voltage in Blue/White wire between connector and heater main relay.
3) Turn ignition on. Check for voltage between A/C control assembly 23-pin connector terminal HR (Blue/White wire) and body ground. If battery voltage does not exist, go to next step. If battery voltage exists, circuit is okay.
4) Remove heater main relay, located behind glove box on right side. Check for continuity between terminals No. 1 and 4. *See Fig. 18.* Continuity should not exist. Check for continuity between terminals No. 2 and 4. Continuity should exist. Measure resistance between terminals No. 3 and 5. Resistance should be 62.5-90.9 ohms.
5) Apply battery voltage to terminal No. 3, and connect terminal No. 5 to ground. Check for continuity between terminals No. 1 and 2. Continuity should exist. Check for continuity between terminals No. 2 and 4. Continuity should not exist. Replace relay if it does not operate as specified. If relay is okay, repair wiring between 8-pin connector and battery.

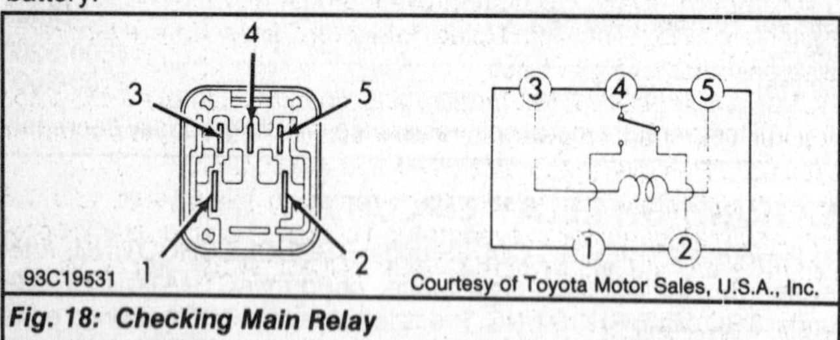
4
3
5
1
2
3
4
5
1
2
93C19531
Courtesy of Toyota Motor Sales, U.S.A., Inc.

Fig. 18: Checking Main Relay

IGNITION POWER & GROUND CIRCUITS

1) Turn ignition on. Check GAUGE fuse at fuse block under left side of instrument panel. If fuse is okay, go next step. If fuse is blown, correct cause and replace fuse.
2) Remove console upper panel. Remove A/C control assembly, leaving harness connectors attached. Turn ignition on. Using DVOM, backprobe 8-pin connector terminals IG+ (Red/Blue wire) and GND (White/Black wire). *See Fig. 5.* If battery voltage does not exist, go to next step. If battery voltage exists, circuit is okay.
3) Turn ignition off. Unplug 8-pin connector from A/C control assembly. Check Red/Blue wire between connector IG+ terminal and GAUGE fuse for continuity or short to ground. Repair wire as necessary. If wire is okay, go to next step.
4) Measure resistance between GND terminal of connector (White/Black wire) and ground. If resistance is less than one ohm, wire is okay. Repair open White/Black wire to ground if resistance is not less than one ohm.

IN-VEHICLE TEMPERATURE SENSOR

Remove in-vehicle temperature sensor. *See Fig. 1.* Measure sensor resistance while heating sensor. See IN-VEHICLE TEMPERATURE SENSOR RESISTANCE SPECIFICATIONS table. If resistance is not as specified, replace sensor.

IN-VEHICLE TEMPERATURE SENSOR RESISTANCE SPECIFICATIONS

Sensor Temperature °F (°C)	[1] Ohms
77 (25)	1600-1800
122 (50)	500-700

[1] - As temperature increases, resistance should gradually decrease.

OUTSIDE TEMPERATURE SENSOR

1) Unplug outside temperature sensor, located behind grille. Measure sensor resistance while heating sensor. See OUTSIDE TEMPERATURE SENSOR RESISTANCE SPECIFICATIONS table.
2) If resistance is not as specified, replace sensor. If resistance is within specification, check wiring harness and connectors between sensor and A/C control assembly. Repair harness and connectors as necessary. If wiring harness and connectors are okay, substitute a known good A/C control assembly. Retest system.

OUTSIDE TEMPERATURE SENSOR RESISTANCE SPECIFICATIONS

Sensor Temperature °F (°C)	[1] Ohms
77 (25)	1600-1800
122 (50)	500-700

[1] - As temperature increases, resistance should gradually decrease.

POWER TRANSISTOR CIRCUIT

1) Remove power transistor. See POWER TRANSISTOR under REMOVAL & INSTALLATION. Unplug power transistor connector. Connect battery voltage to power transistor terminal No. 4. Connect battery voltage, through a 120-ohm resistor, to terminal No. 3. *See Fig. 19.*
2) Connect test light between terminal No. 2 and negative battery terminal. If test light glows, go to next step. If test light does not glow, replace power transistor. Disconnect battery leads.
3) Measure resistance between terminals No. 1 and 4. If resistance is 2000-2400 ohms, power transistor is okay. Replace power transistor if resistance is not as specified.

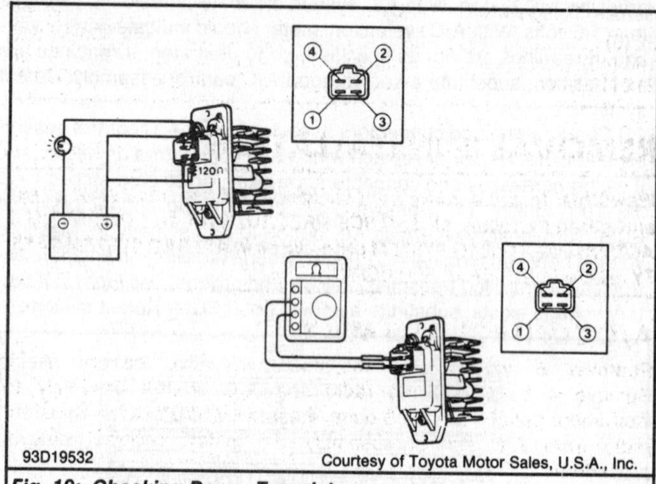
4
2
1
3
120Ω
4
2
1
3
93D19532
Courtesy of Toyota Motor Sales, U.S.A., Inc.

Fig. 19: Checking Power Transistor

SELF-DIAGNOSTIC CIRCUIT

Turn ignition on. Measure voltage between terminals TC and E1 of diagnostic connector, located under left side of instrument panel. *See Fig. 20.* If meter indicates battery voltage, circuit is okay. If meter does not indicate battery voltage, check wiring and connectors associated with A/C control assembly and diagnostic connector. If wiring is okay, substitute a known good A/C control assembly. Retest system.

SOLAR SENSOR

Remove solar sensor from top of instrument panel. Unplug harness connector. Cover sensor using cloth. Measure resistance between sensor terminals. Remove cloth. Subject sensor to bright light and measure resistance between terminals of sensor. See SOLAR SENSOR RESISTANCE SPECIFICATIONS table. If resistance is not as specified, replace sensor.

SOLAR SENSOR RESISTANCE SPECIFICATIONS

Condition	[1] Ohms
Sensor Covered By Cloth	No Continuity
Sensor Subjected To Bright Light	Less Than 10,000

[1] - As light intensity decreases, resistance should increase.

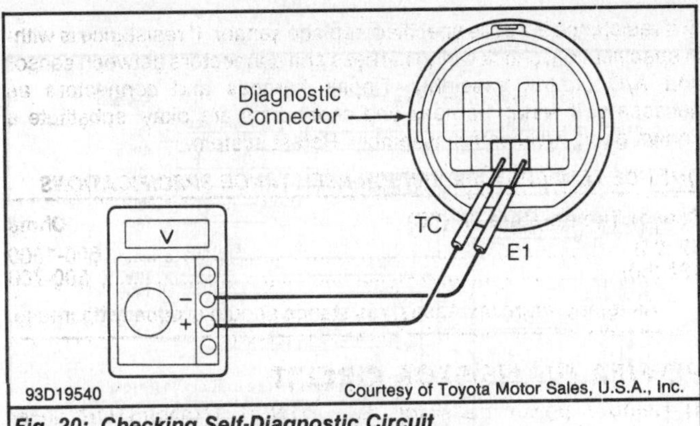
Diagnostic Connector
TC
E1
V
93D19540
Courtesy of Toyota Motor Sales, U.S.A., Inc.

Fig. 20: Checking Self-Diagnostic Circuit

WATER TEMPERATURE SENSOR

Remove coolant temperature sensor, located at heater core. Place sensor and thermometer in water. Measure resistance between sensor terminals as water is heated. If resistance is not as specified, replace water temperature sensor. See WATER TEMPERATURE SENSOR RESISTANCE SPECIFICATIONS table.

WATER TEMPERATURE SENSOR RESISTANCE SPECIFICATIONS

Sensor Temperature °F (°C)	Ohms
32 (0)	48,500-51,500
104 (40)	2500-2700
212 (100)	1900-2100

REMOVAL & INSTALLATION

WARNING: To avoid injury from accidental air bag deployment, read and carefully follow all SERVICE PRECAUTIONS and DISABLING & ACTIVATING AIR BAG SYSTEM procedures in AIR BAG SYSTEM SAFETY article in GENERAL SERVICING.

A/C CONTROL ASSEMBLY

Removal & Installation – Disconnect negative battery cable. Remove 4 bolts retaining radio and A/C control assembly to instrument panel. Remove 8 bolts, 4 screws and brackets. Separate radio from A/C control assembly. To install, reverse removal procedure.

AIR INLET SERVOMOTOR

Removal & Installation – Disconnect negative battery cable. Remove glove box. Remove engine control module and bracket. Unplug servomotor connector. Remove servomotor. To install servomotor, reverse removal procedure.

AIR MIX SERVOMOTOR

Removal & Installation – Disconnect negative battery cable. Remove dashboard lower finish panel, safety pad and air duct. Unplug servomotor connector. Remove servomotor. Disconnect control cable. To install, reverse removal procedure.

AIR OUTLET SERVOMOTOR

Removal & Installation – Disconnect negative battery cable. Remove dashboard lower finish panel, safety pad and air duct. Unplug servomotor connector. Remove servomotor. To install, reverse removal procedure.

BLOWER MOTOR

Removal & Installation – Disconnect negative battery cable. Remove lower dashboard panel and undercover. Remove connector bracket. Remove blower motor. To install, reverse removal procedure.

COMPRESSOR

Removal & Installation – 1) If compressor runs, idle engine for 10 minutes with A/C on. Turn ignition off. Disconnect negative battery cable. Discharge A/C system using approved refrigerant recovery/recycling equipment. Remove battery and tray. Remove radiator fan. Unplug compressor connector.

2) Disconnect and cap refrigerant hoses from compressor. Loosen drive belt. Remove compressor bolts and compressor. If replacing compressor, add 3.5 ounces refrigerant oil to compressor. To install, reverse removal procedure. Evacuate and recharge system. Check system for leaks.

CONDENSER

Removal & Installation – 1) Disconnect negative battery cable. Discharge A/C system using approved refrigerant recovery/recycling equipment. Remove battery, upper cover and radiator fan. Disconnect and plug refrigerant lines at condenser.

2) Remove headlights. Pull condenser upward from between radiator and body. If replacing condenser, add 1.2 ounces refrigerant oil to condenser. To install, reverse removal procedure. Evacuate and recharge system. Check system for leaks.

EVAPORATOR ASSEMBLY

Removal & Installation – 1) Disconnect negative battery cable. Discharge A/C system using approved refrigerant recovery/recycling equipment. Disconnect and plug refrigerant lines from evaporator assembly. Remove glove box.

2) Remove engine control module and bracket. Remove connector bracket. Disconnect blower motor connectors. Remove blower motor assembly. Remove evaporator cover and evaporator.

2) Remove evaporator assembly. If replacing evaporator, add 1.6 ounces of refrigerant oil to evaporator. To install, reverse removal procedure. Evacuate and recharge system. Check system for leaks.

HEATER CORE

Removal & Installation – 1) Disconnect negative battery cable. Drain cooling system. Remove heater shield. Remove 3 retaining screws and clamps. Disconnect heater hoses. Remove heater core.

2) To install, reverse removal procedure. Refill cooling system. Start engine, and warm it to operating temperature. Check system for leaks.

POWER TRANSISTOR

Removal & Installation – Disconnect negative battery cable. Remove dashboard lower finish panel, safety pad and air duct. Unplug power transistor connector. Remove power transistor. To install, reverse removal procedure.

RECEIVER-DRIER

Removal & Installation – 1) Disconnect negative battery cable. Discharge A/C system using approved refrigerant recovery/recycling equipment. Disconnect and plug liquid lines from receiver-drier.

2) Remove receiver-drier from bracket. If replacing receiver-drier, add 0.5 ounce of refrigerant oil to receiver-drier. To install, reverse removal procedure. Evacuate and recharge system. Check system for leaks.

TORQUE SPECIFICATIONS

TORQUE SPECIFICATIONS

Application	Ft. Lbs. (N.m)
A/C Compressor Bolts	18 (25)
A/C Compressor Bracket Bolts	27 (36)
Compressor Hoses	18 (25)
	INCH Lbs. (N.m)
Condenser Lines	88 (10)
Receiver-Drier Lines	88 (10)

1993 AUTOMATIC A/C-HEATER SYSTEMS
ES300 (Cont.)

WIRING DIAGRAM

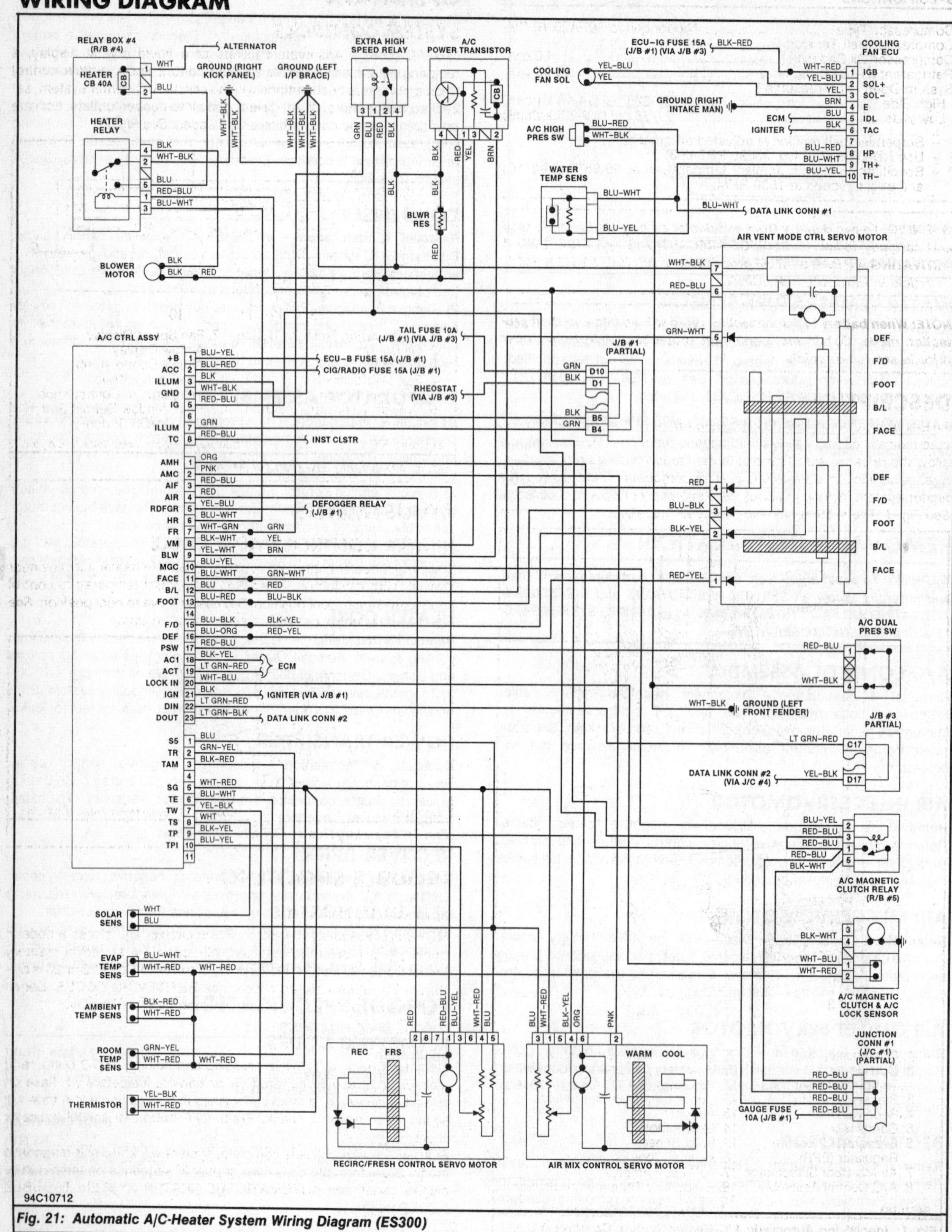
RELAY BOX #4 (R/B #4)
HEATER CB 40A
ALTERNATOR
GROUND (RIGHT KICK PANEL)
GROUND (LEFT I/P BRACE)
EXTRA HIGH SPEED RELAY
A/C POWER TRANSISTOR
ECU-IG FUSE 15A (J/B #1) (VIA J/B #3)
COOLING FAN ECU
COOLING FAN SOL
GROUND (RIGHT INTAKE MAN)
ECM
IGNITER
A/C HIGH PRES SW
IGB
SOL+
SOL−
E
IDL
TAC
HP
TH+
TH−
HEATER RELAY
WATER TEMP SENS
DATA LINK CONN #1
BLWR RES
BLOWER MOTOR
AIR VENT MODE CTRL SERVO MOTOR
A/C CTRL ASSY
TAIL FUSE 10A (J/B #1) (VIA J/B #3)
J/B #1 (PARTIAL)
ECU-B FUSE 15A (J/B #1)
CIG/RADIO FUSE 15A (J/B #1)
RHEOSTAT (VIA J/B #3)
INST CLSTR
DEF
F/D
FOOT
B/L
FACE
+B
ACC
ILLUM
GND
IG
TC
AMH
AMC
AIF
AIR
RDFGR
HR
FR
VM
BLW
MGC
PSW
AC1
ACT
LOCK IN
IGN
DIN
DOUT
DEFOGGER RELAY (J/B #1)
ECM
IGNITER (VIA J/B #1)
DATA LINK CONN #2
A/C DUAL PRES SW
GROUND (LEFT FRONT FENDER)
J/B #3 PARTIAL)
DATA LINK CONN #2 (VIA J/C #4)
S5
TR
TAM
SG
TE
TW
TS
TP
TPI
A/C MAGNETIC CLUTCH RELAY (R/B #5)
SOLAR SENS
EVAP TEMP SENS
AMBIENT TEMP SENS
ROOM TEMP SENS
THERMISTOR
A/C MAGNETIC CLUTCH & A/C LOCK SENSOR
JUNCTION CONN #1 (J/C #1) (PARTIAL)
GAUGE FUSE 10A (J/B #1)
REC
FRS
WARM
COOL
RECIRC/FRESH CONTROL SERVO MOTOR
AIR MIX CONTROL SERVO MOTOR
94C10712

Fig. 21: Automatic A/C-Heater System Wiring Diagram (ES300)

1993 AUTOMATIC A/C-HEATER SYSTEMS GS300

SPECIFICATIONS

Compressor Type .... Nippondenso 10PA20 10-Cyl.
Compressor Belt Tension [1]
Compressor Oil Capacity [2] .... 4.0 ozs.
Refrigerant (R-134a) Capacity .... 28-32 ozs.
System Operating Pressures [3]
High Side .... 199-228 psi (14-16 kg/cm²)
Low Side .... 21-36 psi (1.5-2.5 kg/cm²)

[1] – Serpentine belt tension is adjusted automatically.
[2] – Use ND-Oil 8 (Part No. 38899-PR7-003)
[3] – Specification is with ambient temperature at 86-95°F (30-35°C) and engine speed at 1500 RPM.

WARNING: To avoid injury from accidental air bag deployment, read and carefully follow all SERVICE PRECAUTIONS and DISABLING & ACTIVATING AIR BAG SYSTEM procedures in AIR BAG SYSTEM SAFETY article in GENERAL SERVICING.

NOTE: When battery is disconnected, radio will go into anti-theft protection mode. Obtain radio anti-theft protection code from owner prior to servicing vehicle.

DESCRIPTION

An Electronic Control Unit (ECU), located within A/C control assembly, automatically controls all A/C and heating functions. Manual controls allow the driver to select air distribution mode and desired temperature. In addition to normal A/C system components, automatic A/C-heater system includes various servomotors, controls and sensors. *See Fig. 1.* The system has self-diagnostic capabilities.

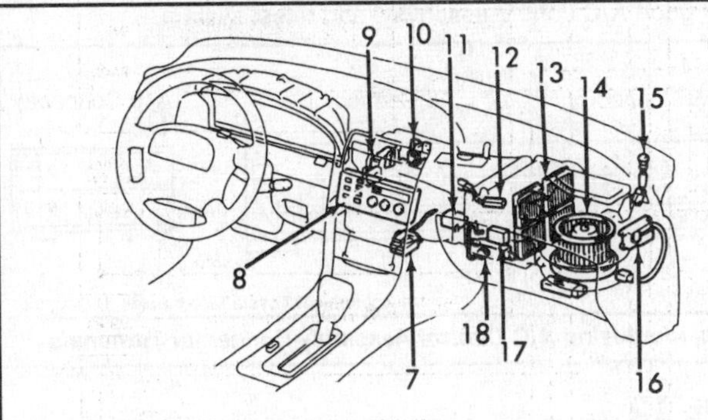
9
10
11
12
13
14
15
8
7
18
17
16

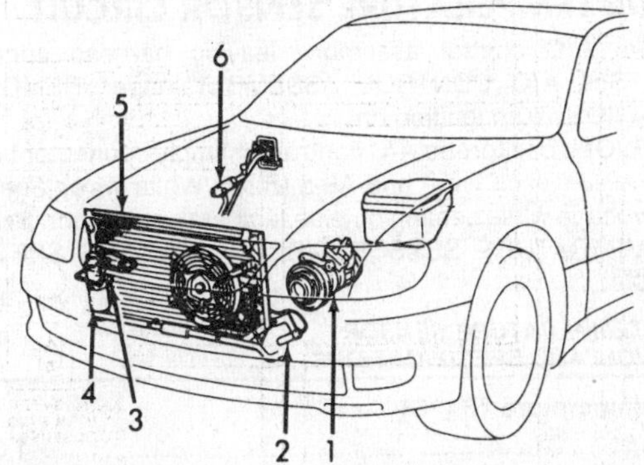
6
5
4
3
2
1

1. Compressor
2. Outside Air Temperature Sensor
3. Pressure Switch
4. Receiver-Drier
5. Condenser
6. Evaporator Pressure Regulator (EPR)
7. Air Mix Door Servomotor
8. A/C Control Assembly
9. Air Outlet Door Servomotor
10. In-Vehicle Temperature Sensor
11. Maximum cool Door Servomotor
12. Coolant Temperature Sensor
13. Air Filter
14. Blower Motor
15. Solar Sensor
16. Air Inlet Door Servomotor
17. A/C Lock Amplifier
18. Evaporator Temperature Sensor

94C10183 Courtesy of Toyota Motor Sales, U.S.A., Inc.

Fig. 1: Identifying Automatic A/C-Heater System Components

OPERATION

SYSTEM CONTROLS

The A/C control assembly consists of a liquid crystal display, a temperature control knob, fan speed control knob, airflow control knob and various push buttons which activate A/C-heater system, set desired temperature, direct discharged air to desired outlets, activate rear defogger and control blower fan speed. *See Fig. 2.*

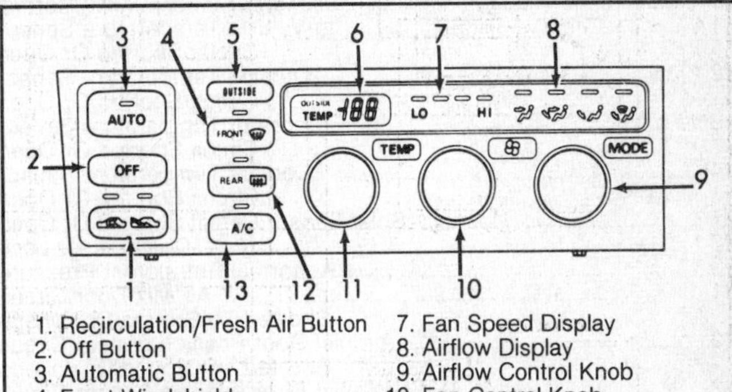
3
4
5
6
7
8
2
9
1
13
12
11
10
AUTO
OFF
OUTSIDE
FRONT
REAR
A/C
TEMP
LO
HI
TEMP
MODE

1. Recirculation/Fresh Air Button
2. Off Button
3. Automatic Button
4. Front Windshield Defogger Button
5. Outside Temperature Button
6. Temperature Display
7. Fan Speed Display
8. Airflow Display
9. Airflow Control Knob
10. Fan Control Knob
11. Temperature Control Knob
12. Rear Window Defrost Button
13. A/C On/Off Button

94D10184 Courtesy of Toyota Motor Sales, U.S.A., Inc.

Fig. 2: Identifying A/C Control Assembly

ADJUSTMENTS

HEATER CONTROL VALVE CABLE

Disconnect heater control valve cable, located in heater inlet line near firewall. Turn ignition on. Press A/C button. Set temperature control knob to maximum cool position. Set heater valve to cool position. *See Fig. 3.* Install control cable, and secure it using clamp.

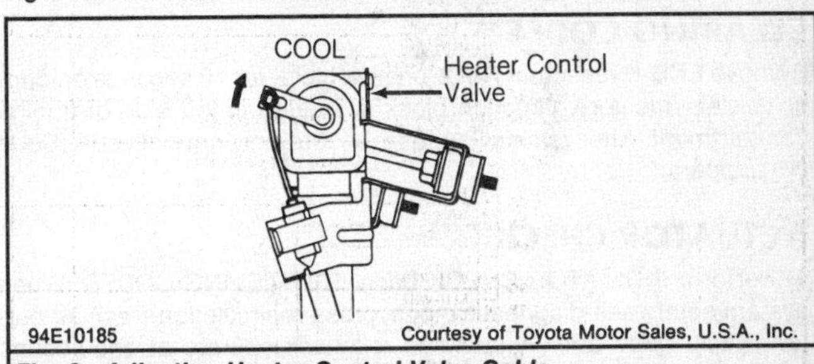
COOL
Heater Control
Valve

94E10185 Courtesy of Toyota Motor Sales, U.S.A., Inc.

Fig. 3: Adjusting Heater Control Valve Cable

TROUBLE SHOOTING

SELF-DIAGNOSTICS

A/C control assembly monitors system circuits and stores a code in memory if a problem is detected. All codes are stored in memory except Codes 22 and 23. Malfunction is current if Code 22 or 23 is displayed. To retrieve stored codes, see RETRIEVING CODES. Codes are displayed at A/C control assembly temperature display.

RETRIEVING CODES

Indicator Check – 1) While pressing and holding AUTO button and recirculation/fresh air button, turn ignition on. Indicators will flash on and off at one second intervals, 4 times in succession and a tone will sound as a indicator check. Press OFF button to cancel indicator check.

2) After indicator check is complete, system will enter self-diagnostic mode. Stored trouble codes will appear in sequence on temperature display panel. See AUTOMATIC A/C-HEATER SYSTEM TROUBLE CODES table.

1993 AUTOMATIC A/C-HEATER SYSTEMS GS300 (Cont.)

3) Press A/C switch button to display codes one at a time. If tone sounds when code is displayed, problem causing code currently exists. If tone does not sound when code is displayed, associated problem is past history and does not currently exist. Press OFF button to exit self-diagnostics.

AUTOMATIC A/C-HEATER SYSTEM TROUBLE CODES

Code Number	Condition/Affected Circuit
00	Normal
11 [1]	In-Vehicle Temperature Sensor Circuit Shorted Or Open
12 [2]	Outside Temperature Sensor Circuit Shorted Or Open
13	Evaporator Temperature Sensor Circuit Shorted Or Open
14	Coolant Temperature Sensor Circuit Shorted Or Open
21 [3]	Solar Sensor Circuit Shorted Or Open
22 [4]	Compressor Lock
23 [4]	Abnormal Refrigerant Pressure
31	Air Mix Door Circuit Shorted To Ground Or Voltage
32	Air Inlet Door Position Sensor Circuit Shorted To Ground Or Voltage
33	Air Outlet Door Position Sensor Circuit Shorted To Ground Or Voltage
41	Air Mix Door Position Sensor Signal Does Not Change
42	Air Inlet Door Position Sensor Signal Does Not Change
43	Air Outlet Door Position Sensor Signal Does Not Change

[1] - If in-vehicle temperature is -4°F (-20°C) or less, Code 11 may occur even though system is normal.
[2] - If outside air temperature is -58°F (-50°C) or less, Code 12 may occur even though system is normal.
[3] - If testing is done in a dark area, Code 21 may occur even though system is normal. Shine a light at solar sensor and recheck codes.
[4] - Malfunction is current. Code is not stored in memory.

CLEARING CODES

Remove ECU-B fuse from No. 2 junction block for 10 seconds or longer to clear memory. Junction block is located in left side of engine compartment. After reinstalling fuse, ensure only normal code (Code 00) appears.

ACTUATOR CHECK

1) Perform INDICATOR CHECK under RETRIEVING CODES. When system enters self-diagnostic mode, press recirculation/fresh air button. Each mode door, motor and relay will operate at one-second intervals. Press A/C switch to display codes one at a time and to step through checks one at a time.

Step No.	Display code	Conditions					
		Blower motor	Air flow vent	Max cool damper	Air inlet damper	Magnetic clutch	Air mix damper
1	20	OFF	(FACE)	0% open	(FRESH)	OFF	Cool side (0% open)
2	21	LO	↑	↑	↑	↑	↑
3	22	MED	(BI-LEVEL)	100% open	(F/R)	ON	↑
4	23	↑	↑	↑	(RECIRC)	↑	↑
5	24	↑	↑	↑	↑	↑	Cool/Hot (50% open)
6	25	↑	(FOOT)	↑	↑	↑	↑
7	26	↑	↑	↑	(FRESH)	↑	Hot side (100% open)
8	27	↑	↑	↑	↑	↑	↑
9	28	↑	(FOOT/DEF)	↑	↑	↑	↑
10	29	HI	(DEF)	↑	↑	↑	↑

94F10186 Courtesy of Toyota Motor Sales, U.S.A., Inc.

Fig. 4: Identifying Actuator Check Display Codes

2) Check airflow and temperature by hand. Tone will sound each time display code changes. Each display code is associated with a system operating condition. *See Fig. 4.* Press OFF button to cancel actuator check mode.

CODE 11
IN-VEHICLE TEMPERATURE SENSOR CIRCUIT

1) Remove A/C control assembly, leaving harness connectors attached. See A/C CONTROL ASSEMBLY under REMOVAL & INSTALLATION. Turn ignition on.

2) Using DVOM, backprobe A/C control assembly connector between terminals A9-2 (Green wire) and A9-5 (Black/White wire). *See Fig. 5.* Measure voltage while heating sensor. See IN-VEHICLE TEMPERATURE SENSOR CIRCUIT VOLTAGE SPECIFICATIONS table.

IN-VEHICLE TEMPERATURE SENSOR CIRCUIT VOLTAGE SPECIFICATIONS

Sensor Temperature °F (°C)	[1] Volts
77 (25)	1.8-2.2
104 (40)	1.2-1.6

[1] - As temperature increases, voltage should gradually decrease.

3) If voltage is as specified, temporarily substitute a known good A/C control assembly, and retest system. If voltage is not as specified, test in-vehicle temperature sensor. See IN-VEHICLE TEMPERATURE SENSOR under TESTING. Replace sensor as necessary. If sensor is okay, go to next step.

4) Check wiring harness and connectors between sensor and A/C control assembly. Repair harness and connectors as necessary. If wiring harness and connectors are okay, temporarily substitute a known good A/C control assembly, and retest system.

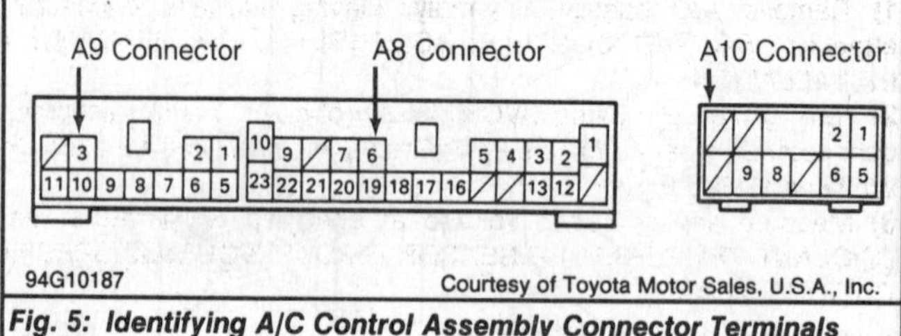
A9 Connector
A8 Connector
A10 Connector

94G10187 Courtesy of Toyota Motor Sales, U.S.A., Inc.

Fig. 5: Identifying A/C Control Assembly Connector Terminals

CODE 12
OUTSIDE TEMPERATURE SENSOR CIRCUIT

1) Remove A/C control assembly, leaving harness connectors attached. See A/C CONTROL ASSEMBLY under REMOVAL & INSTALLATION. Turn ignition on.

2) Using DVOM, backprobe A/C control assembly connector between terminals A9-3 (Black wire) and A9-5 (Black/White wire). *See Fig. 5.* Measure voltage while heating outside temperature sensor. See OUTSIDE TEMPERATURE SENSOR CIRCUIT VOLTAGE SPECIFICATIONS table.

OUTSIDE TEMPERATURE SENSOR CIRCUIT VOLTAGE SPECIFICATIONS

Sensor Temperature °F (°C)	[1] Volts
77 (25)	1.35-1.75
104 (40)	0.85-1.25

[1] - As temperature increases, voltage should gradually decrease.

3) If voltage is as specified, temporarily substitute a known good A/C control assembly, and retest system. If voltage is not as specified, test outside temperature sensor. See OUTSIDE TEMPERATURE SENSOR under TESTING. Replace sensor as necessary. If sensor is okay, go to next step.

4) Check wiring harness and connectors between sensor and A/C control assembly. Repair harness and connectors as necessary. If wiring harness and connectors are okay, temporarily substitute a known good A/C control assembly and, retest system.

CODE 13 EVAPORATOR TEMPERATURE SENSOR CIRCUIT

1) Remove A/C control assembly, leaving harness connectors attached. See A/C CONTROL ASSEMBLY under REMOVAL & INSTALLATION.

2) Turn ignition on. Using DVOM, backprobe A/C control assembly connector between terminals A9-6 (Black/Blue wire) and A9-5 (Black/White wire). *See Fig. 5.*

3) Measure evaporator temperature sensor voltage at specified temperature. See EVAPORATOR TEMPERATURE SENSOR CIRCUIT VOLTAGE SPECIFICATIONS table.

EVAPORATOR TEMPERATURE SENSOR CIRCUIT VOLTAGE SPECIFICATIONS

Sensor Temperature °F (°C)	[1] Volts
32 (0)	2.0-2.4
59 (15)	1.4-1.8

[1] – As temperature increases, voltage should gradually decrease.

4) If voltage is as specified, temporarily substitute a known good A/C control assembly, and retest system. If voltage is not as specified, test evaporator temperature sensor. See EVAPORATOR TEMPERATURE SENSOR under TESTING. Replace sensor as necessary. If sensor is okay, go to next step.

5) Check wiring harness and connectors between sensor and A/C control assembly. Repair harness and connectors as necessary. If wiring harness and connectors are okay, temporarily substitute a known good A/C control assembly, and retest system.

CODE 14 COOLANT TEMPERATURE SENSOR CIRCUIT

1) Remove A/C control assembly, leaving harness connectors attached. See A/C CONTROL ASSEMBLY under REMOVAL & INSTALLATION.

2) Turn ignition on. Using DVOM, backprobe A/C control assembly connector between terminals A9-7 (Green/Red wire) and A9-5 (Black/White wire). *See Fig. 5.*

3) Measure sensor circuit voltage at specified temperature. See COOLANT TEMPERATURE SENSOR CIRCUIT VOLTAGE SPECIFICATIONS table.

COOLANT TEMPERATURE SENSOR CIRCUIT VOLTAGE SPECIFICATIONS

Sensor Temperature °F (°C)	[1] Volts
32 (0)	2.8-3.2
104 (40)	1.8-2.2
158 (70)	1.3-1.5

[1] – As temperature increases, voltage should gradually decrease.

4) If voltage is as specified, temporarily substitute a known good A/C control assembly, and retest system. If voltage is not as specified, test water temperature sensor. See COOLANT (WATER) TEMPERATURE SENSOR under TESTING. Replace sensor as necessary. If sensor is okay, go to next step.

5) Check wiring harness and connectors between sensor and A/C control assembly. Repair harness and connectors as necessary. If wiring harness and connectors are okay, temporarily substitute a known good A/C control assembly, and retest system.

CODE 21 SOLAR SENSOR CIRCUIT

NOTE: If testing is done in a dark area, Code 21 may occur even though system is normal. Shine a light at solar sensor and recheck for Code 21.

1) Remove A/C control assembly, leaving harness connectors attached. See A/C CONTROL ASSEMBLY under REMOVAL & INSTALLATION. Turn ignition on.

2) Using DVOM, backprobe A/C control assembly connector between terminals A9-1 (Red/Yellow wire) and A9-8 (Green/Black wire). *See Fig. 5.* Measure sensor circuit voltage. See SOLAR SENSOR CIRCUIT VOLTAGE SPECIFICATIONS table.

SOLAR SENSOR CIRCUIT VOLTAGE SPECIFICATIONS

Condition	[1] Volts
Sensor Subjected To Bright Light	Less Than 4
Sensor Covered By Cloth	4-4.5

[1] – As light intensity decreases, voltage should increase.

3) If voltage is as specified, temporarily substitute a known good A/C control assembly, and retest system. If voltage is not as specified, test solar sensor. See SOLAR SENSOR under TESTING. Replace sensor as necessary. If sensor is okay, go to next step.

4) Check wiring harness and connectors between sensor and A/C control assembly. Repair harness and connectors as necessary. If wiring harness and connectors are okay, temporarily substitute a known good A/C control assembly, and retest system.

CODE 22 COMPRESSOR LOCK SENSOR CIRCUIT

1) Remove A/C control assembly, leaving harness connectors attached. See A/C CONTROL ASSEMBLY under REMOVAL & INSTALLATION. Start engine. Press AUTO and A/C buttons to on position.

2) Using DVOM, backprobe A/C control assembly connector between terminal A8-20 (Yellow/Red wire) and ground. *See Fig. 5.* Measure sensor circuit voltage.

3) If voltage is 10-14 volts, no problem is indicated at this time. If voltage is not 10-14 volts, test compressor lock sensor. See COMPRESSOR LOCK SENSOR under TESTING. Replace sensor as necessary. If sensor is okay, go to next step.

4) Remove A/C lock amplifier, leaving harness connector attached. Amplifier is located behind glove box. Measure voltage or resistance between specified terminal and ground. See A/C LOCK AMPLIFIER CIRCUIT SPECIFICATIONS table. *See Fig. 6.* If value is as specified, no problem is indicated at this time. If value is not as specified, go to next step.

5) Check wiring harness and connectors between A/C control assembly, A/C lock amplifier and A/C compressor lock sensor. Repair harness and connectors as necessary. If wiring harness and connectors are okay, replace A/C lock amplifier.

A/C LOCK AMPLIFIER CIRCUIT SPECIFICATIONS

Terminal [1]	Condition	Value
No. 1	Engine Running	10-14 Volts
No. 2	Ignition On	10-14 Volts
No. 4	Engine Running	Pulse Voltage
No. 5	Constant	Continuity
No. 6	Engine Running & A/C Switch On	10-14 volts
No. 7	Ignition On & A/C Switch On	10-14 Volts
No. 10	Engine Running & A/C Switch On	Pulse Voltage
No. 11	Engine Running & A/C Switch On	10-14 Volts
No. 12	Constant	Continuity

[1] – Check between specified terminal and ground.

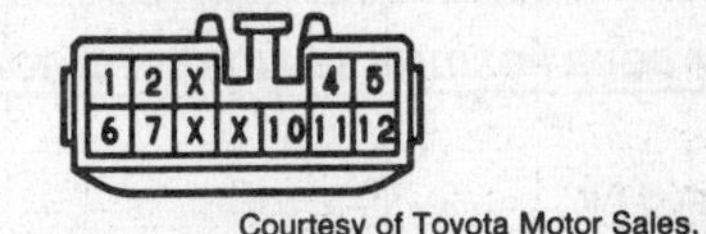

1 2 X 4 5
6 7 X X 10 11 12

94H10253 Courtesy of Toyota Motor Sales, U.S.A., Inc.

Fig. 6: Identifying A/C Lock Amplifier Connector Terminals

1993 AUTOMATIC A/C-HEATER SYSTEMS GS300 (Cont.)

CODE 23
PRESSURE SWITCH CIRCUIT

1) Remove A/C control assembly, leaving harness connectors attached. See A/C CONTROL ASSEMBLY under REMOVAL & INSTALLATION. Install manifold gauge set. Turn ignition on.
2) Using DVOM, backprobe A/C control assembly connector between terminal A8-17 (Blue wire) and ground. *See Fig. 5.*
3) Start engine. Press A/C button to on position. Battery voltage should be present with low side pressure less than 28 psi (2.0 kg/cm²). If voltage is as specified, no problem is indicated at this time.
4) If voltage is not as specified, test pressure switch. See PRESSURE SWITCH under TESTING. Replace pressure switch as necessary. If switch is okay, go to next step.
5) Check wiring harness and connectors between pressure switch and A/C control assembly. Repair harness and connectors as necessary. If wiring harness and connectors are okay, temporarily substitute a known good A/C control assembly, and retest system.

CODE 31 OR 41
AIR MIX DOOR POSITION SENSOR CIRCUIT

NOTE: For Code 41, see CODE 41 AIR MIX SERVOMOTOR CIRCUIT for additional trouble shooting procedures.

1) Remove A/C control assembly, leaving harness connectors attached. See A/C CONTROL ASSEMBLY under REMOVAL & INSTALLATION. Turn ignition on.
2) Using DVOM, backprobe A/C control assembly connector between terminals A9-9 (Blue/Orange wire) and A9-5 (Black/White wire). *See Fig. 5.*
3) Measure sensor circuit voltage while changing set temperature to activate air mix door. See AIR MIX DOOR POSITION SENSOR SPECIFICATIONS table.

AIR MIX DOOR POSITION SENSOR SPECIFICATIONS

Set Temperature	[1] Volts
Maximum Cool	3.5-4.5
Maximum Hot	0.5-1.5

[1] – As set temperature increases, voltage should gradually decrease.

4) If voltage is as specified, temporarily substitute a known good A/C control assembly, and retest system. If voltage is not as specified, test air mix door position sensor. See AIR MIX DOOR POSITION SENSOR under TESTING. If position sensor is defective, replace air mix door servomotor. If position sensor is okay, go to next step.
5) Check wiring harness and connectors between sensor and A/C control assembly. Repair harness and connectors as necessary. If wiring harness and connectors are okay, temporarily substitute a known good A/C control assembly, and retest system.

CODE 32 OR 42
AIR INLET DOOR POSITION SENSOR CIRCUIT

NOTE: For Code 42, see CODE 42 AIR INLET SERVOMOTOR CIRCUIT for additional trouble shooting procedures.

1) Remove A/C control assembly, leaving harness connectors attached. See A/C CONTROL ASSEMBLY under REMOVAL & INSTALLATION. Turn ignition on.
2) Using DVOM, backprobe A/C control assembly connector between terminals A9-10 (Red/Black wire) and A9-5 (Black/White wire). *See Fig. 5.*

AIR INLET DOOR POSITION SENSOR SPECIFICATIONS

Position	[1] Volts
Recirculated Air	3.5-4.5
Fresh Air	0.5-1.5

[1] – As door moves from recirculated air position toward fresh air position, voltage should gradually decrease.

3) Measure sensor voltage while pressing recirculation/fresh air button to change air inlet between recirculated and fresh air. As servomotor operates, note voltage reading. See AIR INLET DOOR POSITION SENSOR SPECIFICATIONS table.
4) If voltage is as specified, temporarily substitute a known good A/C control assembly, and retest system. If voltage is not as specified, test air inlet door position sensor. See AIR INLET DOOR POSITION SENSOR under TESTING. If air inlet door position sensor is defective, replace air inlet door servomotor. If position sensor is okay, go to next step.
5) Check wiring harness and connectors between sensor and A/C control assembly. Repair harness and connectors as necessary. If wiring harness and connectors are okay, temporarily substitute a known good A/C control assembly, and retest system.

CODE 33 OR 43
AIR OUTLET DOOR POSITION SENSOR CIRCUIT

NOTE: For Code 43, see CODE 43 AIR OUTLET SERVOMOTOR CIRCUIT for additional trouble shooting procedures.

1) Remove A/C control assembly, leaving harness connectors attached. See A/C CONTROL ASSEMBLY under REMOVAL & INSTALLATION. Turn ignition on.
2) Using DVOM, backprobe A/C control assembly connector between terminals A9-11 (Yellow/Black wire) and A9-5 (Black/White wire). *See Fig. 5.*
3) Measure sensor circuit voltage while turning airflow control knob from vent to defrost position. As servomotor operates, note voltage reading. See AIR OUTLET DOOR POSITION SENSOR SPECIFICATIONS table.

AIR OUTLET DOOR POSITION SENSOR SPECIFICATIONS

Position	[1] Volts
Vent	3.5-4.5
Defrost	0.5-1.5

[1] – As door moves from defrost position toward vent position, voltage should gradually decrease.

4) If voltage is as specified, temporarily substitute a known good A/C control assembly, and retest system. If voltage is not as specified, test air outlet door position sensor. See AIR OUTLET DOOR POSITION SENSOR under TESTING. If air outlet door position sensor is defective, replace air outlet servomotor. If position sensor is okay, go to next step.
5) Check wiring harness and connectors between sensor and A/C control assembly. Repair harness and connectors as necessary. If wiring harness and connectors are okay, temporarily substitute a known good A/C control assembly, and retest system.

CODE 41
AIR MIX SERVOMOTOR CIRCUIT

NOTE: See CODE 31 OR 41 AIR MIX DOOR POSITION SENSOR CIRCUIT for additional trouble shooting procedures.

1) Warm engine to normal operating temperature. Perform RETRIEVING CODES. After system enters self-diagnostic, perform ACTUATOR CHECK. Press A/C switch button to enter step mode and display codes. See AIR MIX DOOR AIRFLOW table. Air mix door operation should be as specified.

AIR MIX DOOR AIRFLOW

Code	Air Mix Door	Expected Result
20-23	Fully Closed	Cool Air Comes Out
24-25	Half Open	Blend (Cool/Hot) Air Comes Out
26-29	Fully Open	Hot Air Comes Out

2) If air mix door functions as specified, no problem is indicated at this time. If air mix door does not function as specified, test air mix door servomotor. See AIR MIX DOOR SERVOMOTOR under TESTING. Replace air mix door servomotor as necessary. If position sensor is okay, go to next step.

3) Check wiring harness and connectors between servomotor and A/C control assembly. Repair harness and connectors as necessary. If wiring harness and connectors are okay, temporarily substitute a known good A/C control assembly, and retest system.

CODE 42
AIR INLET SERVOMOTOR CIRCUIT

NOTE: See CODE 32 OR 42 AIR INLET DOOR POSITION SENSOR CIRCUIT for additional trouble shooting procedures.

1) Warm engine to normal operating temperature. Perform RETRIEVING CODES. After system enters self-diagnostic code check mode, perform ACTUATOR CHECK. Press A/C button to enter step mode and display codes. See AIR INLET DOOR AIRFLOW table. Air inlet door operation should be as specified.

AIR INLET DOOR AIRFLOW

Code	Door Position
20-21	Fresh Air
22	Fresh/Recirculated Air
23-25	Recirculated Air
26-29	Fresh Air

2) If air inlet door functions as specified, no problem is indicated at this time. If air inlet door does not function as specified, test air inlet servomotor. See AIR INLET DOOR SERVOMOTOR under TESTING. Replace air inlet door servomotor as necessary. If air inlet door servomotor is okay, go to next step.

3) Check wiring harness and connectors between servomotor and A/C control assembly. Repair harness and connectors as necessary. If wiring harness and connectors are okay, temporarily substitute a known good A/C control assembly, and retest system.

CODE 43
AIR OUTLET SERVOMOTOR CIRCUIT

NOTE: See CODE 33 OR 43 AIR OUTLET DOOR POSITION SENSOR CIRCUIT for additional trouble shooting procedures.

1) Warm engine to normal operating temperature. Perform RETRIEVING CODES. After system enters self-diagnostic mode, perform ACTUATOR CHECK. Press A/C button to enter step mode and display codes. See AIR OUTLET DOOR AIRFLOW table. Air outlet door operation should be as specified.

AIR OUTLET DOOR AIRFLOW

Code	Airflow Mode
20-21	Vent
22-24	Bi-Level
25-27	Foot
28	Foot-Defrost
29	Defrost

2) If air outlet door servomotor functions as specified, no problem is indicated at this time. If air outlet door does not function as specified, check air outlet servomotor. See AIR OUTLET DOOR SERVOMOTOR under TESTING. Replace servomotor as necessary. If air outlet servomotor is okay, go to next step.

3) Check wiring harness and connectors between servomotor and A/C control assembly. Repair harness and connectors as necessary. If wiring harness and connectors are okay, temporarily substitute a known good A/C control assembly, and retest system.

TESTING

WARNING: To avoid injury from accidental air bag deployment, read and carefully follow all SERVICE PRECAUTIONS and DISABLING & ACTIVATING AIR BAG SYSTEM procedures in AIR BAG SYSTEM SAFETY article in GENERAL SERVICING.

ACCESSORY POWER CIRCUIT

1) Turn ignition on. Check CIG fuse, located at fuse block under left side of instrument panel. If fuse is okay, go next step. If fuse is blown, correct cause and replace fuse.

2) Turn ignition off. Remove A/C control assembly, leaving harness connectors attached. See A/C CONTROL ASSEMBLY under REMOVAL & INSTALLATION. Turn ignition on.

3) Using DVOM, backprobe between A/C control assembly 10-pin connector terminal A10-2 (Pink/Blue wire) and ground. *See Fig. 5.*

4) If battery voltage is not present, repair Pink/Blue wire between connector and CIG fuse. If battery voltage is present, check wiring harness and connectors between battery and A/C control assembly.

AIR INLET DOOR POSITION SENSOR

1) Remove cooling unit. See COOLING UNIT under REMOVAL & INSTALLATION. Disconnect air inlet servomotor connector. Measure resistance between servomotor connector terminals No. 3 (Black/White wire) and No. 4 (Red/Yellow wire). *See Fig. 7.*

2) Resistance should be 4700-7200 ohms. If resistance is not as specified, replace air inlet servomotor. If resistance is as specified, go to next step.

3) Connect ohmmeter between servomotor terminals No. 3 (Black/White wire) and No. 5 (Red/Black wire). Apply battery voltage to air inlet servomotor connector terminal No. 2 (Red/White wire). Connect terminal No. 1 (Red/Blue wire) to ground. *See Fig. 8.*

4) Note resistance reading as servomotor operates. Reverse power leads and note resistance reading. Resistance should be as specified for each door position. See AIR INLET DOOR POSITION SENSOR SPECIFICATIONS table.

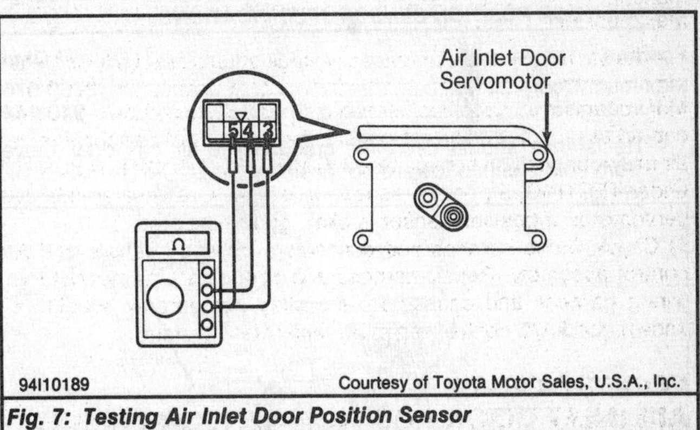
Air Inlet Door
Servomotor
5 4 3
94I10189
Courtesy of Toyota Motor Sales, U.S.A., Inc.

Fig. 7: Testing Air Inlet Door Position Sensor

AIR INLET DOOR POSITION SENSOR SPECIFICATIONS

Position	[1] Ohms
Recirculated Air	3760-5760
Fresh Air	940-1440

[1] – Resistance should decrease gradually as air mix door moves from cold position toward hot position.

AIR INLET DOOR SERVOMOTOR

1) Remove cooling unit. See COOLING UNIT under REMOVAL & INSTALLATION. Disconnect air inlet servomotor connector. Connect battery voltage to terminal No. 2 (Red/White wire). Connect terminal No. 1 (Red/Blue wire) to ground. *See Fig. 8.*

2) Servomotor lever should move smoothly to recirculation position. Reverse power leads. Servomotor lever should move smoothly to fresh air position. If servomotor lever does not function as specified, replace servomotor.

1993 AUTOMATIC A/C-HEATER SYSTEMS GS300 (Cont.)

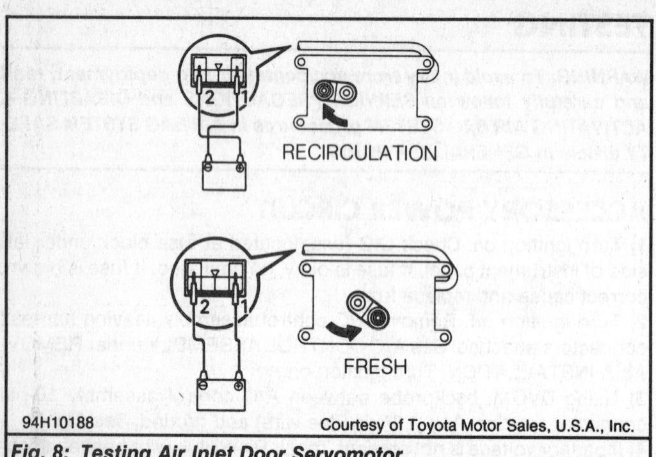

RECIRCULATION
FRESH
94H10188
Courtesy of Toyota Motor Sales, U.S.A., Inc.

Fig. 8: Testing Air Inlet Door Servomotor

AIR MIX DOOR POSITION SENSOR

1) Remove heater unit. See HEATER UNIT under REMOVAL & INSTALLATION. Disconnect air mix servomotor connector. Measure resistance between servomotor connector terminals No. 3 (Black/White wire) and No. 4 (Red/Yellow wire). *See Fig. 9.*

2) Resistance should be 4800-7200 ohms. If resistance is not as specified, replace air mix servomotor. If resistance is as specified, go to next step.

3) Connect ohmmeter between servomotor terminals No. 3 (Black/White wire) and No. 5 (Blue/Orange wire). Apply battery voltage to air mix servomotor connector terminal No. 2 (Pink wire). Connect terminal No. 1 (Pink/Black wire) to ground. *See Fig. 10*

4) As servomotor operates, note resistance reading. Reverse power leads and note resistance reading. Resistance should be as specified for each door position. See AIR MIX DOOR POSITION SENSOR SPECIFICATIONS table. If resistance is not as specified, replace air mix door servomotor.

AIR MIX DOOR POSITION SENSOR SPECIFICATIONS

Position	[1] Ohms
Maximum Cool	3760-5760
Maximum Hot	940-1440

[1] – Resistance should decrease gradually as air mix door moves from cold position toward hot position.

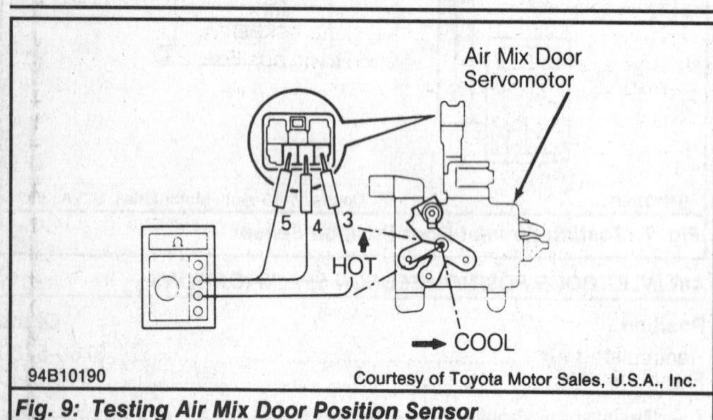

Air Mix Door Servomotor
5
4
3
HOT
COOL
94B10190
Courtesy of Toyota Motor Sales, U.S.A., Inc.

Fig. 9: Testing Air Mix Door Position Sensor

AIR MIX DOOR SERVOMOTOR

1) Remove heater unit. See HEATER UNIT under REMOVAL & INSTALLATION. Disconnect air mix servomotor connector. Apply battery voltage to air mix servomotor connector terminal No. 2 (Pink wire). Connect terminal No. 1 (Pink/Black wire) to ground. *See Fig. 10.* Servomotor lever should turn smoothly to hot side.

2) Reverse power leads. Servomotor lever should move smoothly to cool side. If servomotor lever does not function as specified, replace servomotor.

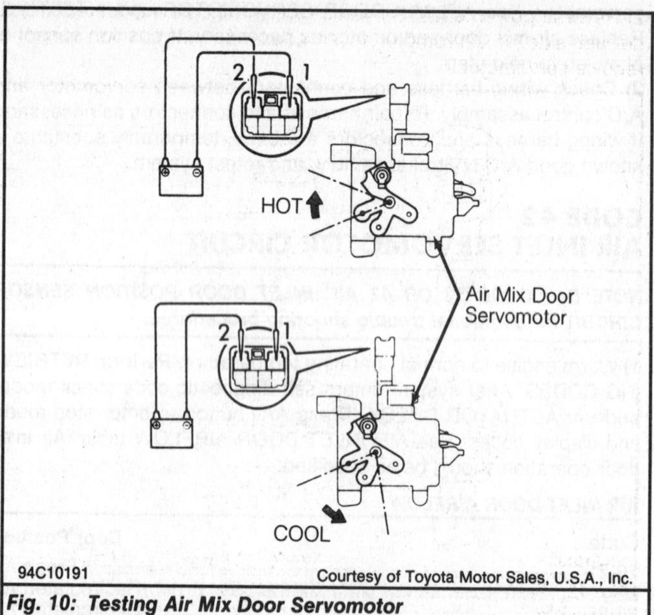

2
1
HOT
Air Mix Door Servomotor
2
1
COOL
94C10191
Courtesy of Toyota Motor Sales, U.S.A., Inc.

Fig. 10: Testing Air Mix Door Servomotor

AIR OUTLET DOOR POSITION SENSOR

1) Remove heater unit. See HEATER UNIT under REMOVAL & INSTALLATION. Disconnect air outlet servomotor connector. Measure resistance between servomotor connector terminals No. 3 (Black/White wire) and No. 4 (Red/Yellow wire). *See Fig. 11.*

2) Resistance should be 4700-7200 ohms. If resistance is not as specified, replace air outlet servomotor. If resistance is as specified, go to next step.

3) Connect ohmmeter between servomotor terminals No. 3 (Black/White wire) and No. 5 (Yellow/Black wire). Apply battery voltage to air outlet servomotor connector terminal No. 2 (Brown/White wire). Connect terminal No. 1 (Yellow/Green wire) to ground. *See Fig. 12*

4) As servomotor operates, note resistance reading. Reverse power leads and note resistance reading. Resistance should be as specified for each door position. See AIR OUTLET DOOR POSITION SENSOR SPECIFICATIONS table.

AIR OUTLET DOOR POSITION SENSOR SPECIFICATIONS

Position	[1] Ohms
Defrost	3760-5760
Vent	940-1440

[1] – Resistance should decrease gradually as air outlet door moves from defrost position toward vent position.

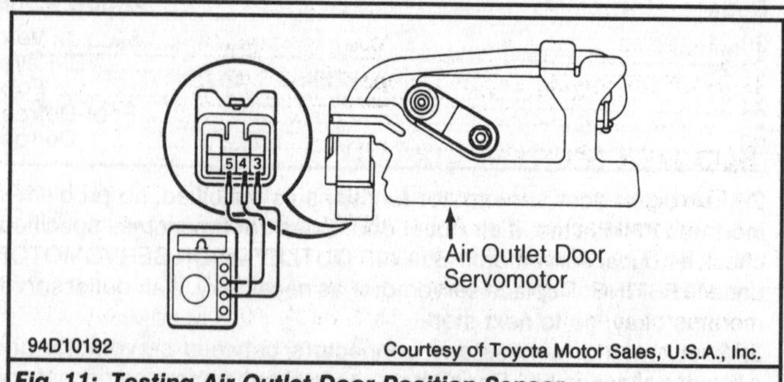

5 4 3
Air Outlet Door Servomotor
94D10192
Courtesy of Toyota Motor Sales, U.S.A., Inc.

Fig. 11: Testing Air Outlet Door Position Sensor

AIR OUTLET DOOR SERVOMOTOR

1) Remove heater unit. See HEATER UNIT under REMOVAL & INSTALLATION. Disconnect air outlet servomotor connector. Apply battery voltage to air mix servomotor connector terminal No. 2 (Brown/White wire). Connect terminal No. 1 (Yellow/Green wire) to ground. *See Fig. 12.* Servomotor lever should turn smoothly to vent side.

1993 AUTOMATIC A/C-HEATER SYSTEMS GS300 (Cont.)

2) Reverse power leads. Servomotor lever should move smoothly to defrost side. If servomotor lever does not function as specified, replace servomotor.

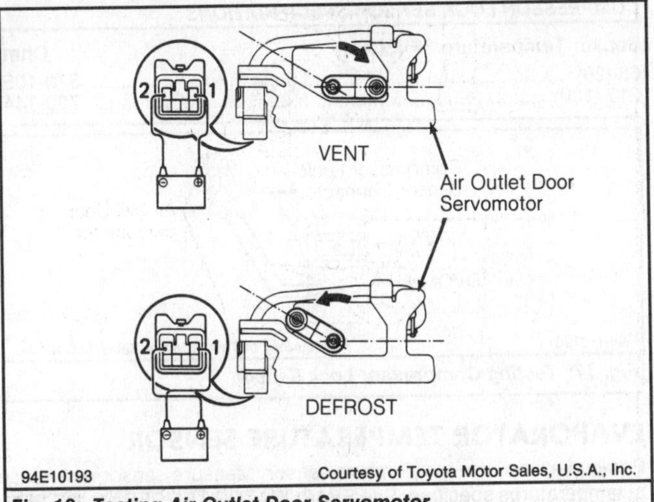
2
1
VENT
Air Outlet Door
Servomotor
2
1
DEFROST
94E10193
Courtesy of Toyota Motor Sales, U.S.A., Inc.

Fig. 12: Testing Air Outlet Door Servomotor

BACK-UP POWER CIRCUIT

1) Turn ignition off. Check ECU-B fuse at engine compartment fuse block. *See Fig. 13.* If fuse is okay, go next step. If fuse is blown, correct cause and replace fuse.

2) Remove A/C control assembly, leaving harness connectors attached. Turn ignition on. Using DVOM, backprobe between A/C control assembly connector terminal A10-1 (White/Red wire) and ground. *See Fig. 5.*

3) If battery voltage is present, no problem is indicated at this time. If battery voltage is not present, repair White/Red wire between connector and ECU-B fuse.

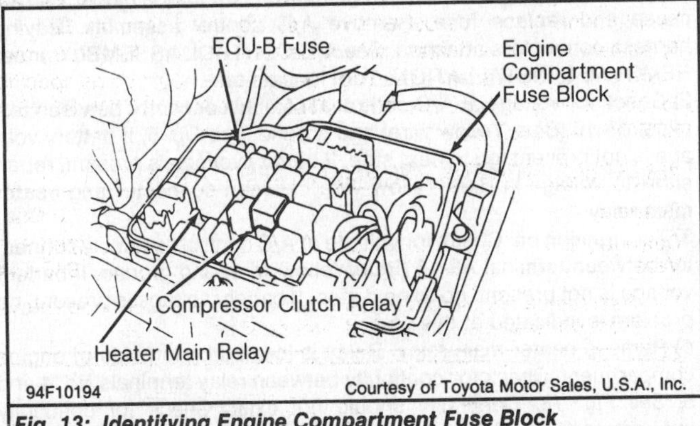
ECU-B Fuse
Engine
Compartment
Fuse Block
Compressor Clutch Relay
Heater Main Relay
94F10194
Courtesy of Toyota Motor Sales, U.S.A., Inc.

Fig. 13: Identifying Engine Compartment Fuse Block

BLOWER MOTOR CIRCUIT

1) Turn ignition off. Remove A/C control assembly, leaving harness connectors attached. See A/C CONTROL ASSEMBLY under REMOVAL & INSTALLATION. Turn ignition on. Operate blower motor.

2) Measure voltage between ground and A/C control assembly connector terminal A8-9 (Pink/Blue wire). Turn ignition on. Operate blower motor. If voltage is 1-3 volts, no problem is indicated at this time. If voltage is not 1-3 volts, go to next step.

3) Remove blower motor. See BLOWER MOTOR under REMOVAL & INSTALLATION. Connect battery voltage to terminal No. 2 (White wire) of blower motor. Connect terminal No. 1 (Black wire) to ground. If blower motor runs smoothly, go to next step. Replace blower motor if it does not run smoothly.

4) Remove blower motor relay, leaving harness connector attached. Relay is mounted to blower motor case. Turn ignition on. Backprobe between relay terminals as specified. See BLOWER MOTOR RELAY SPECIFICATIONS table. *See Fig. 14.* Replace relay as necessary.

5) If relay is okay, check wiring between heater main relay and A/C control assembly. Repair wiring as necessary.

BLOWER MOTOR RELAY SPECIFICATIONS

Measure Between Terminals	Volts
GND & Ground	[1]
+B & Ground	Battery
+M & Ground	Battery
+M & -M	Battery
SI & Ground	1-3

[1] - Continuity should exist.

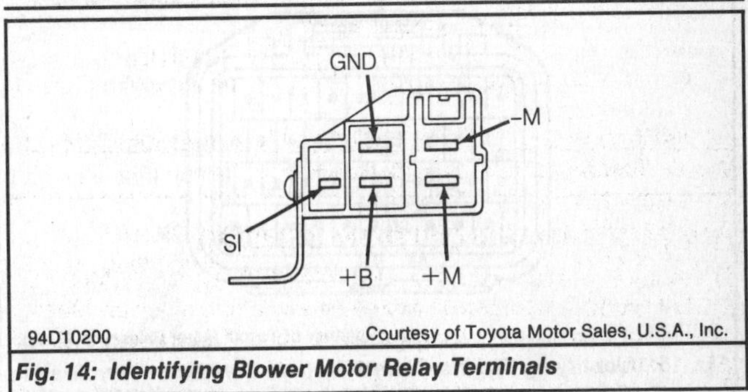
GND
-M
SI
+B
+M
94D10200
Courtesy of Toyota Motor Sales, U.S.A., Inc.

Fig. 14: Identifying Blower Motor Relay Terminals

COMPRESSOR CIRCUIT

1) Turn ignition on. Check GAUGE fuse, at fuse block, under left side of instrument panel. If fuse is okay, go next step. If fuse is blown, correct cause and replace fuse. Remove A/C lock amplifier, leaving harness connector attached. Lock amplifier is located behind glove box.

2) Start engine. Set fan speed control knob to low, medium or high position. Using DVOM, backprobe A/C lock amplifier 12-pin connector between terminal No. 6 (Blue/White wire) and ground. *See Fig. 6.*

3) Press A/C button to on position. Voltmeter should indicate battery voltage. Press A/C button to off position. Voltmeter should indicate zero volts. If voltage is as specified, go to next step. If voltage is as not as specified, go to step **5)**.

4) Disconnect compressor clutch 4-pin connector. Apply battery voltage to compressor clutch terminal No. 4 (Black/Yellow wire). Connect battery ground to compressor. If clutch engages, go to next step. If clutch does not engage, replace clutch.

5) Check wiring and connectors associated with compressor clutch relay and compressor. Repair wiring and connectors as necessary. If wiring and connectors are okay, go to next step.

6) Start engine. Push AUTO button to on position. Using DVOM, backprobe A/C control assembly connector between terminal A8-10 (Blue/White wire) and ground. *See Fig. 5.* Press A/C button to on position. Voltmeter should indicate 10-14 volts. Press A/C button to off position. Voltmeter should indicate zero volts.

7) If voltage is as not as specified, temporarily substitute a known good A/C control assembly, and retest system. Check wiring harness and connectors between A/C control assembly and A/C lock amplifier. Repair or replace wiring and connectors as necessary. If wiring and connectors are okay, go to next step.

8) Remove A/C lock amplifier, leaving harness connector attached. Lock amplifier is located behind glove box. Start engine. Set fan speed control knob to low, medium or high position. Using DVOM, backprobe A/C lock amplifier 12-pin connector between terminal No. 11 (Black wire) and ground. *See Fig. 6.*

9) Press A/C button to on position. Voltmeter should indicate 8-14 volts. Press A/C button to off position. Voltmeter should indicate 0-1.5 volts. If voltage is as specified, go to next step. If voltage is as not as specified, replace A/C lock amplifier.

10) Check wiring harness and connectors between A/C lock amplifier and Engine Control Module (ECM). Repair wiring and connectors as necessary. If wiring and connectors are okay, go to next step.

11) Remove ECM, leaving harness connectors attached. ECM is located behind glove box. Turn ignition on. Set fan speed control knob to low, medium or high position. Using DVOM, backprobe ECM 40-pin

1993 AUTOMATIC A/C-HEATER SYSTEMS GS300 (Cont.)

connector between terminal No. 23 (White wire) and ground. *See Fig. 15.*

12) Press A/C button to on position. Voltmeter should indicate 0-3 volts. Press A/C button to off position. Voltmeter should indicate 9-14 volts. If voltage is as specified, replace compressor clutch relay. If voltage remains 0-3 volts, go to next step. If voltage remains 9-14 volts, temporarily substitute a known good ECM, and retest system.

13) Check wiring harness and connectors between compressor clutch relay and A/C lock amplifier. Repair wiring and connectors as necessary. If wiring and connectors are okay, temporarily substitute a known good ECM, and retest system.

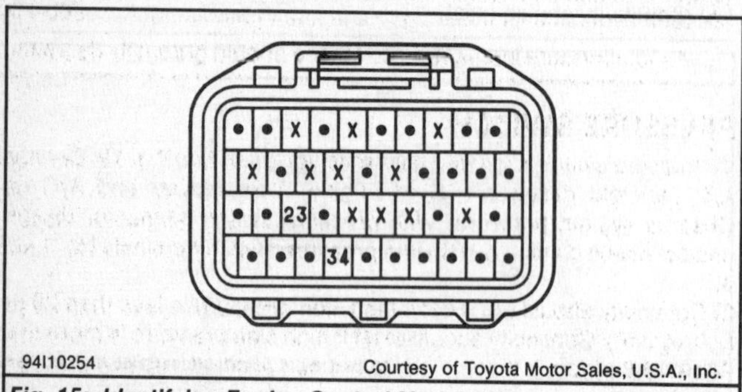
23
34

94I10254 Courtesy of Toyota Motor Sales, U.S.A., Inc.

Fig. 15: Identifying Engine Control Module Connector Terminals

COOLING FANS

1) Cooling fan motors operate at 2 speeds, depending on coolant temperature and A/C switch position. Check cooling fan operation. See COOLING FANS OPERATION table.

2) If fan operation is not as specified, check cooling fan motors, engine coolant temperature switch, cooling fan relays and all related wiring.

COOLING FANS OPERATION

A/C Switch	Compressor Clutch	Coolant Temp. °F (°C)	Fan Speed
Off Or On	Off	181 (83) Or Less	Off
On	On	194 (90)	High
On	On	[1] 181 (83) Or Less	Low
On	On	194 (90) Or More	High

[1] – Or if refrigerant pressure is 455 psi (32 kg/cm²) or more.

COMPRESSOR CLUTCH RELAY

1) Remove compressor clutch relay. Relay is located on left side of engine compartment. Check for continuity between terminals No. 1 and 2. *See Fig. 16.* Continuity should not exist. Check for continuity between terminals No. 3 and 4. Continuity should exist.

2) Connect battery voltage to terminal No. 3. Connect terminal No. 4 to ground. Check for continuity between terminals No. 1 and 2. Continuity should exist. Replace relay if it does not operate as specified.

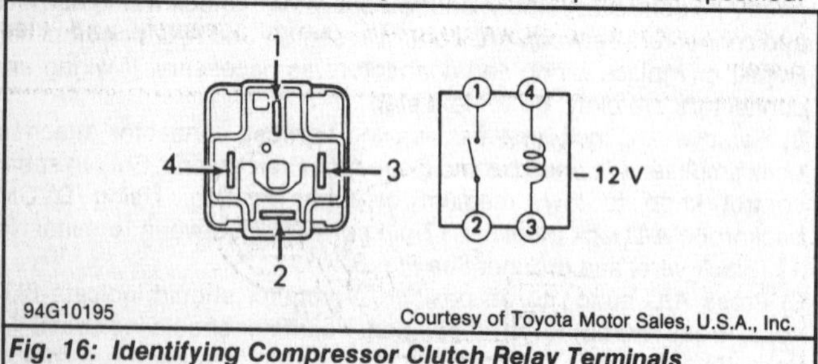
1
4
3
2
1
4
2
3
12 V

94G10195 Courtesy of Toyota Motor Sales, U.S.A., Inc.

Fig. 16: Identifying Compressor Clutch Relay Terminals

COMPRESSOR LOCK SENSOR

Raise and support vehicle. Disconnect compressor lock sensor connector, located at compressor. Measure resistance between terminals No. 1 (Green/Red wire) and No. 2 (Green wire) of sensor at temperatures specified. *See Fig. 17.* See COMPRESSOR LOCK SENSOR SPECIFICATIONS table. Replace sensor if resistance is not as specified.

COMPRESSOR LOCK SENSOR SPECIFICATIONS

Sensor Temperature °F (°C)	Ohms
68 (20)	570-1050
212 (100)	720-1440

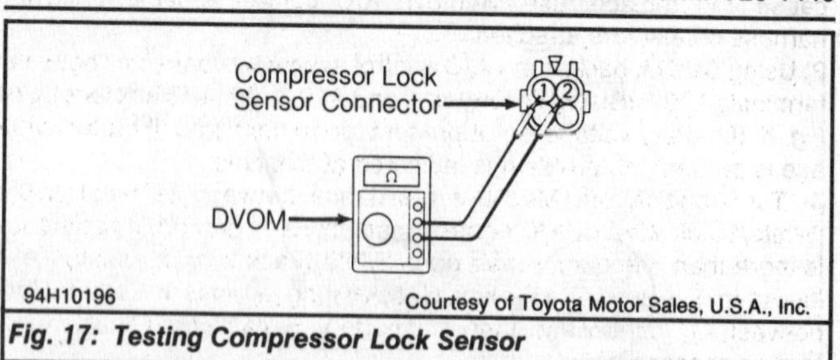
Compressor Lock
Sensor Connector
DVOM

94H10196 Courtesy of Toyota Motor Sales, U.S.A., Inc.

Fig. 17: Testing Compressor Lock Sensor

EVAPORATOR TEMPERATURE SENSOR

Remove evaporator temperature sensor. Measure sensor resistance at temperatures specified. See EVAPORATOR TEMPERATURE SENSOR RESISTANCE SPECIFICATIONS table. If resistance is not as specified, replace sensor.

EVAPORATOR TEMPERATURE SENSOR RESISTANCE SPECIFICATIONS

Sensor Temperature °F (°C)	[1] Ohms
32 (0)	4600-5200
59 (15)	2000-2700

[1] – As temperature increases, resistance should gradually decrease.

HEATER MAIN RELAY CIRCUIT

1) Turn ignition on. Check GAUGE fuse at fuse block under left side of instrument panel. If fuse is okay, go next step. If fuse is blown, correct cause and replace fuse. Remove A/C control assembly, leaving harness connectors attached. See A/C CONTROL ASSEMBLY under REMOVAL & INSTALLATION. Turn ignition off.

2) Check for voltage at A/C control assembly connector between terminal A8-16 (Blue/Yellow wire) and ground. *See Fig. 5.* If battery voltage is not present, go to next step. If battery voltage is present, repair short to voltage in Blue/Yellow wire between connector and heater main relay.

3) Turn ignition on. Check for voltage at A/C control assembly connector between terminal A8-16 (Blue/Yellow wire) and ground. If battery voltage is not present, go to next step. If battery voltage is present, no problem is indicated at this time.

4) Remove heater main relay. Relay is located on left side of engine compartment. Check for continuity between relay terminals No. 4 and 5. *See Fig. 18.* Continuity should not exist. Check for continuity between terminals No. 1 and 3, and between terminals No. 2 and 4. Continuity should exist.

5) Apply battery voltage to relay terminal No. 3, and connect terminal No. 1 to ground. Check for continuity between terminals No. 2 and 4. Continuity should not exist. Check for continuity between terminals

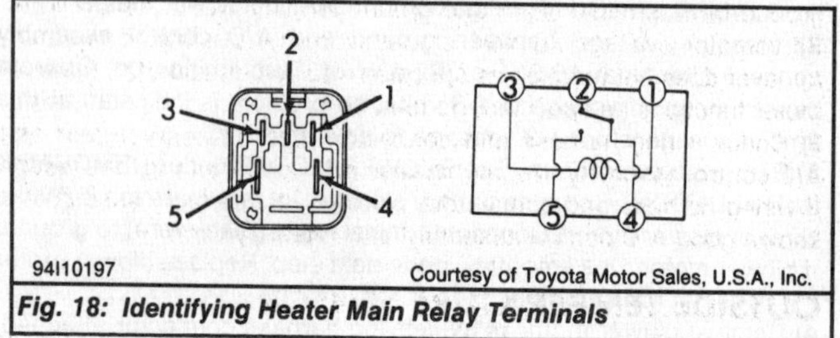
2
3
1
5
4
3
2
1
5
4

94I10197 Courtesy of Toyota Motor Sales, U.S.A., Inc.

Fig. 18: Identifying Heater Main Relay Terminals

1993 AUTOMATIC A/C-HEATER SYSTEMS GS300 (Cont.)

No. 4 and 5. Continuity should exist. Replace relay if it does not operate as specified. If relay is okay, check wiring harness and connectors between A/C control assembly and battery.

IGNITION POWER & GROUND CIRCUITS

1) Turn ignition on. Check GAUGE fuse at fuse block under left side of instrument panel. If fuse is okay, go next step. If fuse is blown, correct cause and replace fuse. Remove A/C control assembly, leaving harness connectors attached.
2) Using DVOM, backprobe A/C control assembly connector between terminals A10-6 (Black/Yellow wire) and A10-5 (White/Black wire). *See Fig. 5.* If battery voltage is not present, go to next step. If battery voltage is present, no problem is indicated at this time.
3) Turn ignition off. Measure resistance between terminal A10-5 (White/Black wire) of A/C control assembly and ground. If resistance is more than one ohm, repair open White/Black wire. If resistance is less than one ohm, wire is okay. Check wiring harness and connectors between A/C control assembly and battery. Repair wiring and connectors as necessary.

IN-VEHICLE TEMPERATURE SENSOR

Remove panel underneath instrument panel. Disconnect in-vehicle temperature sensor. *See Fig. 1.* Measure sensor resistance while heating sensor. See IN-VEHICLE TEMPERATURE SENSOR SPECIFICATIONS table. If resistance is not as specified, replace sensor.

IN-VEHICLE TEMPERATURE SENSOR SPECIFICATIONS

Sensor Temperature °F (°C)	[1] Ohms
77 (25)	1650-1750
122 (50)	550-650

[1] – As temperature increases, resistance should gradually decrease.

MAXIMUM COOL DOOR SERVOMOTOR

1) Warm engine to normal operating temperature. Perform RETRIEVING CODES. After system enters self-diagnostic mode, perform ACTUATOR CHECK. Press A/C button to enter step mode and display codes.
2) Turn temperature control knob and ensure maximum cool door operates with changes in vent blower output and door operation. See MAXIMUM COOLING DOOR SERVOMOTOR OPERATION table.

MAXIMUM COOLING DOOR SERVOMOTOR OPERATION

Code	Door Position
20-21	Open
22-29	Closed

3) If maximum cool door servomotor functions as specified, no problem is indicated at this time. If maximum cool door servomotor does not function as specified, go to next step.
4) Remove heater unit. See HEATER UNIT under REMOVAL & INSTALLATION. Disconnect maximum cool door servomotor connector. Apply battery voltage to maximum cool servomotor connector terminal No. 4 (Black/Yellow wire). Connect terminal No. 1 (Blue/Red wire) to ground. Servomotor lever should turn smoothly to closed position.
5) With battery voltage still connected to terminal No. 4, remove ground from terminal No. 1 and ground terminal No. 3 (Yellow wire). Servomotor lever should move smoothly to open position. If servomotor lever does not function as specified, replace servomotor. If servomotor functions as specified, go to next step.
6) Check wiring harness and connectors between servomotor and A/C control assembly. Repair harness and connectors as necessary. If wiring harness and connectors are okay, temporarily substitute a known good A/C control assembly, and retest system.

OUTSIDE TEMPERATURE SENSOR

1) Remove clip and outside temperature sensor from left side of bumper reinforcement. *See Fig. 1.* Disconnect outside temperature sensor connector. Measure sensor resistance while heating sensor. See OUTSIDE TEMPERATURE SENSOR SPECIFICATIONS table.
2) If resistance is not as specified, replace sensor. If resistance is within specification, check wiring harness and connectors between sensor and A/C control assembly. Repair harness and connectors as necessary. If wiring harness and connectors are okay, substitute a known good A/C control assembly, and retest system.

OUTSIDE TEMPERATURE SENSOR SPECIFICATIONS

Sensor Temperature °F (°C)	[1] Ohms
77 (25)	1600-1800
122 (50)	500-700

[1] – As temperature increases, resistance should gradually decrease.

PRESSURE SWITCH

1) Pressure switch is located near receiver-drier. *See Fig. 19.* Connect A/C manifold gauge set. Start engine. Turn blower and A/C on. Observe system pressure. With pressure switch connector disconnected, check continuity between pressure switch terminals No. 1 and 4.
2) Continuity should not exist if high side pressure is less than 28 psi (2.0 kg/cm²). Continuity should exist if high side pressure is more than 28 psi (2.0 kg/cm²). If continuity is not as specified, replace pressure switch.

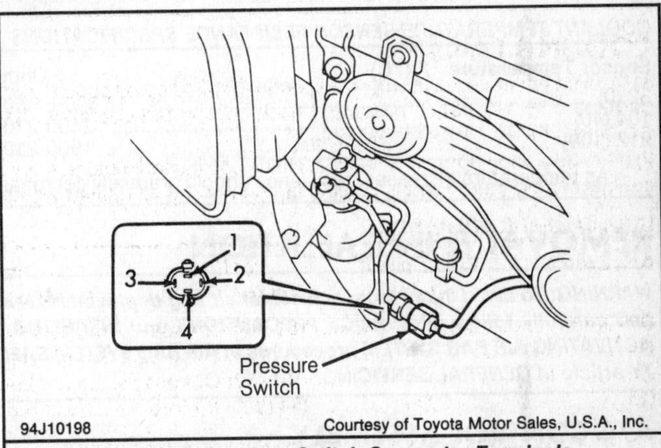
1
3
2
4
Pressure
Switch
94J10198
Courtesy of Toyota Motor Sales, U.S.A., Inc.

Fig. 19: Identifying Pressure Switch Connector Terminals

SELF-DIAGNOSTIC CIRCUIT

1) Turn ignition on. Using a DVOM, measure voltage between Data Link Connector No. 2 (DLC2) terminals TC and AC . *See Fig. 20.* DLC2 is located behind left side of instrument panel. If battery voltage is present, no problem is indicated at this time.
2) If battery voltage is not present, check wiring harness and connectors between A/C control assembly, DLC2 and ground. Repair wiring and connectors as necessary. If wiring and connectors are okay, temporarily substitute a known good A/C control assembly, and retest system.

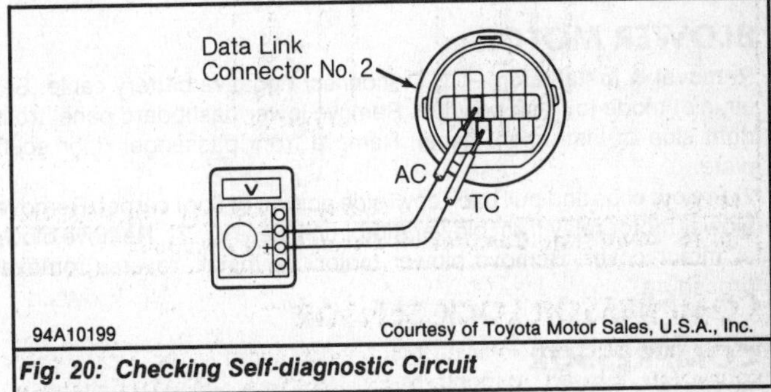
Data Link
Connector No. 2
AC
TC
V
94A10199
Courtesy of Toyota Motor Sales, U.S.A., Inc.

Fig. 20: Checking Self-diagnostic Circuit

1993 AUTOMATIC A/C-HEATER SYSTEMS GS300 (Cont.)

SOLAR SENSOR

1) Remove glove box and solar sensor. Disconnect sensor harness connector. Cover sensor using cloth. Measure and record resistance between sensor terminals. Ensure ohmmeter is connected with positive lead of ohmmeter to Green/Black wire terminal and negative lead to Red/Yellow wire terminal of solar sensor.
2) Remove cloth. Subject sensor to bright light and measure resistance between terminals of sensor. See SOLAR SENSOR RESISTANCE SPECIFICATIONS table. If resistance is not as specified, replace sensor.

SOLAR SENSOR RESISTANCE SPECIFICATIONS

Condition	[1] Ohms
Sensor Covered By Cloth	No Continuity
Sensor Subjected To Bright Light	About 4000

[1] – As light intensity decreases, resistance should increase.

COOLANT (WATER) TEMPERATURE SENSOR

Remove coolant temperature sensor. See COOLANT (WATER) TEMPERATURE SENSOR under REMOVAL & INSTALLATION. Place sensor and thermometer in water. Measure resistance between sensor terminals as water is heated. If resistance is not as specified, replace coolant temperature sensor. See COOLANT TEMPERATURE SENSOR RESISTANCE SPECIFICATIONS table.

COOLANT TEMPERATURE SENSOR RESISTANCE SPECIFICATIONS

Sensor Temperature °F (°C)	[1] Ohms
32 (0)	16,500-51,500
104 (40)	2500-2700
212 (100)	1900-2100

[1] – As temperature increases, resistance should gradually decrease.

REMOVAL & INSTALLATION

WARNING: To avoid injury from accidental air bag deployment, read and carefully follow all SERVICE PRECAUTIONS and DISABLING & ACTIVATING AIR BAG SYSTEM procedures in AIR BAG SYSTEM SAFETY article in GENERAL SERVICING.

A/C CONTROL ASSEMBLY

Removal & Installation – Disconnect negative battery cable. Remove shift lever knob. Remove upper console panel. With ashtray closed, remove ashtray trim panel. Remove center air register. Remove radio and A/C control assembly. Separate radio from A/C control assembly. To install, reverse removal procedure.

AIR OUTLET SERVOMOTOR

Removal & Installation – Disconnect negative battery cable. Remove instrument panel. See INSTRUMENT PANEL. Remove heater-to-No. 2 air duct. Disconnect servomotor connector. Remove wiper relay and power steering electronic control module. Remove servomotor. To install, reverse removal procedure.

BLOWER MOTOR

Removal & Installation – 1) Disconnect negative battery cable. Set air inlet mode to fresh position. Remove lower dashboard panel from right side of instrument panel. Remove front passenger door scuff plate.
2) Pry out clips and pull back cowl side portion of floor carpet. Remove blower motor relay from blower motor unit. *See Fig. 21.* Remove blower motor cover. Remove blower motor. To install, reverse removal procedure.

COMPRESSOR

Removal & Installation – 1) If compressor runs, idle engine for 10 minutes with A/C on. Turn ignition off. Disconnect negative battery cable. Discharge A/C system using approved refrigerant recovery/recycling equipment. Remove battery and tray. Remove drive belt.
2) Remove power steering pump. Disconnect compressor connector. Disconnect and cap refrigerant hoses from compressor. Raise and support vehicle. Remove lower engine splash shield. Remove compressor bolts and compressor.
3) If replacing compressor, ensure compressor is filled with correct amount of refrigerant oil. See COMPRESSOR REFRIGERANT OIL CHECKING article in GENERAL SERVICING. To install, reverse removal procedure. Evacuate and recharge system. Check system for leaks.

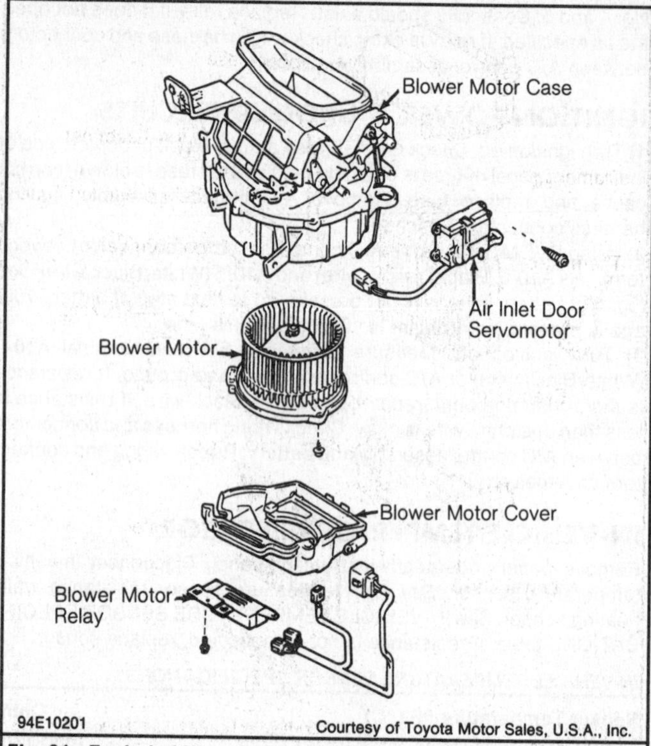
Blower Motor Case
Air Inlet Door Servomotor
Blower Motor
Blower Motor Cover
Blower Motor Relay
94E10201
Courtesy of Toyota Motor Sales, U.S.A., Inc.

Fig. 21: Exploded View Of Blower Motor Assembly

COOLING UNIT

Removal & Installation – 1) Disconnect negative battery cable. Discharge A/C system using approved refrigerant recovery/recycling equipment. Disconnect and plug refrigerant lines from evaporator assembly. Remove lower panel from right side of instrument panel. Remove glove box door.
2) Remove glove box reinforcement. Remove front passenger-side door scuff plate. Remove heater air duct guide. Remove engine control module cover. Remove A/C amplifier and disconnect wiring harness. Remove cooling unit.
3) Disassemble cooling unit and replace components as necessary. *See Fig. 22.* To install, reverse removal procedure. Ensure compressor is filled with correct amount of refrigerant oil. See COMPRESSOR REFRIGERANT OIL CHECKING article in GENERAL SERVICING. Evacuate and recharge system. Check system for leaks.

EXPANSION VALVE

Removal & Installation – Remove evaporator. See COOLING UNIT. Remove equalizer tubes. Remove expansion valve. To install, reverse removal procedure.

HEATER UNIT

Removal & Installation – 1) Disconnect negative battery cable. Drain cooling system. Remove cooling unit. See COOLING UNIT. Disconnect coolant hoses and remove heater control valve. Remove EGR pipe. Disconnect coolant hoses from heater unit. Remove both front seats.

1993 AUTOMATIC A/C-HEATER SYSTEMS GS300 (Cont.)

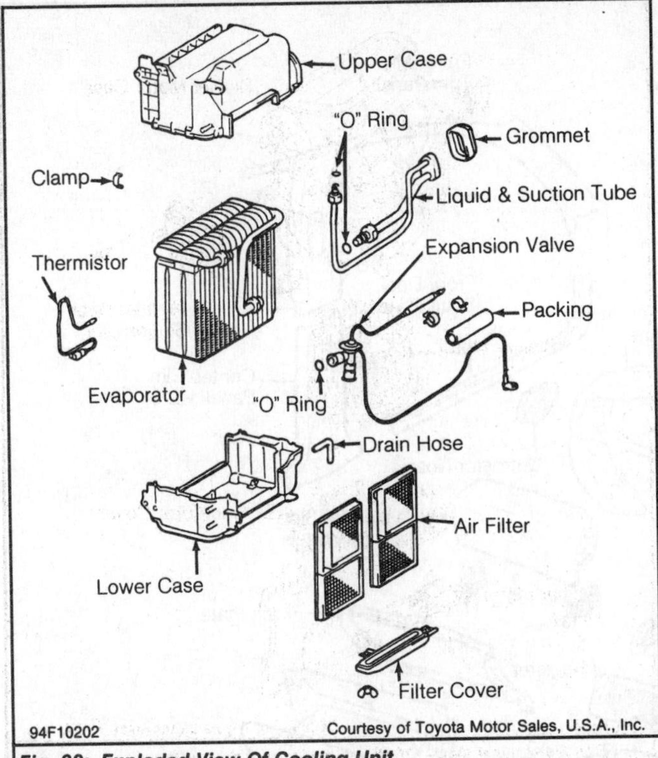
Upper Case
"O" Ring
Grommet
Clamp
Liquid & Suction Tube
Thermistor
Expansion Valve
Packing
Evaporator
"O" Ring
Drain Hose
Air Filter
Lower Case
Filter Cover
94F10202
Courtesy of Toyota Motor Sales, U.S.A., Inc.

Fig. 22: Exploded View Of Cooling Unit

2) Remove instrument panel, console box duct, instrument panel braces and reinforcement. See INSTRUMENT PANEL. Remove heater ducts from passenger and driver floor area. Remove heater-to-register No. 3 center air duct.

3) Remove wiring harness. Remove heater unit. Disassemble heater unit and replace components as necessary. *See Fig. 23.* To install, reverse removal procedure. Refill cooling system. Start engine, and warm it to operating temperature. Check system for leaks.

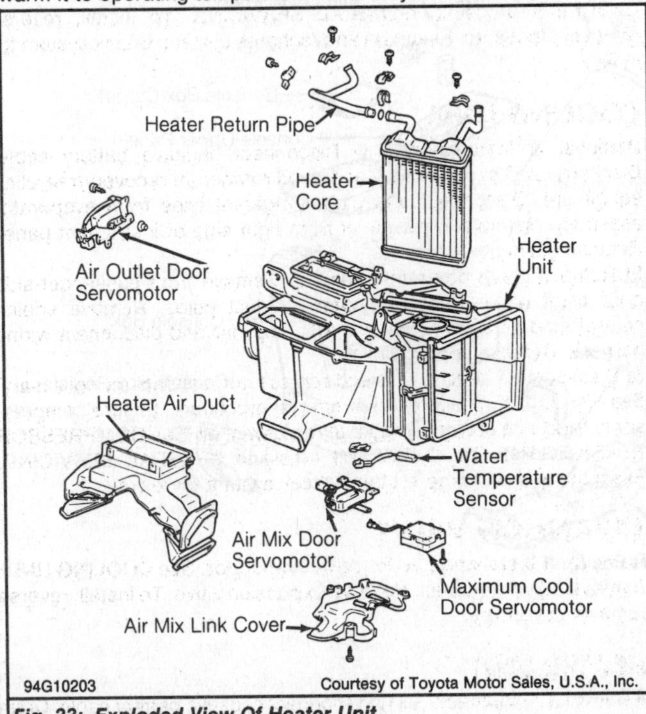
Heater Return Pipe
Heater Core
Heater Unit
Air Outlet Door Servomotor
Heater Air Duct
Water Temperature Sensor
Air Mix Door Servomotor
Maximum Cool Door Servomotor
Air Mix Link Cover
94G10203
Courtesy of Toyota Motor Sales, U.S.A., Inc.

Fig. 23: Exploded View Of Heater Unit

IN-VEHICLE TEMPERATURE SENSOR

Removal & Installation – Disconnect negative battery cable. Remove instrument panel. See INSTRUMENT PANEL. Remove in-vehicle temperature sensor. To install, reverse removal procedure.

INSTRUMENT PANEL

Removal – **1)** Disconnect negative battery cable. Disable air bag system. See AIR BAG SYSTEM SAFETY article in GENERAL SERVICING. Remove front and rear door scuff plates. *See Fig. 24.*

2) Remove center trim panel and seat belt shoulder anchors from center pillar. Remove both front seat belt retractors, located in center pillar. Remove 4 seat track covers. Remove both front seats.

3) Remove roof side inner trim panels and front pillar trim panels. Remove steering wheel pad (driver-side air bag module). Remove steering wheel nut. Mark position of steering wheel on shaft, and remove steering wheel using puller.

4) Remove upper and lower steering column covers. Remove instrument cluster finish panel. Remove both undercover panels. Remove end pads. Remove knee bolster. Remove No. 2 air duct. Remove combination switch. Remove instrument cluster. Open glove box door. Remove finish plate from glove box interior.

5) Disconnect passenger-side air bag connector. Remove glove box door. Remove passenger-side air bag module. Remove No. 3 air register. Remove front ashtray. Remove radio with A/C control assembly. Remove shift knob. Remove console upper panel and register. Remove center console box and mounting brackets.

6) Remove center console air ducts. Remove side defroster nozzles. Remove heater air guide. Disconnect all wiring harness connectors as necessary. Remove nut and antenna cable bracket. Ensure all hoses and connectors necessary for instrument panel removal are disconnected.

7) Remove 9 bolts, 2 screws, one nut and instrument panel. Remove heater-to-air register. Remove steering column assembly. Remove lower mounting bracket, instrument panel braces and instrument panel reinforcement.

Installation – To install instrument panel, reverse removal procedure. Tighten steering wheel pad Torx screws and steering wheel hub nut to specification. See TORQUE SPECIFICATIONS. Activate air bag system and ensure air bag system is functioning properly. See SYSTEM OPERATION CHECK in AIR BAG SYSTEM SAFETY article in GENERAL SERVICING.

COOLANT (WATER) TEMPERATURE SENSOR

Removal & Installation – Disconnect negative battery cable. Remove heater unit. See HEATER UNIT. Disconnect sensor connector and remove sensor from heater unit. To install, reverse removal procedure.

TORQUE SPECIFICATIONS

TORQUE SPECIFICATIONS

Application	Ft. Lbs. (N.m)
A/C Compressor	
Stud Bolt	19 (26)
Bolts	38 (52)
Steering Wheel Nut	26 (35)
Power Steering Pump Bolts	43 (58)
	INCH Lbs. (N.m)
Steering Wheel Pad Torx Screw	65 (7)

1993 AUTOMATIC A/C-HEATER SYSTEMS
GS300 (Cont.)

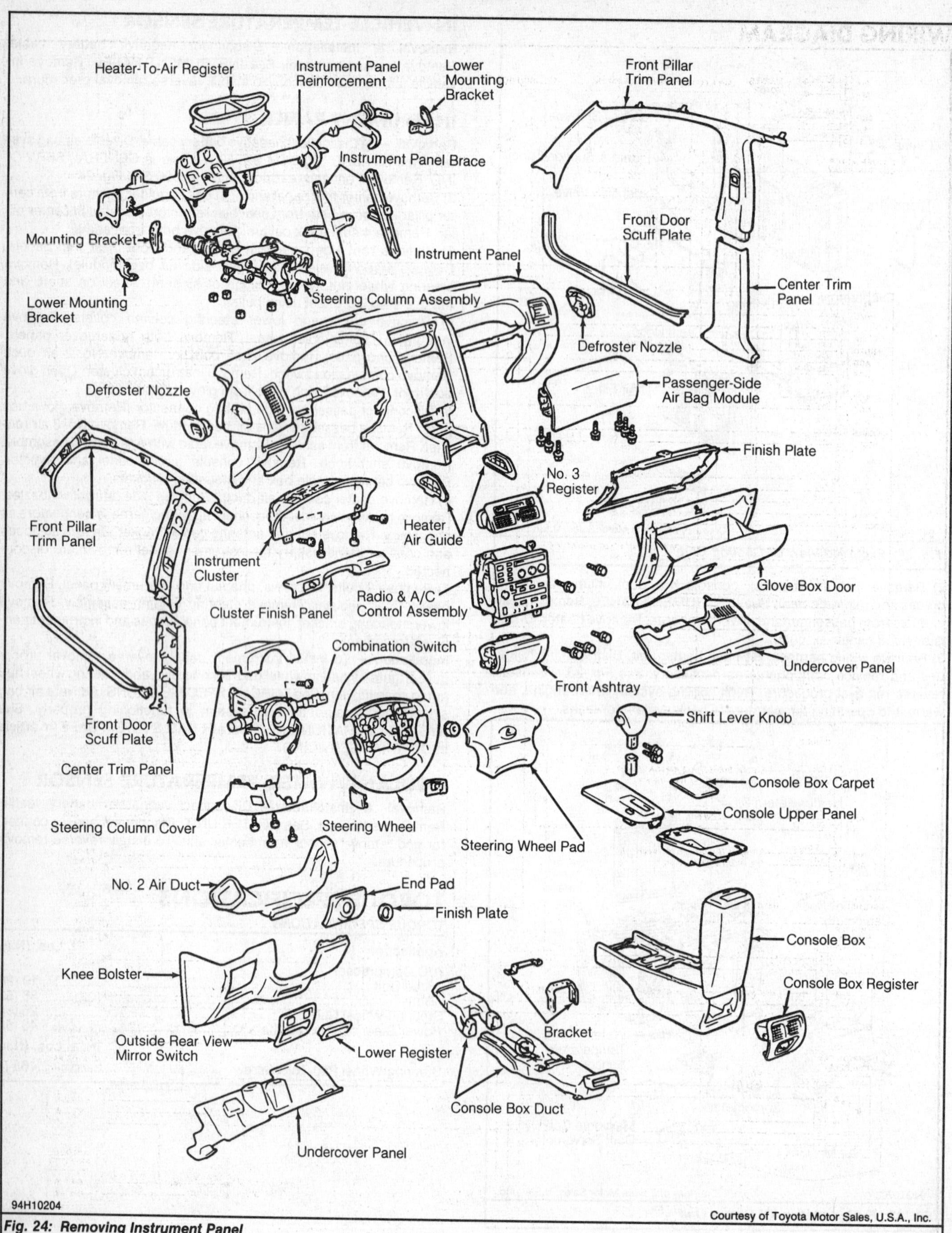
Heater-To-Air Register
Instrument Panel Reinforcement
Lower Mounting Bracket
Front Pillar Trim Panel
Instrument Panel Brace
Mounting Bracket
Lower Mounting Bracket
Steering Column Assembly
Instrument Panel
Front Door Scuff Plate
Center Trim Panel
Defroster Nozzle
Defroster Nozzle
Passenger-Side Air Bag Module
Finish Plate
No. 3 Register
Front Pillar Trim Panel
Heater Air Guide
Instrument Cluster
Radio & A/C Control Assembly
Cluster Finish Panel
Glove Box Door
Undercover Panel
Combination Switch
Front Ashtray
Front Door Scuff Plate
Shift Lever Knob
Center Trim Panel
Console Box Carpet
Console Upper Panel
Steering Column Cover
Steering Wheel
Steering Wheel Pad
No. 2 Air Duct
End Pad
Finish Plate
Console Box
Knee Bolster
Console Box Register
Bracket
Outside Rear View Mirror Switch
Lower Register
Console Box Duct
Undercover Panel
94H10204
Courtesy of Toyota Motor Sales, U.S.A., Inc.

Fig. 24: Removing Instrument Panel

1993 AUTOMATIC A/C-HEATER SYSTEMS GS300 (Cont.)

WIRING DIAGRAM

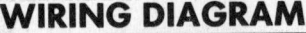

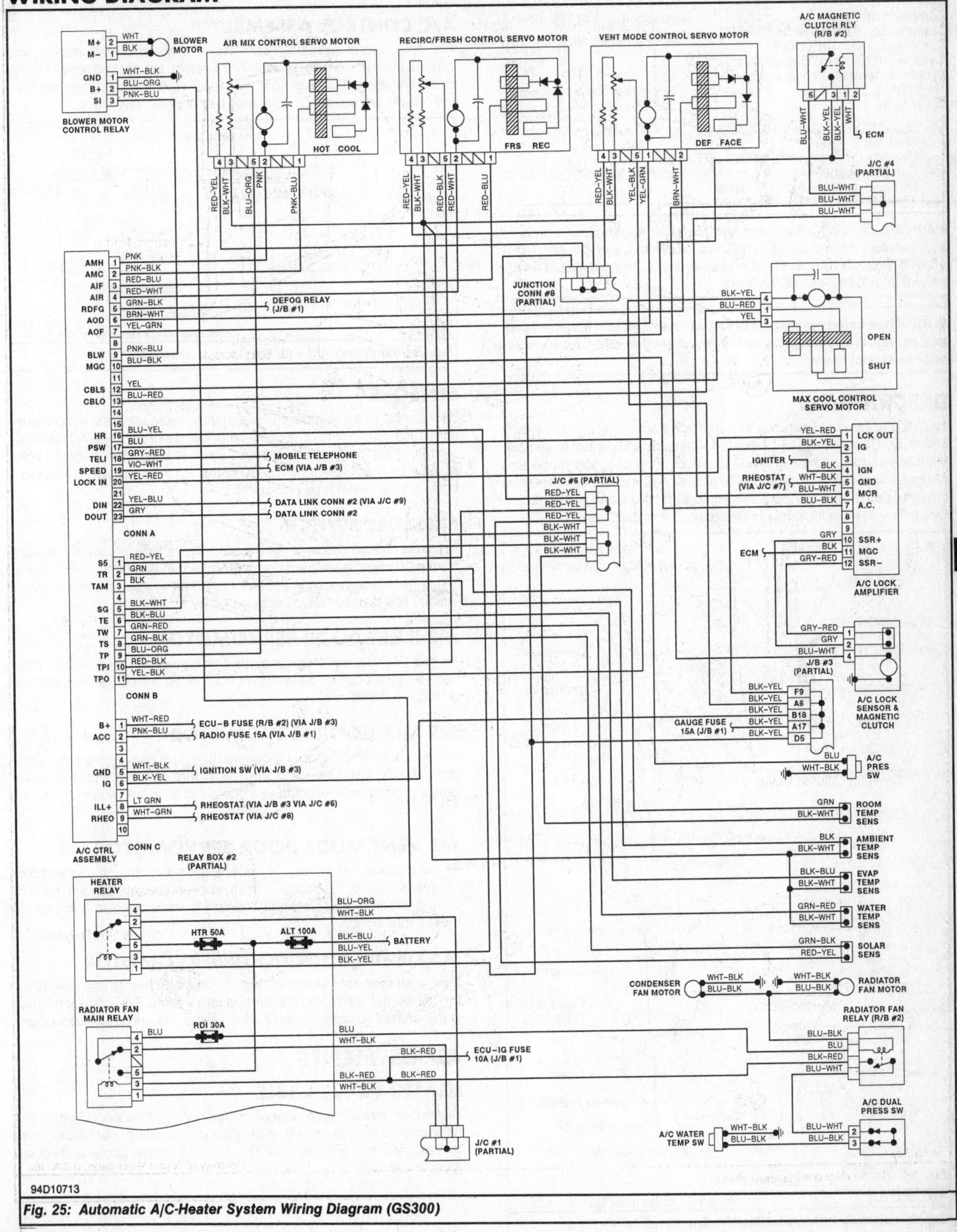
BLOWER MOTOR
AIR MIX CONTROL SERVO MOTOR
RECIRC/FRESH CONTROL SERVO MOTOR
VENT MODE CONTROL SERVO MOTOR
A/C MAGNETIC CLUTCH RLY (R/B #2)
BLOWER MOTOR CONTROL RELAY
HOT COOL
FRS REC
DEF FACE
ECM
J/C #4 (PARTIAL)
JUNCTION CONN #8 (PARTIAL)
DEFOG RELAY (J/B #1)
MAX COOL CONTROL SERVO MOTOR
OPEN
SHUT
MOBILE TELEPHONE
ECM (VIA J/B #3)
DATA LINK CONN #2 (VIA J/C #9)
DATA LINK CONN #2
J/C #6 (PARTIAL)
IGNITER
RHEOSTAT (VIA J/C #7)
A/C LOCK AMPLIFIER
CONN A
CONN B
CONN C
ECU-B FUSE (R/B #2) (VIA J/B #3)
RADIO FUSE 15A (VIA J/B #1)
IGNITION SW (VIA J/B #3)
RHEOSTAT (VIA J/B #3 VIA J/C #6)
RHEOSTAT (VIA J/C #8)
J/B #3 (PARTIAL)
A/C LOCK SENSOR & MAGNETIC CLUTCH
GAUGE FUSE 15A (J/B #1)
A/C PRES SW
ROOM TEMP SENS
AMBIENT TEMP SENS
EVAP TEMP SENS
WATER TEMP SENS
SOLAR SENS
A/C CTRL ASSEMBLY
RELAY BOX #2 (PARTIAL)
HEATER RELAY
HTR 50A
ALT 100A
BATTERY
CONDENSER FAN MOTOR
RADIATOR FAN MOTOR
RADIATOR FAN MAIN RELAY
RDI 30A
ECU-IG FUSE 10A (J/B #1)
RADIATOR FAN RELAY (R/B #2)
A/C DUAL PRESS SW
A/C WATER TEMP SW
J/C #1 (PARTIAL)
94D10713

Fig. 25: Automatic A/C-Heater System Wiring Diagram (GS300)

1993 AUTOMATIC A/C-HEATER SYSTEMS LS400

SPECIFICATIONS

Compressor Type	Nippondenso 10PA20 10-Cyl.
Compressor Belt Deflection	[1]
Compressor Oil Capacity [2]	2.8-3.5 ozs.
Refrigerant (R-134a) Capacity	32 ozs.
System Operating Pressures [3]	
High Side	199-228 psi (14-16 kg/cm²)
Low Side	21-36 psi (1.5-2.5 kg/cm²)

[1] – See CODE 22 COMPRESSOR LOCK SENSOR CIRCUIT under TROUBLE SHOOTING.
[2] – Use ND-Oil 8 (Part No. 38899-PR7-003).
[3] – Specification is with ambient temperature at 86-95°F (30-35°C) and engine speed at 1500 RPM.

WARNING: To avoid injury from accidental air bag deployment, read and carefully follow all SERVICE PRECAUTIONS and DISABLING & ACTIVATING AIR BAG SYSTEM procedures in AIR BAG SYSTEM SAFETY article in GENERAL SERVICING.

NOTE: When battery is disconnected, radio will go into anti-theft protection mode. Obtain radio anti-theft protection code from owner prior to servicing vehicle.

DESCRIPTION

All A/C and heating functions are controlled automatically by an A/C Electronic Control Unit (ECU) located within the A/C control assembly. Manual controls allow the driver to select air distribution mode and desired temperature. In addition to normal A/C system components, the system includes various servomotors, controls and sensors. *See Fig. 1.* The system includes self-diagnostic capabilities.

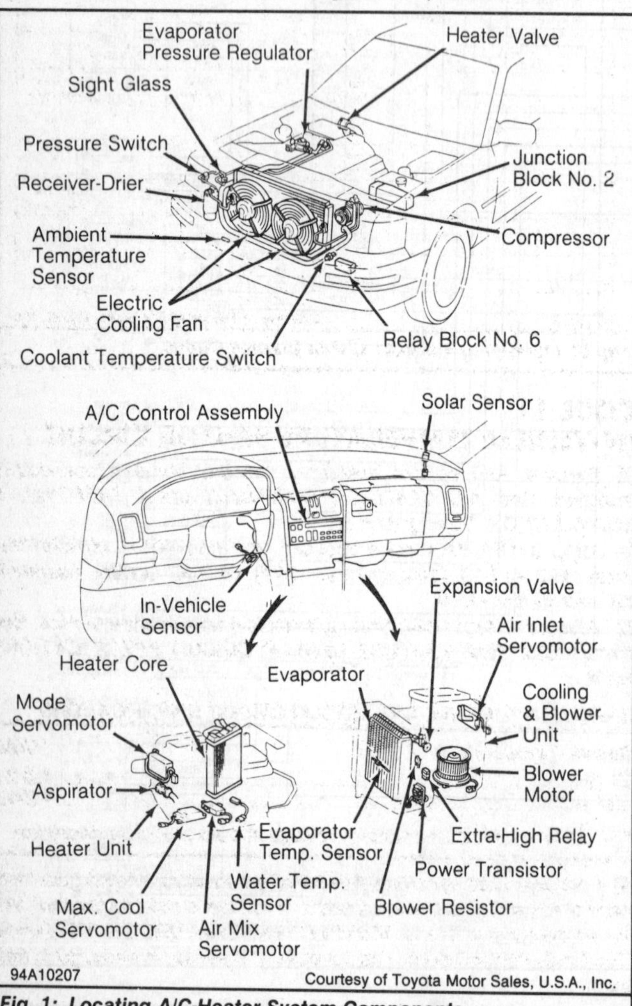
Evaporator Pressure Regulator
Heater Valve
Sight Glass
Pressure Switch
Receiver-Drier
Junction Block No. 2
Ambient Temperature Sensor
Compressor
Electric Cooling Fan
Relay Block No. 6
Coolant Temperature Switch
A/C Control Assembly
Solar Sensor
In-Vehicle Sensor
Expansion Valve
Air Inlet Servomotor
Heater Core
Evaporator
Cooling & Blower Unit
Mode Servomotor
Blower Motor
Aspirator
Heater Unit
Evaporator Temp. Sensor
Extra-High Relay
Water Temp. Sensor
Power Transistor
Max. Cool Servomotor
Air Mix Servomotor
Blower Resistor
94A10207
Courtesy of Toyota Motor Sales, U.S.A., Inc.

Fig. 1: Locating A/C-Heater System Components

OPERATION

A/C CONTROL ASSEMBLY

The A/C control assembly consists of a liquid crystal display and various push buttons to activate A/C system, set desired temperature, direct discharged air to proper vents, activate rear defogger and control blower fan speed. Display also has a clock. *See Fig. 2.*

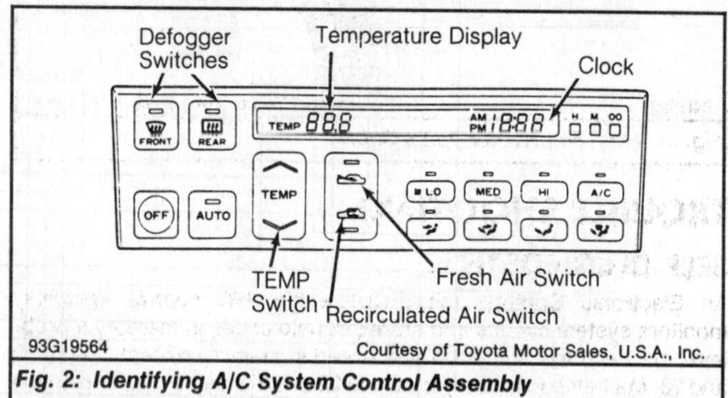
Defogger Switches
Temperature Display
Clock
FRONT
REAR
TEMP 88.8
AM PM 18:88
H
M
00
OFF
AUTO
TEMP
LO
MED
HI
A/C
TEMP Switch
Fresh Air Switch
Recirculated Air Switch
93G19564
Courtesy of Toyota Motor Sales, U.S.A., Inc.

Fig. 2: Identifying A/C System Control Assembly

SENSORS

Resistance of all temperature sensors decreases as temperature increases. Solar sensor resistance is infinite (no continuity) when no light is directed at sensor. When sensor is subjected to bright light, resistance is approximately 4000 ohms. As light intensity decreases, solar sensor resistance increases.

PRESSURE SWITCH

Pressure switch protects A/C system from high pressure resulting from restriction, overcharge or compressor malfunction. If excessively low or high pressure is sensed within the system, pressure switch inhibits compressor clutch engagement.

AIR INLET DOOR SERVOMOTOR

Air inlet door servomotor is mounted on blower unit. Servomotor positions air inlet door so air is drawn from either inside (recirculated air) or outside (fresh air).

AIR MIX DOOR SERVOMOTOR

Air mix door servomotor is mounted on heater unit. Servomotor positions air mix door so air is drawn either through heater core or evaporator. Servomotor rotation is transferred to a link which moves air mix door.

AIR VENT MODE DOOR SERVOMOTOR

Air vent mode servomotor is mounted on heater unit. Servomotor rotates so air is discharged from appropriate outlets set by A/C control assembly. Servomotor rotation is transferred to a link which moves mode door.

MAXIMUM COOL DOOR SERVOMOTOR

Maximum cool door servomotor is mounted on heater unit. Servomotor causes extra air to be discharged into vehicle. Servomotor rotation is transferred to control plates which move the maximum cool doors.

ADJUSTMENTS

HEATER VALVE CABLE

Disconnect heater valve cable. Turn ignition on. Press A/C button. Set temperature control knob to maximum cool position. Set heater valve to maximum cool position. *See Fig. 3.* Install control cable, and secure it using clamp.

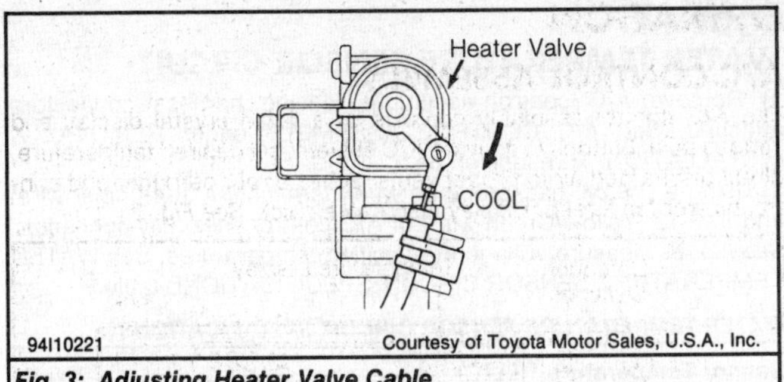
Heater Valve
COOL

94I10221 Courtesy of Toyota Motor Sales, U.S.A., Inc.

Fig. 3: Adjusting Heater Valve Cable

TROUBLE SHOOTING

SELF-DIAGNOSTICS

An Electronic Control Unit (ECU) within A/C control assembly monitors system circuits and stores trouble codes in memory if problems are detected. All codes are stored in memory except Codes 22 and 23. Malfunction is current if Code 22 or 23 is displayed. To retrieve stored codes, see RETRIEVING CODES. Codes are displayed at temperature display. *See Fig. 2.*

RETRIEVING CODES

Indicator Check – 1) Press and hold AUTO and recirculated air buttons. *See Fig. 2.* Turn ignition on. All indicators will flash 4 times at one-second intervals. Tone will sound when indicators flash. Press OFF button to cancel indicator check.

2) After indicator check is complete, system will enter self-diagnostic mode. Stored trouble codes will appear in sequence on temperature display panel. See DIAGNOSTIC CODE IDENTIFICATION table.

3) To slow rate at which codes are displayed, press TEMP (up) switch to change display to step operation. Each time TEMP (up) switch is pressed, display changes by one step.

4) If tone sounds as a code is displayed, problem currently exists. If tone does not sound while code is displayed, problem is past history and does not currently exist. Press OFF button to exit self-diagnostics.

DIAGNOSTIC CODE IDENTIFICATION

Code	Diagnosis
00	Normal
11 [1]	In-Vehicle Temperature Sensor Circuit
12 [2]	Ambient Temperature Sensor Circuit
13	Evaporator Temperature Sensor Circuit
14	Water Temperature Sensor Circuit
21 [3]	Solar Sensor Circuit
22 [4]	Compressor Lock Sensor Circuit
23 [4]	Abnormal Refrigerant Pressure
31	Air Mix Door Position Sensor Circuit
32	Air Inlet Door Position Sensor Circuit
34	Max. Cool Door Position Sensor Circuit
41	Air Mix Door Position Sensor
42	Air Inlet Door Position Sensor
44	Max. Cool Door Position Sensor

[1] – If in-vehicle temperature is -4°F (-20°C) or less, Code 11 may occur even though system is normal.

[2] – If outside air temperature is -58°F (-50°C) or less, Code 12 may occur even though system is normal.

[3] – If testing is done in a dark area, Code 21 may occur even though system is normal. Shine a light at solar sensor and recheck codes.

[4] – Malfunction is current. Code is not stored in memory.

CLEARING CODES

Remove DOME fuse. *See Fig. 4.* Wait at least 10 seconds before installing fuse. Perform RETRIEVING CODES procedure. Ensure only Code 00 is displayed.

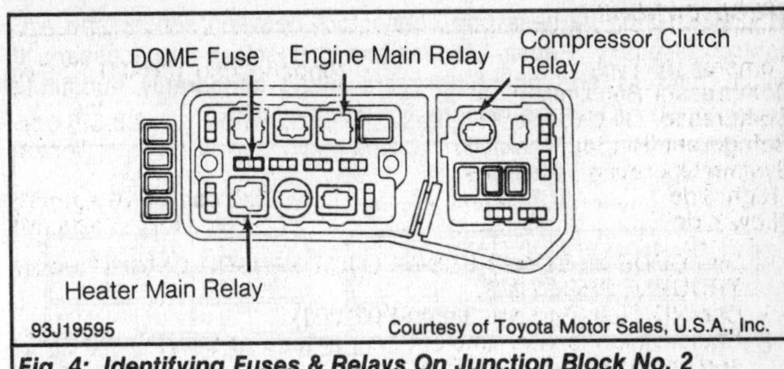
DOME Fuse
Engine Main Relay
Compressor Clutch Relay
Heater Main Relay

93J19595 Courtesy of Toyota Motor Sales, U.S.A., Inc.

Fig. 4: Identifying Fuses & Relays On Junction Block No. 2

ACTUATOR CHECK

1) Perform INDICATOR CHECK under RETRIEVING CODES. When system enters self-diagnostic mode, press recirculation air button. Each mode door, motor and relay will operate at one-second intervals. Press TEMP (up) button to display codes one at a time and to step through checks one at a time.

2) Check airflow and temperature by hand. Tone will sound each time display code changes. Each display code is associated with a system operating condition. *See Fig. 5.* Press OFF button to cancel actuator check mode.

Step No.	Display code	Conditions					
		Blower motor	Air flow vent	Max cool damper	Air inlet damper	Magnetic clutch	Air mix damper
1	20	OFF	(FACE)	0% open	(FRESH)	OFF	Cool side (0% open)
2	21	LO	↑	↑	↑	↑	↑
3	22	MED	↑	50% open	(F/R)	ON	↑
4	23	↑	↑	100% open	(RECIRC)	↑	↑
5	24	↑	(BI-LEVEL)	↑	(FRESH)	↑	Cool/Hot (50% open)
6	25	↑	↑	↑	↑	↑	↑
7	26	↑	(FOOT)	↑	↑	↑	↑
8	27	↑	↑	↑	↑	↑	Hot side (100% open)
9	28	↑	(FOOT/DEF)	↑	↑	↑	↑
10	29	HI	(DEF)	↑	↑	↑	↑

94J10222 Courtesy of Toyota Motor Sales, U.S.A., Inc.

Fig. 5: Identifying Actuator Check Display Codes

CODE 11
IN-VEHICLE TEMPERATURE SENSOR CIRCUIT

1) Remove A/C control assembly, leaving harness connectors attached. See A/C CONTROL ASSEMBLY under REMOVAL & INSTALLATION. Turn ignition on.

2) Using DVOM, backprobe between terminals A15-1 (Yellow/Blue wire) and A15-13 (Yellow/Green wire) of A/C control assembly connector. *See Fig. 6.*

3) Measure voltage while heating in-vehicle temperature sensor. See IN-VEHICLE TEMPERATURE SENSOR CIRCUIT SPECIFICATIONS table.

IN-VEHICLE TEMPERATURE SENSOR CIRCUIT SPECIFICATIONS

Sensor Temperature °F (°C)	[1] Volts
77 (25)	1.8-2.2
104 (40)	1.2-1.6

[1] – As temperature increases, voltage should gradually decrease.

4) If voltage is as specified, temporarily substitute known good A/C control assembly and retest system. If voltage is not as specified, test in-vehicle sensor. See IN-VEHICLE TEMPERATURE SENSOR under TESTING. Replace sensor as necessary. If sensor is okay, go to next step.

1993 AUTOMATIC A/C-HEATER SYSTEMS LS400 (Cont.)

5) Check wiring harness and connectors between sensor and A/C control assembly. Repair harness and connectors as necessary. If wiring harness and connectors are okay, temporarily substitute known good A/C control assembly. Retest system.

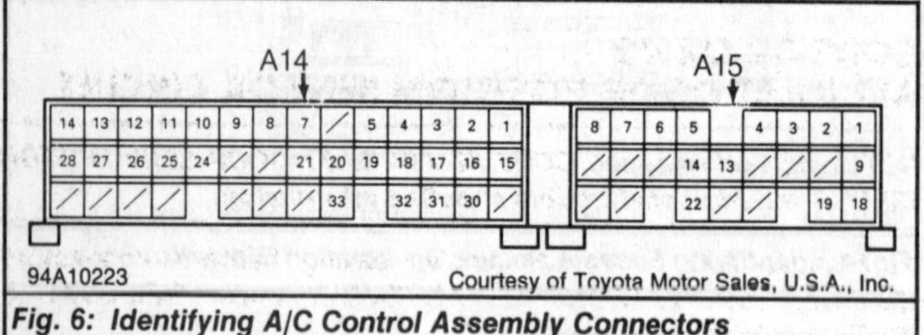
A14
A15
94A10223
Courtesy of Toyota Motor Sales, U.S.A., Inc.

Fig. 6: Identifying A/C Control Assembly Connectors

CODE 12
AMBIENT TEMPERATURE SENSOR CIRCUIT

1) Remove A/C control assembly, leaving harness connectors attached. See A/C CONTROL ASSEMBLY under REMOVAL & INSTALLATION. Turn ignition on.
2) Using DVOM, backprobe between terminals A15-2 (Blue/White wire) and A15-13 (Yellow/Green wire) of A/C control assembly connector. *See Fig. 6.*
3) Measure voltage while heating ambient temperature sensor, located behind grille, on lower right side. See AMBIENT TEMPERATURE SENSOR CIRCUIT SPECIFICATIONS table.

AMBIENT TEMPERATURE SENSOR CIRCUIT SPECIFICATIONS

Sensor Temperature °F (°C)	[1] Volts
77 (25)	1.35-1.75
104 (40)	0.85-1.25

[1] – As temperature increases, voltage should gradually decrease.

4) If voltage is as specified, temporarily substitute known good A/C control assembly and retest system. If voltage is not as specified, test ambient temperature sensor. See AMBIENT TEMPERATURE SENSOR under TESTING. Replace sensor as necessary. If sensor is okay, go to next step.
5) Check wiring harness and connectors between sensor and A/C control assembly. Repair harness and connectors as necessary. If wiring harness and connectors are okay, temporarily substitute known good A/C control assembly. Retest system.

CODE 13
EVAPORATOR TEMPERATURE SENSOR CIRCUIT

1) Remove A/C control assembly, leaving harness connectors attached. See A/C CONTROL ASSEMBLY under REMOVAL & INSTALLATION. Turn ignition on.
2) Using DVOM, backprobe between terminals A15-3 (Yellow/Red wire) and A15-13 (Yellow/Green wire) of A/C control assembly connector. *See Fig. 6.*
3) Measure voltage at specified temperatures. See EVAPORATOR TEMPERATURE SENSOR CIRCUIT SPECIFICATIONS table.

EVAPORATOR TEMPERATURE SENSOR CIRCUIT SPECIFICATIONS

Sensor Temperature °F (°C)	[1] Volts
32 (0)	2.0-2.4
59 (15)	1.4-1.8

[1] – As temperature increases, voltage should gradually decrease.

4) If voltage is as specified, temporarily substitute known good A/C control assembly and retest system. If voltage is not as specified, test evaporator temperature sensor. See EVAPORATOR TEMPERATURE SENSOR under TESTING. Replace sensor as necessary. If sensor is okay, go to next step.
5) Check wiring harness and connectors between sensor and A/C control assembly. Repair harness and connectors as necessary. If wiring harness and connectors are okay, temporarily substitute known good A/C control assembly. Retest system.

CODE 14
WATER TEMPERATURE SENSOR CIRCUIT

1) Remove A/C control assembly, leaving harness connectors attached. See A/C CONTROL ASSEMBLY under REMOVAL & INSTALLATION. Turn ignition on.
2) Using a DVOM, backprobe between terminals A15-4 (Violet wire) and A15-13 (Yellow/Green wire) of A/C control assembly connector. *See Fig. 6.* Measure voltage at specified temperatures. See WATER TEMPERATURE SENSOR CIRCUIT SPECIFICATIONS table.

WATER TEMPERATURE SENSOR CIRCUIT SPECIFICATIONS

Sensor Temperature °F (°C)	[1] Volts
32 (0)	2.8-3.2
104 (40)	1.8-2.2
158 (70)	0.9-1.3

[1] – As temperature increases, voltage should gradually decrease.

3) If voltage is as specified, temporarily substitute known good A/C control assembly and retest system. If voltage is not as specified, test water temperature sensor. See WATER TEMPERATURE SENSOR under TESTING. Replace sensor as necessary. If sensor is okay, go to next step.
4) Check wiring harness and connectors between sensor and A/C control assembly. Repair harness and connectors as necessary. If wiring harness and connectors are okay, temporarily substitute known good A/C control assembly. Retest system.

CODE 21
SOLAR SENSOR CIRCUIT

NOTE: If testing is done in a dark area, Code 21 may occur even though system is normal. Shine a light at solar sensor and recheck for Code 21.

1) Remove A/C control assembly, leaving harness connectors attached. See A/C CONTROL ASSEMBLY under REMOVAL & INSTALLATION. Turn ignition on.
2) Using DVOM, backprobe between terminals A15-9 (Blue wire) and A15-5 (Green/Black wire) of A/C control assembly connector. *See Fig. 6.* Measure voltage at specified temperatures. See SOLAR SENSOR CIRCUIT SPECIFICATIONS table.

SOLAR SENSOR CIRCUIT SPECIFICATIONS

Condition	[1] Volts
Sensor Subjected To Bright Light	Less Than 4.0
Sensor Covered By Cloth	4.0-4.5

[1] – As light intensity decreases, voltage should increase.

3) If voltage is as specified, temporarily substitute known good A/C control assembly and retest system. If voltage is not as specified, test solar sensor. See SOLAR SENSOR under TESTING. Replace sensor as necessary. If sensor is okay, go to next step.
4) Check wiring harness and connectors between sensor and A/C control assembly. Repair harness and connectors as necessary. If wiring harness and connectors are okay, temporarily substitute known good A/C control assembly. Retest system.

CODE 22
COMPRESSOR LOCK SENSOR CIRCUIT

NOTE: When replacing drive belt, new belt tension should be in range "B" on tensioner scale. See Fig. 7.

1) Ensure drive belt fits properly on compressor pulley. If tension is not in range "A" on scale, replace belt. *See Fig. 7.* If tension is okay, go to next step.
2) Start engine. Turn blower and A/C on. Observe compressor. If compressor locks during operation, repair compressor. If compressor does not lock during operation, check compressor lock sensor. See COMPRESSOR LOCK SENSOR under TESTING. Replace sensor as necessary.

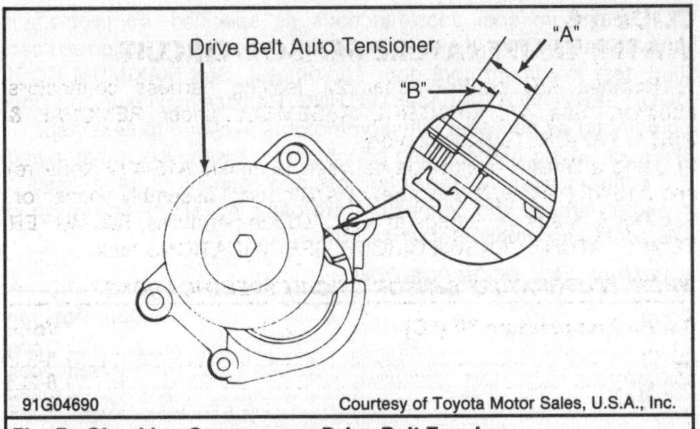

Drive Belt Auto Tensioner
"A"
"B"
91G04690
Courtesy of Toyota Motor Sales, U.S.A., Inc.

Fig. 7: Checking Compressor Drive Belt Tension

3) If sensor is okay, check wiring harness and connectors between sensor and A/C control assembly. Repair harness and connectors as necessary. If wiring harness and connectors are okay, temporarily substitute known good A/C control assembly. Retest system.

CODE 23 PRESSURE SWITCH CIRCUIT

1) Remove A/C control assembly, leaving harness connectors attached. See A/C CONTROL ASSEMBLY under REMOVAL & INSTALLATION. Install manifold gauge set. Turn ignition on.
2) Using DVOM, backprobe A/C control assembly connector between terminal A14-19 (Blue/Black wire) and ground. *See Fig. 6.*
3) Start engine. Turn blower and A/C on. Battery voltage should be present with low side pressure of less than 28 psi (2.0 kg/cm²). If voltage is as specified, temporarily substitute known good A/C control assembly and retest system.
4) If voltage is not as specified, test pressure switch. See PRESSURE SWITCH under TESTING. Replace pressure switch as necessary. If switch is okay, go to next step.
5) Check wiring harness and connectors between pressure switch and A/C control assembly. Repair harness and connectors as necessary. If wiring harness and connectors are okay, temporarily substitute known good A/C control assembly. Retest system.

CODE 31 OR 41 AIR MIX DOOR POSITION SENSOR CIRCUIT

***NOTE:* For Code 41, see CODE 41 AIR MIX SERVOMOTOR CIRCUIT for additional trouble shooting information.**

1) Remove A/C control assembly, leaving harness connectors attached. See A/C CONTROL ASSEMBLY under REMOVAL & INSTALLATION. Turn ignition on.
2) Using DVOM, backprobe between terminals A15-6 (Yellow wire) and A15-13 (Yellow/Green wire) of A/C control assembly connector. *See Fig. 6.*
3) Measure sensor circuit voltage while changing set temperature to activate air mix door. See AIR MIX DOOR POSITION SENSOR CIRCUIT SPECIFICATIONS table.

AIR MIX DOOR POSITION SENSOR CIRCUIT SPECIFICATIONS

Set Temperature	[1] Volts
Maximum Cool	3.76-5.27
Maximum Hot	0.94-1.44

[1] – As set temperature increases, voltage should gradually decrease.

4) If voltage is as specified, temporarily substitute known good A/C control assembly and retest system. If voltage is not as specified, test air mix door position sensor. See AIR MIX DOOR POSITION SENSOR under TESTING. Replace sensor as necessary. If sensor is okay, go to next step.

5) Check wiring harness and connectors between servomotor and A/C control assembly. Repair harness and connectors as necessary. If wiring harness and connectors are okay, temporarily substitute known good A/C control assembly. Retest system.

CODE 32 OR 42 AIR INLET DOOR POSITION SENSOR CIRCUIT

***NOTE:* For Code 42, see CODE 42 AIR INLET DOOR SERVOMOTOR CIRCUIT for additional trouble shooting information.**

1) Remove A/C control assembly, leaving harness connectors attached. See A/C CONTROL ASSEMBLY under REMOVAL & INSTALLATION. Turn ignition on.
2) Using DVOM, backprobe between terminals A15-7 (Blue/Red wire) and A15-13 (Yellow/Green wire) of A/C control assembly connector. *See Fig. 6.*
3) Measure sensor circuit voltage while changing set temperature to activate air inlet door. See AIR INLET DOOR POSITION SENSOR CIRCUIT SPECIFICATIONS table.

AIR INLET DOOR POSITION SENSOR CIRCUIT SPECIFICATIONS

Switch/Inlet Position	[1] Volts
Recirculated Air	3.5-4.5
Fresh Air	0.5-1.8

[1] – Voltage should gradually decrease as air inlet door changes from recirculated air to fresh air position.

4) If voltage is as specified, temporarily substitute known good A/C control assembly and retest system. If voltage is not as specified, test air inlet door position sensor. See AIR INLET DOOR POSITION SENSOR under TESTING. Replace sensor as necessary. If sensor is okay, go to next step.
5) Check wiring harness and connectors between servomotor and A/C control assembly. Repair harness and connectors as necessary. If wiring harness and connectors are okay, temporarily substitute known good A/C control assembly. Retest system.

CODE 33 OR 44 MAXIMUM COOL DOOR POSITION SENSOR CIRCUIT

***NOTE:* For Code 44, see CODE 44 MAXIMUM COOL DOOR SERVOMOTOR CIRCUIT for additional trouble shooting information.**

1) Remove A/C control assembly, leaving harness connectors attached. See A/C CONTROL ASSEMBLY under REMOVAL & INSTALLATION. Turn ignition on.
2) Using DVOM, backprobe A/C control assembly connector between terminals A15-8 (White/Blue wire) and A15-13 (Yellow/Green wire). *See Fig. 6.*
3) Measure sensor circuit voltage while pressing TEMP button up and then down to change set temperature. As servomotor operates, note voltage reading. See MAXIMUM COOL DOOR POSITION SENSOR CIRCUIT SPECIFICATIONS table.

MAXIMUM COOL DOOR POSITION SENSOR CIRCUIT SPECIFICATIONS

Set Temperature	[1] Volts
Maximum Cool	3.5-4.5
Maximum Hot	0.5-1.8

[1] – As set temperature increases, voltage should gradually decrease.

4) If voltage is as specified, temporarily substitute known good A/C control assembly and retest system. If voltage is not as specified, test maximum cool door position sensor. See MAXIMUM COOL DOOR POSITION SENSOR under TESTING. If maximum cool door position sensor is defective, replace maximum cool door servomotor. If position sensor is okay, go to next step.

1993 AUTOMATIC A/C-HEATER SYSTEMS
LS400 (Cont.)

5) Check wiring harness and connectors between servomotor and A/C control assembly. Repair harness and connectors as necessary. If wiring harness and connectors are okay, temporarily substitute known good A/C control assembly. Retest system.

CODE 41
AIR MIX SERVOMOTOR CIRCUIT

NOTE: See CODE 31 OR 41 AIR MIX DOOR POSITION SENSOR CIRCUIT for additional trouble shooting information.

1) Warm engine to normal operating temperature. Perform RETRIEVING CODES. After system enters self-diagnostic mode, perform ACTUATOR CHECK. Press TEMP (up) button to enter step mode and display codes. See AIR MIX DOOR AIRFLOW table. Air mix door operation should be as specified.
2) If air mix door functions as specified, no problem is indicated at this time. If air mix door does not function as specified, test air mix door servomotor. See AIR MIX DOOR SERVOMOTOR under TESTING. Replace air mix door servomotor as necessary. If servomotor is okay, go to next step.
3) Check wiring harness and connectors between servomotor and A/C control assembly. Repair harness and connectors as necessary. If wiring harness and connectors are okay, substitute known good A/C control assembly. Retest system.

AIR MIX DOOR AIRFLOW

Code	Air Mix Door	Specification
20-23	Fully Closed	Cool Air Comes Out
24-26	Half Open	Blend (Cool/Hot) Air Comes Out
27-29	Fully Open	Hot Air Comes Out

CODE 42
AIR INLET DOOR SERVOMOTOR CIRCUIT

NOTE: See CODE 32 OR 42 AIR INLET DOOR POSITION SENSOR CIRCUIT for additional trouble shooting information.

1) Warm engine to normal operating temperature. Perform RETRIEVING CODES. After system enters self-diagnostic mode, perform ACTUATOR CHECK. Press TEMP (up) button to enter step mode and display codes. See AIR INLET DOOR AIRFLOW table. Air inlet door operation should be as specified.
2) If air inlet door functions as specified, no problem is indicated at this time. If air inlet door does not function as specified, test air inlet door servomotor. See AIR INLET DOOR SERVOMOTOR under TESTING. Replace air inlet door servomotor as necessary. If servomotor is okay, go to next step.
3) Check wiring harness and connectors between servomotor and A/C control assembly. Repair harness and connectors as necessary. If wiring harness and connectors are okay, substitute known good A/C control assembly. Retest system.

AIR INLET DOOR AIRFLOW

Code	Door Position
20-21	Fresh Air
22	Fresh/Recirculated Air
23	Recirculated Air
24-29	Fresh Air

CODE 44
MAXIMUM COOL DOOR SERVOMOTOR CIRCUIT

NOTE: See CODE 33 OR 44 MAXIMUM COOL DOOR POSITION SENSOR CIRCUIT for additional trouble shooting information.

1) Warm engine to normal operating temperature. Perform RETRIEVING CODES. After system enters self-diagnostic mode, perform ACTUATOR CHECK. Press TEMP (up) button to enter step mode and display codes. See MAXIMUM COOL DOOR POSITION. Maximum cool door operation should be as specified.
2) If maximum cool door functions as specified, no problem is indicated at this time. If maximum cool door does not function as specified, test maximum cool door servomotor. See MAXIMUM COOL DOOR SERVOMOTOR under TESTING. Replace maximum cool door servomotor as necessary. If servomotor is okay, go to next step.
3) Check wiring harness and connectors between servomotor and A/C control assembly. Repair harness and connectors as necessary. If wiring harness and connectors are okay, substitute known good A/C control assembly. Retest system.

MAXIMUM COOL DOOR POSITION

Code	Door Position
21	Open
22	Half Open
23-29	Closed

TESTING

WARNING: To avoid injury from accidental air bag deployment, read and carefully follow all SERVICE PRECAUTIONS and DISABLING & ACTIVATING AIR BAG SYSTEM procedures in AIR BAG SYSTEM SAFETY article in GENERAL SERVICING.

ACC POWER SOURCE CIRCUIT

1) Remove A/C control assembly, leaving harness connectors attached. See A/C CONTROL ASSEMBLY under REMOVAL & INSTALLATION. Turn ignition on. Using DVOM, backprobe between terminal A14-9 (Green wire) of A/C control assembly connector and ground. *See Fig. 6*.
2) If battery voltage exists, no problem is indicated at this time. If battery voltage is not present, check radio No. 2 fuse in fuse block No. 1, located below instrument panel. If fuse is okay, check wiring between A/C control assembly and battery. Repair wiring as necessary. Replace fuse if blown, and check for short circuit.

AMBIENT TEMPERATURE SENSOR

Remove radiator grille. Disconnect ambient temperature sensor. *See Fig. 1*. Measure resistance between sensor terminals while heating sensor. See AMBIENT TEMPERATURE SENSOR SPECIFICATIONS table. Replace sensor if resistance is not as specified.

AMBIENT TEMPERATURE SENSOR SPECIFICATIONS

Sensor Temperature °F (°C)	[1] Ohms
77 (25)	1600-1800
122 (50)	500-700

[1] – As temperature increases, resistance should gradually decrease.

AIR INLET DOOR POSITION SENSOR

1) Remove heater unit. See HEATER UNIT under REMOVAL & INSTALLATION. Disconnect air inlet servomotor connector. Measure resistance between connector terminals No. 1 (Yellow/Green wire) and No. 3 (Blue wire). *See Fig. 8*.
2) If resistance is not 4700-7200 ohms, replace air inlet servomotor. If resistance is 4700-7200 ohms, apply battery voltage to air inlet servomotor connector terminal No. 5 (Yellow wire). Connect terminal No. 4 (Pink wire) to ground. *See Fig. 9*.
3) As servomotor operates, note resistance reading. Reverse power leads and note resistance reading. Resistance should be as specified for each door position. See AIR INLET DOOR POSITION SENSOR SPECIFICATIONS table. If resistance is not as specified, replace air inlet door servomotor.

AIR INLET DOOR POSITION SENSOR SPECIFICATIONS

Inlet Door Position	[1] Ohms
Recirculated Air	3760-5760
Fresh Air	940-1440

[1] – Resistance should gradually decrease as air inlet door moves from recirculated air position to fresh air position.

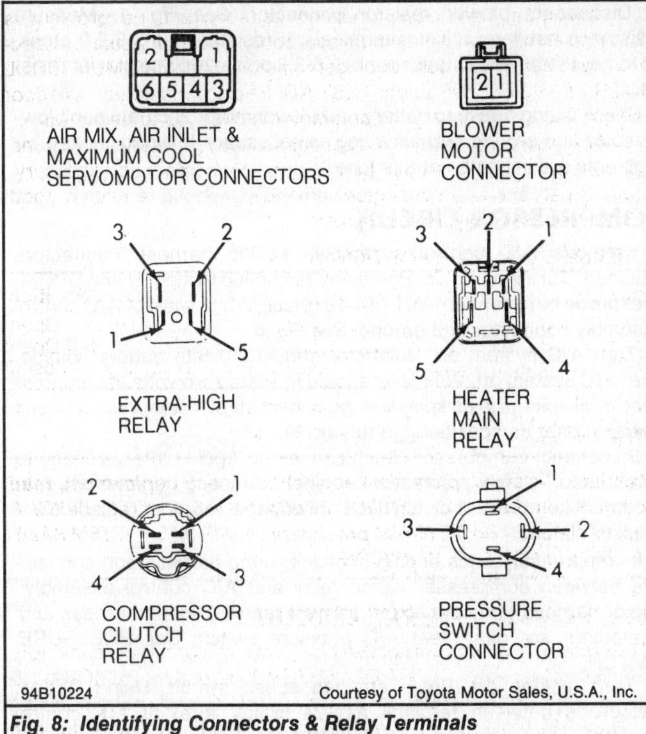
2 1
6 5 4 3
AIR MIX, AIR INLET &
MAXIMUM COOL
SERVOMOTOR CONNECTORS
2 1
BLOWER
MOTOR
CONNECTOR
3
2
1
5
EXTRA-HIGH
RELAY
3
2
1
5
4
HEATER
MAIN
RELAY
2
1
4
3
COMPRESSOR
CLUTCH
RELAY
1
3
2
4
PRESSURE
SWITCH
CONNECTOR
94B10224
Courtesy of Toyota Motor Sales, U.S.A., Inc.

Fig. 8: Identifying Connectors & Relay Terminals

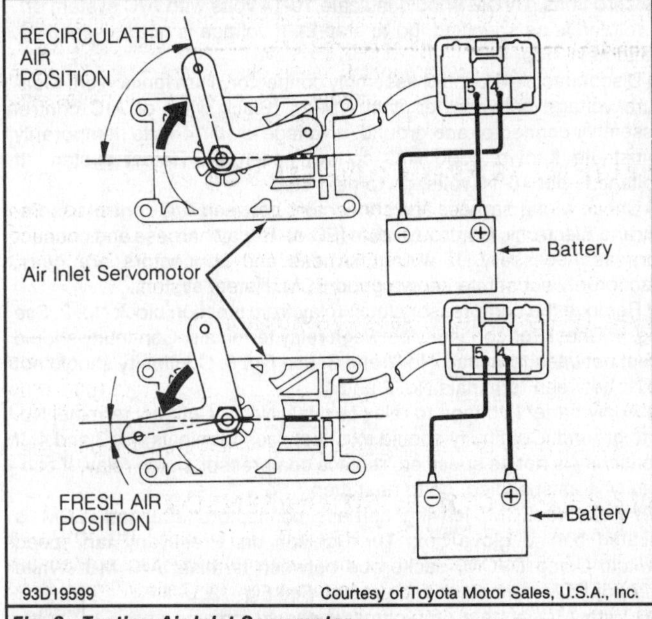
RECIRCULATED
AIR
POSITION
5 4
Battery
Air Inlet Servomotor
5 4
FRESH AIR
POSITION
Battery
93D19599
Courtesy of Toyota Motor Sales, U.S.A., Inc.

Fig. 9: Testing Air Inlet Servomotor

AIR INLET DOOR SERVOMOTOR

1) Remove cooling and blower unit. See COOLING & BLOWER UNIT under REMOVAL & INSTALLATION. Disconnect air inlet servomotor connector. Connect battery voltage to terminal No. 5 (Yellow wire). Connect terminal No. 4 (Pink wire) to ground. *See Fig. 9.*

2) Servomotor lever should move smoothly to recirculation position. Reverse power leads. Servomotor lever should move smoothly to fresh air position. If servomotor lever does not function as specified, replace servomotor.

AIR MIX DOOR POSITION SENSOR

1) Remove heater unit. See HEATER UNIT under REMOVAL & INSTALLATION. Disconnect air mix servomotor connector. Measure resistance between servomotor connector terminals No. 1 (Blue wire) and No. 3 (Yellow/Green wire). *See Fig. 8.*

2) If resistance is not 4700-7200 ohms, replace air mix servomotor. If resistance is 4700-7200 ohms, apply battery voltage to air mix servomotor connector terminal No. 6 (Violet/Red wire). Connect terminal No. 2 (Yellow/Red wire) to ground. *See Fig. 10.*

3) As servomotor operates, note resistance reading. Reverse power leads and note resistance reading. Resistance should be as specified for each door position. See AIR MIX DOOR POSITION SENSOR SPECIFICATIONS table. If resistance is not as specified, replace air mix door servomotor.

AIR MIX DOOR POSITION SENSOR SPECIFICATIONS

Condition	[1] Ohms
Maximum Cold	3760-5760
Maximum Hot	940-1440

[1] – Resistance should gradually decrease as air mix door moves from maximum cold position to maximum hot position.

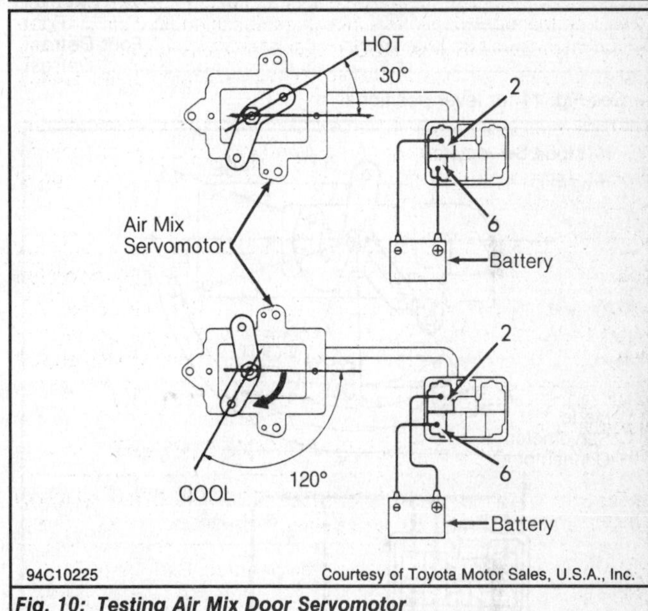
HOT
30°
2
Air Mix
Servomotor
6
Battery
2
6
COOL
120°
Battery
94C10225
Courtesy of Toyota Motor Sales, U.S.A., Inc.

Fig. 10: Testing Air Mix Door Servomotor

AIR MIX DOOR SERVOMOTOR

1) Remove heater unit. See HEATER UNIT under REMOVAL & INSTALLATION. Disconnect air mix servomotor connector. Apply battery voltage to air mix servomotor connector terminal No. 2 (Yellow/Red wire).

2) Connect terminal No. 6 (Violet/Red wire) to ground. *See Fig. 10.* Servomotor lever should turn smoothly to hot side. Reverse power leads. Servomotor lever should move smoothly to cool side. If servomotor lever does not function as specified, replace servomotor.

AIR VENT MODE DOOR SERVOMOTOR CIRCUIT

1) Warm engine to normal operating temperature. Perform RETRIEVING CODES under TROUBLE SHOOTING. After system enters self-diagnostic mode, perform ACTUATOR CHECK under TROUBLE SHOOTING. Press TEMP (up) button to enter step mode and display codes. See AIR VENT MODE DOOR SERVOMOTOR AIRFLOW table. Servomotor door operation should be as specified.

2) If servomotor airflow is as specified, no problem is indicated at this time. If servomotor airflow is not as specified, go to next step.

AIR VENT MODE SERVOMOTOR DOOR AIRFLOW OPERATION

Code	[1] Airflow Mode
20-22	Maximum Face
23	Face
24-25	Bi-Level
26-27	Foot
28	Foot-Defrost
29	Defrost

[1] – Airflow mode should change as display codes change.

1993 AUTOMATIC A/C-HEATER SYSTEMS LS400 (Cont.)

3) Remove heater unit. See HEATER UNIT under REMOVAL & INSTALLATION. Apply battery voltage to air vent mode servomotor connector terminal No. 6 (Red/Blue wire). Connect terminal No. 7 (White/Black wire) to ground. *See Fig. 11.*

4) Air vent mode servomotor lever should move to specified position when appropriate terminal is grounded. See AIR VENT MODE SERVOMOTOR LEVER OPERATING SPECIFICATIONS table. If lever does not function as specified, replace servomotor. If lever functions as specified, check wiring between A/C control assembly and servomotor and between battery, servomotor and ground.

5) Repair or replace wiring as necessary. If wiring is okay, temporarily substitute known good A/C control assembly. Retest system.

AIR VENT MODE SERVOMOTOR LEVER OPERATING SPECIFICATIONS

Ground Terminal No.	[1] Lever Position
1	Face
2	Bi-Level
3	Foot
4	Foot-Defrost
5	Defrost

[1] – *See Fig. 11* for lever positions.

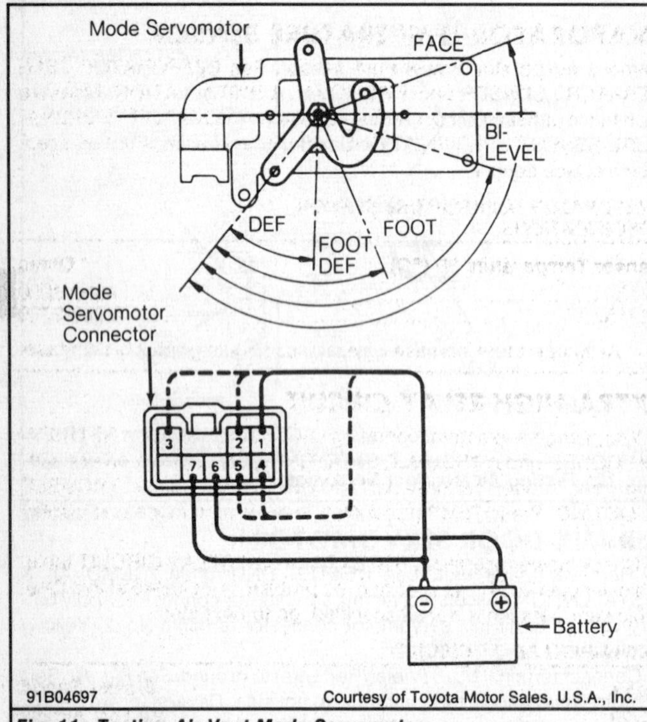
Mode Servomotor
FACE
BI-LEVEL
DEF
FOOT
FOOT DEF
Mode Servomotor Connector
3
2
1
7
6
5
4
Battery
91B04697
Courtesy of Toyota Motor Sales, U.S.A., Inc.

Fig. 11: Testing Air Vent Mode Servomotor

BACK-UP POWER SOURCE CIRCUIT

1) Remove A/C control assembly, leaving harness connectors attached. See A/C CONTROL ASSEMBLY under REMOVAL & INSTALLATION. Turn ignition on. Using DVOM, backprobe terminal A14-8 of A/C control assembly connector and ground. *See Fig. 6.*

2) If battery voltage is present, no problem is indicated at this time. If battery voltage is not present, check DOME fuse in junction block No. 2. *See Fig. 4.* If fuse is okay, check wiring harness between A/C control assembly and battery. Repair wiring as necessary.

BLOWER MOTOR CIRCUIT

1) Remove blower motor. See BLOWER MOTOR under REMOVAL & INSTALLATION. Connect battery voltage to blower motor connector terminal No. 2 (Blue/Red wire). Connect terminal No. 1 (Blue wire) to ground. *See Fig. 8.*

2) Blower motor should operate smoothly. If blower motor does not operate smoothly, replace blower motor. If blower motor operates smoothly, go to next step.

3) Disconnect blower resistor connector. *See Fig. 1.* Measure resistance between resistor terminals. If resistance is 1.8-2.2 ohms, go to next step. If resistance is not 1.8-2.2 ohms, replace blower resistor.

4) Check wiring between battery and blower motor and between blower motor and ground. Repair wiring as necessary. If wiring is okay, no problems are indicated at this time.

COMPRESSOR CIRCUIT

1) Remove A/C control assembly, leaving harness connectors attached. Turn ignition on. Press any fan speed switch. Using DVOM, backprobe between terminal A14-18 (Black/White wire) of A/C control assembly connector and ground. *See Fig. 6.*

2) Turn A/C system on. Voltmeter should indicate battery voltage. Turn A/C system off. Voltmeter should indicate zero volts. If compressor circuit voltage is as specified, go to next step. If compressor circuit voltage is not as specified, go to step **5)**.

3) Disconnect compressor clutch connector. Apply battery voltage to compressor clutch connector terminal. Connect negative lead to ground. If compressor clutch does not engage, repair or replace compressor clutch.

4) If compressor clutch engages, check wiring harness and connectors between compressor clutch relay and A/C control assembly. Repair harness and connectors as necessary. If wiring harness and connectors are okay, test A/C pressure switch. See PRESSURE SWITCH.

5) Turn ignition on. Press any fan speed switch. Using DVOM, backprobe between terminal A14-24 (Black wire) of A/C control assembly connector and ground. With A/C system on, voltage should be zero volts. DVOM should indicate 10-14 volts with A/C system off. If voltage is as specified, go to step **8)**. If voltage is not as specified, go to next step.

6) Disconnect A/C control assembly connector. Turn ignition on. Measure voltage between terminal A14-24 (Black wire) of A/C control assembly connector and ground. If voltage is 10-14 volts, temporarily substitute known good A/C control assembly. Retest system. If voltage is not 10-14 volts, go to next step.

7) Check wiring harness and connectors between A/C control assembly and Electronic Control Module (ECM). Repair harness and connectors as necessary. If wiring harness and connectors are okay, temporarily substitute known good ECM. Retest system.

8) Remove the compressor clutch relay from junction block No. 2. *See Fig. 4.* Check for continuity between relay terminals. Continuity should exist between terminals No. 1 and 3. *See Fig. 8.* Continuity should not exist between terminals No. 2 and 4.

9) Apply battery voltage to relay terminal No. 1. Connect terminal No. 3 to ground. Continuity should exist between terminals No. 2 and 4. If continuity is not as specified, replace compressor clutch relay. If continuity is as specified, go to next step.

10) Remove ECM, leaving harness connectors attached. ECM is located behind glove box. Turn ignition on. Press any fan speed switch. Using DVOM, backprobe between terminal A/C MG (White wire) of ECM connector and ground. *See Fig. 12.*

11) With A/C system on, voltmeter should indicate about 1.3 volts. With A/C system off, voltage should be between 1.3 volts and battery voltage. If voltage is not as specified, temporarily substitute known good ECM. Retest system.

12) If voltage is as specified, check wiring between ECM and A/C control assembly. Repair or replace wiring as necessary. If wiring is okay, temporarily substitute known good A/C control assembly. Retest system.

COMPRESSOR LOCK SENSOR

Raise and support vehicle. Disconnect compressor lock sensor connector. Measure resistance between sensor terminals. If resistance is not as specified, replace sensor. See COMPRESSOR LOCK SENSOR SPECIFICATIONS table.

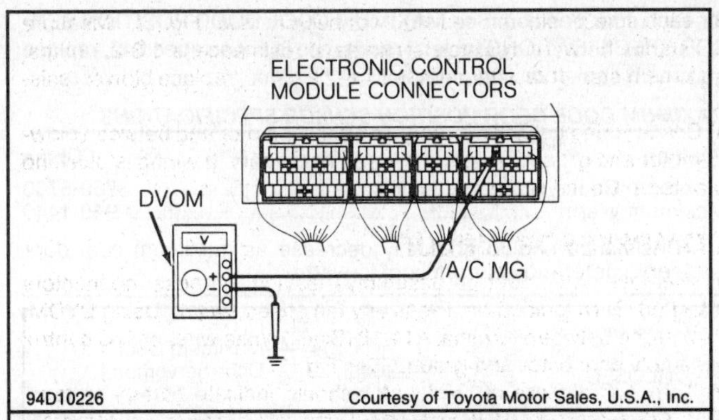
ELECTRONIC CONTROL
MODULE CONNECTORS
DVOM
A/C MG
94D10226
Courtesy of Toyota Motor Sales, U.S.A., Inc.

Fig. 12: Testing Electronic Control Module (ECM) Circuit Voltage

COMPRESSOR LOCK SENSOR SPECIFICATIONS

Sensor Temperature °F (°C)	Ohms
68 (20)	570-1050
212 (100)	720-1440

COOLING FAN SYSTEM

On-Vehicle Inspection – 1) Cooling fan operates at 2 speeds, depending on coolant temperature and A/C switch position. With ignition on and coolant temperature at less than 181°F (83°C), cooling fans should be off. If cooling fans are on, check coolant temperature switch, cooling fan relay and associated wiring.

2) Disconnect coolant temperature switch. Switch is located in lower left side of radiator. Cooling fans should be on. If cooling fans are not on, check for short between cooling fan relay and coolant temperature switch.

3) Reconnect coolant temperature switch. With A/C on, compressor clutch engaged and refrigerant pressure 220 psi (15.5 kg/cm²) or more, cooling fans should rotate at low speed.

4) Start engine. With coolant temperature at 199°F (93°C) or more, cooling fans should rotate at high speed. If cooling fans do not rotate at high speed, replace coolant temperature switch.

Coolant Temperature Switch Check – 1) Remove coolant temperature switch, located at lower left side of radiator. Place switch and thermometer in water. Heat water. Check continuity between terminals of coolant temperature switch.

2) Continuity should exist when water temperature is less than 181°F (83°C). Continuity should not exist when water temperature is greater than 199°F (93°C). Replace switch if continuity is not as specified.

Cooling Fan Relays Check – 1) Remove left headlight. Remove cover from relay block No. 6. *See Fig. 1.* Remove cooling fan relays.

2) Check continuity between relay terminals. On relays No. 1 and 2, continuity should exist between terminals No. 1 and 2 and between terminals No. 3 and 4. *See Fig. 13.* Apply battery voltage to relay terminal No. 1. Ground relay terminal No. 2. Continuity should no longer exist between terminals No. 3 and 4.

3) On relay No. 3, continuity should exist between terminals No. 1 and No. 3 and between terminals No. 2 and 4. *See Fig. 13.* Continuity should not exist between relay terminals No. 4 and 5.

4) Apply battery voltage to relay terminal No. 3. Ground relay terminal No. 1. Continuity should exist between terminals No. 4 and 5. Continuity should no longer exist between terminals No. 2 and 4. Replace relay(s) if continuity is not as specified.

Engine Main Relay Check – 1) Remove engine main relay from junction block No. 2. *See Figs. 1 and 4.* Check continuity at relay terminals. Continuity should exist between relay terminals No. 1 and 3 and between terminals No. 2 and 4. *See Fig. 13.*

2) Continuity should not exist between terminals No. 4 and 5. Apply battery voltage to relay terminal No. 1. Ground relay terminal No. 2. Continuity should exist between terminals No. 4 and 5. Continuity should not exist between terminals No. 2 and 4. Replace relay if continuity is not as specified.

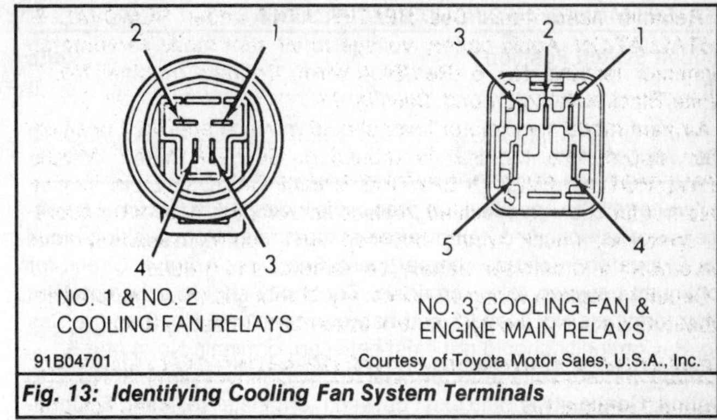
2
1
4
3
NO. 1 & NO. 2
COOLING FAN RELAYS
3
2
1
5
4
NO. 3 COOLING FAN &
ENGINE MAIN RELAYS
91B04701
Courtesy of Toyota Motor Sales, U.S.A., Inc.

Fig. 13: Identifying Cooling Fan System Terminals

Cooling Fan Motor Operational Check – Connect battery voltage through an ammeter to cooling fan motor connector. Connect other connector to ground. Observe cooling fan. Cooling fan should run smoothly and ammeter should indicate 4.2-4.4 amps. Replace cooling fan motor if fan motor does not operate smoothly or current is not as specified.

EVAPORATOR TEMPERATURE SENSOR

Remove evaporator temperature sensor. See EVAPORATOR TEMPERATURE SENSOR under REMOVAL & INSTALLATION. Measure resistance between sensor terminals. See EVAPORATOR TEMPERATURE SENSOR SPECIFICATIONS table. If resistance is not as specified, replace sensor.

EVAPORATOR TEMPERATURE SENSOR SPECIFICATIONS

Sensor Temperature °F (°C)	[1] Ohms
32 (0)	4500-5200
59 (15)	2000-2700

[1] – As temperature increases, resistance should gradually decrease.

EXTRA-HIGH RELAY CIRCUIT

1) Warm engine to normal operating temperature. Perform RETRIEVING CODES under TROUBLE SHOOTING. After system enters self-diagnostic mode, perform ACTUATOR CHECK under TROUBLE SHOOTING. Press TEMP (up) button to enter step mode and display codes.

2) Check blower operation. See EXTRA-HIGH RELAY CIRCUIT table. If blower operation is as specified, no problem is indicated at this time. If blower operation is not as specified, go to next step.

EXTRA-HIGH RELAY CIRCUIT

Code	Blower Speed
21-28	Medium Airflow
29	High Airflow

3) Remove extra-high relay. Relay is mounted on blower unit. Check for continuity between relay terminals. Continuity should exist between terminals No. 2 and 3. *See Fig. 8.* Continuity should not exist between terminals No. 1 and 5.

4) Apply battery voltage to relay terminal No. 2, and connect terminal No. 3 to ground. Continuity should exist between terminals No. 1 and 5. If continuity is not as specified, replace extra-high relay.

5) If continuity is as specified, check wiring between A/C control assembly and extra-high relay and between extra-high relay and battery. Repair wiring as necessary. If wiring is okay, temporarily substitute known good A/C control assembly and retest system.

HEATER MAIN RELAY CIRCUIT

1) Remove A/C control assembly, leaving harness connectors attached. See A/C CONTROL ASSEMBLY under REMOVAL & INSTALLATION. Turn ignition on.

2) Using DVOM, backprobe between terminal A14-33 (Blue/Yellow wire) of A/C control assembly connector and ground. *See Fig. 6.* Turn ignition on. Measure voltage as indicated in HEATER MAIN RELAY CIRCUIT SPECIFICATIONS table.

1993 AUTOMATIC A/C-HEATER SYSTEMS LS400 (Cont.)

HEATER MAIN RELAY CIRCUIT SPECIFICATIONS

Ignition Switch Position	Volts
Off	0
On	
Blower On	0
Blower Off	Battery Voltage

3) If voltage is as specified, no problem is indicated at this time. If voltage is not as specified, remove heater main relay from junction block No. 2, located in engine compartment. *See Figs. 1 and 4*. Check for continuity between relay terminals. Continuity should exist between relay terminals No. 1 and 3 and between terminals No. 2 and 4. *See Fig. 8*. Continuity should not exist between terminals No. 4 and 5.

4) Apply battery voltage to terminal No. 1. Connect terminal No. 3 to ground. Continuity should exist between terminals No. 4 and 5. Continuity should not exist between terminals No. 2 and 4.

5) If continuity is not as specified, replace heater main relay. If continuity is as specified, check heater fuse. If fuse is okay, check wiring between A/C control assembly and battery. Repair wiring as necessary. If fuse is blown, replace fuse and check for short circuit.

IG POWER SOURCE CIRCUIT

1) Remove A/C control assembly, leaving harness connectors attached. See A/C CONTROL ASSEMBLY under REMOVAL & INSTALLATION. Turn ignition on. Using DVOM, backprobe between terminals A14-10 (Red/Yellow wire) and A14-7 (White/Black wire) of A/C control assembly connector. *See Fig. 6*.

2) If battery voltage is present, no problem is indicated at this time. If battery voltage is not present, turn ignition off. Check for continuity between A/C control assembly connector terminal A14-7 (White/Black wire) and ground. If continuity exists, go to next step. If continuity does not exist, repair wiring between terminal A14-7 and body ground.

3) Check heater fuse, in fuse block No. 1, located below instrument panel. If fuse is okay, check wiring harness and connector between A/C control assembly and battery. Repair wiring and connector as necessary. If fuse is blown, replace fuse and check for short circuit.

IGNITOR CIRCUIT

Check tachometer operation. If tachometer does not function properly, repair or replace tachometer. If tachometer functions properly, check wiring harness and connectors between A/C control assembly and ignitor. Ignitor is located on right side of engine compartment. Repair wiring as necessary.

IN-VEHICLE TEMPERATURE SENSOR

Remove left instrument panel undercover. Disconnect in-vehicle temperature sensor. *See Fig. 1*. Measure resistance between in-vehicle temperature sensor terminals while heating sensor. See IN-VEHICLE TEMPERATURE SENSOR SPECIFICATIONS table. If resistance is not as specified, replace sensor.

IN-VEHICLE TEMPERATURE SENSOR SPECIFICATIONS

Sensor Temperature °F (°C)	[1] Ohms
77 (25)	1600-1800
122 (50)	500-700

[1] – As temperature increases, resistance should gradually decrease.

MAXIMUM COOL DOOR POSITION SENSOR

1) Remove heater unit. See HEATER UNIT under REMOVAL & INSTALLATION. Disconnect maximum cool door servomotor connector. Measure resistance between servomotor connector terminals No. 5 (Yellow/Green wire) and No. 4 (Blue wire). *See Fig. 8*.

2) If resistance is not 4700-7200 ohms, replace maximum cool door servomotor. If resistance is 4700-7200 ohms, apply battery voltage to maximum cool door servomotor connector terminal No. 2 (Yellow/Blue wire). *See Fig. 14*. Connect terminal No. 1 (Blue/Red wire) to ground.

3) As servomotor operates, note resistance reading. Reverse power leads and note resistance reading. Resistance should be as specified for each door position. See MAXIMUM COOL DOOR POSITION SENSOR SPECIFICATIONS table. If resistance is not as specified, replace maximum cool door servomotor.

MAXIMUM COOL DOOR POSITION SENSOR SPECIFICATIONS

Position	[1] Ohms
Maximum Cool	3760-5760
Maximum Warm	940-1440

[1] – Resistance should gradually decrease as maximum cool door servomotor moves from cool to warm.

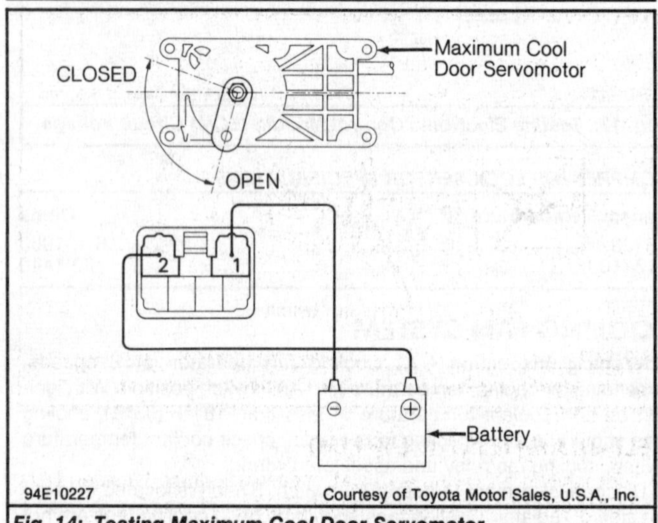
CLOSED
Maximum Cool Door Servomotor
OPEN
2
1
Battery
94E10227
Courtesy of Toyota Motor Sales, U.S.A., Inc.

Fig. 14: Testing Maximum Cool Door Servomotor

MAXIMUM COOL DOOR SERVOMOTOR

1) Remove heater unit. See HEATER UNIT under REMOVAL & INSTALLATION. Disconnect maximum cool door servomotor connector. Connect battery voltage to terminal No. 2 (Yellow/Blue wire). Connect terminal No. 1 (Blue/Red wire) to ground. *See Fig. 14*.

2) Servomotor lever should move smoothly to closed position. Reverse power leads. Servomotor lever should move smoothly to open position. If servomotor lever does not function as specified, replace servomotor.

POWER TRANSISTOR CIRCUIT

1) Remove cooling and blower unit. See COOLING & BLOWER UNIT under REMOVAL & INSTALLATION. Disconnect power transistor connector. *See Fig. 1*. Connect battery voltage to terminal No. 2 of connector A18. Connect battery voltage, through a 120-ohm resistor, to terminal No. 2 of connector A17. *See Fig. 15*.

2) Connect terminal No. 1 of connector A18 to ground through a 12-volt, 3.4-watt test light. If test light does not come on, replace power transistor. If test light comes on, check wiring harness and connectors between A/C control assembly and power transistor.

3) Repair wiring and connectors as necessary. If wiring harness and connectors are okay, no problems are indicated at this time.

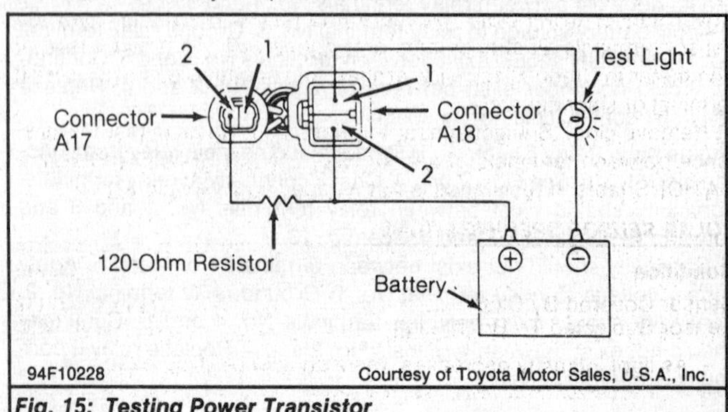
2
1
Connector A17
1
Connector A18
Test Light
2
120-Ohm Resistor
Battery
94F10228
Courtesy of Toyota Motor Sales, U.S.A., Inc.

Fig. 15: Testing Power Transistor

PRESSURE SWITCH

1) Pressure switch is located near receiver-drier. *See Fig. 16.* Install manifold gauge set. Turn ignition on. Start engine. Turn blower and A/C on. Observe system pressure. Disconnect pressure switch connector. Check continuity between pressure switch terminals No. 1 and 4.

2) Continuity should not exist if high side pressure is less than 28 psi (2.0 kg/cm²). Continuity should exist if high side pressure is more than 28 psi (2.0 kg/cm²). If continuity is not as specified, replace pressure switch.

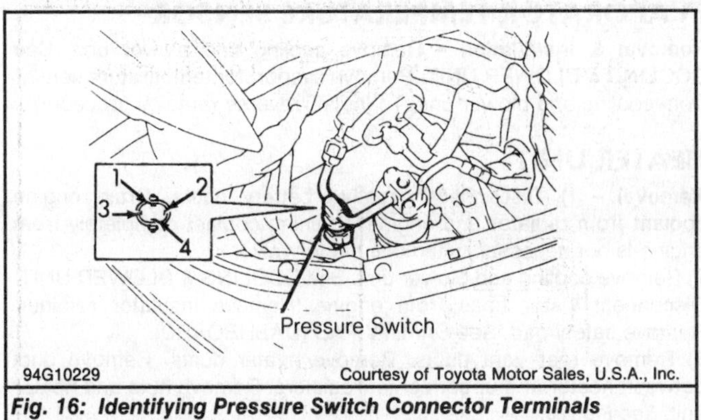
1
2
3
4
Pressure Switch
94G10229
Courtesy of Toyota Motor Sales, U.S.A., Inc.

Fig. 16: Identifying Pressure Switch Connector Terminals

SELF-DIAGNOSTIC CIRCUIT

1) Turn ignition on. Using a DVOM, measure voltage between Data Link Connector No. 2 (DLC2) terminals TC and EI. *See Fig. 17.* DLC2 is located behind left side of instrument panel. If battery voltage is present, no problem is indicated at this time.

2) If battery voltage is not present, check wiring harness and connectors between A/C control panel, DLC2 and ground. Repair wiring and connectors as necessary. If wiring and connectors are okay, temporarily substitute known good A/C control assembly. Retest system.

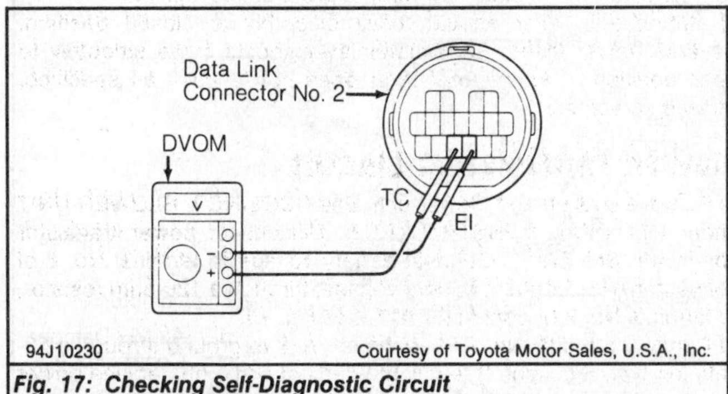
Data Link
Connector No. 2
DVOM
V
TC
EI
94J10230
Courtesy of Toyota Motor Sales, U.S.A., Inc.

Fig. 17: Checking Self-Diagnostic Circuit

SOLAR SENSOR

1) Remove glove box. Disconnect solar sensor harness connector. Cover sensor using cloth. Measure and record resistance between sensor terminals. Ensure ohmmeter is connected with positive lead of ohmmeter to Green/Black wire terminal and negative lead to Blue wire terminal of solar sensor.

2) Remove cloth. Subject sensor to bright light. Again measure resistance between terminals of sensor. See SOLAR SENSOR SPECIFICATIONS table. If resistance is not as specified, replace sensor.

SOLAR SENSOR SPECIFICATIONS

Condition	[1] Ohms
Sensor Covered By Cloth	No Continuity
Sensor Subjected To Bright Light	About 4000

[1] – As light intensity decreases, resistance should increase.

WATER TEMPERATURE SENSOR

Remove heater unit. See HEATER UNIT under REMOVAL & INSTALLATION. Remove water temperature sensor. Place sensor and thermometer in water. Measure resistance between sensor terminals No. 1 and 3 at specified temperatures. *See Fig. 18.* See WATER TEMPERATURE SENSOR RESISTANCE SPECIFICATIONS table. If resistance is not as specified, replace sensor.

WATER TEMPERATURE SENSOR RESISTANCE SPECIFICATIONS

Sensor Temperature °F (°C)	[1] Ohms
32 (0)	16,500-17,500
104 (40)	2400-2800
158 (70)	700-1000

[1] – As temperature increases, resistance should gradually decrease.

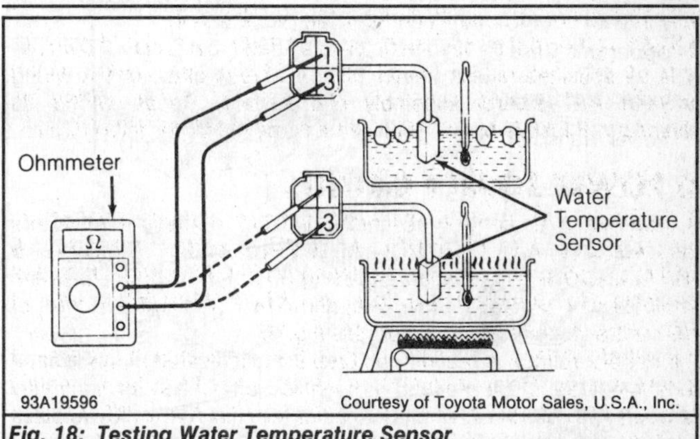
1
3
Ohmmeter
Ω
Water
Temperature
Sensor
93A19596
Courtesy of Toyota Motor Sales, U.S.A., Inc.

Fig. 18: Testing Water Temperature Sensor

REMOVAL & INSTALLATION

WARNING: To avoid injury from accidental air bag deployment, read and carefully follow all SERVICE PRECAUTIONS and DISABLING & ACTIVATING AIR BAG SYSTEM procedures in AIR BAG SYSTEM SAFETY article in GENERAL SERVICING.

A/C COMPRESSOR

Removal – **1)** If compressor operates, idle engine with A/C system on for about 10 minutes. Turn engine off. Remove battery. Discharge A/C system using approved refrigerant recovery/recycling equipment.

2) Disconnect discharge and suction hoses from compressor. Cap open fittings immediately. Remove drive belt. Disconnect wiring from compressor. Remove ground wire bolt from compressor. Remove nut, bolts, bracket and compressor.

Installation – Reverse removal procedure to install compressor. If replacing compressor, ensure compressor is filled with correct amount of refrigerant oil. See COMPRESSOR REFRIGERANT OIL CHECKING article in GENERAL SERVICING. Evacuate and charge A/C system. Check A/C system for leaks and improper operation.

A/C CONTROL ASSEMBLY

Removal & Installation – Remove upper shift console panel. Remove ashtray. Remove register from above radio. Remove 4 screws and radio together with A/C control assembly. Remove 4 screws, and pry apart side claws. Separate A/C control assembly from radio. *See Fig. 1.* To install, reverse removal procedure.

AMBIENT TEMPERATURE SENSOR

Removal & Installation – Remove clip and sensor from right bumper reinforcement. Disconnect harness connector. To install, reverse removal procedure.

BLOWER MOTOR

Removal & Installation – **1)** Set air inlet mode to fresh air. Remove undercover from right side of instrument panel. Disconnect wiring

1993 AUTOMATIC A/C-HEATER SYSTEMS
LS400 (Cont.)

connectors, and remove connector bracket from cooling unit. Remove scuff plate from front passenger door.

2) Pull back carpet. Disconnect control lever shaft from blower case. Remove screws and blower lower case. Disconnect wiring connectors. Remove screws and blower motor. To install blower motor, reverse removal procedure.

BLOWER RESISTOR

Removal & Installation – Remove undercover from right side of instrument panel. Disconnect wiring harness connectors. Remove screws and connector bracket from cooling and blower unit. Remove screws and blower resistor from cooling unit. *See Fig. 19.* Unplug harness connector. To install, reverse removal procedure.

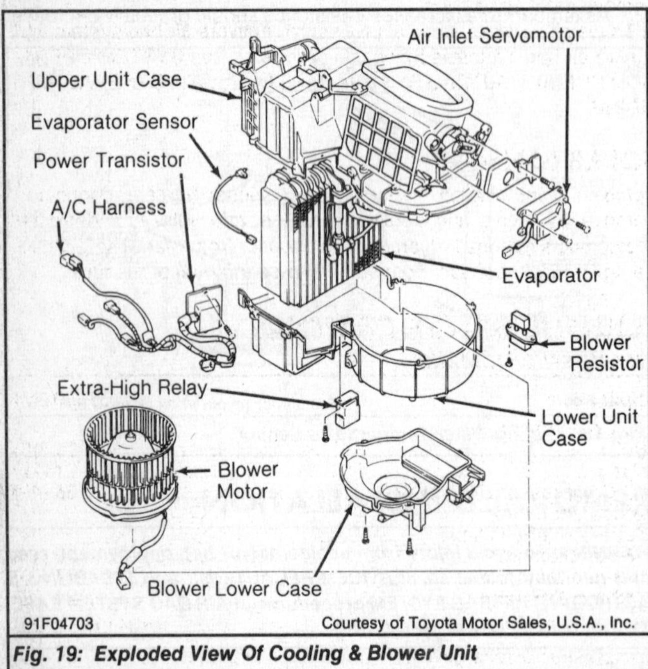
Air Inlet Servomotor
Upper Unit Case
Evaporator Sensor
Power Transistor
A/C Harness
Evaporator
Blower
Resistor
Extra-High Relay
Lower Unit
Case
Blower
Motor
Blower Lower Case
91F04703
Courtesy of Toyota Motor Sales, U.S.A., Inc.

Fig. 19: Exploded View Of Cooling & Blower Unit

CONDENSER

Removal – 1) Remove parking lights and headlights. Remove engine undercover. Remove lower wind guide. Remove fender liner from bumper. Remove bumper and bumper retainer. Remove bumper reinforcement. Remove horns. Remove electric cooling fans. Remove center brace.

2) Discharge A/C system using approved refrigerant recovery/recycling equipment. Disconnect refrigerant lines from condenser. Remove suction tube. Remove nuts and condenser.

Installation – To install, reverse removal procedure. If replacing condenser, add 1.4-1.7 ounces of compressor oil. Evacuate and charge A/C system. Check A/C system for leaks and improper operation.

COOLING & BLOWER UNIT

Removal – 1) Disconnect negative battery cable. Discharge A/C system using approved refrigerant recovery/recycling equipment. Remove cruise control actuator. Disconnect equalizer tubes from cooling and blower unit. Remove liquid and suction tubes.

2) Remove cover plate from firewall. Remove drain hose clamp. Remove necessary ducts. Remove glove box. Remove mirror control ECU from glove box opening.

3) Remove bolts and bracket from cooling and blower unit. Disconnect wiring harness connectors. Remove nuts, screws and cooling and blower unit.

Installation – To install, reverse removal procedure. If replacing evaporator, add 1.4-2.1 ounces of compressor oil. Evacuate and charge A/C system. Check system for leaks and improper operation.

COOLING FAN MOTORS

Removal & Installation – 1) Disconnect negative battery cable. Remove engine splash shield. Remove lower wind guide. Remove clearance lights. Remove headlights and fog lights.

2) Disconnect ambient temperature sensor connector. Remove front bumper. Remove front bumper upper reinforcement. Remove right horn. Disconnect harness connectors from fan motors.

3) Disconnect wire from brackets. Remove hood lock support. Remove cooling fans. To install, reverse removal procedure.

EVAPORATOR TEMPERATURE SENSOR

Removal & Installation – Remove cooling and blower unit. See COOLING & BLOWER UNIT. Remove evaporator temperature sensor from cooling and blower unit. To install, reverse removal procedure.

HEATER UNIT

Removal – 1) Disconnect negative battery cable. Drain engine coolant from radiator and engine. Draining coolant completely from engine is not necessary. Remove heater valve.

2) Remove cooling and blower unit. See COOLING & BLOWER UNIT. Disconnect water hose from engine. Remove insulator retainer. Remove safety pad. See SAFETY PAD (DASHBOARD).

3) Remove rear vent ducts. Remove heater ducts. Remove duct between heater and upper center registers. Remove nuts and heater unit. *See Fig. 20.*

Installation – To install, reverse removal procedure. Refill cooling system. Evacuate and charge A/C system. Check A/C system for leaks and improper operation.

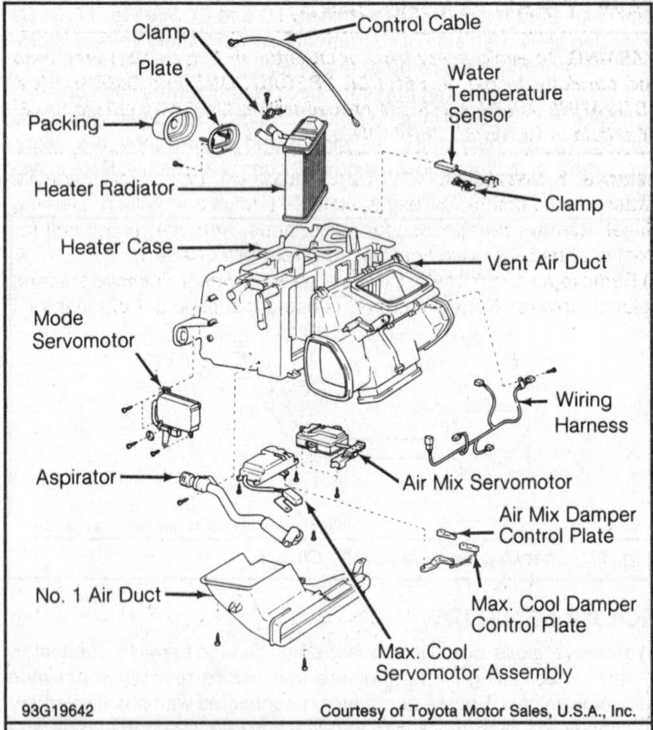
Clamp
Control Cable
Plate
Water
Temperature
Sensor
Packing
Heater Radiator
Clamp
Heater Case
Vent Air Duct
Mode
Servomotor
Wiring
Harness
Aspirator
Air Mix Servomotor
Air Mix Damper
Control Plate
No. 1 Air Duct
Max. Cool Damper
Control Plate
Max. Cool
Servomotor Assembly
93G19642
Courtesy of Toyota Motor Sales, U.S.A., Inc.

Fig. 20: Exploded View Of Heater Unit

IN-VEHICLE TEMPERATURE SENSOR

Removal & Installation – Remove undercover from left side of instrument panel. Remove hood release lever. Disconnect hood release cable from lever. Remove key cylinder pad from steering column. Remove lower left pad. Unplug harness connector. Remove screw and in-vehicle temperature sensor. To install, reverse removal procedure.

1993 AUTOMATIC A/C-HEATER SYSTEMS LS400 (Cont.)

POWER TRANSISTOR

Removal & Installation – 1) Remove undercover from right side of instrument panel. Remove glove box. Remove lower right pad. Remove glove box door. Remove Anti-Lock Brake System (ABS) control unit. Disconnect wiring harness connectors.
2) Remove air duct from heater to registers on passenger side. Remove screw and plate from cooling and blower unit. Disconnect harness connectors. Remove screw and power transistor from cooling and blower unit. *See Fig. 19*. To install power transistor, reverse removal procedure.

PRESSURE SWITCH

Removal – Discharge A/C system using approved refrigerant recovery/recycling equipment. Remove right headlight. Unplug pressure switch harness connector. Remove pressure switch from liquid tube.
Installation – To install pressure switch, reverse removal procedure. Evacuate and charge A/C system. Check A/C system for leaks and improper operation.

RECEIVER-DRIER

Removal – Remove right headlight. Discharge A/C system using approved refrigerant recovery/recycling equipment. Disconnect tubes from receiver-drier. Remove receiver-drier.
Installation – To install, reverse removal procedure. If replacing receiver-drier, add 0.5-1.2 ounces of compressor oil. Evacuate and charge A/C system. Check A/C system for leaks and improper operation. Install headlight.

SAFETY PAD (DASHBOARD)

WARNING: To avoid injury from accidental air bag deployment, read and carefully follow all SERVICE PRECAUTIONS and DISABLING & ACTIVATING AIR BAG SYSTEM procedures in AIR BAG SYSTEM SAFETY article in GENERAL SERVICING.

Removal & Installation – 1) Turn ignition off. Disconnect negative battery cable. Disable air bag system. Tilt down and pull out steering wheel. Remove rear passenger assist grips. Remove anchor bolt for front seat belt. Remove right and left front pillar garnish.
2) Remove air bag module. Remove steering wheel. Remove steering column covers. Remove upper console panel and front ashtray. Remove lower console cover and lower console box. Remove cup holder and console box.
3) Remove hood release lever. Remove instrument panel undercover. Remove key cylinder pad and left lower pad. Remove parking brake lever. Disconnect and remove outer mirror switch assembly.
4) Remove and disconnect cluster finish panel and instrument cluster. Remove registers. Remove radio and A/C control assembly. See A/C CONTROL ASSEMBLY. Remove glove box and door. Remove lower right pad. Remove Anti-Lock Brake System (ABS) control unit.
5) Remove heater ducts. On driver side, disconnect junction block. Remove 3 clips at floor carpet. Remove screws and combination switch. On passenger side, unplug wiring harness connectors under safety pad. Remove bolt and bond cable. Remove carpet clips. Remove safety pad.
6) To install, reverse removal procedure. Activate air bag system and ensure air bag system is functioning properly. See SYSTEM OPERATION CHECK in AIR BAG SYSTEM SAFETY article in GENERAL SERVICING.

SOLAR SENSOR

Removal & Installation – Unplug solar sensor harness connector. Remove 8 screws and defroster front nozzle with side defroster nozzle ducts attached. Push out solar sensor from rear of safety pad. Remove nozzle garnish. To install, reverse removal procedure.

TORQUE SPECIFICATIONS

TORQUE SPECIFICATIONS

Application	Ft. Lbs. (N.m)
A/C Compressor	
Bolt	36 (49)
Nut	21 (29)
A/C Compressor Bracket Bolt	36 (49)
Refrigerant Lines	
Tube-To-Tube Fittings	
8-mm Diameter	10 (14)
13-mm Diameter	17 (23)
16-mm Diameter	24 (32)
	INCH Lbs. (N.m)
Compressor Discharge Tube	89 (10)
Compressor Suction Tube	89 (10)
Condenser Fittings	89 (10)
Cooling & Blower Unit Fittings	89 (10)
Receiver-Drier Fittings	48 (5.4)

1993 AUTOMATIC A/C-HEATER SYSTEMS LS400 (Cont.)

WIRING DIAGRAM

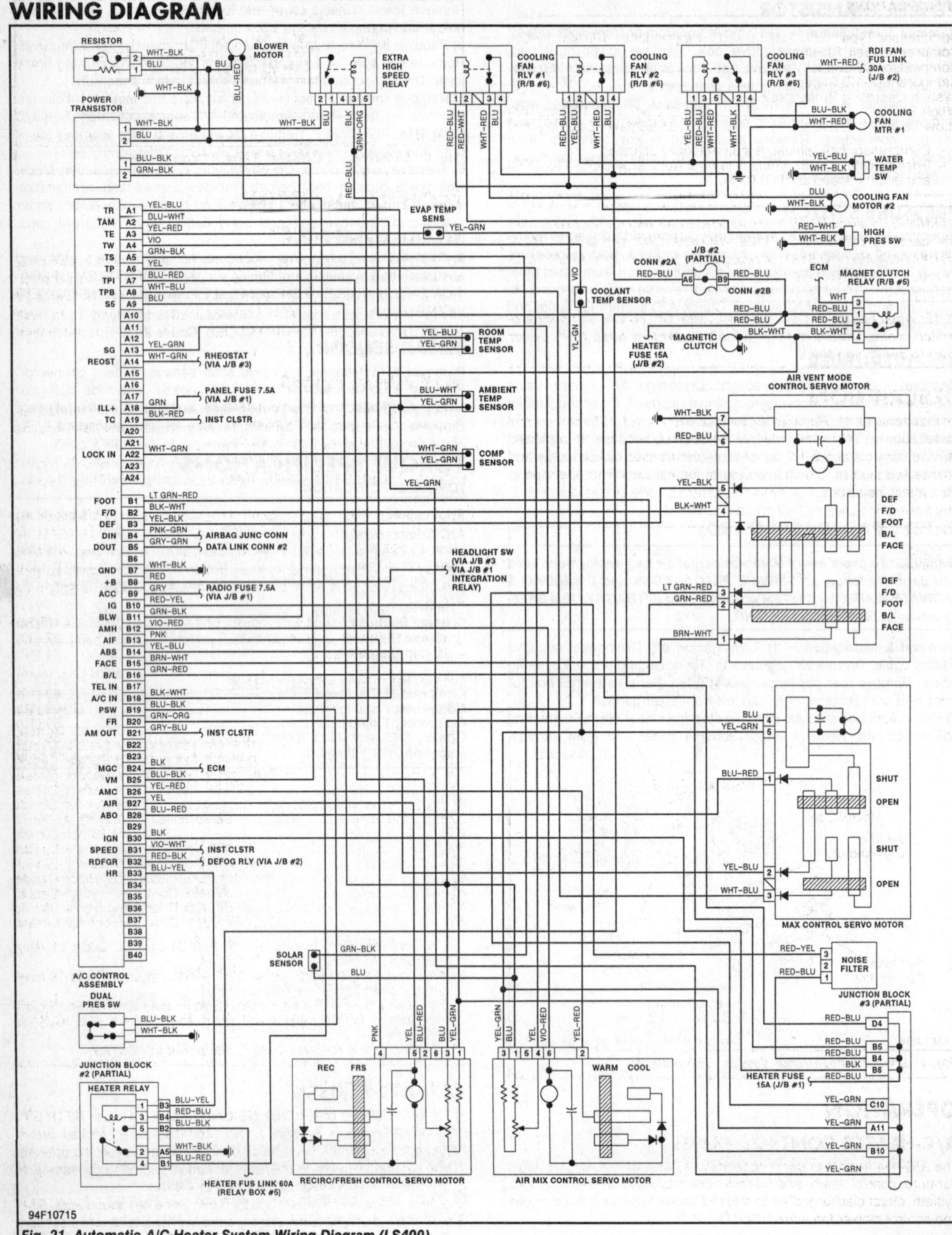
RESISTOR
BLOWER MOTOR
POWER TRANSISTOR
EXTRA HIGH SPEED RELAY
COOLING FAN RLY #1 (R/B #6)
COOLING FAN RLY #2 (R/B #6)
COOLING FAN RLY #3 (R/B #6)
RDI FAN FUS LINK 30A (J/B #2)
COOLING FAN MTR #1
WATER TEMP SW
COOLING FAN MOTOR #2
HIGH PRES SW
EVAP TEMP SENS
CONN #2A
J/B #2 (PARTIAL)
CONN #2B
ECM
MAGNET CLUTCH RELAY (R/B #5)
COOLANT TEMP SENSOR
MAGNETIC CLUTCH
HEATER FUSE 15A (J/B #2)
ROOM TEMP SENSOR
AMBIENT TEMP SENSOR
COMP SENSOR
RHEOSTAT (VIA J/B #3)
PANEL FUSE 7.5A (VIA J/B #1)
INST CLSTR
AIRBAG JUNC CONN
DATA LINK CONN #2
HEADLIGHT SW (VIA J/B #3 VIA J/B #1 INTEGRATION RELAY)
RADIO FUSE 7.5A (VIA J/B #1)
AIR VENT MODE CONTROL SERVO MOTOR
DEF F/D FOOT B/L FACE
MAX CONTROL SERVO MOTOR
SHUT OPEN
DEFOG RLY (VIA J/B #2)
SOLAR SENSOR
NOISE FILTER
JUNCTION BLOCK #3 (PARTIAL)
A/C CONTROL ASSEMBLY
DUAL PRES SW
JUNCTION BLOCK #2 (PARTIAL)
HEATER RELAY
HEATER FUSE 15A (J/B #1)
HEATER FUS LINK 60A (RELAY BOX #5)
REC FRS
RECIRC/FRESH CONTROL SERVO MOTOR
WARM COOL
AIR MIX CONTROL SERVO MOTOR
TR TAM TE TW TS TP TPI TPB S5 SG REOST ILL+ TC LOCK IN
FOOT F/D DEF DIN DOUT GND +B ACC IG BLW AMH AIF ABS FACE B/L TEL IN A/C IN PSW FR AM OUT MGC VM AMC AIR ABO IGN SPEED RDFGR HR
94F10715

Fig. 21 Automatic A/C-Heater System Wiring Diagram (LS400)

1993 AUTOMATIC A/C-HEATER SYSTEMS
SC300 & SC400

SPECIFICATIONS

Compressor Type .... Nippondenso 10PA20 10-Cyl.
Compressor Belt Tension .... [1]
Compressor Oil Capacity .... 4.0 ozs.
Refrigerant (R-12) Capacity .... 32-35 ozs.
System Operating Pressures [2]
High Side .... 206-213 psi (14.5-15.0 kg/cm²)
Low Side .... 21-28 psi (1.5-2.0 kg/cm²)

[1] – Compressor belt tension is automatically adjusted.
[2] – Specification is with ambient temperature at 86-95°F (30-35°C) and engine speed at 2000 RPM.

WARNING: To avoid injury from accidental air bag deployment, read and carefully follow all SERVICE PRECAUTIONS and DISABLING & ACTIVATING AIR BAG SYSTEM procedures in AIR BAG SYSTEM SAFETY article in GENERAL SERVICING.

NOTE: When battery is disconnected, radio will go into anti-theft protection mode. Obtain radio anti-theft protection code from owner prior to servicing vehicle.

DESCRIPTION

An Electronic Control Unit (ECU), located within the A/C-heater control panel, automatically controls all air conditioning and heating functions. Manual controls allow the driver to select air distribution mode and desired temperature. In addition to normal A/C system components, the system includes various motors, controls and sensors. *See Fig. 1.* The system includes self-diagnostic capabilities.

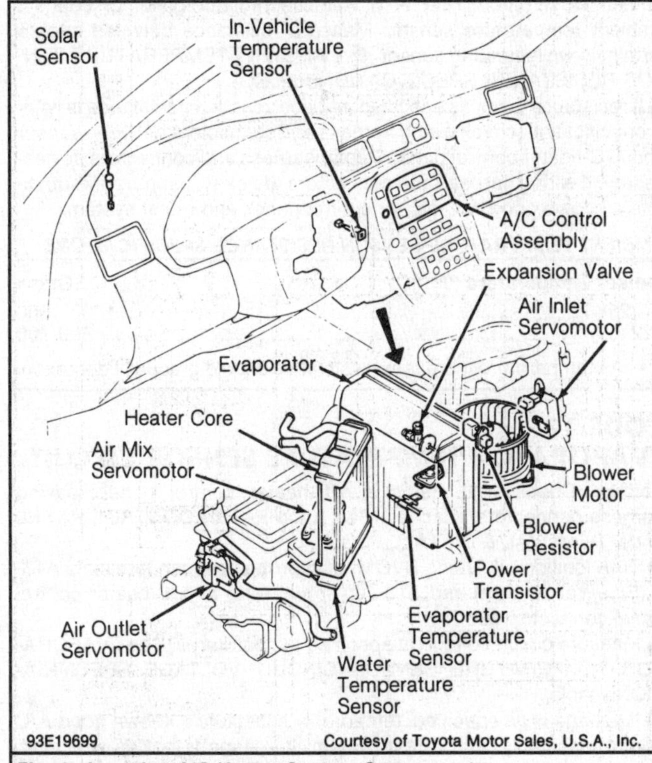
Solar Sensor
In-Vehicle Temperature Sensor
A/C Control Assembly
Expansion Valve
Air Inlet Servomotor
Evaporator
Heater Core
Air Mix Servomotor
Blower Motor
Blower Resistor
Power Transistor
Evaporator Temperature Sensor
Air Outlet Servomotor
Water Temperature Sensor
93E19699
Courtesy of Toyota Motor Sales, U.S.A., Inc.

Fig. 1: Locating A/C-Heater System Components

OPERATION

A/C-HEATER CONTROL PANEL

The A/C-heater control panel consists of a liquid crystal display, temperature control knob and various push buttons to activate A/C system, direct discharged air to desired vents, activate rear defogger and control blower fan speed. *See Fig. 2.*

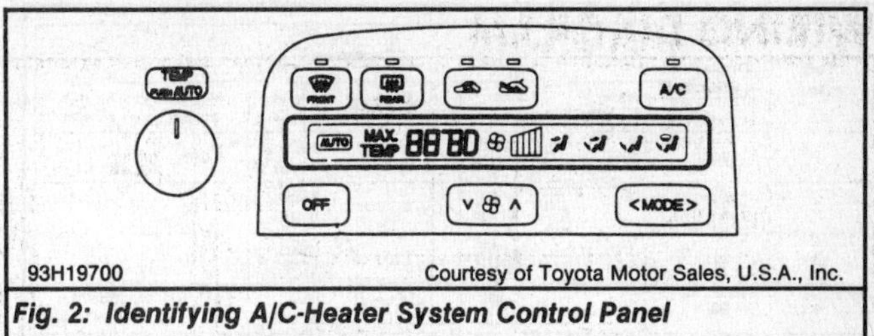
A/C
AUTO
OFF
<MODE>
93H19700
Courtesy of Toyota Motor Sales, U.S.A., Inc.

Fig. 2: Identifying A/C-Heater System Control Panel

TROUBLE SHOOTING

SELF-DIAGNOSTICS

An Electronic Control Unit (ECU) within A/C control assembly monitors system circuits and stores trouble codes in memory if problems are detected. All codes are stored in memory except Codes 22 and 23. Malfunction is current if Code 22 or 23 is displayed. To retrieve stored codes, see RETRIEVING CODES. Codes are displayed at temperature display. *See Fig. 2.*

RETRIEVING CODES

Indicator Check – 1) Press and hold AUTO and recirculated air switches. *See Fig. 2.* Turn ignition on. All indicators will flash 4 times at one-second intervals. Tone will sound when indicators flash.

2) A/C system will enter self-diagnostic mode. To end indicator check, press and release OFF switch. Read codes at temperature display. *See Fig. 2.*

3) If trouble code is displayed, proceed to appropriate trouble shooting procedure. See DIAGNOSTIC CODE IDENTIFICATION table. Codes are displayed in ascending order. To slow rate at which codes are displayed, press fresh air button to change display to step operation. Each time fresh air button is pressed, display changes by one step.

4) If tone sounds as code is displayed, problem currently exists. If tone does not sound as code is displayed, problem occurred in past and does not presently exist.

DIAGNOSTIC CODE IDENTIFICATION

Code	Diagnosis
00	Normal
11 [1]	In-Vehicle Temperature Sensor Circuit
12 [2]	Ambient Temperature Sensor Circuit
13	Evaporator Temperature Sensor Circuit
14	Water Temperature Sensor Circuit
21 [3]	Solar Sensor Circuit
22 [4]	Compressor Lock Sensor Circuit
23 [4]	Pressure Switch Circuit
31	Air Mix Door Position Sensor Circuit
32	Air Inlet Door Position Sensor Circuit
33	Air Outlet Door Position Sensor Circuit
41	Air Mix Door Servomotor Circuit
42	Air Inlet Door Servomotor Circuit
43	Air Outlet Door Servomotor Circuit

[1] – If in-vehicle temperature is -4°F (-20°C) or less, Code 11 may occur even though system is normal.
[2] – If outside air temperature is -58°F (-50°C) or less, Code 12 may occur even though system is normal.
[3] – If testing is done in a dark area, Code 21 may occur even though system is normal. Shine a light at solar sensor and recheck codes.
[4] – Malfunction is current. Code is not stored in memory.

ACTUATOR CHECK

1) Perform indicator check. See INDICATOR CHECK under RETRIEVING CODES. When system enters self-diagnostic mode, press recirculated air button. Each mode door, motor and relay will operate at one-second intervals. Press fresh air button to display codes one at a time and to step through checks one at a time.

2) Check airflow and temperature by hand. Tone will sound each time display code changes. Each display code is associated with a system operating condition. *See Fig. 3.* Press OFF button to cancel actuator check mode.

1993 AUTOMATIC A/C-HEATER SYSTEMS SC300 & SC400 (Cont.)

Step No.	Display code	Conditions					
		Water valve VSV	Blower motor	Air flow vent	Air inlet damper	Magnet clutch	Air mix damper
1	20	OFF	OFF	(FACE)	(FRESH)	OFF	Cool side (0% Open)
2	21	↑	1	↑	(F/R)	↑	↑
3	22	↑	2	↑	(RECIRC)	ON	↑
4	23	ON	3	(BI-LEVEL)	(FRESH)	↑	Cool/Hot (50% open)
5	24	↑	↑	(FOOT)	↑	↑	↑
6	25	↑	4	↑	↑	↑	Hot side (100% open)
7	26	↑	↑	(F/D)	↑	↑	↑
8	27	↑	5	(DEF)	↑	↑	↑

93J19702 Courtesy of Toyota Motor Sales, U.S.A., Inc.

Fig. 3: Identifying Actuator Check Display Codes

CLEARING CODES

Remove DOME fuse, located in relay box No. 2 on left side of engine compartment. Wait at least 10 seconds before installing fuse. Perform RETRIEVING CODES procedure. Ensure only Code 00 is displayed.

CODE 11
IN-VEHICLE TEMPERATURE SENSOR CIRCUIT

Voltage Check – 1) Remove A/C-heater control panel, leaving harness connectors attached. See A/C-HEATER CONTROL PANEL under REMOVAL & INSTALLATION.

2) Turn ignition on.Using DVOM, backprobe between terminals A13-7 (Yellow/Blue wire) and A13-20 (Brown wire) of A/C-heater control panel connector. *See Fig. 4*.

3) Measure circuit voltage while heating in-vehicle temperature sensor. See IN-VEHICLE TEMPERATURE SENSOR CIRCUIT VOLTAGE SPECIFICATIONS table.

4) If voltage is as specified, temporarily substitute a known good A/C control assembly, and retest system. If circuit voltage is not as specified, measure sensor resistance. See SENSOR RESISTANCE TEST.

IN-VEHICLE TEMPERATURE SENSOR CIRCUIT VOLTAGE SPECIFICATIONS

Sensor Temperature °F (°C)	[1] Volts
77 (25)	1.8-2.2
104 (40)	1.2-1.6

[1] – As temperature increases, voltage should gradually decrease.

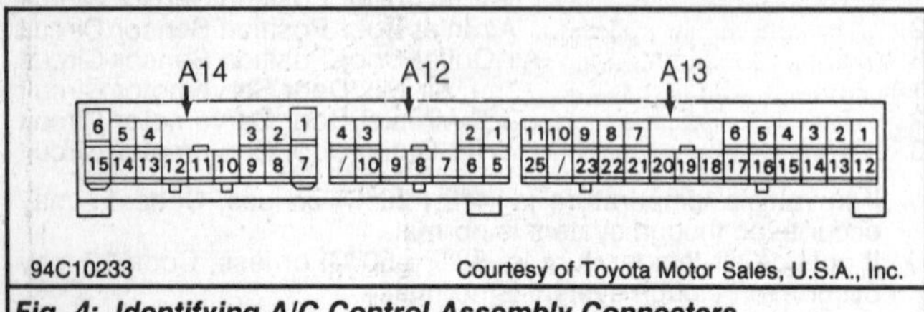
A14
A12
A13

94C10233 Courtesy of Toyota Motor Sales, U.S.A., Inc.

Fig. 4: Identifying A/C Control Assembly Connectors

Sensor Resistance Test – 1) Remove left instrument panel undercover. Disconnect in-vehicle temperature sensor. *See Fig. 1*. Measure resistance between in-vehicle temperature sensor terminals while heating sensor. See IN-VEHICLE TEMPERATURE SENSOR RESISTANCE SPECIFICATIONS table.

2) If resistance is not as specified, replace sensor. If resistance is within specification, check wiring harness and connectors between sensor and A/C-heater control panel. Repair harness and connectors as necessary. If wiring harness and connectors are okay, temporarily substitute a known good A/C-heater control panel, and retest system.

IN-VEHICLE TEMPERATURE SENSOR RESISTANCE SPECIFICATIONS

Sensor Temperature °F (°C)	[1] Ohms
77 (25)	1600-1800
122 (50)	500-700

[1] – As temperature increases, resistance should gradually decrease.

CODE 12
AMBIENT TEMPERATURE SENSOR CIRCUIT

Voltage Check – 1) Remove A/C-heater control panel, leaving harness connectors attached. See A/C-HEATER CONTROL PANEL under REMOVAL & INSTALLATION.

2) Turn ignition on. Using DVOM, backprobe between terminals A13-8 (Pink wire) and A13-20 (Brown wire) of A/C-heater control panel connector. *See Fig. 4*.

3) Measure circuit voltage while heating ambient temperature sensor, located behind grille, on lower right side. See AMBIENT TEMPERATURE SENSOR CIRCUIT VOLTAGE SPECIFICATIONS table.

4) If voltage is as specified, temporarily substitute a known good A/C control assembly, and retest system. If voltage is not as specified, measure sensor resistance. See SENSOR RESISTANCE TEST.

AMBIENT TEMPERATURE SENSOR CIRCUIT VOLTAGE SPECIFICATIONS

Sensor Temperature °F (°C)	[1] Volts
77 (25)	1.35-1.75
104 (40)	0.85-1.25

[1] – As temperature increases, voltage should gradually decrease.

Sensor Resistance Test – 1) Remove radiator grille. Disconnect ambient temperature sensor. Measure resistance between sensor terminals while heating sensor. See AMBIENT TEMPERATURE SENSOR RESISTANCE SPECIFICATIONS table.

2) If resistance is not as specified, replace sensor. If resistance is within specification, check wiring harness and connectors between sensor and A/C-heater control panel. Repair harness and connectors as necessary. If wiring harness and connectors are okay, temporarily substitute a known good A/C-heater control panel, and retest system.

AMBIENT TEMPERATURE SENSOR RESISTANCE SPECIFICATIONS

Sensor Temperature °F (°C)	[1] Ohms
77 (25)	1600-1800
122 (50)	500-700

[1] – As temperature increases, resistance should gradually decrease.

CODE 13
EVAPORATOR TEMPERATURE SENSOR CIRCUIT

Voltage Check – 1) Remove A/C-heater control panel, leaving harness connectors attached. See A/C-HEATER CONTROL PANEL under REMOVAL & INSTALLATION.

2) Turn ignition on. Using DVOM, backprobe between terminals A13-9 (Blue/Yellow wire) and A13-20 (Brown wire) of A/C-heater control panel connector. *See Fig. 4*.

3) Measure circuit voltage at specified temperatures. See EVAPORATOR TEMPERATURE SENSOR CIRCUIT VOLTAGE SPECIFICATIONS table.

4) If voltage is as specified, temporarily substitute a known good A/C control assembly, and retest system. If voltage is not as specified, measure sensor resistance. See SENSOR RESISTANCE TEST.

EVAPORATOR TEMPERATURE SENSOR CIRCUIT VOLTAGE SPECIFICATIONS

Sensor Temperature °F (°C)	[1] Volts
32 (0)	2.0-2.4
59 (15)	1.4-1.8

[1] – As temperature increases, voltage should gradually decrease.

Sensor Resistance Test – 1) Remove evaporator temperature sensor. See EVAPORATOR TEMPERATURE SENSOR under REMOVAL & INSTALLATION. Measure resistance between terminals of sensor. See EVAPORATOR TEMPERATURE SENSOR RESISTANCE SPECIFICATIONS table.

2) If resistance is not as specified, replace sensor. If resistance is within specification, check wiring harness and connectors between sensor and A/C-heater control panel. Repair harness and connectors as necessary. If wiring harness and connectors are okay, temporarily substitute a known good A/C-heater control panel, and retest system.

EVAPORATOR TEMPERATURE SENSOR RESISTANCE SPECIFICATIONS

Sensor Temperature °F (°C)	[1] Ohms
32 (0)	4600-5100
59 (15)	2100-2600

[1] – As temperature increases, resistance should gradually decrease.

CODE 14 WATER TEMPERATURE SENSOR CIRCUIT

Voltage Check – 1) Remove A/C-heater control panel, leaving harness connectors attached. See A/C-HEATER CONTROL PANEL under REMOVAL & INSTALLATION.

2) Turn ignition on. Using DVOM, backprobe between terminals A13-10 (Light Green/Red wire) and A13-20 (Brown wire) of A/C-heater control panel connector. *See Fig. 4*.

3) Measure circuit voltage at specified temperatures. See WATER TEMPERATURE SENSOR CIRCUIT VOLTAGE SPECIFICATIONS table.

4) If voltage is as specified, temporarily substitute a known good A/C control assembly, and retest system. If voltage is not as specified, test sensor resistance. See SENSOR RESISTANCE TEST.

WATER TEMPERATURE SENSOR CIRCUIT VOLTAGE SPECIFICATIONS

Sensor Temperature°F (°C)	[1] Volts
32 (0)	2.8-3.2
104 (40)	1.8-2.2
158 (70)	0.9-1.3

[1] – As temperature increases, voltage should gradually decrease.

Sensor Resistance Test – 1) Remove water temperature sensor. See WATER TEMPERATURE SENSOR under REMOVAL & INSTALLATION. Place sensor and thermometer in water. Measure resistance between sensor terminals No. 1 (Brown wire) and No. 3 (Light Green/Red wire) at specified temperatures. See WATER TEMPERATURE SENSOR RESISTANCE SPECIFICATIONS table.

2) If resistance is not as specified, replace sensor. If resistance is within specification, check wiring harness and connectors between sensor and A/C-heater control panel. Repair or replace harness and connectors as necessary. If wiring harness and connectors are okay, temporarily substitute a known good A/C-heater control panel, and retest system.

WATER TEMPERATURE SENSOR RESISTANCE SPECIFICATIONS

Sensor Temperature °F (°C)	[1] Ohms
32 (0)	16,500-17,500
104 (40)	2400-2800
158 (70)	700-1000

[1] – As temperature increases, resistance should gradually decrease.

CODE 21 SOLAR SENSOR CIRCUIT

Voltage Check – 1) Remove A/C-heater control panel, leaving harness connectors attached. See A/C-HEATER CONTROL PANEL under REMOVAL & INSTALLATION.

2) Turn ignition on. Using DVOM, backprobe between terminals A13-8 (Brown/White wire) and A13-11 (Yellow/Green wire) of A/C-heater control panel connector. *See Fig. 4*.

3) Measure circuit voltage at specified conditions. See SOLAR SENSOR CIRCUIT VOLTAGE SPECIFICATIONS table. If circuit voltage is not as specified, test sensor resistance. See SENSOR RESISTANCE TEST. If circuit voltage is within specification, go to next step.

4) If voltage is as specified, temporarily substitute a known good A/C-heater control panel, and retest system. If voltage is not as specified, test sensor resistance. See SENSOR RESISTANCE TEST.

SOLAR SENSOR CIRCUIT VOLTAGE SPECIFICATIONS

Condition	[1] Volts
Sensor Covered By Cloth	4.0-4.5
Sensor Subjected To Bright Light	Less Than 4.0

[1] – As light intensity increases, voltage should decrease.

Sensor Resistance Test – 1) Remove solar sensor. See SOLAR SENSOR under REMOVAL & INSTALLATION. Disconnect solar sensor harness connector. Cover sensor using cloth. Measure resistance between sensor terminals. Remove cloth. Subject sensor to bright light. Again measure resistance between terminals of sensor. See SOLAR SENSOR RESISTANCE SPECIFICATIONS table.

2) If resistance is not as specified, replace sensor. If resistance is within specification, check wiring harness and connectors between sensor and A/C-heater control panel. Repair or replace harness and connectors as necessary. If wiring harness and connectors are okay, temporarily substitute a known good A/C-heater control panel, and retest system.

SOLAR SENSOR RESISTANCE SPECIFICATIONS

Condition	[1] Ohms
Sensor Covered By Cloth	No Continuity
Sensor Subjected To Bright Light	About 4000

[1] – As light intensity increases, resistance should decrease.

CODE 22 COMPRESSOR LOCK SENSOR CIRCUIT

Compressor Drive Belt Check – 1) Ensure drive belt fits properly on compressor pulley. If pointer is not in range "A" on tensioner scale, replace belt. *See Fig. 5.* If tension is okay, go to next step.

2) Start engine. Turn blower and A/C on. Observe compressor. If compressor locks during operation, repair compressor. If compressor does not lock during operation, measure sensor resistance. See SENSOR RESISTANCE TEST.

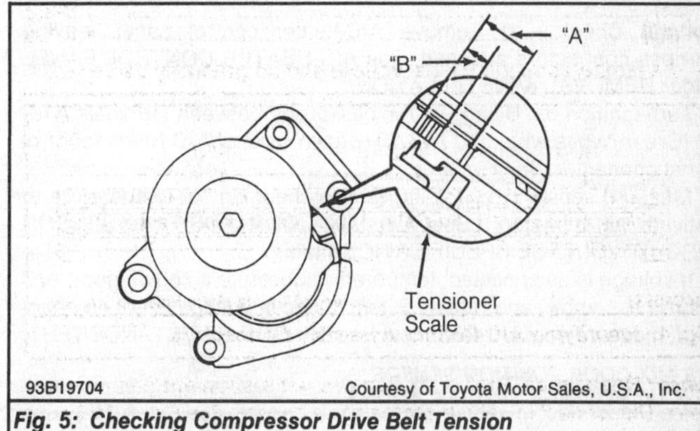

"A"
"B"
Tensioner Scale
93B19704
Courtesy of Toyota Motor Sales, U.S.A., Inc.

Fig. 5: Checking Compressor Drive Belt Tension

Sensor Resistance Test – 1) Disconnect compressor lock sensor connector, located at compressor. Measure resistance between sensor terminals at specified temperatures. See COMPRESSOR LOCK SENSOR RESISTANCE SPECIFICATIONS table.

2) If resistance is not as specified, replace sensor. If resistance is within specification, check wiring harness and connectors between sensor and A/C-heater control panel. Repair or replace harness and connectors as necessary. If wiring harness and connectors are okay, temporarily substitute a known good A/C control assembly, and retest system.

1993 AUTOMATIC A/C-HEATER SYSTEMS SC300 & SC400 (Cont.)

COMPRESSOR LOCK SENSOR RESISTANCE SPECIFICATIONS

Sensor Temperature °F (°C)	Ohms
77 (25)	530-650
212 (100)	670-890

CODE 23
PRESSURE SWITCH CIRCUIT

Pressure Switch Circuit Voltage Check – 1) Remove A/C-heater control panel, leaving harness connectors attached. See A/C-HEATER CONTROL PANEL under REMOVAL & INSTALLATION. Using DVOM, backprobe terminal A13-5 (Blue/Black wire) of A/C-heater control panel connector and ground. *See Fig. 4*.

2) Connect manifold gauge set. Turn ignition and A/C on. Observe voltage and pressure. On low pressure side of system, voltage should switch from 12 to zero volts as pressure increases to more than 30 psi (2.1 kg/cm²). On high pressure side of system, voltage should switch from zero to 12 volts as pressure increases to more than 384 psi (27.0 kg/cm²).

3) If voltage changes as specified, temporarily substitute a known good A/C control assembly, and retest system. If voltage is not as specified, check pressure switch continuity. See PRESSURE SWITCH CONTINUITY CHECK.

Pressure Switch Continuity Check – 1) Disconnect pressure switch connector, located in liquid line on right side of engine compartment. Turn ignition on. Check continuity between switch terminals while varying A/C system pressure.

2) On low pressure side of system, continuity should switch from open circuit to continuity as system pressure increases to more than 30 psi (2.1 kg/cm²). On high pressure side of system, continuity should switch from open circuit to continuity as pressure increases to more than 384 psi (27.0 kg/cm²). If continuity is not as specified, replace pressure switch.

3) If continuity is as specified, check wiring harness and connectors between pressure switch and A/C-heater control panel. Repair or replace harness and connectors as necessary. If wiring harness and connectors are okay, temporarily substitute a known good A/C-heater control panel, and retest system.

CODE 31 OR 41
AIR MIX DOOR POSITION SENSOR CIRCUIT

NOTE: For Code 41, see CODE 41 AIR MIX DOOR SERVOMOTOR CIRCUIT for additional trouble shooting procedures.

Voltage Check – 1) Remove A/C-heater control panel, leaving harness connectors attached. See A/C-HEATER CONTROL PANEL under REMOVAL & INSTALLATION.

2) Turn ignition on. Using DVOM, backprobe between terminals A13-22 (Green/White wire) and A13-20 (Brown wire) of A/C-heater control panel connector. *See Fig. 4*.

3) Measure sensor circuit voltage while changing set temperature to activate air mix door. See AIR MIX DOOR POSITION SENSOR CIRCUIT VOLTAGE SPECIFICATIONS table.

4) If voltage is as specified, temporarily substitute a known good A/C control assembly, and retest system. If circuit voltage is not as specified, measure sensor resistance. See SENSOR RESISTANCE TEST.

AIR MIX DOOR POSITION SENSOR CIRCUIT VOLTAGE SPECIFICATIONS

Set Temperature	[1] Volts
Maximum Cool	3.70-4.27
Maximum Hot	0.88-1.16

[1] – As set temperature increases, voltage should gradually decrease.

Sensor Resistance Test – 1) Remove air mix door servomotor. See AIR MIX DOOR SERVOMOTOR under REMOVAL & INSTALLATION. Disconnect air mix door servomotor connector. Measure resistance between servomotor connector terminals S5 (Brown/White wire) and SG (Brown wire). *See Fig. 6*.

2) Resistance should be 4700-7200 ohms. If resistance is not as specified, replace air mix door servomotor assembly. If resistance is as specified, go to next step.

3) Position air mix door at maximum cold position by applying battery voltage to air mix door servomotor assembly connector terminal No. 4 (Red/Yellow wire) and grounding terminal No. 5 (Violet wire).

4) Measure resistance between terminals TP (Green/White wire) and SG (Brown wire). See AIR MIX DOOR POSITION SENSOR RESISTANCE SPECIFICATIONS table. Position air mix door at maximum hot position by reversing battery voltage and ground leads.

5) If resistance is not as specified, replace air mix door servomotor assembly. If resistance is within specification, check wiring harness and connectors between air mix door servomotor and A/C-heater control panel. Repair or replace harness and connectors as necessary. If wiring harness and connectors are okay, temporarily substitute a known good A/C-heater control panel, and retest system.

AIR MIX DOOR POSITION SENSOR RESISTANCE SPECIFICATIONS

Position	[1] Ohms
Maximum Cold	3760-5760
Maximum Hot	940-1440

[1] – Resistance should gradually decrease as air mix door moves from maximum cold position to maximum hot position.

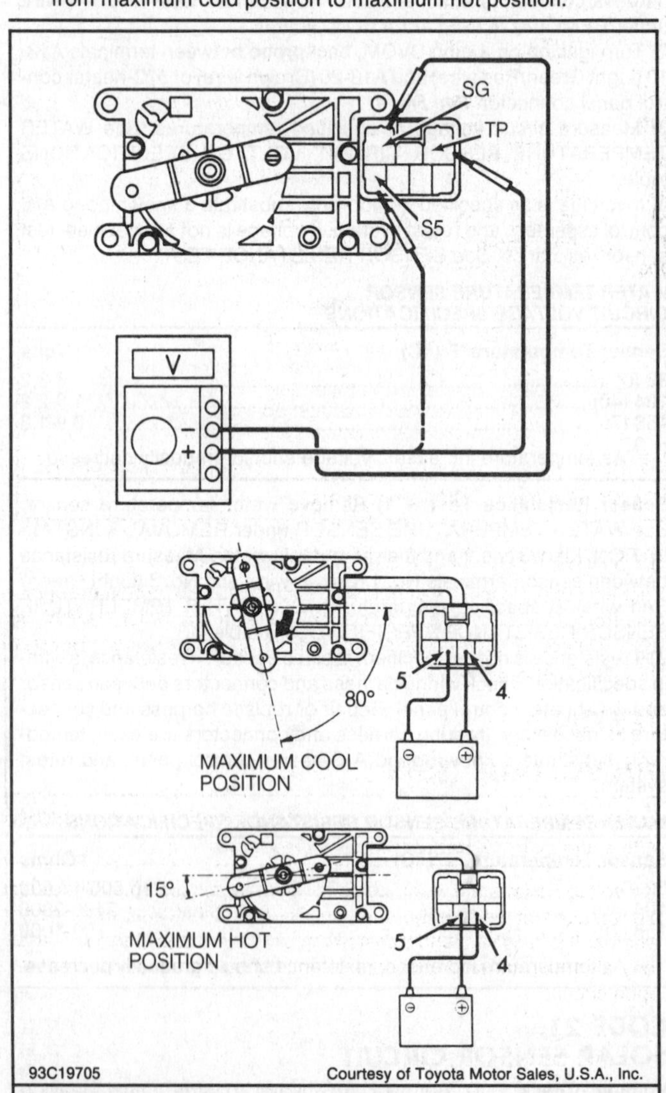
SG
TP
S5
V
–
+
5
4
80°
MAXIMUM COOL POSITION
15°
MAXIMUM HOT POSITION
5
4
93C19705
Courtesy of Toyota Motor Sales, U.S.A., Inc.

Fig. 6: Testing Air Mix Door Servomotor

CODE 32 OR 42
AIR INLET DOOR POSITION SENSOR CIRCUIT

NOTE: For Code 42, see CODE 42 AIR INLET DOOR SERVOMOTOR CIRCUIT for additional trouble shooting procedures.

Voltage Check - 1) Remove A/C-heater control panel, leaving harness connectors attached. See A/C-HEATER CONTROL PANEL under REMOVAL & INSTALLATION.

2) Turn ignition on. Using DVOM, backprobe between terminals A13-23 (Green wire) and A13-20 (Brown wire) of A/C-heater control panel connector. *See Fig. 4*.

3) Measure sensor circuit voltage while alternately pressing fresh air and recirculated air switches to activate air inlet door. See AIR INLET DOOR POSITION SENSOR CIRCUIT VOLTAGE SPECIFICATIONS table.

4) If voltage is as specified, temporarily substitute a known good A/C control assembly, and retest system. If voltage is not as specified, measure sensor resistance. See SENSOR RESISTANCE TEST.

AIR INLET DOOR POSITION SENSOR CIRCUIT VOLTAGE SPECIFICATIONS

Switch/Inlet Position	[1] Volts
Recirculated Air	3.70-4.27
Fresh Air	0.88-1.26

[1] - Voltage should gradually decrease as air inlet door changes from recirculated air to fresh air position.

Sensor Resistance Test - 1) Remove air inlet door servomotor. See AIR INLET DOOR SERVOMOTOR under REMOVAL & INSTALLATION. Disconnect air inlet door servomotor connector. Measure resistance between sensor terminals S5 (Brown/White wire) and SG (Brown wire). *See Fig. 7*.

2) Resistance should be 4700-7200 ohms. If resistance is not as specified, replace air inlet door servomotor. If resistance is 4700-7200 ohms, go to next step.

3) Position servomotor to recirculated air position by applying battery voltage to servomotor connector terminal No. 6 (Green/Red wire) and grounding terminal No. 2. (Light Green wire) *See Fig. 7*.

4) Measure and record resistance between terminals TPI (Green wire) and SG (Brown wire) of air inlet door servomotor connector. Position servomotor to fresh air position by reversing battery and ground leads. Again measure resistance between servomotor connector terminals TPI and SG.

5) See AIR INLET DOOR POSITION SENSOR RESISTANCE SPECIFICATIONS table. If resistance is not as specified, replace air inlet door servomotor. If resistance is within specification, check wiring harness and connectors between air inlet door servomotor and A/C-heater control panel. Repair or replace harness and connectors as necessary. If wiring harness and connectors are okay, temporarily substitute a known good A/C-heater control panel, and retest system.

AIR INLET DOOR POSITION SENSOR RESISTANCE SPECIFICATIONS

Inlet Door Position	[1] Ohms
Recirculated Air	3760-5760
Fresh Air	940-1440

[1] - Resistance should gradually decrease as air inlet door moves from recirculated air position to fresh air position.

CODE 33 OR 43
AIR OUTLET DOOR POSITION SENSOR CIRCUIT

NOTE: For Code 43, see CODE 43 AIR OUTLET DOOR SERVOMOTOR CIRCUIT for additional trouble shooting procedures.

Voltage Check - 1) Remove A/C-heater control panel, leaving harness connectors attached. See A/C-HEATER CONTROL PANEL under REMOVAL & INSTALLATION.

2) Turn ignition on. Using DVOM, backprobe between terminals A13-22 (Yellow/Green wire) and A13-20 (Brown wire) of A/C-heater control panel connector. *See Fig. 4*.

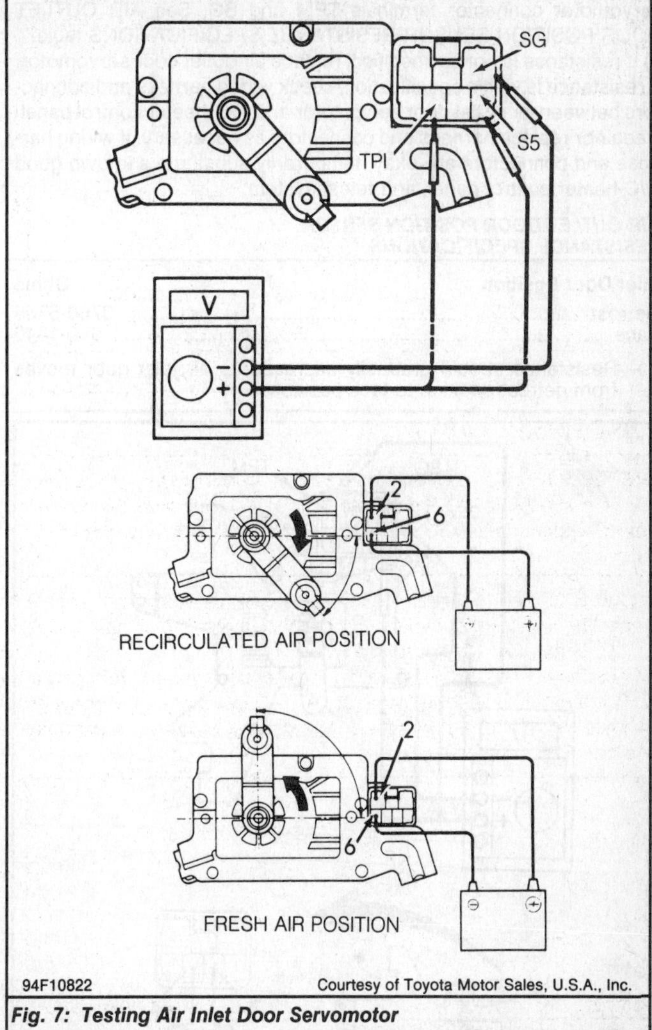
SG
S5
TPI
V
-
+
2
6
RECIRCULATED AIR POSITION
2
6
FRESH AIR POSITION
94F10822
Courtesy of Toyota Motor Sales, U.S.A., Inc.

Fig. 7: Testing Air Inlet Door Servomotor

3) Measure sensor circuit voltage while pressing MODE switch to activate air outlet door servomotor. See AIR OUTLET DOOR POSITION SENSOR CIRCUIT VOLTAGE SPECIFICATIONS table.

4) If voltage is as specified, temporarily substitute a known good A/C control assembly, and retest system. If voltage is not as specified, measure sensor resistance. See SENSOR RESISTANCE TEST.

AIR OUTLET DOOR POSITION SENSOR CIRCUIT VOLTAGE SPECIFICATIONS

Position	[1] Volts
Face	3.70-4.27
Defrost	0.88-1.16

[1] - Voltage should gradually decrease as air outlet door changes from face to defrost position.

Sensor Resistance Test - 1) Remove air outlet door servomotor. See AIR OUTLET DOOR SERVOMOTOR under REMOVAL & INSTALLATION. Disconnect air outlet door servomotor connector. Measure resistance between sensor terminals S5 (Brown/White wire) and SG (Brown wire). *See Fig. 8*.

2) Resistance should be 4700-7200 ohms. If resistance is not as specified, replace air outlet door servomotor. If resistance is as specified, go to next step.

3) Position servomotor to face position by applying battery voltage to servomotor assembly connector terminal No. 4 (White wire) and grounding terminal No. 5 (Yellow/Blue wire). *See Fig. 8*.

4) Measure and record resistance between terminals TPM (Yellow/Red wire) and SG (Brown wire) of air outlet door servomotor connector. *See Fig. 8*. Position servomotor to defrost position by reversing battery and ground leads. Again measure resistance between

1993 AUTOMATIC A/C-HEATER SYSTEMS SC300 & SC400 (Cont.)

servomotor connector terminals TPM and SG. See AIR OUTLET DOOR POSITION SENSOR RESISTANCE SPECIFICATIONS table.

5) If resistance is not as specified, replace air outlet door servomotor. If resistance is within specification, check wiring harness and connectors between air outlet door servomotor and A/C-heater control panel. Repair or replace harness and connectors as necessary. If wiring harness and connectors are okay, temporarily substitute a known good A/C-heater control panel, and retest system.

AIR OUTLET DOOR POSITION SENSOR RESISTANCE SPECIFICATIONS

Inlet Door Position	[1] Ohms
Defrost	3760-5760
Face	940-1440

[1] – Resistance should gradually decrease as air inlet door moves from defrost position to face position.

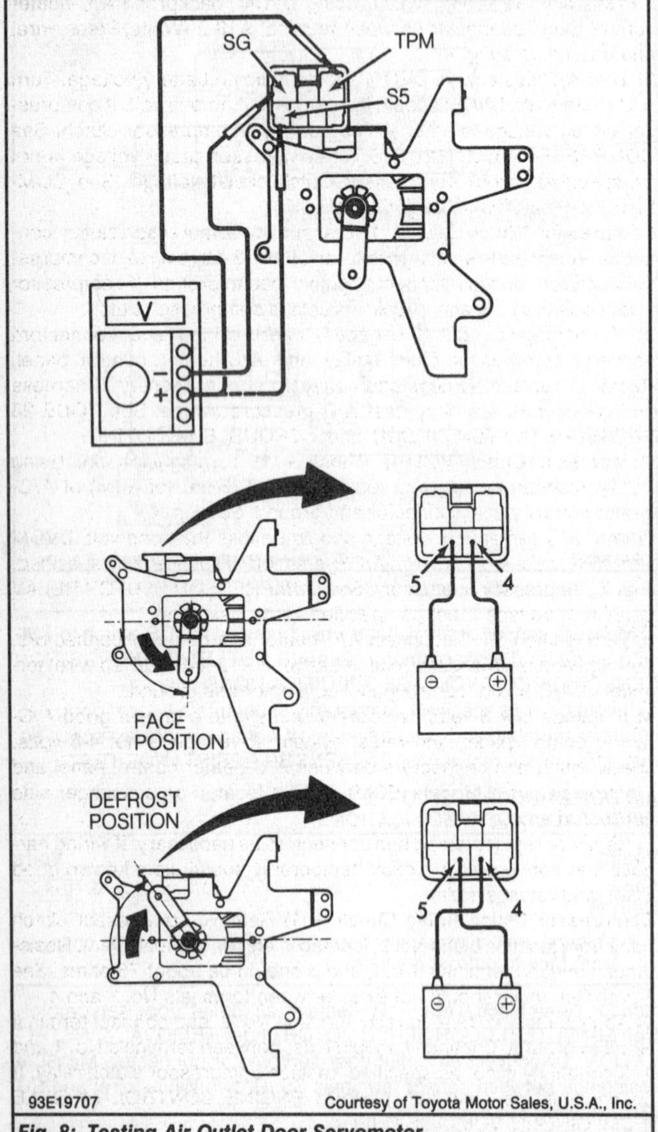
SG
TPM
S5
V
FACE
POSITION
DEFROST
POSITION
5
4
5
4
93E19707
Courtesy of Toyota Motor Sales, U.S.A., Inc.

Fig. 8: Testing Air Outlet Door Servomotor

CODE 41
AIR MIX DOOR SERVOMOTOR CIRCUIT

NOTE: See CODE 31 OR 41 AIR MIX DOOR POSITION SENSOR CIRCUIT for additional trouble shooting procedures.

Actuator Test – 1) Warm engine to normal operating temperature. Perform indicator check. See RETRIEVING CODES under TROUBLE SHOOTING. After system enters diagnostic code check mode, perform actuator check. See ACTUATOR CHECK under TROUBLE SHOOTING. Observe air mix door operation. See AIR MIX DOOR AIRFLOW table.

2) If air mix door functions as specified, no problem is indicated at this time. If air mix door does not function as specified, test air mix door servomotor. See AIR MIX DOOR SERVOMOTOR TEST.

AIR MIX DOOR AIRFLOW

Display Code	Door Position	Condition
20-22	Fully Closed	Cool Air Comes Out
23-24	Half Open	Blend (Cool/Hot) Air Comes Out
25-27	Fully Open	Hot Air Comes Out

Air Mix Door Servomotor Test – 1) Remove air mix door servomotor. See AIR MIX DOOR SERVOMOTOR under REMOVAL & INSTALLATION. Disconnect air mix door servomotor connector.

2) Connect battery voltage to air mix door servomotor connector terminal No. 4 (Red/Yellow wire). Connect terminal No. 5 (Violet wire) to ground. *See Fig. 6*. Air mix door servomotor lever should move to cool air position. Reverse battery and ground leads. Servomotor lever should move to hot air position.

3) Replace air mix door servomotor if it does not function as described. If servomotor functions correctly, check wiring harness and connectors between servomotor and A/C-heater control panel. Repair or replace harness and connectors as necessary. If wiring harness and connectors are okay, temporarily substitute a known good A/C-heater control panel, and retest system.

CODE 42
AIR INLET DOOR SERVOMOTOR CIRCUIT

NOTE: See CODE 32 OR 42 AIR INLET DOOR POSITION SENSOR CIRCUIT for additional trouble shooting procedures.

Actuator Test – 1) Remove glove box. Perform indicator check. See RETRIEVING CODES under TROUBLE SHOOTING. After system enters diagnostic code check mode, perform actuator check. See ACTUATOR CHECK under TROUBLE SHOOTING. Observe air inlet door operation. See AIR INLET DOOR AIRFLOW table.

AIR INLET DOOR AIRFLOW

Display Code	Door Position
20	Fresh Air
21	Fresh/Recirculated Air
22	Recirculated Air
23-27	Fresh Air

2) If air inlet door functions as specified, no problem is indicated at this time. If air inlet door does not function as specified, test air inlet door servomotor. See AIR INLET DOOR SERVOMOTOR TEST.

Air Inlet Door Servomotor Test – 1) Remove A/C unit. See A/C UNIT under REMOVAL & INSTALLATION. Disconnect air inlet door servomotor connector. Connect battery voltage to air inlet door servomotor connector terminal No. 6 (Green/Red wire). Connect terminal No. 2 (Light Green wire) to ground. *See Fig. 7*.

2) Air inlet door servomotor lever should move to recirculated air position. Reverse battery and ground connections. Air inlet door servomotor lever should move to fresh air position.

3) Replace air inlet door servomotor if it does not operate as described. If servomotor operates correctly, check wiring harness and connectors between servomotor and A/C-heater control panel. Repair or replace harness and connectors as necessary.

4) If wiring harness and connectors are okay, substitute a known good A/C-heater control panel, and retest system.

CODE 43
AIR OUTLET DOOR SERVOMOTOR CIRCUIT

NOTE: See CODE 33 OR 43 AIR OUTLET DOOR POSITION SENSOR CIRCUIT for additional trouble shooting procedures.

Actuator Test - 1) Perform indicator check. See RETRIEVING CODES under TROUBLE SHOOTING. After system enters diagnostic code check mode, perform actuator check. See ACTUATOR CHECK under TROUBLE SHOOTING. Observe air outlet door operation. See AIR OUTLET DOOR AIRFLOW table.

2) If air outlet door functions as specified, no problem is indicated at this time. If air outlet door does not function as specified, test air outlet door servomotor. See AIR OUTLET DOOR SERVOMOTOR TEST.

AIR OUTLET DOOR AIRFLOW

Code	Door Position
20-22	Face
23	Bi-Level
24-25	Foot
26	Foot/Defrost
27	Defrost

Air Outlet Door Servomotor Test - 1) Remove air outlet door servomotor. See AIR OUTLET DOOR SERVOMOTOR under REMOVAL & INSTALLATION. Disconnect air outlet door servomotor connector.

2) Connect battery voltage to air outlet door servomotor connector terminal No. 4 (White wire). Connect terminal No. 5 (Yellow/Blue wire) to ground. *See Fig. 8*. Air outlet door servomotor lever should move to face position. Reverse battery and ground connections. Air outlet door servomotor lever should move to defrost position.

3) Replace air outlet door servomotor if it does not operate as described. If servomotor operates correctly, check wiring harness and connectors between servomotor and A/C-heater control panel. Repair or replace harness and connectors as necessary. If wiring harness and connectors are okay, substitute a known good A/C-heater control panel, and retest system.

TESTING

WARNING: To avoid injury from accidental air bag deployment, read and carefully follow all SERVICE PRECAUTIONS and DISABLING & ACTIVATING AIR BAG SYSTEM procedures in AIR BAG SYSTEM SAFETY article in GENERAL SERVICING.

ACC POWER SOURCE CIRCUIT

Voltage Check - 1) Remove A/C-heater control panel, leaving harness connectors attached. See A/C-HEATER CONTROL PANEL under REMOVAL & INSTALLATION. Turn ignition on. Using DVOM, backprobe between terminal A14-15 (Blue/Red wire) of A/C-heater control panel connector and ground. *See Fig. 4*.

2) If battery voltage exists, temporarily substitute a known good A/C control assembly, and retest system. If battery voltage does not exist, check RADIO No. 2 fuse. See RADIO No. 2 FUSE CHECK.

RADIO No. 2 Fuse Check - Check RADIO No. 2 fuse, in fuse block No. 1, located below instrument panel. If fuse is okay, check wiring between A/C-heater control panel and battery. Repair wiring as necessary. Replace fuse if it is blown, and check for short circuit.

BACK-UP POWER SOURCE CIRCUIT

Voltage Check - 1) Remove A/C-heater control panel, leaving harness connectors attached. See A/C-HEATER CONTROL PANEL under REMOVAL & INSTALLATION. Using DVOM, backprobe between terminal A14-1 (Red wire) of A/C-heater control panel connector and ground. *See Fig. 4*.

2) If battery voltage exists, temporarily substitute a known good A/C control assembly, and retest system. If battery voltage does not exist, check DOME fuse in junction block No. 2. If fuse is okay, check wiring and connectors between A/C-heater control panel and battery. Repair wiring and connectors as necessary.

BLOWER MOTOR CIRCUIT

Blower Motor Check - 1) Remove blower motor. See BLOWER MOTOR under REMOVAL & INSTALLATION. Connect battery voltage to blower motor connector terminal No. 2 (Blue/Red wire). Connect terminal No. 1 (Red wire) to ground.

2) Blower motor should operate smoothly. If blower motor does not operate smoothly, replace blower motor. If blower motor operates smoothly, test blower resistor. See BLOWER RESISTOR TEST.

Blower Resistor Test - 1) Disconnect blower resistor connector. See BLOWER RESISTOR under REMOVAL & INSTALLATION. *See Fig. 1*. Measure resistance between blower resistor terminals. Resistance should be 2.6-3.0 ohms. If resistance is not as specified, replace blower resistor.

2) If blower resistor is okay, check wiring and connectors between battery and blower motor and between blower motor and body ground. Repair wiring and connectors as necessary.

COMPRESSOR CIRCUIT

Voltage Check - 1) Remove A/C-heater control panel, leaving harness connectors attached. See A/C-HEATER CONTROL PANEL under REMOVAL & INSTALLATION. Start engine.

2 Press any fan speed switch. Using DVOM, backprobe A/C-heater control panel connector between terminal A13-2 (White/Green wire) and ground. *See Fig. 4*.

3) Turn A/C system on. DVOM should indicate battery voltage. Turn A/C system off. DVOM should indicate less than one volt. If compressor circuit voltage is as specified, test A/C compressor clutch. See COMPRESSOR CLUTCH TEST. If compressor circuit voltage is not as specified, check compressor clutch circuit voltage. See COMPRESSOR CLUTCH VOLTAGE CHECK.

Compressor Clutch Test - 1) Disconnect compressor clutch connector. Apply battery voltage to terminal No. 3 (Blue wire) of compressor clutch connector. Connect negative lead to ground. If compressor clutch does not engage, repair or replace compressor clutch.

2) If compressor clutch engages, check wiring and connectors between compressor clutch relay and A/C-heater control panel. Repair or replace harness and connectors as necessary. If harness and connectors are okay, test A/C pressure switch. See CODE 23 PRESSURE SWITCH CIRCUIT under TROUBLE SHOOTING.

Compressor Clutch Voltage Check - 1) Turn ignition on. Using DVOM, backprobe between terminal A12-4 (Blue/Red wire) of A/C-heater control panel connector and ground. *See Fig. 4*.

2) With A/C system on, voltage should be less than one volt. DVOM should indicate 4-6 volts with A/C system off. If voltage is as specified, check compressor clutch relay. See COMPRESSOR CLUTCH RELAY CHECK. If voltage is not as specified, go to next step.

3) Turn ignition off. Disconnect A/C-heater control panel connectors. Turn ignition on. Measure voltage between A12-4 (Blue/Red wire) terminal of A/C-heater control panel connector and ground.

4) If voltage is 4-6 volts, temporarily substitute a known good A/C-heater control panel, and retest system. If voltage is not 4-6 volts, check wiring and connectors between A/C-heater control panel and Electronic Control Module (ECM). ECM is located on passenger-side floorboard area.

5) Repair or replace wiring and connectors as necessary. If wiring harness and connectors are okay, temporarily substitute a known good ECM, and retest system.

Compressor Clutch Relay Check - 1) Remove compressor clutch relay from junction block No. 2, located in engine compartment. Resistance between terminals No. 2 and 3 should be about 75 ohms. *See Fig. 9*. Continuity should not exist between terminals No. 1 and 4.

2) Apply battery voltage to relay terminal No. 2, and connect terminal No. 3 to ground. Continuity should exist between terminals No. 1 and 4. If continuity is not as specified, replace compressor clutch relay. If continuity is as specified, perform ENGINE CONTROL MODULE (ECM) CIRCUIT VOLTAGE CHECK.

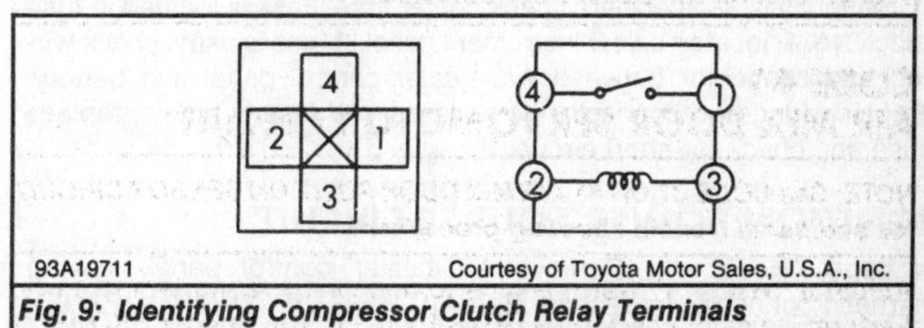

4
2
1
3
4
1
2
3
93A19711
Courtesy of Toyota Motor Sales, U.S.A., Inc.

Fig. 9: Identifying Compressor Clutch Relay Terminals

1993 AUTOMATIC A/C-HEATER SYSTEMS SC300 & SC400 (Cont.)

Engine Control Module (ECM) Circuit Voltage Check – 1) Remove ECM, leaving harness connectors attached. ECM is located on passenger-side floorboard area. Turn ignition on. Using DVOM, backprobe between terminal ACMG (White wire) of ECM connector and ground. *See Fig. 10*.
2) With A/C system on, DVOM should indicate about 1.3 volts. With A/C system off, voltage should be between 1.3 volts and battery voltage. If voltage is not as specified, temporarily substitute a known good ECM, and retest system.
3) If voltage is as specified, check wiring and connectors between ECM and A/C-heater control panel. Repair wiring and connectors as necessary. If wiring and connectors are okay, temporarily substitute a known good A/C-heater control panel, and retest system.

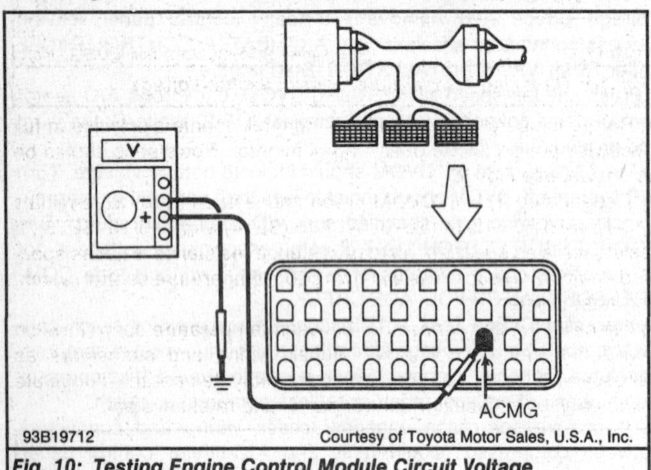
V
ACMG
93B19712
Courtesy of Toyota Motor Sales, U.S.A., Inc.
Fig. 10: Testing Engine Control Module Circuit Voltage

HEATER MAIN RELAY CIRCUIT

Voltage Check – 1) Remove A/C-heater control panel, leaving harness connectors attached. See A/C-HEATER CONTROL PANEL under REMOVAL & INSTALLATION.
2) Turn ignition on. Using DVOM, backprobe between terminal A12-9 (Blue/White wire) of A/C-heater control panel connector and ground. *See Fig. 4*. Turn ignition on. Measure voltage as specified in HEATER MAIN RELAY CIRCUIT SPECIFICATIONS table.
3) If voltage is as specified, temporarily substitute a known good A/C control assembly, and retest system. If voltage is not as specified, test heater main relay. See HEATER MAIN RELAY TEST.

HEATER MAIN RELAY CIRCUIT SPECIFICATIONS

Ignition Switch Position	Volts
OFF	0
ON	
Blower On	0
Blower Off	Battery Voltage

Heater Main Relay Test – 1) Remove heater main relay from junction block No. 2 in engine compartment. Check for continuity between relay terminals. Continuity should exist between relay terminals No. 1 and 3 and between terminals No. 2 and 4. *See Fig. 11*. Continuity should not exist between terminals No. 4 and 5.
2) Apply battery voltage to terminal No. 1. Connect terminal No. 3 to ground. Continuity should exist between terminals No. 4 and 5. Continuity should not exist between terminals No. 2 and 4.
3) If continuity of relay is not as specified, replace heater main relay. If continuity is as specified, check heater fuse. Fuse is located in fuse block No. 1, located below instrument panel. If fuse is okay, check wiring and connector between A/C-heater control panel and battery. Repair wiring and connector as necessary. If fuse is blown, replace fuse and check for short circuit.

IGNITION POWER SOURCE CIRCUIT

Voltage Check – 1) Remove A/C-heater control panel, leaving harness connectors attached. See A/C-HEATER CONTROL PANEL under REMOVAL & INSTALLATION.

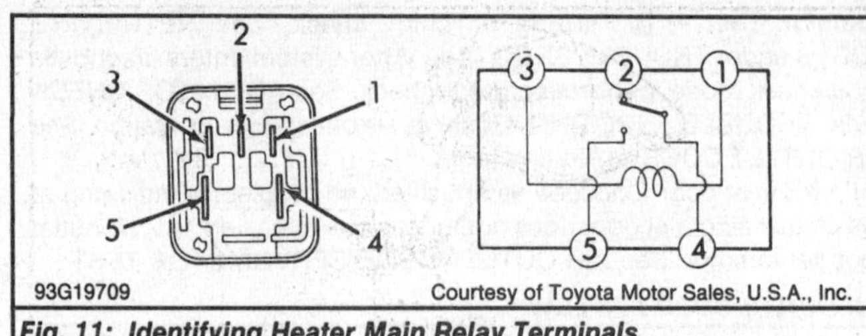
2
3
1
5
4
3
2
1
5
4
93G19709
Courtesy of Toyota Motor Sales, U.S.A., Inc.
Fig. 11: Identifying Heater Main Relay Terminals

2) Turn ignition on. Using DVOM, backprobe between terminals A14-6 (Red/Blue wire) and A14-7 (White/Black wire) of A/C-heater control panel connector. *See Fig. 4*.
3) If battery voltage exists, temporarily substitute a known good A/C control assembly, and retest system. If battery voltage does not exist, go to GROUND WIRE CHECK.
Ground Wire Check – Turn ignition off. Check for continuity between A/C-heater control panel connector terminal "E" (White/Black wire) and ground. If continuity exists, check heater fuse. See HTR FUSE CHECK. If continuity does not exist, repair wiring between GND (ground) terminal and body ground.
HTR Fuse Check – Check HTR fuse, in fuse block No. 1, located below instrument panel. If fuse is okay, check harness and connector between A/C-heater control panel and battery. Repair harness and connector as necessary. If fuse is blown, replace fuse and check for short circuit.

IGNITOR CIRCUIT

Check tachometer operation. If tachometer does not function properly, repair or replace tachometer. If tachometer functions properly, check wiring and connectors between A/C-heater control panel terminal A13-1 (Black wire) and ignitor. Ignitor is located on left side of engine compartment. Repair wiring as necessary.

POWER TRANSISTOR CIRCUIT

Power Transistor Check – 1) Remove power transistor. See POWER TRANSISTOR under REMOVAL & INSTALLATION. Disconnect power transistor connector. Connect battery voltage to terminal No. 2. Connect battery voltage, through a 120-ohm resistor, to terminal No. 4. *See Fig. 12*.
2) Connect terminal No. 1 to ground through a 12-volt, 3.4-watt test light. If test light does not come on, replace power transistor. If test light comes on, go to next step.
3) Disconnect battery and test light. Measure resistance between terminals No. 2 and 3. If resistance is 2000-2400 ohms, transistor is okay. Go to next step. If resistance is not 2000-2400 ohms, replace power transistor.
4) Check wiring harness and connectors between A/C-heater control panel and power transistor. If wiring harness and connectors are defective, repair or replace them as necessary. If wiring harness and connectors are okay, no problem is indicated at this time.

WATER VALVE CIRCUIT

Voltage Check – 1) Remove A/C-heater control panel, leaving harness connectors attached. See A/C-HEATER CONTROL PANEL under REMOVAL & INSTALLATION. Start engine. Using DVOM, backprobe between terminal A12-3 (Black/Yellow wire) of A/C-heater control panel connector and ground. *See Fig. 4*.
2) With temperature control knob set to maximum cold position, DVOM should indicate battery voltage. With temperature control knob set to maximum heat position, DVOM should indicate less than one volt. If voltages are as specified, no problem is indicated at this time. If voltages are not as specified, go to VACUUM SWITCHING VALVE TEST.
Vacuum Switching Valve Test – 1) Disconnect Vacuum Switching Valve (VSV) connector, located next to water valve in hot coolant line to heater core. Measure resistance between valve terminals. If resistance is not 37-44 ohms at 68°F (20°C), replace vacuum switching valve.

1993 AUTOMATIC A/C-HEATER SYSTEMS SC300 & SC400 (Cont.)

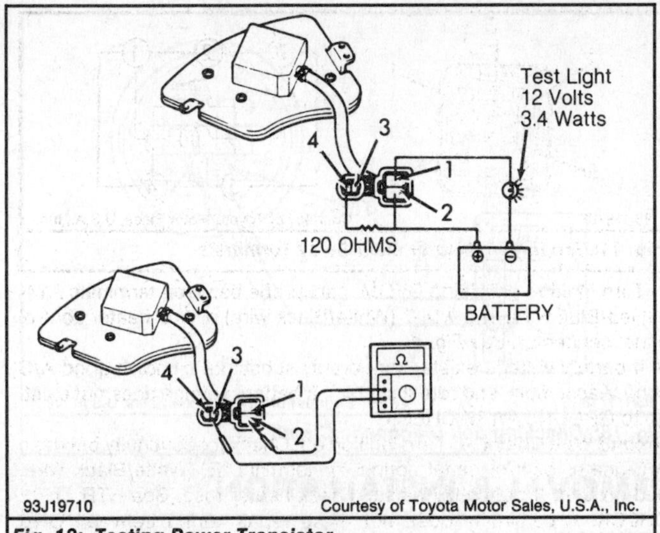

Test Light
12 Volts
3.4 Watts
4
3
1
2
120 OHMS
BATTERY
Ω
4
3
1
2

93J19710 Courtesy of Toyota Motor Sales, U.S.A., Inc.

Fig. 12: Testing Power Transistor

2) Blow through port "A" on valve. *See Fig. 13.* Air should emerge through filter. Apply battery voltage to either valve terminal. Connect remaining valve terminal to ground.

3) Blow through port "A" of valve. Air should emerge through port "B" on valve. If VSV operates as specified, go to next step. Replace VSV if it does not operate as specified.

4) Check wiring and connectors between VSV and A/C-heater control panel. Repair or replace wiring and connectors as necessary. If wiring and connectors are okay, temporarily substitute a known good A/C-heater control panel, and retest system.

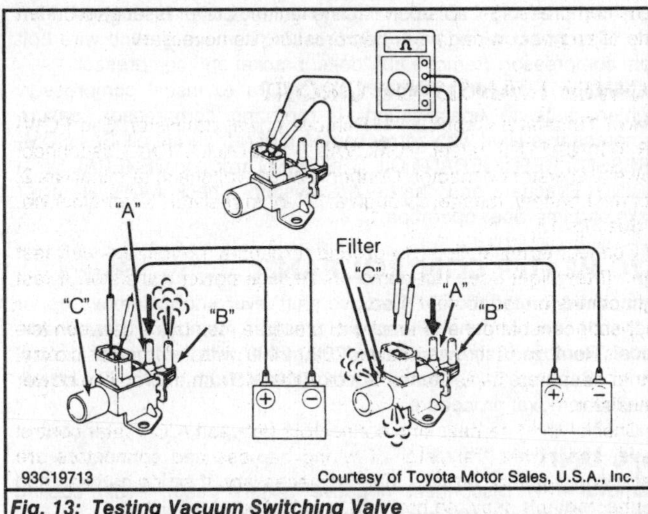

Ω
"A"
Filter
"C"
"C"
"B"
"A"
"B"

93C19713 Courtesy of Toyota Motor Sales, U.S.A., Inc.

Fig. 13: Testing Vacuum Switching Valve

TEMPERATURE CONTROL SWITCH CIRCUIT

Voltage Check – 1) Remove A/C-heater control panel, leaving harness connectors attached. See A/C-HEATER CONTROL PANEL under REMOVAL & INSTALLATION.

2) Turn ignition on. Using DVOM, backprobe between terminals A13-12 (SET1; Violet/Red wire) and A13-20 (Brown wire) of A/C-heater control panel connector and ground. *See Fig. 4.*

3) Rotate temperature control knob from full counterclockwise to full clockwise position while observing DVOM. Voltage should be as shown. *See Fig. 14.*

4) Repeat step **3)** with DVOM probe connected in turn to terminals A13-13 (SET2), A13-14 (SET3), A13-15 (SET4) and A13-16 (SET5). If voltages are as specified, no problem is indicated at this time.

5) If voltages are not as specified, turn ignition off. Disconnect connector from temperature control switch. Connect ohmmeter between terminals SET1 and SG of temperature control switch. *See Fig. 15.*

SW Position / terminal	Most Left → Most Right
SET1	0→5→0→5→0→5→0→5→0→5→0→5
SET2	0 → 5 → 0 → 5 → 0 → 5
SET3	0 → 5 → 0
SET4	5 → 0 → 5
SET5	5 → 0

93D19714 Courtesy of Toyota Motor Sales, U.S.A., Inc.

Fig. 14: Checking Temperature Control Switch Voltage

6) Rotate temperature control knob from full counterclockwise to full clockwise position while observing ohmmeter. Resistance should be as shown. *See Fig. 16.*

7) Repeat step **6)** with DVOM probe connected in turn to terminals A13-13 (SET2), A13-14 (SET3), A13-15 (SET4) and A13-16 (SET5). If resistance is as specified, go to next step. If resistance is not as specified, temporarily substitute a known good temperature control switch, and retest system.

8) Check wiring and connectors between temperature control switch and A/C-heater control panel. Repair wiring and connectors as necessary. If wiring and connectors are okay, temporarily substitute a known good A/C-heater control panel, and retest system.

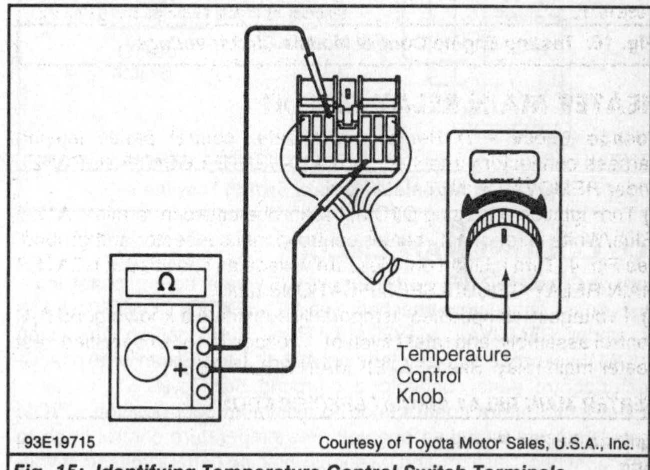

Ω
Temperature
Control
Knob

93E19715 Courtesy of Toyota Motor Sales, U.S.A., Inc.

Fig. 15: Identifying Temperature Control Switch Terminals

SW Position / terminal	Most Left → Most Right
SET1	0→∞→0→∞→0→∞→0→∞→0→∞→0→∞
SET2	0 → ∞ → 0 → ∞ → 0 → ∞
SET3	0 → ∞ → 0
SET4	∞ → 0 → ∞
SET5	∞ → 0

93F19716 Courtesy of Toyota Motor Sales, U.S.A., Inc.

Fig. 16: Checking Temperature Control Switch Resistance

AUTOMATIC CONTROL SWITCH CIRCUIT

Voltage Check – 1) Remove A/C-heater control panel, leaving harness connectors attached. See A/C-HEATER CONTROL PANEL

1993 AUTOMATIC A/C-HEATER SYSTEMS SC300 & SC400 (Cont.)

under REMOVAL & INSTALLATION. Turn ignition on. Using DVOM, backprobe between terminals A13-4 (Violet/White wire) and A13-20 (Brown wire) of A/C-heater control panel. *See Fig. 4.*

2) Press AUTO control knob. With knob pressed, voltage should be less than one volt. With knob released, voltage should be 4-6 volts. If voltage is as specified, no problem is indicated at this time. If voltage is not as specified, go to next step.

3) Turn ignition off. Disconnect connector from automatic control switch. Connect ohmmeter between terminals No. 3 (Violet/White wire) and No. 4 (Brown wire) of automatic control switch. *See Fig. 17.* With AUTO switch pressed, resistance should be less than 500 ohms. Continuity should not exist with switch released. If switch is okay, go to next step. Replace switch if resistance is not as specified.

4) Check wiring and connectors between temperature control switch and A/C-heater control panel. Repair wiring and connectors as necessary. If wiring harness and connectors are okay, temporarily substitute a known good A/C-heater control panel, and retest system.

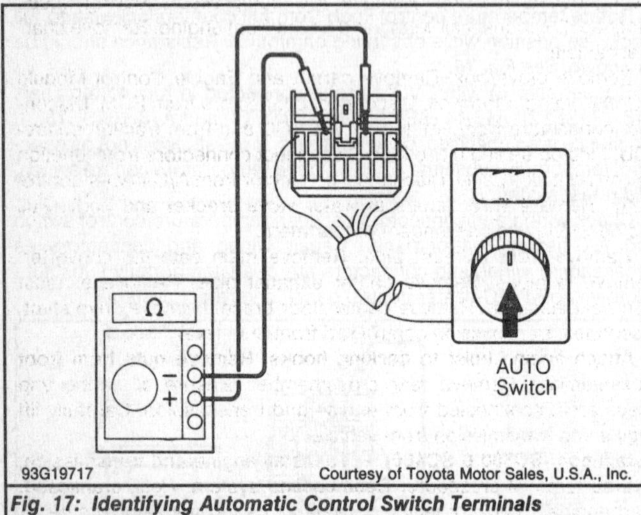
Ω
−
+
AUTO
Switch
93G19717
Courtesy of Toyota Motor Sales, U.S.A., Inc.

Fig. 17: Identifying Automatic Control Switch Terminals

ECU COOLING FAN CIRCUIT

Voltage Check (SC400) – 1) Remove A/C-heater control panel, leaving harness connectors attached. See A/C-HEATER CONTROL PANEL under REMOVAL & INSTALLATION. Turn ignition on. Using DVOM, backprobe between terminal A12-11 (Red/Green wire) of A/C-heater control panel connector and ground. *See Fig. 4.*

2) Set temperature control knob to maximum cool position. DVOM should indicate less than one volt. Set temperature control knob to maximum heat position. DVOM should indicate battery voltage. If voltage is as specified, no problem is indicated at this time. If voltage is not as specified, go to next step.

3) Turn ignition off. Disconnect connectors from A/C-heater control panel. Turn ignition on. Measure voltage between A12-11 (Red/Green wire) terminal of A/C-heater control panel connector and ground. If battery voltage does not exist, go to next step. If battery voltage exists, temporarily substitute a known good A/C-heater control panel, and retest system.

4) Check wiring and connectors between cooling fan ECU and A/C-heater control panel. Cooling fan ECU is located behind A/C-heater control panel. Repair wiring and connectors as necessary. If wiring and connectors are okay, temporarily substitute a known good cooling fan ECU, and retest system.

SELF-DIAGNOSTIC CIRCUIT

1) Turn ignition on. Measure voltage between terminals TC and E1 of diagnostic connector, located under left side of instrument panel. *See Fig. 18.* If battery voltage exists, no problem is indicated at this time. If battery voltage does not exist, go to next step.

2) Check wiring and connectors associated with A/C-heater control panel and diagnostic connector. If wiring and connectors are okay, substitute a known good A/C-heater control panel, and retest system.

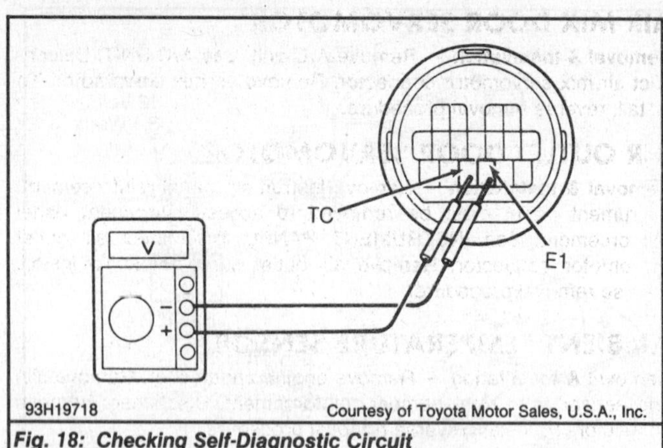
TC
V
E1
−
+
93H19718
Courtesy of Toyota Motor Sales, U.S.A., Inc.

Fig. 18: Checking Self-Diagnostic Circuit

REMOVAL & INSTALLATION

WARNING: To avoid injury from accidental air bag deployment, read and carefully follow all SERVICE PRECAUTIONS and DISABLING & ACTIVATING AIR BAG SYSTEM procedures in AIR BAG SYSTEM SAFETY article in GENERAL SERVICING.

A/C COMPRESSOR

Removal – 1) If compressor operates, idle engine with A/C system on for about 10 minutes. Turn engine off. Remove negative battery cable. Discharge A/C system using approved refrigerant recovery/recycling equipment.

2) Remove splash shield. Disconnect discharge and suction hoses from compressor. Cap open fittings immediately. Disengage drive belt. Disconnect wiring from compressor. Remove ground wire bolt from compressor. Remove nut, bolts, bracket and compressor.

Installation – Reverse removal procedure to install compressor. Tighten bolts to specification. If replacing compressor, ensure compressor is filled with correct amount of refrigerant oil. See COMPRESSOR REFRIGERANT OIL CHECKING article in GENERAL SERVICING. Evacuate and charge A/C system. Check A/C system for leaks and improper operation.

A/C-HEATER CONTROL PANEL

Removal & Installation – Remove shift lever knob. Remove upper rear shift console panel. Remove cup holder. Remove upper console panel. Remove 6 screws and radio together with A/C-heater control panel. Separate A/C-heater control panel from radio. To install, reverse removal procedure.

A/C UNIT

Removal – 1) Disconnect negative battery cable. Drain cooling system. Discharge A/C system using approved refrigerant recovery/recycling equipment. Remove engine. See ENGINE. Remove water valve. See WATER VALVE. Remove brake tube bracket bolts from firewall. Remove evaporator. See EVAPORATOR.

2) Disconnect hoses from heater core fittings. Remove insulator retainer. Remove instrument panel reinforcement. See INSTRUMENT PANEL. Remove carpet. Remove air ducts. Remove connector bracket. Disconnect electrical connectors from A/C unit. Remove A/C unit.

Installation – Pull drain hose forward until painted line on hose is visible in engine compartment. Insert drain hose until match marks align. To complete installation, reverse removal procedure. Evacuate and recharge A/C system. Refill cooling system.

AIR INLET DOOR SERVOMOTOR

Removal & Installation – Remove instrument panel reinforcement. Instrument panel must be removed to access instrument panel reinforcement. See INSTRUMENT PANEL. Disconnect air inlet servomotor connector. Remove control link. Remove air inlet servomotor. To install, reverse removal procedure.

AIR MIX DOOR SERVOMOTOR

Removal & Installation - Remove A/C unit. See A/C UNIT. Disconnect air mix servomotor connector. Remove air mix servomotor. To install, reverse removal procedure.

AIR OUTLET DOOR SERVOMOTOR

Removal & Installation - Remove instrument panel reinforcement. Instrument panel must be removed to access instrument panel reinforcement. See INSTRUMENT PANEL. Disconnect air outlet servomotor connector. Remove air outlet servomotor. To install, reverse removal procedure.

AMBIENT TEMPERATURE SENSOR

Removal & Installation - Remove engine undercover. Remove clip and sensor from right bumper reinforcement. Disconnect harness connector. To install, reverse removal procedure.

BLOWER MOTOR

Removal & Installation - Remove glove box. Lift carpet from passenger footwell. Remove Engine Control Module (ECM) cover. Remove connector bracket. Disconnect wiring connector. Remove screws and blower motor. To install, reverse removal procedure.

BLOWER RESISTOR

Removal & Installation - Remove glove box. Disconnect resistor connector. *See Fig. 1.* Remove screws and blower resistor. To install, reverse removal procedure.

CONDENSER

Removal - Discharge A/C system using approved refrigerant recovery/recycling equipment. Remove battery. Remove covers from above and below condenser. Disconnect refrigerant lines from condenser. Remove suction tube. Cap open fittings immediately. Remove nuts and condenser.

Installation - To install, reverse removal procedure. If replacing condenser, add 1.4-1.7 ounces of compressor oil. Evacuate and charge A/C system. Check A/C system for leaks and improper operation.

ENGINE

Removal (SC300) - **1)** Remove battery. Disable air bag system. See AIR BAG SYSTEM SAFETY article in GENERAL SERVICING. Remove splash shield. Drain cooling system. Disconnect control cables from throttle body. Remove air cleaner.

2) Remove drive belt. Remove fan and fan coupling as an assembly. Remove radiator. Remove charcoal canister. Remove power steering pump, leaving hoses attached. Remove A/C compressor, leaving hoses attached. Disconnect all wiring and hoses from engine. Remove shift lever (M/T models).

3) Remove undercover from right side of instrument panel. Remove glove box. Remove carpet and Engine Control Module (ECM) from right footwell. Disconnect connectors from ECM. Disconnect connectors from anti-lock brake ECU and traction control ECU, located behind glove box. Disconnect connectors from junction box on right kick panel. Pull engine wiring into passenger compartment.

4) Separate power steering lines from bracket on engine. Wrap shop towel around fuel inlet hose in area of starter. Loosen fitting slowly to bleed pressure. Disconnect fuel line. Suspend hose with fitting upward. Disconnect wiring from starter. Disconnect ground wire at transmission.

5) On M/T models, separate clutch slave cylinder from transmission. On all models, remove front exhaust pipe. Remove exhaust pipe heat shield. On A/T models, disconnect transmission control rod from shift lever.

6) On all models, mark drive shaft flanges for installation reference. Remove intermediate drive shaft. Attach engine hoist to decking hooks. Remove engine mount nuts from studs which extend below front crossmember. Remove rear crossmember. Ensure all wiring and hoses are disconnected from engine. Carefully lift engine and transmission from vehicle.

Removal (SC400) - **1)** Remove battery. Disable air bag system. See AIR BAG SYSTEM SAFETY article in GENERAL SERVICING. Remove splash shield. Drain cooling system. Drain engine oil. Remove throttle body cover. Disconnect control cables from throttle body. Remove hood.

2) Wrap shop towel around fuel inlet hose in area of starter. Loosen fitting slowly to bleed pressure. Disconnect fuel line. Remove drive belt. Remove air cleaner and airflow meter. Disconnect hose from power steering air control valve. Disconnect hose from air intake chamber. Disconnect hoses from air intake connector. Remove air intake connector.

3) Remove coolant reservoir. Disconnect coolant and oil cooler hoses from radiator. Remove radiator. Disconnect connectors from ignitor. Disconnect connectors from engine. Disconnect connectors from anti-theft horn and power steering solenoid valve. Remove alternator.

4) Disengage power steering lines from front crossmember. Remove power steering reservoir and bracket. Remove power steering pump, leaving hoses attached. Remove A/C compressor, leaving hoses attached. Disconnect all wiring and hoses from engine. Remove charcoal canister.

5) Remove glove box. Remove carpet and Engine Control Module (ECM) from right footwell. Disconnect connectors from ECM. Disconnect connectors from anti-lock brake ECU and from traction control ECU, located behind glove box. Disconnect connectors from junction box on right kick panel. Disconnect connector from A/C-heater control panel. Remove wire clamps at water valve bracket and body. Pull engine wiring into passenger compartment.

6) Remove front exhaust pipe. Remove main catalytic converter. Remove tailpipes. Remove center exhaust pipe. Remove exhaust pipe heat insulator. Remove center floor brace. Remove drive shaft. Disconnect transmission control rod from shift lever.

7) Attach engine hoist to decking hooks. Remove nuts from front crossmember. Remove rear crossmember. Ensure all wiring and hoses are disconnected from engine and transmission. Carefully lift engine and transmission from vehicle.

Installation (SC300 & SC400) - To install engine and transmission, reverse removal procedure. Refill cooling system. Refill crankcase. Start engine. Check for leaks. Activate air bag system and ensure air bag system is functioning properly. See AIR BAG SYSTEM SAFETY article in GENERAL SERVICING.

EVAPORATOR

Removal - **1)** Disconnect negative battery cable. Discharge A/C system using approved refrigerant recovery/recycling equipment. Remove anti-lock brake (ABS) actuator. Disconnect liquid and suction tubes. Cap open fittings immediately. Disconnect equalizer tube.

2) Remove undercover from right side of instrument panel. Remove power steering relay box, cooling fan Electronic Control Unit (ECU) and traction control ECU. Lift carpet from passenger footwell. Remove evaporator cover. Remove air duct bolt. Remove evaporator housing and evaporator.

Installation - Reverse removal procedure. If replacing evaporator, add 1.4-1.7 ounces of compressor oil. Evacuate and charge A/C system. Check A/C system for leaks and improper operation.

EVAPORATOR TEMPERATURE SENSOR

Removal & Installation - Remove evaporator. See EVAPORATOR. Disconnect sensor connector. Remove evaporator temperature sensor. To install, reverse removal procedure.

HEATER CORE

Removal & Installation - Disconnect negative battery cable. Set temperature control knob to maximum cool position. Drain engine coolant. Remove A/C unit. See A/C UNIT. Remove heater core. To install, reverse removal procedure. Refill cooling system. Check for leaks.

IN-VEHICLE TEMPERATURE SENSOR

Removal & Installation - Remove undercover from left side of instrument panel. Disconnect sensor connector. Remove screw and in-vehicle temperature sensor. To install, reverse removal procedure.

1993 AUTOMATIC A/C-HEATER SYSTEMS SC300 & SC400 (Cont.)

INSTRUMENT PANEL

Removal & Installation – **1)** Turn ignition off. Disconnect negative battery cable. Disable air bag system. See AIR BAG SYSTEM SAFETY article in GENERAL SERVICING. Remove front assist grips, front pillar garnishes and front door scuff plates. *See Fig. 19.* Remove steering column covers. Remove shift lever knob. Open ashtray lid.

2) Lift front of console panel. Pull console panel upward and towards instrument panel, and remove console panel. Remove cup holder. Remove upper console panel. Remove radio with A/C-heater control panel. Remove passenger-side undercover. Remove glove box. Remove passenger-side air bag module.

3) Remove driver-side undercover. Remove console box. Remove center and end pads. Remove engine hood release lever. Disconnect release cable from lever. Remove knee bolster. Remove left and right finish panels. Remove No. 2 and 4 heater-to-register ducts. Remove combination switch.

4) Remove instrument cluster finish panel. Remove instrument cluster. Remove steering column assembly. Ensure all connectors necessary for removal of instrument panel are disconnected.

5) Remove 2 bolts and 2 nuts from instrument panel. Carefully pull instrument panel rearward and remove instrument panel from vehicle. Remove No. 3 heater-to-register duct. Remove all instrument panel reinforcement mounting bolts/nuts and remove panel reinforcement.

6) To install, reverse removal procedure. Activate air bag system and ensure air bag system is functioning properly. See AIR BAG SYSTEM SAFETY article in GENERAL SERVICING.

POWER TRANSISTOR

Removal & Installation – Remove glove box. Remove screws and power transistor. To install, reverse removal procedure.

PRESSURE SWITCH

Removal & Installation – Discharge A/C system using approved refrigerant recovery/recycling equipment. Disconnect pressure switch connector, located in liquid line at right side of engine compartment. Remove pressure switch. To install pressure switch, reverse removal procedure. Evacuate and charge A/C system. Check A/C system for leaks and improper operation.

RECEIVER-DRIER

Removal – Remove left headlight. Discharge A/C system using approved refrigerant recovery/recycling equipment. Disconnect tubes from receiver-drier. Remove receiver-drier.

Installation – To install, reverse removal procedure. If replacing receiver-drier, add 0.7 ounce of compressor oil. Evacuate and charge A/C system. Check A/C system for leaks and improper operation. Install headlight.

SOLAR SENSOR

Removal & Installation – Remove defroster trim molding. Disconnect solar sensor harness connector. Push out solar sensor from rear defroster trim molding. To install, reverse removal procedure.

WATER TEMPERATURE SENSOR

Removal & Installation – Remove A/C unit. See A/C UNIT. Remove clamp and water temperature sensor. To install sensor, reverse removal procedure.

WATER VALVE

Removal & Installation – Drain cooling system. Disconnect coolant hoses and vacuum hose. Disconnect electrical connector. Remove water valve. To install water valve, reverse removal procedure. Refill cooling system. Check for leaks.

TORQUE SPECIFICATIONS

TORQUE SPECIFICATIONS

Application	Ft. Lbs. (N.m)
A/C Compressor	
Bolt	36 (49)
Nut	21 (29)
A/C Compressor Bracket Bolt	36 (49)
Drive Shaft Flange Nut	
SC300	55 (74)
SC400	69 (93)
Front Engine Mount Stud	44 (59)
Rear Crossmember	
Bolt	18 (25)
Nut	10 (14)
Refrigerant Lines	
Compressor Discharge Tube	18 (25)
Compressor Suction Tube	18 (25)
Tube-To-Tube Fittings	
8-mm Diameter	10 (14)
13-mm Diameter	17 (23)
16-mm Diameter	24 (32)
	INCH Lbs. (N.m)
Cooling Unit Fittings	88 (10.0)
Condenser Fittings	88 (10.0)
Receiver-Drier Fittings	48 (5.4)

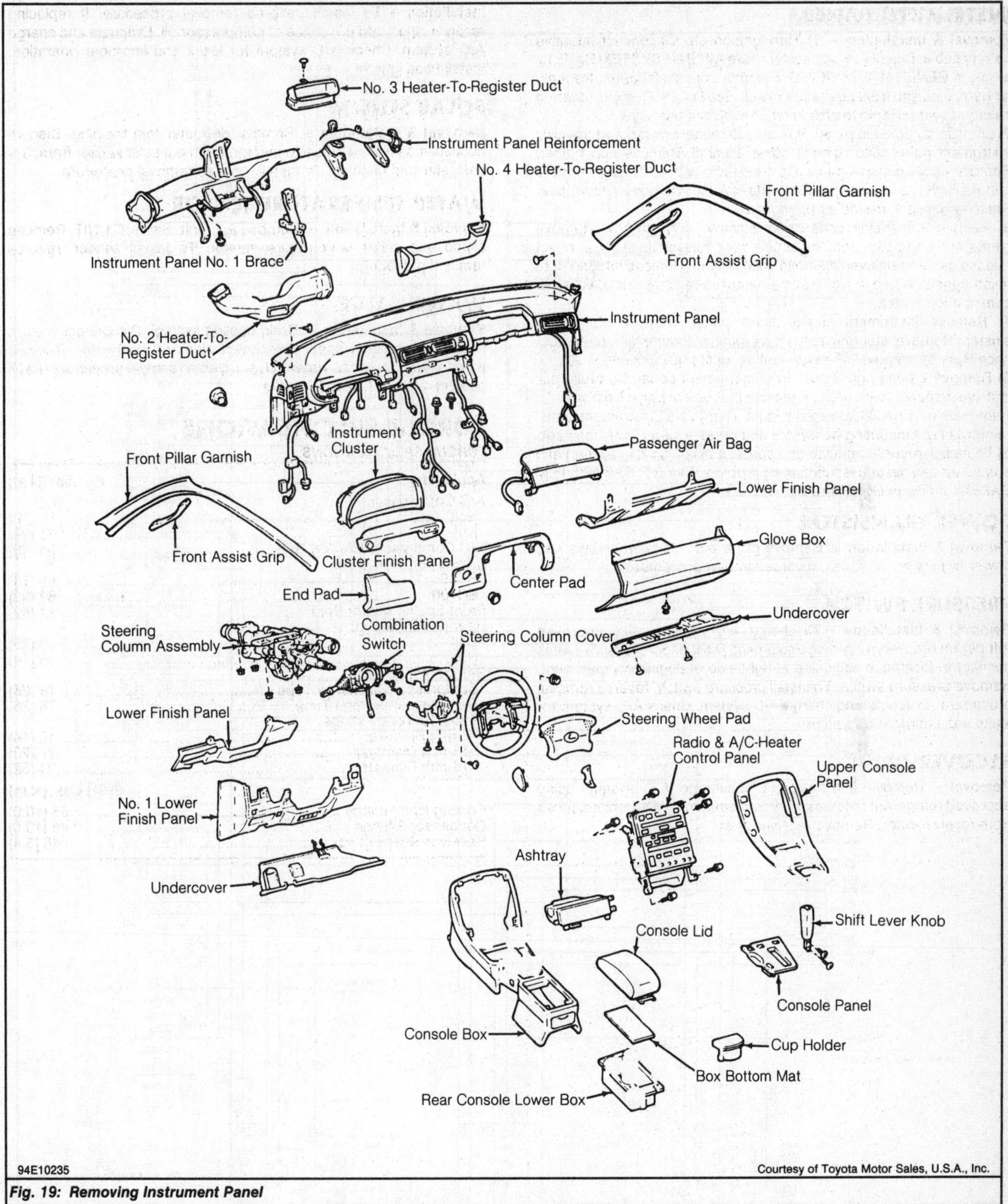
No. 3 Heater-To-Register Duct
Instrument Panel Reinforcement
No. 4 Heater-To-Register Duct
Front Pillar Garnish
Front Assist Grip
Instrument Panel No. 1 Brace
No. 2 Heater-To-Register Duct
Instrument Panel
Instrument Cluster
Passenger Air Bag
Front Pillar Garnish
Lower Finish Panel
Front Assist Grip
Cluster Finish Panel
Glove Box
Center Pad
End Pad
Undercover
Steering Column Assembly
Combination Switch
Steering Column Cover
Lower Finish Panel
Steering Wheel Pad
Radio & A/C-Heater Control Panel
Upper Console Panel
No. 1 Lower Finish Panel
Ashtray
Undercover
Shift Lever Knob
Console Lid
Console Panel
Console Box
Cup Holder
Box Bottom Mat
Rear Console Lower Box
94E10235
Courtesy of Toyota Motor Sales, U.S.A., Inc.

Fig. 19: Removing Instrument Panel

1993 AUTOMATIC A/C-HEATER SYSTEMS SC300 & SC400 (Cont.)

WIRING DIAGRAM

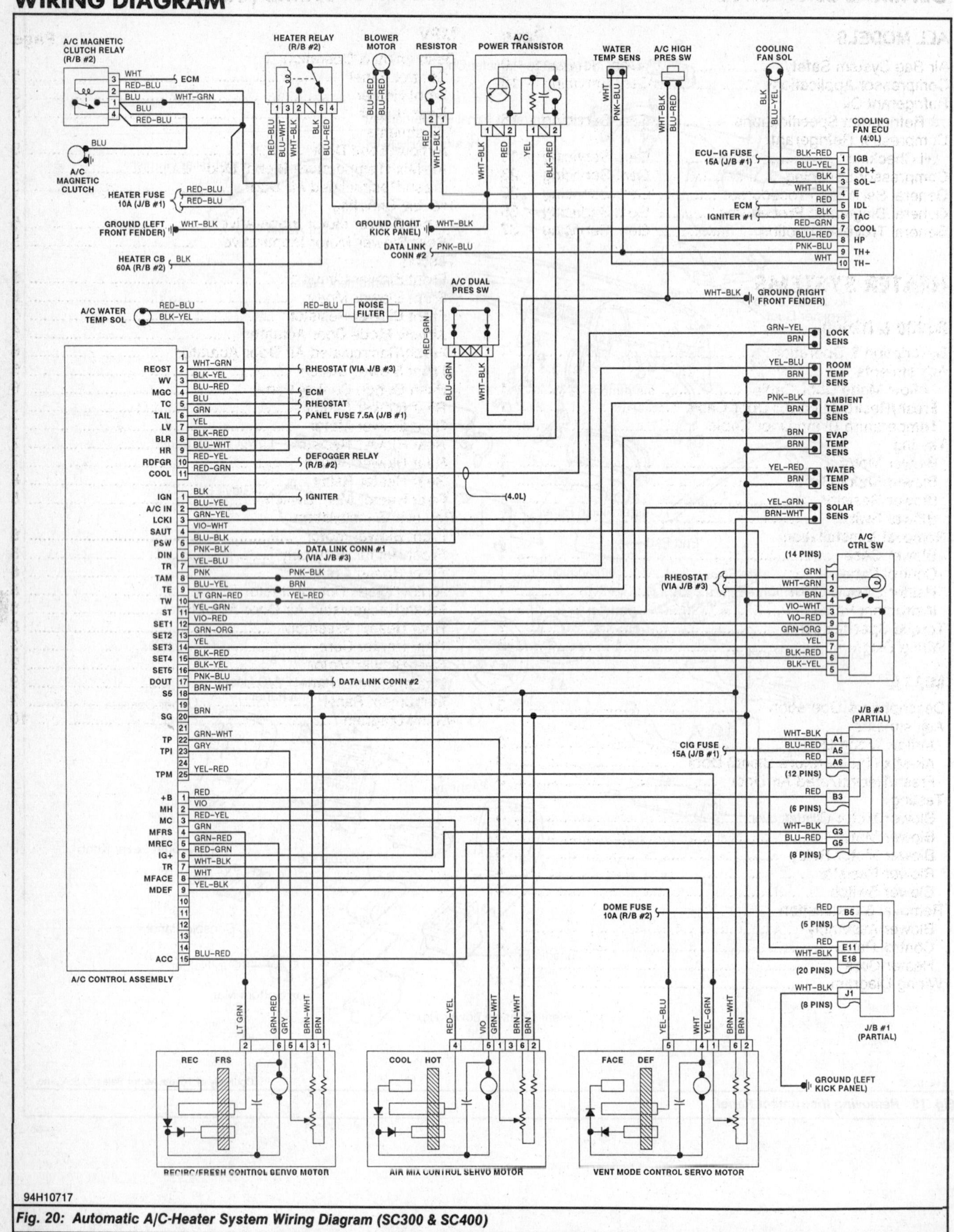
A/C MAGNETIC CLUTCH RELAY (R/B #2)
HEATER RELAY (R/B #2)
BLOWER MOTOR
A/C RESISTOR
A/C POWER TRANSISTOR
WATER TEMP SENS
A/C HIGH PRES SW
COOLING FAN SOL
COOLING FAN ECU (4.0L)
A/C MAGNETIC CLUTCH
HEATER FUSE 10A (J/B #1)
GROUND (LEFT FRONT FENDER)
GROUND (RIGHT KICK PANEL)
DATA LINK CONN #2
ECU-IG FUSE 15A (J/B #1)
ECM
IGNITER #1
HEATER CB 60A (R/B #2)
A/C DUAL PRES SW
NOISE FILTER
GROUND (RIGHT FRONT FENDER)
A/C WATER TEMP SOL
LOCK SENS
ROOM TEMP SENS
AMBIENT TEMP SENS
EVAP TEMP SENS
WATER TEMP SENS
SOLAR SENS
RHEOSTAT (VIA J/B #3)
ECM
RHEOSTAT
PANEL FUSE 7.5A (J/B #1)
DEFOGGER RELAY (R/B #2)
IGNITER
(4.0L)
DATA LINK CONN #1 (VIA J/B #3)
DATA LINK CONN #2
A/C CTRL SW
(14 PINS)
J/B #3 (PARTIAL)
CIG FUSE 15A (J/B #1)
(12 PINS)
(6 PINS)
(8 PINS)
DOME FUSE 10A (R/B #2)
(5 PINS)
(20 PINS)
(8 PINS)
J/B #1 (PARTIAL)
GROUND (LEFT KICK PANEL)
A/C CONTROL ASSEMBLY
REC FRS
COOL HOT
FACE DEF
RECIRC/FRESH CONTROL SERVO MOTOR
AIR MIX CONTROL SERVO MOTOR
VENT MODE CONTROL SERVO MOTOR
94H10717

Fig. 20: Automatic A/C-Heater System Wiring Diagram (SC300 & SC400)

1993 MAZDA CONTENTS

GENERAL SERVICING

HEATER SYSTEMS

HEATER SYSTEMS (Cont.)

1993 MAZDA CONTENTS (Cont.)

HEATER SYSTEMS (Cont.)

MX-3, PROTEGE & 323

MX-6 & 626

NAVAJO

MANUAL A/C-HEATER SYSTEMS

B2200 & B2600i

MIATA

1993 MAZDA CONTENTS (Cont.)

MANUAL A/C-HEATER SYSTEMS (Cont.)

MANUAL A/C-HEATER SYSTEMS (Cont.)

1993 MAZDA CONTENTS (Cont.)

MANUAL A/C-HEATER SYSTEMS (Cont.)

RX7

AUTOMATIC A/C-HEATER SYSTEMS

929

1993 HEATER SYSTEMS
B2200 & B2600i

DESCRIPTION & OPERATION

Heater case, mounted under center of instrument panel, contains airflow mode door and temperature blend (air-mix) door. *See Fig. 3.* Blower case, mounted under right end of instrument panel, contains fresh/recirculated air door. All doors are controlled manually by cables connected to control panel.

ADJUSTMENTS

AIRFLOW MODE DOOR CABLE

Set airflow mode control lever to defrost position. Disconnect cable housing from clip on heater case. Push door lever on heater case fully downward (in cable-extended direction). Reconnect cable housing to clip. Ensure airflow mode control lever moves between defrost and vent positions.

FRESH/RECIRCULATED AIR DOOR CABLE

Set fresh/recirculated air control lever to recirculated position. Disconnect cable housing from clip on blower case. Push fresh/recirculated air door lever on blower case fully forward (in cable-retracted direction). Reconnect cable housing to clip. Ensure fresh/recirculated air control lever moves fully between fresh and recirculated air positions.

TEMPERATURE BLEND DOOR CABLE

Set temperature blend control lever to cold position. Disconnect cable housing from clip on heater case. Push temperature blend door lever on heater case fully upward (in cable-retracted direction). Reconnect cable housing to clip. Ensure temperature blend control lever moves fully between cold and hot positions.

TESTING

BLOWER MOTOR

Remove glove box. Remove electronic control unit. Disconnect blower motor connector from bottom of blower motor. Apply battery voltage across blower motor terminals. Replace blower motor if it does not operate.

BLOWER MOTOR CIRCUIT

NOTE: Leave all connectors attached during blower motor circuit test and backprobe terminals.

1) Check 30-amp HEATER circuit breaker in passenger compartment fuse block. If Red reset button has popped out, repair shorted circuit and reset circuit breaker. If Red reset button has not popped out, turn ignition on.
2) Turn blower switch to highest speed. Check voltage at Blue wire terminal of blower motor connector. If no voltage is present, repair circuit between circuit breaker and blower motor.
3) If battery voltage is present at Blue wire, check voltage at Blue/White wire terminal of blower motor connector. If no voltage is present, replace blower motor. If battery voltage is present, turn off blower switch and A/C switch (if equipped).
4) Turn ignition on. Check voltage at Blue/White, Blue/Black, Blue/Red, Blue and Blue/Yellow wire terminals of blower resistor connector. If battery voltage is present at all terminals, go to next step. If battery voltage is not present at Blue/White wire terminal, repair circuit between blower motor and resistor. If battery voltage is not present at any other terminals, replace blower resistor.
5) Turn ignition on. Turn blower switch to highest speed. Check voltage at Black wire terminal of blower switch connector. If battery voltage is present, repair circuit between blower switch and ground. If no voltage is present, turn off blower switch and A/C switch (if equipped).
6) Turn ignition on. Check voltage at Blue/Black, Blue/Red, Blue and Blue/Yellow wire terminals of blower resistor connector. If battery voltage is present at all terminals, replace blower switch. If voltage is not present at one or more terminals, repair circuit between blower resistor and blower switch.

BLOWER RESISTOR

Remove glove box. Remove resistor from blower case. Using an ohmmeter set at 1000-ohm scale, check continuity between resistor terminals "A" through "E". *See Fig. 1.* If continuity does not exist between any combination of these terminals, replace blower resistor.

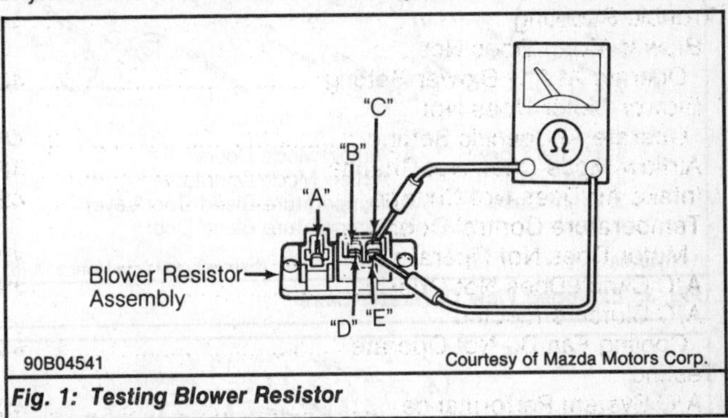
"C"
"B"
"A"
Blower Resistor
Assembly
"D" "E"
90B04541
Courtesy of Mazda Motors Corp.

Fig. 1: Testing Blower Resistor

BLOWER SWITCH

Using an ohmmeter, check continuity between terminal "A" and remaining terminals. *See Fig. 2.* Replace switch if continuity is not present.

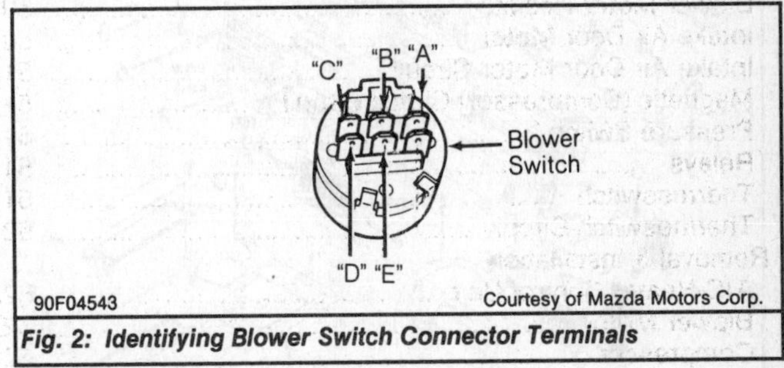
"C"
"B" "A"
Blower
Switch
"D" "E"
90F04543
Courtesy of Mazda Motors Corp.

Fig. 2: Identifying Blower Switch Connector Terminals

REMOVAL & INSTALLATION

BLOWER CASE

Removal & Installation – Remove glove box. Remove electronic control unit from blower case. Disconnect blower motor and blower resistor connectors. Loosen seal plate between blower case and heater case. Remove blower case nuts and blower case. To install, reverse removal procedure.

CONTROL PANEL

Removal & Installation – 1) Remove instrument cluster hood. Pull knobs from blower motor switch. Remove nuts and washers from shafts. Remove hole cover from center panel. *See Fig. 4.* Remove screw from hole. Disconnect connectors from cigarette lighter. Remove center panel of instrument panel.
2) Remove glove box. Disconnect control cables from back of control panel. Remove control panel screws. Pull control panel out and disconnect electrical connectors. To install, reverse removal procedure. Adjust control cables. See ADJUSTMENTS.

HEATER CASE & CORE

Removal & Installation – 1) Drain coolant. Disconnect heater hoses from heater core at engine compartment firewall. Remove firewall grommet. Remove instrument panel. See INSTRUMENT PANEL.
2) Remove nuts and remove heater case. Disassemble heater case to remove heater core. *See Fig. 3.* To install, reverse removal procedure.

1993 HEATER SYSTEMS
B2200 & B2600i (Cont.)

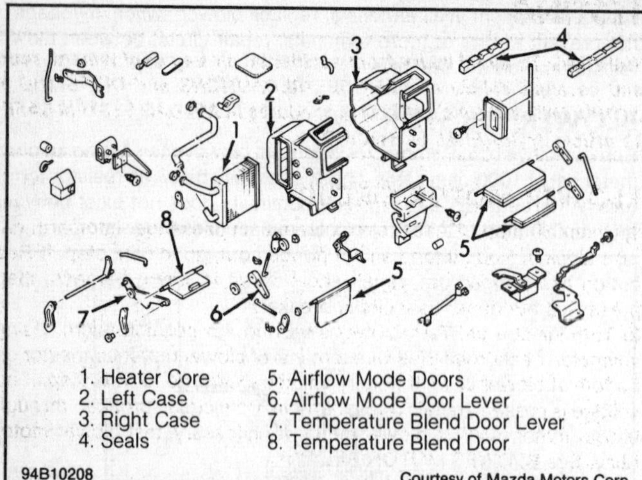
1. Heater Core
2. Left Case
3. Right Case
4. Seals
5. Airflow Mode Doors
6. Airflow Mode Door Lever
7. Temperature Blend Door Lever
8. Temperature Blend Door
94B10208
Courtesy of Mazda Motors Corp.

Fig. 3: Exploded View Of Heater Case

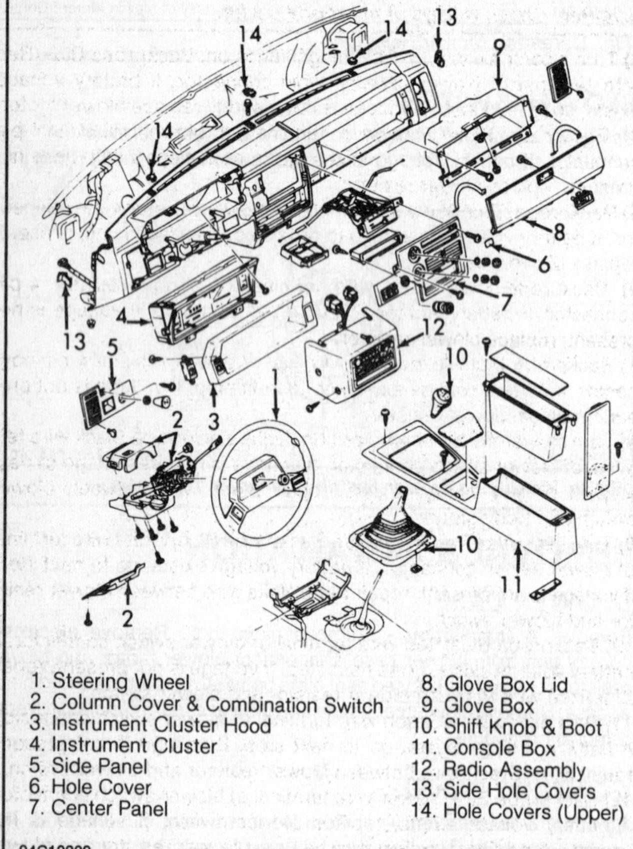
1. Steering Wheel
2. Column Cover & Combination Switch
3. Instrument Cluster Hood
4. Instrument Cluster
5. Side Panel
6. Hole Cover
7. Center Panel
8. Glove Box Lid
9. Glove Box
10. Shift Knob & Boot
11. Console Box
12. Radio Assembly
13. Side Hole Covers
14. Hole Covers (Upper)
94C10209
Courtesy of Mazda Motors Corp.

Fig. 4: Exploded View Of Instrument Panel

INSTRUMENT PANEL

Removal & Installation – Disconnect negative battery cable. Remove instrument panel components in order listed in illustration. *See Fig. 4.* To install, reverse removal procedure.

TORQUE SPECIFICATIONS

TORQUE SPECIFICATIONS

Application	INCH Lbs. (N.m)
Blower Motor Nuts	69-97 (7.8-11)
Instrument Panel Bolts/Nuts	69-97 (7.8-11)
Seal Plate Nuts	69-97 (7.8-11)

WIRING DIAGRAM

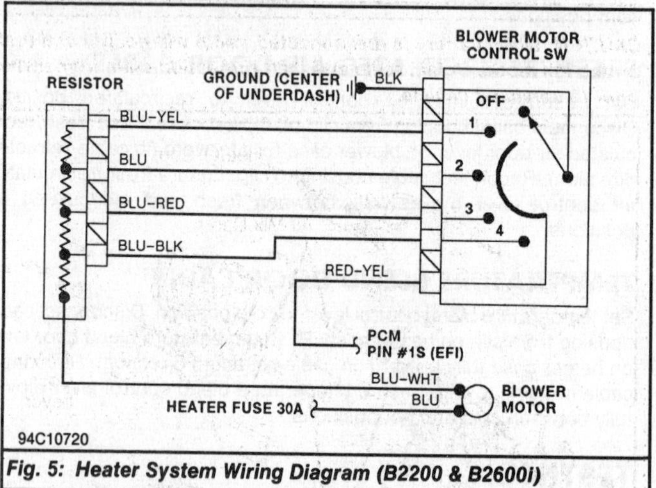
BLOWER MOTOR CONTROL SW
RESISTOR
GROUND (CENTER OF UNDERDASH)
BLK
OFF
1
2
3
4
BLU-YEL
BLU
BLU-RED
BLU-BLK
RED-YEL
PCM PIN #1S (EFI)
BLU-WHT
BLU
BLOWER MOTOR
HEATER FUSE 30A
94C10720

Fig. 5: Heater System Wiring Diagram (B2200 & B2600i)

1993 HEATER SYSTEMS
Miata

DESCRIPTION & OPERATION

Heater case, mounted under center of instrument panel, contains airflow mode doors and air-mix (temperature blend) doors. *See Fig. 1.* Blower case, mounted under right side of instrument panel, contains blower motor, blower resistor and fresh/recirculated air door. All doors are controlled manually from control panel by cable.

Blower motor relay, located in left rear corner of engine compartment (on relay cluster), supplies power to blower motor. Blower resistors, located on bottom of blower case, determine blower speed.

WARNING: To avoid injury from accidental air bag deployment, read and carefully follow all SERVICE PRECAUTIONS and DISABLING & ACTIVATING AIR BAG SYSTEM procedures in AIR BAG SYSTEM SAFETY article in GENERAL SERVICING.

CAUTION: When battery is disconnected, radio will go into anti-theft protection mode. Obtain radio anti-theft protection code from owner prior to servicing vehicle.

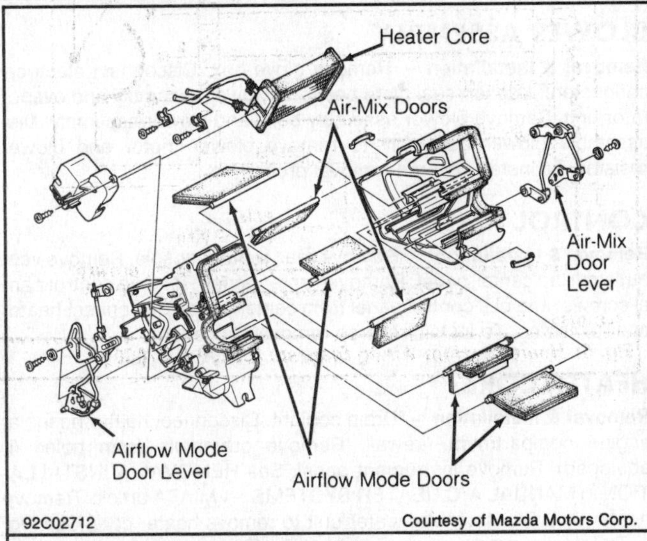
Heater Core
Air-Mix Doors
Air-Mix
Door
Lever
Airflow Mode
Door Lever
Airflow Mode Doors
92C02712
Courtesy of Mazda Motors Corp.

Fig. 1: Exploded View Of Heater Unit

ADJUSTMENTS

AIRFLOW MODE DOOR

Set airflow mode control lever at vent position. Disconnect control cable at airflow mode door lever. *See Fig. 1.* Extend airflow mode door lever until it stops. Attach control cable to door lever. Secure cable using clip. Ensure control lever slides freely between defrost and vent positions.

AIR-MIX (TEMPERATURE BLEND) DOOR

Set temperature control lever at maximum hot setting. Disconnect control cable at air-mix door lever. *See Fig. 1.* Extend air-mix door lever until it stops. Attach control cable to door lever. Secure cable using clip. Ensure control lever slides freely between hot and cold settings.

FRESH/RECIRCULATED AIR DOOR

Set fresh/recirculated air control lever at fresh air setting. Disconnect control cable at fresh/recirculated air door lever. Retract recirculated/fresh air door lever until it stops. Attach control cable to door lever. Secure cable using clip. Ensure control lever slides freely between recirculated air and fresh air settings.

TESTING

WARNING: To avoid injury from accidental air bag deployment, read and carefully follow all SERVICE PRECAUTIONS and DISABLING & ACTIVATING AIR BAG SYSTEM procedures in AIR BAG SYSTEM SAFETY article in GENERAL SERVICING.

BLOWER MOTOR CIRCUIT

1) Check 30-amp HEATER circuit breaker in passenger compartment fuse block. If Red button has not popped out, go to next step. If Red button has popped out, repair short circuit in wiring harness, then press Red button to reset circuit breaker.
2) Turn ignition on. Turn blower switch to 4th position (high). Using voltmeter, backprobe Blue wire terminal of blower motor connector on bottom of blower case. If battery voltage exists, go to next step. If no voltage is present, repair wiring harness from circuit breaker, through blower motor relay, to blower motor. If necessary, test blower motor relay. See BLOWER MOTOR RELAY.

NOTE: Blower resistor uses 1-pin and 4-pin connectors. Wire in 1-pin connector is Blue/Red, and one of the wires in 4-pin connector is also Blue/Red. Check voltage at appropriate wire.

3) Turn blower switch off. Ensure ignition is on. Backprobe Blue/Red wire terminal of blower resistor 1-pin connector. If battery voltage exists, go to next step. If voltage is not present, replace blower motor.
4) Backprobe Blue/White wire terminal of blower resistor 4-pin connector. If battery voltage exists, go to next step. If voltage is not present, replace blower resistor.
5) Backprobe Blue/Red wire terminal of blower resistor 4-pin connector. If battery voltage exists, go to next step. If voltage is not present, replace blower resistor.
6) Backprobe Blue/Green wire terminal of blower resistor 4-pin connector. If battery voltage exists, go to next step. If voltage is not present, replace blower resistor.
7) Backprobe Blue/Yellow wire terminal of blower resistor 4-pin connector. If battery voltage exists, go to next step. If voltage is not present, replace blower resistor.
8) Turn blower switch to 4th position (high). Backprobe Black wire terminal of blower switch connector. If voltage is not present, go to next step. If battery voltage exists, repair Black wire between blower switch and body ground.
9) Turn ignition blower switch off. Backprobe Blue/White wire terminal of blower switch connector. If battery voltage exists, go to next step. If voltage is not present, repair Blue/White wire between blower resistor and blower switch.
10) Backprobe Blue/Red wire terminal of blower switch connector. If battery voltage exists, go to next step. If voltage is not present, repair Blue/Red wire between blower resistor and blower switch.
11) Backprobe Blue/Green wire terminal of blower switch connector. If battery voltage exists, go to next step. If voltage is not present, repair Blue/Green wire between blower resistor and blower switch.
12) Backprobe Blue/Yellow wire terminal of blower switch connector. If battery voltage exists, replace blower switch. If voltage is not present, repair Blue/Yellow wire between blower resistor and blower switch.

BLOWER MOTOR

Disconnect blower motor 2-pin connector from bottom of blower case. Apply battery voltage across blower motor terminals. Replace blower motor if it does not operate.

BLOWER MOTOR RELAY

1) Disconnect blower motor relay connector. Using ohmmeter, check continuity between relay terminals "A" (Blue/White wire) and "B" (Blue wire). *See Fig. 2.* Continuity should not exist.

1993 HEATER SYSTEMS
Miata (Cont.)

2) Check continuity between relay terminals "C" (Blue wire) and "D" (Black/Red wire). Ensure continuity exists. Apply battery voltage between terminals "C" and "D". Ensure continuity exists between terminals "A" and "B" with battery voltage applied. Replace relay if continuity is not as specified.

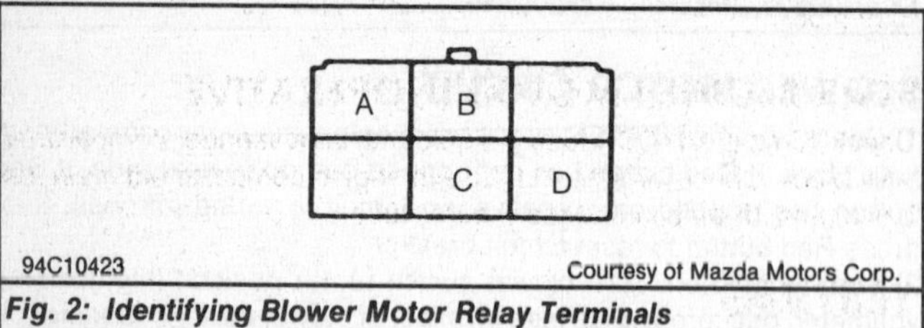
A
B
C
D
94C10423
Courtesy of Mazda Motors Corp.

Fig. 2: Identifying Blower Motor Relay Terminals

BLOWER RESISTOR

Disconnect blower resistor connectors from blower case. Check continuity, in turn, between Blue/Red wire terminal of 1-pin connector and each terminal of 4-pin connector. Ensure continuity exists. Replace resistor if continuity does not exist.

BLOWER SWITCH

Disconnect blower switch connector. Place blower switch in indicated positions, and check continuity between specified blower switch terminals. See BLOWER SWITCH TEST table. *See Fig. 4*. If continuity is not as specified, replace blower switch.

BLOWER SWITCH TEST

Switch Position	Continuity Between Terminals
Off	[1]
Low	"A" & "G"
Medium-Low	"C", "G" & "H"
Medium-High	"E", "G" & "H"
High	"B", "G" & "H"

[1] – There should not be continuity between any terminals.

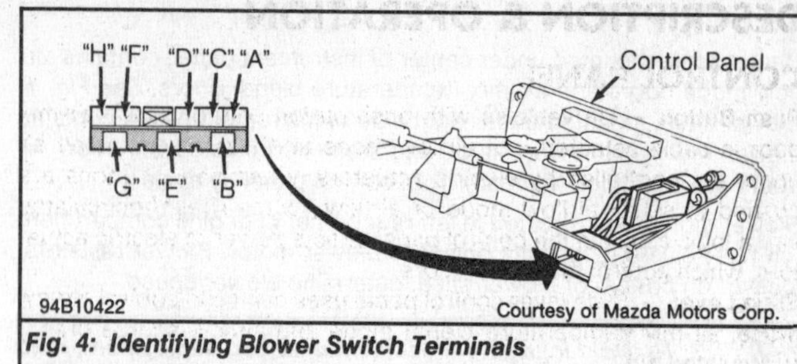
"H" "F" "D" "C" "A"
Control Panel
"G" "E" "B"
94B10422
Courtesy of Mazda Motors Corp.

Fig. 4: Identifying Blower Switch Terminals

REMOVAL & INSTALLATION

WARNING: To avoid injury from accidental air bag deployment, read and carefully follow all SERVICE PRECAUTIONS and DISABLING & ACTIVATING AIR BAG SYSTEM procedures in AIR BAG SYSTEM SAFETY article in GENERAL SERVICING.

BLOWER ASSEMBLY

Removal & Installation – Remove glove box. Disconnect electrical connectors. Loosen seal plate between blower assembly and evaporator unit. Remove blower assembly bolts and blower assembly. Disassemble blower assembly to remove blower motor and blower resistor. To install, reverse removal procedure.

CONTROL PANEL

Removal & Installation – Remove rear center console. Remove vent outlets from center panel. Remove center panel. Remove control panel screws, and pull control panel from center panel. Disconnect heater control cables. To install, reverse removal procedure.

HEATER CORE

Removal & Installation – Drain coolant. Disconnect heater hoses at engine compartment firewall. Remove grommets from holes (if equipped). Remove instrument panel. See REMOVAL & INSTALLATION in MANUAL A/C HEATER SYSTEMS – MIATA article. Remove heater unit. Disassemble heater unit to remove heater core. *See Fig. 1*. To install, reverse removal procedure. Fill cooling system.

WIRING DIAGRAM

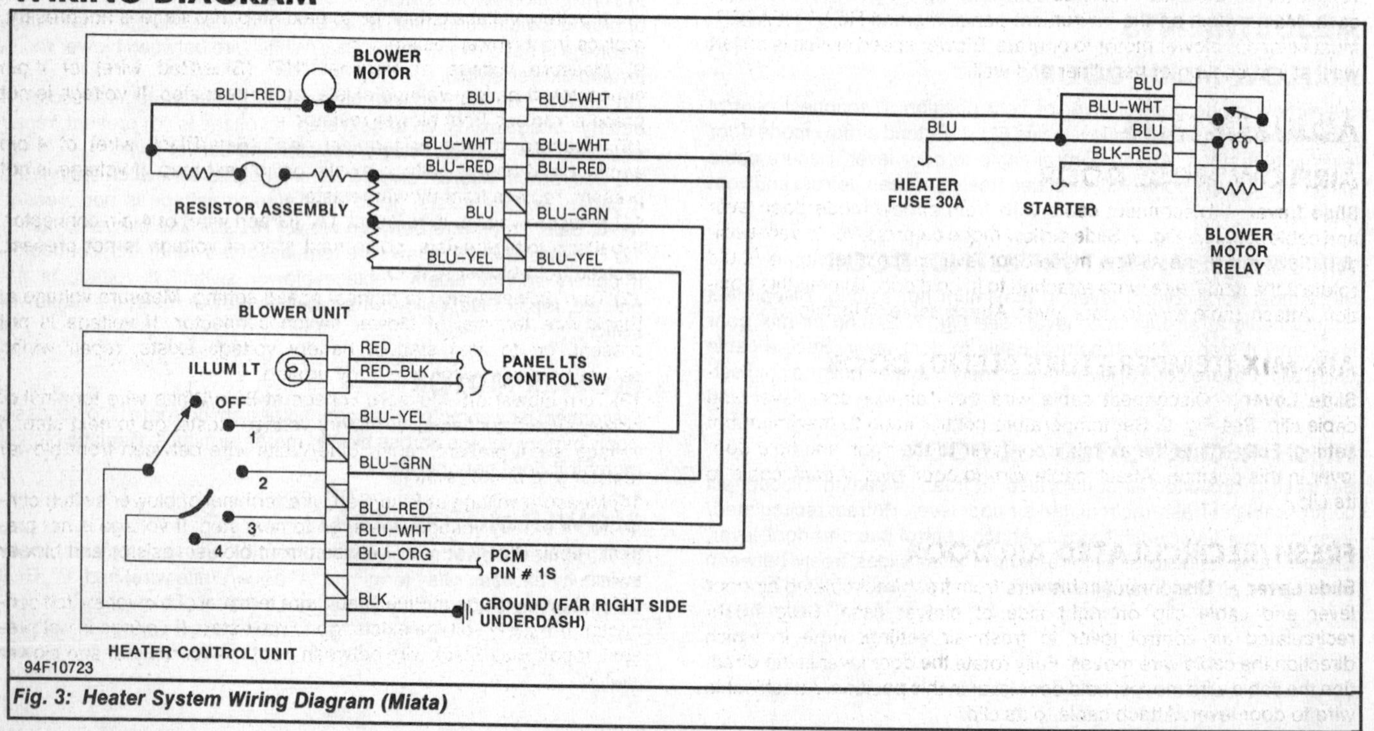
BLOWER MOTOR
BLU-RED
BLU
BLU-WHT
BLU-WHT
BLU-WHT
BLU-RED
BLU-RED
RESISTOR ASSEMBLY
BLU
BLU-GRN
BLU-YEL
BLU-YEL
BLOWER UNIT
BLU
HEATER FUSE 30A
STARTER
BLU
BLU-WHT
BLU
BLK-RED
BLOWER MOTOR RELAY
ILLUM LT
RED
RED-BLK
PANEL LTS CONTROL SW
OFF
1
2
3
4
BLU-YEL
BLU-GRN
BLU-RED
BLU-WHT
BLU-ORG
PCM PIN # 1S
BLK
GROUND (FAR RIGHT SIDE UNDERDASH)
HEATER CONTROL UNIT
94F10723

Fig. 3: Heater System Wiring Diagram (Miata)

1993 HEATER SYSTEMS
MPV

DESCRIPTION & OPERATION

CONTROL PANEL

Push-Button – On vehicles with push-button control panel, air-mix door is cable actuated, but airflow mode and fresh/recirculated air doors are controlled by electric actuators. When panel buttons are pushed to select airflow mode or airflow source (fresh/recirculated air), a logic circuit in the control panel directs power to electric actuators, which control the mode doors.

Slide Lever – Slide lever control panel uses cables to control airflow mode, air-mix (temperature blend) mode and airflow source (fresh/recirculated air).

FRONT HEATER

Heater case, located under center of instrument panel, contains a heater core, airflow mode actuator, airflow mode door and air-mix (temperature blend) door. *See Fig. 9.* Blower case, located under right end of instrument panel, contains blower motor, resistor, and fresh/recirculated air door. Blower motor relay is in left rear corner of engine compartment, in relay block. *See Fig. 1.*

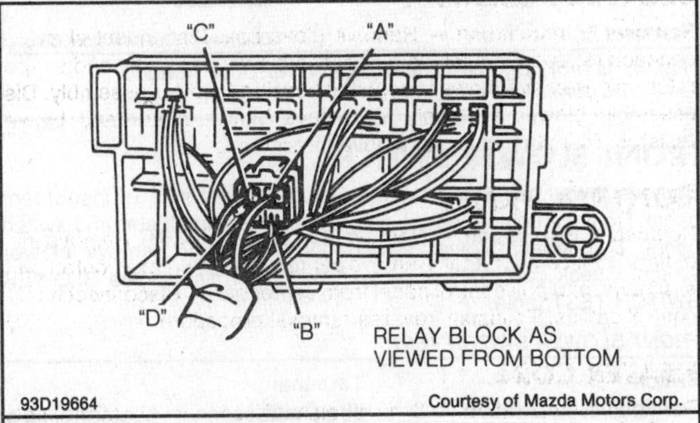
"C"
"A"
"D"
"B"
RELAY BLOCK AS
VIEWED FROM BOTTOM
93D19664
Courtesy of Mazda Motors Corp.

Fig. 1: Identifying Front Blower Motor Relay Connector Terminals

REAR HEATER

Heater case, located under driver's seat, contains a heater core, blower motor, resistor, relay and heater control valve. *See Fig. 10.* Rear in-vehicle temperature can be adjusted by moving control lever on heater case. Main switch on the instrument panel, marked REAR HEATER, must be on for blower motor to operate. Blower speed switch is on left wall, at intersection of headliner and wall.

ADJUSTMENTS

AIRFLOW MODE DOOR

Slide Lever – Disconnect cable wire from airflow mode door lever and cable clip. *See Fig. 9.* Slide airflow mode control lever to vent position. Fully rotate the airflow mode door lever in the direction it would rotate if the cable wire were attached to it; hold door lever in this position. Attach cable wire to door lever. Attach cable to its clip.

AIR-MIX (TEMPERATURE BLEND) DOOR

Slide Lever – Disconnect cable wire from air-mix door lever and cable clip. *See Fig. 9.* Set temperature control knob to maximum hot setting. Fully rotate the air-mix door lever to the right, and hold door lever in this position. Attach cable wire to door lever. Attach cable to its clip.

FRESH/RECIRCULATED AIR DOOR

Slide Lever – Disconnect cable wire from fresh/recirculated air door lever and cable clip on right side of blower case. Slide fresh/recirculated air control lever to fresh air setting. Note in which direction the cable wire moves. Fully rotate the door lever in the direction the cable wire moves; hold door lever in this position. Attach cable wire to door lever. Attach cable to its clip.

TROUBLE SHOOTING

FRONT BLOWER MOTOR INOPERATIVE

Check 15-amp AIR CON fuse (if equipped) in passenger compartment fuse block. Check 40-amp HEATER fuse in engine compartment main fuse block.

REAR BLOWER MOTOR INOPERATIVE

Check 15-amp AIR CON fuse (if equipped) in passenger compartment fuse block. Check 40-amp ALL fuse in engine compartment main fuse block, and 15-amp in-line rear heater fuse.

TESTING

FRONT BLOWER CIRCUIT

1) Check 15-amp AIR CON fuse (if equipped) in passenger compartment fuse block. Check 40-amp HEATER fuse in engine compartment main fuse block. If either fuse is blown, repair wiring and replace fuse. If fuses are okay, go to next step.

2) Turn ignition on. Access engine compartment relay block, leaving connectors attached. *See Fig. 1.* Measure voltage at terminal "A" of blower motor relay connector. If battery voltage is present, go to next step. If voltage does not exist, repair wiring between AIR CON fuse and blower motor relay.

3) Measure voltage at terminal "B" of blower motor relay connector. If voltage does not exist, go to next step. If battery voltage is present, repair wiring between blower motor relay and ground.

4) Measure voltage at terminal "C" of blower motor relay connector. If battery voltage is present, go to next step. If voltage does not exists, repair wiring between HEATER fuse and blower motor relay.

5) Measure voltage at terminal "D" of blower motor relay connector. If battery voltage is present, go to next step. If voltage does not exist, replace blower motor relay.

6) Turn blower switch to highest speed setting. Measure voltage at Blue/Orange wire terminal of blower motor connector, located on bottom of blower case. If voltage does not exist, repair wiring between blower motor relay and blower motor. If battery voltage is present, go to next step.

7) Turn blower off. Measure voltage at terminal "C2" (Blue/Black wire) of 1-pin connector. *See Fig. 2.* If battery voltage exists, go to next step. If voltage is not present, replace blower motor.

8) Measure voltage at terminal "H1" (Blue/White wire) of 4-pin connector. If battery voltage exists, go to next step. If voltage is not present, replace front blower resistor.

9) Measure voltage at terminal "H2" (Blue/Red wire) of 4-pin connector. If battery voltage exists, go to next step. If voltage is not present, replace front blower resistor.

10) Measure voltage at terminal "Me" (Blue/Black wire) of 4-pin connector. If battery voltage exists, go to next step. If voltage is not present, replace front blower resistor.

11) Measure voltage at terminal "Lo" (Green wire) of 4-pin connector. If battery voltage exists, go to next step. If voltage is not present, replace front blower resistor.

12) Turn blower switch to highest speed setting. Measure voltage at Black wire terminal of blower switch connector. If voltage is not present, go to next step. If battery voltage exists, repair wiring between blower switch and body ground.

13) Turn blower off. Measure voltage at Blue/White wire terminal of blower switch connector. If battery voltage exists, go to next step. If voltage is not present, repair Blue/White wire between front blower resistor and blower switch.

14) Measure voltage at Blue/Red wire terminal of blower switch connector. If battery voltage exists, go to next step. If voltage is not present, repair Blue/Red wire between front blower resistor and blower switch.

15) Measure voltage at Blue/Black wire terminal of blower switch connector. If battery voltage exists, go to next step. If voltage is not present, repair Blue/Black wire between front blower resistor and blower switch.

1993 HEATER SYSTEMS
MPV (Cont.)

16) Measure voltage at Green wire terminal of blower switch connector. If battery voltage exists, replace blower switch. If voltage is not present, repair Green wire between front blower resistor and blower switch.

FRONT BLOWER MOTOR

Remove lower panel and undercover from right side of instrument panel. *See Fig. 11.* Disconnect 2-pin connector from blower motor. Apply battery voltage across terminals. Replace blower motor if it does not operate.

FRONT BLOWER RESISTOR

Disconnect resistor connectors on bottom of blower case. *See Fig. 2.* Set ohmmeter to X1000 scale. Check continuity between indicated terminals. See FRONT BLOWER RESISTOR CONTINUITY TEST table. If continuity is not as specified, replace resistor.

FRONT BLOWER RESISTOR CONTINUITY TEST

Terminal	Continuity
"C" & "C1"	Yes
"C1" & "C2"	Yes
"C2" & "H1"	Yes
"C2" & "H2"	Yes
"C2" & "Me"	Yes
"C2" & "Lo"	Yes

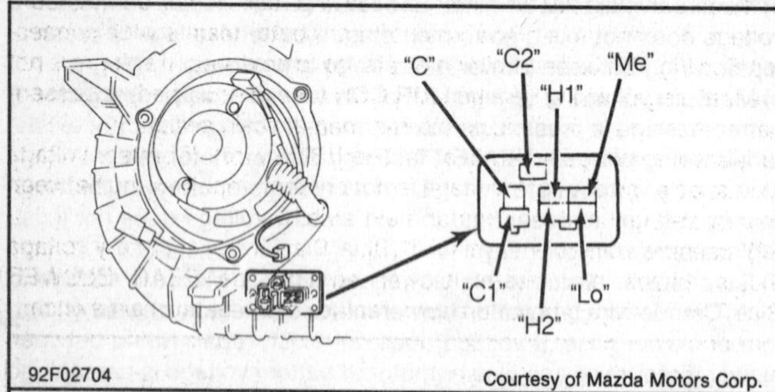
"C"
"C2"
"Me"
"H1"
"C1"
"Lo"
"H2"
92F02704
Courtesy of Mazda Motors Corp.

Fig. 2: Identifying Front Blower Resistor Connector Terminals

AIRFLOW MODE DOOR ACTUATOR

Push-Button – Disconnect negative battery cable. Remove lower panel from driver's side of instrument panel. *See Fig. 11.* Disconnect actuator connector on left side of heater case. *See Fig. 3.* Apply battery voltage across terminals "j" and "k". Ensure actuator rotates door to defrost position. Reverse battery leads, and ensure actuator rotates door to vent position. Replace actuator if it does not function as indicated.

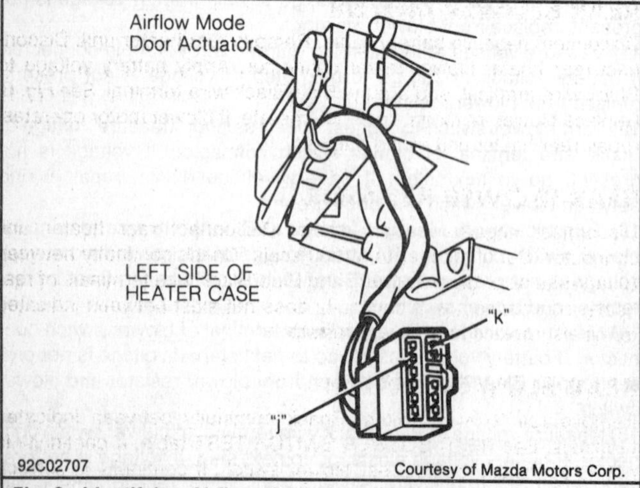
Airflow Mode
Door Actuator
LEFT SIDE OF
HEATER CASE
"k"
"j"
92C02707
Courtesy of Mazda Motors Corp.

Fig. 3: Identifying Airflow Mode Door Actuator Connector Terminals

FRESH/RECIRCULATED AIR DOOR ACTUATOR

Push-Button – Disconnect negative battery cable. Remove lower panel and undercover from passenger's side of instrument panel. *See Fig. 11.* Disconnect actuator connector on right side of blower case. *See Fig. 4.* Apply battery voltage across terminals "f" and "g". Reverse battery leads. Replace actuator if it does not move door in both directions.

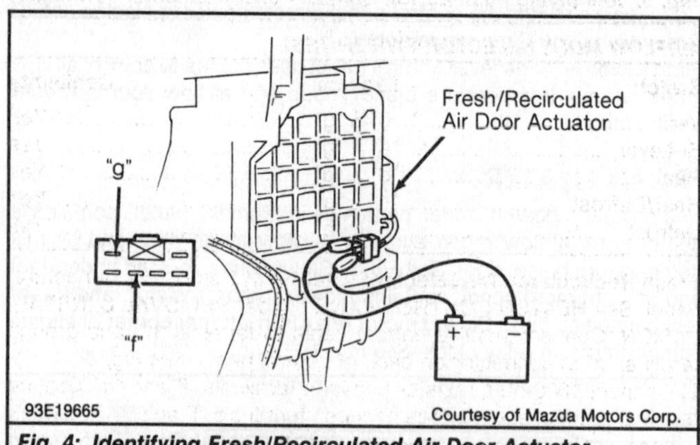
Fresh/Recirculated
Air Door Actuator
"g"
"f"
+
−
93E19665
Courtesy of Mazda Motors Corp.

Fig. 4: Identifying Fresh/Recirculated Air Door Actuator Connector Terminals

FRONT BLOWER SWITCH

Remove lower panel and undercover from right side of instrument panel. Remove column cover. Remove instrument cluster and switch panel. Disconnect blower switch connector, and remove blower switch. Check continuity of blower switch terminals. See BLOWER SWITCH TEST table.

FRONT BLOWER SWITCH TEST

Switch Position	Terminal Wire Color	Continuity
Low	GRN & BLK	Yes
Medium Low	BLU/BLK, BLK & GRN	Yes
Medium High	BLU/RED, BLK & BLU	Yes
High	BLU/WHT, BLK & BLU	Yes

PUSH-BUTTON CONTROL PANEL

NOTE: Ensure test battery used in this test is fully charged.

Airflow Mode Selector – 1) Remove heater control panel. See HEATER CONTROL PANEL under REMOVAL & INSTALLATION. Connect positive battery cable to terminal "h", and ground terminal "g" of connector on back of control panel. *See Fig. 5.*

2) Connect 1000-ohm resistor between terminals "n" and "g" of connector on back of control panel. Connect jumper wire between terminals "l" and "g". Measure voltage between terminals "n" and "g". If battery voltage exists, remove jumper wire and 1000-ohm resistor. Go to next step. If voltage is not present, replace heater control panel.

3) Connect 1000-ohm resistor between terminals "m" and "g". Connect jumper wire between terminals "j" and "g". Measure voltage between terminals "m" and "g". If battery voltage exists, remove jumper wire and 1000-ohm resistor. Go to next step. If voltage is not present, replace heater control panel.

4) Connect 1000-ohm resistor between terminals "h" and "n". Measure voltage between terminals "n" and "g". If voltage is less than one volt, remove jumper wire and 1000-ohm resistor. Go to next step. If voltage is one volt or more, replace heater control panel.

5) Connect 1000-ohm resistor between terminals "h" and "m". Measure voltage between terminals "m" and "g". If voltage is less than one volt, remove jumper wire and 1000-ohm resistor. Go to next step. If voltage is one volt ore more, replace heater control panel.

6) Push indicated switch, and check continuity between appropriate terminals. See AIRFLOW MODE SELECTOR SWITCH TEST table. If continuity is not as specified, replace heater control panel.

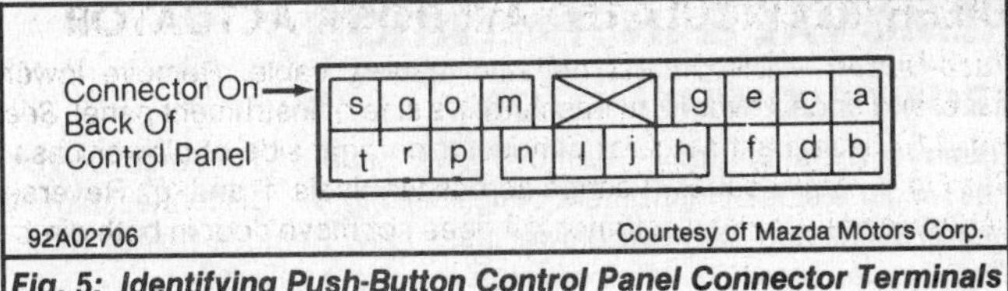
Connector On Back Of Control Panel
s q o m g e c a
t r p n l j h f d b
92A02706
Courtesy of Mazda Motors Corp.

Fig. 5: Identifying Push-Button Control Panel Connector Terminals

AIRFLOW MODE SELECTOR SWITCH TEST

Switch	Terminal	Continuity
Vent	"b" & "g"	Yes
Bi-Level	"a" & "g"	Yes
Heat	"d" & "g"	Yes
Heat/Defrost	"c" & "g"	Yes
Defrost	"e" & "g"	Yes

Fresh/Recirculated Air Selector Switch – 1) Remove heater control panel. See HEATER CONTROL PANEL under REMOVAL & INSTALLATION. Connect positive battery cable to terminal "h", and ground terminal "g" of connector on back of control panel. *See Fig. 5.*

2) Connect 1000-ohm resistor between terminals "f" and "q". Ground terminal "o". Measure voltage between terminals "f" and "g". If battery voltage exists, remove jumper wire and 1000-ohm resistor. Go to next step. If battery voltage is not present, replace heater control panel.

3) Push indicated switch. and check continuity between appropriate terminals. See FRESH/RECIRCULATED AIR SELECTOR SWITCH TEST table. If continuity is not as specified, replace heater control panel.

FRESH/RECIRCULATED AIR SELECTOR SWITCH TEST

Switch	Terminal	Continuity
Recirculated Air	"r" & "g"	Yes
Fresh Air	"p" & "g"	Yes

Light Emitting Diodes (LED) – 1) Remove heater control panel. See HEATER CONTROL PANEL under REMOVAL & INSTALLATION. Connect positive battery cable to terminal "h", and ground terminal "g" of connector on back of control panel. *See Fig. 5.*

2) Push each switch on control panel, and ensure LED comes on. If any LED fails to come on, replace heater control panel. Connect jumper wire between terminals "h" and "s". LEDs should dim. If not, replace heater control panel.

Panel Illumination Light – 1) Remove heater control panel. See HEATER CONTROL PANEL under REMOVAL & INSTALLATION. Connect positive battery cable to terminal "h", and ground terminal "g" of connector on back of control panel. *See Fig. 5.*

2) Connect jumper wire between terminals "h" and "s". Connect a second jumper wire between terminals "g" and "t". Control panel illumination light should come on. If not, replace bulb.

REAR BLOWER CIRCUIT

1) Check 15-amp AIR CON fuse (if equipped) in passenger compartment fuse block. Check 40-amp ALL fuse in engine compartment main fuse block and 10-amp in-line fuse on rear heater unit case. If any fuse is blown, repair wiring and replace fuse.

2) If fuses are okay, disconnect negative battery cable. Disconnect rear heater unit connector. *See Fig. 6.* Apply battery voltage to terminals "a" and "b", and ground terminals "c" and "f". If blower motor operates, go to step **6)**. If blower motor does not operate, go to next step.

3) Check continuity between terminals "b" and "f". If continuity exists, go to next step. If there is no continuity, test rear heater relay. See REAR HEATER RELAY. If relay is okay, test rear blower motor. See REAR BLOWER MOTOR.

4) Check continuity between terminals "c" and "d". If there is no continuity, replace rear blower resistor. If continuity exists, go to next step.

5) Check continuity between terminals "c" and "e". If there is no continuity, replace rear blower resistor. If continuity exists, check rear heater relay. See REAR HEATER RELAY. If relay is okay, test rear blower motor. See REAR BLOWER MOTOR.

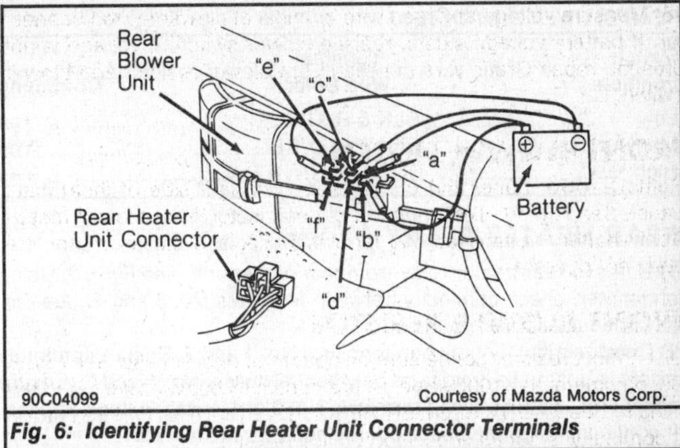
Rear Blower Unit
"e"
"c"
"a"
Battery
Rear Heater Unit Connector
"f"
"b"
"d"
90C04099
Courtesy of Mazda Motors Corp.

Fig. 6: Identifying Rear Heater Unit Connector Terminals

6) Turn ignition on. Turn off rear heater main switch and rear heater blower switch. Reconnect rear heater connector. Measure voltage at Blue wire terminal of rear heater connector. If battery voltage exists, go to next step. If voltage is not present, repair wiring between AIR CON fuse and rear heater unit.

7) Measure voltage at Black/Yellow wire terminal of rear heater connector. If battery voltage exists, go to next step. If voltage is not present, repair wiring between ALL fuse and rear heater unit.

8) Turn rear main heater switch on, leaving rear blower off. Measure voltage at terminal "a" (Blue wire) of rear heater main switch connector. *See Fig. 7.* If battery voltage exists, go to next step. If voltage is not present, repair wiring between AIR CON fuse (if equipped) in passenger compartment fuse block and rear heater main switch.

9) Measure voltage at terminal "h" (Red/Blue wire). If battery voltage exists, go to next step. If voltage is not present, repair wiring between rear heater unit and rear heater main switch.

10) Measure voltage at terminal "i" (Blue/Black wire). If battery voltage exists, check rear heater blower switch. See REAR BLOWER SWITCH. If voltage is not present, replace rear heater main switch.

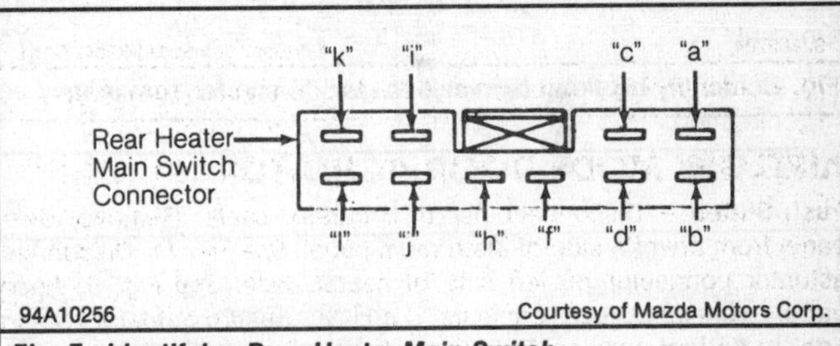
"k"
"i"
"c"
"a"
Rear Heater Main Switch Connector
"l"
"j"
"h"
"f"
"d"
"b"
94A10256
Courtesy of Mazda Motors Corp.

Fig. 7: Identifying Rear Heater Main Switch Connector Terminals

REAR BLOWER MOTOR

Disconnect negative battery cable. Remove rear heater unit. Disconnect rear heater blower motor connector. Apply battery voltage to Black wire terminal, and ground Blue/Black wire terminal. *See Fig. 6.* Replace blower motor if it does not operate. If blower motor operates, repair rear heater unit wiring harness.

REAR BLOWER RESISTOR

Disconnect negative battery cable. Disconnect rear heater unit connector. Set ohmmeter to X1000 scale. Check continuity between Blue/White wire, Blue/Red wire and Blue/Black wire terminals of rear heater unit connector. If continuity does not exist between indicated terminals, replace rear blower resistor.

REAR BLOWER SWITCH

Remove rear blower switch. Check continuity between indicated terminals. See REAR BLOWER SWITCH TEST table. If continuity is not as specified, replace rear blower switch. If continuity is correct, check wiring between rear heater unit, rear blower switch and body ground.

1993 HEATER SYSTEMS
MPV (Cont.)

REAR BLOWER SWITCH TEST

Switch Position	Terminal Wire Color	Continuity
Low	BLK & BLU/BLK	Yes
Medium	BLK & BLU/RED	Yes
High	BLK & BLU/WHT	Yes

REAR HEATER RELAY

1) Remove rear heater relay from rear heater unit. *See Fig. 10.* Using ohmmeter, check continuity between terminals No. 3 and 4. *See Fig. 8.* Continuity should not exist.

2) Check continuity between terminals No. 1 and 2. Ensure continuity exists. Apply battery voltage between terminals No. 1 and 2. Ensure continuity exists between terminals No. 3 and 4 with voltage applied. If continuity is not as specified, replace rear heater relay.

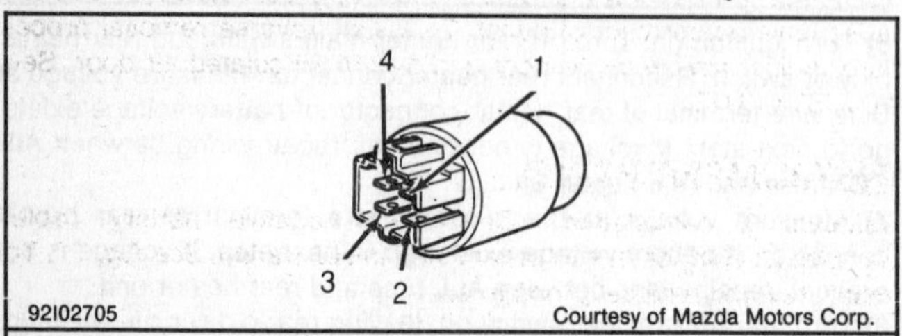
4
1
3
2
92I02705
Courtesy of Mazda Motors Corp.

Fig. 8: Identifying Rear Heater Relay Connector Terminals

REAR HEATER MAIN SWITCH

Remove rear heater main switch. Check continuity between indicated switch terminals. See REAR HEATER MAIN SWITCH TEST table. Replace switch if continuity is not as specified.

REAR HEATER MAIN SWITCH TEST

Switch Position	Terminal	Continuity
Off	"d" & "f"; "h", "i" & "j"	Yes
On	"d" & "f"; "c", "h" & "j"; "h" & "i" [1]	Yes

[1] – Continuity between terminals "h" and "i" should exist in only one direction.

REMOVAL & INSTALLATION

FRONT BLOWER MOTOR

Removal & Installation – Remove lower panel and undercover from passenger's side of instrument panel. *See Fig. 11.* Disconnect blower motor connector. Remove blower assembly. Remove blower motor from blower case. To install, reverse removal procedure.

FRONT HEATER ASSEMBLY

Removal & Installation – Drain coolant. Remove instrument panel. See INSTRUMENT PANEL. Disconnect heater hoses from heater core. Remove instrument panel reinforcement. Carefully remove front heater assembly to prevent spilling coolant from heater core. To install, reverse removal procedure.

FRONT HEATER CORE

Removal & Installation – Remove heater assembly. See FRONT HEATER ASSEMBLY. Disassemble heater assembly, and remove heater core. *See Fig. 9.* To install, reverse removal procedure.

AIRFLOW MODE DOOR ACTUATOR

Removal & Installation (Push-Button) – Disconnect negative battery cable. Remove lower panel from driver's side of instrument panel. *See Fig. 11.* Disconnect electrical connector from airflow mode actuator on left side of heater case. Remove actuator. To install, reverse removal procedure.

FRESH/RECIRCULATED AIR DOOR ACTUATOR

Removal & Installation (Push-Button) – Disconnect negative battery cable. Remove lower panel and undercover from passenger's side of instrument panel. *See Fig. 11.* Disconnect actuator electrical connector on right side of blower case. *See Fig. 4.* Remove actuator. To install, reverse removal procedure.

REAR HEATER ASSEMBLY

Removal & Installation – Disconnect negative battery cable. Set rear heater temperature control knob to warm setting to open heater control valve. Drain coolant. Remove driver's seat. Disconnect heater hoses from heater core. *See Fig. 10.* Disconnect electrical connector. Remove rear heater assembly. To install, reverse removal procedure.

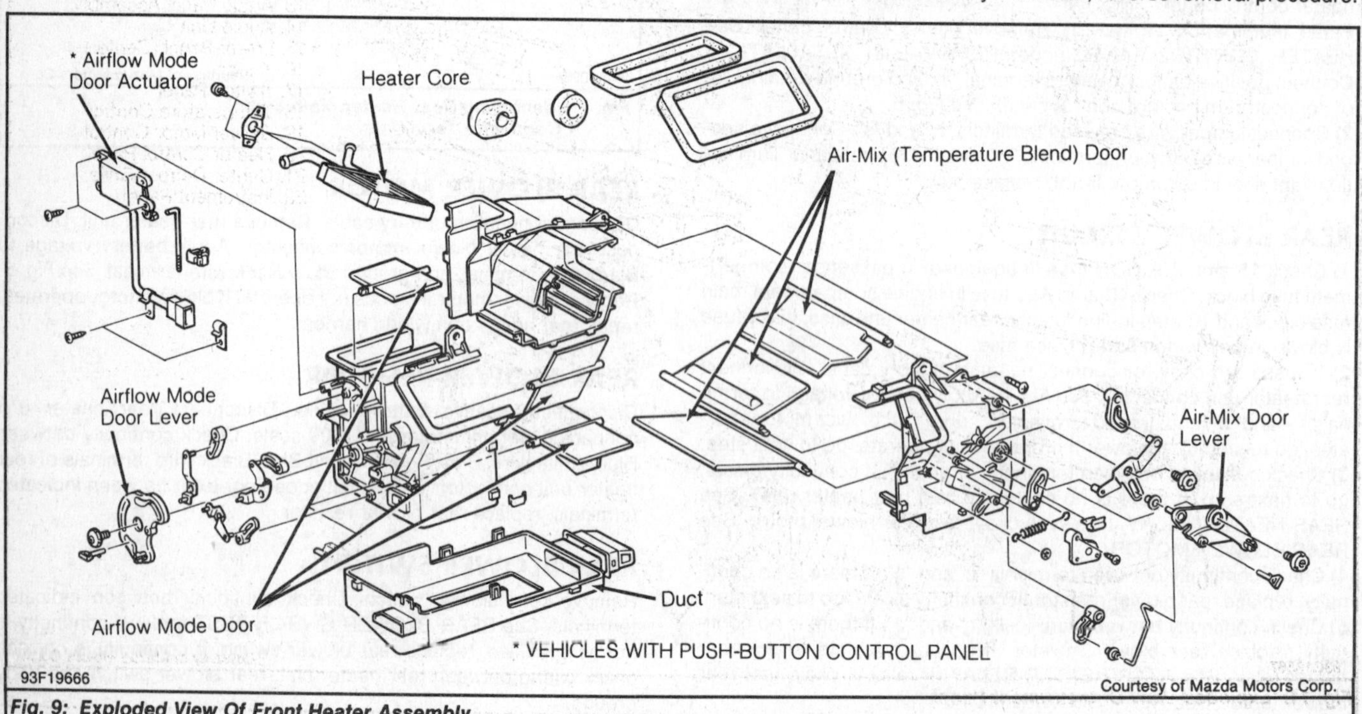
* Airflow Mode
Door Actuator
Heater Core
Air-Mix (Temperature Blend) Door
Airflow Mode
Door Lever
Air-Mix Door
Lever
Duct
Airflow Mode Door
* VEHICLES WITH PUSH-BUTTON CONTROL PANEL
93F19666
Courtesy of Mazda Motors Corp.

Fig. 9: Exploded View Of Front Heater Assembly

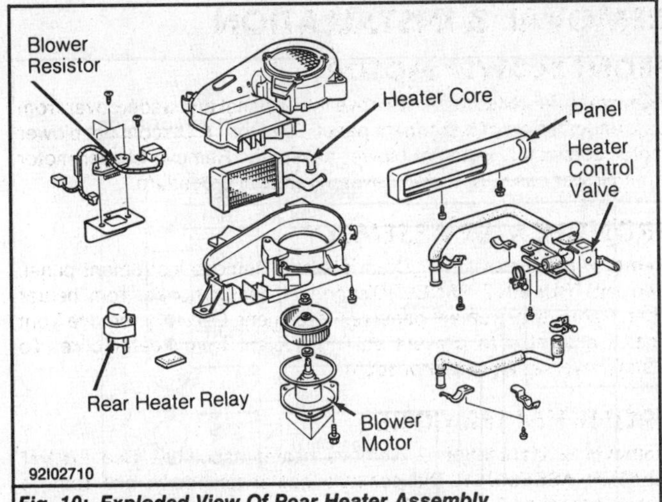
Blower Resistor
Heater Core
Panel
Heater Control Valve
Rear Heater Relay
Blower Motor
92I02710

Fig. 10: Exploded View Of Rear Heater Assembly

REAR HEATER CORE

Removal & Installation – Remove rear heater assembly. See REAR HEATER ASSEMBLY. Disassemble case, and remove rear heater core. *See Fig. 10*. To install, reverse removal procedure.

REAR BLOWER MOTOR

Removal & Installation – Remove rear heater assembly. See REAR HEATER ASSEMBLY. Disassemble case, and remove rear blower motor. *See Fig. 10*. To install, reverse removal procedure.

HEATER CONTROL PANEL

Removal & Installation (Push-Button) – Remove left and right lower panels and undercover from instrument panel. *See Fig. 11*. Remove instrument cluster. Remove switch panel. Remove center lower panel. Pull panel from cavity, and disconnect electrical connector. Remove heater control panel. To install, reverse removal procedure.

Removal & Installation (Slide Lever) – **1)** Remove left and right lower panels and undercover from instrument panel. *See Fig. 11*. If necessary, remove steering column cover. Remove instrument cluster. Remove switch panel and center lower panel. Disconnect control cables from airflow mode door and fresh/recirculated air door.

2) Remove heater control panel. To install, reverse removal procedure. Adjust airflow mode door and fresh/recirculated air door. See ADJUSTMENTS.

INSTRUMENT PANEL

Removal & Installation – Disconnect negative battery cable. Remove all components in order listed in illustration. *See Fig. 11*. To install, reverse removal procedure.

1. Hood Release Knob
2. Steering Column
3. Column Cover
4. Combination Switch
5. Instrument Cluster Cover
6. Instrument Cluster
7. Side Covers (Left & Right)
8. Right Undercover
9. Lower Panel (Right)
10. Lower Panel (Left)
11. Duct
12. Ashtray
13. Audio Panel Assembly
14. Audio Unit
15. Lower Panel (Center)
16. Knobs
17. Switch Panel
18. Temperature Control
19. Blower Motor Control
20. Heater Control Panel
21. Center Defrost Grille
22. Instrument Panel

93G19667

Courtesy of Mazda Motors Corp.

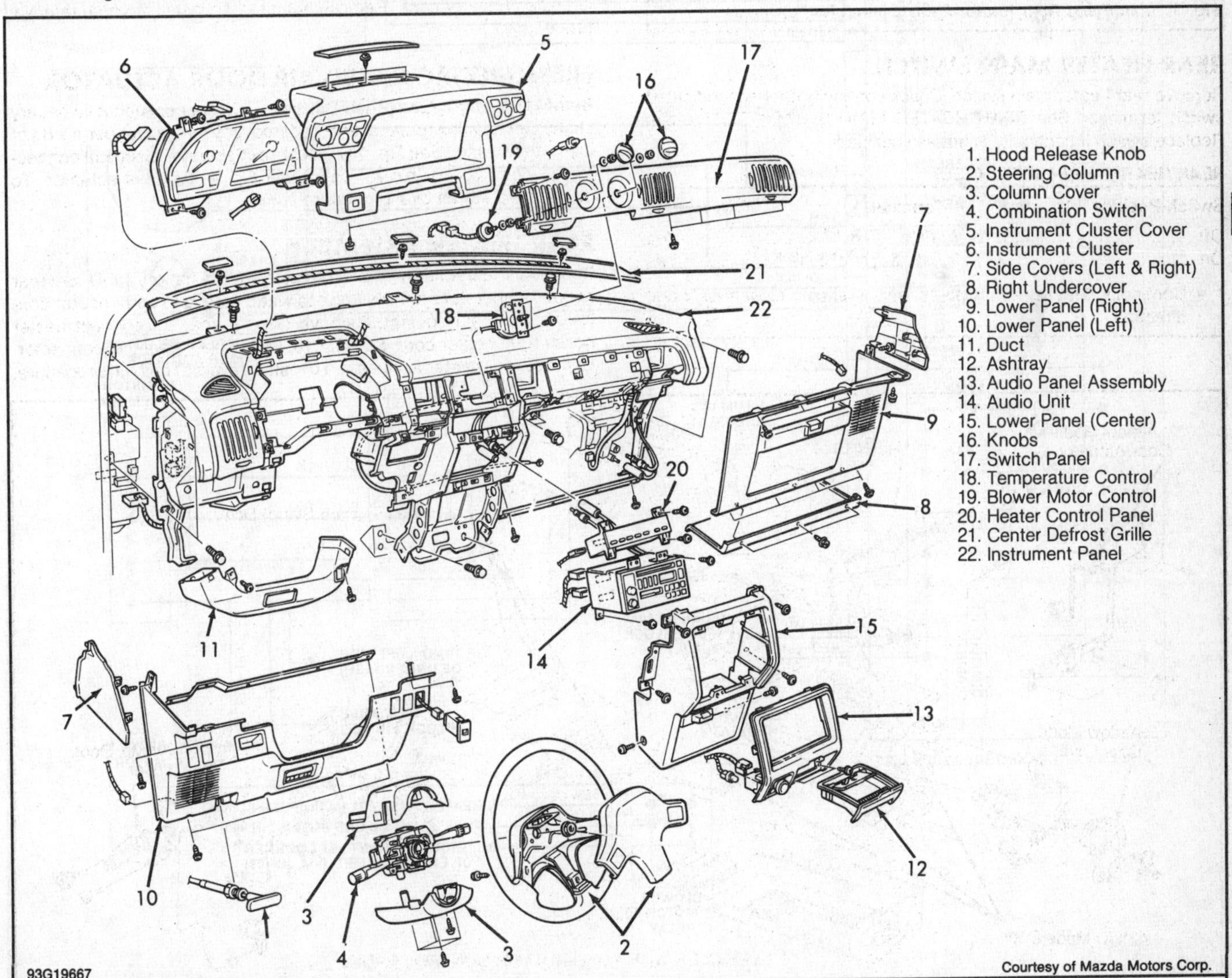

Fig. 11: Exploded View Of Instrument Panel

1993 HEATER SYSTEMS
MPV (Cont.)

WIRING DIAGRAM

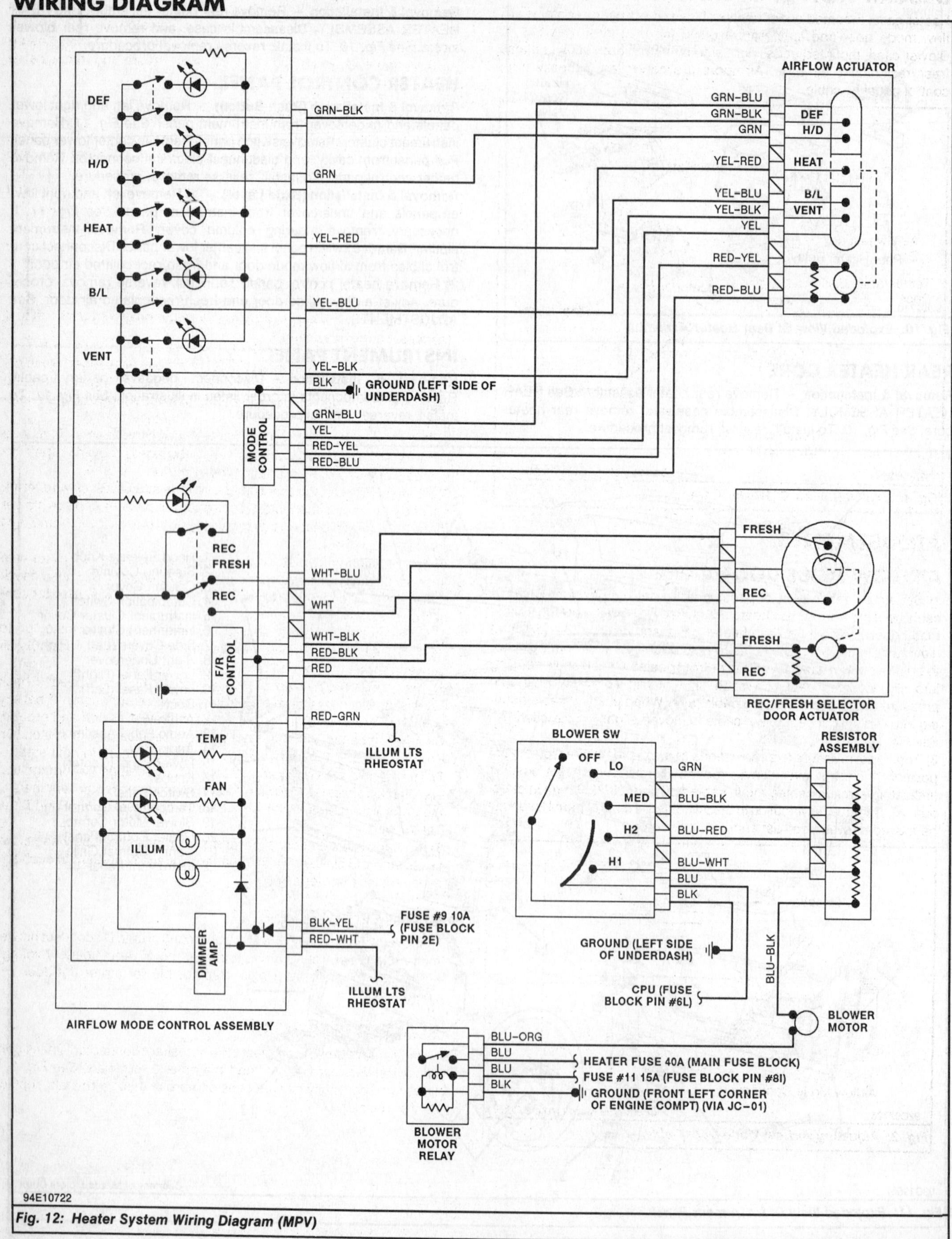
DEF
H/D
HEAT
B/L
VENT
GRN-BLK
GRN
YEL-RED
YEL-BLU
YEL-BLK
BLK
GROUND (LEFT SIDE OF UNDERDASH)
MODE CONTROL
GRN-BLU
YEL
RED-YEL
RED-BLU
AIRFLOW ACTUATOR
GRN-BLU
GRN-BLK
GRN
YEL-RED
YEL-BLU
YEL-BLK
YEL
RED-YEL
RED-BLU
DEF
H/D
HEAT
B/L
VENT
REC
FRESH
REC
WHT-BLU
WHT
WHT-BLK
RED-BLK
RED
F/R CONTROL
FRESH
REC
FRESH
REC
REC/FRESH SELECTOR DOOR ACTUATOR
RED-GRN
ILLUM LTS RHEOSTAT
TEMP
FAN
ILLUM
BLOWER SW
OFF
LO
MED
H2
H1
GRN
BLU-BLK
BLU-RED
BLU-WHT
BLU
BLK
RESISTOR ASSEMBLY
BLK-YEL
RED-WHT
FUSE #9 10A (FUSE BLOCK PIN 2E)
DIMMER AMP
ILLUM LTS RHEOSTAT
GROUND (LEFT SIDE OF UNDERDASH)
CPU (FUSE BLOCK PIN #6L)
BLU-BLK
BLOWER MOTOR
AIRFLOW MODE CONTROL ASSEMBLY
BLU-ORG
BLU
BLU
BLK
HEATER FUSE 40A (MAIN FUSE BLOCK)
FUSE #11 15A (FUSE BLOCK PIN #8I)
GROUND (FRONT LEFT CORNER OF ENGINE COMPT) (VIA JC-01)
BLOWER MOTOR RELAY
94E10722

Fig. 12: Heater System Wiring Diagram (MPV)

1993 HEATER SYSTEMS
MX-3, Protege & 323

DESCRIPTION & OPERATION

Heater case, mounted under center of instrument panel, contains airflow mode door and temperature blend (air-mix) door. *See Fig. 1.* Blower case, mounted under right side of instrument panel, contains fresh/recirculated air door. All doors are controlled manually from control panel by cable.

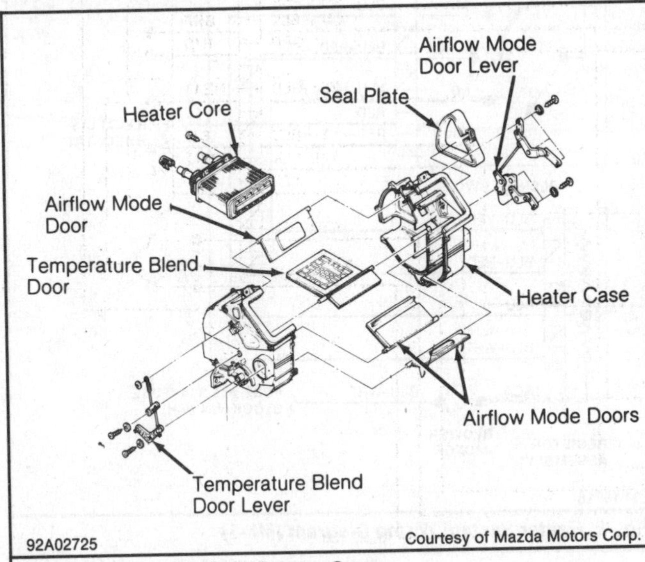
Airflow Mode
Door Lever
Seal Plate
Heater Core
Airflow Mode
Door
Temperature Blend
Door
Heater Case
Airflow Mode Doors
Temperature Blend
Door Lever
92A02725
Courtesy of Mazda Motors Corp.

Fig. 1: Exploded View Of Heater Case

ADJUSTMENTS

AIRFLOW MODE DOOR CABLE

1) Set airflow mode control panel lever to defrost position. Remove cable housing from clip on heater case. *See Fig. 2.* Align hole in airflow mode door lever with hole in heater case, and insert a .24" (6.1 mm) diameter pin through both holes to hold door lever in proper position.
2) Ensure control panel lever is in defrost position. Push cable housing into clip, pushing cable on each side of clip to evenly distribute pressure and prevent bending cable wire. When pushing cable housing into clip, it is acceptable if cable is moved slightly in direction "A". *See Fig. 2.*
3) Apply light pressure to airflow mode control lever in direction of vent position. If control lever can be moved slightly toward vent position (indicating slack in cable), move cable housing .08" (2.0 mm) in direction "A". Remove pin installed in step **1)**. Ensure control panel lever can be moved between defrost and vent positions.

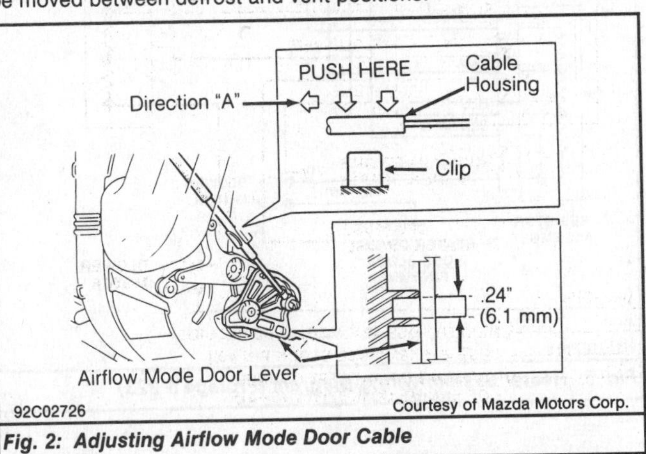
PUSH HERE
Cable
Housing
Direction "A"
Clip
.24"
(6.1 mm)
Airflow Mode Door Lever
92C02726
Courtesy of Mazda Motors Corp.

Fig. 2: Adjusting Airflow Mode Door Cable

FRESH/RECIRCULATED AIR DOOR CABLE

Set control panel lever to fresh position. Disconnect cable housing from clip on blower case. Rotate fresh/recirculated air door lever in cable-retracted direction. Reconnect cable housing to clip. Ensure control panel lever moves fully between fresh and recirculated positions.

TEMPERATURE BLEND DOOR CABLE

Set temperature blend control panel lever to cold position. Disconnect cable housing from clip on heater case. Rotate temperature blend door lever in cable-extended direction. Attach cable housing to clip. Ensure control panel lever moves fully between cold and hot positions.

TESTING

BLOWER MOTOR CIRCUIT

NOTE: Leave all connectors attached during blower motor circuit test (backprobe the terminals).

1) Check 30-amp heater circuit breaker above passenger compartment fuse block. If Red reset button has popped out, repair short and reset circuit breaker. If Red reset button has not popped out, turn ignition on.
2) Turn blower switch to highest speed. Check voltage at Blue wire terminal of blower motor connector. If no voltage is present, repair circuit between circuit breaker and blower motor.
3) If battery voltage is present, check voltage at Blue/Black wire terminal of blower motor connector. If no voltage is present, replace blower motor. If battery voltage is present, turn off blower switch and A/C switch (if equipped).
4) Turn ignition on. On all models, check voltage at Blue/White wire terminal of blower resistor connector. On Protege and 323, also check Blue/Red, Blue and Blue/Yellow wire terminals of blower resistor connector.
5) On all models, if battery voltage is present at each terminal, go to next step. If battery voltage is not present at any terminal, repair circuit between blower motor and resistor.
6) Turn ignition on. Turn blower switch to highest speed. Check voltage at Black wire terminal of blower switch connector. If battery voltage is present, repair circuit between blower switch and ground. On MX-3, if battery voltage is not present, replace blower switch. On Protege and 323, if battery voltage is not present, go to next step.
7) Turn off blower switch and A/C switch (if equipped). Turn ignition on. Check voltage at following blower switch connector terminals in the order listed: Blue/White wire, Blue/Red wire, Blue wire and Blue/Yellow wire.
8) If voltage is not present at any terminal, repair circuit between blower resistor and blower switch. If battery voltage is present at each terminal, replace blower switch.

BLOWER MOTOR

Remove glove box. Remove electronic control unit. Disconnect blower motor connector from bottom of blower motor. Apply battery voltage across blower motor terminals. Replace blower motor if it does not operate.

BLOWER RESISTOR

Remove glove box. Disconnect blower resistor connector. Check continuity between terminal "A" and the other 3 terminals. *See Fig. 3.* If there is no continuity between one or more of these terminals, replace blower resistor.

1993 HEATER SYSTEMS
MX-3, Protege & 323 (Cont.)

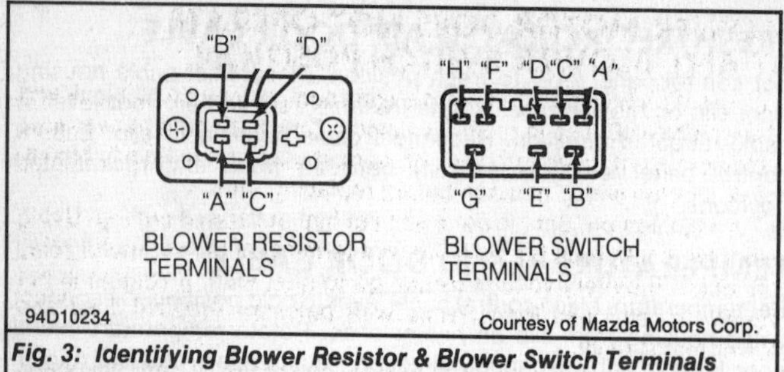
"B" "D"
"A" "C"
BLOWER RESISTOR TERMINALS
"H" "F" "D" "C" "A"
"G" "E" "B"
BLOWER SWITCH TERMINALS
94D10234
Courtesy of Mazda Motors Corp.

Fig. 3: Identifying Blower Resistor & Blower Switch Terminals

BLOWER SWITCH

Remove control panel. See CONTROL PANEL under REMOVAL & INSTALLATION. Check continuity between specified blower switch terminals. See BLOWER SWITCH CONTINUITY TEST table. *See Fig. 3.* If continuity is not as specified, replace blower switch.

BLOWER SWITCH CONTINUITY TEST

Blower Switch Position	Continuity Between Terminals
All Positions	"A" & "C"
Off	"A" & "C"
1	"B" & "F"
2	"B", "D" & "H"
3	"B", "D" & "E"
4	"B", "D" & "G"

REMOVAL & INSTALLATION

BLOWER CASE

Removal & Installation – Remove glove box. Remove electronic control unit from blower case. Disconnect blower motor and blower resistor connectors. Loosen seal plate between blower case and heater case. Remove blower case nuts and blower case. To install, reverse removal procedure.

CONTROL PANEL

Removal & Installation – **1)** Disconnect negative battery cable. Remove side panel from right side of instrument panel. Remove right lower panel, center lower panel and instrument cluster cover.

2) Remove glove box and glove box cover. Disconnect air control door cables from control panel. Remove control panel. To install, reverse removal procedure.

HEATER CASE & CORE

Removal & Installation – **1)** Drain coolant. Disconnect heater hoses from heater core at engine compartment firewall. Remove firewall grommet. Remove side panels from left and right sides of instrument panel.

2) Remove right lower panel, center lower panel and instrument cluster cover. Remove glove box and cover. Remove control panel. See CONTROL PANEL. Remove nuts and heater case. Disassemble heater case to remove heater core. *See Fig. 1.* To install, reverse removal procedure.

INSTRUMENT PANEL

Removal & Installation – See REMOVAL & INSTALLATION in MANUAL A/C HEATER SYSTEMS – MX-3, PROTEGE & 323 article.

TORQUE SPECIFICATIONS

TORQUE SPECIFICATIONS

Application	INCH Lbs. (N.m)
Blower Motor Nut	69-106 (7.8-12)
Instrument Panel Bolt/Nut	69-106 (7.8-12)
Seal Plate Bolt	69-106 (7.8-12)

WIRING DIAGRAMS

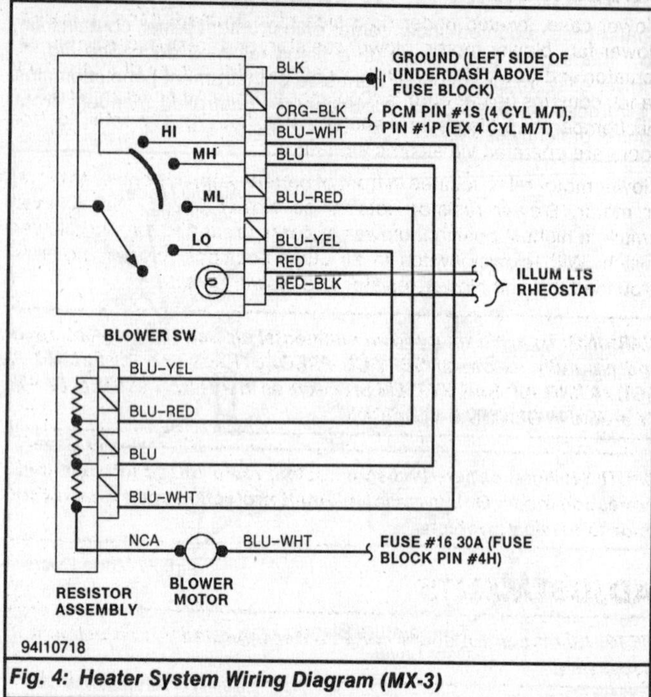
BLK
GROUND (LEFT SIDE OF UNDERDASH ABOVE FUSE BLOCK)
ORG-BLK
PCM PIN #1S (4 CYL M/T), PIN #1P (EX 4 CYL M/T)
BLU-WHT
HI
MH
BLU
ML
BLU-RED
LO
BLU-YEL
RED
RED-BLK
ILLUM LTS RHEOSTAT
BLOWER SW
BLU-YEL
BLU-RED
BLU
BLU-WHT
NCA
BLU-WHT
FUSE #16 30A (FUSE BLOCK PIN #4H)
RESISTOR ASSEMBLY
BLOWER MOTOR
94I10718

Fig. 4: Heater System Wiring Diagram (MX-3)

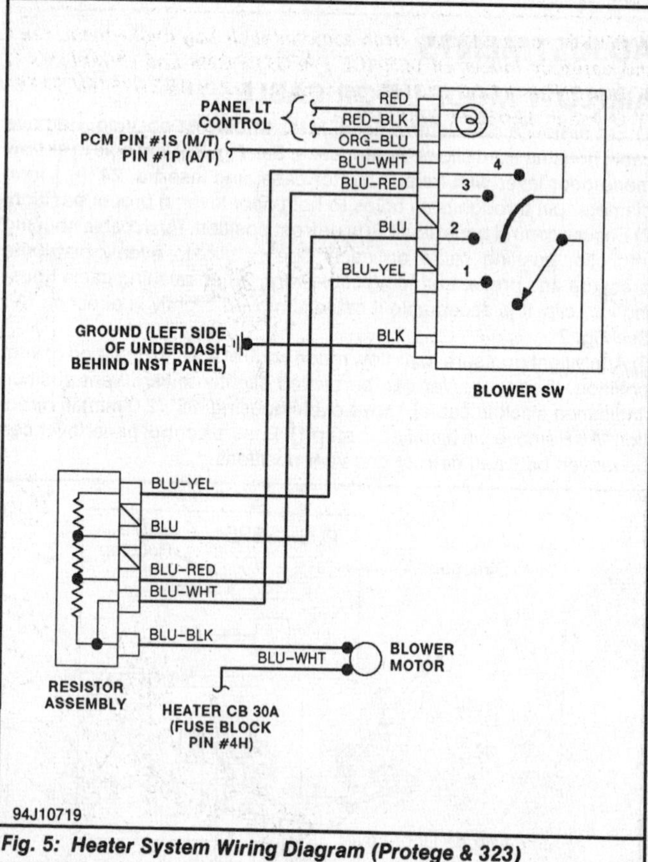
PANEL LT CONTROL
RED
RED-BLK
ORG-BLU
PCM PIN #1S (M/T) PIN #1P (A/T)
BLU-WHT
BLU-RED
4
3
BLU
2
BLU-YEL
1
GROUND (LEFT SIDE OF UNDERDASH BEHIND INST PANEL)
BLK
BLOWER SW
BLU-YEL
BLU
BLU-RED
BLU-WHT
BLU-BLK
BLU-WHT
BLOWER MOTOR
RESISTOR ASSEMBLY
HEATER CB 30A (FUSE BLOCK PIN #4H)
94J10719

Fig. 5: Heater System Wiring Diagram (Protege & 323)

1993 HEATER SYSTEMS
MX-6 & 626

DESCRIPTION & OPERATION

Blower case, located under right side of instrument panel, contains blower fan, blower motor, blower resistor, and fresh/recirculated air actuator and door. Heater case, located under center of instrument panel, contains heater core, airflow mode door and actuator, and air-mix (temperature-blend) door and actuator. *See Fig. 1*. Heater control doors are operated via electric actuators.

Blower motor relay, located in front of battery, supplies power to blower motor. Blower resistor determines blower speed. With blower switch in highest position, blower motor is grounded through blower switch. With blower switch in all other positions, blower motor is grounded through blower resistor and blower switch.

WARNING: To avoid injury from accidental air bag deployment, read and carefully follow all SERVICE PRECAUTIONS and DISABLING & ACTIVATING AIR BAG SYSTEM procedures in AIR BAG SYSTEM SAFETY article in GENERAL SERVICING.

CAUTION: When battery is disconnected, radio will go into anti-theft protection mode. Obtain radio anti-theft protection code from owner prior to servicing vehicle.

ADJUSTMENTS

NOTE: All air control doors are actuator operated. No adjustment is necessary.

TESTING

WARNING: To avoid injury from accidental air bag deployment, read and carefully follow all SERVICE PRECAUTIONS and DISABLING & ACTIVATING AIR BAG SYSTEM procedures in AIR BAG SYSTEM SAFETY article in GENERAL SERVICING.

BLOWER MOTOR DOES NOT OPERATE AT ANY BLOWER SWITCH POSITION

1) Check 30-amp HEATER fuse in engine compartment fuse block and 15-amp ENGINE fuse in dash fuse block. Check 30-amp blower fuse in blower unit. If fuses are okay, go to next step. If any fuse is blown, check shorted wiring harness before replacing fuse.

2) Turn ignition on. Set blower switch at highest speed setting. Using voltmeter, backprobe Black/White wire terminal of blower motor relay connector. If battery voltage exists, go to next step. If voltage is not present, repair open Black/White wire between ENGINE fuse and blower motor relay.

3) Backprobe Blue wire terminal of relay connector. If battery voltage exists, go to next step. If voltage is not present, repair open Blue wire between HEATER fuse and blower motor relay.

4) Backprobe Black/Blue wire terminal of relay connector. If voltage is not present, go to next step. If battery voltage exists, repair wiring harness. Check starting system.

5) Backprobe Blue/Red wire terminal of relay connector. If battery voltage exists, go to next step. If voltage is not present, replace blower motor relay.

6) Ensure ignition is on and blower switch is at highest speed setting. Backprobe Blue/Red wire terminal of blower motor connector. If battery voltage exists, go to next step. If voltage is not present, repair open Blue/Red wire between blower motor relay and blower motor.

7) Backprobe Blue/White wire terminal of blower motor connector. If battery voltage exists, check Blue/White wire between blower motor, blower resistor and blower switch. If wire is okay, go to BLOWER MOTOR DOES NOT OPERATE AT SPECIFIC BLOWER SWITCH POSITION test. If voltage does not exist, replace blower motor.

BLOWER MOTOR DOES NOT OPERATE AT SPECIFIC BLOWER SWITCH POSITION

1) Turn ignition on. Ensure blower is off. Using voltmeter, backprobe Blue/White wire terminal of blower resistor. If voltage exists, go to

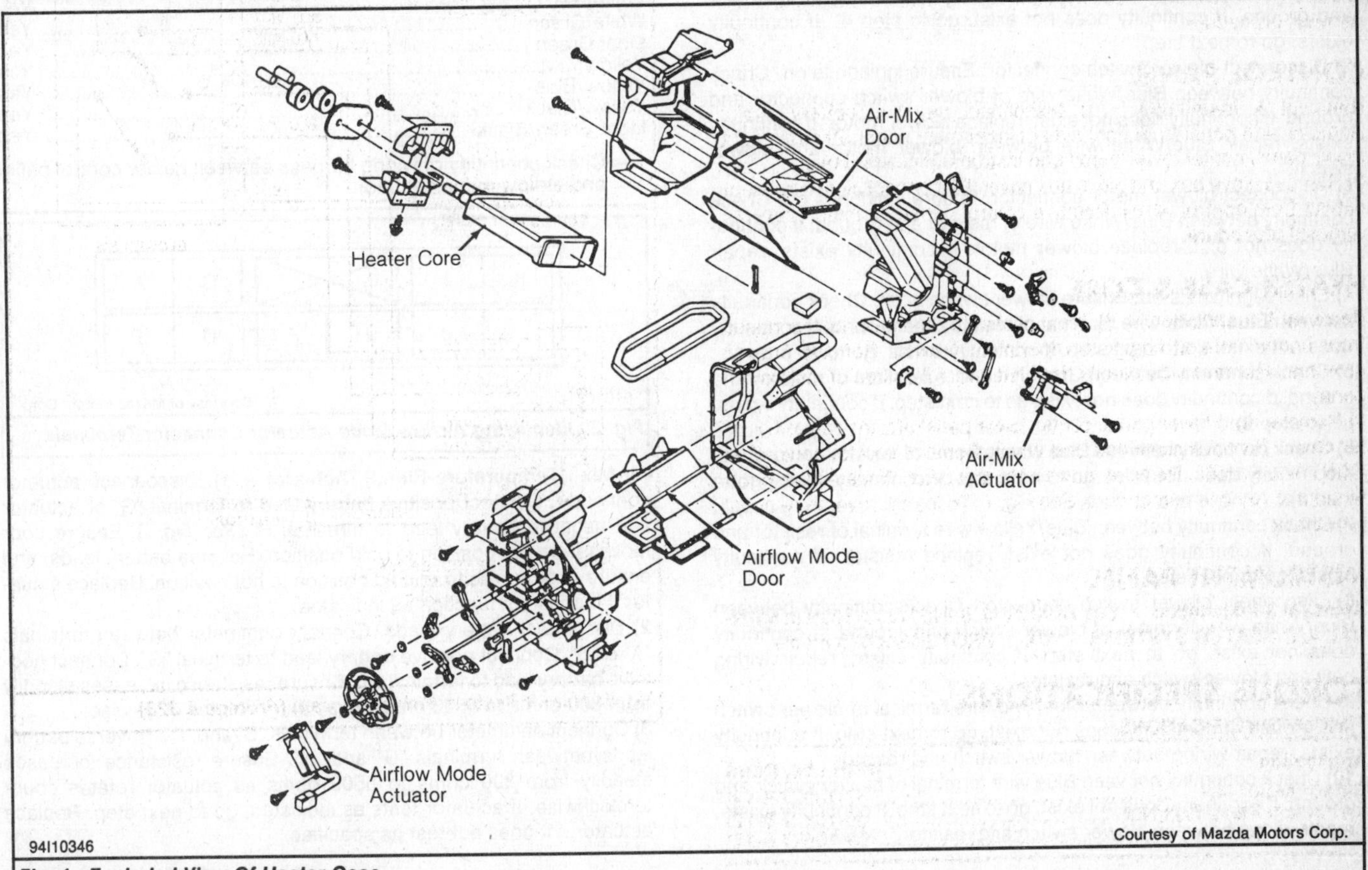
Air-Mix Door
Heater Core
Air-Mix Actuator
Airflow Mode Door
Airflow Mode Actuator
94I10346
Courtesy of Mazda Motors Corp.

Fig. 1: Exploded View Of Heater Case

1993 HEATER SYSTEMS
MX-6 & 626 (Cont.)

next step. If voltage is not present, check Blue/White wire between blower motor and blower resistor. If wire is okay, replace resistor.

2) Backprobe Green/Red wire terminal of resistor. If voltage exists, go to next step. If voltage is not present, replace resistor.

3) Backprobe Blue wire terminal of resistor. If voltage exists, go to next step. If voltage is not present, replace resistor.

4) Backprobe Blue/Yellow wire terminal of resistor. If voltage exists, go to next step. If voltage does not exist, replace resistor.

5) Disconnect blower switch connector. Measure voltage at Blue/White wire terminal of blower switch connector. If voltage exists, go to next step. If voltage does not exist, repair open Blue/White wire between blower resistor and blower switch.

6) Measure voltage at Blue/Red wire terminal of blower switch connector. If voltage exists, go to next step. If voltage does not exist, repair open Blue/Red wire between blower resistor and blower switch.

7) Measure voltage at Blue wire terminal of blower switch connector. If voltage exists, go to next step. If voltage does not exist, repair open Blue wire between blower resistor and blower switch.

8) Measure voltage at Blue/Yellow wire terminal of blower switch connector. If voltage exists, replace blower switch. If voltage is not present, repair open Blue/Yellow wire between resistor and blower switch. Go to next step.

9) Reconnect blower switch connector. Ensure blower switch is off and ignition is on. Backprobe Blue/White wire terminal of blower switch. If battery voltage exists, go to next step. If voltage is not present, check Blue/White wire between blower motor and blower switch. If wire is okay, replace blower switch.

10) Check continuity between Black wire terminal of blower switch connector and ground. If continuity exists, replace blower switch. If continuity does not exist, repair ground circuit.

BLOWER MOTOR OPERATES WITH BLOWER SWITCH IN OFF POSITION

1) Disconnect resistor connector. Turn ignition off. Turn blower switch off. Check continuity between Blue/White wire of resistor connector and ground. If continuity does not exist, go to step **4)**. If continuity exists, go to next step.

2) Disconnect blower switch connector. Ensure ignition is off. Check continuity between Blue/White wire of blower switch connector and ground. If continuity does not exist, replace blower motor. If continuity exists, repair Blue/White wire between blower motor and blower switch.

3) Disconnect blower motor connector. Ensure ignition is off. Check continuity between Blue/White wire of resistor and ground. If continuity does not exit, replace blower motor. If continuity exists, repair Blue/White wire.

4) Ensure ignition is off. Ensure blower switch is off. Check continuity between Blue/White wire terminal of resistor and ground. If continuity does not exist, go to next step. If continuity exists, go to step **8)**.

5) Check continuity between Green/Red wire terminal of resistor and ground. If continuity does not exist, go to next step. If continuity exists, go to step **8)**.

6) Check continuity between Blue wire terminal of resistor and ground. If continuity does not exist, go to next step. If continuity exists, go to step **8)**.

7) Check continuity between Blue/Yellow wire terminal of resistor and ground. If continuity does not exist, replace resistor. If continuity exists, go to next step.

8) Disconnect blower switch connector. Check continuity between Blue/White wire terminal of blower switch and ground. If continuity does not exist, go to next step. If continuity exists, repair wiring between blower switch and resistor.

9) Check continuity between Blue/Red wire terminal of blower switch and ground. If continuity does not exist, go to next step. If continuity exists, repair wiring between blower switch and resistor.

10) Check continuity between Blue wire terminal of blower switch and ground. If continuity does not exist, go to next step. If continuity exists, repair wiring between blower switch and resistor.

11) Check continuity between Blue/Yellow wire terminal of blower switch and ground. If continuity does not exist, replace blower switch. If continuity exists, repair wiring between blower switch and resistor.

ACTUATOR DOOR INOPERATIVE

Airflow Mode Actuator – 1) Disconnect actuator connector. Connect positive battery lead to terminal "J" of actuator and negative battery lead to terminal "I" of actuator. *See Fig. 2.* Ensure actuator moves door from vent position to defrost position. Reverse battery leads, and ensure door moves from defrost position to vent position. Replace actuator if it does not function as indicated.

2) Press appropriate push button on airflow mode panel, and check continuity between indicated terminals of actuator. See AIRFLOW MODE ACTUATOR TEST table. If continuity is as specified, go to next step. If continuity is not as specified, replace actuator.

3) Disconnect heater control panel connector. Check continuity of indicated wires between heater control panel connector and airflow mode actuator connector. See AIRFLOW MODE ACTUATOR WIRING HARNESS TEST table. If wiring harness continuity is as specified, replace heater control panel. If continuity does not exist, repair appropriate open wire.

AIRFLOW MODE ACTUATOR TEST

Switch Position	Terminal	Continuity
Vent	"C", "D", "F", "H" & "K"	Yes
Bi-Level	"A" & "B"; "D", "F", "H" & "K"	Yes
Heat	"A", "B" & "C"; "F", "H" & "K"	Yes
Heat/Defrost	"A", "B", "C" & "D"; "H" & "K"	Yes
Defrost	"A", "B", "C", "D" & "F"	Yes

AIRFLOW MODE ACTUATOR WIRING HARNESS TEST

Wire Color [1]	Continuity
White	Yes
White/Black	Yes
White/Red	Yes
White/Green	Yes
Light Green	Yes
Yellow	Yes
Yellow/Blue	Yes
Yellow/Black	Yes
Light Green/Black	Yes

[1] – Check continuity of wiring harness between heater control panel and airflow mode actuator.

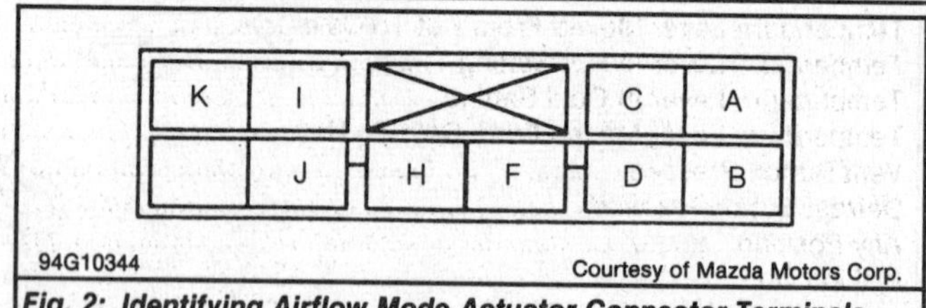
K
I
C
A
J
H
F
D
B
94G10344
Courtesy of Mazda Motors Corp.

Fig. 2: Identifying Airflow Mode Actuator Connector Terminals

Air-Mix (Temperature-Blend) Actuator – 1) Disconnect actuator connector. Connect positive battery lead to terminal "G" of actuator and negative battery lead to terminal "H". *See Fig. 3.* Ensure door moves from hot position to cold position. Reverse battery leads, and ensure door moves from cold position to hot position. Replace actuator if it does not function as indicated.

2) Disconnect battery leads. Connect ohmmeter between terminals "A" & "B". Connect positive battery lead to terminal "G". Connect negative battery lead to terminal "H". Ensure resistance increases steadily from 800 ohms to 5500 ohms as actuator rotates clockwise.

3) Connect ohmmeter between terminals "B" and "D". Reverse battery leads between terminals "G" and "H". Ensure resistance increases steadily from 800 ohms to 5500 ohms as actuator rotates counterclockwise. If actuator tests as indicated, go to next step. Replace actuator if it does not test as specified.

4) Disconnect heater control panel connector. Check continuity of indicated wires between heater control panel connector and air-mix actuator connector. See AIR-MIX ACTUATOR WIRING HARNESS TEST table. If wiring harness continuity is as specified, replace heater control panel. If continuity does not exist, repair appropriate open wire.

AIR-MIX ACTUATOR WIRING HARNESS TEST

Wire Color [1]	Continuity
Brown	Yes
Green	Yes
Green/White	Yes
Pink	Yes
Green/Yellow	Yes

[1] – Check continuity of wiring harness between heater control panel and air-mix actuator.

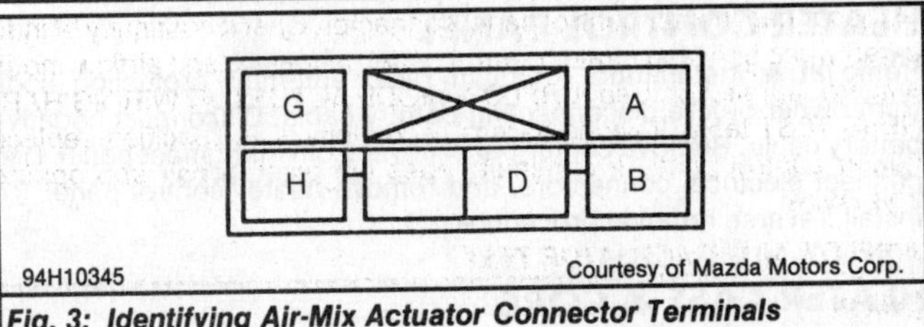
G
A
H
D
B
94H10345
Courtesy of Mazda Motors Corp.

Fig. 3: Identifying Air-Mix Actuator Connector Terminals

Fresh/Recirculated Air Actuator – 1) Disconnect actuator connector. Connect positive battery lead to Blue/Orange wire terminal of actuator. Connect negative battery lead to Light Green/Red wire terminal of actuator. Ensure actuator moves door from fresh air position to recirculated air position.

2) Move negative battery lead to Blue wire terminal of actuator. Ensure door moves from recirculated air position to fresh air position. If actuator functions as indicated, go to next step. Replace actuator if it does not function as indicated.

3) Disconnect heater control panel connector. Check continuity of indicated wire between heater control panel connector and fresh/recirculated air actuator connector. See FRESH/RECIRCULATED AIR ACTUATOR WIRING HARNESS TEST table. If wiring harness continuity is as specified, replace heater control panel. If continuity does not exist, repair appropriate open wire.

FRESH/RECIRCULATED AIR ACTUATOR WIRING HARNESS TEST

Wire Color [1]	Continuity
Blue/Orange [2]	Yes
Blue [3]	Yes
Light Green/Red	Yes

[1] – Check continuity of wiring harness between heater control panel and fresh/recirculated air actuator.
[2] – Blue/Orange wire at fresh/recirculated air actuator; Blue wire at heater control panel.
[3] – There are 2 Blue wires at heater control panel; ensure correct wire is tested.

HEATER CONTROL PANEL

Remove heater control panel. See HEATER CONTROL PANEL under REMOVAL & INSTALLATION. Measure voltage at indicated terminals on back of heater control panel. See HEATER CONTROL PANEL TEST table. If voltage is not as specified, check related components and wiring harness. If components and wiring harness are okay, replace heater control panel.

HEATER CONTROL PANEL TEST

Test Condition	Terminal Wire Color	Volts
6-Pin Connector		
Blower Switch In Medium-High Setting	BLU/RED (Resistor)	0
Blower Switch In Medium-High Or High Setting	BLU/WHT (Resistor – Blower Motor)	0
Blower Switch In Medium-Low Setting	BLU (Resistor)	0
Blower Switch In High Setting	BLU/BLK (ECU)	0
Blower Switch In Low Setting	BLU/YEL (Resistor – A/C Amplifier)	0
Any Position	BLK (Body Ground)	0
10-Pin Connector		
Any Position	GRN/WHT (Air-Mix Actuator)	About 5
Any Position	BRN (Air-Mix Actuator)	0
Temperature Lever Moved From Hot To Cold	GRN/BLK (Air-Mix Actuator)	0
Temperature Lever In Hot Setting	GRN (Air-Mix Actuator)	5
Temperature Lever In Cold Setting	GRN (Air-Mix Actuator)	0
Temperature Lever Moved From Cold To Hot	GRN/YEL (Air-Mix Actuator)	0
Vent Button Pressed	YEL/BLK (Airflow Mode Actuator)	12
Defrost Button Pressed	YEL/GRN (Airflow Mode Actuator)	12
Any Position	BLK (Body Ground)	0
Ignition On	BLU (Ignition Switch)	12
14-Pin Connector		
Defrost Button Pressed	WHT (Airflow Mode Actuator)	0
Vent Button Pressed	WHT/BLK (Airflow Mode Actuator)	About 10
Light Switch On	ORN (Tail No. Side Relay)	12
Blower Switch Off	RED (A/C Amplifier)	12
A/C Switch & Blower Switch On	BLU/WHT (A/C Amplifier)	12
Fresh Air Button Pressed	GRN/BLU (Intake Actuator)	12
Recirculated Air Button Pressed	BLU (Intake Actuator)	12
Defrost Button Pressed	YEL/WHT (Airflow Mode Actuator)	0
Heat/Defrost Button Pressed	YEL (Airflow Mode Actuator)	0
Heat Button Pressed	WHT/BLU (Airflow Mode Actuator)	0
Vent Button Pressed	WHT/YEL (Airflow Mode Actuator)	0
Bi-Level Button Pressed	WHT/GRN (Airflow Mode Actuator)	0
Ignition On	BRN/RED (Swing Louver)	12
Swing Louver On	BRN/RED (Swing Louver)	About 1

1993 HEATER SYSTEMS
MX-6 & 626 (Cont.)

BLOWER MOTOR

Disconnect blower motor connector on bottom of blower case. Connect battery voltage across blower motor connector terminals. Replace blower motor if it does not operate.

BLOWER MOTOR RELAY

1) Disconnect blower motor relay. Using ohmmeter, check continuity between Blue wire and Blue/Red wire terminals of relay. Continuity should not exist. Check continuity between Black/White wire and Black/Blue wire terminals of relay. Ensure continuity exists.

2) Apply battery voltage between Black/White wire and Black/Blue wire terminals of relay. Ensure continuity exists between Blue wire and Blue/Red wire terminals with voltage applied. If continuity is not as specified, replace relay.

BLOWER MOTOR RESISTOR

Disconnect resistor connector. Using ohmmeter, check continuity between indicated resistor terminals. See BLOWER MOTOR RESISTOR TEST table. Replace resistor if continuity is not as specified.

BLOWER MOTOR RESISTOR TEST

Terminal (Wire Color)	Continuity
Blue/White & Green/Red	Yes
Blue/White & Blue	Yes
Blue/White & Blue/Yellow	Yes

REMOVAL & INSTALLATION

WARNING: To avoid injury from accidental air bag deployment, read and carefully follow all SERVICE PRECAUTIONS and DISABLING & ACTIVATING AIR BAG SYSTEM procedures in AIR BAG SYSTEM SAFETY article in GENERAL SERVICING.

BLOWER ASSEMBLY

Removal & Installation – Remove instrument panel. See REMOVAL & INSTALLATION in MANUAL A/C-HEATER SYSTEMS – MX-6 & 626 article. Disconnect electrical connectors from blower assembly. Remove blower assembly nuts, and remove blower assembly. Disassemble blower assembly to remove blower motor and blower resistor. To install, reverse removal procedure.

HEATER CONTROL PANEL

Removal & Installation – Obtain radio anti-theft protection code from owner before disconnecting battery cable. Disconnect negative battery cable. Remove center panel cover from instrument panel. Disconnect electrical connectors, and remove heater control panel. To install, reverse removal procedure.

HEATER CASE & CORE

Removal & Installation – **1)** Drain engine coolant. Disconnect heater hoses at engine compartment firewall. Remove instrument panel. See REMOVAL & INSTALLATION in MANUAL A/C-HEATER SYSTEMS – MX-6 & 626 article.

2) Remove nuts and bolts from heater case. Remove heater case. Disassemble heater case to remove heater core. *See Fig. 1.* To install, reverse removal procedure. Fill cooling system.

WIRING DIAGRAM

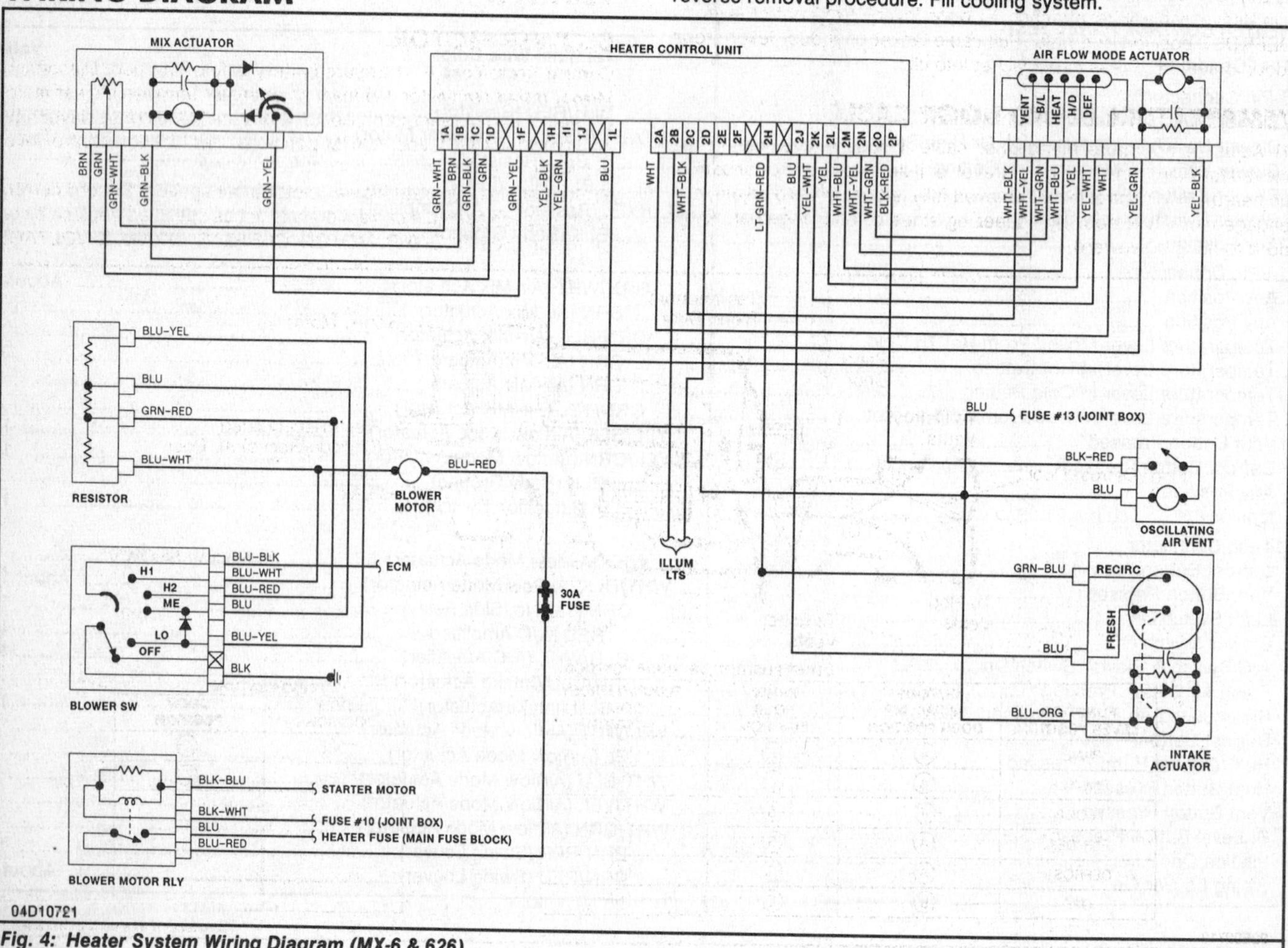
MIX ACTUATOR
HEATER CONTROL UNIT
AIR FLOW MODE ACTUATOR
VENT
B/L
HEAT
H/D
DEF
BRN
GRN
GRN-WHT
GRN-BLK
GRN-YEL
YEL-BLK
YEL-GRN
BLU
WHT
WHT-BLK
LT GRN-RED
YEL-WHT
YEL
WHT-BLU
WHT-YEL
WHT-GRN
BLK-RED
YEL-BLK
BLU-YEL
GRN-RED
BLU-WHT
RESISTOR
BLU-RED
BLOWER MOTOR
FUSE #13 (JOINT BOX)
OSCILLATING AIR VENT
BLU-BLK
ECM
H1
H2
ME
LO
OFF
BLK
BLOWER SW
30A FUSE
ILLUM LTS
GRN-BLU
RECIRC
FRESH
BLU-ORG
INTAKE ACTUATOR
BLK-BLU
STARTER MOTOR
BLK-WHT
FUSE #10 (JOINT BOX)
HEATER FUSE (MAIN FUSE BLOCK)
BLOWER MOTOR RLY
04D10721

Fig. 4: Heater System Wiring Diagram (MX-6 & 626)

1993 HEATER SYSTEMS
Navajo

DESCRIPTION & OPERATION

Blower case, containing blower motor and blower resistor, is mounted on engine compartment firewall. Air flows through the fresh/recirculated air, temperature blend, panel and floor/defrost doors in heater case (plenum assembly). *See Fig. 1*. The fresh/recirculated air door is vacuum-actuated. All other doors are cable actuated.

When function lever is in OFF position, a vacuum valve on the control panel allows vacuum to reach the fresh/recirculated air door vacuum motor on right side of heater case, closeing the door and shutting off outside air. When function lever is in all other positions, vacuum valve denies vacuum to vacuum motor, opening the door and allowing outside air to enter vehicle. *See Fig. 2*.

Temperature blend door controls amount of air that flows through or around heater core. Function lever uses one cable to control positions of panel and floor/defrost doors.

A 30-amp fuse in passenger compartment fuse block protects power supply circuit to blower motor. With blower switch in highest position, blower motor is grounded through blower switch. With blower switch in all other positions, blower motor is grounded through blower resistor and blower switch.

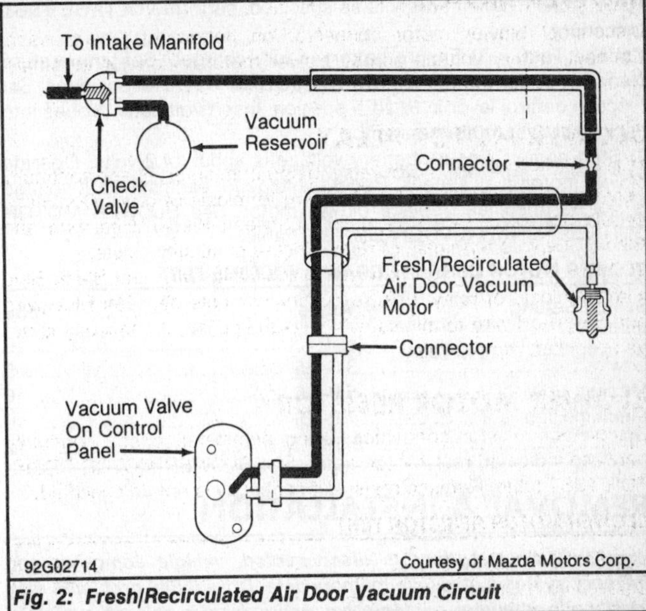
To Intake Manifold
Vacuum Reservoir
Connector
Check Valve
Fresh/Recirculated Air Door Vacuum Motor
Connector
Vacuum Valve On Control Panel
92G02714
Courtesy of Mazda Motors Corp.

Fig. 2: Fresh/Recirculated Air Door Vacuum Circuit

ADJUSTMENTS

PANEL & FLOOR/DEFROST DOOR CABLE

1) Adjust cable if control lever cannot be moved fully through its range of travel, or if airflow through vents does not match setting on control panel. To adjust, disengage glove box door by squeezing sides of door together. Allow door to hang downward.

2) Depress cable clip tab on top of heater case, and pull cable out of clip (leave cable wire attached to door lever). Set control lever to DEFROST position and hold. Pull cable jacket until door lever stops (door is seated). Press cable jacket into clip.

TEMPERATURE BLEND DOOR CABLE

1) Adjust temperature blend door cable if control lever cannot be moved fully through its range of travel, or if firm seating of door cannot be heard when control lever is moved fully left or right. To adjust, disengage glove box door by squeezing sides of door together. Allow door to hang downward.

2) Depress cable clip tab on top of heater case, and pull cable out of clip (leave cable wire attached to door lever). Set control lever to COOL position and hold. Gently push cable jacket until door lever stops (door is seated). Press cable jacket into clip.

TESTING

BLOWER MOTOR

Current Draw Test - 1) Ensure battery is fully charged. Disconnect blower motor connector. Connect an ammeter between blower motor connector and blower motor. Set temperature blend control lever halfway between COOL and WARM positions. Set function control lever in PANEL position.

2) Start engine. Operate blower motor in all speeds. Record current draw for each speed. If current draw is not as specified, replace blower motor. See BLOWER MOTOR CURRENT DRAW & VOLTAGE

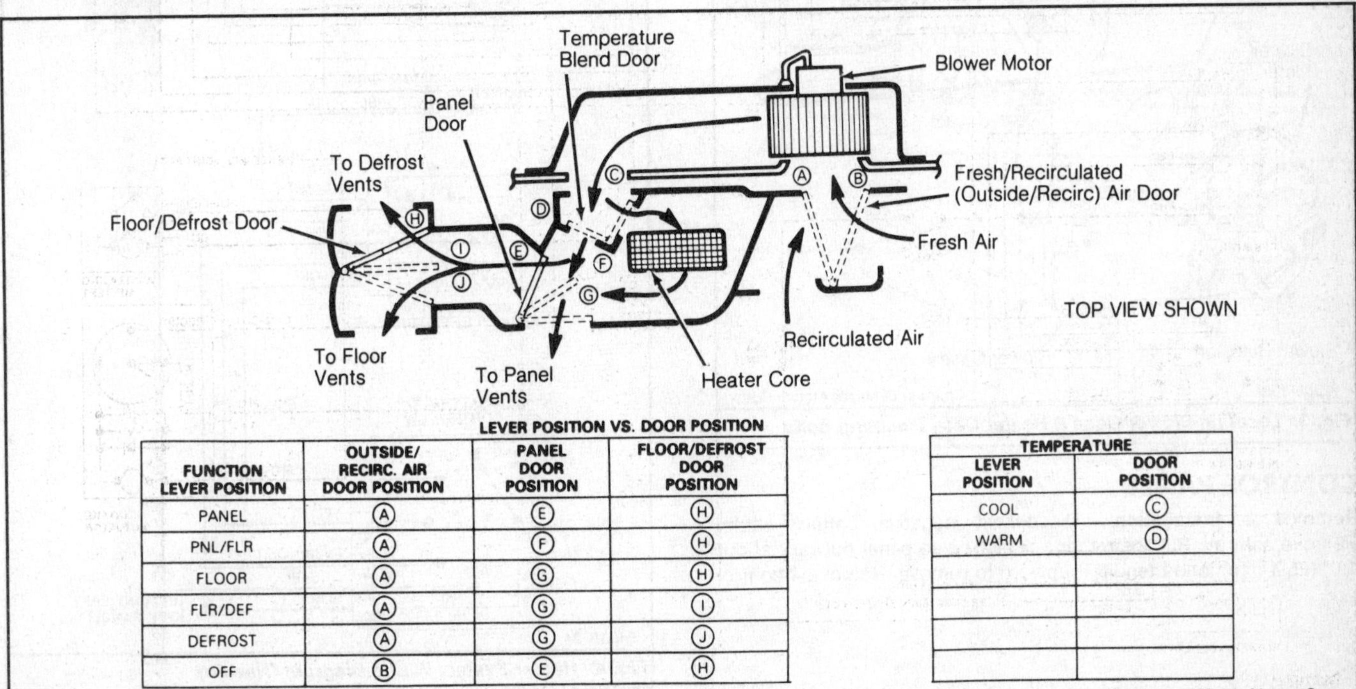
Temperature Blend Door
Blower Motor
Panel Door
To Defrost Vents
Fresh/Recirculated (Outside/Recirc) Air Door
Floor/Defrost Door
Fresh Air
TOP VIEW SHOWN
Recirculated Air
To Floor Vents
To Panel Vents
Heater Core
92E02713
Courtesy of Mazda Motors Corp.

LEVER POSITION VS. DOOR POSITION

FUNCTION LEVER POSITION	OUTSIDE/ RECIRC. AIR DOOR POSITION	PANEL DOOR POSITION	FLOOR/DEFROST DOOR POSITION
PANEL	Ⓐ	Ⓔ	Ⓗ
PNL/FLR	Ⓐ	Ⓕ	Ⓗ
FLOOR	Ⓐ	Ⓖ	Ⓗ
FLR/DEF	Ⓐ	Ⓖ	Ⓘ
DEFROST	Ⓐ	Ⓖ	Ⓙ
OFF	Ⓑ	Ⓔ	Ⓗ

TEMPERATURE	
LEVER POSITION	DOOR POSITION
COOL	Ⓒ
WARM	Ⓓ

Fig. 1: Heater System Airflow Circuits

1993 HEATER SYSTEMS
Navajo (Cont.)

TEST table. If current draw is as specified, perform VOLTAGE TEST procedure.

Voltage Test – 1) Ensure battery is fully charged. Set temperature blend control lever halfway between COOL and WARM positions. Set function control lever in PANEL position. Insert voltmeter probes into back of blower motor connector.

2) Start engine. Ensure battery voltage is about 14.2 volts. Operate blower motor in all speeds. Record voltage for each speed. If voltage is not as specified, replace blower motor. See BLOWER MOTOR CURRENT DRAW & VOLTAGE TEST table.

BLOWER MOTOR CURRENT DRAW & VOLTAGE TEST

Switch Setting	Amps	Volts
OFF	0	0
Low	3.5-5.5	5
Medium Low	5.0-7.5	8
Medium High	7.0-9.5	10
HI	9.5-11.5	12

REMOVAL & INSTALLATION

WARNING: When battery is disconnected, vehicle computer and memory systems may lose memory data. Driveability problems may exist until computer systems have completed a relearn cycle. To complete a relearn cycle, drive vehicle for 10 miles after connecting battery.

BLOWER CASE

Removal & Installation – Disconnect negative battery cable. Remove one nut from blower case in passenger compartment. *See Fig. 3.* Disconnect electrical connectors from blower motor and blower resistor. Disconnect vacuum hose from check valve and intake manifold. Remove 3 remaining nuts from blower case. Remove blower case. Disassemble blower case to remove blower motor. To install, reverse removal procedure.

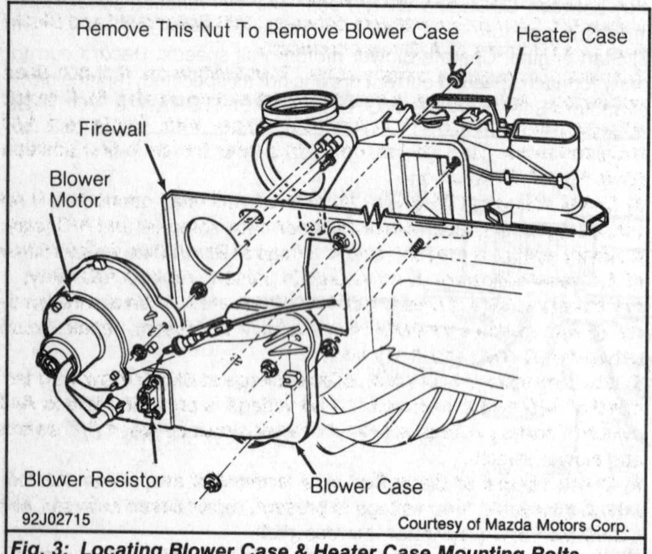
Remove This Nut To Remove Blower Case
Heater Case
Firewall
Blower Motor
Blower Resistor
Blower Case
92J02715
Courtesy of Mazda Motors Corp.

Fig. 3: Locating Blower Case & Heater Case Mounting Bolts

CONTROL PANEL

Removal & Installation – Disconnect negative battery cable. Remove ashtray. Pull instrument cluster finish panel outward about 1.0" (25.4 mm), and then lift it upward to remove. Remove 4 control panel-to-instrument panel screws. Pull control panel out, disconnect electrical and vacuum connectors, and remove control panel. To install, reverse removal procedure.

HEATER CASE

Removal & Installation – Disconnect negative battery cable. Disconnect heater hoses. Remove blower case. See BLOWER CASE. At engine compartment firewall, remove all other nuts securing heater case to firewall. *See Fig. 3.* Remove instrument panel. See INSTRUMENT PANEL. Remove heater case. To install, reverse removal procedure.

HEATER CORE

Removal & Installation – Disconnect heater hoses from heater core. Remove 4 heater core access cover bolts from bottom of heater case. Pull heater core rearward and then down. To install, reverse removal procedure.

INSTRUMENT PANEL

Removal & Installation – 1) Disconnect negative battery cable. Disconnect all necessary electrical connectors. Remove ashtray. Pull instrument cluster finish panel outward about 1.0" (25.4 mm), and then lift it upward to remove. Remove instrument cluster. Remove hood release cable from bottom of steering column cover.

2) Disengage steering column cover at top corners and remove. Remove instrument panel-to-brake/clutch pedal bracket screw. Remove upper and lower shrouds from steering column. Disconnect electrical connectors from steering column switches. Remove right and left covers from ends of instrument panel.

3) Remove 2 bolts securing right and left sides of instrument panel lower corners to cowl sides. Remove left and right kick panels. Remove 4 screws retaining top of instrument panel. Remove instrument panel. To install, reverse removal procedure.

WIRING DIAGRAM

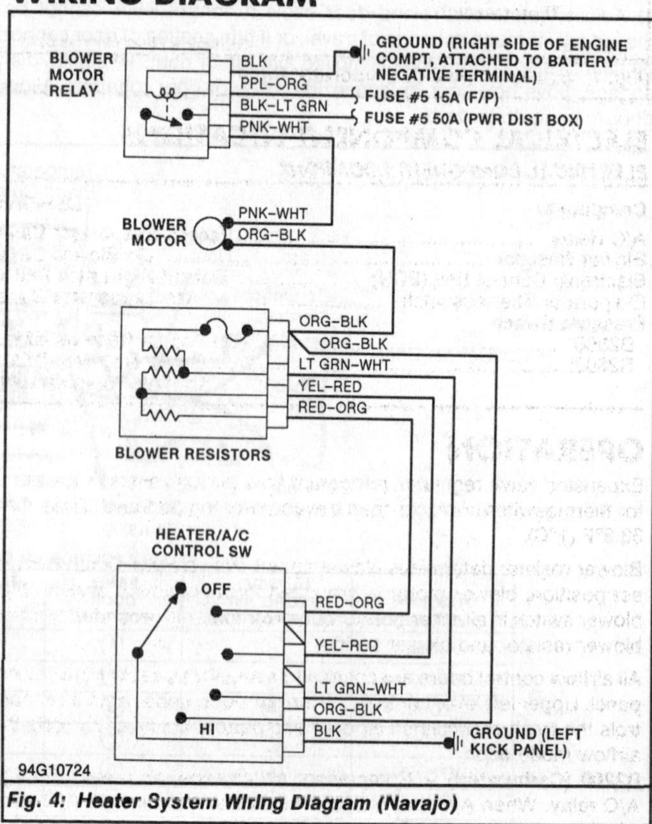
BLOWER MOTOR RELAY
BLK
PPL-ORG
BLK-LT GRN
PNK-WHT
GROUND (RIGHT SIDE OF ENGINE COMPT, ATTACHED TO BATTERY NEGATIVE TERMINAL)
FUSE #5 15A (F/P)
FUSE #5 50A (PWR DIST BOX)
BLOWER MOTOR
PNK-WHT
ORG-BLK
ORG-BLK
ORG-BLK
LT GRN-WHT
YEL-RED
RED-ORG
BLOWER RESISTORS
HEATER/A/C CONTROL SW
OFF
RED-ORG
YEL-RED
LT GRN-WHT
ORG-BLK
HI
BLK
GROUND (LEFT KICK PANEL)
94G10724

Fig. 4: Heater System Wiring Diagram (Navajo)

1993 MANUAL A/C-HEATER SYSTEMS
B2200 & B2600i

SPECIFICATIONS

Compressor Type	Sanden 5-Cyl.
Compressor Belt Deflection [1]	
B2200	
New	25/64-15/32" (10-12 mm)
Used	5/32-35/64" (12-14 mm)
B2600i	
New	21/64-15/32" (8.5-10.0 mm)
Used	15/32-29/64" (10.0-11.5 mm)
Compressor Oil Capacity	4.5 ozs.
Refrigerant (R-12) Capacity	28 ozs.
System Operating Pressures [2]	
High Side	150-184 psi (10.5-12.9 kg/cm²)
Low Side	14-24 psi (1.0-1.7 kg/cm²)

[1] – Measure with 22 lb. (10 kg) pressure applied to center of belt.
[2] – Specification is with ambient temperature at about 77°F (25°C).

DESCRIPTION

Blower case contains blower motor, blower resistor and fresh/recirculated air door. Heater case contains heater core, airflow mode door and air-mix (temperature blend) door. Evaporator case contains evaporator, evaporator thermoswitch and expansion valve. *See Fig. 1.*

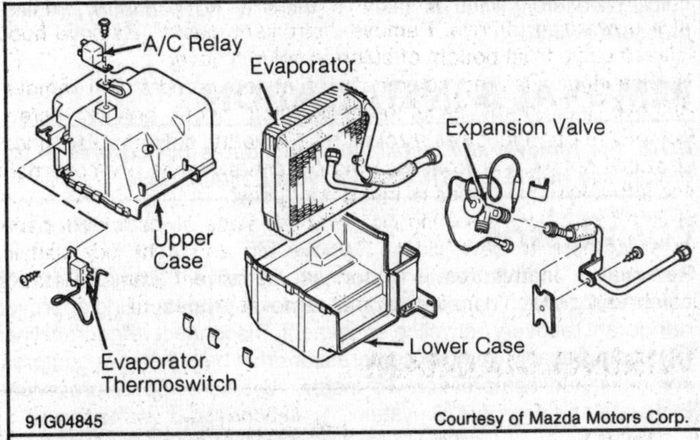
A/C Relay
Evaporator
Expansion Valve
Upper Case
Lower Case
Evaporator Thermoswitch
91G04845
Courtesy of Mazda Motors Corp.

Fig. 1: Exploded View Of Evaporator Case

ELECTRICAL COMPONENT LOCATIONS

ELECTRICAL COMPONENT LOCATIONS

Component	Location
A/C Relay	On Top Of Evaporator Case
Blower Resistor	On Blower Case
Electronic Control Unit (ECU)	Behind Right Kick Panel
Evaporator Thermoswitch	On Evaporator Case
Pressure Switch	
B2200	On Top Of Receiver-Drier
B2600i	Below Receiver-Drier, In High-Pressure Line

OPERATION

Expansion valve regulates refrigerant flow through system. Evaporator thermoswitch contacts open if evaporator temperature is less than 33.8°F (1°C).

Blower resistor determines blower speed. With blower switch in highest position, blower motor is grounded through blower switch. With blower switch in all other positions, blower motor is grounded through blower resistor and blower switch.

All airflow control doors are controlled manually by cable from control panel. Upper left lever controls the air-mix door, upper right lever controls the fresh/recirculated air door and bottom left lever controls the airflow mode door.

B2200 (Carbureted) – Compressor clutch receives power through A/C relay. When A/C and blower switches are turned on, A/C relay windings are grounded. This energizes A/C relay, allowing power to compressor clutch. If contacts in evaporator thermoswitch or pressure switch open, power to compressor clutch is interrupted. Pressure switch contacts open if high-side pressure is less than 40 psi (2.8 kg/cm²).

B2200 (Fuel Injected) & B2600i – Compressor clutch receives power when A/C relay is energized. Electronic Control Unit (ECU) grounds A/C relay windings to energize A/C relay. ECU stops energizing A/C relay if it senses open contacts in evaporator thermoswitch. If pressure switch contacts open, power to compressor clutch is interrupted. Pressure switch contacts open if high-side pressure is less than 30 psi (2.1 kg/cm²) or greater than 256 psi (18 kg/cm²).

ADJUSTMENTS

***NOTE:** For cable adjustments, see HEATER SYSTEMS – B2200 & B2600i article.*

TESTING

***NOTE:** For testing procedures not covered in this article, see HEATER SYSTEMS – B2200 & B2600i article.*

A/C SYSTEM PERFORMANCE

1) Park vehicle out of direct sunlight. Install A/C gauge set. Start engine and allow it to idle at 1500 RPM. Set A/C controls to recirculate air, panel (vent) mode, full cold, and A/C button on.

2) Set blower/fan on high speed and close doors and windows. Insert thermometer in center vent. Operate system for 20 minutes to allow system to stabilize. Measure temperature. Temperature should be 37-42°F (3-6°C) at center vent, with high side and low side pressures within specification. See SPECIFICATIONS table at beginning of article.

COMPRESSOR CLUTCH CIRCUIT

B2200 (Carbureted) – **1)** Check 10-amp AIR COND fuse in passenger compartment fuse block. If fuse is blown, repair short circuit. If fuse is okay, disconnect negative battery cable. Disconnect A/C relay connector. Connect jumper wire between Light Green/Red and Black/Red wire terminals of A/C relay connector.

2) Reconnect negative battery cable. Turn ignition on. If clutch does not engage, leave jumper wire connected and go to step **6)**. If clutch engages, turn ignition off. Disconnect jumper wire. Reconnect A/C relay connector. Turn ignition on. Turn blower switch to first position (low). Turn A/C switch on.

3) Check voltage at Blue wire terminal of A/C relay connector. If no voltage is present, repair circuit between circuit breaker and A/C relay. If battery voltage is present, check voltage at Blue/White wire terminal of A/C relay connector. If no voltage is present, replace A/C relay.

4) If battery voltage is present, check voltage at Blue/White wire terminal of A/C switch connector. If no voltage is present, repair circuit between A/C relay and A/C switch.

5) If battery voltage is present, check voltage at Blue/Yellow wire terminal of A/C switch connector. If no voltage is present, replace A/C switch. If battery voltage is present, repair circuit between A/C switch and blower switch.

6) Check voltage at Black/Red wire terminal of evaporator thermoswitch connector. If no voltage is present, repair circuit between AIR COND fuse and evaporator thermoswitch.

7) If battery voltage is present, check voltage at Black/Yellow wire terminal of evaporator thermoswitch connector. If no voltage is present, replace evaporator thermoswitch.

8) If battery voltage is present, disconnect jumper wire. Disconnect compressor clutch connector. Set ohmmeter to X1000 scale. Check continuity between ground and compressor clutch connector. If there is no continuity, replace compressor clutch.

9) If there is continuity, reconnect compressor clutch connector. Disconnect pressure switch connector. Check continuity between terminals of pressure switch connector. If there is continuity, repair circuit between evaporator thermoswitch and compressor clutch.

10) If there is no continuity, reconnect pressure switch connector. Connect manifold gauge set. If high-side pressure is more than 40 psi

1993 MANUAL A/C-HEATER SYSTEMS B2200 & B2600i (Cont.)

(2.8 kg/cm²), replace pressure switch. If high-side pressure is less than 40 psi (2.8 kg/cm²), check refrigerant system for proper charge.

B2200 (Fuel Injected) & B2600i - 1) Check 10-amp AIR COND fuse in passenger compartment fuse block. If fuse is blown, repair short circuit. If fuse is okay, go to next step.

2) Start and run engine at idle. Connect jumper wire between ground and Blue/White wire terminal of A/C relay connector. Turn blower switch and A/C switch on. If clutch does not engage, disconnect jumper wire and go to step **6)**. If clutch engages, disconnect jumper wire and go to next step.

3) Disconnect evaporator thermoswitch connector. Check continuity between evaporator thermoswitch terminals. If there is no continuity, replace evaporator thermoswitch. If there is continuity, reconnect evaporator thermoswitch connector.

4) Turn ignition off. Turn blower and A/C switches on. Check voltage at Black/Red wire terminal of evaporator thermoswitch connector. If no voltage is present, ECU or related system is faulty. If battery voltage is present, check voltage at Black/Red wire terminal of A/C switch connector.

5) If no voltage is present, repair circuit between evaporator thermoswitch and A/C switch. If battery voltage is present, check voltage at Blue/Yellow wire terminal of A/C switch connector. If battery voltage is present, repair circuit between A/C switch and blower switch. If no voltage is present, replace A/C switch.

6) Start and run engine at idle. Turn blower and A/C switches on. Check voltage at Blue/White wire terminal of A/C relay connector. If battery voltage is present, return to step **3)**. If no voltage is present, check voltage at Blue wire terminal of A/C relay connector.

7) If no voltage is present, repair circuit between 30-amp HEATER circuit breaker and A/C relay. If battery voltage is present, check voltage at Light Green/Red wire terminal of A/C relay connector.

8) If no voltage is present, repair circuit between AIR COND fuse and A/C relay. If battery voltage is present, check voltage at Black/Yellow wire terminal of A/C relay connector. If no voltage is present, replace A/C relay.

9) If battery voltage is present, disconnect pressure switch connector. Check for continuity between pressure switch terminals. If there is continuity, go to step **11)**. If there is no continuity, check high-side pressure.

10) If high-side pressure is 30-256 psi (2.1-18 kg/cm²), replace pressure switch. If high-side pressure is less than 30 psi (2.1 kg/cm²) or more than 256 psi (18 kg/cm²), check refrigerant system for proper charge.

11) Disconnect compressor clutch connector. Set ohmmeter to X1000 scale. Check continuity between ground and compressor clutch connector. If there is no continuity, replace compressor clutch. If there is continuity, repair circuit between A/C relay and compressor clutch.

A/C RELAY

Remove A/C relay. Check continuity between terminals No. 3 and 4. *See Fig. 2.* If there is continuity, replace relay. If there is no continuity, attach battery positive lead to terminal No. 1 and negative lead to terminal No. 2. Check continuity between terminals No. 3 and 4. If there is no continuity, replace relay. If there is continuity, relay is okay.

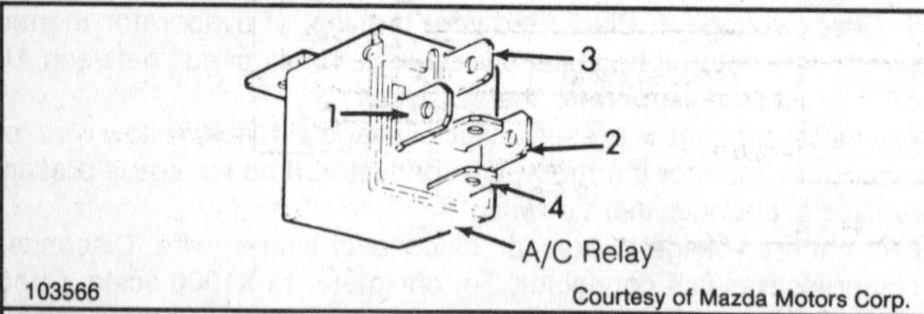
3
1
2
4
A/C Relay
103566
Courtesy of Mazda Motors Corp.

Fig. 2: Identifying A/C Relay Connector Terminals

A/C SWITCH

Remove A/C switch. With switch off, there should be no continuity between Black/Red and Blue/Yellow wire terminals. With switch on, there should be continuity between Black/Red and Blue/Yellow wire terminals. Replace switch if continuity is not as specified.

BLOWER MOTOR

Disconnect blower motor connector. Connect battery voltage across blower motor connector terminals. Replace blower motor if it does not operate.

EVAPORATOR THERMOSWITCH

Remove glove box. Start engine. Turn blower switch to low speed. Turn A/C on. Block air inlet at blower case to speed-up evaporator cooling. If compressor clutch does not disengage after a few minutes, check continuity between evaporator thermoswitch terminals. If there is continuity, replace evaporator thermoswitch. If continuity is not present, evaporator thermoswitch is okay.

PRESSURE SWITCH

1) Connect manifold gauge set. On B2200 (carbureted), ensure high-side pressure is more than 40 psi (2.8 kg/cm²). On B2200 (fuel injected) and B2600i, ensure high-side pressure is 30-256 psi (2.1-18 kg/cm²). On all models, if pressure is not as specified, check refrigerant charge.

2) If pressure is as specified, disconnect pressure switch connector. Check continuity between pressure switch terminals. If there is continuity, pressure switch is okay. If there is no continuity, replace pressure switch.

REMOVAL & INSTALLATION

NOTE: For removal and installation procedures not covered in this article, see HEATER SYSTEMS - B2200 & B2600i article.

COMPRESSOR

Removal & Installation - Disconnect negative battery cable and compressor clutch connector. Discharge A/C system using approved refrigerant recovery/recycling equipment. Disconnect refrigerant lines from compressor. Remove compressor drive belt. Remove compressor bolts and compressor. To install, reverse removal procedure. Evacuate and charge A/C system.

CONDENSER

Removal & Installation - Discharge A/C system using approved refrigerant recovery/recycling equipment. Remove radiator grille and front combination lights. Remove condenser pipe-to-center brace clip. Disconnect pipe nuts, and remove lower pipe. Remove center brace and hood lock brace. Disconnect discharge hose and liquid tube. Remove condenser nuts and condenser. To install, reverse removal procedure. Evacuate and charge A/C system.

CONTROL PANEL

Removal & Installation - 1) Remove instrument cluster cover. Pull knobs from blower motor switch and A/C switch. Remove nuts and washers from shafts. Remove hole cover from center panel. *See Fig. 3.* Remove screw from hole. Disconnect connectors from cigarette lighter and A/C switch. Remove center panel of instrument panel.

2) Remove glove box. Disconnect control cables from back of control panel. Remove control panel screws. Pull control panel out and disconnect electrical connectors. To install, reverse removal procedure. Adjust control cables. See HEATER SYSTEMS - B2200 & B2600i article.

EVAPORATOR CASE

Removal & Installation - 1) Discharge A/C system using approved refrigerant recovery/recycling equipment. Disconnect refrigerant lines from evaporator tubes at engine compartment firewall. Remove right side undercover and glove box.

2) Disconnect electrical connectors from evaporator case. Loosen left seal plate between heater case and evaporator case. Loosen right seal plate between evaporator case and blower motor case. Remove evaporator case nuts. Disconnect drain hose. Remove evaporator case.

3) Disassemble evaporator case to remove evaporator, evaporator thermoswitch and expansion valve. *See Fig. 1*. To install, reverse removal procedure. Evacuate and charge A/C system.

RECEIVER-DRIER

Removal & Installation – Discharge A/C system using approved refrigerant recovery/recycling equipment. Remove radiator grille. Remove receiver-drier nuts. Disconnect refrigerant lines from receiver-drier. Remove receiver-drier. To install, reverse removal procedure. Evacuate and charge A/C system.

INSTRUMENT PANEL

Removal & Installation – Disconnect negative battery cable. Remove all components in order listed in illustration. *See Fig. 4*. To install, reverse removal procedure.

TORQUE SPECIFICATIONS

TORQUE SPECIFICATIONS

Application	Ft. Lbs. (N.m)
Compressor Bolt/Nut	
B2200 (Carbureted)	29-40 (39-54)
B2200 (Fuel Injected) & B2600i	14-22 (19-30)
Refrigerant Hose-To-Compressor Bolt	
B2200 (Carbureted)	29-33 (39-45)
B2200 (Fuel Injected) & B2600i	
High Pressure (Discharge)	14-18 (19-24)
Low Pressure (Suction)	22-25 (30-34)
Steering Wheel Nut	29-36 (39-49)
	INCH Lbs. (N.m)
Instrument Panel Bolts/Nuts	69-97 (7.8-11)

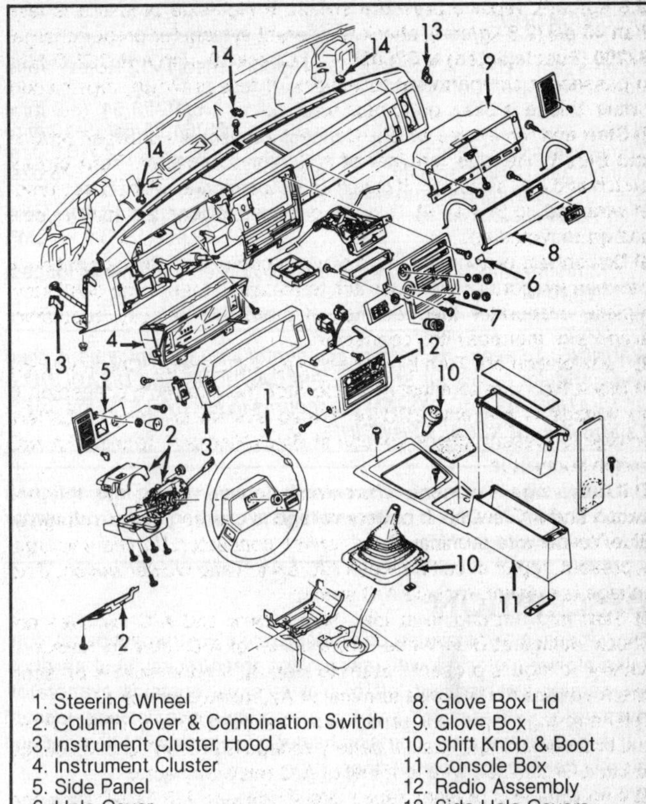
1. Steering Wheel
2. Column Cover & Combination Switch
3. Instrument Cluster Hood
4. Instrument Cluster
5. Side Panel
6. Hole Cover
7. Center Panel
8. Glove Box Lid
9. Glove Box
10. Shift Knob & Boot
11. Console Box
12. Radio Assembly
13. Side Hole Covers
14. Hole Covers (Upper)
94C10209
Courtesy of Mazda Motors Corp.

Fig. 4: Exploded View Of Instrument Panel

WIRING DIAGRAM

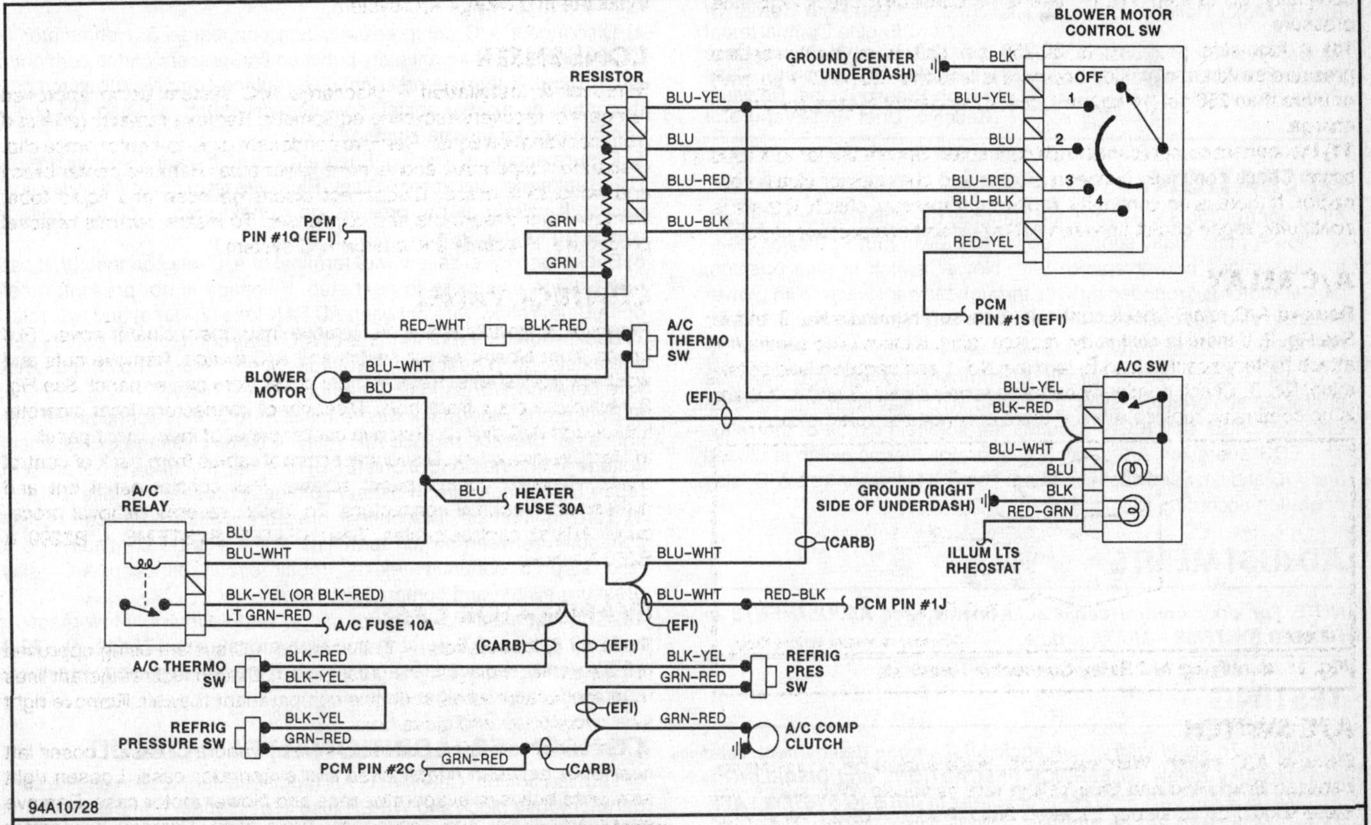

94A10728

Fig. 3: Manual A/C-Heater System Wiring Diagram (B2200 & B2600i)

1993 MANUAL A/C-HEATER SYSTEMS
Miata

SPECIFICATIONS

Specification	Value
Compressor Type	Nippondenso TV12 Rotary Vane
Compressor Belt Deflection [1]	
New	5/16-23/64" (8-9 mm)
Used	23/64-25/64" (9-10 mm)
Compressor Oil Capacity	2.7-3.3 ozs.
Refrigerant (R-12) Capacity	28 ozs.
System Operating Pressures	
High Side	171-235 psi (12.0-16.5 kg/cm²)
Low Side	21-43 psi (1.5-3.0 kg/cm²)

[1] – Measure with 22-lb. (10 kg) pressure applied to center of longest belt run.

WARNING: To avoid injury from accidental air bag deployment, read and carefully follow all SERVICE PRECAUTIONS and DISABLING & ACTIVATING AIR BAG SYSTEM procedures in AIR BAG SYSTEM SAFETY article in GENERAL SERVICING.

CAUTION: When battery is disconnected, radio will go into anti-theft protection mode. Obtain radio anti-theft protection code from owner prior to servicing vehicle.

DESCRIPTION

Blower assembly, mounted under right side of instrument panel, contains blower motor, blower resistor and fresh/recirculated air door. Evaporator unit, located left of blower case, contains evaporator, evaporator thermoswitch and expansion valve. Heater unit, located left of evaporator case, contains heater core, airflow mode door and air-mix (temperature blend) door.

ELECTRICAL COMPONENT LOCATIONS

ELECTRICAL COMPONENT LOCATIONS

Component	Location
A/C Relay	Right Front Corner Of Engine Compartment
Blower Motor Relay	Left Rear Corner Of Engine Compartment
Blower Resistor	Bottom Of Blower Case
Evaporator Thermoswitch	Left Side Of Evaporator Case
Pressure Switch	In High-Pressure Line, Between Receiver-Drier And Evaporator

OPERATION

All air control doors are controlled manually by cable from control panel. Blower motor relay supplies power to blower motor. Blower resistor determines blower speed. With blower switch in high position, blower motor is grounded directly through blower switch. With blower switch in all other positions, blower motor is grounded through blower resistor and blower switch.

A/C compressor clutch circuit is completed when A/C relay is energized and pressure switch is closed. A/C relay is energized when Engine Control Unit (ECU) grounds the solenoid circuit of the relay. The ECU energizes A/C relay if evaporator thermoswitch is closed and A/C and blower switches are on. The ECU also controls A/C relay operation according to engine load.

ADJUSTMENTS

NOTE: For door control cable adjustments, see ADJUSTMENTS in HEATER SYSTEMS – MIATA article.

TESTING

WARNING: To avoid injury from accidental air bag deployment, read and carefully follow all SERVICE PRECAUTIONS and DISABLING & ACTIVATING AIR BAG SYSTEM procedures in AIR BAG SYSTEM SAFETY article in GENERAL SERVICING.

NOTE: For test procedures not covered in this article, see TESTING in HEATER SYSTEMS – MIATA article.

A/C SYSTEM PERFORMANCE

1) Connect manifold gauge set. Operate engine at 1500 RPM. Operate A/C at maximum cooling. Open all doors and windows. Place thermometers at center vent outlet and blower inlet.

2) Allow A/C to stabilize. Ensure blower inlet temperature is 77-95°F (25-35°C), and high pressure is 171-234 psi (12-16.5 kg/cm²). Calculate difference between blower inlet temperature and center vent outlet temperature. Compare temperature difference to relative humidity. Ensure values are within specified range. See A/C SYSTEM PERFORMANCE table.

A/C SYSTEM PERFORMANCE

Temperature °F (°C) [1]	Relative Humidity (%)
70-81 (21-27)	40
63-73 (17-23)	50
57-68 (14-20)	60
52-63 (11-17)	70

[1] – Difference between blower inlet temperature and center vent outlet temperature.

A/C COMPRESSOR CLUTCH CIRCUIT

1) Turn ignition on. Check 20-amp WIPER fuse in passenger compartment fuse block. Check 20-amp AD FAN (additional fan) fuse in engine compartment fuse block. If fuses are okay, go to next step. If any fuse is blown, check for shorted wiring harness before replacing fuse.

2) Operate engine at idle. Turn A/C and blower switches on. Using voltmeter, backprobe Black/Red wire terminal of compressor clutch connector. If battery voltage exists, go to next step. If voltage is not present, go to step **5)**.

3) Turn ignition off. Disconnect evaporator thermoswitch connector. Check continuity between evaporator thermoswitch terminals. If continuity exists, go to next step. If there is no continuity, replace evaporator thermoswitch.

4) Disconnect A/C compressor clutch connector. Set ohmmeter to X1000 scale. Check continuity between compressor clutch connector and ground. If there is no continuity, replace compressor clutch coil. If continuity exists, adjust compressor clutch air gap or check compressor for internal damage.

5) Ensure engine is running. Ensure A/C and blower switches are on. Using voltmeter, backprobe Black/Blue wire terminal of A/C relay connector. If voltage is not present, go to next step. If battery voltage exists, go to step **9)**.

6) Backprobe Blue/Yellow wire terminal of A/C relay connector. If battery voltage exists, go to next step. If voltage is not present, repair open Blue/Yellow wire between AD FAN fuse (20-amp) and A/C relay.

7) Backprobe Blue wire terminal of A/C relay connector. If battery voltage exists, go to next step. If voltage is not present, repair open Blue wire between WIPER fuse (20-amp) and A/C relay.

8) Backprobe Blue/Black wire terminal of A/C relay connector. If voltage is not present, replace A/C relay. If battery voltage exists, check voltage at Engine Control Unit (ECU) terminal. If voltage is not present, repair Blue/Black wire. If battery voltage is present, replace ECU.

9) Turn ignition off. Disconnect pressure switch connector. Check continuity between switch terminals. If there is no continuity, go to next step. If continuity exists, repair circuit between A/C relay, pressure switch and compressor clutch.

10) Connect manifold pressure gauge set to system. If low pressure is 21-43 psi (1.5-3.0 kg/cm²) and high pressure is 171-235 psi (12.0-16.5 kg/cm²), replace pressure switch. If pressure readings are not as specified, check refrigerant level.

CONDENSER (ADDITIONAL) FAN CIRCUIT

1) Turn ignition on. Check AD FAN (additional fan) fuse in engine compartment fuse block and WIPER fuse in passenger compartment fuse block. If fuses are okay, go to next step. If either fuse is blown, check for shorted wiring harness before replacing fuse.

1993 MANUAL A/C-HEATER SYSTEMS
Miata (Cont.)

2) Ensure wiring harness between fuses and A/C relay is okay. Repair if necessary. Check A/C relay and replace if necessary. See A/C RELAY. If wiring harness and A/C relay are okay, go to next step.
3) Turn A/C and blower switches on. Using voltmeter, backprobe Black/Blue wire terminal of condenser fan connector. If battery voltage exists, go to next step. If voltage is not present, repair open Black/Blue wire between A/C relay and condenser fan.
4) Backprobe Black wire terminal of condenser fan connector. If voltage is not present, replace condenser fan motor. If battery voltage exists, repair open Black wire between condenser fan and ground.

A/C SWITCH

Disconnect A/C switch connector. Turn A/C switch on. Check continuity between indicated terminals. See A/C SWITCH TEST table. *See Fig. 1.* Replace A/C switch if continuity is not as specified.

A/C SWITCH TEST

Terminal	Continuity
"D" & "A"	[1] Yes
"F" & "A"	[1] Yes

[1] – Continuity exists in only one direction.

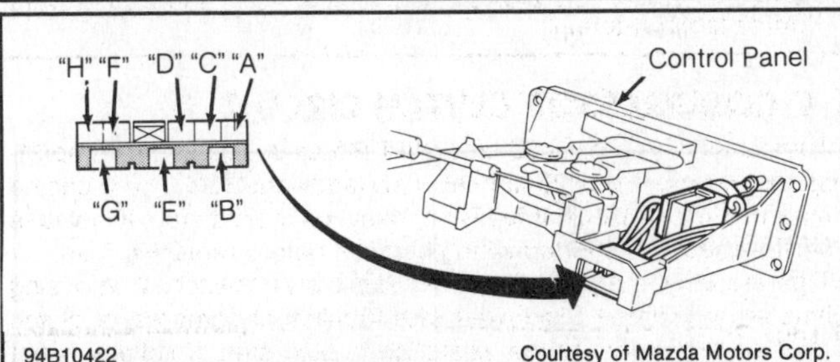
"H" "F" "D" "C" "A"
Control Panel
"G" "E" "B"
94B10422
Courtesy of Mazda Motors Corp.

Fig. 1: Identifying A/C Switch Terminals

A/C RELAY

Remove relay. Check continuity between indicated relay terminals. See A/C RELAY TEST table. *See Fig. 2.* Replace relay if continuity is not as specified.

A/C RELAY TEST

Application	Continuity
No Voltage Applied	
Terminals "B" & "A"	[1] Yes
Terminals "D" & "A"	[1] Yes
Terminals "C" & "F"	Yes
Terminals "C" & "E"	No
Terminals "C" & "E"	[2] Yes

[1] – Continuity exists in only one direction.
[2] – With voltage applied to terminals "D" and "A".

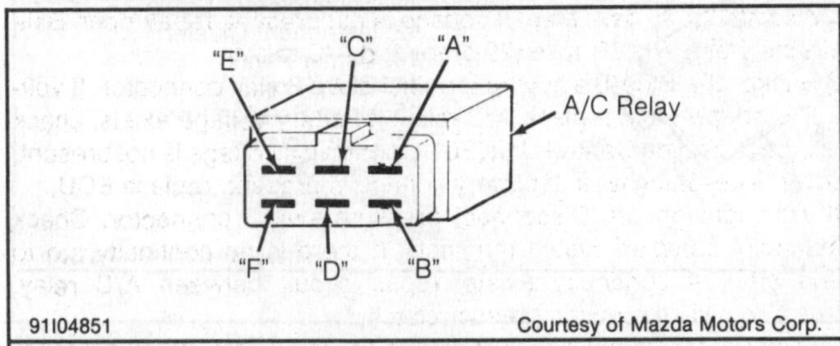
"E"
"C"
"A"
A/C Relay
"F"
"D"
"B"
91I04851
Courtesy of Mazda Motors Corp.

Fig. 2: Identifying A/C Relay Terminals

CONDENSER (ADDITIONAL) FAN MOTOR

Disconnect condenser fan motor connector. Connect positive battery lead to condenser fan motor Black/Blue wire terminal, and ground Black wire terminal. Replace condenser fan motor if it does not operate.

EVAPORATOR THERMOSWITCH

1) Remove glove box. Operate engine at idle. Turn A/C switch off. Turn blower switch to 4th position (high) for a few minutes to ensure evaporator temperature is greater than 32°F (0°C). Turn blower switch and engine off.
2) Disconnect evaporator thermoswitch connector. Check continuity between thermoswitch terminals. If continuity exists, go to next step. If there is no continuity, replace thermoswitch.
3) Immerse thermoswitch sensing bulb in ice cold water of less than 32°F (0°C). Ensure continuity exists between thermoswitch terminals. Replace thermoswitch if continuity does not exist.

PRESSURE SWITCH

1) Turn ignition off. Connect manifold pressure gauge set to system. If high-side pressure is greater than 31 psi (2.2 kg/cm²), go to next step. If pressure is less than 31.2 psi (2.2 kg/cm²), check refrigerant level.
2) Disconnect pressure switch connector. Check continuity between switch terminals. If continuity exists, pressure switch is okay. If there is no continuity, replace pressure switch.

REMOVAL & INSTALLATION

WARNING: To avoid injury from accidental air bag deployment, read and carefully follow all SERVICE PRECAUTIONS and DISABLING & ACTIVATING AIR BAG SYSTEM procedures in AIR BAG SYSTEM SAFETY article in GENERAL SERVICING.

NOTE: For removal and installation procedures not covered in this article, see HEATER SYSTEMS – MIATA article.

COMPRESSOR

Removal & Installation – 1) Before disconnecting negative battery cable, obtain radio anti-theft code from vehicle owner. Disconnect negative battery cable.
2) Raise and support front of vehicle with safety stands. Discharge A/C system using approved refrigerant recovery/recycling equipment. Remove splash shield and air guide.
3) Disconnect compressor clutch connector. Disconnect refrigerant lines from compressor. Remove compressor drive belt. Remove compressor bolts and compressor. To install, reverse removal procedure. Adjust drive belt deflection. Evacuate and charge A/C system.

CONDENSER & RECEIVER-DRIER

Removal – Raise and support front of vehicle with safety stands. Discharge A/C system using approved refrigerant recovery/recycling equipment. Remove splash shield and air guide. Remove condenser and receiver-drier as an assembly.
Installation – To install, reverse removal procedure. Apply clean compressor oil to "O" rings before connecting fittings. DO NOT apply compressor oil to fitting nuts. If installing new compressor, add one ounce of new compressor oil. If installing new receiver-drier, add .34 ounce of new compressor oil. Evacuate and charge A/C system.

EVAPORATOR UNIT

Removal – 1) Discharge A/C system using approved refrigerant recovery/recycling equipment. Disconnect refrigerant pipes from evaporator tubes at engine compartment firewall. Remove passenger-side instrument panel undercover. Remove glove box.
2) Disconnect electrical connectors. Loosen seal plates between evaporator unit, heater unit and blower assembly. Remove evaporator unit. Disassemble evaporator unit to remove evaporator core and thermoswitch. *See Fig. 3.*
Installation – To install, reverse removal procedure. Apply clean compressor oil to "O" rings before connecting fittings. DO NOT apply compressor oil to fitting nuts. Evacuate and charge A/C system.

1993 MANUAL A/C-HEATER SYSTEMS
Miata (Cont.)

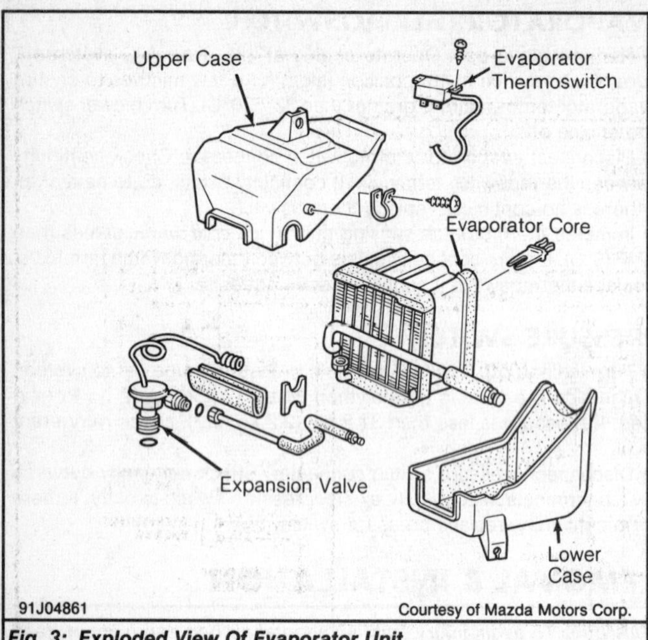
Upper Case
Evaporator
Thermoswitch
Evaporator Core
Expansion Valve
Lower
Case
91J04861
Courtesy of Mazda Motors Corp.

Fig. 3: Exploded View Of Evaporator Unit

INSTRUMENT PANEL

Removal & Installation – Before disconnecting negative battery cable, obtain radio anti-theft code from vehicle owner. Disconnect negative battery cable. Remove components in the order listed in illustration. *See Fig. 4*. To install, reverse removal procedure.

TORQUE SPECIFICATIONS

TORQUE SPECIFICATIONS

Application	Ft. Lbs. (N.m)
Compressor Bracket-To-Engine Bolt	28-38 (38-51)
Compressor-To-Compressor Bracket Bolt	11-15 (15-21)
Refrigerant Pipe Fittings	
Condenser Inlet	11-18 (15-24)
Evaporator Outlet	15-21 (20-29)
Steering Wheel Nut	29-36 (40-49)
	INCH Lbs. (N.m)
Evaporator Unit Nut	71-97 (8-11)
Refrigerant Pipe Fittings	
Compressor Inlet & Outlet	89-132 (10-15)
Evaporator Inlet	89-168 (10-19)
Receiver-Drier Inlet & Outlet	89-168 (10-19)

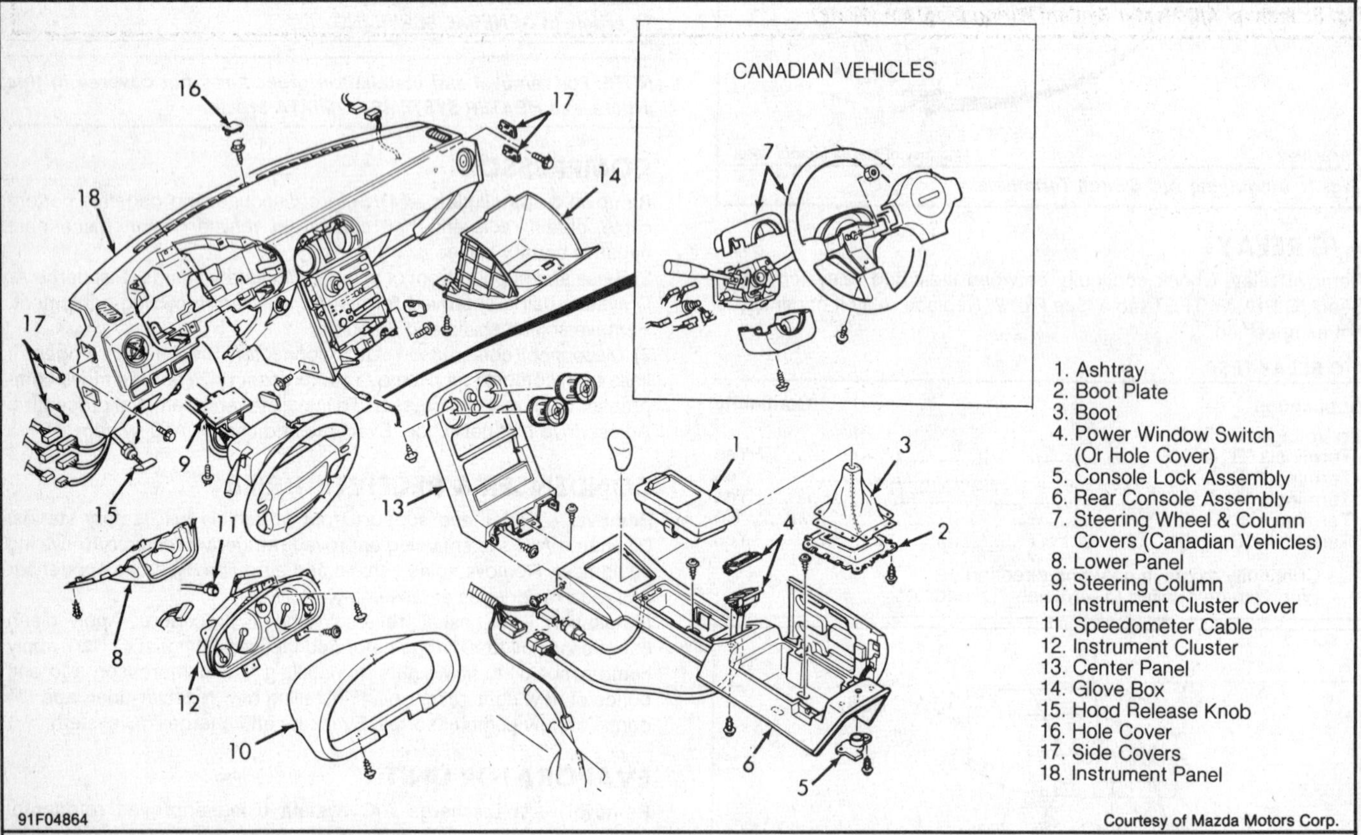

CANADIAN VEHICLES

1. Ashtray
2. Boot Plate
3. Boot
4. Power Window Switch (Or Hole Cover)
5. Console Lock Assembly
6. Rear Console Assembly
7. Steering Wheel & Column Covers (Canadian Vehicles)
8. Lower Panel
9. Steering Column
10. Instrument Cluster Cover
11. Speedometer Cable
12. Instrument Cluster
13. Center Panel
14. Glove Box
15. Hood Release Knob
16. Side Cover
17. Side Covers
18. Instrument Panel

91F04864

Courtesy of Mazda Motors Corp.

Fig. 4: Exploded View Of Instrument Panel

1993 MANUAL A/C-HEATER SYSTEMS
Miata (Cont.)

WIRING DIAGRAM

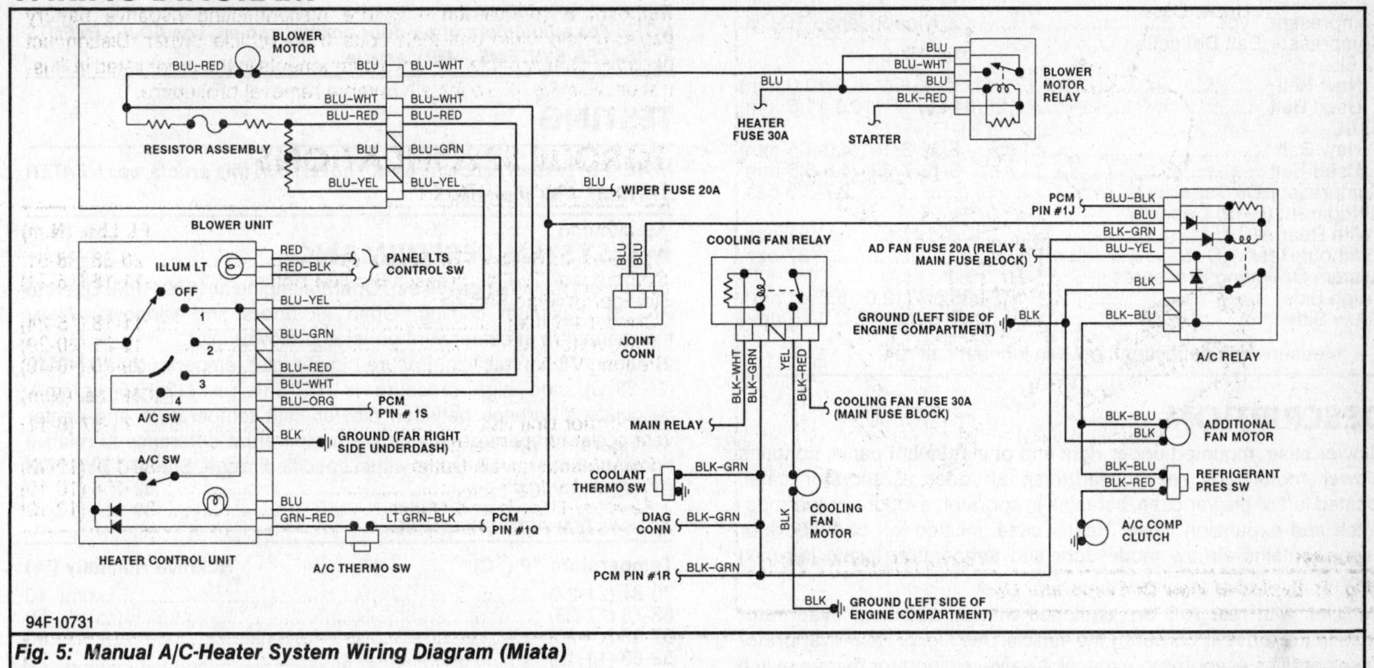
BLOWER MOTOR
BLU-RED
BLU
BLU-WHT
BLU-WHT
BLU-WHT
BLU-RED
BLU-RED
RESISTOR ASSEMBLY
BLU
BLU-GRN
BLU-YEL
BLU-YEL
BLOWER UNIT
BLU
HEATER FUSE 30A
STARTER
BLU
BLU-WHT
BLU
BLK-RED
BLOWER MOTOR RELAY
BLU
WIPER FUSE 20A
BLU
BLU
JOINT CONN
COOLING FAN RELAY
ILLUM LT
RED
RED-BLK
PANEL LTS CONTROL SW
OFF
1
2
3
4
BLU-YEL
BLU-GRN
BLU-RED
BLU-WHT
BLU-ORG
PCM PIN # 1S
A/C SW
BLK
GROUND (FAR RIGHT SIDE UNDERDASH)
A/C SW
BLU
GRN-RED
LT GRN-BLK
PCM PIN #1Q
HEATER CONTROL UNIT
A/C THERMO SW
BLK-WHT
BLK-GRN
YEL
BLK-RED
COOLING FAN FUSE 30A (MAIN FUSE BLOCK)
MAIN RELAY
COOLANT THERMO SW
BLK-GRN
DIAG CONN
BLK-GRN
BLK
COOLING FAN MOTOR
PCM PIN #1R
BLK-GRN
BLK
GROUND (LEFT SIDE OF ENGINE COMPARTMENT)
PCM PIN #1J
BLU-BLK
BLU
BLK-GRN
BLU-YEL
AD FAN FUSE 20A (RELAY & MAIN FUSE BLOCK)
BLK
GROUND (LEFT SIDE OF ENGINE COMPARTMENT)
BLK
BLK-BLU
A/C RELAY
BLK-BLU
BLK
ADDITIONAL FAN MOTOR
BLK-BLU
BLK-RED
REFRIGERANT PRES SW
A/C COMP CLUTCH
94F10731

Fig. 5: Manual A/C-Heater System Wiring Diagram (Miata)

1993 MANUAL A/C-HEATER SYSTEMS
MPV

SPECIFICATIONS

Compressor Type .... Nippondenso 10-Cyl.
Compressor Belt Deflection [1]
2.6L
New Belt .... 11/32-25/64" (8.5-10.0 mm)
Used Belt .... 25/64-29/64" (10.0-11.5 mm)
3.0L
New Belt .... 5/32-3/16" (4.0-4.5 mm)
Used Belt .... 3/16-7/32" (4.5-5.5 mm)
Compressor Oil Capacity .... 2.7-3.3 ozs.
Refrigerant (R-12) Capacity
With Rear A/C .... 51 ozs.
Without Rear A/C .... 37 ozs.
System Operating Pressures
High Side .... 171-235 psi (12.0-16.5 kg/cm²)
Low Side .... 21-43 psi (1.5-3.0 kg/cm²)

[1] - Measure belt deflection between longest belt run.

DESCRIPTION

Blower case, mounted under right end of instrument panel, contains blower motor and recirculated/fresh air door. Evaporator case, located left of blower case, contains evaporator, evaporator thermoswitch and expansion valve. Heater case, located left of evaporator case, contains airflow mode door and temperature blend (air-mix) door.

Vehicles with rear A/C are equipped with an additional evaporator case in the left rear corner of the vehicle. *See Fig. 5.* Rear evaporator case contains evaporator, expansion valve, evaporator thermoswitch and blower motor.

ELECTRICAL COMPONENT LOCATIONS

ELECTRICAL COMPONENT LOCATIONS

Component	Location
A/C Relay(s)	
Front	Right Rear Corner Of Engine Compartment
Rear	Top Of Rear Evaporator Case
Blower Resistor	
Front	Bottom Of Blower Case
Rear	Top Of Rear Evaporator Case
Condenser Fan Relay	Right Rear Corner Of Engine Compartment
ECU	At Front Passenger Floor, Under Cover
Evaporator Thermoswitch	
Front	Top Of Front Evaporator Case
Rear	Top Of Rear Evaporator Case
In-Line Fuse (15-Amp)	Right Rear Corner Of Engine Compartment
Magnetic Solenoid Valve	Under Vehicle, Below Driver Seat
Pressure Switch	Near Receiver-Drier, In High-Pressure Line

OPERATION

FRONT A/C-HEATER SYSTEM

On vehicles with push-button control panel, the airflow mode and fresh/recirculated air doors are controlled by electric actuators, but air-mix door is cable actuated. Vehicles with slide lever control panel use cables to control all 3 doors.

Based on engine load, Electronic Control Unit (ECU) controls operation of compressor clutch and condenser fan by grounding the energizing circuit of the A/C relay.

REAR A/C SYSTEM

Front A/C must be on in order for rear A/C system to operate. Main switch for rear A/C is on instrument panel. Rear A/C blower switch is in left rear corner of vehicle, near ceiling. Magnetic solenoid valve allows or denies refrigerant flow from front A/C refrigerant system to rear A/C system. Rear evaporator thermoswitch controls power to magnetic solenoid valve.

ADJUSTMENTS

NOTE: For adjustment of air door control cables, see ADJUSTMENTS in HEATER SYSTEMS - MPV article.

TESTING

NOTE: For testing procedures not covered in this article, see HEATER SYSTEMS - MPV article.

A/C SYSTEM PERFORMANCE

1) Connect manifold gauge set. Operate engine at 1500 RPM. Operate A/C at maximum cooling. Open all doors and windows. Place thermometers at center vent outlet and blower inlet.

2) Allow A/C to stabilize. Ensure blower inlet temperature is 77-95°F (25-35°C), and high pressure is 171-234 psi (12-16.5 kg/cm²). Calculate difference between blower inlet temperature and center vent outlet temperature. Compare temperature difference to relative humidity. Ensure values are within specified range. See A/C SYSTEM PERFORMANCE table.

A/C SYSTEM PERFORMANCE

Temperature °F (°C) [1]	Relative Humidity (%)
70-81 (21-27)	40
63-73 (17-23)	50
57-68 (14-20)	60
52-63 (11-17)	70

[1] - Difference between blower inlet temperature and center vent outlet temperature.

COMPRESSOR CLUTCH CIRCUIT

1) Run engine at idle. Turn A/C and blower on. Measure voltage at Green wire terminal of compressor clutch connector. If no voltage is present, check circuit between pressure switch and compressor clutch.

2) If battery voltage exists, check compressor clutch ground circuit and connection. If okay, replace compressor clutch.

CONDENSER FAN CIRCUIT

NOTE: Vehicles with 2.6L engine are equipped with 2 condenser fans.

1) Check 15-amp AIR CON fuse in passenger compartment fuse block, 40-amp DEFOG fuse in engine compartment fuse block, and 15-amp COOLER in-line fuse next to A/C relay. If fuses are okay, go to next step. If any fuse is blown, check for short circuit and repair.

2) Disconnect negative battery cable. Disconnect condenser fan relay connector. Connect jumper wire between Black/White wire and Blue wire terminals of condenser fan relay connector.

3) Reconnect negative battery cable. If condenser fan(s) operates, disconnect jumper wire, and go to step **5)**. If condenser fan(s) does not operate, disconnect jumper wire, and go to next step.

4) Measure voltage at Black/White wire terminal of condenser fan relay connector. If no voltage is present, repair circuit between DEFOG fuse and condenser fan relay. If battery voltage exists, test condenser fan motor(s). See MOTORS. If condenser fan motor is okay, repair circuit between condenser fan relay, condenser fan and body ground.

5) Reconnect condenser fan relay connector. Disconnect negative battery cable. Disconnect A/C relay connector. Connect a jumper wire between Black/White wire and Yellow wire terminals of A/C relay connector. Reconnect negative battery cable.

6) If condenser fan(s) does not operate, leave jumper wire connected, and go to next step. If condenser fan(s) operates, remove jumper wire. Reconnect A/C relay connector. Test A/C switch. See SWITCHES. If A/C switch is okay, go to step **10)**.

7) Disconnect pressure switch connector. Measure voltage at Yellow wire terminal of pressure switch connector. If battery voltage is present, go to next step. If no voltage is present, repair circuit between A/C relay and pressure switch.

8) Using ohmmeter, check continuity between pressure switch connector terminals. If there is no continuity, go to next step. If there is continuity, reconnect pressure switch connector. Test condenser fan relay. See RELAYS. If relay is okay, repair circuit between condenser fan relay and body ground. Test A/C switch. See SWITCHES. If A/C switch is okay, go to step **11)**.

9) Reconnect pressure switch connector. Turn ignition off. Check refrigerant high-side pressure. Pressure switch normal operating range is 33.4-299 psi (2.35-21.0 kg/cm²). If pressure is not within range, service refrigerant system. If pressure is within range, replace pressure switch.

10) Turn ignition and blower on. Measure voltage at Green wire terminal of A/C switch connector. If no voltage is present, go to next step. If battery voltage exists, repair circuit between A/C switch and blower switch.

11) Measure voltage at Blue/White wire terminal of thermoswitch connector. If no voltage is present, go to next step. If battery voltage exists, repair circuit between evaporator thermoswitch and A/C switch.

12) Measure voltage at Red/Black wire terminal of evaporator thermoswitch connector. If voltage is not present, check ECU operation. If battery voltage exists, ensure temperature at evaporator surface is less than 32°F (0°C), system is okay. If temperature is greater 32°F (0°C), replace thermoswitch.

REAR A/C BLOWER CIRCUIT

NOTE: During testing procedures, be aware of difference between A/C switch and rear A/C switch on instrument panel.

1) Check 40-amp ALL fuse in engine compartment fuse block, and 15-amp AIR CON fuse in passenger compartment fuse block. If any fuse is blown, repair short circuit and replace fuse. If fuses are okay, test A/C switch. See SWITCHES. If A/C switch is okay, go to next step.

2) Turn ignition on. Turn front blower switch to low speed setting. Turn front A/C on. Measure voltage at Green wire terminal of A/C switch connector. If battery voltage exists, repair circuit between A/C switch and front blower switch. If no voltage is present, test rear A/C switch. See SWITCHES. If rear A/C switch is okay, go to next step.

3) Ensure ignition and A/C are on. Ensure front blower switch is at low speed setting. Turn rear A/C on. Measure voltage at Black/Blue wire terminal of rear A/C switch connector. If battery voltage exists, repair circuit between rear A/C switch and A/C switch. If no voltage is present, test rear A/C blower switch. See SWITCHES. If rear A/C blower switch is okay, go to next step.

4) Turn rear A/C blower switch to low speed setting. Measure voltage at Black wire terminal of rear evaporator case connector. If no voltage is present, go to next step. If battery voltage exists, repair circuit between evaporator case and body ground.

5) Measure voltage at Blue wire terminal of evaporator case connector. If battery voltage exists, go to next step. If no voltage is present, repair circuit between AIR CON fuse and evaporator case.

6) Measure voltage at Black/Yellow wire terminal of evaporator case connector. If no voltage is present, repair circuit between ALL fuse and evaporator case. If battery voltage exists, go to next step.

7) Test rear A/C blower motor. See MOTORS. If rear A/C blower motor is okay, test rear A/C relay No. 1. See RELAYS. If rear A/C relay No. 1 is okay, test rear A/C blower resistor. See RESISTOR. If rear A/C blower resistor is okay, repair wiring harness between rear evaporator case and rear A/C switch.

REAR A/C REFRIGERANT CIRCUIT

1) Operate engine at idle. Turn on front blower switch, A/C switch, rear A/C switch and rear A/C blower switch. Measure voltage at Blue/White wire terminal of rear A/C relay No. 2 connector. If battery voltage exists, go to next step. If voltage is not present, repair circuit between rear A/C relays No. 1 and 2.

2) Measure voltage at Green/Yellow wire terminal of rear A/C relay No. 2 connector. If no voltage is present, replace rear A/C relay No. 2. If battery voltage exists, repair circuit between rear A/C relay No. 2 and rear A/C blower switch, and then go to next step.

3) Measure voltage at Black wire terminal of rear A/C relay No. 2 connector. If no voltage is present, go to next step. If battery voltage exists, repair circuit between rear A/C relay No. 2 and body ground.

4) Measure voltage at Green/Red wire terminal of rear A/C relay No. 2 connector. If no voltage is present, go to next step. If battery voltage exists, replace rear A/C relay No. 2.

5) Measure voltage at Green/Red wire terminal of rear evaporator thermoswitch connector. If no voltage is present, go to next step. If battery voltage exists, repair circuit between rear evaporator thermoswitch and rear A/C relay No. 2.

6) Measure voltage at Blue/Green wire terminal of rear evaporator thermoswitch connector. If no voltage is present, go to next step. If battery voltage exists, test rear evaporator thermoswitch. See SWITCHES. If rear evaporator thermoswitch is okay, system is functional.

7) Disconnect magnetic solenoid valve connector. Measure voltage at Blue wire terminal of connector. If battery voltage exists, go to next step. If no voltage is present, repair circuit between 15-amp AIR CON fuse and magnetic solenoid valve.

8) Apply positive battery lead to Blue wire terminal, and ground Blue/Green wire terminal of magnetic solenoid valve connector. Operate rear A/C system. If air output from rear A/C is not cold, go to next step. If air output is cold, repair circuit between magnetic solenoid valve and rear evaporator thermoswitch.

9) Measure resistance between magnetic solenoid valve connector terminals. Resistance should be about 20 ohms. If resistance is not as specified, replace magnetic solenoid valve. If resistance is as specified, check rear evaporator surface. If surface is not cold, replace rear evaporator expansion valve. If surface is cold, system is okay.

MOTORS

Condenser Fan Motor – Disconnect condenser fan motor connector. Apply battery voltage across condenser fan motor terminals. Replace condenser fan motor if fan does not operate.

Rear A/C Blower Motor – Ensure negative battery cable is disconnected. Remove interior trim from left rear corner of vehicle. Disconnect rear A/C blower motor connector. Apply battery voltage across motor terminals. Replace blower motor if it does not operate.

RELAYS

4-Pin Relay – Remove relay. Using ohmmeter, check continuity between indicated terminals. See 4-PIN RELAY TEST table. Replace relay if continuity is not as specified.

4-PIN RELAY TEST

Terminal (Wire Color)	Continuity
Front A/C Relay	
BLU & GRN	[1] No
BLK/WHT & YEL	[1] Yes
BLU & GRN	[2] Yes
Condenser Fan Relay	
BLK/WHT & BLU	[1] No
GRN & BLK	[1] Yes
BLK/WHT & BLU	[2] Yes
Rear A/C Relay No. 1	
BLK/YEL & BLU/WHT	[1] No
BLU & BLK/RED	[1] Yes
BLK/YEL & BLU/WHT	[2] Yes
Rear A/C Relay No. 2	
GRN/RED & BLK	[1] No
BLU/WHT & GRN/YEL	[1] Yes
GRN/RED & BLK	[2] Yes
Rear A/C Relay No. 3	
BLU & VIO	[1] No
BLU/WHT & GRN/YEL	[1] Yes
BLU & VIO	[2] Yes

[1] – With no voltage applied.
[2] – With battery voltage applied between remaining terminals.

RESISTOR

Rear A/C Blower Resistor - Disconnect negative battery cable. Remove left rear trim. Disconnect resistor connector. Set ohmmeter to X1000 scale. Ensure continuity exists between Red/White wire, Blue/Red wire and Green/Yellow wire terminals of resistor. If continuity is not as specified, replace resistor.

SWITCHES

A/C Switch - Remove switch. Check continuity between specified A/C switch terminals. *See Fig. 1.* Replace switch if continuity is not as specified.

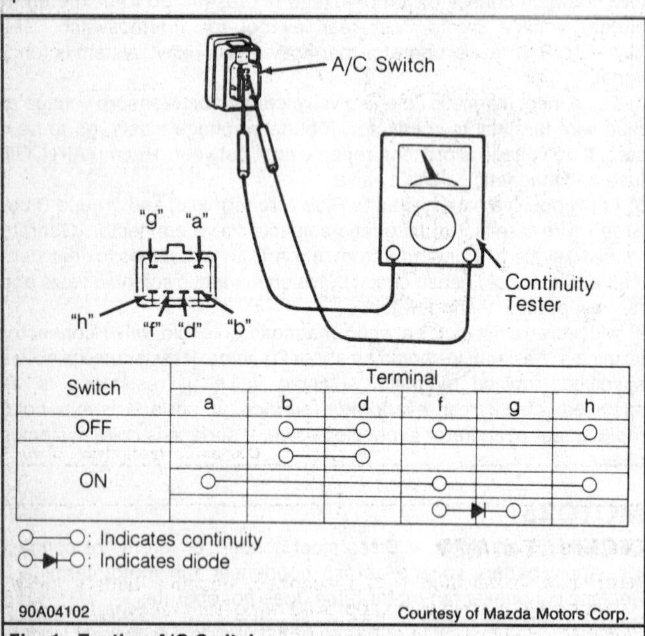
A/C Switch
"g" "a"
"h" "f" "d" "b"
Continuity Tester
Switch
Terminal
a b d f g h
OFF
ON
O—O: Indicates continuity
O-▶|-O: Indicates diode
90A04102
Courtesy of Mazda Motors Corp.

Fig. 1: Testing A/C Switch

Rear A/C Switch - Remove switch. Check continuity between specified terminals of rear A/C switch. See REAR A/C SWITCH TEST table. *See Fig. 2.* Replace switch if continuity is not as specified.

REAR A/C SWITCH TEST

Switch Position	Terminal No.	Continuity
Off	"d", "f", "h" & "j"	Yes
On	"d" & "f"; "c", "h" & "j"	Yes
On	"h" & "i"	[1] Yes

[1] - Ensure continuity exists in only one direction.

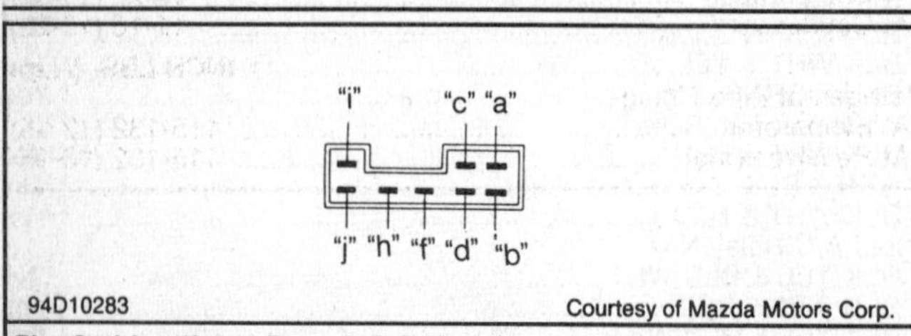
"i" "c" "a"
"j" "h" "f" "d" "b"
94D10283
Courtesy of Mazda Motors Corp.

Fig. 2: Identifying Rear A/C Switch Terminals

Rear A/C Blower Switch - Remove switch. Place switch in indicated position, and check continuity between specified terminals. See REAR A/C BLOWER SWITCH TEST table. Replace switch if continuity is not as specified.

REAR A/C BLOWER SWITCH TEST

Switch Position	Terminals	Continuity
Off	[1]	No
Low	Black & Green/Yellow	Yes
Medium	Black & Blue/Red	Yes
High	Black & Red/White	Yes

[1] - There should be no continuity between any terminals.

Evaporator Thermoswitch - Remove thermoswitch. Immerse sensing bulb in ice cold water. Check continuity between thermoswitch terminals. Continuity should exist when temperature of water is about 32°F (0°C) or more. Continuity should not exist when temperature of water is less than 32°F (0°C). Replace thermoswitch if continuity is not as specified.

REMOVAL & INSTALLATION

NOTE: For removal and installation procedures not covered in this article, see HEATER SYSTEMS - MPV article.

CONDENSER FAN

Removal & Installation - Disconnect negative battery cable. Remove lower grille and radiator grille. Remove hood lock assembly. Disconnect condenser fan connector(s). Remove condenser fan(s). To install, reverse removal procedure.

NOTE: On vehicles with 2 condenser fans, install fans in following order: right condenser fan, hood lock assembly, and left condenser fan.

EVAPORATOR CASE

Removal & Installation (Front) - 1) Disconnect negative battery cable. Discharge A/C system using approved refrigerant recovery/recycling equipment. Disconnect refrigerant lines from evaporator at engine compartment firewall. Plug open fittings to prevent contamination system. Remove grommet from firewall.

2) Remove glove box and undercover. Disconnect electrical connectors from evaporator case. Loosen seal plates on each side of evaporator case (seal plates connect evaporator case to blower and heater cases). Remove evaporator case nuts and evaporator case.

3) Disassemble evaporator case to remove evaporator, evaporator thermoswitch and expansion valve. *See Fig. 3.* To install, reverse removal procedure. Evacuate and charge A/C system.

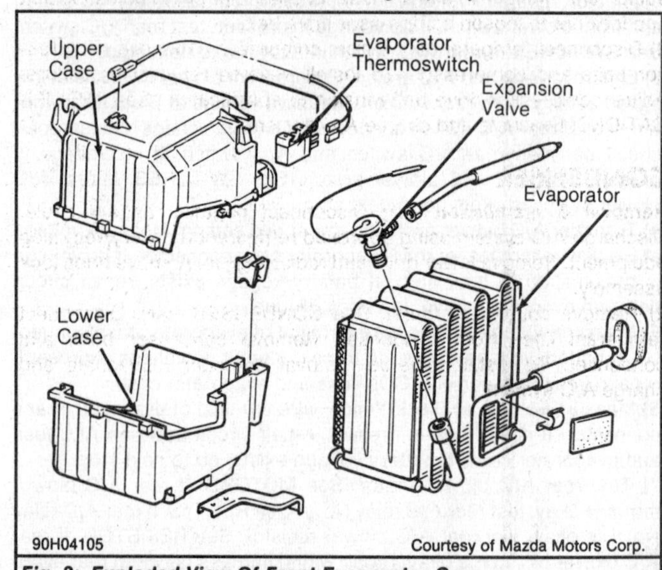
Upper Case
Evaporator Thermoswitch
Expansion Valve
Evaporator
Lower Case
90H04105
Courtesy of Mazda Motors Corp.

Fig. 3: Exploded View Of Front Evaporator Case

Removal & Installation (Rear) - 1) Disconnect negative battery cable. Discharge A/C system using approved refrigerant recovery/recycling equipment. Remove interior trim from left rear corner of vehicle. Disconnect refrigerant lines from evaporator. Plug open fittings to prevent contaminating system.

2) Disconnect electrical connectors from evaporator case. Remove rear evaporator case nuts and bolts. Remove rear evaporator case. Disassemble evaporator case to remove evaporator, evaporator thermoswitch and expansion valve. *See Fig. 4.* To install, reverse removal procedure. Evacuate and charge A/C system.

1993 MANUAL A/C-HEATER SYSTEMS
MPV (Cont.)

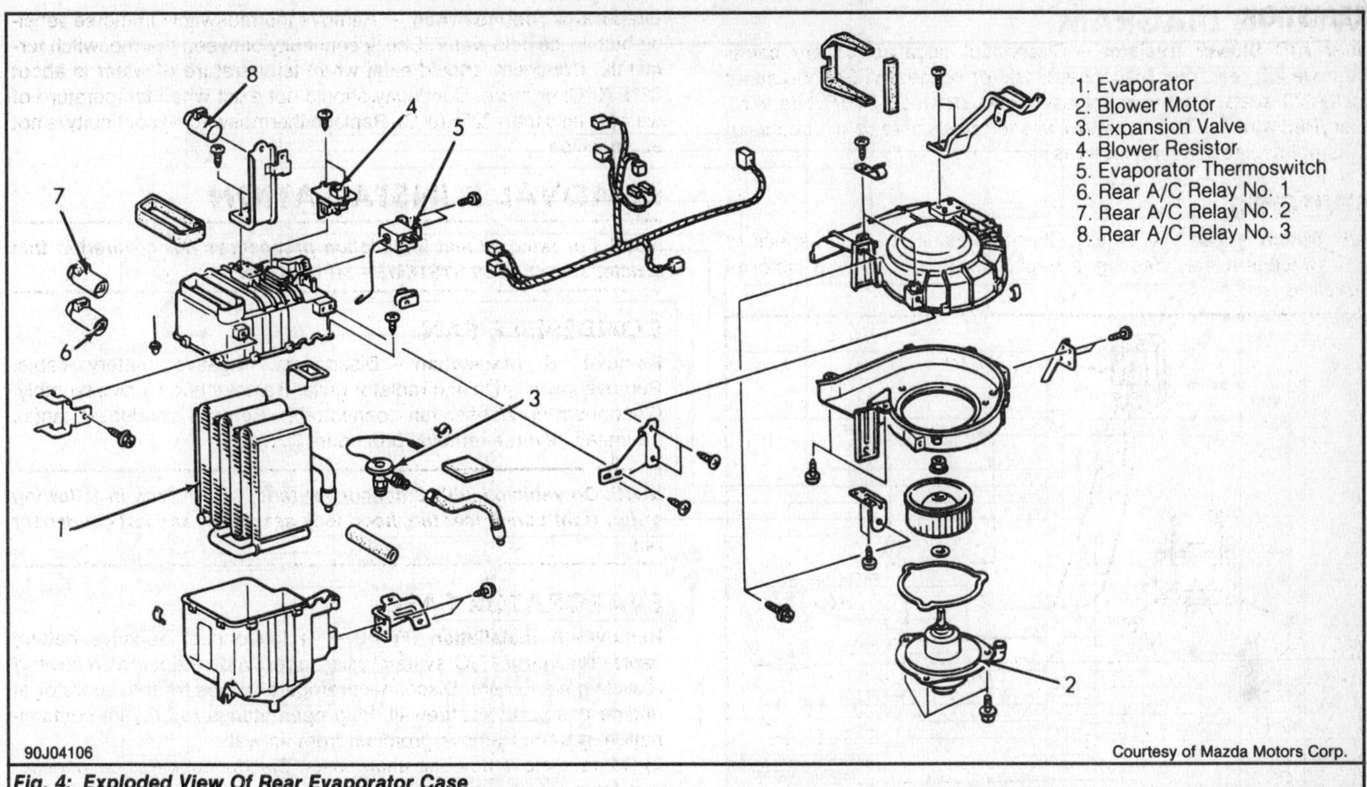
1. Evaporator
2. Blower Motor
3. Expansion Valve
4. Blower Resistor
5. Evaporator Thermoswitch
6. Rear A/C Relay No. 1
7. Rear A/C Relay No. 2
8. Rear A/C Relay No. 3
90J04106
Courtesy of Mazda Motors Corp.

Fig. 4: Exploded View Of Rear Evaporator Case

COMPRESSOR

Removal & Installation – 1) Disconnect negative battery cable. Discharge A/C system using approved refrigerant recovery/recycling equipment. Remove intake air hose. Loosen idler pulley adjusting bolt and lock nut to loosen compressor drive belt.

2) Disconnect refrigerant lines from compressor. Remove compressor bolts and compressor. To install, reverse removal procedure. Adjust compressor drive belt tension to specification. See SPECIFICATIONS. Evacuate and charge A/C system.

CONDENSER

Removal & Installation – 1) Disconnect negative battery cable. Discharge A/C system using approved refrigerant recovery/recycling equipment. Remove lower grille and radiator grille. Remove hood lock assembly.

2) Remove condenser fan(s). See CONDENSER FAN. Disconnect refrigerant lines from condenser. Remove condenser bolts and condenser. To install, reverse removal procedure. Evacuate and charge A/C system.

RECEIVER-DRIER

Removal & Installation – 1) Disconnect negative battery cable. Discharge A/C system using approved refrigerant recovery/recycling equipment. Remove lower grille and radiator grille. Disconnect electrical connectors.

2) Remove right front combination light and headlight. Disconnect refrigerant lines from receiver-drier. Remove receiver-drier. To install, reverse removal procedure. Evacuate and charge A/C system.

TORQUE SPECIFICATIONS

TORQUE SPECIFICATIONS

Application	Ft. Lbs. (N.m)
Compressor Bolt	14-19 (19-26)
Refrigerant Pipe Fittings	
At Compressor	14-22 (19-30)
At Condenser	11-16 (15-22)
	INCH LBS. (N.m)
Refrigerant Pipe Fittings	
At Evaporator	115-132 (13-15)
At Receiver-Drier	115-132 (13-15)

1993 MANUAL A/C-HEATER SYSTEMS MPV (Cont.)

WIRING DIAGRAM

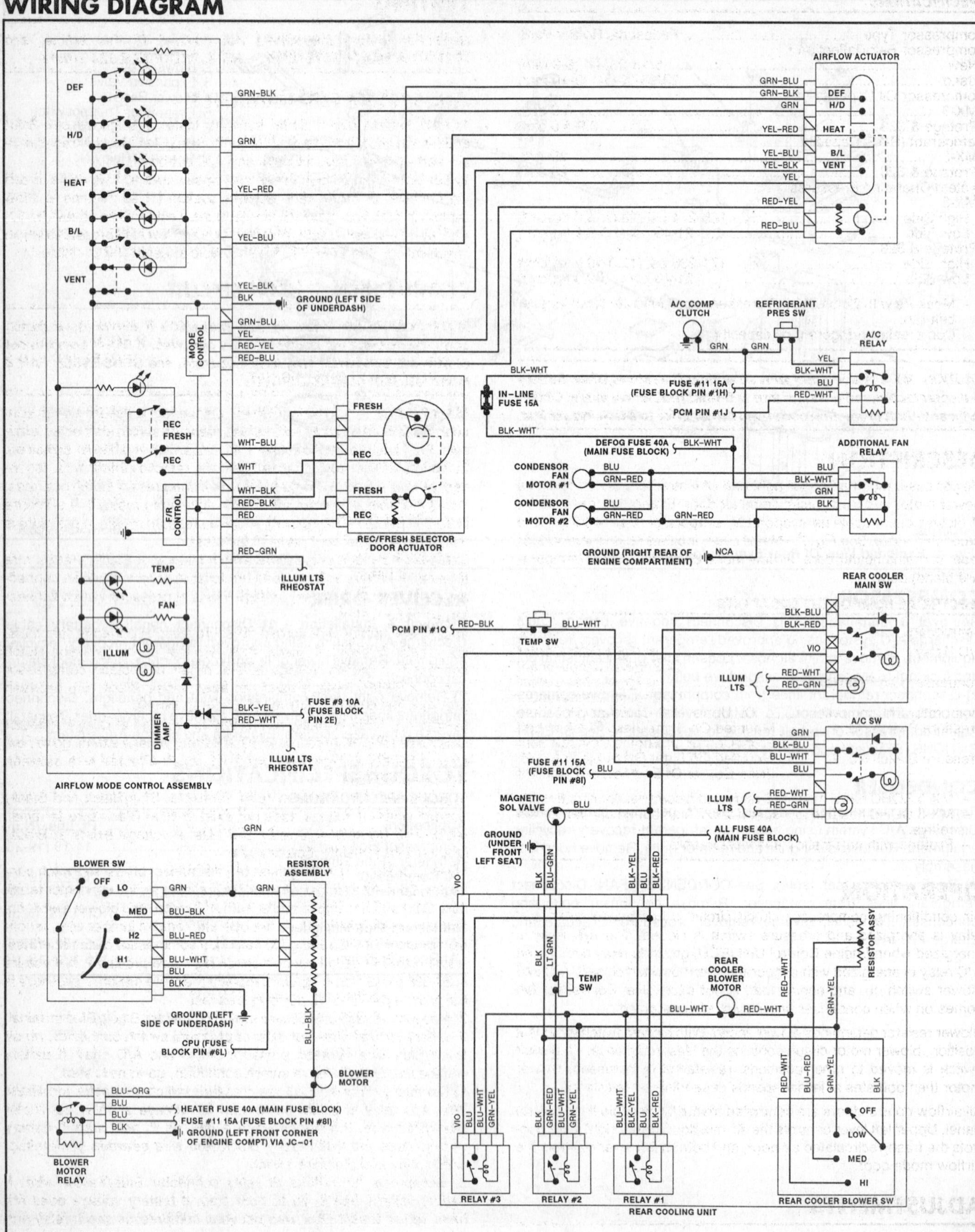
DEF
H/D
HEAT
B/L
VENT
GRN-BLK
GRN
YEL-RED
YEL-BLU
YEL-BLK
BLK
GROUND (LEFT SIDE OF UNDERDASH)
GRN-BLU
YEL
RED-YEL
RED-BLU
MODE CONTROL
AIRFLOW ACTUATOR
GRN-BLU
GRN-BLK
GRN
DEF
H/D
YEL-RED
HEAT
YEL-BLU
B/L
YEL-BLK
VENT
YEL
RED-YEL
RED-BLU
A/C COMP CLUTCH
REFRIGERANT PRES SW
GRN
A/C RELAY
YEL
BLK-WHT
BLU
RED-WHT
FUSE #11 15A (FUSE BLOCK PIN #1H)
PCM PIN #1J
BLK-WHT
IN-LINE FUSE 15A
DEFOG FUSE 40A (MAIN FUSE BLOCK)
ADDITIONAL FAN RELAY
CONDENSOR FAN MOTOR #1
CONDENSOR FAN MOTOR #2
BLU
GRN-RED
BLK
GROUND (RIGHT REAR OF ENGINE COMPARTMENT)
NCA
REC
FRESH
WHT-BLU
WHT
WHT-BLK
RED-BLK
RED
F/R CONTROL
REC/FRESH SELECTOR DOOR ACTUATOR
RED-GRN
ILLUM LTS RHEOSTAT
TEMP
FAN
ILLUM
DIMMER AMP
BLK-YEL
RED-WHT
FUSE #9 10A (FUSE BLOCK PIN 2E)
AIRFLOW MODE CONTROL ASSEMBLY
PCM PIN #1Q
TEMP SW
BLU-WHT
REAR COOLER MAIN SW
BLK-BLU
BLK-RED
VIO
ILLUM LTS
A/C SW
BLK-BLU
BLU-WHT
FUSE #11 15A (FUSE BLOCK PIN #8I)
MAGNETIC SOL VALVE
ALL FUSE 40A (MAIN FUSE BLOCK)
GROUND (UNDER FRONT LEFT SEAT)
BLOWER SW
OFF
LO
MED
H2
H1
RESISTOR ASSEMBLY
BLU-BLK
BLU-RED
GROUND (LEFT SIDE OF UNDERDASH)
CPU (FUSE BLOCK PIN #6L)
BLOWER MOTOR
BLU-ORG
HEATER FUSE 40A (MAIN FUSE BLOCK)
FUSE #11 15A (FUSE BLOCK PIN #8I)
GROUND (LEFT FRONT CORNER OF ENGINE COMPT) VIA JC-01
BLOWER MOTOR RELAY
LT GRN
BLK-GRN
BLK-YEL
BLK-RED
RESISTOR ASSY
REAR COOLER BLOWER MOTOR
GRN-YEL
RELAY #3
RELAY #2
RELAY #1
REAR COOLING UNIT
HI
REAR COOLER BLOWER SW
94J10727

Fig. 5: Manual A/C-Heater System Wiring Diagram (MPV)

1993 MANUAL A/C-HEATER SYSTEMS
MX-3, Protege & 323

SPECIFICATIONS

Compressor Type .... Panasonic Rotary Vane
Compressor Belt Deflection [1]
New .... 5/16-23/64" (8-9 mm)
Used .... 23/64-25/64" (9-10 mm)
Compressor Oil Capacity [2]
MX-3 .... 5.0 ozs.
Protege & 323 .... 3.9-4.6 ozs.
Refrigerant (R-12) Capacity
MX-3 .... 28 ozs.
Protege & 323 .... 28 ozs.
System Operating Pressures
MX-3
High Side .... 185-214 psi (13.0-15.0 kg/cm²)
Low Side .... 21-43 psi (1.5-3.0 kg/cm²)
Protege & 323
High Side .... 171-235 psi (12.0-16.5 kg/cm²)
Low Side .... 21-43 psi (1.5-3.0 kg/cm²)

[1] - Measure with 22 lbs. (10 kg) pressure applied to center of longest belt run.
[2] - Compressor refrigerant oil capacity.

CAUTION: MX-3 is equipped with an anti-theft system. When battery is disconnected, radio will go into anti-theft protection mode. Obtain radio anti-theft protection code from owner prior to servicing vehicle.

DESCRIPTION

Blower case, mounted under right end of instrument panel, contains blower motor and fresh/recirculated air door. Evaporator case, to left of blower case, contains evaporator, evaporator thermoswitch and expansion valve. *See Fig. 7.* Heater case, located next to evaporator case, contains heater core, airflow mode door and air-mix (temperature blend) door.

ELECTRICAL COMPONENT LOCATIONS

Component	Location
A/C Relay [1]	In Right Rear Corner Of Engine Compartment
Condenser Fan Relay(s) [2]	In Right Rear Corner Of Engine Compartment
Evaporator Thermoswitch	On Upper Half Of Evaporator Case
Pressure Switch No. 1	Mounted On Sight Glass Block In Left Front Corner Of Engine Compartment
Pressure Switch No. 2 [3]	Mounted On Sight Glass Block In Left Front Corner Of Engine Compartment

[1] - MX-3 SOHC has a main A/C relay and a compressor clutch relay.
[2] - MX-3 DOHC has one low speed and 2 high speed condenser fan relays.
[3] - Protege with automatic transmission only.

OPERATION

Air conditioning compressor clutch circuit is completed when A/C relay is energized and pressure switch is closed. The A/C relay is energized when Engine Control Unit (ECU) grounds relay circuit. The A/C relay is energized with evaporator thermoswitch closed, A/C and blower switch on, and engine load is not excessive. Condenser fan comes on when condenser fan relay(s) are energized.

Blower resistor determines blower speed. With blower switch in highest position, blower motor circuit contains the least resistance. As blower switch is moved to other positions, resistance is increased. Blower motor then operates at lesser speeds depending on resistance.

All airflow control doors are controlled manually by cable from control panel. Upper left lever controls the air-mix door, upper right lever controls the fresh/recirculated air door, and bottom left lever controls the airflow mode door.

ADJUSTMENTS

NOTE: For control cable adjustments, see ADJUSTMENTS in HEATER SYSTEMS - MX-3, PROTEGE & 323 article.

TESTING

NOTE: For testing procedures not covered in this article, see TESTING in HEATER SYSTEMS - MX-3, PROTEGE & 323 article.

A/C SYSTEM PERFORMANCE

1) Park vehicle out of direct sunlight. Install A/C gauge set. Start engine and allow it to idle at 1500 RPM. Set A/C controls to recirculate air, panel (vent) mode, full cold, and A/C button on.

2) Set blower/fan on high speed and close doors and windows. Insert thermometer in center vent. Operate system for 20 minutes to allow system to stabilize. Measure temperature. Temperature should be 37-42°F (3-6°C) at center vent, with high side and low side pressures within specification. See SPECIFICATIONS table at beginning of article.

COMPRESSOR CLUTCH CIRCUIT

NOTE: Perform the following test procedure if compressor clutch does not operate but condenser fan operates. If BOTH compressor clutch and condenser fan do not operate, see CONDENSER FAN & COMPRESSOR CLUTCH CIRCUIT.

MX-3 (DOHC) - 1) With ignition off, disconnect pressure switch connector. Connect a jumper wire across pressure switch connector terminals. Start and run engine at idle. Turn A/C switch and blower switch on.

2) If compressor clutch does not operate, remove jumper wire, reconnect pressure switch and go to step **3)**. If compressor clutch operates, install manifold gauge set and check high-side pressure. If pressure is 30-298 psi (2.1-21.0 kg/cm²), replace pressure switch. If pressure is not within specification, perform leak test.

3) Measure voltage at pressure switch connector Black/Orange wire terminal. If battery voltage does not exist at pressure switch connector, go to step **5)**. If battery voltage exists at pressure switch connector, go to next step.

4) Connect jumper wire across pressure switch connector terminals, and check voltage at Black wire terminal of compressor clutch connector. If battery voltage exists, repair or replace compressor clutch. If battery voltage does not exist, repair Black wire between pressure switch and compressor clutch terminals.

5) With A/C relay in place, backprobe for voltage at relay connector Blue/Green and Blue/Yellow wires. If battery voltage exists, go to next step. If battery voltage does not exist, repair affected wire between A/C relay and fuse.

6) Backprobe for voltage at relay connector Blue/Black and Black/Orange wires. If voltage does not exist at Blue/Black wire terminal, repair wire between A/C relay and fuse. If voltage exists at Black/Orange wire terminal, replace relay.

MX-3 (SOHC) - 1) With ignition off, disconnect pressure switch connector. Connect a jumper wire across pressure switch connector terminals. Start and run engine at idle. Turn A/C switch and blower switch on.

2) If compressor clutch does not operate, remove jumper wire, reconnect pressure switch and go to step **3)**. If compressor clutch operates, install manifold gauge set and check high-side pressure. If pressure is 30-298 psi (2.1-21.0 kg/cm²), replace pressure switch. If pressure is not within specification, perform leak test.

3) Measure voltage at pressure switch connector Black/Blue terminal. If battery voltage does not exist at pressure switch connector, repair Black/Blue wire between pressure switch and A/C relay. If battery voltage exists at pressure switch connector, go to next step.

4) Connect jumper wire across pressure switch connector terminals. With A/C relay in place, backprobe for voltage at relay connector Black/Red wire. If battery voltage exists, go to next step. If battery voltage does not exist, repair Black/Red wire between compressor clutch relay and pressure switch.

5) Backprobe for voltage at relay connector Blue/Yellow wire. If battery voltage exists, go to next step. If battery voltage does not exist, repair Blue/Yellow wire between compressor clutch relay and fuse.

1993 MANUAL A/C-HEATER SYSTEMS
MX-3, Protege & 323 (Cont.)

6) Backprobe for voltage at relay connector Black wire. If no voltage exists, go to next step. If voltage exists, repair short to voltage on Black wire between compressor clutch relay and body ground.
7) Backprobe for voltage at relay connector Red wire. If battery voltage exists, go to next step. If battery voltage does not exist, replace compressor clutch relay.
8) Backprobe for voltage at compressor clutch connector Red wire. If battery voltage exists, repair or replace compressor clutch. If battery voltage does not exist, repair Red wire between compressor clutch relay and compressor clutch.
Protege & 323 - 1) Start and run engine at idle. Turn A/C switch and blower switch on. Check voltage at Black/Red wire terminal of compressor clutch connector. If no voltage exists, go to step **5)**.
2) If battery voltage exists, check voltage at Black wire terminal of compressor clutch connector. If no voltage exists, go to step **4)**. If battery voltage exists, disconnect compressor clutch connector.
3) Check continuity between compressor clutch and ground. If there is continuity, adjust compressor clutch air gap or check compressor for internal damage. If there is no continuity, check ground wire. If ground wire is okay, replace compressor clutch.
4) Turn A/C off. After 10 minutes, check continuity between wire terminals of compressor thermal protector. If there is continuity, go to next step. If there is no continuity, replace thermal protector.
5) Check voltage at Black/Red wire terminal of No. 1 pressure switch connector. If battery voltage exists, repair Black/Red wire. If no voltage exists, check voltage at Black/Blue wire terminal of No. 1 pressure switch connector. If no voltage exists, repair Black/Blue wire. If battery voltage exists, go to next step.
6) Turn ignition off. Connect pressure gauge set to system. If high-side pressure is less than 65 psi (4.6 kg/cm²), check system for proper refrigerant charge. If high-side pressure is greater than 65 psi (4.6 kg/cm²), test pressure switches. See PRESSURE SWITCHES.

CONDENSER FAN CIRCUIT

NOTE: Perform the following test procedure if condenser fan does not operate but compressor clutch operates. If BOTH condenser fan and compressor clutch do not operate, see CONDENSER FAN & COMPRESSOR CLUTCH CIRCUIT.

MX-3 (DOHC) - 1) Start and run engine at idle. Turn A/C switch and blower switch on. Starting with Blue/Green wire, backprobe for voltage at specified wire terminals of condenser fan low speed relay connector. Perform indicated action as specified in table. See CONDENSER FAN LOW SPEED RELAY VOLTAGE TEST (MX-3 DOHC) table.

CONDENSER FAN LOW SPEED RELAY VOLTAGE TEST (MX-3 DOHC)

Terminal	Voltage	Action
Blue/Green	12	Check Voltage On Next Wire
	0	[1] Repair Blue/Green Wire
Blue/Black	0	Check Voltage On Next Wire
	0-12	[2] Repair Blue/Black Wire
Blue/Yellow	12	Check Voltage On Next Wire
	0	[1] Repair Blue/Yellow Wire
Blue	12	Go To Step **2)**
	0	Replace Condenser Fan Low Speed Relay

[1] - Between fuse and low speed relay.
[2] - Between low speed relay and ECU.

2) Start and run engine at idle. Turn A/C switch and blower switch on. Backprobe for voltage at Blue wire terminal of condenser fan connector. If no voltage exists, repair Blue wire between condenser fan low speed relay and condenser fan. If battery voltage exists, go to next step.
3) Backprobe for voltage at Black wire terminal of condenser fan relay connector. If no voltage exists, replace condenser fan motor. If voltage exists, repair Black wire between condenser fan and ground.

MX-3 (SOHC) - 1) Start and run engine at idle. Turn A/C switch and blower switch on. Backprobe for voltage at Black/Blue wire terminal of condenser fan connector. If no voltage exists, repair Black/Blue wire between A/C relay and condenser fan. If battery voltage exists, go to next step.
2) Backprobe for voltage at Black wire terminal of condenser fan relay connector. If no voltage exists, replace condenser fan motor. If voltage exists, repair Black wire between condenser fan and ground.
Protege & 323 - 1) Disconnect condenser fan connector. Connect battery positive lead to Blue/White wire terminal and negative lead to Black wire terminal of condenser fan connector. If condenser fan does not operate, replace condenser fan motor. If condenser fan operates, go to next step.
2) Start and run engine at idle. Turn A/C switch and blower switch on. With fan motor disconnected, check voltage at Blue/White wire terminal of condenser fan connector. If battery voltage exists, replace condenser fan. If no voltage exists, go to next step.
3) Starting with Blue/White wire, check voltage at specified wire terminals of condenser fan relay connector, and perform indicated action as specified in table. See appropriate CONDENSER FAN RELAY VOLTAGE TEST table.

CONDENSER FAN RELAY VOLTAGE TEST (PROTEGE WITH AUTOMATIC TRANSMISSION)

Terminal	Voltage	Action
Blue/White	12	Repair Blue/White Wire
	0	Check Voltage On Next Wire
Blue/Yellow	12	Check Voltage On Next Wire
	0	Repair Blue/Yellow Wire
Black/Blue	12	Check Voltage On Next Wire
	0	Repair Black/Blue Wire
Black/Orange	12	Go To Step **4)**
	0	Replace Condenser Fan Relay

CONDENSER FAN RELAY VOLTAGE TEST (PROTEGE WITH MANUAL TRANSMISSION & 323)

Terminal	Voltage	Action
Blue/White	12	Repair Blue/White Wire
	0	Check Voltage On Next Wire
Blue/Yellow	12	Repair Blue/Yellow Wire
	0	Check Voltage On Next Wire
Black/Blue	12	Repair Black/Blue Wire
	0	Check Voltage On Next Wire
Black	12	Repair Black Wire
	0	Replace Condenser Fan Relay

4) Check voltage at Black/Orange wire terminal of pressure switch No. 2 connector (Protege with A/T only). If no voltage exists, repair Black/Orange wire. If battery voltage exists, check voltage at Black wire terminal of pressure switch No. 2 connector.
5) If battery voltage exists, repair Black wire. If no voltage exists, connect manifold pressure gauge set. Turn on A/C with temperature lever set at coldest position and engine at 2000 RPM.
6) If high-side pressure is less than 171 psi (12.0 kg/cm²), pressure switch No. 2 is okay. Recheck wiring harness for intermittent. If high-side pressure is greater than 171 psi (12.0 kg/cm²), replace pressure switch No. 2.

CONDENSER FAN & COMPRESSOR CLUTCH CIRCUIT

NOTE: Perform the following test procedures only if BOTH condenser fan and compressor clutch do not operate.

1) Check 20-amp AD FAN (condenser fan) fuse in engine compartment fuse block. Check 10-amp REAR WIPER fuse in passenger compartment fuse block. If fuse is blown, repair short in wiring harness as necessary. If fuse is okay, start and run engine at idle.

2) Turn A/C switch and blower switch on. Starting with Blue/Green wire, backprobe for voltage at specified wire terminals of A/C relay connector, and perform indicated action as specified in table. See appropriate A/C RELAY VOLTAGE TEST table.

A/C RELAY VOLTAGE TEST (MX-3 DOHC)

Terminal	Voltage	Action
Blue/Green	12	Check Voltage On Next Wire
	0	Repair Blue/Green Wire
Blue/Yellow	12	Go To Step 3)
	0	Repair Blue/Yellow Wire

A/C RELAY VOLTAGE TEST (EXCEPT MX-3 DOHC)

Terminal	Voltage	Action
Blue/Green	12	Check Voltage On Next Wire
	0	Repair Blue/Green Wire
Blue/Yellow	12	Check Voltage On Next Wire
	0	Repair Blue/Yellow Wire
Black/Blue	12	Repair Black/Blue Wire
	0	Check Voltage On Next Wire
Blue/Black	12	Go To Step 3)
	0	Replace A/C Relay

3) Backprobe for voltage at Black wire (Blue/Yellow wire on MX-3) terminal of A/C switch connector. If battery voltage exists, repair Black wire (Blue/Yellow on MX-3). If no voltage exists, check voltage at Green/Red wire terminal of A/C switch connector. If battery voltage exists, replace A/C switch.

4) If no voltage exists, check voltage at Green/Red wire terminal of evaporator thermoswitch connector. If battery voltage exists, repair Green/Red wire. If no voltage exists, backprobe for voltage at Green/Black wire (Brown/Red wire on MX-3) of evaporator thermoswitch connector.

5) If no voltage exists, check operation of Engine Control Unit (ECU). If battery voltage exists, turn off A/C switch. Turn blower switch to 4th position (high). Operate blower for a few minutes. Turn off blower switch and engine. Disconnect evaporator thermoswitch connector.

6) Check continuity between terminals of evaporator thermoswitch connector. If there is continuity, thermoswitch is okay. Recheck wiring harness for intermittent. If there is no continuity, replace thermoswitch.

A/C RELAY

MX-3 (DOHC) – 1) Remove relay from right rear corner of engine compartment. Check continuity between relay terminals "A" and "B". *See Fig. 1.* If continuity does not exist, replace relay. If continuity exists, go to next step.

2) Repeat test on relay terminals "C" and "D". If continuity does not exist, replace relay. If continuity exists, go to next step.

3) Attach battery positive lead to terminal "A" and negative lead to terminal "B". Check continuity between terminals "C" and "D". If continuity does not exist, replace relay. If continuity exists, relay is okay.

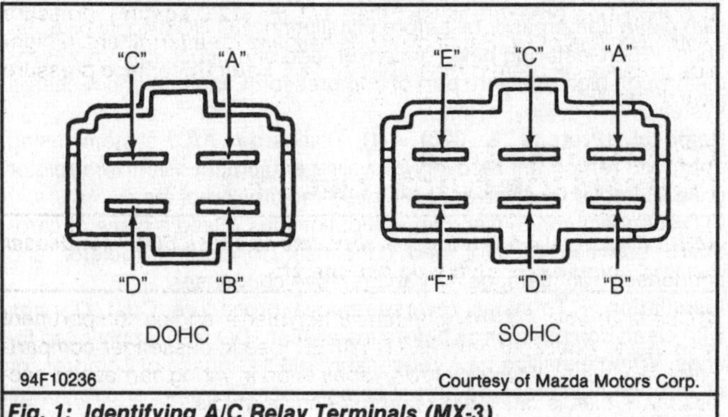

"C"
"A"
"D"
"B"
DOHC
"E"
"C"
"A"
"F"
"D"
"B"
SOHC
94F10236
Courtesy of Mazda Motors Corp.

Fig. 1: Identifying A/C Relay Terminals (MX-3)

MX-3 (SOHC) – 1) Remove relay from right rear corner of engine compartment. Check continuity between relay terminals "A" and "B". *See Fig. 1.* Reverse ohmmeter leads and check continuity. There should be continuity in one direction only.

2) If there is continuity in both directions or no continuity in either direction, replace relay. Repeat test on relay terminals "A" and "D". Repeat test on relay terminals "E" and "C". Ensure there is continuity in one direction only. If there is continuity in both directions or no continuity in either direction, replace relay.

3) If continuity is okay, attach battery positive lead to terminal "D" and negative lead to terminal "A". Check continuity between terminals "E" and "C". There should be continuity in both directions. If there is no continuity, replace relay.

Protege & 323 – 1) Remove relay from right rear corner of engine compartment. Check continuity between specified terminals of relay connector. See A/C RELAY TEST table. *See Fig. 2.* Ensure test lead polarity is correct. If continuity is not as specified, replace relay.

2) If continuity is as specified, apply battery positive lead to terminal "D" and negative lead to terminal "A". Check continuity between terminals "E" and "C". If there is continuity, relay is okay. If there is no continuity, replace relay.

A/C RELAY TEST

Terminal (+) [1]	Terminal (-) [2]	Continuity
"A"	"B"	Yes
"A"	"D"	Yes
"B"	"A"	No
"C"	"E"	No
"D"	"A"	No
"E"	"C"	Yes

[1] – Connect ohmmeter positive lead to this terminal.
[2] – Connect ohmmeter negative lead to this terminal.

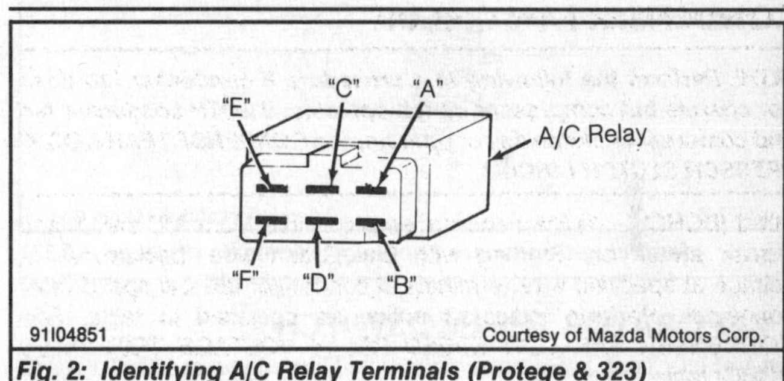

"C"
"A"
"E"
A/C Relay
"F"
"D"
"B"
91I04851
Courtesy of Mazda Motors Corp.

Fig. 2: Identifying A/C Relay Terminals (Protege & 323)

A/C SWITCH

1) Remove switch. Turn switch off. If continuity does not exist between switch terminals "B" and "H", replace switch. *See Fig. 3 or 4.* Turn switch on. Continuity should exist between terminals "A" and "F". On MX-3, continuity should also exist between terminals "B" and "H".

2) On all models, place one ohmmeter lead on terminal "D". Place other ohmmeter lead on terminal "F" and then on terminal "A". Continuity should exist in one direction only.

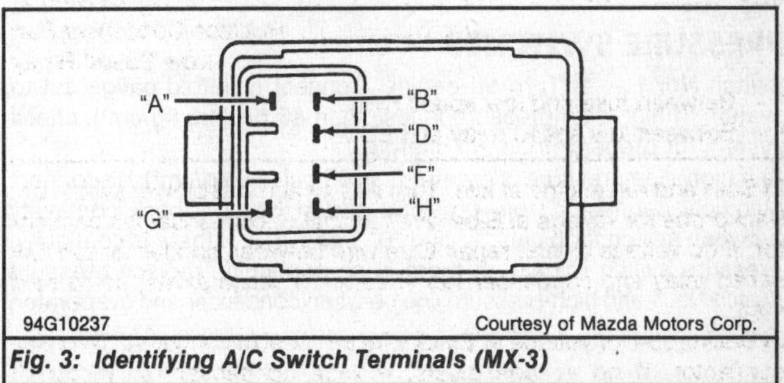

"A"
"B"
"D"
"F"
"G"
"H"
94G10237
Courtesy of Mazda Motors Corp.

Fig. 3: Identifying A/C Switch Terminals (MX-3)

1993 MANUAL A/C-HEATER SYSTEMS MX-3, Protege & 323 (Cont.)

3) Reverse ohmmeter leads, placing opposite ohmmeter lead onto terminal "D". Check continuity at terminal "F" and "A" again. Continuity should exist in one direction only. If continuity is not as specified, replace switch.

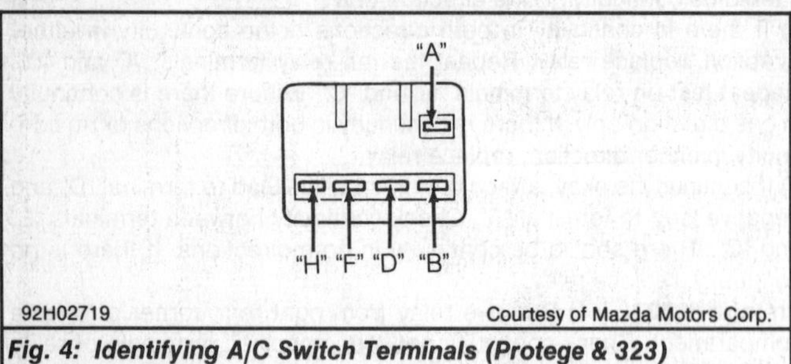
"A"
"H" "F" "D" "B"
92H02719
Courtesy of Mazda Motors Corp.

Fig. 4: Identifying A/C Switch Terminals (Protege & 323)

CONDENSER FAN RELAY

NOTE: On MX-3 (SOHC), condenser fan is controlled by A/C system relay. On MX-3 (DOHC), condenser fan relay, high and low speed relays are identical to A/C system relay. See A/C RELAY under TESTING.

Protege & 323 - 1) Remove relay from right rear corner of engine compartment. Check continuity between terminals No. 3 and 4. *See Fig. 5.* If continuity exists, replace relay.
2) If continuity does not exist, attach battery positive lead to terminal No. 1 and negative lead to terminal No. 2. Check continuity between terminals No. 3 and 4. If continuity exists, relay is okay. If continuity does not exist, replace relay.

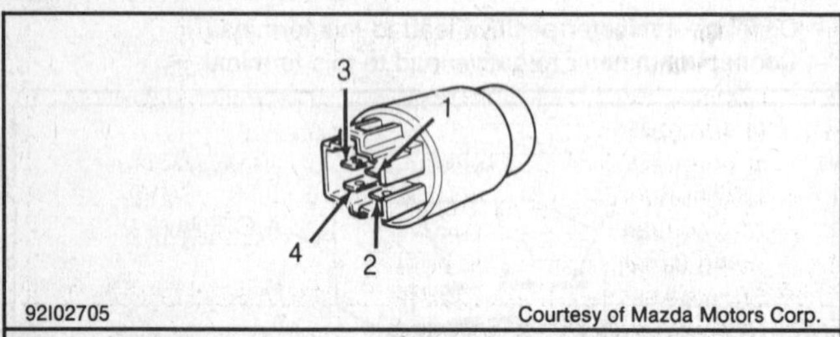
3
1
4
2
92I02705
Courtesy of Mazda Motors Corp.

Fig. 5: Identifying Condenser Fan Relay Terminals (Protege & 323)

EVAPORATOR THERMOSWITCH

On-Vehicle Test - Remove glove box. Run engine at idle. Turn A/C switch off. Operate blower at high speed for a few minutes. Turn off blower and engine. Disconnect evaporator thermoswitch connector. *See Fig. 7.* Check continuity between thermoswitch terminals. If there is continuity, thermoswitch is okay. If there is no continuity, replace thermoswitch.
Off-Vehicle Test - Submerge thermoswitch sensing bulb into ice cold water. There should be continuity between thermoswitch terminals at temperatures above 41°F (5°C). At temperatures below 32°F (0°C), there should be no continuity. If continuity is not as specified, replace thermoswitch.

PRESSURE SWITCHES

Switch No. 1 - 1) Turn off engine. Connect manifold gauge set to system. If high-side pressure is less than 65 psi (4.6 kg/cm²), check system for proper refrigerant charge.
2) If high-side pressure is greater than 65 psi (4.6 kg/cm²), disconnect electrical connector from pressure switch No. 1. Check continuity between switch terminals "A" and "B". *See Fig. 6.* If there is continuity, pressure switch is okay. If there is no continuity, replace pressure switch No. 1 and high-pressure line between condenser and evaporator.

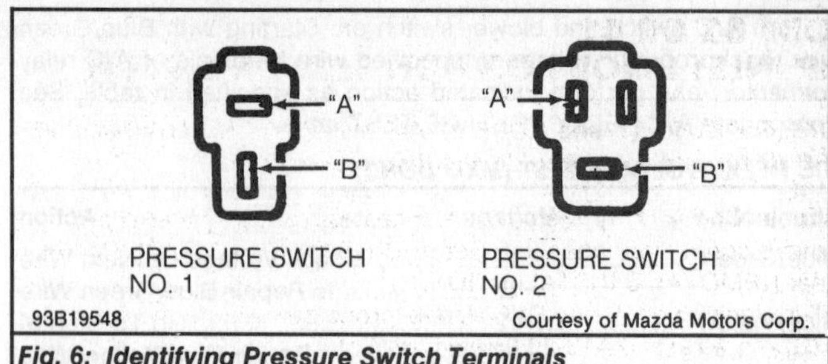
"A"
"B"
"A"
"B"
PRESSURE SWITCH NO. 1
PRESSURE SWITCH NO. 2
93B19548
Courtesy of Mazda Motors Corp.

Fig. 6: Identifying Pressure Switch Terminals

WARNING: If high-side pressure exceeds 256 psi (18 kg/cm²) while testing pressure switch No. 2, stop testing procedure.

Switch No. 2 (Protege With A/T) - 1) Turn ignition off. Connect manifold gauge set to system. Ensure high-side pressure is less than 171 psi (12 kg/cm²). Disconnect electrical connector from pressure switch No. 2. Check continuity between switch terminals "A" and "B". *See Fig. 6.* If there is continuity, replace pressure switch No. 2 and high-pressure line between condenser and evaporator.
2) If there is no continuity, disconnect condenser fan connector. Operate engine at 2000 RPM. Turn on A/C with temperature lever set at coldest position. Turn on blower switch. When high-side pressure reaches 213-242 psi (15-17 kg/cm²), check continuity of pressure switch No. 2. If there is continuity, pressure switch No. 2 is okay. If there is no continuity, replace pressure switch No. 2 and high-pressure line between condenser and evaporator.

REMOVAL & INSTALLATION

NOTE: For removal and installation procedures not covered in this article, see REMOVAL & INSTALLATION in HEATER SYSTEMS - MX-3, PROTEGE & 323 article.

COMPRESSOR

Removal & Installation - Disconnect negative battery cable. Discharge A/C system using approved refrigerant recovery/recycling equipment. Loosen idler pulley or power steering pump (if equipped). Remove drive belt. Disconnect compressor clutch connector. Working from under vehicle, disconnect refrigerant lines from compressor. Remove compressor bolts and compressor. To install, reverse removal procedure. Evacuate and recharge system.

CONDENSER

Removal (MX-3) - 1) Discharge A/C system using approved refrigerant recovery/recycling equipment. Remove front undercover. Remove fresh air duct. Remove radiator mount. Remove airflow meter.
2) Remove condenser brackets. Disconnect condenser inlet and outlet lines. Place a piece of cardboard between radiator and condenser to protect radiator and condenser from damage. Lift and remove condenser.
Installation - To install, reverse removal procedure. Coat "O" rings with clean compressor oil before installation. DO NOT apply oil to fittings. When installing new condenser, add one ounce of compressor oil through high pressure port of compressor. Evacuate and recharge system.
Removal (Protege & 323) - 1) Discharge A/C system using approved refrigerant recovery/recycling equipment. Remove radiator grille. Remove receiver-drier. Remove radiator brackets.
2) Disconnect condenser inlet and outlet lines. Place a piece of cardboard between radiator and condenser to protect radiator and condenser from damage. Lift and remove condenser.
Installation - To install, reverse removal procedure. Coat "O" rings with clean compressor oil before installation. DO NOT apply oil to fittings. When installing new condenser, add 1/3 ounce of compressor oil through high pressure port of compressor. Evacuate and recharge system.

CONTROL PANEL

Removal & Installation (MX-3) – Disconnect negative battery cable. Remove side panel from right end of instrument panel. *See Fig. 8*. Remove front and rear console. Remove ventilation grille. Remove right lower panel (under glove box), glove box and glove box cover. Remove center panel, and radio/cassette unit. Disconnect air control door cables from control panel. Remove control panel. To install, reverse removal procedure. Ensure cables operate properly.

Removal & Installation (Protege & 323) – Disconnect negative battery cable. Remove side panel from right end of instrument panel. *See Fig. 9*. Remove right lower panel, center lower panel, instrument cluster cover, glove box and glove box cover. Disconnect air control door cables from control panel. Remove control panel. To install, reverse removal procedure. Ensure cables operate properly.

EVAPORATOR CASE

Removal – **1)** Discharge A/C system using approved refrigerant recovery/recycling equipment. Remove instrument panel undercover. Remove glove box and glove box cover. *See Fig. 8 or 9*. Disconnect electrical connectors from evaporator case.

2) Disconnect refrigerant lines from evaporator at engine compartment firewall. Loosen seal plate between heater case and evaporator case. Loosen seal plate between evaporator case and blower motor case.

3) Remove evaporator case nuts and evaporator case. Disassemble evaporator case to remove evaporator, thermoswitch and expansion valve. *See Fig. 7*.

Installation – To install, reverse removal procedure. Coat "O" rings with clean compressor oil before installation. DO NOT apply oil to fittings. When installing new evaporator, add 2 ounces (1 3/4 ounces on Protege and 323) of compressor oil through high pressure port of compressor. Evacuate and recharge system.

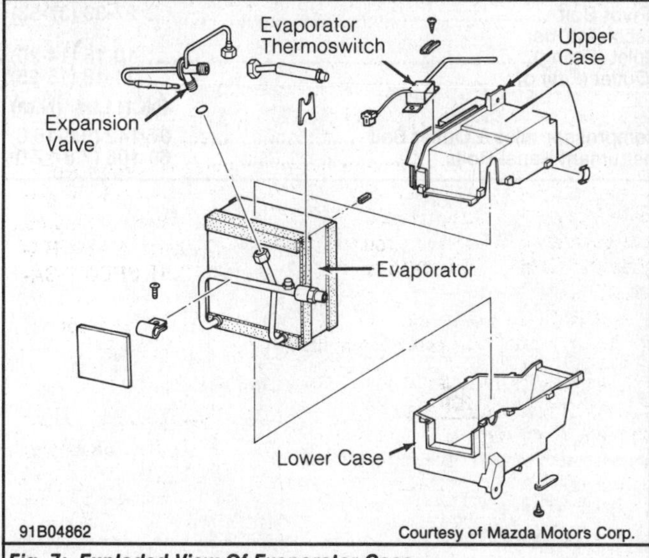

Evaporator Thermoswitch
Upper Case
Expansion Valve
Evaporator
Lower Case
91B04862
Courtesy of Mazda Motors Corp.

Fig. 7: Exploded View Of Evaporator Case

INSTRUMENT PANEL

Removal & Installation – Disconnect negative battery cable. Remove all components in order listed in illustration. *See Fig. 8 or 9*. To install, reverse removal procedure.

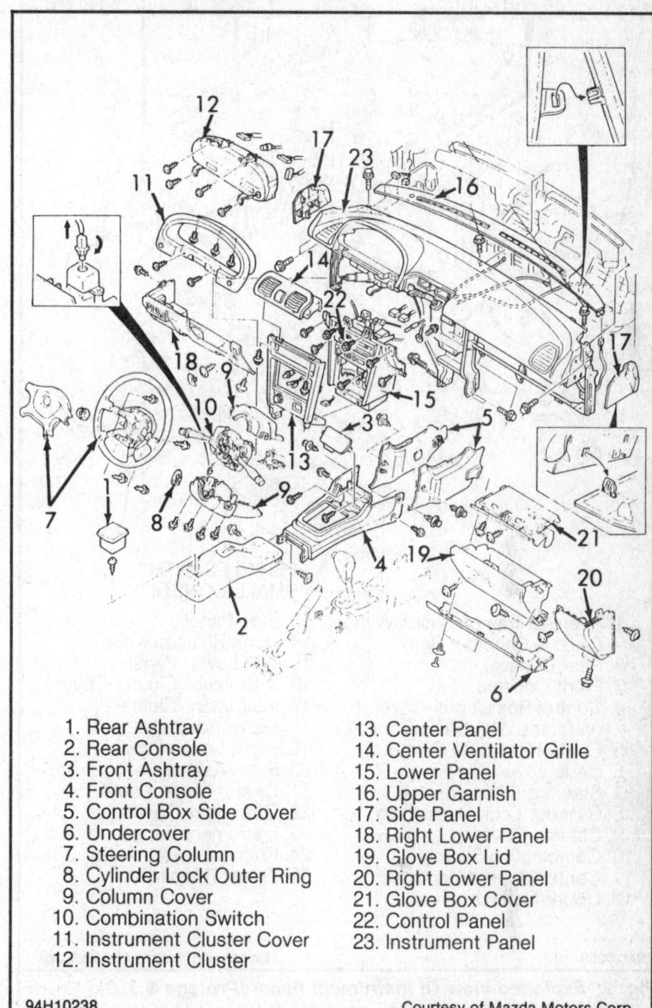

1. Rear Ashtray
2. Rear Console
3. Front Ashtray
4. Front Console
5. Control Box Side Cover
6. Undercover
7. Steering Column
8. Cylinder Lock Outer Ring
9. Column Cover
10. Combination Switch
11. Instrument Cluster Cover
12. Instrument Cluster
13. Center Panel
14. Center Ventilator Grille
15. Lower Panel
16. Upper Garnish
17. Side Panel
18. Right Lower Panel
19. Glove Box Lid
20. Right Lower Panel
21. Glove Box Cover
22. Control Panel
23. Instrument Panel
94H10238
Courtesy of Mazda Motors Corp.

Fig. 8: Exploded View Of Instrument Panel (MX-3)

1993 MANUAL A/C-HEATER SYSTEMS
MX-3, Protege & 323 (Cont.)

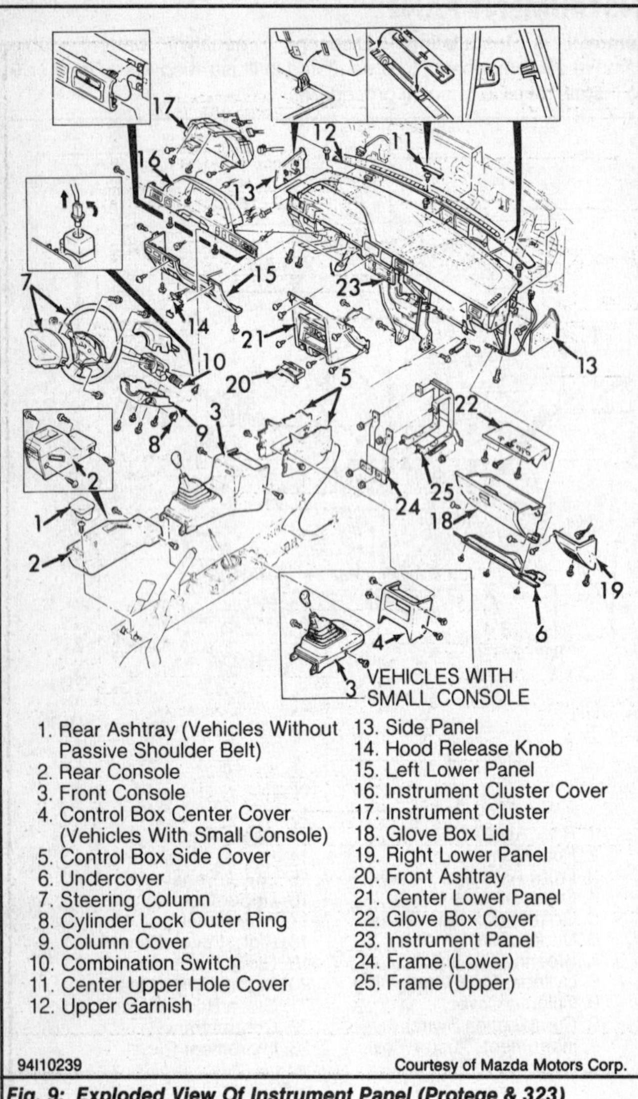
VEHICLES WITH
SMALL CONSOLE
1. Rear Ashtray (Vehicles Without Passive Shoulder Belt)
2. Rear Console
3. Front Console
4. Control Box Center Cover (Vehicles With Small Console)
5. Control Box Side Cover
6. Undercover
7. Steering Column
8. Cylinder Lock Outer Ring
9. Column Cover
10. Combination Switch
11. Center Upper Hole Cover
12. Upper Garnish
13. Side Panel
14. Hood Release Knob
15. Left Lower Panel
16. Instrument Cluster Cover
17. Instrument Cluster
18. Glove Box Lid
19. Right Lower Panel
20. Front Ashtray
21. Center Lower Panel
22. Glove Box Cover
23. Instrument Panel
24. Frame (Lower)
25. Frame (Upper)
94I10239
Courtesy of Mazda Motors Corp.

Fig. 9: Exploded View Of Instrument Panel (Protege & 323)

RECEIVER-DRIER

Removal (MX-3) – Discharge A/C system using approved refrigerant recovery/recycling equipment. Remove airflow meter. Disconnect pressure switch. Disconnect receiver-drier inlet and outlet lines. Remove receiver-drier with bracket from vehicle. Remove receiver-drier bracket.

Removal (Protege & 323) – Discharge A/C system using approved refrigerant recovery/recycling equipment. Remove front grille. Disconnect inlet and outlet lines from receiver-drier. Remove receiver-drier.

Installation (All Models) – To install, reverse removal procedure. Coat "O" rings with clean compressor oil before installation. DO NOT apply oil to fittings. When installing new receiver-drier, add 1/3 ounce of compressor oil through high pressure port of compressor. Evacuate and recharge system.

TORQUE SPECIFICATIONS

TORQUE SPECIFICATIONS

Application	Ft. Lbs. (N.m)
A/C Compressor Belt	
Idler Pulley Nut	23-25 (31-34)
A/C Compressor Bolt	18-26 (25-35)
Condenser	
Inlet (Fitting)	11-18 (15-25)
Outlet (Fitting)	10-14 (14-19)
Evaporator Assembly	
MX-3	
Inlet (Fitting)	10-11 (14-15)
Outlet (Fitting)	21-25 (29-34)
Protege & 323	
Inlet (Fitting)	10-14 (14-19)
Outlet (Fitting)	15-21 (20-29)
Power Steering Pump	
Bracket Pivot Bolt/Nut	24-34 (32-46)
Pivot Bolt	27-39 (37-53)
Receiver-Drier	
Inlet (Fitting)	10-15 (14-20)
Outlet (Fitting)	11-18 (15-25)
	INCH Lbs. (N.m)
Compressor Inlet & Outlet Bolt	87-142 (9.8-16.0)
Instrument Panel Bolts	69-106 (7.8-12.0)

1993 MANUAL A/C-HEATER SYSTEMS MX-3, Protege & 323 (Cont.)

WIRING DIAGRAMS

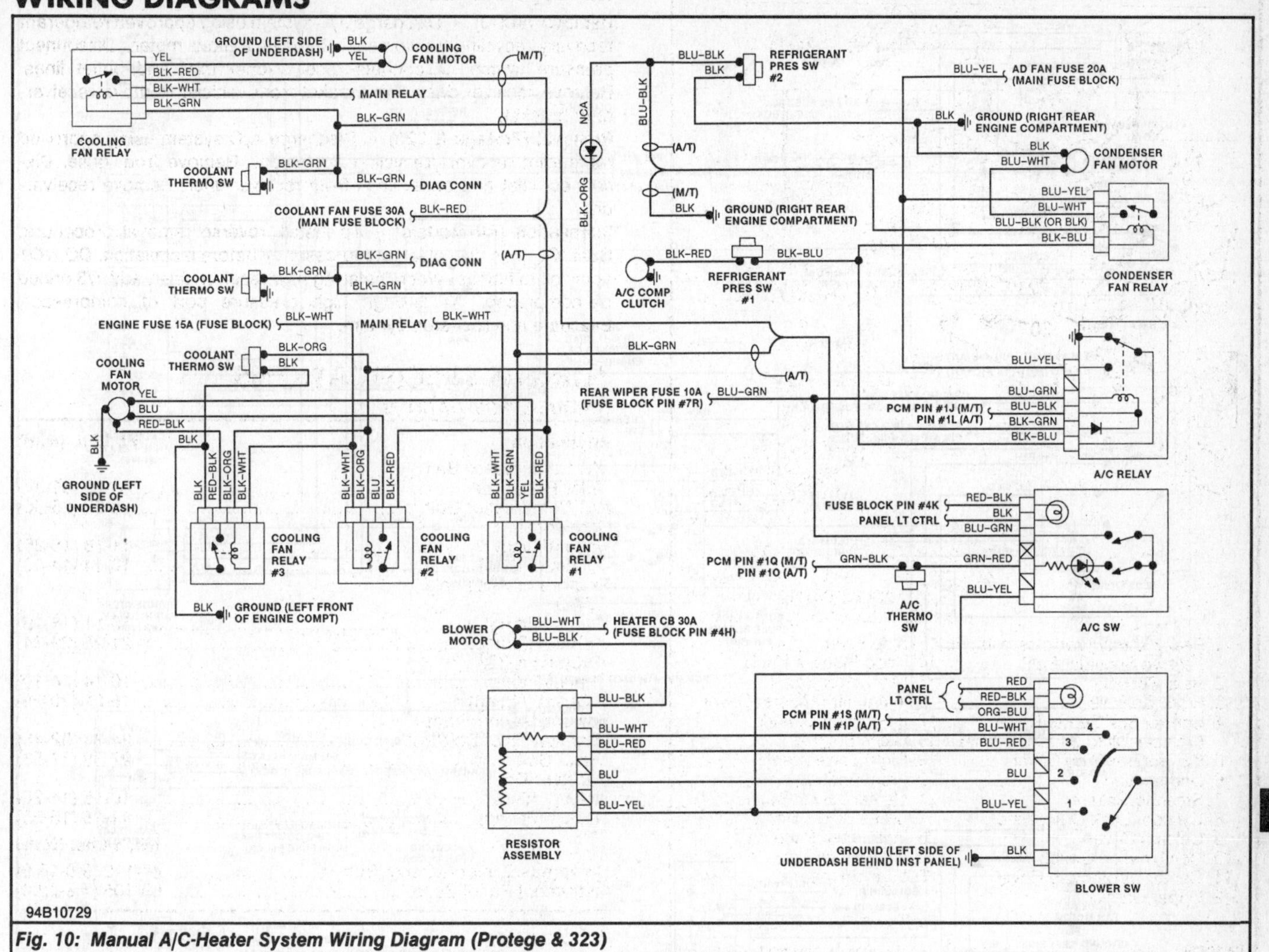

GROUND (LEFT SIDE OF UNDERDASH)
BLK
YEL
COOLING FAN MOTOR
COOLING FAN RELAY
BLK-RED
BLK-WHT
BLK-GRN
MAIN RELAY
COOLANT THERMO SW
DIAG CONN
COOLANT FAN FUSE 30A (MAIN FUSE BLOCK)
ENGINE FUSE 15A (FUSE BLOCK)
COOLING FAN MOTOR
BLU
RED-BLK
GROUND (LEFT SIDE OF UNDERDASH)
COOLING FAN RELAY #3
COOLING FAN RELAY #2
COOLING FAN RELAY #1
GROUND (LEFT FRONT OF ENGINE COMPT)
BLK-ORG
(M/T)
(A/T)
NCA
BLU-BLK
REFRIGERANT PRES SW #2
GROUND (RIGHT REAR ENGINE COMPARTMENT)
A/C COMP CLUTCH
REFRIGERANT PRES SW #1
BLK-BLU
REAR WIPER FUSE 10A (FUSE BLOCK PIN #7R)
BLU-GRN
AD FAN FUSE 20A (MAIN FUSE BLOCK)
BLU-YEL
CONDENSER FAN MOTOR
BLU-WHT
BLU-BLK (OR BLK)
CONDENSER FAN RELAY
PCM PIN #1J (M/T) PIN #1L (A/T)
A/C RELAY
FUSE BLOCK PIN #4K
PANEL LT CTRL
PCM PIN #1Q (M/T) PIN #1O (A/T)
GRN-BLK
GRN-RED
A/C THERMO SW
A/C SW
BLOWER MOTOR
HEATER CB 30A (FUSE BLOCK PIN #4H)
RESISTOR ASSEMBLY
BLU-RED
PCM PIN #1S (M/T) PIN #1P (A/T)
ORG-BLU
RED
GROUND (LEFT SIDE OF UNDERDASH BEHIND INST PANEL)
BLOWER SW
94B10729

Fig. 10: Manual A/C-Heater System Wiring Diagram (Protege & 323)

1993 MANUAL A/C-HEATER SYSTEMS
MX-3, Protege & 323 (Cont.)

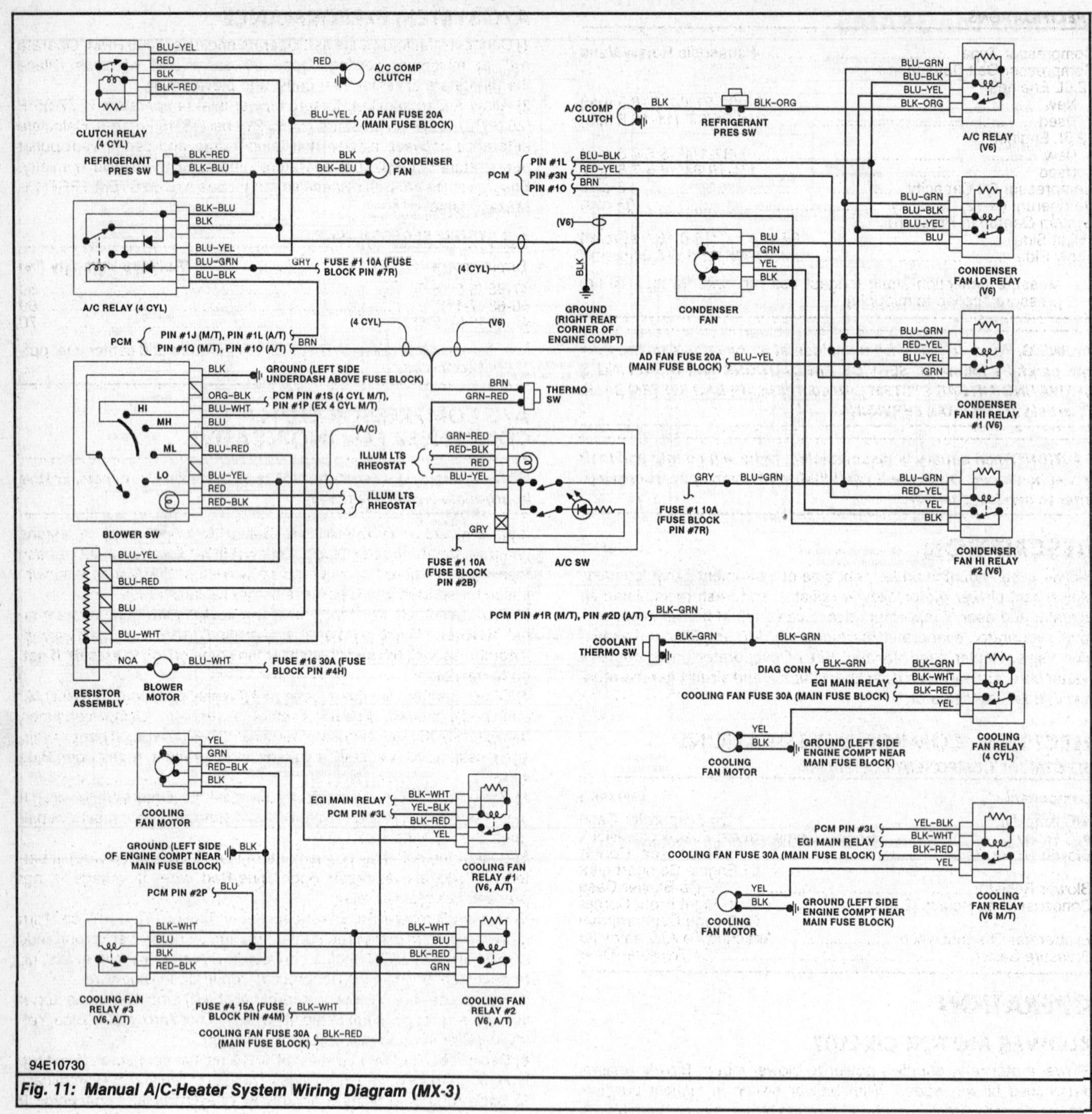
BLU-YEL
RED
BLK
BLK-RED
CLUTCH RELAY (4 CYL)
RED
A/C COMP CLUTCH
BLU-YEL
AD FAN FUSE 20A (MAIN FUSE BLOCK)
REFRIGERANT PRES SW
BLK-RED
BLK-BLU
BLK
BLK-BLU
CONDENSER FAN
BLK-BLU
BLK
BLU-YEL
BLU-GRN
BLU-BLK
GRY
FUSE #1 10A (FUSE BLOCK PIN #7R)
A/C RELAY (4 CYL)
PCM
PIN #1J (M/T), PIN #1L (A/T)
PIN #1Q (M/T), PIN #1O (A/T)
BRN
(4 CYL)
(V6)
BLK
GROUND (LEFT SIDE UNDERDASH ABOVE FUSE BLOCK)
ORG-BLK
BLU-WHT
PCM PIN #1S (4 CYL M/T), PIN #1P (EX 4 CYL M/T)
HI
MH
ML
LO
BLU
BLU-RED
BLU-YEL
RED
RED-BLK
ILLUM LTS RHEOSTAT
BLOWER SW
BLU-YEL
BLU-RED
BLU
BLU-WHT
NCA
BLU-WHT
FUSE #16 30A (FUSE BLOCK PIN #4H)
RESISTOR ASSEMBLY
BLOWER MOTOR
A/C COMP CLUTCH
BLK
BLK-ORG
REFRIGERANT PRES SW
PCM
PIN #1L
PIN #3N
PIN #1O
BLU-BLK
RED-YEL
BRN
(V6)
(4 CYL)
BLK
GROUND (RIGHT REAR CORNER OF ENGINE COMPT)
BLU
GRN
YEL
BLK
CONDENSER FAN
AD FAN FUSE 20A (MAIN FUSE BLOCK)
BLU-YEL
BRN
GRN-RED
THERMO SW
(A/C)
GRN-RED
RED-BLK
RED
BLU-YEL
ILLUM LTS RHEOSTAT
GRY
FUSE #1 10A (FUSE BLOCK PIN #2B)
A/C SW
GRY
BLU-GRN
FUSE #1 10A (FUSE BLOCK PIN #7R)
BLU-GRN
BLU-BLK
BLU-YEL
BLK-ORG
A/C RELAY (V6)
BLU-GRN
BLU-BLK
BLU-YEL
BLU
CONDENSER FAN LO RELAY (V6)
BLU-GRN
RED-YEL
BLU-YEL
GRN
CONDENSER FAN HI RELAY #1 (V6)
BLU-GRN
RED-YEL
YEL
BLK
CONDENSER FAN HI RELAY #2 (V6)
PCM PIN #1R (M/T), PIN #2D (A/T)
BLK-GRN
COOLANT THERMO SW
BLK-GRN
BLK-GRN
DIAG CONN
BLK-GRN
EGI MAIN RELAY
COOLING FAN FUSE 30A (MAIN FUSE BLOCK)
BLK-GRN
BLK-WHT
BLK-RED
YEL
COOLING FAN RELAY (4 CYL)
YEL
BLK
GROUND (LEFT SIDE ENGINE COMPT NEAR MAIN FUSE BLOCK)
COOLING FAN MOTOR
YEL
GRN
RED-BLK
BLK
COOLING FAN MOTOR
GROUND (LEFT SIDE OF ENGINE COMPT NEAR MAIN FUSE BLOCK)
BLK
EGI MAIN RELAY
PCM PIN #3L
BLK-WHT
YEL-BLK
BLK-RED
YEL
COOLING FAN RELAY #1 (V6, A/T)
PCM PIN #2P
BLU
BLK-WHT
BLU
BLK
RED-BLK
COOLING FAN RELAY #3 (V6, A/T)
BLK-WHT
BLU
BLK-RED
GRN
COOLING FAN RELAY #2 (V6, A/T)
FUSE #4 15A (FUSE BLOCK PIN #4M)
BLK-WHT
COOLING FAN FUSE 30A (MAIN FUSE BLOCK)
BLK-RED
PCM PIN #3L
EGI MAIN RELAY
COOLING FAN FUSE 30A (MAIN FUSE BLOCK)
YEL-BLK
BLK-WHT
BLK-RED
YEL
COOLING FAN RELAY (V6 M/T)
YEL
BLK
GROUND (LEFT SIDE ENGINE COMPT NEAR MAIN FUSE BLOCK)
COOLING FAN MOTOR
94E10730

Fig. 11: Manual A/C-Heater System Wiring Diagram (MX-3)

1993 MANUAL A/C-HEATER SYSTEMS MX-6 & 626

SPECIFICATIONS

Compressor Type	Panasonic Rotary Vane
Compressor Belt Deflection [1]	
2.0L Engines	
New	9/32-21/64" (7-8.5 mm)
Used	7/16-31/64" (11-12.5 mm)
2.5L Engines	
New	7/32-1/4" (5.5-6.5 mm)
Used	1/4-19/64" (6.5-7.5 mm)
Compressor Oil Capacity	4.3 ozs.
Refrigerant (R-12) Capacity	26 ozs.
System Operating Pressures	
High Side	185-214 psi (13.0-15.0 kg/cm²)
Low Side	21-43 psi (1.5-3.0 kg/cm²)

[1] – Measure deflection along longest belt run, with 22 lbs. (10 kg) pressure applied to midpoint.

WARNING: To avoid injury from accidental air bag deployment, read and carefully follow all SERVICE PRECAUTIONS and DISABLING & ACTIVATING AIR BAG SYSTEM procedures in AIR BAG SYSTEM SAFETY article in GENERAL SERVICING.

CAUTION: When battery is disconnected, radio will go into anti-theft protection mode. Obtain radio anti-theft protection code from owner prior to servicing vehicle.

DESCRIPTION

Blower case, mounted under right side of instrument panel, contains blower fan, blower motor, blower resistor, and fresh/recirculated air actuator and door. Evaporator case, located left of blower case, contains evaporator, evaporator thermoswitch, A/C amplifier and expansion valve. Heater case, located left of evaporator case, contains heater core, airflow mode door and actuator, and air-mix (temperature blend) door and actuator.

ELECTRICAL COMPONENT LOCATIONS

ELECTRICAL COMPONENT LOCATIONS

Component	Location
A/C Amplifier	On Evaporator Case
A/C Relay	Engine Compartment Fuse/Relay Block
Blower Motor Relay	In Right Front Corner Of Engine Compartment
Blower Resistor	On Blower Case
Condenser Fan Relays (2.5L)	In Right Front Corner Of Engine Compartment
Evaporator Thermoswitch	Attached To A/C Amplifier
Pressure Switch	On Receiver-Drier

OPERATION

BLOWER MOTOR CIRCUIT

Blower motor relay supplies power to blower motor. Blower resistor determines blower speed. With blower switch in highest position, blower motor is directly grounded through blower switch. With blower switch in all other positions, blower motor is grounded through blower resistor and blower switch.

A/C COMPRESSOR CLUTCH CIRCUIT

Circuit through A/C compressor clutch is completed when A/C relay is energized and pressure switch is closed. A/C relay is energized when Engine Control Unit (ECU) grounds the solenoid circuit of the A/C relay.

TESTING

NOTE: For testing procedures not covered in this article, see TESTING in HEATER SYSTEMS – MX-6 & 626 article.

A/C SYSTEM PERFORMANCE

1) Connect manifold gauge set. Operate engine at 2000 RPM. Operate A/C at maximum cooling. Open all doors and windows. Place thermometers at center vent outlet and blower inlet.

2) Allow A/C to stabilize. Ensure blower inlet temperature is 77-95°F (25-35°C), and high pressure is 185-214 psi (13-15 kg/cm²). Calculate difference between blower inlet temperature and center vent outlet temperature. Compare temperature difference to relative humidity. Ensure values are within specified range. See A/C SYSTEM PERFORMANCE table.

A/C SYSTEM PERFORMANCE

Temperature °F (°C) [1]	Relative Humidity (%)
47-65 (8.5-18.5)	50
45-63 (7-17)	60
42-60 (5.5-15.5)	70

[1] – Difference between blower inlet temperature and center vent outlet temperature.

A/C COMPRESSOR CLUTCH & CONDENSER FAN INOPERATIVE

NOTE: A/C relay connector has 2 Green/White wire terminals. Ensure appropriate terminal is tested.

2.0L Engines – 1) Check AIR COND fuse (40-amp) in engine compartment fuse/relay block. Check WIPER fuse (20-amp) in dash fuse block. If fuses are okay, go to next step. If any fuse is blown, check for shorted wiring harness before replacing fuse.

2) Turn ignition off. Connect jumper wire to A/C relay connector terminal "A" (Green/White wire) and body ground. *See Fig. 1.* Start engine. If compressor clutch and condenser fan come on, go to step **6)**. If not, go to next step.

3) Check jumper wire connection at A/C relay connector terminal "A" and body ground. Ensure engine is running. Using voltmeter, backprobe A/C relay connector terminal "D" (Blue wire). If battery voltage exists, go to next step. If voltage is not present, repair open Blue wire.

4) Backprobe A/C relay connector terminal "E" (Green/White wire). If battery voltage exists, go to next step. If voltage is not present, repair open Green/White wire.

5) Backprobe A/C relay connector terminal "C" (Blue/Red wire). If battery voltage exists, repair open Blue/Red wire. If voltage is not present, replace A/C relay.

6) Remove jumper wire. Ensure engine is running. Turn A/C on. Turn blower switch to low speed setting. Using voltmeter, backprobe Blue wire terminal of A/C amplifier connector. If battery voltage exists, go to next step. If voltage is not present, repair open Blue wire.

7) Backprobe Blue/Yellow wire terminal of A/C amplifier connector. If voltage is zero, go to next step. If voltage is not zero, repair Blue/Yellow wire for short to power (battery voltage).

8) Backprobe Red wire terminal of A/C amplifier connector. If voltage is zero, go to next step. If voltage is not zero, replace A/C amplifier.

9) Backprobe Blue/White wire terminal of A/C amplifier connector. If voltage is zero, go to next step. If voltage is not zero, go to step **12)**.

10) Backprobe Green/Black wire terminal of A/C amplifier connector. If voltage is zero, check ECU operation. If voltage is not zero, go to next step.

11) Turn A/C off. Operate blower fan at high speed. After a few minutes, turn A/C on. Backprobe Green/Black wire terminal of A/C amplifier. If voltage is zero, system is normal. If voltage is not zero, replace A/C amplifier.

12) Ensure engine is running. Ensure A/C is on and blower switch is at low speed setting. Backprobe Red wire terminal of A/C-heater control panel. If voltage is zero, go to next step. If voltage is not zero, repair Red wire for short to power (battery voltage).

13) Backprobe Blue/White wire terminal of A/C-heater control panel. If voltage is zero, repair open Blue/White wire. If voltage is not zero, replace A/C-heater control panel.

1993 MANUAL A/C-HEATER SYSTEMS MX-6 & 626 (Cont.)

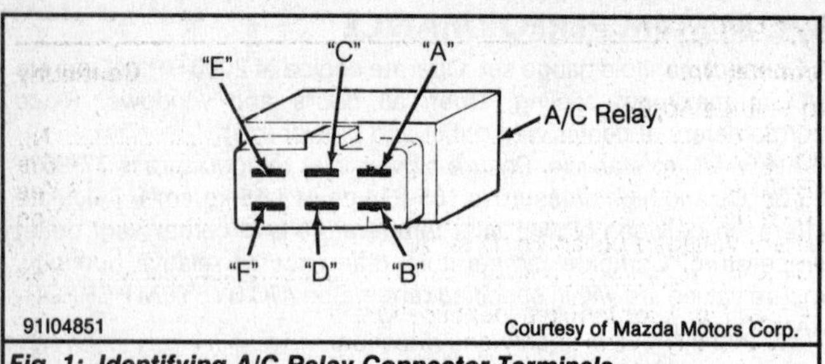
"E"
"C"
"A"
A/C Relay
"F"
"D"
"B"
91I04851
Courtesy of Mazda Motors Corp.

Fig. 1: Identifying A/C Relay Connector Terminals

A/C COMPRESSOR CLUTCH INOPERATIVE

NOTE: A/C relay connector has 2 Green/White wire terminals. Ensure appropriate terminal is tested.

2.0L Engines - 1) Check AIR COND fuse (40-amp) in engine compartment fuse/relay block. Check WIPER fuse (20-amp) in dash fuse block. If fuses are okay, go to next step. If any fuse is blown, check for shorted wiring harness before replacing fuse.

2) Turn ignition off. Disconnect refrigerant pressure switch connector. Connect jumper wire to Blue/Red wire and Red wire terminals of pressure switch connector. Start engine. Turn A/C and blower on. If compressor clutch engages, go to next step. If not, go to step **4)**.

3) Connect manifold gauge set. Measure high-side pressure. If pressure is 29.9-298 psi (2.1-21 kg/cm²), replace pressure switch. If pressure is not 29.9-298 psi (2.1-21 kg/cm²), check refrigerant level and correct if necessary.

4) Disconnect jumper wire. Reconnect pressure switch connector. Ensure ignition, A/C and blower are on. Using voltmeter, backprobe Red wire terminal of compressor clutch connector. If battery voltage exists, replace compressor clutch. If voltage is not present, repair open Red wire between compressor clutch and pressure switch.

2.5L Engines - 1) Check AIR COND fuse (40-amp) in engine compartment fuse/relay block. Check WIPER fuse (20-amp) in dash fuse block. If fuses are okay, go to next step. If any fuse is blown, check for shorted wiring harness before replacing fuse.

2) Turn ignition off. Disconnect refrigerant pressure switch connector. Connect jumper wire to Blue/Red wire and Red wire terminals of pressure switch connector. Start engine. Turn A/C and blower on. If compressor clutch comes on, go to next step. If not, go to step **4)**.

3) Connect manifold gauge set. Measure high-side pressure. If pressure is 29.9-298 psi (2.1-21 kg/cm²), replace pressure switch. If pressure is not 29.9-298 psi (2.1-21 kg/cm²), check refrigerant level and correct as necessary.

4) Disconnect jumper wire. Reconnect pressure switch connector. Ensure ignition, A/C and blower are on. Using voltmeter, backprobe Blue/Red wire terminal of pressure switch connector. If battery voltage exists, go to next step. If voltage is not present, go to step **6)**.

5) Backprobe Red wire terminal of compressor clutch connector. If battery voltage exists, replace compressor clutch. If voltage is not present, repair open Red wire between pressure switch and compressor clutch.

6) Backprobe A/C relay connector terminal "D" (Blue wire). *See Fig. 1.* If battery voltage exists, go to next step. If voltage is not present, repair open Blue wire between WIPER fuse (20-amp) and A/C relay.

7) Backprobe A/C relay connector terminal "A" (Green/White wire). If battery voltage exists, ensure Green/White wire to ECU is okay, then go to next step. If voltage is not present, replace defective A/C relay.

8) Backprobe A/C relay connector terminal "E" (Green/White wire). If battery voltage exists, go to next step. If voltage is not present, repair Green/White wire between AIR COND fuse and A/C relay.

9) Backprobe A/C relay connector terminal "C" (Blue/Red wire). If voltage is zero, replace A/C relay. If voltage is not zero, repair Blue/Red wire between A/C relay and pressure switch.

CONDENSER FAN INOPERATIVE

2.0L Engines - 1) Check AIR COND fuse (40-amp) in engine compartment fuse/relay block. Check WIPER fuse (20-amp) in dash fuse block. If fuses are okay, go to next step. If any fuse is blown, check for shorted wiring harness before replacing fuse.

2) Start engine. Turn A/C and blower on. Using voltmeter, backprobe Blue/Red wire terminal of condenser fan connector. If battery voltage exists, go to next step. If voltage is not present, repair Blue/Red wire between A/C relay and condenser fan.

3) Backprobe Black/Yellow wire terminal of condenser fan connector. If battery voltage exists, repair wiring harness between condenser fan and body ground. If voltage is not present, replace condenser fan.

NOTE: Condenser fan low relay connector has 2 Green/White wire terminals. Check voltage at appropriate wire.

2.5L Engines - 1) Check AIR COND fuse (40-amp) in engine compartment fuse/relay block. Check WIPER fuse (20-amp) in dash fuse block. If fuses are okay, go to next step. If any fuse is blown, check for shorted wiring harness before replacing fuse.

2) Start engine. Turn A/C and blower on. Using voltmeter, backprobe condenser fan low relay connector terminal No. 2 (Blue wire). *See Fig. 2.* If battery voltage exists, go to next step. If voltage is not present, repair open Blue wire between WIPER fuse and condenser fan low relay.

3) Backprobe condenser fan low relay connector terminal No. 4 (Green/White wire). If battery voltage exists, ensure Green/White wire to ECU is okay, then go to next step. If voltage is not present, replace defective relay.

4) Backprobe condenser fan low relay connector terminal No. 1 (Green/White wire). If battery voltage exists, go to next step. If voltage is not present, repair open Green/White wire between AIR COND fuse and condenser fan low relay.

5) Backprobe condenser fan low relay connector terminal No. 3 (Blue/Black wire). If battery voltage exists, go to next step. If voltage is not present, replace condenser fan relay.

6) Backprobe Blue/Black wire terminal of condenser fan connector. If battery voltage exists, go to next step. If voltage is not present, repair open Blue/Black wire between condenser fan low relay and condenser fan.

7) Backprobe Black/Yellow wire terminal of condenser fan connector. If battery voltage exists, repair wiring harness between condenser fan and body ground. If voltage is not present, replace condenser fan.

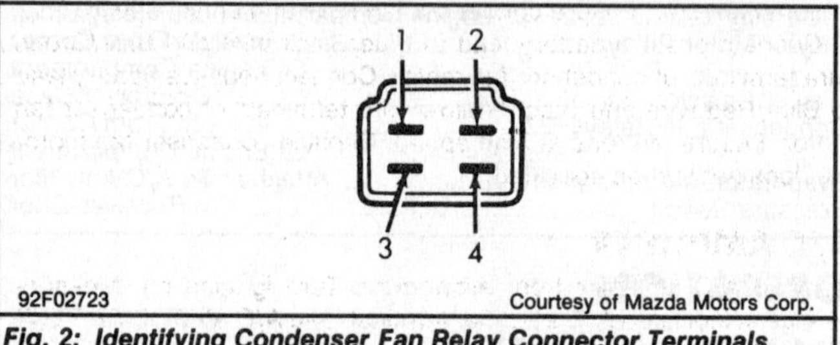
1
2
3
4
92F02723
Courtesy of Mazda Motors Corp.

Fig. 2: Identifying Condenser Fan Relay Connector Terminals

ENGINE OVERHEATS UNDER HIGH LOAD (A/C FUNCTIONS NORMALLY)

2.5L Engines - 1) Check AIR COND fuse (40-amp) in engine compartment fuse/relay block. Check WIPER fuse (20-amp) in dash fuse block. If fuses are okay, go to next step. If any fuse is blown, check for shorted wiring harness before replacing fuse.

2) Connect jumper wire to terminal No. 3 (Red wire) of condenser fan high relay No. 1 connector and body ground. *See Fig. 2.* Turn ignition on. If condenser fan does not operate, go to next step. If condenser fan operates at low speed, go to step **7)**. If condenser fan operates at high speed, check voltage at ECU terminal. Repair Red wire between ECU, high relay No. 1 and high relay No. 2 as necessary.

3) Leave jumper wire connected. Using voltmeter, backprobe Blue/Green wire terminal of condenser fan connector. If battery voltage exists, replace condenser fan. If voltage is not present, go to next step.

4) Leave jumper wire connected. Backprobe terminal No. 2 (Green/White wire) of condenser fan high relay No. 1 connector. If battery voltage exists, go to next step. If voltage is not present, repair open Green/White wire between AIR COND fuse and high relay No. 1.

5) Backprobe terminal No. 1 (Blue wire) of high relay No. 1 connector. If battery voltage exists, go to next step. If voltage is not present, repair open Blue wire between WIPER fuse and high relay No. 1.

6) Backprobe terminal No. 4 (Blue/Green wire) of high relay No. 1 connector. If battery voltage exists, repair open Blue/Green wire between high relay No. 1 and condenser fan. If voltage is not present, replace condenser fan high relay No. 1.

7) Leave jumper wire connected. Backprobe Blue/Red wire terminal of condenser fan. If battery voltage exists, go to next step. If voltage is not present, replace condenser fan.

8) Leave jumper wire connected. Backprobe terminal No. 1 (Blue wire) of condenser fan high relay No. 2 connector. If battery voltage exists, go to next step. If voltage is not present, repair open Blue wire between WIPER fuse and high relay No. 2.

9) Backprobe terminal No. 2 (Blue/Red wire) of high relay No. 2 connector. If battery voltage exists, go to next step. If voltage is not present, repair open Blue/Red wire between condenser fan and condenser fan high relay No. 2.

10) Backprobe terminal No. 3 (Red wire) of condenser fan high relay No. 2 connector. If battery voltage exists, ensure Red wire to ECU is okay, then go to next step. If voltage is not present, replace condenser fan high relay No. 2.

11) Backprobe terminal No. 4 (Black/Yellow wire) of condenser fan high relay No. 2 connector. If voltage is zero, replace condenser fan high relay No. 2. If voltage is not zero, repair open Black/Yellow wire between condenser fan high relay No. 2 and body ground.

CONDENSER FAN MOTOR

2.0L Engines – Disconnect condenser fan motor connector. Apply battery voltage across condenser fan motor terminals. Replace condenser fan motor if it does not operate.

2.5L Engines – **1)** Disconnect condenser fan motor connector. Connect positive battery lead to Blue/Black wire terminal of condenser fan motor. Connect negative battery lead to Black/Yellow wire terminal of motor. Ensure condenser fan runs at low speed.

2) Connect positive battery lead to Blue/Green wire terminal of condenser fan motor connector. Connect negative battery lead to Black/Yellow wire and Blue/Red wire terminals of condenser fan motor connector. Ensure condenser fan runs at medium speed.

3) Connect positive battery lead to Blue/Black wire and Blue/Green wire terminals of condenser fan motor. Connect negative battery lead to Blue/Red wire and Black/Yellow wire terminals of condenser fan motor. Ensure fan runs at high speed. Replace condenser fan motor if it does not test as specified.

A/C AMPLIFIER

Remove A/C amplifier from evaporator. Turn ignition on. Measure voltage at indicated A/C amplifier terminal. See A/C AMPLIFIER TEST table. Replace A/C amplifier if it does not test as specified.

A/C AMPLIFIER TEST

Terminal (Wire Color)	Condition	Volts
Blue	Ignition On	12
Blue	Ignition Off	0
Green/Black	Compressor On	0
Green/Black	Compressor Off	12
Blue/White	A/C & Blower On	0
Blue/White	A/C & Blower Off	12
Red	Blower Off	12
Red	Blower On	0
Blue/Yellow	Blower On	12
Blue/Yellow	Blower Off	0

A/C RELAY

Remove relay. Using ohmmeter, check continuity between indicated terminals. See A/C RELAY TEST table. Replace relay if continuity is not as specified.

A/C RELAY TEST

Terminal No. [1]	Continuity
No Voltage Applied	
"C" & "E"	No
"D" & "A"	[2] Yes
"B" & "A"	[2] Yes
"C" & "F"	Yes
Battery Voltage Applied To "D" & "A"	
"C" & "E"	Yes

[1] – *See Fig. 1* for terminal identification.
[2] – Continuity exists in only one direction.

CONDENSER FAN RELAY

2.5L Engines – Remove relay. Using ohmmeter, check continuity between indicated terminals. See CONDENSER FAN RELAY TEST table. Replace relay if continuity is not as specified.

CONDENSER FAN RELAY TEST

Terminal (Wire Color)	Continuity
Condenser Fan Low Relay	
Green/White & Blue/Black	[1] No
Blue & Green/White	[1] Yes
Green/White & Blue/Black	[2] Yes
Condenser Fan High Relay No. 1	
Green/White & Blue/Green	[1] No
Blue & Red	[1] Yes
Green/White & Blue/Green	[2] Yes
Condenser Fan High Relay No. 2	
Blue/Red & Black/Yellow	[1] No
Blue & Red	[1] Yes
Blue/Red & Black/Yellow	[2] Yes

[1] – With no voltage applied.
[2] – With battery voltage applied between remaining terminals.

PRESSURE SWITCH

1) Connect manifold gauge set. Ensure high-side pressure is 29.9-299 psi (2.1-21 kg/cm²). Disconnect pressure switch. Check continuity between Blue/Red wire and Red wire terminals of pressure switch. Replace pressure switch if continuity does not exist.

2) On 2.5L engines, check continuity between Green/White wire and Black/Yellow wire terminals. Continuity should exist with high-side pressure greater than 213 psi (15 kg/cm²). Continuity should not exist with high-side pressure less than 156 psi (11 kg/cm²). If continuity is not as specified, replace pressure switch.

REMOVAL & INSTALLATION

NOTE: For removal and installation procedures not covered in this article, see HEATER SYSTEMS – MX-6 & 626 article.

COMPRESSOR

Removal – Discharge A/C system using approved refrigerant recovery/recycling equipment. Remove compressor drive belt. Remove engine undercover. Disconnect flexible hose from compressor. Remove bolts and compressor.

Installation – If installing a new compressor, measure oil amount in old compressor. Subtract this amount and .5 ounce from 4.4 ounces. Remove calculated amount from new compressor. To install, reverse removal procedure. Adjust drive belt deflection.

CONDENSER

Removal – Discharge A/C system using approved refrigerant recovery/recycling equipment. Remove engine undercover and air ducts. Remove radiator upper mount. Disconnect refrigerant lines from condenser. Insert protector between radiator and condenser. Remove condenser bolts and condenser.

Installation – If installing a new condenser, add .5 ounce of compressor oil through high-pressure side of compressor. To install,

1993 MANUAL A/C-HEATER SYSTEMS MX-6 & 626 (Cont.)

reverse removal procedure. Apply clean compressor oil to "O" rings before connecting fittings. DO NOT apply compressor oil to fitting nuts.

EVAPORATOR CASE & CORE

Removal – 1) Discharge A/C system using approved refrigerant recovery/recycling equipment. Disconnect refrigerant lines from evaporator at engine compartment firewall.

2) Remove undercover, glove box and instrument panel support. Disconnect electrical connectors from evaporator case. Loosen left seal plate between heater case and evaporator case. Loosen right seal plate between evaporator case and blower motor case.

3) Remove evaporator case nuts. Disconnect drain hose. Remove evaporator case. Disassemble evaporator case to remove evaporator, expansion valve, thermosensor and A/C amplifier. To install, reverse removal procedure. Evacuate and charge A/C system.

Installation – If installing a new evaporator, add 1.7 ounces of compressor oil through high-pressure side of compressor. To install, reverse removal procedure. Apply clean compressor oil to "O" rings before connecting fittings. DO NOT apply compressor oil to fitting nuts.

RECEIVER-DRIER

Removal – Discharge A/C system using approved refrigerant recovery/recycling equipment. Disconnect refrigerant lines from receiver-drier. Remove receiver-drier.

Installation – If installing a new receiver-drier, add .34 ounce of compressor oil through high-pressure side of compressor. To install, reverse removal procedure. Apply clean compressor oil to "O" rings before connecting fittings.

INSTRUMENT PANEL

Removal & Installation – Obtain radio anti-theft code before servicing vehicle. Disconnect negative battery cable. Remove all components in order listed in illustration. *See Fig. 3.* To install, reverse removal procedure.

TORQUE SPECIFICATIONS

TORQUE SPECIFICATIONS

Application	Ft. Lbs. (N.m)
Compressor Bolt	34 (46)
Refrigerant Pipe Fittings	
Condenser Inlet	11-18 (15-24)
Evaporator Outlet	15-21 (20-29)
	INCH Lbs. (N.m)
Refrigerant Pipe Fittings	
Condenser Outlet	87-168 (10-14)
Evaporator Inlet	87-174 (10-20)
Receiver-Drier Inlet & Outlet	70-104 (8-12)

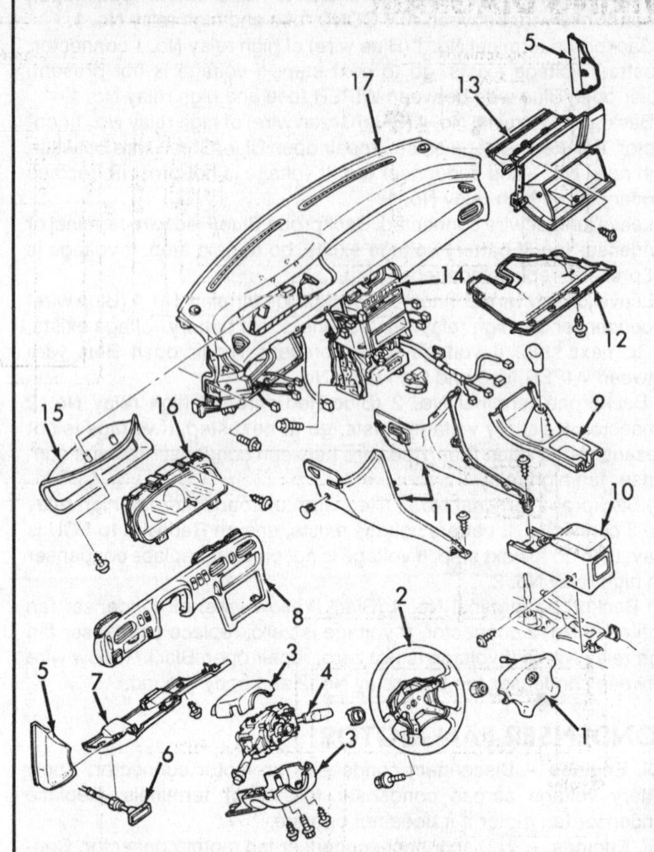
1. Steering Wheel Cover
2. Steering Wheel
3. Steering Column Covers
4. Combination Switch
5. Side Covers
6. Hood Release Knob
7. Knee Protector
8. Switch Panel
9. Front Console
10. Rear Console
11. Console Side Covers
12. Instrument Panel Undercover (Right)
13. Glove Compartment
14. A/C-Heater Control Panel
15. Instrument Cluster Cover (626)
16. Instrument Cluster
17. Instrument Panel
94J10396
Courtesy of Mazda Motors Corp.

Fig. 3: Exploded View Of Instrument Panel (626 Shown; MX-6 Similar)

WIRING DIAGRAM

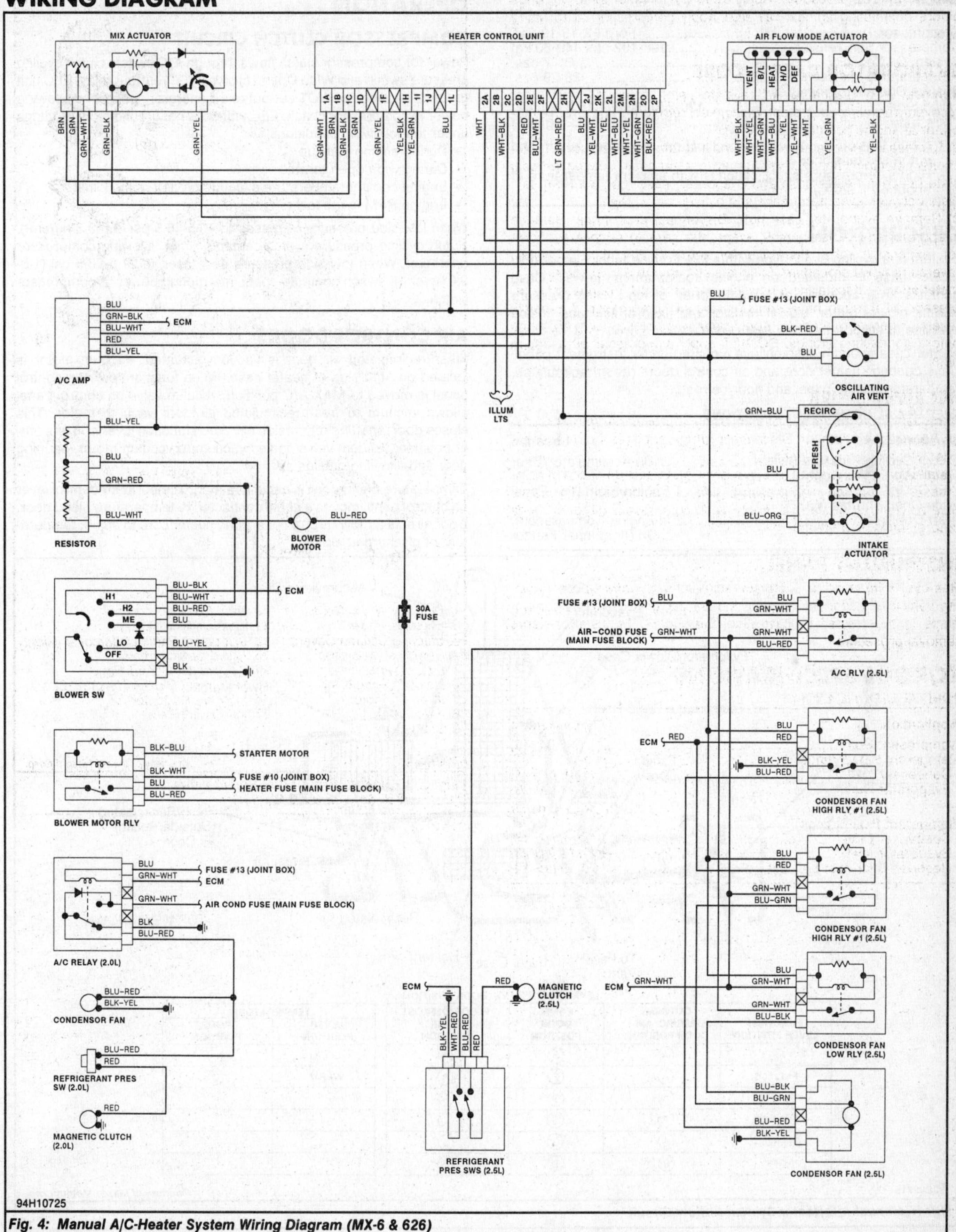
MIX ACTUATOR
HEATER CONTROL UNIT
AIR FLOW MODE ACTUATOR
VENT
B/L
HEAT
H/D
DEF
1A 1B 1C 1D 1F 1H 1I 1J 1L
2A 2B 2C 2D 2E 2F 2H 2J 2K 2L 2M 2N 2O 2P
BRN
GRN
GRN-WHT
GRN-BLK
GRN-YEL
YEL-BLK
YEL-GRN
BLU
WHT
WHT-BLK
RED
BLU-WHT
LT GRN-RED
YEL-WHT
YEL
WHT-BLU
WHT-YEL
WHT-GRN
BLK-RED
YEL-GRN
WHT-RED
FUSE #13 (JOINT BOX)
ECM
A/C AMP
ILLUM LTS
OSCILLATING AIR VENT
RECIRC
FRESH
GRN-BLU
BLU-ORG
INTAKE ACTUATOR
BLU-YEL
RESISTOR
BLOWER MOTOR
BLU-RED
30A FUSE
BLU-BLK
H1
H2
ME
LO
OFF
BLK
BLOWER SW
BLK-BLU
STARTER MOTOR
BLK-WHT
FUSE #10 (JOINT BOX)
HEATER FUSE (MAIN FUSE BLOCK)
BLOWER MOTOR RLY
AIR COND FUSE (MAIN FUSE BLOCK)
A/C RELAY (2.0L)
BLK-YEL
CONDENSOR FAN
REFRIGERANT PRES SW (2.0L)
MAGNETIC CLUTCH (2.0L)
AIR-COND FUSE (MAIN FUSE BLOCK)
A/C RLY (2.5L)
CONDENSOR FAN HIGH RLY #1 (2.5L)
BLU-GRN
BLU-BLK
CONDENSOR FAN LOW RLY (2.5L)
MAGNETIC CLUTCH (2.5L)
REFRIGERANT PRES SWS (2.5L)
CONDENSOR FAN (2.5L)
94H10725

Fig. 4: Manual A/C-Heater System Wiring Diagram (MX-6 & 626)

1993 MANUAL A/C-HEATER SYSTEMS
Navajo

SPECIFICATIONS

Compressor Type .... Ford FX-15 10-Cyl.
Compressor Belt Tension .... [1] 108-132 Lbs. (49-60 kg)
System Oil Capacity .... 7 ozs.
Refrigerant (R-12) Capacity .... 28-29 ozs.
System Operating Pressures [2]
High Side .... 130-230 psi (9.1-16.2 kg/cm²)
Low Side .... 18-45 psi (1.3-3.2 kg/cm²)

[1] – If belt tension is not within specification, check belt length and automatic tensioner.
[2] – High side pressure specification is with ambient temperature at about 68°F (20°C).

DESCRIPTION

System is a cycling-clutch type with a fixed orifice tube. Evaporator/blower case is mounted on engine compartment firewall. Case contains an evaporator, accumulator/drier, clutch cycling pressure switch, blower motor, blower resistor and fixed orifice tube (inside inlet line to evaporator). *See Figs. 1 and 3.*

Heater case (plenum assembly) is mounted under instrument panel. Case contains heater core and air control doors (fresh/recirculated, temperature blend, panel and floor/defrost).

ELECTRICAL COMPONENT LOCATIONS

Component	Location
Clutch Cycling Pressure Switch	On Accumulator/Drier
Electronic Engine Control (EEC) Unit	Behind Right Kick Panel
Wide Open Throttle (WOT) Cut-Out Relay	In Engine Compartment, On Right Inner Fender

OPERATION

COMPRESSOR CLUTCH CIRCUIT

Power for compressor clutch flows through A/C switch, clutch cycling pressure switch and Wide Open Throttle (WOT) cut-out relay. EEC unit grounds windings of WOT cut-out relay, energizing relay and allowing power to compressor clutch. EEC unit does not ground relay windings under the following conditions.

- During engine start-up
- During wide open throttle
- Engine coolant temperature exceeds predetermined limit
- Engine RPM is too low

When low-side pressure increases to 40.5-46.5 psi (2.8-3.3 kg/cm²), clutch cycling pressure switch contacts close, allowing compressor operation. When low-side pressure decreases to 21.5-28.5 psi (1.5-2.0 kg/cm²), switch contacts open, interrupting power to compressor clutch.

AIR CONTROL DOORS

Fresh/recirculated air door is vacuum actuated. Vacuum motor is located on right side of heater case. When function lever on control panel is moved to MAX A/C position, vacuum valve on control panel allows vacuum to fresh/recirculated air door vacuum motor. This closes door, shutting off outside air. When function lever is in any other position, vacuum valve denies vacuum to vacuum motor, opening door and allowing outside air.

Temperature blend door is cable actuated. Temperature control lever on control panel moves a cable connected to temperature blend door. Door directs airflow through or around heater core to adjust temperature of discharged airflow.

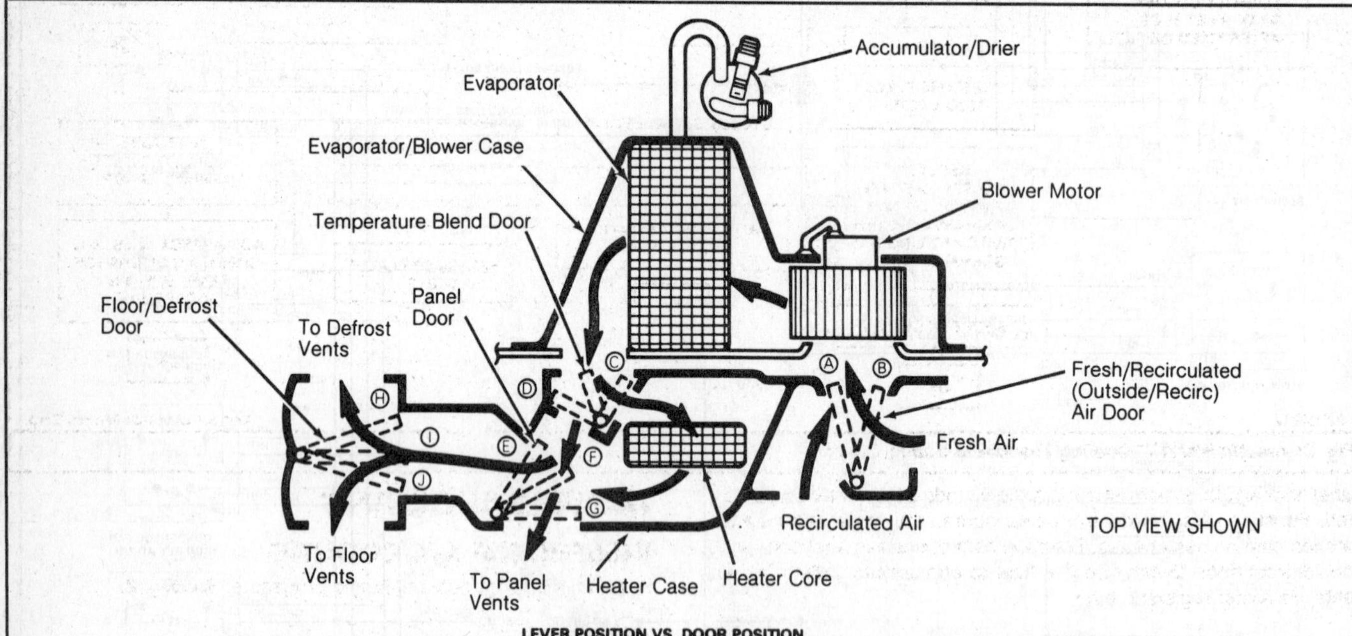
Accumulator/Drier
Evaporator
Evaporator/Blower Case
Blower Motor
Temperature Blend Door
Floor/Defrost Door
To Defrost Vents
Panel Door
Fresh/Recirculated (Outside/Recirc) Air Door
Fresh Air
Recirculated Air
TOP VIEW SHOWN
To Floor Vents
To Panel Vents
Heater Case
Heater Core
A
B
C
D
E
F
G
H
I
J

LEVER POSITION VS. DOOR POSITION

FUNCTION LEVER POSITION	OUTSIDE/ RECIRC. AIR DOOR POSITION	PANEL DOOR POSITION	FLOOR/DEFROST DOOR POSITION
PANEL	A	E	H
PNL/FLR	A	F	H
FLOOR	A	G	H
FLR/DEF	A	G	I
DEFROST	A	G	J
OFF	B	E	H

TEMPERATURE	
LEVER POSITION	DOOR POSITION
COOL	C
WARM	D

92B02716

Courtesy of Mazda Motors Corp.

Fig. 1: Manual A/C-Heater System Airflow Circuit

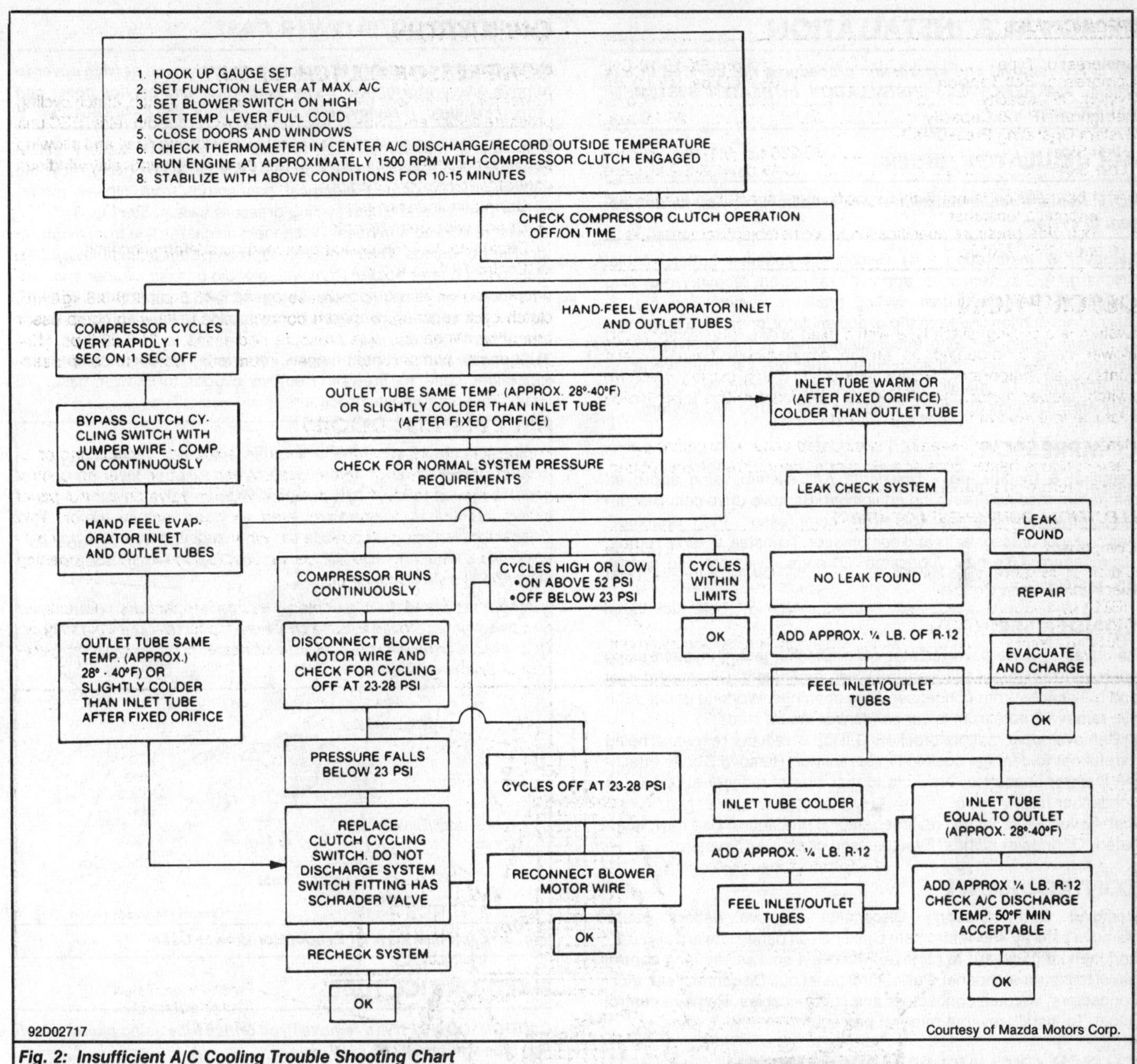
1. HOOK UP GAUGE SET
2. SET FUNCTION LEVER AT MAX. A/C
3. SET BLOWER SWITCH ON HIGH
4. SET TEMP. LEVER FULL COLD
5. CLOSE DOORS AND WINDOWS
6. CHECK THERMOMETER IN CENTER A/C DISCHARGE/RECORD OUTSIDE TEMPERATURE
7. RUN ENGINE AT APPROXIMATELY 1500 RPM WITH COMPRESSOR CLUTCH ENGAGED
8. STABILIZE WITH ABOVE CONDITIONS FOR 10-15 MINUTES
CHECK COMPRESSOR CLUTCH OPERATION OFF/ON TIME
COMPRESSOR CYCLES VERY RAPIDLY 1 SEC ON 1 SEC OFF
HAND-FEEL EVAPORATOR INLET AND OUTLET TUBES
BYPASS CLUTCH CYCLING SWITCH WITH JUMPER WIRE - COMP. ON CONTINUOUSLY
OUTLET TUBE SAME TEMP. (APPROX. 28°-40°F) OR SLIGHTLY COLDER THAN INLET TUBE (AFTER FIXED ORIFICE)
INLET TUBE WARM OR (AFTER FIXED ORIFICE) COLDER THAN OUTLET TUBE
CHECK FOR NORMAL SYSTEM PRESSURE REQUIREMENTS
LEAK CHECK SYSTEM
HAND FEEL EVAPORATOR INLET AND OUTLET TUBES
LEAK FOUND
COMPRESSOR RUNS CONTINUOUSLY
CYCLES HIGH OR LOW •ON ABOVE 52 PSI •OFF BELOW 23 PSI
CYCLES WITHIN LIMITS
NO LEAK FOUND
REPAIR
OK
ADD APPROX. ¼ LB. OF R-12
EVACUATE AND CHARGE
OUTLET TUBE SAME TEMP. (APPROX.) 28° - 40°F) OR SLIGHTLY COLDER THAN INLET TUBE AFTER FIXED ORIFICE
DISCONNECT BLOWER MOTOR WIRE AND CHECK FOR CYCLING OFF AT 23-28 PSI
FEEL INLET/OUTLET TUBES
OK
PRESSURE FALLS BELOW 23 PSI
CYCLES OFF AT 23-28 PSI
INLET TUBE COLDER
INLET TUBE EQUAL TO OUTLET (APPROX. 28°-40°F)
REPLACE CLUTCH CYCLING SWITCH. DO NOT DISCHARGE SYSTEM SWITCH FITTING HAS SCHRADER VALVE
ADD APPROX. ¼ LB. R-12
RECONNECT BLOWER MOTOR WIRE
FEEL INLET/OUTLET TUBES
ADD APPROX ¼ LB. R-12 CHECK A/C DISCHARGE TEMP. 50°F MIN ACCEPTABLE
OK
RECHECK SYSTEM
OK
OK
92D02717
Courtesy of Mazda Motors Corp.

Fig. 2: Insufficient A/C Cooling Trouble Shooting Chart

Panel door and floor/defrost door (airflow mode doors) are cable actuated. Function lever on control panel operates a cable attached to function cam on heater case. Function cam operates panel door and floor/defrost door. Doors direct airflow to appropriate outlets (panel vents, defroster registers, etc.).

BLOWER MOTOR CIRCUIT

With blower switch in highest position, blower motor is grounded directly through blower switch. With blower switch in all other positions, blower motor is grounded through blower resistor and blower switch. Blower resistor contains a thermal limiter. Blower resistor must be replaced if contacts in thermal limiter open due to excessive heat in resistor.

ADJUSTMENTS

NOTE: For adjustment procedures, see HEATER SYSTEMS - NAVAJO article.

TROUBLE SHOOTING

INSUFFICIENT A/C COOLING

Refer to chart for trouble shooting procedure. *See Fig. 2.*

TESTING

A/C SYSTEM PERFORMANCE

1) Park vehicle out of direct sunlight. Connect manifold gauge set. Start and run engine at 1500 RPM. Set A/C controls to recirculate air, panel (vent) mode, full cold, and A/C button at MAX.

2) Set blower/fan on high speed and close doors and windows. Insert thermometer in center vent. Operate system for 10-15 minutes to allow system to stabilize. Measure temperature.

3) Temperature must be 37-42°F (3-6°C) at center vent, with high side and low side pressures within specification. See SPECIFICATIONS table at beginning of article.

1993 MANUAL A/C-HEATER SYSTEMS
Navajo (Cont.)

REMOVAL & INSTALLATION

NOTE: For removal and installation procedures not covered in this article, see REMOVAL & INSTALLATION in HEATER SYSTEMS - NAVAJO article.

ACCUMULATOR/DRIER

NOTE: Replace accumulator/drier when replacing any major component of system.

Removal & Installation - 1) Disconnect negative battery cable. Discharge A/C system using approved refrigerant recovery/recycling equipment. Remove clutch cycling pressure switch. *See Fig. 3.* Disconnect suction line from top of accumulator/drier. Plug openings.
2) Loosen fitting securing accumulator/drier to top of evaporator. Remove screws securing accumulator/drier bracket. Remove accumulator/drier. To install, reverse removal procedure. Use new, lubricated "O" rings at fittings. Evacuate and charge A/C system.

COMPRESSOR

Removal & Installation - Discharge A/C system using approved refrigerant recovery/recycling equipment. Remove drive belt. Disconnect refrigerant line manifold from compressor. Plug openings. Remove compressor bolts and compressor. To install, reverse removal procedure. Use new, lubricated "O" rings. Evacuate and charge A/C system.

CONDENSER

Removal - 1) Remove radiator grille. Discharge A/C system using approved refrigerant recovery/recycling equipment. Disconnect inlet and outlet lines from condenser. Plug openings. Working under vehicle, remove 2 nuts from lower condenser mount studs.
2) Remove upper radiator brackets. Tilt top of radiator rearward, being careful not to damage cooling fan or radiator. Remove 2 bolts attaching 2 upper condenser brackets to rear side of radiator support. Lift condenser from vehicle.
Installation - To install, reverse removal procedure. Use new, lubricated "O" rings at fittings. Evacuate and charge A/C system.

CONTROL PANEL

Removal & Installation - Disconnect negative battery cable. Remove ashtray. Pull instrument cluster finish panel outward about 1", and then lift it upward to remove. Remove 4 screws securing control panel to instrument panel. Pull control panel out. Disconnect electrical connectors, vacuum connectors and control cables. Remove control panel. To install, reverse removal procedure.

CLUTCH CYCLING PRESSURE SWITCH

Removal & Installation - Disconnect electrical connector from clutch cycling pressure switch. *See Fig. 3.* Remove switch. To install, lubricate new "O" ring with refrigerant oil and install on switch fitting on accumulator/drier. Install and tighten switch. Connect electrical connector.

EVAPORATOR

Removal & Installation - 1) Disconnect negative battery cable. Discharge A/C system using approved refrigerant recovery/recycling equipment. Remove clutch cycling pressure switch. *See Fig. 3.* Disconnect refrigerant lines from accumulator/drier. Plug openings.
2) Remove vacuum reservoir. Remove screws securing evaporator/blower case to evaporator service cover. Remove nuts securing evaporator service cover to firewall. Remove evaporator service cover.
3) Remove evaporator and accumulator/drier. Remove accumulator/drier and discard. To install, reverse removal procedure. Install new accumulator/drier. Evacuate and charge A/C system.

EVAPORATOR/BLOWER CASE

NOTE: It is not necessary to remove evaporator and service cover to remove evaporator/blower case; evaporator and service cover can remain installed. If removing evaporator only, see EVAPORATOR.

Removal & Installation - 1) Disconnect negative battery cable. Discharge A/C system using approved refrigerant recovery/recycling equipment. Disconnect electrical connectors from blower motor, blower resistor and clutch cycling pressure switch. *See Fig. 3.*
2) Disconnect vacuum hose. Disconnect discharge line from evaporator. Plug openings. Disconnect suction line from accumulator/drier. Disconnect heater hoses. Remove solenoid box, air cleaner and vacuum reservoir (if equipped). At passenger compartment firewall, remove nut securing evaporator/blower case to firewall (nut is at bottom of heater case).
3) At engine compartment firewall, remove 3 nuts securing evaporator/blower case to firewall. Remove evaporator/blower case. To install, reverse removal procedure.

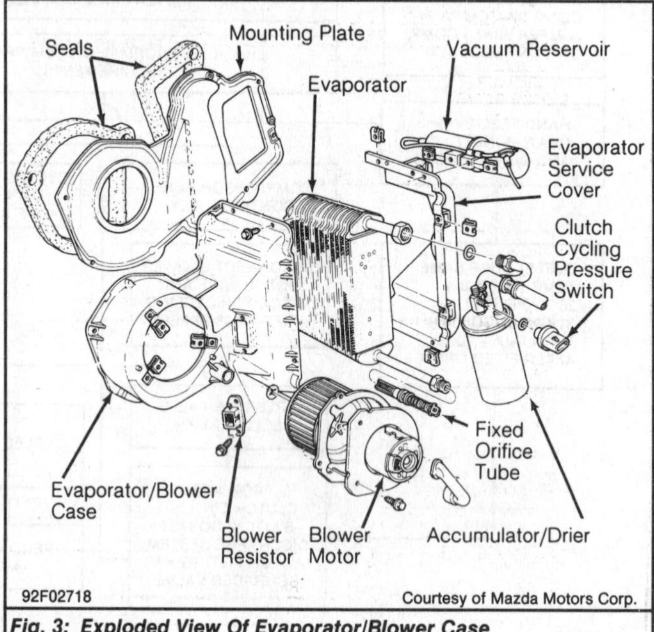
Seals
Mounting Plate
Vacuum Reservoir
Evaporator
Evaporator Service Cover
Clutch Cycling Pressure Switch
Fixed Orifice Tube
Evaporator/Blower Case
Blower Resistor
Blower Motor
Accumulator/Drier
92F02718
Courtesy of Mazda Motors Corp.

Fig. 3: Exploded View Of Evaporator/Blower Case

FIXED ORIFICE TUBE

CAUTION: DO NOT try to remove fixed orifice tube using pliers, as orifice tube will break.

Removal - 1) Discharge A/C system using approved refrigerant recovery/recycling equipment. Disconnect inlet line from evaporator. Plug end of line. Spray refrigerant oil into evaporator inlet to lubricate tube and "O" rings. *See Fig. 3.*
2) Position Orifice Tube Remover/Installer (49-UN01-060) on inlet tube threads. While holding "T" handle stationary, screw hex portion of tube remover/installer onto inlet tube threads. If fixed orifice tube breaks in inlet tube, remove it using Orifice Tube Extractor (49-UN01-061).
Installation - Liberally lubricate new fixed orifice tube "O" rings with refrigerant oil. Position fixed orifice tube in slot in remover/installer. Install fixed orifice tube. Connect inlet line using new, lubricated "O" ring. Evacuate and charge A/C system.

1993 MANUAL A/C-HEATER SYSTEMS
Navajo (Cont.)

TORQUE SPECIFICATIONS

Application	Ft. Lbs. (N.m)
Accumulator-To-Evaporator Fitting	26-31 (35-42)
Compressor Bolt	25-35 (34-47)
Refrigerant Line Bolt/Fitting	
To Compressor	21-27 (28-37)
To Evaporator (Inlet)	15-20 (20-27)
	INCH Lbs. (N.m)
Clutch Cycling Pressure Switch	60-120 (7-14)

WIRING DIAGRAM

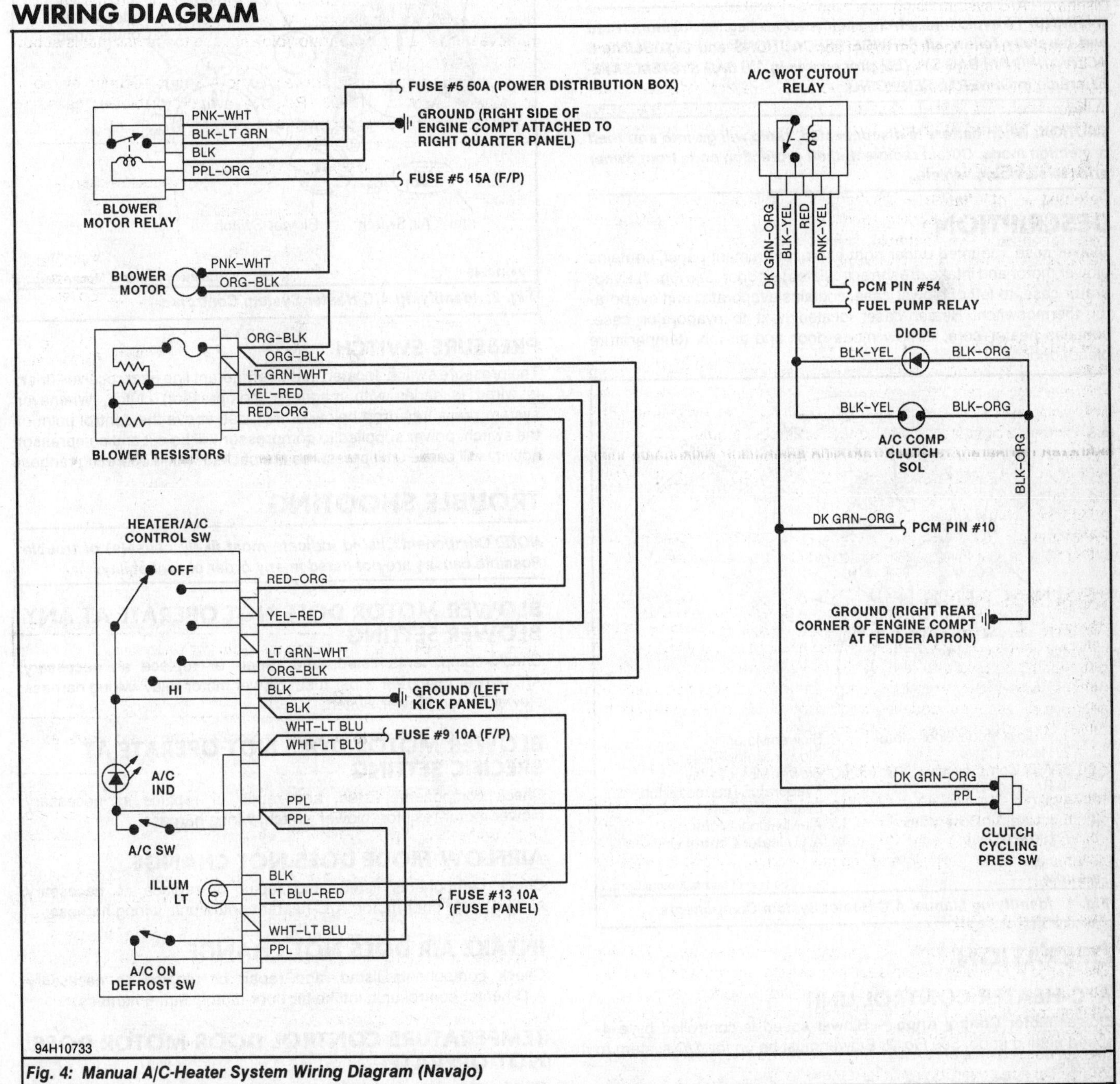
FUSE #5 50A (POWER DISTRIBUTION BOX)
GROUND (RIGHT SIDE OF ENGINE COMPT ATTACHED TO RIGHT QUARTER PANEL)
FUSE #5 15A (F/P)
PNK-WHT
BLK-LT GRN
BLK
PPL-ORG
BLOWER MOTOR RELAY
BLOWER MOTOR
ORG-BLK
ORG-BLK
LT GRN-WHT
YEL-RED
RED-ORG
BLOWER RESISTORS
HEATER/A/C CONTROL SW
OFF
HI
GROUND (LEFT KICK PANEL)
WHT-LT BLU
FUSE #9 10A (F/P)
A/C IND
PPL
A/C SW
ILLUM LT
LT BLU-RED
FUSE #13 10A (FUSE PANEL)
A/C ON DEFROST SW
A/C WOT CUTOUT RELAY
DK GRN-ORG
BLK-YEL
RED
PNK-YEL
PCM PIN #54
FUEL PUMP RELAY
DIODE
BLK-ORG
A/C COMP CLUTCH SOL
PCM PIN #10
GROUND (RIGHT REAR CORNER OF ENGINE COMPT AT FENDER APRON)
CLUTCH CYCLING PRES SW
94H10733

Fig. 4: Manual A/C-Heater System Wiring Diagram (Navajo)

1993 MANUAL A/C-HEATER SYSTEMS RX7

SPECIFICATIONS

Compressor Type	Panasonic Rotary Vane
Compressor Belt Deflection [1]	
New	9/64-11/64" (3.5-4.5 mm)
Used	11/64-13/64" (4.5-5.0 mm)
System Oil Capacity	3.4-4.7 ozs.
Refrigerant (R-12) Capacity	21 ozs.
System Operating Pressures [2]	
High Side	142-192 psi (10-13.5 kg/cm²)
Low Side	15-27 psi (1.1-1.9 kg/cm²)

[1] – Measure with 22 lb. (10 kg) pressure applied to center of belt.
[2] – Specification is with ambient temperature at about 68°F (20°C).

WARNING: To avoid injury from accidental air bag deployment, read and carefully follow all SERVICE PRECAUTIONS and DISABLING & ACTIVATING AIR BAG SYSTEM procedures in AIR BAG SYSTEM SAFETY article in GENERAL SERVICING.

CAUTION: When battery is disconnected, radio will go into anti-theft protection mode. Obtain radio anti-theft protection code from owner prior to servicing vehicle.

DESCRIPTION

Blower case, mounted under right end of instrument panel, contains blower motor and intake (fresh/recirculated) air door. *See Fig. 1*. Evaporator case, to left of blower case, contains evaporator and evaporator thermoswitch. Heater case, located next to evaporator case, contains heater core, airflow mode door and air-mix (temperature blend) door.

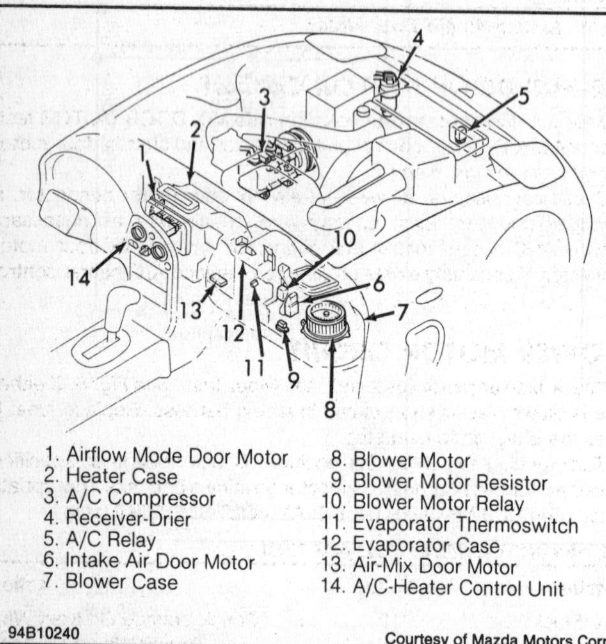
1. Airflow Mode Door Motor
2. Heater Case
3. A/C Compressor
4. Receiver-Drier
5. A/C Relay
6. Intake Air Door Motor
7. Blower Case
8. Blower Motor
9. Blower Motor Resistor
10. Blower Motor Relay
11. Evaporator Thermoswitch
12. Evaporator Case
13. Air-Mix Door Motor
14. A/C-Heater Control Unit
94B10240
Courtesy of Mazda Motors Corp.

Fig. 1: Identifying Manual A/C-Heater System Components

OPERATION

A/C-HEATER CONTROL UNIT

Blower Motor Control Knob – Blower speed is controlled by a 4-speed setting knob. *See Fig. 2*. Blower must be on for A/C system to operate.

Temperature Control Knob – Temperature control knob operates air-mix door in evaporator case to achieve desired temperature. System will provide cooled air when A/C switch is on and blower switch is in any position other than off. Rotate knob counterclockwise for cooler air. Temperature control knob should be in maximum cool setting for maximum A/C performance.

A/C Switch – Push switch to engage A/C compressor. Compressor will not engage with ambient temperature less than 38°F (3°C).

Airflow Mode Control Knob – Control knob selects distribution of incoming air. Going clockwise from 9 o'clock position , air distribution positions of control knob are as follows: vent, floor and vent, floor, floor and defrost, defrost.

Intake (Fresh/Recirculated) Air Switch – Use this switch when maximum cooling is required. To recirculate air inside vehicle, press intake air button. Indicator light will come on, and outside air will be shut off.

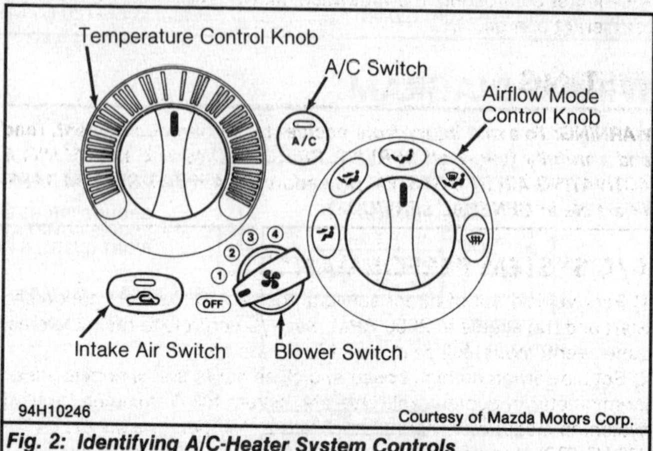
Temperature Control Knob
A/C Switch
Airflow Mode
Control Knob
A/C
OFF
Intake Air Switch
Blower Switch
94H10246
Courtesy of Mazda Motors Corp.

Fig. 2: Identifying A/C-Heater System Controls

PRESSURE SWITCH

The pressure switch, located in the refrigerant line near receiver-drier, is wired in series with magnetic (compressor) clutch. Whenever system pressures drop below or increase above the control point of the switch, power supplied to compressor will be cut and compressor activity will cease until pressures are back to within operating ranges.

TROUBLE SHOOTING

NOTE: Components listed indicate most likely cause(s) of trouble. Possible causes are not listed in any order of probability.

BLOWER MOTOR DOES NOT OPERATE AT ANY BLOWER SETTING

Check components listed, and repair or replace as necessary: A/C blower fuse; rear wiper fuse; blower motor relay; wiring harness; blower motor; blower switch.

BLOWER MOTOR DOES NOT OPERATE AT SPECIFIC SETTING

Check components listed, and repair or replace as necessary: blower motor resistor; blower switch; wiring harness.

AIRFLOW MODE DOES NOT CHANGE

Check components listed, and repair or replace as necessary: airflow mode door motor; A/C-heater control unit; wiring harness.

INTAKE AIR DOES NOT CHANGE

Check components listed, and repair or replace as necessary: A/C-heater control unit; intake air door motor; wiring harness.

TEMPERATURE CONTROL DOOR MOTOR DOES NOT OPERATE

Check components listed, and repair or replace as necessary: A/C-heater control unit; temperature control door motor; wiring harness.

A/C CLUTCH DOES NOT OPERATE

Check components listed, and repair or replace as necessary: A/C clutch; refrigerant pressure switch; A/C relay; A/C fuse; cigar fuse; wiring harness.

A/C CLUTCH & ELECTRIC COOLING FAN DO NOT OPERATE

Check components listed, and repair or replace as necessary: A/C-heater control unit; thermoswitch; blower switch; wiring harness; refrigerant charge.

TESTING

WARNING: To avoid injury from accidental air bag deployment, read and carefully follow all SERVICE PRECAUTIONS and DISABLING & ACTIVATING AIR BAG SYSTEM procedures in AIR BAG SYSTEM SAFETY article in GENERAL SERVICING.

A/C SYSTEM PERFORMANCE

1) Park vehicle out of direct sunlight. Install A/C manifold gauge set. Start and run engine at 2000 RPM. Set A/C controls to recirculate air, panel (vent) mode, full cold, and A/C button on.

2) Set blower/fan on high speed and close doors and windows. Insert thermometer in center vent. Operate system for 20 minutes to allow system to stabilize. Measure temperature. Temperature should be 37-42°F (3-6°C) at center vent, with high side and low side pressures within specification. See SPECIFICATIONS table at beginning of article.

AIRFLOW MODE DOOR MOTOR

1) Disconnect airflow mode door motor connector. Apply battery voltage to terminal "J" and ground terminal "K". *See Fig. 3.* Ensure motor operates.

2) Check continuity between specified terminals. See AIRFLOW MODE SPECIFICATIONS table. If continuity does not exist, replace motor.

AIRFLOW MODE SPECIFICATIONS

Switch Setting	Terminals
Vent	"C", "D", "F", "H" & "I"
Floor & Vent	"A" & "B"; "D", "F", "H" & "I"
Floor	"A", "B" & "C"; "F", "H" & "I"
Floor & Defrost	"A", "B", "C" & "D"; "H" & "I"
Defrost	"A", "B", "C", "D" & "F"

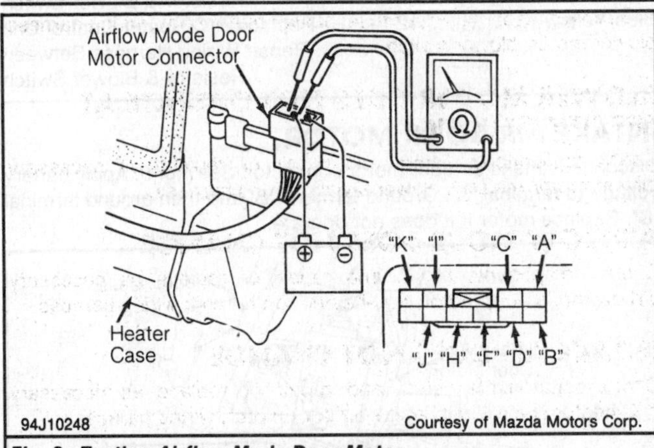
Airflow Mode Door
Motor Connector
Heater
Case
"K" "I" "C" "A"
"J" "H" "F" "D" "B"
94J10248
Courtesy of Mazda Motors Corp.

Fig. 3: Testing Airflow Mode Door Motor

AIRFLOW MODE DOOR CIRCUIT

1) If airflow mode door motor tested okay in AIRFLOW MODE DOOR MOTOR test, disconnect A/C-heater control unit connector and airflow mode door motor connector. *See Figs. 3 and 7.*

2) Check continuity on all wires at airflow mode door motor connector. If continuity does not exist on any wire, repair wire as necessary between A/C-heater control unit connector and airflow door motor connector. If continuity exists on all wires, replace A/C-heater control unit.

AIR-MIX DOOR MOTOR

1) Disconnect air-mix door motor connector. *See Fig. 4.* Apply battery voltage to terminal "G" and ground terminal "H". Verify motor operation. Check resistance between terminals "F" and "B". Resistance should increase from 1000 ohms to 5500 ohms as temperature control knob is moved from hot to cold setting.

2) Apply battery voltage to terminal "H" and ground terminal "G". Verify motor operation. Check resistance between terminals "F" and "A". Resistance should decrease from 5500 ohms to 1000 ohms as temperature control knob is moved from cold to hot setting. Replace motor if it does not test as specified.

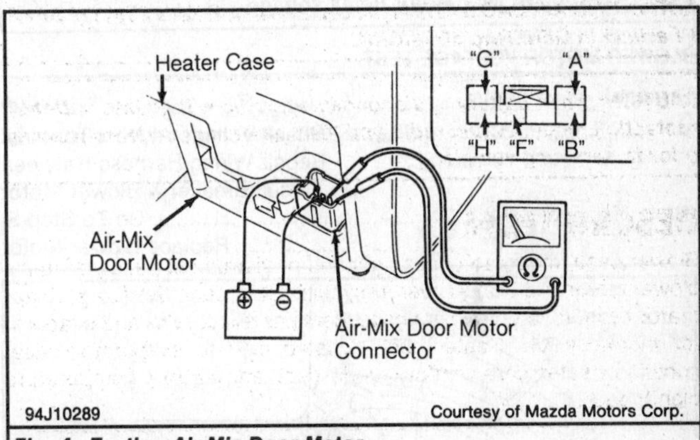
Heater Case
"G" "A"
"H" "F" "B"
Air-Mix
Door Motor
Air-Mix Door Motor
Connector
94J10289
Courtesy of Mazda Motors Corp.

Fig. 4: Testing Air-Mix Door Motor

AIR-MIX DOOR MOTOR CIRCUIT

1) If air-mix door motor tested okay in AIR-MIX DOOR MOTOR test, disconnect A/C-heater control unit connector and air-mix door motor connector. *See Figs. 4 and 7.*

2) Check continuity on all wires at air-mix door motor connector. If continuity does not exist on any wire, repair wire as necessary between A/C-heater control unit connector and air-mix door motor connector. If continuity exists on all wires, replace A/C-heater control unit.

BLOWER MOTOR CIRCUIT

1) Check blower motor fuse and rear wiper fuse. *See Fig. 5.* If either fuse is blown, repair short circuit in wiring harness. Replace fuse. If fuses are okay, go to next step.

2) Turn ignition switch to ON position. Check voltage at specified blower motor relay harness connector terminals and take appropriate action. See BLOWER MOTOR RELAY VOLTAGE TEST table.

BLOWER MOTOR RELAY VOLTAGE TEST

Terminal	Volts	Action
Blue/Black	12	Check Voltage On Next Wire
	0	Repair Wiring Harness
Blue/Green	12	Check Voltage On Next Wire
	0	Repair Wiring Harness
Red	12	Go To Step 4)
	0	Go To Step 3)

3) Turn ignition switch to OFF position. Check for continuity between chassis ground and blower motor relay harness connector Black wire. If continuity exists, replace blower motor relay. If continuity does not exist, repair wiring harness.

4) Turn ignition switch to ON position. Ensure blower switch is in OFF position. Check voltage at specified blower motor harness connector terminals and take appropriate action. See BLOWER MOTOR VOLTAGE TEST table. *See Fig. 6.*

1993 MANUAL A/C-HEATER SYSTEMS
RX7 (Cont.)

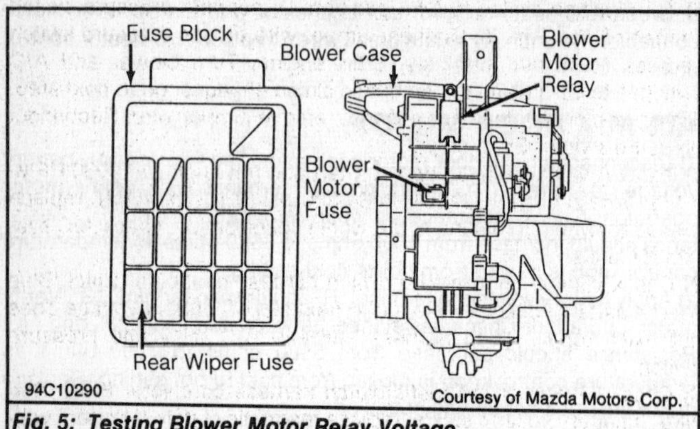
Fuse Block
Blower Case
Blower
Motor
Relay
Blower
Motor
Fuse
Rear Wiper Fuse
94C10290
Courtesy of Mazda Motors Corp.

Fig. 5: Testing Blower Motor Relay Voltage

BLOWER MOTOR VOLTAGE TEST

Terminal	Volts	Action
"A"	12	Check Voltage At Next Terminal
	0	Repair Wiring Harness Between Circuit Breaker & Blower Motor
"B"	12	Go To Step **5)**
	0	Replace Blower Motor

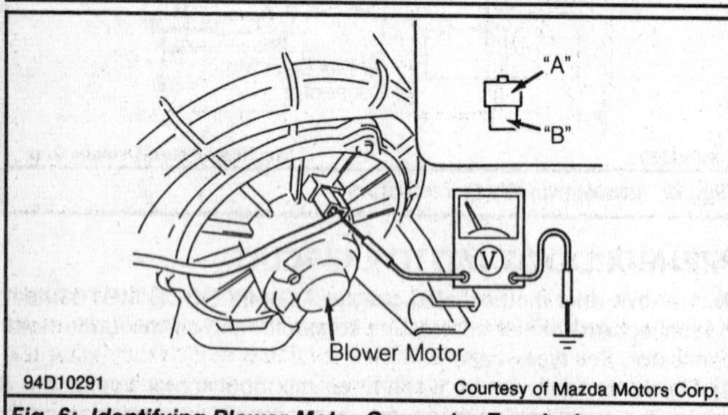
"A"
"B"
Blower Motor
94D10291
Courtesy of Mazda Motors Corp.

Fig. 6: Identifying Blower Motor Connector Terminals

5) Remove A/C-heater control unit. See A/C-HEATER CONTROL UNIT under REMOVAL & INSTALLATION. Check voltage at blower switch connector Blue/White wire. *See Fig. 7*. If 12 volts exist, go next step. If 12 volts do not exist, repair wiring harness between blower motor and blower switch.

6) Turn ignition switch to ON position. Turn blower switch to position No. 4. Check voltage at blower switch connector Black wire. *See Fig. 7*. If no voltage exists, replace A/C-heater control unit. If voltage exists, repair wiring harness between blower switch and chassis ground.

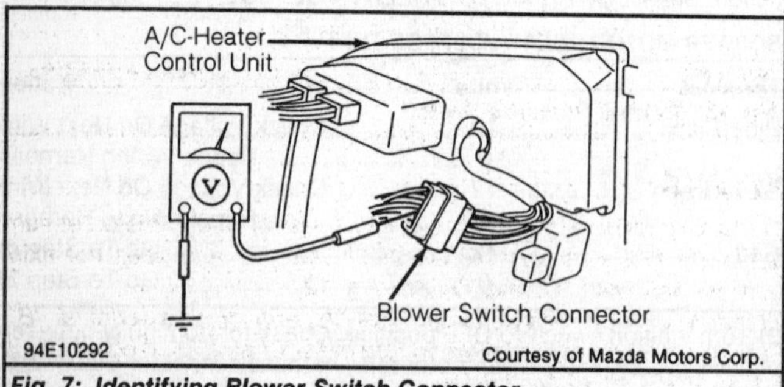
A/C-Heater
Control Unit
Blower Switch Connector
94E10292
Courtesy of Mazda Motors Corp.

Fig. 7: Identifying Blower Switch Connector

BLOWER MOTOR RESISTOR

1) Turn ignition switch to ON position. Ensure blower switch and A/C switch are in OFF position. Check voltage at specified resistor connector terminals and take appropriate action. See BLOWER MOTOR RESISTOR VOLTAGE TEST table. *See Figs. 1 and 8*.

BLOWER MOTOR RESISTOR VOLTAGE TEST

Terminal	Volts	Action
"A"	12	Check Voltage At Next Terminal
	0	Replace Resistor
"B"	12	Check Voltage At Next Terminal
	0	Replace Resistor
"C"	12	Check Voltage At Next Terminal
	0	Replace Resistor
"D"	12	Go To Step **2)**
	0	Replace Resistor

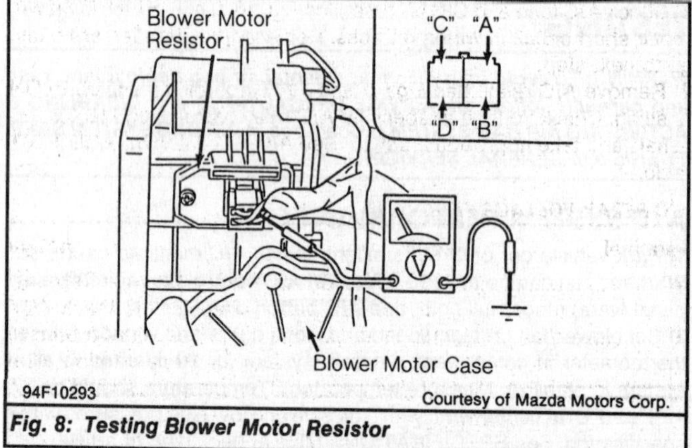
Blower Motor
Resistor
"C"
"A"
"D"
"B"
Blower Motor Case
94F10293
Courtesy of Mazda Motors Corp.

Fig. 8: Testing Blower Motor Resistor

2) Turn ignition switch to ON position. Ensure blower switch and A/C switch are in OFF position. Check voltage at specified blower switch connector terminal and take appropriate action. See BLOWER SWITCH VOLTAGE TEST table. *See Fig. 7*.

BLOWER SWITCH VOLTAGE TEST

Terminal	Volts	Action
Blue/White	12	Check Voltage At Next Wire
	0	Repair Wiring Harness Between Resistor & Blower Switch
Blue/Red	12	Check Voltage At Next Wire
	0	Repair Wiring Harness Between Resistor & Blower Switch
Blue	12	Check Voltage At Next Wire
	0	Repair Wiring Harness Between Resistor & Blower Switch
Blue/Yellow	12	Replace A/C-Heater Control Unit
	0	Repair Wiring Harness Between Resistor & Blower Switch

INTAKE AIR DOOR MOTOR

Disconnect intake air door motor connector. *See Fig. 9*. Apply battery voltage to terminal "A". Ground terminal "B" and then ground terminal "C". Replace motor if it does not operate.

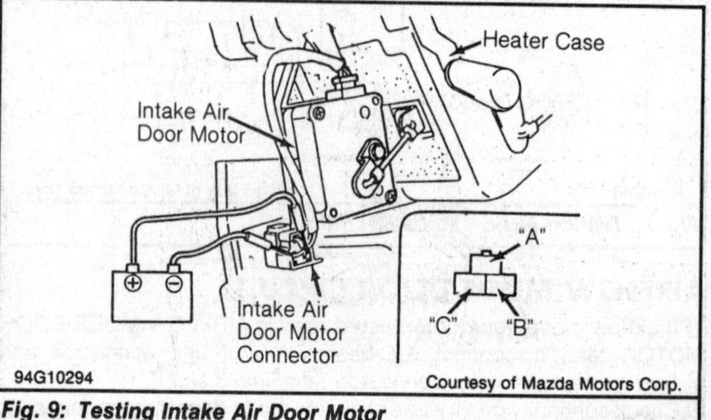
Heater Case
Intake Air
Door Motor
"A"
"C"
"B"
Intake Air
Door Motor
Connector
94G10294
Courtesy of Mazda Motors Corp.

Fig. 9: Testing Intake Air Door Motor

1993 MANUAL A/C-HEATER SYSTEMS RX7 (Cont.)

INTAKE AIR DOOR MOTOR CIRCUIT

1) If intake air door motor tested okay in INTAKE AIR DOOR MOTOR test, disconnect A/C-heater control unit connector and intake air door motor connector. *See Figs. 7 and 9*.

2) Check continuity on all wires at intake air door motor connector. If continuity does not exist on any wire, repair wire as necessary between A/C-heater control unit connector and intake air door motor connector. If continuity exists on all wires, replace A/C-heater control unit.

MAGNETIC (COMPRESSOR) CLUTCH CIRCUIT

1) Check A/C fuse and CIGAR fuse. *See Fig. 10*. If either fuse is blown, repair short circuit in wiring harness. Replace fuse. If fuses are okay, go to next step.

2) Remove A/C relay. *See Figs. 1 and 11*. Turn ignition switch to ON position. Check voltage at specified A/C relay harness connector terminals and take appropriate action. See A/C RELAY VOLTAGE TEST table.

A/C RELAY VOLTAGE TEST

Terminal	Volts	Action
"A"	12	Check Voltage On Next Terminal
	0	Repair Blue/Black Wire
"B"	12	Go To Step **3)**
	0	Repair Yellow Wire

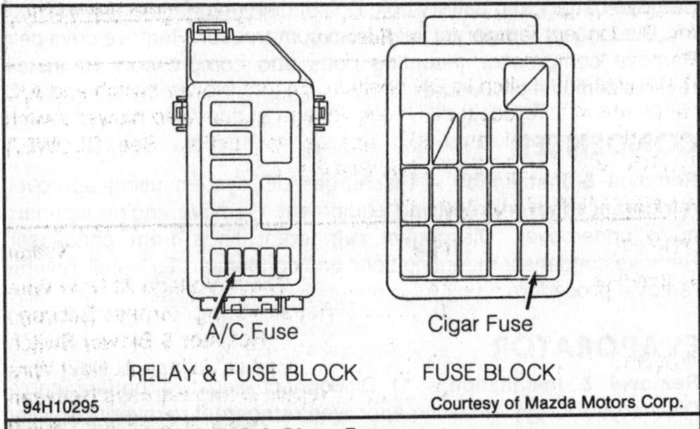
A/C Fuse
Cigar Fuse
RELAY & FUSE BLOCK
FUSE BLOCK
94H10295
Courtesy of Mazda Motors Corp.

Fig. 10: Identifying A/C & Cigar Fuses

3) Apply battery voltage to A/C relay terminal "A" and ground terminal "B". *See Fig. 12*. Check continuity between terminals "C" and "D". If continuity does not exist, replace relay. If continuity exists, go to next step.

4) Ensure ignition switch is in OFF position. Connect a jumper wire between A/C relay connector terminals "A" and "B". *See Fig. 11*. Start engine. Turn blower and A/C switches to ON position. If magnetic clutch engages, repair wiring harness between A/C relay connector and Electronic Control Unit (ECU). If magnetic clutch does not engage, remove jumper wire and go to next step.

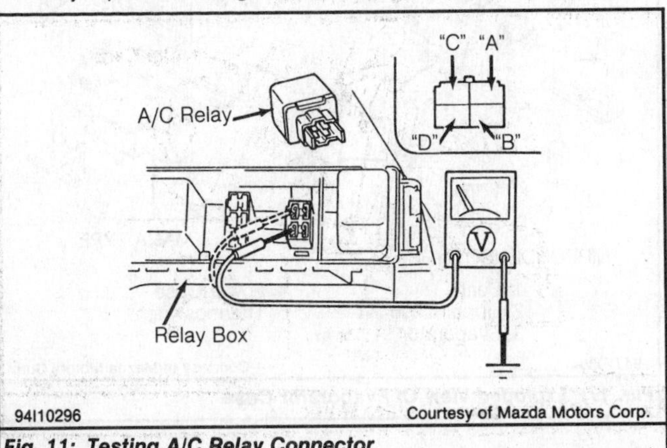
"C"
"A"
A/C Relay
"D"
"B"
Relay Box
94I10296
Courtesy of Mazda Motors Corp.

Fig. 11: Testing A/C Relay Connector

5) Turn ignition switch to OFF position. Disconnect pressure switch connector. *See Fig. 13*. Connect jumper wire across pressure switch harness connector terminals. Start engine. Turn blower and A/C switches to ON position. If magnetic clutch engages, go to next step. If magnetic clutch does not engage, remove jumper wire. Reconnect pressure switch. Go to step **7)**.

6) Install A/C manifold gauge set. Start and run engine at 2000 RPM. If high side pressure reading is 30-299 psi (2.1-21 kg/cm²), replace pressure switch. If reading is not within specification, check A/C system for leaks.

7) Check voltage on pressure switch harness connector Black/Blue wire. If battery voltage exists, go to next step. If battery voltage does not exist, repair wiring harness between A/C relay and pressure switch.

8) Check voltage on magnetic clutch harness connector Black/Red wire. If battery voltage exists, replace magnetic clutch. If battery voltage does not exist, repair wiring harness between magnetic clutch and pressure switch.

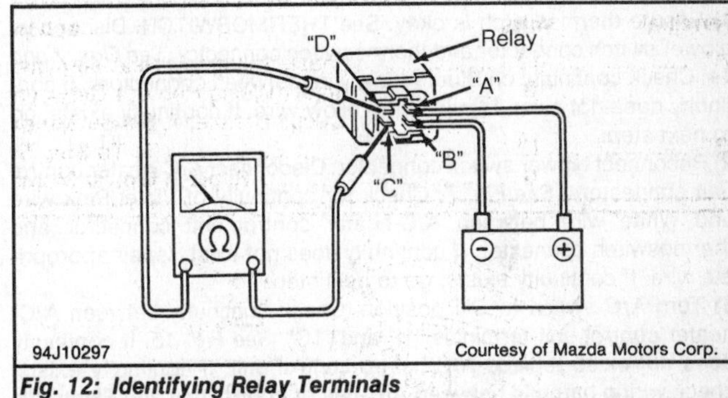
"D"
Relay
"A"
"B"
"C"
94J10297
Courtesy of Mazda Motors Corp.

Fig. 12: Identifying Relay Terminals

PRESSURE SWITCH

Turn engine off. Connect A/C manifold gauge set. Ensure system pressure reads 30-299 psi (2.1-21 kg/cm²). Disconnect pressure switch connector. *See Fig. 13*. Check continuity across connector terminals. If continuity does not exist, replace pressure switch.

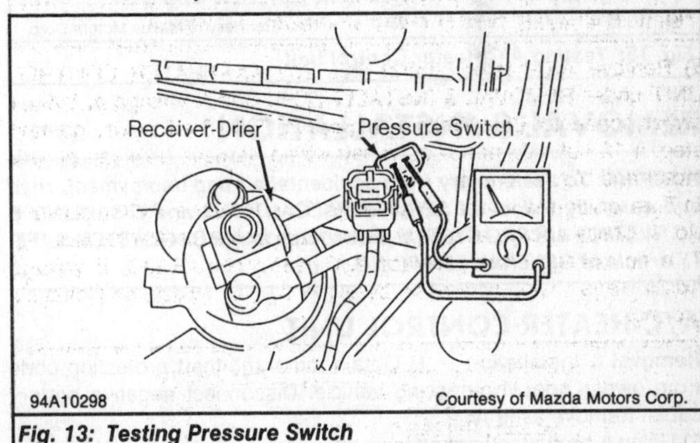
Receiver-Drier
Pressure Switch
94A10298
Courtesy of Mazda Motors Corp.

Fig. 13: Testing Pressure Switch

RELAYS

1) Remove relay to be tested. *See Fig. 1*. Using an ohmmeter, ensure continuity exists between terminals "A" and "B" and does not exist between terminals "C" and "D". *See Fig. 12*.

2) Apply battery voltage to terminal "A" and ground terminal "B". Ensure continuity exists between terminals "C" and "D". If continuity is not as specified, replace relay.

THERMOSWITCH

Ensure ignition switch is in OFF position. Disconnect thermoswitch connector. *See Fig. 14*. Check continuity between specified thermoswitch connector terminals. Continuity should exist between terminals "A" and "B", and terminals "C" and "D". If continuity is not as specified, replace thermoswitch.

1993 MANUAL A/C-HEATER SYSTEMS RX7 (Cont.)

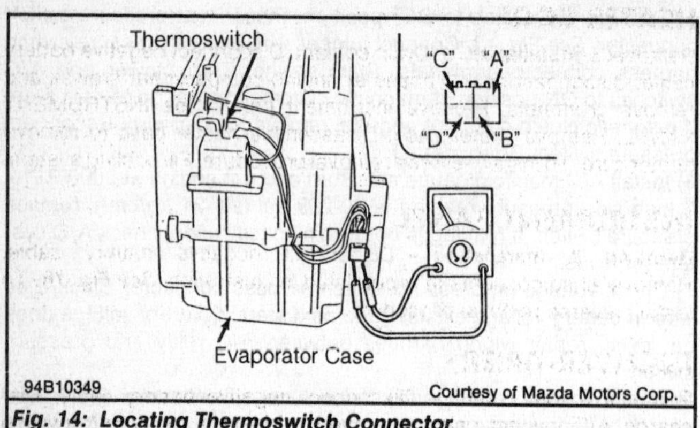
Thermoswitch
"C"
"A"
"D"
"B"
Evaporator Case
94B10349
Courtesy of Mazda Motors Corp.

Fig. 14: Locating Thermoswitch Connector

THERMOSWITCH CIRCUIT

1) Ensure thermoswitch is okay. See THERMOSWITCH. Disconnect blower switch connector and thermoswitch connector. *See Figs. 7 and 14.* Check continuity on Blue/Yellow wire between connectors. If continuity does not exist, repair Blue/Yellow wire. If continuity exists, go to next step.

2) Reconnect blower switch connector. Disconnect A/C-heater control unit connectors. *See Fig. 7.* Check for continuity of Violet/Pink wire and White wire between A/C-heater control unit connector and thermoswitch connector. If continuity does not exist, repair appropriate wire. If continuity exists, go to next step.

3) Turn A/C switch to ON position. Check continuity between A/C-heater control unit terminals "1I" and "1G". *See Fig. 15.* If continuity does not exist, replace A/C-heater control unit. If continuity exists, check wiring harness between A/C-heater control unit and Electronic Control Unit (ECU).

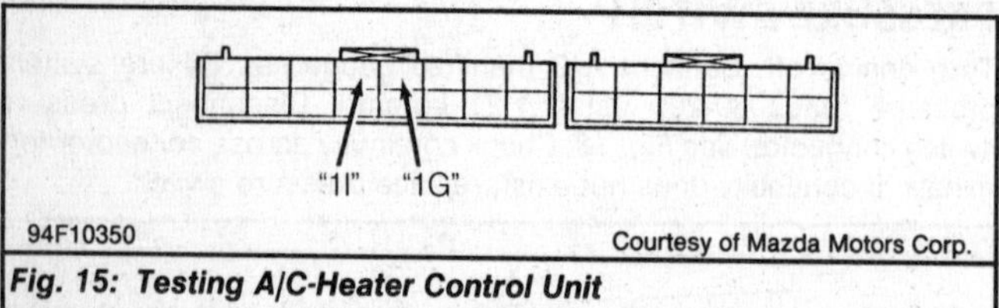
"1I"
"1G"
94F10350
Courtesy of Mazda Motors Corp.

Fig. 15: Testing A/C-Heater Control Unit

REMOVAL & INSTALLATION

WARNING: To avoid injury from accidental air bag deployment, read and carefully follow all SERVICE PRECAUTIONS and DISABLING & ACTIVATING AIR BAG SYSTEM procedures in AIR BAG SYSTEM SAFETY article in GENERAL SERVICING.

A/C-HEATER CONTROL UNIT

Removal & Installation – 1) Obtain radio anti-theft protection code from owner prior to servicing vehicle. Disconnect negative battery cable. Remove ashtray.

2) Using a protected screwdriver, lift center console panel at location indicated. *See Fig. 16.* Pull console panel upward to disengage clips from center console.

3) Remove center panel screws and center panel. Disconnect electrical connectors from A/C-heater control unit. Remove A/C-heater control unit screws and control unit. To install, reverse removal procedure.

BLOWER MOTOR

Removal & Installation – Remove instrument panel. See INSTRUMENT PANEL. Remove evaporator case. See EVAPORATOR CASE. Remove blower case mounting nuts and blower case. Disassemble blower case to remove blower motor. To install, reverse removal procedure.

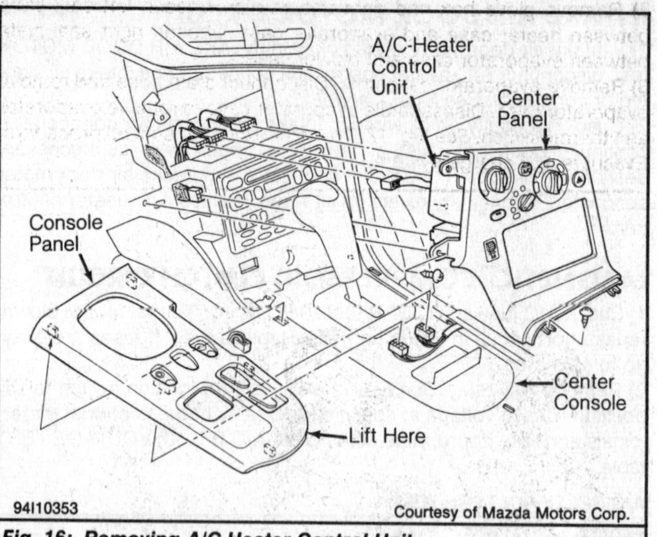
A/C-Heater
Control
Unit
Center
Panel
Console
Panel
Center
Console
Lift Here
94I10353
Courtesy of Mazda Motors Corp.

Fig. 16: Removing A/C-Heater Control Unit

COMPRESSOR

Removal & Installation – Discharge A/C system using approved refrigerant recovery/recycling equipment. Disconnect battery. Remove battery and battery box. Disconnect magnetic clutch connector. Disconnect refrigerant lines from compressor. Remove drive belt. Remove compressor mounting bolts and compressor. To install, reverse removal procedure.

CONDENSER

Removal & Installation – Discharge A/C system using approved refrigerant recovery/recycling equipment. Remove engine compartment undercover. Disconnect refrigerant lines from condenser. Remove condenser mounting bolts and condenser. To install, reverse removal procedure.

EVAPORATOR

Removal & Installation – 1) Disconnect negative battery cable. Discharge A/C system using approved refrigerant recovery/recycling equipment. Disconnect refrigerant lines from evaporator tubes at engine compartment firewall.

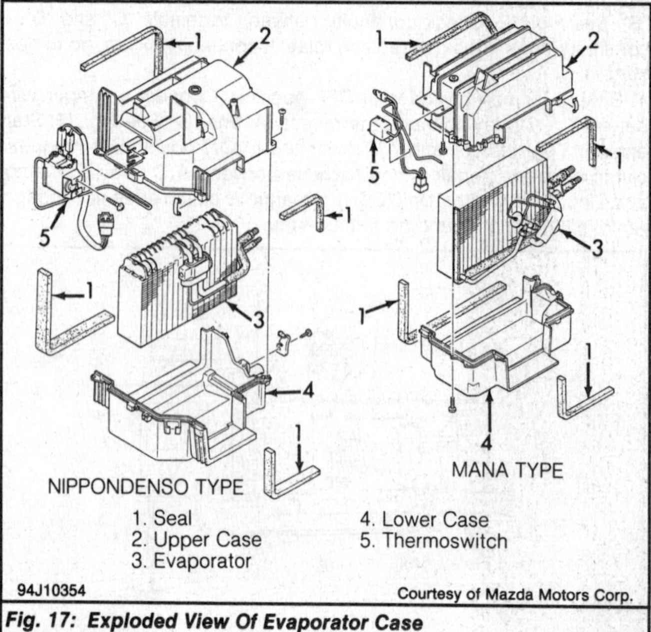
NIPPONDENSO TYPE
MANA TYPE
1. Seal
2. Upper Case
3. Evaporator
4. Lower Case
5. Thermoswitch
94J10354
Courtesy of Mazda Motors Corp.

Fig. 17: Exploded View Of Evaporator Case

2) Remove glove box and right undercover. Loosen left seal plate between heater case and evaporator case. Loosen right seal plate between evaporator case and blower case.
3) Remove evaporator case nuts. Disconnect drain hose and remove evaporator case. Disassemble evaporator case to remove evaporator and thermoswitch. *See Fig. 17*. To install, reverse removal procedure. Evacuate and charge system.

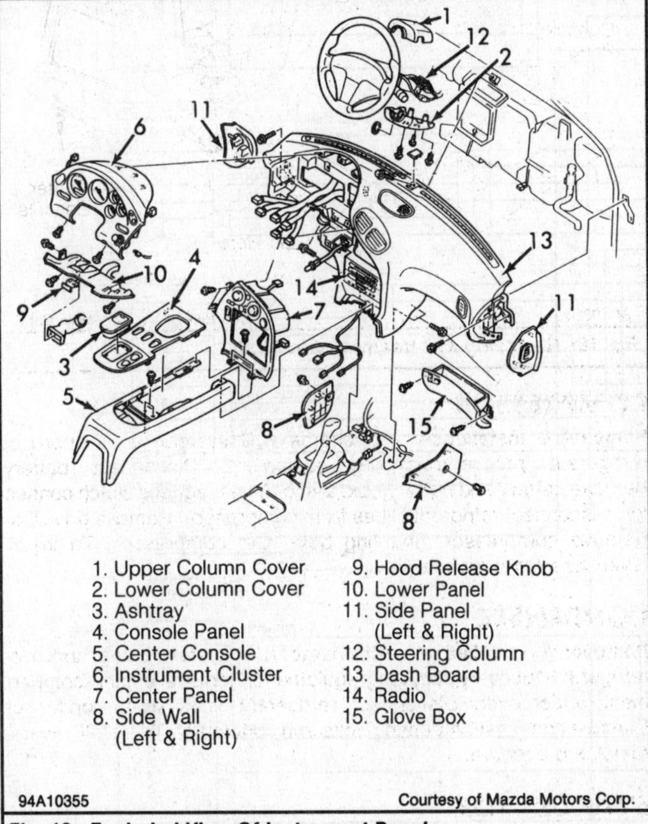

1
12
2
11
6
13
4
10
14
7
9
11
3
5
8
15
8
1. Upper Column Cover
2. Lower Column Cover
3. Ashtray
4. Console Panel
5. Center Console
6. Instrument Cluster
7. Center Panel
8. Side Wall (Left & Right)
9. Hood Release Knob
10. Lower Panel
11. Side Panel (Left & Right)
12. Steering Column
13. Dash Board
14. Radio
15. Glove Box
94A10355
Courtesy of Mazda Motors Corp.

Fig. 18: Exploded View Of Instrument Panel

HEATER CORE

Removal & Installation – Drain coolant. Disconnect negative battery cable. Disconnect heater hoses at engine compartment firewall and remove grommets. Remove instrument panel. See INSTRUMENT PANEL. Remove heater case. Disassemble heater case to remove heater core. To install, reverse removal procedure. Fill cooling system.

INSTRUMENT PANEL

Removal & Installation – Disconnect negative battery cable. Remove all components in order listed in illustration. *See Fig. 18*. To install, reverse removal procedure.

RECEIVER-DRIER

Removal & Installation – Disconnect negative battery cable. Discharge A/C system using approved refrigerant recovery/recycling equipment. Disconnect refrigerant lines from receiver-drier. Remove receiver-drier. To install, reverse removal procedure. Evacuate and charge system.

TORQUE SPECIFICATIONS

TORQUE SPECIFICATIONS

Application	Ft. Lbs. (N.m)
A/C Compressor Bolts	14-19 (19-26)
A/C Compressor Lines	15-21 (20-29)
A/C Condenser Lines	
Inlet	11-18 (15-24)
Outlet	[1]
	INCH Lbs. (N.m)
Evaporator Hoses	108-120 (12.2-13.6)
Receiver-Drier Hoses	40-56 (4.5-6.3)

[1] – Specification is 84-168 INCH lbs. (9.5-19 N.m).

1993 MANUAL A/C-HEATER SYSTEMS
RX7 (Cont.)

WIRING DIAGRAM

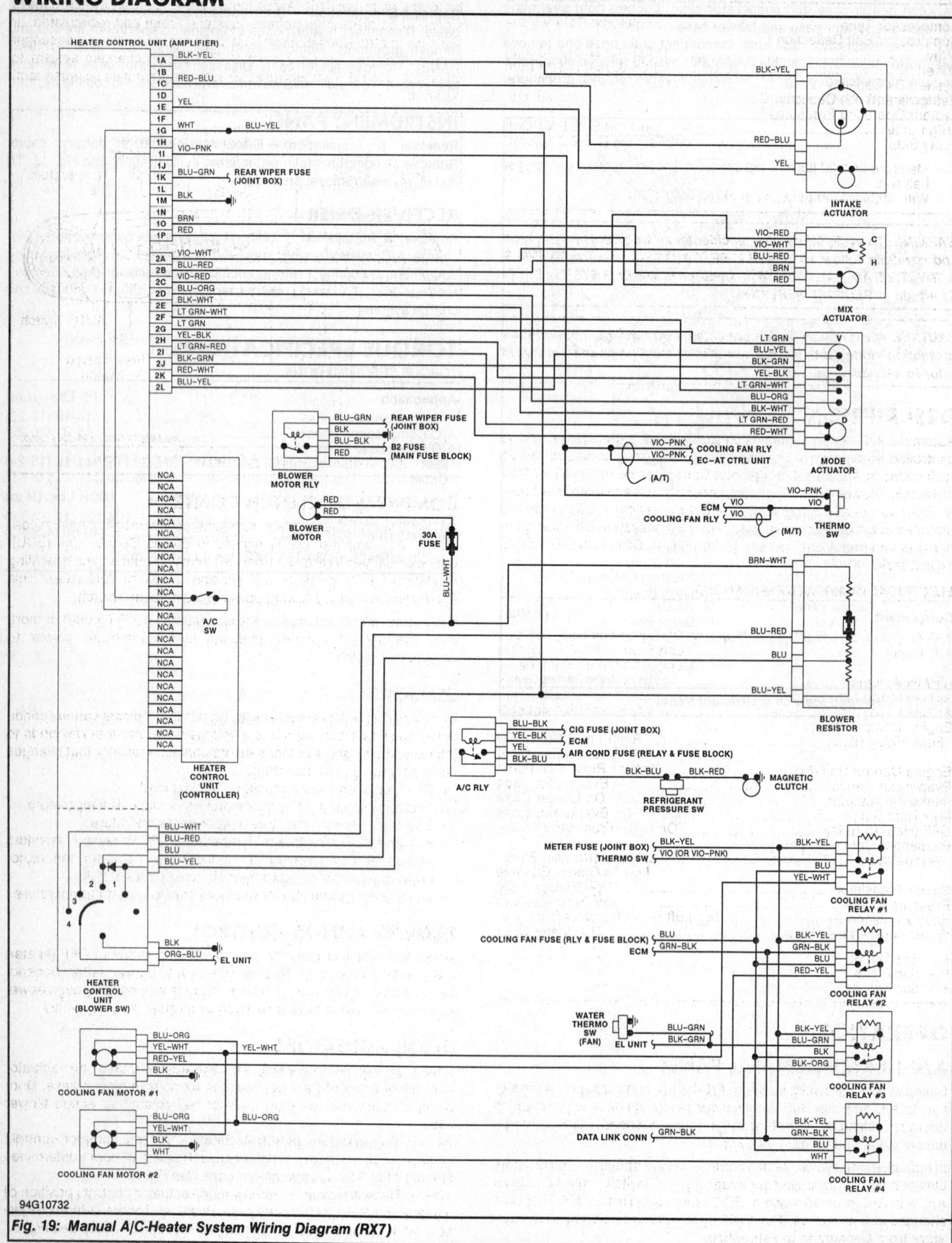
HEATER CONTROL UNIT (AMPLIFIER)
INTAKE ACTUATOR
MIX ACTUATOR
MODE ACTUATOR
REAR WIPER FUSE (JOINT BOX)
B2 FUSE (MAIN FUSE BLOCK)
BLOWER MOTOR RLY
BLOWER MOTOR
30A FUSE
COOLING FAN RLY
EC-AT CTRL UNIT
THERMO SW
BLOWER RESISTOR
A/C SW
HEATER CONTROL UNIT (CONTROLLER)
CIG FUSE (JOINT BOX)
ECM
AIR COND FUSE (RELAY & FUSE BLOCK)
A/C RLY
REFRIGERANT PRESSURE SW
MAGNETIC CLUTCH
METER FUSE (JOINT BOX)
COOLING FAN RELAY #1
COOLING FAN FUSE (RLY & FUSE BLOCK)
COOLING FAN RELAY #2
EL UNIT
HEATER CONTROL UNIT (BLOWER SW)
WATER THERMO SW (FAN)
COOLING FAN RELAY #3
COOLING FAN MOTOR #1
COOLING FAN MOTOR #2
DATA LINK CONN
COOLING FAN RELAY #4
94G10732

Fig. 19: Manual A/C-Heater System Wiring Diagram (RX7)

1993 AUTOMATIC A/C-HEATER SYSTEMS
929

SPECIFICATIONS

Compressor Type	Panasonic Rotary Vane
Compressor Belt Deflection [1]	
New	15/32-33/64" (12-13 mm)
Used	33/64-35/64" (13-14 mm)
System Oil Capacity	3.6 ozs.
Refrigerant (R-12) Capacity	28 ozs.
System Operating Pressures [2]	
High Side	149-178 psi (10.5-12.5 kg/cm²)
Low Side	23-32 psi (1.6-2.2 kg/cm²)

[1] – Measure with 22 lbs. (10 kg) pressure applied midway on longest belt run.
[2] – With ambient temperature at about 86°F (30°C).

WARNING: To avoid injury from accidental air bag deployment, read and carefully follow all SERVICE PRECAUTIONS and DISABLING & ACTIVATING AIR BAG SYSTEM procedures in AIR BAG SYSTEM SAFETY article in GENERAL SERVICING.

CAUTION: When battery is disconnected, radio will go into anti-theft protection mode. Obtain radio anti-theft protection code from owner prior to servicing vehicle.

DESCRIPTION

Automatic A/C-heater system is a cycling clutch type. System can be controlled automatically or manually. Self-diagnostic feature stores fault codes in A/C amplifier memory. Codes can be retrieved for fault diagnosis. Blower case is mounted under right side of instrument panel. Evaporator case is mounted to left of blower case. Heater case is mounted to left of evaporator case. For a list of system electrical components and their locations, see ELECTRICAL COMPONENT LOCATIONS table.

ELECTRICAL COMPONENT LOCATIONS

Component	Location
A/C Amplifier	Forward Of Center Console, At Floor
A/C Relay	Left Front Corner Of Engine Compartment, In Relay Block
Air Mix Actuator	[1] On Heater Case
Airflow Mode Actuator	[1] On Heater Case
Ambient Temperature Sensor	On Front Grille Support
Engine Compartment Fuse/Relay Block	Right Front Corner Of Engine Compartment
Engine Control Unit (ECU)	Behind Right Kick Panel
Evaporator Sensor	[2] In Evaporator Case
Intake Air Actuator	On Blower Case
Max High Relay	[2] On Evaporator Case
OFF (Heater) Relay	On Right Front Strut Tower
Passenger Compartment Temperature (PCT) Sensor	On Instrument Panel, Left Of Center Console
Power Transistor	[3] On Blower Case
Pressure Switch	On Receiver-Drier
Solar Radiation Sensor	Top Left Side Of Instrument Panel
Water Temperature Sensor	On Heater Case

[1] – *See Fig. 5.*
[2] – *See Fig. 6.*
[3] – *See Fig. 2.*

OPERATION

A/C-HEATER CONTROL PANEL

Based on control switch settings, A/C-heater control panel sends signals to A/C amplifier. A/C amplifier sends signals back to panel which displays selected control settings (blower speed, airflow mode, temperature setting, etc.). *See Fig. 1.*

In manual mode, blower switch controls blower speed. In AUTO mode, blower speed is controlled automatically. A/C switch controls whether A/C is in A/C (normal) mode or ECON (economy) mode. MODE switch changes airflow modes. The °C/°F switch changes displayed temperature from Centigrade to Fahrenheit. Ambient switch changes displayed temperature from set (SET) temperature to ambient (AMB) temperature. Defrost switch causes airflow to be diverted to defrost registers. Fresh and recirculated air switches control whether fresh (outside) air or recirculated (passenger compartment) air enters system. AUTO switch changes system to automatic control. Temperature dial setting determines selected temperature.

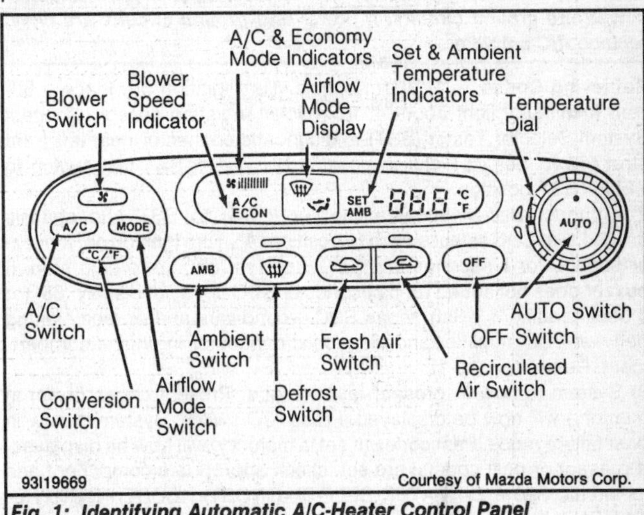
A/C & Economy Mode Indicators
Set & Ambient Temperature Indicators
Blower Speed Indicator
Airflow Mode Display
Blower Switch
Temperature Dial
A/C
ECON
SET
AMB
A/C
MODE
°C/°F
AMB
OFF
AUTO
A/C Switch
AUTO Switch
Ambient Switch
Fresh Air Switch
OFF Switch
Recirculated Air Switch
Airflow Mode Switch
Defrost Switch
Conversion Switch
93I19669
Courtesy of Mazda Motors Corp.

Fig. 1: Identifying Automatic A/C-Heater Control Panel

COMPRESSOR CLUTCH CONTROL

A/C amplifier receives signals from sensors that monitor system conditions. A/C amplifier sends signals to Engine Control Unit (ECU). Based on signals it receives from A/C amplifier (and engine operating conditions), ECU grounds coil winding circuit of A/C relay. This energizes A/C relay, allowing power to compressor clutch.

If high side refrigerant pressure is less than 30 psi (2 kg/cm²) or more than 299 psi (21 kg/cm²), pressure switch interrupts power to compressor clutch.

SENSORS

Sensors provide A/C amplifier with signals that indicate various conditions. Solar radiation sensor is a voltage generator that responds to intensity of sunlight. All other sensors contain a resistor that changes value according to temperature.

- Solar radiation sensor monitors sunlight load.
- Ambient temperature sensor monitors outside air temperature.
- Evaporator sensor monitors evaporator temperature.
- Passenger Compartment Temperature (PCT) sensor monitors passenger compartment air temperature. Aspirator fan motor draws passenger compartment air across sensor bulb.
- Water temperature sensor monitors engine coolant temperature.

BLOWER MOTOR CONTROL

When A/C amplifier grounds the coil winding circuit of OFF (heater) relay, relay is energized. This allows power to blower motor. Depending on blower speed setting, blower motor is grounded through power transistor (similar to blower resistor) or through max high relay.

DOOR ACTUATORS

Intake (Fresh/Recirculated) Air Actuator – Intake air actuator controls position of fresh/recirculated air door in blower case. Door position determines whether fresh or recirculated air enters blower case.

Air Mix (Temperature Blend) Actuator – Air mix actuator controls position of air mix doors in heater case. Position of doors determines amount of airflow through heater core. *See Fig. 5.*

Airflow Mode Actuator – Airflow mode actuator controls position of 3 airflow mode doors in heater case. Position of doors determines airflow mode (vent, bi-level, heat, heat/defrost and defrost). *See Fig. 5.*

1993 AUTOMATIC A/C-HEATER SYSTEMS
929 (Cont.)

TROUBLE SHOOTING

SELF-DIAGNOSTIC SYSTEM CHECK

***NOTE:** If no light strikes solar radiation sensor, self-diagnostic system will falsely indicate a fault in solar radiation sensor circuit (Code 02). If self-diagnostics cannot be entered, check A/C amplifier power and ground circuits. If power and ground circuits are okay, replace A/C amplifier.*

Retrieving Codes – 1) Warm engine. Turn ignition off. Place a 60-watt (minimum) light about 4" from solar radiation sensor. Connect System Selector Tester (SST) to diagnostic connector near left front strut tower. Set SST dial to position No. 4. Set SST test switch to SELF-TEST position.

2) Connect Self-Diagnostic Checker (SDC) to SST and chassis ground. Set SDC select switch to position "A". Turn ignition on. If buzzer sounds for 5 seconds and SDC displays "88", go to next step. If buzzer does not sound for 5 seconds or SDC does not display "88" (or if both conditions exist), repair SDC ground wire and/or repair wiring between A/C amplifier and diagnostic connector in engine compartment. Return to step **1)**.

3) System is now in present failure mode. Present codes (if set in memory) will now be displayed. Press A/C switch. System is now in past failure mode. Past codes (if set in memory) will now be displayed. If present or past code(s) are set, check appropriate component and its circuit. See A/C-HEATER SELF-DIAGNOSTIC CODE INTERPRETATION table.

A/C-HEATER SELF-DIAGNOSTIC CODE INTERPRETATION

Present Code	Past Code	Component/Circuit
02		Solar Radiation Sensor
06	07	PCT Sensor
10	11	Evaporator Sensor
12	13	Ambient Temp. Sensor
14	15	Water Temperature Sensor
18	19	Air Mix Actuator
21	22	Airflow Mode Actuator
47		Idle-Up Signal
46		A/C Relay Signal

Output Inspection Mode – 1) In output inspection mode, A/C amplifier sends signals to blower motor, door actuators, idle speed control motor and compressor clutch. This tests each output device and its circuit.

2) To start output inspection mode, enter self-diagnostics. See RETRIEVING CODES. While in present failure mode, press AUTO switch. Output devices should now begin operating and conditions of output devices should be indicated on A/C-heater control panel.

3) Begin output inspection with mode step No. 1. See OUTPUT INSPECTION MODE DESCRIPTION table. Pressing recirculated air switch changes mode to next step. Pressing fresh air switch returns mode to previous step.

4) Check operation of each output device. Each component should be heard or seen operating. If output devices operate, system is okay. If output devices do not operate, check appropriate output device and/or its circuit.

OUTPUT INSPECTION MODE DESCRIPTION

Mode Step No.	Device(s) Operated
1	Blower Motor
2	Air Mix Actuator
3	Airflow Mode Actuator
4	Intake Air Actuator & Idle Speed Control Valve (Idle-Up)

CLEARING PAST CODES FROM MEMORY

Enter self-diagnostics. Enter past failure mode. See RETRIEVING CODES under SELF-DIAGNOSTIC SYSTEM CHECK. Simultaneously press AUTO and recirculated air switches. Verify Code 01 is momentarily indicated on display, then Code 00. Past codes are now cleared.

TESTING

***WARNING:** To avoid injury from accidental air bag deployment, read and carefully follow all SERVICE PRECAUTIONS and DISABLING & ACTIVATING AIR BAG SYSTEM procedures in AIR BAG SYSTEM SAFETY article in GENERAL SERVICING.*

***CAUTION:** When measuring voltage at specified wire terminals, back-probe connector terminals whenever possible to prevent terminal damage. When checking continuity of wiring between components, turn off ignition and disconnect connectors as necessary.*

A/C SYSTEM PERFORMANCE

1) Park vehicle out of direct sunlight. Connect manifold gauge set. Start engine and run at 2000 RPM. Set A/C controls to recirculate air, panel (vent) mode, full cold, and A/C button on.

2) Set blower/fan on high speed and close doors and windows. Insert thermometer in center vent. Operate system for 20 minutes to allow system to stabilize. Measure temperature. Temperature should be 37-42°F (3-6°C) at center vent, with high side and low side pressures within specification. See SPECIFICATIONS table at beginning of article.

SOLAR RADIATION SENSOR

1) Turn ignition off. Pry solar radiation sensor from instrument panel with a small screwdriver. Disconnect solar radiation sensor connector. Place a 60-watt (minimum) light about 4" from solar radiation sensor. Measure voltage between solar radiation sensor connector terminals. If less than 0.3 volt is present, replace solar radiation sensor.

2) If 0.3 volt or more is present, reconnect sensor connector. Disconnect A/C amplifier connectors. At A/C amplifier connectors, measure voltage between Gray wire terminal of 26-pin connector and Blue/Orange wire terminal of 22-pin connector.

3) If less than 0.3 volt is present, repair wiring between A/C amplifier and solar radiation sensor. If 0.3 volt or more is present, replace A/C amplifier.

PASSENGER COMPARTMENT TEMPERATURE (PCT) SENSOR

1) Turn ignition off. Remove lower cover from driver-side of instrument panel. Disconnect PCT sensor connector. Measure resistance across PCT sensor terminals. Measure air temperature near PCT sensor. Compare measured resistance and temperature readings with specifications listed in PCT SENSOR RESISTANCE SPECIFICATIONS table. If readings do not match specifications, replace PCT sensor.

2) If readings match specifications, reconnect PCT sensor connector. Disconnect A/C amplifier connectors. Measure resistance between Pink and Blue/Orange wire terminals of A/C amplifier 22-pin connector. Measure air temperature near PCT sensor. Compare measured resistance and temperature readings with specifications listed in PCT SENSOR RESISTANCE SPECIFICATIONS table.

3) If readings do not match specifications, repair wiring harness between A/C amplifier and PCT sensor. If readings match specifications, replace A/C amplifier.

PCT SENSOR RESISTANCE SPECIFICATIONS

Temperature °F (°C)	Ohms
32 (0)	7500
50 (10)	4500
68 (20)	3000
86 (30)	2000
104 (40)	1250
122 (50)	750

EVAPORATOR SENSOR

1) Turn ignition off. Remove glove box. Disconnect evaporator sensor connector. Measure resistance across evaporator sensor terminals. Measure air temperature near evaporator sensor. Compare measured resistance and temperature readings with specifications listed in EVAPORATOR SENSOR RESISTANCE SPECIFICATIONS table. If readings do not match specifications, replace evaporator sensor.

2) If readings match specifications, reconnect evaporator sensor connector. Disconnect A/C amplifier connectors. At A/C amplifier, measure resistance between Yellow/Black wire terminal of 26-pin connector and Blue/Orange wire terminal of 22-pin connector. Measure air temperature near evaporator sensor. Compare measured resistance and temperature readings with specifications listed in EVAPORATOR SENSOR RESISTANCE SPECIFICATIONS table.

3) If readings do not match specifications, repair wiring harness between A/C amplifier and evaporator sensor. If readings match specifications, replace A/C amplifier.

EVAPORATOR SENSOR RESISTANCE SPECIFICATIONS

Temperature °F (°C)	Ohms
14 (10)	12,000
32 (0)	7000
50 (10)	4000
68 (20)	2800
86 (30)	1800
104 (40)	1000
122 (50)	800

AMBIENT TEMPERATURE SENSOR

1) Turn ignition off. Disconnect ambient temperature sensor connector. Measure resistance across ambient temperature sensor terminals. Measure air temperature near ambient temperature sensor. Compare measured resistance and temperature readings with specifications listed in AMBIENT TEMPERATURE SENSOR RESISTANCE SPECIFICATIONS table. If readings do not match specifications, replace ambient temperature sensor.

2) If readings match specifications, reconnect ambient temperature sensor connector. Disconnect A/C amplifier connectors. Measure resistance between Blue/Yellow and Blue/Orange wire terminals of A/C amplifier 22-pin connector. Measure air temperature near ambient temperature sensor. Compare measured resistance and temperature readings with specifications listed in AMBIENT TEMPERATURE SENSOR RESISTANCE SPECIFICATIONS table.

3) If readings do not match specifications, repair wiring harness between A/C amplifier and ambient temperature sensor. If readings match specifications, replace A/C amplifier.

AMBIENT TEMPERATURE SENSOR RESISTANCE SPECIFICATIONS

Temperature °F (°C)	Ohms
14 (10)	12,000
32 (0)	7000
50 (10)	4000
68 (20)	2800
86 (30)	1800
104 (40)	1000
122 (50)	800

WATER TEMPERATURE SENSOR

1) Turn ignition off. Remove center console for access to water temperature sensor. Disconnect water temperature sensor connector. Measure resistance across water temperature sensor terminals. Measure air temperature near water temperature sensor. Compare measured resistance and temperature readings with specifications listed in WATER TEMPERATURE SENSOR RESISTANCE SPECIFICATIONS table. If readings do not match specifications, replace water temperature sensor.

2) If readings match specifications, reconnect water temperature sensor connector. Disconnect A/C amplifier connectors. Measure resistance between Black/White and Blue/Orange wire terminals of A/C amplifier 22-pin connector. Measure air temperature near water temperature sensor. Compare measured resistance and temperature readings with specifications listed in WATER TEMPERATURE SENSOR RESISTANCE SPECIFICATIONS table.

3) If readings do not match specifications, repair wiring harness between A/C amplifier and water temperature sensor. If readings match specifications, replace A/C amplifier.

WATER TEMPERATURE SENSOR RESISTANCE SPECIFICATIONS

Temperature °F (°C)	Ohms
32 (0)	35,000
50 (10)	20,000
68 (20)	12,500
86 (30)	8000
104 (40)	6000
122 (50)	3000

AIR MIX ACTUATOR

1) Disconnect air mix actuator connector. Apply battery voltage to air mix actuator Black/Yellow wire terminal and ground Gray wire terminal. Verify actuator operation. Check resistance between Green/Red wire and Blue/Orange wire terminals. Resistance should increase from 1000 ohms to 5500 ohms as temperature control knob is moved from cold to hot setting.

2) Apply battery voltage to Gray wire terminal and ground Black/Yellow wire terminal. Verify actuator operation. Check resistance between Black/Red wire and Green/Red wire terminals. Resistance should increase from 1000 to 5500 ohms as temperature control knob is moved from hot to cold setting. Replace actuator if it does not test as specified.

3) If actuator tests as specified, disconnect A/C amplifier connectors. Check continuity on A/C amplifier connector wires. If continuity does not exist on any wire, repair wire as necessary between A/C amplifier connector and actuator connector. If continuity exists on all wires, replace A/C amplifier.

AIRFLOW MODE ACTUATOR

1) Disconnect airflow mode actuator connector. Apply battery voltage to airflow mode actuator Yellow/Red wire terminal and ground Gray/White wire terminal. Verify actuator operation. Check resistance between White /Blue wire and Blue/Orange wire terminals. Resistance should increase from 1000 ohms to 5500 ohms as airflow mode changes from defrost to vent mode.

2) Apply battery voltage to Gray/White wire terminal and ground Yellow/Red wire terminal. Verify actuator operation. Check resistance between Black/Red wire and White/Blue wire terminals. Resistance should increase from 1000 to 5000 ohms as airflow mode changes from vent to defrost mode. Replace actuator if it does not test as specified.

3) If actuator tests as specified, disconnect A/C amplifier connectors. Check continuity on A/C amplifier connector wires. If continuity does not exist on any wire, repair wire as necessary between A/C amplifier connector and actuator connector. If continuity exists on all wires, replace A/C amplifier.

INTAKE AIR ACTUATOR

1) Disconnect intake air actuator connector. Apply battery voltage to intake air actuator Yellow wire terminal and ground Black wire terminal. Verify actuator operation. Check continuity between specified terminals of intake air actuator connector (door position sensor circuit). See INTAKE AIR DOOR POSITION SENSOR CONTINUITY table. If there is no continuity, replace intake air actuator.

2) If actuator tests as specified, disconnect A/C amplifier connectors. Check continuity on A/C amplifier connector wires. If continuity does not exist on any wire, repair wire as necessary between A/C amplifier connector and actuator connector. If continuity exists on all wires, replace A/C amplifier.

INTAKE AIR DOOR POSITION SENSOR CONTINUITY

Door Position	Terminals (Wire Colors)
Fresh	White/Red, Black/Blue & Green/Black
Recirculated	White/Red, Green & Green/Black
1/3 Fresh	White/Red, Green & Black/Blue

IDLE-UP SIGNAL

1) Turn ignition on. Press AUTO switch. Operate blower motor in first speed (low speed). Measure voltage at Yellow wire terminal of A/C amplifier 26-pin connector. If battery voltage is present, go to next

1993 AUTOMATIC A/C-HEATER SYSTEMS
929 (Cont.)

step. If battery voltage is not present, check wiring between Engine Control Unit (ECU) and A/C amplifier. If wiring is okay, check ECU.
2) Ensure ignition switch and AUTO switch are on. Operate blower motor in fourth speed (high speed). Measure voltage at Yellow wire terminal of A/C amplifier 26-pin connector. If battery voltage is present, replace A/C amplifier. If battery voltage is not present, check ECU.

A/C RELAY SIGNAL (COMPRESSOR CONTROL)

1) Turn ignition on. Press AUTO switch. Press defrost switch. Turn blower switch to manual first speed (low speed). If engine speed does not increase (idle-up control does not operate), go to step **8)**. If engine speed increases (idle-up control operates), check AIR CON (15-amp) and HEATER (40-amp) fuses in engine compartment fuse block.
2) If fuses are okay, remove A/C relay. Turn ignition on. Press AUTO switch. Check voltage at Red and Red/White wire terminals of A/C relay connector. If battery voltage is not present, repair wiring harness.
3) If battery voltage is present, check A/C relay. See RELAYS under TESTING. If A/C relay is okay, install relay. Connect jumper wire between chassis ground and Blue/White wire terminal of A/C relay connector. Turn ignition and AUTO switch on.
4) If compressor operates, check wiring between A/C relay and Engine Control Unit (ECU), and check ECU. If compressor does not operate, disconnect pressure switch connector. By-pass pressure switch by connecting jumper wire across pressure switch connector terminals.
5) Turn ignition and AUTO switch on. Set temperature dial to 64°F (18°C). If compressor does not operate, go to next step. If compressor operates, check refrigerant pressure. If pressure is okay, replace pressure switch.
6) Disconnect pressure switch connector. Turn ignition and AUTO switch on. Set temperature dial to 64°F (18°C). Check voltage at Blue/Green wire terminal of pressure switch connector. If battery voltage is not present, repair wiring between A/C relay and pressure switch.
7) If battery voltage is present, turn ignition and AUTO switch on. Set temperature dial to 64°F (18°C). Check voltage at Green/White wire terminal of compressor clutch connector. If battery voltage is not present, repair wiring between pressure switch and compressor clutch. If battery voltage is present, replace compressor clutch.
8) Turn ignition and AUTO switch on. Set temperature dial to 64°F (18°C). Check voltage at Black/Orange wire terminal of A/C amplifier connector. If 5 volts is present, replace A/C amplifier. If 5 volts is not present, check wiring between ECU and A/C amplifier, and check ECU.

BLOWER MOTOR CIRCUIT

Blower Motor Always Inoperative – 1) Check AIR CON (15-amp) and HEATER (40-amp) fuses in engine compartment fuse block. If fuses are okay, check OFF (heater) relay. See RELAYS under TESTING.
2) If relay is okay, connect jumper wire between chassis ground and Pink/Black wire terminal of OFF (heater) relay connector. Turn ignition and AUTO switch on. If blower motor does not operate, go to step **4)**.
3) If blower motor operates, check continuity of Pink/Black wire between OFF (heater) relay and A/C amplifier. If there is no continuity, repair Pink/Black wire. If there is continuity, replace A/C amplifier.
4) Connect jumper wire between chassis ground and Pink/Black wire terminal of OFF (heater) relay connector. Turn ignition and AUTO switch on. Check voltage at Red wire terminal of blower motor connector.
5) If battery voltage is not present, repair Red wire. If battery voltage is present, check voltage at Blue/White wire terminal of blower motor connector. If battery voltage is not present, replace blower motor.
6) If battery voltage is present, connect jumper wire between chassis ground and Pink/Black wire terminal of OFF (heater) relay connector. Turn ignition and AUTO switch on. Check voltage at Blue/White wire terminal of power transistor connector.
7) If battery voltage is not present, repair Blue/White wire. If battery voltage is present, check continuity of Black wire between power transistor and chassis ground. If there is no continuity, repair Black wire. If there is continuity, replace A/C amplifier.

NOTE: Blower motor should operate at high speed if blower switch is in fourth position with A/C in manual mode, or if temperature dial is set to 64°F (18°C) with A/C in AUTO mode.

Blower Motor Inoperative In High Speed – 1) Check max high relay. See RELAYS under TESTING. If max high relay is okay, disconnect power transistor connector. Turn ignition and AUTO switch on. Operate blower motor in fourth position (high speed).
2) Check voltage at Light Green/Red wire terminal of max high relay connector. If battery voltage is not present, repair Light Green/Red wire. If battery voltage is present, check voltage at Red/Blue wire terminal of max high relay connector. If battery voltage is present, go to step **4)**.
3) If battery voltage is not present, check voltage at Blue/White wire terminal of max high relay connector. If battery voltage is present, repair Black wire between max high relay and chassis ground. If battery voltage is not present, repair Blue/White wire between max high relay and blower motor.
4) Check continuity of Red/Blue wire between max high relay and A/C amplifier. If there is no continuity, repair Red/Blue wire. If there is continuity, replace A/C amplifier.
Blower Motor Operates In High Speed Only – 1) Disconnect power transistor connector. Measure resistance across specified terminals of power transistor connector. See POWER TRANSISTOR RESISTANCE SPECIFICATIONS table. *See Fig. 2.* If resistance is not as specified, replace power transistor.
2) If resistance is as specified, turn ignition and AUTO switch on. Operate blower motor in first position (low speed). Check voltage at Blue/White wire terminal of power transistor connector. If battery voltage is not present, repair Blue/White wire between A/C amplifier and power transistor.
3) If battery voltage is present, check voltage at Black wire terminal of power transistor connector. If more than zero volts is present, repair Black wire between A/C amplifier and chassis ground. If zero volts is present, replace A/C amplifier.

POWER TRANSISTOR RESISTANCE SPECIFICATIONS

Terminals [1]	Ohms
"A" & "B"	1900
"A" & "C"	Infinite
"B" & "A"	1900
"B" & "C"	Infinite
"C" & "A"	2400
"C" & "B"	2700

[1] – Connect ohmmeter positive lead to first terminal specified, and negative lead to second terminal specified.

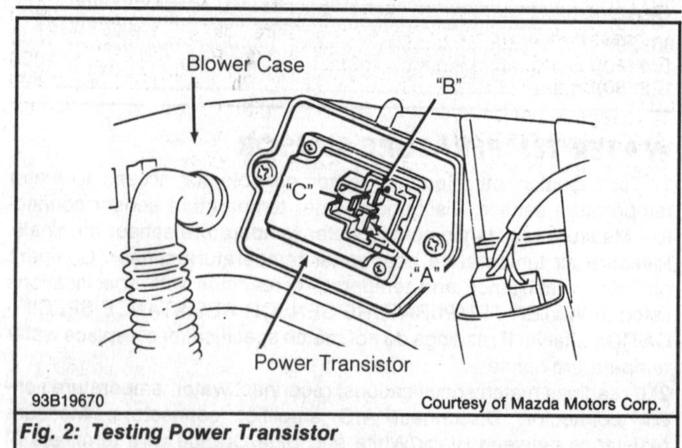
Blower Case
"B"
"C"
"A"
Power Transistor
93B19670
Courtesy of Mazda Motors Corp.
Fig. 2: Testing Power Transistor

RELAYS

A/C Relay – Check continuity between relay terminals "A" and "D". *See Fig. 3.* If there is continuity, replace relay. If there is no continuity, apply battery voltage to terminals "B" and "C". Check continuity between relay terminals "A" and "D". If there is no continuity, replace relay. If there is continuity, relay is okay.

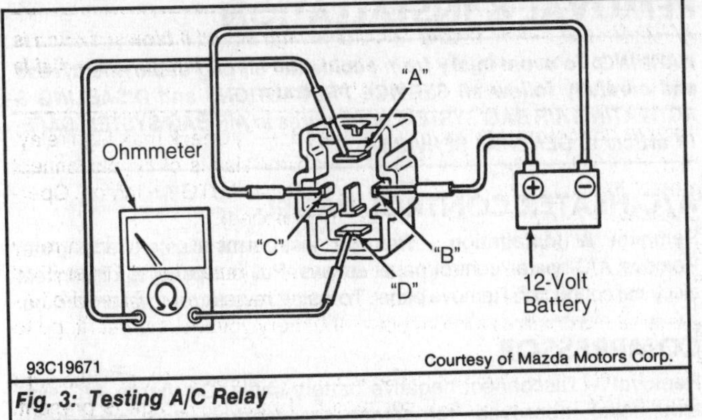
"A"
Ohmmeter
"C"
"B"
"D"
12-Volt
Battery
93C19671
Courtesy of Mazda Motors Corp.

Fig. 3: Testing A/C Relay

Max High & OFF (Heater) Relays – Check continuity between relay terminals "A" and "B". *See Fig. 4.* If there is continuity, replace relay. If there is no continuity, apply battery voltage to terminals "C" and "D". Check continuity between relay terminals "A" and "B". If there is no continuity, replace relay. If there is continuity, relay is okay.

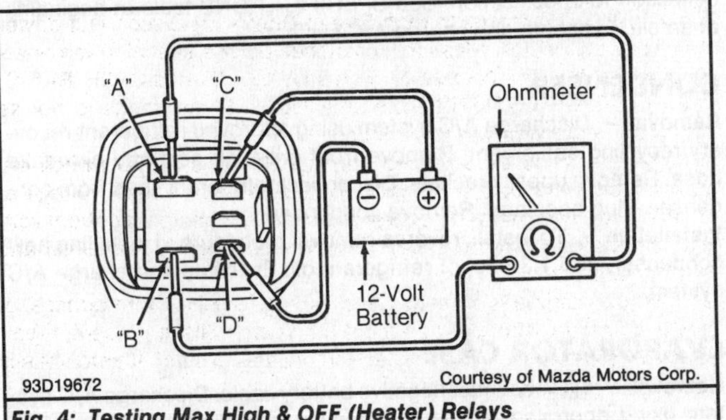
"A"
"C"
Ohmmeter
12-Volt
Battery
"B"
"D"
93D19672
Courtesy of Mazda Motors Corp.

Fig. 4: Testing Max High & OFF (Heater) Relays

PRESSURE SWITCH

Ensure high side refrigerant pressure is 30-299 psi (2-21 kg/cm²). Check continuity across pressure switch terminals. If there is no continuity, replace pressure switch. If there is continuity, pressure switch is okay.

A/C AMPLIFIER PIN VOLTAGE TEST

Remove center console to gain access to A/C amplifier. With wiring harness connected to A/C amplifier, ensure voltages are as specified. See A/C AMPLIFIER PIN VOLTAGE TEST (22-PIN CONNECTOR) and A/C AMPLIFIER PIN VOLTAGE TEST (26-PIN CONNECTOR) tables. If voltage is not as specified, check circuit and input/output device. See WIRING DIAGRAM. Repair or replace as necessary. If circuit and input/output device are okay, replace A/C amplifier.

A/C AMPLIFIER PIN VOLTAGE TEST (22-PIN CONNECTOR)

Wire Color & Test Condition	Volts
Orange/Black	
1st Blower Speed	1.3
2nd Blower Speed	1.4
3rd Blower Speed	1.6
4th Blower Speed	1.3
Blue/White	
Blower Switch Off	5.0
1st Blower Speed	8.5
2nd Blower Speed	5.5
3rd Blower Speed	3.0
4th Blower Speed	0.4
Red/Blue	
4th Blower Speed	0
Any Other Blower Speed	12.0
Pink/Black (OFF Relay)	
OFF Switch On	12.0
OFF Switch Off	0
Red/White	
Ignition Switch On	4.0
Ignition Switch Off	0
Brown/Yellow	
Ignition Switch On	4.0
Ignition Switch Off	0
Blue	
Ignition Switch On	3.0
Ignition Switch Off	0
Green/Yellow	
Ignition Switch On	3.0
Ignition Switch Off	0
Green/Orange	
Ignition Switch On	3.0
Ignition Switch Off	0
White	
Ignition Switch On	4.0
Ignition Switch Off	0
Gray/Red	
Ignition Switch On	12.0
Ignition Switch Off	0
Blue/Black	
Wiper Switch On	12.0
Wiper Switch Off	0
Red	0
Pink/Black	
OFF Switch On	5.0
OFF Switch Off	0
Black/Red	
OFF Switch On	5.0
OFF Switch Off	0
Blue/Orange	0
White/Blue	
Mode Switch In Vent Position	4.3
Mode Switch In Bi-level Position	3.5
Mode Switch In Heat Position	2.5
Mode Switch In Heat/Defrost Position	1.5
Mode Switch In Defrost Position	0.6

1993 AUTOMATIC A/C-HEATER SYSTEMS
929 (Cont.)

A/C AMPLIFIER PIN VOLTAGE TEST (26-PIN CONNECTOR)

Wire Color & Test Condition	Volts
Green/Red	
Temperature Set At 90°F (32°C)	4.4
Temperature Set At 64°F (18°C)	0.6
Yellow/Black	
A/C Switch In Normal Position	2.2-2.5
A/C Switch In ECON Position	1.6-2.1
Black/Orange	
Compressor Clutch On	1.4-3.4
Compressor Clutch Off	5.0
White/Red	
Ignition Switch On	5.0
Ignition Switch Off	0
Yellow/Red	
Ignition Switch On	12.0
Ignition Switch Off	0
Yellow	
Intake Air Actuator Operating	12.0
Intake Air Actuator Not Operating	0
Blue/Black	
Rear Vent Switch On	0
Rear Vent Switch Off	12.0
Green/Black	
Intake Air Actuator In 1/3 Fresh Position	0
Intake Air Actuator In Any Other Position	12.0
Black/Blue	
Intake Air Actuator In Recirculated Position	0
Intake Air Actuator In Fresh Position	5.0
Brown	
Ignition Switch On	3.5
Ignition Switch Off	0
Green	
Intake Air Actuator In Fresh Position	0
Intake Air Actuator In Recirculated Position	5.0
Green/Yellow	
Rear Vent Switch In Position No. 2 Or No. 3	7.5
Rear Vent Switch Off Or In Position No. 1	0
Brown/White	
Ignition Switch On	3.5
Ignition Switch Off	0
Green/Red	
Rear Vent Switch In Position No. 1 Or 3	7.5
Rear Vent Switch Off Or In Position No. 2	0
Black/Yellow	
Air Mix Actuator From Cold To Hot Position	12.0
Air Mix Actuator Off	
In Maximum Hot Position	12.0
In Any Other Position	0
Gray	
Air Mix Actuator From Hot To Cold Position	12.0
Air Mix Actuator Off	
In Maximum Cold Position	12.0
In Any Other Position	0
Yellow/Red	
Airflow Mode Actuator From Defrost To Vent Position	12.0
Airflow Mode Actuator Off	
In Vent Position	12.0
In Any Other Position	0
Green/White	
Airflow Mode Actuator From Vent To Defrost Position	12.0
Airflow Mode Actuator Off	
In Defrost Position	0
In Any Other Position	12.0
Green/Orange	
Rear Switch On	0
Rear Switch Off	12.0
Yellow	
Compressor On With Blower Speed High	0
Compressor On With Blower Speed Low	9.0
Black	0
Red	
Swing Switch On	0
Swing Switch Off	12.0
Blue/Red	12.0
Light Green/Red	
Ignition Switch On	12.0
Ignition Switch Off	0

REMOVAL & INSTALLATION

WARNING: To avoid injury from accidental air bag deployment, read and carefully follow all SERVICE PRECAUTIONS and DISABLING & ACTIVATING AIR BAG SYSTEM procedures in AIR BAG SYSTEM SAFETY article in GENERAL SERVICING.

A/C-HEATER CONTROL PANEL

Removal & Installation – Remove instrument cluster face plate. Remove A/C-heater control panel screws. Pull out panel to disconnect electrical connector. Remove panel. To install, reverse removal procedure.

COMPRESSOR

Removal – Disconnect negative battery cable. Discharge A/C system using approved refrigerant recovery/recycling equipment. Remove air cleaner assembly and air intake hose. Disconnect refrigerant lines from compressor. Plug openings. Disconnect compressor clutch connector. Remove drive belt. Remove compressor bolts, nuts and compressor.

Installation – To install, reverse removal procedure. Adjust drive belt deflection to specification. See SPECIFICATIONS table at beginning of article. Evacuate and charge A/C system.

CONDENSER

Removal – Discharge A/C system using approved refrigerant recovery/recycling equipment. Remove front grille, air seal and air intake hose. Remove upper brackets. Disconnect refrigerant lines from condenser. Plug openings. Remove condenser.

Installation – To install, reverse removal procedure. If installing new condenser, add 1.3 ozs. of refrigerant oil. Evacuate and charge A/C system.

EVAPORATOR CASE

Removal – **1)** Disconnect negative battery cable. Discharge A/C system using approved refrigerant recovery/recycling equipment. Disconnect refrigerant lines from evaporator at engine compartment firewall.

2) Remove glove box, glove box cover and instrument panel lower cover. In passenger compartment, remove 2 nuts securing evaporator case to firewall. Remove evaporator case. Disassemble case to remove evaporator and expansion valve. *See Fig. 5.*

Installation – To install, reverse removal procedure. If installing new evaporator, add 2 ounces of refrigerant oil. Evacuate and charge A/C system.

EVAPORATOR SENSOR

Removal & Installation – Remove and disassemble evaporator case. See EVAPORATOR CASE under REMOVAL & INSTALLATION. Remove evaporator sensor. To install, reverse removal procedure.

HEATER CASE & CORE

Removal & Installation – **1)** Drain coolant. Remove instrument panel. See INSTRUMENT PANEL under REMOVAL & INSTALLATION. Remove evaporator case. See EVAPORATOR CASE under REMOVAL & INSTALLATION.

2) In passenger compartment, remove 3 nuts securing heater case to firewall. Remove heater case. Disassemble case to remove heater core and air doors. *See Fig. 6.* To install, reverse removal procedure. Fill cooling system.

INSTRUMENT PANEL

Removal & Installation – Remove instrument panel components in order listed in illustration. *See Fig. 7.* To install, reverse removal procedure.

1993 AUTOMATIC A/C-HEATER SYSTEMS 929 (Cont.)

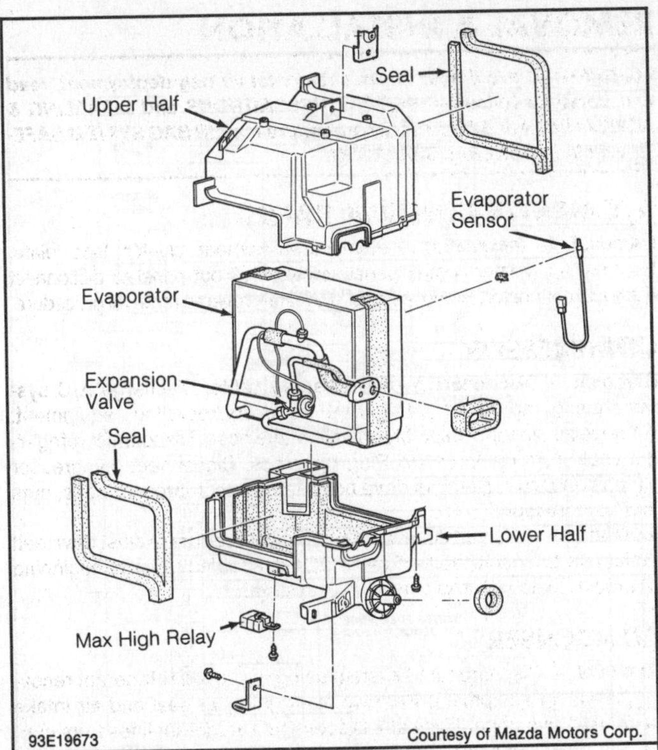
Seal
Upper Half
Evaporator Sensor
Evaporator
Expansion Valve
Seal
Lower Half
Max High Relay
93E19673
Courtesy of Mazda Motors Corp.

Fig. 5: Exploded View Of Evaporator Case

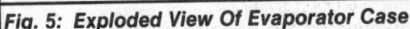

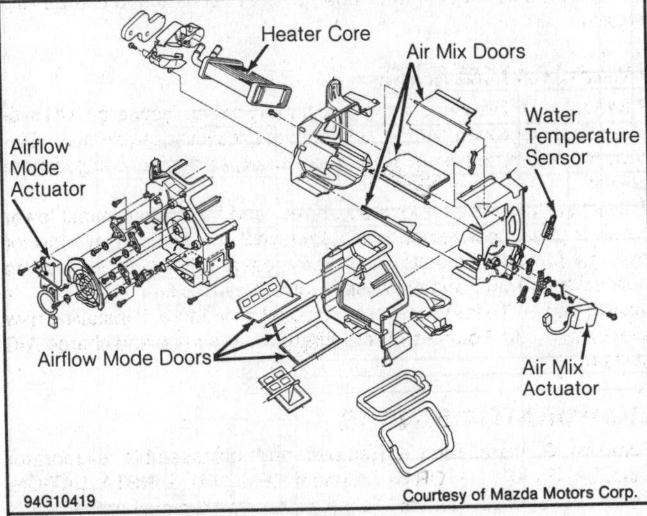
Heater Core
Air Mix Doors
Water Temperature Sensor
Airflow Mode Actuator
Airflow Mode Doors
Air Mix Actuator
94G10419
Courtesy of Mazda Motors Corp.

Fig. 6: Exploded View Of Heater Case

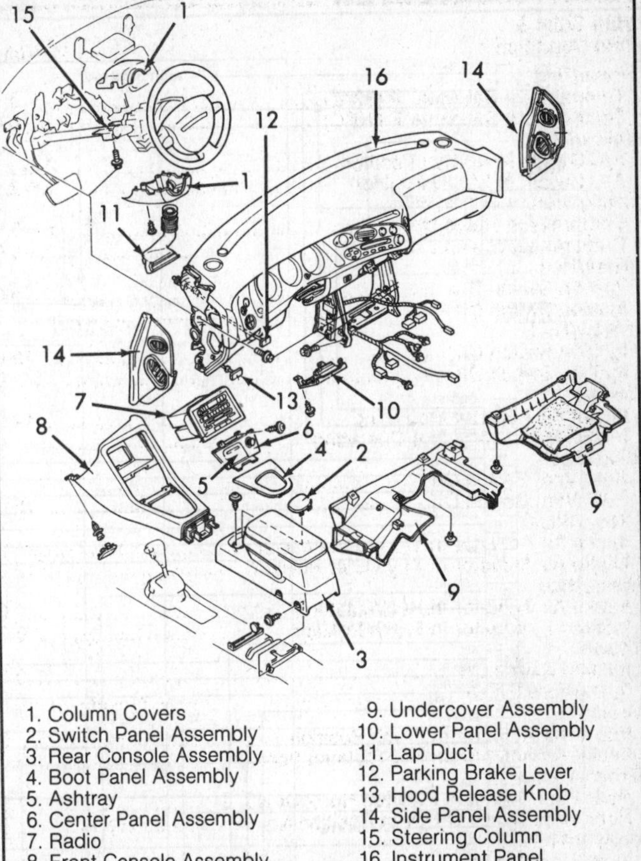
1. Column Covers
2. Switch Panel Assembly
3. Rear Console Assembly
4. Boot Panel Assembly
5. Ashtray
6. Center Panel Assembly
7. Radio
8. Front Console Assembly
9. Undercover Assembly
10. Lower Panel Assembly
11. Lap Duct
12. Parking Brake Lever
13. Hood Release Knob
14. Side Panel Assembly
15. Steering Column
16. Instrument Panel
93I19677
Courtesy of Mazda Motors Corp.

Fig. 7: Exploded View Of Instrument Panel

BLOWER CASE

Removal & Installation - Remove instrument panel. See INSTRUMENT PANEL under REMOVAL & INSTALLATION. Remove evaporator case. See EVAPORATOR CASE under REMOVAL & INSTALLATION. In passenger compartment, remove 3 nuts securing blower case to firewall. Remove blower case. To install, reverse removal procedure.

PCT SENSOR

Removal & Installation - Remove driver-side cover from below instrument panel. Disconnect PCT sensor connector. Remove duct hose and PCT sensor. To install, reverse removal procedure.

RECEIVER-DRIER

Removal - Disconnect negative battery cable. Disconnect pressure switch connector. Discharge A/C system using approved refrigerant recovery/recycling equipment. Disconnect refrigerant lines from receiver-drier. Plug openings. Remove receiver-drier.

Installation - To install, reverse removal procedure. If installing new receiver-drier, add 0.3 ozs. of refrigerant oil. Evacuate and charge A/C system.

SOLAR RADIATION SENSOR

Removal & Installation - Pry sensor out of instrument panel with small screwdriver. Disconnect sensor connector. To install, reverse removal procedure.

WATER TEMPERATURE SENSOR

Removal & Installation - Remove center console. Disconnect water temperature sensor connector. Remove water temperature sensor. To install, reverse removal procedure.

TORQUE SPECIFICATIONS

TORQUE SPECIFICATIONS

Application	Ft. Lbs. (N.m)
Compressor Bolt	17-26 (23-35)
Compressor Belt Idler Pulley Lock Nut	27-38 (37-52)
Refrigerant Line Bolt/Fitting	
To Compressor (Inlet & Outlet)	14-22 (19-30)
To Condenser (Inlet)	15-18 (20-24)
To Evaporator (Outlet)	14-22 (19-30)
Steering Column Bracket Bolt	12-17 (16-23)
	INCH Lbs. (N.m)
Refrigerant Line Bolt/Fitting	
To Condenser (Outlet)	57-82 (6.4-9.3)
To Evaporator (Inlet)	69-104 (7.8-11.8)
To Receiver-Drier (Inlet & Outlet)	69-104 (7.8-11.8)

1993 AUTOMATIC A/C-HEATER SYSTEMS
929 (Cont.)

WIRING DIAGRAM

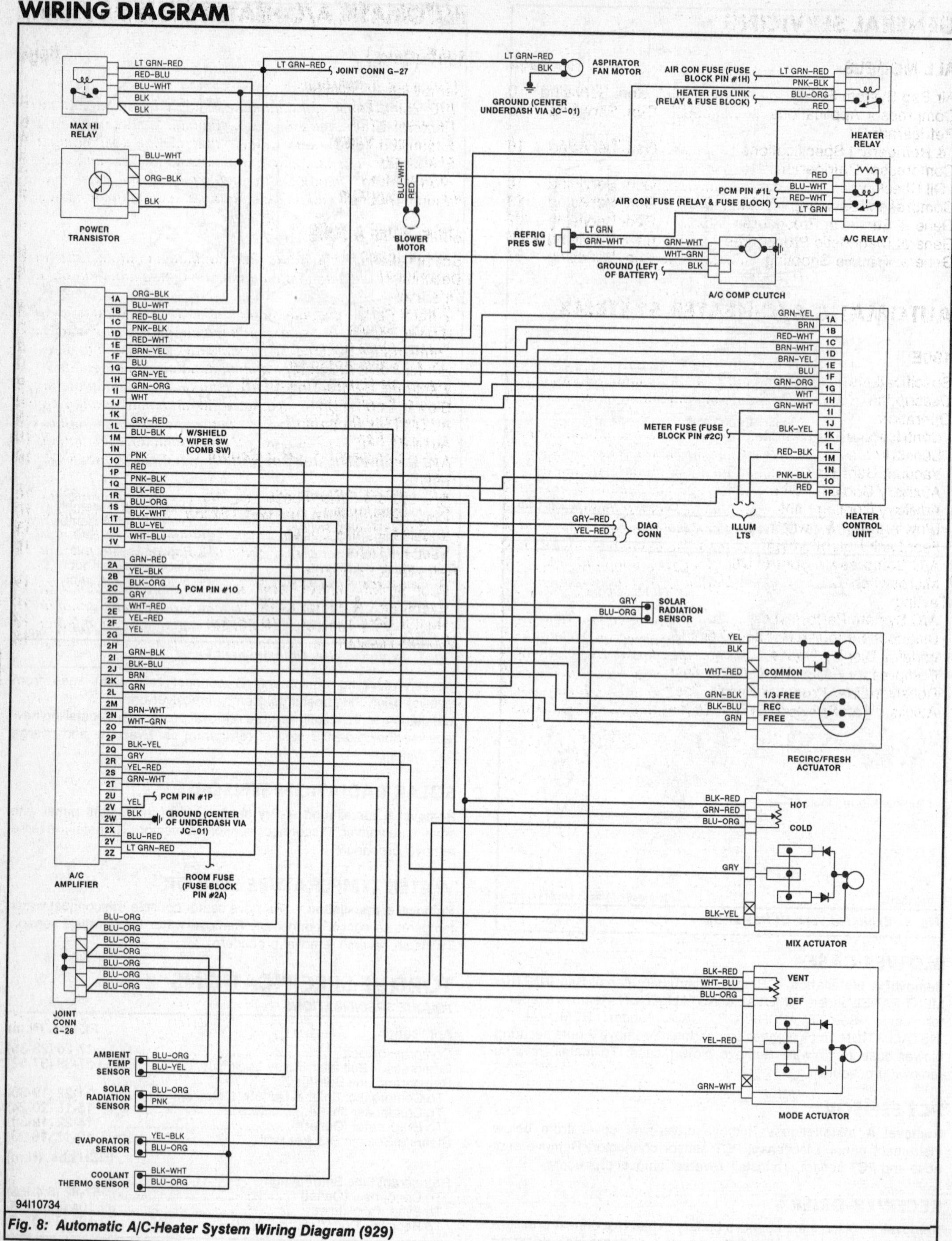
MAX HI RELAY
LT GRN-RED
RED-BLU
BLU-WHT
BLK
JOINT CONN G-27
ASPIRATOR FAN MOTOR
GROUND (CENTER UNDERDASH VIA JC-01)
AIR CON FUSE (FUSE BLOCK PIN #1H)
HEATER FUS LINK (RELAY & FUSE BLOCK)
HEATER RELAY
POWER TRANSISTOR
BLOWER MOTOR
PCM PIN #1L
AIR CON FUSE (RELAY & FUSE BLOCK)
A/C RELAY
REFRIG PRES SW
GROUND (LEFT OF BATTERY)
A/C COMP CLUTCH
W/SHIELD WIPER SW (COMB SW)
METER FUSE (FUSE BLOCK PIN #2C)
HEATER CONTROL UNIT
DIAG CONN
ILLUM LTS
PCM PIN #1O
SOLAR RADIATION SENSOR
COMMON
1/3 FREE
REC
FREE
RECIRC/FRESH ACTUATOR
PCM PIN #1P
GROUND (CENTER OF UNDERDASH VIA JC-01)
ROOM FUSE (FUSE BLOCK PIN #2A)
A/C AMPLIFIER
HOT
COLD
MIX ACTUATOR
VENT
DEF
MODE ACTUATOR
JOINT CONN G-28
AMBIENT TEMP SENSOR
SOLAR RADIATION SENSOR
EVAPORATOR SENSOR
COOLANT THERMO SENSOR
94I10734

Fig. 8: Automatic A/C-Heater System Wiring Diagram (929)

1993 MERCEDES-BENZ CONTENTS

GENERAL SERVICING

ALL MODELS

AUTOMATIC A/C-HEATER SYSTEMS

190E

AUTOMATIC A/C-HEATER SYSTEMS (Cont.)

190E (Cont.)

300E, 400E & 500E

1993 MERCEDES-BENZ CONTENTS (Cont.)

AUTOMATIC A/C-HEATER SYSTEMS (Cont.)

300SE, 300SD, 400SE & 500SEL

AUTOMATIC A/C-HEATER SYSTEMS (Cont.)

300SE, 300SD, 400SE & 500SEL (Cont.)

1993 AUTOMATIC A/C-HEATER SYSTEMS
190E

SPECIFICATIONS

Compressor Type	Nippondenso 10PA15 10-Cyl.
Compressor Belt Tension	[1]
System Oil Capacity	4.0 ozs.
Refrigerant (R-12) Capacity	36 ozs.
System Operating Pressures	
High Side	230-275 psi (16.2-19.3 kg/cm²)
Low Side	24-34 psi (1.7-2.4 kg/cm²)

[1] - Belt tension is maintained by automatic belt tensioner.

WARNING: To avoid injury from accidental air bag deployment, read and carefully follow all SERVICE PRECAUTIONS and DISABLING & ACTIVATING AIR BAG SYSTEM procedures in AIR BAG SYSTEM SAFETY article in GENERAL SERVICING.

DESCRIPTION

The A/C-heater system automatically controls interior cooling and heating temperature through the A/C control unit. Blower can be adjusted manually or automatically.

System consists of push button control panel, in-vehicle and ambient temperature sensors, electric (auxiliary) coolant pump, solenoid-controlled heater valve, A/C compressor control unit, switchover valves and basic A/C system components.

OPERATION

CONTROL PANEL

Temperature Selector Wheel - Interior temperature can be set to 62-90°F (16-32°C) with temperature control wheel. *See Fig. 1.* If the temperature wheel is set at minimum position, system operates at full cooling capacity, provided A/C has been switched on. If wheel is set at maximum position, the system operates at full heating capacity. Rotating temperature wheel changes the electrical resistance (potentiometer), transmitting new resistance value to temperature control system.

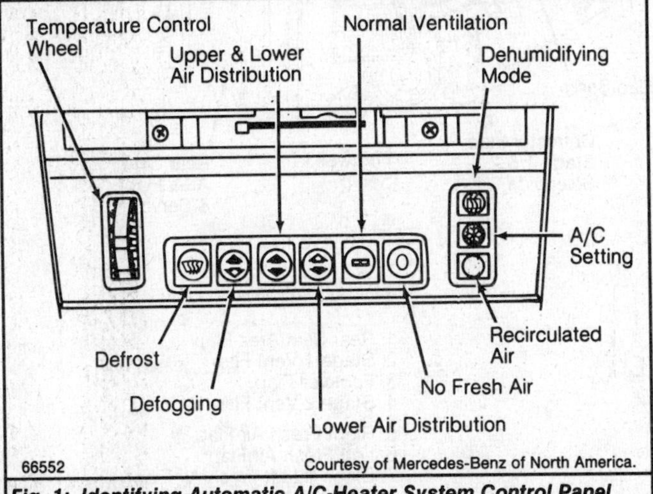
Temperature Control Wheel
Upper & Lower Air Distribution
Normal Ventilation
Dehumidifying Mode
A/C Setting
Recirculated Air
Defrost
Defogging
No Fresh Air
Lower Air Distribution
66552
Courtesy of Mercedes-Benz of North America.

Fig. 1: Identifying Automatic A/C-Heater System Control Panel

Defrost Mode - In this position, the blower runs at maximum (4th) speed with 100 percent fresh air, unless the fresh air/recirculated air switch is in the recirculated air position.

The blower switch and temperature wheel are by-passed, and the auxiliary coolant pump runs continuously. Maximum heated air, depending on coolant temperature, is directed to the windshield. The air feed to center and side outlets can be manually set using the levers. Center outlets should be closed.

The functions of the air conditioning mode switch are by-passed and the A/C system operates at maximum capacity (if outside or evaporator temperature is above the freeze protection setting). For proper operation, the fresh air/recirculated air switch must always be set in the fresh air position.

Defogging Mode - Blower runs at speed to which blower switch has been set (or 1st speed). Heating and cooling capacity is controlled by setting on temperature wheel and mode switch of A/C system.

If A/C system has been switched on, and temperature difference between temperature wheel and outside temperature is greater than 45°F (8°C), the system will automatically switch to recirculating air.

Upper & Lower Air Distribution Mode - This mode is similar to defogging mode except for air distribution. Legroom and defroster flaps are fully open.

Lower Air Distribution Mode - In this mode, air distribution is directed to legroom area. The legroom flaps should open fully, and defroster flaps should open partially.

Normal Ventilation Mode - This mode is similar to the upper level mode, except air is delivered out of center and side outlets only, with manual control levers.

Fresh Air Off Mode - In this mode, blower is switched off and the fresh air/recirculating air flap is closed (no outside air). The A/C system will be off and the auxiliary coolant pump will not be running. Temperature control will continue to operate and the heater valve is open or closed as controlled.

NOTE: If none of the mode buttons are depressed, only upper level air circulation will be present.

A/C Normal Mode - In this mode, the A/C compressor is engaged only as necessary for cooling. During the heating operation, the system operates without air conditioning (if no cooling is required).

If in-vehicle temperature exceeds selected temperature, the A/C compressor engages. The air conditioning output is then regulated according to cooling requirements.

A/C Recirculated Air Mode - In this position, the outside air temperature must exceed 59°F (15°C) for the system to remain in the recirculated air mode for 30 minutes.

Dehumidifying Mode - This selection dehumidifies the incoming fresh air and vehicle's interior. The A/C compressor remains on until evaporator temperature reaches 41°F (5°C). The interior temperature sensor does not affect A/C operation.

SENSORS

In-Vehicle Temperature Sensor - The in-vehicle temperature sensor is located near the front dome light. Resistance of current flow is affected by temperatures in the passenger compartment. Resistance is fed into the electronic system by A/C control unit.

An aspirator blower, connected to the sensor by a hose, provides continuous airflow past the in-vehicle temperature sensor. This increases the accuracy of temperature control inside the vehicle.

Ambient Temperature Sensor - The ambient temperature sensor is located on top of the evaporator housing. Resistance of sensor is affected by outside temperature. Resistance value is transmitted into the electronic system of the A/C control unit to provide input for fresh/recirculated air flap and in-vehicle temperature control.

Evaporator Temperature Sensors - This sensor is located in the evaporator housing. The sensor probes evaporator-fin temperature and transmits its resistance into the electronic system of the A/C control unit.

The resistance values provide input for temperature regulation and evaporator ice-up protection.

RPM Sensors - Inductive RPM sensors for the flywheel ring gear and compressor shaft are used. Sensors induce alternating voltage, which is used as an input signal to the A/C compressor control unit. Voltage alternates, depending on RPM, to increase or decrease input frequency to the control unit.

VACUUM CONTROLS

Vacuum Control Elements - Three vacuum control elements (actuators) are located on heater box. Two vacuum elements actuate the air

1993 AUTOMATIC A/C-HEATER SYSTEMS
190E (Cont.)

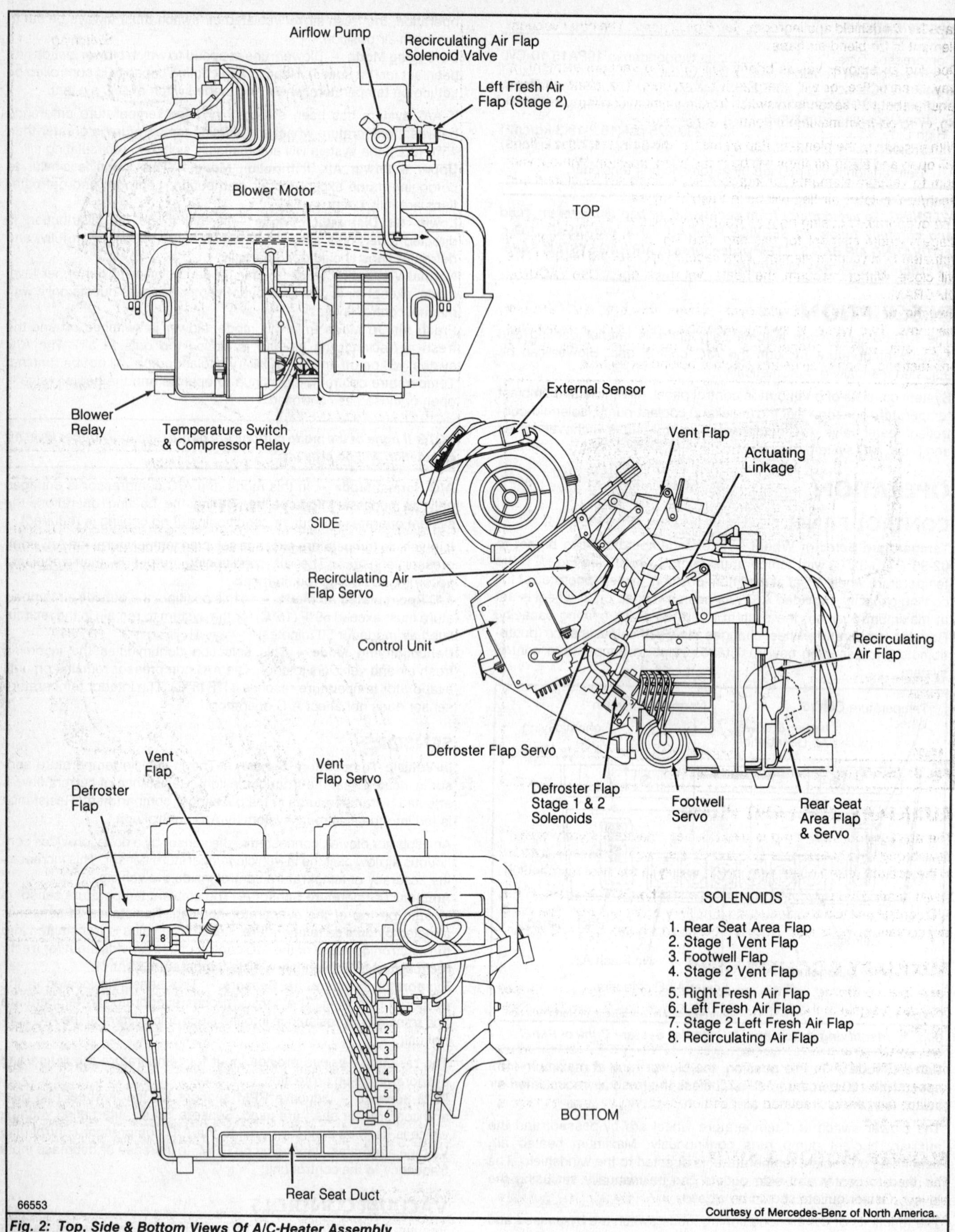
Airflow Pump
Recirculating Air Flap
Solenoid Valve
Left Fresh Air
Flap (Stage 2)
Blower Motor
TOP
Blower
Relay
Temperature Switch
& Compressor Relay
External Sensor
Vent Flap
Actuating
Linkage
SIDE
Recirculating Air
Flap Servo
Control Unit
Recirculating
Air Flap
Defroster Flap Servo
Defroster Flap
Stage 1 & 2
Solenoids
Footwell
Servo
Rear Seat
Area Flap
& Servo
Vent
Flap
Vent
Flap Servo
Defroster
Flap
SOLENOIDS
1. Rear Seat Area Flap
2. Stage 1 Vent Flap
3. Footwell Flap
4. Stage 2 Vent Flap
5. Right Fresh Air Flap
6. Left Fresh Air Flap
7. Stage 2 Left Fresh Air Flap
8. Recirculating Air Flap
BOTTOM
Rear Seat Duct
66553
Courtesy of Mercedes-Benz of North America.

Fig. 2: Top, Side & Bottom Views Of A/C-Heater Assembly

flaps for windshield and legroom. *See Figs. 2 and 7*. The other vacuum element is for blend-air flaps.

Opening switchover valves briefly will vent the vacuum element by way of an orifice, or will energize it by vacuum. The blend-air flaps require about 20 seconds to switch from maximum cooling to no cooling, or to go from maximum heating to no heating.

With vacuum in the blend-air flap elements, the defroster nozzle flaps will open and blend-air flaps will be in the warm position. Without vacuum to vacuum elements for legroom flaps, flaps will be closed and fresh/recirculated air flap will be in fresh air mode.

The evaporator housing houses fresh/recirculated air flap and the 2-stage vacuum element for this flap. *See Fig. 3*. The heater valve is actuated by a vacuum element. With vacuum applied, the heater valve will close. Without vacuum, the heater valve will open. See VACUUM DIAGRAM.

Switchover Valves – Switchover valves control the vacuum elements. Two types of switchover valves are used: a switchover valve unit with 4 connections and a switchover valve with 5 connections. These valves are stacked behind glove box.

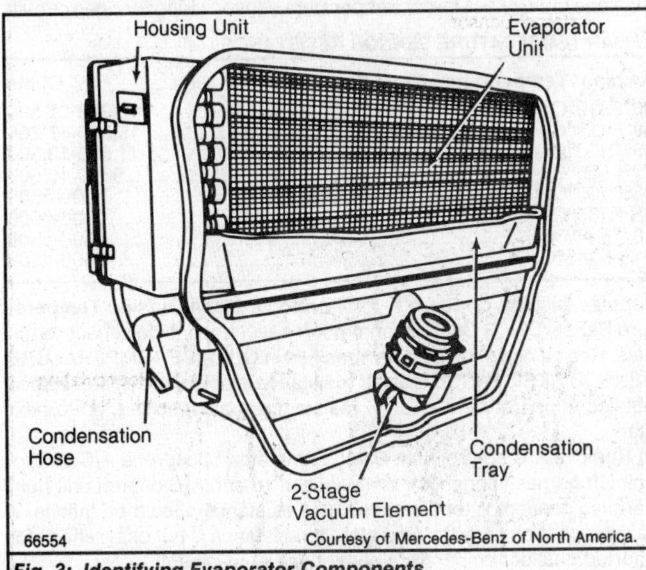
Housing Unit
Evaporator Unit
Condensation Hose
Condensation Tray
2-Stage Vacuum Element
66554
Courtesy of Mercedes-Benz of North America.

Fig. 3: Identifying Evaporator Components

AUXILIARY COOLANT PUMP

The auxiliary coolant pump is used to help maintain steady coolant flow through the heater core at low engine speeds. The pump, located in the coolant return hose, runs continuously in the heating mode.

When heating stops, with blend-air flaps and heater valve closed, the A/C control unit will disconnect the auxiliary coolant pump. The auxiliary coolant pump is also switched off when system is in A/C mode.

AUXILIARY COOLING FANS

Fans are controlled by the coolant temperature sensor. Sensor provides a signal to the A/C control unit to activate the auxiliary cooling fans.

Fans switch on at coolant temperatures of 225°F (107°C) and switches off at 212°F (100°C). The auxiliary cooling fans will also come on at temperatures greater than 77°F (25°C), if an open circuit exists in the coolant temperature sensor or if the coolant temperature sensor is disconnected.

BLOWER MOTOR & SWITCH

The blower motor is controlled by a 4-speed blower switch. With control lever at left-hand stop, blower motor runs in 1st speed when control buttons are engaged.

The blower assembly consists of dual centrifugal fans (4 fluted squirrel cages). The blower motor draws about 21 amps in 4th speed with 13 volts applied. *See Fig. 4*.

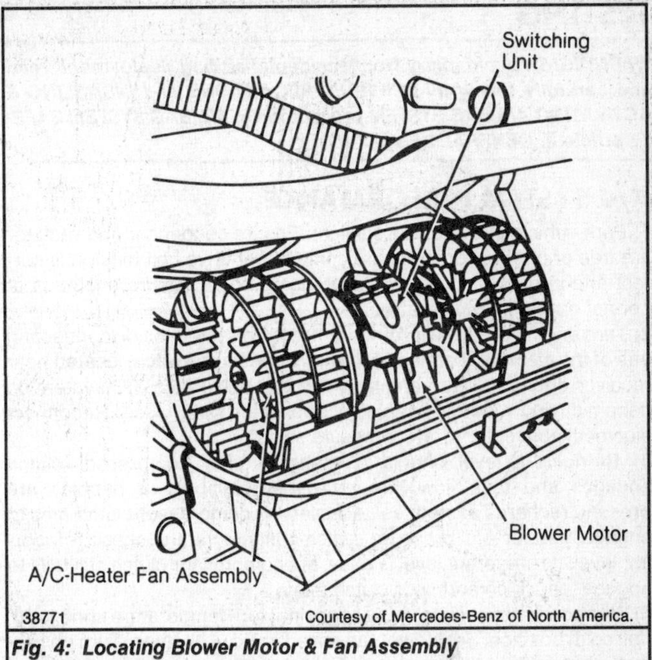
Switching Unit
Blower Motor
A/C-Heater Fan Assembly
38771
Courtesy of Mercedes-Benz of North America.

Fig. 4: Locating Blower Motor & Fan Assembly

FEEDBACK POTENTIOMETER

The feedback potentiometer is located on top of heater box. It is actuated by a vacuum unit and the blend-air flap. Accuracy of temperature control depends on adjustment of feedback potentiometer, especially during cooling mode. *See Fig. 5*.

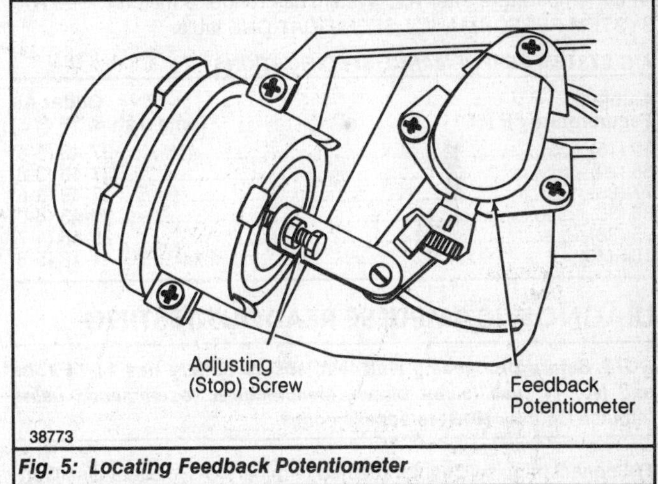
Adjusting (Stop) Screw
Feedback Potentiometer
38773

Fig. 5: Locating Feedback Potentiometer

A/C COMPRESSOR CONTROL UNIT

The protective cut-out control (A/C compressor control) unit compares speed of flywheel and compressor. If speeds vary more than 30 percent, compressor clutch will disengage. If ignition and A/C system are on and the engine is not running, A/C compressor will remain off.

Compressor is activated after engine speed reaches 500 RPM. The control unit compares engine and compressor speeds 2 seconds after compressor activation. If there is an RPM difference of more than 30 percent as the compressor comes on, the compressor will disengage. If engine speed and compressor speed are equal, the compressor will remain engaged.

MICROSWITCH

Automatic Transmission – At full throttle, the A/C compressor is cut out at 1050-2150 RPM by the microswitch. The microswitch is controlled by the protective cut-out control unit. This system is designed to improve engine performance.

1993 AUTOMATIC A/C-HEATER SYSTEMS 190E (Cont.)

TESTING

WARNING: To avoid injury from accidental air bag deployment, read and carefully follow all SERVICE PRECAUTIONS and DISABLING & ACTIVATING AIR BAG SYSTEM procedures in AIR BAG SYSTEM SAFETY article in GENERAL SERVICING.

A/C SYSTEM PERFORMANCE

1) Park vehicle out of direct sunlight. Ensure condenser and radiator are free of obstructions. Ensure compressor drive belt tension is correct and in good condition. Close engine hood. Ensure engine is at normal operating temperature.

2) Turn engine off. Check refrigerant level in system by disconnecting one of the electrical connector from A/C pressure switch, located near receiver-drier unit. Start engine and run at idle. Place A/C system on dehumidifying mode. Observe receiver-drier sight glass. Reconnect electrical connector to A/C pressure switch.

3) Refrigerant level should rise shortly after compressor clutch engages and then flow through without bubbles. If bubbles are present, recharge system as necessary. If compressor clutch fails to engage, jumper A/C pressure switch connectors and check refrigerant level. If refrigerant level is okay, but compressor clutch still fails to engage, check compressor clutch relay.

4) With compressor clutch now engaging, turn temperature knob to "0" (full cold) position. Set blower fan speed to No. 4 position. Turn on normal cooling/fresh air button. Move volume control lever (located between center vents) for adjustable air outlets in up position.

5) Open left and right side outlets. Insert thermometer in left or right center vent outlet. Position another thermometer in work area, about 8 feet from driver's side, to monitor ambient temperature.

6) Open all of vehicle's windows and close all doors. Operate engine at 2000 RPM. Record ambient temperature and check center vent outlet air temperature after A/C system has run for 5 minutes. See A/C SYSTEM PERFORMANCE SPECIFICATIONS table.

A/C SYSTEM PERFORMANCE SPECIFICATIONS

Ambient Temperature °F (°C)	Outlet Air Temperature °F (°C)
59 (15)	37-43 (3-6)
68 (20)	37-43 (3-6)
77 (25)	37-43 (3-6)
86 (30)	37-43 (3-6)
95 (35)	39-45 (4-7)
104 (40)	41-48 (5-8)

DIAGNOSTIC/IMPULSE READOUT TESTING

NOTE: Before proceeding with test, ensure battery has 11-14 volts and No. 11 fuse is not blown. Manufacturer recommends using Impulse Counter (013) to access codes.

1) Connect Impulse Counter (013) to terminal No. 7 of Data Link Connector (DLC), located in engine compartment. Turn ignition switch on. LED U BATT indicator (LED) on impulse counter should be displayed. If LED does not light up, check voltage between DLC terminal No. 1 (ground) and positive battery terminal. Voltage should be 11-14 volts.

2) Check voltage between DLC terminals No. 1 and 7. Voltage should be 6-12 volts. If voltage is not 6-12 volts, check wiring circuit.

3) Start impulse testing procedure. Press start button for 2-4 seconds. Record impulse code(s).

4) Press start button again for 2-4 seconds. If there are no further system malfunctions, the first indicated code will reappear. If trouble codes are present, repair as indicated. See IMPULSE DISPLAY CODES.

IMPULSE DISPLAY CODES

NOTE: Ensure fuse No. 7 is okay, battery voltage is 11-14 volts and temperature control wheel is set at 22°C.

Impulse Display Code 1 – No malfunction detected.

Impulse Display Codes 2 & 3 (Shorted In-Car Temp. Sensor) – **1)** Connect ohmmeter between temperature sensor terminals. Ensure resistance is as specified. See IN-CAR TEMPERATURE SENSOR RESISTANCE table. If resistance is not as specified, replace in-car temperature sensor. If resistance is as specified, go to next step.

2) Remove A/C control unit. Using ohmmeter, check resistance between A/C control unit terminal No. 9 on left harness connector and control unit terminal No. 12 on right harness connector. Resistance should be infinite. If resistance is okay, go to next step. If resistance is not okay, check in-car temperature sensor wiring for short to ground.

3) Connect ohmmeter to A/C control unit terminal No. 9 on left harness connector and Brown/Yellow wire at in-car temperature sensor terminal. Resistance should be less than one ohm. If resistance is not less than one ohm, check in-car temperature sensor wiring for open circuit.

IN-CAR TEMPERATURE SENSOR RESISTANCE

Ambient Temperature	Ohms
50°F (10°C)	18,300-21,500
59°F (15°C)	15,200-17,200
68°F (20°C)	11,500-13,500
77°F (25°C)	9500-10,500
86°F (30°C)	7500-8500
95°F (35°C)	6000-7000
104°F (40°C)	4500-5500
113°F (45°C)	3500-4500

Impulse Display Codes 4 & 5 (Shorted Or Open Outside Temperature Sensor) – **1)** Connect ohmmeter between outside sensor terminals. Resistance should be as specified in OUTSIDE TEMPERATURE SENSOR RESISTANCE table. If resistance is not as specified, replace outside temperature sensor. If resistance is as specified, go to next step.

2) Remove A/C control unit. Using ohmmeter, backprobe A/C control unit left harness connector terminal No. 10 and A/C control unit right harness connector terminal No. 12. Resistance should be infinite. If resistance is okay, go to next step. If resistance is not okay, check for shorted outside temperature sensor wiring to ground.

3) Backprobe A/C control unit left harness connector terminal No. 10 and Brown/Green terminal connector of outside temperature sensor. Resistance should be less than one ohm. If resistance is not less than one ohm, check outside temperature sensor wiring for open circuit.

OUTSIDE TEMPERATURE SENSOR RESISTANCE

Ambient Temperature	Ohms
50°F (10°C)	5000-6000
59°F (15°C)	4000-4600
68°F (20°C)	3100-3900
77°F (25°C)	2400-3000
86°F (30°C)	1900-2300
95°F (35°C)	1600-2000
104°F (40°C)	1400-1600
113°F (45°C)	1100-1300

Impulse Display Codes 6 & 7 (Shorted Or Open Evaporator Temperature Sensor) – **1)** Connect ohmmeter between evaporator temperature sensor terminals. Resistance should be as specified in EVAPORATOR TEMPERATURE SENSOR RESISTANCE table. If resistance is not as specified, replace evaporator temperature sensor. If resistance is as specified, go to next step.

2) Remove A/C control unit. Using ohmmeter, backprobe A/C control unit terminal No. 7 on left harness connector and terminal No. 12 on right harness connector. Resistance should be infinite. If resistance is okay, go to next step. If resistance is not okay, check evaporator temperature sensor wiring for short to ground.

3) Backprobe A/C control unit terminal No. 7 on left harness connector and Brown/Blue terminal connector of evaporator sensor. Resistance should be less than one ohm. If resistance is not as specified, check sensor for open circuit.

EVAPORATOR TEMPERATURE SENSOR RESISTANCE

Ambient Temperature	Ohms
32°F (0°C)	57,000-67,000
41°F (5°C)	46,000-54,000
50°F (10°C)	37,000-45,000
59°F (15°C)	31,000-36,000
68°F (20°C)	24,000-28,000
77°F (25°C)	20,000-24,000
86°F (30°C)	14,000-16,000
95°F (35°C)	13,000-15,000

Impulse Display Codes 12 & 13 (Shorted Or Open Coolant Temperature Sensor) – 1) Connect ohmmeter between coolant temperature sensor terminals. Resistance should be as specified in COOLANT TEMPERATURE SENSOR RESISTANCE table. If resistance is not as specified, replace coolant temperature sensor. If resistance is as specified, go to next step.

2) Remove A/C control unit. Using an ohmmeter, backprobe A/C control unit terminal No. 3 on left harness connector and A/C control unit terminal No. 12 on right harness connector. Resistance should be infinite. If resistance is okay, go to next step. If resistance is not okay, check coolant temperature sensor for short to ground.

3) Connect ohmmeter to A/C control unit terminal No. 3 on left harness connector and Green terminal connector of coolant temperature sensor. Resistance should be less than one ohm. If resistance is not less than one ohm, check coolant temperature sensor wiring for an open circuit.

COOLANT TEMPERATURE SENSOR RESISTANCE

Coolant Temperature	Ohms
68°F (20°C)	5000-8000
140°F (60°C)	900-1800
185°F (85°C)	460-650
212°F (100°C)	300-400

Impulse Display Codes 14 & 15 (Short Or Open Feedback Potentiometer) – 1) Connect ohmmeter between feedback potentiometer terminals No. 1 (Brown wire) and No. 2 (Blue wire). Measure resistance while moving feedback potentiometer from stop to stop. Resistance should be 8-5100 ohms. If okay, go to next step. If not, replace feedback potentiometer.

2) Remove A/C control unit. Using an ohmmeter, backprobe A/C control unit terminal No. 5 on left harness connector and A/C control unit terminal No. 12 on right harness connector. Resistance should be infinite. If resistance is infinite, go to next step. If resistance is not infinite, check Green/Red wire to feedback potentiometer for short to ground.

3) Connect ohmmeter on A/C control unit harness connector terminal No. 5 and feedback potentiometer Green/Red wire connector. Resistance should be less than one ohm. If resistance is not as specified, check Green/Red wire to feedback potentiometer for an open circuit.

Impulse Display Code 30 (Shorted Auxiliary Coolant Pump) – Turn ignition on and press defrost button. Connect ammeter to auxiliary coolant pump terminals. Reading should be less than one amp. If reading is not less than one amp, replace auxiliary coolant pump.

Impulse Display Code 33 – Shorted A/C compressor control unit. Replace A/C control unit.

Impulse Display Code 34 (Shorted 2nd Speed Auxiliary Fan Relay) – Connect ohmmeter between auxiliary fan relay terminal No. 85 (Black/Blue or Black/Red wire) and No. 86 (Brown/Blue wire). Resistance should be 50-80 ohms. If resistance is not as specified, replace auxiliary fan relay.

Impulse Display Code 50 (Shorted Switchover Valve To Defroster Long Stroke Flaps) – Connect ohmmeter between switchover valve unit terminals No. 4 (Gray/Violet wire) and No. 5 (Black/Red wire). Resistance should be 50-80 ohms. If resistance is not 50-80 ohms, replace switchover valve unit.

Impulse Display Code 51 (Shorted Switchover Valve To Defroster Short Stroke Flaps) – Connect ohmmeter between switchover valve terminals No. 5 (Black/Red wire) and No. 6 (Gray/White wire). Resistance should be 50-80 ohms. If resistance is not 50-80 ohms, replace switchover valve unit.

Impulse Display Code 52 (Shorted Switchover Valve To Legroom Flaps) – Connect ohmmeter between switchover valve terminals No. 2 (Gray/Red wire) and No. 5 (Black/Red wire). Resistance should be 50-80 ohms. If resistance is not 50-80 ohms, replace switchover valve unit.

Impulse Display Code 56 (Shorted Switchover Valve Fresh/Recirculated Air Long Stroke Flap) – Connect ohmmeter between switchover valve terminals No. 3 (Gray/Green wire) and No. 5 (Black/Red wire). Resistance should be 50-80 ohms. If resistance is not 50-80 ohms, replace switchover valve unit.

Impulse Display Code 57 (Shorted Switchover Valve To Fresh/Recirculated Air Short Stroke Flap) – Connect ohmmeter between switchover valve terminals No. 1 (Gray/Yellow wire) and No. 5 (Black/Red wire). Resistance should be 50-80 ohms. If resistance is not 50-80 ohms, replace switchover valve unit.

Impulse Display Code 58 (Shorted Switchover Valve To Warm Blend-Air Flaps) – Connect ohmmeter between switchover valve terminals No. 2 (Blue/Yellow wire) and No. 5 (Black/Red wire). Resistance should be 50-80 ohms. If resistance is not 50-80 ohms, replace switchover valve unit.

Impulse Display Code 59 (Shorted Switchover Valve To Cold Blend-Air Flaps) – Connect ohmmeter between switchover valve terminals No. 1 (Blue/Red wire) and No. 5 (Black/Red wire). Resistance should be 50-80 ohms. If resistance is not as specified, replace switchover valve unit.

Impulse Display Code 60 (Shorted Switchover Valve To Heater Valve) – Connect ohmmeter between switchover valve terminals No. 3 (Blue/Black wire) and No. 5 (Black/Red wire). Resistance should be 50-80 ohms. If resistance is not 50-80 ohms, replace switchover valve unit.

Impulse Display Code 61 (Shorted Blower Switch Relay For 1st Speed) – Connect ohmmeter between blower switch terminals No. 1 (Black/Green/White wire) and No. 3 (White/Blue wire). Resistance should be 50-80 ohms. If resistance is not 50-80 ohms, replace defective blower switch.

Impulse Display Code 62 (Shorted Blower Switch Relay For Maximum Speed) – Connect ohmmeter between blower switch terminals No. 1 (Black/Green/White wire) and No. 2 (White/Yellow wire). Resistance should be 50-80 ohms. If resistance is not 50-80 ohms, replace defective blower switch.

COMPRESSOR PROTECTIVE CUT-OUT TEST

NOTE: Verify compressor is functioning correctly before testing compressor protective cut-out system.

A/C Compressor Clutch Check – 1) Turn ignition on and press maximum cooling mode button. Using a voltmeter, connect positive lead to the Blue/Red wire of refrigerant pressure switch, and ground negative lead. Voltage should be approximately 12 volts. If there is no voltage, test A/C system for an open circuit.

2) Using a voltmeter, connect positive lead to Blue/Red wire at spade connector of refrigerant pressure switch, and ground negative lead. Voltage should be approximately 12 volts. If there is no voltage, check low refrigerant charge or defective pressure switch.

Non-Engagement Of Compressor Clutch – 1) Disconnect A/C compressor control unit from 12-pin connector. Connect positive lead of voltmeter to terminal No. 5 and negative lead to terminal No. 1 of 12-pin connector. Turn ignition on. If 12 volts exist, go to next step. If voltage does not exist, check wiring for open circuit.

1993 AUTOMATIC A/C-HEATER SYSTEMS
190E (Cont.)

2) Test control voltage from refrigerant pressure switch to A/C compressor control unit by pressing maximum cooling mode button. Connect positive lead of voltmeter to terminal No. 10 and negative lead to terminal No. 1 of 12-pin connector. If 12 volts are present, go to next step. If voltage is not present, check wiring from terminal No. 10 to refrigerant low pressure switch for open circuit.
3) Test compressor clutch and wiring by jumping terminals No. 5 and 7 on 12-pin connector. Start engine briefly to see if compressor runs (clutch engaging). If clutch is engaging, go to next step. If clutch is not engaging, check compressor clutch and repair or replace as necessary.
4) Test compressor RPM sensor by connecting voltmeter to terminals No. 9 and 11 of A/C compressor control unit 12-pin connector. Set voltmeter to read AC. Run engine at idle speed (approximately 750 RPM). Reading should be 0.3 volt minimum. If voltage is okay, go to next step. If voltage is not okay, stop engine. Test resistance of RPM sensor on terminals No. 9 and 11. Resistance should be approximately 530-650 ohms. If resistance is not approximately 530-650 ohms, replace compressor RPM sensor.
5) Test engine (flywheel) RPM sensor by connecting voltmeter to terminals No. 1 and 2 of A/C compressor control unit 12-pin connector. Run engine at approximately 750 RPM. Reading should be 4 volts AC. If voltage is okay, replace A/C compressor control unit. If voltage is not okay, stop engine. Check resistance of RPM sensor on terminals No. 1 and 2. Replace RPM sensor if resistance reading is not approximately 2000 ohms.

RECEIVER-DRIER PRESSURE SWITCH TEST

Operational Check – 1) Start engine, and switch on A/C system. If A/C compressor clutch does not engage, backprobe each of the 2 flat connectors on refrigerant pressure switch to check for voltage (DO NOT pull connector from pressure switch). *See Fig. 6.*

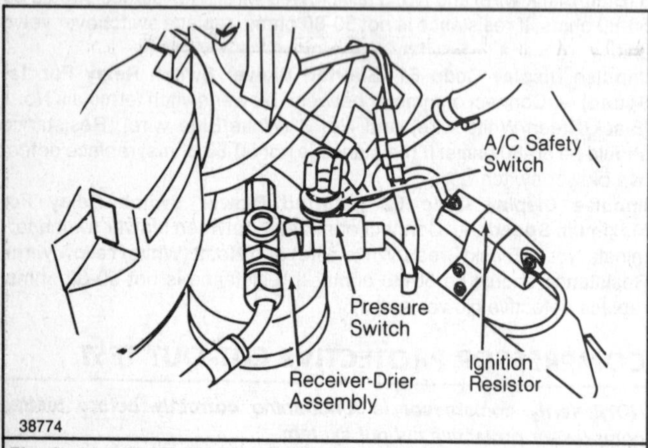
A/C Safety
Switch
Pressure
Switch
Receiver-Drier
Assembly
Ignition
Resistor
38774

Fig. 6: Identifying Receiver-Drier Assembly

2) If voltage is present on both pressure switch connectors, the fault is on clutch coil, or in wiring between pressure switch and compressor clutch coil.
3) If voltage is present at only one of the pressure switch connectors, there is not enough refrigerant in A/C system. Check sight glass on receiver-drier or check for defective pressure switch.
4) Using a fused jumper wire, jumper pressure switch connectors to check refrigerant level. Run A/C system for approximately 2-3 minutes. Check compressor clutch immediately after making connection to verify refrigerant flows past sight glass on receiver-drier free of bubbles. If refrigerant in system is adequate, the pressure switch is defective.
Cut-Out Pressure Check – 1) Connect a pressure gauge to service valve (pressure end). Disconnect electrical connectors from pressure switch, and connect an ohmmeter to pressure switch.
2) Slowly discharge refrigerant using approved refrigerant recovery/recycling equipment. At approximately 30 psi (2.1 kg/cm²), the cut-out point of the pressure switch must have continuity. If pressure switch does not cut out, replace pressure switch.

AUXILIARY FAN PRESSURE SWITCH TEST

Operational Check – 1) Turn ignition on, and connect 2 connectors of pressure switch to each other. If auxiliary fan (in front of condenser) and A/C compressor clutch do not engage, problem is outside of pressure switch.
2) If fan and compressor engage, unscrew closing caps. Connect hose line of high-pressure gauge to service valve. Ensure connecting nipple of hose line has a pressure pin in center.
3) Move heater switch to the "O" position. Turn fresh/recirculating air switch to fresh air position. Move airflow slide switch to stage 2. Slide temperature slide control to maximum position. If system does not operate correctly, go to CUT-OUT PRESSURE CHECK.
Cut-Out Pressure Check – Run engine at idle until refrigerant pressure has attained approximately 175 psi (12.3 kg/cm²) at pressure switch. If necessary, disconnect pressure switch connector. If auxiliary fan and electromagnetic clutch do not disengage at specified pressure reading, pressure switch is defective.

REMOVAL & INSTALLATION

WARNING: To avoid injury from accidental air bag deployment, read and carefully follow all SERVICE PRECAUTIONS and DISABLING & ACTIVATING AIR BAG SYSTEM procedures in AIR BAG SYSTEM SAFETY article in GENERAL SERVICING.

A/C COMPRESSOR

Removal – 1) Disconnect battery and remove alternator. Discharge A/C system using approved refrigerant recovery/recycling equipment. Disconnect connector from compressor clutch. Loosen mounting and tensioning bolt. Remove drive belt.
2) Remove mounting bolt for right torsion bar, and pull torsion bar downward. Remove A/C compressor mounting bracket bolts. Remove A/C compressor downward with mounting bracket attached.
3) Remove nuts and bolts on mounting bracket. Remove hex-headed bolts from mounting bracket. Remove A/C compressor from mounting bracket.
Installation – To install, reverse removal procedure. Replace "O" rings on A/C compressor. Evacuate and recharge A/C system. Run engine at idle for at least 4 minutes to circulate A/C system refrigerant oil.

RECEIVER-DRIER

Removal – Discharge A/C system using approved refrigerant recovery/recycling equipment. Remove electrical connectors from receiver-drier. Remove receiver-drier hoses, and plug lines.
Installation – Before installing new receiver-drier, fill with 0.3 oz. (10 cc) of fresh compressor oil. Evacuate and recharge A/C system. Check for leaks and proper operation.

EXPANSION VALVE

NOTE: If expansion valve is heavily contaminated, replace receiver-drier and expansion valve.

Removal – Discharge A/C system using approved refrigerant recovery/recycling equipment. Remove cover on air inlet. Unscrew hex bolt on expansion valve and remove lines. Remove both screws and expansion valve. Plug all open connections.
Installation – To install, reverse removal procedure. Replace "O" rings on evaporator pipes and pipe lines. Lubricate lines with A/C compressor oil. Evacuate and recharge A/C system. Check for leaks and improper operation.

EVAPORATOR

Removal – 1) Discharge A/C system using approved refrigerant recovery/recycling equipment. Remove cover at air inlet. Loosen bulkhead, unscrewing screws at left and right on bulkhead. Pull bulkhead forward, up to engine.

2) Remove expansion valve and blower motor. Remove screws for housing mounting bracket, and lift out housing lower half. Pull temperature sensor out of guide tube.

3) Remove clamps for evaporator. Remove frame. Lift evaporator, with pan and drain hoses attached, out of evaporator housing. *See Fig. 3.*

Installation – **1)** To install, reverse removal procedure. Clean pan and check drain hose passages. Insert evaporator into pan.

2) Insert evaporator, with pan attached, into evaporator housing. Mount rubber grommets of drain hoses. Attach frame to evaporator housing and clip down with clamps.

NOTE: When replacing evaporator, add 1.3 ounces of refrigerant oil.

3) Insert temperature sensor into guide tube, up to stop. Mount housing lower half with screws. Install blower motor. Remove closing cap of new evaporator from evaporator pipes.

4) Install expansion valve. Mount bulkhead and fasten with screws. Install cover on air inlet. Evacuate and recharge A/C system. Check for leaks and proper operation.

BLOWER MOTOR

Removal – **1)** Remove cover at air inlet. Loosen firewall, unscrewing screws at left and right for this purpose. Pull firewall forward, up to engine. Remove wiper arm.

2) Unscrew screws on wiper linkage. Set wiper linkage, with motor, aside. Loosen clamping straps and unclip clamps laterally and at top. Lift out cover in upward direction.

3) Unclip holding strap. Pull off connector and lift out blower motor. *See Fig. 4.*

Installation – To install, reverse removal procedure. Insert blower motor into holder so connections point in driving direction, and motor housing is engaged in motor holder.

WIRING DIAGRAM

NOTE: Information is not available from manufacturer.

VACUUM DIAGRAM

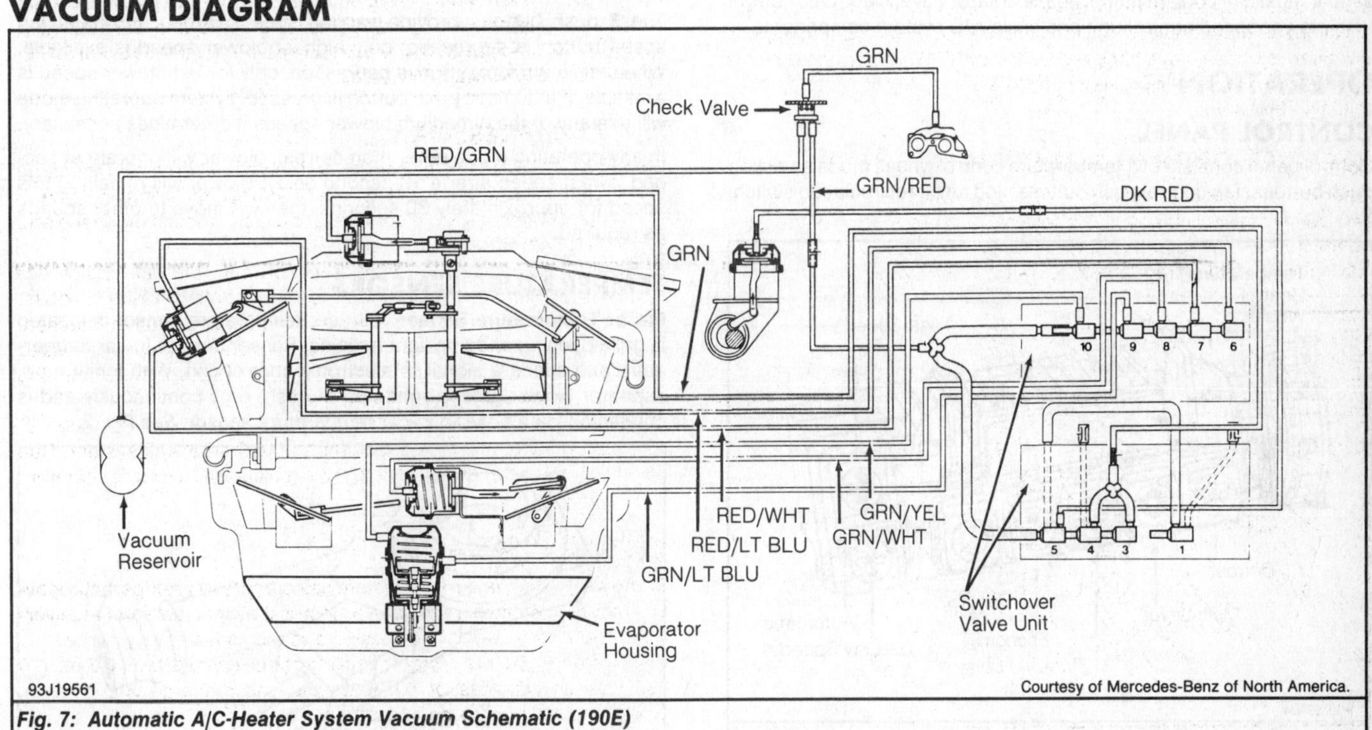
GRN
Check Valve
RED/GRN
GRN/RED
DK RED
GRN
10
9
8
7
6
Vacuum Reservoir
RED/WHT
RED/LT BLU
GRN/YEL
GRN/WHT
GRN/LT BLU
5
4
3
1
Switchover Valve Unit
Evaporator Housing
93J19561
Courtesy of Mercedes-Benz of North America.

Fig. 7: Automatic A/C-Heater System Vacuum Schematic (190E)

1993 AUTOMATIC A/C-HEATER SYSTEMS 300E, 400E & 500E

SPECIFICATIONS

Compressor Type	Nippondenso 10PA17 10-Cyl.
Compressor Belt Tension	[1]
Compressor Oil Capacity	[2] 5.4 ozs.
Refrigerant (R-134a) Capacity	36 ozs.
System Operating Pressures	[3]

[1] – Belt tension is automatically adjusted by belt tensioner.
[2] – Use Densooil 8 (Part No. A 001 989 08 03).
[3] – Information not available from manufacturer. To check system operation, see A/C SYSTEM PERFORMANCE under TESTING.

WARNING: To avoid injury from accidental air bag deployment, read and carefully follow all SERVICE PRECAUTIONS and DISABLING & ACTIVATING AIR BAG SYSTEM procedures in AIR BAG SYSTEM SAFETY article in GENERAL SERVICING.

DESCRIPTION

Automatic Climate Control (ACC) system uses a variety of sensors to maintain selected temperature. System consists of push button control panel, in-car temperature sensor, heater core temperature sensor, auxiliary coolant pump, heater control valve, electronic control unit, blower speed control unit and basic A/C system components.

OPERATION

CONTROL PANEL

Control panel consists of a temperature control wheel, mode selection push buttons, fan control push buttons, and an air recirculation switch. *See Fig. 1*.

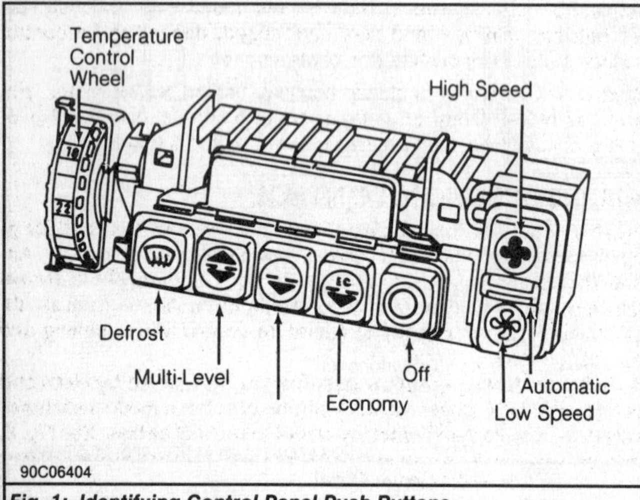
Temperature Control Wheel
High Speed
Defrost
Multi-Level
Off
Economy
Automatic
Low Speed
90C06404

Fig. 1: Identifying Control Panel Push Buttons

Temperature Control Wheel – Temperature control wheel provides interior temperature control in a temperature range of 62°F (16°C) to 90°F (32°C). If temperature wheel is set at MIN detent, peak cooling performance is attained. If temperature wheel is set at MAX detent, system will operate at full heating capacity.

A basic setting of 72°F (22°C) is recommended (represented by "22" on wheel). To avoid undesirable temperature fluctuations, readjustment of temperature setting should be made in small increments.

Air Recirculation Mode – Pressing air recirculation switch causes air to be recirculated without additional fresh air. Air recirculation mode switch automatically shuts off after a specified period of time. Air recirculation mode cannot be turned on if defrost button is pressed.

"0" (Air Supply Off) Mode – In this setting, fresh air supply to car interior is shut off. Use setting only temporarily while driving.

EC (Economy) Mode – In economy setting, A/C compressor remains off. In any other setting, A/C compressor comes on when ambient temperature is greater than 41°F (5°C).

In ventilation mode, air is supplied from center and side dash panel registers. In heating mode, warm air is primarily supplied to foot area. Enough air is supplied to windshield and dash panel side registers to keep glass defogged in normal weather conditions. Air will be emitted from center dash panel register depending on interior temperature.

With low outside temperatures, fan operation is delayed until engine coolant temperature rises above set temperature.

Normal Setting Mode – This setting is recommended when interior cooling is desired or for use in humid weather. Setting corresponds with economy setting. Air can be cooled as necessary.

Multi-Level Mode – Setting is used for clearing fogged windshield. In heating mode, warm air is supplied to windshield, foot area and dash panel side registers. Additional warm air may be emitted periodically from center dash panel register, depending on interior temperature. In cooling mode, cool air is supplied to windshield, foot area and dash panel center and side registers.

BLOWER SWITCH

The 3 push buttons provide varying speeds. When maximum fan speed button is depressed, only highest blower speed is available. When minimum fan button is depressed, only lowest blower speed is available. If automatic push button is pressed, system operating mode will use any of the 3 medium blower speeds it determines necessary.

In any operating mode other than defrost, blower will operate at second lowest speed after a 10-second delay. Blower will remain at this speed for approximately 30 seconds, then will move to other speeds as required.

TEMPERATURE SENSORS

In-Car Temperature Sensor – In-car temperature sensor is located in grille opening of dome light housing. Sensor detects in-car temperature and sends a signal to electronic control unit. With ignition on, aspirator blower (under right side of dash) runs continuously and is connected via a hose to in-car temperature sensor. *See Fig. 2*.

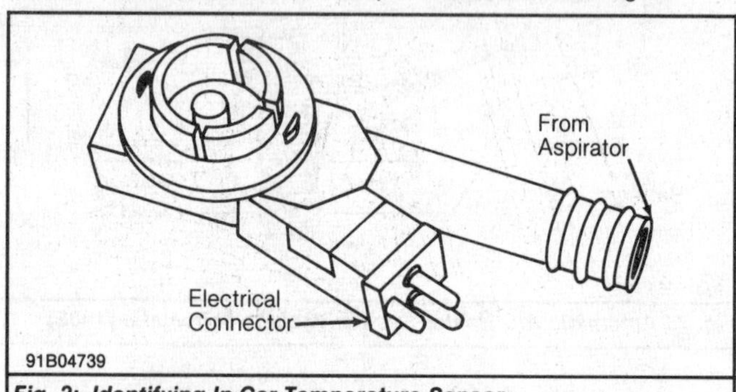
From Aspirator
Electrical Connector
91B04739

Fig. 2: Identifying In-Car Temperature Sensor

Outside Temperature Sensor – Outside (ambient) temperature sensor transmits varying voltage (depending on outside temperature) to electronic control panel assembly. Sensor is located on right side of blower housing, under air inlet grille.

Evaporator Temperature Sensor – Sensor is located on left side of evaporator housing, just above accelerator pedal. Sensor monitors evaporator fin temperature and provides input for temperature regulation and evaporator freeze protection. Sensor also helps prevent icing-up of evaporator.

Heater Temperature Sensor – Sensor is located in heater housing and monitors heater outlet temperature. Variations in heater temperature cause a varying voltage signal sent to electronic control unit. *See Fig. 3*.

1993 AUTOMATIC A/C-HEATER SYSTEMS 300E, 400E & 500E (Cont.)

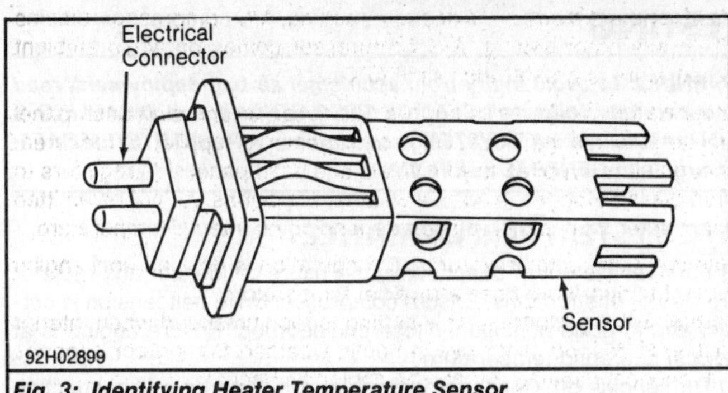
Electrical
Connector
Sensor
92H02899

Fig. 3: Identifying Heater Temperature Sensor

HEATER VALVE ASSEMBLY

Valve assembly includes heater control valve, auxiliary coolant pump and cold engine lock-out switch.

Heater Control Valve - Heater control valve is located in right front section of engine compartment, right of battery. *See Fig. 4*. Valve controls flow rate of coolant into heater core. Signal from electronic control unit (in response to temperature sensor signals) activates solenoid of heater valve to open or close valve as necessary. When de-energized, heater valve is open. A 5-second cycle opens valve to fill heater core with coolant. A check valve prevents over-filling of core.

NOTE: Auxiliary coolant pump is activated by signal from control unit which also opens floor (heater) air doors.

Auxiliary Coolant Pump - Auxiliary coolant pump is located in heated coolant return flow circuit. *See Fig. 4*. Coolant pump operates in heating mode when heater control valve is fully open or operating in regulating cycles.

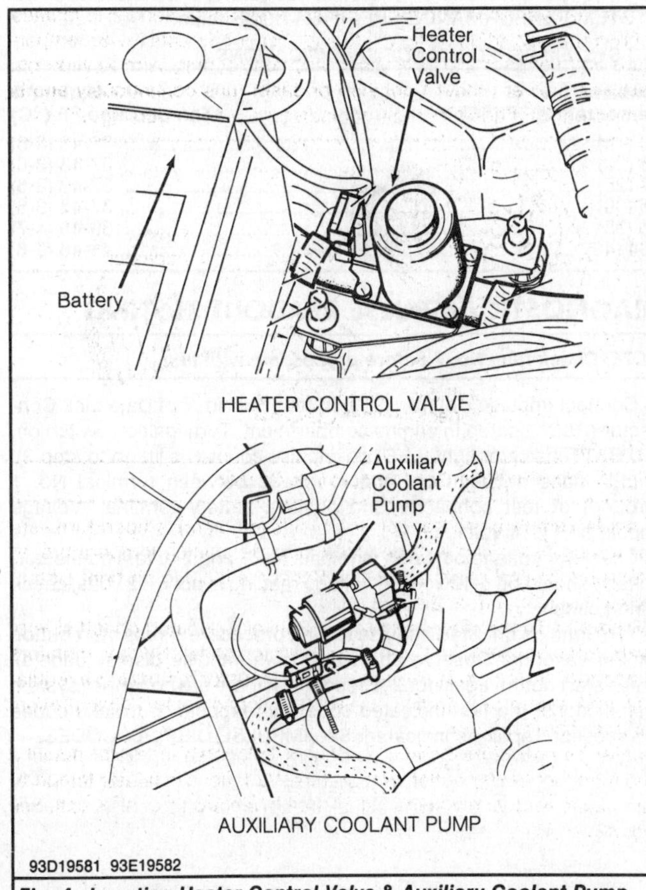
Heater
Control
Valve
Battery
HEATER CONTROL VALVE
Auxiliary
Coolant
Pump
AUXILIARY COOLANT PUMP
93D19581 93E19582

Fig. 4: Locating Heater Control Valve & Auxiliary Coolant Pump

Cold Engine Lock-Out Switch - Switch is located in coolant passage on engine block. It prevents blower operation when heating mode is selected and coolant temperature is less than 95°F (35°C).

ELECTRONIC CONTROL UNIT (ECU)

Sensor signals and temperature control wheel settings are processed in ECU (A/C control unit). *See Fig. 5*. ECU controls coolant flow through heater valve, mode change (heating to cooling) and position of fresh/recirculated air door. ECU signals to blower speed control unit. ECU also controls compressor clutch engagement.

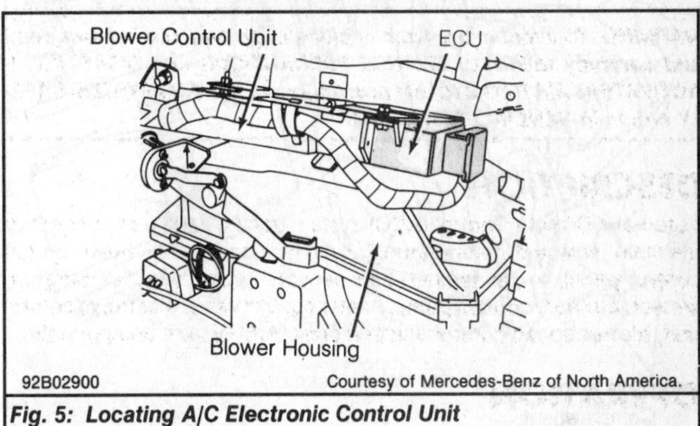
Blower Control Unit
ECU
Blower Housing
92B02900
Courtesy of Mercedes-Benz of North America.

Fig. 5: Locating A/C Electronic Control Unit

BLOWER CONTROL UNIT

300E - Blower control unit consists of a transistorized current regulator and a heat sink. In automatic mode, control unit provides stepless control of blower speeds. Blower speed is continuously varied between minimum and maximum speed, depending on control voltage supplied by push button control panel.

Control unit is located in blower housing, behind blower motor, and switches blower motor off in the event of a short circuit. *See Fig. 5*. Unit is constantly cooled when the blower motor is running.

AIR DISTRIBUTION CONTROL

Fresh air from inlet located below screen on cowl area is used for all operations except maximum cooling, which uses recirculated air. Airflow through lower ducts to rear passenger compartment is always the same temperature as outside air temperature. Airflow from all other outlets is determined by temperature control wheel setting and operating mode.

Switchover Valves - Airflow patterns are maintained by electronic control unit. Unit causes vacuum portion of various mode switchover valves to operate their respective doors to redirect airflow. *See Fig. 6*.

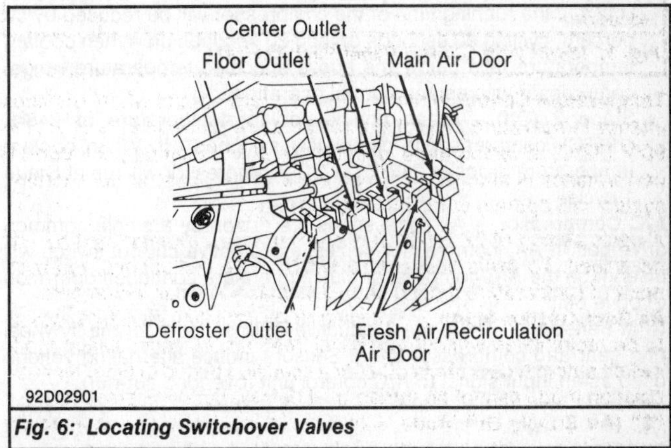
Center Outlet
Floor Outlet
Main Air Door
Defroster Outlet
Fresh Air/Recirculation
Air Door
92D02901

Fig. 6: Locating Switchover Valves

Vacuum Actuators - Actuators are located on heater-evaporator assembly. Vacuum signal from respective switchover valve causes actuator to open or close associated air door. *See Fig. 7*.

1993 AUTOMATIC A/C-HEATER SYSTEMS 300E, 400E & 500E (Cont.)

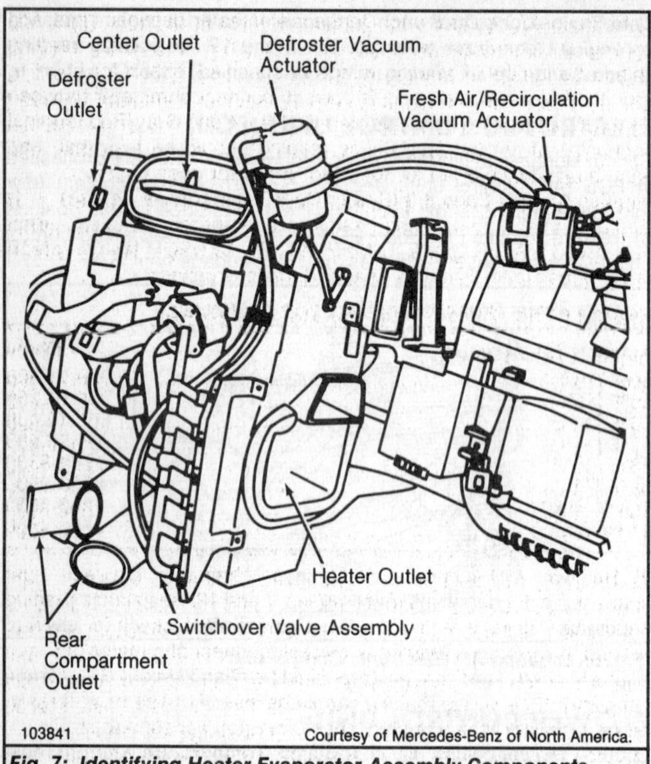
Center Outlet
Defroster Vacuum Actuator
Defroster Outlet
Fresh Air/Recirculation Vacuum Actuator
Heater Outlet
Switchover Valve Assembly
Rear Compartment Outlet
103841
Courtesy of Mercedes-Benz of North America.

Fig. 7: Identifying Heater-Evaporator Assembly Components

AUXILIARY FAN

Engine coolant temperature sensor controls auxiliary fan. Sensor provides a signal to control panel to activate second (high speed) stage of auxiliary fan when coolant temperature reaches 225°F (107°C). Second stage is switched off when coolant temperature drops to 212°F (100°C). At ambient temperatures greater than 77°F (25°C), auxiliary fan will switch to high speed if open circuit is detected in coolant temperature sensor or harness connector is disconnected.

A/C COMPRESSOR CUT-OUT CONTROL

NOTE: A/C Compressor Control unit activates compressor engagement 4 seconds after the engine is started.

A/C Compressor Overheating Cut-Out – To prevent engine from overheating, A/C compressor will shut off in 2 stages:

- Stage 1 (Cycling) – At an engine coolant temperature of 243°F (117°C), the running time of the compressor will be reduced by 50 percent, cycling 20 seconds off and 20 seconds on. When coolant temperature falls below the above specified temperature range, compressor will resume normal operation.
- Stage 2 (Off) – At an engine coolant temperature of 248°F (120°C), compressor is completely switched off. When coolant temperature drops to 243°F (117°C), compressor will run at Stage 1 cycle.

A/C Compressor – All accessories are driven by a single common drive belt. If A/C compressor seizes, a protective cut-out switch will disengage the A/C compressor clutch to ensure continued operation of drive belt.

RPM Sensors – There are 2 inductive RPM sensors for the flywheel ring gear and compressor shaft. Sensors induce alternating voltage used as an input signal to A/C control unit (overload cut-out).

TESTING

WARNING: To avoid injury from accidental air bag deployment, read and carefully follow all SERVICE PRECAUTIONS and DISABLING & ACTIVATING AIR BAG SYSTEM procedures in AIR BAG SYSTEM SAFETY article in GENERAL SERVICING.

A/C SYSTEM PERFORMANCE

1) Park vehicle out of direct sunlight. Ensure condenser and radiator are free of obstructions. Ensure compressor drive belt tension is correct and in good condition. Close engine hood. Ensure engine is at normal operating temperature.

2) Turn engine off. Check refrigerant level in system by disconnecting one of the electrical connector from A/C pressure switch, located near receiver-drier unit. Start engine and run at idle. Place A/C system on dehumidifying mode. Observe receiver-drier sight glass. Reconnect electrical connector to A/C pressure switch.

3) Refrigerant level should rise shortly after compressor clutch engages and then flow through without bubbles. If bubbles are present, recharge system as necessary. If compressor clutch fails to engage, jumper A/C pressure switch connectors and check refrigerant level. If refrigerant level is okay, but compressor clutch still fails to engage, check compressor clutch relay.

4) With compressor clutch now engaging, turn temperature knob to "0" (full cold) position. Set blower fan speed to No. 4 position. Turn on normal cooling/fresh air button. Move volume control lever (located between center vents) for adjustable air outlets in up position.

5) Open left and right side outlets. Insert thermometer in left or right center vent outlet. Position another thermometer in work area, about 8 feet from driver's side, to monitor ambient temperature.

6) Open all of vehicle's windows and close all doors. Operate engine at 2000 RPM. Record ambient temperature and check center vent outlet air temperature after A/C system has run for 5 minutes. See A/C SYSTEM PERFORMANCE SPECIFICATIONS table.

A/C SYSTEM PERFORMANCE SPECIFICATIONS

Ambient Temperature °F (°C)	Outlet Air Temperature °F (°C)
59 (15)	37-43 (3-6)
68 (20)	37-43 (3-6)
77 (25)	37-43 (3-6)
86 (30)	37-43 (3-6)
95 (35)	39-45 (4-7)
104 (40)	41-48 (5-8)

DIAGNOSTIC/IMPULSE READOUT TESTING

NOTE: Check fuse No. 7 before proceeding with test.

1) Connect Impulse Counter (013) to terminal No. 7 of Data Link Connector (DLC) located in engine compartment. Turn ignition switch on. If U BATT indicator light (LED) on impulse counter is lit, go to step **3)**. If LED does not light up, check voltage between terminal No. 1 (ground) of test connector and positive battery terminal. Voltage should be 11-14 volts.

2) Check for voltage between terminals No. 1 and 7 of test connector, voltage should be 6-12 volts. If voltage reading is not 6-12 volts, check wiring circuit.

3) Turn ignition on. Start impulse testing procedure. Press start button for 2-4 seconds. Observe and write down impulse display code(s). Press start button again for 2-4 seconds. If there are no further system malfunctions, the first indicated code will reappear. If trouble codes are present, repair as indicated. See IMPULSE DISPLAY CODES.

IMPULSE DISPLAY CODES

NOTE: Ensure fuse No. 7 is okay, battery voltage is 11-14 volts and temperature control wheel is set at 22°C.

Impulse Display Code 1 – No malfunction detected.

Impulse Display Code 2/3 (In-Car Temperature Sensor) – **1)** Using an ohmmeter, check resistance on in-car temperature sensor. See IN-CAR TEMPERATURE SENSOR RESISTANCE table. If resistance is not as specified, replace sensor.

IN-CAR TEMPERATURE SENSOR RESISTANCE

Ambient Temperature	Ohms
50°F (10°C)	18,300-21,500
59°F (15°C)	15,200-17,200
68°F (20°C)	11,500-13,500
77°F (25°C)	9500-10,500
86°F (30°C)	7500-8500
95°F (35°C)	6000-7000
104°F (40°C)	4500-5500
113°F (45°C)	3500-4500

2) Remove A/C control unit. Connect ohmmeter between A/C control unit right connector terminals No. 2 and 12. Resistance reading should be infinite. If resistance is not as specified, check for grounded wiring to in-car temperature sensor.

3) Connect ohmmeter between A/C control unit right connector terminal No. 2 and in-car temperature sensor terminal Green/Yellow wire. Resistance reading should be less than one ohm. If resistance is greater than one ohm, check wiring to in-car temperature sensor for an open circuit.

Impulse Display Code 4/5 (Outside Temperature Sensor) – **1)** Connect ohmmeter between outside temperature sensor terminals. See OUTSIDE TEMPERATURE SENSOR RESISTANCE table. If resistance is not as specified, replace sensor.

OUTSIDE TEMPERATURE SENSOR RESISTANCE

Ambient Temperature	Ohms
50°F (10°C)	5000-6000
59°F (15°C)	4000-4600
68°F (20°C)	3100-3900
77°F (25°C)	2400-3000
86°F (30°C)	1900-2300
95°F (35°C)	1600-2000
104°F (40°C)	1400-1600
113°F (45°C)	1100-1300

2) Remove A/C control unit. Connect ohmmeter between right A/C control unit connector terminals No. 9 and 12. Ohmmeter should read infinity. If resistance reading is not as specified, check for short to ground. If reading is correct, connect ohmmeter between right A/C control unit connector terminal No. 9 and outside temperature sensor Gray/Black terminal connector. Resistance reading should be less than one ohm. If resistance is not as specified, check outside temperature sensor for an open circuit.

Impulse Display Code 6/7 (Evaporator Temperature Sensor) – **1)** Connect ohmmeter between evaporator temperature sensor terminals. See EVAPORATOR TEMPERATURE SENSOR RESISTANCE table. If resistance is not as specified, replace sensor.

EVAPORATOR TEMPERATURE SENSOR RESISTANCE

Ambient Temperature	Ohms
50°F (10°C)	18,200-21,500
59°F (15°C)	15,300-17,200
68°F (20°C)	11,500-13,500
77°F (25°C)	9500-10,500
86°F (30°C)	7500-8500
95°F (35°C)	6000-7000
104°F (40°C)	4500-5500
113°F (45°C)	3500-4500

2) Remove A/C control unit. Connect ohmmeter between right A/C control unit connector terminals No. 4 and 12. Resistance reading should be infinite. If reading is not as specified, check for short to ground. If resistance reading is correct, connect ohmmeter between right A/C control unit connector terminal No. 4 and Gray/Red terminal connector of sensor. Resistance reading should be less than one ohm. If resistance is not as specified, check for open circuit.

Impulse Display Code 8/9 (Heater Core Temperature Sensor) – **1)** Connect ohmmeter between heater core temperature sensor terminals. See HEATER CORE TEMPERATURE SENSOR RESISTANCE table. If resistance is not as specified, replace sensor.

HEATER CORE TEMPERATURE SENSOR RESISTANCE

Ambient Temperature	Ohms
50°F (10°C)	18,300-21,500
59°F (15°C)	15,200-17,200
68°F (20°C)	11,500-13,500
77°F (25°C)	9500-10,500
86°F (30°C)	7500-8500
95°F (35°C)	6000-7000
104°F (40°C)	4500-5500
113°F (45°C)	3500-4500

2) Remove A/C control unit. Connect ohmmeter between right connector A/C control unit terminals No. 7 and 12. Resistance reading should be infinite. If resistance is not as specified, check for short to ground. If resistance reading is correct, connect ohmmeter between right A/C control unit connector terminal No. 7 and sensor Gray/Green connector. Resistance reading should be less than one ohm. If resistance is greater than one ohm, check for open sensor circuit.

Impulse Display Code 12/13 (Coolant Temperature Sensor) – **1)** Connect ohmmeter between coolant temperature sensor terminals. See COOLANT TEMPERATURE SENSOR RESISTANCE table. If resistance is not as specified, replace sensor.

COOLANT TEMPERATURE SENSOR RESISTANCE

Coolant Temperature	Ohms
68°F (20°C)	5000-8000
140°F (60°C)	900-1800
185°F (85°C)	460-650
212°F (100°C)	300-400
230°F (110°C)	230-290
248°F (120°C)	180-220
266°F (130°C)	135-175

2) Remove A/C control unit. Connect ohmmeter between right A/C control unit connector terminals No. 8 and 12. Resistance reading should be infinite. If resistance is not as specified, check for short to ground. If resistance reading is correct, connect ohmmeter between right A/C control unit connector terminal No. 8 and sensor Blue/Gray connector. Resistance reading should be less than one ohm. If resistance is greater than one ohm, check for open circuit in wiring harness.

NOTE: It is possible for Impulse Display 30 to be displayed even though coolant pump and control unit are okay. In this instance, coolant pump function must be checked by hand. Turn ignition off and on again and depress DEF button. If coolant pump is operating, no fault is present.

Impulse Display Code 30 (Coolant Pump) – Connect ammeter to coolant pump. Turn ignition on and press DEF function selector. Amperage reading should be less than one amp. If reading is not as specified, replace coolant pump.

Impulse Display Code 31 (Mono Valve) – Connect ohmmeter between mono valve terminals. Resistance should be 11-19 ohms. If resistance is not as specified, replace mono valve.

Impulse Display Code 33 – A/C compressor control unit defective.

Impulse Display Code 34 (Shorted 2nd Speed Auxiliary Fan Control) – Connect ohmmeter between auxiliary fan relay pins No. 85 and 86. Resistance reading should be 50-80 ohms. If resistance is not as specified, replace fan relay.

1993 AUTOMATIC A/C-HEATER SYSTEMS 300E, 400E & 500E (Cont.)

Impulse Display Code 50 (Shorted Long Stroke Defroster Flap Switchover Valve) – Connect ohmmeter between switchover valve pins No. 5 and 8. Resistance reading should be 50-80 ohms. If resistance reading is not as specified, replace switchover valve unit.
Impulse Display Code 51 (Shorted Short Stroke Defroster Flap Switchover Valve) – Connect ohmmeter between switchover valve pins No. 7 and 8. Resistance reading should be 50-80 ohms. If resistance reading is not as specified, replace switchover valve unit.
Impulse Display Code 52 (Shorted Legroom Flap Switchover Valve) – Connect ohmmeter between switchover valve pins No. 3 and 8. Resistance reading should be 50-80 ohms. If resistance reading is not as specified, replace switchover valve unit.
Impulse Display Code 54 (Shorted Center Outlet Flap Switchover Valve) – Connect ohmmeter between switchover valve pins No. 4 and 8. Resistance reading should be 50-80 ohms. If reading is not as specified, replace switchover valve unit.
Impulse Display Code 55 (Shorted Diverter Flap Switchover Valve) – Connect ohmmeter between switchover valve pins No. 6 and 8. Resistance reading should be 50-80 ohms. If resistance is not as specified, replace switchover valve unit.
Impulse Display Code 56 (Shorted Long Stroke Fresh/Recirculated Air Flap Switchover Valve) – Connect ohmmeter between switchover valve pins No. 2 and 8. Resistance reading should be 50-80 ohms. If resistance is not as specified, replace switchover valve unit.
Impulse Display Code 57 (Shorted Short Stroke Fresh/Recirculated Air Flap Switchover Valve) – Connect ohmmeter between switchover valve pins No. 1 and 8. Resistance reading should be 50-80 ohms. If resistance is not as specified, replace switchover valve.

VACUUM TESTS

Before beginning tests, run engine until it is at full operating temperature (cold engine lock-out switch is off), then turn engine off. Depress economy push button.
Check Valve – Detach vacuum line from check valve (in-line from manifold vacuum source). Attach vacuum tester to check valve port and apply vacuum. If vacuum leaks down, replace check valve.
Vacuum Reservoir – Detach vacuum line from check valve leading to vacuum reservoir. Connect vacuum tester to vacuum line, and apply vacuum. If reservoir does not hold vacuum, replace vacuum reservoir gasket or reservoir.

REMOVAL & INSTALLATION

WARNING: To avoid injury from accidental air bag deployment, read and carefully follow all SERVICE PRECAUTIONS and DISABLING & ACTIVATING AIR BAG SYSTEM procedures in AIR BAG SYSTEM SAFETY article in GENERAL SERVICING.

PUSH BUTTON CONTROL PANEL

Removal & Installation – **1)** Disconnect battery. Remove radio. Remove optional switch (if equipped). Remove 2 screws in radio opening, and carefully pull out and remove wooden cover panel from bottom.
2) Remove 2 screws retaining control assembly, and pull assembly forward. Remove instrument lamps. Detach 12-pin connector from control unit. Temperature control wheel and blower switch can be removed independently at this time.
3) To remove push buttons or blower switch from control panel, remove screw near blower switch. Remove plastic cover from control panel assembly. Remove push buttons or blower switch as necessary. To install, reverse removal procedure.

EVAPORATOR & HEATER CORE

Removal – **1)** Disable air bag system. See AIR BAG SYSTEM SAFETY article in GENERAL SERVICING. Discharge A/C system using approved refrigerant recovery/recycling equipment. Drain engine coolant. Disconnect battery. Cover both front seats and slide them back. Remove floor mats and carpets.
2) Remove glove box light and disconnect wiring. Pry top half of expanding rivets with a screwdriver. Pry bottom half of expanding rivets out of glove box, and remove glove box.
3) Remove screws from left and right panels under dash. Turn plastic clip on center console 90 degrees to the left, and remove panel. Pull left and right side interior windshield moldings. Release molding from roof frame or remove windshield.
4) Remove speaker covers. Remove screws under speaker cut-outs. Remove steering wheel. Release instrument cluster panel from dash by pulling out using hands only.
5) Disconnect speedometer cable, 2 wire connectors and oil pressure line. Remove instrument cluster from vehicle. Remove in-car temperature sensor from top of dash. Pull light switch knob and remove retaining nut. Pull light switch cover and disconnect wiring.
6) Disconnect parking brake cable. Remove left and right side panel vent ducts. Remove radio and slightly lift control panel from center console. Pull 12-pin connector from electrical switch gear. Pull 5-pin and 6-pin connectors from temperature control wheel.
7) Remove 2-pin connectors from temperature sensor, air volume control and air distribution switch. Remove control panel. Remove center console-to-dash screws. Remove control cable(s) for fresh air vents.
8) Push plastic defroster nozzle on top of dash and remove. Remove dash mounting screw at top center of dash. Remove screws beneath left and right side of dash. Remove glove box light switch wiring. Slightly raise dash and make sure defroster ducts come out of heater box.
9) Pull remaining cable(s) from A/C-heater housing. Disconnect hose for in-car temperature sensor, and remove dash. Remove screws from transmission tunnel sides, center tray and near floor shifter. Move center console to rear. Remove 3 supporting straps and all heater hoses.
10) Remove air ducts on transmission tunnel. Remove all remaining vacuum hoses, electrical connectors and control cable(s) as necessary. Remove screws from transmission tunnel brace. Pull air ducts for left and right fresh air vents. Remove electronic switching unit.
11) Pull expansion valve housing to remove A/C hoses from fittings. Plug all openings. Pull drain hoses from both sides of A/C-heater housing. Pull electrical lead from switchover valve.
12) Remove remaining screws and nuts from support brackets. Pull A/C-heater unit housing complete with heater hoses from vehicle. Hold heater hoses up so coolant will not spill.
13) Remove clips from top of A/C-heater case. Remove heater core case and core unit. Pry 2 clamps from lateral member. Pull vacuum line to vacuum control motor. Disconnect actuator control rod and vacuum motor mounting screw.
14) Remove lateral member. Pull plastic shaft and shaft bearing rod out of A/C-heater housing. Pull temperature sensor from A/C-heater housing near expansion valve. Disconnect vacuum controls on main air flap.
15) Pry clips holding main flap housing, and remove flap. Pry remaining clips around evaporator-to-heater core housing. Remove screws holding vacuum switchover valve to case. Remove left side panel. Remove main air flap shaft. Separate A/C-heater housing, and remove evaporator.
Installation – To install, reverse removal procedure. Ensure evaporator housing joining surfaces are well sealed during reassembly.

HEATER CORE TEMPERATURE SENSOR

Removal & Installation – **1)** Remove radio. Remove ashtray. Detach 2-pin connector from sensor. Pull sensor from heater housing.
2) Using a screwdriver, remove sensor from guide tube. Ensure screwdriver is inserted between guide tube and sensor, not between guide tube and center air duct. *See Fig. 3.* To install, reverse removal procedure.

VACUUM DIAGRAM

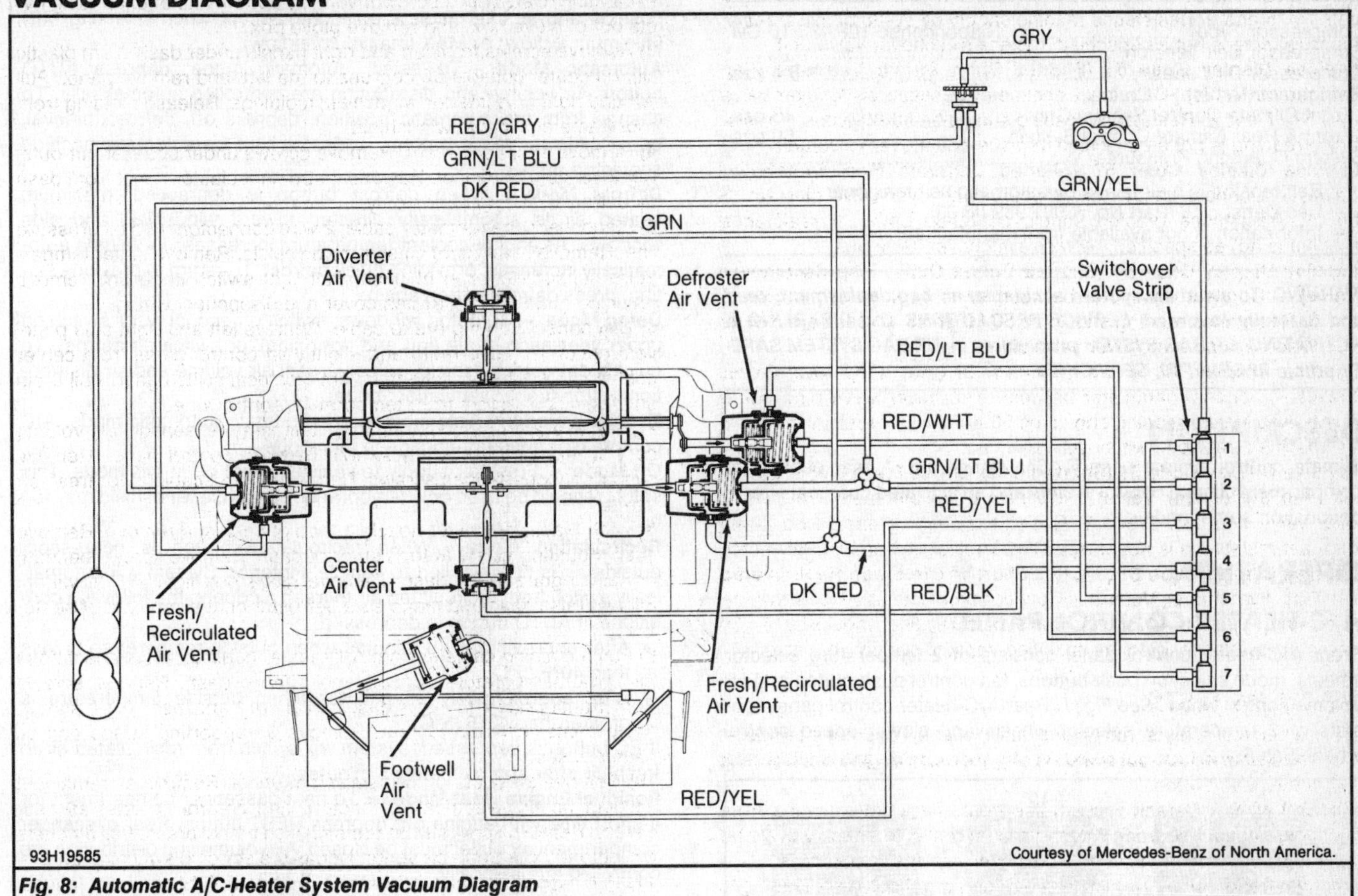
GRY
RED/GRY
GRN/LT BLU
DK RED
GRN
GRN/YEL
Diverter
Air Vent
Defroster
Air Vent
Switchover
Valve Strip
RED/LT BLU
RED/WHT
GRN/LT BLU
RED/YEL
1
2
3
4
5
6
7
Center
Air Vent
DK RED
RED/BLK
Fresh/
Recirculated
Air Vent
Fresh/Recirculated
Air Vent
Footwell
Air
Vent
RED/YEL
93H19585
Courtesy of Mercedes-Benz of North America.

Fig. 8: Automatic A/C-Heater System Vacuum Diagram

WIRING DIAGRAM

NOTE: Information is not available from manufacturer.

1993 AUTOMATIC A/C-HEATER SYSTEMS
300SE, 300SD, 400SE & 500SEL

SPECIFICATIONS

Compressor Type	Nippondenso 10PA20 10-Cyl.
Compressor Belt Tension	[1]
Compressor Oil Capacity	[2] 5.4 ozs.
Refrigerant (R-134a) Capacity	
Front Climate Control System Only	43 ozs.
Front & Rear Climate Control System	50 ozs.
System Operating Pressures	[3]

[1] – Belt tension is maintained by automatic belt tensioner.
[2] – Use Densooil 8 (Part No. A 001 989 08 03).
[3] – Information is not available from manufacturer.

WARNING: To avoid injury from accidental air bag deployment, read and carefully follow all SERVICE PRECAUTIONS and DISABLING & ACTIVATING AIR BAG SYSTEM procedures in AIR BAG SYSTEM SAFETY article in GENERAL SERVICING.

DESCRIPTION

Climate control system uses R-134a refrigerant. A rear passenger compartment climate control system and an activated charcoal filter is optional on some models.

OPERATION

A/C-HEATER CONTROL PANEL

Front A/C-heater control panel consists of 2 temperature selector wheels, mode selection push buttons, fan control push button and air volume control wheel. *See Fig. 1.* Rear A/C-heater control panel consists of 2 temperature selector wheels and blower speed control wheel. *See Fig. 2.*

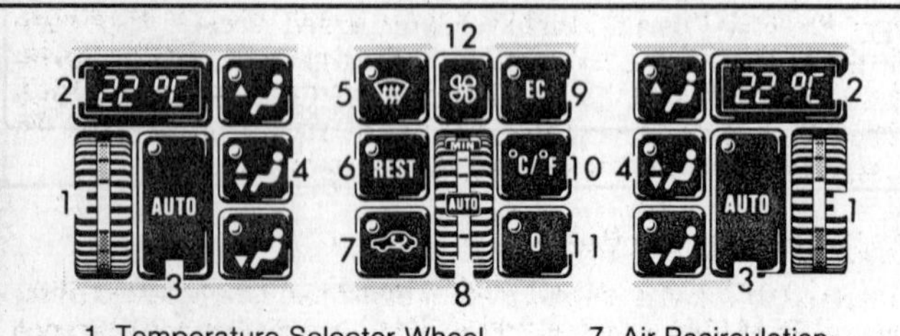
12
2
22 °C
5
9
EC
22 °C
2
4
6
REST
C/°F
10
4
1
AUTO
AUTO
AUTO
1
7
0
11
3
8
3

1. Temperature Selector Wheel
2. Temperature Display
3. Automatic Mode
4. Air Distribution Buttons
5. Defrost Switch
6. Residual Engine Heat Mode
7. Air Recirculation
8. Air Volume Wheel
9. Economy Switch
10. Selection Switch
11. Off Switch
12. Fan Switch

93I19735 Courtesy of Mercedes-Benz of North America.

Fig. 1: Identifying Front Climate Control System Control Panel

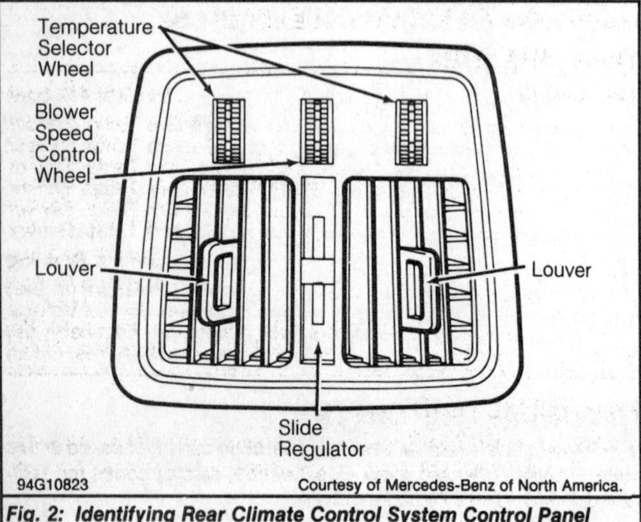
Temperature Selector Wheel
Blower Speed Control Wheel
Louver
Louver
Slide Regulator

94G10823 Courtesy of Mercedes-Benz of North America.

Fig. 2: Identifying Rear Climate Control System Control Panel

Air Volume Selector – Air volume is automatically regulated in AUTO position and all intermediate positions, except when selecting MIN (minimum airflow) or MAX (maximum airflow).

Automatic Mode – To select automatic mode, depress AUTO button. Air volume and distribution are controlled automatically. To change from the automatic position, depress off, defrost, bi-level, upper or lower mode buttons. Indicator light for automatic position should go off.

Defrost Mode – When defrost button is depressed, maximum heated air is automatically directed toward windshield and side windows. As engine coolant temperature increases, air volume automatically increases, providing quick defrost. To return to previous setting, press defrost button again.

Defog Mode – To defog windows, switch off economy, or switch on upper ventilation mode (left and right side), or switch on defrost. To quickly defrost windshield, select largest air volume and air distribution button (upper ventilation mode).

Economy Mode – This mode corresponds to automatic mode. A/C compressor does not engage in this mode.

Off Mode – Fresh air supply to vehicle is shut off in this mode. This setting should be used only temporarily, otherwise windshield may fog up.

Recirculation Mode – When recirculation button is depressed, outside air is not supplied to vehicle's interior. System will automatically switch from recirculated air to fresh air during the following conditions, if AUTO button is depressed.

- After approximately 5 minutes when outside temperature is less than 40°F (5°C).
- After approximately 20 minutes when outside temperature is greater than 40°F (5°C).

If EC button is depressed, system will switch from recirculated air to fresh air after approximately 5 minutes.

Residual Engine Heat Mode – To heat passenger compartment for a short time with engine off, depress REST button. Rear passenger compartment air outlet must be closed. Air volume and distribution are controlled automatically.

To select this mode, turn ignition switch to position "1", "0" or remove key. Press REST button. This mode will not activate if engine coolant is less than 122°F (50°C) or battery charge is insufficient.

To cancel this mode, press REST button. Turn ignition switch to position "2". System will automatically turn off after about 30 minutes, if engine coolant temperature is less than 122°F (50°C), or battery voltage drops.

Temperature Selector Wheels – Temperature selector wheels provide separate interior temperature control for driver and passenger. A basic setting in White field is recommended for year-round driving. Selected temperature is shown in display window in °F or °C.

TROUBLE SHOOTING

WARNING: To avoid injury from accidental air bag deployment, read and carefully follow all SERVICE PRECAUTIONS and DISABLING & ACTIVATING AIR BAG SYSTEM procedures in AIR BAG SYSTEM SAFETY article in GENERAL SERVICING.

FUNCTION TEST

1) Check fuses No. 20, 21 and 18. Check in-vehicle temperature sensor ventilation blower by placing a small piece of paper over blower vent grille with ignition on. Vent grille is located near dome light. *See Fig. 3.* If sufficient ventilation is present, paper will remain on vent grille. If not, check ventilation blower voltage supply.

2) Put shift lever in "P" and engage parking brake. Run engine until it reaches normal operating temperature. Manually open center and side air outlets. Ensure recirculation button is not depressed.

3) To check defrost, put temperature selector wheel at a random setting. Press defrost button. Put fan speed wheel in AUTO position. If defrost mode does not operate sufficiently, see VOLTAGE SUPPLY CIRCUIT CHECK, BLOWER SELECTOR CIRCUIT, WARM AIR SWITCH CIRCUIT and COOL AIR SWITCH CIRCUIT under TESTING.

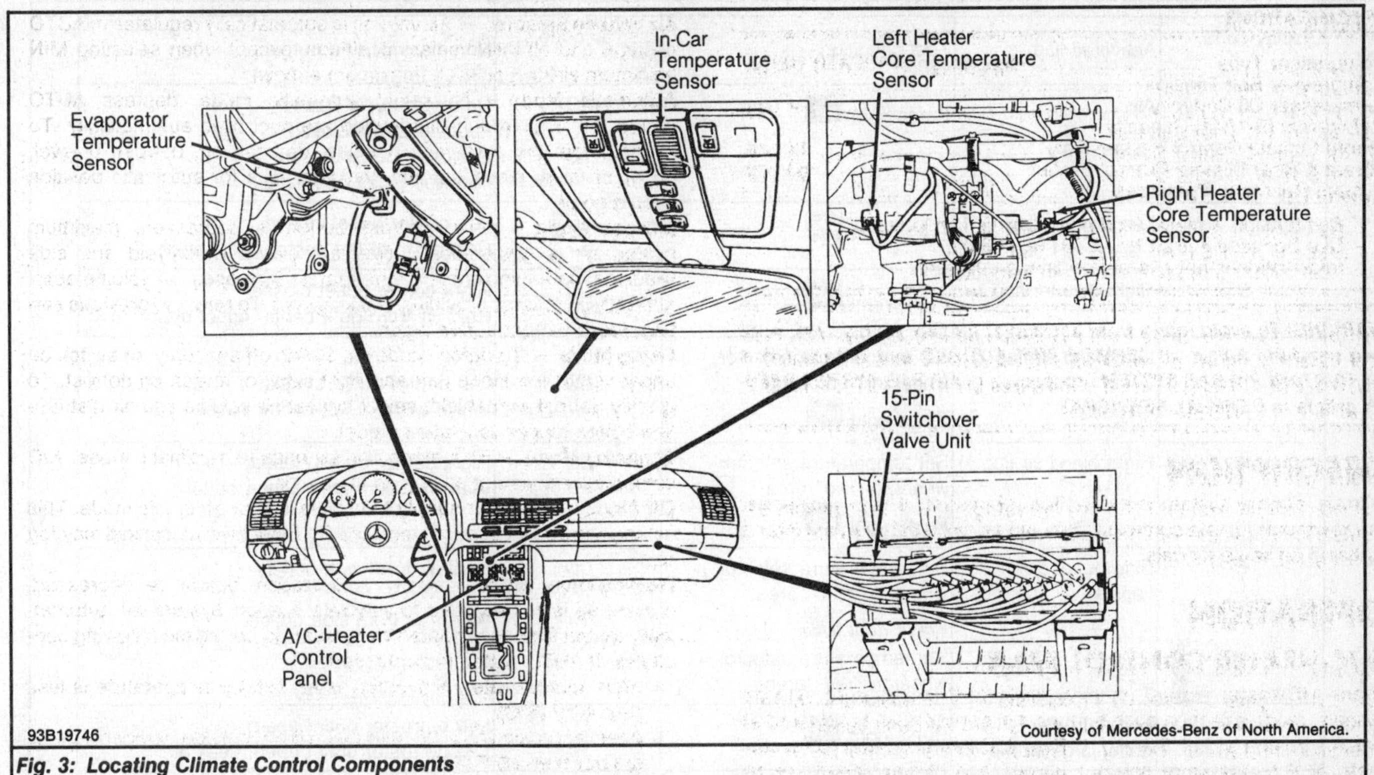

In-Car Temperature Sensor
Left Heater Core Temperature Sensor
Evaporator Temperature Sensor
Right Heater Core Temperature Sensor
15-Pin Switchover Valve Unit
A/C-Heater Control Panel
93B19746
Courtesy of Mercedes-Benz of North America.

Fig. 3: Locating Climate Control Components

4) To check total ventilation in cooling mode, put temperature selector wheel in Blue area. Press AUTO button. Put fan speed wheel in AUTO position. If this mode does not operate sufficiently, see BLOWER SELECTOR CIRCUIT and CODES E088-E091, A/C COMPRESSOR GROUND CIRCUIT under TESTING.

5) To check normal ventilation in regulating mode, put temperature selector wheel at present in-vehicle temperature. Press AUTO button. Put fan speed wheel in AUTO position. If this mode does not operate sufficiently, see BLOWER SELECTOR CIRCUIT; CODES E072-E075, HEATER CIRCULATION PUMP CIRCUIT; CODES E084-E087, RIGHT HEATER CONTROL VALVE CIRCUIT; CODES E080-E083, LEFT HEATER CONTROL VALVE CIRCUIT; and CODES E088-E091, A/C COMPRESSOR GROUND CIRCUIT under TESTING.

6) To check center air outlet warm air, put temperature selector wheel in Red area. Press Red switch on center outlet. Put fan speed wheel in AUTO position. If this mode does not operate sufficiently, see BLOWER SELECTOR CIRCUIT, WARM AIR SWITCH CIRCUIT and COOL AIR SWITCH CIRCUIT under TESTING.

7) To check center air outlet cold air, put temperature selector wheel in Red area. Press Blue switch on center outlet. Put fan speed wheel in AUTO position. Press AUTO button. If this mode does not operate sufficiently, see CODES E0108-E111, AFTER-RUN PUMP CONTROL RELAY CIRCUIT and CODES E116-E123, CHARCOAL FILTER SWITCH CIRCUIT under TESTING.

8) To check air recirculation mode, put temperature selector wheel in White area. Put fan speed wheel in AUTO position. Press recirculation button. If this mode does not operate sufficiently, see BLOWER SELECTOR CIRCUIT and CODES E108-E111, AFTER-RUN PUMP CONTROL RELAY CIRCUIT under TESTING.

9) To check economy in heating mode, put temperature selector wheel in Red area. Press EC button. Put fan speed wheel in AUTO position. If this mode does not operate sufficiently, see BLOWER SELECTOR CIRCUIT under TESTING.

10) To check minimum blower speed, put temperature selector wheel in 72°F position. Press EC button. Put fan speed wheel in MIN position. If this mode does not operate sufficiently, see CODES E048-E051, LEFT TEMPERATURE SELECTOR WHEEL CIRCUIT; CODES E052-E055, RIGHT TEMPERATURE SELECTOR WHEEL CIRCUIT; and BLOWER SELECTOR CIRCUIT under TESTING.

11) To check maximum blower speed, put temperature selector wheel in 72°F position. Press EC button. Put fan speed wheel in MAX position. If this mode does not operate sufficiently, see CODES E048-E051, LEFT TEMPERATURE SELECTOR WHEEL CIRCUIT; CODES E052-E055, RIGHT TEMPERATURE SELECTOR WHEEL CIRCUIT; and BLOWER SELECTOR CIRCUIT under TESTING.

SENSOR VALUE CHECK

1) Display areas in A/C-heater control panel can be utilized to show temperature sensor readings. This is useful in checking the tolerance range of temperature sensors and coolant pressure. Temperature control is maintained during test.

2) Set temperature selector wheel to White area. Press AUTO button. Turn ignition on. Press REST button for at least 5 seconds. Numeral "1" will appear in left display area. Right display area will show in-vehicle temperature, HI (if a short circuit is present), or LO (if an open circuit is present).

3) Press left AUTO button to access sensor codes and refrigerant pressure codes. See SENSOR VALUE CODES table.

SENSOR VALUE CODES

Code Number	System Affected
1	In-Vehicle Temp. Sensor
2	Outside Temp. Sensor
3	Left Heater Core Temp. Sensor
4	Right Heater Core Temp. Sensor
5	Evaporator Temp. Sensor
6	Coolant Temp. Sensor
	Sensor Reading
7	Coolant Pressure (In Bar)
8	Blower Control Voltage
9	Software Type (Bosch-60, Kammerer-06)
16	Charcoal Filter Switch (A-Yes, O-No)

INDIVIDUAL FLAP CHECK

1) Individual climate control vent flap operation can be checked in this mode. Display areas will show, in sequence, display codes for each activated flap as well as flap position.

1993 AUTOMATIC A/C-HEATER SYSTEMS 300SE, 300SD, 400SE & 500SEL (Cont.)

Display code, left	Activated flap	Test condition	Display code, right	Nominal value/Air output
0	All	Press right AUTO	LO HI	Defroster outlet open, Footwell outlet closed. Defroster outlet closed, Footwell outlet open.
1	Left diverter flap 1)	Press right AUTO	LO HI	Left center outlet closed, Cold air from left center outlet open.
2	Right diverter flap 1)	Press right AUTO	LO HI	Right center outlet closed, Cold air from right center outlet open.
3	Left blend air flap 1)	Set temperature selector wheel to "red" area, Press right AUTO	LO HI	Left center outlet closed, Warm air from left center outlet.
4	Right blend air flap 1)	Set temperature selector wheel to "red" area, Press right AUTO	LO HI	Right center outlet closed, Warm air from right center outlet.
5	Side outlet diverter flaps 1)	Set temperature selector wheel to "blue" area, Press right AUTO, Set temperature selector wheel to "red" area	LO HI	Cool air from side outlet, Warm air from side outlet.
6	Left defroster outlet,large stroke 2)	Press right AUTO	LO HI	Left defroster outlet open, Left defroster outlet open, Leak air.

1) The left and right defroster outlets will also be activated (large and small stroke).
2) The right defroster outlet will also be activated (large and small stroke).
3) The left defroster outlet will also be activated (large and small stroke).

93A19729

Courtesy of Mercedes-Benz of North America.

Fig. 4: Vent Flap Test (1 Of 2)

Display code, left	Activated flap	Test condition	Display code, right	Nominal value/Air output
7	Left defroster outlet (large and small stroke) 2)	Press right AUTO	LO HI	Left defroster outlet open, Left defroster outlet closed.
8	Right defroster outlet (large stroke) 3)	Press right AUTO	LO HI	Right defroster outlet open, Right defroster outlet open, Leak air.
9	Right defroster outlet (large and small stroke) 3)	Press right AUTO	LO HI	Right defroster outlet open, Right defroster outlet closed.
10	Main air flap (large stroke) 4)	Press right AUTO	LO HI	
11	Main air flap (large and small stroke) 4)	Press right AUTO	LO HI	
12	Left footwell flap (large stroke) 1)	Press right AUTO	LO HI	Left footwell outlet closed, Left footwell outlet open, Leak air.
13	Left footwell flap (large and small stroke) 1)	Press right AUTO	LO HI	Left footwell outlet closed, Left footwell outlet open.
14	Right footwell flap (large stroke) 1)	Press right AUTO	LO HI	Right footwell outlet closed, Leak air, Right footwell outlet open.
15	Right footwell flap (large and small stroke) 1)	Press right AUTO	LO HI	Right footwell outlet closed, Right footwell outlet open.

1) The left and right defroster outlets will also be activated (large and small stroke).
2) The right defroster outlet will also be activated (large and small stroke).
3) The left defroster outlet will also be activated (large and small stroke).
4) The left and right blend air flaps will also be activated.

93D19730

Courtesy of Mercedes-Benz of North America.

Fig. 5: Vent Flap Test (2 Of 2)

2) Set temperature wheel to White area. Manually open center and side air outlets. Start and run engine at idle. Press AUTO button. Ensure warm and cold buttons on center outlet are not depressed.
3) Simultaneously press "C" and "F" buttons, and press REST button for more than 5 seconds. Number "0" should appear in left display area. Either HI or LO should appear in right display area.
4) Press left AUTO button to individually display stored codes 0-15. *See Figs. 4 and 5.* Press right AUTO button to switch flaps (HI activated, LO not activated). When last flap position is indicated, first flap position will display. Press REST button to end individual flap check.

TESTING

A/C SYSTEM PERFORMANCE

NOTE: For A/C SYSTEM PERFORMANCE, refer to FUNCTION TEST under TROUBLE SHOOTING.

SELF-DIAGNOSTICS

Retrieving Fault Codes – 1) Automatic Climate Control (ACC) unit has fault code memory and capability to display fault codes on temperature display area of A/C-heater control panel. System can display codes relating to permanent or intermittent malfunctions. Stored fault codes remain in memory even with vehicle battery disconnected.
2) To access fault codes, turn left temperature wheel to Red area. Turn right temperature wheel to Blue area. Turn ignition on and press AUTO button on A/C-heater control panel. Within 20 seconds, simultaneously press REST and "0" buttons for at least 2 seconds.
3) Display will show fault codes stored in memory. See FRONT CLIMATE CONTROL FAULT CODES and REAR CLIMATE CONTROL SYSTEM FAULT CODES tables. Press AUTO until all stored fault codes are displayed.
4) Each malfunction has a specific code. The letter "E" and hundredth digit of display code will appear in left display. Tenth and single digit of code will display in right display area. Press right AUTO button to display each subsequent fault code (if necessary). Turn ignition off and repair recorded fault codes as directed

Erasing Fault Codes – To erase fault codes, press left AUTO button. Letter "d" will appear in left display area. By pressing right AUTO button, display code will be erased from memory. Continue to press left and right buttons until all codes are erased from memory. Display will show E0 00.

FRONT CLIMATE CONTROL FAULT CODES

Code Number	Possible Cause/System Affected
E001	[1] No Malfunction Stored In Memory
E002	[1] A/C-Heater Push-Button Control Unit
E003	[1] Rear Climate Control Unit
E006	[1] Switchover Valve Unit Connection
E007 & 08	[1] Data Exchange Short
E009	[1] Data Exchange Open
E010	[1] Repeat Display Of Malfunction Readout
E011 & 12	[1] Data Exchange Open
E013	[1] Rear Climate Control Unit Connection
E014	[1] Rear Climate Control Open
E015	[1] Rear Climate Control Open
E016	[2] In-Car Temp. Sensor Blower Short
E017	[3] In-Car Temp. Sensor Blower Short
E018	[2] In-Car Temp. Sensor Blower Open
E019	[3] In-Car Temp. Sensor Blower Open
E024	[2] Left Heater Core Temp. Sensor Short
E025	[3] Left Heater Core Temp. Sensor Short
E026	[2] Left Heater Core Temp. Sensor Open/Short
E027	[3] Left Heater Core Temp. Sensor Open/Short
E028	[2] Right Heater Core Temp. Sensor Short
E029	[2] Right Heater Core Temp. Sensor Short
E030	[2] Right Heater Core Temp. Sensor Open/Short

[1] – Diagnostics not supplied by manufacturer. Diagnose system or circuit affected.
[2] – A permanent failure is detected.
[3] – An intermittent failure is detected.

FRONT CLIMATE CONTROL FAULT CODES (Cont.)

Code Number	Possible Cause/System Affected
E031	[3] Right Heater Core Temp. Sensor Open/Short
E032	[2] Outside Temp. Sensor Short
E033	[3] Outside Temp. Sensor Short
E034	[2] Outside Temp. Sensor Open/Short
E035	[3] Outside Temp. Sensor Open/Short
E036	[2] Evaporator Temp. Sensor Short
E037	[3] Evaporator Temp. Sensor Short
E038	[2] Evaporator Temp. Sensor Open/Short
E039	[3] Evaporator Temp. Sensor Open/Short
E040	[2] Coolant Temp. Sensor Short
E041	[3] Coolant Temp. Sensor Short
E042	[2] Coolant Temp. Sensor Open/Short
E043	[3] Coolant Temp. Sensor Open/Short
E044	[2] Refrigerant Pressure Switch Short
E045	[3] Refrigerant Pressure Switch Short
E046	[2] Refrigerant Pressure Switch Open/Short
E047	[3] Refrigerant Pressure Switch Open/Short
E048	[2] Left Temp. Selector Wheel Short
E049	[3] Left Temp. Selector Wheel Short
E050	[2] Left Temp. Selector Wheel Open/Short
E051	[3] Left Temp. Selector Wheel Open/Short
E052	[2] Right Temp. Selector Wheel Short
E053	[3] Right Temp. Selector Wheel Short
E054	[2] Right Temp. Selector Wheel Open/Short
E055	[3] Right Temp. Selector Wheel Open/Short
E072	[2] Heater Circulation Pump Short
E073	[3] Heater Circulation Pump Short
E074	[2] Heater Circulation Pump Open/Short
E075	[3] Heater Circulation Pump Open/Short
E076	[1 2] Heater Circulation Pump Overload
E077	[1 3] Heater Circulation Pump Overload
E080	[2] Left Heater Valve Short
E081	[3] Left Heater Valve Short
E082	[2] Left Heater Valve Open/Short
E083	[3] Left Heater Valve Open/Short
E084	[2] Right Heater Valve Short
E085	[3] Right Heater Valve Short
E086	[2] Right Heater Valve Open/Short
E087	[3] Right Heater Valve Open/Short
E088	[2] A/C Compressor Ground
E089	[3] A/C Compressor Ground
E090	[2] A/C Compressor Ground Open/Short
E091	[3] A/C Compressor Ground Open/Short
E096	[2] Auxiliary Fan, 1st Stage Short
E097	[3] Auxiliary Fan, 1st Stage Short
E098	[2] Auxiliary Fan, 1st Stage Open/Short
E099	[3] Auxiliary Fan, 1st Stage Open/Short
E100	[2] Auxiliary Fan, 2nd Stage Short
E101	[3] Auxiliary Fan, 2nd Stage Short
E102	[2] Auxiliary Fan, 2nd Stage Open/Short
E103	[3] Auxiliary Fan, 2nd Stage Open/Short
E104	[2] Auxiliary Fan, 3rd Stage Short
E105	[3] Auxiliary Fan, 3rd Stage Short
E106	[2] Auxiliary Fan, 3rd Stage Open/Short
E107	[3] Auxiliary Fan, 3rd Stage Open/Short
E108	[2] After-Run Pump Relay Short
E109	[3] After-Run Pump Relay Short
E110	[2] After-Run Pump Relay Open/Short
E111	[3] After-Run Pump Relay Open/Short
E112	[2] Diode Matrix, RPM Increase Short
E113	[3] Diode Matrix, RPM Increase Short
E114	[2] Diode Matrix, RPM Increase Open/Short
E115	[3] Diode Matrix, RPM Increase Open/Short
E116	[2] Charcoal Filter Open, Short
E117	[3] Charcoal Filter Open, Short
E118	[2] Charcoal Filter Open, Open/Short
E119	[3] Charcoal Filter Open, Open/Short
E120	[2] Charcoal Filter Closed, Short
E121	[3] Charcoal Filter Closed, Short
E122	[2] Charcoal Filter Closed, Open/Short
E123	[3] Charcoal Filter Closed, Open/Short

[1] – Diagnostics not supplied by manufacturer. Diagnose system or circuit affected.
[2] – A permanent failure is detected.
[3] – An intermittent failure is detected.

REAR CLIMATE CONTROL SYSTEM FAULT CODES [1]

Code Number	Possible Cause/System Affected
E128	[2] Left Heater Core Temperature Sensor
E129	[3] Left Heater Core Temperature Sensor Short
E130	[2] Left Heater Core Temperature Sensor Open/Short
E131	[3] Left Heater Core Temperature Sensor Open/Short
E132	[2] Right Heater Core Temperature Sensor Short
E133	[3] Right Heater Core Temperature Sensor Short
E134	[2] Right Heater Core Temperature Sensor Open/Short
E135	[3] Right Heater Core Temperature Sensor Open/Short
E136	[2] Left Temperature Selector Wheel Short
E137	[3] Left Temperature Selector Wheel Short
E138	[3] Left Temperature Selector Wheel Open/Short
E139	[3] Left Temperature Selector Wheel Open/Short
E140	[2] Right Temperature Selector Wheel Short
E141	[3] Right Temperature Selector Wheel Short
E142	[2] Right Temperature Selector Wheel Open/Short
E143	[3] Right Temperature Selector Wheel Open/Short
E144	[2] Drier Temperature Sensor Short
E145	[3] Drier Temperature Sensor Short
E146	[2] Drier Temperature Sensor Open/Short
E147	[3] Drier Temperature Sensor Open/Short
E148	[2] Heater Circulation Pump Short
E149	[3] Heater Circulation Pump Short
E150	[2] Heater Circulation Pump Open/Short
E151	[3] Heater Circulation Pump Open/Short
E152	[2] Heater Circulation Pump Overloaded
E153	[3] Heater Circulation Pump Overloaded
E156	[2] Heater Left Valve Short
E157	[3] Heater Left Valve Short
E158	[2] Heater Left Valve Open/Short
E159	[3] Heater Left Valve Open/Short
E160	[2] Heater Right Valve Short
E161	[3] Heater Right Valve Short
E162	[2] Heater Right Valve Open/Short
E163	[3] Heater Right Valve Open/Short
E164	[2] Refrigerant Shut-Off Valve Short
E165	[3] Refrigerant Shut-Off Valve Short
E166	[2] Refrigerant Shut-Off Valve Open/Short
E167	[3] Refrigerant Shut-Off Valve Open/Short
E168	[2] Tunnel Flap Vacuum Valve Short
E169	[3] Tunnel Flap Vacuum Valve Short
E170	[2] Tunnel Flap Vacuum Valve Open/Short
E171	[3] Tunnel Flap Vacuum Valve Open/Short

[1] – Testing procedures not provided by manufacturer.
[2] – A permanent failure is detected.
[3] – An intermittent failure is detected.

NOTE: Manufacturer recommends use of Socket Box (124 589 00 21 00) to test climate control circuits. Connect socket box to A/C-heater control panel connectors No. 1 or 2 as directed in individual test. See Fig. 6.

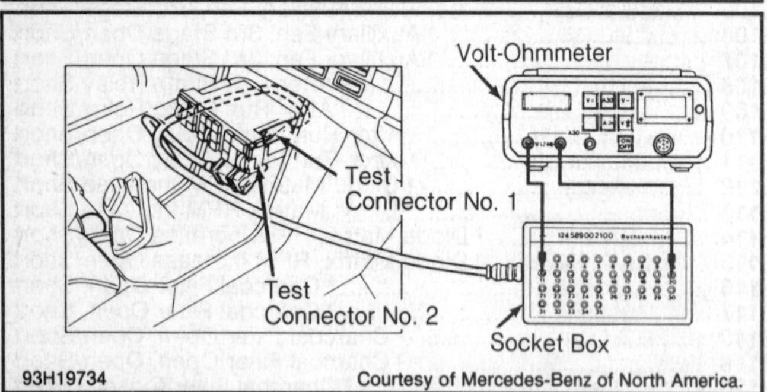
Volt-Ohmmeter
Test Connector No. 1
Test Connector No. 2
Socket Box
93H19734
Courtesy of Mercedes-Benz of North America.

Fig. 6: Connecting Socket Box (124 589 00 21 00) To A/C-Heater Control Panel

VOLTAGE SUPPLY CIRCUIT CHECK

1) Connect socket box to A/C-heater control panel connector No. 2. Connect voltmeter negative lead to socket box terminal No. 1 and voltmeter positive lead to socket box terminal No. 11. About 11-14 volts should be present. If voltage is not as specified, check wiring.

2) Connect voltmeter negative lead to ground and voltmeter positive lead to socket box terminal No. 11. About 11-14 volts should be present. If voltage is not as specified check wiring.

3) Connect voltmeter negative lead to socket box terminal No. 1 and voltmeter positive lead to socket box terminal No. 2. Turn ignition on. About 11-14 volts should be present. If voltage is not as specified, check wiring.

4) Connect voltmeter negative lead to socket box terminal No. 1 and voltmeter positive lead to socket box terminal No. 20. Turn ignition on. About 11-14 volts should be present. If voltage is not as specified, check wiring.

CODES E016-E019, IN-CAR TEMPERATURE SENSOR CIRCUIT

1) Connect socket box to A/C-heater control panel connector No. 2. Connect voltmeter negative lead to socket box terminal No. 10 and voltmeter positive lead to terminal No. 8. Turn ignition on and measure in-car temperature sensor circuit voltage. See IN-CAR TEMPERATURE & OUTSIDE TEMPERATURE SENSOR CIRCUIT SPECIFICATIONS table.

2) If voltage readings are incorrect, check in-car temperature sensor circuit and A/C-heater control panel. If okay, go to next step.

IN-CAR TEMPERATURE & OUTSIDE TEMPERATURE SENSOR CIRCUIT SPECIFICATIONS

Temperature °F (°C)	Specifications
With Ignition On	
50 (10)	3.2-3.5 Volts
68 (20)	2.6-2.9 Volts
86 (30)	2.0-2.4 Volts
113 (45)	1.3-1.7 Volts
With Ignition Off	
50 (10)	5200-5800 Ohms
68 (20)	3200-3600 Ohms
86 (30)	2050-2300 Ohms
113 (45)	1100-1250 Ohms

3) Connect ohmmeter negative lead to socket box terminal No. 10 and ohmmeter positive lead to terminal No. 8. Disconnect A/C-heater control panel connector.

4) Turn ignition off and measure in-car temperature sensor circuit resistance. See IN-CAR TEMPERATURE & OUTSIDE TEMPERATURE SENSOR CIRCUIT SPECIFICATIONS table. If resistance is not as specified, repair in-car temperature sensor circuit. If circuit is okay, replace in-car temperature sensor.

CODES E032-E035, OUTSIDE TEMPERATURE SENSOR CIRCUIT

1) Connect socket box to A/C-heater control panel connector No. 2. Connect voltmeter negative lead to socket box terminal No. 10 and voltmeter positive lead to terminal No. 26. Turn ignition on and measure outside temperature sensor circuit voltage. See IN-CAR TEMPERATURE & OUTSIDE TEMPERATURE SENSOR CIRCUIT SPECIFICATIONS table.

2) If voltage readings are incorrect, check outside temperature sensor circuit and A/C-heater control panel. Outside temperature sensor is located in engine compartment, on center of firewall. If okay, go to next step.

3) Connect ohmmeter negative lead to socket box terminal No. 10 and positive lead to terminal No. 26. Disconnect A/C-heater control panel connector.

4) Turn ignition off and measure outside temperature sensor circuit resistance. See IN-CAR TEMPERATURE & OUTSIDE TEMPERATURE SENSOR CIRCUIT SPECIFICATIONS table. If resistance is not as specified, repair outside temperature sensor circuit. If circuit is okay, replace outside temperature sensor.

CODES E036-E039, EVAPORATOR TEMPERATURE SENSOR CIRCUIT

1) Connect socket box to A/C-heater control panel connector No. 2. Connect voltmeter negative lead to socket box terminal No. 10 and positive lead to terminal No. 25. Turn ignition on and measure evaporator temperature sensor circuit voltage. See EVAPORATOR TEMPERATURE SENSOR CIRCUIT SPECIFICATIONS table.

2) If voltage readings are incorrect, check outside temperature sensor circuit and A/C-heater control panel. Outside temperature sensor is located in engine compartment, on center of firewall.

EVAPORATOR TEMPERATURE SENSOR CIRCUIT SPECIFICATIONS

Temperature °F (°C)	Specifications
With Ignition On	
32 (0)	2.2-2.6 Volts
50 (10)	1.6-2.0 Volts
68 (20)	1.2-1.5 Volts
86 (30)	0.8-1.1 Volts
113 (45)	0.5-0.7 Volts
With Ignition Off	
32 (0)	7300-10,000 Ohms
50 (10)	4200-6000 Ohms
68 (20)	2800-3900 Ohms
86 (30)	1700-2600 Ohms
113 (45)	1000-1500 Ohms

3) Connect ohmmeter negative lead to socket box terminal No. 10 and ohmmeter positive lead to terminal No. 25. Disconnect A/C-heater control panel connector.

4) Turn ignition off and measure outside temperature sensor circuit resistance. See EVAPORATOR TEMPERATURE SENSOR CIRCUIT SPECIFICATIONS table. If resistance is not as specified, repair evaporator temperature sensor circuit. If circuit is okay, replace evaporator temperature sensor.

CODES E024-E027, LEFT HEATER CORE TEMPERATURE SENSOR CIRCUIT

1) Connect socket box to A/C-heater control panel connector No. 2. Connect voltmeter negative lead to socket box terminal No. 10 and positive lead to terminal No. 16. Turn ignition on and measure left heater core temperature sensor circuit voltage. See LEFT & RIGHT HEATER CORE TEMPERATURE SENSOR CIRCUIT SPECIFICATIONS table.

2) If voltage readings are incorrect, check left heater core temperature sensor circuit and A/C-heater control panel. *See Fig. 3.*

LEFT & RIGHT HEATER CORE TEMPERATURE SENSOR CIRCUIT SPECIFICATIONS

Temperature °F (°C)	Specifications
With Ignition On	
50 (10)	3.1-3.5 Volts
68 (20)	2.6-2.9 Volts
86 (30)	2.0-2.4 Volts
113 (45)	1.3-1.7 Volts
With Ignition Off	
50 (10)	19,000-21,200 Ohms
68 (20)	11,900-13,200 Ohms
86 (30)	7700-8400 Ohms
113 (45)	4200-4600 Ohms

3) Connect ohmmeter negative lead to socket box terminal No. 10 and ohmmeter positive lead to terminal No. 16. Disconnect A/C-heater control panel connector.

4) Turn ignition off and measure left heater core temperature sensor circuit resistance. See LEFT & RIGHT HEATER CORE TEMPERATURE SENSOR CIRCUIT SPECIFICATIONS table. If resistance is not as specified, repair left heater core temperature sensor circuit. If circuit is okay, replace left heater core temperature sensor.

CODES E028-E031, RIGHT HEATER CORE TEMPERATURE SENSOR CIRCUIT

1) Connect socket box to A/C-heater control panel connector No. 2. Connect voltmeter negative lead to socket box terminal No. 10 and positive lead to terminal No. 7. Turn ignition on and measure right heater core temperature sensor circuit voltage. See LEFT & RIGHT HEATER CORE TEMPERATURE SENSOR CIRCUIT SPECIFICATIONS table.

2) If voltage readings are incorrect, check heater core temperature sensor circuit and A/C-heater control panel. *See Fig. 3.* Connect ohmmeter negative lead to socket box terminal No. 10 and ohmmeter positive lead to terminal No. 7. Disconnect A/C-heater control panel connector.

3) Turn ignition off and measure right heater core temperature sensor circuit resistance. See LEFT & RIGHT HEATER CORE TEMPERATURE SENSOR CIRCUIT SPECIFICATIONS table. If resistance is not as specified, repair right heater core temperature sensor circuit. If circuit is okay, replace right heater core temperature sensor.

CODES E040-E043, COOLANT TEMPERATURE SENSOR CIRCUIT

1) Connect socket box to A/C-heater control panel connector No. 2. Connect voltmeter negative lead to socket box terminal No. 10 and positive lead to terminal No. 6. Turn ignition on and measure coolant temperature sensor circuit voltage. See COOLANT TEMPERATURE SENSOR CIRCUIT SPECIFICATIONS table.

2) If voltage readings are incorrect, check coolant temperature sensor circuit and A/C-heater control panel. *See Figs. 7-9.*

COOLANT TEMPERATURE SENSOR CIRCUIT SPECIFICATIONS

Temperature °F (°C)	Specifications
With Ignition On	
68 (20)	3.1-3.5 Volts
140 (60)	2.6-2.9 Volts
185 (85)	2.0-2.4 Volts
212 (100)	1.3-1.7 Volts
248 (120)	1.3-1.7 Volts
With Ignition Off	
68 (20)	19,000-21,200 Ohms
140 (60)	11,900-13,200 Ohms
185 (85)	7700-8400 Ohms
212 (100)	4200-4600 Ohms
248 (120)	4200-4600 Ohms

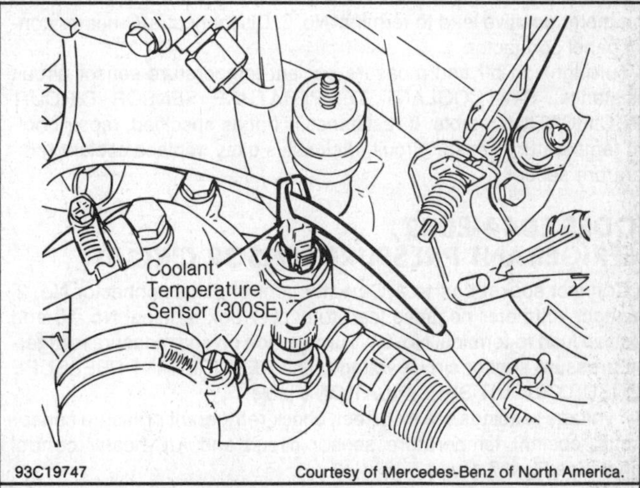
Coolant
Temperature
Sensor (300SE)
93C19747
Courtesy of Mercedes-Benz of North America.

Fig. 7: Locating Coolant Temperature Sensor (300SE)

1993 AUTOMATIC A/C-HEATER SYSTEMS 300SE, 300SD, 400SE & 500SEL (Cont.)

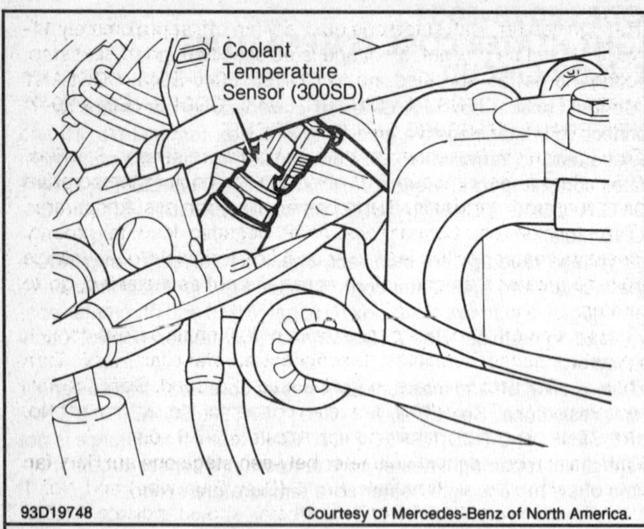
Coolant
Temperature
Sensor (300SD)
93D19748
Courtesy of Mercedes-Benz of North America.

Fig. 8: Locating Coolant Temperature Sensor (300SD)

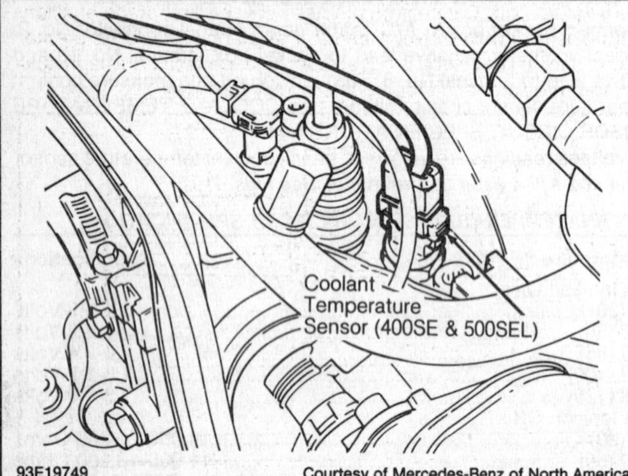
Coolant
Temperature
Sensor (400SE & 500SEL)
93E19749
Courtesy of Mercedes-Benz of North America.

Fig. 9: Locating Coolant Temperature Sensor (400SE & 500SEL)

3) Connect ohmmeter negative lead to socket box terminal No. 10 and ohmmeter positive lead to terminal No. 6. Disconnect A/C-heater control panel connector.

4) Turn ignition off and measure coolant temperature sensor circuit resistance. See COOLANT TEMPERATURE SENSOR CIRCUIT SPECIFICATIONS table. If resistance is not as specified, repair coolant temperature sensor circuit. If circuit is okay, replace coolant temperature sensor.

CODES E044-E047, REFRIGERANT PRESSURE SENSOR CIRCUIT

1) Connect socket box to A/C-heater control panel connector No. 2. Connect voltmeter negative lead to socket box terminal No. 10 and positive lead to terminal No. 24. Turn ignition on and measure refrigerant pressure sensor circuit voltage. See REFRIGERANT PRESSURE SENSOR CIRCUIT SPECIFICATIONS table.

2) If voltage readings are incorrect, check refrigerant pressure sensor circuit, coolant temperature sensor circuit and A/C-heater control panel. *See Figs. 7-10.*

REFRIGERANT PRESSURE SENSOR CIRCUIT SPECIFICATIONS

PSI (kg/cm^2)	Volts
With Ignition On	
29 (2.1)	0.5-.75
145 (10.6)	1.4-1.8
261 (19.1)	2.4-2.8
406 (29.7)	3.5-4.0

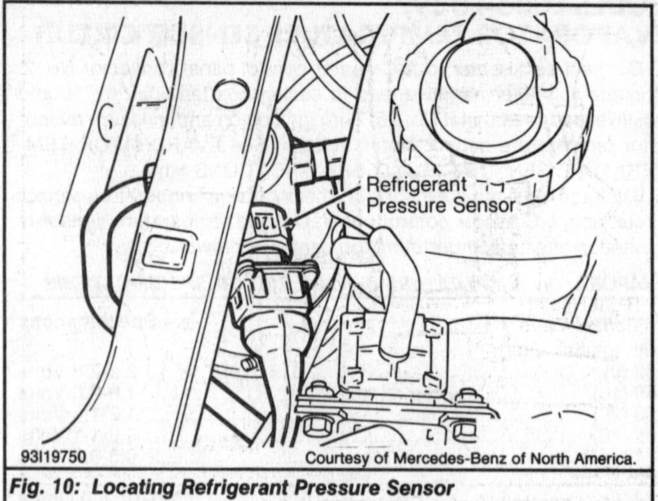
Refrigerant
Pressure Sensor
93I19750
Courtesy of Mercedes-Benz of North America.

Fig. 10: Locating Refrigerant Pressure Sensor

3) Connect voltmeter negative lead to socket box terminal No. 10 and positive lead to terminal No. 19. Turn ignition on and measure refrigerant pressure sensor voltage supply. Voltage should be 4.75-5.25 volts. If not, check wiring, refrigerant pressure sensor and A/C-heater control panel.

CODES E048-E051, LEFT TEMPERATURE SELECTOR WHEEL CIRCUIT

1) Connect socket box to A/C-heater control panel connector No. 2. Connect voltmeter negative lead to socket box terminal No. 1 and positive lead to terminal No. 3. Turn ignition on and put temperature selector wheel in Blue area. Voltage should be less than one volt.

2) Put temperature selector wheel in Red area. Voltage should be greater than 3.5 volts. If voltages are not as indicated, replace A/C-heater control panel. See BLOWER SELECTOR CIRCUIT test.

CODES E052-E055, RIGHT TEMPERATURE SELECTOR WHEEL CIRCUIT

1) Connect socket box to A/C-heater control panel connector No. 2. Connect voltmeter negative lead to socket box terminal No. 1 and positive lead to terminal No. 12. Turn ignition on and put temperature selector wheel in Blue area. Voltage should be less than one volt.

2) Put temperature selector wheel in Red area. Voltage should be greater than 3.5 volts. If voltages are not as indicated, replace A/C-heater control panel. See BLOWER SELECTOR CIRCUIT test.

BLOWER SELECTOR CIRCUIT

Connect socket box to A/C-heater control panel terminal No. 2. Turn ignition on. Connect a voltmeter between socket box terminals No. 1 and 21. Set blower speed on MIN. Voltage should be less than one volt. Set blower speed to MAX. Voltage should be more than 4 volts. If voltages are not as indicated, replace A/C-heater control panel.

CODES E072-E075, HEATER CIRCULATION PUMP CIRCUIT

1) Connect socket box to A/C-heater control panel connector No. 1. Connect voltmeter negative lead to ground. Connect positive lead to socket box terminal No. 12. Turn ignition on and put temperature selector wheel in Red area. Voltage should be 11-14 volts.

2) Put temperature selector wheel in Blue area. Voltage should be less than one volt. If voltages are not as indicated, check wiring and A/C-heater control panel.

3) Turn ignition off. Disconnect heater circulation pump connector. *See Fig. 11.* Connect ohmmeter negative lead to socket box terminal No. 1. Connect positive lead to terminal No. 2. Resistance should be about 2-4 ohms. If resistance is not as specified, replace heater circulation pump.

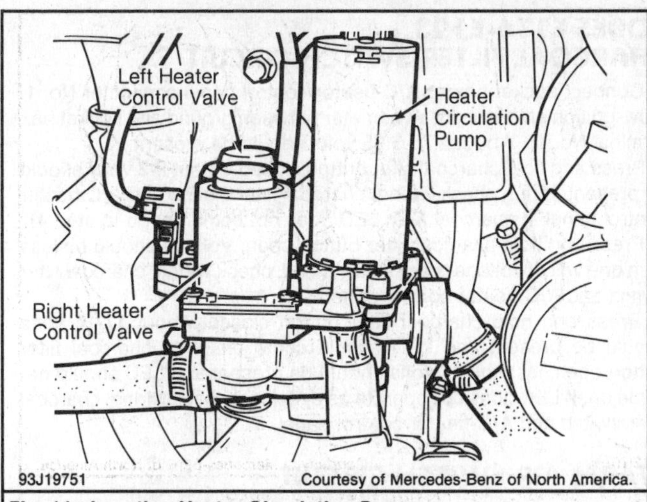
Left Heater
Control Valve
Heater
Circulation
Pump
Right Heater
Control Valve
93J19751
Courtesy of Mercedes-Benz of North America.

Fig. 11: Locating Heater Circulation Pump

CODES E080-E083, LEFT HEATER CONTROL VALVE CIRCUIT

1) Connect socket box to A/C-heater control panel connector No. 1. Connect voltmeter negative lead to ground. Connect positive lead to socket box terminal No. 21. Turn ignition on and press AUTO button. Put both temperature selector wheels in Blue area. Voltage should be less than one volt.

2) Put temperature selector wheels in Red area. Voltage should be 11-14 volts. If voltages are not as indicated, check wiring, A/C-heater control panel, and left and right heater control valves. *See Fig. 11.*

CODES E084-E087, RIGHT HEATER CONTROL VALVE CIRCUIT

1) Connect socket box to A/C-heater control panel connector No. 1. Connect voltmeter negative lead to ground. Connect positive lead to socket box terminal No. 3. Turn ignition on. Put both temperature selector wheels in Blue area. Voltage should be less than one volt.

2) Put temperature selector wheels in Red area. Voltage should be 11-14 volts. If voltages are not as indicated, check wiring, A/C-heater control panel, and left and right heater control valves. *See Fig. 11.*

3) Turn ignition off. Disconnect A/C-heater control panel connector. Connect ohmmeter negative lead to terminal No. 3. Connect positive lead to terminal No. 21. Resistance should be 20-35 ohms. If resistance is not as specified, check heater control valves. *See Fig. 11.*

CODES E088-E091, A/C COMPRESSOR GROUND CIRCUIT

1) Connect socket box to A/C-heater control panel connector No. 1. Connect voltmeter negative lead to ground. Connect positive lead to socket box terminal No. 17. Turn ignition on. With A/C compressor off, less than one volt should be present. With A/C compressor on, 11-14 volts should be present. If voltages are not as indicated, check wiring, fuses and A/C-heater control panel.

2) Connect voltmeter negative lead to ground. Connect positive lead to socket box terminal No. 23. Start and run engine at idle. Set parking brake and put transmission selector in "P". Press AUTO button.

3) With compressor off, voltage should be less than one volt. With compressor on, voltage should be 11-14 volts. If voltages are not as indicated, check wiring, fuses, left front wheel speed sensor, A/C compressor and A/C-heater control panel.

CODES E096-E099, STAGE ONE AUXILIARY FAN CIRCUIT

1) Connect socket box to A/C-heater control panel connector No. 1. Connect voltmeter negative lead to ground. Connect positive lead to socket box terminal No. 5.

2) Turn ignition on. With stage one auxiliary fan off, approximately 11-14 volts should be present. If voltage is as specified, go to next step. If voltage is not as specified, go to CODES E040-E043, COOLANT TEMPERATURE SENSOR CIRCUIT and CODES E044-E047, REFRIGERANT PRESSURE SENSOR CIRCUIT.

3) Turn ignition off. Disconnect coolant temperature sensor. *See Figs. 7-9.* Simulate a resistance of 310 ohms across coolant temperature sensor connector terminals. Stage one auxiliary fan should operate.

4) Turn ignition on. Connect voltmeter negative lead to ground. Connect voltmeter positive lead to socket box terminal No. 5. Voltage should be greater than one volt. If voltage is not as indicated, go to next step.

5) Turn ignition off. Simulate a resistance of 310 ohms across coolant temperature sensor terminals. Disconnect auxiliary fan relay. Turn ignition on. Connect voltmeter negative lead to ground. Connect voltmeter positive lead to auxiliary fan relay connector No. 2, terminal No. 5 (Gray/Blue wire). Voltmeter should indicate 6.5-7.5 volts.

6) With ignition on, connect voltmeter between stage one auxiliary fan relay connector No. 2, terminals No. 5 (Gray/Blue wire) and No. 1 (Brown/Green wire). *See Fig. 12.* Voltmeter should indicate 6.5-7.5 volts. If voltage is not as specified, check wiring, auxiliary fan, and auxiliary fan preresistor. *See Fig. 13.*

7) Turn ignition off. Connect ohmmeter between first stage auxiliary fan preresistor terminals No. 1 and 2. Resistance should be greater than one ohm. If resistance is not as specified, replace first stage auxiliary fan preresistor and stage one auxiliary fan relay.

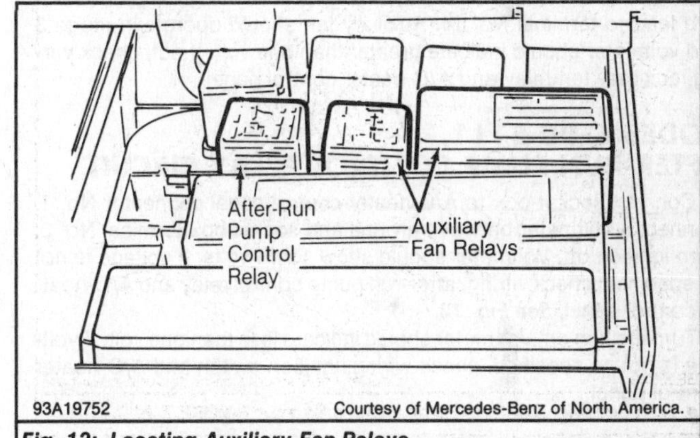
After-Run
Pump
Control
Relay
Auxiliary
Fan Relays
93A19752
Courtesy of Mercedes-Benz of North America.

Fig. 12: Locating Auxiliary Fan Relays

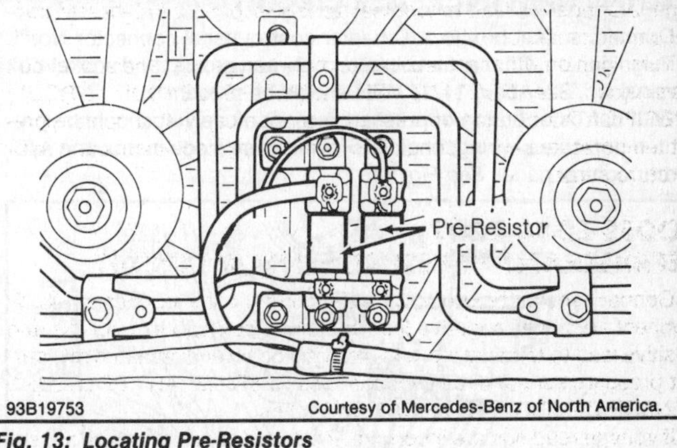
Pre-Resistor
93B19753
Courtesy of Mercedes-Benz of North America.

Fig. 13: Locating Pre-Resistors

CODES E100-E103, STAGE 2 AUXILIARY FAN CIRCUIT

1) Connect socket box to A/C-heater control panel connector No. 1. Connect voltmeter negative lead to ground. Connect positive lead to socket box terminal No. 14. Turn ignition on. With stage 2 auxiliary fan off, approximately 11-14 volts should be present. If voltage is as indicated, go to next step. If voltage is not as indicated, go to step **3)**.

1993 AUTOMATIC A/C-HEATER SYSTEMS 300SE, 300SD, 400SE & 500SEL (Cont.)

2) Turn ignition off. Disconnect coolant temperature sensor. Simulate a resistance of 250 ohms across coolant temperature sensor connector terminals. Turn ignition on. Connect voltmeter negative lead to ground and positive lead to terminal No. 14. Auxiliary fan should operate and greater than one volt should be present. If not, go to next step.
3) Turn ignition off. Disconnect auxiliary fan relay. *See Fig. 12.* Connector a voltmeter between ground and auxiliary fan relay terminal No. 1 (Black/White wire). Turn ignition on. Approximately 11-14 volts should be present. If not, check wiring and auxiliary fan relay.
4) If wiring and auxiliary fan relay are okay, turn ignition off. Disconnect auxiliary fan relay connector No. 2. Connect an ohmmeter between terminals No. 1 (Black/White wire) and No. 5 (Gray/Blue wire). Resistance should be greater than one ohm. If resistance is not as specified, check wiring and stage 2 auxiliary fan pre-resistor. *See Fig. 13.*

CODES E104-E107, STAGE 3 AUXILIARY FAN CIRCUIT

1) Connect socket box to A/C-heater control panel connector No. 1. Connect voltmeter negative lead to ground. Connect positive lead to socket box terminal No. 4. Turn ignition on. With stage 3 auxiliary fan off, approximately 11-14 volts should be present. If voltage is not as indicated, check auxiliary fan relay. *See Fig. 12.*
2) Disconnect coolant temperature sensor. Simulate a resistance of 200 ohms between coolant temperature sensor connector terminals. Turn ignition on. Connect voltmeter negative lead to ground and positive lead to terminal No. 14. Auxiliary fan should operate in stage 3 and voltmeter should indicate greater than one volt. If not, check wiring, auxiliary fan relay and A/C-heater control panel.

CODES E108-E111, AFTER-RUN PUMP CONTROL RELAY CIRCUIT

1) Connect socket box to A/C-heater control panel connector No. 1. Connect a voltmeter between ground and socket box terminal No. 2. Turn ignition off. Voltmeter should show 11-14 volts. If voltage is not as specified, check wiring, after-run pump control relay and A/C-heater control panel. *See Fig. 12.*
2) Turn ignition on. Voltmeter should indicate less than one volt. If voltage is not as specified, check wiring, ignition switch and A/C-heater control panel.

CODES E112-E115, ENGINE RPM INCREASE CIRCUIT

1) Connect socket box to A/C-heater control panel connector No. 1. Turn ignition on. Connect a voltmeter between ground and socket box terminal No. 22. About 11-14 volts should be present.
2) With defroster button depressed, less than one volt should be present. If not, check wiring, engine RPM increase diode matrix and A/C-heater control panel. *See Fig. 14.*

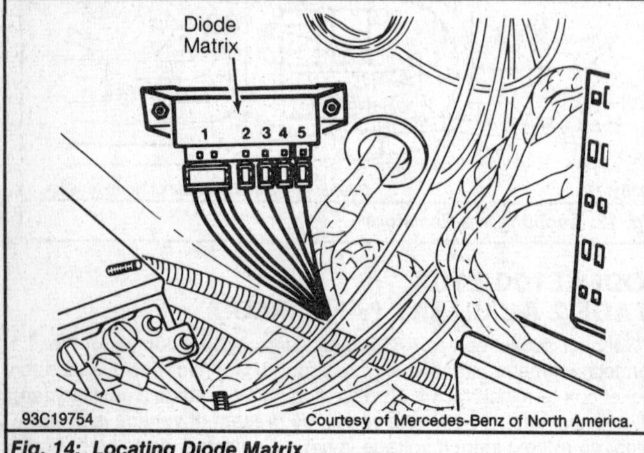
Diode
Matrix
1
2 3 4 5
93C19754
Courtesy of Mercedes-Benz of North America.

Fig. 14: Locating Diode Matrix

CODES E116-E123, CHARCOAL FILTER SWITCH CIRCUIT

1) Connect socket box to A/C-heater control panel connector No. 1. Turn ignition on. Connect a voltmeter between ground and socket box terminal No. 16. About 4.75-5.25 volts should be present.
2) Press and hold charcoal filter button closed. About 2-3 volts should be present. If not, check wiring, charcoal filter switch and A/C-heater control panel. If charcoal filter LED does not come on, go to step **4)**.
3) Press and hold charcoal filter button open. Voltage should be less than one volt. If voltage is not as specified, check wiring, charcoal filter switch and A/C-heater control panel.
4) Press and hold charcoal filter button closed. About 11-14 volts should be present and LED should come on. With charcoal filter button open, less than 2 volts should be present and LED should not come on. If LED does not operate as specified, check wiring, charcoal filter switch and A/C-heater control panel.

WARM AIR SWITCH CIRCUIT

1) Connect socket box to A/C-heater control panel connector No. 1. Turn ignition on. Connect voltmeter negative lead to ground and positive lead to socket box terminal No. 6. About 4.75-5.25 volts should be present. If voltage is not as specified, check wiring, warm/cool air switch and A/C-heater control panel.
2) Set blower wheel to AUTO. Press and hold Red warm air button on. About 2-3 volts should be present and Red LED should come on. If voltage is not as specified, go to next step.
3) Connect voltmeter negative lead to ground and positive lead to socket box terminal No. 1. Turn warm air button off. About 11-14 volts should be present and LED should not come on.
4) Turn warm air button on. Less than 2 volts should be present and Red LED should come on. If voltage is not as specified, check wiring, warm/cool air switch and A/C-heater control panel.

COOL AIR SWITCH CIRCUIT

1) Connect socket box to A/C-heater control panel connector No. 1. Turn ignition on. Connect voltmeter negative lead to ground and positive lead to socket box terminal No. 6. About 4.75-5.25 volts should be present. If voltage is not as specified, check wiring, warm/cool air switch and A/C-heater control panel.
2) Set blower wheel to AUTO. Press and hold Blue cool air button on. Less than one volt should be present and Blue LED should come on. If voltage is not as specified, go to next step.
3) Connect voltmeter negative lead to ground and positive lead to socket box terminal No. 19. Turn cool air button off. About 11-14 volts should be present and LED should not come on.
4) Turn cool air button on. Less than 2 volts should be present and Blue LED should come on. If voltage is not as specified, check wiring, warm/cool air switch and A/C-heater control panel.

REMOVAL & INSTALLATION

NOTE: Removal and installation information is not available from manufacturer.

VACUUM DIAGRAMS

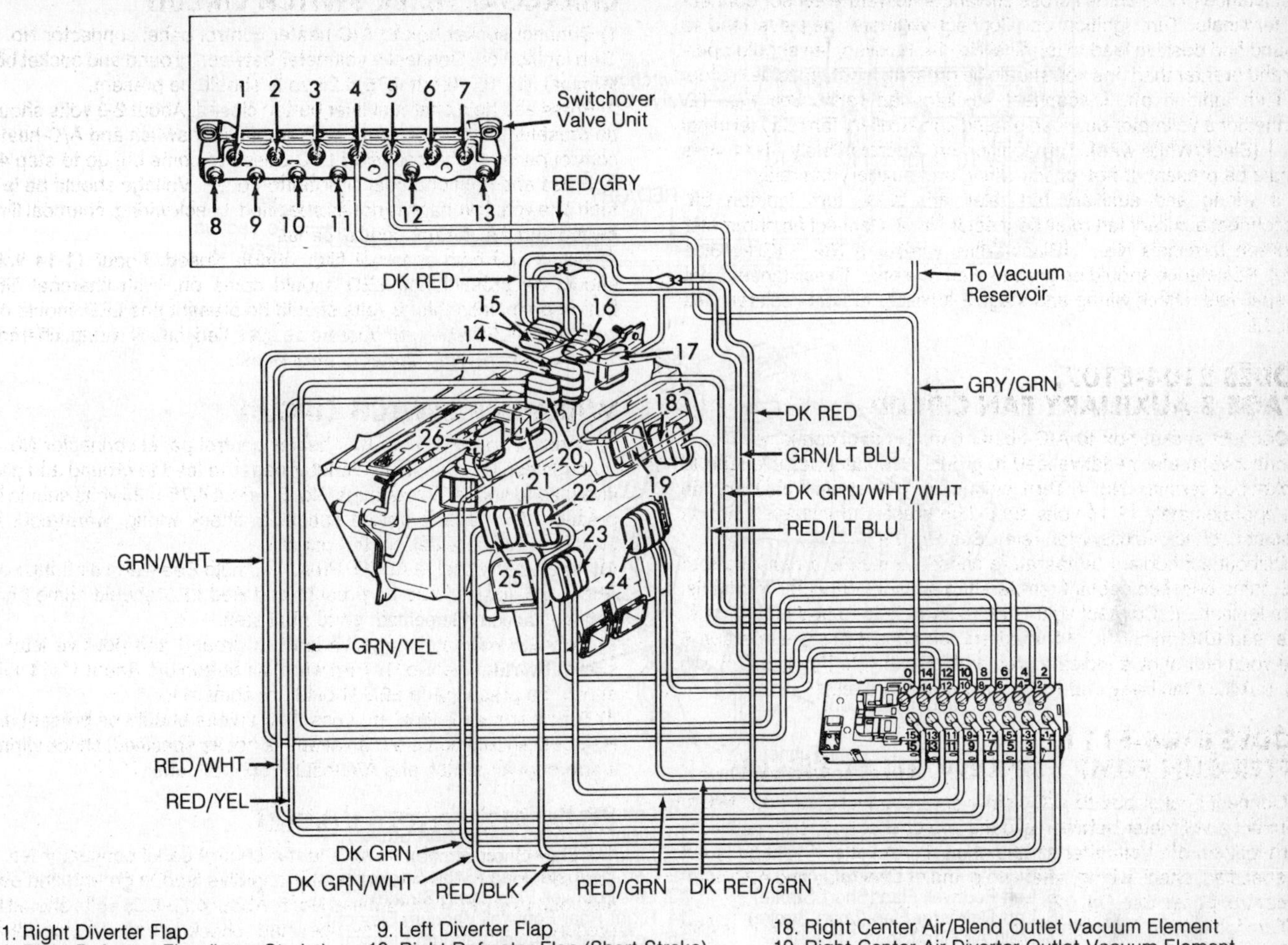
Switchover Valve Unit
1 2 3 4 5 6 7
8 9 10 11 12 13
RED/GRY
DK RED
To Vacuum Reservoir
15 16 14 17
GRY/GRN
18
DK RED
26
20
GRN/LT BLU
21
22 19
DK GRN/WHT/WHT
RED/LT BLU
23
GRN/WHT
25 24
GRN/YEL
RED/WHT
RED/YEL
DK GRN
DK GRN/WHT
RED/BLK
RED/GRN
DK RED/GRN

1. Right Diverter Flap
2. Right Defroster Flap (Long Stroke)
3. Right Blend Air Flap
4. Side Air Outlet Diverter Flap
5. Left Footwell Flap (Short Stroke)
6. Left Defroster Flap (Long Stroke)
7. Main Air Flap (Short Stroke)
8. Left Blend Air Flap
9. Left Diverter Flap
10. Right Defroster Flap (Short Stroke)
11. Main Air Flap (Short Stroke)
12. Left Defroster Flap (Short Stroke)
13. Left Footwell Flap (Long Stroke)
14. Right Defroster Flap Vacuum Element
15. Front Main Air Flap Vacuum Element
16. Rear Main Air Flap Vacuum Element
17. Air Recirculation Flap Vacuum Element
18. Right Center Air/Blend Outlet Vacuum Element
19. Right Center Air Diverter Outlet Vacuum Element
20. Left Defroster Flap Vacuum Element
21. Right Side Air Outlet Flap Vacuum Element
22. Left Center Air Outlet Vacuum Element
23. Left Footwell Flap Vacuum Element
24. Right Footwell Flap Vacuum Element
25. Left Center Air Outlet Diverter Flap Vacuum Element
26. Left Side Air Outlet Diverter Flap Vacuum Element

93F19732

Courtesy of Mercedes-Benz of North America.

Fig. 15: Front Climate Control System Vacuum Diagram (300SE, 300SD, 400SE & 500SEL)

1993 AUTOMATIC A/C-HEATER SYSTEMS 300SE, 300SD, 400SE & 500SEL (Cont.)

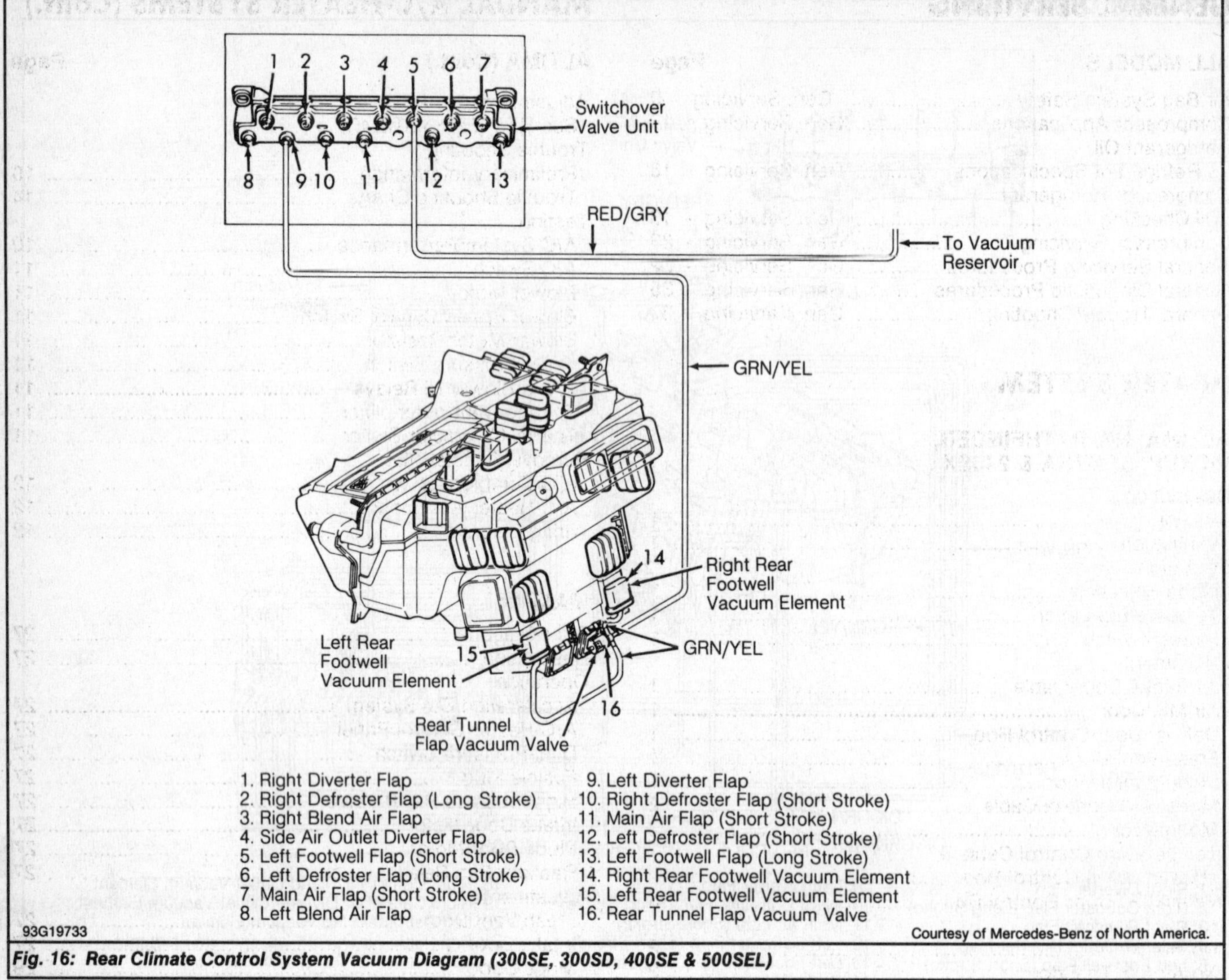
1
2
3
4
5
6
7
Switchover
Valve Unit
8
9
10
11
12
13
RED/GRY
To Vacuum
Reservoir
GRN/YEL
14
Right Rear
Footwell
Vacuum Element
Left Rear
Footwell
Vacuum Element
15
GRN/YEL
16
Rear Tunnel
Flap Vacuum Valve
1. Right Diverter Flap
2. Right Defroster Flap (Long Stroke)
3. Right Blend Air Flap
4. Side Air Outlet Diverter Flap
5. Left Footwell Flap (Short Stroke)
6. Left Defroster Flap (Long Stroke)
7. Main Air Flap (Short Stroke)
8. Left Blend Air Flap
9. Left Diverter Flap
10. Right Defroster Flap (Short Stroke)
11. Main Air Flap (Short Stroke)
12. Left Defroster Flap (Short Stroke)
13. Left Footwell Flap (Long Stroke)
14. Right Rear Footwell Vacuum Element
15. Left Rear Footwell Vacuum Element
16. Rear Tunnel Flap Vacuum Valve
93G19733
Courtesy of Mercedes-Benz of North America.

Fig. 16: Rear Climate Control System Vacuum Diagram (300SE, 300SD, 400SE & 500SEL)

WIRING DIAGRAM

NOTE: Information is not available from manufacturer.

1993 NISSAN CONTENTS

GENERAL SERVICING

HEATER SYSTEMS

MANUAL A/C-HEATER SYSTEMS

MANUAL A/C-HEATER SYSTEMS (Cont.)

1993 NISSAN CONTENTS (Cont.)

MANUAL A/C-HEATER SYSTEMS (Cont.)

MANUAL A/C-HEATER SYSTEMS (Cont.)

1993 NISSAN CONTENTS (Cont.)

MANUAL A/C-HEATER SYSTEMS (Cont.)

AUTOMATIC A/C-HEATER SYSTEMS

AUTOMATIC A/C-HEATER SYSTEMS (Cont.)

1993 NISSAN CONTENTS (Cont.)

AUTOMATIC A/C-HEATER SYSTEMS (Cont.)

AUTOMATIC A/C-HEATER SYSTEMS (Cont.)

1993 HEATER SYSTEMS
Except Quest, Maxima & 300ZX

Altima, NX, Pathfinder, Pickup, Sentra & 240SX

DESCRIPTION

HEATER

Heater assembly is contained in a housing beneath instrument panel. Assembly consists of blower motor, heater housing and core, heater valve, and control panel.

VENTILATION

Ventilation is a separate function from heating and is combined with the heating unit to obtain fresh air ventilation when required. Separate selector lever, push button or position setting on mode lever permits fresh air to enter passenger compartment. Blower switch position determines airflow volume.

WARNING: To avoid injury from accidental air bag deployment, read and carefully follow all SERVICE PRECAUTIONS and DISABLING & ACTIVATING AIR BAG SYSTEM procedures in AIR BAG SYSTEM SAFETY article in GENERAL SERVICING.

OPERATION

MODE SELECTION

Mode lever or push button controls airflow doors (intake, blend-air, heat, defrost and ventilation). Lever setting on control panel determines door positions.

Recirculation/Fresh Door – With door in the open position, outside air flows into heater system after passing through blower motor fan. With door in closed position, inside air is recirculated through heater system.

Ventilation Door – Ventilation door (fresh vent door on some models) permits fresh air to flow from dash panel registers.

Defrost Door – Controls air delivery or defroster outlets when this mode is selected. This separate door opens when mode door closes off floor and dash panel outlets to direct air to windshield.

Blend-Air Door – See TEMPERATURE LEVER.

TEMPERATURE LEVER

This lever setting positions blend-air door to direct flow of air through heater core (hot setting), around heater core (cold setting) or mixture of both. The lever also controls opening and closing of heater valve. At any setting except cold, heater valve is open, allowing engine coolant into heater.

BLOWER SWITCH

Switch controls speed of blower motor through resistor assembly. Either a dial knob or control lever may be used to select blower speeds.

ADJUSTMENTS

AIR INTAKE DOOR CABLE

NX, Pathfinder, Pickup & Sentra – Place air intake door and control lever to recirculation setting. Remove cable retaining clip. Ensure intake door and cable are in full recirculation position. *See Fig. 1.* Attach control cable retaining clip, and check air intake door operation.

AIR MIX DOOR

Altima – **1)** Move air mix link by hand and hold air mix door in full cold position. Install air mix door motor on heater unit, and connect wiring harness connector. *See Fig. 2.* Turn ignition on.

2) Slide temperature control lever to full cold. Attach air mix door motor rod to air mix door link rod holder. Ensure air mix door and heater valve operates properly when temperature control lever is in full hot and full cold positions.

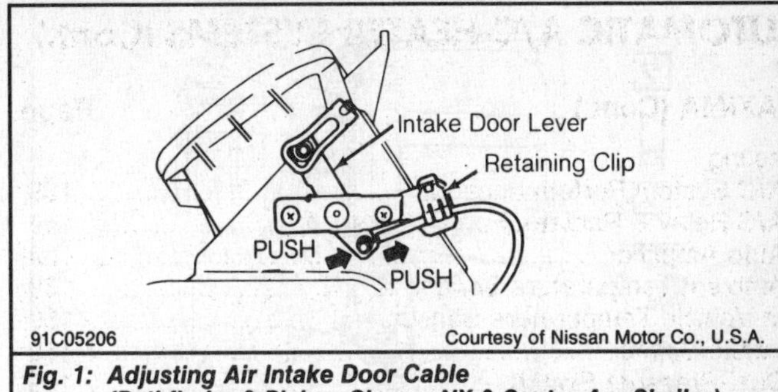
Intake Door Lever
Retaining Clip
PUSH
PUSH
91C05206
Courtesy of Nissan Motor Co., U.S.A.

Fig. 1: Adjusting Air Intake Door Cable (Pathfinder & Pickup Shown; NX & Sentra Are Similar)

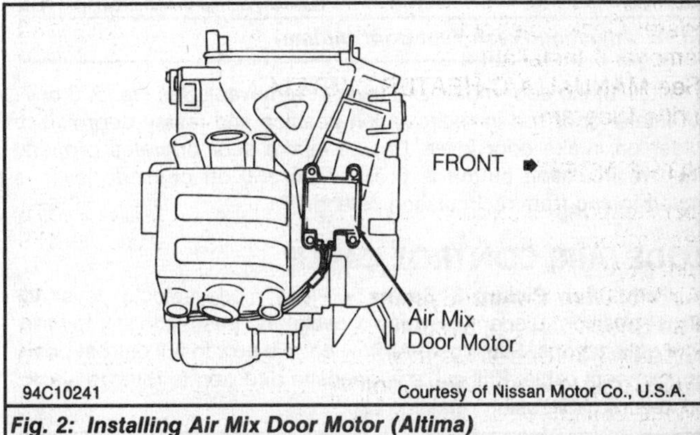
FRONT
Air Mix
Door Motor
94C10241
Courtesy of Nissan Motor Co., U.S.A.

Fig. 2: Installing Air Mix Door Motor (Altima)

DEFROST DOOR CONTROL ROD

Pathfinder & Pickup – Disconnect mode control cable from side link. Push side link and defrost door in direction of arrow. *See Fig. 3.* Connect rod to side link. Connect mode control cable, and adjust it as necessary. See MODE (AIR) CONTROL CABLE.

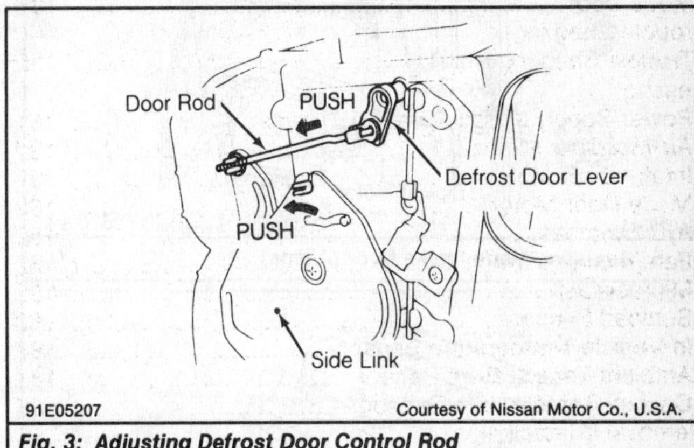
Door Rod
PUSH
Defrost Door Lever
PUSH
Side Link
91E05207
Courtesy of Nissan Motor Co., U.S.A.

Fig. 3: Adjusting Defrost Door Control Rod (Pathfinder & Pickup)

FRESH VENT DOOR

Altima – Before installing fresh vent door motor, connect vent door motor wiring harness connector. Turn ignition on. Slide fresh air vent switch down to off position. *See Fig. 4.* Install fresh vent door motor. Attach fresh vent door rod to fresh vent door link rod holder. Ensure fresh vent door operates properly.

NX & Sentra – Pull fresh ventilation lever down to off position. Pull cable to remove any slack. Attach control cable and retaining clip. Check air intake door operation.

MODE INTAKE DOOR

Altima, NX, Sentra & 240SX – **1)** Before installing intake door motor, ensure wiring harness connector of intake door motor is connected. Turn ignition on. Depress recirculation button or move mode lever to recirculation setting.

1993 HEATER SYSTEMS
Except Quest, Maxima & 300ZX (Cont.)

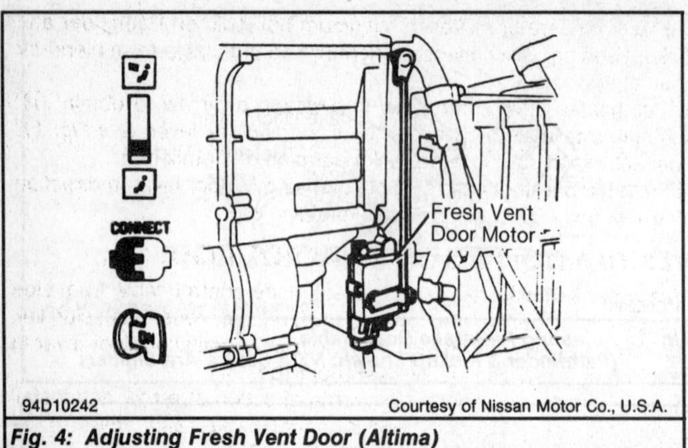
Fresh Vent
Door Motor
CONNECT
ON
94D10242
Courtesy of Nissan Motor Co., U.S.A.

Fig. 4: Adjusting Fresh Vent Door (Altima)

2) Install intake door motor and lever (if removed). *See Fig. 5, 6 or 7.* Set intake door rod in recirculation position and fasten door rod to holder on intake door lever. Ensure intake door operates properly when recirculation button is pressed on and off or mode lever is moved to and from recirculation setting.

MODE (AIR) CONTROL CABLE

NX, Pathfinder, Pickup & Sentra – Place mode selector lever to defrost position. Disconnect control cable and push side link toward cable until it stops. *See Fig. 8.* Airflow door is now in full defrost position. Connect cable. Pull cable in opposite direction to remove slack, and secure cable using retaining clip.

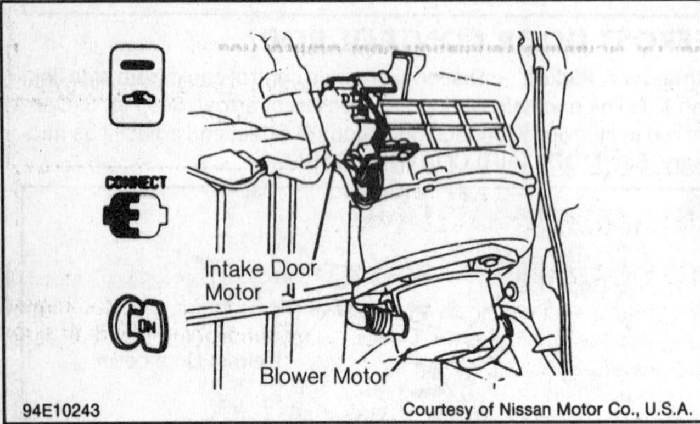
CONNECT
Intake Door
Motor
ON
Blower Motor
94E10243
Courtesy of Nissan Motor Co., U.S.A.

Fig. 5: Adjusting Mode Intake Door (Altima)

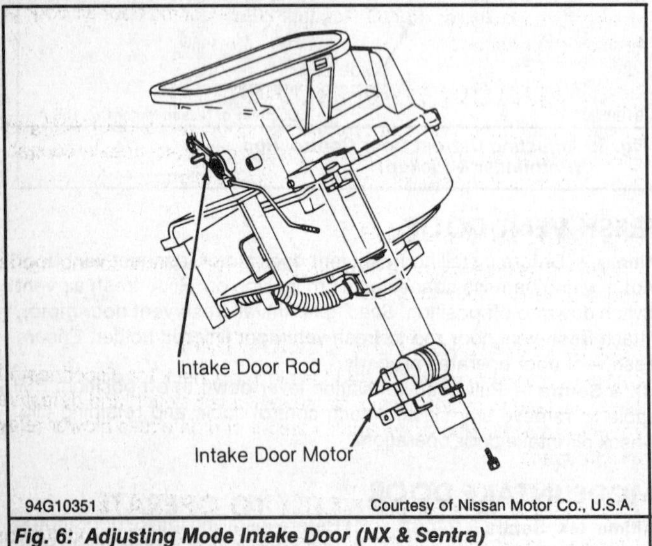
Intake Door Rod
Intake Door Motor
94G10351
Courtesy of Nissan Motor Co., U.S.A.

Fig. 6: Adjusting Mode Intake Door (NX & Sentra)

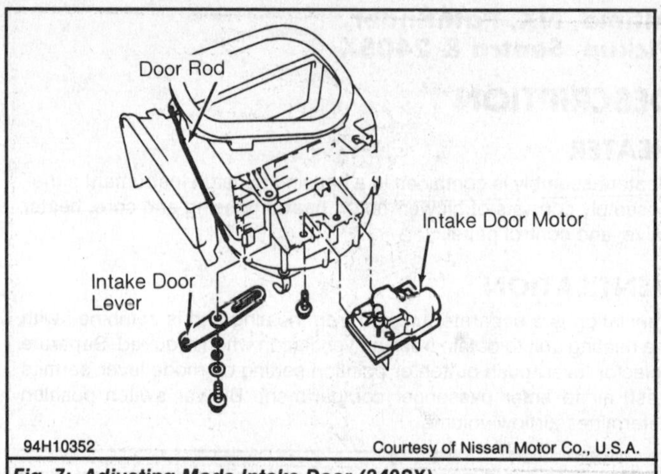
Door Rod
Intake Door Motor
Intake Door
Lever
94H10352
Courtesy of Nissan Motor Co., U.S.A.

Fig. 7: Adjusting Mode Intake Door (240SX)

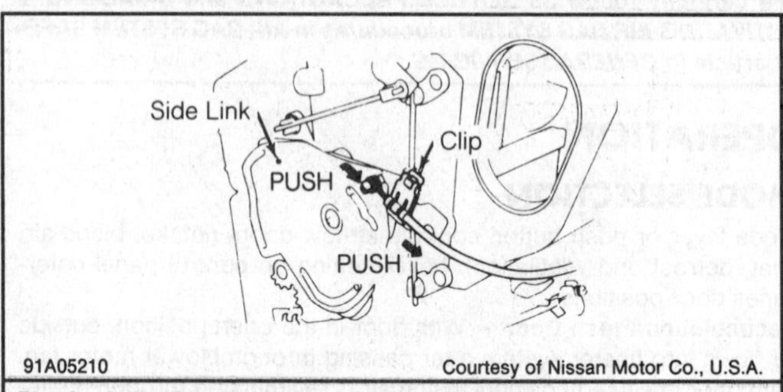
Side Link
Clip
PUSH
PUSH
91A05210
Courtesy of Nissan Motor Co., U.S.A.

Fig. 8: Adjusting Mode (Air) Control Cable (Pathfinder & Pickup Shown; NX & Sentra Are Similar)

MODE DOOR

Altima, NX, Sentra & 240SX – 1) Rotate side link clockwise and hold mode door in vent position. *See Fig. 9 or 10.* Install mode door motor on heater assembly, and connect wiring harness connector. Turn ignition on. Depress vent button or move mode lever to vent setting.
2) Install rod of mode door motor to side link rod holder. Depress defrost button (or move mode lever to defrost setting), and ensure side link operates at fully open position. Depress vent button (or move mode lever to vent setting), and ensure side link operates at fully open position.

TEMPERATURE CONTROL CABLE & HEATER VALVE CONTROL ROD

NOTE: Before adjusting heater valve control rod, disconnect temperature control cable from blend-air door. After adjusting control rod, install temperature control cable and adjust it as necessary.

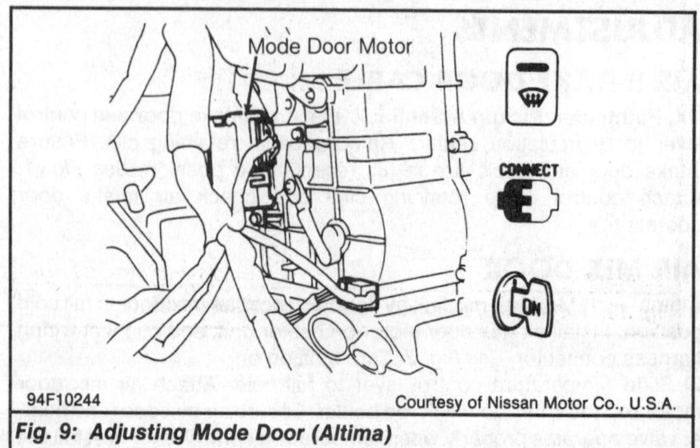
Mode Door Motor
CONNECT
ON
94F10244
Courtesy of Nissan Motor Co., U.S.A.

Fig. 9: Adjusting Mode Door (Altima)

1993 HEATER SYSTEMS Except Quest, Maxima & 300ZX (Cont.)

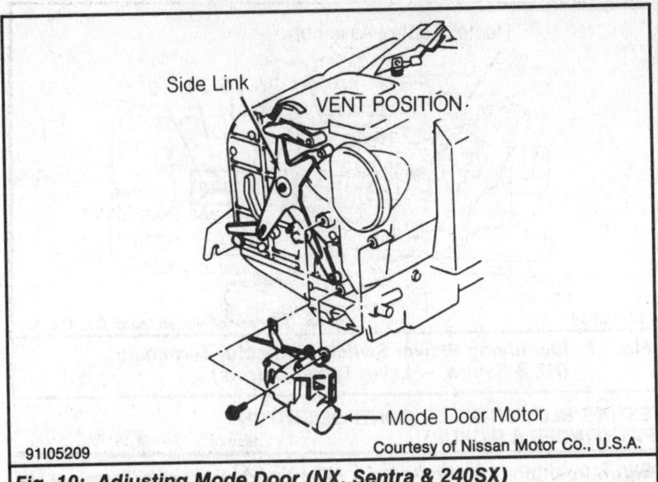
Side Link
VENT POSITION
Mode Door Motor
91I05209
Courtesy of Nissan Motor Co., U.S.A.

Fig. 10: Adjusting Mode Door (NX, Sentra & 240SX)

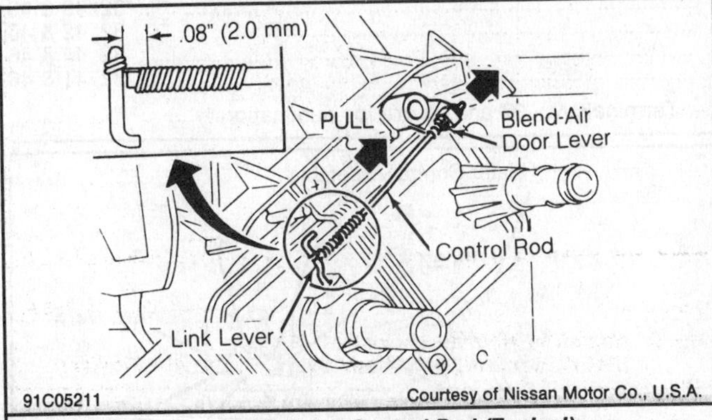
.08" (2.0 mm)
PULL
Blend-Air
Door Lever
Control Rod
Link Lever
91C05211
Courtesy of Nissan Motor Co., U.S.A.

Fig. 11: Adjusting Heater Valve Control Rod (Typical)

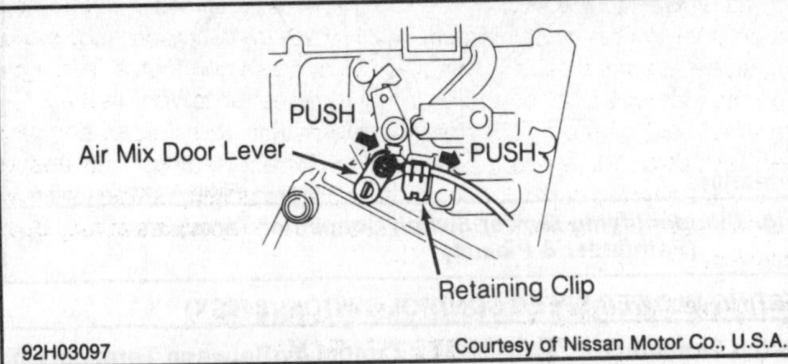
PUSH
Air Mix Door Lever
PUSH
Retaining Clip
92H03097
Courtesy of Nissan Motor Co., U.S.A.

Fig. 12: Adjusting Temperature Control Cable (Pathfinder & Pickup Shown; NX & Sentra Are Similar)

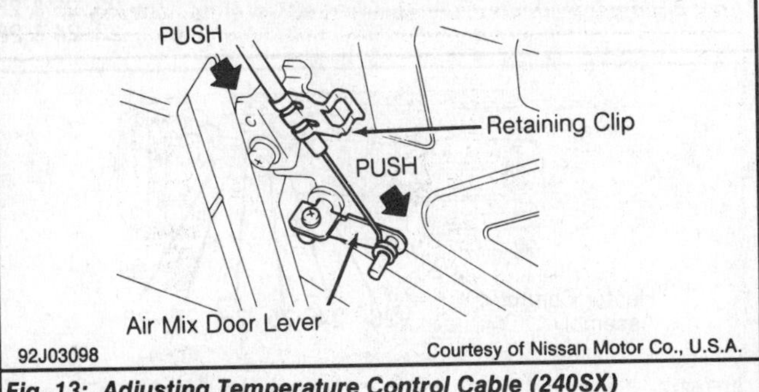
PUSH
Retaining Clip
PUSH
Air Mix Door Lever
92J03098
Courtesy of Nissan Motor Co., U.S.A.

Fig. 13: Adjusting Temperature Control Cable (240SX)

1) Place temperature lever to maximum hot (cold on Pathfinder and Pickup) setting. Disconnect temperature control cable from blend-air door lever.
2) Pull heater valve control rod in direction of arrow to obtain .08" (2.0 mm) clearance between ends of rod and link lever. *See Fig. 11.* Connect rod to door lever. Check operation of air mix door.
3) Push temperature control cable and air mix door lever in direction of arrow. *See Fig. 12 or 13.* Install retaining clip.

VENTILATION DOOR CONTROL ROD

Pathfinder & Pickup – 1) Disconnect mode control cable from side link. Disconnect upper and lower ventilation door rods. Push side link in direction of arrow. *See Fig. 14.* Hold lower ventilation door lever in direction of arrow and install lower door rod.
2) Hold upper ventilation door lever in direction of arrow and install upper door rod. Connect mode control cable, and adjust it as necessary. See MODE (AIR) CONTROL CABLE.

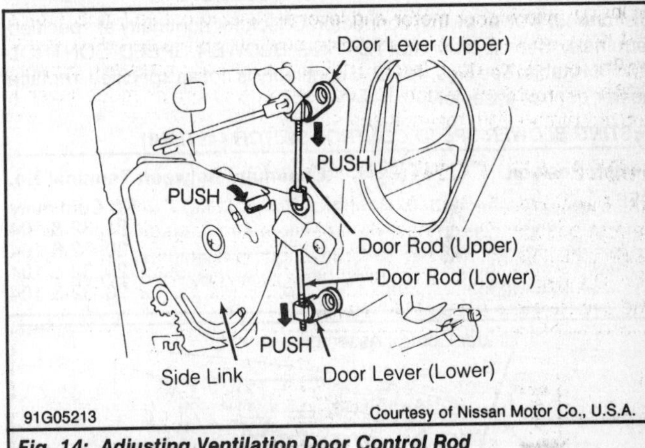
Door Lever (Upper)
PUSH
PUSH
Door Rod (Upper)
Door Rod (Lower)
PUSH
Side Link
Door Lever (Lower)
91G05213
Courtesy of Nissan Motor Co., U.S.A.

Fig. 14: Adjusting Ventilation Door Control Rod (Pathfinder & Pickup)

TROUBLE SHOOTING

NO HOT AIR

Check for malfunctioning engine coolant thermostat, plugged heater core, and low coolant level. Check for malfunctioning blend-air door and heater valve not opening.

NO AIRFLOW TO FLOOR

Check for low blower motor speed, poor electrical connection or blower switch and faulty resistor. Check for malfunctioning floor air door or floor air door actuator.

LOW AIRFLOW TO DEFROSTER

Check for malfunctioning floor/defroster door, faulty door seal and plugged defroster nozzle. Check for leaking duct-to-nozzle connection. Check for defroster door actuator malfunction.

HOT AIR AT ALL TIMES

Check for heater valve not closing. Check for malfunctioning mode door and faulty mode door seal.

NO BLOWER MOTOR OPERATION

Check for blown fuse and melted fusible link. Check for disconnected electrical lead to motor. Check for defective fan switch and defective blower motor. Check for defective resistor and defective blower relay (if equipped).

CONTROL LEVER DIFFICULT TO OPERATE

Check for inner wire rubbing on outer case end. Check for kinked or bent cable. Check for sticking doors or lever.

1993 HEATER SYSTEMS
Except Quest, Maxima & 300ZX (Cont.)

OUTSIDE AIR ENTERING WHEN FAN IS OFF

Check air intake door adjustment. Check control cable adjustment. Check for air intake door actuator malfunction.

BLOWER MOTOR/FAN NOISE

Check for loose bolt and foreign objects in blower fan. Check for broken blower fan blades.

TESTING

WARNING: To avoid injury from accidental air bag deployment, read and carefully follow all SERVICE PRECAUTIONS and DISABLING & ACTIVATING AIR BAG SYSTEM procedures in AIR BAG SYSTEM SAFETY article in GENERAL SERVICING.

BLOWER SPEED CONTROL SWITCH

Disconnect blower switch connector. Check for continuity at specified terminals. See appropriate TESTING BLOWER SPEED CONTROL SWITCH table. *See Figs. 15-19.* If continuity is not as specified, replace heater control assembly.

TESTING BLOWER SPEED CONTROL SWITCH (ALTIMA)

Switch Position	Continuity Between Terminal No.
OFF	No Continuity
1	31, 32 & 104
2	30, 32 & 104
3	29, 32 & 104
4	28, 32 & 104

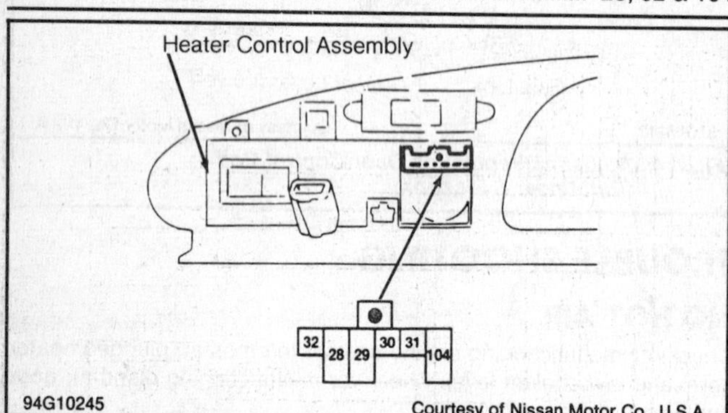
Heater Control Assembly
32
28
29
30
31
104
94G10245
Courtesy of Nissan Motor Co., U.S.A.

Fig. 15: Identifying Blower Switch Connector Terminals (Altima)

TESTING BLOWER SPEED CONTROL SWITCH (NX & SENTRA)

Switch Position	Continuity Between Terminal No.
OFF	No Continuity
1	12, 23 & 27
2	12, 23 & 26
3	12, 23 & 25
4	12, 23 & 24

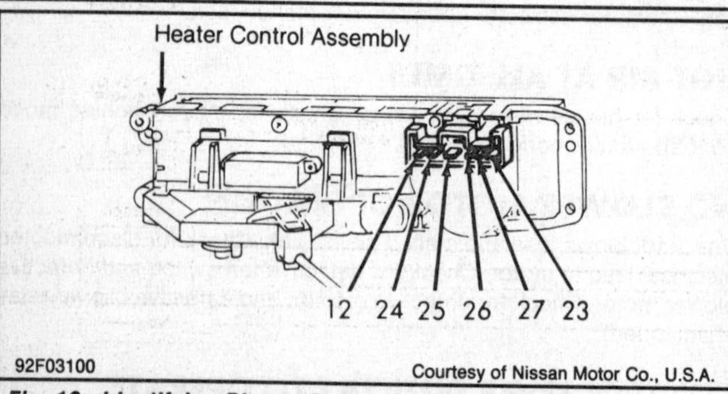
Heater Control Assembly
12 24 25 26 27 23
92F03100
Courtesy of Nissan Motor Co., U.S.A.

Fig. 16: Identifying Blower Switch Connector Terminals (NX & Sentra - Push Button Controls)

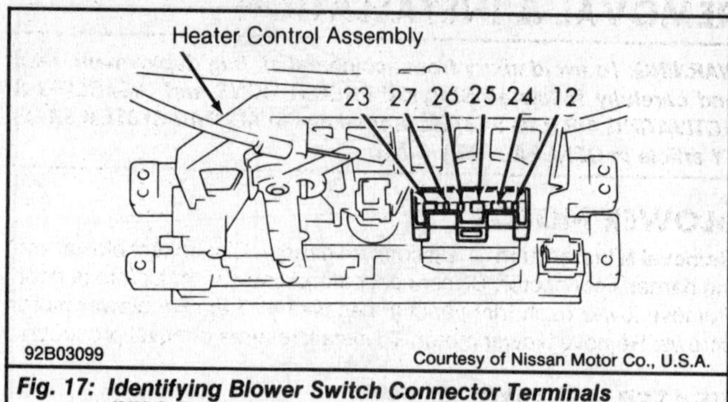
Heater Control Assembly
23 27 26 25 24 12
92B03099
Courtesy of Nissan Motor Co., U.S.A.

Fig. 17: Identifying Blower Switch Connector Terminals (NX & Sentra - Lever Type Controls)

TESTING BLOWER SPEED CONTROL SWITCH (PATHFINDER & PICKUP)

Switch Position	[1] Continuity Between Terminal No.
OFF	No Continuity
1	32, 43 & 46
2	32, 42 & 46
3	32, 44 & 46
4	32, 41 & 46

[1] - Terminals No. 37 and 38 are for illumination.

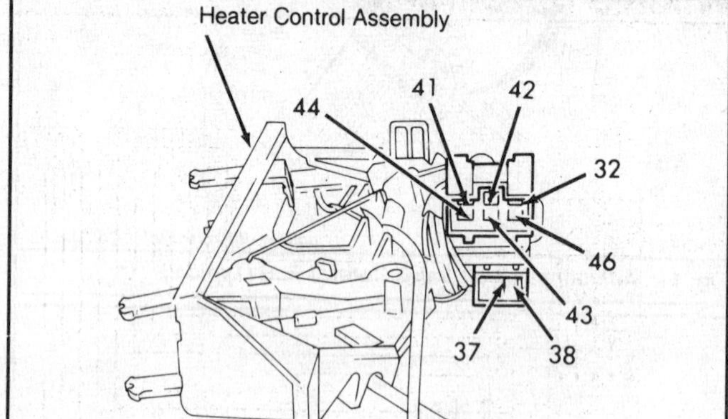
Heater Control Assembly
41
42
44
32
46
43
37
38
92H03101
Courtesy of Nissan Motor Co., U.S.A.

Fig. 18: Identifying Blower Switch Connector Terminals (Pathfinder & Pickup)

TESTING BLOWER SPEED CONTROL SWITCH (240SX)

Switch Position	Continuity Between Terminal No.
OFF	No Continuity
1	23, 27 & 28
2	23, 26 & 28
3	23, 25 & 28
4	23, 24 & 28

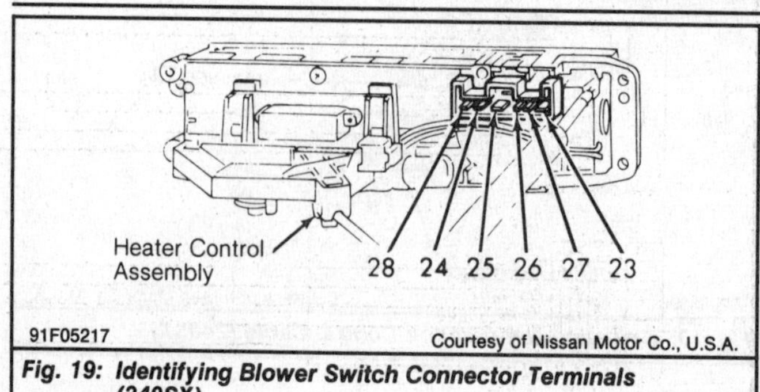
Heater Control
Assembly
28 24 25 26 27 23
91F05217
Courtesy of Nissan Motor Co., U.S.A.

Fig. 19: Identifying Blower Switch Connector Terminals (240SX)

REMOVAL & INSTALLATION

***WARNING:** To avoid injury from accidental air bag deployment, read and carefully follow all SERVICE PRECAUTIONS and DISABLING & ACTIVATING AIR BAG SYSTEM procedures in AIR BAG SYSTEM SAFETY article in GENERAL SERVICING.*

BLOWER MOTOR

Removal & Installation – Disconnect battery. Disconnect blower wiring harness connector. Disconnect control cable from air intake door. Remove lower dash trim panel (if necessary). Remove blower motor screws. Remove blower motor. To install, reverse removal procedure.

HEATER ASSEMBLY

Removal & Installation – See EVAPORATOR & HEATER CORE ASSEMBLY under REMOVAL & INSTALLATION in appropriate MANUAL A/C-HEATER SYSTEMS article.

HEATER CONTROL ASSEMBLY

***NOTE:** Altima removal and installation procedures are not available from manufacturer.*

Removal & Installation (Except Altima) – **1)** Remove heater control bezel (if necessary). Remove radio. Remove control unit screws. Remove control cables by unfastening clamps at door levers. Remove heater control assembly bolts.

2) Disconnect wiring harness connector, and remove heater control assembly. To install, reverse removal procedure. Adjust cables, and check system operation.

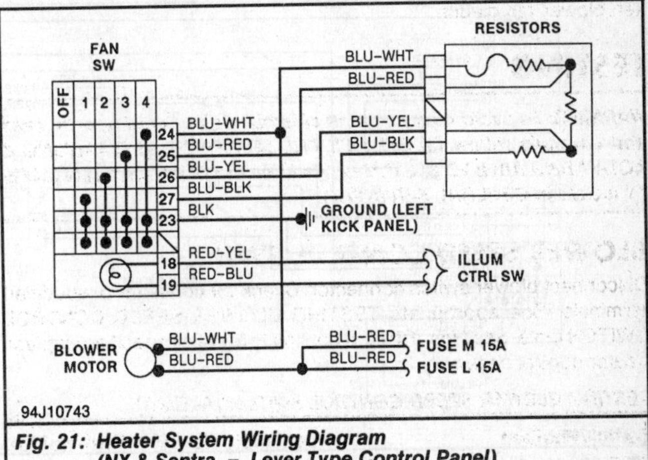
RESISTORS
FAN SW
OFF
1
2
3
4
BLU-WHT
BLU-RED
BLU-YEL
BLU-BLK
BLK
24
25
26
27
23
GROUND (LEFT KICK PANEL)
RED-YEL
RED-BLU
18
19
ILLUM CTRL SW
BLOWER MOTOR
FUSE M 15A
FUSE L 15A
94J10743

Fig. 21: Heater System Wiring Diagram (NX & Sentra – Lever Type Control Panel)

WIRING DIAGRAMS

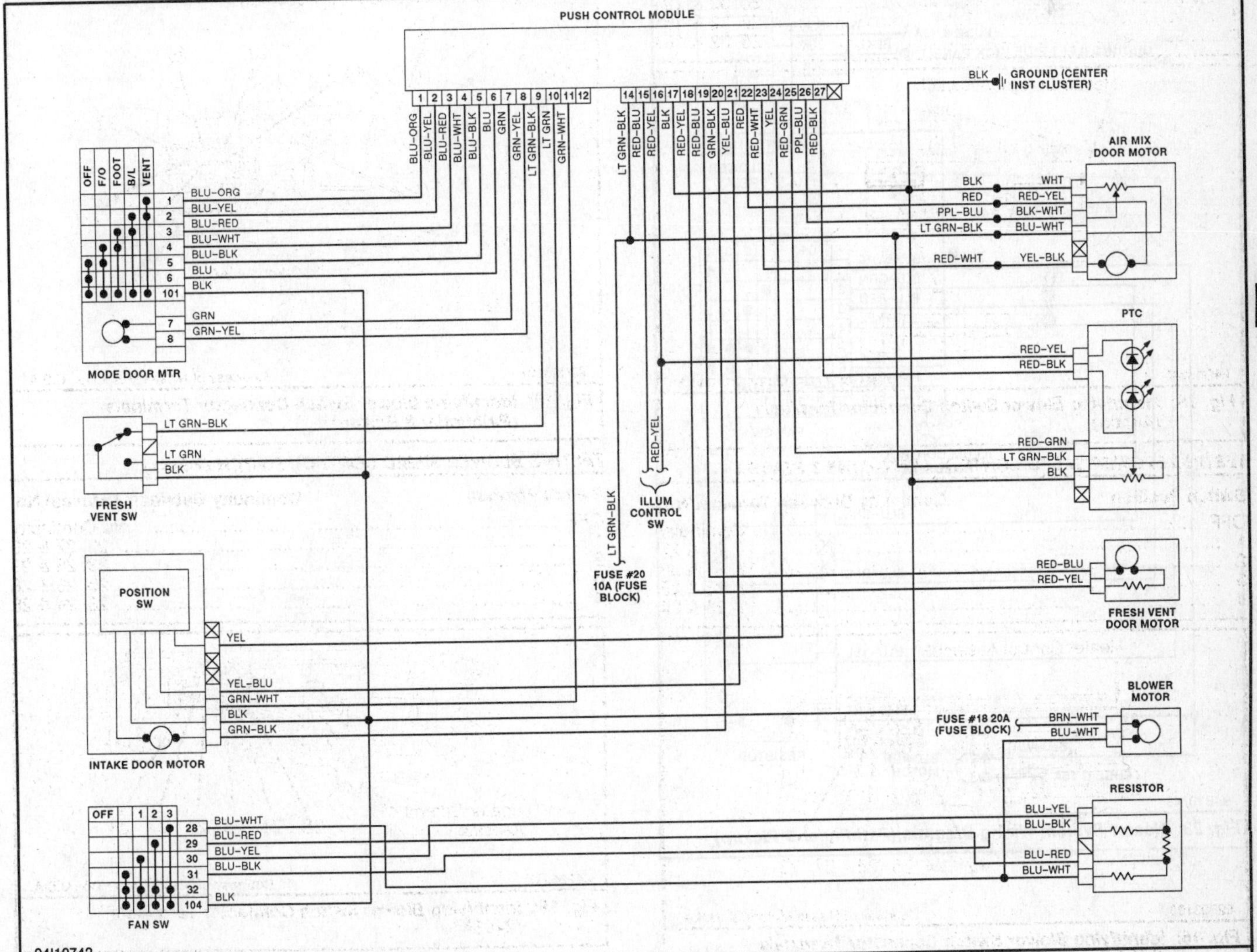

PUSH CONTROL MODULE

GROUND (CENTER INST CLUSTER)

AIR MIX DOOR MOTOR

MODE DOOR MTR

PTC

FRESH VENT SW

ILLUM CONTROL SW

FUSE #20 10A (FUSE BLOCK)

FRESH VENT DOOR MOTOR

POSITION SW

INTAKE DOOR MOTOR

BLOWER MOTOR

FUSE #18 20A (FUSE BLOCK)

RESISTOR

FAN SW

94I10742

Fig. 20: Heater System Wiring Diagram (Altima)

1993 HEATER SYSTEMS
Except Quest, Maxima & 300ZX (Cont.)

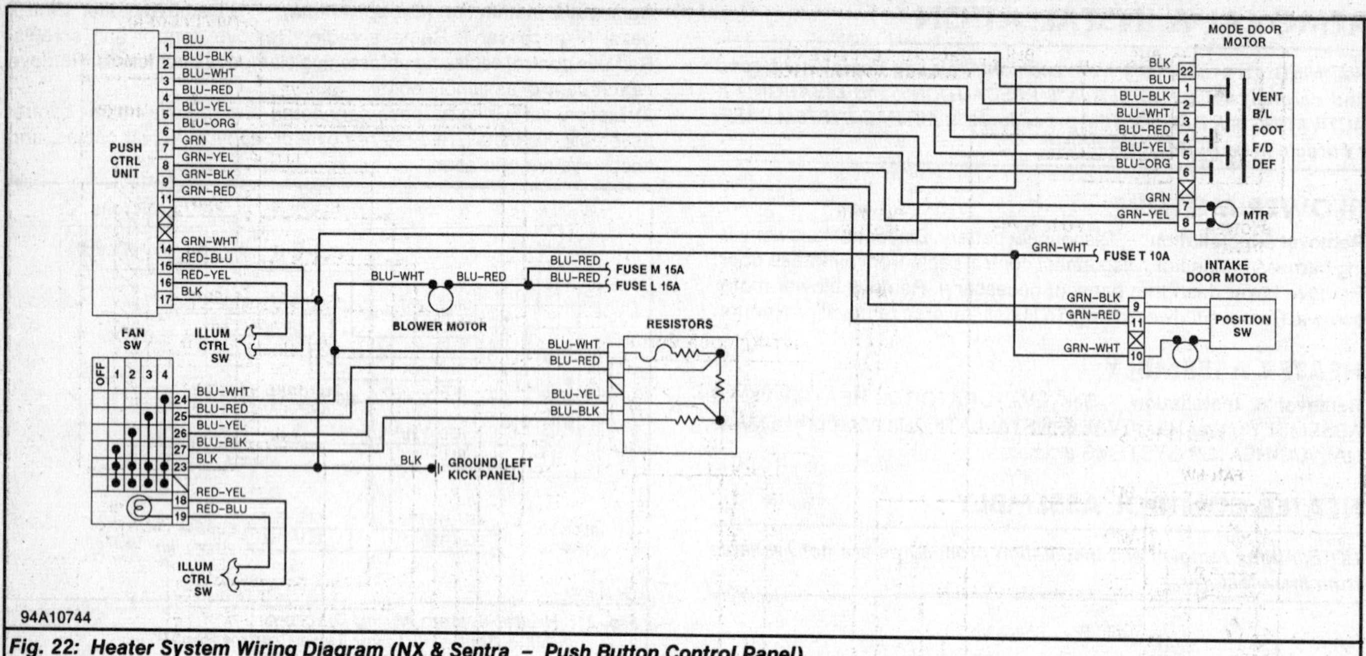
PUSH CTRL UNIT
BLU
BLU-BLK
BLU-WHT
BLU-RED
BLU-YEL
BLU-ORG
GRN
GRN-YEL
GRN-BLK
GRN-RED
GRN-WHT
RED-BLU
RED-YEL
BLK
FAN SW
OFF 1 2 3 4
ILLUM CTRL SW
BLU-WHT
BLU-RED
BLU-YEL
BLU-BLK
RED-YEL
RED-BLU
BLOWER MOTOR
FUSE M 15A
FUSE L 15A
RESISTORS
GROUND (LEFT KICK PANEL)
MODE DOOR MOTOR
VENT
B/L
FOOT
F/D
DEF
MTR
GRN-WHT
FUSE T 10A
INTAKE DOOR MOTOR
POSITION SW
94A10744
Fig. 22: Heater System Wiring Diagram (NX & Sentra – Push Button Control Panel)

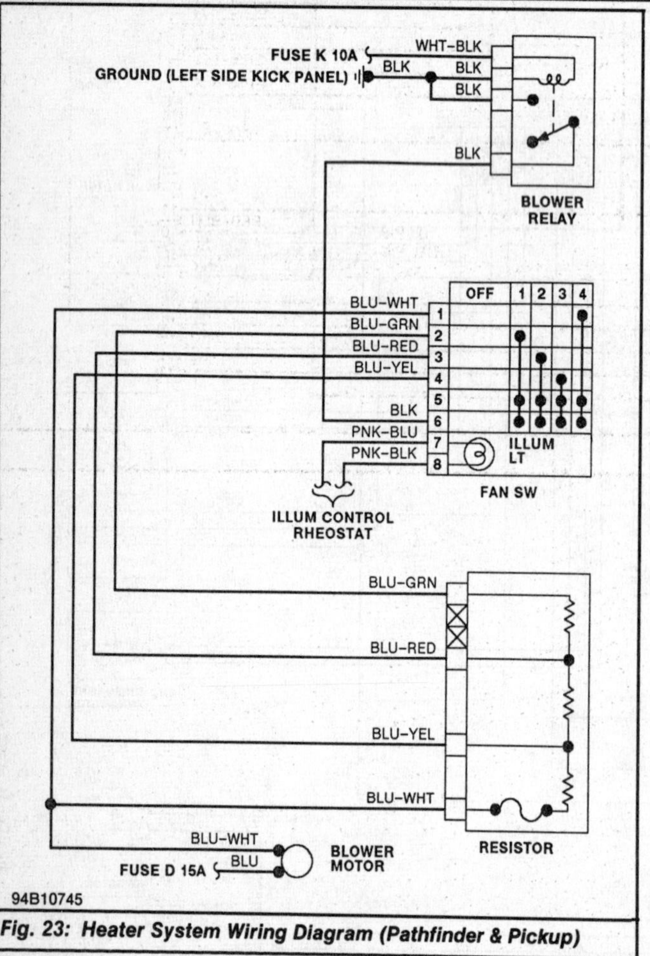
FUSE K 10A
WHT-BLK
GROUND (LEFT SIDE KICK PANEL)
BLK
BLOWER RELAY
BLU-WHT
BLU-GRN
BLU-RED
BLU-YEL
PNK-BLU
PNK-BLK
OFF 1 2 3 4
ILLUM LT
FAN SW
ILLUM CONTROL RHEOSTAT
RESISTOR
FUSE D 15A
BLU
BLOWER MOTOR
94B10745
Fig. 23: Heater System Wiring Diagram (Pathfinder & Pickup)

1993 HEATER SYSTEMS
Except Quest, Maxima & 300ZX (Cont.)

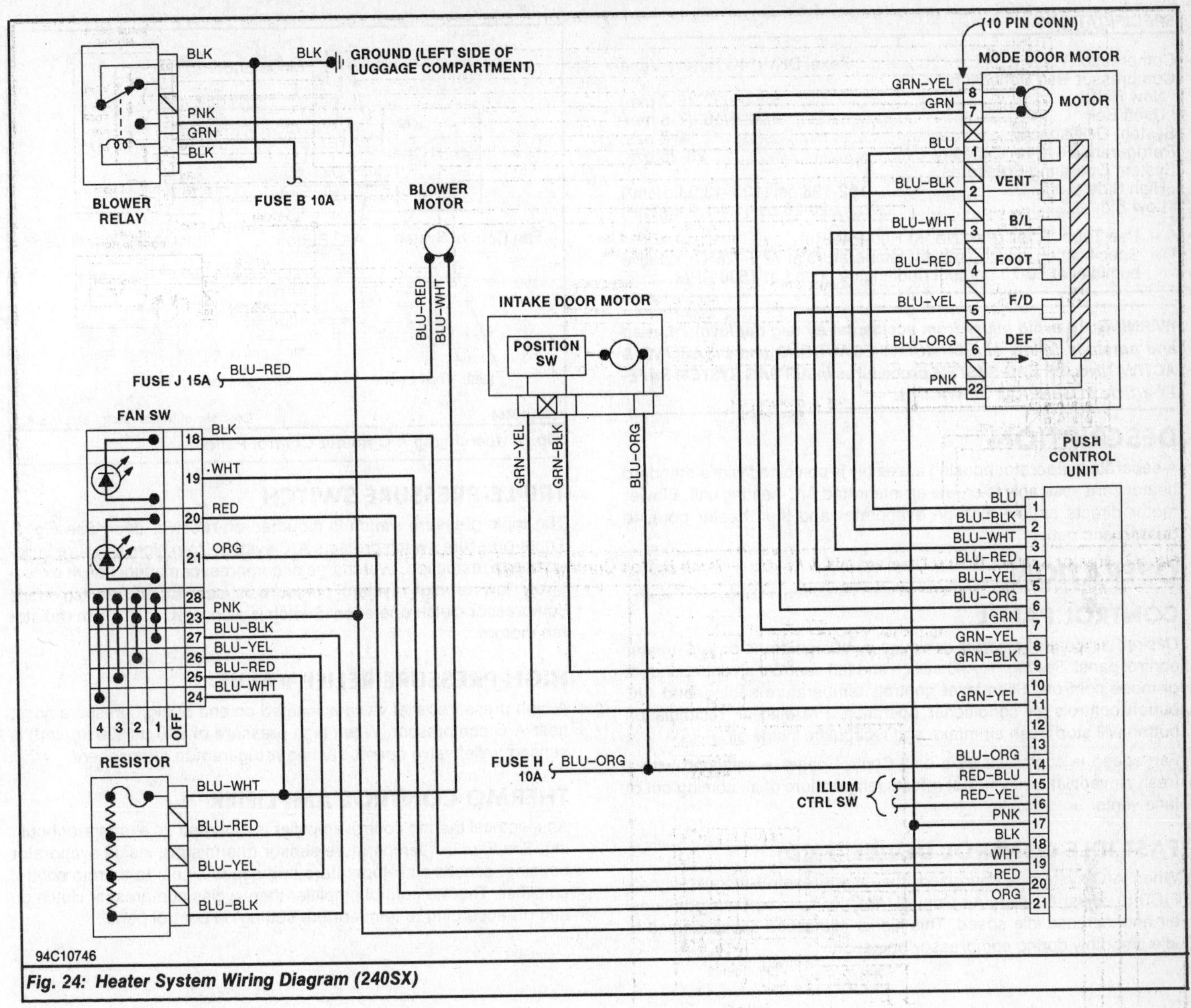
BLK
BLK
GROUND (LEFT SIDE OF LUGGAGE COMPARTMENT)
PNK
GRN
BLK
BLOWER RELAY
FUSE B 10A
BLOWER MOTOR
BLU-RED
BLU-WHT
FUSE J 15A
BLU-RED
INTAKE DOOR MOTOR
POSITION SW
GRN-YEL
GRN-BLK
BLU-ORG
FAN SW
18 BLK
19 WHT
20 RED
21 ORG
28 PNK
23 BLU-BLK
27 BLU-YEL
26 BLU-RED
25 BLU-WHT
24
4 3 2 1 OFF
RESISTOR
BLU-WHT
BLU-RED
BLU-YEL
BLU-BLK
FUSE H 10A
BLU-ORG
ILLUM CTRL SW
(10 PIN CONN)
MODE DOOR MOTOR
MOTOR
GRN-YEL 8
GRN 7
BLU 1
BLU-BLK 2 VENT
BLU-WHT 3 B/L
BLU-RED 4 FOOT
BLU-YEL 5 F/D
BLU-ORG 6 DEF
PNK 22
PUSH CONTROL UNIT
BLU 1
BLU-BLK 2
BLU-WHT 3
BLU-RED 4
BLU-YEL 5
BLU-ORG 6
GRN 7
GRN-YEL 8
GRN-BLK 9
10
GRN-YEL 11
12
13
BLU-ORG 14
RED-BLU 15
RED-YEL 16
PNK 17
BLK 18
WHT 19
RED 20
ORG 21
94C10746
Fig. 24: Heater System Wiring Diagram (240SX)

1993 MANUAL A/C-HEATER SYSTEMS
Altima

SPECIFICATIONS

Compressor Type .... Zexel DKV-14C Rotary Vane
Compressor Belt Deflection
New Belt .... 5/64-9/32" (6-7 mm)
Used Belt .... 9/32-5/16" (7-8 mm)
System Oil Capacity .... [1] 6.8 ozs.
Refrigerant (R-134a) Capacity .... 25-28 ozs.
System Operating Pressures [2]
High Side .... 152-198 psi (10.7-13.9 kg/cm²)
Low Side .... 20-26 psi (1.4-1.9 kg/cm²)

[1] – Use Type "R" oil (Part No. KLH00-PAGR0).
[2] – Specification is with ambient temperature at 77°F (25°C), relative humidity at 50-70 percent and engine speed at 1500 RPM.

WARNING: To avoid injury from accidental air bag deployment, read and carefully follow all SERVICE PRECAUTIONS and DISABLING & ACTIVATING AIR BAG SYSTEM procedures in AIR BAG SYSTEM SAFETY article in GENERAL SERVICING.

DESCRIPTION

A separate evaporator housing assembly is combined with a standard heater core assembly to create an integrated A/C-heating unit. Blower motor directs airflow through evaporator and then heater core, to ducting and outlets.

OPERATION

CONTROL PANEL

Desired air control mode is achieved by push buttons on A/C-heater control panel. *See Fig. 1.* A/C switch and fan controls are independent of mode controls. Slide lever controls temperature setting, and A/C button controls air conditioner operation. Pressing air recirculation button will stop fresh air intake and recirculate inside air.

Fan speed is controlled by a dial. Control panel is equipped with a fresh air ventilation lever that affects temperature of air coming out of face vents.

FAST IDLE CONTROL DEVICE (FICD)

When A/C system is energized, the engine control module signals FICD to adjust Auxiliary Air Control (AAC) valve to by-pass additional air and increase idle speed. This higher idle speed allows engine to idle smoothly during compressor operation.

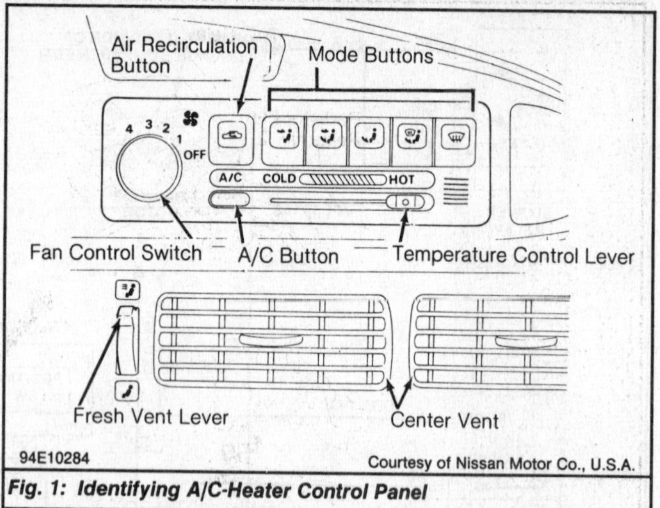
Air Recirculation Button
Mode Buttons
4 3 2 1
OFF
A/C
COLD
HOT
Fan Control Switch
A/C Button
Temperature Control Lever
Fresh Vent Lever
Center Vent
94E10284
Courtesy of Nissan Motor Co., U.S.A.
Fig. 1: Identifying A/C-Heater Control Panel

TRIPLE-PRESSURE SWITCH

The triple-pressure switch is mounted on receiver-drier. *See Fig. 2.* Triple-pressure switch protects A/C system from high pressure build-up due to restriction, overcharge or compressor malfunction. If excessively low or high system pressure is sensed, the switch stops compressor clutch operation. Switch is also used to activate radiator fan motors.

HIGH PRESSURE RELIEF VALVE

A high pressure relief valve is located on end of high pressure hose, near A/C compressor. When high pressure of 540 psi (38 kg/cm²) is sensed, relief valve opens, venting refrigerant to atmosphere.

THERMO CONTROL AMPLIFIER

An electrical thermo control amplifier is mounted on evaporator housing. *See Fig. 3.* A temperature sensor (thermistor), inside evaporator housing, senses air temperature and sends signal to thermo control amplifier. Thermo control amplifier then cycles compressor clutch on and off according to temperature setting on control panel.

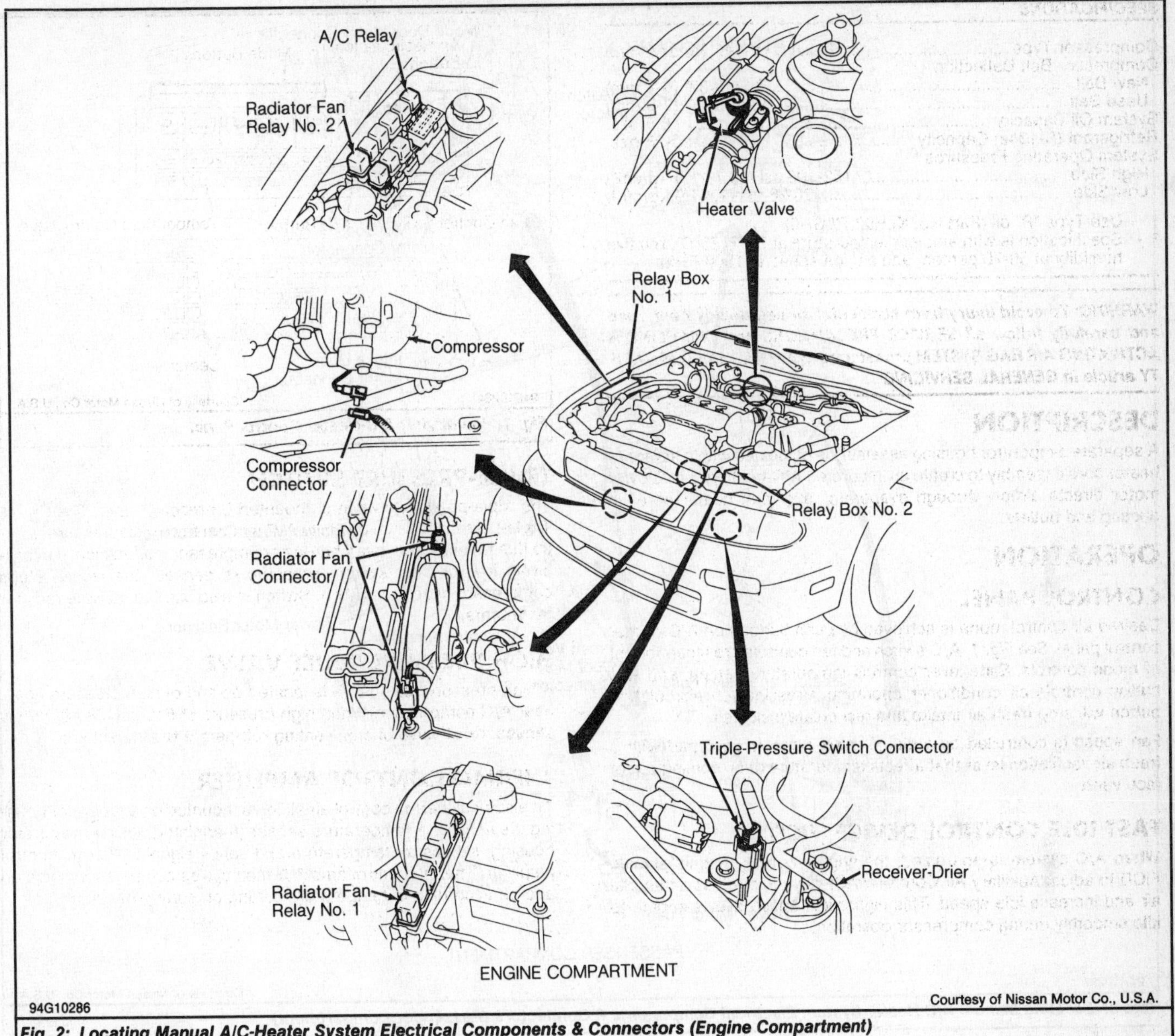
A/C Relay
Radiator Fan Relay No. 2
Heater Valve
Relay Box No. 1
Compressor
Compressor Connector
Relay Box No. 2
Radiator Fan Connector
Triple-Pressure Switch Connector
Receiver-Drier
Radiator Fan Relay No. 1
ENGINE COMPARTMENT
94G10286
Courtesy of Nissan Motor Co., U.S.A.

Fig. 2: Locating Manual A/C-Heater System Electrical Components & Connectors (Engine Compartment)

1993 MANUAL A/C-HEATER SYSTEMS
Altima (Cont.)

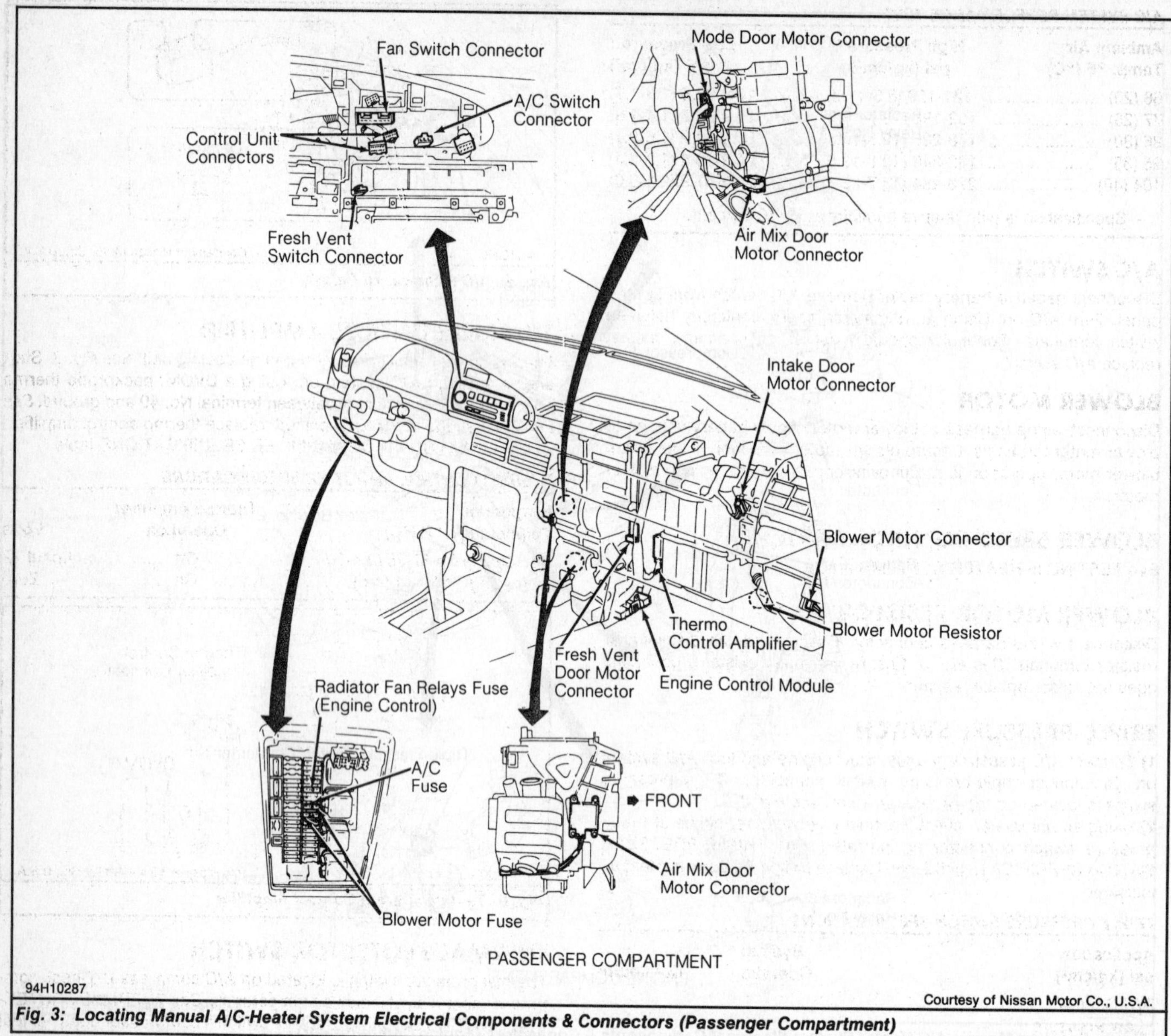
Fan Switch Connector
Mode Door Motor Connector
A/C Switch Connector
Control Unit Connectors
Fresh Vent Switch Connector
Air Mix Door Motor Connector
Intake Door Motor Connector
Blower Motor Connector
Blower Motor Resistor
Thermo Control Amplifier
Fresh Vent Door Motor Connector
Engine Control Module
Radiator Fan Relays Fuse (Engine Control)
A/C Fuse
FRONT
Air Mix Door Motor Connector
Blower Motor Fuse
PASSENGER COMPARTMENT
94H10287
Courtesy of Nissan Motor Co., U.S.A.

Fig. 3: Locating Manual A/C-Heater System Electrical Components & Connectors (Passenger Compartment)

ADJUSTMENTS

NOTE: For control cable and door rod adjustments, see HEATER SYSTEMS article.

TROUBLE SHOOTING

NOTE: See TROUBLE SHOOTING - ALTIMA charts following this article.

Preliminary Information - The Engine Control Module (ECM) may be referred to as Engine Concentrated Control System (ECCS) control unit and the A/C-heater control panel may also be referred to as push control module in the trouble shooting charts.

Altima is equipped with a diagnostic connector for use with Nissan Consult Tester (J-38465). Consult tester may be used to diagnose radiator fan control circuit. Connector is located on driver's side of center console (above accelerator pedal).

TESTING

WARNING: To avoid injury from accidental air bag deployment, read and carefully follow all SERVICE PRECAUTIONS and DISABLING & ACTIVATING AIR BAG SYSTEM procedures in AIR BAG SYSTEM SAFETY article in GENERAL SERVICING.

A/C SYSTEM PERFORMANCE

1) Park vehicle out of direct sunlight. Close all doors and open engine hood and windows. Connect A/C pressure gauges to the high and low side pressure ports of system. Determine relative humidity and ambient air temperature.

2) Set temperature control to maximum cold, mode control to face vent and recirculation switch to recirculation positions. Turn blower fan switch to highest position. Start and run engine at 1500 RPM.

3) After running A/C for 10 minutes, check high and low side system pressures. Refer to A/C-HEATER PERFORMANCE TEST table to determine if system is operating within range.

1993 MANUAL A/C-HEATER SYSTEMS
Altima (Cont.)

A/C SYSTEM PERFORMANCE TEST

Ambient Air Temp. °F (°C)	High Pressure [1] psi (kg/cm²)	Low Pressure [1] psi (kg/cm²)
68 (20)	121-159 (8.5-11.2)	17.8-23.5 (1.3-1.7)
77 (25)	152-198 (10.7-13.9)	19.9-26.3 (1.4-1.9)
86 (30)	178-235 (12.5-16.5)	22.0-29.2 (1.6-2.1)
95 (35)	182-249 (12.8-17.5)	24.2-33.4 (1.7-2.4)
104 (40)	223-294 (15.7-20.7)	29.2-41.9 (2.1-3.0)

[1] – Specification is with relative humidity at 50-70 percent.

A/C SWITCH

Disconnect negative battery cable. Remove A/C switch from control panel. Turn A/C on. Using an ohmmeter, check continuity between switch terminals. Continuity should exist. If no continuity exists, replace A/C switch.

BLOWER MOTOR

Disconnect wiring harness at blower motor. Apply battery voltage to blower motor terminals. Ensure blower motor operation is smooth. If blower motor operation is rough or not up to speed, replace blower motor.

BLOWER SPEED CONTROL SWITCH

See TESTING in HEATER SYSTEMS article.

BLOWER MOTOR RESISTOR

Disconnect wiring harness connector. Check continuity between all resistor terminals. *See Fig. 3.* Ensure continuity exists. If continuity does not exist, replace resistor.

TRIPLE-PRESSURE SWITCH

1) Connect A/C pressure gauges. Start engine and turn A/C system on. Disconnect triple-pressure switch connector. Triple-pressure switch is located on top of receiver-drier. *See Fig. 2.*

2) Using an ohmmeter, check continuity between terminals of triple-pressure switch connector as indicated. See TRIPLE-PRESSURE SWITCH SPECIFICATIONS table. Replace switch if it does not test as indicated.

TRIPLE-PRESSURE SWITCH SPECIFICATIONS

Application psi (kg/cm²)	System Operation	Continuity
A/C Control [1]		
Low Pressure		
Decreasing To 22-29 (1.6-2.1)	Off	No
Increasing To 23-33 (1.6-2.3)	On	Yes
High Pressure		
Increasing To 356-412 (25-29)	Off	No
Decreasing To 242-299 (17-21)	On	Yes
Radiator Fan Control [2]		
Increasing To 206-235 (14.5-16.6)	On	Yes
Decreasing To 164-206 (11.5-14.5)	Off	No

[1] – Check continuity between Black and Light Green/Red wires.
[2] – Check continuity between Light Green/Black and Yellow wires.

A/C & BLOWER HI RELAYS

Remove relay to be tested. *See Fig. 4.* Apply battery voltage between terminals No. 1 and No. 3. Check for continuity between remaining relay terminals. Continuity should exist. If no continuity exists, replace relay.

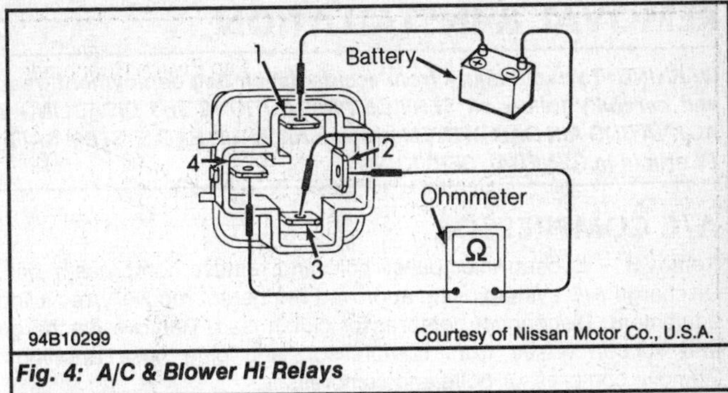
1
Battery
2
4
Ohmmeter
Ω
3
94B10299
Courtesy of Nissan Motor Co., U.S.A.

Fig. 4: A/C & Blower Hi Relays

THERMO CONTROL AMPLIFIER

Thermo control amplifier is mounted on cooling unit. *See Fig. 3.* Start engine and turn A/C system on. Using a DVOM, backprobe thermo control amplifier connector between terminal No. 40 and ground. *See Fig. 5.* If voltage is not as specified, replace thermo control amplifier. See THERMO CONTROL AMPLIFIER SPECIFICATIONS table.

THERMO CONTROL AMPLIFIER SPECIFICATIONS

Evaporator Temperature °F (°C)	Thermo Amplifier Operation	Volts
Decreasing To 37-38 (2.5-3.5)	Off	About 12
Increasing To 39-41 (4-5)	On	Zero

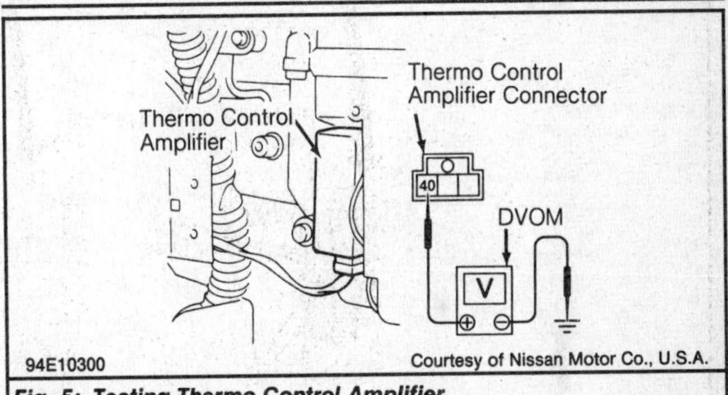
Thermo Control
Amplifier Connector
Thermo Control
Amplifier
40
DVOM
V
94E10300
Courtesy of Nissan Motor Co., U.S.A.

Fig. 5: Testing Thermo Control Amplifier

THERMAL PROTECTOR SWITCH

Thermal protector switch is located on A/C compressor. Check compressor operation at indicated temperature. See THERMAL PROTECTOR SWITCH TEST table. Replace switch if compressor does not test as specified.

THERMAL PROTECTOR SWITCH TEST

Compressor Temperature °F (°C)	Compressor Operation
Increasing To 293-311 (145-155)	Off
Decreasing To 266-284 (130-140)	On

1993 MANUAL A/C-HEATER SYSTEMS
Altima (Cont.)

REMOVAL & INSTALLATION

WARNING: To avoid injury from accidental air bag deployment, read and carefully follow all SERVICE PRECAUTIONS and DISABLING & ACTIVATING AIR BAG SYSTEM procedures in AIR BAG SYSTEM SAFETY article in GENERAL SERVICING.

A/C COMPRESSOR

Removal – Loosen idler pulley bolt, and remove compressor belt. Discharge A/C system using approved refrigerant recovery/recycling equipment. Disconnect compressor clutch lead. Remove discharge and suction hoses from compressor, and plug hose openings. Remove compressor bolts and compressor.

Installation – To install, reverse removal procedure. Tighten compressor bolts to 33-44 ft. lbs. (45-60 N.m). Coat new "O" rings with refrigerant oil when attaching hoses to compressor. Evacuate and recharge system.

A/C-HEATER ASSEMBLY

Removal & Installation – Removal and installation procedures are not available from manufacturer. See illustration to aid in removal and installation. *See Fig. 6.*

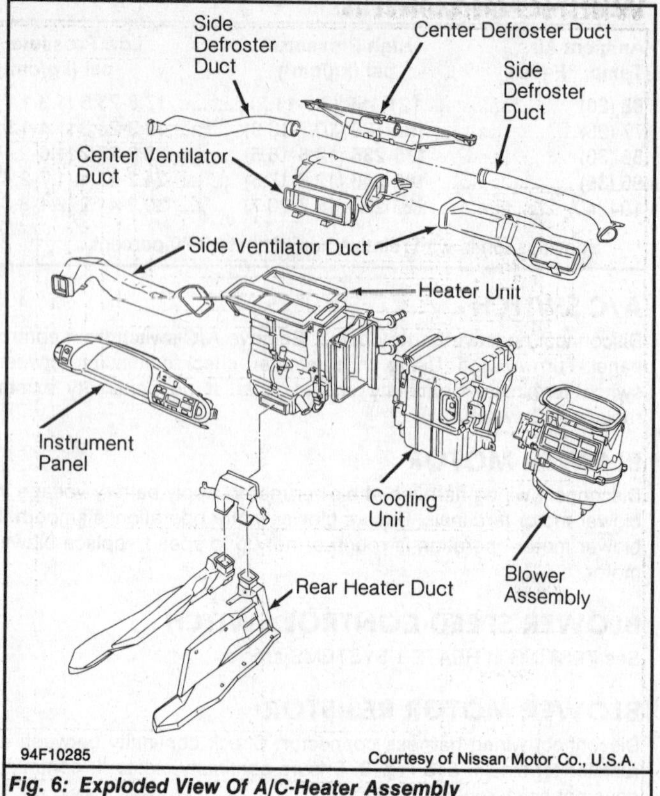
Side Defroster Duct
Center Defroster Duct
Side Defroster Duct
Center Ventilator Duct
Side Ventilator Duct
Heater Unit
Instrument Panel
Cooling Unit
Rear Heater Duct
Blower Assembly
94F10285
Courtesy of Nissan Motor Co., U.S.A.

Fig. 6: Exploded View Of A/C-Heater Assembly

1993 MANUAL A/C-HEATER SYSTEMS
Altima (Cont.)

WIRING DIAGRAM

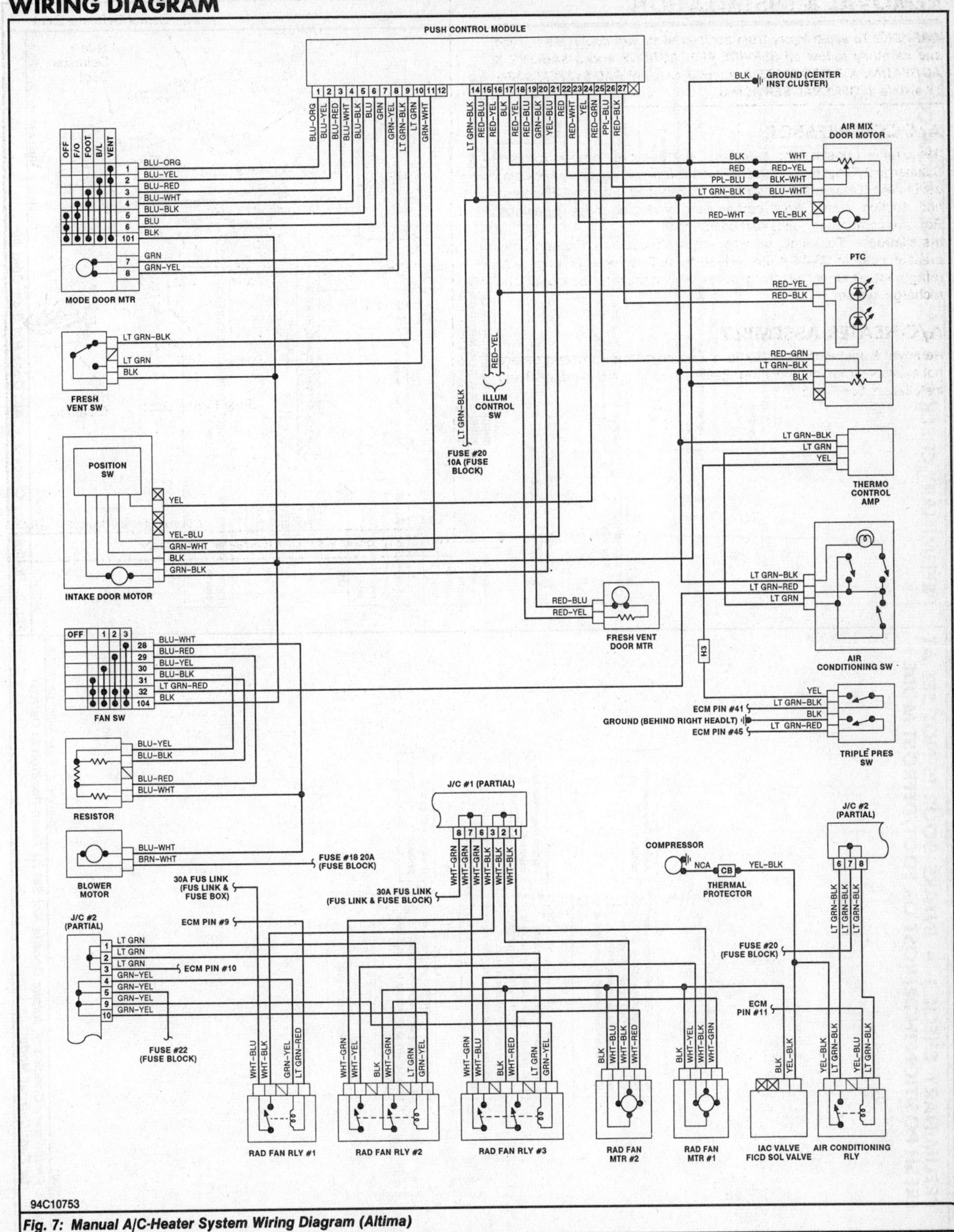

PUSH CONTROL MODULE
GROUND (CENTER INST CLUSTER)
AIR MIX DOOR MOTOR
PTC
MODE DOOR MTR
OFF
F/O
FOOT
B/L
VENT
FRESH VENT SW
ILLUM CONTROL SW
FUSE #20 10A (FUSE BLOCK)
THERMO CONTROL AMP
POSITION SW
INTAKE DOOR MOTOR
FRESH VENT DOOR MTR
AIR CONDITIONING SW
FAN SW
ECM PIN #41
GROUND (BEHIND RIGHT HEADLT)
ECM PIN #45
TRIPLE PRES SW
RESISTOR
J/C #1 (PARTIAL)
J/C #2 (PARTIAL)
BLOWER MOTOR
FUSE #18 20A (FUSE BLOCK)
COMPRESSOR
NCA
CB
THERMAL PROTECTOR
30A FUS LINK (FUS LINK & FUSE BOX)
30A FUS LINK (FUS LINK & FUSE BLOCK)
ECM PIN #9
ECM PIN #10
FUSE #20 (FUSE BLOCK)
ECM PIN #11
FUSE #22 (FUSE BLOCK)
RAD FAN RLY #1
RAD FAN RLY #2
RAD FAN RLY #3
RAD FAN MTR #2
RAD FAN MTR #1
IAC VALVE FICD SOL VALVE
AIR CONDITIONING RLY
94C10753

Fig. 7: Manual A/C-Heater System Wiring Diagram (Altima)

1993 MANUAL A/C-HEATER SYSTEMS
Trouble Shooting – Altima

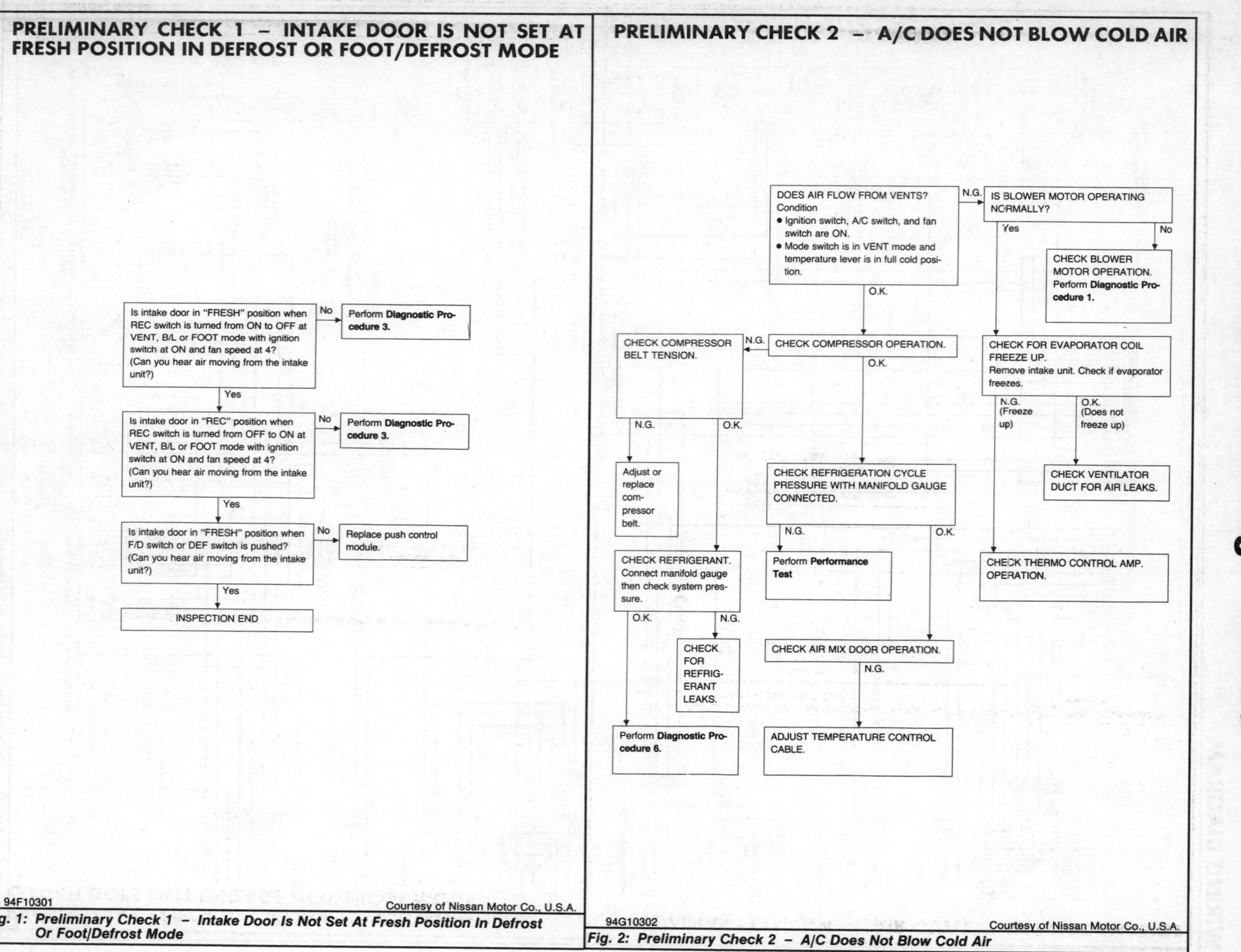
PRELIMINARY CHECK 1 – INTAKE DOOR IS NOT SET AT FRESH POSITION IN DEFROST OR FOOT/DEFROST MODE
Is intake door in "FRESH" position when REC switch is turned from ON to OFF at VENT, B/L or FOOT mode with ignition switch at ON and fan speed at 4? (Can you hear air moving from the intake unit?)
No
Perform Diagnostic Procedure 3.
Yes
Is intake door in "REC" position when REC switch is turned from OFF to ON at VENT, B/L or FOOT mode with ignition switch at ON and fan speed at 4? (Can you hear air moving from the intake unit?)
No
Perform Diagnostic Procedure 3.
Yes
Is intake door in "FRESH" position when F/D switch or DEF switch is pushed? (Can you hear air moving from the intake unit?)
No
Replace push control module.
Yes
INSPECTION END
94F10301
Courtesy of Nissan Motor Co., U.S.A.
PRELIMINARY CHECK 2 – A/C DOES NOT BLOW COLD AIR
DOES AIR FLOW FROM VENTS? Condition
• Ignition switch, A/C switch, and fan switch are ON.
• Mode switch is in VENT mode and temperature lever is in full cold position.
N.G.
IS BLOWER MOTOR OPERATING NORMALLY?
Yes
No
CHECK BLOWER MOTOR OPERATION. Perform Diagnostic Procedure 1.
O.K.
CHECK COMPRESSOR OPERATION.
N.G.
CHECK COMPRESSOR BELT TENSION.
CHECK FOR EVAPORATOR COIL FREEZE UP. Remove intake unit. Check if evaporator freezes.
N.G. (Freeze up)
O.K. (Does not freeze up)
CHECK VENTILATOR DUCT FOR AIR LEAKS.
CHECK THERMO CONTROL AMP. OPERATION.
N.G.
O.K.
Adjust or replace compressor belt.
O.K.
CHECK REFRIGERATION CYCLE PRESSURE WITH MANIFOLD GAUGE CONNECTED.
N.G.
Perform Performance Test
O.K.
CHECK REFRIGERANT. Connect manifold gauge then check system pressure.
O.K.
N.G.
CHECK FOR REFRIGERANT LEAKS.
Perform Diagnostic Procedure 6.
CHECK AIR MIX DOOR OPERATION.
N.G.
ADJUST TEMPERATURE CONTROL CABLE.
94G10302
Courtesy of Nissan Motor Co., U.S.A.

Fig. 1: Preliminary Check 1 – Intake Door Is Not Set At Fresh Position In Defrost Or Foot/Defrost Mode

Fig. 2: Preliminary Check 2 – A/C Does Not Blow Cold Air

PRELIMINARY CHECK 3 – COMPRESSOR (MAGNET) CLUTCH DOES NOT ENGAGE IN DEFROST MODE

- Perform PRELIMINARY CHECK 2 before referring to the following flow chart.

With engine running, does magnet clutch engage normally when A/C switch and fan switch are ON?

No → Perform **Diagnostic Procedure 6.**

Yes ↓

Push A/C switch and turn A/C system OFF. Make sure that magnet clutch is disengaged.

↓

With engine running, does magnet clutch engage normally when DEF switch and fan switch are ON?

No → Replace push control module.

Yes ↓

INSPECTION END

4H10303

Courtesy of Nissan Motor Co., U.S.A.

Fig. 3: Preliminary Check 3 – Compressor (Magnet) Clutch Does Not Engage In Defrost Mode

PRELIMINARY CHECK 4 – AIR OUTLET DOES NOT CHANGE

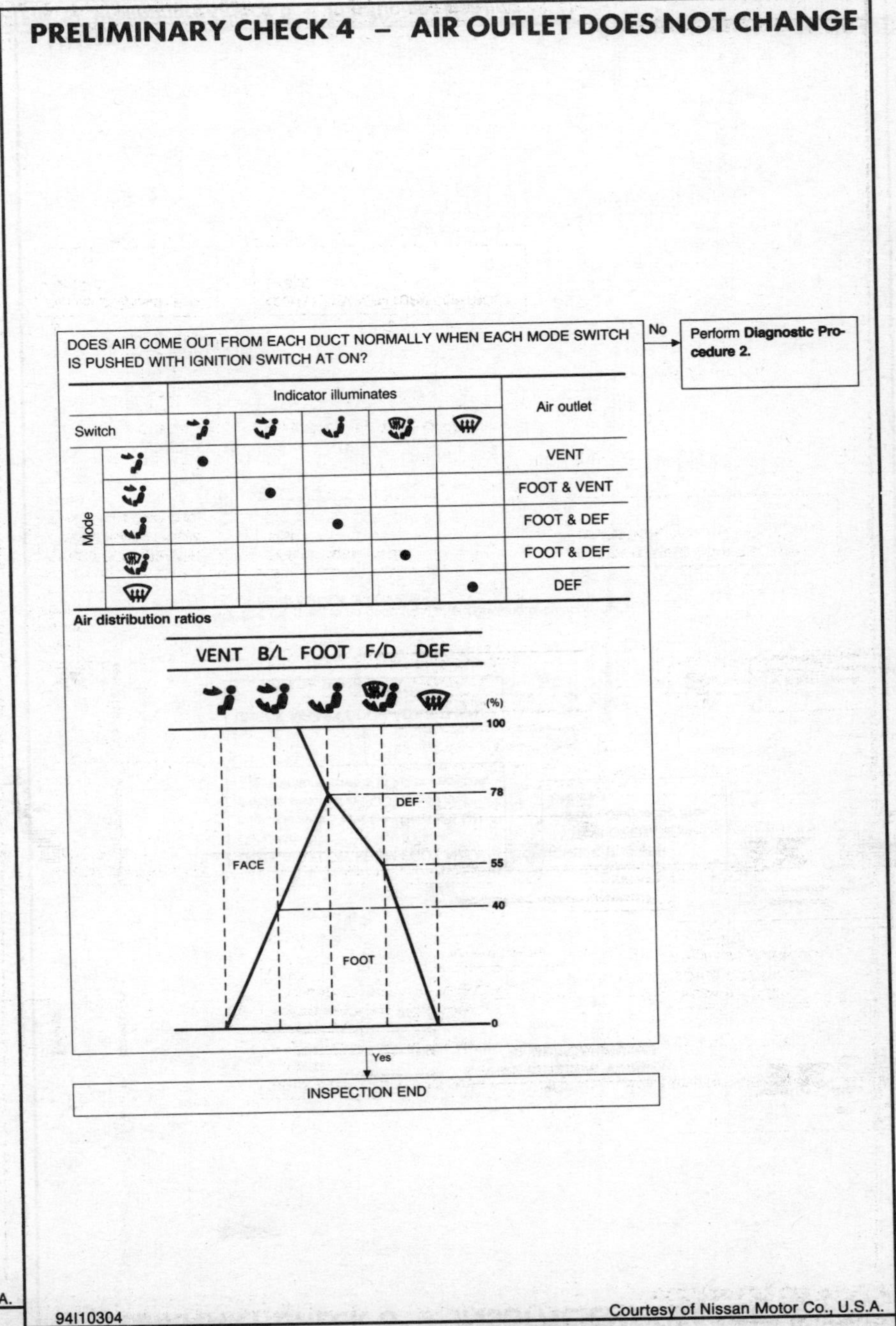

DOES AIR COME OUT FROM EACH DUCT NORMALLY WHEN EACH MODE SWITCH IS PUSHED WITH IGNITION SWITCH AT ON?
No
Perform Diagnostic Procedure 2.
Switch
Indicator illuminates
Air outlet
Mode
VENT
FOOT & VENT
FOOT & DEF
FOOT & DEF
DEF
Air distribution ratios
VENT B/L FOOT F/D DEF
(%)
100
78
55
40
0
FACE
DEF
FOOT
Yes
INSPECTION END

94I10304

Courtesy of Nissan Motor Co., U.S.A.

Fig. 4: Preliminary Check 4 – Air Outlet Does Not Change

1993 MANUAL A/C-HEATER SYSTEMS
Trouble Shooting – Altima (Cont.)

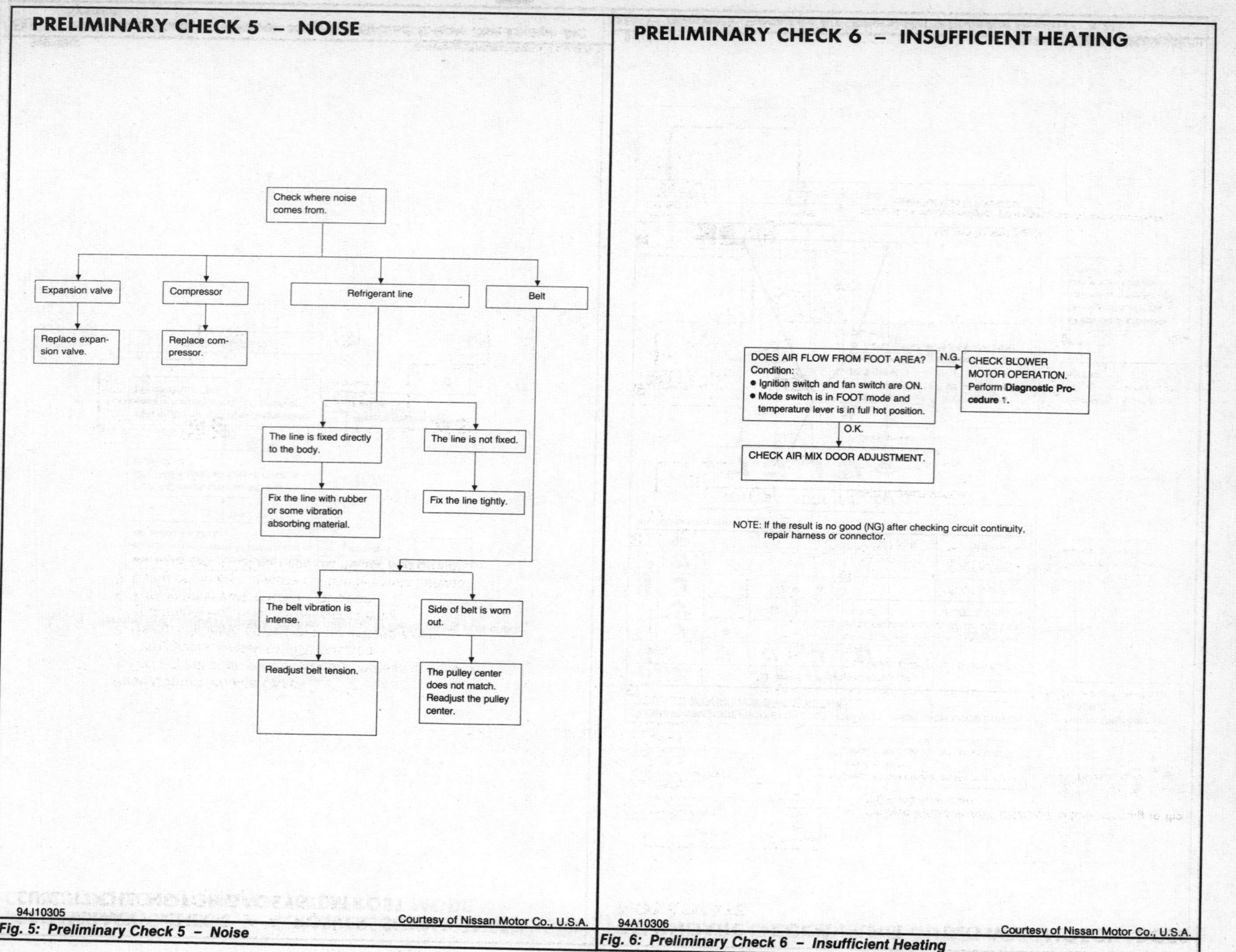
PRELIMINARY CHECK 5 – NOISE
Check where noise comes from.
Expansion valve
Compressor
Refrigerant line
Belt
Replace expansion valve.
Replace compressor.
The line is fixed directly to the body.
The line is not fixed.
Fix the line with rubber or some vibration absorbing material.
Fix the line tightly.
The belt vibration is intense.
Side of belt is worn out.
Readjust belt tension.
The pulley center does not match. Readjust the pulley center.
94J10305
Courtesy of Nissan Motor Co., U.S.A.
PRELIMINARY CHECK 6 – INSUFFICIENT HEATING
DOES AIR FLOW FROM FOOT AREA?
Condition:
● Ignition switch and fan switch are ON.
● Mode switch is in FOOT mode and temperature lever is in full hot position.
N.G.
CHECK BLOWER MOTOR OPERATION. Perform Diagnostic Procedure 1.
O.K.
CHECK AIR MIX DOOR ADJUSTMENT.
NOTE: If the result is no good (NG) after checking circuit continuity, repair harness or connector.
94A10306
Courtesy of Nissan Motor Co., U.S.A.

Fig. 5: Preliminary Check 5 – Noise

Fig. 6: Preliminary Check 6 – Insufficient Heating

PRELIMINARY CHECK 7 – POWER SUPPLY & GROUND CIRCUIT CHECKS FOR A/C SYSTEM

Push Control Module Check

1. Disconnect push control module harness connector.
2. Turn ignition switch to ACC position.
3. Using voltmeter, ensure battery voltage exists at terminal No. 14 of harness connector.
4. Turn ignition switch to OFF position.
5. Using ohmmeter, ensure continuity exists between terminal No. 17 of harness connector and ground.

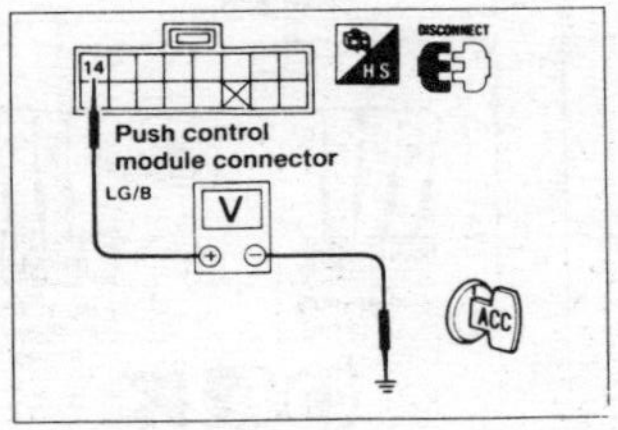

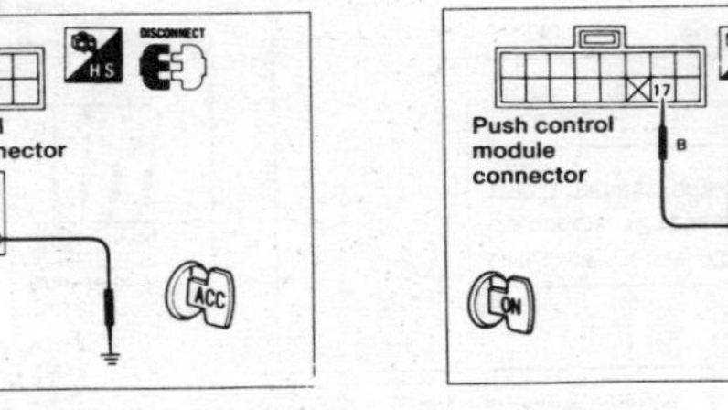
14
Push control
module connector
LG/B
V
HS
DISCONNECT
ACC

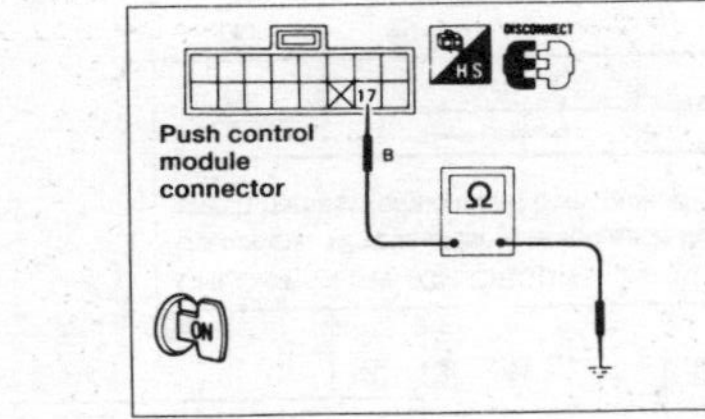
17
Push control
module
connector
B
Ω
HS
DISCONNECT
ON

94B10307 Courtesy of Nissan Motor Co., U.S.A.

Fig. 7: Preliminary Check 7 – Power Supply & Ground Circuit Checks For A/C System

DIAGNOSTIC PROCEDURE 1 – BLOWER MOTOR DOES NOT ROTATE

	INCIDENT	Flow chart No.
1	Fan fails to rotate.	1
2	Fan does not rotate at 1-speed.	2
3	Fan does not rotate at 2-speed.	3
4	Fan does not rotate at 3-speed.	4
5	Fan does not rotate at 4-speed.	5

- **Perform PRELIMINARY CHECK 2 before referring to the following flow chart.**

Check if blower motor rotates properly at each fan speed. Conduct check as per flow chart at left.

2 3 4 5 Go To Next Figure → B

1 ↓

A CHECK POWER SUPPLY FOR BLOWER MOTOR. Disconnect blower motor harness connector. Do approx. 12 volts exist between blower motor harness terminal No. 45 and body ground?

- N.G. → Check 20A fuses at fuse block.
- O.K. ↓

B Check circuit continuity between blower motor harness terminal No. 46 and body ground.

- N.G. → Reconnect blower motor harness connector.
- O.K. ↓

CHECK BLOWER MOTOR.

- N.G. ↓ Replace blower motor.

C CHECK BLOWER MOTOR CIRCUIT BETWEEN BLOWER MOTOR AND RESISTOR. Do approx. 12 volts exist between resistor harness terminal No. 28 and body ground?

- N.G. → Disconnect blower motor and resistor harness connectors. ↓ D (Note) Check circuit continuity between blower motor harness terminal No. 46 and resistor harness terminal No. 28.
- O.K. ↓ A Go To Next Figure

NOTE: If the result is no good (NG) after checking circuit continuity, repair harness or connector.

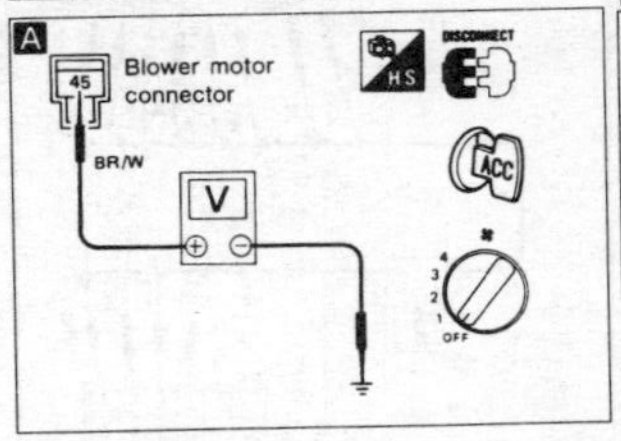

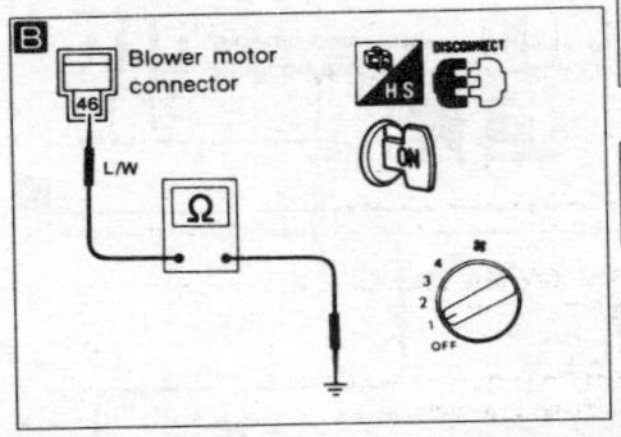

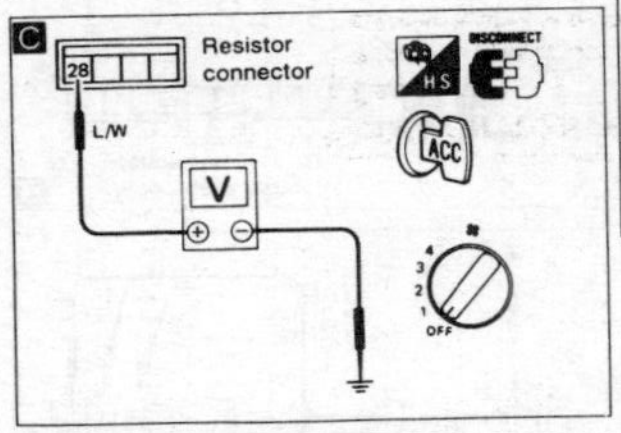

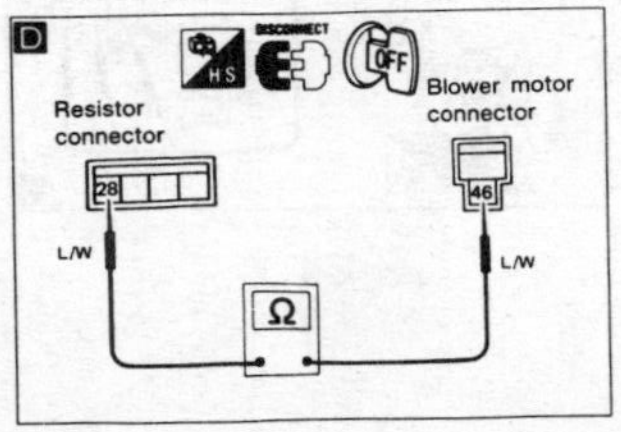

A: Blower motor connector, 45, BR/W, V, HS, DISCONNECT, ACC
B: Blower motor connector, 46, L/W, Ω, HS, DISCONNECT, ON
C: Resistor connector, 28, L/W, V, HS, DISCONNECT, ACC
D: Resistor connector, 28, L/W, Blower motor connector, 46, L/W, Ω, HS, DISCONNECT, OFF

94C10308 Courtesy of Nissan Motor Co., U.S.A.

Fig. 8: Diagnostic Procedure 1 – Blower Motor Does Not Rotate (1 Of 2)

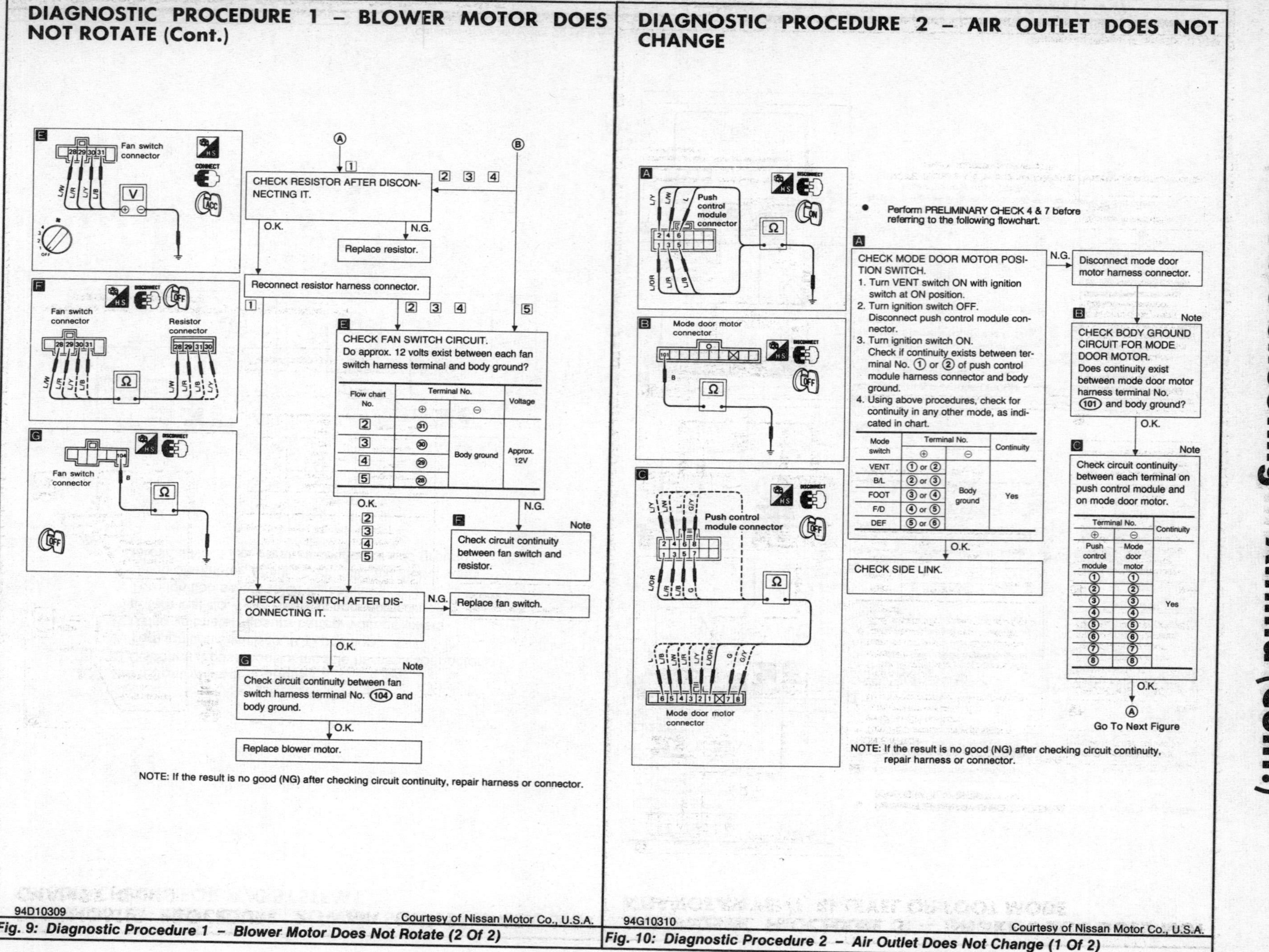
DIAGNOSTIC PROCEDURE 1 – BLOWER MOTOR DOES NOT ROTATE (Cont.)
Fan switch connector
Resistor connector
CHECK RESISTOR AFTER DISCONNECTING IT.
Replace resistor.
Reconnect resistor harness connector.
CHECK FAN SWITCH CIRCUIT.
Do approx. 12 volts exist between each fan switch harness terminal and body ground?
Flow chart No.
Terminal No.
Voltage
Body ground
Approx. 12V
Check circuit continuity between fan switch and resistor.
CHECK FAN SWITCH AFTER DISCONNECTING IT.
Replace fan switch.
Check circuit continuity between fan switch harness terminal No. 104 and body ground.
Replace blower motor.
O.K.
N.G.
Note
NOTE: If the result is no good (NG) after checking circuit continuity, repair harness or connector.
94D10309
Courtesy of Nissan Motor Co., U.S.A.
DIAGNOSTIC PROCEDURE 2 – AIR OUTLET DOES NOT CHANGE
Push control module connector
Mode door motor connector
Perform PRELIMINARY CHECK 4 & 7 before referring to the following flowchart.
CHECK MODE DOOR MOTOR POSITION SWITCH.
1. Turn VENT switch ON with ignition switch at ON position.
2. Turn ignition switch OFF. Disconnect push control module connector.
3. Turn ignition switch ON. Check if continuity exists between terminal No. 1 or 2 of push control module harness connector and body ground.
4. Using above procedures, check for continuity in any other mode, as indicated in chart.
Mode switch
VENT
B/L
FOOT
F/D
DEF
1 or 2
2 or 3
3 or 4
4 or 5
5 or 6
Body ground
Continuity
Yes
CHECK SIDE LINK.
Disconnect mode door motor harness connector.
CHECK BODY GROUND CIRCUIT FOR MODE DOOR MOTOR.
Does continuity exist between mode door motor harness terminal No. 101 and body ground?
Check circuit continuity between each terminal on push control module and on mode door motor.
Go To Next Figure
NOTE: If the result is no good (NG) after checking circuit continuity, repair harness or connector.
94G10310
Courtesy of Nissan Motor Co., U.S.A.

Fig. 9: Diagnostic Procedure 1 – Blower Motor Does Not Rotate (2 Of 2)

Fig. 10: Diagnostic Procedure 2 – Air Outlet Does Not Change (1 Of 2)

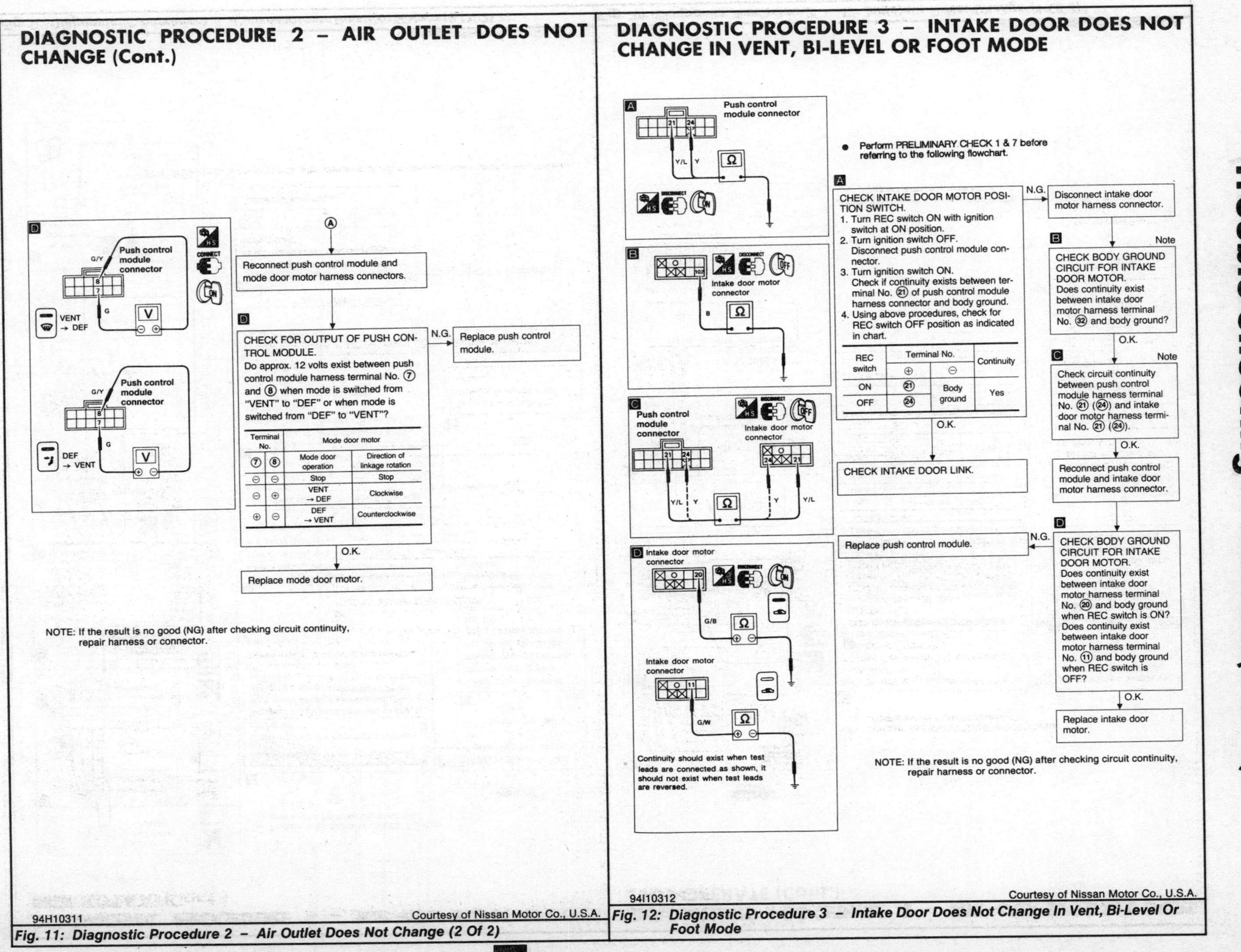

DIAGNOSTIC PROCEDURE 2 – AIR OUTLET DOES NOT CHANGE (Cont.)
D
Push control module connector
G/Y
8
7
G
V
VENT → DEF
HS
CONNECT
ON
DEF → VENT
A
Reconnect push control module and mode door motor harness connectors.
D
CHECK FOR OUTPUT OF PUSH CONTROL MODULE.
Do approx. 12 volts exist between push control module harness terminal No. ⑦ and ⑧ when mode is switched from "VENT" to "DEF" or when mode is switched from "DEF" to "VENT"?
N.G.
Replace push control module.
O.K.
Replace mode door motor.
NOTE: If the result is no good (NG) after checking circuit continuity, repair harness or connector.
94H10311
Courtesy of Nissan Motor Co., U.S.A.
DIAGNOSTIC PROCEDURE 3 – INTAKE DOOR DOES NOT CHANGE IN VENT, BI-LEVEL OR FOOT MODE
A
Push control module connector
21
24
Y/L
Y
Ω
DISCONNECT
ON
B
Intake door motor connector
102
B
OFF
C
Push control module connector
Intake door motor connector
D
Intake door motor connector
20
G/B
11
G/W
Continuity should exist when test leads are connected as shown, it should not exist when test leads are reversed.
• Perform PRELIMINARY CHECK 1 & 7 before referring to the following flowchart.
A
CHECK INTAKE DOOR MOTOR POSITION SWITCH.
1. Turn REC switch ON with ignition switch at ON position.
2. Turn ignition switch OFF. Disconnect push control module connector.
3. Turn ignition switch ON. Check if continuity exists between terminal No. ㉑ of push control module harness connector and body ground.
4. Using above procedures, check for REC switch OFF position as indicated in chart.
N.G.
Disconnect intake door motor harness connector.
B
Note
CHECK BODY GROUND CIRCUIT FOR INTAKE DOOR MOTOR.
Does continuity exist between intake door motor harness terminal No. ㉜ and body ground?
O.K.
C
Note
Check circuit continuity between push control module harness terminal No. ㉑ (㉔) and intake door motor harness terminal No. ㉑ (㉔).
O.K.
Reconnect push control module and intake door motor harness connector.
D
CHECK BODY GROUND CIRCUIT FOR INTAKE DOOR MOTOR.
Does continuity exist between intake door motor harness terminal No. ⑳ and body ground when REC switch is ON?
Does continuity exist between intake door motor harness terminal No. ⑪ and body ground when REC switch is OFF?
O.K.
Replace intake door motor.
N.G.
Replace push control module.
O.K.
CHECK INTAKE DOOR LINK.
NOTE: If the result is no good (NG) after checking circuit continuity, repair harness or connector.
94I10312
Courtesy of Nissan Motor Co., U.S.A.

Terminal No.		Mode door motor	
⑦	⑧	Mode door operation	Direction of linkage rotation
⊖	⊖	Stop	Stop
⊖	⊕	VENT → DEF	Clockwise
⊕	⊖	DEF → VENT	Counterclockwise

REC switch	Terminal No. ⊕	Terminal No. ⊖	Continuity
ON	㉑	Body ground	Yes
OFF	㉔	Body ground	Yes

Fig. 11: Diagnostic Procedure 2 – Air Outlet Does Not Change (2 Of 2)

Fig. 12: Diagnostic Procedure 3 – Intake Door Does Not Change In Vent, Bi-Level Or Foot Mode

1993 MANUAL A/C-HEATER SYSTEMS
Trouble Shooting – Altima (Cont.)

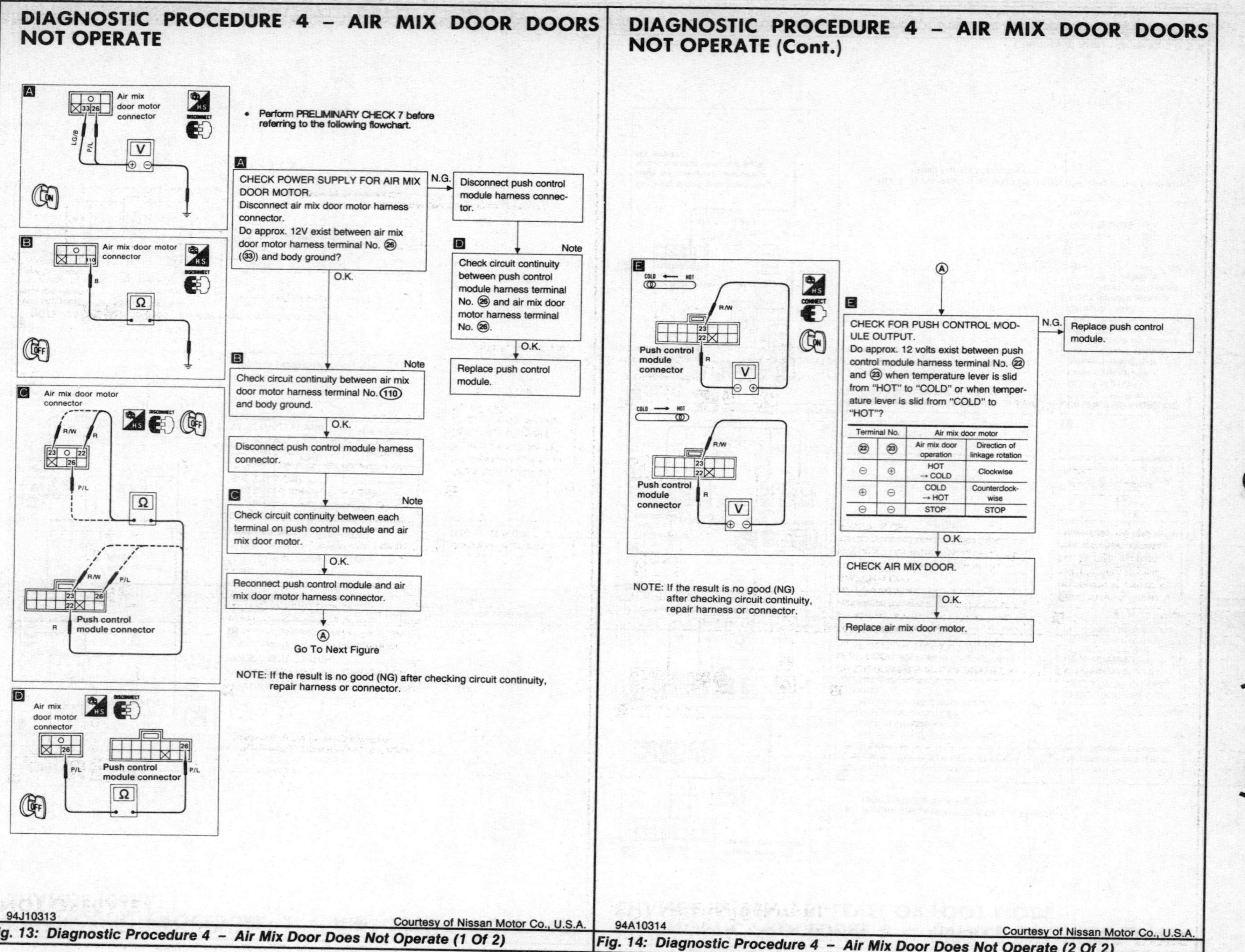
DIAGNOSTIC PROCEDURE 4 – AIR MIX DOOR DOORS NOT OPERATE
A
Air mix door motor connector
33
26
LG/B
P/L
V
B
Air mix door motor connector
110
B
Ω
C
Air mix door motor connector
23
22
26
R/W
R
P/L
Ω
Push control module connector
D
Air mix door motor connector
26
P/L
Push control module connector
Ω
• Perform PRELIMINARY CHECK 7 before referring to the following flowchart.
A
CHECK POWER SUPPLY FOR AIR MIX DOOR MOTOR.
Disconnect air mix door motor harness connector.
Do approx. 12V exist between air mix door motor harness terminal No. 26 (33) and body ground?
N.G.
Disconnect push control module harness connector.
D
Note
Check circuit continuity between push control module harness terminal No. 26 and air mix door motor harness terminal No. 26.
O.K.
Replace push control module.
O.K.
B
Note
Check circuit continuity between air mix door motor harness terminal No. 110 and body ground.
O.K.
Disconnect push control module harness connector.
C
Note
Check circuit continuity between each terminal on push control module and air mix door motor.
O.K.
Reconnect push control module and air mix door motor harness connector.
A
Go To Next Figure
NOTE: If the result is no good (NG) after checking circuit continuity, repair harness or connector.
94J10313
Courtesy of Nissan Motor Co., U.S.A.
DIAGNOSTIC PROCEDURE 4 – AIR MIX DOOR DOORS NOT OPERATE (Cont.)
E
COLD ← HOT
R/W
23
22
R
Push control module connector
V
COLD → HOT
R/W
23
22
R
Push control module connector
V
NOTE: If the result is no good (NG) after checking circuit continuity, repair harness or connector.
A
E
CHECK FOR PUSH CONTROL MODULE OUTPUT.
Do approx. 12 volts exist between push control module harness terminal No. 22 and 23 when temperature lever is slid from "HOT" to "COLD" or when temperature lever is slid from "COLD" to "HOT"?
N.G.
Replace push control module.
O.K.
CHECK AIR MIX DOOR.
O.K.
Replace air mix door motor.
94A10314
Courtesy of Nissan Motor Co., U.S.A.

Terminal No.		Air mix door motor	
22	23	Air mix door operation	Direction of linkage rotation
⊖	⊕	HOT → COLD	Clockwise
⊕	⊖	COLD → HOT	Counterclockwise
⊖	⊖	STOP	STOP

Fig. 13: Diagnostic Procedure 4 – Air Mix Door Does Not Operate (1 Of 2)

Fig. 14: Diagnostic Procedure 4 – Air Mix Door Does Not Operate (2 Of 2)

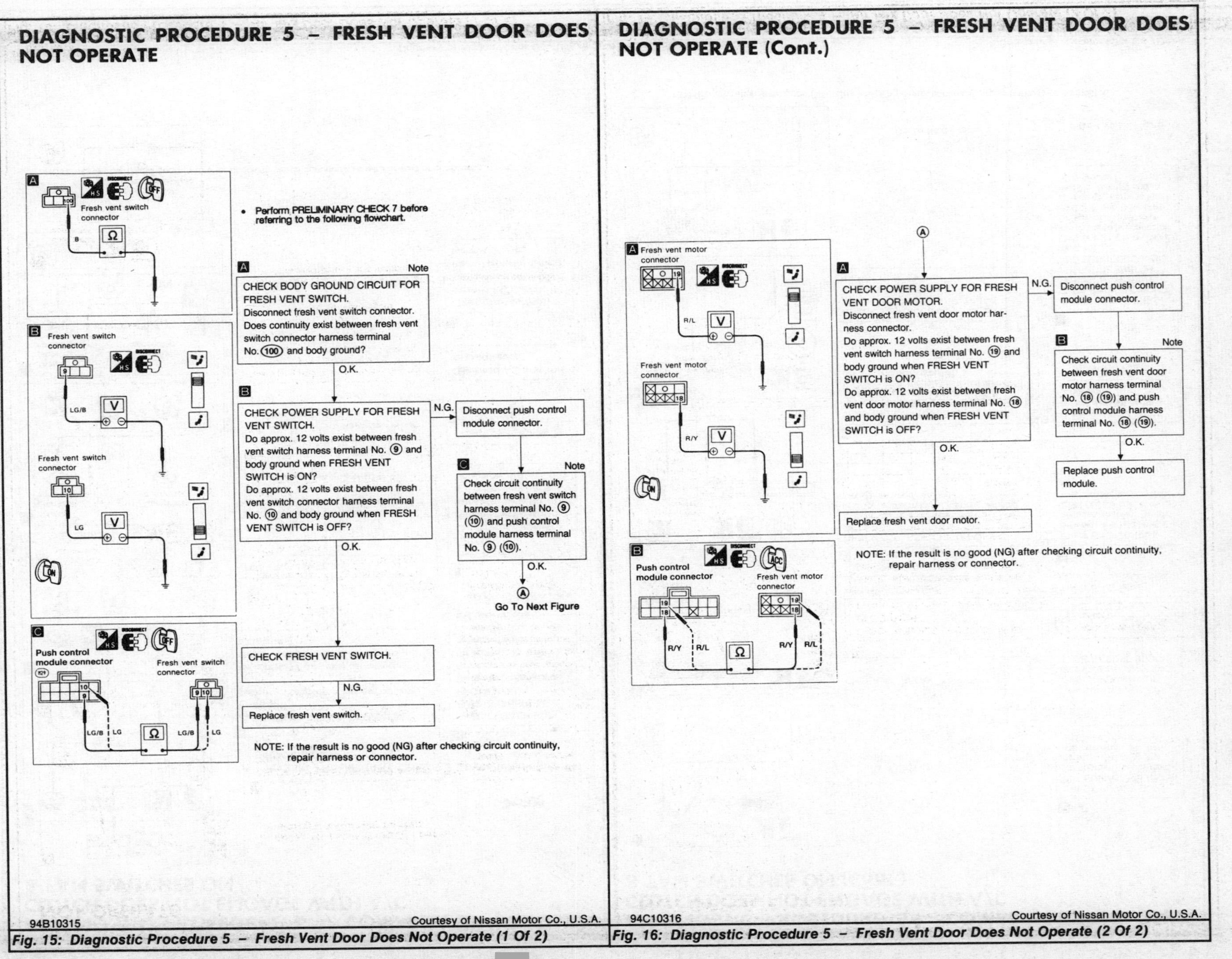
DIAGNOSTIC PROCEDURE 5 – FRESH VENT DOOR DOES NOT OPERATE
A
Fresh vent switch connector
B
• Perform PRELIMINARY CHECK 7 before referring to the following flowchart.
A
Note
CHECK BODY GROUND CIRCUIT FOR FRESH VENT SWITCH.
Disconnect fresh vent switch connector.
Does continuity exist between fresh vent switch connector harness terminal No. (100) and body ground?
O.K.
B
Fresh vent switch connector
LG/B
Fresh vent switch connector
LG
B
CHECK POWER SUPPLY FOR FRESH VENT SWITCH.
Do approx. 12 volts exist between fresh vent switch harness terminal No. (9) and body ground when FRESH VENT SWITCH is ON?
Do approx. 12 volts exist between fresh vent switch connector harness terminal No. (10) and body ground when FRESH VENT SWITCH is OFF?
N.G.
Disconnect push control module connector.
C
Note
Check circuit continuity between fresh vent switch harness terminal No. (9) ((10)) and push control module harness terminal No. (9) ((10)).
O.K.
(A)
Go To Next Figure
O.K.
C
Push control module connector
Fresh vent switch connector
LG/B
LG
CHECK FRESH VENT SWITCH.
N.G.
Replace fresh vent switch.
NOTE: If the result is no good (NG) after checking circuit continuity, repair harness or connector.
94B10315
Courtesy of Nissan Motor Co., U.S.A.
DIAGNOSTIC PROCEDURE 5 – FRESH VENT DOOR DOES NOT OPERATE (Cont.)
A
Fresh vent motor connector
R/L
Fresh vent motor connector
R/Y
(A)
A
CHECK POWER SUPPLY FOR FRESH VENT DOOR MOTOR.
Disconnect fresh vent door motor harness connector.
Do approx. 12 volts exist between fresh vent switch harness terminal No. (19) and body ground when FRESH VENT SWITCH is ON?
Do approx. 12 volts exist between fresh vent door motor harness terminal No. (18) and body ground when FRESH VENT SWITCH is OFF?
N.G.
Disconnect push control module connector.
B
Note
Check circuit continuity between fresh vent door motor harness terminal No. (18) ((19)) and push control module harness terminal No. (18) ((19)).
O.K.
Replace push control module.
O.K.
Replace fresh vent door motor.
B
Push control module connector
Fresh vent motor connector
R/Y
R/L
NOTE: If the result is no good (NG) after checking circuit continuity, repair harness or connector.
94C10316
Courtesy of Nissan Motor Co., U.S.A.

Fig. 15: Diagnostic Procedure 5 – Fresh Vent Door Does Not Operate (1 Of 2)

Fig. 16: Diagnostic Procedure 5 – Fresh Vent Door Does Not Operate (2 Of 2)

1993 MANUAL A/C-HEATER SYSTEMS
Trouble Shooting – Altima (Cont.)

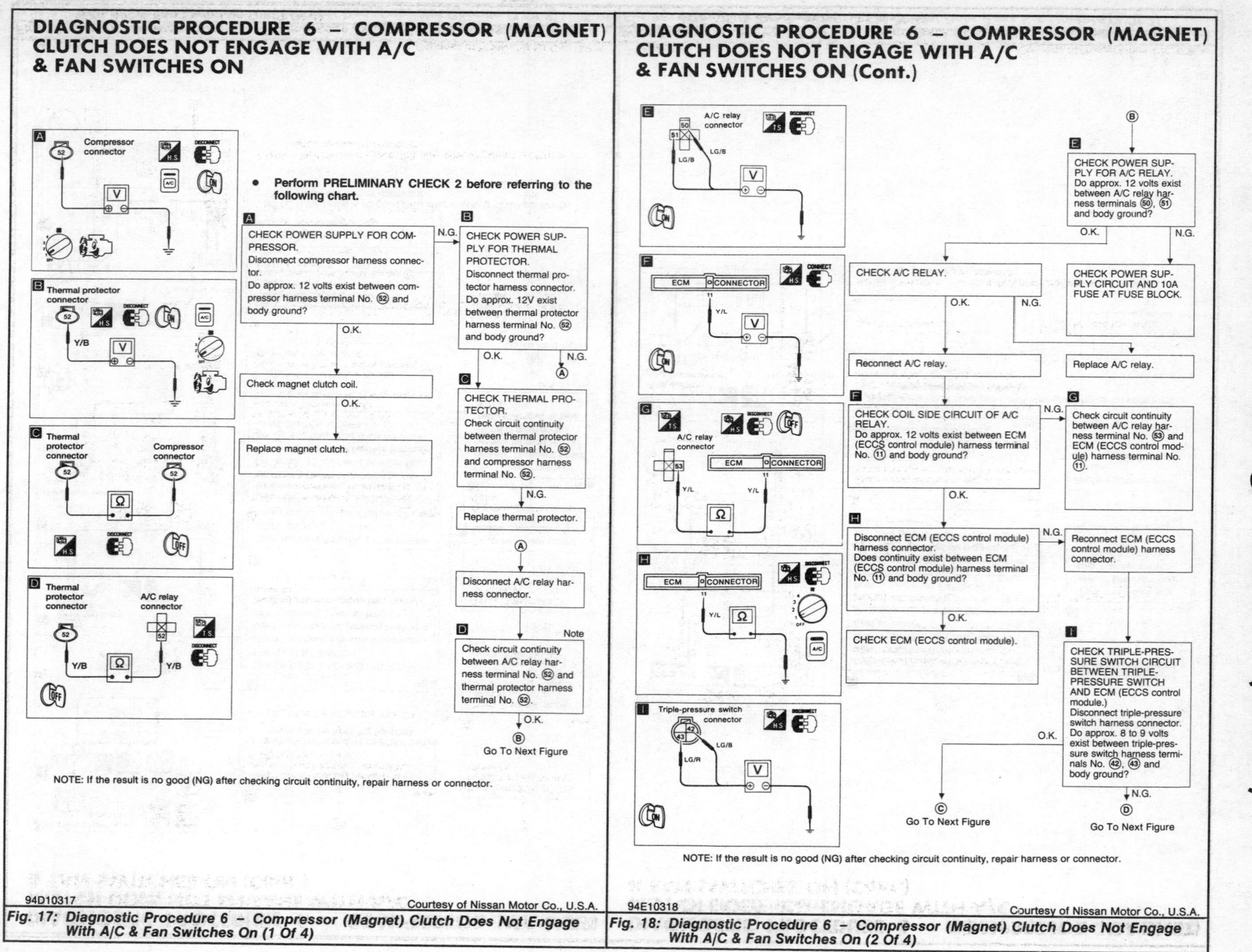
DIAGNOSTIC PROCEDURE 6 – COMPRESSOR (MAGNET) CLUTCH DOES NOT ENGAGE WITH A/C & FAN SWITCHES ON
A Compressor connector
B Thermal protector connector
Y/B
C Thermal protector connector
Compressor connector
D Thermal protector connector
A/C relay connector
Y/B
Y/B
• Perform PRELIMINARY CHECK 2 before referring to the following chart.
A CHECK POWER SUPPLY FOR COMPRESSOR.
Disconnect compressor harness connector.
Do approx. 12 volts exist between compressor harness terminal No. 52 and body ground?
N.G.
O.K.
Check magnet clutch coil.
O.K.
Replace magnet clutch.
B CHECK POWER SUPPLY FOR THERMAL PROTECTOR.
Disconnect thermal protector harness connector.
Do approx. 12V exist between thermal protector harness terminal No. 52 and body ground?
O.K.
N.G.
A
C CHECK THERMAL PROTECTOR.
Check circuit continuity between thermal protector harness terminal No. 52 and compressor harness terminal No. 52.
N.G.
Replace thermal protector.
A
Disconnect A/C relay harness connector.
D Note
Check circuit continuity between A/C relay harness terminal No. 52 and thermal protector harness terminal No. 52.
O.K.
B
Go To Next Figure
NOTE: If the result is no good (NG) after checking circuit continuity, repair harness or connector.
94D10317
Courtesy of Nissan Motor Co., U.S.A.
DIAGNOSTIC PROCEDURE 6 – COMPRESSOR (MAGNET) CLUTCH DOES NOT ENGAGE WITH A/C & FAN SWITCHES ON (Cont.)
E A/C relay connector
50
51
LG/B
LG/B
F ECM CONNECTOR
11
Y/L
G A/C relay connector
53
ECM CONNECTOR
11
Y/L
Y/L
H ECM CONNECTOR
11
Y/L
I Triple-pressure switch connector
42
43
LG/B
LG/R
B
E CHECK POWER SUPPLY FOR A/C RELAY.
Do approx. 12 volts exist between A/C relay harness terminals 50, 51 and body ground?
O.K.
N.G.
CHECK A/C RELAY.
O.K.
N.G.
CHECK POWER SUPPLY CIRCUIT AND 10A FUSE AT FUSE BLOCK.
Reconnect A/C relay.
Replace A/C relay.
F CHECK COIL SIDE CIRCUIT OF A/C RELAY.
Do approx. 12 volts exist between ECM (ECCS control module) harness terminal No. 11 and body ground?
N.G.
G Check circuit continuity between A/C relay harness terminal No. 53 and ECM (ECCS control module) harness terminal No. 11.
O.K.
H Disconnect ECM (ECCS control module) harness connector.
Does continuity exist between ECM (ECCS control module) harness terminal No. 11 and body ground?
N.G.
Reconnect ECM (ECCS control module) harness connector.
O.K.
CHECK ECM (ECCS control module).
I CHECK TRIPLE-PRESSURE SWITCH CIRCUIT BETWEEN TRIPLE-PRESSURE SWITCH AND ECM (ECCS control module.)
Disconnect triple-pressure switch harness connector.
Do approx. 8 to 9 volts exist between triple-pressure switch harness terminals No. 42, 43 and body ground?
O.K.
N.G.
C
Go To Next Figure
D
Go To Next Figure
NOTE: If the result is no good (NG) after checking circuit continuity, repair harness or connector.
94E10318
Courtesy of Nissan Motor Co., U.S.A.

Fig. 17: Diagnostic Procedure 6 – Compressor (Magnet) Clutch Does Not Engage With A/C & Fan Switches On (1 Of 4)

Fig. 18: Diagnostic Procedure 6 – Compressor (Magnet) Clutch Does Not Engage With A/C & Fan Switches On (2 Of 4)

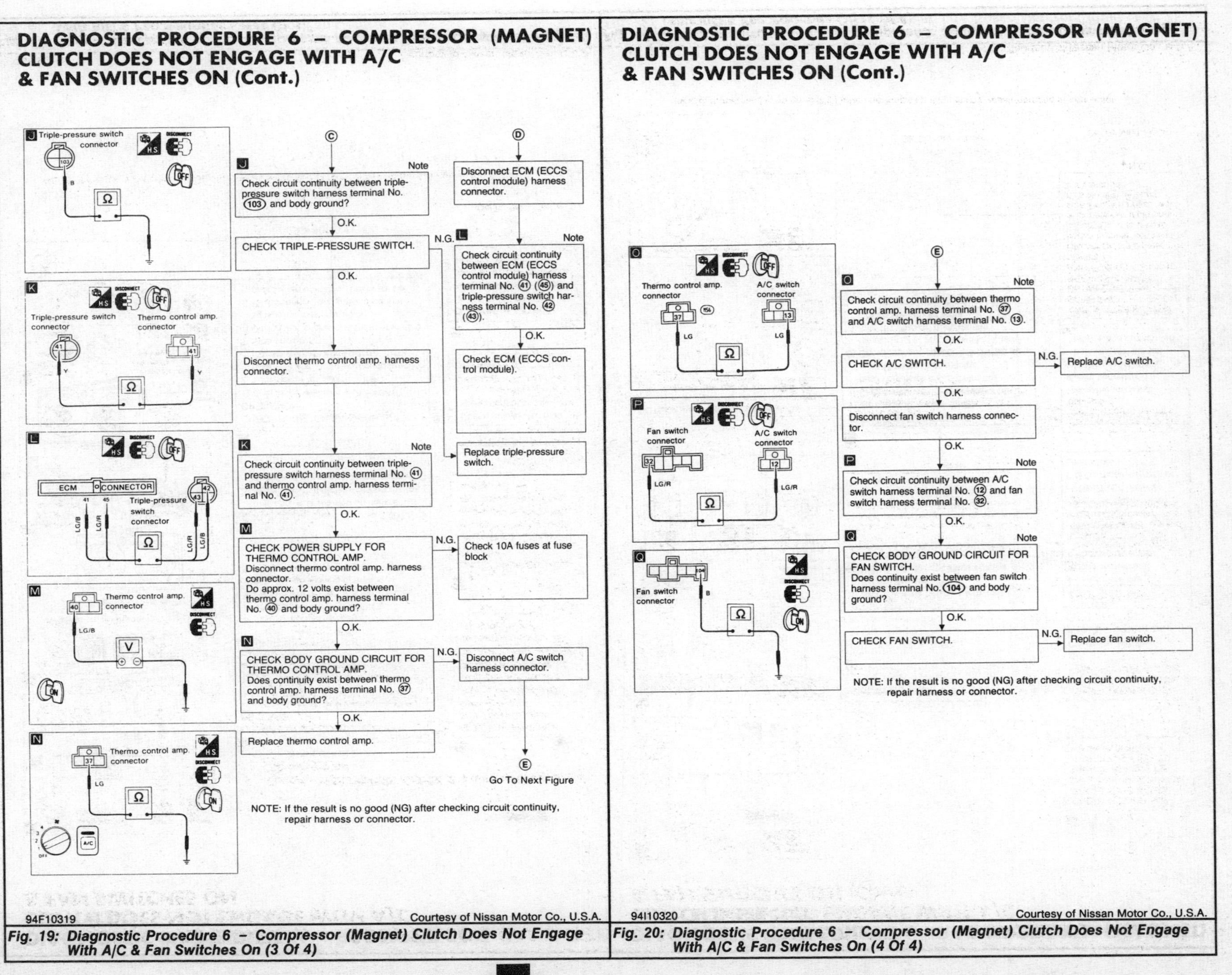
DIAGNOSTIC PROCEDURE 6 – COMPRESSOR (MAGNET) CLUTCH DOES NOT ENGAGE WITH A/C & FAN SWITCHES ON (Cont.)
J Triple-pressure switch connector
103
B
Ω
K
Triple-pressure switch connector
Thermo control amp. connector
41
Y
Ω
L
ECM
CONNECTOR
41
45
LG/B
LG/R
Triple-pressure switch connector
42
43
Ω
M
Thermo control amp. connector
40
LG/B
V
N
Thermo control amp. connector
37
LG
Ω
A/C
C
J
Note
Check circuit continuity between triple-pressure switch harness terminal No. 103 and body ground?
O.K.
CHECK TRIPLE-PRESSURE SWITCH.
O.K.
Disconnect thermo control amp. harness connector.
K
Note
Check circuit continuity between triple-pressure switch harness terminal No. 41 and thermo control amp. harness terminal No. 41.
O.K.
M
CHECK POWER SUPPLY FOR THERMO CONTROL AMP.
Disconnect thermo control amp. harness connector.
Do approx. 12 volts exist between thermo control amp. harness terminal No. 40 and body ground?
O.K.
N
CHECK BODY GROUND CIRCUIT FOR THERMO CONTROL AMP.
Does continuity exist between thermo control amp. harness terminal No. 37 and body ground?
O.K.
Replace thermo control amp.
D
Disconnect ECM (ECCS control module) harness connector.
N.G.
L
Note
Check circuit continuity between ECM (ECCS control module) harness terminal No. 41 (45) and triple-pressure switch harness terminal No. 42 (43).
O.K.
Check ECM (ECCS control module).
Replace triple-pressure switch.
N.G.
Check 10A fuses at fuse block
N.G.
Disconnect A/C switch harness connector.
E
Go To Next Figure
NOTE: If the result is no good (NG) after checking circuit continuity, repair harness or connector.
94F10319
Courtesy of Nissan Motor Co., U.S.A.
DIAGNOSTIC PROCEDURE 6 – COMPRESSOR (MAGNET) CLUTCH DOES NOT ENGAGE WITH A/C & FAN SWITCHES ON (Cont.)
O
Thermo control amp. connector
A/C switch connector
37
13
LG
Ω
P
Fan switch connector
A/C switch connector
32
12
LG/R
Ω
Q
Fan switch connector
104
B
Ω
E
O
Note
Check circuit continuity between thermo control amp. harness terminal No. 37 and A/C switch harness terminal No. 13.
O.K.
CHECK A/C SWITCH.
N.G.
Replace A/C switch.
O.K.
Disconnect fan switch harness connector.
O.K.
P
Note
Check circuit continuity between A/C switch harness terminal No. 12 and fan switch harness terminal No. 32.
O.K.
Q
Note
CHECK BODY GROUND CIRCUIT FOR FAN SWITCH.
Does continuity exist between fan switch harness terminal No. 104 and body ground?
O.K.
CHECK FAN SWITCH.
N.G.
Replace fan switch.
NOTE: If the result is no good (NG) after checking circuit continuity, repair harness or connector.
94I10320
Courtesy of Nissan Motor Co., U.S.A.

Fig. 19: Diagnostic Procedure 6 – Compressor (Magnet) Clutch Does Not Engage With A/C & Fan Switches On (3 Of 4)

Fig. 20: Diagnostic Procedure 6 – Compressor (Magnet) Clutch Does Not Engage With A/C & Fan Switches On (4 Of 4)

1993 MANUAL A/C-HEATER SYSTEMS
Trouble Shooting – Altima (Cont.)

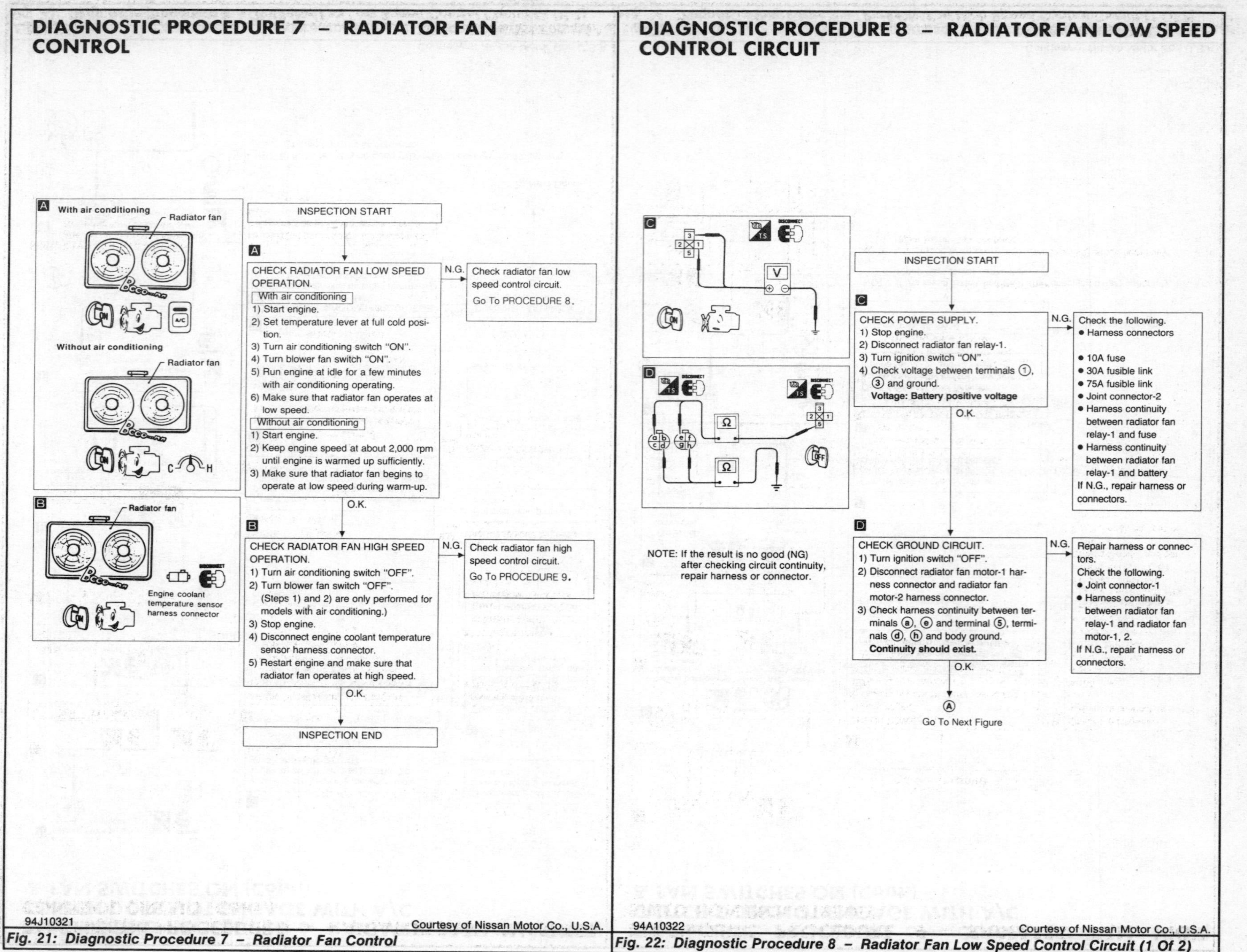
DIAGNOSTIC PROCEDURE 7 – RADIATOR FAN CONTROL
A With air conditioning
Radiator fan
Without air conditioning
Radiator fan
B
Radiator fan
Engine coolant temperature sensor harness connector
INSPECTION START
A
CHECK RADIATOR FAN LOW SPEED OPERATION.
With air conditioning
1) Start engine.
2) Set temperature lever at full cold position.
3) Turn air conditioning switch "ON".
4) Turn blower fan switch "ON".
5) Run engine at idle for a few minutes with air conditioning operating.
6) Make sure that radiator fan operates at low speed.
Without air conditioning
1) Start engine.
2) Keep engine speed at about 2,000 rpm until engine is warmed up sufficiently.
3) Make sure that radiator fan begins to operate at low speed during warm-up.
N.G.
Check radiator fan low speed control circuit.
Go To PROCEDURE 8.
O.K.
B
CHECK RADIATOR FAN HIGH SPEED OPERATION.
1) Turn air conditioning switch "OFF".
2) Turn blower fan switch "OFF".
(Steps 1) and 2) are only performed for models with air conditioning.)
3) Stop engine.
4) Disconnect engine coolant temperature sensor harness connector.
5) Restart engine and make sure that radiator fan operates at high speed.
N.G.
Check radiator fan high speed control circuit.
Go To PROCEDURE 9.
O.K.
INSPECTION END
94J10321
Courtesy of Nissan Motor Co., U.S.A.
DIAGNOSTIC PROCEDURE 8 – RADIATOR FAN LOW SPEED CONTROL CIRCUIT
C
D
NOTE: If the result is no good (NG) after checking circuit continuity, repair harness or connector.
INSPECTION START
C
CHECK POWER SUPPLY.
1) Stop engine.
2) Disconnect radiator fan relay-1.
3) Turn ignition switch "ON".
4) Check voltage between terminals ①, ③ and ground.
Voltage: Battery positive voltage
N.G.
Check the following.
• Harness connectors
• 10A fuse
• 30A fusible link
• 75A fusible link
• Joint connector-2
• Harness continuity between radiator fan relay-1 and fuse
• Harness continuity between radiator fan relay-1 and battery
If N.G., repair harness or connectors.
O.K.
D
CHECK GROUND CIRCUIT.
1) Turn ignition switch "OFF".
2) Disconnect radiator fan motor-1 harness connector and radiator fan motor-2 harness connector.
3) Check harness continuity between terminals ⓐ, ⓔ and terminal ⑤, terminals ⓓ, ⓗ and body ground.
Continuity should exist.
N.G.
Repair harness or connectors.
Check the following.
• Joint connector-1
• Harness continuity between radiator fan relay-1 and radiator fan motor-1, 2.
If N.G., repair harness or connectors.
O.K.
Ⓐ
Go To Next Figure
94A10322
Courtesy of Nissan Motor Co., U.S.A.

Fig. 21: Diagnostic Procedure 7 – Radiator Fan Control

Fig. 22: Diagnostic Procedure 8 – Radiator Fan Low Speed Control Circuit (1 Of 2)

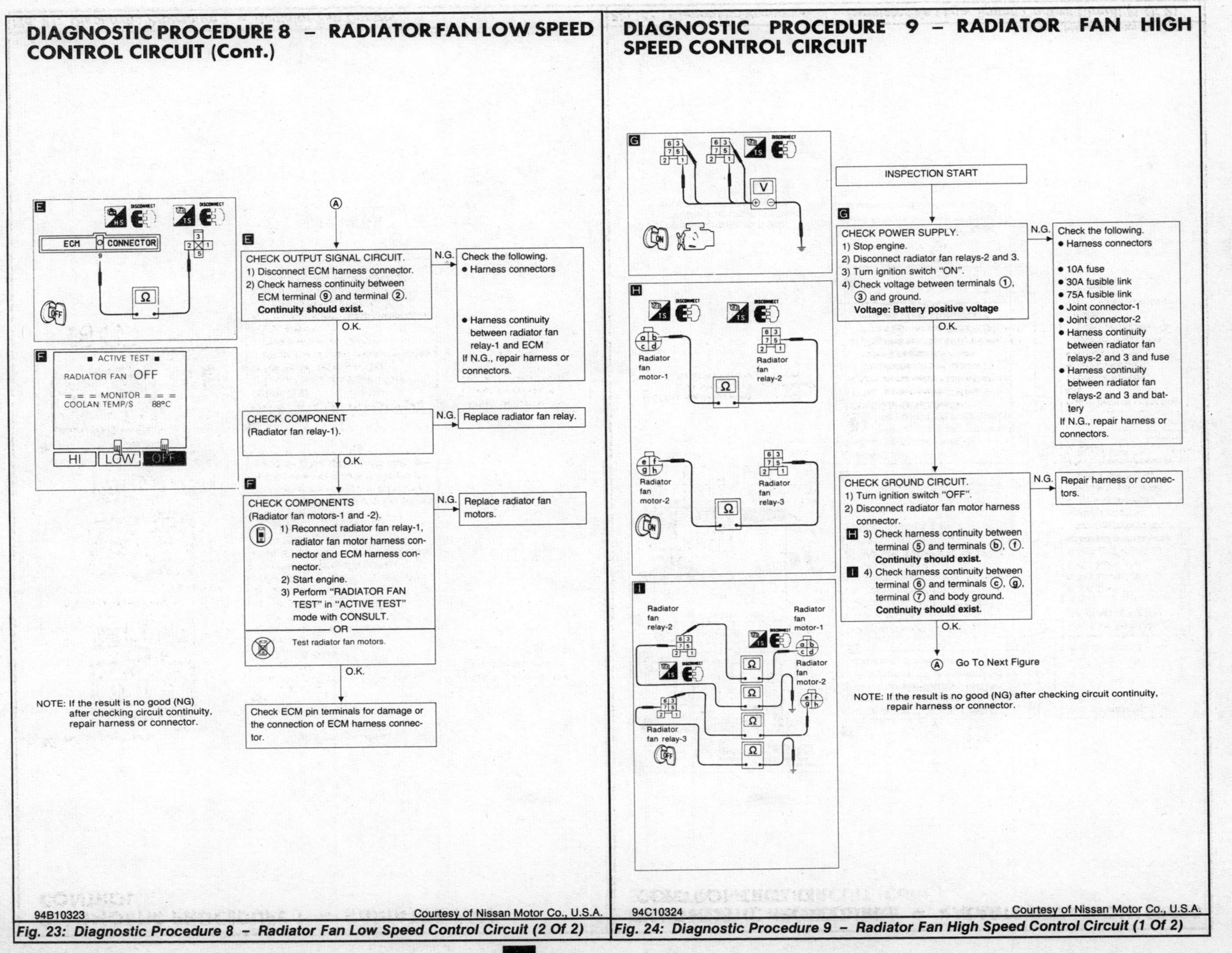
DIAGNOSTIC PROCEDURE 8 – RADIATOR FAN LOW SPEED CONTROL CIRCUIT (Cont.)
E
ECM
CONNECTOR
9
DISCONNECT
HS
TS
OFF
F
■ ACTIVE TEST ■
RADIATOR FAN OFF
= = = MONITOR = = =
COOLAN TEMP/S 88°C
HI
LOW
OFF
Ⓐ
E
CHECK OUTPUT SIGNAL CIRCUIT.
1) Disconnect ECM harness connector.
2) Check harness continuity between ECM terminal ⑨ and terminal ②.
Continuity should exist.
N.G.
Check the following.
• Harness connectors
• Harness continuity between radiator fan relay-1 and ECM
If N.G., repair harness or connectors.
O.K.
CHECK COMPONENT
(Radiator fan relay-1).
N.G.
Replace radiator fan relay.
O.K.
F
CHECK COMPONENTS
(Radiator fan motors-1 and -2).
1) Reconnect radiator fan relay-1, radiator fan motor harness connector and ECM harness connector.
2) Start engine.
3) Perform "RADIATOR FAN TEST" in "ACTIVE TEST" mode with CONSULT.
OR
Test radiator fan motors.
N.G.
Replace radiator fan motors.
O.K.
Check ECM pin terminals for damage or the connection of ECM harness connector.
NOTE: If the result is no good (NG) after checking circuit continuity, repair harness or connector.
94B10323
Courtesy of Nissan Motor Co., U.S.A.
DIAGNOSTIC PROCEDURE 9 – RADIATOR FAN HIGH SPEED CONTROL CIRCUIT
G
DISCONNECT
TS
V
ON
INSPECTION START
G
CHECK POWER SUPPLY.
1) Stop engine.
2) Disconnect radiator fan relays-2 and 3.
3) Turn ignition switch "ON".
4) Check voltage between terminals ①, ③ and ground.
Voltage: Battery positive voltage
N.G.
Check the following.
• Harness connectors
• 10A fuse
• 30A fusible link
• 75A fusible link
• Joint connector-1
• Joint connector-2
• Harness continuity between radiator fan relays-2 and 3 and fuse
• Harness continuity between radiator fan relays-2 and 3 and battery
If N.G., repair harness or connectors.
O.K.
H
Radiator fan motor-1
Radiator fan relay-2
Radiator fan motor-2
Radiator fan relay-3
CHECK GROUND CIRCUIT.
1) Turn ignition switch "OFF".
2) Disconnect radiator fan motor harness connector.
H 3) Check harness continuity between terminal ⑤ and terminals ⓑ, ⓕ.
Continuity should exist.
I 4) Check harness continuity between terminal ⑥ and terminals ⓒ, ⓖ, terminal ⑦ and body ground.
Continuity should exist.
N.G.
Repair harness or connectors.
O.K.
Ⓐ Go To Next Figure
I
Radiator fan relay-2
Radiator fan motor-1
Radiator fan motor-2
Radiator fan relay-3
NOTE: If the result is no good (NG) after checking circuit continuity, repair harness or connector.
94C10324
Courtesy of Nissan Motor Co., U.S.A.

Fig. 23: Diagnostic Procedure 8 – Radiator Fan Low Speed Control Circuit (2 Of 2)

Fig. 24: Diagnostic Procedure 9 – Radiator Fan High Speed Control Circuit (1 Of 2)

1993 MANUAL A/C-HEATER SYSTEMS
Trouble Shooting – Altima (Cont.)

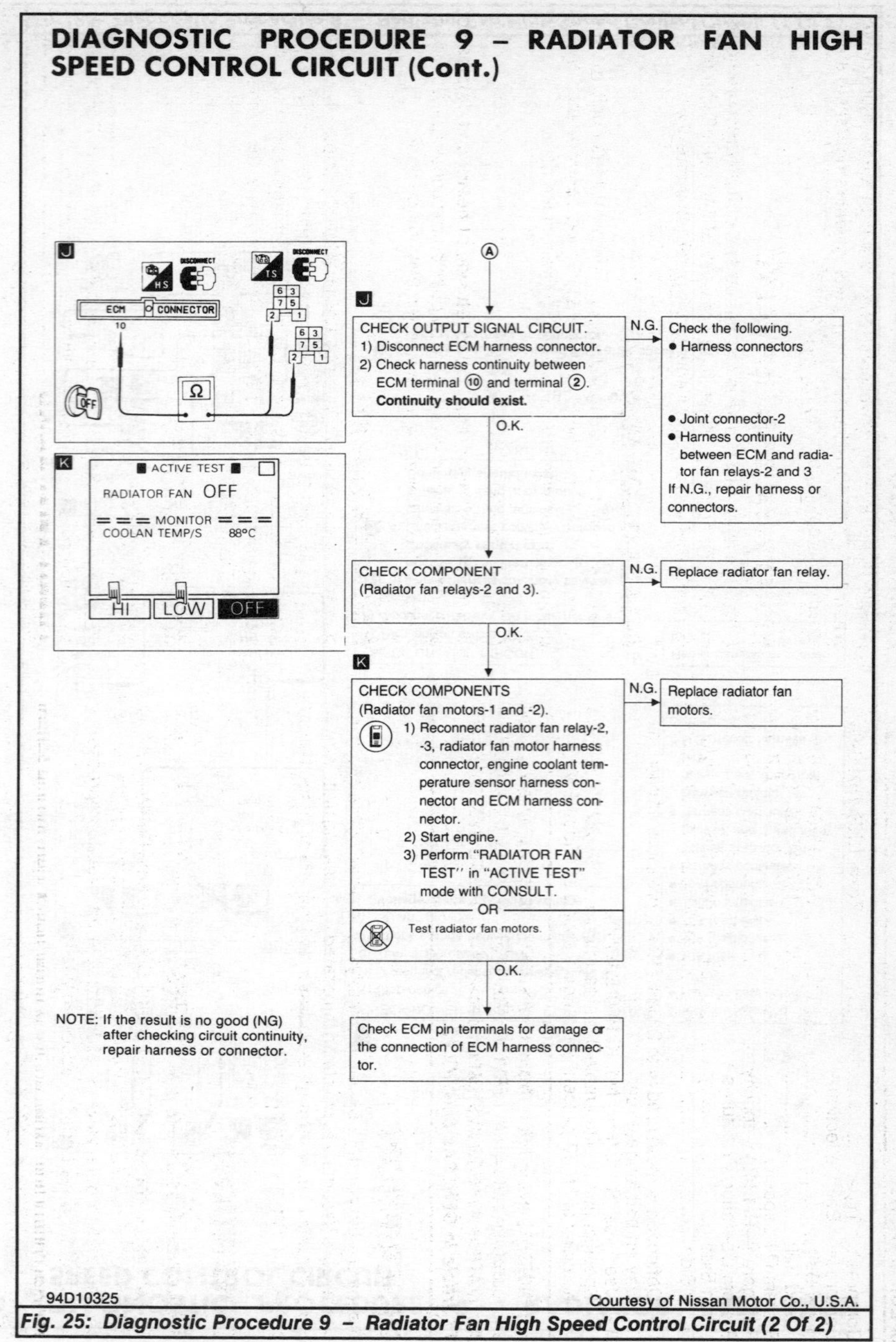
DIAGNOSTIC PROCEDURE 9 – RADIATOR FAN HIGH SPEED CONTROL CIRCUIT (Cont.)
J
ECM
CONNECTOR
10
DISCONNECT
HS
TS
6 3
7 5
2 1
Ω
OFF
K
ACTIVE TEST
RADIATOR FAN OFF
=== MONITOR ===
COOLAN TEMP/S 88°C
HI
LOW
OFF
A
J
CHECK OUTPUT SIGNAL CIRCUIT.
1) Disconnect ECM harness connector.
2) Check harness continuity between ECM terminal ⑩ and terminal ②.
Continuity should exist.
N.G.
Check the following.
• Harness connectors
• Joint connector-2
• Harness continuity between ECM and radiator fan relays-2 and 3
If N.G., repair harness or connectors.
O.K.
CHECK COMPONENT
(Radiator fan relays-2 and 3).
N.G.
Replace radiator fan relay.
O.K.
K
CHECK COMPONENTS
(Radiator fan motors-1 and -2).
1) Reconnect radiator fan relay-2, -3, radiator fan motor harness connector, engine coolant temperature sensor harness connector and ECM harness connector.
2) Start engine.
3) Perform "RADIATOR FAN TEST" in "ACTIVE TEST" mode with CONSULT.
OR
Test radiator fan motors.
N.G.
Replace radiator fan motors.
O.K.
Check ECM pin terminals for damage or the connection of ECM harness connector.
NOTE: If the result is no good (NG) after checking circuit continuity, repair harness or connector.
94D10325
Courtesy of Nissan Motor Co., U.S.A.

Fig. 25: Diagnostic Procedure 9 – Radiator Fan High Speed Control Circuit (2 Of 2)

SPECIFICATIONS

Compressor Type	Zexel DKS-16H 6-Cyl.
Compressor Belt Deflection [1]	
New Belt	5/32-15/64" (4-6 mm)
Used Belt	13/64-9/32" (5-7 mm)
System Oil Capacity [2]	6.8 ozs.
Refrigerant (R-134a) Capacity	30-33 ozs.
System Operating Pressures [3]	
High Side	151-213 psi (10.6-15.0 kg/cm²)
Low Side	16-27 psi (1.1-1.9 kg/cm²)

[1] – Deflection is measured with 22 lbs. (10 kg) pressure applied mid-way on belt longest run.
[2] – Use Type "S" oil (Part No. KLH00-PAGS0).
[3] – Specification is with ambient temperature at 77°F (25°C), relative humidity at 50-70 percent and engine speed at 1500 RPM.

WARNING: To avoid injury from accidental air bag deployment, read and carefully follow all SERVICE PRECAUTIONS and DISABLING & ACTIVATING AIR BAG SYSTEM procedures in AIR BAG SYSTEM SAFETY article in GENERAL SERVICING.

DESCRIPTION

A separate evaporator housing assembly is combined with a standard heater core assembly to create an integrated A/C-heating unit. Blower motor directs airflow through evaporator and then through the heater core to ducting and outlets.

OPERATION

ACCELERATION CUT SYSTEM

This system is controlled by the Engine Concentrated Control System (ECCS) control unit. When engine is under heavy load, throttle sensor senses that throttle valve is at full throttle and A/C compressor is turned off for 5 seconds to reduce engine load.

A/C-HEATER CONTROL PANEL

Desired air control mode is achieved by push buttons and lever-type controls on A/C-heater control assembly. Air intake control can be set for recirculation or outside air entry. A/C switch and fan controls are independent of mode controls. *See Fig. 1.*

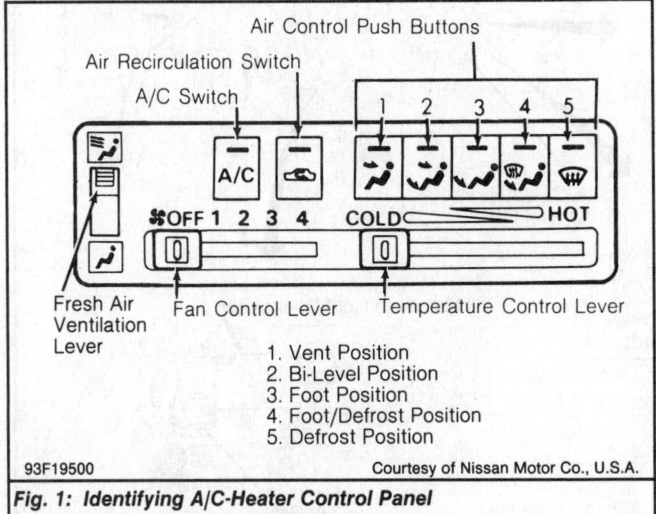

Air Control Push Buttons
Air Recirculation Switch
A/C Switch
1
2
3
4
5
A/C
OFF 1 2 3 4
COLD
HOT
Fresh Air Ventilation Lever
Fan Control Lever
Temperature Control Lever
1. Vent Position
2. Bi-Level Position
3. Foot Position
4. Foot/Defrost Position
5. Defrost Position
93F19500
Courtesy of Nissan Motor Co., U.S.A.

Fig. 1: Identifying A/C-Heater Control Panel

DUAL-PRESSURE SWITCH

The dual-pressure switch is mounted on the receiver-drier to protect A/C system from high pressure build-up (due to restriction, overcharge or compressor malfunction). *See Fig. 3.* If excessively low or high pressure is sensed within system, dual-pressure switch stops compressor clutch operation.

FUSIBLE PLUG

Fusible plug, mounted on receiver-drier, is a high temperature relief. When 221°F (105°C) is sensed, plug melts to vent refrigerant to atmosphere, thereby protecting the A/C system.

HIGH PRESSURE RELIEF VALVE

A high pressure relief valve is located on end of high pressure hose, near A/C compressor. When high pressure of 540 psi (38 kg/cm²) is sensed, relief valve opens, venting refrigerant to atmosphere.

INTAKE DOOR MOTOR

The intake door motor, attached to front portion of heater unit, rotates so air is drawn from inlets set by push button control panel. Motor rotation is transferred to a link which moves intake door.

MODE DOOR MOTOR

The mode door motor, attached to left side of heater unit, rotates so air is discharged from outlet(s) set by push button control panel. Motor rotation is transferred to a link which moves mode door.

RADIATOR FAN RELAYS

Radiator fan relays are located within engine compartment relay boxes. *See Fig. 3.* The 2 radiator cooling fans are controlled by 3 relays. Relay No. 1 is used for low-speed operation, while relay No. 2 and 3 are for high-speed operation. Relay grounds are controlled by Engine Concentrated Control System (ECCS).

ADJUSTMENTS

FRESH VENT DOOR

Push fresh vent shaft in direction indicated. *See Fig. 2.* Pull on outer cable and secure cable using clamp.

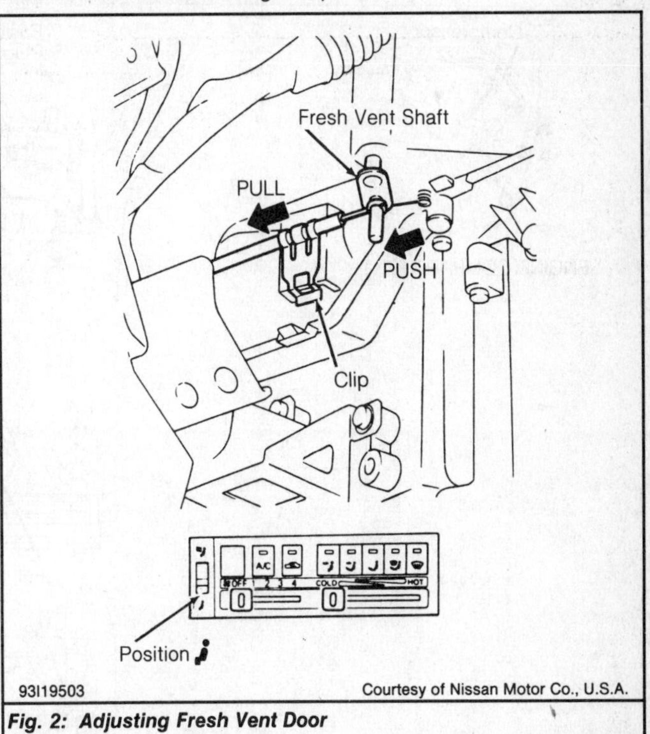

Fresh Vent Shaft
PULL
PUSH
Clip
Position
93I19503
Courtesy of Nissan Motor Co., U.S.A.

Fig. 2: Adjusting Fresh Vent Door

INTAKE DOOR

1) Turn ignition on. Ensure air recirculation button is on. Install intake door motor on intake unit (connect harness before installing motor). Install intake door link.

1993 MANUAL A/C-HEATER SYSTEMS
Maxima (Cont.)

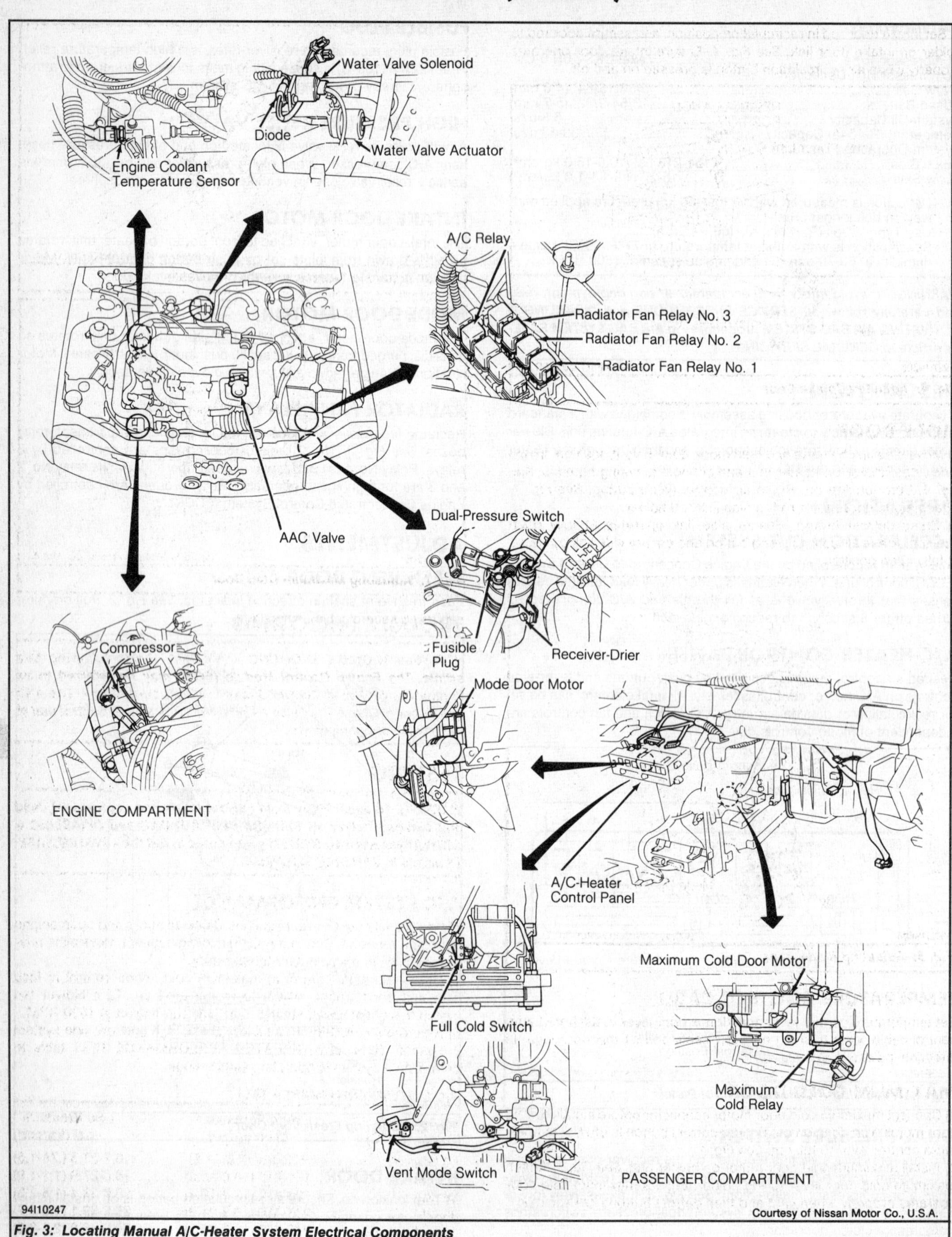
Water Valve Solenoid
Diode
Water Valve Actuator
Engine Coolant
Temperature Sensor
A/C Relay
Radiator Fan Relay No. 3
Radiator Fan Relay No. 2
Radiator Fan Relay No. 1
Dual-Pressure Switch
AAC Valve
Fusible
Plug
Receiver-Drier
Compressor
Mode Door Motor
ENGINE COMPARTMENT
A/C-Heater
Control Panel
Maximum Cold Door Motor
Full Cold Switch
Maximum
Cold Relay
Vent Mode Switch
PASSENGER COMPARTMENT
94I10247
Courtesy of Nissan Motor Co., U.S.A.

Fig. 3: Locating Manual A/C-Heater System Electrical Components

2) Set intake door rod in recirculation position, and secure door rod to holder on intake door link. *See Fig. 4*. Ensure intake door operates properly when air recirculation button is pressed on and off.

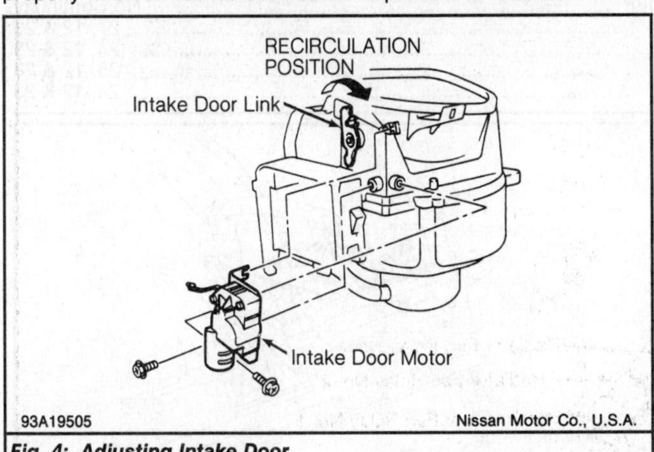
RECIRCULATION
POSITION
Intake Door Link
Intake Door Motor
93A19505
Nissan Motor Co., U.S.A.

Fig. 4: Adjusting Intake Door

MODE DOOR

1) Move side link by hand and hold mode door in vent position. Install mode door motor on heater unit and connect to wiring harness. *See Fig. 5*. Turn ignition on. Press air control (vent) button. *See Fig. 1*. Attach mode door motor rod to side link rod holder.
2) Press defrost button. Ensure side link operates at fully open position. Press air control (vent) button and ensure side link operates at fully open position.

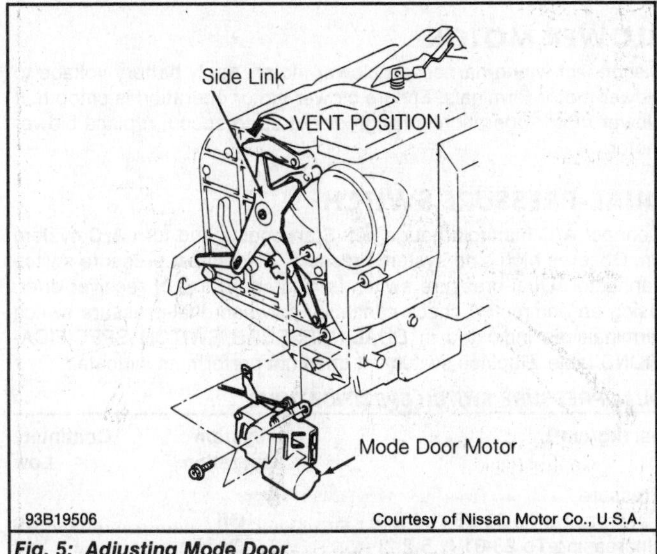
Side Link
VENT POSITION
Mode Door Motor
93B19506
Courtesy of Nissan Motor Co., U.S.A.

Fig. 5: Adjusting Mode Door

TEMPERATURE CONTROL CABLE

Set temperature control lever and air mix door lever to full hot. Clamp control cable while pushing on outer cable and air mix door lever in direction indicated. *See Fig. 6*.

MAXIMUM COLD DOOR

1) Connect maximum cold door motor connector before installing cold door motor. Turn ignition on. Ensure defrost button is off. Set temperature control lever to full hot. *See Fig. 1*.
2) Install maximum cold door motor on heater unit. *See Fig. 7*. Attach maximum cold door lever to rod holder. Ensure maximum cold door operates properly when vent and then defrost buttons are selected.

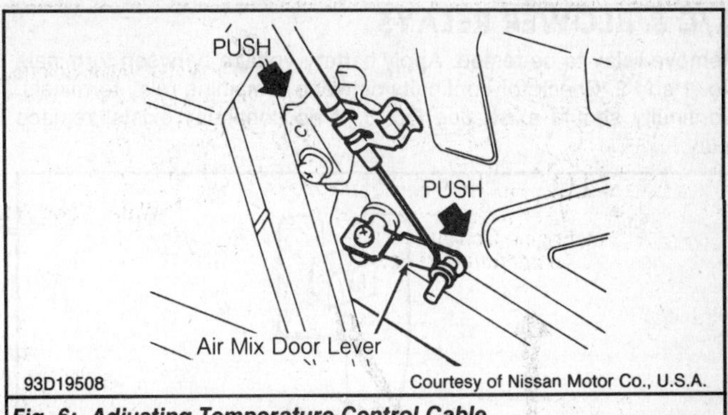
PUSH
PUSH
Air Mix Door Lever
93D19508
Courtesy of Nissan Motor Co., U.S.A.

Fig. 6: Adjusting Temperature Control Cable

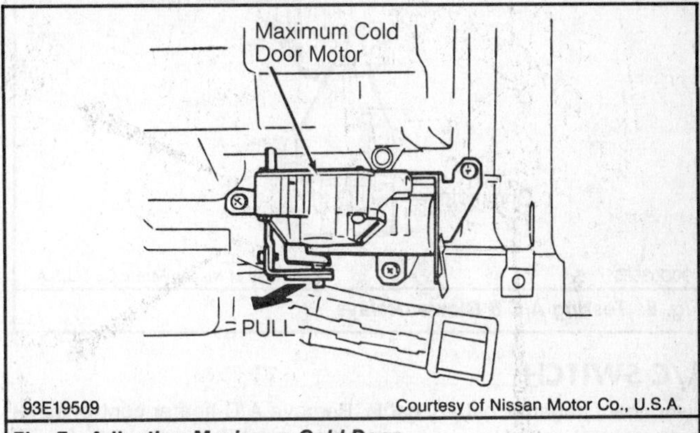
Maximum Cold
Door Motor
PULL
93E19509
Courtesy of Nissan Motor Co., U.S.A.

Fig. 7: Adjusting Maximum Cold Door

TROUBLE SHOOTING

NOTE: See TROUBLE SHOOTING – MAXIMA charts following this article. The Engine Control Module (ECM) may be referred to as Engine Concentrated Control System (ECCS) control unit. The A/C-heater control panel may also be referred to as a push control unit in the trouble shooting charts.

TESTING

WARNING: To avoid injury from accidental air bag deployment, read and carefully follow all SERVICE PRECAUTIONS and DISABLING & ACTIVATING AIR BAG SYSTEM procedures in AIR BAG SYSTEM SAFETY article in GENERAL SERVICING.

A/C SYSTEM PERFORMANCE

1) Park vehicle out of direct sunlight. Close all doors and open engine hood and windows. Connect A/C manifold gauge set. Determine relative humidity and ambient air temperature.
2) Set temperature control to maximum cold, mode control to face vent and, recirculation switch to recirculated air. Turn blower fan switch to highest speed setting. Start and run engine at 1500 RPM.
3) After running A/C for 10 minutes, check high and low side system pressures. Refer to A/C-HEATER PERFORMANCE TEST table to determine if system is operating within range.

A/C SYSTEM PERFORMANCE TEST

Ambient Air Temp. °F (°C)	High Pressure [1] psi (kg/cm^2)	Low Pressure [1] psi (kg/cm^2)
68 (20)	108-164 (7.6-11.5)	10.7-21.3 (.75-1.5)
77 (25)	151-213 (10.6-15.0)	16.0-27.0 (1.1-1.9)
86 (30)	193-262 (13.6-18.4)	20.6-33.4 (1.5-2.3)
95 (35)	236-310 (16.6-21.8)	25.6-39.1 (1.8-2.7)
104 (40)	279-358 (19.6-25.2)	30.0-46.0 (2.1-3.2)

[1] – Specification is with relative humidity at 50-70 percent.

1993 MANUAL A/C-HEATER SYSTEMS
Maxima (Cont.)

A/C & BLOWER RELAYS

Remove relay to be tested. Apply battery voltage between terminals No. 1 and 2. Check for continuity between remaining relay terminals. Continuity should exist. *See Fig. 8*. If no continuity exists, replace relay.

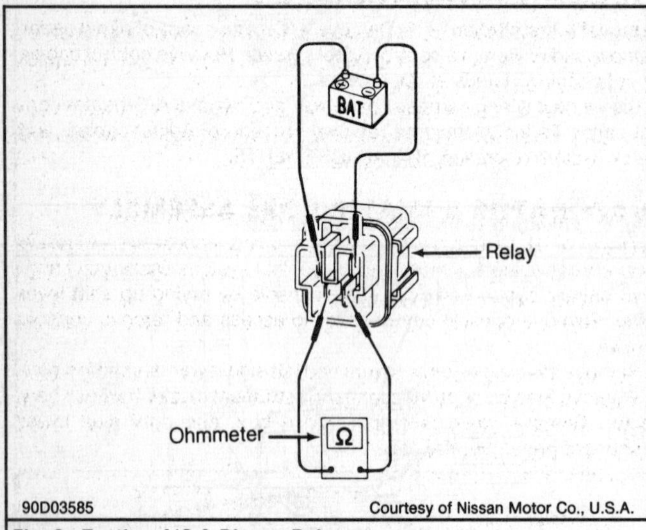
BAT
Relay
Ohmmeter
Ω
90D03585
Courtesy of Nissan Motor Co., U.S.A.

Fig. 8: Testing A/C & Blower Relays

A/C SWITCH

Disconnect negative battery cable. Remove A/C-heater control panel (push control unit). Using an ohmmeter, check for continuity at push control unit connector with A/C switch in specified position. *See Fig. 9*. If A/C switch does not test as specified, replace switch.

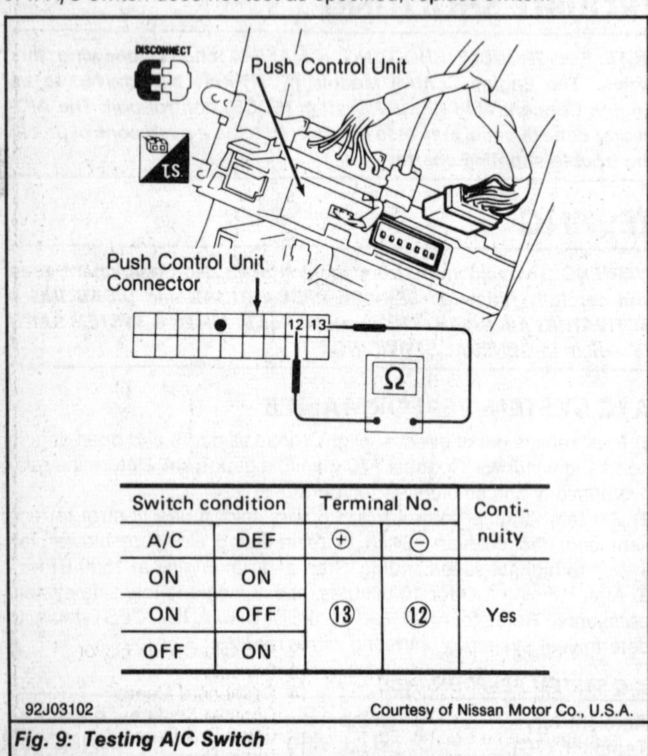
DISCONNECT
T.S.
Push Control Unit
Push Control Unit Connector
12
13
Ω
92J03102
Courtesy of Nissan Motor Co., U.S.A.

Switch condition		Terminal No.		Conti-nuity
A/C	DEF	⊕	⊖	
ON	ON	⑬	⑫	Yes
ON	OFF			
OFF	ON			

Fig. 9: Testing A/C Switch

BLOWER SPEED CONTROL SWITCH

Disconnect blower switch connector. Check for continuity at specified terminals. *See Fig. 10*. See TESTING BLOWER SPEED CONTROL SWITCH table. If continuity is not as specified, replace switch.

TESTING BLOWER SPEED CONTROL SWITCH

Switch Position	Continuity Between Terminal No.
OFF	No Continuity
1	27, 12 & 23
2	26, 12 & 23
3	25, 12 & 23
4	24, 12 & 23

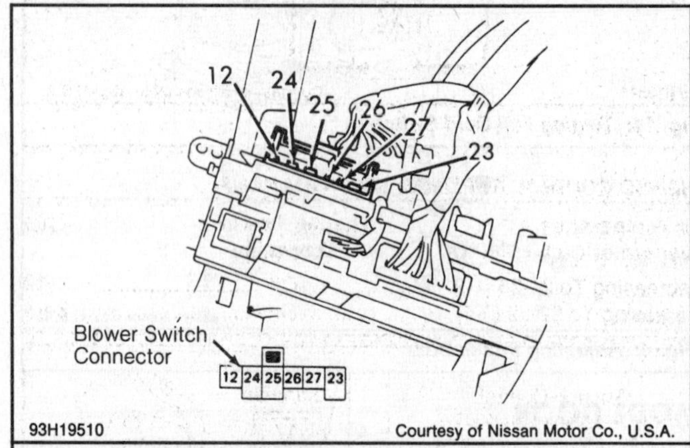
12
24
25
26
27
23
Blower Switch Connector
12 24 25 26 27 23
93H19510
Courtesy of Nissan Motor Co., U.S.A.

Fig. 10: Identifying Blower Switch Connector Terminals

BLOWER MOTOR RESISTOR

To check blower motor resistor for proper operation, disconnect harness connector and ensure continuity exists between resistor terminals. If continuity does not exist, replace resistor.

BLOWER MOTOR

Disconnect wiring harness at blower motor. Apply battery voltage to blower motor terminals. Ensure blower motor operation is smooth. If blower motor operation is rough or not up to speed, replace blower motor.

DUAL-PRESSURE SWITCH

Connect A/C manifold gauge set. Start engine and turn A/C system on. Observe high side system pressure. Disconnect pressure switch connector. Dual-pressure switch is located on top of receiver-drier. Using an ohmmeter, check continuity between dual-pressure switch terminals as indicated in DUAL-PRESSURE SWITCH SPECIFICATIONS table. Replace switch if it does not perform as indicated.

DUAL-PRESSURE SWITCH SPECIFICATIONS

psi (kg/cm^2)	System Operation	Continuity Low
Pressure		
Decreasing To 23-28 (1.6-2.0)	Off	No
Increasing To 23-31 (1.6-2.2)	On	Yes
High Pressure		
Increasing To 356-412 (25-29)	Off	No
Decreasing To 57-114 (4.0-8.0)	On	Yes

FULL COLD SWITCH

Disconnect full cold switch connector. Check for continuity between terminals No. 106 and 83 with temperature control lever in full cold position. *See Fig. 11*. If continuity does not exist, replace A/C-heater control panel.

THERMO CONTROL AMPLIFIER

Start engine and turn A/C system on. Using a DVOM, backprobe thermo control amplifier connector between terminal No. 59 (Pink/Black wire) and ground. *See Fig. 12*. If voltage is not as specified, replace thermo control amplifier. See THERMO CONTROL AMPLIFIER SPECIFICATIONS table.

1993 MANUAL A/C-HEATER SYSTEMS
Maxima (Cont.)

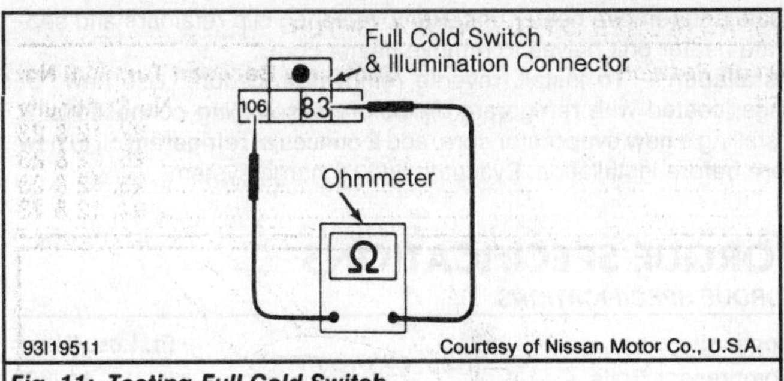
Full Cold Switch
& Illumination Connector
106
83
Ohmmeter
Ω
93I19511
Courtesy of Nissan Motor Co., U.S.A.

Fig. 11: Testing Full Cold Switch

THERMO CONTROL AMPLIFIER SPECIFICATIONS

Air Temperature At Evaporator Outlet °F (°C)	Thermo Amplifier Operation	Volts
Decreasing To 34-36 (1-2)	Off	12
Increasing To 37-39 (3-4)	On	Zero

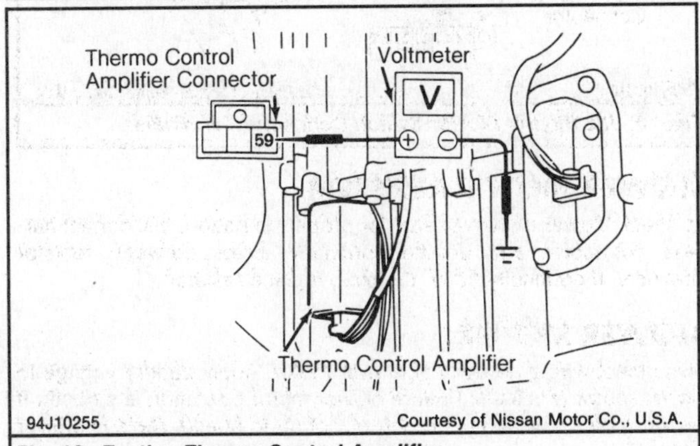
Thermo Control
Amplifier Connector
59
Voltmeter
V
Thermo Control Amplifier
94J10255
Courtesy of Nissan Motor Co., U.S.A.

Fig. 12: Testing Thermo Control Amplifier

VENT MODE SWITCH

Disconnect vent mode switch connector. Check for continuity between terminals No. 89 and 88 with vent mode button on. *See Fig. 13.* If continuity does not exist, replace switch.

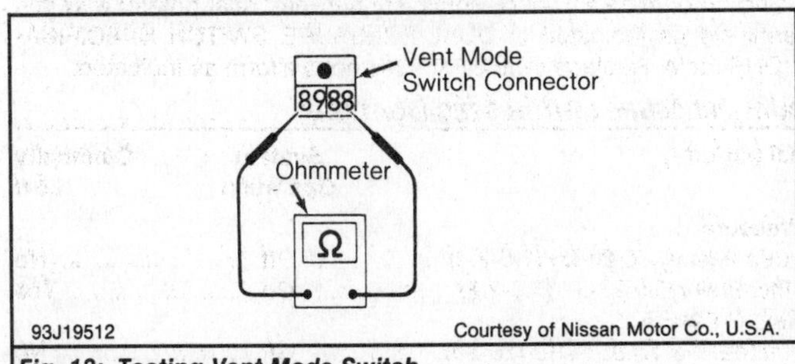
Vent Mode
Switch Connector
89
88
Ohmmeter
Ω
93J19512
Courtesy of Nissan Motor Co., U.S.A.

Fig. 13: Testing Vent Mode Switch

REMOVAL & INSTALLATION

WARNING: To avoid injury from accidental air bag deployment, read and carefully follow all SERVICE PRECAUTIONS and DISABLING & ACTIVATING AIR BAG SYSTEM procedures in AIR BAG SYSTEM SAFETY article in GENERAL SERVICING.

A/C COMPRESSOR

Removal – Loosen idler pulley bolt and remove compressor belt. Discharge A/C system using approved refrigerant recovery/recycling equipment. Disconnect compressor clutch lead. Remove discharge and suction hoses from compressor and plug hose openings. Remove compressor bolts and compressor.

Installation – To install, reverse removal procedure. Tighten bolts to specification. See TORQUE SPECIFICATIONS. Use new "O" rings, coated with refrigerant oil, when attaching hoses to compressor. Evacuate and recharge system.

A/C-HEATER CONTROL PANEL

Removal & Installation – **1)** Remove A/C-heater control panel bezel. Remove radio. Remove control panel screws. Remove control cables by unfastening clamps at door levers.

2) Disconnect wiring harness connector, and remove A/C-heater control panel. To install, reverse removal procedure. Adjust cables, and check system operation. See ADJUSTMENTS.

EVAPORATOR & HEATER CORE ASSEMBLY

Removal – **1)** Discharge A/C system using approved refrigerant recovery/recycling equipment. Drain cooling system. Disconnect negative battery cable. Remove center console by prying up shift lever cover. Remove console center cover to access and remove console screws.

2) Remove steering column covers and left side lower dashboard panel. Remove fuse block and disconnect instrument cluster harness connector. Remove glove box door, glove box, and right side lower dashboard panel. *See Fig. 14.*

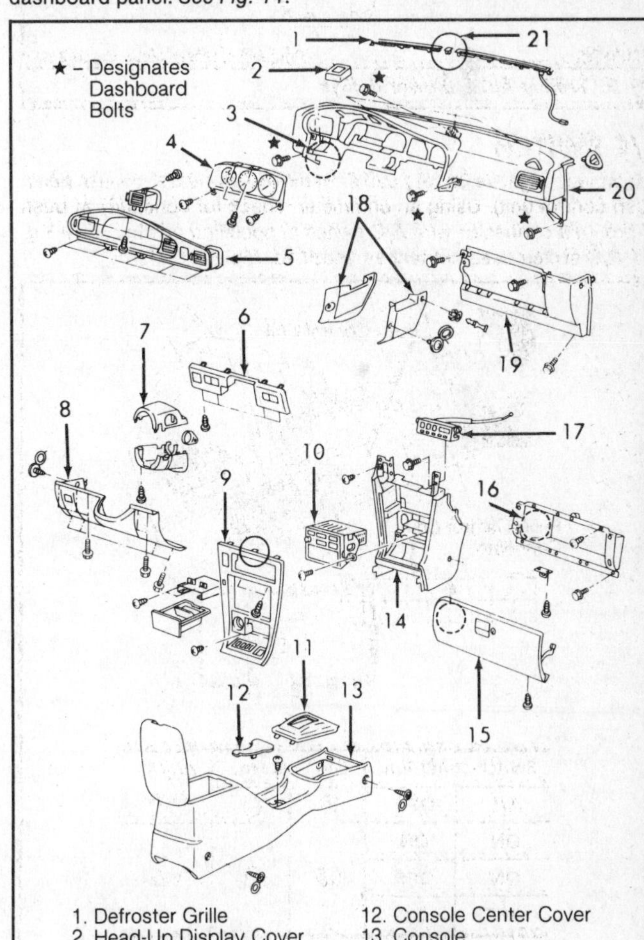
★ - Designates
Dashboard
Bolts
1. Defroster Grille
2. Head-Up Display Cover
3. Harness Connector
4. Instrument Cluster
5. Instrument Cluster Lid/
Air Outlet Vent Assembly
6. Switches Panel
7. Steering Column Covers
8. Lower Dashboard Panel
9. Radio Faceplate
10. Radio
11. Shift Lever Cover
12. Console Center Cover
13. Console
14. Dashboard Center
Console Section
15. Glove Box Door
16. Glove Box
17. A/C-Heater Control Panel
18. Side Covers
19. Lower Dashboard Panel
20. Dashboard
21. Defroster Grille
Center Pawl
93A19513
Courtesy of Nissan Motor Co., U.S.A.

Fig. 14: Removing Dashboard & Components

1993 MANUAL A/C-HEATER SYSTEMS
Maxima (Cont.)

3) Remove instrument switches panel. Remove instrument cluster lid and air vent outlet assembly, ashtray, radio faceplate and radio. Cover Head-Up display reflective surface on windshield.

4) Remove instrument cluster and Head-Up display cover. Remove defroster grilles by carefully prying center pawl upward, then slide grilles toward center and lift out. Remove dashboard screws from under defroster grilles and from both outside lower corners.

5) Remove A/C-heater control panel screws. Remove dashboard center console section and side covers. Note all wiring harnesses and A/C-heater control cable locations. Lift upward and outward on right side dashboard to remove blower and intake housing assembly.

6) In engine compartment, disconnect A/C lines from evaporator and remove heater hoses from heater core. Lift upward and outward on right side dashboard to remove evaporator assembly. Disconnect all ducts and remove heater unit. Remove spring clip retainers and separate heater unit halves to remove heater core.

Installation - To install, reverse removal procedure. Use new "O" rings, coated with refrigerant oil, before assembling connections. If installing a new evaporator core, add 2 ounces of refrigerant oil to new core before installation. Evacuate and recharge system.

TORQUE SPECIFICATIONS

TORQUE SPECIFICATIONS

Application	Ft. Lbs. (N.m)
Compressor Bolts	44 (60)
Compressor Bracket Bolts	26 (35)

WIRING DIAGRAM

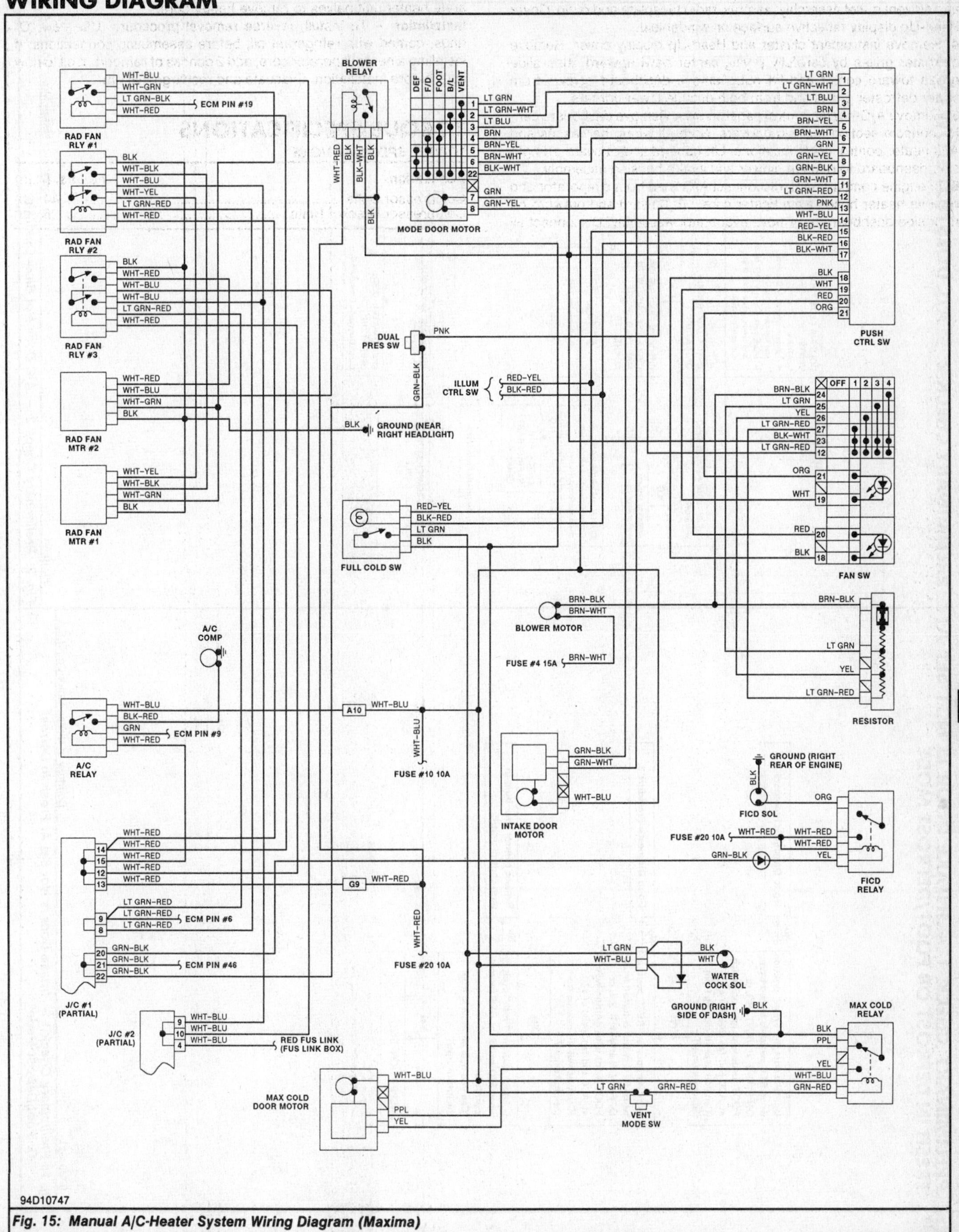
RAD FAN RLY #1
WHT-BLU
WHT-GRN
LT GRN-BLK
WHT-RED
ECM PIN #19
RAD FAN RLY #2
BLK
WHT-BLK
WHT-BLU
WHT-YEL
LT GRN-RED
WHT-RED
RAD FAN RLY #3
RAD FAN MTR #2
RAD FAN MTR #1
BLOWER RELAY
WHT-RED
BLK
BLK-WHT
DEF
F/D
FOOT
B/L
VENT
LT GRN
LT GRN-WHT
LT BLU
BRN
BRN-YEL
BRN-WHT
BLK-WHT
GRN
GRN-YEL
MODE DOOR MOTOR
PUSH CTRL SW
GRN-BLK
GRN-WHT
LT GRN-RED
PNK
WHT-BLU
RED-YEL
BLK-RED
BLK-WHT
WHT
RED
ORG
DUAL PRES SW
ILLUM CTRL SW
GRN-BLK
GROUND (NEAR RIGHT HEADLIGHT)
OFF
BRN-BLK
YEL
FAN SW
FULL COLD SW
BLOWER MOTOR
FUSE #4 15A
RESISTOR
A/C COMP
A/C RELAY
BLK-RED
ECM PIN #9
A10
FUSE #10 10A
INTAKE DOOR MOTOR
GROUND (RIGHT REAR OF ENGINE)
FICD SOL
FUSE #20 10A
FICD RELAY
G9
J/C #1 (PARTIAL)
ECM PIN #6
ECM PIN #46
WATER COCK SOL
GROUND (RIGHT SIDE OF DASH)
MAX COLD RELAY
PPL
J/C #2 (PARTIAL)
RED FUS LINK (FUS LINK BOX)
MAX COLD DOOR MOTOR
VENT MODE SW
94D10747

Fig. 15: Manual A/C-Heater System Wiring Diagram (Maxima)

1993 MANUAL A/C-HEATER SYSTEMS
Trouble Shooting – Maxima

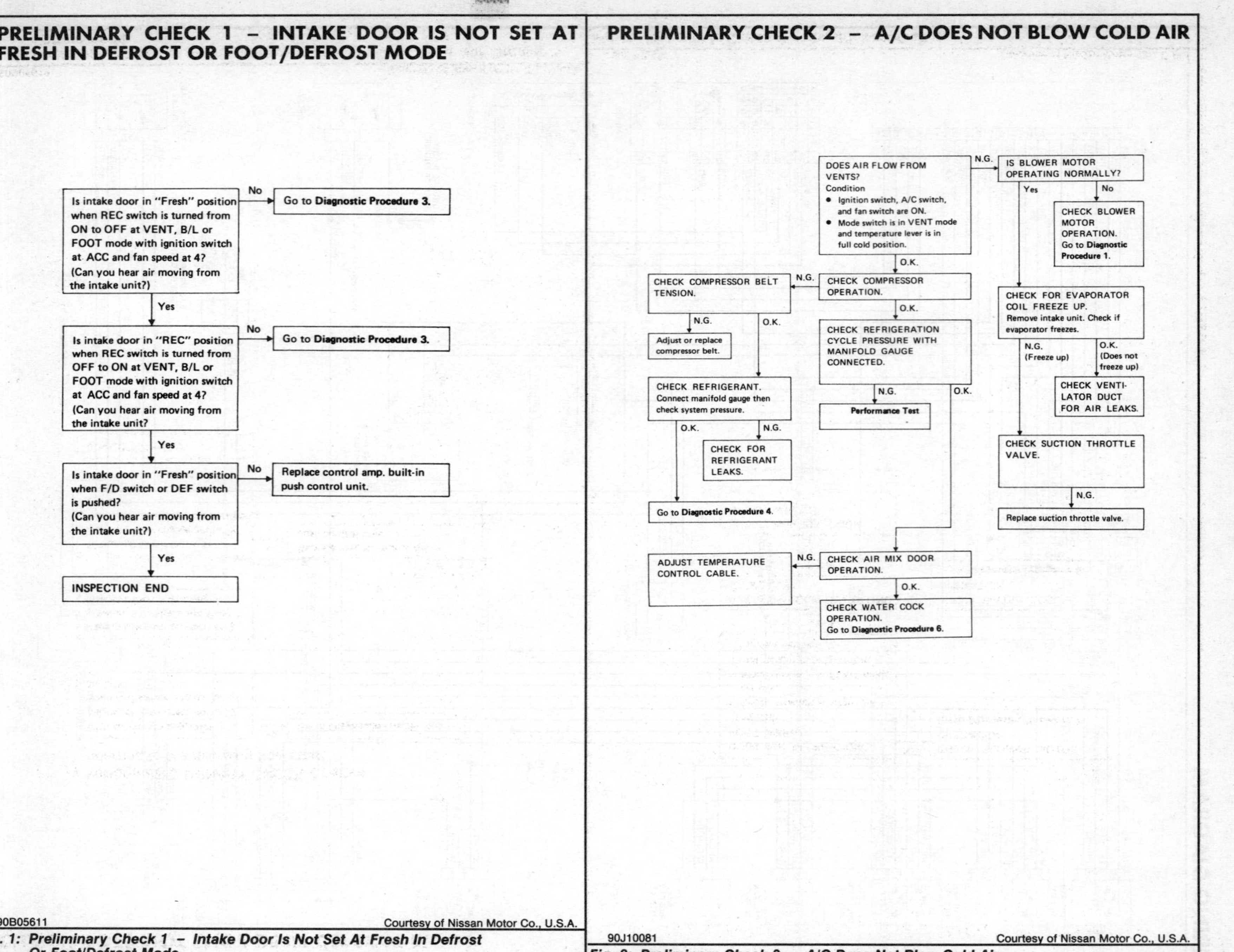
PRELIMINARY CHECK 1 – INTAKE DOOR IS NOT SET AT FRESH IN DEFROST OR FOOT/DEFROST MODE
Is intake door in "Fresh" position when REC switch is turned from ON to OFF at VENT, B/L or FOOT mode with ignition switch at ACC and fan speed at 4? (Can you hear air moving from the intake unit?)
No
Go to Diagnostic Procedure 3.
Yes
Is intake door in "REC" position when REC switch is turned from OFF to ON at VENT, B/L or FOOT mode with ignition switch at ACC and fan speed at 4? (Can you hear air moving from the intake unit?)
No
Go to Diagnostic Procedure 3.
Yes
Is intake door in "Fresh" position when F/D switch or DEF switch is pushed? (Can you hear air moving from the intake unit?)
No
Replace control amp. built-in push control unit.
Yes
INSPECTION END
90B05611
Courtesy of Nissan Motor Co., U.S.A.
PRELIMINARY CHECK 2 – A/C DOES NOT BLOW COLD AIR
DOES AIR FLOW FROM VENTS?
Condition
• Ignition switch, A/C switch, and fan switch are ON.
• Mode switch is in VENT mode and temperature lever is in full cold position.
N.G.
IS BLOWER MOTOR OPERATING NORMALLY?
Yes
No
CHECK BLOWER MOTOR OPERATION. Go to Diagnostic Procedure 1.
CHECK FOR EVAPORATOR COIL FREEZE UP. Remove intake unit. Check if evaporator freezes.
N.G. (Freeze up)
O.K. (Does not freeze up)
CHECK VENTI-LATOR DUCT FOR AIR LEAKS.
CHECK SUCTION THROTTLE VALVE.
N.G.
Replace suction throttle valve.
O.K.
CHECK COMPRESSOR OPERATION.
N.G.
CHECK COMPRESSOR BELT TENSION.
N.G.
Adjust or replace compressor belt.
O.K.
CHECK REFRIGERANT. Connect manifold gauge then check system pressure.
O.K.
N.G.
CHECK FOR REFRIGERANT LEAKS.
Go to Diagnostic Procedure 4.
O.K.
CHECK REFRIGERATION CYCLE PRESSURE WITH MANIFOLD GAUGE CONNECTED.
N.G.
Performance Test
O.K.
CHECK AIR MIX DOOR OPERATION.
N.G.
ADJUST TEMPERATURE CONTROL CABLE.
O.K.
CHECK WATER COCK OPERATION. Go to Diagnostic Procedure 6.
90J10081
Courtesy of Nissan Motor Co., U.S.A.

Fig. 1: Preliminary Check 1 – Intake Door Is Not Set At Fresh In Defrost Or Foot/Defrost Mode

Fig. 2: Preliminary Check 2 – A/C Does Not Blow Cold Air

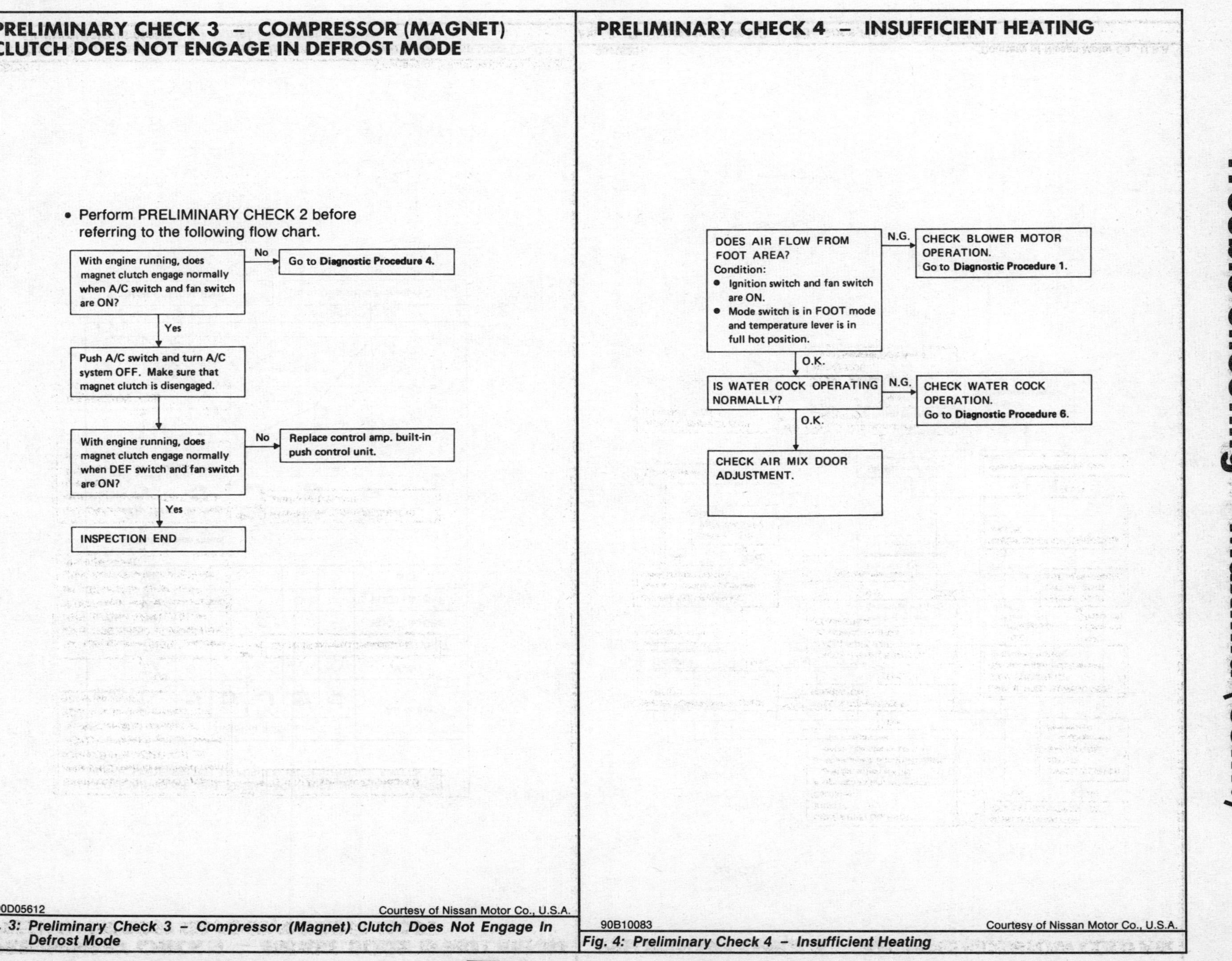
PRELIMINARY CHECK 3 – COMPRESSOR (MAGNET) CLUTCH DOES NOT ENGAGE IN DEFROST MODE
• Perform PRELIMINARY CHECK 2 before referring to the following flow chart.
With engine running, does magnet clutch engage normally when A/C switch and fan switch are ON?
No
Go to Diagnostic Procedure 4.
Yes
Push A/C switch and turn A/C system OFF. Make sure that magnet clutch is disengaged.
With engine running, does magnet clutch engage normally when DEF switch and fan switch are ON?
No
Replace control amp. built-in push control unit.
Yes
INSPECTION END
90D05612
Courtesy of Nissan Motor Co., U.S.A.
PRELIMINARY CHECK 4 – INSUFFICIENT HEATING
DOES AIR FLOW FROM FOOT AREA?
Condition:
• Ignition switch and fan switch are ON.
• Mode switch is in FOOT mode and temperature lever is in full hot position.
N.G.
CHECK BLOWER MOTOR OPERATION.
Go to Diagnostic Procedure 1.
O.K.
IS WATER COCK OPERATING NORMALLY?
N.G.
CHECK WATER COCK OPERATION.
Go to Diagnostic Procedure 6.
O.K.
CHECK AIR MIX DOOR ADJUSTMENT.
90B10083
Courtesy of Nissan Motor Co., U.S.A.

Fig. 3: Preliminary Check 3 – Compressor (Magnet) Clutch Does Not Engage In Defrost Mode

Fig. 4: Preliminary Check 4 – Insufficient Heating

1993 MANUAL A/C-HEATER SYSTEMS
Trouble Shooting – Maxima (Cont.)

PRELIMINARY CHECK 5 – AIR OUTLET DOES NOT CHANGE

DOES AIR COME OUT FROM EACH DUCT NORMALLY WHEN EACH MODE SWITCH IS PUSHED WITH IGNITION SWITCH AT ACC?

Switch: Mode	Indicator illuminates: VENT	B/L	FOOT	F/D	DEF	Air outlet
VENT	O					VENT
B/L		O				FOOT & VENT
FOOT			O			FOOT & DEF
F/D				O		FOOT & DEF
DEF					O	DEF

Air distribution ratios

VENT
B/L
FOOT
F/D
DEF
(%)
100
70
50
35
0
FACE
FOOT
DEF

Yes → INSPECTION END

No → Go to **Diagnostic Procedure 2.**

90A10082 Courtesy of Nissan Motor Co., U.S.A.

Fig. 5: Preliminary Check 5 – Air Outlet Does Not Change

PRELIMINARY CHECK 6 – NOISE

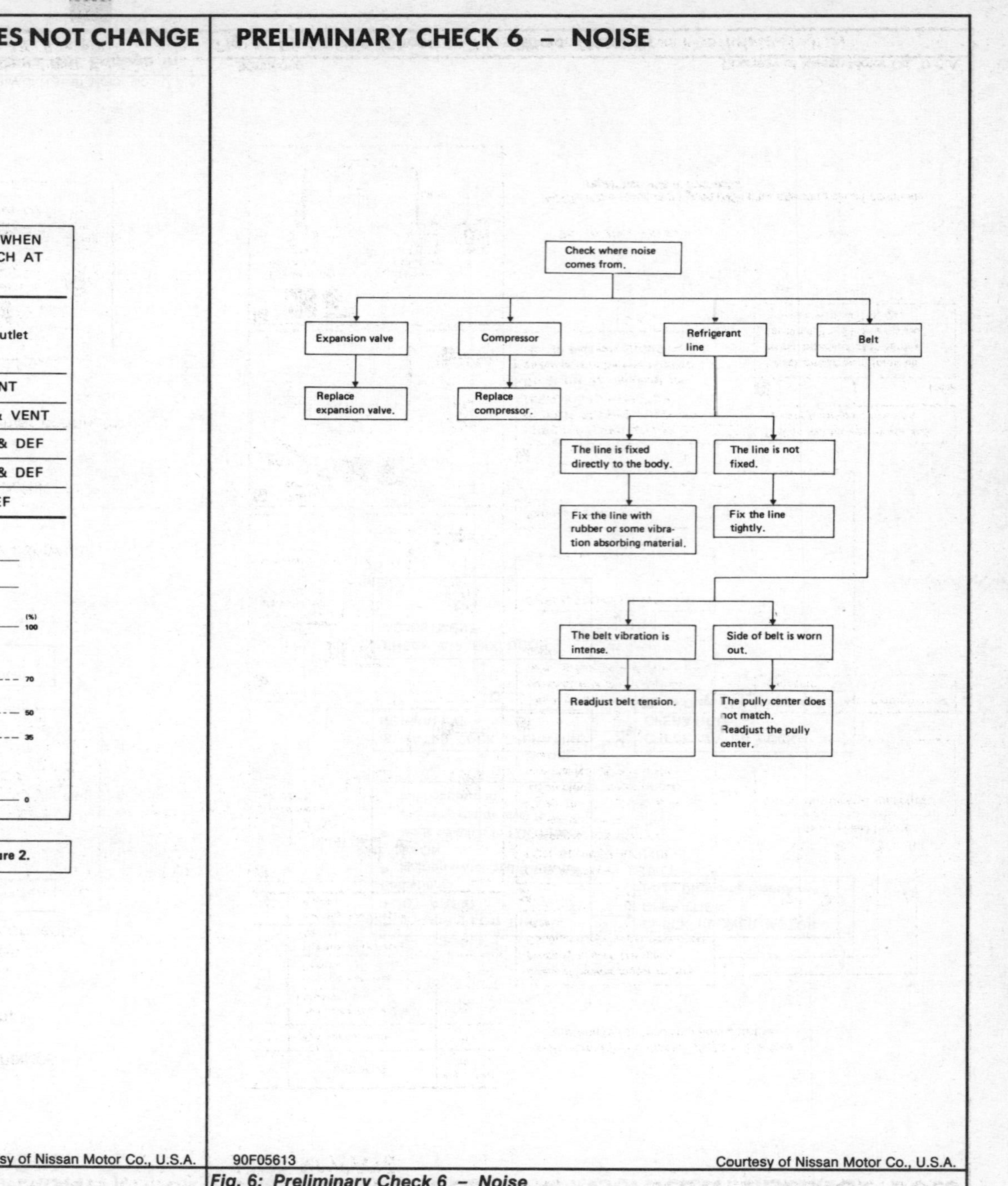
Check where noise comes from.
Expansion valve
Compressor
Refrigerant line
Belt
Replace expansion valve.
Replace compressor.
The line is fixed directly to the body.
The line is not fixed.
Fix the line with rubber or some vibration absorbing material.
Fix the line tightly.
The belt vibration is intense.
Side of belt is worn out.
Readjust belt tension.
The pully center does not match. Readjust the pully center.

90F05613 Courtesy of Nissan Motor Co., U.S.A.

Fig. 6: Preliminary Check 6 – Noise

PRELIMINARY CHECK 7 – POWER SUPPLY CIRCUIT CHECK FOR A/C SYSTEM

Push Control Unit Check

1. Disconnect push control unit wiring harness connector.
2. Turn ignition on.
3. Using voltmeter, ensure battery voltage is present at terminal No. 14 of harness connector.
4. Turn ignition off.
5. Using ohmmeter, ensure continuity exists between ground and terminal No. 17 of push control unit connector.

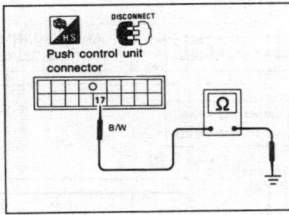

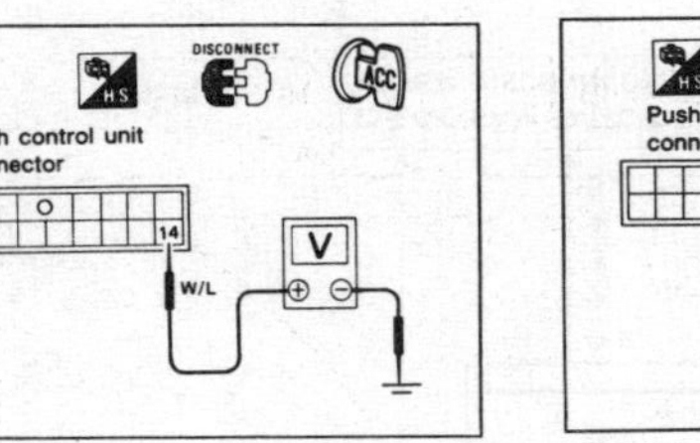
DISCONNECT
Push control unit connector
14
W/L
V

Thermo Control Amplifier Check

1. Disconnect thermo control amplifier wiring harness connector.
2. Turn ignition on.
3. Using voltmeter, ensure battery voltage is present at terminal No. 34 of thermo control amplifier connector.
4. Turn ignition off. Turn A/C and fan switches on.
5. Using ohmmeter, ensure continuity exists between ground and terminal No. 13 of thermo control amplifier connector.

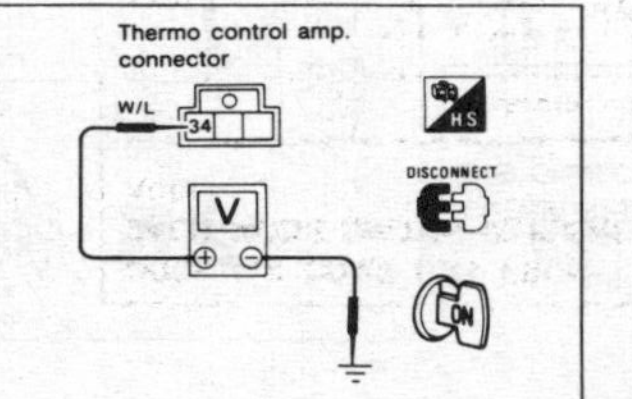
Thermo control amp. connector
W/L
34
DISCONNECT
V

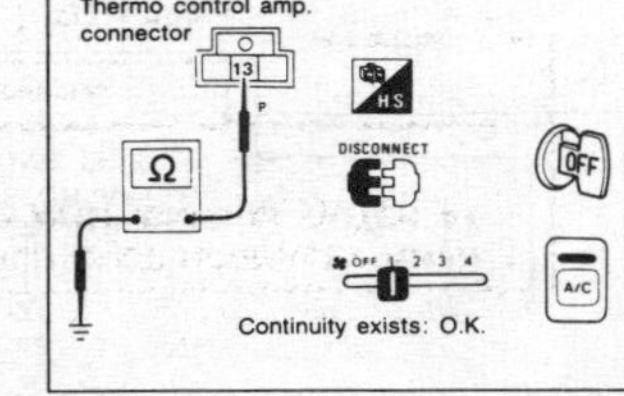
Thermo control amp. connector
13
DISCONNECT
Ω
Continuity exists: O.K.

94G10260 Courtesy of Nissan Motor Co., U.S.A.

Fig. 7: Preliminary Check 7 – Power Supply Circuit Check For A/C System

DIAGNOSTIC PROCEDURE 1 – BLOWER MOTOR DOES NOT ROTATE

	INCIDENT	Flow chart No.
1	Fan fails to rotate.	1
2	Fan does not rotate at 1-speed.	2
3	Fan does not rotate at 2-speed.	3
4	Fan does not rotate at 3-speed.	4
5	Fan does not rotate at 4-speed.	5

- Perform PRELIMINARY CHECK 2 before referring to the following flow chart.

Check if blower motor rotates properly at each fan speed. Conduct check as per flow chart at left.
- 2 → (B), 3 → (C), 4 → (D), 5 → (E): Go To Next Figure
- 1 ↓

A CHECK POWER SUPPLY FOR BLOWER MOTOR. Disconnect blower motor harness connector. Do approx. 12 volts exist between blower motor harness terminal No. 30 and body ground?
- N.G. → Check 15A fuses at fuse block.
- O.K. ↓

B Check circuit continuity between blower motor harness terminal No. 24 and body ground.
- N.G. → Reconnect blower motor harness connector. → (to C)
- O.K. ↓

CHECK BLOWER MOTOR.
- N.G. → Replace blower motor.

C CHECK BLOWER MOTOR CIRCUIT BETWEEN BLOWER MOTOR AND RESISTOR. Do approx. 12 volts exist between resistor harness terminal No. 24 and body ground?
- N.G. → Disconnect blower motor and resistor harness connectors. → D Check circuit continuity between blower motor harness terminal No. 24 and resistor harness terminal No. 24. (Note)
- O.K. → (A) Go To Next Figure

NOTE: If the result is no good (NG) after checking circuit continuity, repair harness or connector.

A: Blower motor connector, 30, BR/W, V
B: Blower motor connector, 24, BR/B, Ω, Continuity exists: O.K.
C: Resistor connector, BR/B, 24, CONNECT, V
D: Blower motor connector, Resistor connector, 24, BR/B, Ω

90H05614 Courtesy of Nissan Motor Co., U.S.A.

Fig. 8: Diagnostic Procedure 1 – Blower Motor Does Not Rotate (1 Of 3)

1993 MANUAL A/C-HEATER SYSTEMS
Trouble Shooting – Maxima (Cont.)

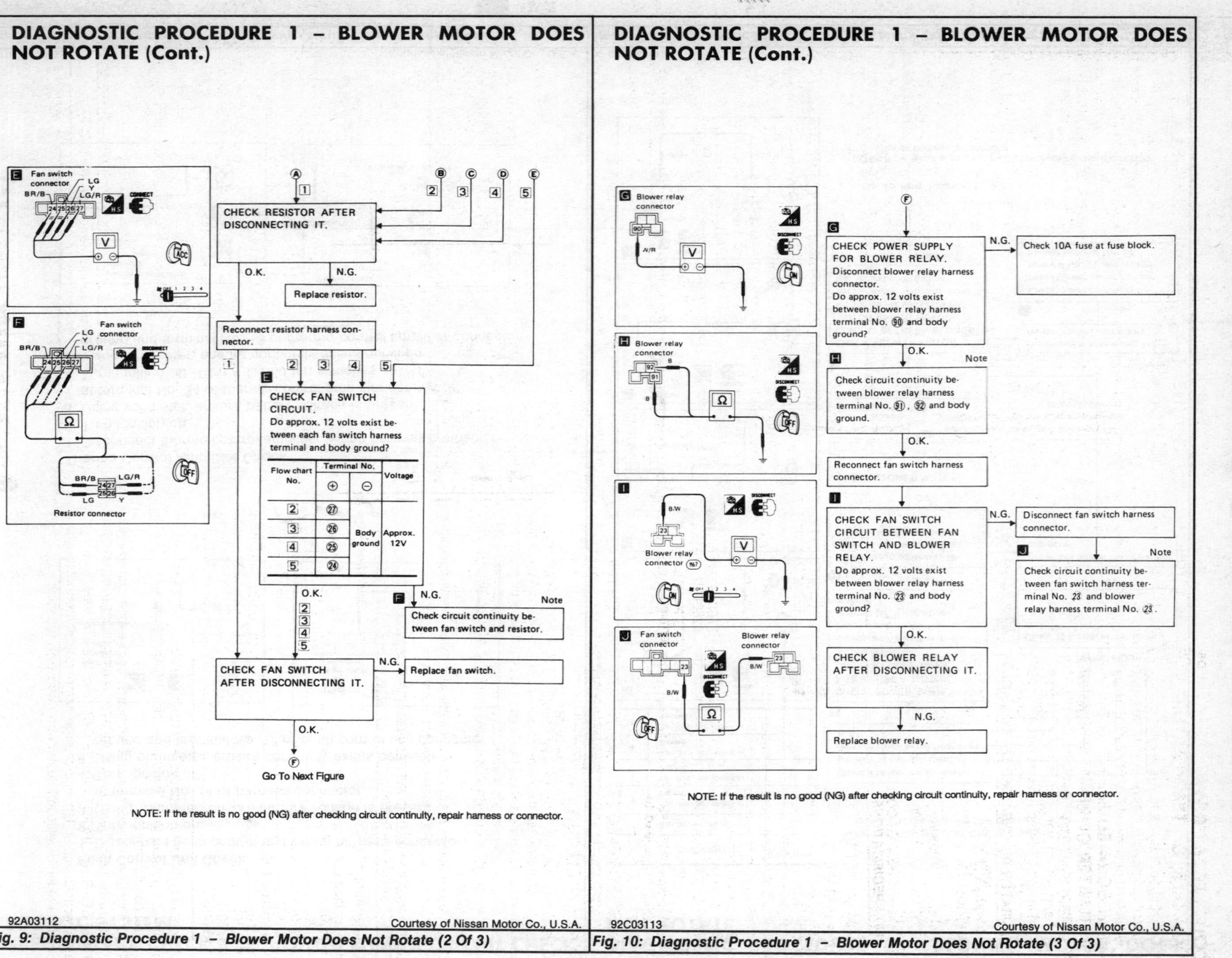
DIAGNOSTIC PROCEDURE 1 – BLOWER MOTOR DOES NOT ROTATE (Cont.)
E Fan switch connector
LG
Y
BR/B
LG/R
24 25 26 27
V
ACC
F
Fan switch connector
Resistor connector
CHECK RESISTOR AFTER DISCONNECTING IT.
O.K.
N.G.
Replace resistor.
Reconnect resistor harness connector.
E CHECK FAN SWITCH CIRCUIT.
Do approx. 12 volts exist between each fan switch harness terminal and body ground?
Flow chart No.
Terminal No.
Voltage
Body ground
Approx. 12V
F Check circuit continuity between fan switch and resistor.
Note
CHECK FAN SWITCH AFTER DISCONNECTING IT.
Replace fan switch.
Go To Next Figure
NOTE: If the result is no good (NG) after checking circuit continuity, repair harness or connector.
92A03112
Courtesy of Nissan Motor Co., U.S.A.
DIAGNOSTIC PROCEDURE 1 – BLOWER MOTOR DOES NOT ROTATE (Cont.)
G Blower relay connector
H Blower relay connector
I Blower relay connector
J Fan switch connector
Blower relay connector
B/W
G CHECK POWER SUPPLY FOR BLOWER RELAY.
Disconnect blower relay harness connector.
Do approx. 12 volts exist between blower relay harness terminal No. 90 and body ground?
Check 10A fuse at fuse block.
H Check circuit continuity between blower relay harness terminal No. 91, 92 and body ground.
Reconnect fan switch harness connector.
I CHECK FAN SWITCH CIRCUIT BETWEEN FAN SWITCH AND BLOWER RELAY.
Do approx. 12 volts exist between blower relay harness terminal No. 23 and body ground?
Disconnect fan switch harness connector.
J Check circuit continuity between fan switch harness terminal No. 23 and blower relay harness terminal No. 23.
CHECK BLOWER RELAY AFTER DISCONNECTING IT.
Replace blower relay.
NOTE: If the result is no good (NG) after checking circuit continuity, repair harness or connector.
92C03113
Courtesy of Nissan Motor Co., U.S.A.

Flow chart No.	Terminal No. ⊕	Terminal No. ⊖	Voltage
2	27	Body ground	Approx. 12V
3	26	Body ground	Approx. 12V
4	25	Body ground	Approx. 12V
5	24	Body ground	Approx. 12V

Fig. 9: Diagnostic Procedure 1 – Blower Motor Does Not Rotate (2 Of 3)

Fig. 10: Diagnostic Procedure 1 – Blower Motor Does Not Rotate (3 Of 3)

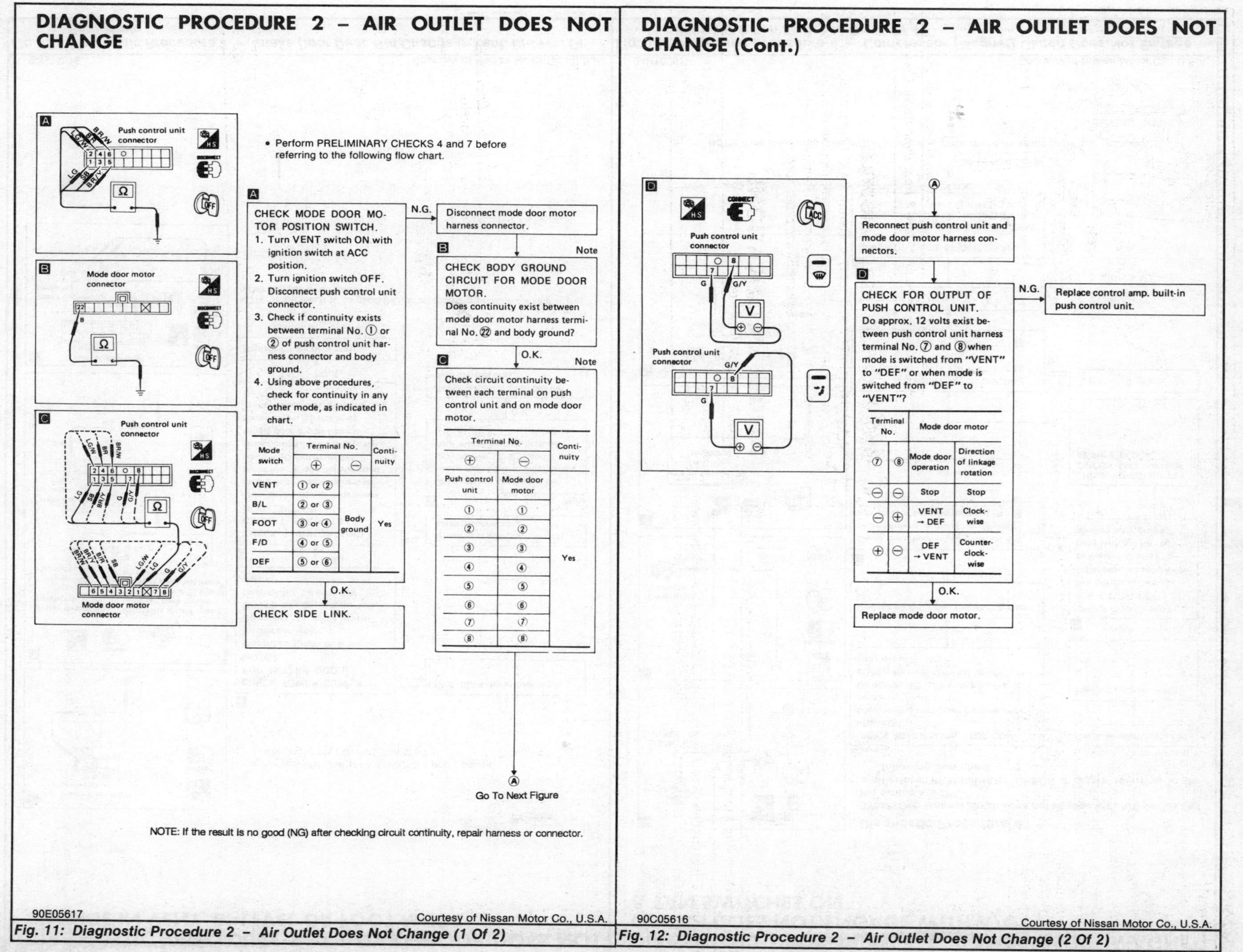
DIAGNOSTIC PROCEDURE 2 – AIR OUTLET DOES NOT CHANGE
A
Push control unit connector
BR/W
BR
LG/W
LG
SB
BR/Y
Ω
HS
DISCONNECT
OFF
B
Mode door motor connector
22
B
Ω
C
Push control unit connector
G/Y
G
Mode door motor connector
• Perform PRELIMINARY CHECKS 4 and 7 before referring to the following flow chart.
A
CHECK MODE DOOR MOTOR POSITION SWITCH.
1. Turn VENT switch ON with ignition switch at ACC position.
2. Turn ignition switch OFF. Disconnect push control unit connector.
3. Check if continuity exists between terminal No. ① or ② of push control unit harness connector and body ground.
4. Using above procedures, check for continuity in any other mode, as indicated in chart.
N.G.
Disconnect mode door motor harness connector.
B
Note
CHECK BODY GROUND CIRCUIT FOR MODE DOOR MOTOR.
Does continuity exist between mode door motor harness terminal No. ㉒ and body ground?
O.K.
C
Note
Check circuit continuity between each terminal on push control unit and on mode door motor.
O.K.
CHECK SIDE LINK.
Ⓐ
Go To Next Figure
NOTE: If the result is no good (NG) after checking circuit continuity, repair harness or connector.
DIAGNOSTIC PROCEDURE 2 – AIR OUTLET DOES NOT CHANGE (Cont.)
D
HS
CONNECT
ACC
Push control unit connector
G
G/Y
V
Ⓐ
Reconnect push control unit and mode door motor harness connectors.
D
CHECK FOR OUTPUT OF PUSH CONTROL UNIT.
Do approx. 12 volts exist between push control unit harness terminal No. ⑦ and ⑧ when mode is switched from "VENT" to "DEF" or when mode is switched from "DEF" to "VENT"?
N.G.
Replace control amp. built-in push control unit.
O.K.
Replace mode door motor.

Mode switch	Terminal No. ⊕	Terminal No. ⊖	Continuity
VENT	① or ②	Body ground	Yes
B/L	② or ③		
FOOT	③ or ④		
F/D	④ or ⑤		
DEF	⑤ or ⑥		

Terminal No. ⊕ Push control unit	Terminal No. ⊖ Mode door motor	Continuity
①	①	Yes
②	②	
③	③	
④	④	
⑤	⑤	
⑥	⑥	
⑦	⑦	
⑧	⑧	

Terminal No. ⑦	Terminal No. ⑧	Mode door operation	Direction of linkage rotation
⊖	⊖	Stop	Stop
⊖	⊕	VENT → DEF	Clockwise
⊕	⊖	DEF → VENT	Counterclockwise

90E05617 Courtesy of Nissan Motor Co., U.S.A.

Fig. 11: Diagnostic Procedure 2 – Air Outlet Does Not Change (1 Of 2)

90C05616 Courtesy of Nissan Motor Co., U.S.A.

Fig. 12: Diagnostic Procedure 2 – Air Outlet Does Not Change (2 Of 2)

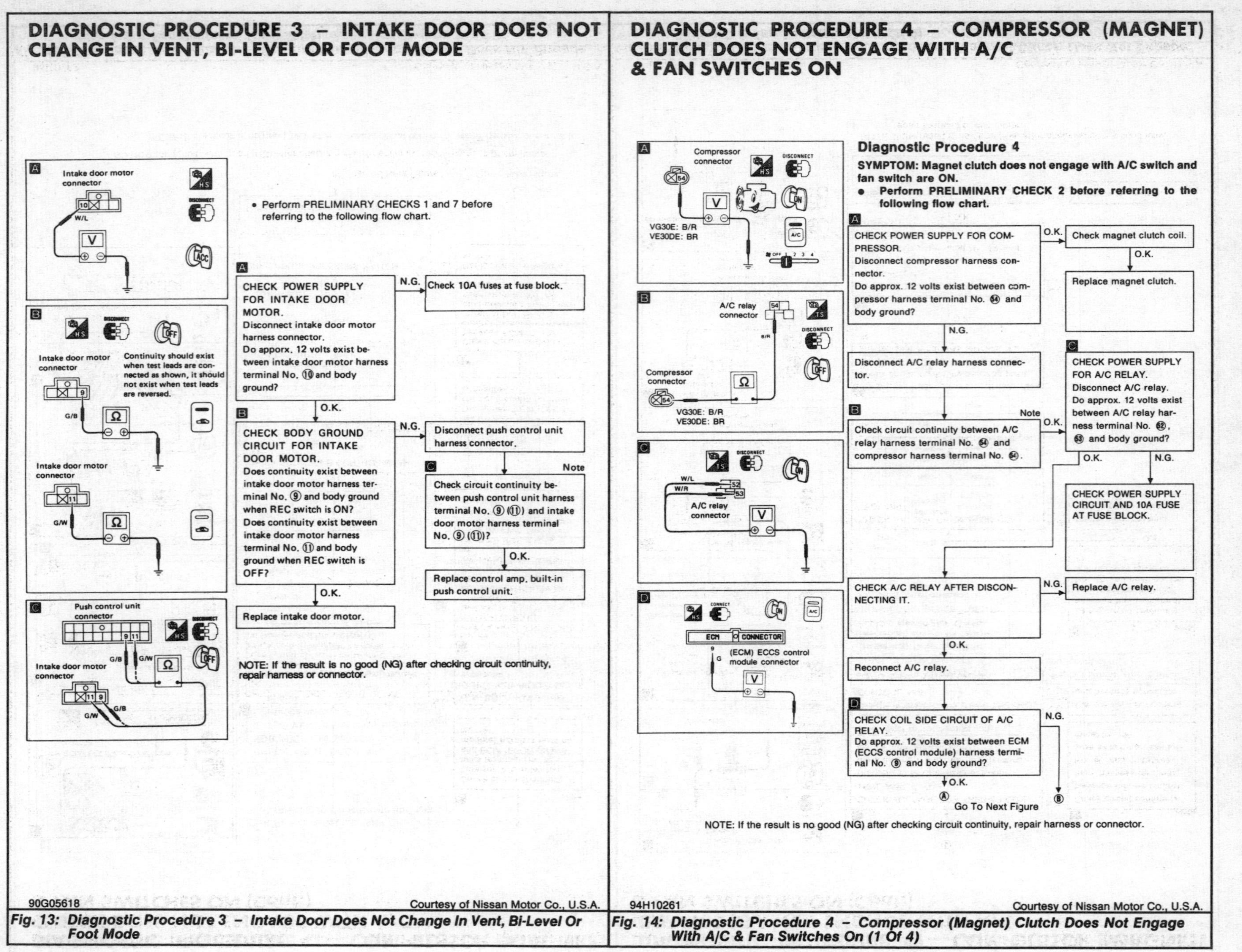
DIAGNOSTIC PROCEDURE 3 – INTAKE DOOR DOES NOT CHANGE IN VENT, BI-LEVEL OR FOOT MODE
A
Intake door motor connector
W/L
B
Intake door motor connector
Continuity should exist when test leads are connected as shown, it should not exist when test leads are reversed.
G/B
Intake door motor connector
G/W
C
Push control unit connector
Intake door motor connector
G/B
G/W
• Perform PRELIMINARY CHECKS 1 and 7 before referring to the following flow chart.
A
CHECK POWER SUPPLY FOR INTAKE DOOR MOTOR.
Disconnect intake door motor harness connector.
Do apporx. 12 volts exist between intake door motor harness terminal No. ⑩ and body ground?
N.G.
Check 10A fuses at fuse block.
O.K.
B
CHECK BODY GROUND CIRCUIT FOR INTAKE DOOR MOTOR.
Does continuity exist between intake door motor harness terminal No. ⑨ and body ground when REC switch is ON?
Does continuity exist between intake door motor harness terminal No. ⑪ and body ground when REC switch is OFF?
N.G.
Disconnect push control unit harness connector.
C
Note
Check circuit continuity between push control unit harness terminal No. ⑨ (⑪) and intake door motor harness terminal No. ⑨ (⑪)?
O.K.
Replace control amp. built-in push control unit.
O.K.
Replace intake door motor.
NOTE: If the result is no good (NG) after checking circuit continuity, repair harness or connector.
90G05618
Courtesy of Nissan Motor Co., U.S.A.
DIAGNOSTIC PROCEDURE 4 – COMPRESSOR (MAGNET) CLUTCH DOES NOT ENGAGE WITH A/C & FAN SWITCHES ON
A
Compressor connector
VG30E: B/R
VE30DE: BR
B
A/C relay connector
B/R
Compressor connector
VG30E: B/R
VE30DE: BR
C
W/L
W/R
A/C relay connector
D
ECM
CONNECTOR
(ECM) ECCS control module connector
Diagnostic Procedure 4
SYMPTOM: Magnet clutch does not engage with A/C switch and fan switch are ON.
• Perform PRELIMINARY CHECK 2 before referring to the following flow chart.
A
CHECK POWER SUPPLY FOR COMPRESSOR.
Disconnect compressor harness connector.
Do approx. 12 volts exist between compressor harness terminal No. ⑭ and body ground?
O.K.
Check magnet clutch coil.
O.K.
Replace magnet clutch.
N.G.
Disconnect A/C relay harness connector.
B
Note
Check circuit continuity between A/C relay harness terminal No. ⑭ and compressor harness terminal No. ⑭.
O.K.
C
CHECK POWER SUPPLY FOR A/C RELAY.
Disconnect A/C relay.
Do approx. 12 volts exist between A/C relay harness terminal No. ㊾, ㊿ and body ground?
O.K.
N.G.
CHECK POWER SUPPLY CIRCUIT AND 10A FUSE AT FUSE BLOCK.
CHECK A/C RELAY AFTER DISCONNECTING IT.
N.G.
Replace A/C relay.
O.K.
Reconnect A/C relay.
D
CHECK COIL SIDE CIRCUIT OF A/C RELAY.
Do approx. 12 volts exist between ECM (ECCS control module) harness terminal No. ⑨ and body ground?
N.G.
O.K.
Ⓐ
Ⓑ
Go To Next Figure
NOTE: If the result is no good (NG) after checking circuit continuity, repair harness or connector.
94H10261
Courtesy of Nissan Motor Co., U.S.A.

Fig. 13: Diagnostic Procedure 3 – Intake Door Does Not Change In Vent, Bi-Level Or Foot Mode

Fig. 14: Diagnostic Procedure 4 – Compressor (Magnet) Clutch Does Not Engage With A/C & Fan Switches On (1 Of 4)

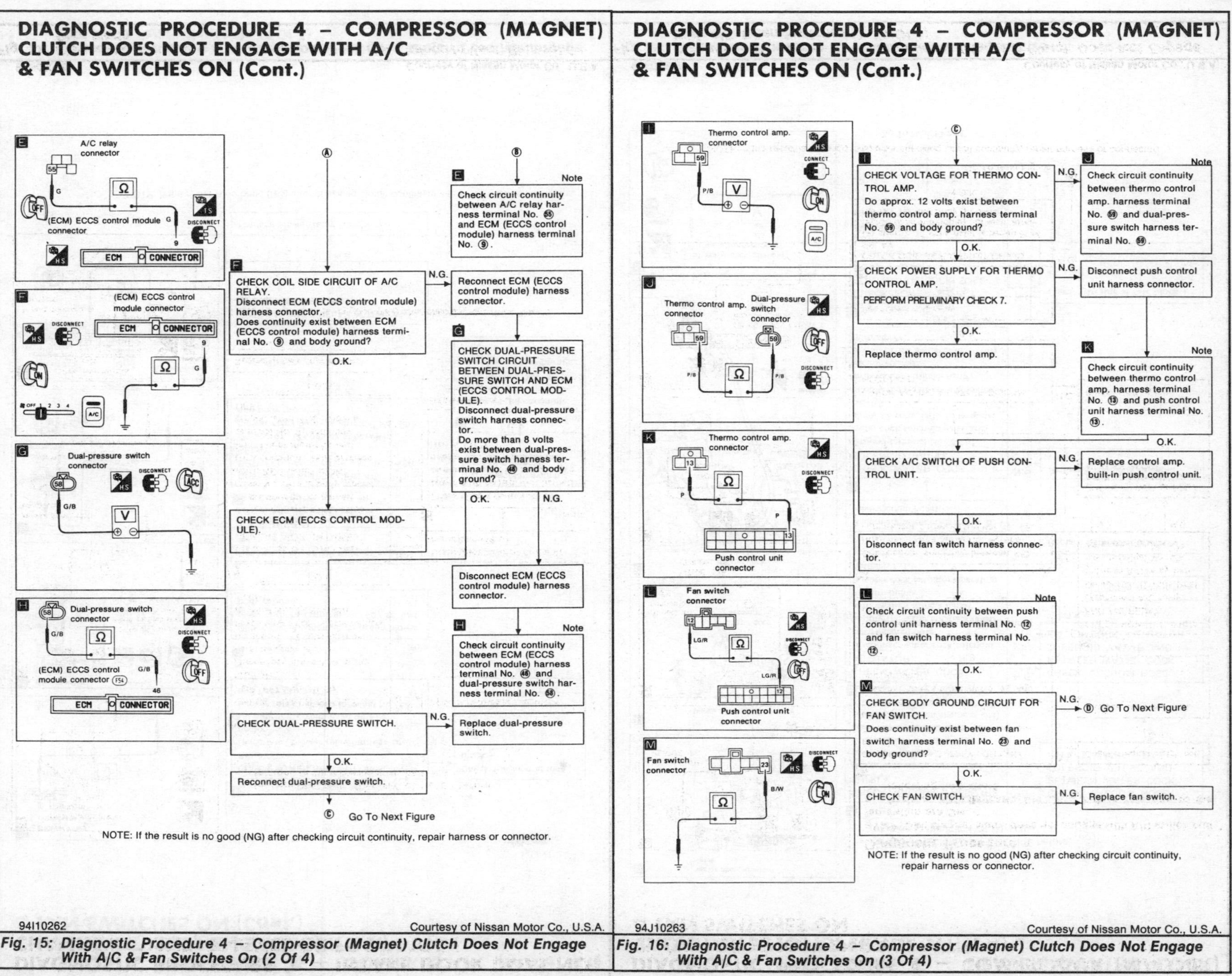
DIAGNOSTIC PROCEDURE 4 – COMPRESSOR (MAGNET) CLUTCH DOES NOT ENGAGE WITH A/C & FAN SWITCHES ON (Cont.)
E
A/C relay connector
55
G
(ECM) ECCS control module connector
9
DISCONNECT
ECM
CONNECTOR
F
(ECM) ECCS control module connector
DISCONNECT
G
G
Dual-pressure switch connector
58
DISCONNECT
G/B
H
Dual-pressure switch connector
58
G/B
DISCONNECT
(ECM) ECCS control module connector F54
46
A
B
F
CHECK COIL SIDE CIRCUIT OF A/C RELAY.
Disconnect ECM (ECCS control module) harness connector.
Does continuity exist between ECM (ECCS control module) harness terminal No. 9 and body ground?
N.G.
O.K.
E
Note
Check circuit continuity between A/C relay harness terminal No. 55 and ECM (ECCS control module) harness terminal No. 9.
Reconnect ECM (ECCS control module) harness connector.
G
CHECK DUAL-PRESSURE SWITCH CIRCUIT BETWEEN DUAL-PRESSURE SWITCH AND ECM (ECCS CONTROL MODULE).
Disconnect dual-pressure switch harness connector.
Do more than 8 volts exist between dual-pressure switch harness terminal No. 46 and body ground?
CHECK ECM (ECCS CONTROL MODULE).
Disconnect ECM (ECCS control module) harness connector.
H
Note
Check circuit continuity between ECM (ECCS control module) harness terminal No. 46 and dual-pressure switch harness terminal No. 58.
CHECK DUAL-PRESSURE SWITCH.
Replace dual-pressure switch.
Reconnect dual-pressure switch.
C Go To Next Figure
NOTE: If the result is no good (NG) after checking circuit continuity, repair harness or connector.
94I10262
Courtesy of Nissan Motor Co., U.S.A.
DIAGNOSTIC PROCEDURE 4 – COMPRESSOR (MAGNET) CLUTCH DOES NOT ENGAGE WITH A/C & FAN SWITCHES ON (Cont.)
I
Thermo control amp. connector
59
P/B
CONNECT
J
Thermo control amp. connector
Dual-pressure switch connector
59
P/B
DISCONNECT
K
Thermo control amp. connector
13
P
DISCONNECT
Push control unit connector
L
Fan switch connector
12
LG/R
DISCONNECT
Push control unit connector
M
Fan switch connector
23
B/W
DISCONNECT
C
I
CHECK VOLTAGE FOR THERMO CONTROL AMP.
Do approx. 12 volts exist between thermo control amp. harness terminal No. 59 and body ground?
J
Note
Check circuit continuity between thermo control amp. harness terminal No. 59 and dual-pressure switch harness terminal No. 59.
CHECK POWER SUPPLY FOR THERMO CONTROL AMP.
PERFORM PRELIMINARY CHECK 7.
Disconnect push control unit harness connector.
Replace thermo control amp.
K
Note
Check circuit continuity between thermo control amp. harness terminal No. 13 and push control unit harness terminal No. 13.
CHECK A/C SWITCH OF PUSH CONTROL UNIT.
Replace control amp. built-in push control unit.
Disconnect fan switch harness connector.
L
Note
Check circuit continuity between push control unit harness terminal No. 12 and fan switch harness terminal No. 12.
M
CHECK BODY GROUND CIRCUIT FOR FAN SWITCH.
Does continuity exist between fan switch harness terminal No. 23 and body ground?
D Go To Next Figure
CHECK FAN SWITCH.
Replace fan switch.
N.G.
O.K.
NOTE: If the result is no good (NG) after checking circuit continuity, repair harness or connector.
94J10263
Courtesy of Nissan Motor Co., U.S.A.

Fig. 15: Diagnostic Procedure 4 – Compressor (Magnet) Clutch Does Not Engage With A/C & Fan Switches On (2 Of 4)

Fig. 16: Diagnostic Procedure 4 – Compressor (Magnet) Clutch Does Not Engage With A/C & Fan Switches On (3 Of 4)

1993 MANUAL A/C-HEATER SYSTEMS
Trouble Shooting – Maxima (Cont.)

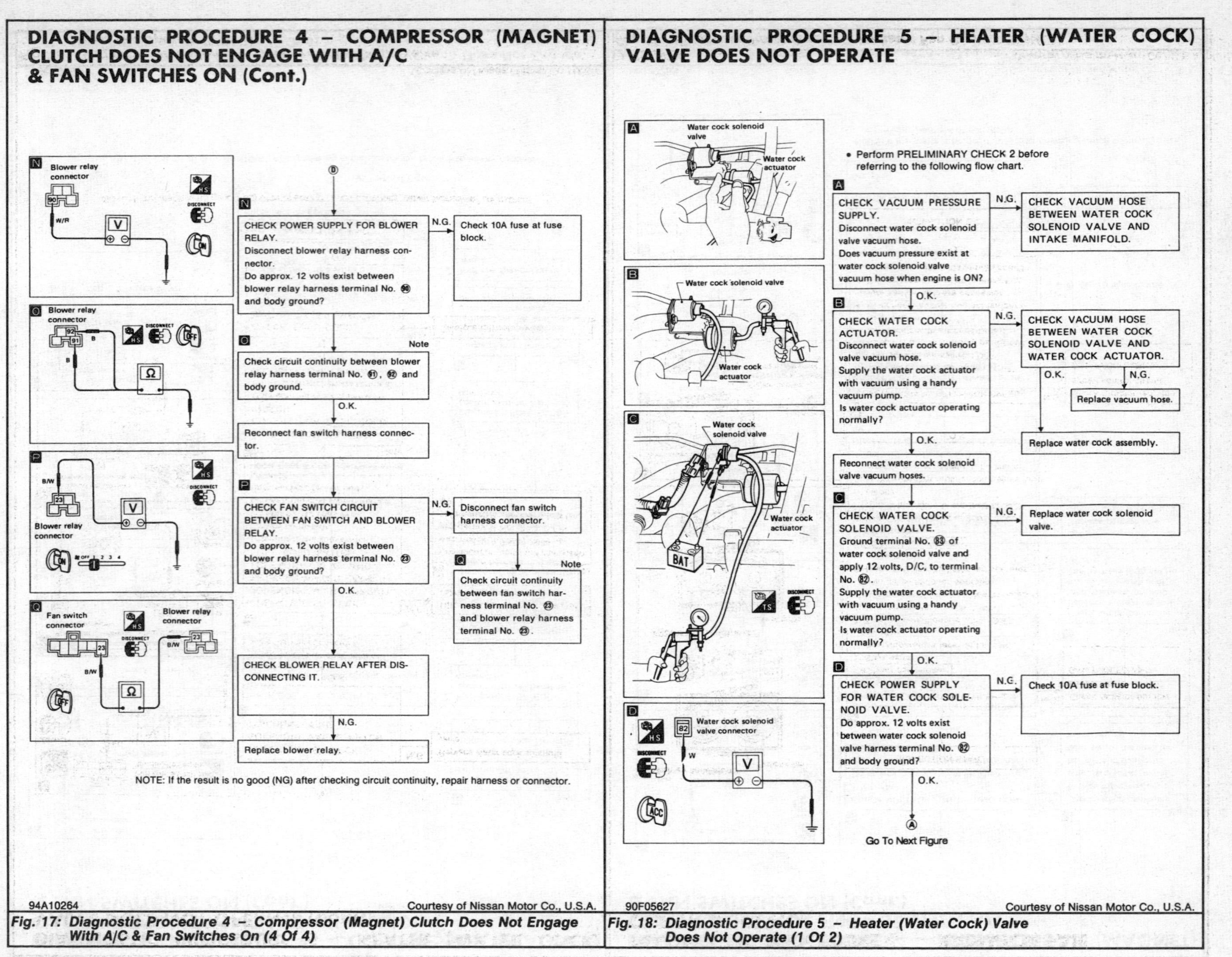
DIAGNOSTIC PROCEDURE 4 – COMPRESSOR (MAGNET) CLUTCH DOES NOT ENGAGE WITH A/C & FAN SWITCHES ON (Cont.)
N Blower relay connector
90
W/R
V
D
N CHECK POWER SUPPLY FOR BLOWER RELAY. Disconnect blower relay harness connector. Do approx. 12 volts exist between blower relay harness terminal No. 90 and body ground?
N.G.
Check 10A fuse at fuse block.
O Blower relay connector
92
91
B
Ω
O Check circuit continuity between blower relay harness terminal No. 91, 92 and body ground.
Note
O.K.
Reconnect fan switch harness connector.
P
B/W
23
Blower relay connector
OFF 1 2 3 4
V
P CHECK FAN SWITCH CIRCUIT BETWEEN FAN SWITCH AND BLOWER RELAY. Do approx. 12 volts exist between blower relay harness terminal No. 23 and body ground?
N.G.
Disconnect fan switch harness connector.
Q Check circuit continuity between fan switch harness terminal No. 23 and blower relay harness terminal No. 23.
Note
O.K.
Q Fan switch connector
Blower relay connector
23
B/W
Ω
CHECK BLOWER RELAY AFTER DISCONNECTING IT.
N.G.
Replace blower relay.
NOTE: If the result is no good (NG) after checking circuit continuity, repair harness or connector.
94A10264
Courtesy of Nissan Motor Co., U.S.A.
DIAGNOSTIC PROCEDURE 5 – HEATER (WATER COCK) VALVE DOES NOT OPERATE
A Water cock solenoid valve
Water cock actuator
• Perform PRELIMINARY CHECK 2 before referring to the following flow chart.
A CHECK VACUUM PRESSURE SUPPLY. Disconnect water cock solenoid valve vacuum hose. Does vacuum pressure exist at water cock solenoid valve vacuum hose when engine is ON?
N.G.
CHECK VACUUM HOSE BETWEEN WATER COCK SOLENOID VALVE AND INTAKE MANIFOLD.
O.K.
B Water cock solenoid valve
Water cock actuator
B CHECK WATER COCK ACTUATOR. Disconnect water cock solenoid valve vacuum hose. Supply the water cock actuator with vacuum using a handy vacuum pump. Is water cock actuator operating normally?
N.G.
CHECK VACUUM HOSE BETWEEN WATER COCK SOLENOID VALVE AND WATER COCK ACTUATOR.
O.K.
N.G.
Replace vacuum hose.
Replace water cock assembly.
O.K.
Reconnect water cock solenoid valve vacuum hoses.
C Water cock solenoid valve
Water cock actuator
BAT
C CHECK WATER COCK SOLENOID VALVE. Ground terminal No. 83 of water cock solenoid valve and apply 12 volts, D/C, to terminal No. 82. Supply the water cock actuator with vacuum using a handy vacuum pump. Is water cock actuator operating normally?
N.G.
Replace water cock solenoid valve.
O.K.
D Water cock solenoid valve connector
82
W
V
D CHECK POWER SUPPLY FOR WATER COCK SOLENOID VALVE. Do approx. 12 volts exist between water cock solenoid valve harness terminal No. 82 and body ground?
N.G.
Check 10A fuse at fuse block.
O.K.
A
Go To Next Figure
90F05627
Courtesy of Nissan Motor Co., U.S.A.

Fig. 17: Diagnostic Procedure 4 – Compressor (Magnet) Clutch Does Not Engage With A/C & Fan Switches On (4 Of 4)

Fig. 18: Diagnostic Procedure 5 – Heater (Water Cock) Valve Does Not Operate (1 Of 2)

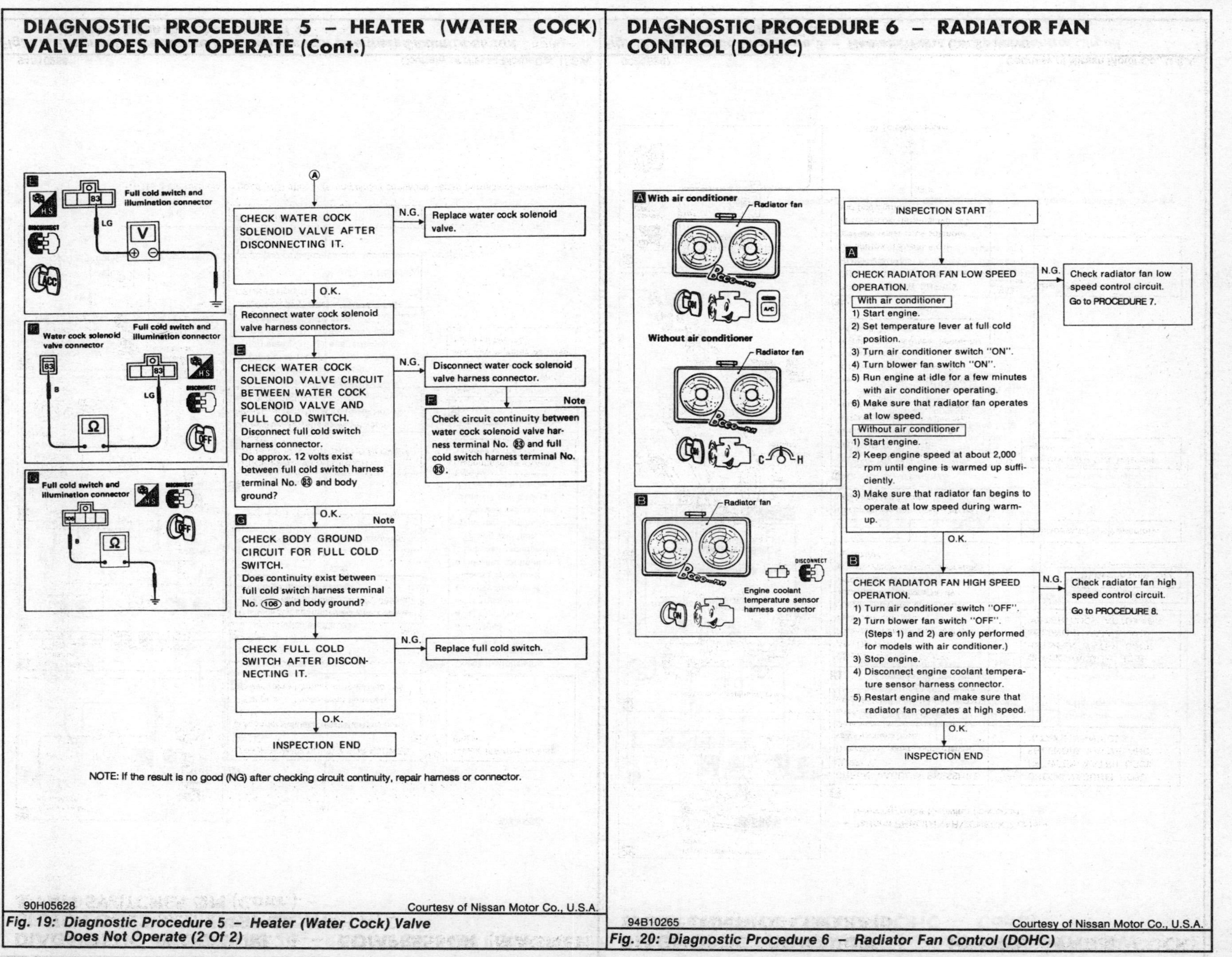
DIAGNOSTIC PROCEDURE 5 – HEATER (WATER COCK) VALVE DOES NOT OPERATE (Cont.)
E
Full cold switch and illumination connector
83
LG
V
DISCONNECT
ACC
F
Water cock solenoid valve connector
Full cold switch and illumination connector
83
B
LG
Ω
DISCONNECT
OFF
G
Full cold switch and illumination connector
106
B
Ω
DISCONNECT
OFF
A
CHECK WATER COCK SOLENOID VALVE AFTER DISCONNECTING IT.
N.G.
Replace water cock solenoid valve.
O.K.
Reconnect water cock solenoid valve harness connectors.
E
CHECK WATER COCK SOLENOID VALVE CIRCUIT BETWEEN WATER COCK SOLENOID VALVE AND FULL COLD SWITCH.
Disconnect full cold switch harness connector.
Do approx. 12 volts exist between full cold switch harness terminal No. 83 and body ground?
N.G.
Disconnect water cock solenoid valve harness connector.
F
Note
Check circuit continuity between water cock solenoid valve harness terminal No. 83 and full cold switch harness terminal No. 83.
O.K.
G
Note
CHECK BODY GROUND CIRCUIT FOR FULL COLD SWITCH.
Does continuity exist between full cold switch harness terminal No. 106 and body ground?
CHECK FULL COLD SWITCH AFTER DISCONNECTING IT.
N.G.
Replace full cold switch.
O.K.
INSPECTION END
NOTE: If the result is no good (NG) after checking circuit continuity, repair harness or connector.
90H05628
Courtesy of Nissan Motor Co., U.S.A.
DIAGNOSTIC PROCEDURE 6 – RADIATOR FAN CONTROL (DOHC)
A With air conditioner
Radiator fan
A/C
Without air conditioner
Radiator fan
C H
B
Radiator fan
DISCONNECT
Engine coolant temperature sensor harness connector
INSPECTION START
A
CHECK RADIATOR FAN LOW SPEED OPERATION.
With air conditioner
1) Start engine.
2) Set temperature lever at full cold position.
3) Turn air conditioner switch "ON".
4) Turn blower fan switch "ON".
5) Run engine at idle for a few minutes with air conditioner operating.
6) Make sure that radiator fan operates at low speed.
Without air conditioner
1) Start engine.
2) Keep engine speed at about 2,000 rpm until engine is warmed up sufficiently.
3) Make sure that radiator fan begins to operate at low speed during warm-up.
N.G.
Check radiator fan low speed control circuit.
Go to PROCEDURE 7.
O.K.
B
CHECK RADIATOR FAN HIGH SPEED OPERATION.
1) Turn air conditioner switch "OFF".
2) Turn blower fan switch "OFF".
(Steps 1) and 2) are only performed for models with air conditioner.)
3) Stop engine.
4) Disconnect engine coolant temperature sensor harness connector.
5) Restart engine and make sure that radiator fan operates at high speed.
N.G.
Check radiator fan high speed control circuit.
Go to PROCEDURE 8.
O.K.
INSPECTION END
94B10265
Courtesy of Nissan Motor Co., U.S.A.

Fig. 19: Diagnostic Procedure 5 – Heater (Water Cock) Valve Does Not Operate (2 Of 2)

Fig. 20: Diagnostic Procedure 6 – Radiator Fan Control (DOHC)

1993 MANUAL A/C-HEATER SYSTEMS
Trouble Shooting – Maxima (Cont.)

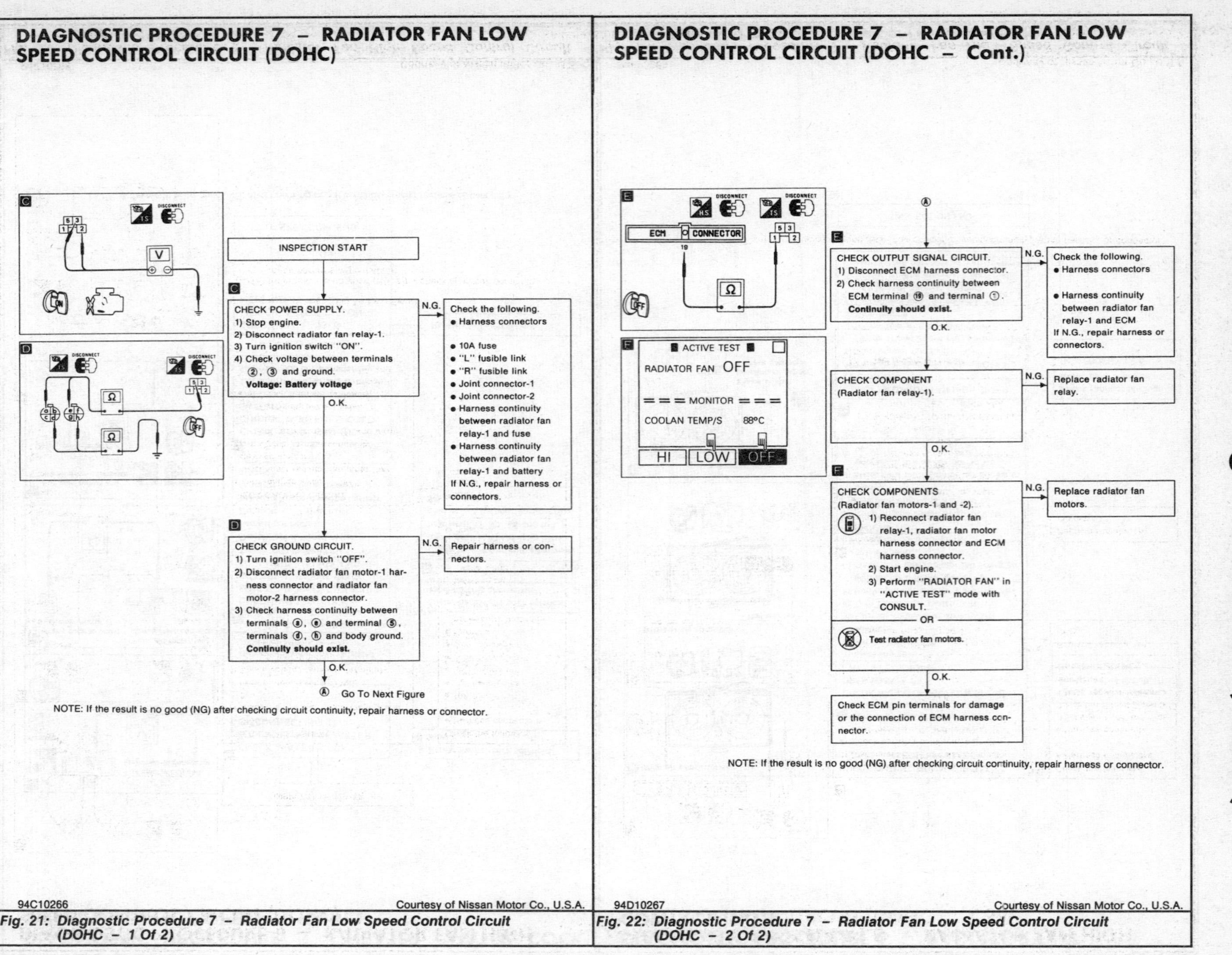
DIAGNOSTIC PROCEDURE 7 – RADIATOR FAN LOW SPEED CONTROL CIRCUIT (DOHC)
INSPECTION START
C CHECK POWER SUPPLY.
1) Stop engine.
2) Disconnect radiator fan relay-1.
3) Turn ignition switch "ON".
4) Check voltage between terminals ②, ③ and ground.
Voltage: Battery voltage
N.G.
Check the following.
• Harness connectors
• 10A fuse
• "L" fusible link
• "R" fusible link
• Joint connector-1
• Joint connector-2
• Harness continuity between radiator fan relay-1 and fuse
• Harness continuity between radiator fan relay-1 and battery
If N.G., repair harness or connectors.
O.K.
D CHECK GROUND CIRCUIT.
1) Turn ignition switch "OFF".
2) Disconnect radiator fan motor-1 harness connector and radiator fan motor-2 harness connector.
3) Check harness continuity between terminals ⓐ, ⓔ and terminal ⑤, terminals ⓓ, ⓗ and body ground.
Continuity should exist.
N.G.
Repair harness or connectors.
O.K.
Ⓐ Go To Next Figure
NOTE: If the result is no good (NG) after checking circuit continuity, repair harness or connector.
94C10266
Courtesy of Nissan Motor Co., U.S.A.
DIAGNOSTIC PROCEDURE 7 – RADIATOR FAN LOW SPEED CONTROL CIRCUIT (DOHC – Cont.)
ECM
CONNECTOR
19
DISCONNECT
ACTIVE TEST
RADIATOR FAN OFF
=== MONITOR ===
COOLAN TEMP/S 88°C
HI
LOW
OFF
Ⓐ
E CHECK OUTPUT SIGNAL CIRCUIT.
1) Disconnect ECM harness connector.
2) Check harness continuity between ECM terminal ⑲ and terminal ①.
Continuity should exist.
N.G.
Check the following.
• Harness connectors
• Harness continuity between radiator fan relay-1 and ECM
If N.G., repair harness or connectors.
O.K.
CHECK COMPONENT
(Radiator fan relay-1).
N.G.
Replace radiator fan relay.
O.K.
F CHECK COMPONENTS
(Radiator fan motors-1 and -2).
1) Reconnect radiator fan relay-1, radiator fan motor harness connector and ECM harness connector.
2) Start engine.
3) Perform "RADIATOR FAN" in "ACTIVE TEST" mode with CONSULT.
OR
Test radiator fan motors.
N.G.
Replace radiator fan motors.
O.K.
Check ECM pin terminals for damage or the connection of ECM harness connector.
NOTE: If the result is no good (NG) after checking circuit continuity, repair harness or connector.
94D10267
Courtesy of Nissan Motor Co., U.S.A.

Fig. 21: Diagnostic Procedure 7 – Radiator Fan Low Speed Control Circuit (DOHC – 1 Of 2)

Fig. 22: Diagnostic Procedure 7 – Radiator Fan Low Speed Control Circuit (DOHC – 2 Of 2)

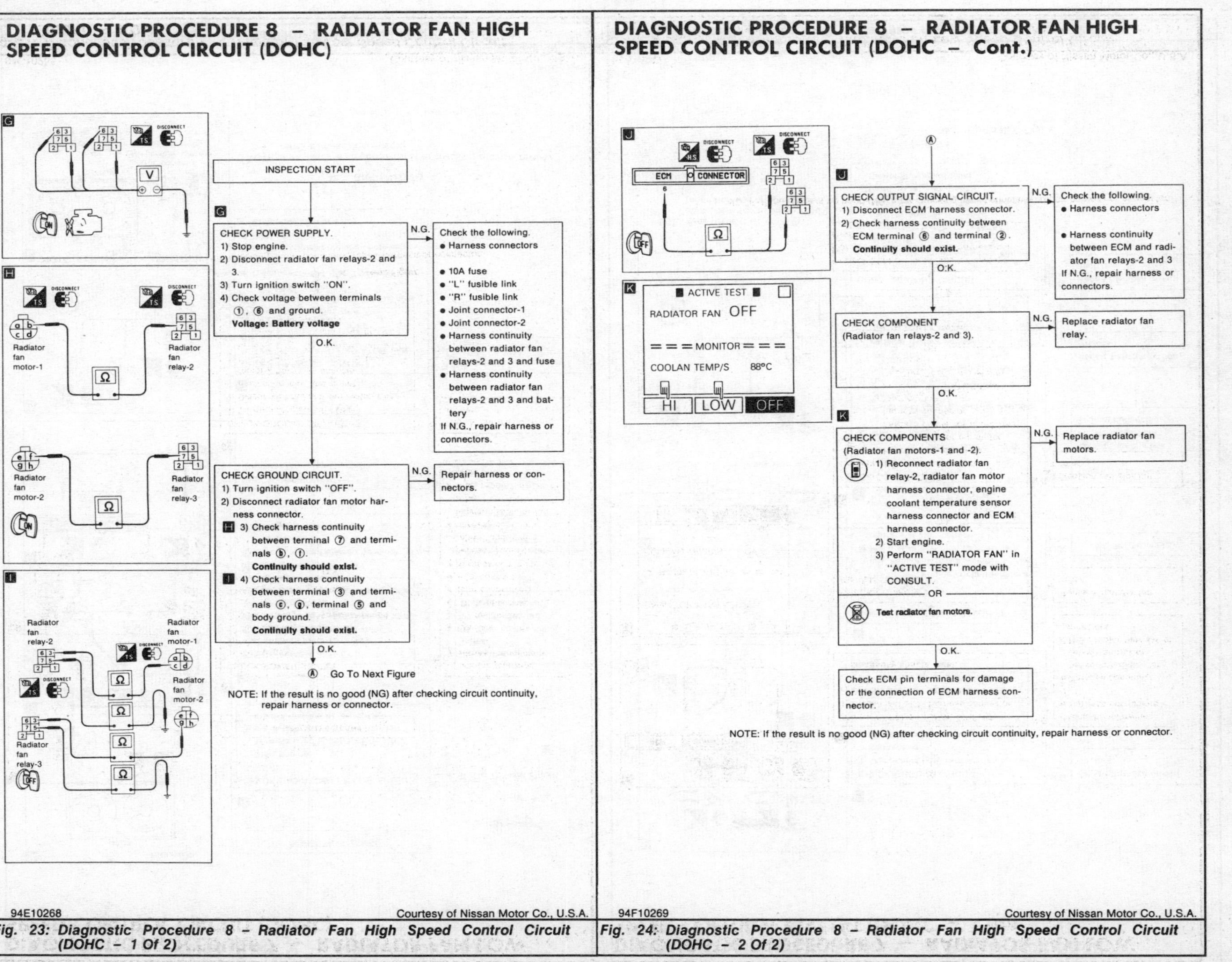
DIAGNOSTIC PROCEDURE 8 – RADIATOR FAN HIGH SPEED CONTROL CIRCUIT (DOHC)
INSPECTION START
G
CHECK POWER SUPPLY.
1) Stop engine.
2) Disconnect radiator fan relays-2 and 3.
3) Turn ignition switch "ON".
4) Check voltage between terminals ①, ⑥ and ground.
Voltage: Battery voltage
N.G.
Check the following.
• Harness connectors
• 10A fuse
• "L" fusible link
• "R" fusible link
• Joint connector-1
• Joint connector-2
• Harness continuity between radiator fan relays-2 and 3 and fuse
• Harness continuity between radiator fan relays-2 and 3 and battery
If N.G., repair harness or connectors.
O.K.
CHECK GROUND CIRCUIT.
1) Turn ignition switch "OFF".
2) Disconnect radiator fan motor harness connector.
H 3) Check harness continuity between terminal ⑦ and terminals ⓑ, ⓕ.
Continuity should exist.
I 4) Check harness continuity between terminal ③ and terminals ⓒ, ⓖ, terminal ⑤ and body ground.
Continuity should exist.
N.G.
Repair harness or connectors.
O.K.
Ⓐ Go To Next Figure
NOTE: If the result is no good (NG) after checking circuit continuity, repair harness or connector.
G
H
I
DISCONNECT
Radiator fan motor-1
Radiator fan motor-2
Radiator fan relay-2
Radiator fan relay-3
Radiator fan motor-1
Radiator fan motor-2
94E10268
Courtesy of Nissan Motor Co., U.S.A.
DIAGNOSTIC PROCEDURE 8 – RADIATOR FAN HIGH SPEED CONTROL CIRCUIT (DOHC – Cont.)
Ⓐ
J
CHECK OUTPUT SIGNAL CIRCUIT.
1) Disconnect ECM harness connector.
2) Check harness continuity between ECM terminal ⑥ and terminal ②.
Continuity should exist.
N.G.
Check the following.
• Harness connectors
• Harness continuity between ECM and radiator fan relays-2 and 3
If N.G., repair harness or connectors.
O.K.
CHECK COMPONENT
(Radiator fan relays-2 and 3).
N.G.
Replace radiator fan relay.
O.K.
K
CHECK COMPONENTS
(Radiator fan motors-1 and -2).
1) Reconnect radiator fan relay-2, radiator fan motor harness connector, engine coolant temperature sensor harness connector and ECM harness connector.
2) Start engine.
3) Perform "RADIATOR FAN" in "ACTIVE TEST" mode with CONSULT.
OR
Test radiator fan motors.
N.G.
Replace radiator fan motors.
O.K.
Check ECM pin terminals for damage or the connection of ECM harness connector.
NOTE: If the result is no good (NG) after checking circuit continuity, repair harness or connector.
J
ECM
CONNECTOR
DISCONNECT
K
ACTIVE TEST
RADIATOR FAN OFF
=== MONITOR ===
COOLAN TEMP/S 88°C
HI
LOW
OFF
94F10269
Courtesy of Nissan Motor Co., U.S.A.

Fig. 23: Diagnostic Procedure 8 – Radiator Fan High Speed Control Circuit (DOHC – 1 Of 2)

Fig. 24: Diagnostic Procedure 8 – Radiator Fan High Speed Control Circuit (DOHC – 2 Of 2)

1993 MANUAL A/C-HEATER SYSTEMS
Trouble Shooting – Maxima (Cont.)

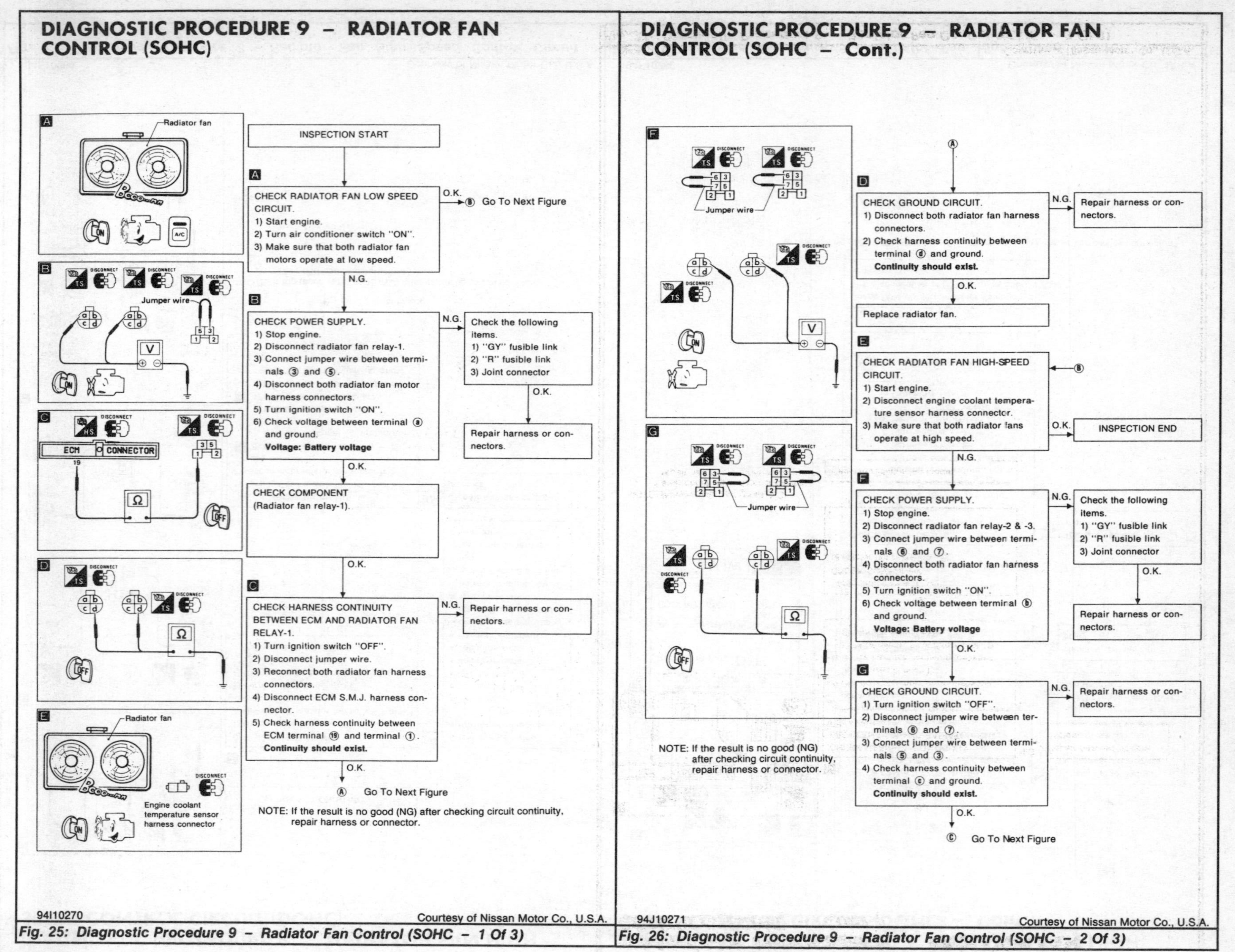
DIAGNOSTIC PROCEDURE 9 – RADIATOR FAN CONTROL (SOHC)
Radiator fan
ON
A/C
DISCONNECT
T.S
Jumper wire
ECM
CONNECTOR
19
H.S
OFF
Engine coolant temperature sensor harness connector
INSPECTION START
A
CHECK RADIATOR FAN LOW SPEED CIRCUIT.
1) Start engine.
2) Turn air conditioner switch "ON".
3) Make sure that both radiator fan motors operate at low speed.
O.K.
Ⓑ Go To Next Figure
N.G.
B
CHECK POWER SUPPLY.
1) Stop engine.
2) Disconnect radiator fan relay-1.
3) Connect jumper wire between terminals ③ and ⑤.
4) Disconnect both radiator fan motor harness connectors.
5) Turn ignition switch "ON".
6) Check voltage between terminal ⓐ and ground.
Voltage: Battery voltage
N.G.
Check the following items.
1) "GY" fusible link
2) "R" fusible link
3) Joint connector
O.K.
Repair harness or connectors.
O.K.
CHECK COMPONENT
(Radiator fan relay-1).
O.K.
C
CHECK HARNESS CONTINUITY BETWEEN ECM AND RADIATOR FAN RELAY-1.
1) Turn ignition switch "OFF".
2) Disconnect jumper wire.
3) Reconnect both radiator fan harness connectors.
4) Disconnect ECM S.M.J. harness connector.
5) Check harness continuity between ECM terminal ⑲ and terminal ①.
Continuity should exist.
N.G.
Repair harness or connectors.
O.K.
Ⓐ Go To Next Figure
NOTE: If the result is no good (NG) after checking circuit continuity, repair harness or connector.
94I10270
Courtesy of Nissan Motor Co., U.S.A.
DIAGNOSTIC PROCEDURE 9 – RADIATOR FAN CONTROL (SOHC – Cont.)
Jumper wire
DISCONNECT
T.S
ON
OFF
Ⓐ
D
CHECK GROUND CIRCUIT.
1) Disconnect both radiator fan harness connectors.
2) Check harness continuity between terminal ⓓ and ground.
Continuity should exist.
N.G.
Repair harness or connectors.
O.K.
Replace radiator fan.
E
CHECK RADIATOR FAN HIGH-SPEED CIRCUIT.
1) Start engine.
2) Disconnect engine coolant temperature sensor harness connector.
3) Make sure that both radiator fans operate at high speed.
Ⓑ
O.K.
INSPECTION END
N.G.
F
CHECK POWER SUPPLY.
1) Stop engine.
2) Disconnect radiator fan relay-2 & -3.
3) Connect jumper wire between terminals ⑥ and ⑦.
4) Disconnect both radiator fan harness connectors.
5) Turn ignition switch "ON".
6) Check voltage between terminal ⓑ and ground.
Voltage: Battery voltage
N.G.
Check the following items.
1) "GY" fusible link
2) "R" fusible link
3) Joint connector
O.K.
Repair harness or connectors.
O.K.
G
CHECK GROUND CIRCUIT.
1) Turn ignition switch "OFF".
2) Disconnect jumper wire between terminals ⑥ and ⑦.
3) Connect jumper wire between terminals ⑤ and ③.
4) Check harness continuity between terminal ⓒ and ground.
Continuity should exist.
N.G.
Repair harness or connectors.
O.K.
Ⓒ Go To Next Figure
NOTE: If the result is no good (NG) after checking circuit continuity, repair harness or connector.
94J10271
Courtesy of Nissan Motor Co., U.S.A.

Fig. 25: Diagnostic Procedure 9 – Radiator Fan Control (SOHC – 1 Of 3)

Fig. 26: Diagnostic Procedure 9 – Radiator Fan Control (SOHC – 2 Of 3)

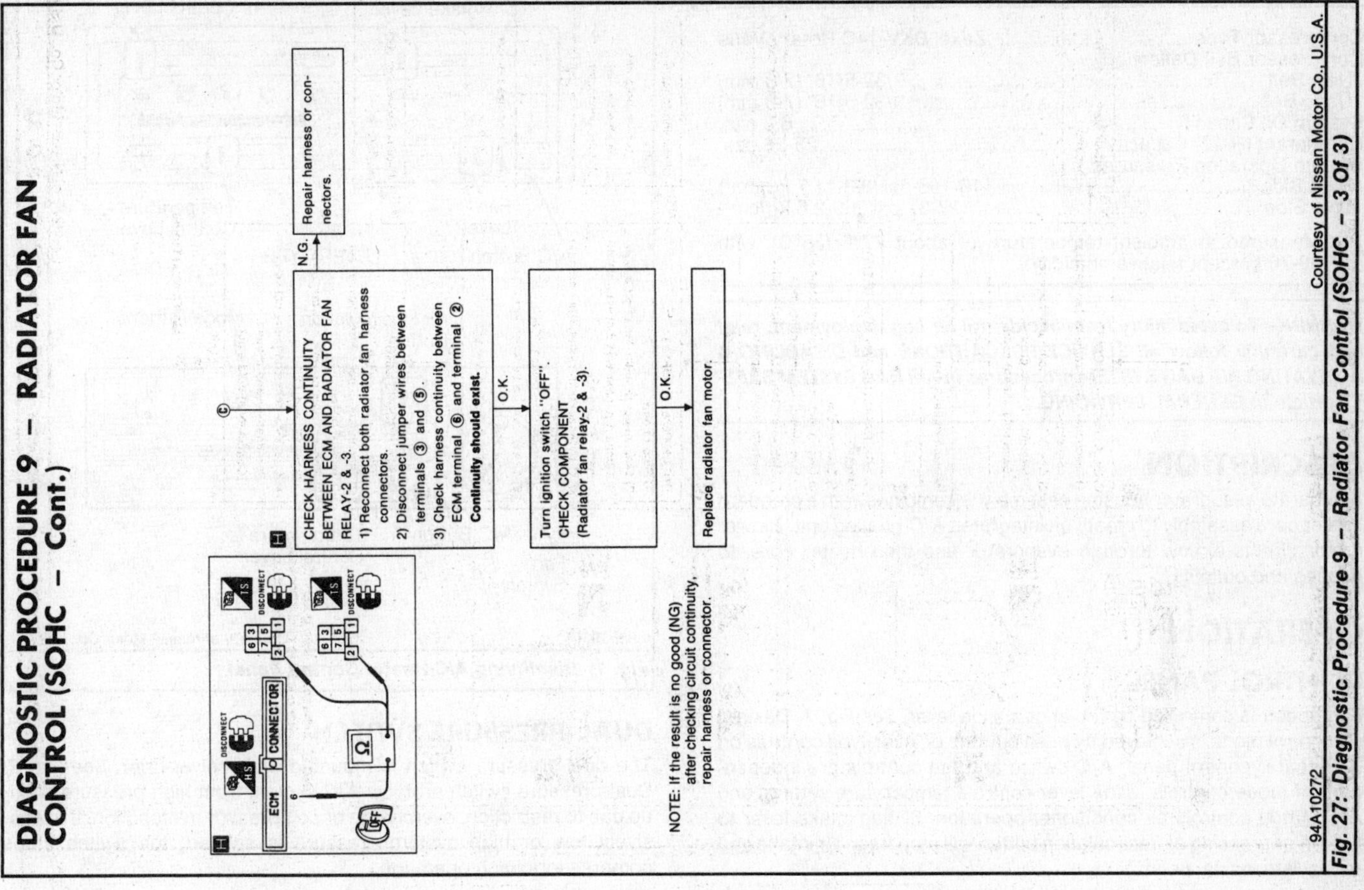
DIAGNOSTIC PROCEDURE 9 – RADIATOR FAN CONTROL (SOHC – Cont.)
H
ECM
CONNECTOR
DISCONNECT
H.S.
6
OFF
Ω
6 3
7 5
2 1
DISCONNECT
H
CHECK HARNESS CONTINUITY BETWEEN ECM AND RADIATOR FAN RELAY-2 & -3.
1) Reconnect both radiator fan harness connectors.
2) Disconnect jumper wires between terminals ③ and ⑤.
3) Check harness continuity between ECM terminal ⑥ and terminal ②.
Continuity should exist.
N.G.
Repair harness or connectors.
O.K.
Turn ignition switch "OFF".
CHECK COMPONENT
(Radiator fan relay-2 & -3).
O.K.
Replace radiator fan motor.
NOTE: If the result is no good (NG) after checking circuit continuity, repair harness or connector.
94A10272
Courtesy of Nissan Motor Co., U.S.A.

Fig. 27: Diagnostic Procedure 9 – Radiator Fan Control (SOHC – 3 Of 3)

1993 MANUAL A/C-HEATER SYSTEMS
NX & Sentra

SPECIFICATIONS

Compressor Type .... Zexel DKV-14C Rotary Vane
Compressor Belt Deflection
  New Belt .... 9/32-5/16" (7-8 mm)
  Used Belt .... 9/32-5/16" (7-8 mm)
System Oil Capacity .... 6.8 ozs.
Refrigerant (R-12) Capacity .... 23-26 ozs.
System Operating Pressures [1]
  High Side .... 118-166 psi (8.3-11.7 kg/cm²)
  Low Side .... 27-37 psi (1.9-2.6 kg/cm²)

[1] – Measured at ambient temperature of about 77°F (25°C), with 50-70 percent relative humidity.

WARNING: To avoid injury from accidental air bag deployment, read and carefully follow all SERVICE PRECAUTIONS and DISABLING & ACTIVATING AIR BAG SYSTEM procedures in AIR BAG SYSTEM SAFETY article in GENERAL SERVICING.

DESCRIPTION

A separate evaporator housing assembly is combined with a standard heater core assembly to create an integrated A/C-heating unit. Blower motor directs airflow through evaporator and then heater core, to ducting and outlets.

OPERATION

CONTROL PANEL

Fan speed is controlled by a dial or a slide lever. *See Fig. 1.* Desired air control mode is achieved by push buttons or lever-type controls on A/C-heater control panel. A/C switch and fan controls are independent of mode controls. Slide lever controls temperature setting, and A/C button controls air conditioner operation. Sliding intake lever to the left or pressing air recirculation button will stop fresh air intake and recirculate inside air.

FUSIBLE PLUG

Fusible plug, mounted on receiver-drier, is a high temperature relief valve. When temperature is 221°F (105°C), plug melts to vent refrigerant to atmosphere, thereby protecting the system.

FAST IDLE CONTROL DEVICE (FICD)

When A/C system is energized, the engine control module signals FICD to adjust Auxiliary Air Control (AAC) valve to by-pass additional air and increase idle speed. This higher idle speed allows engine to idle smoothly during compressor operation.

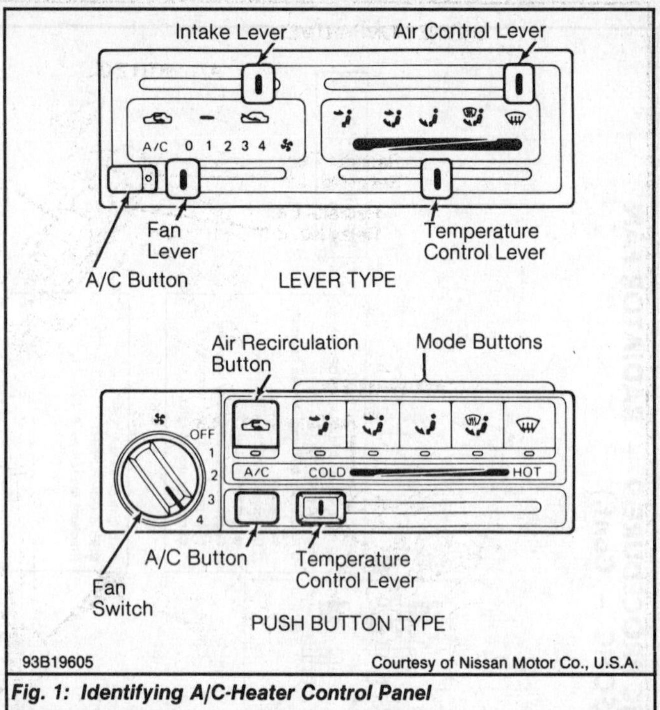
Intake Lever
Air Control Lever
A/C 0 1 2 3 4
Fan Lever
Temperature Control Lever
A/C Button
LEVER TYPE
Air Recirculation Button
Mode Buttons
OFF
1
2
3
4
A/C
COLD
HOT
A/C Button
Temperature Control Lever
Fan Switch
PUSH BUTTON TYPE
93B19605
Courtesy of Nissan Motor Co., U.S.A.

Fig. 1: Identifying A/C-Heater Control Panel

DUAL-PRESSURE SWITCH

The dual-pressure switch is mounted on receiver-drier. *See Fig. 2.* Dual-pressure switch protects A/C system from high pressure build-up due to restriction, overcharge or compressor malfunction. If excessively low or high system pressure is sensed, the switch stops compressor clutch operation.

HIGH PRESSURE RELIEF VALVE

A high pressure relief valve is located on end of high pressure hose, near A/C compressor. When high pressure of 540 psi (38 kg/cm²) is sensed, relief valve opens, venting refrigerant to atmosphere.

THERMO CONTROL AMPLIFIER

An electrical thermo control amplifier is mounted on evaporator housing. *See Fig. 3.* A temperature sensor (thermistor), inside evaporator housing, senses air temperature and sends signal to thermo control amplifier. Thermo control amplifier then cycles compressor clutch on and off according to temperature setting on control panel.

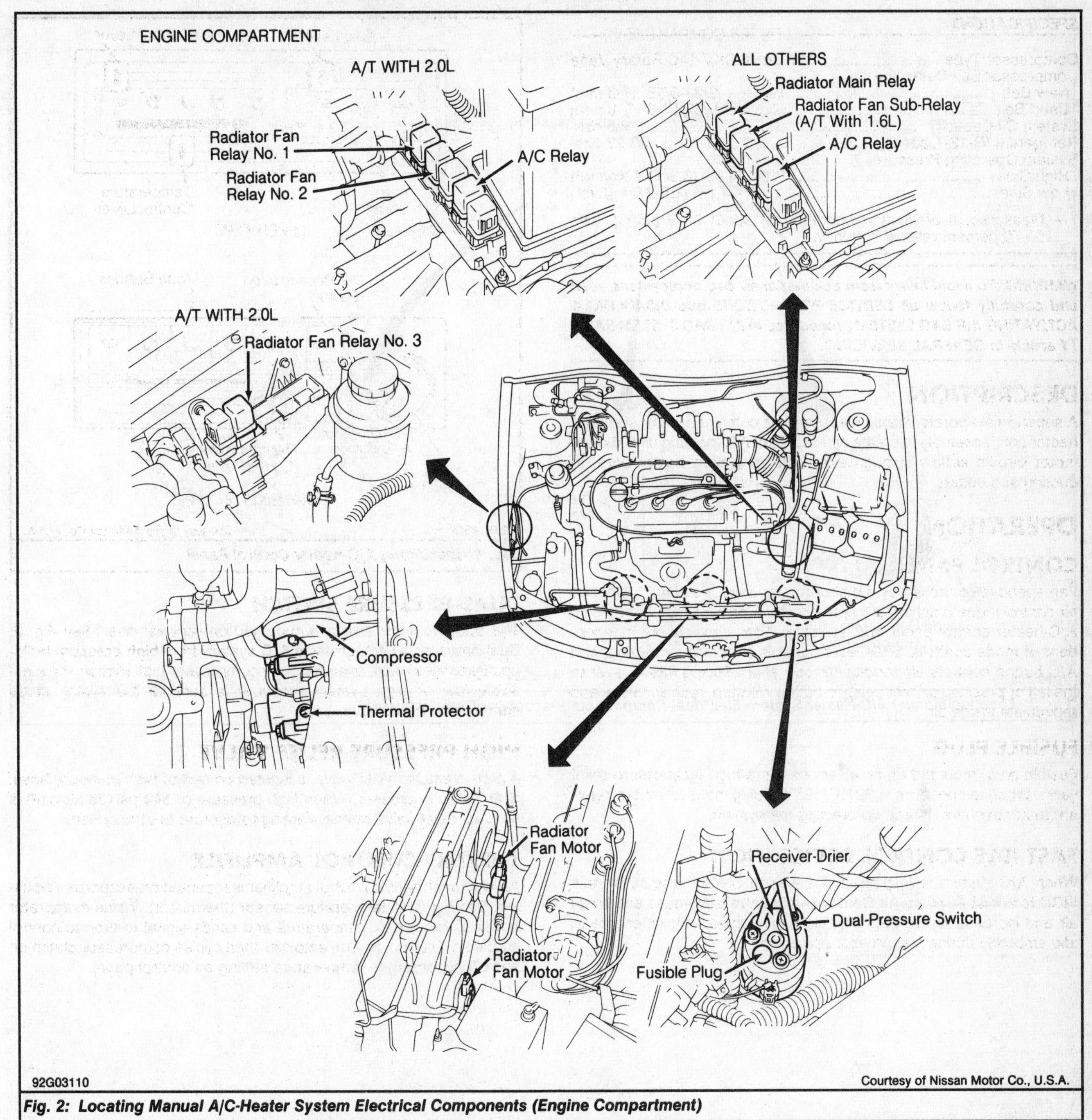
ENGINE COMPARTMENT
A/T WITH 2.0L
Radiator Fan Relay No. 1
Radiator Fan Relay No. 2
A/C Relay
ALL OTHERS
Radiator Main Relay
Radiator Fan Sub-Relay (A/T With 1.6L)
A/C Relay
A/T WITH 2.0L
Radiator Fan Relay No. 3
Compressor
Thermal Protector
Radiator Fan Motor
Radiator Fan Motor
Receiver-Drier
Dual-Pressure Switch
Fusible Plug
92G03110
Courtesy of Nissan Motor Co., U.S.A.

Fig. 2: Locating Manual A/C-Heater System Electrical Components (Engine Compartment)

1993 MANUAL A/C-HEATER SYSTEMS
NX & Sentra (Cont.)

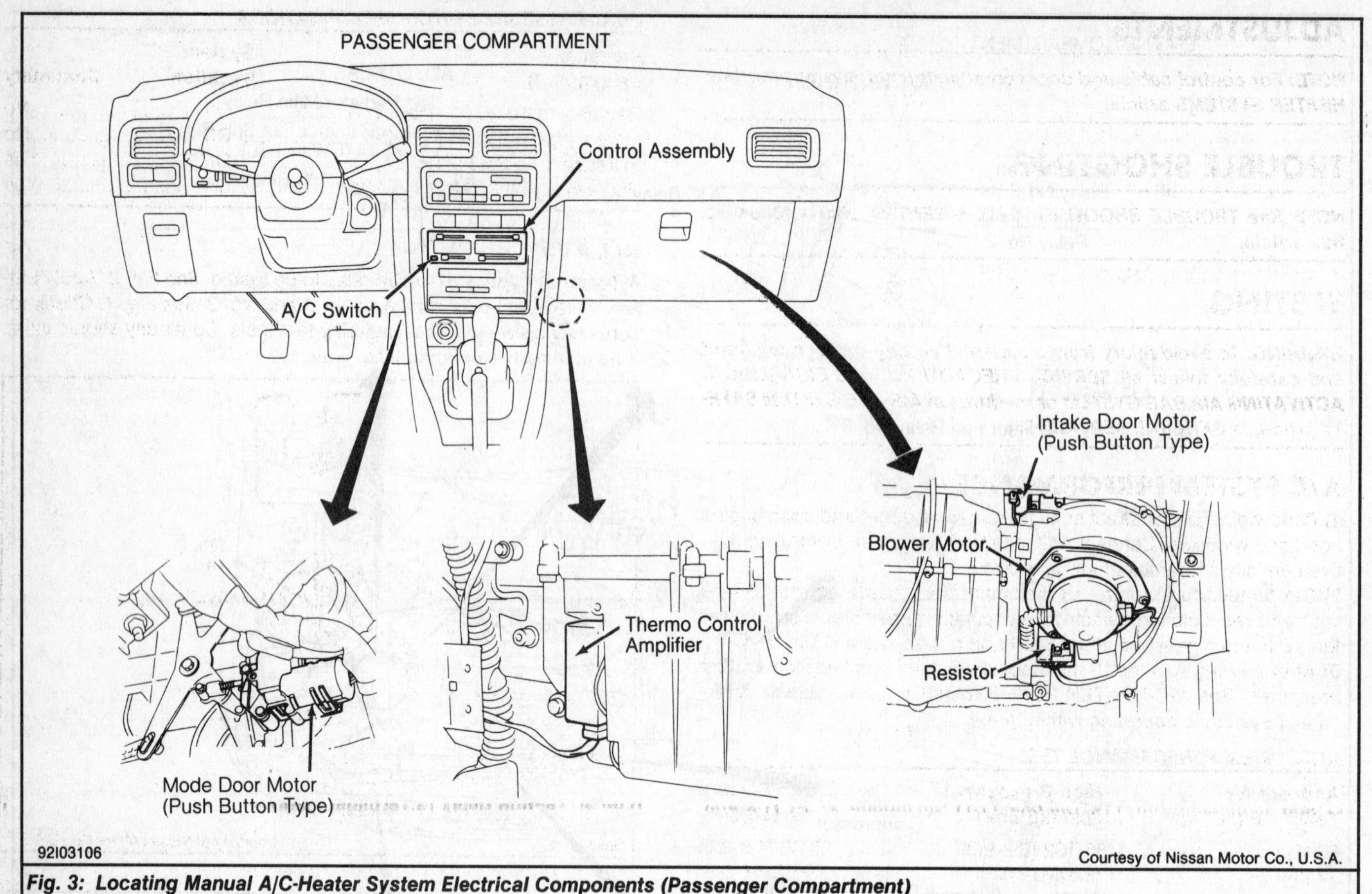
PASSENGER COMPARTMENT
Control Assembly
A/C Switch
Intake Door Motor
(Push Button Type)
Blower Motor
Thermo Control
Amplifier
Resistor
Mode Door Motor
(Push Button Type)
92I03106
Courtesy of Nissan Motor Co., U.S.A.

Fig. 3: Locating Manual A/C-Heater System Electrical Components (Passenger Compartment)

ADJUSTMENTS

NOTE: *For control cable and door rod adjustments, see appropriate HEATER SYSTEMS article.*

TROUBLE SHOOTING

NOTE: *See TROUBLE SHOOTING – NX & SENTRA charts following this article.*

TESTING

WARNING: *To avoid injury from accidental air bag deployment, read and carefully follow all SERVICE PRECAUTIONS and DISABLING & ACTIVATING AIR BAG SYSTEM procedures in AIR BAG SYSTEM SAFETY article in GENERAL SERVICING.*

A/C SYSTEM PERFORMANCE

1) Park vehicle out of direct sunlight. Close all doors and open engine hood and windows. Connect A/C manifold gauge set. Determine relative humidity and ambient air temperature.
2) Set temperature control to maximum cold, mode control to face vent and recirculation switch to recirculation positions. Turn blower fan switch to highest position. Start and run engine at 1500 RPM.
3) After running A/C for 10 minutes, check high and low side system pressures. See A/C-HEATER PERFORMANCE TEST table to determine if system is operating within range.

A/C SYSTEM PERFORMANCE TEST

Ambient Air Temp. °F (°C) [1]	High Pressure psi (kg/cm²)	Low Pressure psi (kg/cm²)
68 (20)	88-132 (6.2-9.3)	26-36 (1.8-2.5)
77 (25)	118-166 (8.3-11.7)	27-37 (1.9-2.6)
86 (30)	148-203 (10.4-14.3)	28-38 (2.0-2.7)
95 (35)	179-237 (12.6-16.7)	33-46 (2.3-3.2)

[1] – Specification is with relative humidity at 50-70 percent.

A/C SWITCH

Disconnect negative battery cable. Remove A/C switch from control panel. Turn A/C on. Using an ohmmeter, check continuity between switch terminals. Continuity should exist. If no continuity exists, replace A/C switch.

BLOWER MOTOR

Disconnect wiring harness at blower motor. Apply battery voltage to blower motor terminals. Ensure blower motor operation is smooth. If blower motor operation is rough or not up to speed, replace blower motor.

BLOWER SPEED CONTROL SWITCH

See TESTING in appropriate HEATER SYSTEMS article.

BLOWER MOTOR RESISTOR

Disconnect harness connector. Check continuity between all resistor terminals. *See Fig. 3.* Ensure continuity exists. If continuity does not exist, replace resistor.

DUAL-PRESSURE SWITCH

Remove dual-pressure switch connector. Dual-pressure switch is located on top of receiver-drier. Using an ohmmeter, check continuity across switch terminals. See DUAL-PRESSURE SWITCH SPECIFICATIONS table. Replace switch if it does not test as indicated.

DUAL-PRESSURE SWITCH SPECIFICATIONS

Pressure psi (kg/cm²)	System Operation	Continuity
Decreasing To 26-31 (1.8-2.2)	Off	No
Increasing To 356-412 (25-29)	Off	No
Increasing To 26-34 (1.8-2.4)	On	Yes
Decreasing To 270-327 (19-23)	On	Yes

RELAYS

4-Terminal Type – Remove relay to be tested. *See Fig. 2.* Apply battery voltage between terminals No. 1 and No. 2. *See Fig. 4.* Check for continuity between remaining relay terminals. Continuity should exist. If no continuity exists, replace relay.

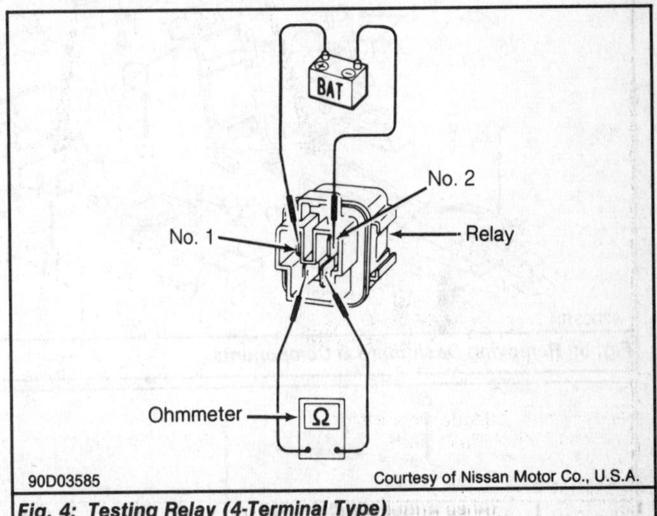

BAT
No. 2
No. 1
Relay
Ohmmeter
Ω
90D03585
Courtesy of Nissan Motor Co., U.S.A.

Fig. 4: Testing Relay (4-Terminal Type)

THERMO CONTROL AMPLIFIER

Check thermo control amplifier as indicated. See THERMO CONTROL AMPLIFIER SPECIFICATIONS table. Replace amplifier if it does not test as specified.

THERMO CONTROL AMPLIFIER SPECIFICATIONS

Evaporator Temperature °F (°C)	Thermo Amplifier Operation	Volts
Decreasing To 37-38 (2.5-3.5)	Off	About 12
Increasing To 39-41 (4-5)	On	Zero

THERMAL PROTECTOR SWITCH

Check compressor operation at indicated temperature. See THERMAL PROTECTOR SWITCH TEST table. Replace switch if compressor does not test as specified.

THERMAL PROTECTOR SWITCH TEST

Compressor Temperature °F (°C)	Compressor Operation
Increasing To 275-293 (135-145)	Off
Decreasing To 248-266 (120-130)	On

1993 MANUAL A/C-HEATER SYSTEMS
NX & Sentra (Cont.)

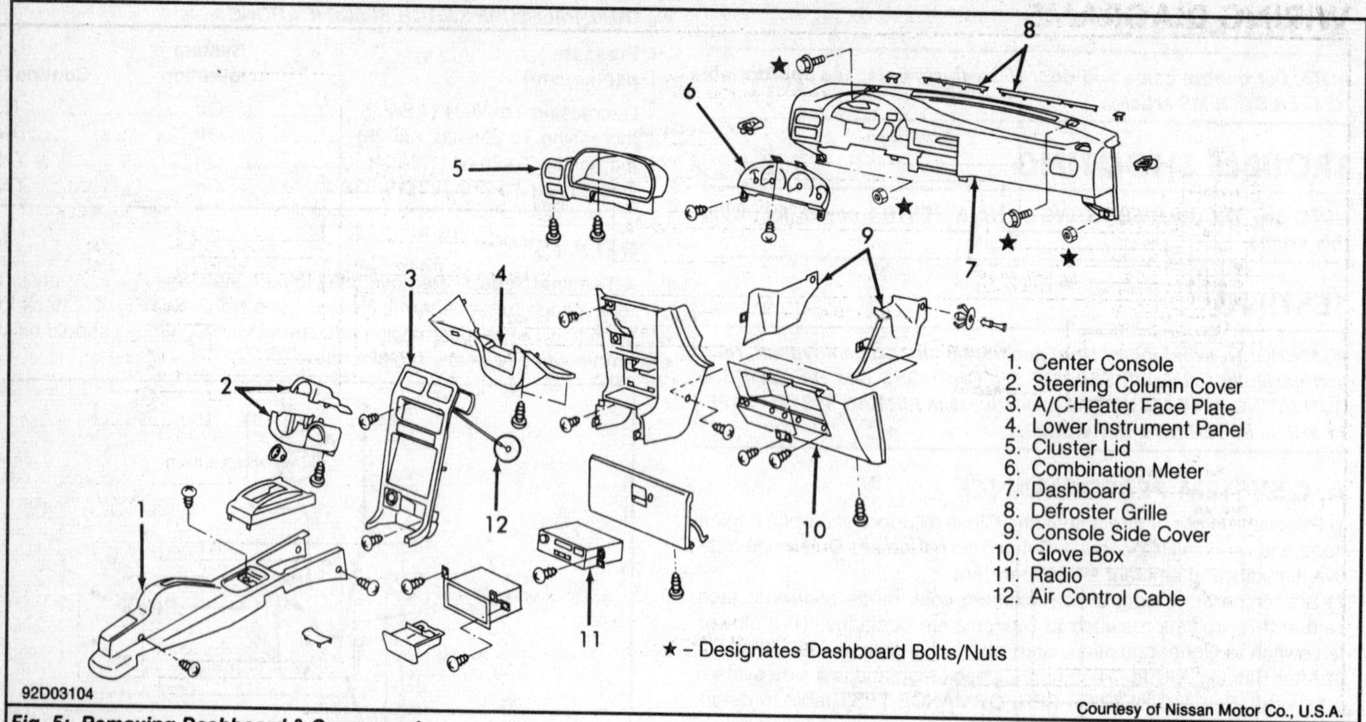
1. Center Console
2. Steering Column Cover
3. A/C-Heater Face Plate
4. Lower Instrument Panel
5. Cluster Lid
6. Combination Meter
7. Dashboard
8. Defroster Grille
9. Console Side Cover
10. Glove Box
11. Radio
12. Air Control Cable
★ - Designates Dashboard Bolts/Nuts
92D03104
Courtesy of Nissan Motor Co., U.S.A.

Fig. 5: Removing Dashboard & Components

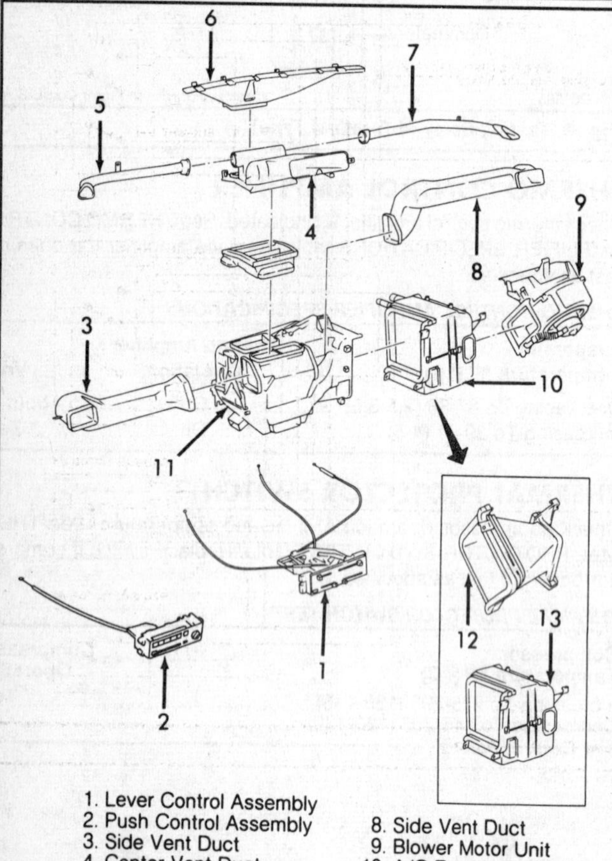
1. Lever Control Assembly
2. Push Control Assembly
3. Side Vent Duct
4. Center Vent Duct
5. Side Defroster Duct
6. Center Defroster Duct
7. Side Defroster Duct
8. Side Vent Duct
9. Blower Motor Unit
10. A/C Evaporator Unit
11. Heater Unit
12. Heater Duct (Sedan)
13. Heater Duct (Coupe)
92G03105
Courtesy of Nissan Motor Co., U.S.A.

Fig. 6: Exploded View Of A/C-Heater System Components

REMOVAL & INSTALLATION

WARNING: To avoid injury from accidental air bag deployment, read and carefully follow all SERVICE PRECAUTIONS and DISABLING & ACTIVATING AIR BAG SYSTEM procedures in AIR BAG SYSTEM SAFETY article in GENERAL SERVICING.

A/C COMPRESSOR

Removal – Loosen idler pulley bolt, and remove compressor belt. Discharge A/C system using approved refrigerant recovery/recycling equipment. Disconnect compressor clutch lead. Remove discharge and suction hoses from compressor, and plug hose openings. Remove compressor bolts and compressor.

Installation – To install, reverse removal procedure. Tighten compressor bolts to 33-44 ft. lbs. (45-60 N.m). Coat new "O" rings with refrigerant oil when attaching hoses to compressor. Evacuate and recharge system.

EVAPORATOR & HEATER CORE ASSEMBLY

Removal – Discharge A/C system using approved refrigerant recovery/recycling equipment. Drain cooling system. Disconnect negative battery cable. Deactivate air bag. See AIR BAG SYSTEM SAFETY article in GENERAL SERVICING. Remove components in order listed in illustrations. *See Figs. 5 and 6.*

Installation – To install, reverse removal procedure. Coat NEW "O" rings with refrigerant oil before assembling connections. If installing a new evaporator core, add 2 ounces of refrigerant oil to new core before installation. Evacuate and recharge system.

INSTRUMENT PANEL

Disconnect negative battery cable. Deactivate air bag. See AIR BAG SYSTEM SAFETY article in GENERAL SERVICING. Remove components in order listed in illustration. *See Fig. 5.*

1993 MANUAL A/C-HEATER SYSTEMS
NX & Sentra (Cont.)

WIRING DIAGRAMS

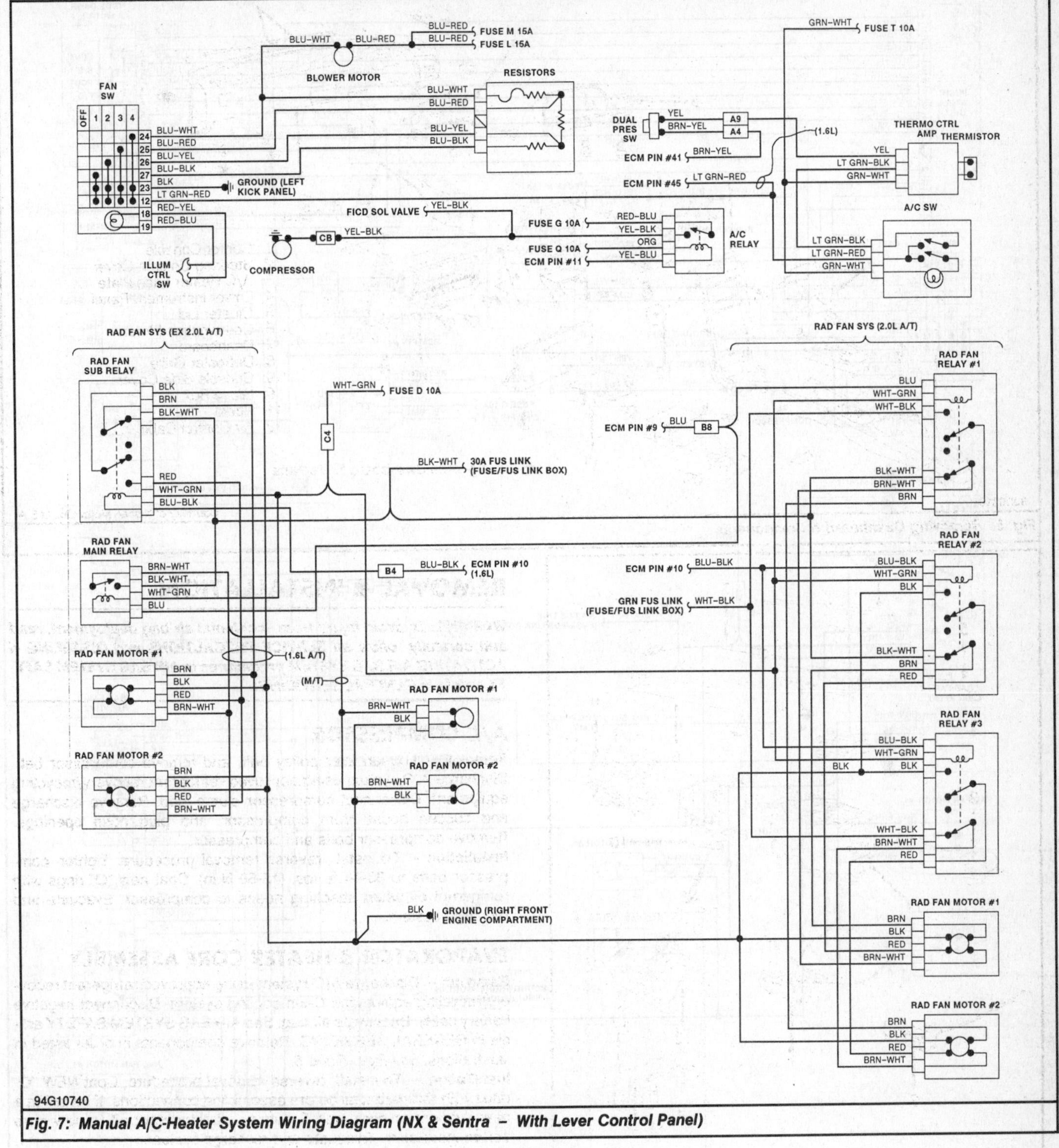
FAN SW
OFF 1 2 3 4
24 BLU-WHT
25 BLU-RED
26 BLU-YEL
27 BLU-BLK
23 BLK
12 LT GRN-RED
18 RED-YEL
19 RED-BLU
GROUND (LEFT KICK PANEL)
ILLUM CTRL SW
BLU-WHT
BLU-RED
BLU-RED FUSE M 15A
BLU-RED FUSE L 15A
BLOWER MOTOR
RESISTORS
BLU-WHT
BLU-RED
BLU-YEL
BLU-BLK
FICD SOL VALVE
YEL-BLK
CB
COMPRESSOR
DUAL PRES SW
YEL
BRN-YEL
A9
A4
ECM PIN #41
BRN-YEL
ECM PIN #45
LT GRN-RED
FUSE G 10A
FUSE Q 10A
ECM PIN #11
RED-BLU
YEL-BLK
ORG
YEL-BLU
A/C RELAY
GRN-WHT
FUSE T 10A
(1.6L)
THERMO CTRL AMP
THERMISTOR
YEL
LT GRN-BLK
GRN-WHT
A/C SW
LT GRN-BLK
LT GRN-RED
GRN-WHT
RAD FAN SYS (EX 2.0L A/T)
RAD FAN SUB RELAY
BLK
BRN
BLK-WHT
RED
WHT-GRN
BLU-BLK
WHT-GRN
FUSE D 10A
C4
BLK-WHT
30A FUS LINK (FUSE/FUS LINK BOX)
RAD FAN MAIN RELAY
BRN-WHT
BLK-WHT
WHT-GRN
BLU
B4
BLU-BLK
ECM PIN #10 (1.6L)
RAD FAN MOTOR #1
(1.6L A/T)
(M/T)
BRN
BLK
RED
BRN-WHT
RAD FAN MOTOR #2
BRN
BLK
RED
BRN-WHT
RAD FAN MOTOR #1
BRN-WHT
BLK
RAD FAN MOTOR #2
BRN-WHT
BLK
BLK
GROUND (RIGHT FRONT ENGINE COMPARTMENT)
RAD FAN SYS (2.0L A/T)
ECM PIN #9
BLU
B8
RAD FAN RELAY #1
BLU
WHT-GRN
WHT-BLK
BLK-WHT
BRN-WHT
BRN
ECM PIN #10
BLU-BLK
GRN FUS LINK (FUSE/FUS LINK BOX)
WHT-BLK
RAD FAN RELAY #2
BLU-BLK
WHT-GRN
BLK
BLK-WHT
BRN
RED
RAD FAN RELAY #3
BLU-BLK
WHT-GRN
BLK
BLK
WHT-BLK
BRN-WHT
RED
RAD FAN MOTOR #1
BRN
BLK
RED
BRN-WHT
RAD FAN MOTOR #2
BRN
BLK
RED
BRN-WHT
94G10740

Fig. 7: Manual A/C-Heater System Wiring Diagram (NX & Sentra – With Lever Control Panel)

1993 MANUAL A/C-HEATER SYSTEMS
NX & Sentra (Cont.)

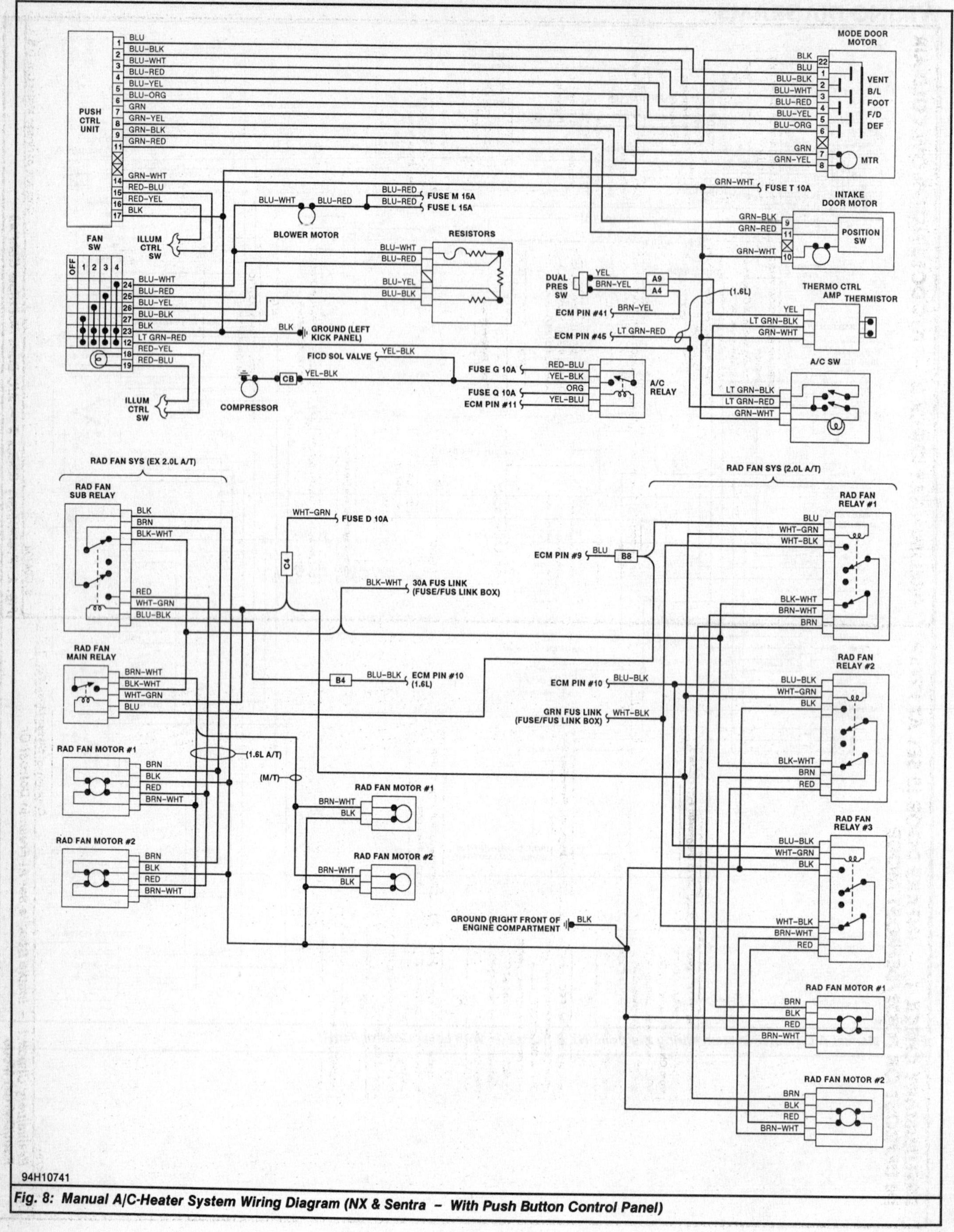
PUSH CTRL UNIT
BLU
BLU-BLK
BLU-WHT
BLU-RED
BLU-YEL
BLU-ORG
GRN
GRN-YEL
GRN-BLK
GRN-RED
GRN-WHT
RED-BLU
RED-YEL
BLK
MODE DOOR MOTOR
VENT
B/L
FOOT
F/D
DEF
MTR
FUSE T 10A
FUSE M 15A
FUSE L 15A
BLOWER MOTOR
INTAKE DOOR MOTOR
POSITION SW
FAN SW
OFF 1 2 3 4
ILLUM CTRL SW
RESISTORS
DUAL PRES SW
ECM PIN #41
ECM PIN #45
(1.6L)
THERMO CTRL AMP
THERMISTOR
LT GRN-BLK
LT GRN-RED
GROUND (LEFT KICK PANEL)
FICD SOL VALVE
YEL-BLK
COMPRESSOR
CB
FUSE G 10A
FUSE Q 10A
ECM PIN #11
A/C RELAY
A/C SW
RAD FAN SYS (EX 2.0L A/T)
RAD FAN SUB RELAY
RAD FAN SYS (2.0L A/T)
RAD FAN RELAY #1
WHT-GRN
FUSE D 10A
ECM PIN #9
30A FUS LINK (FUSE/FUS LINK BOX)
RAD FAN MAIN RELAY
ECM PIN #10 (1.6L)
ECM PIN #10
RAD FAN RELAY #2
GRN FUS LINK (FUSE/FUS LINK BOX)
RAD FAN MOTOR #1
(1.6L A/T)
(M/T)
RAD FAN MOTOR #2
RAD FAN RELAY #3
GROUND (RIGHT FRONT OF ENGINE COMPARTMENT)
94H10741

Fig. 8: Manual A/C-Heater System Wiring Diagram (NX & Sentra – With Push Button Control Panel)

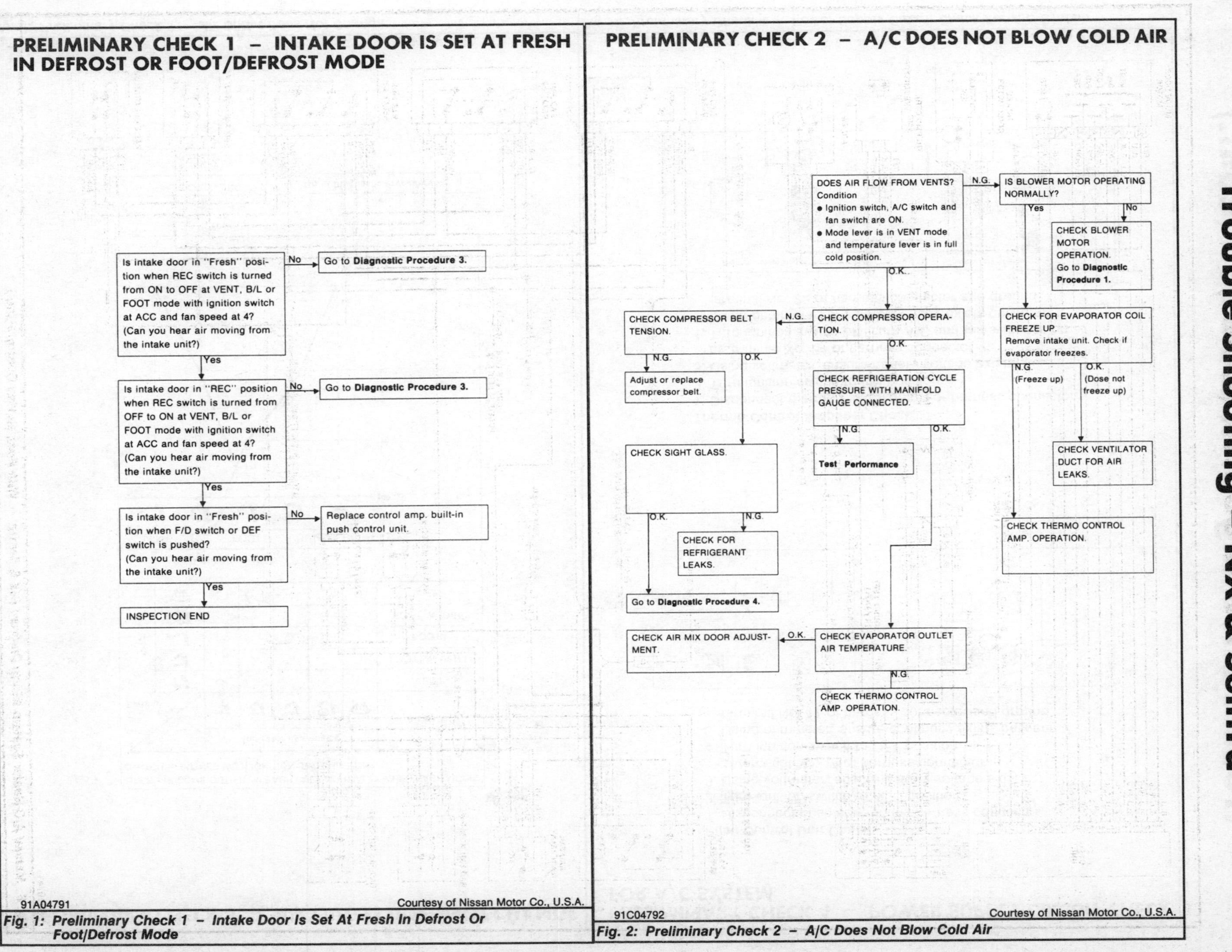
PRELIMINARY CHECK 1 – INTAKE DOOR IS SET AT FRESH IN DEFROST OR FOOT/DEFROST MODE
Is intake door in "Fresh" position when REC switch is turned from ON to OFF at VENT, B/L or FOOT mode with ignition switch at ACC and fan speed at 4? (Can you hear air moving from the intake unit?)
No
Go to Diagnostic Procedure 3.
Yes
Is intake door in "REC" position when REC switch is turned from OFF to ON at VENT, B/L or FOOT mode with ignition switch at ACC and fan speed at 4? (Can you hear air moving from the intake unit?)
No
Go to Diagnostic Procedure 3.
Yes
Is intake door in "Fresh" position when F/D switch or DEF switch is pushed? (Can you hear air moving from the intake unit?)
No
Replace control amp. built-in push control unit.
Yes
INSPECTION END
91A04791
Courtesy of Nissan Motor Co., U.S.A.
PRELIMINARY CHECK 2 – A/C DOES NOT BLOW COLD AIR
DOES AIR FLOW FROM VENTS?
Condition
• Ignition switch, A/C switch and fan switch are ON.
• Mode lever is in VENT mode and temperature lever is in full cold position.
N.G.
IS BLOWER MOTOR OPERATING NORMALLY?
Yes
No
CHECK BLOWER MOTOR OPERATION. Go to Diagnostic Procedure 1.
CHECK FOR EVAPORATOR COIL FREEZE UP.
Remove intake unit. Check if evaporator freezes.
N.G. (Freeze up)
O.K. (Dose not freeze up)
CHECK VENTILATOR DUCT FOR AIR LEAKS.
CHECK THERMO CONTROL AMP. OPERATION.
O.K.
CHECK COMPRESSOR OPERATION.
N.G.
CHECK COMPRESSOR BELT TENSION.
N.G.
Adjust or replace compressor belt.
O.K.
CHECK SIGHT GLASS.
N.G.
CHECK FOR REFRIGERANT LEAKS.
O.K.
Go to Diagnostic Procedure 4.
O.K.
CHECK REFRIGERATION CYCLE PRESSURE WITH MANIFOLD GAUGE CONNECTED.
N.G.
Test Performance
O.K.
CHECK EVAPORATOR OUTLET AIR TEMPERATURE.
O.K.
CHECK AIR MIX DOOR ADJUSTMENT.
N.G.
CHECK THERMO CONTROL AMP. OPERATION.
91C04792
Courtesy of Nissan Motor Co., U.S.A.

Fig. 1: Preliminary Check 1 – Intake Door Is Set At Fresh In Defrost Or Foot/Defrost Mode

Fig. 2: Preliminary Check 2 – A/C Does Not Blow Cold Air

1993 MANUAL A/C-HEATER SYSTEMS
Trouble Shooting – NX & Sentra (Cont.)

PRELIMINARY CHECK 3 – AIR OUTLET DOES NOT CHANGE

DOES AIR COME OUT FROM EACH DUCT NORMALLY WHEN EACH MODE SWITCH IS PUSHED WITH IGNITION SWITCH AT ON?

Mode Switch	Indicator illuminates: VENT	B/L	FOOT	F/D	DEF	Air outlet
VENT	○					VENT
B/L		○				FOOT & VENT
FOOT			○			FOOT
F/D				○		FOOT & DEF
DEF					○	DEF

Air distribution ratios

VENT B/L FOOT F/D DEF

(%)
100
70
50
40
0

VENT
FOOT
DEF

Yes → INSPECTION END

No → Go to **Diagnostic Procedure 2.**

94E10458

Courtesy of Nissan Motor Co., U.S.A.

Fig. 3: Preliminary Check 3 – Air Outlet Does Not Change

PRELIMINARY CHECK 4 – POWER SUPPLY CIRCUIT CHECK FOR A/C SYSTEM

Push Control Unit Check

1. Disconnect push control unit harness connector.
2. Turn ignition switch to ACC position.
3. Using voltmeter, ensure battery voltage exists at terminal No. 14 of harness connector.
4. Turn ignition switch to OFF position.
5. Using ohmmeter, ensure continuity exists between terminal No. 17 of harness connector and ground.

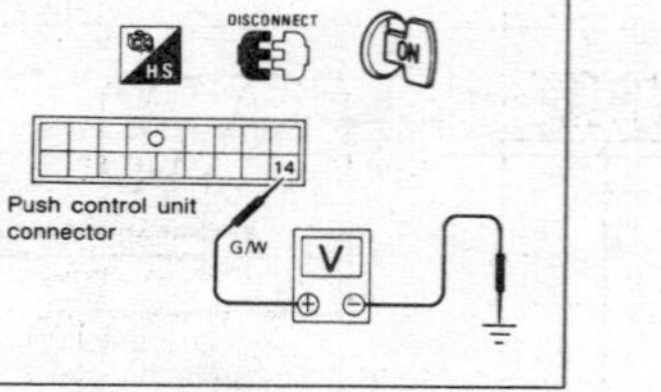
DISCONNECT
H.S
ON
14
Push control unit
connector
G/W
V

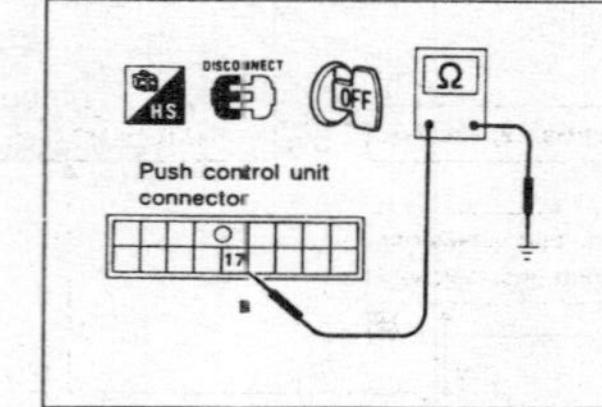
DISCONNECT
H.S
OFF
Ω
Push control unit
connector
17

Thermo Control Amplifier Check

1. Disconnect thermo control amplifier harness connector.
2. Turn ignition switch to ON position.
3. Using voltmeter, ensure battery voltage exists at terminal No. 34 of harness connector.
4. Turn ignition switch off. Turn A/C and fan switches on.
5. Using ohmmeter, ensure continuity exists between terminal No. 22 of harness connector and ground.

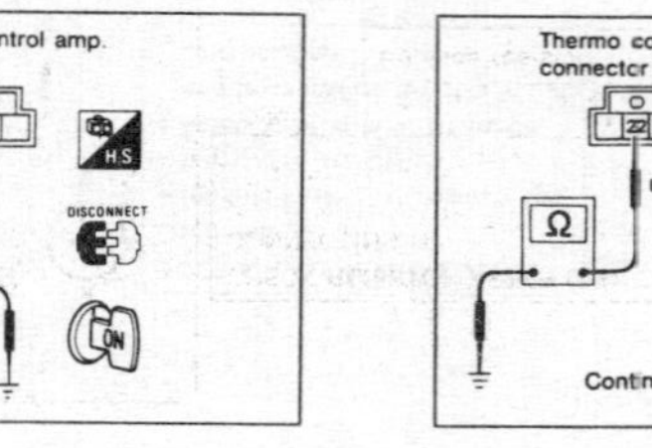
Thermo control amp.
connector
34
G/W
H.S
DISCONNECT
V
ON

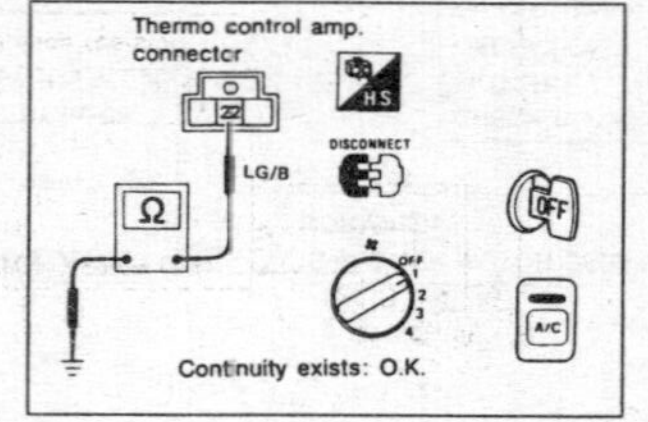
Thermo control amp.
connector
22
H.S
DISCONNECT
LG/B
Ω
OFF
A/C
Continuity exists: O.K.

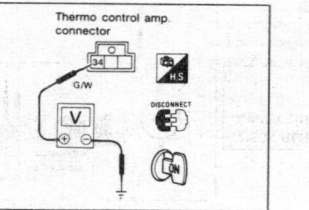

94F10459

Courtesy of Nissan Motor Co., U.S.A.

Fig. 4: Preliminary Check 4 – Power Supply Circuit Check For A/C System

1993 MANUAL A/C-HEATER SYSTEMS
Trouble Shooting – NX & Sentra (Cont.)

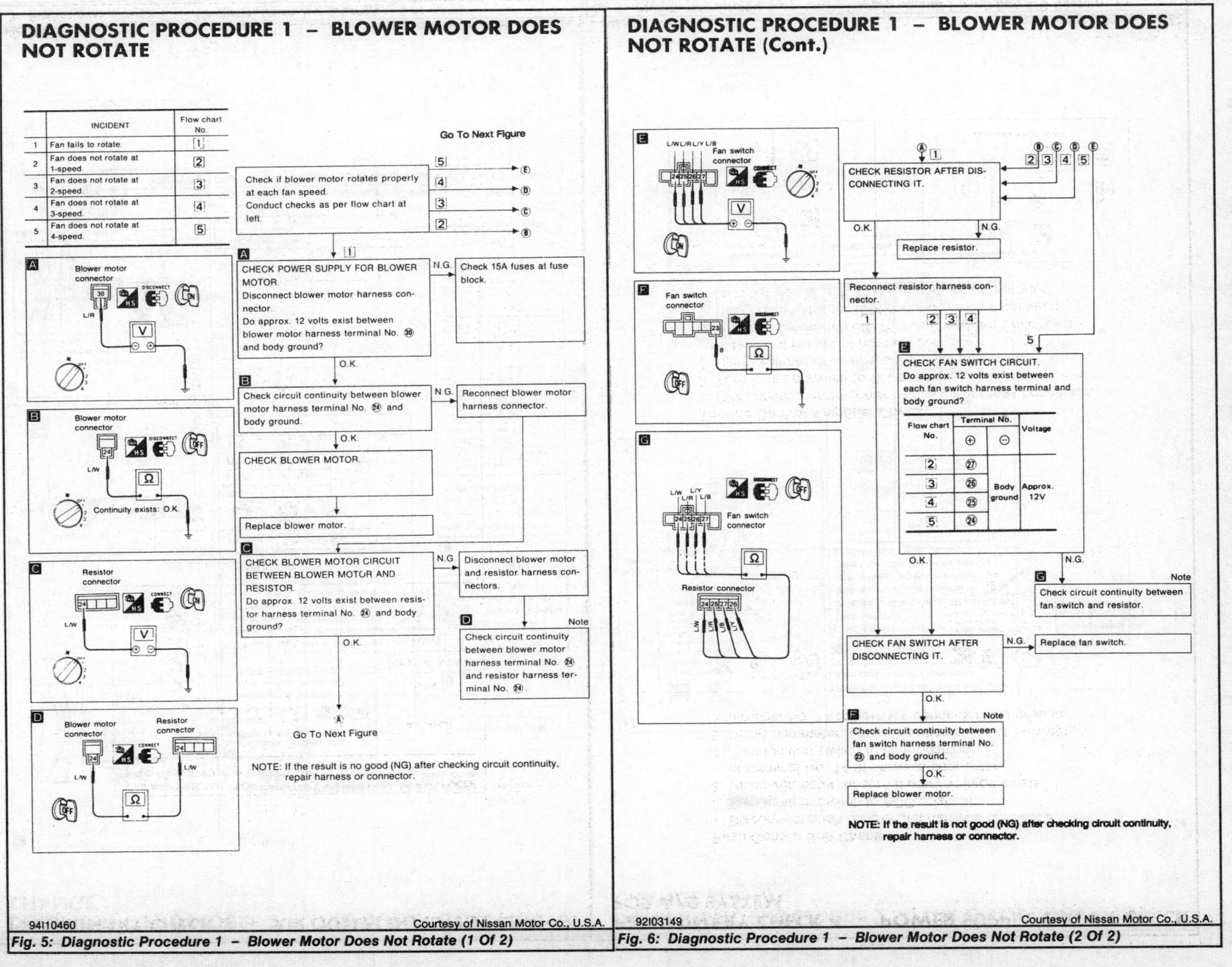
DIAGNOSTIC PROCEDURE 1 – BLOWER MOTOR DOES NOT ROTATE
INCIDENT
Flow chart No.
1 Fan fails to rotate. 1
2 Fan does not rotate at 1-speed. 2
3 Fan does not rotate at 2-speed. 3
4 Fan does not rotate at 3-speed. 4
5 Fan does not rotate at 4-speed. 5
Go To Next Figure
Check if blower motor rotates properly at each fan speed.
Conduct checks as per flow chart at left.
A CHECK POWER SUPPLY FOR BLOWER MOTOR.
Disconnect blower motor harness connector.
Do approx. 12 volts exist between blower motor harness terminal No. 30 and body ground?
N.G.
Check 15A fuses at fuse block.
O.K.
B Check circuit continuity between blower motor harness terminal No. 24 and body ground.
N.G.
Reconnect blower motor harness connector.
O.K.
CHECK BLOWER MOTOR.
Replace blower motor.
C CHECK BLOWER MOTOR CIRCUIT BETWEEN BLOWER MOTOR AND RESISTOR.
Do approx. 12 volts exist between resistor harness terminal No. 24 and body ground?
N.G
Disconnect blower motor and resistor harness connectors.
D Check circuit continuity between blower motor harness terminal No. 24 and resistor harness terminal No. 24.
Note
O.K.
Go To Next Figure
NOTE: If the result is no good (NG) after checking circuit continuity, repair harness or connector.
Blower motor connector
Resistor connector
Continuity exists: O.K.
DISCONNECT
CONNECT
94I10460
Courtesy of Nissan Motor Co., U.S.A.
DIAGNOSTIC PROCEDURE 1 – BLOWER MOTOR DOES NOT ROTATE (Cont.)
Fan switch connector
Resistor connector
CHECK RESISTOR AFTER DISCONNECTING IT.
N.G.
Replace resistor.
O.K.
Reconnect resistor harness connector.
E CHECK FAN SWITCH CIRCUIT.
Do approx. 12 volts exist between each fan switch harness terminal and body ground?
Flow chart No.
Terminal No.
Voltage
2 27
3 26
4 25
5 24
Body ground
Approx. 12V
N.G.
G Check circuit continuity between fan switch and resistor.
Note
O.K.
CHECK FAN SWITCH AFTER DISCONNECTING IT.
N.G.
Replace fan switch.
F Check circuit continuity between fan switch harness terminal No. 23 and body ground.
Note
O.K.
Replace blower motor.
NOTE: If the result is not good (NG) after checking circuit continuity, repair harness or connector.
92I03149
Courtesy of Nissan Motor Co., U.S.A.

Fig. 5: Diagnostic Procedure 1 – Blower Motor Does Not Rotate (1 Of 2)

Fig. 6: Diagnostic Procedure 1 – Blower Motor Does Not Rotate (2 Of 2)

1993 MANUAL A/C-HEATER SYSTEMS
Trouble Shooting – NX & Sentra (Cont.)

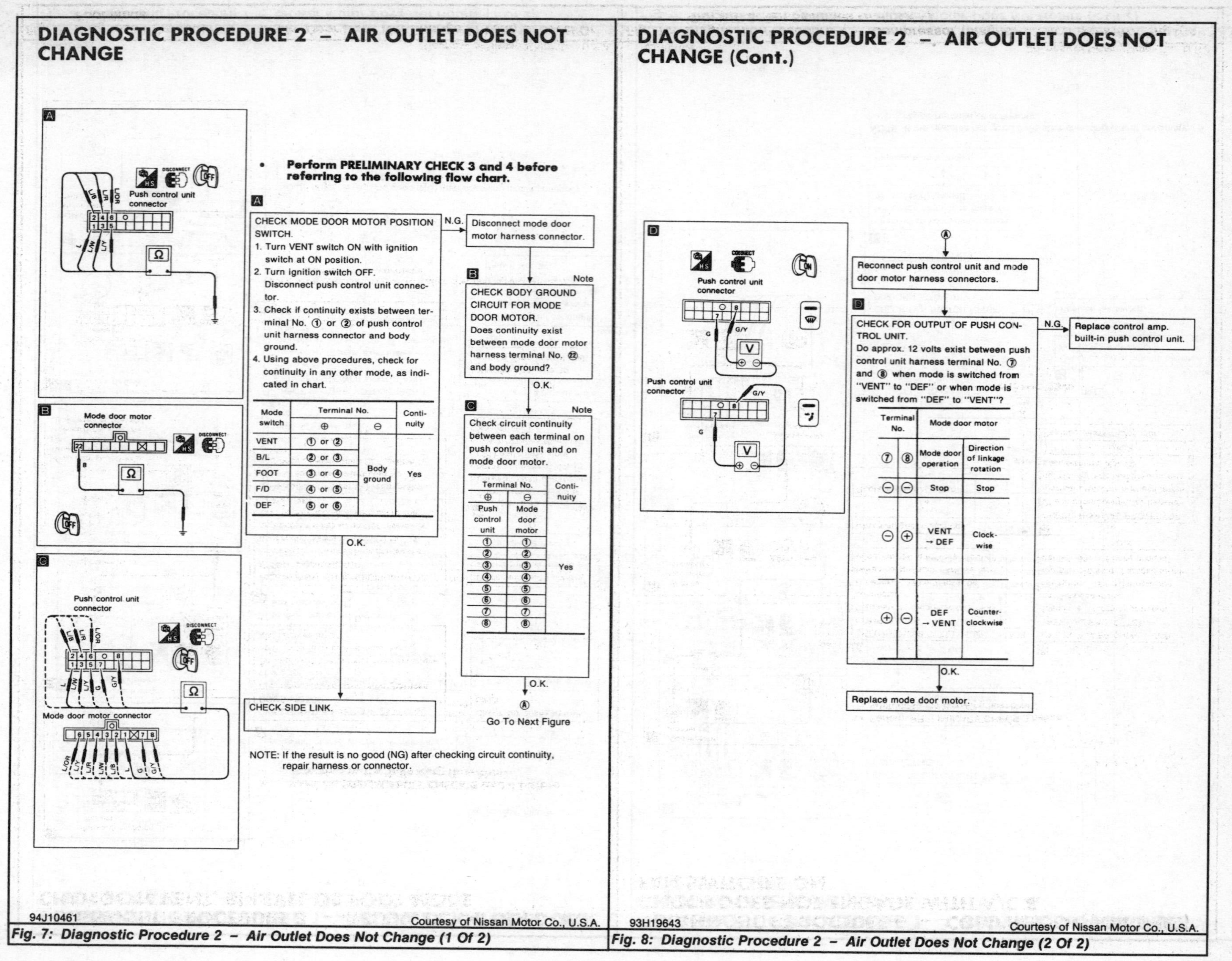
DIAGNOSTIC PROCEDURE 2 – AIR OUTLET DOES NOT CHANGE
A
Push control unit connector
DISCONNECT
OFF
L/OR
L/R
L/B
L
L/W
L/Y
B
Mode door motor connector
DISCONNECT
OFF
C
Push control unit connector
DISCONNECT
OFF
L/B
L/R
L/OR
L
L/W
L/Y
G
G/Y
Mode door motor connector
L/OR
L/Y
L/R
L/W
L/B
L
G
G/Y
• Perform PRELIMINARY CHECK 3 and 4 before referring to the following flow chart.
A
CHECK MODE DOOR MOTOR POSITION SWITCH.
1. Turn VENT switch ON with ignition switch at ON position.
2. Turn ignition switch OFF. Disconnect push control unit connector.
3. Check if continuity exists between terminal No. ① or ② of push control unit harness connector and body ground.
4. Using above procedures, check for continuity in any other mode, as indicated in chart.
Mode switch | Terminal No. ⊕ | ⊖ | Continuity
VENT | ① or ② | Body ground | Yes
B/L | ② or ③
FOOT | ③ or ④
F/D | ④ or ⑤
DEF | ⑤ or ⑥
N.G.
Disconnect mode door motor harness connector.
B
Note
CHECK BODY GROUND CIRCUIT FOR MODE DOOR MOTOR.
Does continuity exist between mode door motor harness terminal No. ㉒ and body ground?
O.K.
C
Note
Check circuit continuity between each terminal on push control unit and on mode door motor.
Terminal No. ⊕ Push control unit | ⊖ Mode door motor | Continuity
① | ① | Yes
② | ②
③ | ③
④ | ④
⑤ | ⑤
⑥ | ⑥
⑦ | ⑦
⑧ | ⑧
O.K.
Ⓐ
Go To Next Figure
O.K.
CHECK SIDE LINK.
NOTE: If the result is no good (NG) after checking circuit continuity, repair harness or connector.
94J10461
Courtesy of Nissan Motor Co., U.S.A.
DIAGNOSTIC PROCEDURE 2 – AIR OUTLET DOES NOT CHANGE (Cont.)
D
CONNECT
ON
Push control unit connector
G
G/Y
Push control unit connector
Ⓐ
Reconnect push control unit and mode door motor harness connectors.
D
CHECK FOR OUTPUT OF PUSH CONTROL UNIT.
Do approx. 12 volts exist between push control unit harness terminal No. ⑦ and ⑧ when mode is switched from "VENT" to "DEF" or when mode is switched from "DEF" to "VENT"?
Terminal No. ⑦ | ⑧ | Mode door motor: Mode door operation | Direction of linkage rotation
⊖ | ⊖ | Stop | Stop
⊖ | ⊕ | VENT → DEF | Clockwise
⊕ | ⊖ | DEF → VENT | Counterclockwise
N.G.
Replace control amp. built-in push control unit.
O.K.
Replace mode door motor.
93H19643
Courtesy of Nissan Motor Co., U.S.A.

Fig. 7: Diagnostic Procedure 2 – Air Outlet Does Not Change (1 Of 2)

Fig. 8: Diagnostic Procedure 2 – Air Outlet Does Not Change (2 Of 2)

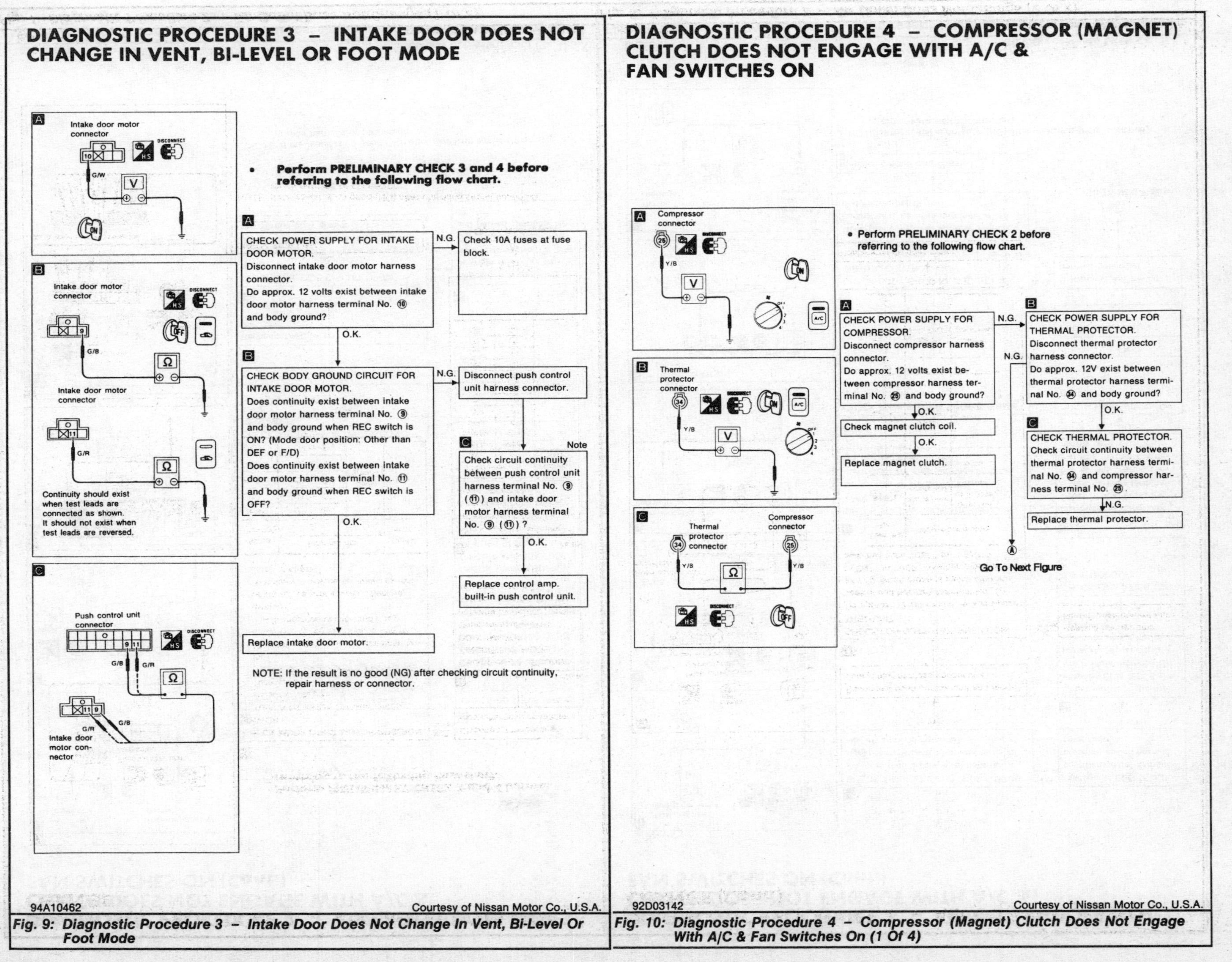
DIAGNOSTIC PROCEDURE 3 – INTAKE DOOR DOES NOT CHANGE IN VENT, BI-LEVEL OR FOOT MODE
A
Intake door motor connector
DISCONNECT
HS
G/W
V
ON
• Perform PRELIMINARY CHECK 3 and 4 before referring to the following flow chart.
A
CHECK POWER SUPPLY FOR INTAKE DOOR MOTOR.
Disconnect intake door motor harness connector.
Do approx. 12 volts exist between intake door motor harness terminal No. ⑩ and body ground?
N.G.
Check 10A fuses at fuse block.
O.K.
B
Intake door motor connector
G/B
Intake door motor connector
G/R
OFF
Continuity should exist when test leads are connected as shown.
It should not exist when test leads are reversed.
B
CHECK BODY GROUND CIRCUIT FOR INTAKE DOOR MOTOR.
Does continuity exist between intake door motor harness terminal No. ⑨ and body ground when REC switch is ON? (Mode door position: Other than DEF or F/D)
Does continuity exist between intake door motor harness terminal No. ⑪ and body ground when REC switch is OFF?
N.G.
Disconnect push control unit harness connector.
C
Note
Check circuit continuity between push control unit harness terminal No. ⑨ (⑪) and intake door motor harness terminal No. ⑨ (⑪) ?
O.K.
Replace control amp. built-in push control unit.
O.K.
Replace intake door motor.
C
Push control unit connector
G/B
G/R
Intake door motor connector
NOTE: If the result is no good (NG) after checking circuit continuity, repair harness or connector.
94A10462
Courtesy of Nissan Motor Co., U.S.A.
DIAGNOSTIC PROCEDURE 4 – COMPRESSOR (MAGNET) CLUTCH DOES NOT ENGAGE WITH A/C & FAN SWITCHES ON
A
Compressor connector
Y/B
V
A/C
• Perform PRELIMINARY CHECK 2 before referring to the following flow chart.
A
CHECK POWER SUPPLY FOR COMPRESSOR.
Disconnect compressor harness connector.
Do approx. 12 volts exist between compressor harness terminal No. ㉕ and body ground?
N.G.
B
CHECK POWER SUPPLY FOR THERMAL PROTECTOR.
Disconnect thermal protector harness connector.
Do approx. 12V exist between thermal protector harness terminal No. ㉞ and body ground?
N.G.
O.K.
Check magnet clutch coil.
O.K.
Replace magnet clutch.
B
Thermal protector connector
Y/B
O.K.
C
CHECK THERMAL PROTECTOR.
Check circuit continuity between thermal protector harness terminal No. ㉞ and compressor harness terminal No. ㉕.
N.G.
Replace thermal protector.
A
Go To Next Figure
C
Thermal protector connector
Compressor connector
Y/B
OFF
92D03142
Courtesy of Nissan Motor Co., U.S.A.

Fig. 9: Diagnostic Procedure 3 – Intake Door Does Not Change In Vent, Bi-Level Or Foot Mode

Fig. 10: Diagnostic Procedure 4 – Compressor (Magnet) Clutch Does Not Engage With A/C & Fan Switches On (1 Of 4)

1993 MANUAL A/C-HEATER SYSTEMS
Trouble Shooting – NX & Sentra (Cont.)

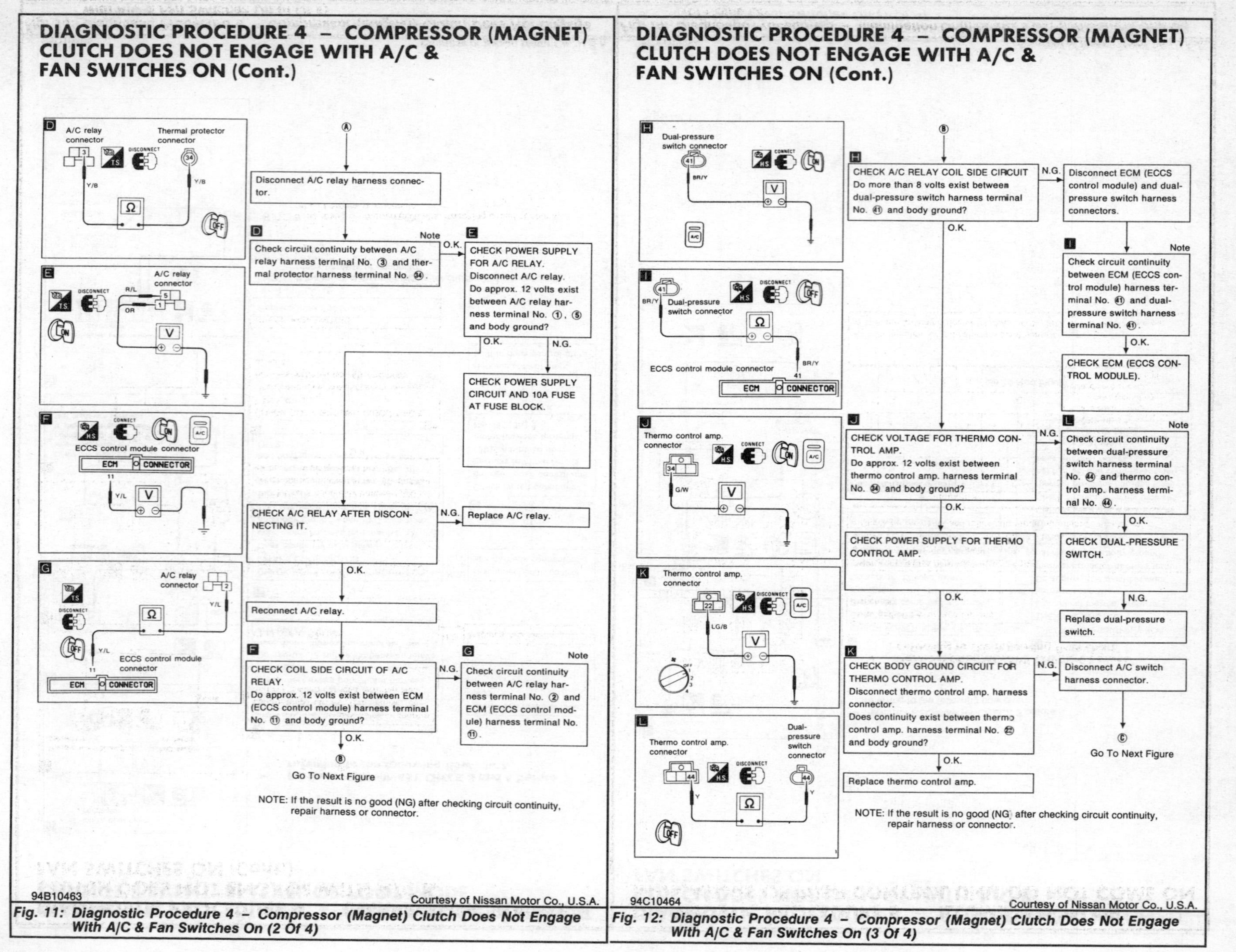
DIAGNOSTIC PROCEDURE 4 – COMPRESSOR (MAGNET) CLUTCH DOES NOT ENGAGE WITH A/C & FAN SWITCHES ON (Cont.)
D A/C relay connector
Thermal protector connector
DISCONNECT
Y/B
E A/C relay connector
R/L
OR
F ECCS control module connector
ECM CONNECTOR
Y/L
G A/C relay connector
ECCS control module connector
A
Disconnect A/C relay harness connector.
D Check circuit continuity between A/C relay harness terminal No. ③ and thermal protector harness terminal No. ㉞.
Note
O.K.
E CHECK POWER SUPPLY FOR A/C RELAY. Disconnect A/C relay. Do approx. 12 volts exist between A/C relay harness terminal No. ①, ⑤ and body ground?
N.G.
CHECK POWER SUPPLY CIRCUIT AND 10A FUSE AT FUSE BLOCK.
CHECK A/C RELAY AFTER DISCONNECTING IT.
Replace A/C relay.
Reconnect A/C relay.
F CHECK COIL SIDE CIRCUIT OF A/C RELAY. Do approx. 12 volts exist between ECM (ECCS control module) harness terminal No. ⑪ and body ground?
G Check circuit continuity between A/C relay harness terminal No. ② and ECM (ECCS control module) harness terminal No. ⑪.
B
Go To Next Figure
NOTE: If the result is no good (NG) after checking circuit continuity, repair harness or connector.
94B10463
Courtesy of Nissan Motor Co., U.S.A.
DIAGNOSTIC PROCEDURE 4 – COMPRESSOR (MAGNET) CLUTCH DOES NOT ENGAGE WITH A/C & FAN SWITCHES ON (Cont.)
H Dual-pressure switch connector
BR/Y
CONNECT
I Dual-pressure switch connector
ECCS control module connector
ECM CONNECTOR
J Thermo control amp. connector
G/W
K Thermo control amp. connector
LG/B
L Thermo control amp. connector
Dual-pressure switch connector
Y
B
H CHECK A/C RELAY COIL SIDE CIRCUIT Do more than 8 volts exist between dual-pressure switch harness terminal No. ㊶ and body ground?
Disconnect ECM (ECCS control module) and dual-pressure switch harness connectors.
I Check circuit continuity between ECM (ECCS control module) harness terminal No. ㊶ and dual-pressure switch harness terminal No. ㊶.
CHECK ECM (ECCS CONTROL MODULE).
J CHECK VOLTAGE FOR THERMO CONTROL AMP. Do approx. 12 volts exist between thermo control amp. harness terminal No. ㉞ and body ground?
L Check circuit continuity between dual-pressure switch harness terminal No. ㊹ and thermo control amp. harness terminal No. ㊹.
CHECK POWER SUPPLY FOR THERMO CONTROL AMP.
CHECK DUAL-PRESSURE SWITCH.
Replace dual-pressure switch.
K CHECK BODY GROUND CIRCUIT FOR THERMO CONTROL AMP. Disconnect thermo control amp. harness connector. Does continuity exist between thermo control amp. harness terminal No. ㉒ and body ground?
Disconnect A/C switch harness connector.
Replace thermo control amp.
C
Go To Next Figure
NOTE: If the result is no good (NG) after checking circuit continuity, repair harness or connector.
94C10464
Courtesy of Nissan Motor Co., U.S.A.

Fig. 11: Diagnostic Procedure 4 – Compressor (Magnet) Clutch Does Not Engage With A/C & Fan Switches On (2 Of 4)

Fig. 12: Diagnostic Procedure 4 – Compressor (Magnet) Clutch Does Not Engage With A/C & Fan Switches On (3 Of 4)

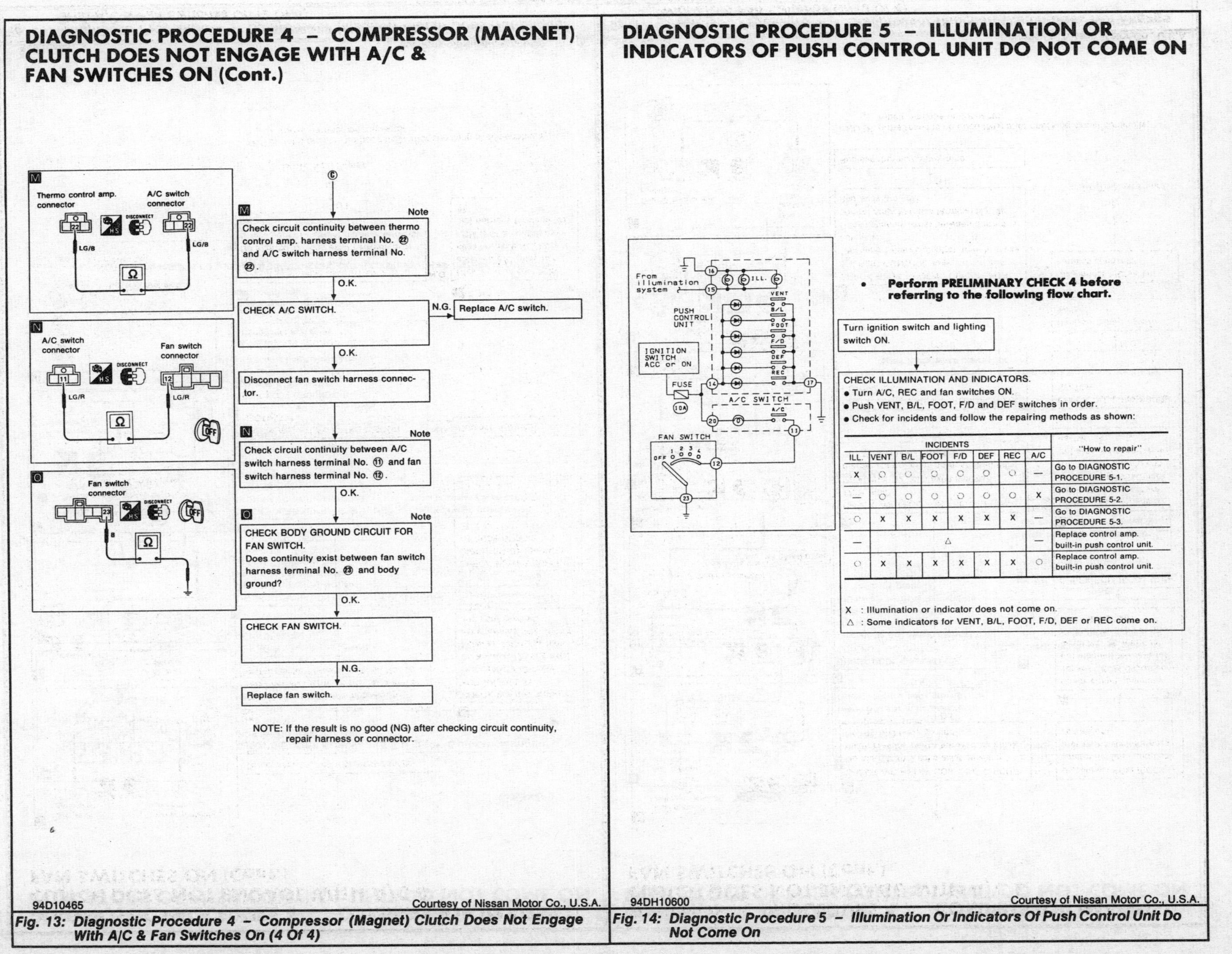

DIAGNOSTIC PROCEDURE 4 – COMPRESSOR (MAGNET) CLUTCH DOES NOT ENGAGE WITH A/C & FAN SWITCHES ON (Cont.)
M
Thermo control amp. connector
A/C switch connector
DISCONNECT
LG/B
LG/B
N
A/C switch connector
Fan switch connector
LG/R
LG/R
O
Fan switch connector
B
C
M Note
Check circuit continuity between thermo control amp. harness terminal No. 22 and A/C switch harness terminal No. 22.
O.K.
CHECK A/C SWITCH.
N.G.
Replace A/C switch.
O.K.
Disconnect fan switch harness connector.
N Note
Check circuit continuity between A/C switch harness terminal No. 11 and fan switch harness terminal No. 12.
O.K.
O Note
CHECK BODY GROUND CIRCUIT FOR FAN SWITCH.
Does continuity exist between fan switch harness terminal No. 23 and body ground?
O.K.
CHECK FAN SWITCH.
N.G.
Replace fan switch.
NOTE: If the result is no good (NG) after checking circuit continuity, repair harness or connector.
94D10465
Courtesy of Nissan Motor Co., U.S.A.
DIAGNOSTIC PROCEDURE 5 – ILLUMINATION OR INDICATORS OF PUSH CONTROL UNIT DO NOT COME ON
From illumination system
PUSH CONTROL UNIT
IGNITION SWITCH ACC or ON
FUSE
10A
ILL.
VENT
B/L
FOOT
F/D
DEF
REC
A/C SWITCH
A/C
FAN SWITCH
OFF 1 2 3 4
Perform PRELIMINARY CHECK 4 before referring to the following flow chart.
Turn ignition switch and lighting switch ON.
CHECK ILLUMINATION AND INDICATORS.
Turn A/C, REC and fan switches ON.
Push VENT, B/L, FOOT, F/D and DEF switches in order.
Check for incidents and follow the repairing methods as shown:
94DH10600
Courtesy of Nissan Motor Co., U.S.A.

INCIDENTS								"How to repair"
ILL.	VENT	B/L	FOOT	F/D	DEF	REC	A/C	
X	○	○	○	○	○	○	—	Go to DIAGNOSTIC PROCEDURE 5-1.
—	○	○	○	○	○	○	X	Go to DIAGNOSTIC PROCEDURE 5-2.
○	X	X	X	X	X	X	—	Go to DIAGNOSTIC PROCEDURE 5-3.
—	△						—	Replace control amp. built-in push control unit.
○	X	X	X	X	X	X	○	Replace control amp. built-in push control unit.

X : Illumination or indicator does not come on.
△ : Some indicators for VENT, B/L, FOOT, F/D, DEF or REC come on.

Fig. 13: Diagnostic Procedure 4 – Compressor (Magnet) Clutch Does Not Engage With A/C & Fan Switches On (4 Of 4)

Fig. 14: Diagnostic Procedure 5 – Illumination Or Indicators Of Push Control Unit Do Not Come On

1993 MANUAL A/C-HEATER SYSTEMS
Trouble Shooting – NX & Sentra (Cont.)

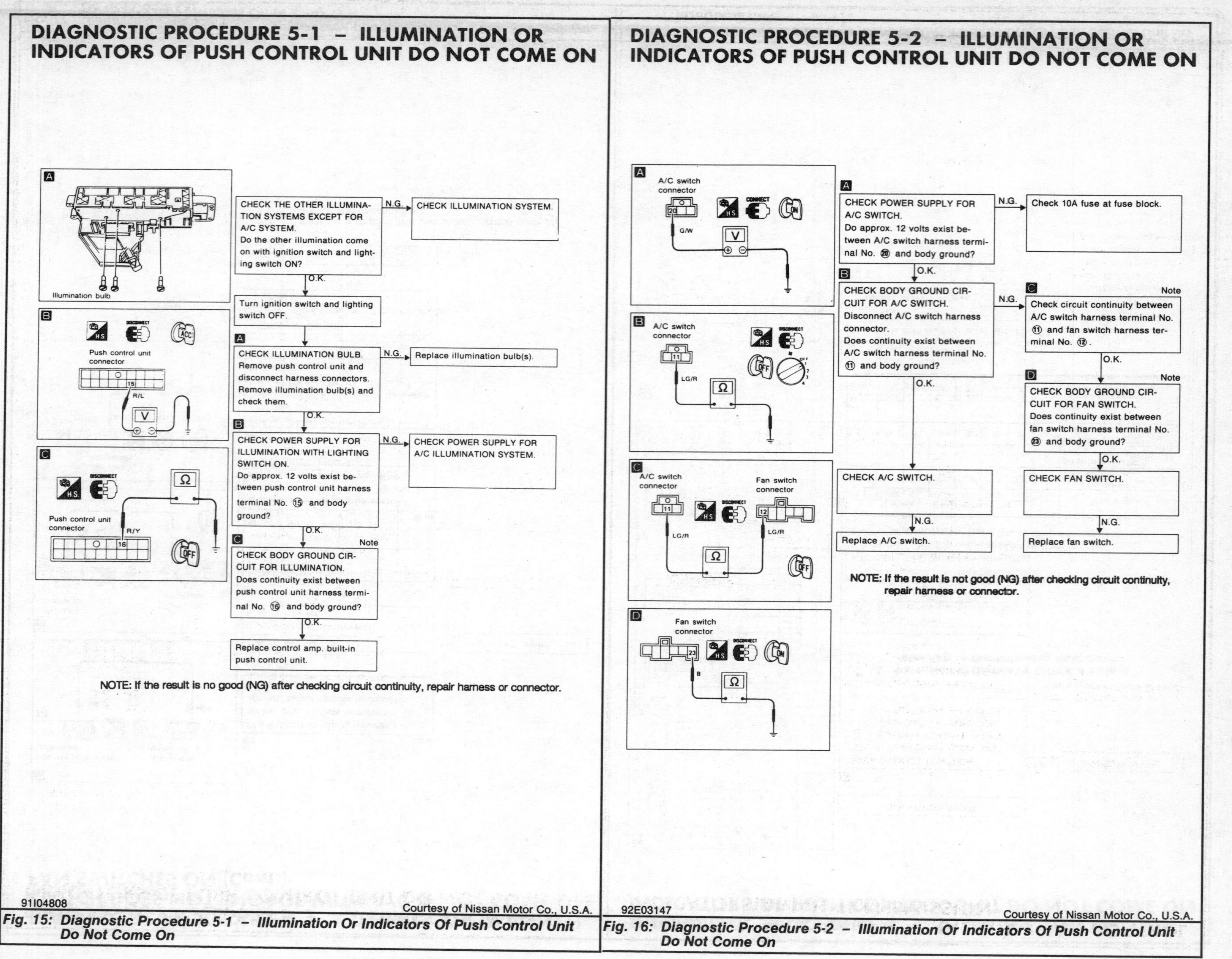
DIAGNOSTIC PROCEDURE 5-1 – ILLUMINATION OR INDICATORS OF PUSH CONTROL UNIT DO NOT COME ON
A
Illumination bulb
B
Push control unit connector
15
R/L
V
C
Push control unit connector
R/Y
16
Ω
CHECK THE OTHER ILLUMINATION SYSTEMS EXCEPT FOR A/C SYSTEM.
Do the other illumination come on with ignition switch and lighting switch ON?
N.G.
CHECK ILLUMINATION SYSTEM.
O.K.
Turn ignition switch and lighting switch OFF.
A
CHECK ILLUMINATION BULB.
Remove push control unit and disconnect harness connectors.
Remove illumination bulb(s) and check them.
N.G.
Replace illumination bulb(s).
O.K.
B
CHECK POWER SUPPLY FOR ILLUMINATION WITH LIGHTING SWITCH ON.
Do approx. 12 volts exist between push control unit harness terminal No. ⑮ and body ground?
N.G.
CHECK POWER SUPPLY FOR A/C ILLUMINATION SYSTEM.
O.K.
C
Note
CHECK BODY GROUND CIRCUIT FOR ILLUMINATION.
Does continuity exist between push control unit harness terminal No. ⑯ and body ground?
O.K.
Replace control amp. built-in push control unit.
NOTE: If the result is no good (NG) after checking circuit continuity, repair harness or connector.
91I04808
DIAGNOSTIC PROCEDURE 5-2 – ILLUMINATION OR INDICATORS OF PUSH CONTROL UNIT DO NOT COME ON
A
A/C switch connector
20
G/W
V
B
A/C switch connector
11
LG/R
Ω
C
A/C switch connector
11
LG/R
Fan switch connector
12
LG/R
Ω
D
Fan switch connector
23
B
Ω
A
CHECK POWER SUPPLY FOR A/C SWITCH.
Do approx. 12 volts exist between A/C switch harness terminal No. ⑳ and body ground?
N.G.
Check 10A fuse at fuse block.
O.K.
B
CHECK BODY GROUND CIRCUIT FOR A/C SWITCH.
Disconnect A/C switch harness connector.
Does continuity exist between A/C switch harness terminal No. ⑪ and body ground?
N.G.
C
Note
Check circuit continuity between A/C switch harness terminal No. ⑪ and fan switch harness terminal No. ⑫.
O.K.
D
Note
CHECK BODY GROUND CIRCUIT FOR FAN SWITCH.
Does continuity exist between fan switch harness terminal No. ㉓ and body ground?
O.K.
CHECK FAN SWITCH.
N.G.
Replace fan switch.
O.K.
CHECK A/C SWITCH.
N.G.
Replace A/C switch.
NOTE: If the result is not good (NG) after checking circuit continuity, repair harness or connector.
92E03147

Courtesy of Nissan Motor Co., U.S.A.

Fig. 15: Diagnostic Procedure 5-1 – Illumination Or Indicators Of Push Control Unit Do Not Come On

Courtesy of Nissan Motor Co., U.S.A.

Fig. 16: Diagnostic Procedure 5-2 – Illumination Or Indicators Of Push Control Unit Do Not Come On

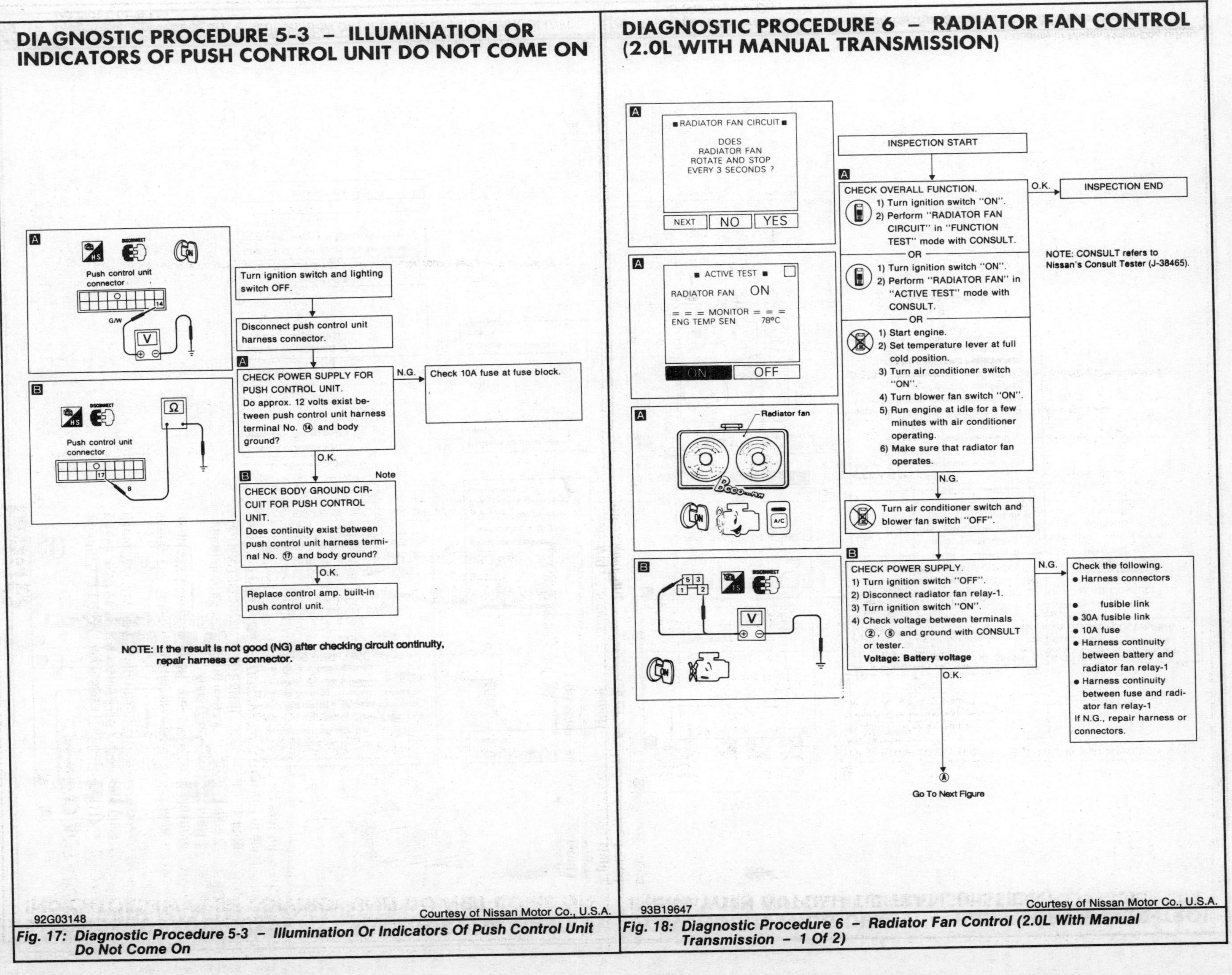
DIAGNOSTIC PROCEDURE 5-3 – ILLUMINATION OR INDICATORS OF PUSH CONTROL UNIT DO NOT COME ON
A
Push control unit connector
14
G/W
V
B
Push control unit connector
Ω
17
B
Turn ignition switch and lighting switch OFF.
Disconnect push control unit harness connector.
A
CHECK POWER SUPPLY FOR PUSH CONTROL UNIT.
Do approx. 12 volts exist between push control unit harness terminal No. ⑭ and body ground?
N.G.
Check 10A fuse at fuse block.
O.K.
B
Note
CHECK BODY GROUND CIRCUIT FOR PUSH CONTROL UNIT.
Does continuity exist between push control unit harness terminal No. ⑰ and body ground?
O.K.
Replace control amp. built-in push control unit.
NOTE: If the result is not good (NG) after checking circuit continuity, repair harness or connector.
92G03148
Courtesy of Nissan Motor Co., U.S.A.
DIAGNOSTIC PROCEDURE 6 – RADIATOR FAN CONTROL (2.0L WITH MANUAL TRANSMISSION)
A
■ RADIATOR FAN CIRCUIT ■
DOES RADIATOR FAN ROTATE AND STOP EVERY 3 SECONDS ?
NEXT
NO
YES
A
■ ACTIVE TEST ■
RADIATOR FAN ON
= = = MONITOR = = =
ENG TEMP SEN 78°C
ON
OFF
A
Radiator fan
Bcoo...nn
A/C
B
5 3
1 2
V
INSPECTION START
A
CHECK OVERALL FUNCTION.
1) Turn ignition switch "ON".
2) Perform "RADIATOR FAN CIRCUIT" in "FUNCTION TEST" mode with CONSULT.
OR
1) Turn ignition switch "ON".
2) Perform "RADIATOR FAN" in "ACTIVE TEST" mode with CONSULT.
OR
1) Start engine.
2) Set temperature lever at full cold position.
3) Turn air conditioner switch "ON".
4) Turn blower fan switch "ON".
5) Run engine at idle for a few minutes with air conditioner operating.
6) Make sure that radiator fan operates.
O.K.
INSPECTION END
NOTE: CONSULT refers to Nissan's Consult Tester (J-38465).
N.G.
Turn air conditioner switch and blower fan switch "OFF".
B
CHECK POWER SUPPLY.
1) Turn ignition switch "OFF".
2) Disconnect radiator fan relay-1.
3) Turn ignition switch "ON".
4) Check voltage between terminals ②, ⑤ and ground with CONSULT or tester.
Voltage: Battery voltage
N.G.
Check the following.
• Harness connectors
• fusible link
• 30A fusible link
• 10A fuse
• Harness continuity between battery and radiator fan relay-1
• Harness continuity between fuse and radiator fan relay-1
If N.G., repair harness or connectors.
O.K.
Ⓐ
Go To Next Figure
93B19647
Courtesy of Nissan Motor Co., U.S.A.

Fig. 17: Diagnostic Procedure 5-3 – Illumination Or Indicators Of Push Control Unit Do Not Come On

Fig. 18: Diagnostic Procedure 6 – Radiator Fan Control (2.0L With Manual Transmission – 1 Of 2)

1993 MANUAL A/C-HEATER SYSTEMS
Trouble Shooting – NX & Sentra (Cont.)

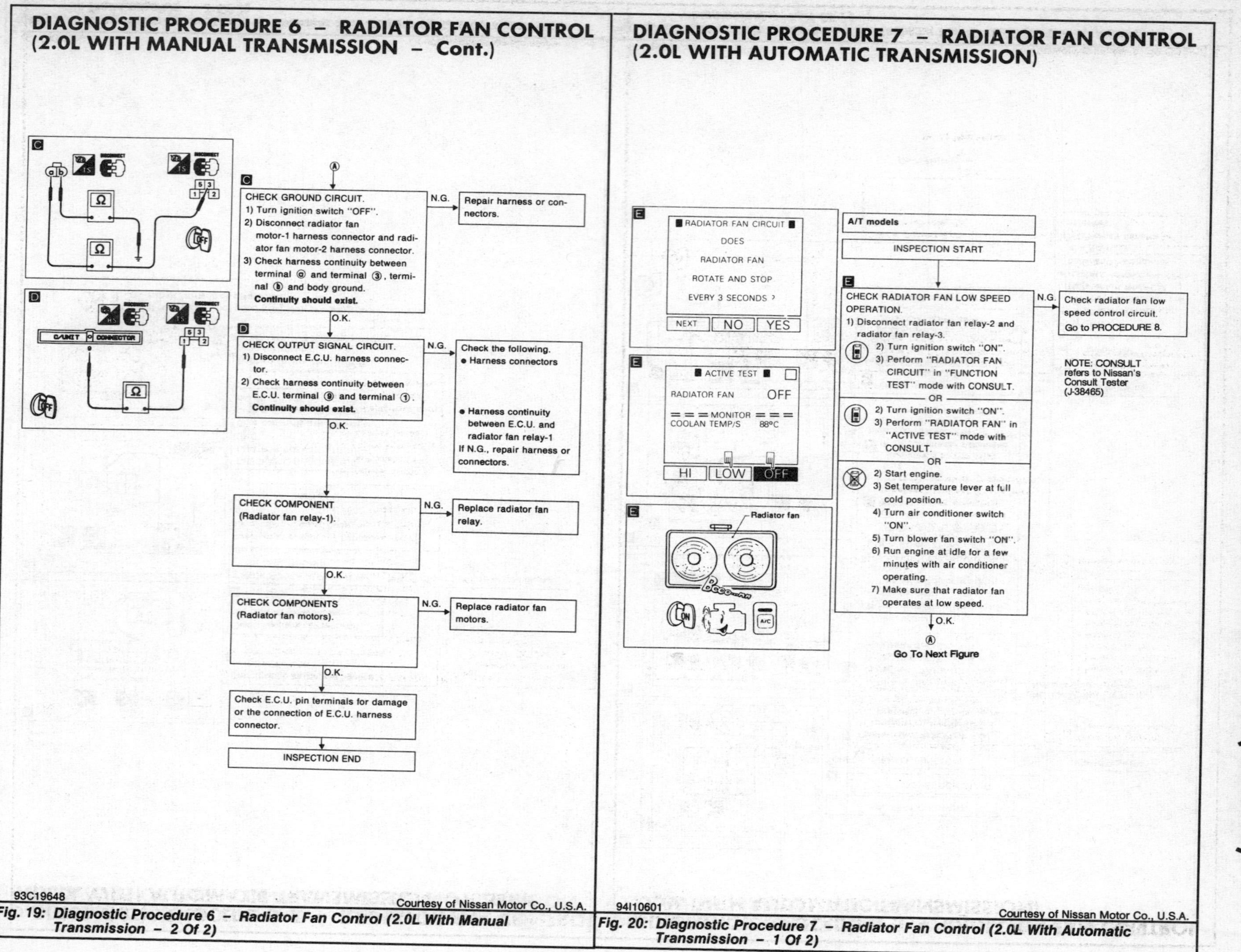
DIAGNOSTIC PROCEDURE 6 – RADIATOR FAN CONTROL
(2.0L WITH MANUAL TRANSMISSION – Cont.)
C
D
C/UNIT CONNECTOR
A
C CHECK GROUND CIRCUIT.
1) Turn ignition switch "OFF".
2) Disconnect radiator fan motor-1 harness connector and radiator fan motor-2 harness connector.
3) Check harness continuity between terminal ⓐ and terminal ③, terminal ⓑ and body ground.
Continuity should exist.
N.G.
Repair harness or connectors.
O.K.
D CHECK OUTPUT SIGNAL CIRCUIT.
1) Disconnect E.C.U. harness connector.
2) Check harness continuity between E.C.U. terminal ⑨ and terminal ①.
Continuity should exist.
N.G.
Check the following.
• Harness connectors
• Harness continuity between E.C.U. and radiator fan relay-1
If N.G., repair harness or connectors.
O.K.
CHECK COMPONENT
(Radiator fan relay-1).
N.G.
Replace radiator fan relay.
O.K.
CHECK COMPONENTS
(Radiator fan motors).
N.G.
Replace radiator fan motors.
O.K.
Check E.C.U. pin terminals for damage or the connection of E.C.U. harness connector.
INSPECTION END
93C19648
Courtesy of Nissan Motor Co., U.S.A.
DIAGNOSTIC PROCEDURE 7 – RADIATOR FAN CONTROL
(2.0L WITH AUTOMATIC TRANSMISSION)
E
RADIATOR FAN CIRCUIT
DOES
RADIATOR FAN
ROTATE AND STOP
EVERY 3 SECONDS ?
NEXT
NO
YES
E
ACTIVE TEST
RADIATOR FAN OFF
MONITOR
COOLAN TEMP/S 88°C
HI
LOW
OFF
E
Radiator fan
A/C
A/T models
INSPECTION START
E CHECK RADIATOR FAN LOW SPEED OPERATION.
1) Disconnect radiator fan relay-2 and radiator fan relay-3.
2) Turn ignition switch "ON".
3) Perform "RADIATOR FAN CIRCUIT" in "FUNCTION TEST" mode with CONSULT.
OR
2) Turn ignition switch "ON".
3) Perform "RADIATOR FAN" in "ACTIVE TEST" mode with CONSULT.
OR
2) Start engine.
3) Set temperature lever at full cold position.
4) Turn air conditioner switch "ON".
5) Turn blower fan switch "ON".
6) Run engine at idle for a few minutes with air conditioner operating.
7) Make sure that radiator fan operates at low speed.
N.G.
Check radiator fan low speed control circuit.
Go to PROCEDURE 8.
NOTE: CONSULT refers to Nissan's Consult Tester (J-38465)
O.K.
A
Go To Next Figure
94I10601
Courtesy of Nissan Motor Co., U.S.A.

Fig. 19: Diagnostic Procedure 6 – Radiator Fan Control (2.0L With Manual Transmission – 2 Of 2)

Fig. 20: Diagnostic Procedure 7 – Radiator Fan Control (2.0L With Automatic Transmission – 1 Of 2)

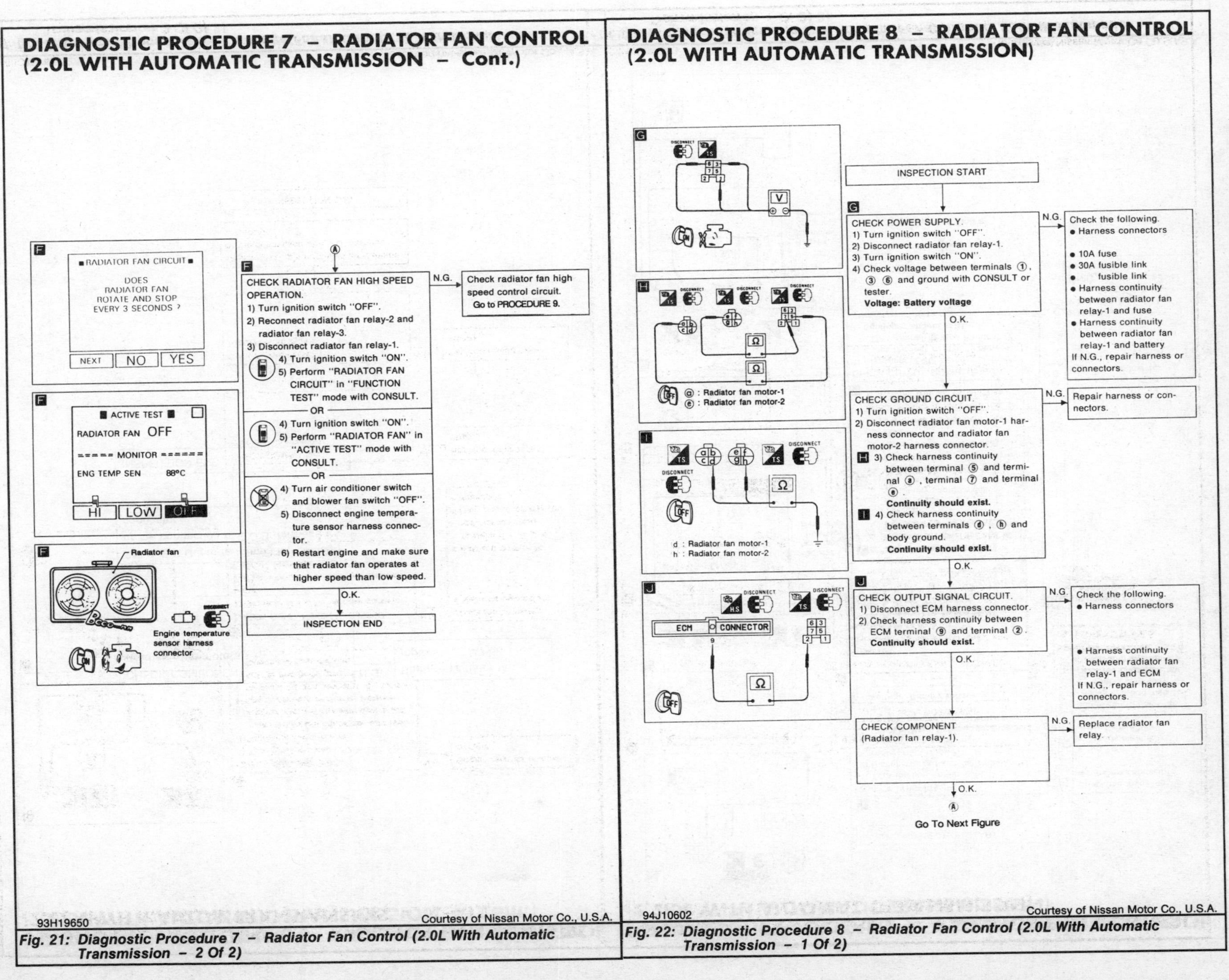
DIAGNOSTIC PROCEDURE 7 – RADIATOR FAN CONTROL
(2.0L WITH AUTOMATIC TRANSMISSION – Cont.)
F
■ RADIATOR FAN CIRCUIT ■
DOES RADIATOR FAN ROTATE AND STOP EVERY 3 SECONDS ?
NEXT
NO
YES
F
■ ACTIVE TEST ■
RADIATOR FAN OFF
===== MONITOR ======
ENG TEMP SEN 88ºC
HI
LOW
OFF
F
Radiator fan
Engine temperature sensor harness connector
DISCONNECT
Ⓐ
F
CHECK RADIATOR FAN HIGH SPEED OPERATION.
1) Turn ignition switch "OFF".
2) Reconnect radiator fan relay-2 and radiator fan relay-3.
3) Disconnect radiator fan relay-1.
4) Turn ignition switch "ON".
5) Perform "RADIATOR FAN CIRCUIT" in "FUNCTION TEST" mode with CONSULT.
OR
4) Turn ignition switch "ON".
5) Perform "RADIATOR FAN" in "ACTIVE TEST" mode with CONSULT.
OR
4) Turn air conditioner switch and blower fan switch "OFF".
5) Disconnect engine temperature sensor harness connector.
6) Restart engine and make sure that radiator fan operates at higher speed than low speed.
N.G.
Check radiator fan high speed control circuit.
Go to PROCEDURE 9.
O.K.
INSPECTION END
93H19650
Courtesy of Nissan Motor Co., U.S.A.
DIAGNOSTIC PROCEDURE 8 – RADIATOR FAN CONTROL
(2.0L WITH AUTOMATIC TRANSMISSION)
G
H
ⓐ : Radiator fan motor-1
ⓔ : Radiator fan motor-2
I
d : Radiator fan motor-1
h : Radiator fan motor-2
J
ECM
CONNECTOR
INSPECTION START
G
CHECK POWER SUPPLY.
1) Turn ignition switch "OFF".
2) Disconnect radiator fan relay-1.
3) Turn ignition switch "ON".
4) Check voltage between terminals ①, ③ ⑥ and ground with CONSULT or tester.
Voltage: Battery voltage
N.G.
Check the following.
• Harness connectors
• 10A fuse
• 30A fusible link
• fusible link
• Harness continuity between radiator fan relay-1 and fuse
• Harness continuity between radiator fan relay-1 and battery
If N.G., repair harness or connectors.
O.K.
CHECK GROUND CIRCUIT.
1) Turn ignition switch "OFF".
2) Disconnect radiator fan motor-1 harness connector and radiator fan motor-2 harness connector.
H 3) Check harness continuity between terminal ⑤ and terminal ⓐ, terminal ⑦ and terminal ⓔ.
Continuity should exist.
I 4) Check harness continuity between terminals ⓓ, ⓗ and body ground.
Continuity should exist.
N.G.
Repair harness or connectors.
O.K.
J
CHECK OUTPUT SIGNAL CIRCUIT.
1) Disconnect ECM harness connector.
2) Check harness continuity between ECM terminal ⑨ and terminal ②.
Continuity should exist.
N.G.
Check the following.
• Harness connectors
• Harness continuity between radiator fan relay-1 and ECM
If N.G., repair harness or connectors.
O.K.
CHECK COMPONENT
(Radiator fan relay-1).
N.G.
Replace radiator fan relay.
O.K.
Ⓐ
Go To Next Figure
94J10602
Courtesy of Nissan Motor Co., U.S.A.

Fig. 21: Diagnostic Procedure 7 – Radiator Fan Control (2.0L With Automatic Transmission – 2 Of 2)

Fig. 22: Diagnostic Procedure 8 – Radiator Fan Control (2.0L With Automatic Transmission – 1 Of 2)

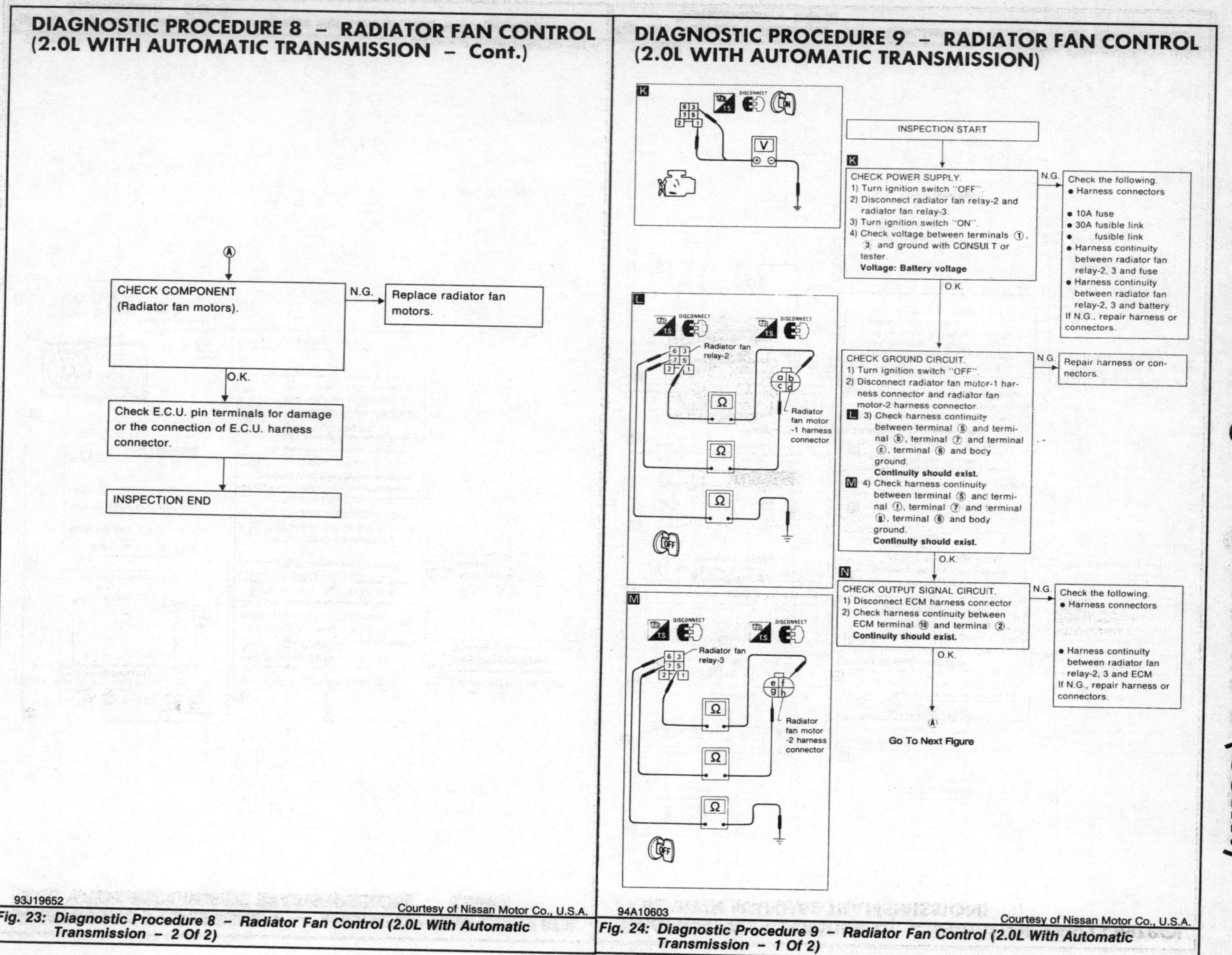
DIAGNOSTIC PROCEDURE 8 – RADIATOR FAN CONTROL (2.0L WITH AUTOMATIC TRANSMISSION – Cont.)
Ⓐ
CHECK COMPONENT (Radiator fan motors).
N.G.
Replace radiator fan motors.
O.K.
Check E.C.U. pin terminals for damage or the connection of E.C.U. harness connector.
INSPECTION END
93J19652
Courtesy of Nissan Motor Co., U.S.A.
DIAGNOSTIC PROCEDURE 9 – RADIATOR FAN CONTROL (2.0L WITH AUTOMATIC TRANSMISSION)
INSPECTION START
K
CHECK POWER SUPPLY.
1) Turn ignition switch "OFF".
2) Disconnect radiator fan relay-2 and radiator fan relay-3.
3) Turn ignition switch "ON".
4) Check voltage between terminals ①, ③ and ground with CONSULT or tester.
Voltage: Battery voltage
N.G.
Check the following.
• Harness connectors
• 10A fuse
• 30A fusible link
• fusible link
• Harness continuity between radiator fan relay-2, 3 and fuse
• Harness continuity between radiator fan relay-2, 3 and battery
If N.G., repair harness or connectors.
O.K.
CHECK GROUND CIRCUIT.
1) Turn ignition switch "OFF".
2) Disconnect radiator fan motor-1 harness connector and radiator fan motor-2 harness connector.
L 3) Check harness continuity between terminal ⑤ and terminal ⓑ, terminal ⑦ and terminal ⓒ, terminal ⑥ and body ground.
Continuity should exist.
M 4) Check harness continuity between terminal ⑤ and terminal ⓕ, terminal ⑦ and terminal ⓖ, terminal ⑥ and body ground.
Continuity should exist.
N.G.
Repair harness or connectors.
O.K.
N
CHECK OUTPUT SIGNAL CIRCUIT.
1) Disconnect ECM harness connector
2) Check harness continuity between ECM terminal ⑩ and terminal ②.
Continuity should exist.
N.G.
Check the following.
• Harness connectors
• Harness continuity between radiator fan relay-2, 3 and ECM
If N.G., repair harness or connectors.
O.K.
Ⓐ
Go To Next Figure
Radiator fan relay-2
Radiator fan motor -1 harness connector
Radiator fan relay-3
Radiator fan motor -2 harness connector
DISCONNECT
T.S.
V
Ω
OFF
ON
94A10603
Courtesy of Nissan Motor Co., U.S.A.

Fig. 23: Diagnostic Procedure 8 – Radiator Fan Control (2.0L With Automatic Transmission – 2 Of 2)

Fig. 24: Diagnostic Procedure 9 – Radiator Fan Control (2.0L With Automatic Transmission – 1 Of 2)

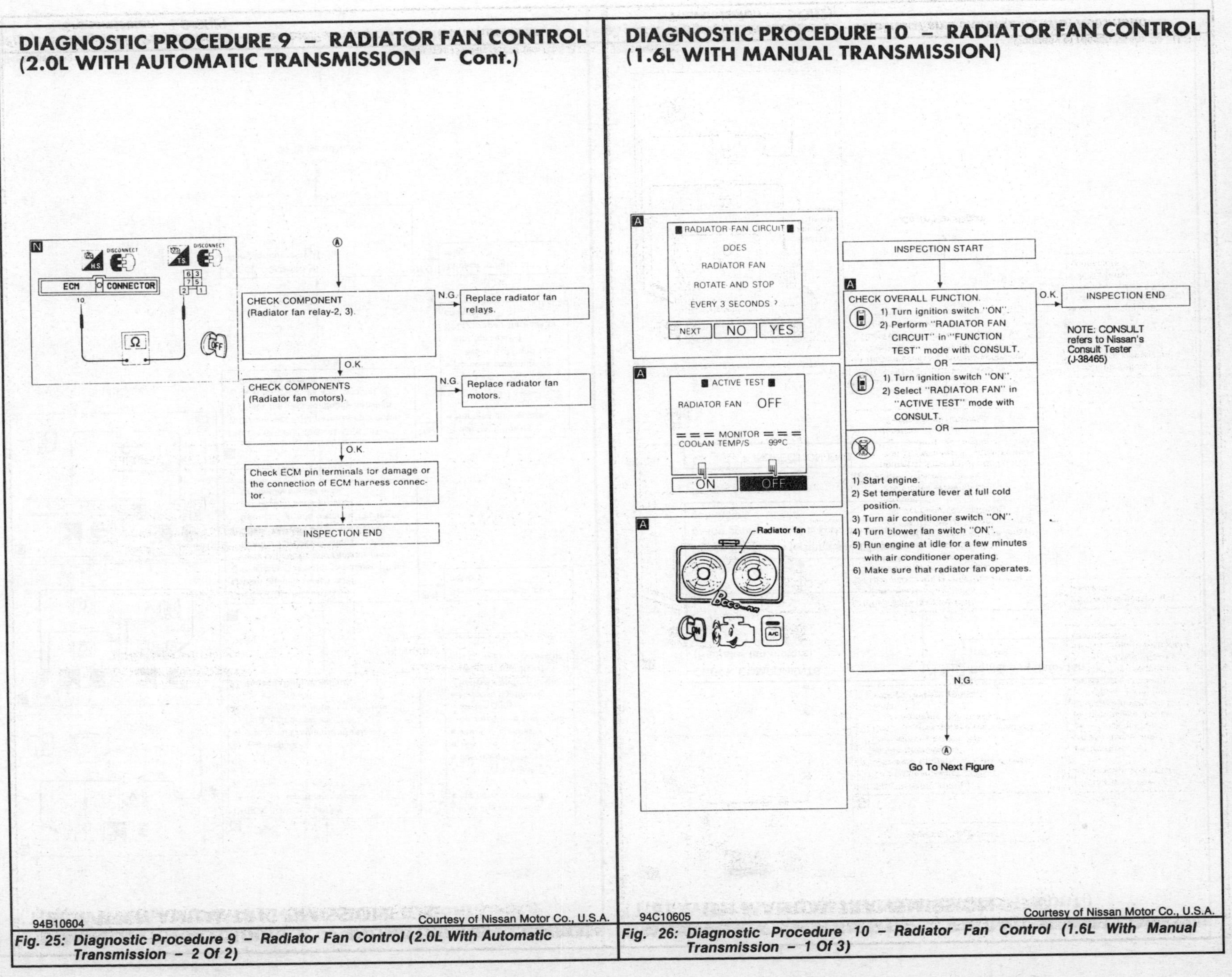
DIAGNOSTIC PROCEDURE 9 – RADIATOR FAN CONTROL (2.0L WITH AUTOMATIC TRANSMISSION – Cont.)
N
DISCONNECT
H.S.
T.S.
ECM
CONNECTOR
10
Ω
OFF
Ⓐ
CHECK COMPONENT (Radiator fan relay-2, 3).
N.G.
Replace radiator fan relays.
O.K.
CHECK COMPONENTS (Radiator fan motors).
N.G.
Replace radiator fan motors.
O.K.
Check ECM pin terminals for damage or the connection of ECM harness connector.
INSPECTION END
94B10604
Courtesy of Nissan Motor Co., U.S.A.
DIAGNOSTIC PROCEDURE 10 – RADIATOR FAN CONTROL (1.6L WITH MANUAL TRANSMISSION)
A
RADIATOR FAN CIRCUIT
DOES RADIATOR FAN ROTATE AND STOP EVERY 3 SECONDS ?
NEXT
NO
YES
ACTIVE TEST
RADIATOR FAN OFF
MONITOR
COOLAN TEMP/S 99°C
ON
OFF
Radiator fan
INSPECTION START
CHECK OVERALL FUNCTION.
1) Turn ignition switch "ON".
2) Perform "RADIATOR FAN CIRCUIT" in "FUNCTION TEST" mode with CONSULT.
OR
1) Turn ignition switch "ON".
2) Select "RADIATOR FAN" in "ACTIVE TEST" mode with CONSULT.
OR
1) Start engine.
2) Set temperature lever at full cold position.
3) Turn air conditioner switch "ON".
4) Turn blower fan switch "ON".
5) Run engine at idle for a few minutes with air conditioner operating.
6) Make sure that radiator fan operates.
O.K.
INSPECTION END
NOTE: CONSULT refers to Nissan's Consult Tester (J-38465)
N.G.
Ⓐ
Go To Next Figure
94C10605
Courtesy of Nissan Motor Co., U.S.A.

Fig. 25: Diagnostic Procedure 9 – Radiator Fan Control (2.0L With Automatic Transmission – 2 Of 2)

Fig. 26: Diagnostic Procedure 10 – Radiator Fan Control (1.6L With Manual Transmission – 1 Of 3)

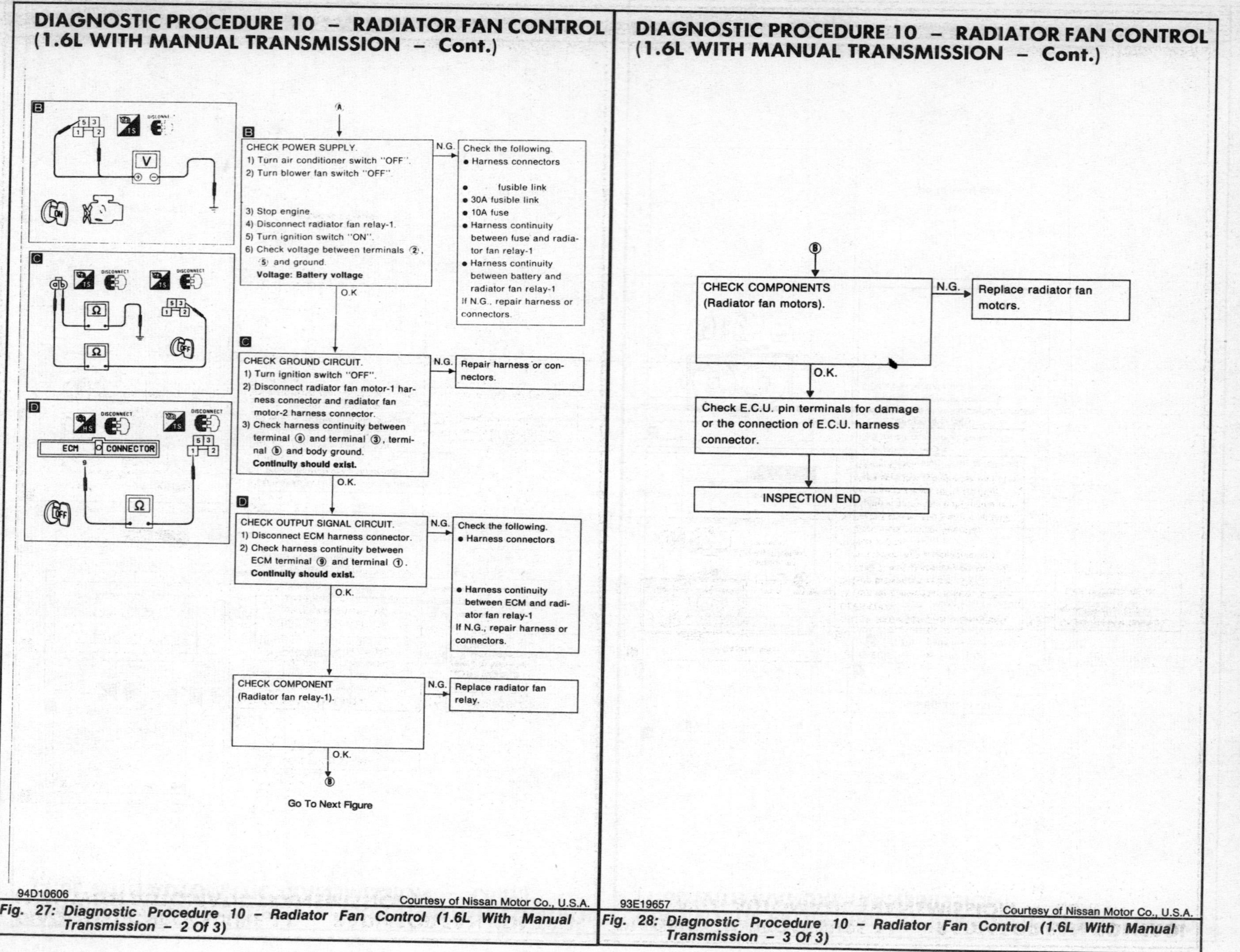
DIAGNOSTIC PROCEDURE 10 – RADIATOR FAN CONTROL (1.6L WITH MANUAL TRANSMISSION – Cont.)
B
CHECK POWER SUPPLY.
1) Turn air conditioner switch "OFF".
2) Turn blower fan switch "OFF".
3) Stop engine.
4) Disconnect radiator fan relay-1.
5) Turn ignition switch "ON".
6) Check voltage between terminals ②, ⑤ and ground.
Voltage: Battery voltage
N.G.
Check the following.
• Harness connectors
• fusible link
• 30A fusible link
• 10A fuse
• Harness continuity between fuse and radiator fan relay-1
• Harness continuity between battery and radiator fan relay-1
If N.G., repair harness or connectors.
O.K.
C
CHECK GROUND CIRCUIT.
1) Turn ignition switch "OFF".
2) Disconnect radiator fan motor-1 harness connector and radiator fan motor-2 harness connector.
3) Check harness continuity between terminal ⓐ and terminal ③, terminal ⓑ and body ground.
Continuity should exist.
N.G.
Repair harness or connectors.
O.K.
D
CHECK OUTPUT SIGNAL CIRCUIT.
1) Disconnect ECM harness connector.
2) Check harness continuity between ECM terminal ⑨ and terminal ①.
Continuity should exist.
N.G.
Check the following.
• Harness connectors
• Harness continuity between ECM and radiator fan relay-1
If N.G., repair harness or connectors.
O.K.
CHECK COMPONENT
(Radiator fan relay-1).
N.G.
Replace radiator fan relay.
O.K.
Go To Next Figure
ECM
CONNECTOR
DISCONNECT
V
Ω
94D10606
Courtesy of Nissan Motor Co., U.S.A.
DIAGNOSTIC PROCEDURE 10 – RADIATOR FAN CONTROL (1.6L WITH MANUAL TRANSMISSION – Cont.)
CHECK COMPONENTS
(Radiator fan motors).
N.G.
Replace radiator fan motcrs.
O.K.
Check E.C.U. pin terminals for damage or the connection of E.C.U. harness connector.
INSPECTION END
93E19657
Courtesy of Nissan Motor Co., U.S.A.

Fig. 27: Diagnostic Procedure 10 – Radiator Fan Control (1.6L With Manual Transmission – 2 Of 3)

Fig. 28: Diagnostic Procedure 10 – Radiator Fan Control (1.6L With Manual Transmission – 3 Of 3)

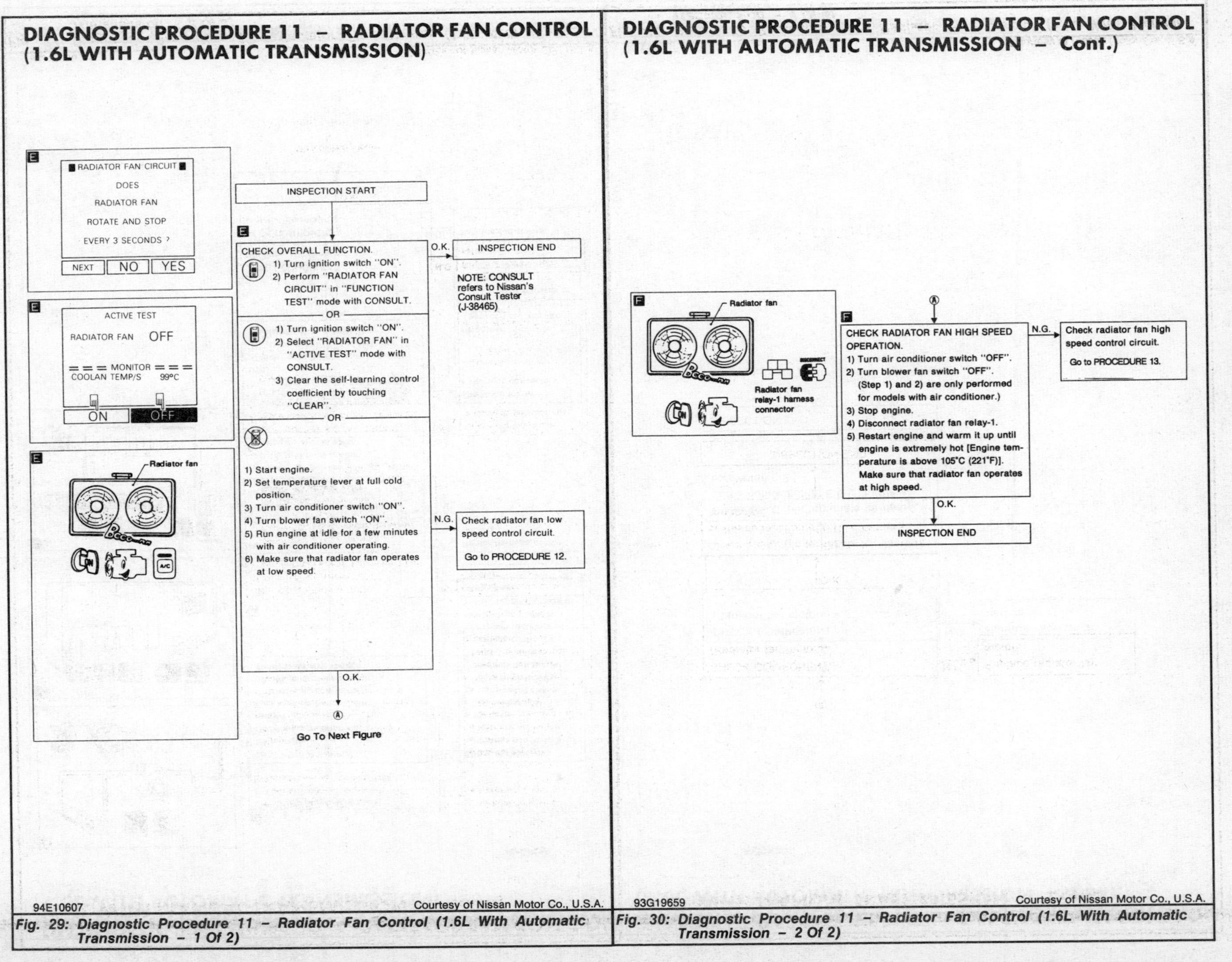
DIAGNOSTIC PROCEDURE 11 – RADIATOR FAN CONTROL (1.6L WITH AUTOMATIC TRANSMISSION)
RADIATOR FAN CIRCUIT
DOES RADIATOR FAN ROTATE AND STOP EVERY 3 SECONDS ?
NEXT
NO
YES
ACTIVE TEST
RADIATOR FAN OFF
=== MONITOR ===
COOLAN TEMP/S 99°C
ON
OFF
Radiator fan
INSPECTION START
CHECK OVERALL FUNCTION.
1) Turn ignition switch "ON".
2) Perform "RADIATOR FAN CIRCUIT" in "FUNCTION TEST" mode with CONSULT.
OR
1) Turn ignition switch "ON".
2) Select "RADIATOR FAN" in "ACTIVE TEST" mode with CONSULT.
3) Clear the self-learning control coefficient by touching "CLEAR".
OR
1) Start engine.
2) Set temperature lever at full cold position.
3) Turn air conditioner switch "ON".
4) Turn blower fan switch "ON".
5) Run engine at idle for a few minutes with air conditioner operating.
6) Make sure that radiator fan operates at low speed.
O.K.
INSPECTION END
NOTE: CONSULT refers to Nissan's Consult Tester (J-38465)
N.G.
Check radiator fan low speed control circuit.
Go to PROCEDURE 12.
O.K.
Go To Next Figure
94E10607
Courtesy of Nissan Motor Co., U.S.A.
DIAGNOSTIC PROCEDURE 11 – RADIATOR FAN CONTROL (1.6L WITH AUTOMATIC TRANSMISSION – Cont.)
Radiator fan
Radiator fan relay-1 harness connector
CHECK RADIATOR FAN HIGH SPEED OPERATION.
1) Turn air conditioner switch "OFF".
2) Turn blower fan switch "OFF".
(Step 1) and 2) are only performed for models with air conditioner.)
3) Stop engine.
4) Disconnect radiator fan relay-1.
5) Restart engine and warm it up until engine is extremely hot [Engine temperature is above 105°C (221°F)].
Make sure that radiator fan operates at high speed.
N.G.
Check radiator fan high speed control circuit.
Go to PROCEDURE 13.
O.K.
INSPECTION END
93G19659
Courtesy of Nissan Motor Co., U.S.A.
Fig. 29: Diagnostic Procedure 11 – Radiator Fan Control (1.6L With Automatic Transmission – 1 Of 2)

Fig. 30: Diagnostic Procedure 11 – Radiator Fan Control (1.6L With Automatic Transmission – 2 Of 2)

1993 MANUAL A/C-HEATER SYSTEMS
Trouble Shooting – NX & Sentra (Cont.)

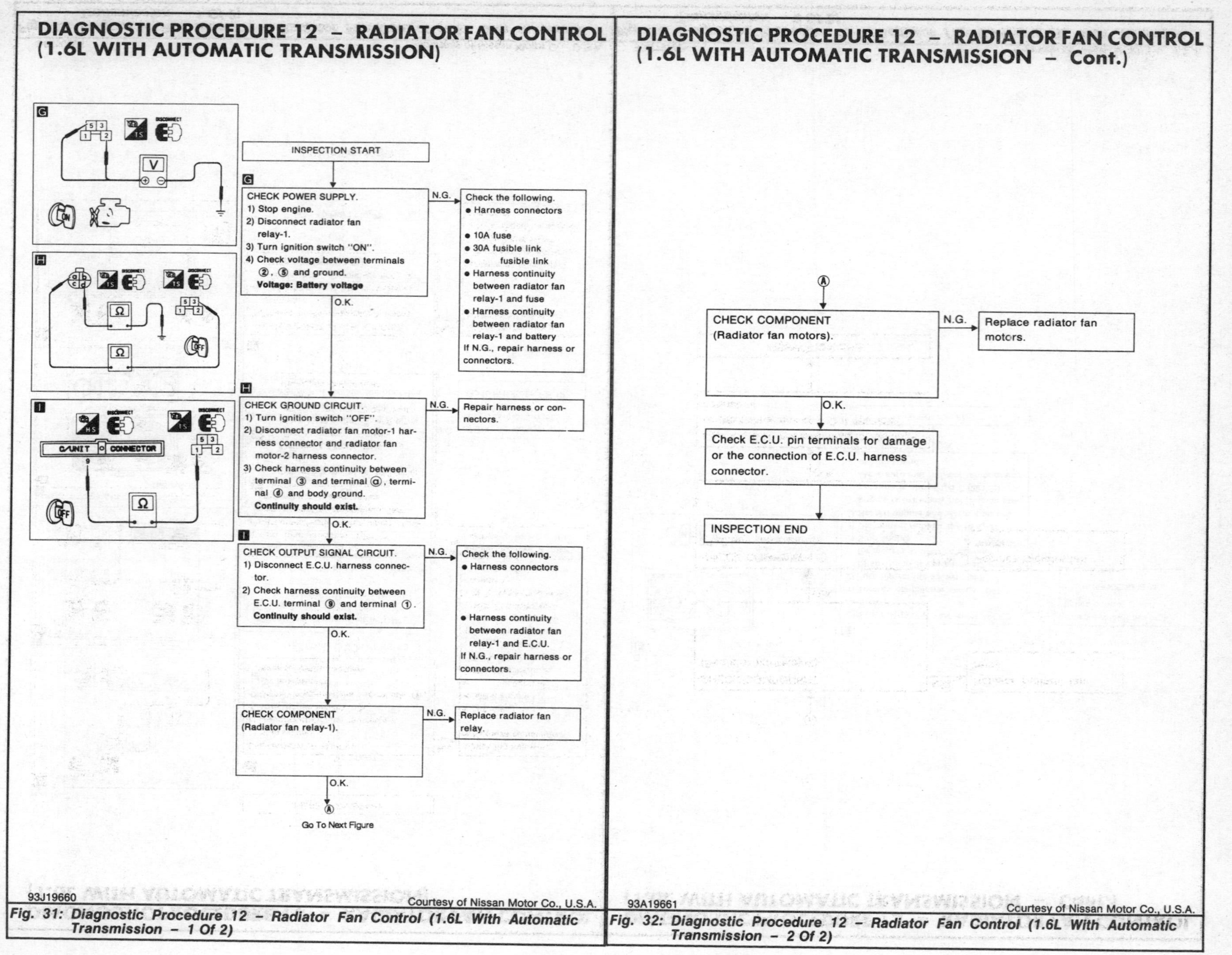
DIAGNOSTIC PROCEDURE 12 – RADIATOR FAN CONTROL (1.6L WITH AUTOMATIC TRANSMISSION)
G
H
I
C/UNIT CONNECTOR
INSPECTION START
G
CHECK POWER SUPPLY.
1) Stop engine.
2) Disconnect radiator fan relay-1.
3) Turn ignition switch "ON".
4) Check voltage between terminals ②, ⑤ and ground.
Voltage: Battery voltage
N.G.
Check the following.
• Harness connectors
• 10A fuse
• 30A fusible link
• fusible link
• Harness continuity between radiator fan relay-1 and fuse
• Harness continuity between radiator fan relay-1 and battery
If N.G., repair harness or connectors.
O.K.
H
CHECK GROUND CIRCUIT.
1) Turn ignition switch "OFF".
2) Disconnect radiator fan motor-1 harness connector and radiator fan motor-2 harness connector.
3) Check harness continuity between terminal ③ and terminal ⓐ, terminal ⓓ and body ground.
Continuity should exist.
N.G.
Repair harness or connectors.
O.K.
I
CHECK OUTPUT SIGNAL CIRCUIT.
1) Disconnect E.C.U. harness connector.
2) Check harness continuity between E.C.U. terminal ⑨ and terminal ①.
Continuity should exist.
N.G.
Check the following.
• Harness connectors
• Harness continuity between radiator fan relay-1 and E.C.U.
If N.G., repair harness or connectors.
O.K.
CHECK COMPONENT
(Radiator fan relay-1).
N.G.
Replace radiator fan relay.
O.K.
Ⓐ
Go To Next Figure
93J19660
Courtesy of Nissan Motor Co., U.S.A.
DIAGNOSTIC PROCEDURE 12 – RADIATOR FAN CONTROL (1.6L WITH AUTOMATIC TRANSMISSION – Cont.)
Ⓐ
CHECK COMPONENT
(Radiator fan motors).
N.G.
Replace radiator fan motors.
O.K.
Check E.C.U. pin terminals for damage or the connection of E.C.U. harness connector.
INSPECTION END
93A19661
Courtesy of Nissan Motor Co., U.S.A.

Fig. 31: Diagnostic Procedure 12 – Radiator Fan Control (1.6L With Automatic Transmission – 1 Of 2)

Fig. 32: Diagnostic Procedure 12 – Radiator Fan Control (1.6L With Automatic Transmission – 2 Of 2)

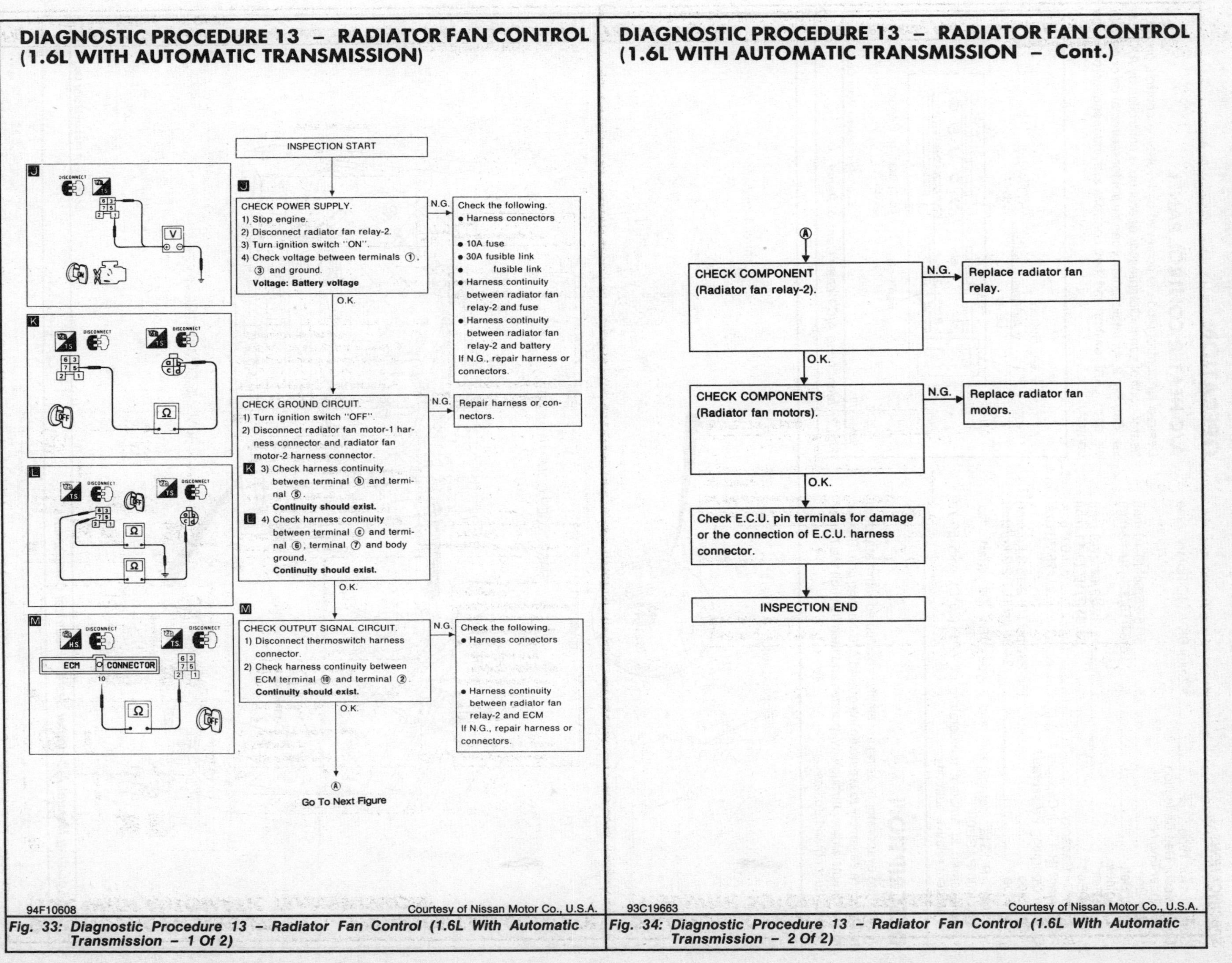
DIAGNOSTIC PROCEDURE 13 – RADIATOR FAN CONTROL
(1.6L WITH AUTOMATIC TRANSMISSION)
INSPECTION START
J
CHECK POWER SUPPLY.
1) Stop engine.
2) Disconnect radiator fan relay-2.
3) Turn ignition switch "ON".
4) Check voltage between terminals ①, ③ and ground.
Voltage: Battery voltage
N.G.
Check the following.
• Harness connectors
• 10A fuse
• 30A fusible link
• fusible link
• Harness continuity between radiator fan relay-2 and fuse
• Harness continuity between radiator fan relay-2 and battery
If N.G., repair harness or connectors.
O.K.
CHECK GROUND CIRCUIT.
1) Turn ignition switch "OFF".
2) Disconnect radiator fan motor-1 harness connector and radiator fan motor-2 harness connector.
K 3) Check harness continuity between terminal ⓑ and terminal ⑤.
Continuity should exist.
L 4) Check harness continuity between terminal ⓒ and terminal ⑥, terminal ⑦ and body ground.
Continuity should exist.
N.G.
Repair harness or connectors.
O.K.
M
CHECK OUTPUT SIGNAL CIRCUIT.
1) Disconnect thermoswitch harness connector.
2) Check harness continuity between ECM terminal ⑩ and terminal ②.
Continuity should exist.
N.G.
Check the following.
• Harness connectors
• Harness continuity between radiator fan relay-2 and ECM
If N.G., repair harness or connectors.
O.K.
Ⓐ
Go To Next Figure
DISCONNECT
T.S.
H.S.
ECM
CONNECTOR
10
ON
OFF
V
Ω
94F10608
Courtesy of Nissan Motor Co., U.S.A.
DIAGNOSTIC PROCEDURE 13 – RADIATOR FAN CONTROL
(1.6L WITH AUTOMATIC TRANSMISSION – Cont.)
Ⓐ
CHECK COMPONENT
(Radiator fan relay-2).
N.G.
Replace radiator fan relay.
O.K.
CHECK COMPONENTS
(Radiator fan motors).
N.G.
Replace radiator fan motors.
O.K.
Check E.C.U. pin terminals for damage or the connection of E.C.U. harness connector.
INSPECTION END
93C19663
Courtesy of Nissan Motor Co., U.S.A.

Fig. 33: Diagnostic Procedure 13 – Radiator Fan Control (1.6L With Automatic Transmission – 1 Of 2)

Fig. 34: Diagnostic Procedure 13 – Radiator Fan Control (1.6L With Automatic Transmission – 2 Of 2)

1993 MANUAL A/C-HEATER SYSTEMS
Pathfinder & Pickup

SPECIFICATIONS

Compressor Type	Zexel DKV-14C Rotary Vane
Compressor Belt Deflection	
4-Cylinder Engines	
New Belt	5/16-25/64" (8-10 mm)
Used Belt	25/64-15/32" (10-12 mm)
V6 Engines	
New Belt	9/32-23/64" (7-9 mm)
Used Belt	23/64-7/16" (9-11 mm)
System Oil Capacity	6.8 ozs.
Refrigerant (R-134a) Capacity [1]	26-30 ozs.
System Operating Pressures [2]	
High Side	188-232 psi (13.2-16.3 kg/cm²)
Low Side	24-31 psi (1.7-2.2 kg/cm²)

[1] – Use R-134a refrigerant and Type "R" Oil (Part No. KLH00-PAGR0).

[2] – Measured at ambient temperature of 77°F (25°C), with 50-70 percent relative humidity.

DESCRIPTION

A separate evaporator housing assembly is combined with a standard heater core assembly to create an integrated A/C-heating unit. Blower motor directs airflow through evaporator and then through the heater core to ducting and outlets.

OPERATION

A/C-HEATER CONTROL PANEL

Desired air control mode is achieved by lever-type controls on A/C-heater control panel. Compressor operation is controlled by A/C button. *See Fig. 2.* Air intake control can be set for recirculation or outside air entry. A/C switch and fan controls are independent of mode controls.

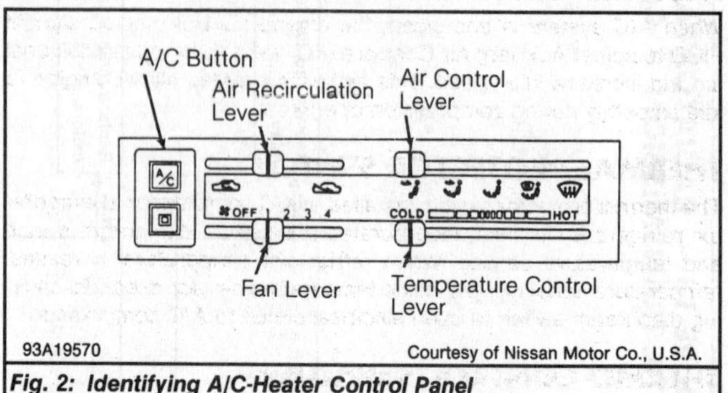
A/C Button
Air Recirculation Lever
Air Control Lever
OFF 1 2 3 4
COLD
HOT
Fan Lever
Temperature Control Lever
93A19570
Courtesy of Nissan Motor Co., U.S.A.

Fig. 2: Identifying A/C-Heater Control Panel

Blower Switch
A/C Switch
Cooling Unit
Control Amplifier
Resistor
PASSENGER COMPARTMENT
Blower Relay
A/C Relay
Dual-Pressure Switch
ENGINE COMPARTMENT
94H10428
Courtesy of Nissan Motor Co., U.S.A.

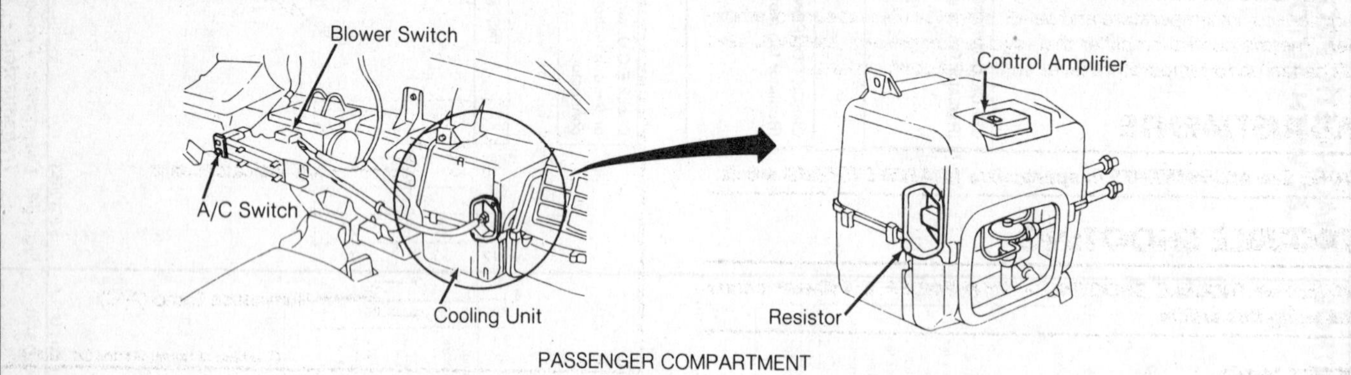

Fig. 1: Locating Manual A/C-Heater System Electrical Components

DUAL-PRESSURE SWITCH

Dual-pressure switch is mounted on receiver-drier. *See Fig. 1.* The switch protects A/C system from high pressure build-up due to restriction, overcharge or compressor malfunction. If excessively low or high system pressure is sensed, the switch electrically stops compressor clutch operation.

FAST IDLE CONTROL DEVICE (FICD)

When A/C system is energized, the engine control module signals FICD to adjust Auxiliary Air Control (AAC) valve to by-pass additional air and increase idle speed. This higher idle speed allows engine to idle smoothly during compression operation.

THERMAL PROTECTOR SWITCH

The thermal protector switch, installed in A/C compressor at evaporator refrigerant line inlet, incorporates a pressure diaphragm switch and temperature sensor. When refrigerant temperature increases, temperature-sensitive gas inside temperature sensor expands, causing diaphragm switch to open electrical circuit to A/C compressor.

THERMO CONTROL AMPLIFIER

Thermo control amplifier is mounted on evaporator housing. *See Fig. 1.* A temperature sensor (thermistor), located inside evaporator housing, senses air temperature and sends signal to thermo control amplifier. Thermo control amplifier then cycles compressor clutch on and off based on to temperature lever setting on control panel.

ADJUSTMENTS

NOTE: ***See ADJUSTMENTS in appropriate HEATER SYSTEMS article.***

TROUBLE SHOOTING

NOTE: ***See TROUBLE SHOOTING – PATHFINDER & PICKUP charts following this article.***

TESTING

NOTE: ***For test procedures not covered in this article, see appropriate HEATER SYSTEMS article.***

A/C SYSTEM PERFORMANCE

1) Park vehicle out of direct sunlight. Close all doors, and open engine hood and windows. Connect A/C manifold gauge set. Determine relative humidity and ambient air temperature.

2) Set temperature control to maximum cold setting, mode control to vent position, and air recirculation lever to recirculated air position. Turn blower fan switch to highest position. Operate engine at 1500 RPM.

3) After running A/C for 10 minutes, check high- and low-side system pressures. Ensure system is operating within specified range. See A/C-HEATER PERFORMANCE TEST table.

A/C SYSTEM PERFORMANCE TEST

Ambient Air Temp. °F (°C)	High Pressure [1] psi (kg/cm²)	Low Pressure [1] psi (kg/cm²)
68 (20)	139-172 (9.8-12.1)	16-23 (1.1-1.6)
77 (25)	188-232 (13.2-16.3)	23.5-31.3 (1.65-2.2)
86 (30)	186-228 (13.1-16)	24-31 (1.7-2.2)
95 (35)	220-270 (15.5-19)	34-41 (2.4-2.9)
104 (40)	256-313 (18-22)	41.9-51.2 (2.95-3.6)

[1] – Specification is with relative humidity at 50-70 percent.

POWER SUPPLY & GROUND CIRCUITS

Thermo Control Amplifier – 1) Disconnect thermo control amplifier connector. Turn ignition on. Measure voltage at Green/Blue wire terminal of thermo control amplifier harness connector. If battery voltage exists, go to next step. If voltage is not present, repair open Green/Blue wire.

2) Turn blower fan switch on. Using ohmmeter, check continuity between Green/Black wire terminal of thermo control amplifier harness connector and body ground. Ensure continuity exists. If there is no continuity, repair open Green/Black wire.

A/C SWITCH

Disconnect negative battery cable. Remove A/C switch. Using an ohmmeter, check continuity between A/C switch terminals with switch in specified position. *See Fig. 3.*

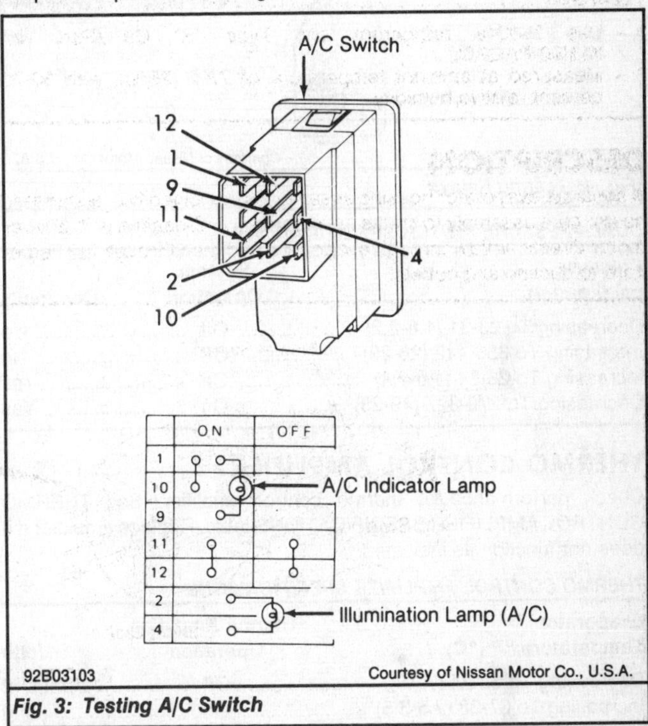

A/C Switch
12
1
9
11
4
2
10
ON
OFF
1
10
9
11
12
2
4
A/C Indicator Lamp
Illumination Lamp (A/C)
92B03103
Courtesy of Nissan Motor Co., U.S.A.

Fig. 3: Testing A/C Switch

BLOWER MOTOR RESISTOR

Disconnect blower motor resistor connector. Check continuity between all resistor terminals. Ensure continuity exists. If continuity does not exist, replace resistor.

RELAYS

1) Remove relay to be tested. *See Fig. 1.* Check continuity between coil side terminals of relay. Ensure continuity exists. Check continuity between remaining terminals of relay. Continuity should not exist.

2) Apply battery voltage between coil side terminals of relay, and check continuity between remaining terminals. *See Fig. 4.* Ensure continuity exists with battery voltage applied. If continuity is not as specified, replace relay.

BLOWER MOTOR

Disconnect wiring harness at blower motor. Apply battery voltage to blower motor terminals. Ensure blower motor operates smoothly. If blower motor operation is rough or not up to speed, replace blower motor.

DUAL-PRESSURE SWITCH

Remove dual-pressure switch connector. Dual-pressure switch is on top of receiver-drier. Using ohmmeter, check continuity between dual-pressure switch terminals. See DUAL-PRESSURE SWITCH SPECIFICATIONS table. Replace switch if it does not perform as indicated.

1993 MANUAL A/C-HEATER SYSTEMS
Pathfinder & Pickup (Cont.)

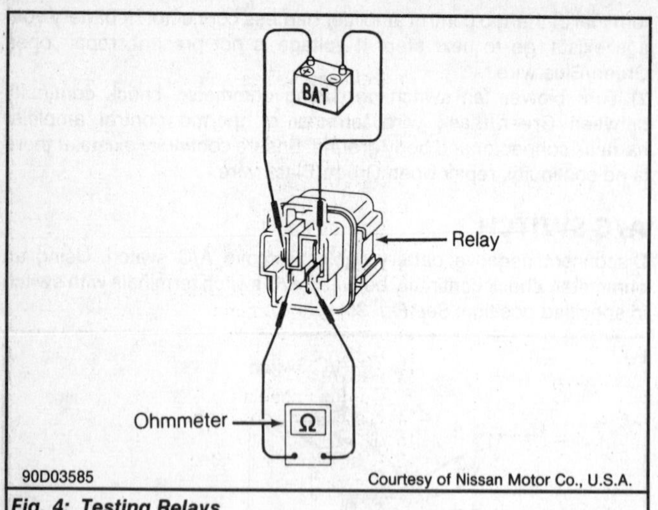
BAT
Relay
Ohmmeter
Ω
90D03585
Courtesy of Nissan Motor Co., U.S.A.

Fig. 4: Testing Relays

DUAL-PRESSURE SWITCH SPECIFICATIONS

Pressure psi (kg/cm²)	System Operation	Continuity
Decreasing To 23-31 (1.6-2.2)	Off	No
Increasing To 356-412 (25-29)	Off	No
Increasing To 23-34 (1.6-2.4)	On	Yes
Decreasing To 270-327 (19-23)	On	Yes

THERMO CONTROL AMPLIFIER

Check performance of thermo control amplifier. See THERMO CONTROL AMPLIFIER SPECIFICATIONS table. Replace amplifier if it does not function as indicated.

THERMO CONTROL AMPLIFIER SPECIFICATIONS

Evaporator Temperature °F (°C)	Thermo Amplifier Operation	Volts
Decreasing To 32-34 (.1-.9)	Off	About 12
Increasing To 37-38 (2.5-3.5)	On	0

THERMAL PROTECTOR SWITCH

Check compressor operation at indicated compressor temperatures. See THERMAL PROTECTOR SWITCH SPECIFICATIONS table. Replace switch if it does not perform as indicated.

THERMAL PROTECTOR SWITCH SPECIFICATIONS

Compressor Temperature °F (°C)	Compressor Operation
Increasing To 293-311 (145-155)	Off
Decreasing To 266-284 (130-140)	On

REMOVAL & INSTALLATION

A/C COMPRESSOR

Removal – Loosen idler pulley bolt, and remove compressor belt. Discharge A/C system using approved refrigerant recovery/recycling equipment. Disconnect compressor clutch connector. Remove discharge and suction hoses from compressor. Remove compressor bolts and compressor.

Installation – To install, reverse removal procedure. Tighten bolts to specification. See TORQUE SPECIFICATIONS. When connecting hoses to compressor, use new "O" rings coated with refrigerant oil. Evacuate and recharge system.

EVAPORATOR & HEATER CORE ASSEMBLY

Removal – **1)** Discharge A/C system using approved refrigerant recovery/recycling equipment. Drain cooling system. In engine compartment, disconnect A/C lines from evaporator and remove drain tube bolt. If removing heater core, remove heater hoses from core tubes. Plug all line openings.

2) Remove steering column covers and column bolts. Lower steering column and steering wheel onto seat. Remove instrument cluster bezel/cover and cluster, noting all wiring harness connector locations. *See Fig. 5.*

3) Remove center section lower panel. Remove radio faceplate, center air vent outlet, ashtray and radio. Pry out A/C-heater control panel and temporarily leave in this position. Remove glove box and door as a unit by removing bottom swivel pins. Remove rear glove box panel.

4) Remove front pillar (windshield posts) support covers to enable top dash pad removal. Top dash pad unit must be removed before dashboard can be removed. Dash pad is attached to dashboard from underneath and behind dashboard. *See Fig. 5.* Remove dashboard bolts, and lift dashboard upward and outward.

5) Remove evaporator unit, blower motor unit, and intake air box. *See Fig. 6.* Remove all air duct and control cable connections from heater unit. Remove heater unit. Remove spring clip retainers, and separate heater unit halves to remove heater core.

Installation – To install, reverse removal procedure. When assembling connections, use new "O" rings coated with refrigerant oil. If installing a new evaporator core, add 2.5 ounces of refrigerant oil to new core. Evacuate and recharge system.

CONDENSER

Removal – **1)** Discharge A/C system using approved refrigerant recovery/recycling equipment. Drain cooling system. Remove cooling fan from water pump. Remove radiator hoses, lines and shroud. Disconnect wiring harness connectors. Remove radiator.

2) Remove front grille. Detach right headlight assembly. Disconnect refrigerant lines from condenser and receiver-drier. Remove refrigerant lines from condenser and plug openings. Remove condenser.

Installation – To install, reverse removal procedure. When assembling connections, use new "O" rings coated with refrigerant oil. If installing new condenser, add 2.5 ounces of refrigerant oil to system. Evacuate, recharge and leak test system.

RECEIVER-DRIER

Removal – Discharge A/C system using approved refrigerant recovery/recycling equipment. Remove front grille to access receiver-drier. Disconnect dual-pressure switch connector. Disconnect A/C lines from receiver-drier, and plug openings. Remove screws and receiver-drier.

Installation – To install, reverse removal procedure. When assembling connections, use new "O" rings coated with refrigerant oil. If installing new receiver-drier, add .2 ounce of refrigerant oil. Evacuate, recharge and leak test system.

TORQUE SPECIFICATIONS

TORQUE SPECIFICATIONS

Application	Ft. Lbs. (N.m)
A/C Compressor Bolts	33-44 (45-60)
Compressor Bracket Bolts	33-44 (45-60)

1993 MANUAL A/C-HEATER SYSTEMS
Pathfinder & Pickup (Cont.)

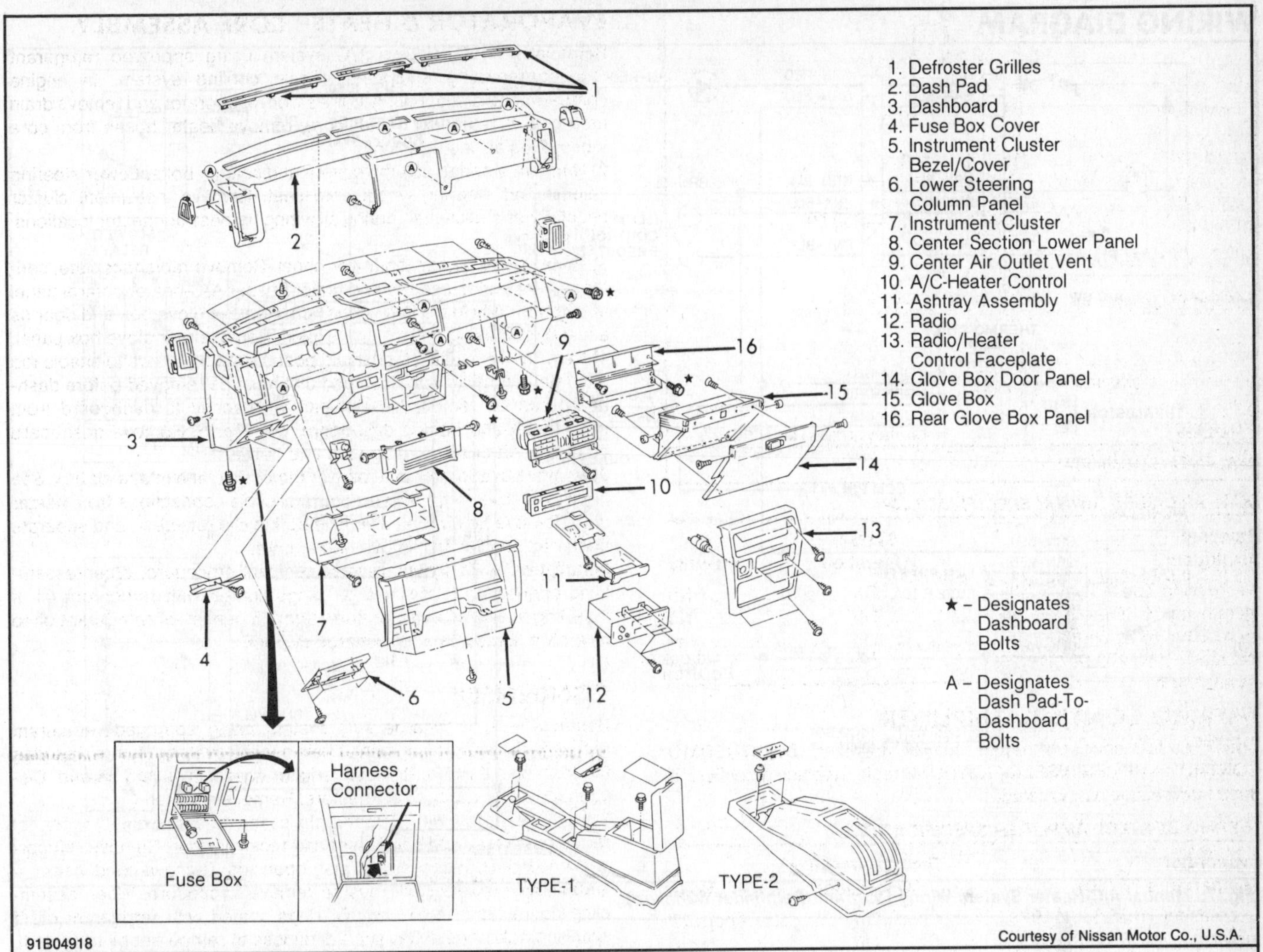

1. Defroster Grilles
2. Dash Pad
3. Dashboard
4. Fuse Box Cover
5. Instrument Cluster Bezel/Cover
6. Lower Steering Column Panel
7. Instrument Cluster
8. Center Section Lower Panel
9. Center Air Outlet Vent
10. A/C-Heater Control
11. Ashtray Assembly
12. Radio
13. Radio/Heater Control Faceplate
14. Glove Box Door Panel
15. Glove Box
16. Rear Glove Box Panel

★ - Designates Dashboard Bolts

A - Designates Dash Pad-To-Dashboard Bolts

Fuse Box

Harness Connector

TYPE-1

TYPE-2

91B04918

Courtesy of Nissan Motor Co., U.S.A.

Fig. 5: Removing Dashboard For Access To Evaporator & Heater Core

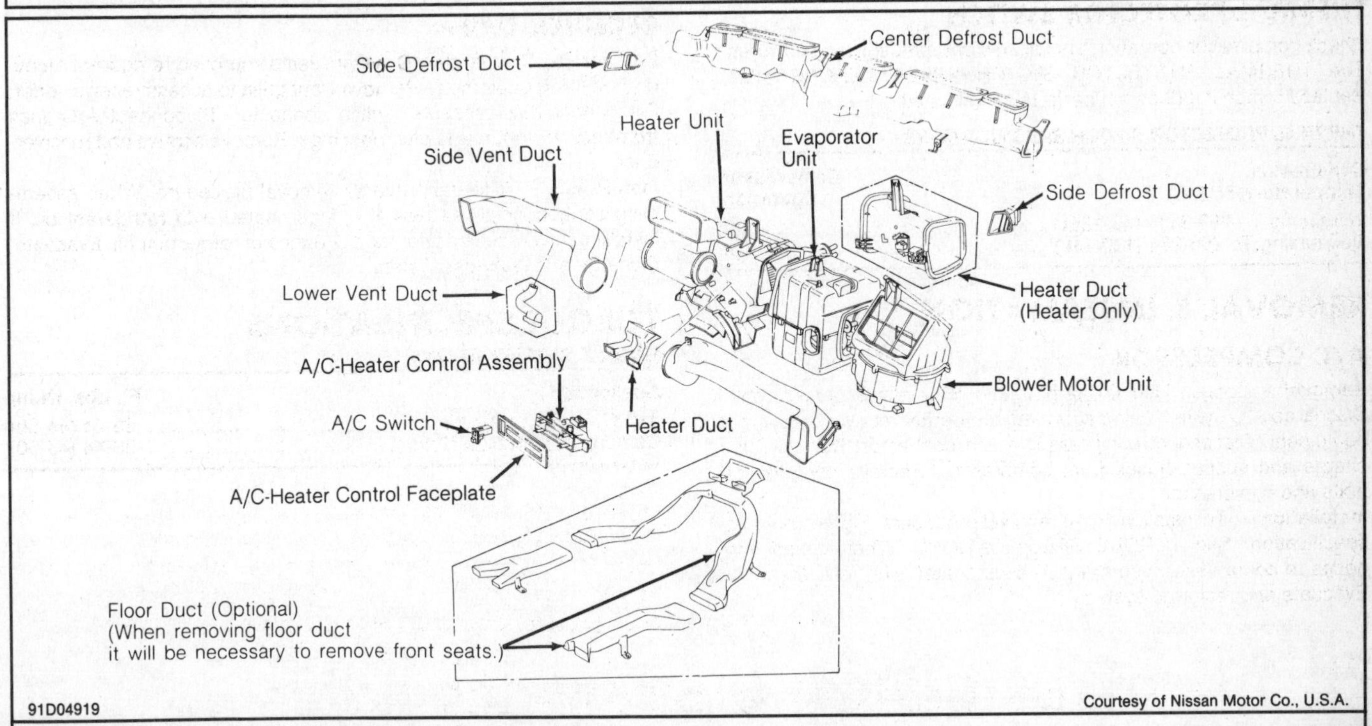
Center Defrost Duct
Side Defrost Duct
Heater Unit
Evaporator Unit
Side Vent Duct
Side Defrost Duct
Heater Duct (Heater Only)
Lower Vent Duct
A/C-Heater Control Assembly
Blower Motor Unit
A/C Switch
Heater Duct
A/C-Heater Control Faceplate
Floor Duct (Optional)
(When removing floor duct
it will be necessary to remove front seats.)
91D04919
Courtesy of Nissan Motor Co., U.S.A.

Fig. 6: Exploded View Of A/C-Heater System Components

1993 MANUAL A/C-HEATER SYSTEMS
Pathfinder & Pickup (Cont.)

WIRING DIAGRAM

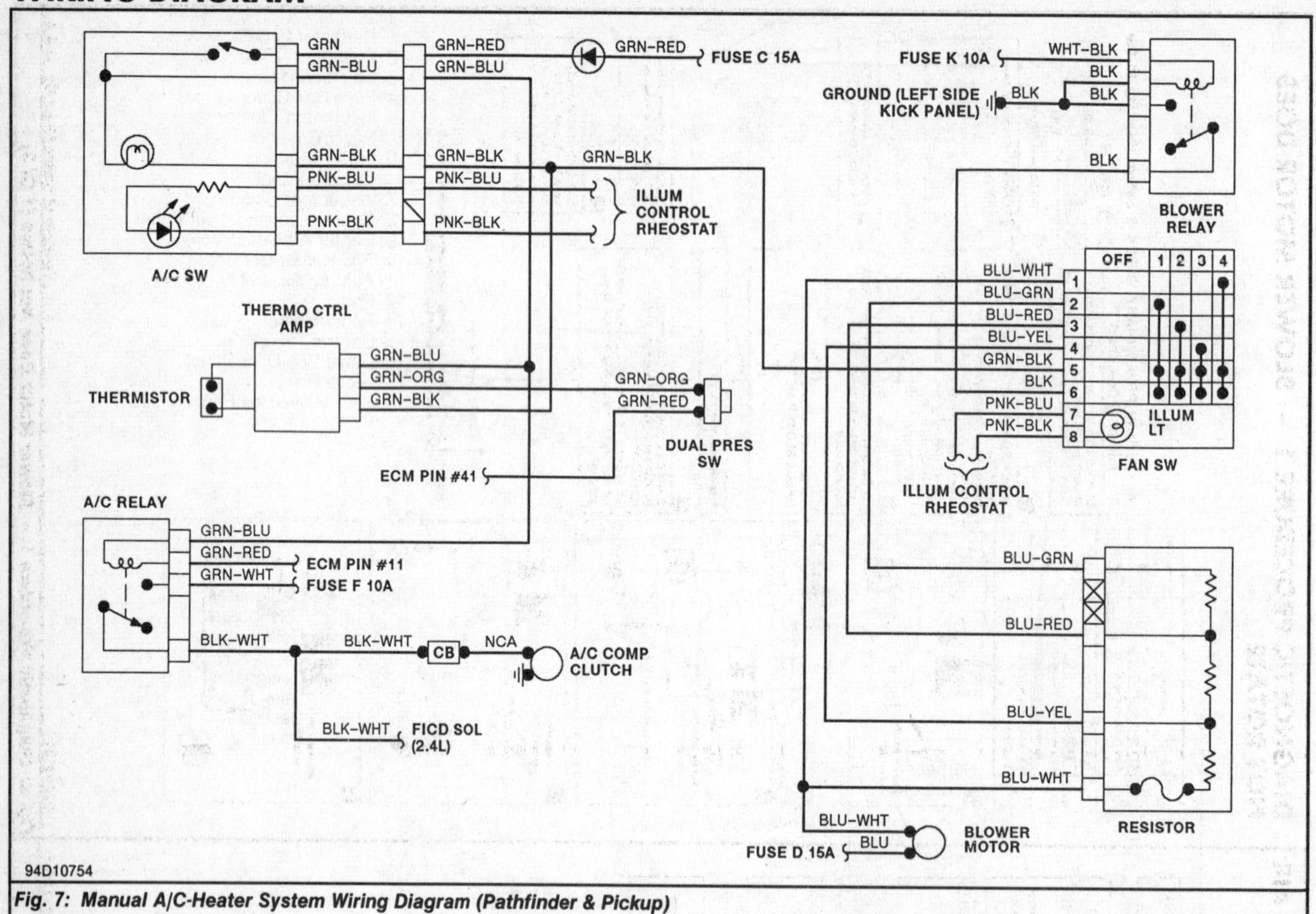
GRN
GRN-BLU
GRN-RED
GRN-BLU
GRN-RED
FUSE C 15A
GRN-BLK
PNK-BLU
PNK-BLK
GRN-BLK
PNK-BLU
PNK-BLK
GRN-BLK
ILLUM CONTROL RHEOSTAT
A/C SW
THERMO CTRL AMP
THERMISTOR
GRN-BLU
GRN-ORG
GRN-BLK
GRN-ORG
GRN-RED
DUAL PRES SW
ECM PIN #41
A/C RELAY
GRN-BLU
GRN-RED
GRN-WHT
ECM PIN #11
FUSE F 10A
BLK-WHT
BLK-WHT
CB
NCA
A/C COMP CLUTCH
BLK-WHT
FICD SOL (2.4L)
FUSE K 10A
WHT-BLK
BLK
GROUND (LEFT SIDE KICK PANEL)
BLK
BLK
BLK
BLOWER RELAY
OFF
1
2
3
4
BLU-WHT
BLU-GRN
BLU-RED
BLU-YEL
GRN-BLK
BLK
PNK-BLU
PNK-BLK
5
6
7
8
ILLUM LT
FAN SW
ILLUM CONTROL RHEOSTAT
BLU-GRN
BLU-RED
BLU-YEL
BLU-WHT
RESISTOR
BLU-WHT
BLU
FUSE D 15A
BLOWER MOTOR
94D10754

Fig. 7: Manual A/C-Heater System Wiring Diagram (Pathfinder & Pickup)

1993 MANUAL A/C-HEATER SYSTEMS
Trouble Shooting – Pathfinder & Pickup

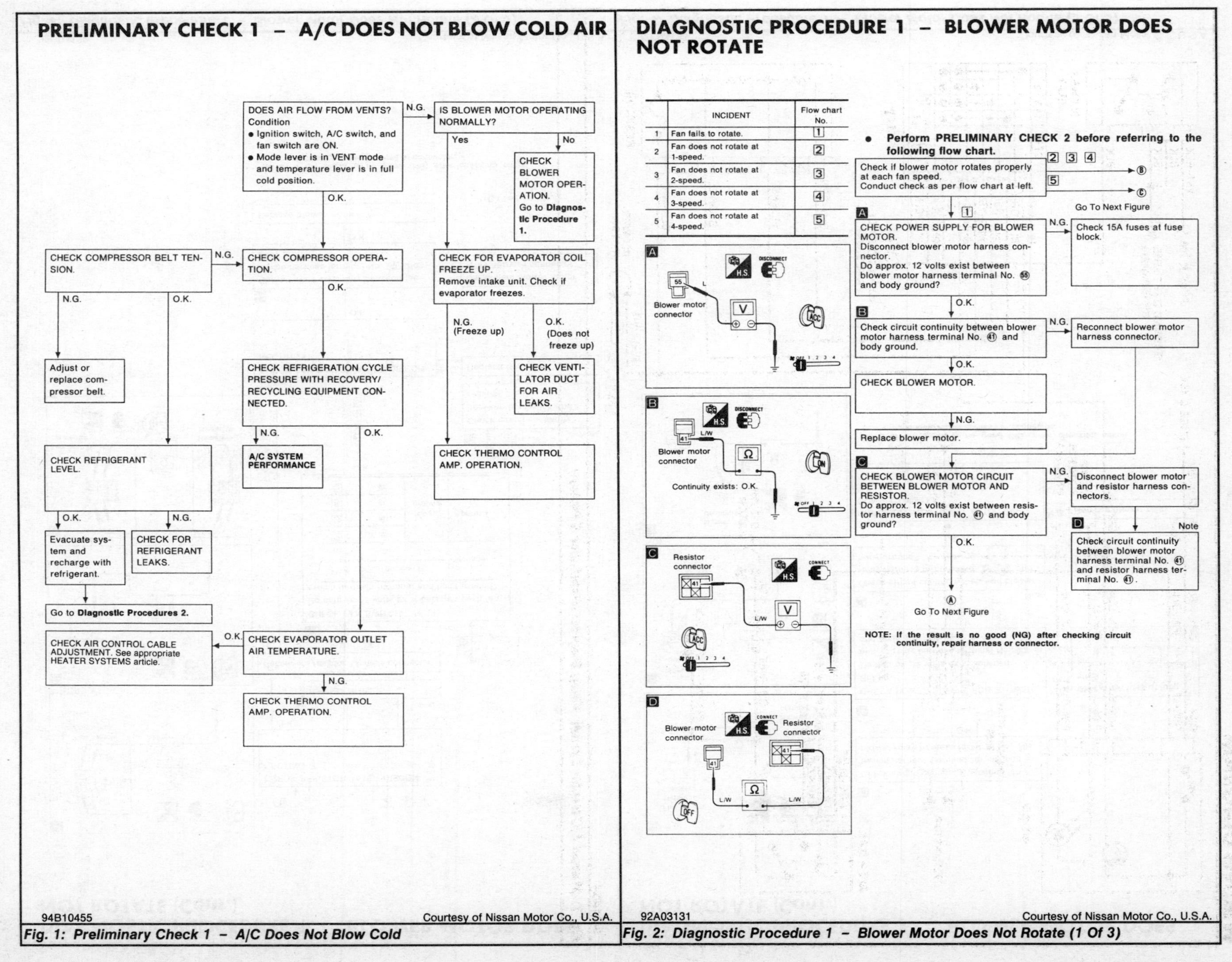
PRELIMINARY CHECK 1 – A/C DOES NOT BLOW COLD AIR
DOES AIR FLOW FROM VENTS? Condition
• Ignition switch, A/C switch, and fan switch are ON.
• Mode lever is in VENT mode and temperature lever is in full cold position.
N.G.
IS BLOWER MOTOR OPERATING NORMALLY?
Yes
No
CHECK BLOWER MOTOR OPERATION. Go to Diagnostic Procedure 1.
O.K.
CHECK COMPRESSOR BELT TENSION.
N.G.
CHECK COMPRESSOR OPERATION.
CHECK FOR EVAPORATOR COIL FREEZE UP. Remove intake unit. Check if evaporator freezes.
N.G.
O.K.
Adjust or replace compressor belt.
N.G. (Freeze up)
O.K. (Does not freeze up)
CHECK REFRIGERATION CYCLE PRESSURE WITH RECOVERY/ RECYCLING EQUIPMENT CONNECTED.
CHECK VENTILATOR DUCT FOR AIR LEAKS.
N.G.
O.K.
A/C SYSTEM PERFORMANCE
CHECK REFRIGERANT LEVEL.
CHECK THERMO CONTROL AMP. OPERATION.
O.K.
N.G.
Evacuate system and recharge with refrigerant.
CHECK FOR REFRIGERANT LEAKS.
Go to Diagnostic Procedures 2.
CHECK AIR CONTROL CABLE ADJUSTMENT. See appropriate HEATER SYSTEMS article.
O.K.
CHECK EVAPORATOR OUTLET AIR TEMPERATURE.
N.G.
CHECK THERMO CONTROL AMP. OPERATION.
94B10455
Courtesy of Nissan Motor Co., U.S.A.
DIAGNOSTIC PROCEDURE 1 – BLOWER MOTOR DOES NOT ROTATE
• Perform PRELIMINARY CHECK 2 before referring to the following flow chart.
Check if blower motor rotates properly at each fan speed. Conduct check as per flow chart at left.
2 3 4
5
B
C
Go To Next Figure
1
A
CHECK POWER SUPPLY FOR BLOWER MOTOR. Disconnect blower motor harness connector. Do approx. 12 volts exist between blower motor harness terminal No. 55 and body ground?
N.G.
Check 15A fuses at fuse block.
O.K.
B
Check circuit continuity between blower motor harness terminal No. 41 and body ground.
N.G.
Reconnect blower motor harness connector.
O.K.
CHECK BLOWER MOTOR.
N.G.
Replace blower motor.
C
CHECK BLOWER MOTOR CIRCUIT BETWEEN BLOWER MOTOR AND RESISTOR. Do approx. 12 volts exist between resistor harness terminal No. 41 and body ground?
N.G.
Disconnect blower motor and resistor harness connectors.
D
Note
Check circuit continuity between blower motor harness terminal No. 41 and resistor harness terminal No. 41.
O.K.
A
Go To Next Figure
NOTE: If the result is no good (NG) after checking circuit continuity, repair harness or connector.
A
Blower motor connector
55
L
DISCONNECT
H.S.
V
ACC
OFF 1 2 3 4
B
DISCONNECT
H.S.
41
L/W
Blower motor connector
Ω
ON
Continuity exists: O.K.
C
Resistor connector
41
CONNECT
H.S.
V
L/W
ACC
OFF 1 2 3 4
D
Blower motor connector
CONNECT
H.S.
Resistor connector
41
Ω
L/W
L/W
OFF
92A03131
Courtesy of Nissan Motor Co., U.S.A.

	INCIDENT	Flow chart No.
1	Fan fails to rotate.	1
2	Fan does not rotate at 1-speed.	2
3	Fan does not rotate at 2-speed.	3
4	Fan does not rotate at 3-speed.	4
5	Fan does not rotate at 4-speed.	5

Fig. 1: Preliminary Check 1 – A/C Does Not Blow Cold

Fig. 2: Diagnostic Procedure 1 – Blower Motor Does Not Rotate (1 Of 3)

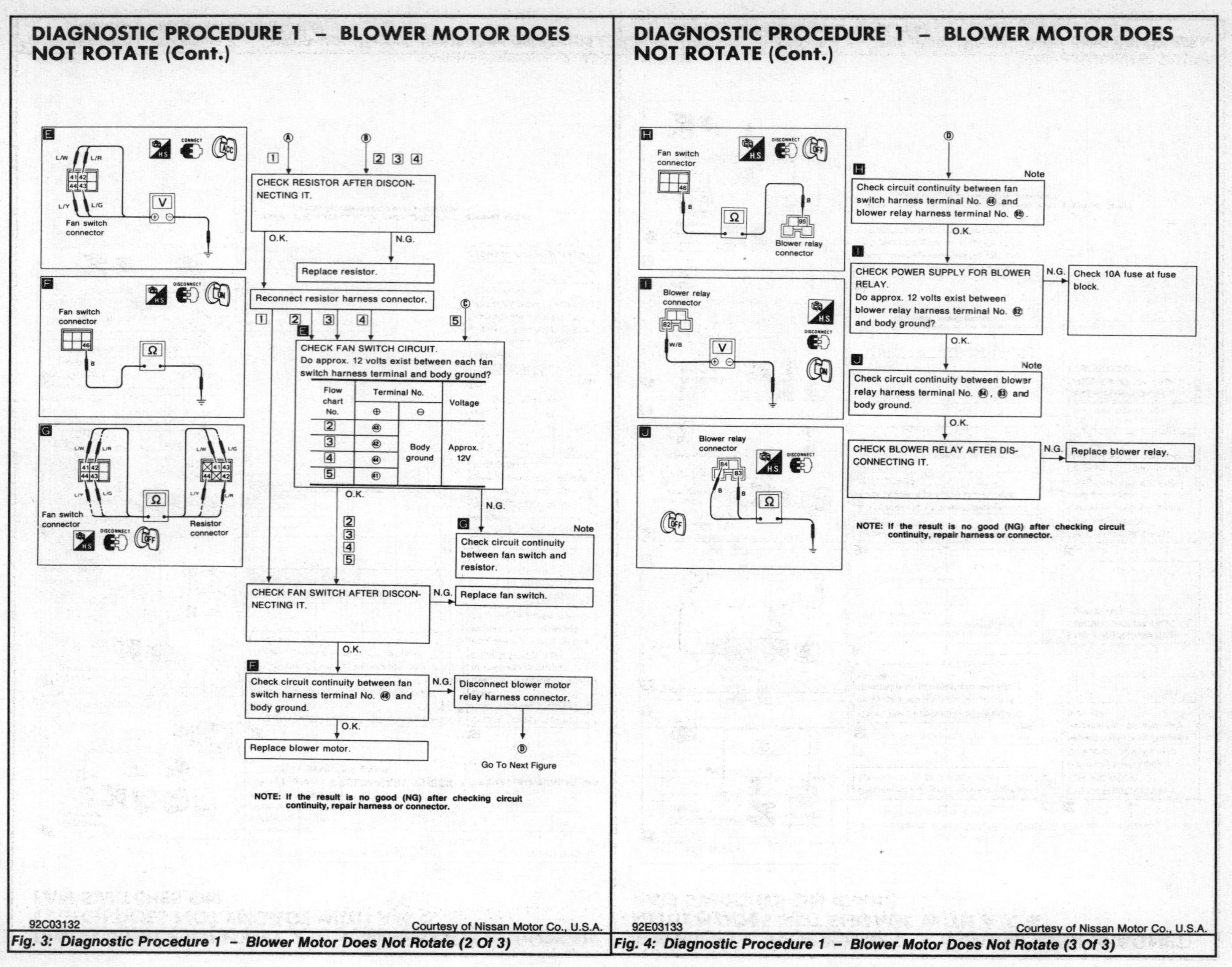
DIAGNOSTIC PROCEDURE 1 – BLOWER MOTOR DOES NOT ROTATE (Cont.)
E
L/W
L/R
41 42
44 43
L/Y
L/G
Fan switch connector
V
CONNECT
ACC
F
Fan switch connector
46
B
Ω
DISCONNECT
ON
G
Fan switch connector
Resistor connector
DISCONNECT
OFF
A
B
1
2 3 4
CHECK RESISTOR AFTER DISCONNECTING IT.
O.K.
N.G.
Replace resistor.
Reconnect resistor harness connector.
C
1
2
3
4
5
E
CHECK FAN SWITCH CIRCUIT.
Do approx. 12 volts exist between each fan switch harness terminal and body ground?
Flow chart No.
Terminal No.
Voltage
⊕
⊖
2
43
3
42
4
44
5
41
Body ground
Approx. 12V
O.K.
N.G.
2
3
4
5
G
Note
Check circuit continuity between fan switch and resistor.
CHECK FAN SWITCH AFTER DISCONNECTING IT.
N.G.
Replace fan switch.
O.K.
F
Check circuit continuity between fan switch harness terminal No. 46 and body ground.
N.G.
Disconnect blower motor relay harness connector.
O.K.
Replace blower motor.
D
Go To Next Figure
NOTE: If the result is no good (NG) after checking circuit continuity, repair harness or connector.
92C03132
Courtesy of Nissan Motor Co., U.S.A.
DIAGNOSTIC PROCEDURE 1 – BLOWER MOTOR DOES NOT ROTATE (Cont.)
H
Fan switch connector
46
B
Ω
95
Blower relay connector
DISCONNECT
OFF
I
Blower relay connector
82
W/B
V
DISCONNECT
ON
J
Blower relay connector
84
83
B
Ω
DISCONNECT
OFF
D
H
Note
Check circuit continuity between fan switch harness terminal No. 46 and blower relay harness terminal No. 95.
O.K.
I
CHECK POWER SUPPLY FOR BLOWER RELAY.
Do approx. 12 volts exist between blower relay harness terminal No. 82 and body ground?
N.G.
Check 10A fuse at fuse block.
O.K.
J
Note
Check circuit continuity between blower relay harness terminal No. 84, 83 and body ground.
O.K.
CHECK BLOWER RELAY AFTER DISCONNECTING IT.
N.G.
Replace blower relay.
NOTE: If the result is no good (NG) after checking circuit continuity, repair harness or connector.
92E03133
Courtesy of Nissan Motor Co., U.S.A.

Fig. 3: Diagnostic Procedure 1 – Blower Motor Does Not Rotate (2 Of 3)

Fig. 4: Diagnostic Procedure 1 – Blower Motor Does Not Rotate (3 Of 3)

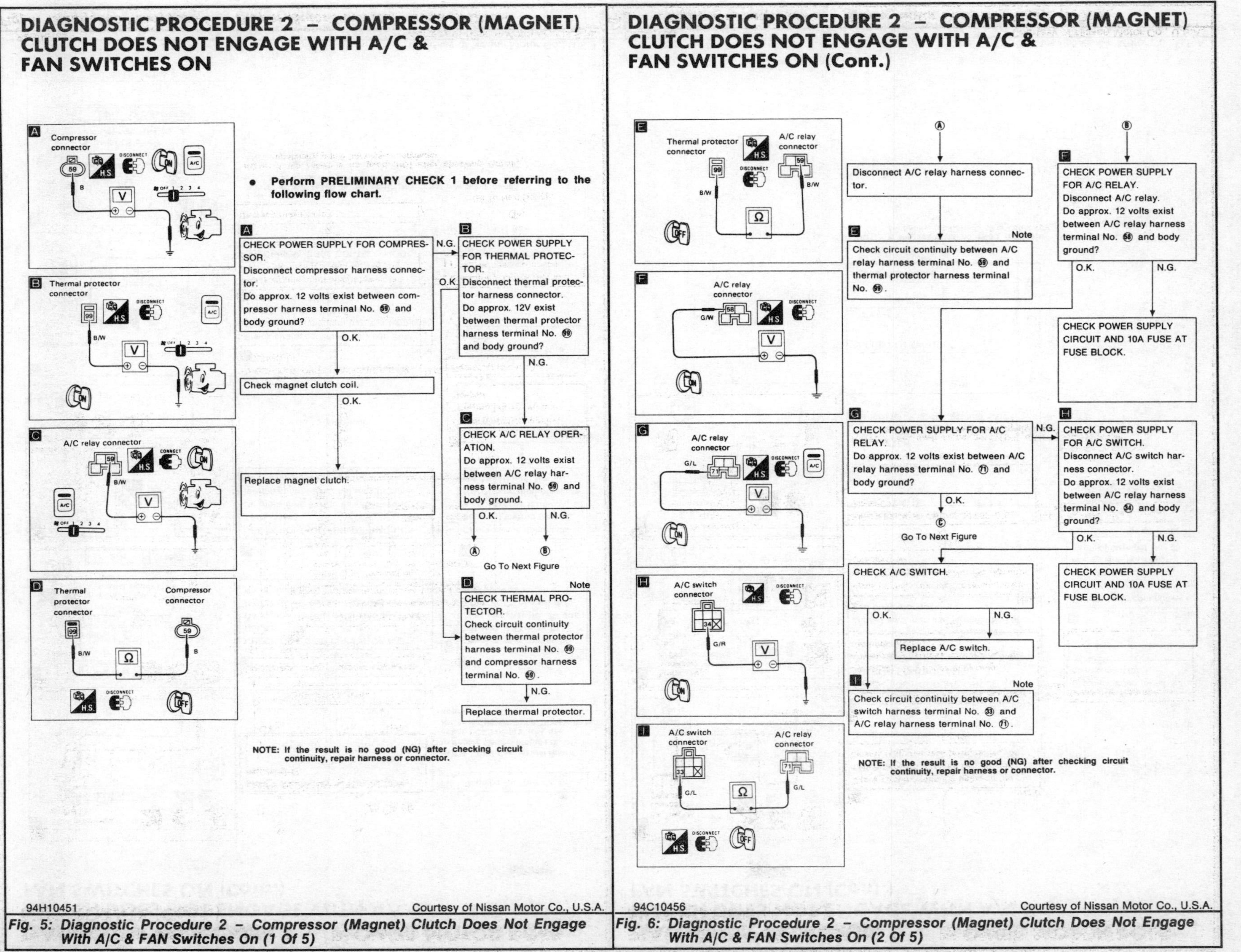
DIAGNOSTIC PROCEDURE 2 – COMPRESSOR (MAGNET) CLUTCH DOES NOT ENGAGE WITH A/C & FAN SWITCHES ON
A Compressor connector
59
B
V
B Thermal protector connector
99
B/W
V
C A/C relay connector
59
B/W
V
D Thermal protector connector
Compressor connector
99
59
B/W
B
Ω
• Perform PRELIMINARY CHECK 1 before referring to the following flow chart.
A CHECK POWER SUPPLY FOR COMPRESSOR.
Disconnect compressor harness connector.
Do approx. 12 volts exist between compressor harness terminal No. 59 and body ground?
O.K.
Check magnet clutch coil.
O.K.
Replace magnet clutch.
N.G.
O.K.
B CHECK POWER SUPPLY FOR THERMAL PROTECTOR.
Disconnect thermal protector harness connector.
Do approx. 12V exist between thermal protector harness terminal No. 99 and body ground?
N.G.
C CHECK A/C RELAY OPERATION.
Do approx. 12 volts exist between A/C relay harness terminal No. 59 and body ground.
O.K.
N.G.
A
B
Go To Next Figure
D CHECK THERMAL PROTECTOR.
Note
Check circuit continuity between thermal protector harness terminal No. 99 and compressor harness terminal No. 59.
N.G.
Replace thermal protector.
NOTE: If the result is no good (NG) after checking circuit continuity, repair harness or connector.
94H10451
Courtesy of Nissan Motor Co., U.S.A.
DIAGNOSTIC PROCEDURE 2 – COMPRESSOR (MAGNET) CLUTCH DOES NOT ENGAGE WITH A/C & FAN SWITCHES ON (Cont.)
E Thermal protector connector
A/C relay connector
99
59
B/W
B/W
Ω
F A/C relay connector
58
G/W
V
G A/C relay connector
71
G/L
V
H A/C switch connector
34
G/R
V
I A/C switch connector
A/C relay connector
33
71
G/L
G/L
Ω
A
Disconnect A/C relay harness connector.
E Check circuit continuity between A/C relay harness terminal No. 59 and thermal protector harness terminal No. 99.
Note
B
F CHECK POWER SUPPLY FOR A/C RELAY.
Disconnect A/C relay.
Do approx. 12 volts exist between A/C relay harness terminal No. 58 and body ground?
O.K.
N.G.
CHECK POWER SUPPLY CIRCUIT AND 10A FUSE AT FUSE BLOCK.
G CHECK POWER SUPPLY FOR A/C RELAY.
Do approx. 12 volts exist between A/C relay harness terminal No. 71 and body ground?
N.G.
O.K.
C
Go To Next Figure
H CHECK POWER SUPPLY FOR A/C SWITCH.
Disconnect A/C switch harness connector.
Do approx. 12 volts exist between A/C relay harness terminal No. 34 and body ground?
O.K.
N.G.
CHECK A/C SWITCH.
O.K.
N.G.
Replace A/C switch.
CHECK POWER SUPPLY CIRCUIT AND 10A FUSE AT FUSE BLOCK.
I Check circuit continuity between A/C switch harness terminal No. 33 and A/C relay harness terminal No. 71.
Note
NOTE: If the result is no good (NG) after checking circuit continuity, repair harness or connector.
94C10456
Courtesy of Nissan Motor Co., U.S.A.

Fig. 5: Diagnostic Procedure 2 – Compressor (Magnet) Clutch Does Not Engage With A/C & FAN Switches On (1 Of 5)

Fig. 6: Diagnostic Procedure 2 – Compressor (Magnet) Clutch Does Not Engage With A/C & FAN Switches On (2 Of 5)

1993 MANUAL A/C-HEATER SYSTEMS
Trouble Shooting – Pathfinder & Pickup (Cont.)

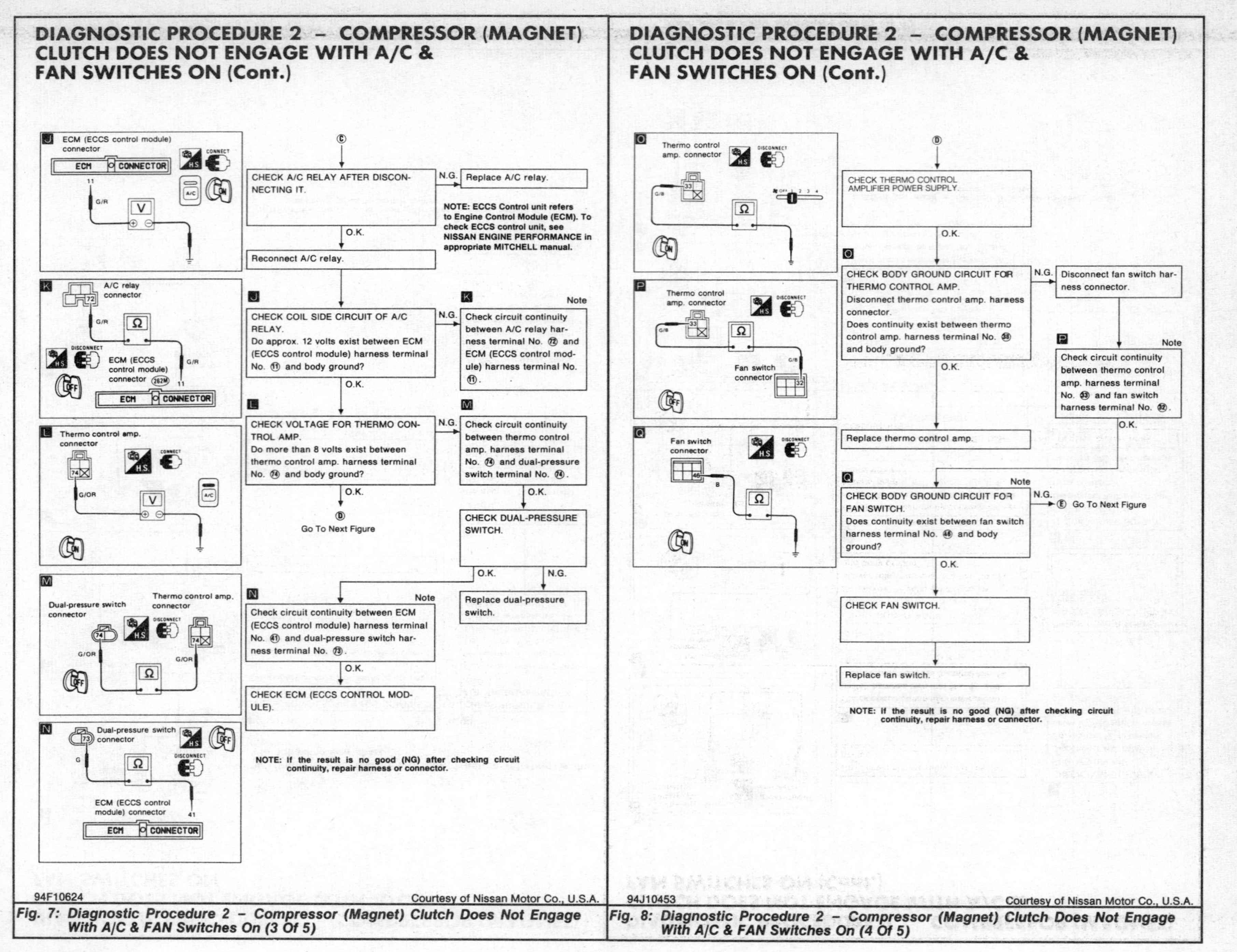
DIAGNOSTIC PROCEDURE 2 – COMPRESSOR (MAGNET) CLUTCH DOES NOT ENGAGE WITH A/C & FAN SWITCHES ON (Cont.)
J ECM (ECCS control module) connector
ECM CONNECTOR
11
G/R
V
CONNECT
H.S.
A/C
ON
K A/C relay connector
72
G/R
Ω
DISCONNECT
H.S.
ECM (ECCS control module) connector 262M
G/R
11
OFF
ECM CONNECTOR
L Thermo control amp. connector
74
G/OR
V
CONNECT
H.S.
A/C
ON
M Dual-pressure switch connector
Thermo control amp. connector
74
G/OR
DISCONNECT
H.S.
74
G/OR
Ω
OFF
N Dual-pressure switch connector
73
G
Ω
H.S.
OFF
DISCONNECT
ECM (ECCS control module) connector
41
ECM CONNECTOR
C
CHECK A/C RELAY AFTER DISCONNECTING IT.
N.G.
Replace A/C relay.
NOTE: ECCS Control unit refers to Engine Control Module (ECM). To check ECCS control unit, see NISSAN ENGINE PERFORMANCE in appropriate MITCHELL manual.
O.K.
Reconnect A/C relay.
J
CHECK COIL SIDE CIRCUIT OF A/C RELAY.
Do approx. 12 volts exist between ECM (ECCS control module) harness terminal No. ⑪ and body ground?
N.G.
K
Note
Check circuit continuity between A/C relay harness terminal No. ⑫ and ECM (ECCS control module) harness terminal No. ⑪.
O.K.
L
CHECK VOLTAGE FOR THERMO CONTROL AMP.
Do more than 8 volts exist between thermo control amp. harness terminal No. ⑭ and body ground?
N.G.
M
Check circuit continuity between thermo control amp. harness terminal No. ⑭ and dual-pressure switch terminal No. ⑭.
O.K.
D
Go To Next Figure
O.K.
CHECK DUAL-PRESSURE SWITCH.
O.K.
N.G.
Replace dual-pressure switch.
N
Note
Check circuit continuity between ECM (ECCS control module) harness terminal No. ㊶ and dual-pressure switch harness terminal No. ⑬.
O.K.
CHECK ECM (ECCS CONTROL MODULE).
NOTE: If the result is no good (NG) after checking circuit continuity, repair harness or connector.
94F10624
Courtesy of Nissan Motor Co., U.S.A.
DIAGNOSTIC PROCEDURE 2 – COMPRESSOR (MAGNET) CLUTCH DOES NOT ENGAGE WITH A/C & FAN SWITCHES ON (Cont.)
O Thermo control amp. connector
H.S.
DISCONNECT
33
G/B
Ω
OFF 1 2 3 4
ON
P Thermo control amp. connector
H.S.
DISCONNECT
33
G/B
Ω
G/B
Fan switch connector
32
OFF
Q Fan switch connector
H.S.
DISCONNECT
46
B
Ω
ON
D
CHECK THERMO CONTROL AMPLIFIER POWER SUPPLY.
O.K.
O
CHECK BODY GROUND CIRCUIT FOR THERMO CONTROL AMP.
Disconnect thermo control amp. harness connector.
Does continuity exist between thermo control amp. harness terminal No. ㊳ and body ground?
N.G.
Disconnect fan switch harness connector.
P
Note
Check circuit continuity between thermo control amp. harness terminal No. ㊳ and fan switch harness terminal No. ㉜.
O.K.
O.K.
Replace thermo control amp.
Q
Note
CHECK BODY GROUND CIRCUIT FOR FAN SWITCH.
Does continuity exist between fan switch harness terminal No. ㊻ and body ground?
N.G.
E Go To Next Figure
O.K.
CHECK FAN SWITCH.
Replace fan switch.
NOTE: If the result is no good (NG) after checking circuit continuity, repair harness or connector.
94J10453
Courtesy of Nissan Motor Co., U.S.A.

Fig. 7: Diagnostic Procedure 2 – Compressor (Magnet) Clutch Does Not Engage With A/C & FAN Switches On (3 Of 5)

Fig. 8: Diagnostic Procedure 2 – Compressor (Magnet) Clutch Does Not Engage With A/C & FAN Switches On (4 Of 5)

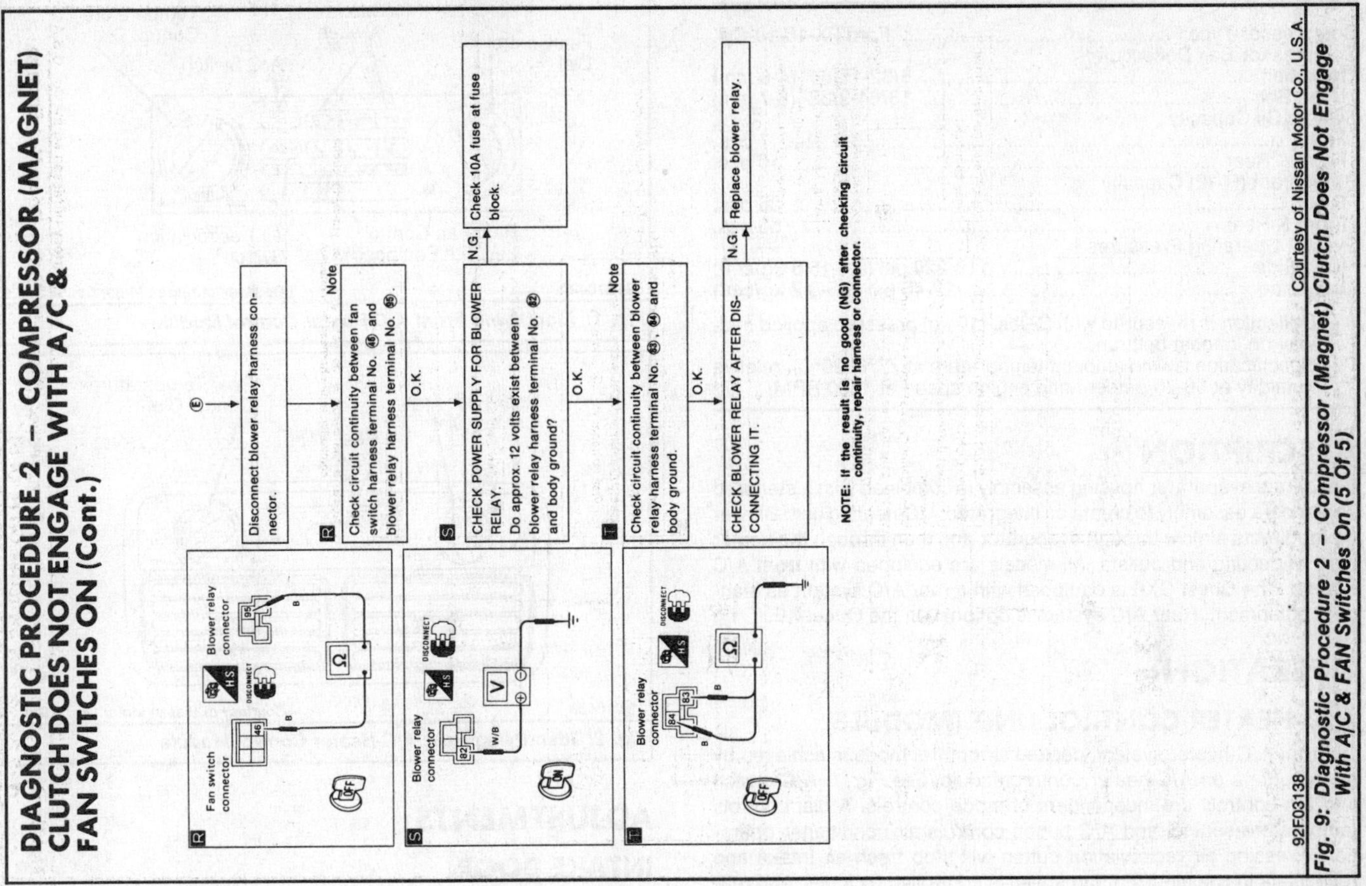
DIAGNOSTIC PROCEDURE 2 – COMPRESSOR (MAGNET) CLUTCH DOES NOT ENGAGE WITH A/C & FAN SWITCHES ON (Cont.)
R
Fan switch connector
48
Blower relay connector
95
DISCONNECT
H.S.
B
Ω
OFF
S
Blower relay connector
82
W/B
V
DISCONNECT
H.S.
ON
T
Blower relay connector
84
83
B
Ω
DISCONNECT
H.S.
OFF
E
Disconnect blower relay harness connector.
R
Check circuit continuity between fan switch harness terminal No. 48 and blower relay harness terminal No. 95.
Note
O.K.
S
CHECK POWER SUPPLY FOR BLOWER RELAY.
Do approx. 12 volts exist between blower relay harness terminal No. 82 and body ground?
N.G.
Check 10A fuse at fuse block.
O.K.
T
Check circuit continuity between blower relay harness terminal No. 83, 84 and body ground.
Note
O.K.
CHECK BLOWER RELAY AFTER DISCONNECTING IT.
N.G.
Replace blower relay.
NOTE: If the result is no good (NG) after checking circuit continuity, repair harness or connector.
92F03138
Courtesy of Nissan Motor Co., U.S.A.

Fig. 9: Diagnostic Procedure 2 – Compressor (Magnet) Clutch Does Not Engage With A/C & FAN Switches On (5 Of 5)

1993 MANUAL A/C-HEATER SYSTEMS
Quest

SPECIFICATIONS

Compressor Type	Ford FX-15 10-Cyl.
Compressor Belt Deflection [1]	
New Belt	5/32-15/64" (4-6 mm)
Used Belt	13/64-9/32" (5-7 mm)
System Oil Capacity	
Front	7 ozs.
Front & Rear	10 ozs.
Refrigerant (R-12) Capacity	
Front	36 ozs.
Front & Rear	56 ozs.
System Operating Pressures [2]	
High Side	119-220 psi (8.4-15.5 kg/cm²)
Low Side	22-46 psi (1.5-3.2 kg/cm²)

[1] – Deflection is measured with 22 lbs. (10 kg) pressure applied midway on longest belt run.

[2] – Specification is with ambient temperature at 77°F (25°C), relative humidity at 50-70 percent and engine speed at 1500 RPM.

DESCRIPTION

A separate evaporator housing assembly is combined with a standard heater core assembly to create an integrated A/C-heating unit. Blower motor directs airflow through evaporator and then through the heater core to ducting and outlets. All models are equipped with front A/C system. The Quest GXE is equipped with a rear A/C system as standard equipment. Rear A/C system is optional on the Quest XE.

OPERATION

A/C-HEATER CONTROL UNIT (MODULE)

On front A/C-heater system, desired air control mode is achieved by push buttons on A/C-heater control module. *See Fig. 1.* A/C switch and fan controls are independent of mode controls. A dial controls temperature setting, and A/C button controls air conditioner operation. Pressing air recirculation button will stop fresh air intake and recirculate inside air. Front fan speed is controlled by a dial, and rear fan speed (if equipped with rear A/C) is controlled by a lever.

On models equipped with rear A/C-heater system, fan speed and temperature settings are controlled by dials. *See Fig. 2.* Upper and lower vent selection is controlled by a vent switch. Rear A/C-heater system can be turned off from front controls.

If rear fan control lever on front A/C-heater control module is set to OFF, rear A/C-heater system will be off. If rear fan control lever is set to any fan speed, air will be discharged from rear vents at the corresponding speed. When rear fan control lever is set to REAR, rear A/C-heater system can be controlled by rear A/C-heater control module. Rear A/C system will only operate when front A/C system is on.

FAST IDLE CONTROL DEVICE (FICD)

When A/C system is energized, the engine control module signals FICD to adjust Auxiliary Air Control (AAC) valve to by-pass additional air and increase idle speed. This higher idle speed allows engine to idle smoothly during compressor operation.

HIGH-PRESSURE SWITCH

The high-pressure switch protects A/C system from high pressure build-up (due to restriction, overcharge or compressor malfunction). High-pressure switch is located at rear of compressor. *See Fig. 4.* If high pressure exceeds 404 psi (28.4 kg/cm²), high-pressure switch opens and interrupts compressor clutch operation.

LOW-PRESSURE SWITCH

Low-pressure switch is located on top of accumulator. *See Fig. 4.* A/C system is protected against excessively low system pressure. If low pressure drops to 24 psi (1.7 kg/cm²) or less, low-pressure switch opens and interrupts compressor clutch operation.

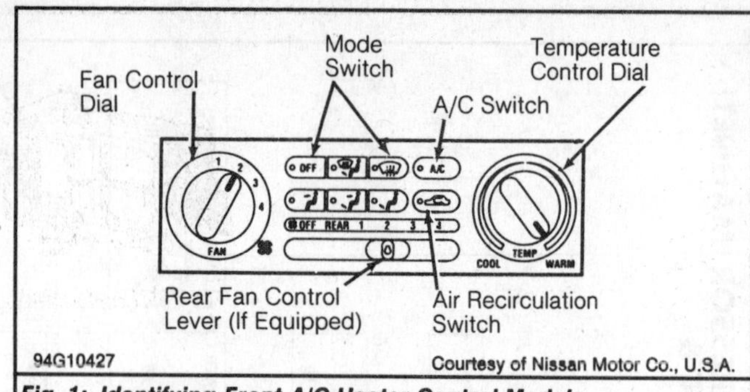
Fan Control Dial
Mode Switch
Temperature Control Dial
A/C Switch
OFF
A/C
OFF REAR 1 2 3
FAN
COOL
TEMP
WARM
Rear Fan Control Lever (If Equipped)
Air Recirculation Switch
94G10427
Courtesy of Nissan Motor Co., U.S.A.

Fig. 1: Identifying Front A/C-Heater Control Module

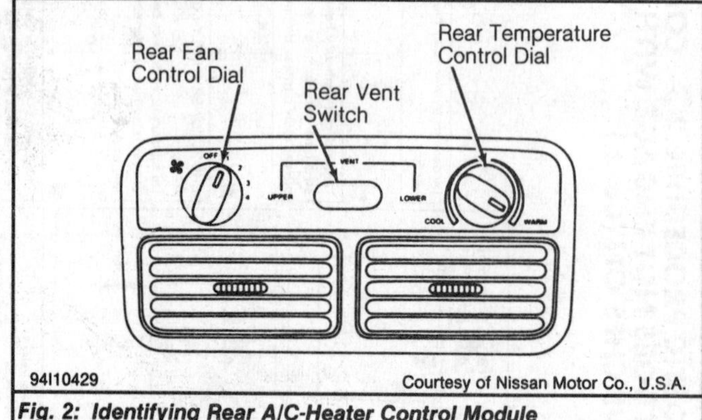
Rear Fan Control Dial
Rear Temperature Control Dial
Rear Vent Switch
OFF
VENT
UPPER
LOWER
COOL
WARM
94I10429
Courtesy of Nissan Motor Co., U.S.A.

Fig. 2: Identifying Rear A/C-Heater Control Module

ADJUSTMENTS

INTAKE DOOR

1) Turn ignition on. Ensure air recirculation button is on. Connect intake door motor connector. Install intake door lever and intake door motor. *See Fig. 3.*

2) Set intake door rod in recirculation position, and secure door rod to holder on intake door lever. Ensure intake door operates properly when air recirculation button is pressed on and off.

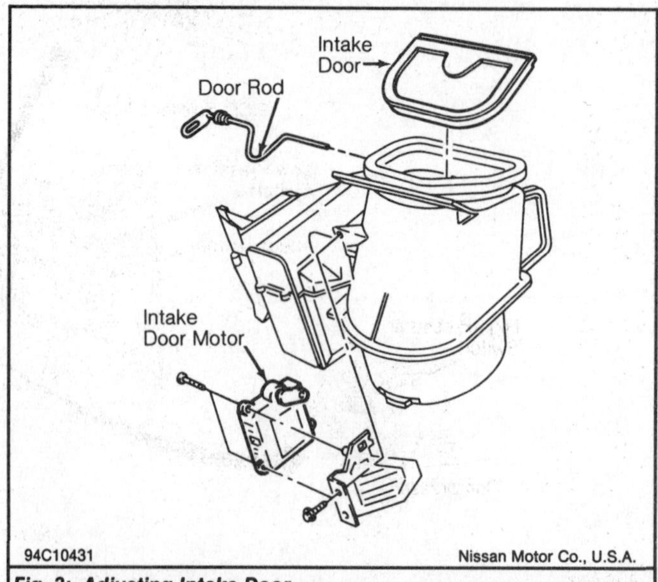
Intake Door
Door Rod
Intake Door Motor
94C10431
Nissan Motor Co., U.S.A.

Fig. 3: Adjusting Intake Door

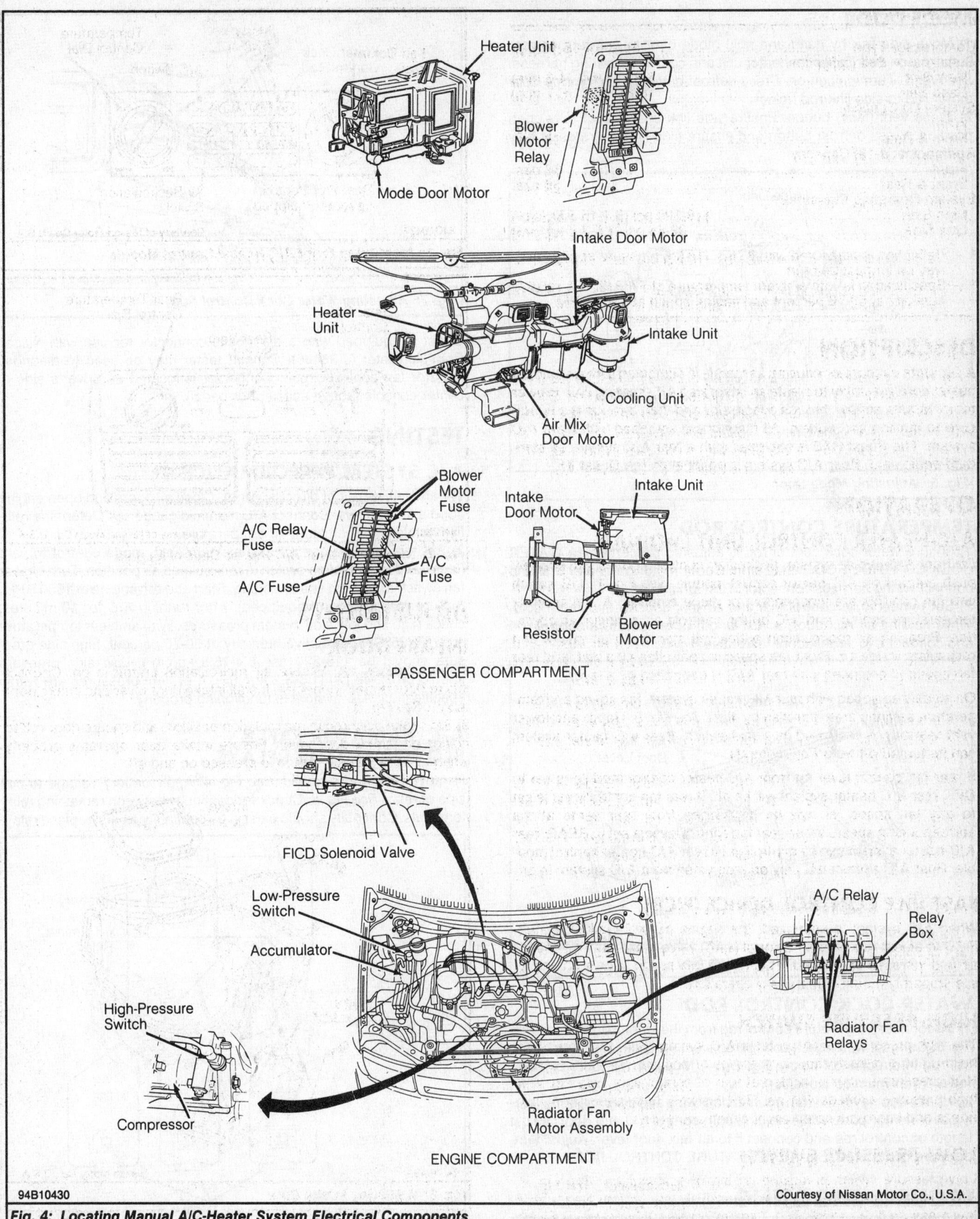

Heater Unit
Blower
Motor
Relay
Mode Door Motor
Intake Door Motor
Heater
Unit
Intake Unit
Cooling Unit
Air Mix
Door Motor
Blower
Motor
Fuse
A/C Relay
Fuse
A/C
Fuse
A/C Fuse
Intake
Door Motor
Intake Unit
Resistor
Blower
Motor
PASSENGER COMPARTMENT
FICD Solenoid Valve
Low-Pressure
Switch
Accumulator
A/C Relay
Relay
Box
High-Pressure
Switch
Radiator Fan
Relays
Compressor
Radiator Fan
Motor Assembly
ENGINE COMPARTMENT
94B10430
Courtesy of Nissan Motor Co., U.S.A.

Fig. 4: Locating Manual A/C-Heater System Electrical Components

1993 MANUAL A/C-HEATER SYSTEMS
Quest (Cont.)

MODE DOOR

1) Move side link by hand and hold mode door in defrost position. Install mode door motor on heater unit and connect to wiring harness. *See Fig. 5.* Turn ignition on. Press defrost button. Attach mode door motor rod to side link rod holder.
2) Press vent (face) button. Ensure side link operates at fully open position. Press defrost button and ensure side link operates at fully open position.

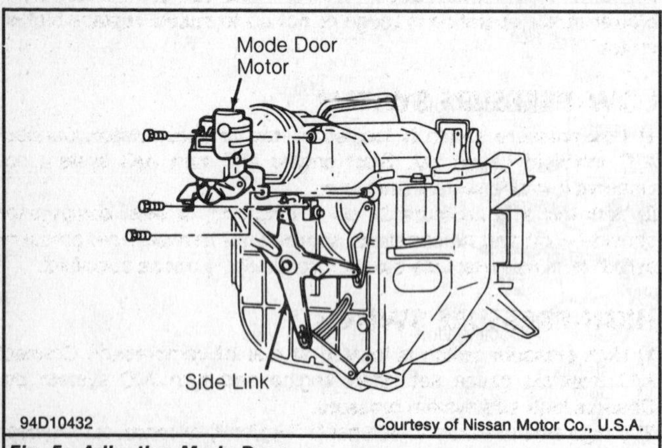
Mode Door
Motor
Side Link
94D10432
Courtesy of Nissan Motor Co., U.S.A.

Fig. 5: Adjusting Mode Door

TEMPERATURE CONTROL ROD

1) Ensure water cock control rod is adjusted properly. See WATER COCK CONTROL ROD. Install air mix door motor on heater unit and connect wiring harness connector. Turn ignition on.
2) Set temperature control dial and air mix door to maximum cold. While holding air mix door, adjust length of temperature control rod and connect it to air mix door lever. *See Fig. 6.*

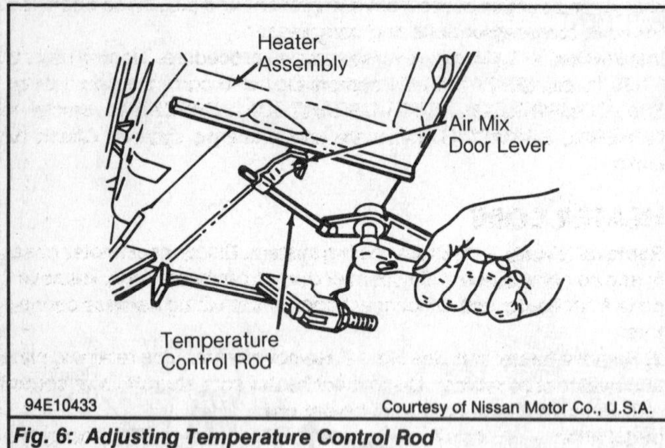
Heater
Assembly
Air Mix
Door Lever
Temperature
Control Rod
94E10433
Courtesy of Nissan Motor Co., U.S.A.

Fig. 6: Adjusting Temperature Control Rod

WATER COCK CONTROL ROD

1) Disconnect temperature control rod from the air mix door lever. *See Fig. 6.* Connect water cock control rod to water cock lever. Push control rod in direction of arrow. *See Fig. 7.* Move air mix door by hand toward maximum cold position.
2) Air mix door lever will turn counterclockwise and door will completely cover heater core. While holding both control rod and door, adjust length of control rod and connect it to air mix door lever. Adjust temperature control rod. See TEMPERATURE CONTROL ROD.

TROUBLE SHOOTING

NOTE: See TROUBLE SHOOTING - QUEST charts following this article. The Engine Control Module (ECM) may be referred to as Engine Concentrated Control System (ECCS) control unit.

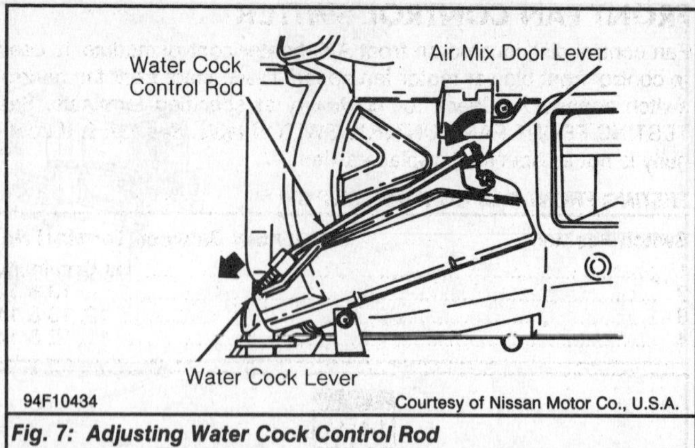
Water Cock
Control Rod
Air Mix Door Lever
Water Cock Lever
94F10434
Courtesy of Nissan Motor Co., U.S.A.

Fig. 7: Adjusting Water Cock Control Rod

Quest is equipped with a diagnostic connector for use with Nissan Consult Tester (J-38465). Consult tester may be used to diagnose radiator fan control circuit. Connector is located on driver's side of center console (above accelerator pedal).

TESTING

A/C SYSTEM PERFORMANCE

1) Park vehicle out of direct sunlight. Close all doors and open engine hood and windows. Connect A/C manifold gauge set. Determine relative humidity and ambient air temperature.
2) Set temperature control to maximum cold, mode control to vent (face), and recirculation switch to recirculated air position. Turn blower fan switch to highest speed setting. Start and run engine at 1500 RPM.
3) Turn rear A/C on (if equipped). After running A/C for 10 minutes, check high and low side system pressures. With ambient temperature at 77°F (25°C) and relative humidity at 50-70 percent, high side pressure should be 119-220 psi (8.4-15.5 kg/cm²). Low side pressure should be 22-46 psi (1.5-3.2 kg/cm²). If system pressures are within specification, A/C system is functioning properly.

A/C, RADIATOR FAN & BLOWER MOTOR RELAYS

Remove relay to be tested. *See Fig. 4.* Apply battery voltage to coil side of relay. *See Fig. 8.* Check for continuity between remaining relay terminals. Continuity should exist. If no continuity exists, replace relay.

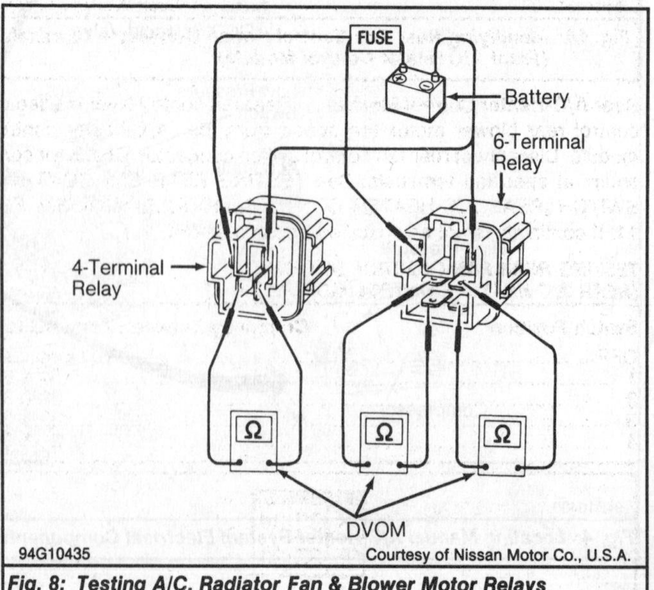
FUSE
Battery
6-Terminal
Relay
4-Terminal
Relay
Ω
Ω
Ω
DVOM
94G10435
Courtesy of Nissan Motor Co., U.S.A.

Fig. 8: Testing A/C, Radiator Fan & Blower Motor Relays

FRONT FAN CONTROL SWITCH

Fan control dial, located on front A/C-heater control module, is used to control front blower motor fan speed. Disconnect front fan control switch connector. Check for continuity at specified terminals. See TESTING FRONT FAN CONTROL SWITCH table. *See Fig. 9.* If continuity is not as specified, replace switch.

TESTING FRONT FAN CONTROL SWITCH

Switch Position	Continuity Between Terminal No.
1	No Continuity
2	13 & 14
3	12, 13 & 14
4	11, 12 & 14

14 11
12 13

94H10436 Courtesy of Nissan Motor Co., U.S.A.

Fig. 9: Identifying Front Fan Control Switch Connector

REAR FAN CONTROL SWITCH

Front A/C-Heater Control Module – Rear fan control lever is used to control rear blower motor fan speed from front A/C-heater control module. Disconnect rear fan control switch connector. Check for continuity at specified terminals. See TESTING REAR FAN CONTROL SWITCH (FRONT A/C-HEATER CONTROL MODULE) table. *See Fig. 10.* If continuity is not as specified, replace switch.

TESTING REAR FAN CONTROL SWITCH (FRONT A/C-HEATER CONTROL MODULE)

Switch Position	Continuity Between Terminal No.
OFF	No Continuity
REAR	25 & 26
1	24 & 26
2	23 & 26
3	22 & 26
4	21 & 26

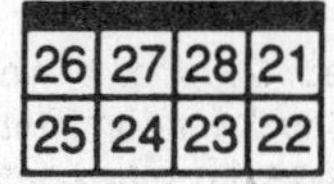

26 27 28 21
25 24 23 22

94I10437 Courtesy of Nissan Motor Co., U.S.A.

Fig. 10: Identifying Rear Fan Control Switch Connector Terminals (Front A/C-Heater Control Module)

Rear A/C-Heater Control Module – Rear fan control lever is used to control rear blower motor fan speed from rear A/C-heater control module. Disconnect rear fan control switch connector. Check for continuity at specified terminals. See TESTING REAR FAN CONTROL SWITCH (REAR A/C-HEATER CONTROL MODULE) table. *See Fig. 11.* If continuity is not as specified, replace switch.

TESTING REAR FAN CONTROL SWITCH (REAR A/C-HEATER CONTROL MODULE)

Switch Position	Continuity Between Terminal No.
OFF	No Continuity
1	34 & 35
2	33 & 35
3	32 & 35
4	31 & 35

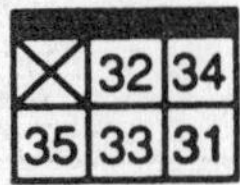

32 34
35 33 31

94J10438 Courtesy of Nissan Motor Co., U.S.A.

Fig. 11: Identifying Rear Fan Control Switch Connector Terminals (Rear A/C-Heater Control Module)

BLOWER MOTOR RESISTOR

Disconnect blower motor resistor connector. Using an ohmmeter, ensure continuity exists between resistor terminals. If continuity does not exist, replace resistor.

BLOWER MOTOR

Disconnect wiring harness at blower motor. Apply battery voltage to blower motor terminals. Ensure blower motor operation is smooth. If blower motor operation is rough or not up to speed, replace blower motor.

LOW-PRESSURE SWITCH

1) Low-pressure switch is located on top of accumulator. Connect A/C manifold gauge set. Start engine and turn A/C system on. Observe low side system pressure.

2) With low side pressure 24 psi (1.7 kg/cm²) or less, compressor should be off and no continuity should exist between low pressure switch terminals. Replace switch if continuity is not as specified.

HIGH-PRESSURE SWITCH

1) High-pressure switch is located at rear of compressor. Connect A/C manifold gauge set. Start engine and turn A/C system on. Observe high side system pressure.

2) If high side pressure is 404 psi (1.7 kg/cm²) or more, compressor should be off and no continuity should exist between high pressure switch terminals. Replace switch if continuity is not as specified.

REMOVAL & INSTALLATION

A/C COMPRESSOR

Removal – Loosen idler pulley bolt and remove compressor belt. Discharge A/C system using approved refrigerant recovery/recycling equipment. Disconnect compressor clutch connector. Remove discharge and suction hoses from compressor and plug hose openings. Remove compressor bolts and compressor.

Installation – To install, reverse removal procedure. Tighten bolts to 17-20 ft. lbs. (23-77 N.m) Fill compressor with correct amount of oil. See COMPRESSOR REFRIGERANT OIL CHECKING article in GENERAL SERVICING. Evacuate and recharge system. Check for leaks.

HEATER CORE

Removal (Front) – **1)** Drain cooling system. Disconnect heater hoses in engine compartment. Disconnect ducts from heater unit. Remove 2 bolts from heater unit. Disconnect door motor wiring harness connectors.

2) Remove heater unit. *See Fig. 12.* Remove heater pipe retaining plate and heater core retainer. Disconnect heater core shutoff valve control rod. Remove heater core from heater unit.

Installation – To install, reverse removal procedure. Fill cooling system. Start vehicle and check for coolant leaks.

Removal & Installation (Rear) – Removal and installation procedure is not available from manufacturer. To aid in removal and installation, see illustration. *See Fig. 14.*

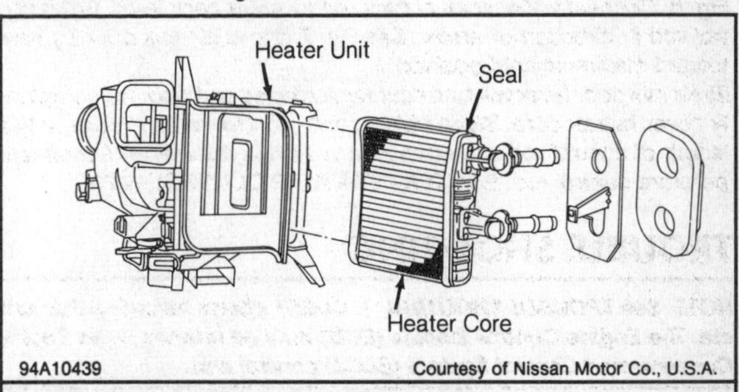

Heater Unit
Seal
Heater Core

94A10439 Courtesy of Nissan Motor Co., U.S.A.

Fig. 12: Removing Front Heater Core

1993 MANUAL A/C-HEATER SYSTEMS
Quest (Cont.)

EVAPORATOR CORE

Removal (Front) – **1)** Discharge A/C system using approved refrigerant recovery/recycling equipment. Disconnect A/C lines from evaporator (in engine compartment). Remove right-side lower instrument panel cover.

2) Disconnect air duct from heater unit-to-right register. Disconnect wiring harness connectors as necessary. Remove evaporator upper case. *See Fig. 13* Remove evaporator core.

Installation – To install, reverse removal procedure. Fill compressor with correct amount of oil. See COMPRESSOR REFRIGERANT OIL CHECKING article in GENERAL SERVICING. Evacuate and recharge system. Check for leaks.

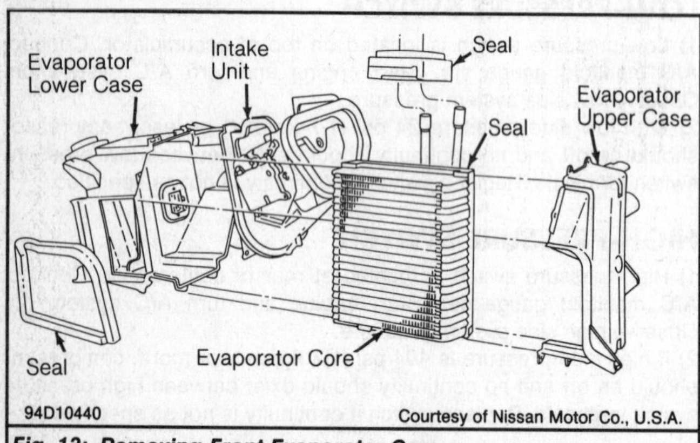
Evaporator
Lower Case
Intake
Unit
Seal
Evaporator
Upper Case
Seal
Seal
Evaporator Core
94D10440
Courtesy of Nissan Motor Co., U.S.A.

Fig. 13: Removing Front Evaporator Core

Removal & Installation (Rear) – Removal and installation procedure is not available from manufacturer. To aid in removal and installation, see illustration. *See Fig. 14.*

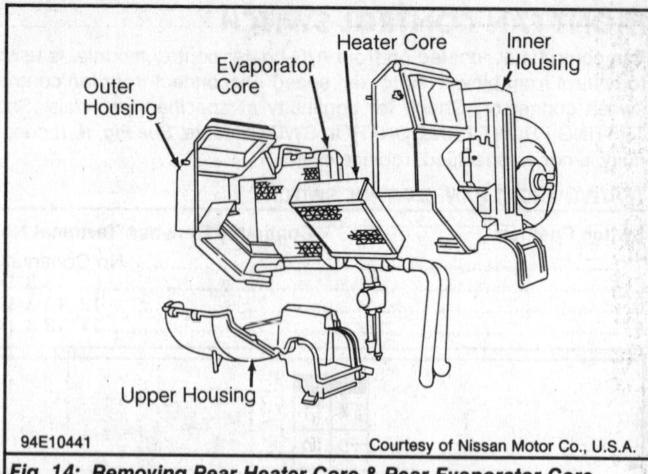
Heater Core
Inner
Housing
Evaporator
Core
Outer
Housing
Upper Housing
94E10441
Courtesy of Nissan Motor Co., U.S.A.

Fig. 14: Removing Rear Heater Core & Rear Evaporator Core

A/C-HEATER CONTROL MODULE

Removal & Installation (Front) – Remove A/C-heater control module trim panel. Remove 4 A/C-heater control module retaining screws. Disconnect wiring harness connectors. Remove A/C-heater control module. To install, reverse removal procedure.

TORQUE SPECIFICATIONS

TORQUE SPECIFICATIONS

Application	Ft. Lbs. (N.m)
Compressor Bolts	17-20 (23-27)

WIRING DIAGRAM

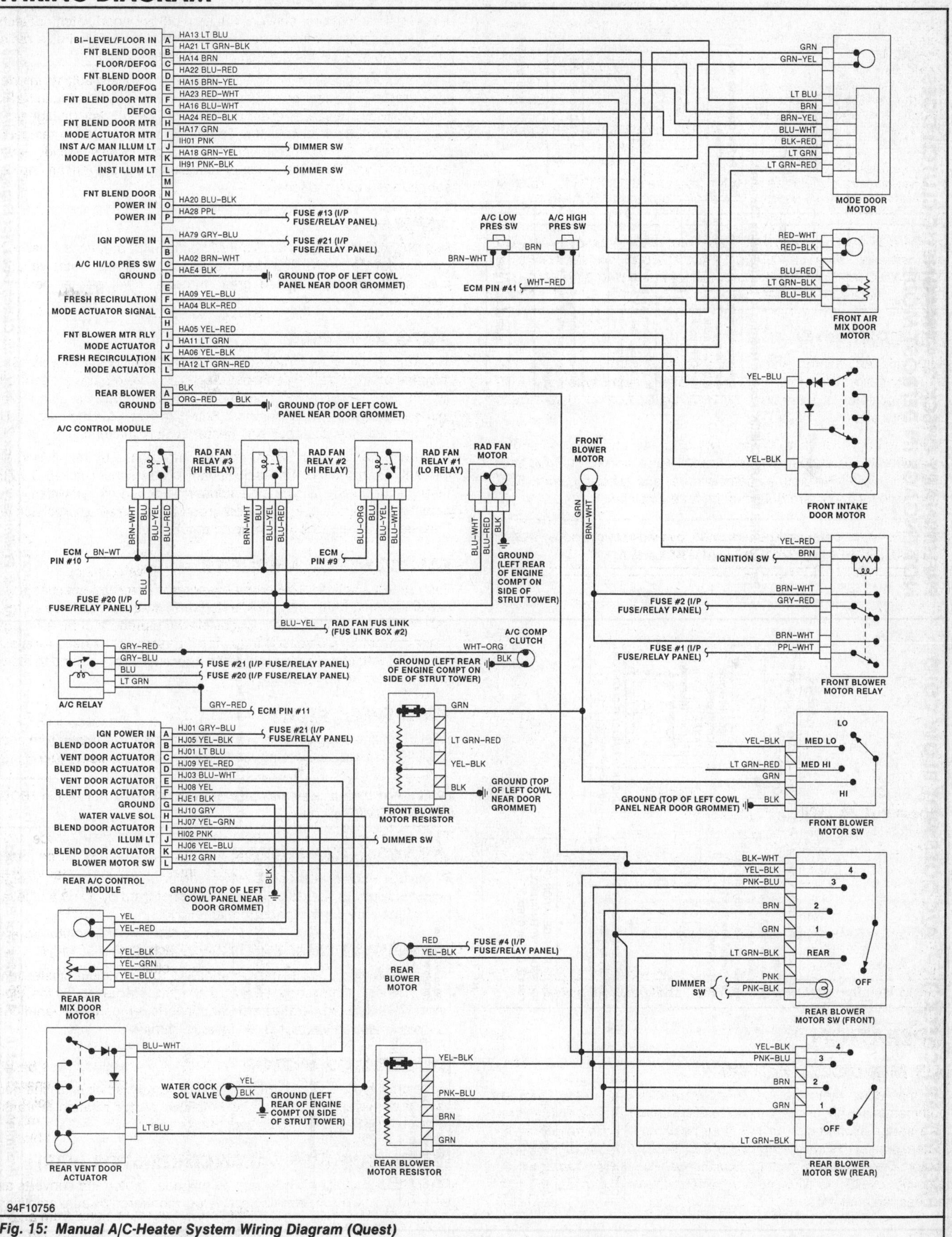
BI-LEVEL/FLOOR IN
FNT BLEND DOOR
FLOOR/DEFOG
FNT BLEND DOOR
FLOOR/DEFOG
FNT BLEND DOOR MTR
DEFOG
FNT BLEND DOOR MTR
MODE ACTUATOR MTR
INST A/C MAN ILLUM LT
MODE ACTUATOR MTR
INST ILLUM LT
FNT BLEND DOOR
POWER IN
POWER IN
IGN POWER IN
A/C HI/LO PRES SW
GROUND
FRESH RECIRULATION
MODE ACTUATOR SIGNAL
FNT BLOWER MTR RLY
MODE ACTUATOR
FRESH RECIRCULATION
MODE ACTUATOR
REAR BLOWER
GROUND
A/C CONTROL MODULE
DIMMER SW
FUSE #13 (I/P FUSE/RELAY PANEL)
FUSE #21 (I/P FUSE/RELAY PANEL)
GROUND (TOP OF LEFT COWL PANEL NEAR DOOR GROMMET)
A/C LOW PRES SW
A/C HIGH PRES SW
ECM PIN #41
MODE DOOR MOTOR
FRONT AIR MIX DOOR MOTOR
FRONT INTAKE DOOR MOTOR
RAD FAN RELAY #3 (HI RELAY)
RAD FAN RELAY #2 (HI RELAY)
RAD FAN RELAY #1 (LO RELAY)
RAD FAN MOTOR
FRONT BLOWER MOTOR
ECM PIN #10
ECM PIN #9
FUSE #20 (I/P FUSE/RELAY PANEL)
GROUND (LEFT REAR OF ENGINE COMPT ON SIDE OF STRUT TOWER)
RAD FAN FUS LINK (FUS LINK BOX #2)
IGNITION SW
FUSE #2 (I/P FUSE/RELAY PANEL)
FUSE #1 (I/P FUSE/RELAY PANEL)
FRONT BLOWER MOTOR RELAY
A/C RELAY
FUSE #21 (I/P FUSE/RELAY PANEL)
FUSE #20 (I/P FUSE/RELAY PANEL)
ECM PIN #11
A/C COMP CLUTCH
GROUND (LEFT REAR OF ENGINE COMPT ON SIDE OF STRUT TOWER)
FRONT BLOWER MOTOR RESISTOR
GROUND (TOP OF LEFT COWL NEAR DOOR GROMMET)
FRONT BLOWER MOTOR SW
LO
MED LO
MED HI
HI
GROUND (TOP OF LEFT COWL PANEL NEAR DOOR GROMMET)
IGN POWER IN
BLEND DOOR ACTUATOR
VENT DOOR ACTUATOR
BLEND DOOR ACTUATOR
VENT DOOR ACTUATOR
BLENT DOOR ACTUATOR
GROUND
WATER VALVE SOL
BLEND DOOR ACTUATOR
ILLUM LT
BLEND DOOR ACTUATOR
BLOWER MOTOR SW
REAR A/C CONTROL MODULE
GROUND (TOP OF LEFT COWL PANEL NEAR DOOR GROMMET)
REAR AIR MIX DOOR MOTOR
FUSE #4 (I/P FUSE/RELAY PANEL)
REAR BLOWER MOTOR
REAR BLOWER MOTOR SW (FRONT)
DIMMER SW
REAR
OFF
REAR VENT DOOR ACTUATOR
WATER COCK SOL VALVE
GROUND (LEFT REAR OF ENGINE COMPT ON SIDE OF STRUT TOWER)
REAR BLOWER MOTOR RESISTOR
REAR BLOWER MOTOR SW (REAR)
94F10756

Fig. 15: Manual A/C-Heater System Wiring Diagram (Quest)

1993 MANUAL A/C-HEATER SYSTEMS
Trouble Shooting – Quest

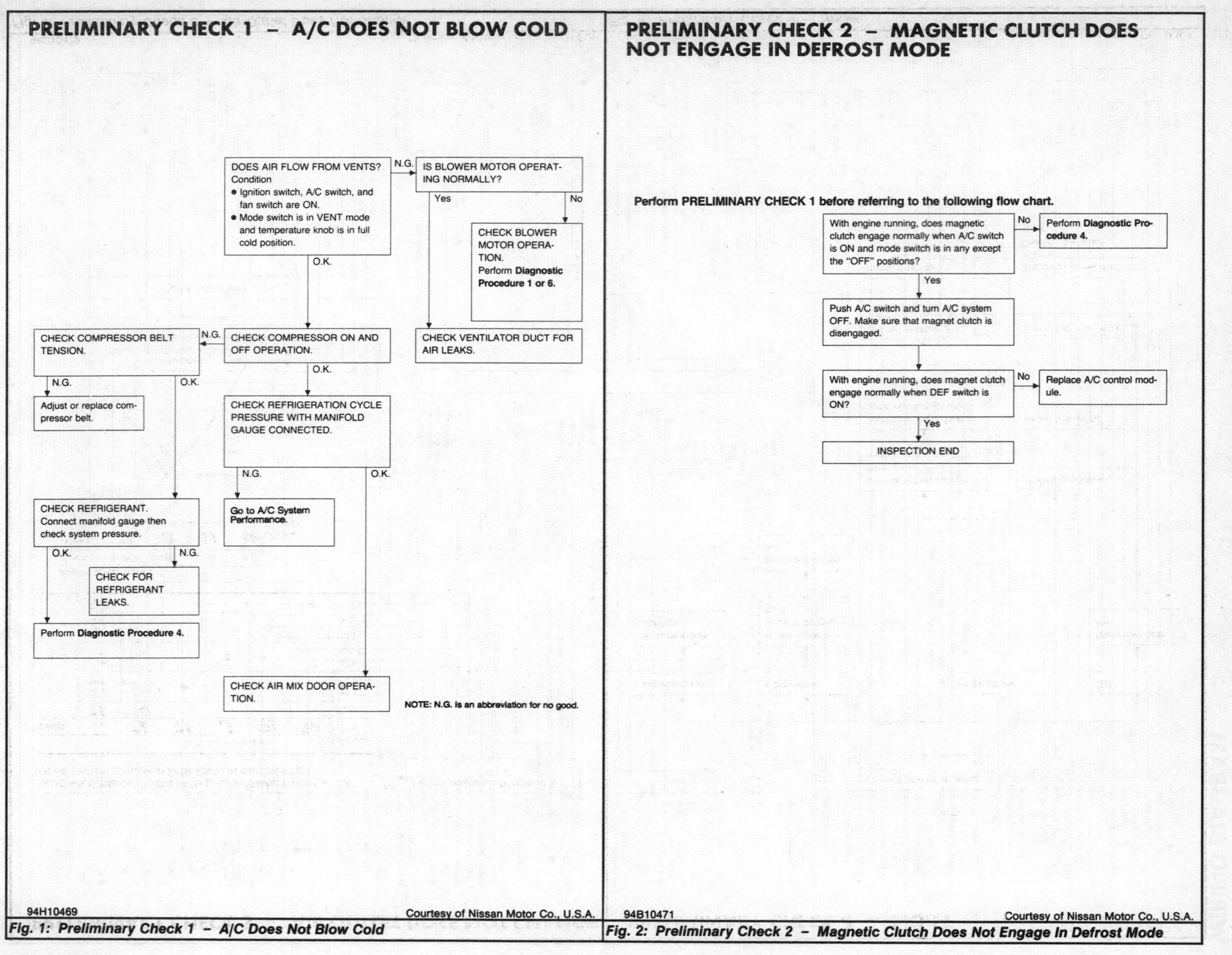
PRELIMINARY CHECK 1 – A/C DOES NOT BLOW COLD
DOES AIR FLOW FROM VENTS? Condition
• Ignition switch, A/C switch, and fan switch are ON.
• Mode switch is in VENT mode and temperature knob is in full cold position.
N.G.
IS BLOWER MOTOR OPERATING NORMALLY?
Yes
No
CHECK BLOWER MOTOR OPERATION. Perform Diagnostic Procedure 1 or 6.
O.K.
CHECK COMPRESSOR ON AND OFF OPERATION.
CHECK VENTILATOR DUCT FOR AIR LEAKS.
N.G.
CHECK COMPRESSOR BELT TENSION.
N.G.
O.K.
Adjust or replace compressor belt.
O.K.
CHECK REFRIGERATION CYCLE PRESSURE WITH MANIFOLD GAUGE CONNECTED.
N.G.
O.K.
CHECK REFRIGERANT. Connect manifold gauge then check system pressure.
Go to A/C System Performance.
O.K.
N.G.
CHECK FOR REFRIGERANT LEAKS.
Perform Diagnostic Procedure 4.
CHECK AIR MIX DOOR OPERATION.
NOTE: N.G. is an abbreviation for no good.
94H10469
Courtesy of Nissan Motor Co., U.S.A.
PRELIMINARY CHECK 2 – MAGNETIC CLUTCH DOES NOT ENGAGE IN DEFROST MODE
Perform PRELIMINARY CHECK 1 before referring to the following flow chart.
With engine running, does magnetic clutch engage normally when A/C switch is ON and mode switch is in any except the "OFF" positions?
No
Perform Diagnostic Procedure 4.
Yes
Push A/C switch and turn A/C system OFF. Make sure that magnet clutch is disengaged.
With engine running, does magnet clutch engage normally when DEF switch is ON?
No
Replace A/C control module.
Yes
INSPECTION END
94B10471
Courtesy of Nissan Motor Co., U.S.A.

Fig. 1: Preliminary Check 1 – A/C Does Not Blow Cold

Fig. 2: Preliminary Check 2 – Magnetic Clutch Does Not Engage In Defrost Mode

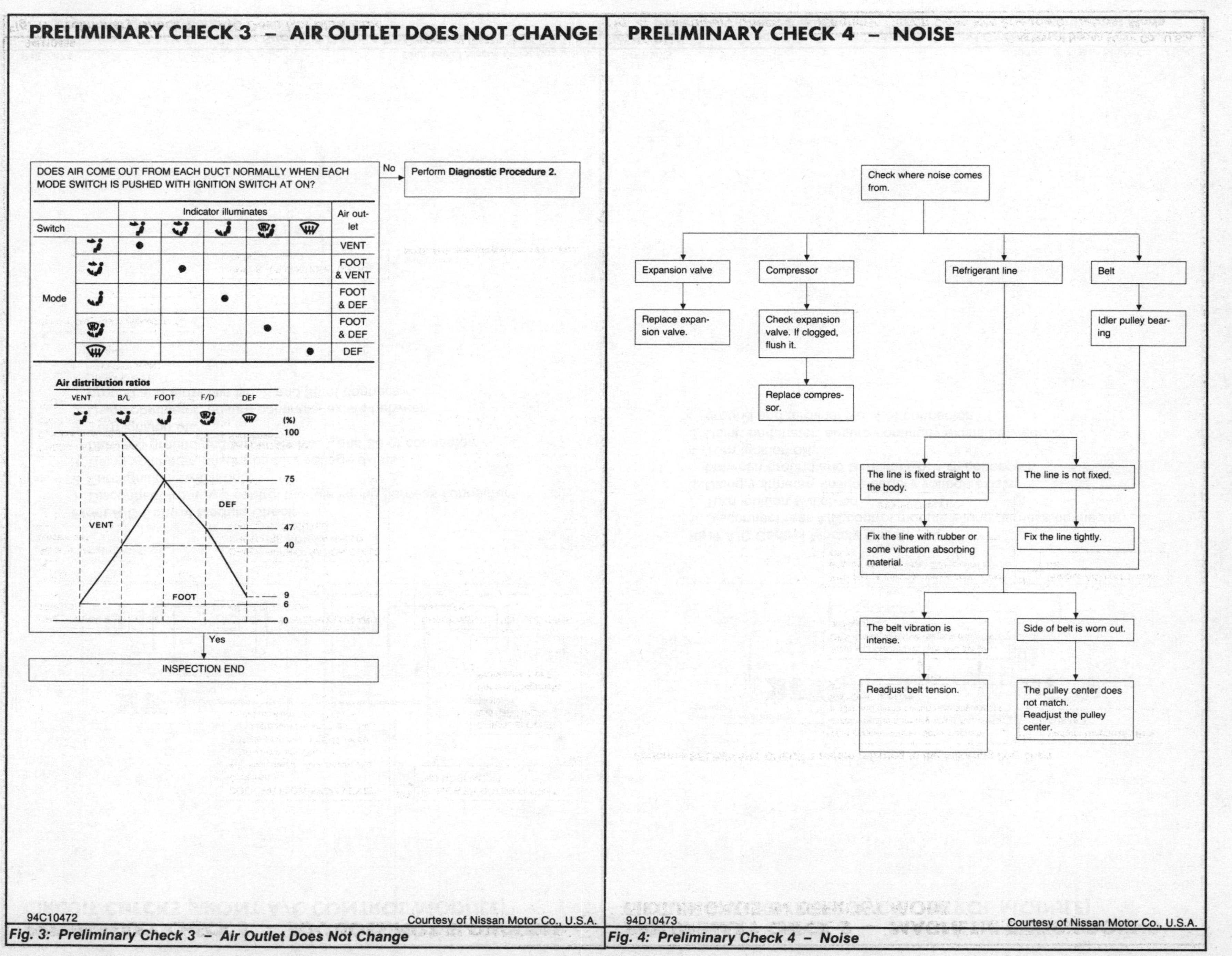

PRELIMINARY CHECK 3 – AIR OUTLET DOES NOT CHANGE
DOES AIR COME OUT FROM EACH DUCT NORMALLY WHEN EACH MODE SWITCH IS PUSHED WITH IGNITION SWITCH AT ON?
No
Perform Diagnostic Procedure 2.
Indicator illuminates
Air outlet
Switch
Mode
VENT
FOOT & VENT
FOOT & DEF
FOOT & DEF
DEF
Air distribution ratios
VENT
B/L
FOOT
F/D
DEF
(%)
100
75
47
40
9
6
0
VENT
DEF
FOOT
Yes
INSPECTION END
94C10472
Courtesy of Nissan Motor Co., U.S.A.
PRELIMINARY CHECK 4 – NOISE
Check where noise comes from.
Expansion valve
Compressor
Refrigerant line
Belt
Replace expansion valve.
Check expansion valve. If clogged, flush it.
Idler pulley bearing
Replace compressor.
The line is fixed straight to the body.
The line is not fixed.
Fix the line with rubber or some vibration absorbing material.
Fix the line tightly.
The belt vibration is intense.
Side of belt is worn out.
Readjust belt tension.
The pulley center does not match. Readjust the pulley center.
94D10473
Courtesy of Nissan Motor Co., U.S.A.

Fig. 3: Preliminary Check 3 – Air Outlet Does Not Change

Fig. 4: Preliminary Check 4 – Noise

1993 MANUAL A/C-HEATER SYSTEMS
Trouble Shooting – Quest (Cont.)

PRELIMINARY CHECK 5 – POWER SUPPLY & GROUND CIRCUIT CHECKS (FRONT A/C CONTROL MODULE)

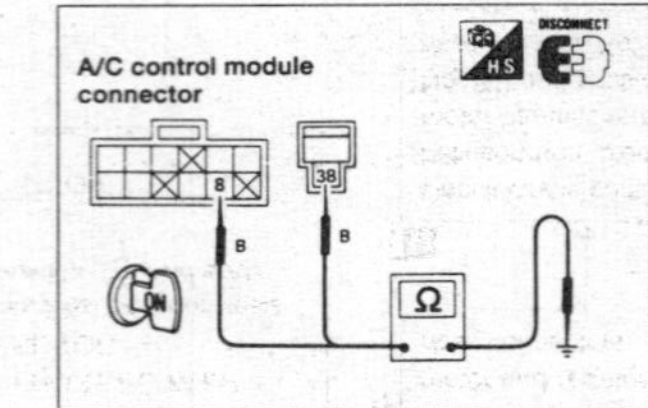
A/C control module
connector
8
38
B
B
Ω

Front A/C Control Module Check

1. Disconnect front A/C control module wiring harness connector.
2. Turn ignition switch on.
3. Using voltmeter, ensure battery voltage exists between ground and terminals No. 1 and 28 of connector.
4. Turn ignition off.
5. Using ohmmeter, ensure continuity exists between ground and terminals No. 8 and 38 of connector.

94E10474 Courtesy of Nissan Motor Co., U.S.A.

Fig. 5: Preliminary Check 5 – Power Supply & Ground Circuit Checks (Front A/C Control Module)

PRELIMINARY CHECK 6 – POWER SUPPLY & GROUND CIRCUIT CHECKS (REAR A/C CONTROL MODULE)

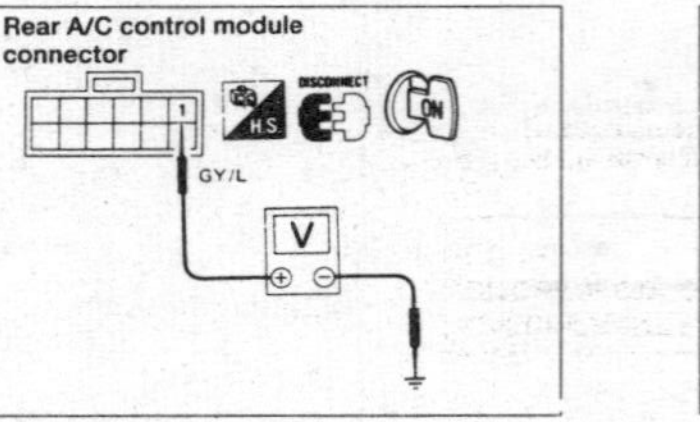
Rear A/C control module
connector
1
GY/L
V

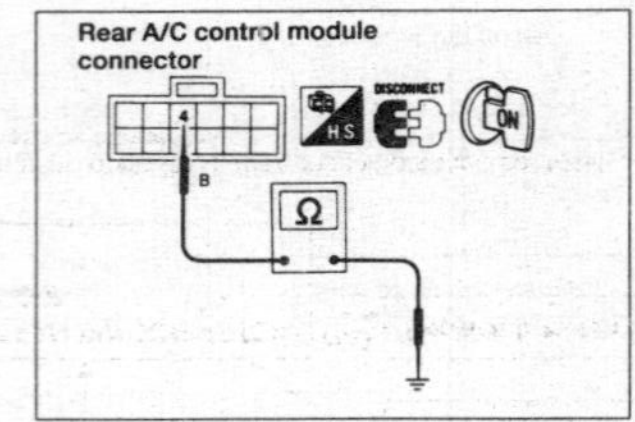
Rear A/C control module
connector
4
B
Ω

Rear A/C Control Module Check

1. Disconnect rear A/C control module wiring harness connector.
2. Turn ignition switch on.
3. Using voltmeter, ensure battery voltage exists between ground and terminal No. 1 of connector.
4. Turn ignition off.
5. Using ohmmeter, ensure continuity exists between ground and terminal No. 4 of connector.

94F10475 Courtesy of Nissan Motor Co., U.S.A.

Fig. 6: Preliminary Check 6 – Power Supply & Ground Circuit Checks (Rear A/C Control Module)

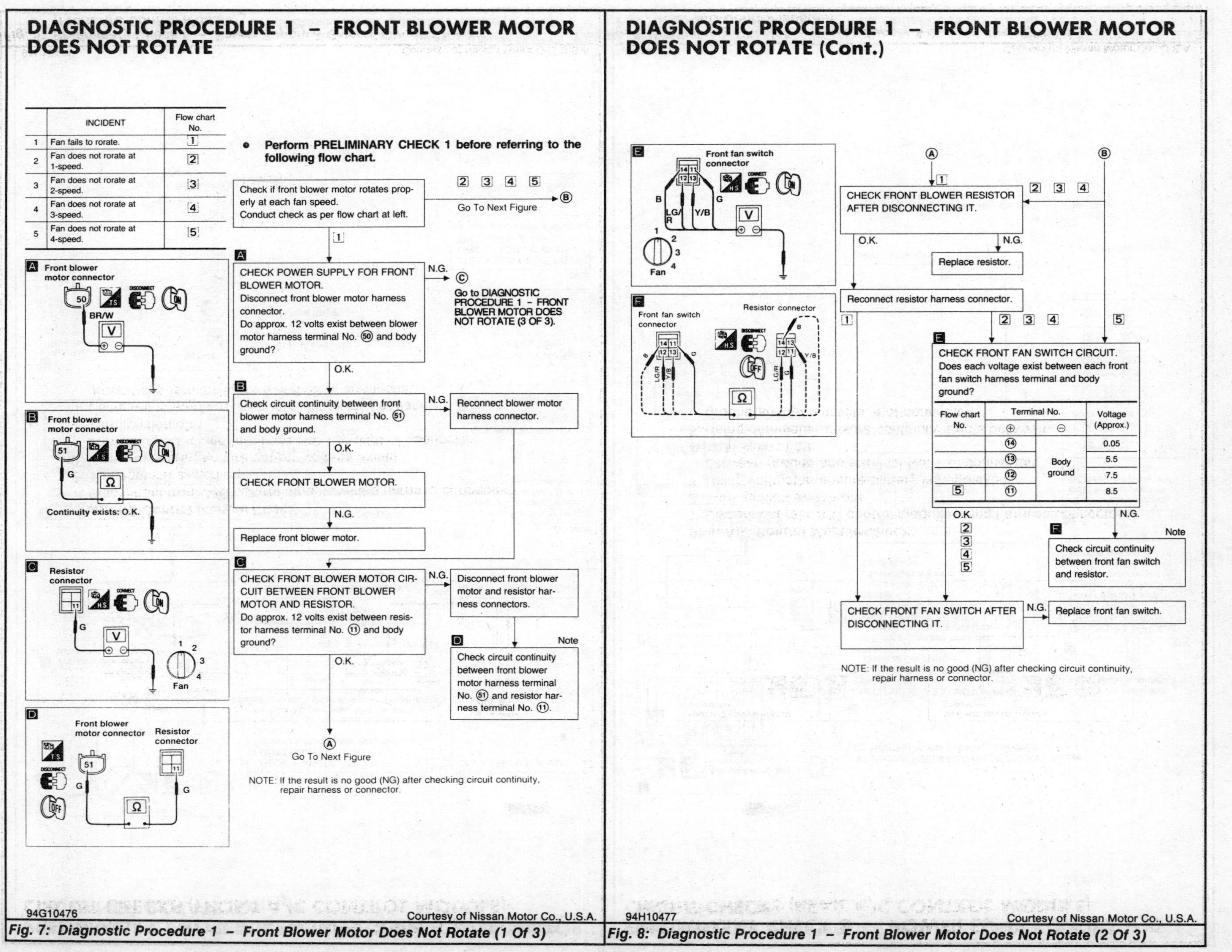
DIAGNOSTIC PROCEDURE 1 – FRONT BLOWER MOTOR DOES NOT ROTATE
INCIDENT | Flow chart No.
1 Fan fails to rorate. | 1
2 Fan does not rorate at 1-speed. | 2
3 Fan does not rorate at 2-speed. | 3
4 Fan does not rorate at 3-speed. | 4
5 Fan does not rorate at 4-speed. | 5
A Front blower motor connector
50
BR/W
V
B Front blower motor connector
51
G
Ω
Continuity exists: O.K.
C Resistor connector
11
G
V
1 2 3 4
Fan
D Front blower motor connector
Resistor connector
51
11
G
G
Ω
Perform PRELIMINARY CHECK 1 before referring to the following flow chart.
Check if front blower motor rotates properly at each fan speed. Conduct check as per flow chart at left.
2 3 4 5
Go To Next Figure
B
1
A CHECK POWER SUPPLY FOR FRONT BLOWER MOTOR. Disconnect front blower motor harness connector. Do approx. 12 volts exist between blower motor harness terminal No. 50 and body ground?
N.G.
C Go to DIAGNOSTIC PROCEDURE 1 – FRONT BLOWER MOTOR DOES NOT ROTATE (3 OF 3).
O.K.
B Check circuit continuity between front blower motor harness terminal No. 51 and body ground.
N.G.
Reconnect blower motor harness connector.
O.K.
CHECK FRONT BLOWER MOTOR.
N.G.
Replace front blower motor.
C CHECK FRONT BLOWER MOTOR CIRCUIT BETWEEN FRONT BLOWER MOTOR AND RESISTOR. Do approx. 12 volts exist between resistor harness terminal No. 11 and body ground?
N.G.
Disconnect front blower motor and resistor harness connectors.
D Check circuit continuity between front blower motor harness terminal No. 51 and resistor harness terminal No. 11.
Note
O.K.
A
Go To Next Figure
NOTE: If the result is no good (NG) after checking circuit continuity, repair harness or connector.
94G10476
Courtesy of Nissan Motor Co., U.S.A.
DIAGNOSTIC PROCEDURE 1 – FRONT BLOWER MOTOR DOES NOT ROTATE (Cont.)
E Front fan switch connector
14 11
12 13
B
LG/R
Y/B
G
V
1 2 3 4
Fan
F Front fan switch connector
Resistor connector
LG/R
Y/B
G
B
Ω
A
B
1
CHECK FRONT BLOWER RESISTOR AFTER DISCONNECTING IT.
2 3 4
O.K.
N.G.
Replace resistor.
Reconnect resistor harness connector.
1
2 3 4
5
E CHECK FRONT FAN SWITCH CIRCUIT. Does each voltage exist between each front fan switch harness terminal and body ground?
Flow chart No. | Terminal No. ⊕ | Terminal No. ⊖ | Voltage (Approx.)
 | 14 | Body ground | 0.05
 | 13 | Body ground | 5.5
 | 12 | Body ground | 7.5
5 | 11 | Body ground | 8.5
O.K.
2
3
4
5
N.G.
F Check circuit continuity between front fan switch and resistor.
Note
CHECK FRONT FAN SWITCH AFTER DISCONNECTING IT.
N.G.
Replace front fan switch.
NOTE: If the result is no good (NG) after checking circuit continuity, repair harness or connector.
94H10477
Courtesy of Nissan Motor Co., U.S.A.

Fig. 7: Diagnostic Procedure 1 – Front Blower Motor Does Not Rotate (1 Of 3)

Fig. 8: Diagnostic Procedure 1 – Front Blower Motor Does Not Rotate (2 Of 3)

1993 MANUAL A/C-HEATER SYSTEMS
Trouble Shooting – Quest (Cont.)

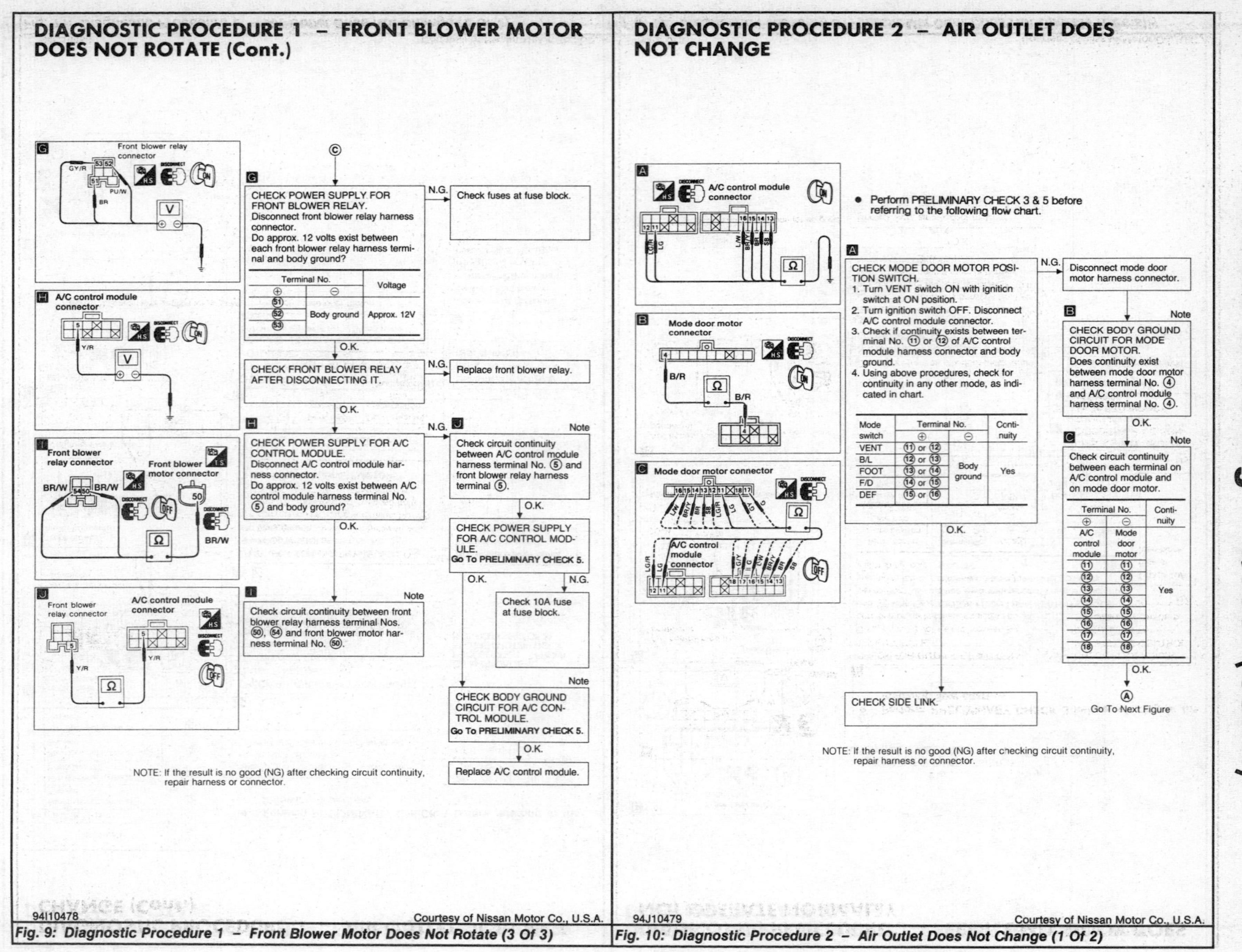
DIAGNOSTIC PROCEDURE 1 – FRONT BLOWER MOTOR DOES NOT ROTATE (Cont.)
G Front blower relay connector
GY/R
PU/W
BR
H A/C control module connector
Y/R
I Front blower relay connector
Front blower motor connector
BR/W
J Front blower relay connector
A/C control module connector
Y/R
C
G CHECK POWER SUPPLY FOR FRONT BLOWER RELAY.
Disconnect front blower relay harness connector.
Do approx. 12 volts exist between each front blower relay harness terminal and body ground?
Terminal No. ⊕ ⊖ Voltage
51 52 53 Body ground Approx. 12V
N.G.
Check fuses at fuse block.
O.K.
CHECK FRONT BLOWER RELAY AFTER DISCONNECTING IT.
N.G.
Replace front blower relay.
O.K.
H CHECK POWER SUPPLY FOR A/C CONTROL MODULE.
Disconnect A/C control module harness connector.
Do approx. 12 volts exist between A/C control module harness terminal No. 5 and body ground?
N.G.
J Note
Check circuit continuity between A/C control module harness terminal No. 5 and front blower relay harness terminal 5.
O.K.
CHECK POWER SUPPLY FOR A/C CONTROL MODULE.
Go To PRELIMINARY CHECK 5.
O.K.
N.G.
Check 10A fuse at fuse block.
O.K.
I Note
Check circuit continuity between front blower relay harness terminal Nos. 50, 54 and front blower motor harness terminal No. 50.
Note
CHECK BODY GROUND CIRCUIT FOR A/C CONTROL MODULE.
Go To PRELIMINARY CHECK 5.
O.K.
Replace A/C control module.
NOTE: If the result is no good (NG) after checking circuit continuity, repair harness or connector.
94I10478
Courtesy of Nissan Motor Co., U.S.A.
DIAGNOSTIC PROCEDURE 2 – AIR OUTLET DOES NOT CHANGE
A A/C control module connector
LG/R LG L/W BR/Y BR SB
B Mode door motor connector
B/R
C Mode door motor connector
A/C control module connector
• Perform PRELIMINARY CHECK 3 & 5 before referring to the following flow chart.
A CHECK MODE DOOR MOTOR POSITION SWITCH.
1. Turn VENT switch ON with ignition switch at ON position.
2. Turn ignition switch OFF. Disconnect A/C control module connector.
3. Check if continuity exists between terminal No. 11 or 12 of A/C control module harness connector and body ground.
4. Using above procedures, check for continuity in any other mode, as indicated in chart.
Mode switch | Terminal No. ⊕ | ⊖ | Continuity
VENT | 11 or 12 | Body ground | Yes
B/L | 12 or 13
FOOT | 13 or 14
F/D | 14 or 15
DEF | 15 or 16
N.G.
Disconnect mode door motor harness connector.
B Note
CHECK BODY GROUND CIRCUIT FOR MODE DOOR MOTOR.
Does continuity exist between mode door motor harness terminal No. 4 and A/C control module harness terminal No. 4.
O.K.
C Note
Check circuit continuity between each terminal on A/C control module and on mode door motor.
Terminal No. ⊕ A/C control module | ⊖ Mode door motor | Continuity
11 | 11 | Yes
12 | 12
13 | 13
14 | 14
15 | 15
16 | 16
17 | 17
18 | 18
O.K.
A Go To Next Figure
O.K.
CHECK SIDE LINK.
NOTE: If the result is no good (NG) after checking circuit continuity, repair harness or connector.
94J10479
Courtesy of Nissan Motor Co., U.S.A.

Fig. 9: Diagnostic Procedure 1 – Front Blower Motor Does Not Rotate (3 Of 3)

Fig. 10: Diagnostic Procedure 2 – Air Outlet Does Not Change (1 Of 2)

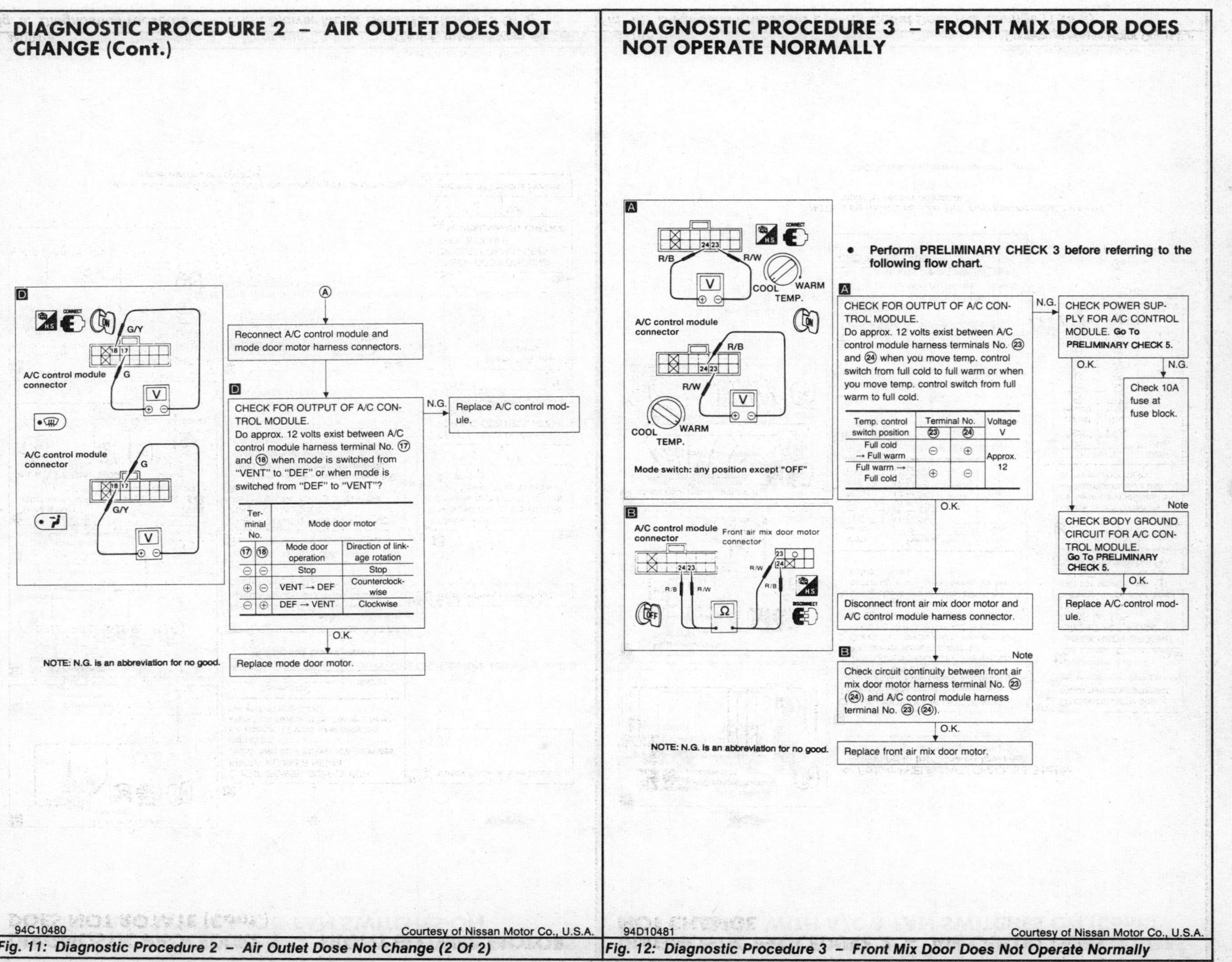
DIAGNOSTIC PROCEDURE 2 – AIR OUTLET DOES NOT CHANGE (Cont.)
D
A/C control module connector
G/Y
G
V
A/C control module connector
A
Reconnect A/C control module and mode door motor harness connectors.
D
CHECK FOR OUTPUT OF A/C CONTROL MODULE.
Do approx. 12 volts exist between A/C control module harness terminal No. ⑰ and ⑱ when mode is switched from "VENT" to "DEF" or when mode is switched from "DEF" to "VENT"?
N.G.
Replace A/C control module.
O.K.
Replace mode door motor.
NOTE: N.G. is an abbreviation for no good.
94C10480
Courtesy of Nissan Motor Co., U.S.A.
DIAGNOSTIC PROCEDURE 3 – FRONT MIX DOOR DOES NOT OPERATE NORMALLY
A
R/B
R/W
COOL
WARM
TEMP.
A/C control module connector
Mode switch: any position except "OFF"
B
A/C control module connector
Front air mix door motor connector
R/B
R/W
Ω
• Perform PRELIMINARY CHECK 3 before referring to the following flow chart.
A
CHECK FOR OUTPUT OF A/C CONTROL MODULE.
Do approx. 12 volts exist between A/C control module harness terminals No. ㉓ and ㉔ when you move temp. control switch from full cold to full warm or when you move temp. control switch from full warm to full cold.
N.G.
CHECK POWER SUPPLY FOR A/C CONTROL MODULE. Go To PRELIMINARY CHECK 5.
O.K.
N.G.
Check 10A fuse at fuse block.
Note
CHECK BODY GROUND CIRCUIT FOR A/C CONTROL MODULE. Go To PRELIMINARY CHECK 5.
O.K.
Replace A/C control module.
O.K.
Disconnect front air mix door motor and A/C control module harness connector.
B
Note
Check circuit continuity between front air mix door motor harness terminal No. ㉓ (㉔) and A/C control module harness terminal No. ㉓ (㉔).
O.K.
Replace front air mix door motor.
NOTE: N.G. is an abbreviation for no good.
94D10481
Courtesy of Nissan Motor Co., U.S.A.

Terminal No. ⑰	Terminal No. ⑱	Mode door operation	Direction of linkage rotation
⊖	⊖	Stop	Stop
⊕	⊖	VENT → DEF	Counterclockwise
⊖	⊕	DEF → VENT	Clockwise

Temp. control switch position	Terminal No. ㉓	Terminal No. ㉔	Voltage V
Full cold → Full warm	⊖	⊕	Approx. 12
Full warm → Full cold	⊕	⊖	

Fig. 11: Diagnostic Procedure 2 – Air Outlet Dose Not Change (2 Of 2)

Fig. 12: Diagnostic Procedure 3 – Front Mix Door Does Not Operate Normally

1993 MANUAL A/C-HEATER SYSTEMS
Trouble Shooting – Quest (Cont.)

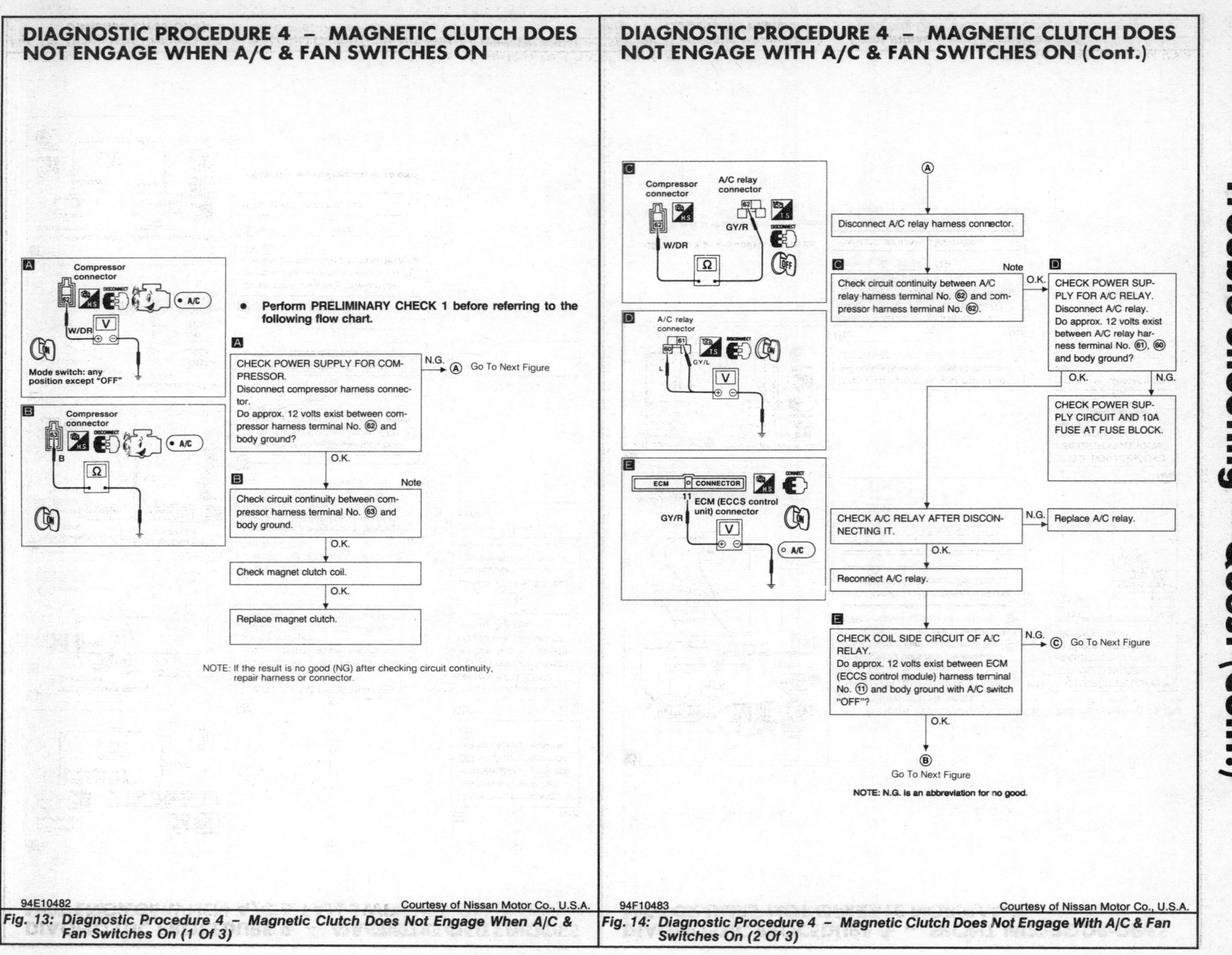
DIAGNOSTIC PROCEDURE 4 – MAGNETIC CLUTCH DOES NOT ENGAGE WHEN A/C & FAN SWITCHES ON
A
Compressor connector
62
H.S
DISCONNECT
A/C
W/DR
V
ON
Mode switch: any position except "OFF"
B
Compressor connector
63
H.S
DISCONNECT
A/C
B
Ω
ON
• Perform PRELIMINARY CHECK 1 before referring to the following flow chart.
A
CHECK POWER SUPPLY FOR COMPRESSOR.
Disconnect compressor harness connector.
Do approx. 12 volts exist between compressor harness terminal No. 62 and body ground?
N.G.
A Go To Next Figure
O.K.
B
Note
Check circuit continuity between compressor harness terminal No. 63 and body ground.
O.K.
Check magnet clutch coil.
O.K.
Replace magnet clutch.
NOTE: If the result is no good (NG) after checking circuit continuity, repair harness or connector.
94E10482
Courtesy of Nissan Motor Co., U.S.A.
DIAGNOSTIC PROCEDURE 4 – MAGNETIC CLUTCH DOES NOT ENGAGE WITH A/C & FAN SWITCHES ON (Cont.)
C
Compressor connector
A/C relay connector
62
H.S
T.S
GY/R
DISCONNECT
W/DR
Ω
OFF
D
A/C relay connector
61
60
T.S
DISCONNECT
GY/L
L
V
ON
E
ECM
CONNECTOR
11
ECM (ECCS control unit) connector
H.S
CONNECT
GY/R
V
ON
A/C
A
Disconnect A/C relay harness connector.
C
Note
Check circuit continuity between A/C relay harness terminal No. 62 and compressor harness terminal No. 62.
O.K.
D
CHECK POWER SUPPLY FOR A/C RELAY.
Disconnect A/C relay.
Do approx. 12 volts exist between A/C relay harness terminal No. 61, 60 and body ground?
O.K.
N.G.
CHECK POWER SUPPLY CIRCUIT AND 10A FUSE AT FUSE BLOCK.
CHECK A/C RELAY AFTER DISCONNECTING IT.
N.G.
Replace A/C relay.
O.K.
Reconnect A/C relay.
E
CHECK COIL SIDE CIRCUIT OF A/C RELAY.
Do approx. 12 volts exist between ECM (ECCS control module) harness terminal No. 11 and body ground with A/C switch "OFF"?
N.G.
C Go To Next Figure
O.K.
B
Go To Next Figure
NOTE: N.G. is an abbreviation for no good.
94F10483
Courtesy of Nissan Motor Co., U.S.A.

Fig. 13: Diagnostic Procedure 4 – Magnetic Clutch Does Not Engage When A/C & Fan Switches On (1 Of 3)

Fig. 14: Diagnostic Procedure 4 – Magnetic Clutch Does Not Engage With A/C & Fan Switches On (2 Of 3)

DIAGNOSTIC PROCEDURE 4 – MAGNETIC CLUTCH DOES NOT ENGAGE WHEN A/C & FAN SWITCHES ON (Cont.)

DIAGNOSTIC PROCEDURE 5 – FRONT INTAKE DOOR MOTOR DOES NOT OPERATE NORMALLY

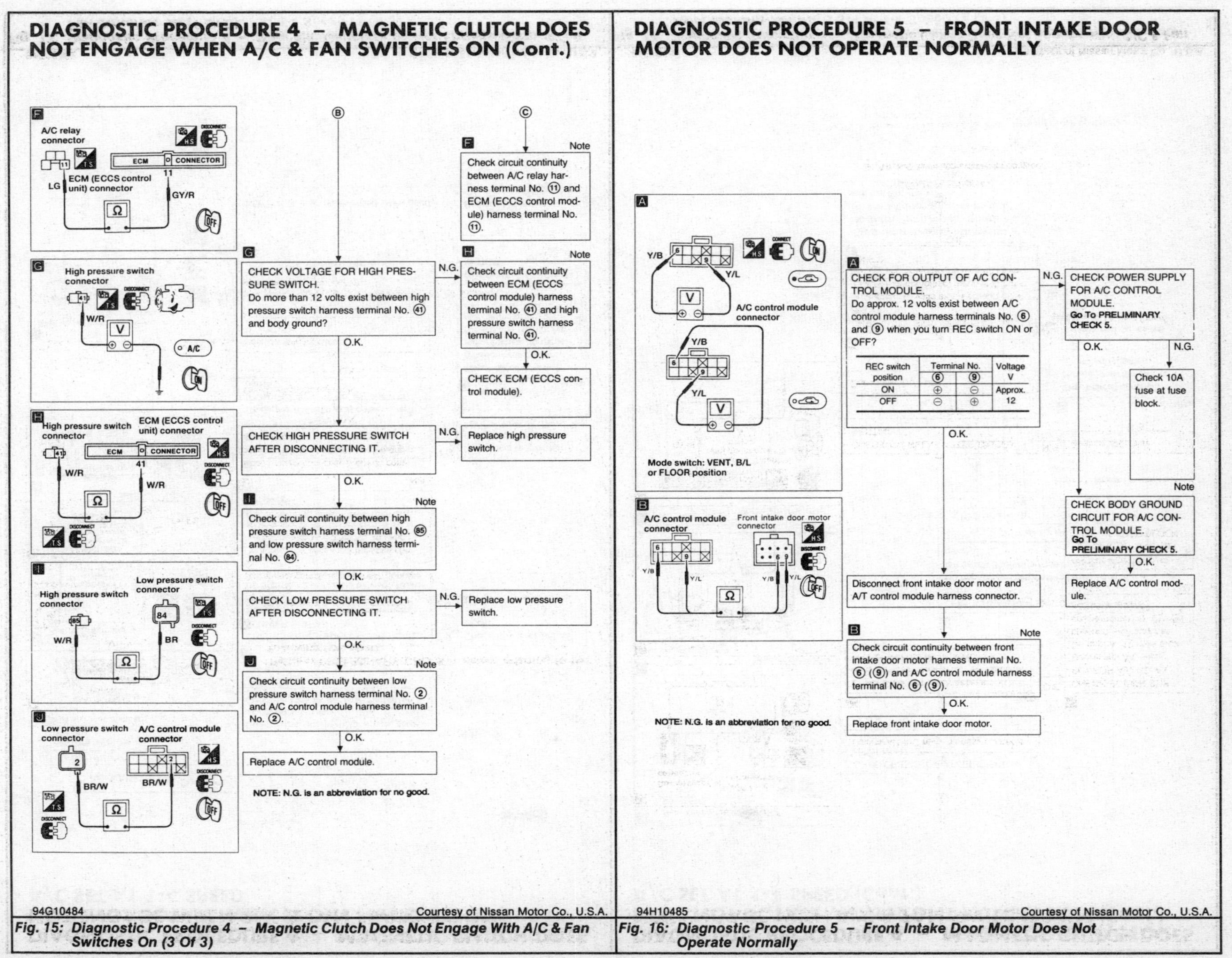
F
A/C relay connector
ECM (ECCS control unit) connector
LG
11
ECM
CONNECTOR
GY/R
G
High pressure switch connector
41
W/R
V
A/C
H
High pressure switch connector
ECM (ECCS control unit) connector
ECM
CONNECTOR
41
W/R
W/R
I
High pressure switch connector
Low pressure switch connector
85
84
W/R
BR
J
Low pressure switch connector
A/C control module connector
2
BR/W
BR/W
B
C
G
CHECK VOLTAGE FOR HIGH PRESSURE SWITCH.
Do more than 12 volts exist between high pressure switch harness terminal No. 41 and body ground?
N.G.
O.K.
F
Note
Check circuit continuity between A/C relay harness terminal No. 11 and ECM (ECCS control module) harness terminal No. 11.
H
Note
Check circuit continuity between ECM (ECCS control module) harness terminal No. 41 and high pressure switch harness terminal No. 41.
O.K.
CHECK ECM (ECCS control module).
CHECK HIGH PRESSURE SWITCH AFTER DISCONNECTING IT.
N.G.
Replace high pressure switch.
O.K.
I
Note
Check circuit continuity between high pressure switch harness terminal No. 85 and low pressure switch harness terminal No. 84.
O.K.
CHECK LOW PRESSURE SWITCH AFTER DISCONNECTING IT.
N.G.
Replace low pressure switch.
O.K.
J
Note
Check circuit continuity between low pressure switch harness terminal No. 2 and A/C control module harness terminal No. 2.
O.K.
Replace A/C control module.
NOTE: N.G. is an abbreviation for no good.
94G10484
Courtesy of Nissan Motor Co., U.S.A.
A
Y/B
6
9
Y/L
V
A/C control module connector
Y/B
6
9
Y/L
V
Mode switch: VENT, B/L or FLOOR position
B
A/C control module connector
Front intake door motor connector
6
9
Y/B
Y/L
Y/B
Y/L
A
CHECK FOR OUTPUT OF A/C CONTROL MODULE.
Do approx. 12 volts exist between A/C control module harness terminals No. 6 and 9 when you turn REC switch ON or OFF?
REC switch position | Terminal No. 6 | Terminal No. 9 | Voltage V
ON | ⊕ | ⊖ | Approx. 12
OFF | ⊖ | ⊕ |
N.G.
CHECK POWER SUPPLY FOR A/C CONTROL MODULE.
Go To PRELIMINARY CHECK 5.
O.K.
N.G.
Check 10A fuse at fuse block.
Note
CHECK BODY GROUND CIRCUIT FOR A/C CONTROL MODULE.
Go To PRELIMINARY CHECK 5.
O.K.
Replace A/C control module.
O.K.
Disconnect front intake door motor and A/T control module harness connector.
B
Note
Check circuit continuity between front intake door motor harness terminal No. 6 (9) and A/C control module harness terminal No. 6 (9).
O.K.
Replace front intake door motor.
NOTE: N.G. is an abbreviation for no good.
94H10485
Courtesy of Nissan Motor Co., U.S.A.

Fig. 15: Diagnostic Procedure 4 – Magnetic Clutch Does Not Engage With A/C & Fan Switches On (3 Of 3)

Fig. 16: Diagnostic Procedure 5 – Front Intake Door Motor Does Not Operate Normally

1993 MANUAL A/C-HEATER SYSTEMS
Trouble Shooting – Quest (Cont.)

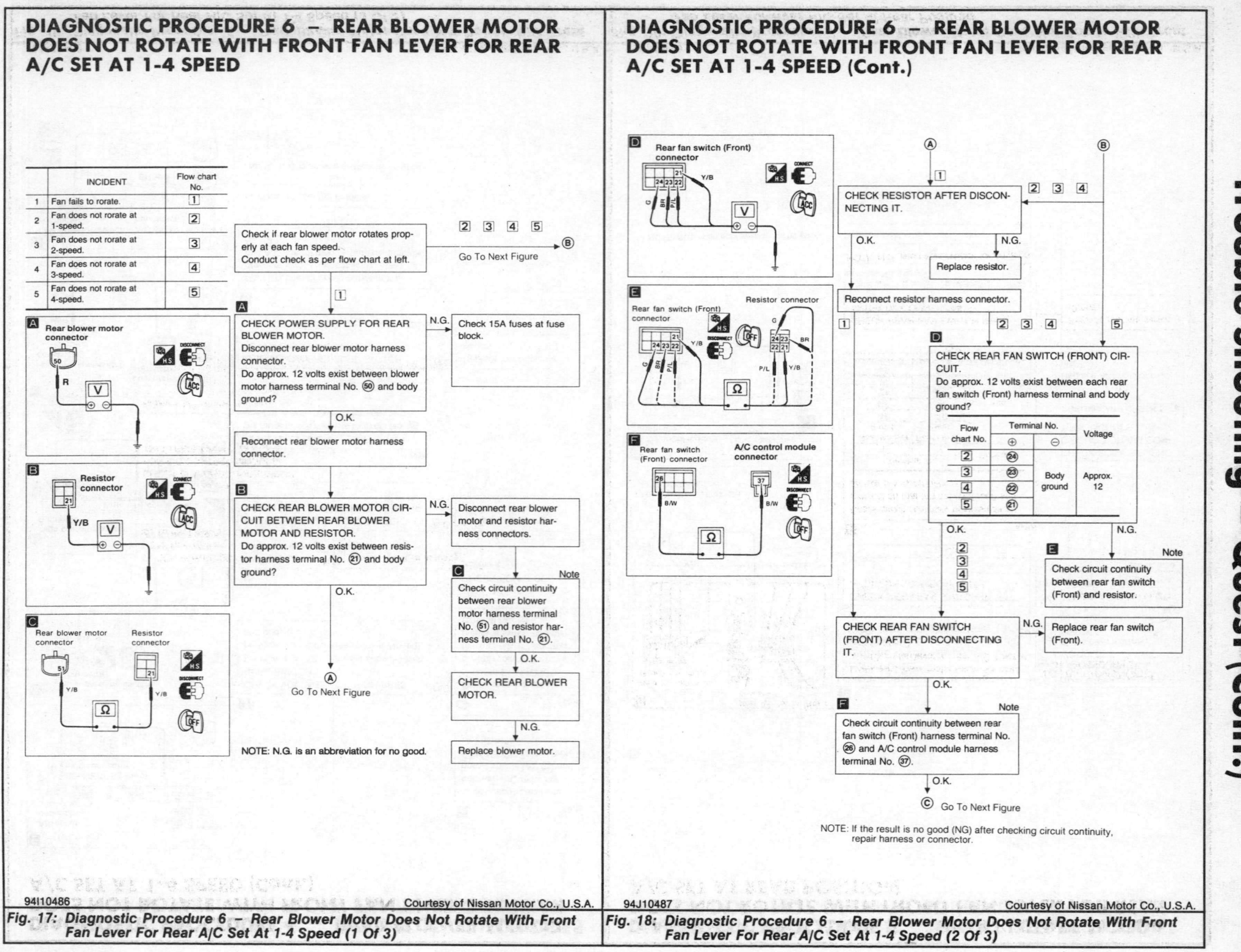
DIAGNOSTIC PROCEDURE 6 – REAR BLOWER MOTOR DOES NOT ROTATE WITH FRONT FAN LEVER FOR REAR A/C SET AT 1-4 SPEED
INCIDENT | Flow chart No.
1 Fan fails to rorate. | 1
2 Fan does not rorate at 1-speed. | 2
3 Fan does not rorate at 2-speed. | 3
4 Fan does not rorate at 3-speed. | 4
5 Fan does not rorate at 4-speed. | 5
Check if rear blower motor rotates properly at each fan speed. Conduct check as per flow chart at left.
2 3 4 5
Go To Next Figure
B
1
A
CHECK POWER SUPPLY FOR REAR BLOWER MOTOR. Disconnect rear blower motor harness connector. Do approx. 12 volts exist between blower motor harness terminal No. 50 and body ground?
N.G.
Check 15A fuses at fuse block.
O.K.
Reconnect rear blower motor harness connector.
B
CHECK REAR BLOWER MOTOR CIRCUIT BETWEEN REAR BLOWER MOTOR AND RESISTOR. Do approx. 12 volts exist between resistor harness terminal No. 21 and body ground?
N.G.
Disconnect rear blower motor and resistor harness connectors.
C
Note
Check circuit continuity between rear blower motor harness terminal No. 51 and resistor harness terminal No. 21.
O.K.
CHECK REAR BLOWER MOTOR.
N.G.
Replace blower motor.
O.K.
A
Go To Next Figure
NOTE: N.G. is an abbreviation for no good.
A Rear blower motor connector
50
R
V
B Resistor connector
21
Y/B
V
C Rear blower motor connector
Resistor connector
51
21
Y/B
Ω
HS
CONNECT
DISCONNECT
ACC
OFF
94I10486
Courtesy of Nissan Motor Co., U.S.A.
DIAGNOSTIC PROCEDURE 6 – REAR BLOWER MOTOR DOES NOT ROTATE WITH FRONT FAN LEVER FOR REAR A/C SET AT 1-4 SPEED (Cont.)
A
1
CHECK RESISTOR AFTER DISCONNECTING IT.
B
2 3 4
N.G.
Replace resistor.
O.K.
Reconnect resistor harness connector.
1
2 3 4
5
D
CHECK REAR FAN SWITCH (FRONT) CIRCUIT. Do approx. 12 volts exist between each rear fan switch (Front) harness terminal and body ground?
Flow chart No. | Terminal No. ⊕ | Terminal No. ⊖ | Voltage
2 | 24 | Body ground | Approx. 12
3 | 23 | |
4 | 22 | |
5 | 21 | |
N.G.
E
Note
Check circuit continuity between rear fan switch (Front) and resistor.
O.K.
2 3 4 5
CHECK REAR FAN SWITCH (FRONT) AFTER DISCONNECTING IT.
N.G.
Replace rear fan switch (Front).
O.K.
F
Note
Check circuit continuity between rear fan switch (Front) harness terminal No. 26 and A/C control module harness terminal No. 37.
O.K.
C
Go To Next Figure
NOTE: If the result is no good (NG) after checking circuit continuity, repair harness or connector.
D Rear fan switch (Front) connector
24 23 22 21
G BR P/L Y/B
V
E Rear fan switch (Front) connector
Resistor connector
Ω
F Rear fan switch (Front) connector
A/C control module connector
26
37
B/W
Ω
94J10487
Courtesy of Nissan Motor Co., U.S.A.

Fig. 17: Diagnostic Procedure 6 – Rear Blower Motor Does Not Rotate With Front Fan Lever For Rear A/C Set At 1-4 Speed (1 Of 3)

Fig. 18: Diagnostic Procedure 6 – Rear Blower Motor Does Not Rotate With Front Fan Lever For Rear A/C Set At 1-4 Speed (2 Of 3)

DIAGNOSTIC PROCEDURE 6 – REAR BLOWER MOTOR DOES NOT ROTATE WITH FRONT FAN LEVER FOR REAR A/C SET AT 1-4 SPEED (Cont.)

DIAGNOSTIC PROCEDURE 7 – REAR BLOWER MOTOR DOES NOT ROTATE WITH FRONT FAN LEVER FOR REAR A/C SET AT REAR POSITION

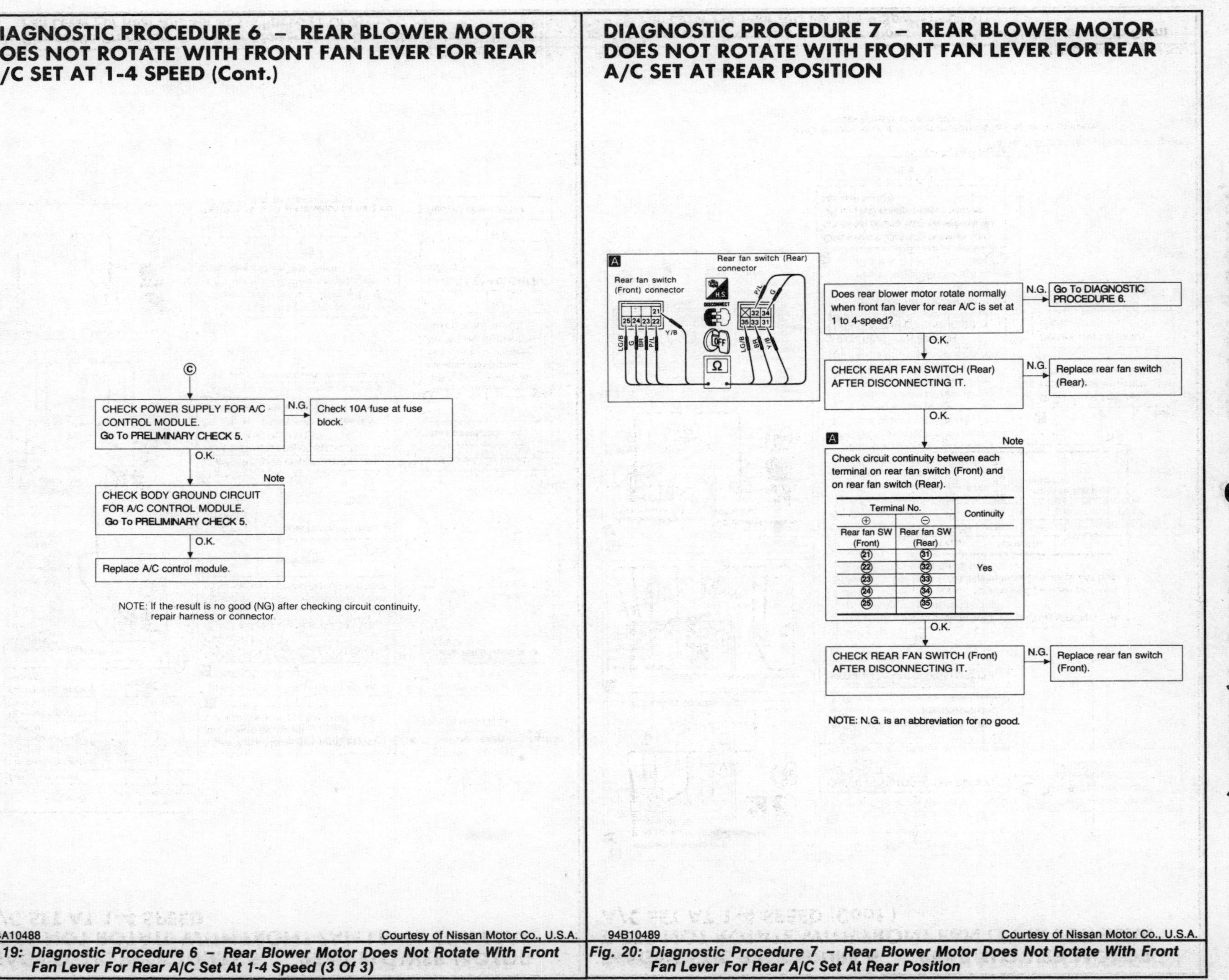
C
CHECK POWER SUPPLY FOR A/C CONTROL MODULE.
Go To PRELIMINARY CHECK 5.
N.G.
Check 10A fuse at fuse block.
O.K.
Note
CHECK BODY GROUND CIRCUIT FOR A/C CONTROL MODULE.
Go To PRELIMINARY CHECK 5.
O.K.
Replace A/C control module.
NOTE: If the result is no good (NG) after checking circuit continuity, repair harness or connector.
94A10488
Courtesy of Nissan Motor Co., U.S.A.
A
Rear fan switch (Front) connector
Rear fan switch (Rear) connector
21
25 24 23 22
LG/B
G
BR
P/L
Y/B
32 34
35 33 31
Ω
Does rear blower motor rotate normally when front fan lever for rear A/C is set at 1 to 4-speed?
N.G.
Go To DIAGNOSTIC PROCEDURE 6.
O.K.
CHECK REAR FAN SWITCH (Rear) AFTER DISCONNECTING IT.
N.G.
Replace rear fan switch (Rear).
O.K.
A
Note
Check circuit continuity between each terminal on rear fan switch (Front) and on rear fan switch (Rear).
O.K.
CHECK REAR FAN SWITCH (Front) AFTER DISCONNECTING IT.
N.G.
Replace rear fan switch (Front).
NOTE: N.G. is an abbreviation for no good.
94B10489
Courtesy of Nissan Motor Co., U.S.A.

Terminal No. ⊕ Rear fan SW (Front)	Terminal No. ⊖ Rear fan SW (Rear)	Continuity
21	31	Yes
22	32	
23	33	
24	34	
25	35	

Fig. 19: Diagnostic Procedure 6 – Rear Blower Motor Does Not Rotate With Front Fan Lever For Rear A/C Set At 1-4 Speed (3 Of 3)

Fig. 20: Diagnostic Procedure 7 – Rear Blower Motor Does Not Rotate With Front Fan Lever For Rear A/C Set At Rear Position

1993 MANUAL A/C-HEATER SYSTEMS
Trouble Shooting – Quest (Cont.)

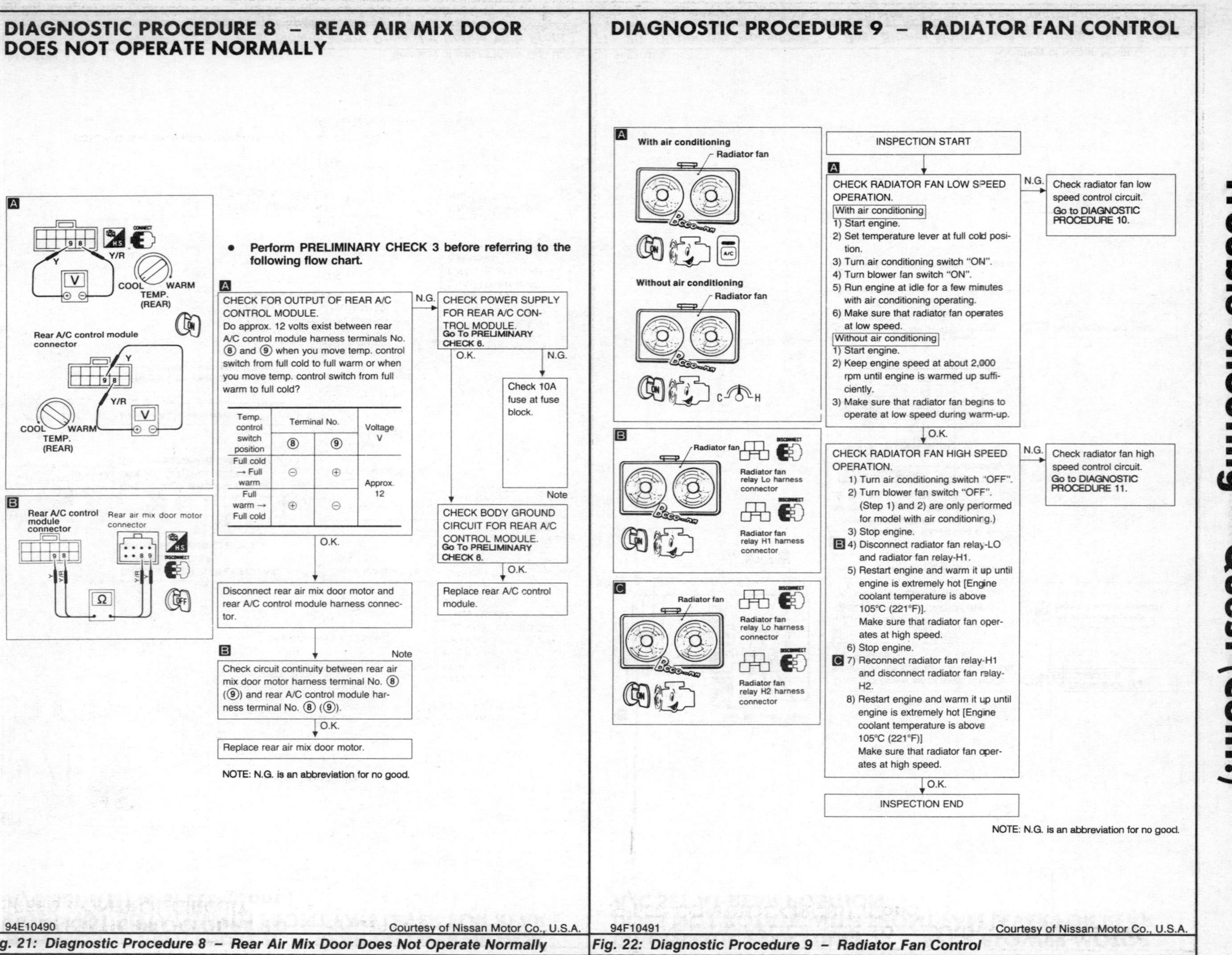
DIAGNOSTIC PROCEDURE 8 – REAR AIR MIX DOOR DOES NOT OPERATE NORMALLY
A
Y/R
Y
V
COOL
WARM
TEMP. (REAR)
Rear A/C control module connector
B
Rear A/C control module connector
Rear air mix door motor connector
Ω
• Perform PRELIMINARY CHECK 3 before referring to the following flow chart.
A CHECK FOR OUTPUT OF REAR A/C CONTROL MODULE.
Do approx. 12 volts exist between rear A/C control module harness terminals No. ⑧ and ⑨ when you move temp. control switch from full cold to full warm or when you move temp. control switch from full warm to full cold?
Temp. control switch position | Terminal No. ⑧ | ⑨ | Voltage V
Full cold → Full warm | ⊖ | ⊕ | Approx. 12
Full warm → Full cold | ⊕ | ⊖ |
N.G.
CHECK POWER SUPPLY FOR REAR A/C CONTROL MODULE.
Go To PRELIMINARY CHECK 6.
O.K.
N.G.
Check 10A fuse at fuse block.
Note
CHECK BODY GROUND CIRCUIT FOR REAR A/C CONTROL MODULE.
Go To PRELIMINARY CHECK 6.
O.K.
Replace rear A/C control module.
O.K.
Disconnect rear air mix door motor and rear A/C control module harness connector.
B
Note
Check circuit continuity between rear air mix door motor harness terminal No. ⑧ (⑨) and rear A/C control module harness terminal No. ⑧ (⑨).
O.K.
Replace rear air mix door motor.
NOTE: N.G. is an abbreviation for no good.
94E10490
Courtesy of Nissan Motor Co., U.S.A.
DIAGNOSTIC PROCEDURE 9 – RADIATOR FAN CONTROL
A
With air conditioning
Radiator fan
Without air conditioning
Radiator fan
B
Radiator fan
Radiator fan relay Lo harness connector
Radiator fan relay H1 harness connector
C
Radiator fan
Radiator fan relay Lo harness connector
Radiator fan relay H2 harness connector
INSPECTION START
A CHECK RADIATOR FAN LOW SPEED OPERATION.
With air conditioning
1) Start engine.
2) Set temperature lever at full cold position.
3) Turn air conditioning switch "ON".
4) Turn blower fan switch "ON".
5) Run engine at idle for a few minutes with air conditioning operating.
6) Make sure that radiator fan operates at low speed.
Without air conditioning
1) Start engine.
2) Keep engine speed at about 2,000 rpm until engine is warmed up sufficiently.
3) Make sure that radiator fan begins to operate at low speed during warm-up.
N.G.
Check radiator fan low speed control circuit.
Go to DIAGNOSTIC PROCEDURE 10.
O.K.
CHECK RADIATOR FAN HIGH SPEED OPERATION.
1) Turn air conditioning switch "OFF".
2) Turn blower fan switch "OFF".
(Step 1) and 2) are only performed for model with air conditioning.)
3) Stop engine.
B 4) Disconnect radiator fan relay-LO and radiator fan relay-H1.
5) Restart engine and warm it up until engine is extremely hot [Engine coolant temperature is above 105°C (221°F)].
Make sure that radiator fan operates at high speed.
6) Stop engine.
C 7) Reconnect radiator fan relay-H1 and disconnect radiator fan relay-H2.
8) Restart engine and warm it up until engine is extremely hot [Engine coolant temperature is above 105°C (221°F)]
Make sure that radiator fan operates at high speed.
N.G.
Check radiator fan high speed control circuit.
Go to DIAGNOSTIC PROCEDURE 11.
O.K.
INSPECTION END
NOTE: N.G. is an abbreviation for no good.
94F10491
Courtesy of Nissan Motor Co., U.S.A.

Fig. 21: Diagnostic Procedure 8 – Rear Air Mix Door Does Not Operate Normally

Fig. 22: Diagnostic Procedure 9 – Radiator Fan Control

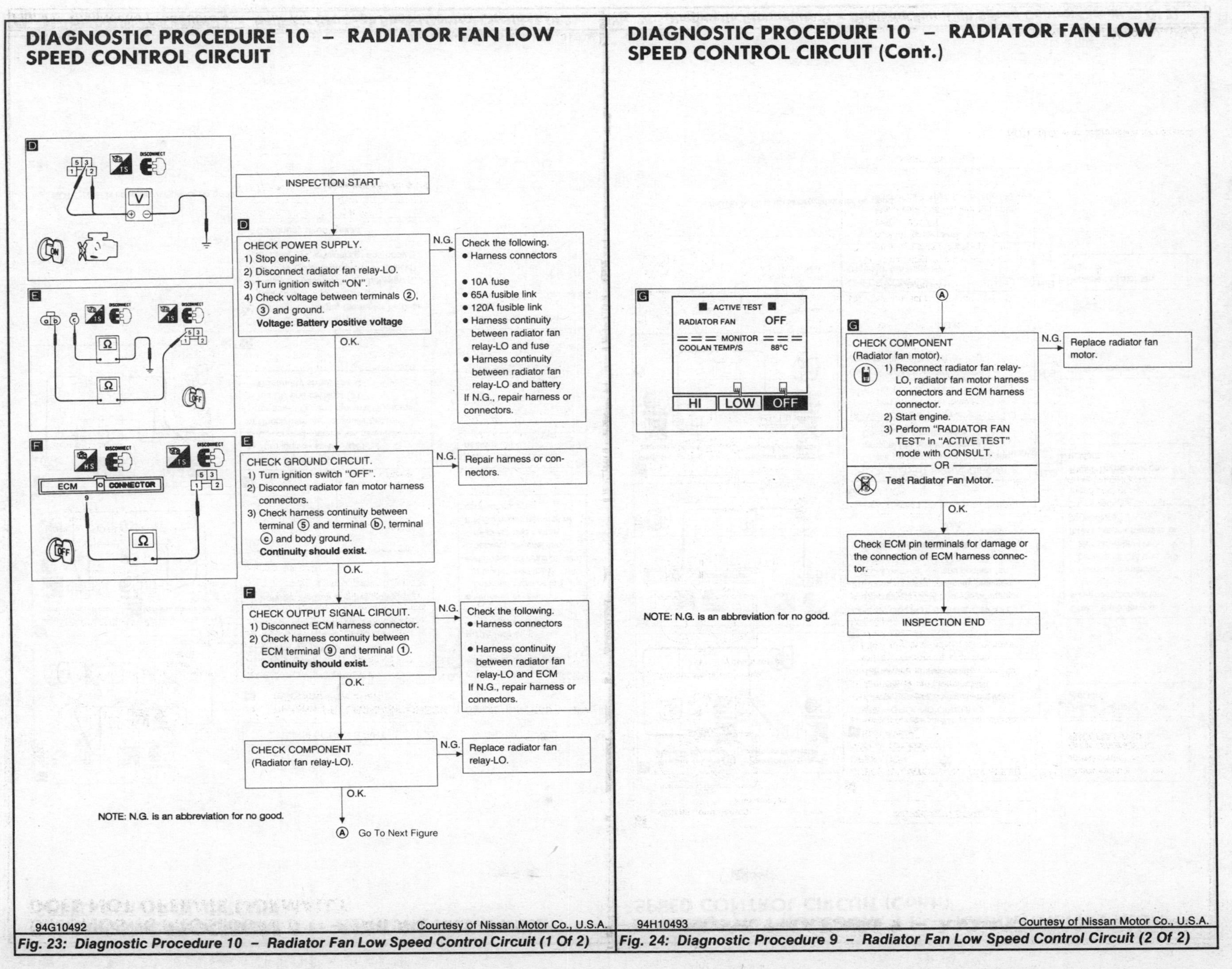
DIAGNOSTIC PROCEDURE 10 – RADIATOR FAN LOW SPEED CONTROL CIRCUIT
INSPECTION START
D
CHECK POWER SUPPLY.
1) Stop engine.
2) Disconnect radiator fan relay-LO.
3) Turn ignition switch "ON".
4) Check voltage between terminals ②, ③ and ground.
Voltage: Battery positive voltage
N.G.
Check the following.
● Harness connectors
● 10A fuse
● 65A fusible link
● 120A fusible link
● Harness continuity between radiator fan relay-LO and fuse
● Harness continuity between radiator fan relay-LO and battery
If N.G., repair harness or connectors.
O.K.
E
CHECK GROUND CIRCUIT.
1) Turn ignition switch "OFF".
2) Disconnect radiator fan motor harness connectors.
3) Check harness continuity between terminal ⑤ and terminal ⓑ, terminal ⓒ and body ground.
Continuity should exist.
N.G.
Repair harness or connectors.
O.K.
F
CHECK OUTPUT SIGNAL CIRCUIT.
1) Disconnect ECM harness connector.
2) Check harness continuity between ECM terminal ⑨ and terminal ①.
Continuity should exist.
N.G.
Check the following.
● Harness connectors
● Harness continuity between radiator fan relay-LO and ECM
If N.G., repair harness or connectors.
O.K.
CHECK COMPONENT
(Radiator fan relay-LO).
N.G.
Replace radiator fan relay-LO.
O.K.
Ⓐ Go To Next Figure
NOTE: N.G. is an abbreviation for no good.
ECM
CONNECTOR
DISCONNECT
HS
IS
V
Ω
ON
OFF
9
94G10492
Courtesy of Nissan Motor Co., U.S.A.
DIAGNOSTIC PROCEDURE 10 – RADIATOR FAN LOW SPEED CONTROL CIRCUIT (Cont.)
G
ACTIVE TEST
RADIATOR FAN OFF
MONITOR
COOLAN TEMP/S 88°C
HI
LOW
OFF
Ⓐ
CHECK COMPONENT
(Radiator fan motor).
1) Reconnect radiator fan relay-LO, radiator fan motor harness connectors and ECM harness connector.
2) Start engine.
3) Perform "RADIATOR FAN TEST" in "ACTIVE TEST" mode with CONSULT.
OR
Test Radiator Fan Motor.
N.G.
Replace radiator fan motor.
O.K.
Check ECM pin terminals for damage or the connection of ECM harness connector.
INSPECTION END
NOTE: N.G. is an abbreviation for no good.
94H10493
Courtesy of Nissan Motor Co., U.S.A.

Fig. 23: Diagnostic Procedure 10 – Radiator Fan Low Speed Control Circuit (1 Of 2)

Fig. 24: Diagnostic Procedure 9 – Radiator Fan Low Speed Control Circuit (2 Of 2)

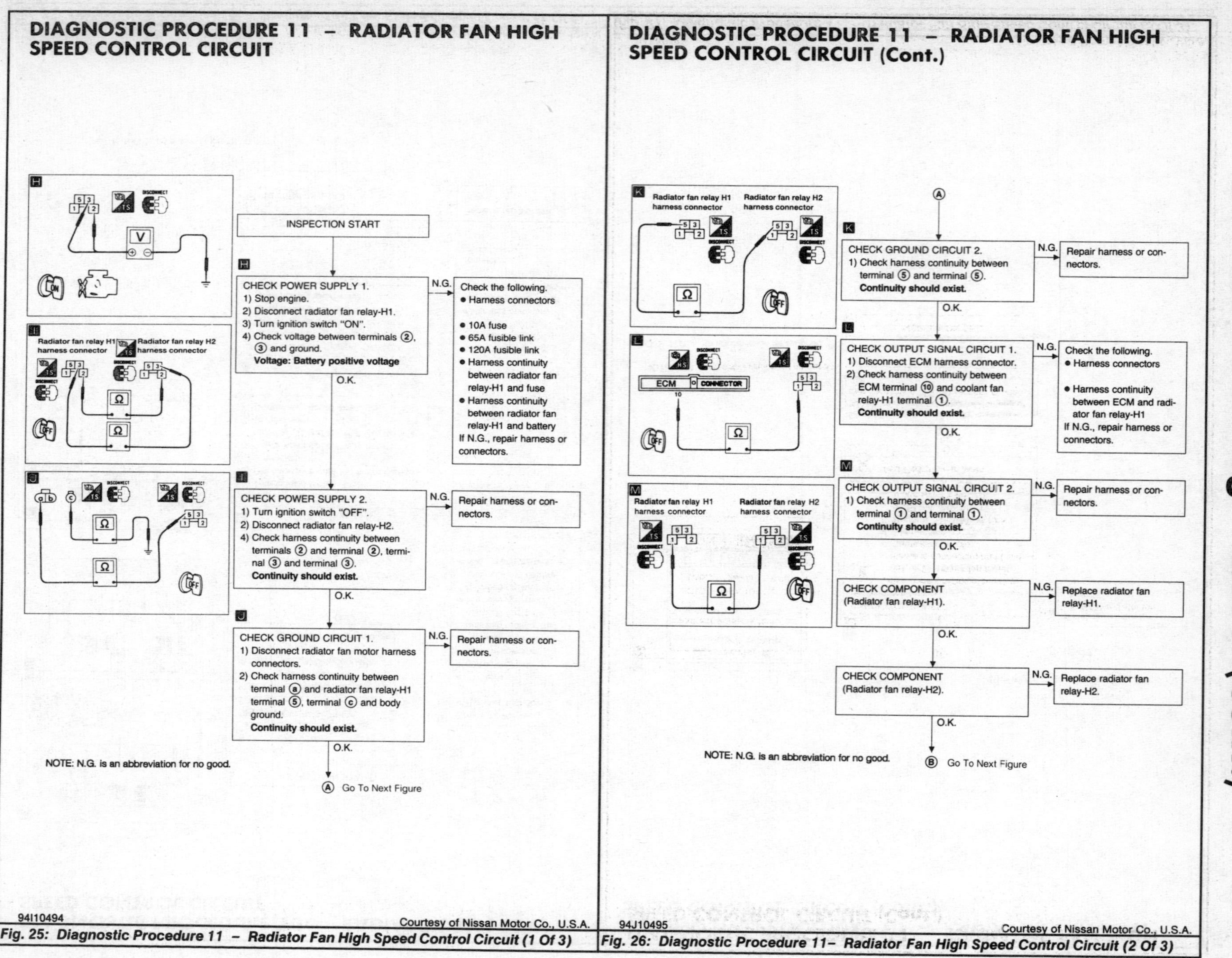
DIAGNOSTIC PROCEDURE 11 – RADIATOR FAN HIGH SPEED CONTROL CIRCUIT
Radiator fan relay H1 harness connector
Radiator fan relay H2 harness connector
INSPECTION START
H
CHECK POWER SUPPLY 1.
1) Stop engine.
2) Disconnect radiator fan relay-H1.
3) Turn ignition switch "ON".
4) Check voltage between terminals ②, ③ and ground.
Voltage: Battery positive voltage
N.G.
Check the following.
• Harness connectors
• 10A fuse
• 65A fusible link
• 120A fusible link
• Harness continuity between radiator fan relay-H1 and fuse
• Harness continuity between radiator fan relay-H1 and battery
If N.G., repair harness or connectors.
O.K.
I
CHECK POWER SUPPLY 2.
1) Turn ignition switch "OFF".
2) Disconnect radiator fan relay-H2.
4) Check harness continuity between terminals ② and terminal ②, terminal ③ and terminal ③.
Continuity should exist.
N.G.
Repair harness or connectors.
O.K.
J
CHECK GROUND CIRCUIT 1.
1) Disconnect radiator fan motor harness connectors.
2) Check harness continuity between terminal ⓐ and radiator fan relay-H1 terminal ⑤, terminal ⓒ and body ground.
Continuity should exist.
N.G.
Repair harness or connectors.
O.K.
Ⓐ Go To Next Figure
NOTE: N.G. is an abbreviation for no good.
94I10494
Courtesy of Nissan Motor Co., U.S.A.
DIAGNOSTIC PROCEDURE 11 – RADIATOR FAN HIGH SPEED CONTROL CIRCUIT (Cont.)
Radiator fan relay H1 harness connector
Radiator fan relay H2 harness connector
ECM
CONNECTOR
Ⓐ
K
CHECK GROUND CIRCUIT 2.
1) Check harness continuity between terminal ⑤ and terminal ⑤.
Continuity should exist.
N.G.
Repair harness or connectors.
O.K.
L
CHECK OUTPUT SIGNAL CIRCUIT 1.
1) Disconnect ECM harness connector.
2) Check harness continuity between ECM terminal ⑩ and coolant fan relay-H1 terminal ①.
Continuity should exist.
N.G.
Check the following.
• Harness connectors
• Harness continuity between ECM and radiator fan relay-H1
If N.G., repair harness or connectors.
O.K.
M
CHECK OUTPUT SIGNAL CIRCUIT 2.
1) Check harness continuity between terminal ① and terminal ①.
Continuity should exist.
N.G.
Repair harness or connectors.
O.K.
CHECK COMPONENT
(Radiator fan relay-H1).
N.G.
Replace radiator fan relay-H1.
O.K.
CHECK COMPONENT
(Radiator fan relay-H2).
N.G.
Replace radiator fan relay-H2.
O.K.
Ⓑ Go To Next Figure
NOTE: N.G. is an abbreviation for no good.
94J10495
Courtesy of Nissan Motor Co., U.S.A.

Fig. 25: Diagnostic Procedure 11 – Radiator Fan High Speed Control Circuit (1 Of 3)

Fig. 26: Diagnostic Procedure 11– Radiator Fan High Speed Control Circuit (2 Of 3)

1993 MANUAL A/C-HEATER SYSTEMS
Trouble Shooting – Quest (Cont.)

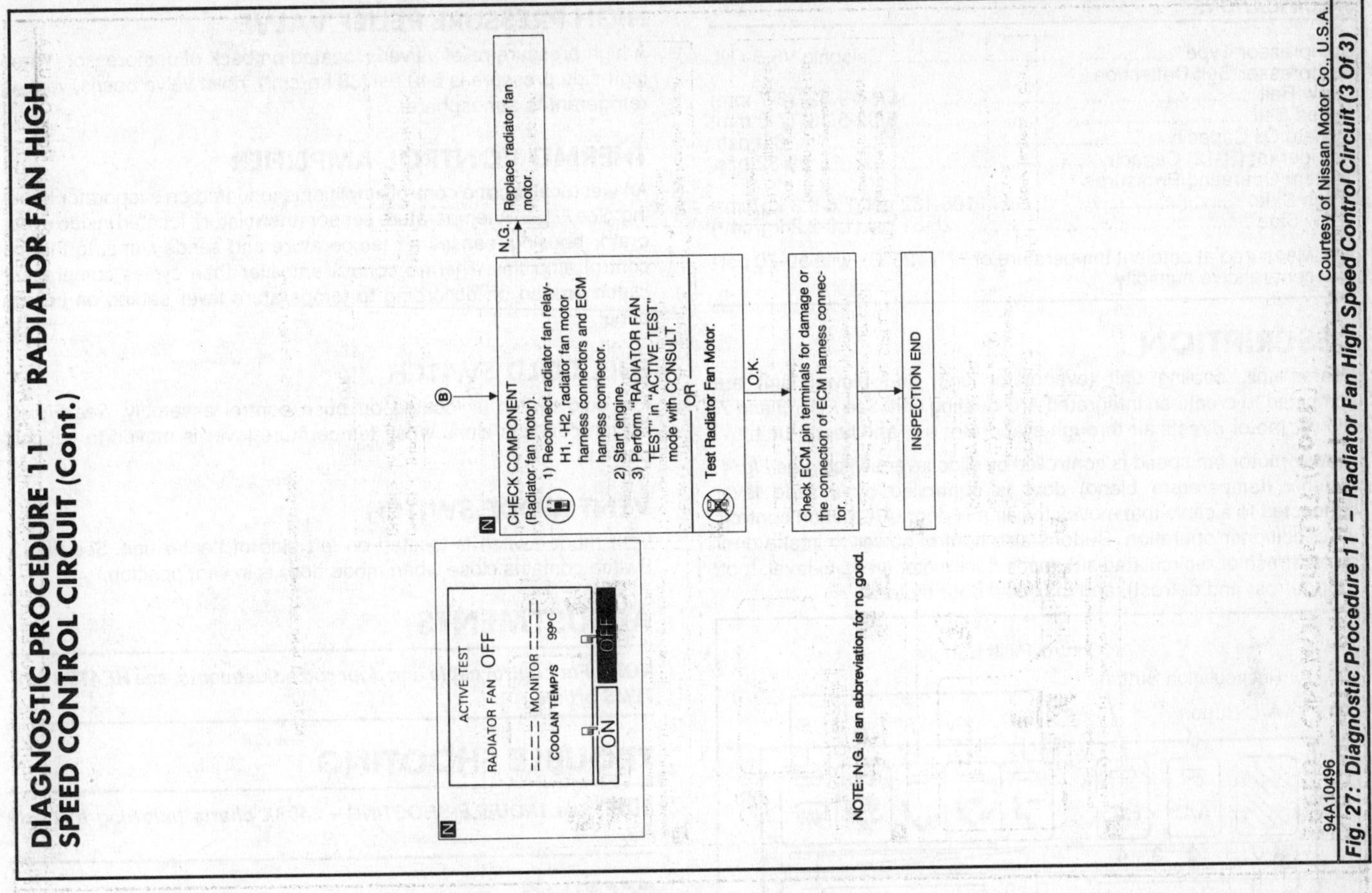
DIAGNOSTIC PROCEDURE 11 – RADIATOR FAN HIGH SPEED CONTROL CIRCUIT (Cont.)
N
ACTIVE TEST
RADIATOR FAN OFF
==== MONITOR ====
COOLAN TEMP/S 99°C
ON
OFF
B
N
CHECK COMPONENT
(Radiator fan motor).
1) Reconnect radiator fan relay-H1, -H2, radiator fan motor harness connectors and ECM harness connector.
2) Start engine.
3) Perform "RADIATOR FAN TEST" in "ACTIVE TEST" mode with CONSULT.
OR
Test Radiator Fan Motor.
N.G.
Replace radiator fan motor.
O.K.
Check ECM pin terminals for damage or the connection of ECM harness connector.
INSPECTION END
NOTE: N.G. is an abbreviation for no good.
94A10496
Courtesy of Nissan Motor Co., U.S.A.

Fig. 27: Diagnostic Procedure 11 – Radiator Fan High Speed Control Circuit (3 Of 3)

1993 MANUAL A/C-HEATER SYSTEMS 240SX

SPECIFICATIONS

Compressor Type	Calsonic V5 5-Cyl.
Compressor Belt Deflection	
New Belt	15/64-9/32" (6-7 mm)
Used Belt	9/32-5/16" (7-8 mm)
System Oil Capacity	8.0 ozs.
Refrigerant (R-12) Capacity	29-32 ozs.
System Operating Pressures [1]	
High Side	108-132 psi (7.6-9.3 kg/cm²)
Low Side	26-31 psi (1.8-2.2 kg/cm²)

[1] – Measured at ambient temperature of 77°F (25°C), with 50-70 percent relative humidity.

DESCRIPTION

Heater unit, cooling unit (evaporator unit) and blower unit are combined to create an integrated A/C-heating unit. *See Figs. 3 and 7.* Blower motor directs air through evaporator unit and heater unit.

Blower motor fan speed is controlled by slide lever switch. *See Fig. 1.* Air mix (temperature blend) door is controlled by a slide lever connected to a cable that moves the air mix door. A/C button controls air conditioner operation. Buttons also control power to intake door motor (fresh or recirculated air), mode door motor (vent, bi-level, foot, foot/defrost and defrost), and max cold door motor.

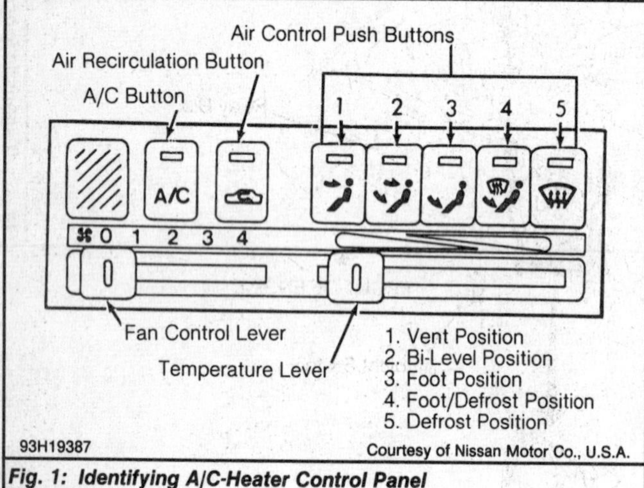
Air Control Push Buttons
Air Recirculation Button
A/C Button
1 2 3 4 5
A/C
0 1 2 3 4
Fan Control Lever
Temperature Lever
1. Vent Position
2. Bi-Level Position
3. Foot Position
4. Foot/Defrost Position
5. Defrost Position
93H19387
Courtesy of Nissan Motor Co., U.S.A.

Fig. 1: Identifying A/C-Heater Control Panel

OPERATION

ACCELERATION CUT SYSTEM

This system is controlled by the Engine Concentrated Control System (ECCS) control unit. When engine is under heavy load (full throttle), A/C compressor is turned off for 5 seconds to reduce engine load. Also, when engine coolant temperature is greater than 235°F (113°C), A/C compressor is turned off.

DUAL-PRESSURE SWITCH

Dual-pressure switch, mounted on receiver-drier, prevents A/C clutch operation if system pressure is too high (due to restriction, overcharge or compressor malfunction) or too low. *See Fig. 2.*

FAST IDLE CONTROL DEVICE (FICD)

When engine speed decreases due to A/C clutch engagement, the engine control module signals FICD to increase idle speed, allowing engine to idle smoothly.

FUSIBLE PLUG

Fusible plug, mounted on receiver-drier, is a high temperature relief. When temperature is 221°F (105°C), plug melts to vent refrigerant to atmosphere, thereby protecting the A/C system.

HIGH PRESSURE RELIEF VALVE

A high pressure relief valve is located on back of compressor. When high-side pressure is 540 psi (38 kg/cm²), relief valve opens, venting refrigerant to atmosphere.

THERMO CONTROL AMPLIFIER

An electrical thermo control amplifier is mounted on evaporator housing. *See Fig. 3.* A temperature sensor (thermistor), located inside evaporator housing, senses air temperature and sends signal to thermo control amplifier. Thermo control amplifier then cycles compressor clutch on and off according to temperature lever setting on control panel.

FULL COLD SWITCH

Full cold switch is located on push control assembly. *See Fig. 3.* Switch contacts close when temperature lever is moved to full cold position.

VENT MODE SWITCH

Vent mode switch is located on left side of heater unit. *See Fig. 3.* Switch contacts close when mode door is in vent position.

ADJUSTMENTS

NOTE: For control cable and door rod adjustments, see HEATER SYSTEMS article.

TROUBLE SHOOTING

NOTE: See TROUBLE SHOOTING – 240SX charts following this article.

TESTING

A/C SYSTEM PERFORMANCE

1) Park vehicle out of direct sunlight. Close all doors. Open engine hood and windows. Connect A/C manifold gauge set. Determine relative humidity and ambient air temperature. Select maximum cold temperature, face vent mode and recirculated air.

2) Turn blower fan switch to highest position. Run engine at 1500 RPM for 10 minutes. Check A/C system pressures. System is operating correctly if pressures are as specified. See A/C SYSTEM PERFORMANCE TEST table.

A/C SYSTEM PERFORMANCE TEST

Ambient Air Temp. °F (°C)	High Pressure [1] psi (kg/cm²)	[1] Low Pressure psi (kg/cm²)
77 (25)	108-132 (7.6-9.3)	26-31 (1.8-2.2)
86 (30)	128-158 (9.0-11.1)	23-28 (1.6-2.0)
95 (35)	151-185 (10.6-13.0)	24-31 (1.7-2.2)
104 (40)	173-210 (12.2-14.8)	26-37 (1.8-2.6)

[1] – Specification is with relative humidity at 50-70 percent.

A/C SWITCH

Disconnect negative battery cable. Remove push control assembly. Connect ohmmeter between indicated push control assembly connector terminals, and check for continuity with A/C and defrost switches in specified positions. *See Fig. 4.*

BLOWER MOTOR

Disconnect wiring harness at blower motor. Apply battery voltage to blower motor terminals. Ensure blower motor operation is smooth. If blower motor operation is rough or not up to speed, replace blower motor.

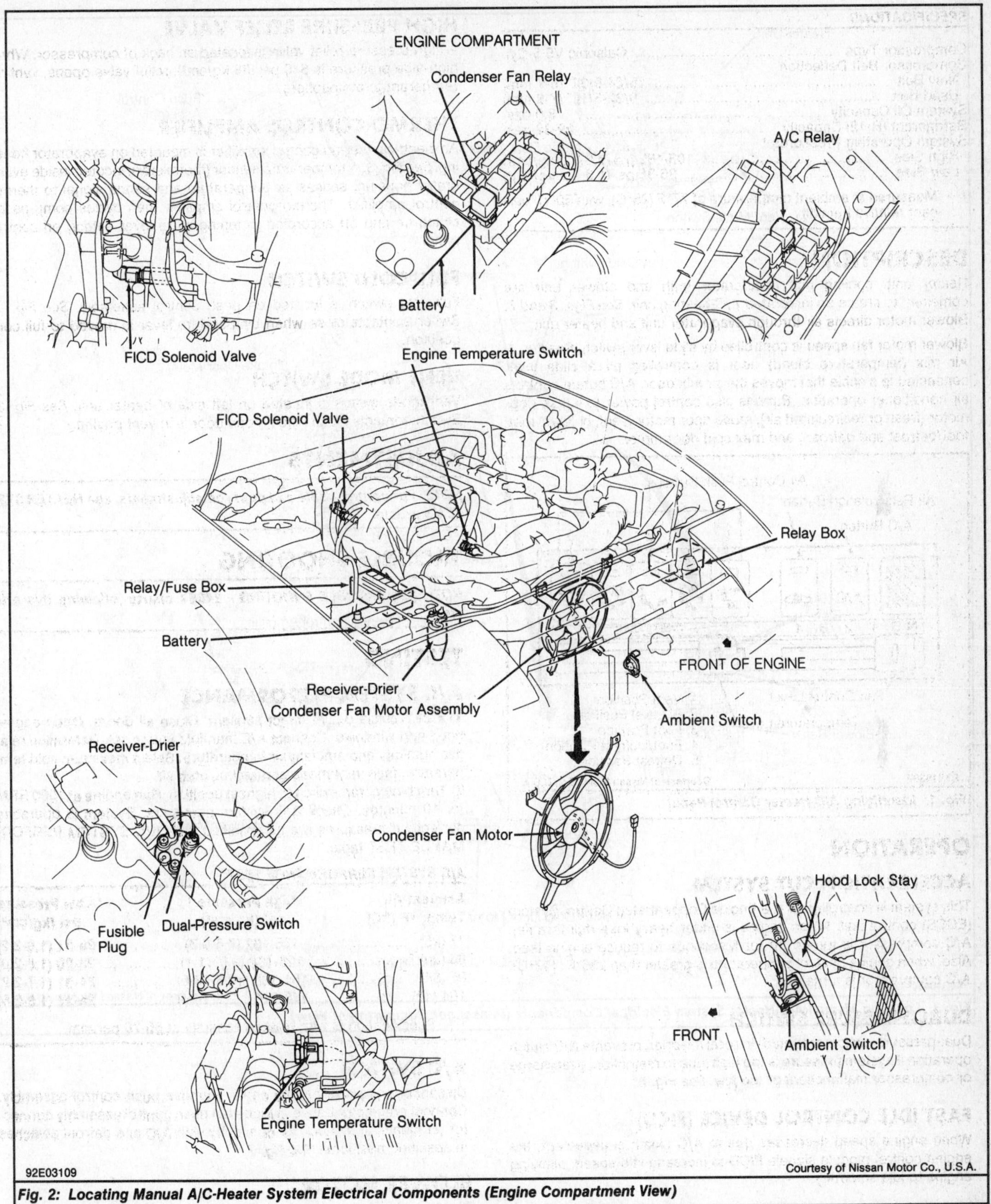
ENGINE COMPARTMENT
Condenser Fan Relay
A/C Relay
Battery
FICD Solenoid Valve
Engine Temperature Switch
FICD Solenoid Valve
Relay Box
Relay/Fuse Box
Battery
FRONT OF ENGINE
Receiver-Drier
Condenser Fan Motor Assembly
Ambient Switch
Receiver-Drier
Condenser Fan Motor
Hood Lock Stay
Fusible Plug
Dual-Pressure Switch
FRONT
Ambient Switch
Engine Temperature Switch
92E03109
Courtesy of Nissan Motor Co., U.S.A.

Fig. 2: Locating Manual A/C-Heater System Electrical Components (Engine Compartment View)

1993 MANUAL A/C-HEATER SYSTEMS
240SX (Cont.)

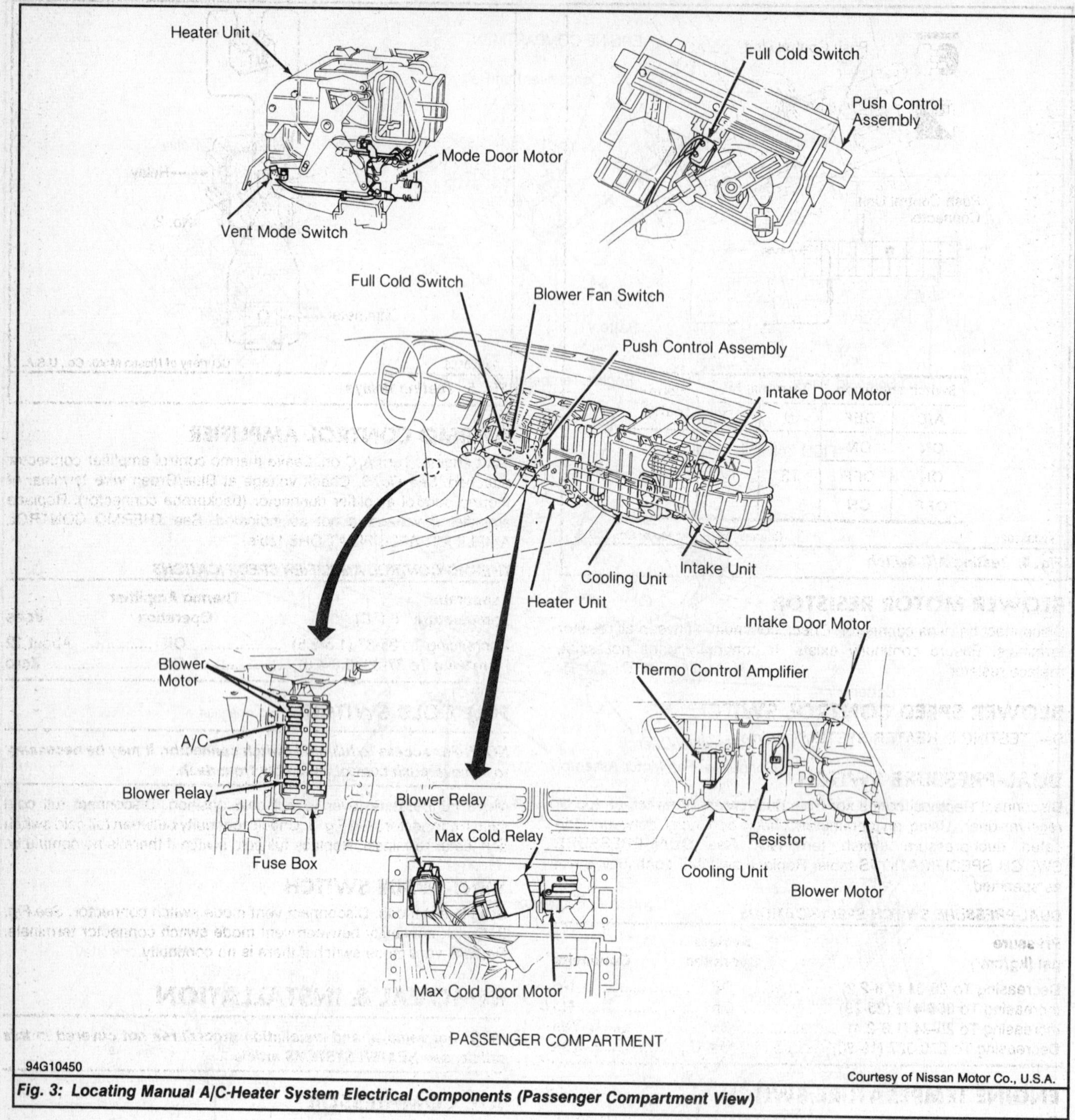
Heater Unit
Full Cold Switch
Push Control Assembly
Mode Door Motor
Vent Mode Switch
Full Cold Switch
Blower Fan Switch
Push Control Assembly
Intake Door Motor
Cooling Unit
Intake Unit
Heater Unit
Intake Door Motor
Thermo Control Amplifier
Blower Motor
A/C
Blower Relay
Fuse Box
Blower Relay
Max Cold Relay
Resistor
Cooling Unit
Blower Motor
Max Cold Door Motor
PASSENGER COMPARTMENT
94G10450
Courtesy of Nissan Motor Co., U.S.A.

Fig. 3: Locating Manual A/C-Heater System Electrical Components (Passenger Compartment View)

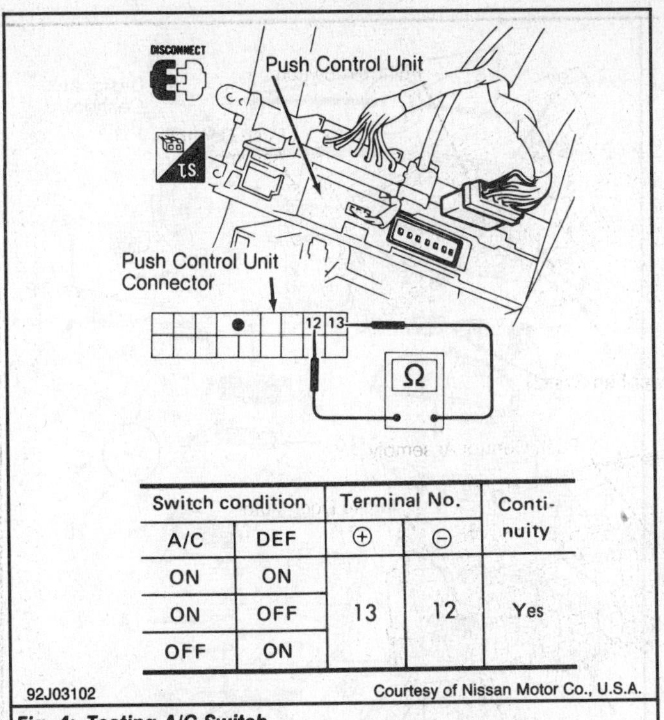
DISCONNECT
T.S.
Push Control Unit
Push Control Unit
Connector
12
13
Ω
92J03102
Courtesy of Nissan Motor Co., U.S.A.

Switch condition		Terminal No.		Continuity
A/C	DEF	⊕	⊖	
ON	ON	13	12	Yes
ON	OFF			
OFF	ON			

Fig. 4: Testing A/C Switch

BLOWER MOTOR RESISTOR

Disconnect harness connector. Check continuity between all resistor terminals. Ensure continuity exists. If continuity does not exist, replace resistor.

BLOWER SPEED CONTROL SWITCH

See TESTING in HEATER SYSTEMS article.

DUAL-PRESSURE SWITCH

Disconnect electrical connector from dual-pressure switch on top of receiver-drier. Using an ohmmeter, check continuity between indicated dual-pressure switch terminals. See DUAL-PRESSURE SWITCH SPECIFICATIONS table. Replace switch if continuity is not as specified.

DUAL-PRESSURE SWITCH SPECIFICATIONS

Pressure psi (kg/cm²)	System Operation	Continuity
Decreasing To 26-31 (1.8-2.2)	Off	No
Increasing To 356-412 (25-29)	Off	No
Increasing To 26-34 (1.8-2.4)	On	Yes
Decreasing To 270-327 (19-23)	On	Yes

ENGINE TEMPERATURE SWITCH

Remove engine temperature switch connector. *See Fig. 2.* Using an ohmmeter, check continuity between indicated engine temperature switch terminals. See ENGINE TEMPERATURE SWITCH SPECIFICATIONS table. Replace switch if it does not test as indicated.

ENGINE TEMPERATURE SWITCH SPECIFICATIONS

Coolant Temperature °F (°C)	Operation	Continuity
Decreasing To 185-196 (85-91)	Off	No
Increasing To 198-208 (92-98)	Off	No

RELAYS

Remove relay to be tested. *See Fig. 2 or 3.* Apply battery voltage between terminals No. 1 and 2. *See Fig. 5.* Check for continuity between remaining relay terminals. Continuity should exist. If no continuity exists, replace relay.

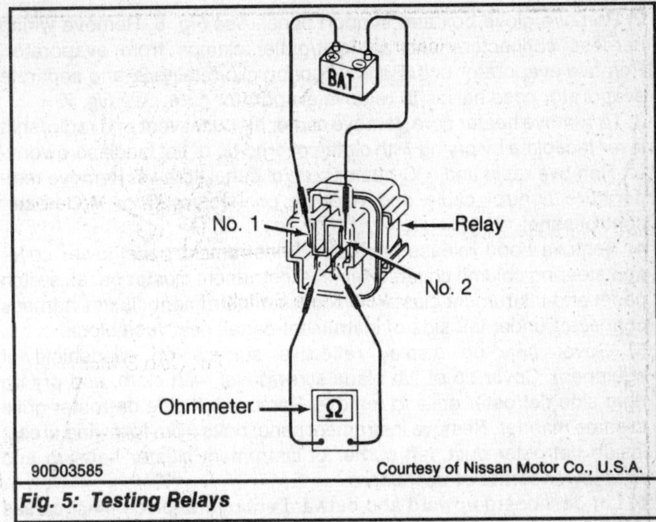
BAT
No. 1
Relay
No. 2
Ohmmeter
Ω
90D03585
Courtesy of Nissan Motor Co., U.S.A.

Fig. 5: Testing Relays

THERMO CONTROL AMPLIFIER

Start engine. Turn A/C on. Leave thermo control amplifier connector attached. *See Fig. 3.* Check voltage at Blue/Green wire terminal of thermo control amplifier connector (backprobe connector). Replace amplifier if voltage is not as indicated. See THERMO CONTROL AMPLIFIER SPECIFICATIONS table.

THERMO CONTROL AMPLIFIER SPECIFICATIONS

Evaporator Temperature °F (°C)	Thermo Amplifier Operation	Volts
Decreasing To 35-37 (1.5-2.5)	Off	About 12
Increasing To 37-39 (3.0-4.0)	On	Zero

FULL COLD SWITCH

NOTE: For access to full cold switch connector, it may be necessary to remove push control assembly from dash.

Move temperature lever to full cold position. Disconnect full cold switch connector. *See Fig. 3.* Check continuity between full cold switch connector terminals. Replace full cold switch if there is no continuity.

VENT MODE SWITCH

Select vent mode. Disconnect vent mode switch connector. *See Fig. 3.* Check continuity between vent mode switch connector terminals. Replace vent mode switch if there is no continuity.

REMOVAL & INSTALLATION

NOTE: For removal and installation procedures not covered in this article, see HEATER SYSTEMS article.

A/C COMPRESSOR

Removal – Loosen idler pulley bolt, and remove compressor belt. Discharge A/C system using approved refrigerant recovery/recycling equipment. Disconnect compressor clutch lead. Remove discharge and suction hoses from compressor, and plug hose openings. Remove compressor bolts and compressor.

Installation – To install, reverse removal procedure. Tighten compressor bolts to 33-44 ft. lbs. (45-60 N.m). Coat new "O" rings with refrigerant oil when attaching hoses to compressor. Evacuate and recharge system.

EVAPORATOR & HEATER CORE ASSEMBLY

Removal – **1)** Discharge A/C system using approved refrigerant recovery/recycling equipment. Drain cooling system. In engine compartment, disconnect A/C lines from evaporator. Remove heater hoses from heater core.

1993 MANUAL A/C-HEATER SYSTEMS
240SX (Cont.)

2) Remove glove box and support panel. *See Fig. 6.* Remove wiring harness connectors and air inlet/outlet clamps from evaporator. Remove evaporator unit. Remove spring clip retainers, and separate evaporator case halves to remove evaporator core. *See Fig. 7.*
3) To remove heater core, remove center air outlet vent and radio/shift lever faceplate by prying with cloth-covered tip of flat blade screwdriver. Remove radio and A/C-heater control panel screws. Remove temperature control cable and harness connectors from A/C-heater control panel.
4) Remove hood release bracket, left instrument panel lower cover and steering column covers. Remove instrument cluster bezel, switch panel and instrument cluster. Disconnect instrument cluster harness connector under left side of instrument panel, near fuse block.
5) Cover head-up display reflective surface on windshield (if equipped). Cover tip of flat blade screwdriver with cloth, and pry up right side defroster grille to remove. Remove left side defroster grille in same manner. Remove instrument panel bolts from following areas: inside defroster duct, left corner of instrument cluster housing and right lower corner of dashboard.
6) Lift dashboard upward and outward enough to disconnect cables and wiring harness from heater. Disconnect all air ducts, and remove heater unit. Remove spring clip retainers, and separate heater case halves to remove heater core.
Installation – To install, reverse removal procedure. Coat new "O" rings with refrigerant oil before assembling connections. If installing new evaporator core, add 2 ounces of refrigerant oil to new core before installation. Evacuate, recharge and leak test system.

MAX COLD DOOR MOTOR

Removal & Installation – Remove max cold door motor screws and door motor. *See Fig. 3.* Pull out door motor, and disconnect electrical connector. To install, connect door motor connector. Turn ignition switch to ACC position. Turn on defroster. Move temperature control lever to full hot position. Install door motor, engaging door lever and rod holder. Tighten screws. Select vent and defrost positions. Door should move back and forth.

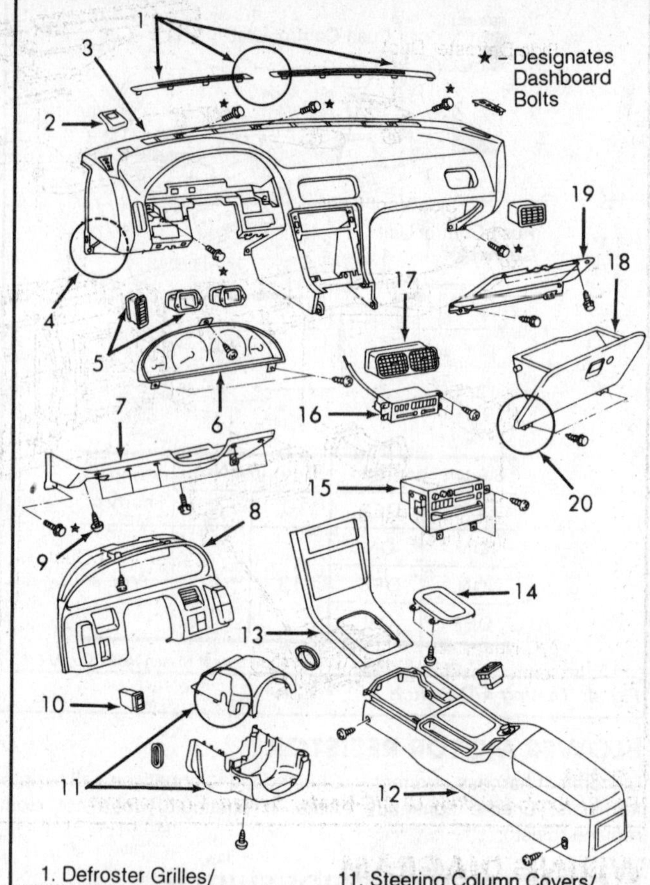
★ - Designates Dashboard Bolts
1. Defroster Grilles/ Pawl Locations
2. Head-Up Display Cover
3. Dashboard
4. Harness Connector
5. Air Vent Ducts
6. Instrument Cluster
7. Instrument Panel
8. Instrument Cluster Bezel/ Switches Panel
9. Hood Release Bracket Bolt
10. Panel Brightness Control
11. Steering Column Covers/ Pawl Location
12. Center Console
13. Radio/Shift Lever Faceplate
14. Shift Lever Cover
15. Radio
16. A/C-Heater Control Assembly
17. Center Air Outlet Vent
18. Glove Box
19. Glove Box Support Panel
20. Locating Pin
91D04924
Courtesy of Nissan Motor Co., U.S.A.

Fig. 6: Removing Dashboard For Access To Evaporator & Heater Core

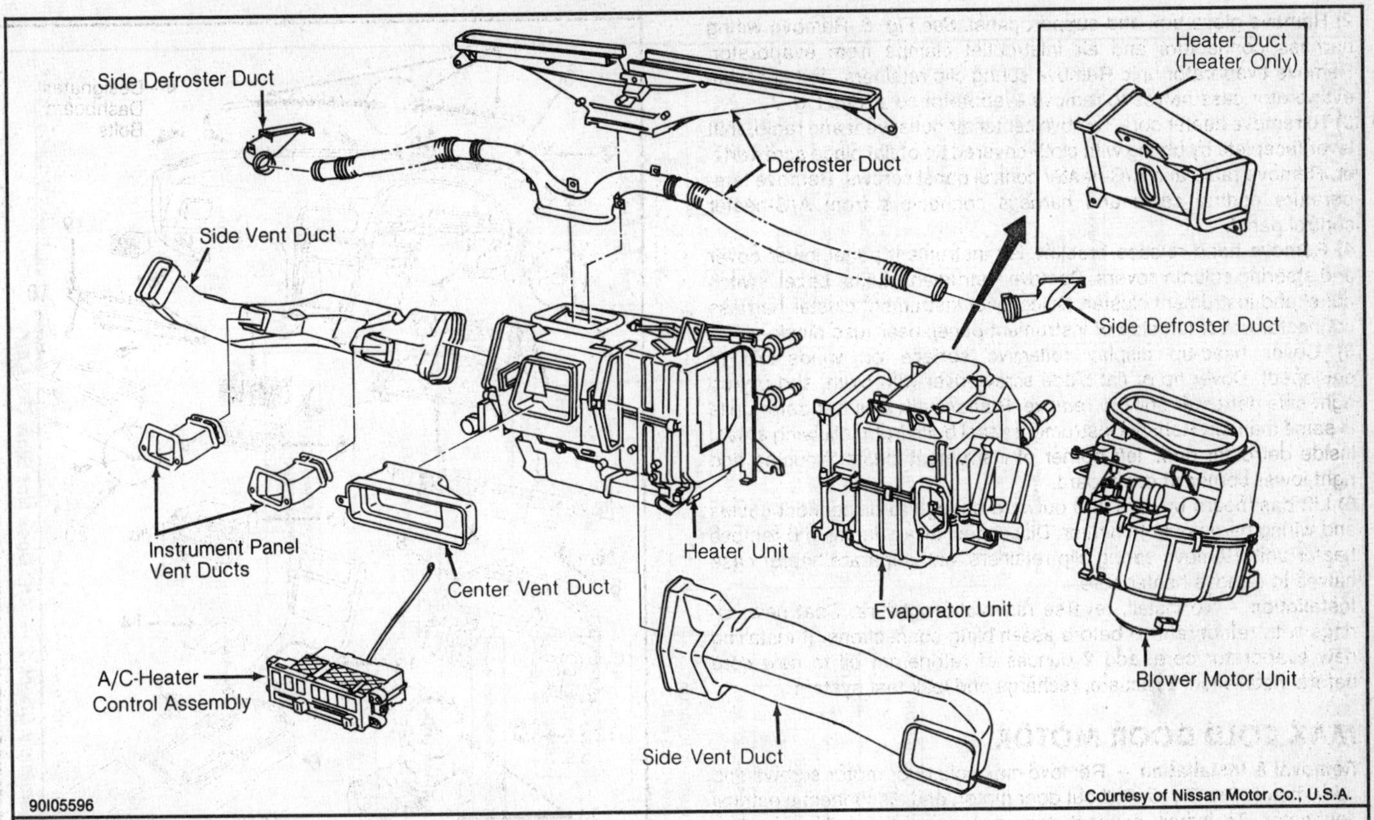

1993 MANUAL A/C-HEATER SYSTEMS
240SX (Cont.)

Side Defroster Duct
Heater Duct
(Heater Only)
Defroster Duct
Side Vent Duct
Side Defroster Duct
Instrument Panel
Vent Ducts
Heater Unit
Center Vent Duct
Evaporator Unit
A/C-Heater
Control Assembly
Blower Motor Unit
Side Vent Duct
90I05596
Courtesy of Nissan Motor Co., U.S.A.

Fig. 7: Exploded View Of A/C-Heater System Components

WIRING DIAGRAM

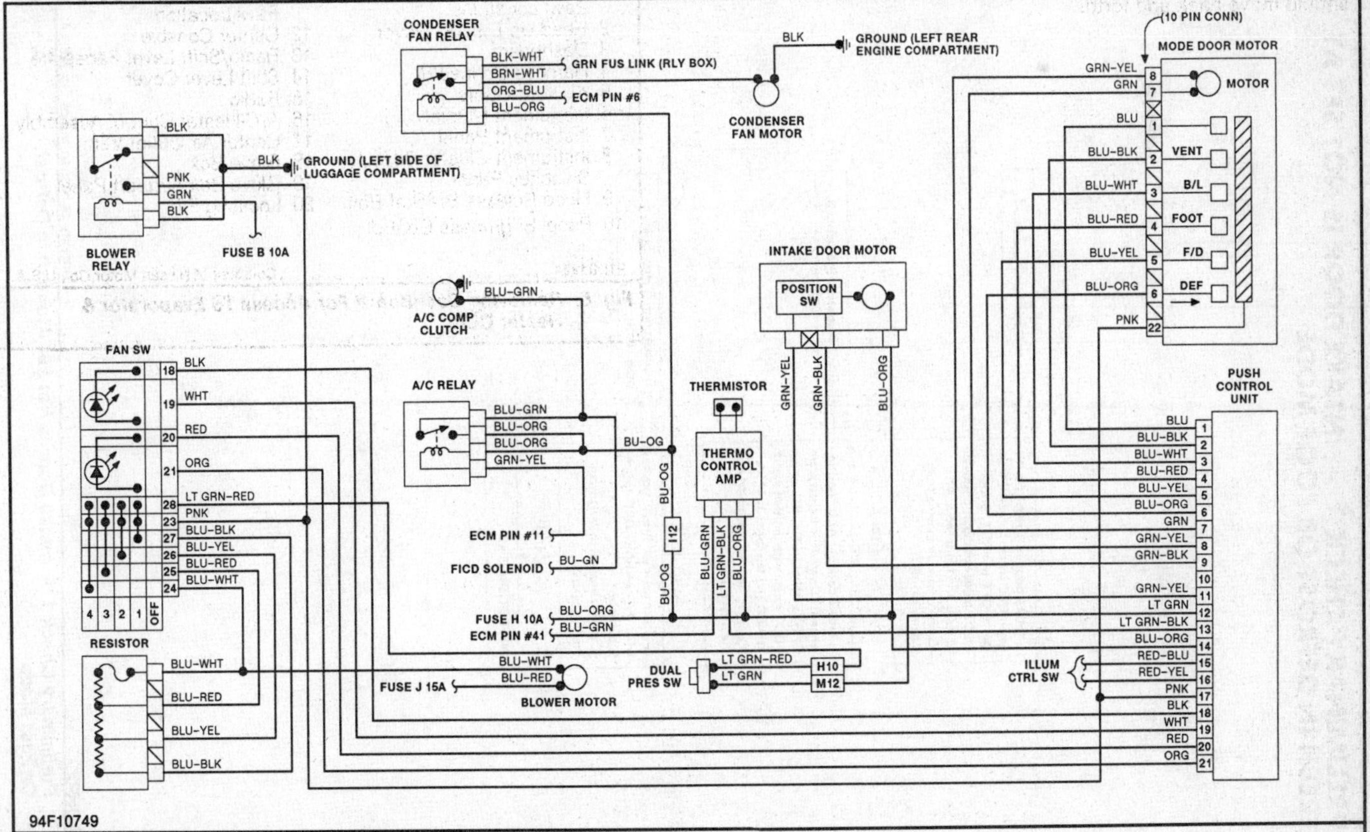

CONDENSER
FAN RELAY
GRN FUS LINK (RLY BOX)
ECM PIN #6
GROUND (LEFT REAR
ENGINE COMPARTMENT)
CONDENSER
FAN MOTOR
(10 PIN CONN)
MODE DOOR MOTOR
MOTOR
VENT
B/L
FOOT
F/D
DEF
GROUND (LEFT SIDE OF
LUGGAGE COMPARTMENT)
BLOWER
RELAY
FUSE B 10A
INTAKE DOOR MOTOR
POSITION
SW
A/C COMP
CLUTCH
FAN SW
A/C RELAY
THERMISTOR
THERMO
CONTROL
AMP
PUSH
CONTROL
UNIT
ECM PIN #11
FICD SOLENOID
FUSE H 10A
ECM PIN #41
RESISTOR
FUSE J 15A
BLOWER MOTOR
DUAL
PRES SW
ILLUM
CTRL SW
94F10749

Fig. 8: Manual A/C-Heater System Wiring Diagram (240SX)

1993 MANUAL A/C-HEATER SYSTEMS
Trouble Shooting – 240SX

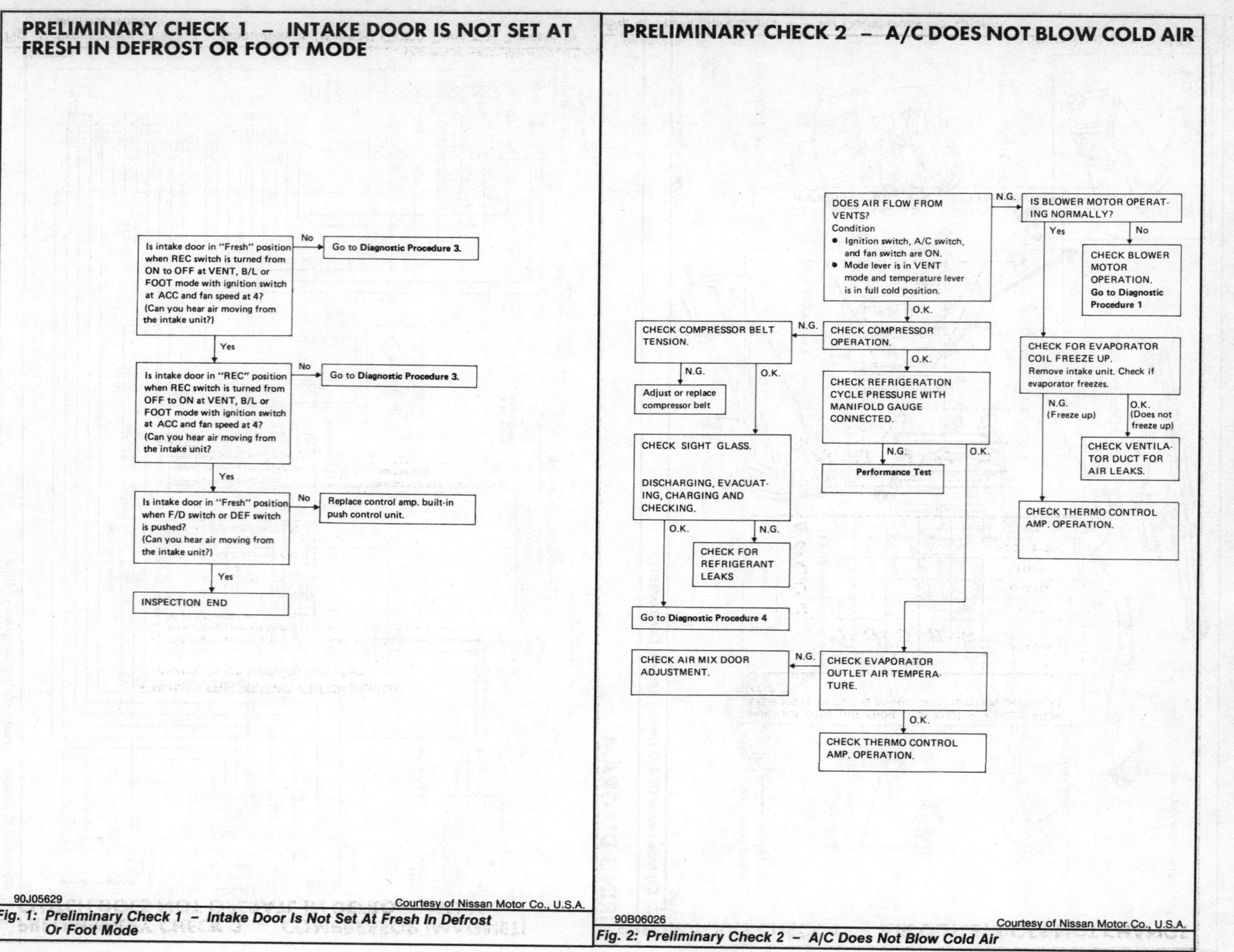
PRELIMINARY CHECK 1 – INTAKE DOOR IS NOT SET AT FRESH IN DEFROST OR FOOT MODE
Is intake door in "Fresh" position when REC switch is turned from ON to OFF at VENT, B/L or FOOT mode with ignition switch at ACC and fan speed at 4? (Can you hear air moving from the intake unit?)
No
Go to Diagnostic Procedure 3.
Yes
Is intake door in "REC" position when REC switch is turned from OFF to ON at VENT, B/L or FOOT mode with ignition switch at ACC and fan speed at 4? (Can you hear air moving from the intake unit?)
No
Go to Diagnostic Procedure 3.
Yes
Is intake door in "Fresh" position when F/D switch or DEF switch is pushed? (Can you hear air moving from the intake unit?)
No
Replace control amp. built-in push control unit.
Yes
INSPECTION END
90J05629
Courtesy of Nissan Motor Co., U.S.A.
PRELIMINARY CHECK 2 – A/C DOES NOT BLOW COLD AIR
DOES AIR FLOW FROM VENTS?
Condition
• Ignition switch, A/C switch, and fan switch are ON.
• Mode lever is in VENT mode and temperature lever is in full cold position.
N.G.
IS BLOWER MOTOR OPERATING NORMALLY?
Yes
No
CHECK BLOWER MOTOR OPERATION. Go to Diagnostic Procedure 1
CHECK FOR EVAPORATOR COIL FREEZE UP. Remove intake unit. Check if evaporator freezes.
N.G. (Freeze up)
O.K. (Does not freeze up)
CHECK VENTILATOR DUCT FOR AIR LEAKS.
CHECK THERMO CONTROL AMP. OPERATION.
O.K.
CHECK COMPRESSOR OPERATION.
N.G.
CHECK COMPRESSOR BELT TENSION.
N.G.
Adjust or replace compressor belt
O.K.
CHECK SIGHT GLASS.
DISCHARGING, EVACUATING, CHARGING AND CHECKING.
O.K.
N.G.
CHECK FOR REFRIGERANT LEAKS
Go to Diagnostic Procedure 4
O.K.
CHECK REFRIGERATION CYCLE PRESSURE WITH MANIFOLD GAUGE CONNECTED.
N.G.
Performance Test
O.K.
CHECK EVAPORATOR OUTLET AIR TEMPERATURE.
N.G.
CHECK AIR MIX DOOR ADJUSTMENT.
O.K.
CHECK THERMO CONTROL AMP. OPERATION.
90B06026
Courtesy of Nissan Motor Co., U.S.A.

Fig. 1: Preliminary Check 1 – Intake Door Is Not Set At Fresh In Defrost Or Foot Mode

Fig. 2: Preliminary Check 2 – A/C Does Not Blow Cold Air

PRELIMINARY CHECK 3 – COMPRESSOR (MAGNET) CLUTCH DOES NOT OPERATE IN DEFROST MODE

- Perform PRELIMINARY CHECK 2 before referring to the following flow chart.

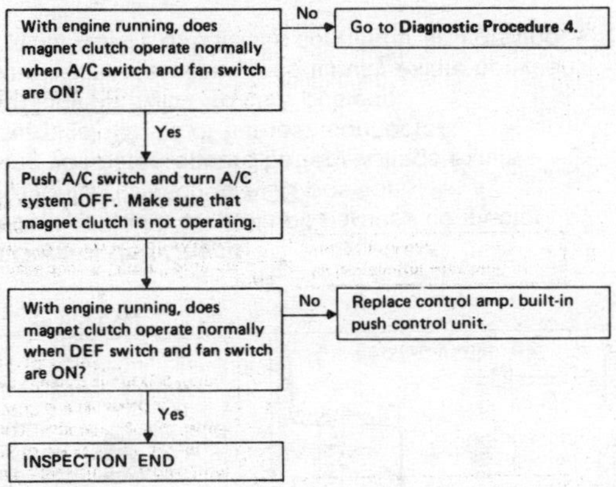

With engine running, does magnet clutch operate normally when A/C switch and fan switch are ON?
- No → Go to **Diagnostic Procedure 4.**
- Yes → Push A/C switch and turn A/C system OFF. Make sure that magnet clutch is not operating.

With engine running, does magnet clutch operate normally when DEF switch and fan switch are ON?
- No → Replace control amp. built-in push control unit.
- Yes → INSPECTION END

90B05630 Courtesy of Nissan Motor Co., U.S.A.

Fig. 3: Preliminary Check 3 – Compressor (Magnet) Clutch Does Not Operate In Defrost Mode

PRELIMINARY CHECK 4 – AIR OUTLET DOES NOT CHANGE

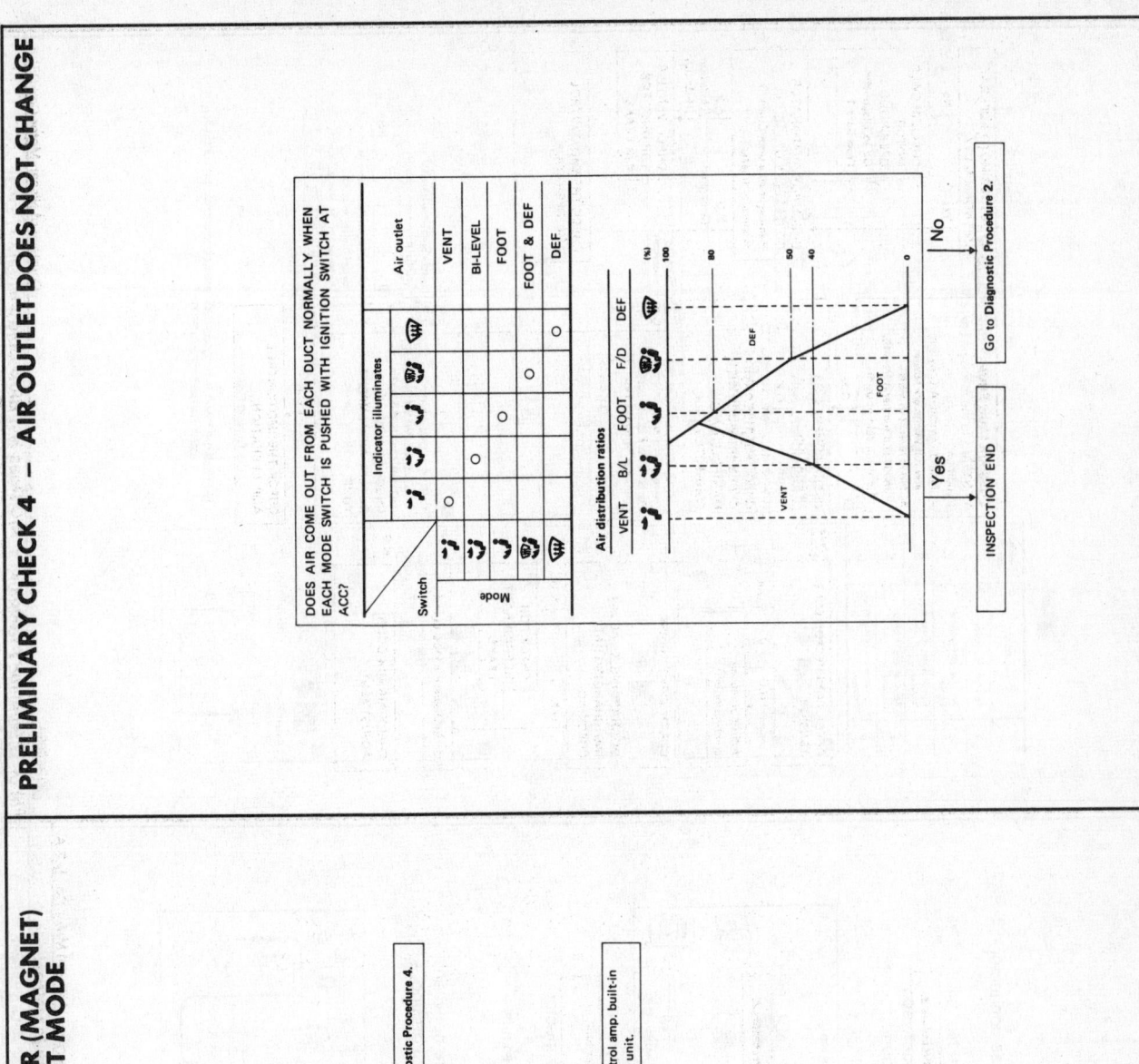

DOES AIR COME OUT FROM EACH DUCT NORMALLY WHEN EACH MODE SWITCH IS PUSHED WITH IGNITION SWITCH AT ACC?

Switch (Mode)	Indicator illuminates: VENT	B/L	FOOT	F/D	DEF	Air outlet
VENT	O					VENT
B/L		O				BI-LEVEL
FOOT			O			FOOT
F/D				O		FOOT & DEF
DEF					O	DEF

Air distribution ratios

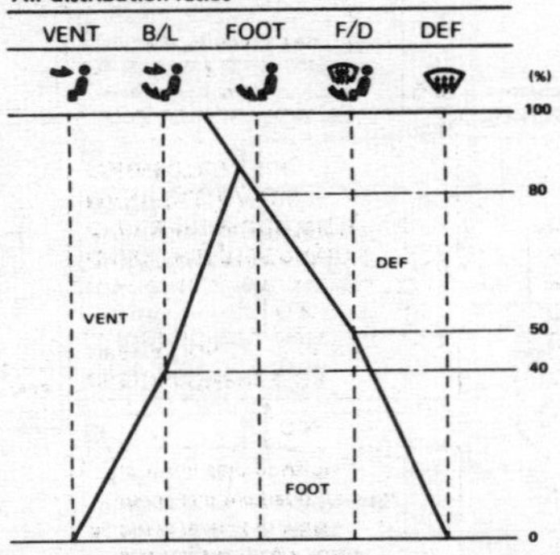

VENT B/L FOOT F/D DEF

(%) 100, 80, 50, 40, 0

VENT, FOOT, DEF

- Yes → INSPECTION END
- No → Go to **Diagnostic Procedure 2.**

90D06027 Courtesy of Nissan Motor Co., U.S.A.

Fig. 4: Preliminary Check 4 – Air Outlet Does Not Change

PRELIMINARY CHECK 5 – POWER SUPPLY CIRCUIT CHECK FOR A/C SYSTEM

Thermo Control Amplifier Check

1. Disconnect thermo control amplifier harness connector.
2. Turn ignition on. Using voltmeter, ensure battery voltage exists at connector terminal No. 34.
3. Turn ignition off. Turn A/C and fan switch on. Using ohmmeter, ensure continuity exists between harness connector terminal No. 13 and ground.

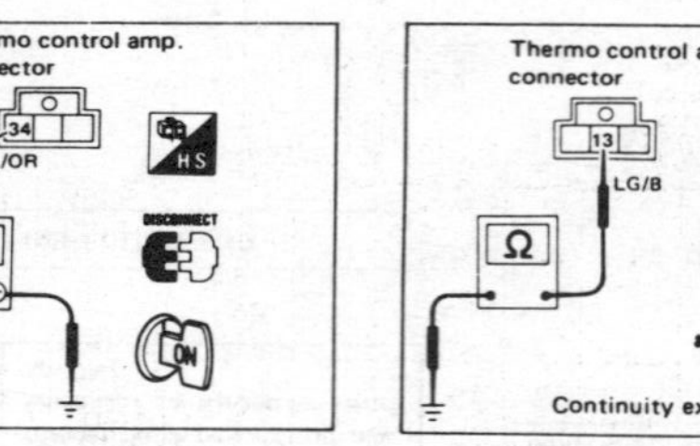
Thermo control amp. connector
34
L/OR
V
HS
DISCONNECT
ON

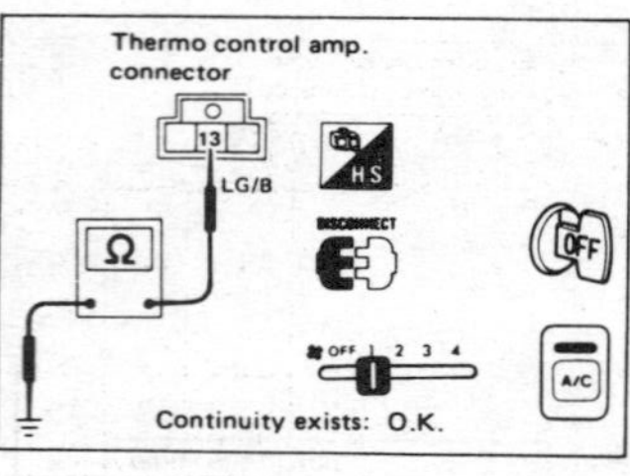
Thermo control amp. connector
13
LG/B
Ω
HS
DISCONNECT
OFF
OFF 1 2 3 4
A/C
Continuity exists: O.K.

Push Control Unit Check

1. Disconnect push control unit harness connector.
2. Turn ignition switch to ACC position.
3. Using voltmeter, ensure battery voltage exists at terminal No. 14 of harness connector.
4. Turn ignition switch to OFF position.
5. Using ohmmeter, ensure continuity exists between terminal No. 17 of harness connector and ground.

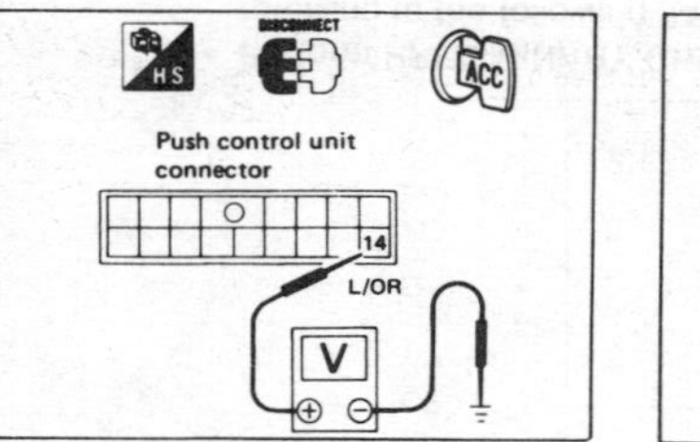
HS
DISCONNECT
ACC
Push control unit connector
14
L/OR
V

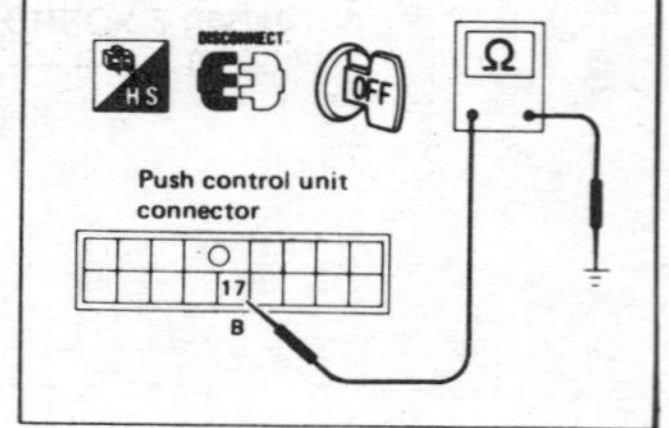
HS
DISCONNECT
OFF
Ω
Push control unit connector
17
B

91I04813 Courtesy of Nissan Motor Co., U.S.A.

Fig. 5: Preliminary Check 5 – Power Supply Circuit Check For A/C System

DIAGNOSTIC PROCEDURE 1 – BLOWER MOTOR DOES NOT ROTATE

	INCIDENT	Flow chart No.
1	Fan fails to rotate.	1
2	Fan does not rotate at 1-speed.	2
3	Fan does not rotate at 2-speed.	3
4	Fan does not rotate at 3-speed.	4
5	Fan does not rotate at 4-speed.	5

- Perform PRELIMINARY CHECK 2 before referring to the following flow chart.

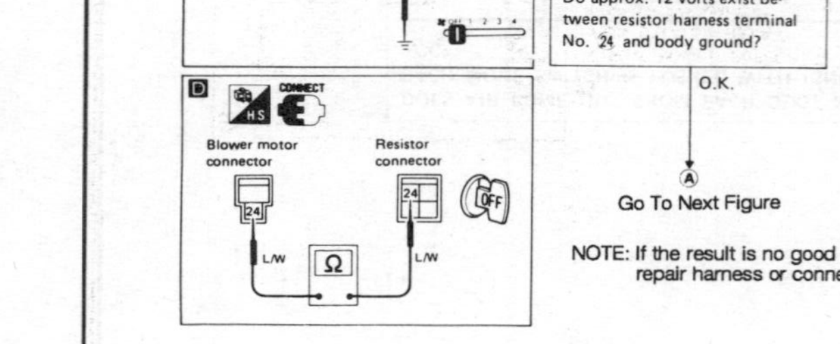
A
Blower motor connector
30
L/R
HS
V
ACC
B
24
L/W
Blower motor connector
Ω
ON
Continuity exists: O.K.
C
Resistor connector
L/W
24
HS
CONNECT
V
ACC
D
HS
CONNECT
Blower motor connector
Resistor connector
24
L/W
Ω
OFF

Check if blower motor rotates properly at each fan speed. Conduct check as per flow chart at left.

1 → A; 2 → B, 3 → C, 4 → D, 5 → E: Go To Next Figure

A CHECK POWER SUPPLY FOR BLOWER MOTOR. Disconnect blower motor harness connector. Do approx. 12 volts exist between blower motor harness terminal No. 30 and body ground?
- N.G. → Check 15A fuses at fuse block.
- O.K. → B

B Check circuit continuity between blower motor harness terminal No. 24 and body ground.
- N.G. → Reconnect blower motor harness connector. → C
- O.K. → CHECK BLOWER MOTOR. → N.G. → Replace blower motor.

C CHECK BLOWER MOTOR CIRCUIT BETWEEN BLOWER MOTOR AND RESISTOR. Do approx. 12 volts exist between resistor harness terminal No. 24 and body ground?
- N.G. → Disconnect blower motor and resistor harness connectors. → **D** Check circuit continuity between blower motor harness terminal No. 24 and resistor harness terminal No. 24. (Note)
- O.K. → A: Go To Next Figure

NOTE: If the result is no good (NG) after checking circuit continuity, repair harness or connector.

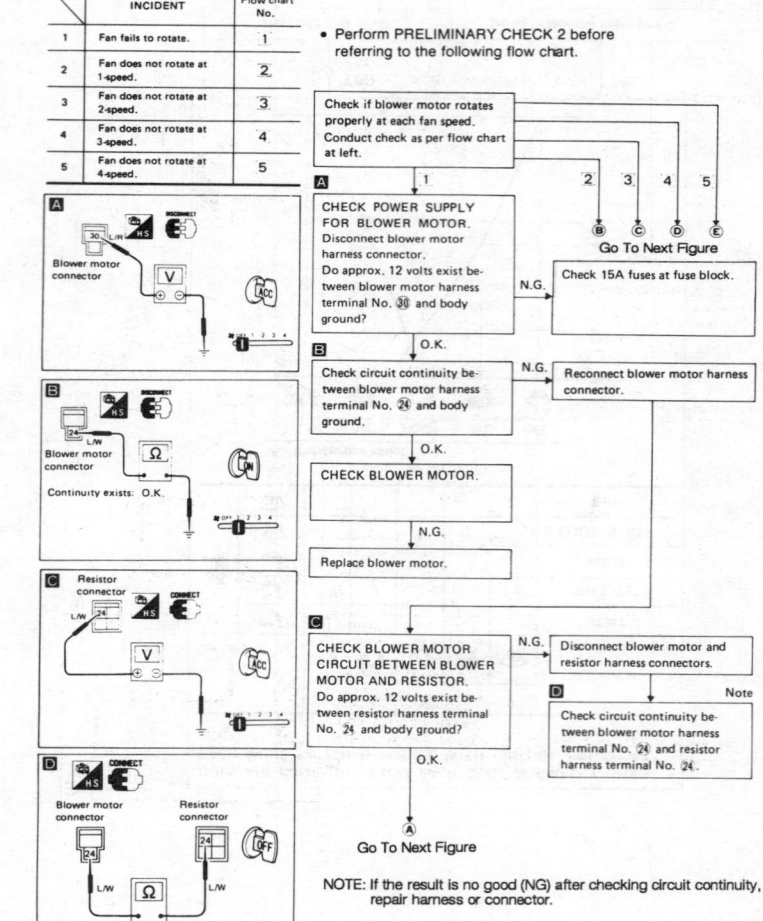

90F05632 Courtesy of Nissan Motor Co., U.S.A.

Fig. 6: Diagnostic Procedure 1 – Blower Motor Does Not Rotate (1 Of 3)

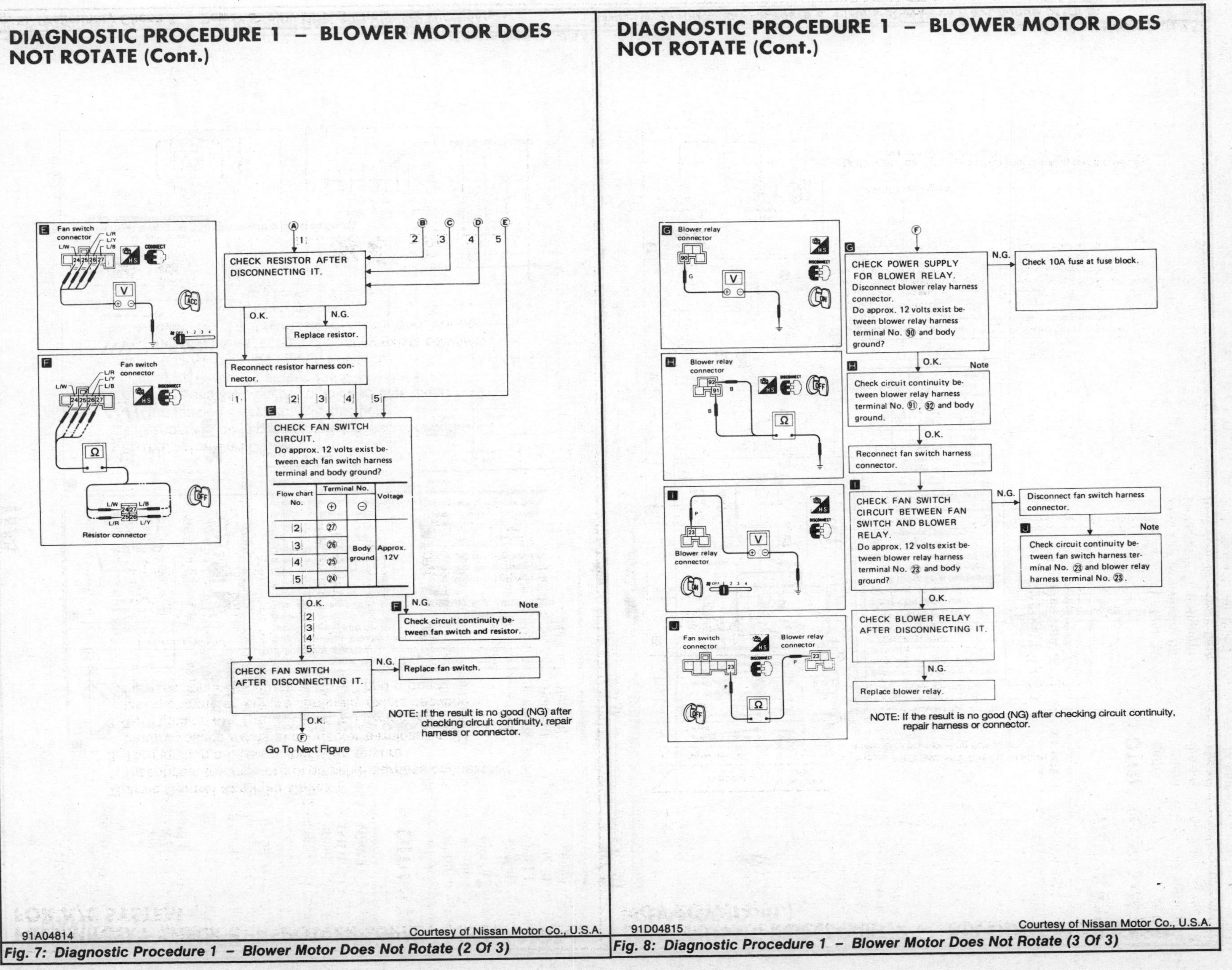
DIAGNOSTIC PROCEDURE 1 – BLOWER MOTOR DOES NOT ROTATE (Cont.)
E Fan switch connector
L/R
L/Y
L/B
L/W
CONNECT
ACC
F Fan switch connector
DISCONNECT
OFF
L/W
L/B
L/R
L/Y
Resistor connector
CHECK RESISTOR AFTER DISCONNECTING IT.
O.K.
N.G.
Replace resistor.
Reconnect resistor harness connector.
E CHECK FAN SWITCH CIRCUIT.
Do approx. 12 volts exist between each fan switch harness terminal and body ground?
Flow chart No.
Terminal No.
Voltage
Body ground
Approx. 12V
F Check circuit continuity between fan switch and resistor.
Note
CHECK FAN SWITCH AFTER DISCONNECTING IT.
Replace fan switch.
NOTE: If the result is no good (NG) after checking circuit continuity, repair harness or connector.
Go To Next Figure
Courtesy of Nissan Motor Co., U.S.A.
91A04814
DIAGNOSTIC PROCEDURE 1 – BLOWER MOTOR DOES NOT ROTATE (Cont.)
G Blower relay connector
H Blower relay connector
I Blower relay connector
J Fan switch connector
Blower relay connector
G CHECK POWER SUPPLY FOR BLOWER RELAY.
Disconnect blower relay harness connector.
Do approx. 12 volts exist between blower relay harness terminal No. 90 and body ground?
Check 10A fuse at fuse block.
H Check circuit continuity between blower relay harness terminal No. 91, 92 and body ground.
Reconnect fan switch harness connector.
I CHECK FAN SWITCH CIRCUIT BETWEEN FAN SWITCH AND BLOWER RELAY.
Do approx. 12 volts exist between blower relay harness terminal No. 23 and body ground?
Disconnect fan switch harness connector.
J Check circuit continuity between fan switch harness terminal No. 23 and blower relay harness terminal No. 23.
CHECK BLOWER RELAY AFTER DISCONNECTING IT.
Replace blower relay.
NOTE: If the result is no good (NG) after checking circuit continuity, repair harness or connector.
Courtesy of Nissan Motor Co., U.S.A.
91D04815

Fig. 7: Diagnostic Procedure 1 – Blower Motor Does Not Rotate (2 Of 3)

Fig. 8: Diagnostic Procedure 1 – Blower Motor Does Not Rotate (3 Of 3)

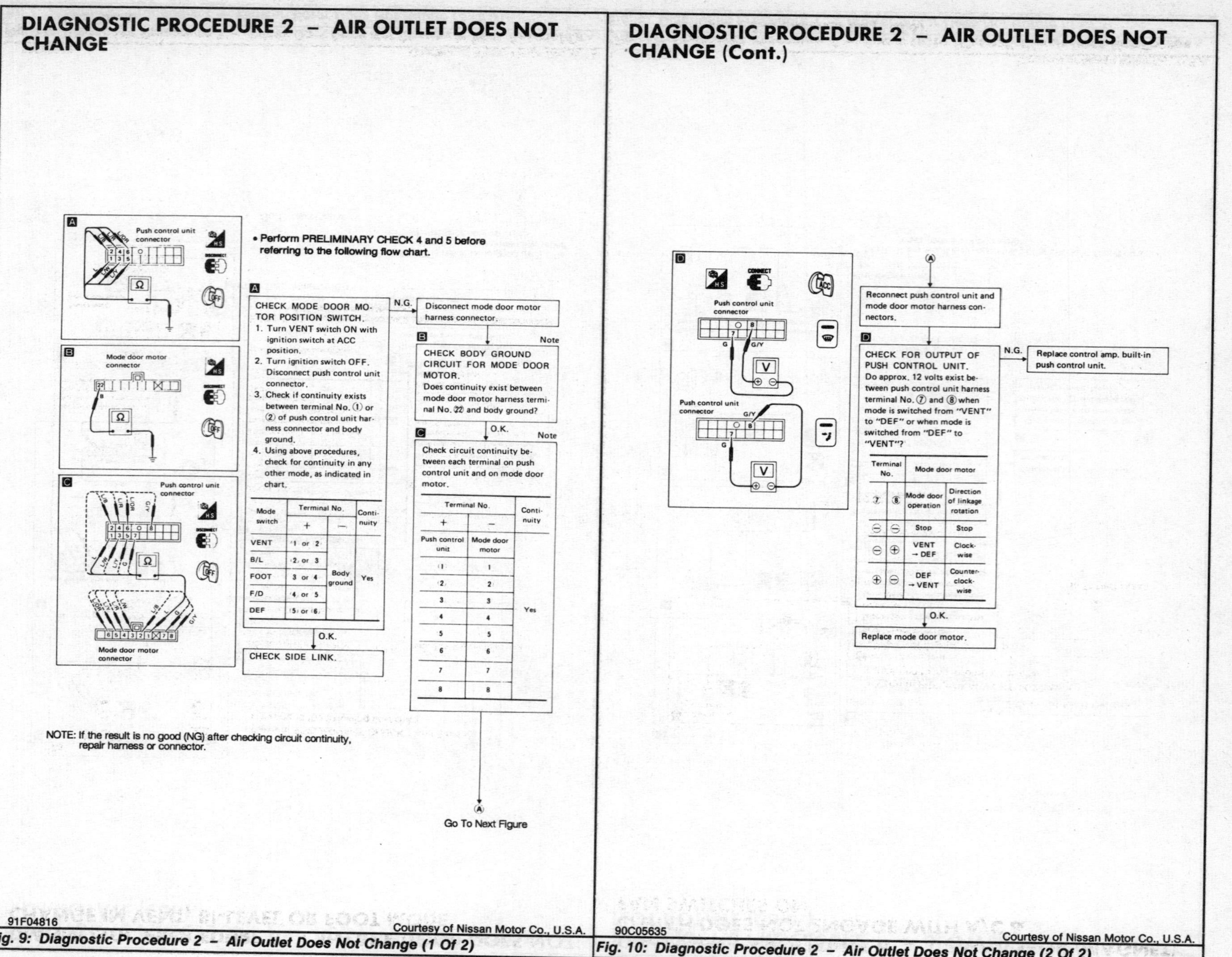
DIAGNOSTIC PROCEDURE 2 – AIR OUTLET DOES NOT CHANGE
A
Push control unit connector
B
Mode door motor connector
C
Push control unit connector
Mode door motor connector
• Perform PRELIMINARY CHECK 4 and 5 before referring to the following flow chart.
A
CHECK MODE DOOR MOTOR POSITION SWITCH.
1. Turn VENT switch ON with ignition switch at ACC position.
2. Turn ignition switch OFF. Disconnect push control unit connector.
3. Check if continuity exists between terminal No. ① or ② of push control unit harness connector and body ground.
4. Using above procedures, check for continuity in any other mode, as indicated in chart.
N.G.
Disconnect mode door motor harness connector.
B
Note
CHECK BODY GROUND CIRCUIT FOR MODE DOOR MOTOR.
Does continuity exist between mode door motor harness terminal No. ㉒ and body ground?
O.K.
C
Note
Check circuit continuity between each terminal on push control unit and on mode door motor.
O.K.
CHECK SIDE LINK.
Go To Next Figure
NOTE: If the result is no good (NG) after checking circuit continuity, repair harness or connector.
DIAGNOSTIC PROCEDURE 2 – AIR OUTLET DOES NOT CHANGE (Cont.)
D
Push control unit connector
Push control unit connector
Reconnect push control unit and mode door motor harness connectors.
D
CHECK FOR OUTPUT OF PUSH CONTROL UNIT.
Do approx. 12 volts exist between push control unit harness terminal No. ⑦ and ⑧ when mode is switched from "VENT" to "DEF" or when mode is switched from "DEF" to "VENT"?
N.G.
Replace control amp. built-in push control unit.
O.K.
Replace mode door motor.

Mode switch	Terminal No. +	Terminal No. –	Continuity
VENT	1 or 2	Body ground	Yes
B/L	2 or 3		
FOOT	3 or 4		
F/D	4 or 5		
DEF	5 or 6		

Terminal No. + Push control unit	Terminal No. – Mode door motor	Continuity
1	1	Yes
2	2	
3	3	
4	4	
5	5	
6	6	
7	7	
8	8	

Terminal No. ⑦	Terminal No. ⑧	Mode door operation	Direction of linkage rotation
⊖	⊖	Stop	Stop
⊖	⊕	VENT → DEF	Clockwise
⊕	⊖	DEF → VENT	Counterclockwise

91F04816 Courtesy of Nissan Motor Co., U.S.A.

Fig. 9: Diagnostic Procedure 2 – Air Outlet Does Not Change (1 Of 2)

90C05635 Courtesy of Nissan Motor Co., U.S.A.

Fig. 10: Diagnostic Procedure 2 – Air Outlet Does Not Change (2 Of 2)

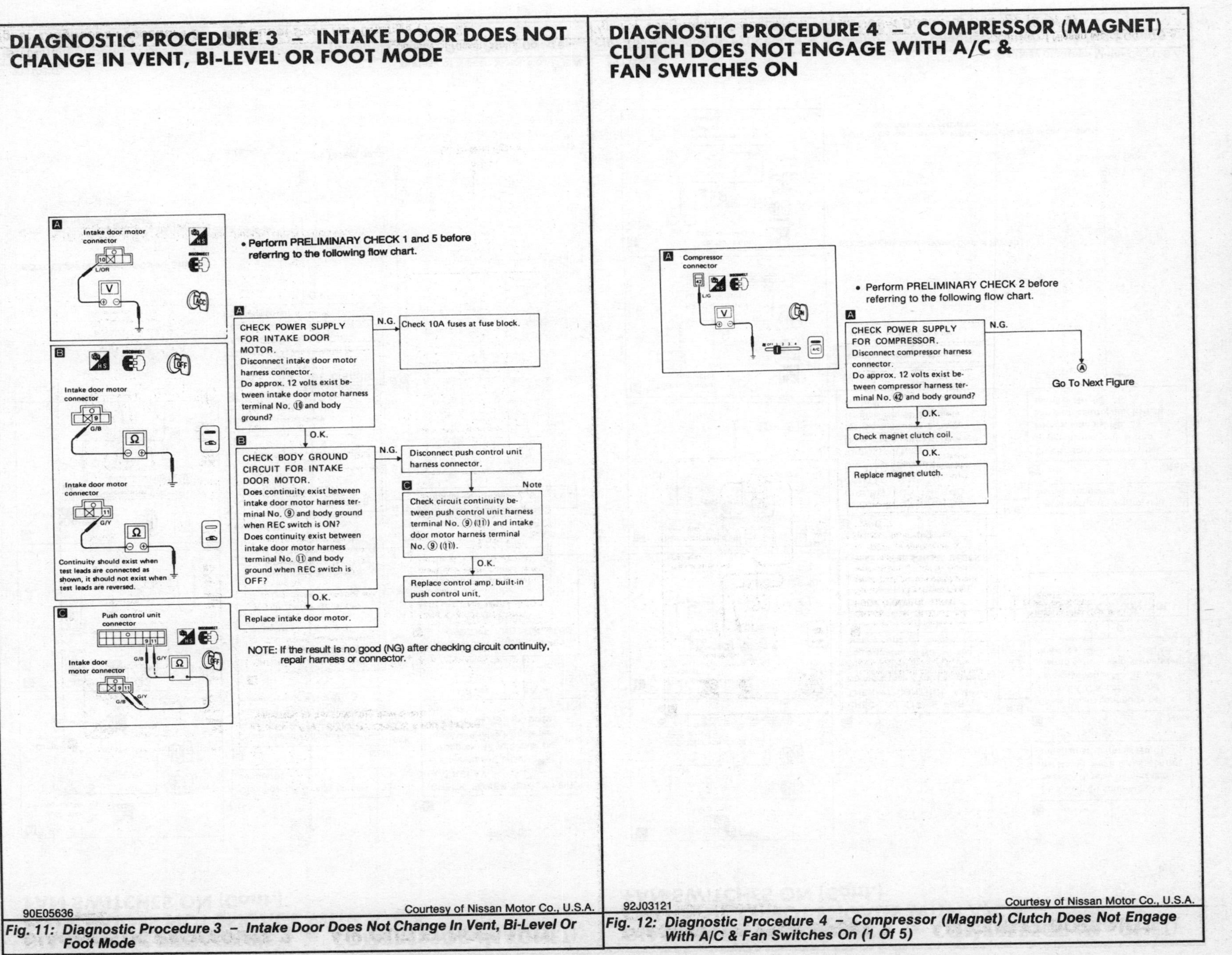
DIAGNOSTIC PROCEDURE 3 – INTAKE DOOR DOES NOT CHANGE IN VENT, BI-LEVEL OR FOOT MODE
• Perform PRELIMINARY CHECK 1 and 5 before referring to the following flow chart.
A
Intake door motor connector
L/OR
V
B
Intake door motor connector
G/B
Ω
Intake door motor connector
G/Y
Ω
Continuity should exist when test leads are connected as shown, it should not exist when test leads are reversed.
C
Push control unit connector
Intake door motor connector
G/B
G/Y
Ω
A
CHECK POWER SUPPLY FOR INTAKE DOOR MOTOR.
Disconnect intake door motor harness connector.
Do approx. 12 volts exist between intake door motor harness terminal No. ⑩ and body ground?
N.G.
Check 10A fuses at fuse block.
O.K.
B
CHECK BODY GROUND CIRCUIT FOR INTAKE DOOR MOTOR.
Does continuity exist between intake door motor harness terminal No. ⑨ and body ground when REC switch is ON?
Does continuity exist between intake door motor harness terminal No. ⑪ and body ground when REC switch is OFF?
N.G.
Disconnect push control unit harness connector.
C
Note
Check circuit continuity between push control unit harness terminal No. ⑨ (⑪) and intake door motor harness terminal No. ⑨ (⑪).
O.K.
Replace control amp. built-in push control unit.
O.K.
Replace intake door motor.
NOTE: If the result is no good (NG) after checking circuit continuity, repair harness or connector.
90E05636
Courtesy of Nissan Motor Co., U.S.A.
DIAGNOSTIC PROCEDURE 4 – COMPRESSOR (MAGNET) CLUTCH DOES NOT ENGAGE WITH A/C & FAN SWITCHES ON
A
Compressor connector
L/G
V
A/C
• Perform PRELIMINARY CHECK 2 before referring to the following flow chart.
A
CHECK POWER SUPPLY FOR COMPRESSOR.
Disconnect compressor harness connector.
Do approx. 12 volts exist between compressor harness terminal No. ㊷ and body ground?
N.G.
Ⓐ
Go To Next Figure
O.K.
Check magnet clutch coil.
O.K.
Replace magnet clutch.
92J03121
Courtesy of Nissan Motor Co., U.S.A.

Fig. 11: Diagnostic Procedure 3 – Intake Door Does Not Change In Vent, Bi-Level Or Foot Mode

Fig. 12: Diagnostic Procedure 4 – Compressor (Magnet) Clutch Does Not Engage With A/C & Fan Switches On (1 Of 5)

1993 MANUAL A/C-HEATER SYSTEMS
Trouble Shooting – 240SX (Cont.)

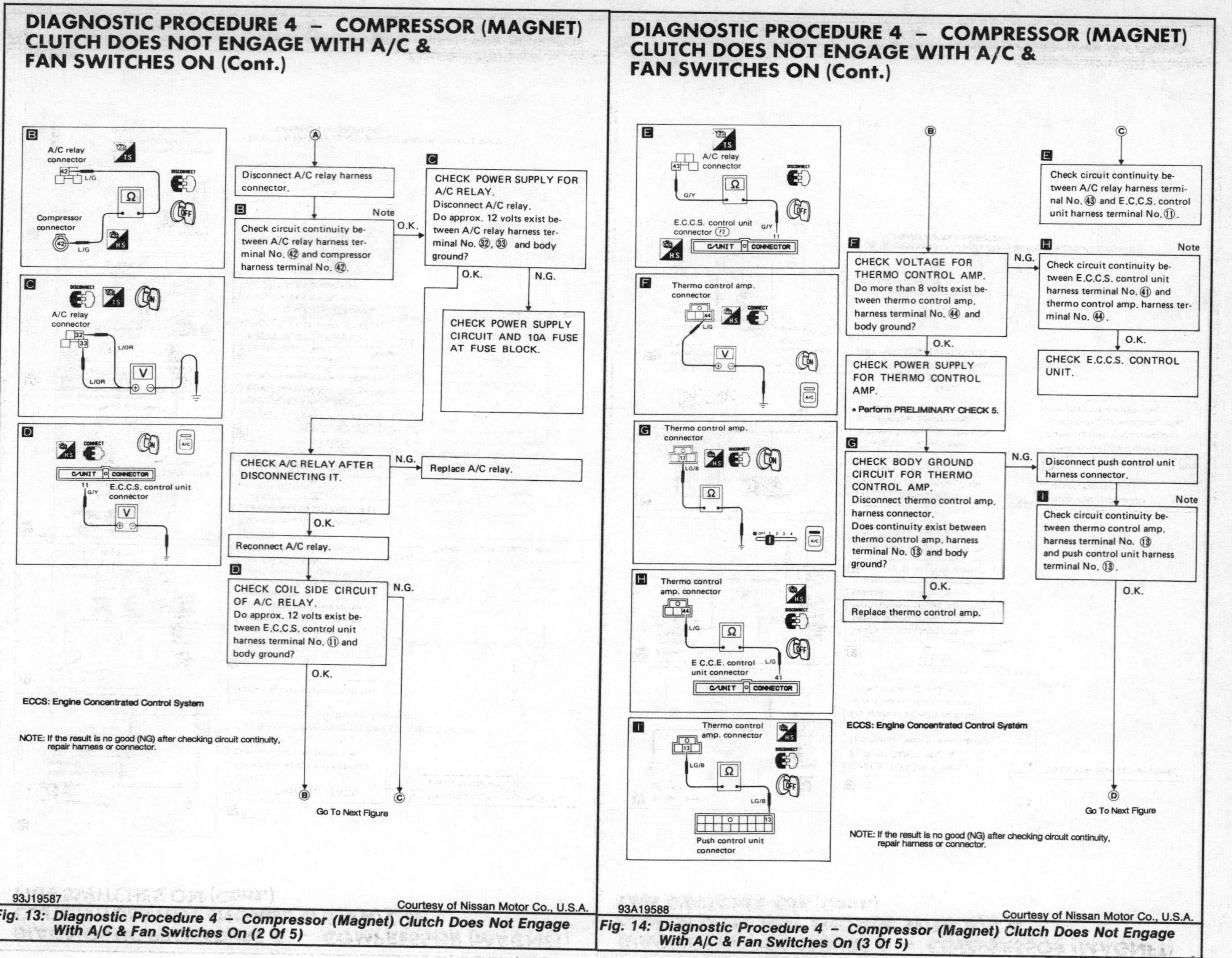
DIAGNOSTIC PROCEDURE 4 – COMPRESSOR (MAGNET) CLUTCH DOES NOT ENGAGE WITH A/C & FAN SWITCHES ON (Cont.)
B
A/C relay connector
Compressor connector
L/G
A
Disconnect A/C relay harness connector.
B
Note
Check circuit continuity between A/C relay harness terminal No. 42 and compressor harness terminal No. 42.
O.K.
C
CHECK POWER SUPPLY FOR A/C RELAY.
Disconnect A/C relay.
Do approx. 12 volts exist between A/C relay harness terminal No. 32, 33 and body ground?
O.K.
N.G.
CHECK POWER SUPPLY CIRCUIT AND 10A FUSE AT FUSE BLOCK.
C
A/C relay connector
L/OR
D
E.C.C.S. control unit connector
G/Y
CHECK A/C RELAY AFTER DISCONNECTING IT.
N.G.
Replace A/C relay.
O.K.
Reconnect A/C relay.
D
CHECK COIL SIDE CIRCUIT OF A/C RELAY.
Do approx. 12 volts exist between E.C.C.S. control unit harness terminal No. 11 and body ground?
N.G.
O.K.
ECCS: Engine Concentrated Control System
NOTE: If the result is no good (NG) after checking circuit continuity, repair harness or connector.
B
C
Go To Next Figure
93J19587
Courtesy of Nissan Motor Co., U.S.A.
DIAGNOSTIC PROCEDURE 4 – COMPRESSOR (MAGNET) CLUTCH DOES NOT ENGAGE WITH A/C & FAN SWITCHES ON (Cont.)
E
A/C relay connector
G/Y
E.C.C.S. control unit connector
F
Thermo control amp. connector
L/G
G
Thermo control amp. connector
LG/B
H
Thermo control amp. connector
E C.C.E. control unit connector
I
Thermo control amp. connector
LG/B
Push control unit connector
B
F
CHECK VOLTAGE FOR THERMO CONTROL AMP.
Do more than 8 volts exist between thermo control amp. harness terminal No. 44 and body ground?
O.K.
CHECK POWER SUPPLY FOR THERMO CONTROL AMP.
• Perform PRELIMINARY CHECK 5.
G
CHECK BODY GROUND CIRCUIT FOR THERMO CONTROL AMP.
Disconnect thermo control amp. harness connector.
Does continuity exist between thermo control amp. harness terminal No. 13 and body ground?
O.K.
Replace thermo control amp.
ECCS: Engine Concentrated Control System
C
E
Check circuit continuity between A/C relay harness terminal No. 43 and E.C.C.S. control unit harness terminal No. 11.
N.G.
H
Note
Check circuit continuity between E.C.C.S. control unit harness terminal No. 41 and thermo control amp. harness terminal No. 44.
O.K.
CHECK E.C.C.S. CONTROL UNIT.
N.G.
Disconnect push control unit harness connector.
I
Note
Check circuit continuity between thermo control amp. harness terminal No. 13 and push control unit harness terminal No. 13.
O.K.
D
Go To Next Figure
NOTE: If the result is no good (NG) after checking circuit continuity, repair harness or connector.
93A19588
Courtesy of Nissan Motor Co., U.S.A.

Fig. 13: Diagnostic Procedure 4 – Compressor (Magnet) Clutch Does Not Engage With A/C & Fan Switches On (2 Of 5)

Fig. 14: Diagnostic Procedure 4 – Compressor (Magnet) Clutch Does Not Engage With A/C & Fan Switches On (3 Of 5)

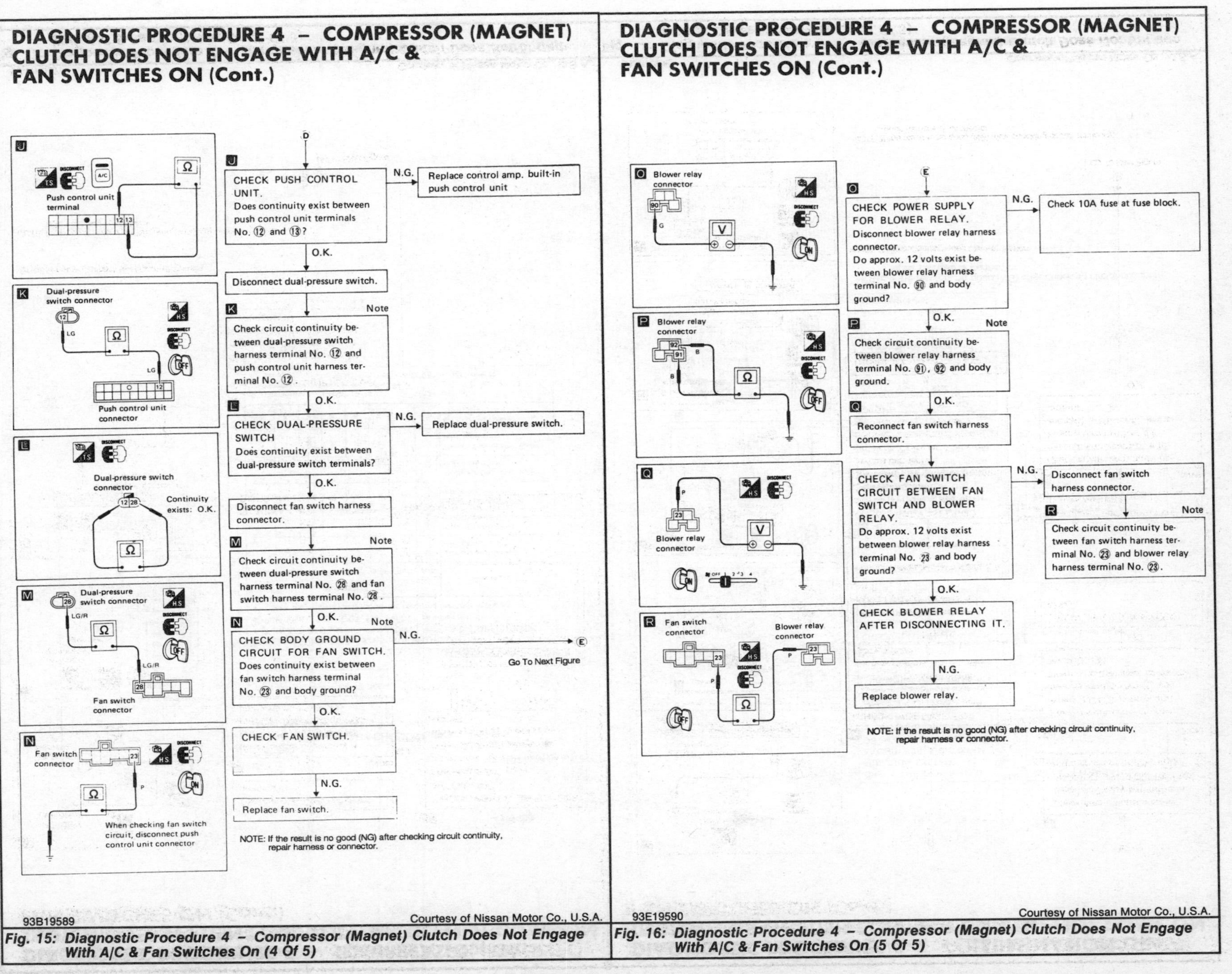
DIAGNOSTIC PROCEDURE 4 – COMPRESSOR (MAGNET) CLUTCH DOES NOT ENGAGE WITH A/C & FAN SWITCHES ON (Cont.)
J
Push control unit terminal
K
Dual-pressure switch connector
Push control unit connector
L
Dual-pressure switch connector
Continuity exists: O.K.
M
Dual-pressure switch connector
Fan switch connector
N
Fan switch connector
When checking fan switch circuit, disconnect push control unit connector
D
J CHECK PUSH CONTROL UNIT.
Does continuity exist between push control unit terminals No. 12 and 13?
N.G.
Replace control amp. built-in push control unit
O.K.
Disconnect dual-pressure switch.
K Check circuit continuity between dual-pressure switch harness terminal No. 12 and push control unit harness terminal No. 12.
Note
O.K.
L CHECK DUAL-PRESSURE SWITCH
Does continuity exist between dual-pressure switch terminals?
N.G.
Replace dual-pressure switch.
O.K.
Disconnect fan switch harness connector.
M Check circuit continuity between dual-pressure switch harness terminal No. 28 and fan switch harness terminal No. 28.
Note
O.K.
N CHECK BODY GROUND CIRCUIT FOR FAN SWITCH.
Does continuity exist between fan switch harness terminal No. 23 and body ground?
Note
N.G.
E
Go To Next Figure
O.K.
CHECK FAN SWITCH.
N.G.
Replace fan switch.
NOTE: If the result is no good (NG) after checking circuit continuity, repair harness or connector.
93B19589
Courtesy of Nissan Motor Co., U.S.A.
DIAGNOSTIC PROCEDURE 4 – COMPRESSOR (MAGNET) CLUTCH DOES NOT ENGAGE WITH A/C & FAN SWITCHES ON (Cont.)
O
Blower relay connector
P
Blower relay connector
Q
Blower relay connector
R
Fan switch connector
Blower relay connector
E
O CHECK POWER SUPPLY FOR BLOWER RELAY.
Disconnect blower relay harness connector.
Do approx. 12 volts exist between blower relay harness terminal No. 90 and body ground?
N.G.
Check 10A fuse at fuse block.
O.K.
P Check circuit continuity between blower relay harness terminal No. 91, 92 and body ground.
Note
O.K.
Q Reconnect fan switch harness connector.
CHECK FAN SWITCH CIRCUIT BETWEEN FAN SWITCH AND BLOWER RELAY.
Do approx. 12 volts exist between blower relay harness terminal No. 23 and body ground?
N.G.
Disconnect fan switch harness connector.
R Check circuit continuity between fan switch harness terminal No. 23 and blower relay harness terminal No. 23.
Note
O.K.
CHECK BLOWER RELAY AFTER DISCONNECTING IT.
N.G.
Replace blower relay.
NOTE: If the result is no good (NG) after checking circuit continuity, repair harness or connector.
93E19590
Courtesy of Nissan Motor Co., U.S.A.

Fig. 15: Diagnostic Procedure 4 – Compressor (Magnet) Clutch Does Not Engage With A/C & Fan Switches On (4 Of 5)

Fig. 16: Diagnostic Procedure 4 – Compressor (Magnet) Clutch Does Not Engage With A/C & Fan Switches On (5 Of 5)

1993 MANUAL A/C-HEATER SYSTEMS
Trouble Shooting – 240SX (Cont.)

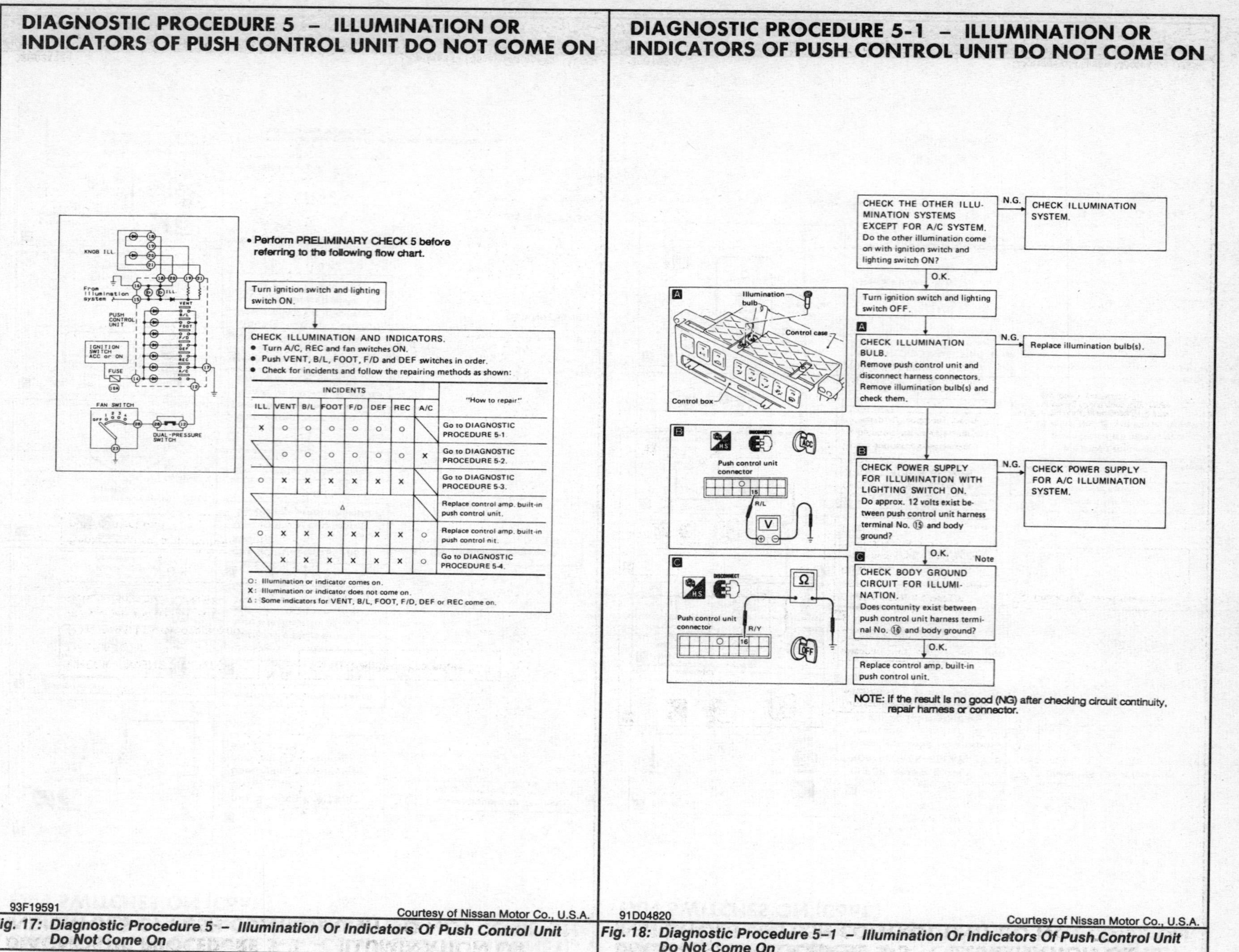
DIAGNOSTIC PROCEDURE 5 – ILLUMINATION OR INDICATORS OF PUSH CONTROL UNIT DO NOT COME ON
KNOB ILL.
From illumination system
PUSH CONTROL UNIT
IGNITION SWITCH ACC or ON
FUSE
FAN SWITCH
OFF
DUAL-PRESSURE SWITCH
• Perform PRELIMINARY CHECK 5 before referring to the following flow chart.
Turn ignition switch and lighting switch ON.
CHECK ILLUMINATION AND INDICATORS.
• Turn A/C, REC and fan switches ON.
• Push VENT, B/L, FOOT, F/D and DEF switches in order.
• Check for incidents and follow the repairing methods as shown:
○: Illumination or indicator comes on.
X: Illumination or indicator does not come on.
Δ: Some indicators for VENT, B/L, FOOT, F/D, DEF or REC come on.
DIAGNOSTIC PROCEDURE 5-1 – ILLUMINATION OR INDICATORS OF PUSH CONTROL UNIT DO NOT COME ON
A
Illumination bulb
Control case
Control box
B
DISCONNECT
Push control unit connector
R/L
C
Push control unit connector
R/Y
CHECK THE OTHER ILLUMINATION SYSTEMS EXCEPT FOR A/C SYSTEM. Do the other illumination come on with ignition switch and lighting switch ON?
N.G.
CHECK ILLUMINATION SYSTEM.
O.K.
Turn ignition switch and lighting switch OFF.
CHECK ILLUMINATION BULB. Remove push control unit and disconnect harness connectors. Remove illumination bulb(s) and check them.
N.G.
Replace illumination bulb(s).
CHECK POWER SUPPLY FOR ILLUMINATION WITH LIGHTING SWITCH ON. Do approx. 12 volts exist between push control unit harness terminal No. 15 and body ground?
N.G.
CHECK POWER SUPPLY FOR A/C ILLUMINATION SYSTEM.
O.K.
Note
CHECK BODY GROUND CIRCUIT FOR ILLUMINATION. Does contunity exist between push control unit harness terminal No. 16 and body ground?
O.K.
Replace control amp. built-in push control unit.
NOTE: If the result is no good (NG) after checking circuit continuity, repair harness or connector.

INCIDENTS								"How to repair"
ILL.	VENT	B/L	FOOT	F/D	DEF	REC	A/C	
X	○	○	○	○	○	○		Go to DIAGNOSTIC PROCEDURE 5-1.
	○	○	○	○	○	○	X	Go to DIAGNOSTIC PROCEDURE 5-2.
○	X	X	X	X	X	X		Go to DIAGNOSTIC PROCEDURE 5-3.
	Δ							Replace control amp. built-in push control unit.
○	X	X	X	X	X	X	○	Replace control amp. built-in push control nit.
	X	X	X	X	X	X	○	Go to DIAGNOSTIC PROCEDURE 5-4.

93F19591 Courtesy of Nissan Motor Co., U.S.A.

Fig. 17: Diagnostic Procedure 5 – Illumination Or Indicators Of Push Control Unit Do Not Come On

91D04820 Courtesy of Nissan Motor Co., U.S.A.

Fig. 18: Diagnostic Procedure 5-1 – Illumination Or Indicators Of Push Control Unit Do Not Come On

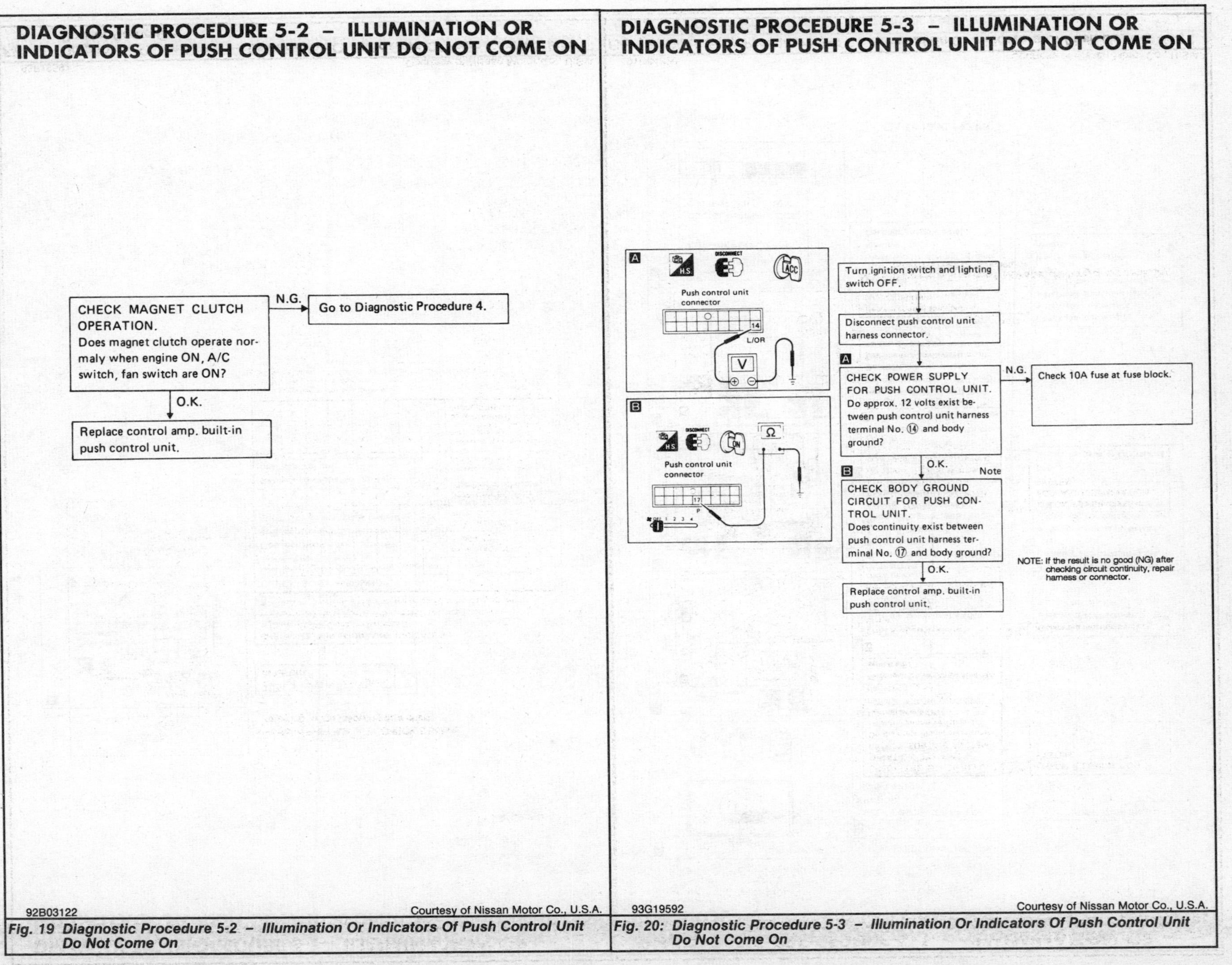
DIAGNOSTIC PROCEDURE 5-2 – ILLUMINATION OR INDICATORS OF PUSH CONTROL UNIT DO NOT COME ON
CHECK MAGNET CLUTCH OPERATION.
Does magnet clutch operate normaly when engine ON, A/C switch, fan switch are ON?
N.G.
Go to Diagnostic Procedure 4.
O.K.
Replace control amp. built-in push control unit.
92B03122
Courtesy of Nissan Motor Co., U.S.A.
DIAGNOSTIC PROCEDURE 5-3 – ILLUMINATION OR INDICATORS OF PUSH CONTROL UNIT DO NOT COME ON
A
DISCONNECT
ACC
Push control unit connector
14
L/OR
V
B
DISCONNECT
ON
Ω
Push control unit connector
17
P
1 2 3 4
Turn ignition switch and lighting switch OFF.
Disconnect push control unit harness connector.
A
CHECK POWER SUPPLY FOR PUSH CONTROL UNIT.
Do approx. 12 volts exist between push control unit harness terminal No. ⑭ and body ground?
N.G.
Check 10A fuse at fuse block.
O.K.
Note
B
CHECK BODY GROUND CIRCUIT FOR PUSH CONTROL UNIT.
Does continuity exist between push control unit harness terminal No. ⑰ and body ground?
O.K.
Replace control amp. built-in push control unit.
NOTE: If the result is no good (NG) after checking circuit continuity, repair harness or connector.
93G19592
Courtesy of Nissan Motor Co., U.S.A.

Fig. 19 Diagnostic Procedure 5-2 – Illumination Or Indicators Of Push Control Unit Do Not Come On

Fig. 20: Diagnostic Procedure 5-3 – Illumination Or Indicators Of Push Control Unit Do Not Come On

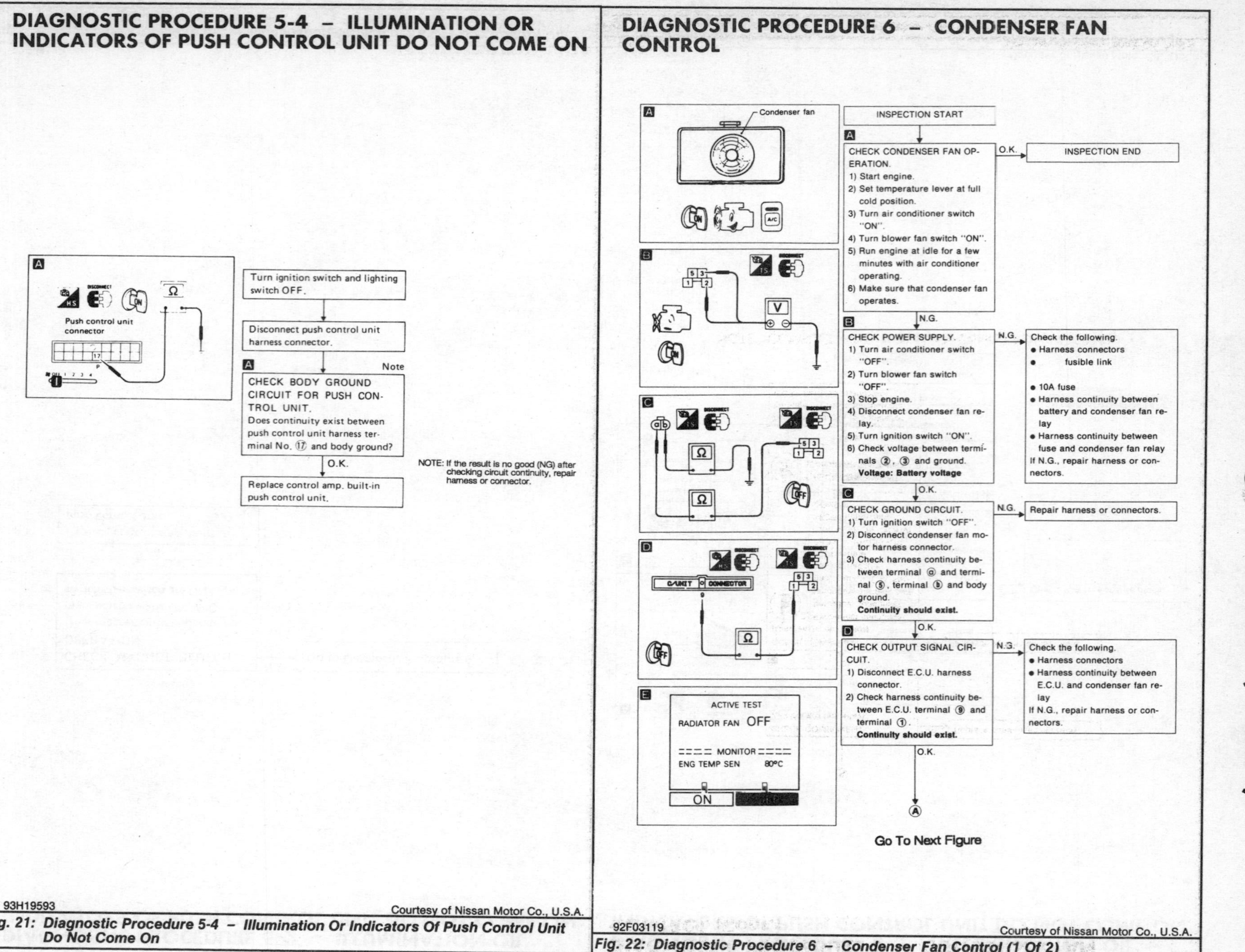
DIAGNOSTIC PROCEDURE 5-4 – ILLUMINATION OR INDICATORS OF PUSH CONTROL UNIT DO NOT COME ON
A
Push control unit connector
Turn ignition switch and lighting switch OFF.
Disconnect push control unit harness connector.
A
Note
CHECK BODY GROUND CIRCUIT FOR PUSH CONTROL UNIT.
Does continuity exist between push control unit harness terminal No. ⑰ and body ground?
O.K.
Replace control amp. built-in push control unit.
NOTE: If the result is no good (NG) after checking circuit continuity, repair harness or connector.
93H19593
Courtesy of Nissan Motor Co., U.S.A.
DIAGNOSTIC PROCEDURE 6 – CONDENSER FAN CONTROL
A
Condenser fan
B
C
D
E
ACTIVE TEST
RADIATOR FAN OFF
==== MONITOR ====
ENG TEMP SEN 80°C
ON
INSPECTION START
A
CHECK CONDENSER FAN OPERATION.
1) Start engine.
2) Set temperature lever at full cold position.
3) Turn air conditioner switch "ON".
4) Turn blower fan switch "ON".
5) Run engine at idle for a few minutes with air conditioner operating.
6) Make sure that condenser fan operates.
O.K.
INSPECTION END
N.G.
B
CHECK POWER SUPPLY.
1) Turn air conditioner switch "OFF".
2) Turn blower fan switch "OFF".
3) Stop engine.
4) Disconnect condenser fan relay.
5) Turn ignition switch "ON".
6) Check voltage between terminals ②, ③ and ground.
Voltage: Battery voltage
N.G.
Check the following.
• Harness connectors
• fusible link
• 10A fuse
• Harness continuity between battery and condenser fan relay
• Harness continuity between fuse and condenser fan relay
If N.G., repair harness or connectors.
O.K.
C
CHECK GROUND CIRCUIT.
1) Turn ignition switch "OFF".
2) Disconnect condenser fan motor harness connector.
3) Check harness continuity between terminal ⓐ and terminal ⑤, terminal ⓑ and body ground.
Continuity should exist.
N.G.
Repair harness or connectors.
O.K.
D
CHECK OUTPUT SIGNAL CIRCUIT.
1) Disconnect E.C.U. harness connector.
2) Check harness continuity between E.C.U. terminal ⑨ and terminal ①.
Continuity should exist.
N.G.
Check the following.
• Harness connectors
• Harness continuity between E.C.U. and condenser fan relay
If N.G., repair harness or connectors.
O.K.
Ⓐ
Go To Next Figure
92F03119
Courtesy of Nissan Motor Co., U.S.A.

Fig. 21: Diagnostic Procedure 5-4 – Illumination Or Indicators Of Push Control Unit Do Not Come On

Fig. 22: Diagnostic Procedure 6 – Condenser Fan Control (1 Of 2)

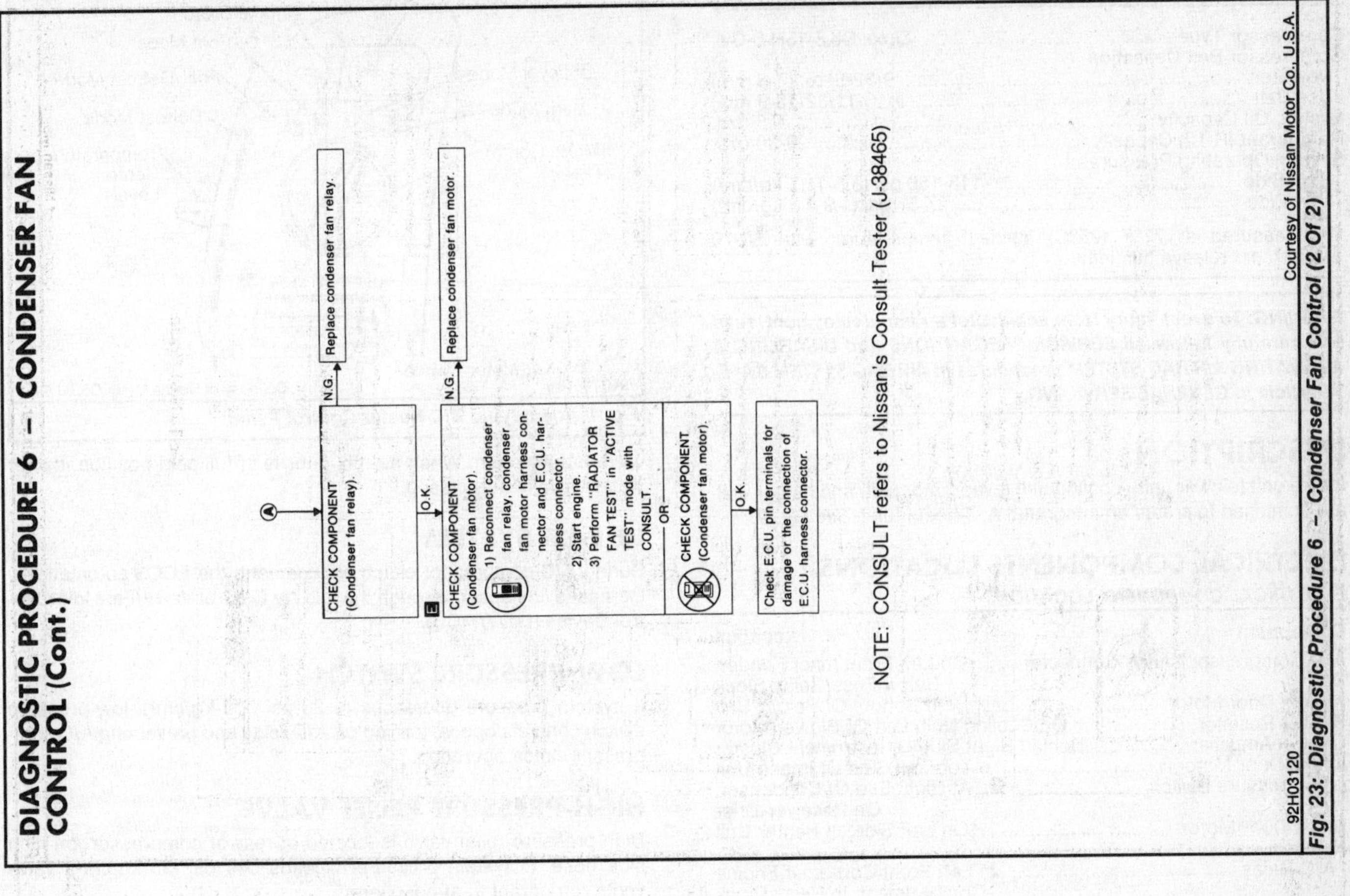

DIAGNOSTIC PROCEDURE 6 – CONDENSER FAN CONTROL (Cont.)
A
CHECK COMPONENT (Condenser fan relay).
N.G.
Replace condenser fan relay.
O.K.
E
CHECK COMPONENT (Condenser fan motor).
1) Reconnect condenser fan relay, condenser fan motor harness connector and E.C.U. harness connector.
2) Start engine.
3) Perform "RADIATOR FAN TEST" in "ACTIVE TEST" mode with CONSULT.
OR
CHECK COMPONENT (Condenser fan motor).
N.G.
Replace condenser fan motor.
O.K.
Check E.C.U. pin terminals for damage or the connection of E.C.U. harness connector.
NOTE: CONSULT refers to Nissan's Consult Tester (J-38465)
92H03120
Courtesy of Nissan Motor Co., U.S.A.

Fig. 23: Diagnostic Procedure 6 – Condenser Fan Control (2 Of 2)

1993 MANUAL A/C-HEATER SYSTEMS
300ZX

SPECIFICATIONS

Compressor Type	Zexel DKS-16H 6-Cyl.
Compressor Belt Deflection	
New Belt	9/32-5/16" (7-8 mm)
Use Belt	5/16-11/32" (8-9 mm)
System Oil Capacity	6.8 ozs.
Refrigerant (R-12) Capacity	26-30 ozs.
System Operating Pressures [1]	
High Side	118-166 psi (8.3-11.7 kg/cm²)
Low Side	27-37 psi (1.9-2.6 kg/cm²)

[1] – Measured at 77°F (25°C) ambient temperature, with 50-70 percent relative humidity.

WARNING: To avoid injury from accidental air bag deployment, read and carefully follow all SERVICE PRECAUTIONS and DISABLING & ACTIVATING AIR BAG SYSTEM procedures in AIR BAG SYSTEM SAFETY article in GENERAL SERVICING.

DESCRIPTION

Intake unit (blower unit), cooling unit (evaporator unit) and heater unit are combined to create an integrated A/C-heater unit. *See Fig. 9.*

ELECTRICAL COMPONENTS LOCATIONS

ELECTRICAL COMPONENT LOCATIONS

Component	Location
A/C Compressor Clutch Connector	On Left Front Inner Fender, Below Fuse/Relay Block
Air Mix Door Motor	On Bottom Of Heater Unit
Blower Resistor	On Cooling Unit, Left Of Blower Motor
Control Amplifier	Behind Right Side Of Instrument Cluster
Intake Door Motor	n Top Left Side Of Intake Unit
Low-Pressure Switch	At Right End Of Condenser, On Receiver-Drier
Mode Door Motor	On Left Side Of Heater Unit
Relays	
A/C Relay	In Left Front Corner Of Engine Compartment, In Relay Block
A/C Ignition (Blower) Relay	Behind Left Side Of Dash, On Fuse/Relay Block
Blower Relay No. 1	Left Of Blower Motor
Blower Relays No. 2 & 3	[1] Behind Right Kick Panel
Radiator Fan Relay	In Left Front Corner Of Engine Compartment, In Relay Block
Thermal Transmitter	Forward Of Timing Belt Cover, On Coolant Outlet
Thermo Control Amplifier	On Left Side Of Cooling Unit

[1] – Blower relay No. 2 is closest to passenger door opening.

OPERATION

A/C COMPRESSOR CLUTCH CONTROL

Engine Concentrated Control System (ECCS) control unit monitors evaporator temperature through thermistor inside evaporator housing (signal is amplified by thermo control amplifier).

The ECCS cycles the A/C compressor clutch on and off as needed. The ECCS turns off A/C compressor clutch when engine is under heavy load (full throttle) or if engine coolant temperature exceeds predetermined value.

AIRFLOW CONTROL

Airflow control doors are controlled by electric motors. These include intake door motor (fresh or recirculated air), air mix door motor (temperature blend) and mode door motor (vent, bi-level, foot, foot/defrost and defrost positions). *See Figs. 2-4.* Control amplifier receives inputs from A/C-heater control panel buttons and applies voltage to appropriate door control motors. *See Fig. 1.*

HEATER WATER VALVE

Heater water valve is controlled by a cable from the air mix door motor. *See Fig. 2.* When air mix door is in full hot position, heater water valve is fully open. When air mix door is in full cold position, heater water valve is fully closed.

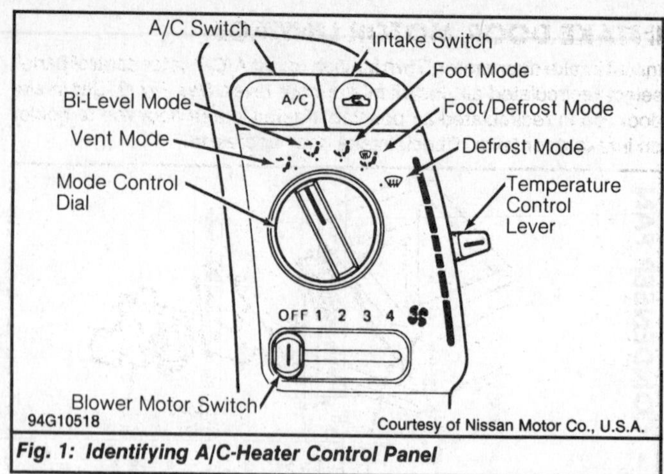
A/C Switch
Intake Switch
Foot Mode
Bi-Level Mode
Foot/Defrost Mode
Vent Mode
Defrost Mode
Mode Control
Dial
Temperature
Control
Lever
A/C
OFF 1 2 3 4
Blower Motor Switch
94G10518
Courtesy of Nissan Motor Co., U.S.A.

Fig. 1: Identifying A/C-Heater Control Panel

IDLE-UP SYSTEM

During A/C compressor clutch engagement, the ECCS automatically increases idle speed through the Idle Air Control Valve/Fast Idle Control Device (IACV/FICD).

LOW-PRESSURE SWITCH

If system pressure decreases to 28 psi (2.0 kg/cm²), low-pressure switch contacts opens, turning off A/C relay and preventing A/C compressor clutch operation.

HIGH-PRESSURE RELIEF VALVE

High-pressure relief valve is located at rear of compressor, on high side hose. If system pressure exceeds 540 psi (38 kg/cm²), valve vents refrigerant to atmosphere.

FUSIBLE PLUG

Fusible plug, mounted on receiver-drier, is a high temperature relief. If temperature exceeds 221°F (105°C), plug melts to vent refrigerant to atmosphere, protecting the A/C system.

ADJUSTMENTS

AIR MIX DOOR MOTOR LINKAGE

Install air mix door motor. Turn ignition on. Move A/C-heater control panel temperature control lever to full cold position. Move air mix doors to full cold position. *See Fig. 2.* Fasten door rod to air mix door motor. Install air mix door motor.

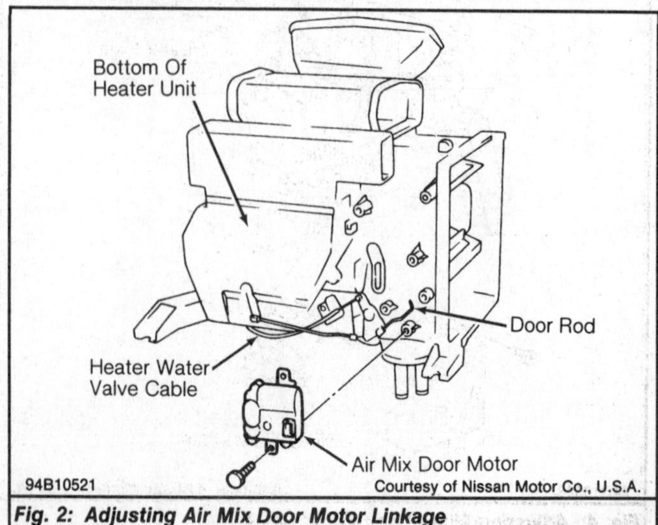
Bottom Of
Heater Unit
Door Rod
Heater Water
Valve Cable
Air Mix Door Motor
94B10521
Courtesy of Nissan Motor Co., U.S.A.

Fig. 2: Adjusting Air Mix Door Motor Linkage

INTAKE DOOR MOTOR LINKAGE

Install intake door motor. Turn ignition on. At A/C-heater control panel, select recirculated air. Install intake door lever. *See Fig. 3.* Set intake door rod in recirculated air position. Fasten intake door rod to holder on intake door lever. Check intake door operation.

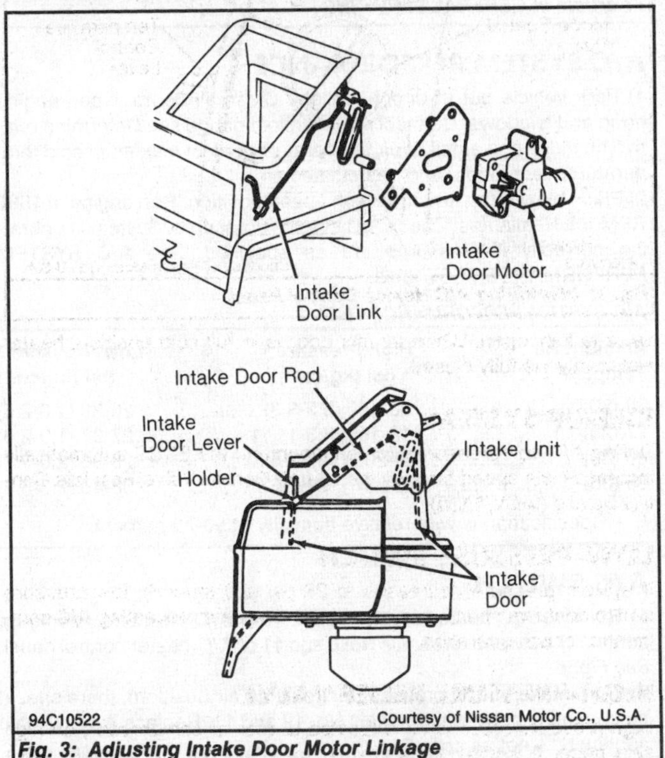

Intake
Door Motor
Intake
Door Link
Intake Door Rod
Intake
Door Lever
Intake Unit
Holder
Intake
Door
94C10522
Courtesy of Nissan Motor Co., U.S.A.

Fig. 3: Adjusting Intake Door Motor Linkage

MODE DOOR MOTOR LINKAGE

1) Install mode door motor. Turn ignition on. At A/C-heater control panel, select vent position. Move side link by hand and hold mode door in vent mode. *See Fig. 4.*

2) Attach mode door rod to side link rod holder. Ensure defrost door only is at fully open position when defrost mode is selected, and vent door only is at fully open position when vent mode is selected.

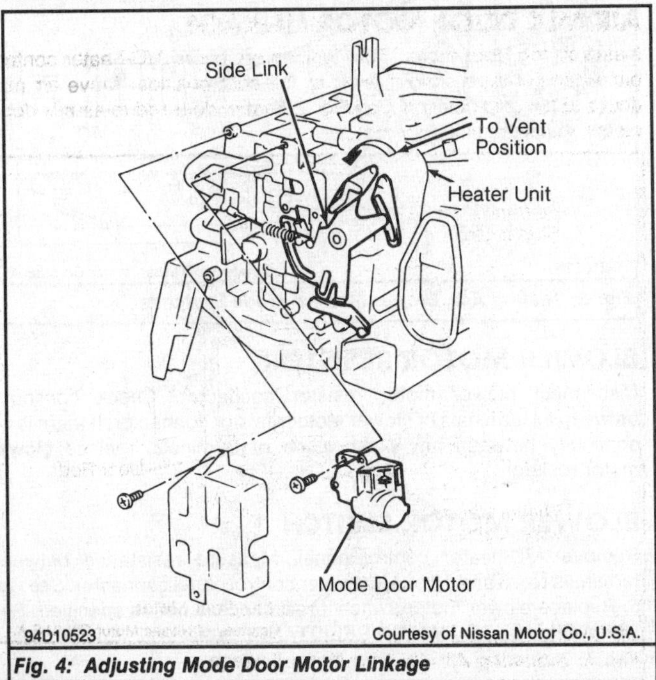

Side Link
To Vent
Position
Heater Unit
Mode Door Motor
94D10523
Courtesy of Nissan Motor Co., U.S.A.

Fig. 4: Adjusting Mode Door Motor Linkage

HEATER WATER VALVE CABLE

Clamp cable at fully closed position with both air mix doors in full cold position. In fully opened position, both air mix doors should be in full hot position.

TROUBLE SHOOTING

Perform PRELIMINARY CHECKS prior to using TROUBLE SHOOTING - 300ZX charts following this article. The 300ZX is equipped with a diagnostic connector for use with Nissan Consult Tester (J-38465). Consult tester may be used to diagnose radiator fan control circuit. Connector is located on driver's side of instrument panel, above hood release handle.

NOTE: Diagnostic procedures are found in TROUBLE SHOOTING - 300ZX charts following this article.

PRELIMINARY CHECK 1

NOTE: When vent mode is selected, intake door must be in fresh/ recirculated air position (halfway point).

Intake Door Is Not Set At Fresh In Defrost Mode - 1) Turn ignition on. Place blower motor on high speed. While in vent, bi-level, foot or foot/defrost mode, turn intake (fresh/recirculated air) switch from on to off. Check intake door position. If intake door is not in fresh air position, go to DIAGNOSTIC PROCEDURE 3.

2) If intake door is in fresh air position, turn intake switch from off to on. Check intake door position. If intake door is not in recirculated air position, go to DIAGNOSTIC PROCEDURE 3.

3) If intake door is in recirculated air position, select defrost mode. Check intake door position. If intake door is not in fresh air position, replace control amplifier. If intake door is in fresh air position, no problem is indicated at this time.

PRELIMINARY CHECK 2

A/C Does Not Blow Cold Air - 1) Turn ignition on. Turn on A/C and blower motor. Select vent mode. Move temperature control lever to full cold position. If air does not flow from vents, go to step **4)**. If air flows from vents, check compressor clutch engagement.

2) If compressor clutch does not engage, go to next step. If compressor clutch engages, check refrigerant pressures. See A/C SYSTEM PERFORMANCE under TESTING. If pressures are within specification, go to DIAGNOSTIC PROCEDURE 6. If pressures are not within specification, check for mechanical problem in refrigerant system.

3) Check belt tension. Adjust or replace belt as necessary. If belt is okay, check refrigerant pressures. See A/C SYSTEM PERFORMANCE under TESTING. If pressures are within specification, go to DIAGNOSTIC PROCEDURE 6. If pressures are not within specification, check for leak in refrigerant system.

4) If air did not flow from vents in step **1)**, check blower motor operation. If blower motor does not operate, go to DIAGNOSTIC PROCEDURE 1. If blower motor operates, check for leaks in ducting. If ducting is okay, check thermo control amplifier. See THERMO CONTROL AMPLIFIER under TESTING. If thermo control amplifier is okay, remove intake unit and check for evaporator freezing.

PRELIMINARY CHECK 3

Compressor Clutch Does Not Operate In Foot/Defrost Or Defrost Mode - Start engine. Turn on A/C and blower motor. If compressor clutch does not engage, go to DIAGNOSTIC PROCEDURE 4. If compressor clutch engages, turn off A/C. Ensure compressor clutch disengages. Leave engine and blower motor running. Select foot/ defrost and defrost modes. If compressor clutch does not engage in both modes, replace control amplifier. If compressor clutch engages in both modes, no problem is indicated at this time.

1993 MANUAL A/C-HEATER SYSTEMS 300ZX (Cont.)

PRELIMINARY CHECK 4

Air Outlet (Mode) Does Not Change – Turn ignition on. If air does not come out of correct duct, or if air distribution ratio is not as specified, go to DIAGNOSTIC PROCEDURE 2. See AIR DISTRIBUTION RATIOS table. If air comes out of correct duct and air distribution ratio is as specified, no problem is indicated at this time.

AIR DISTRIBUTION RATIOS

Switch Position	Distribution
Vent	100% Vent
Bi-Level	65% Vent; 35% Foot
Foot	70% Foot; 30% Defrost
Foot/Defrost	50% Foot; 50% Defrost
Defrost	100% Defrost

PRELIMINARY CHECK 5

Noisy Blower Motor – Replace blower motor.
Noisy Expansion Valve – Replace expansion valve.
Noisy Compressor – Replace compressor.
Noisy Refrigerant Line – Ensure line is secured. If necessary, attach rubber or other vibration-absorbing material to line.
Noisy Belt – If belt vibration is intense, adjust belt tension. If side of belt is worn, align pulleys. Replace belt if necessary

PRELIMINARY CHECK 6

Insufficient Heating – Turn ignition on. Turn blower motor on. Select foot mode. Move temperature control lever to full hot position. If air does not flow from foot ducts, go to DIAGNOSTIC PROCEDURE 1. If air flows from foot ducts, go to DIAGNOSTIC PROCEDURE 6.

MAIN POWER SUPPLY & GROUND CIRCUIT CHECK

1) Remove instrument panel lower lid from driver's side. Remove vent duct. Remove control amplifier, leaving harness connected. Disconnect control amplifier harness connector. Turn ignition on. Check voltage at terminals No. 13 and 14 of control amplifier harness connector. *See Fig. 5.*
2) If battery voltage is not present, repair wiring harness. If battery voltage is present, turn ignition off. Check continuity between terminal No. 23 and ground. If there is no continuity, repair wiring harness. If there is continuity, power supply circuit is okay.

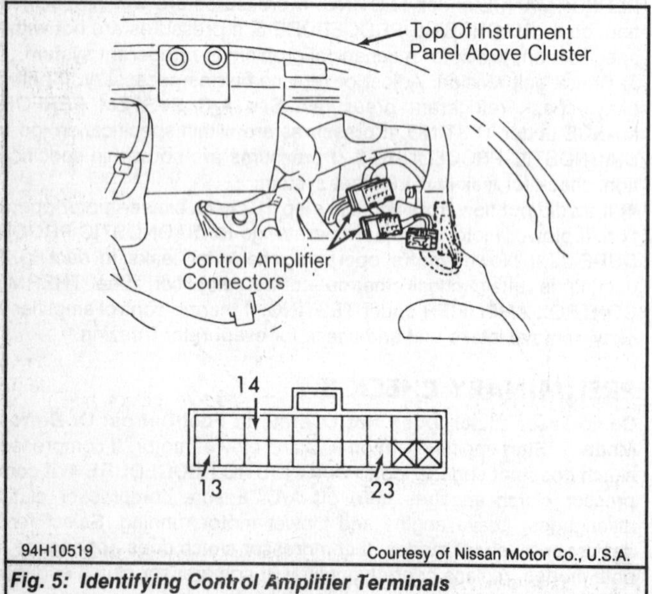
Top Of Instrument
Panel Above Cluster
Control Amplifier
Connectors
14
13
23
94H10519
Courtesy of Nissan Motor Co., U.S.A.

Fig. 5: Identifying Control Amplifier Terminals

TESTING

WARNING: To avoid injury from accidental air bag deployment, read and carefully follow all SERVICE PRECAUTIONS and DISABLING & ACTIVATING AIR BAG SYSTEM procedures in AIR BAG SYSTEM SAFETY article in GENERAL SERVICING.

A/C SYSTEM PERFORMANCE

1) Park vehicle out of direct sunlight. Close all doors. Open engine hood and windows. Connect A/C manifold gauge set. Determine relative humidity and ambient air temperature. Select maximum cold temperature, vent mode, and recirculated air.
2) Place blower fan switch to high speed position. Run engine at 1500 RPM for 10 minutes. Check A/C system pressures. System is operating correctly if pressures are as specified. See A/C SYSTEM PERFORMANCE TEST table.

A/C SYSTEM PERFORMANCE TEST

Ambient Air Temp. °F (°C)	High Pressure [1] psi (kg/cm²)	Low Pressure [1] psi (kg/cm²)
68 (20)	88-132 (6.2-9.3)	26-36 (1.8-2.5)
77 (25)	118-166 (8.3-11.7)	27-37 (1.9-2.6)
86 (30)	148-203 (10.4-14.3)	28-38 (2.0-2.7)
95 (35)	179-237 (12.6-16.7)	33-46 (2.3-3.2)

[1] – Specification is with relative humidity at 50-70 percent.

A/C SWITCH

1) Remove A/C-heater control panel. With A/C on, there should be continuity between terminals No. 6 and 11 of A/C-heater control panel. *See Fig. 6.*
2) With intake button pressed (recirculated air position), there should be continuity between terminals No. 12 and 11. Replace A/C switch if continuity is not as specified.

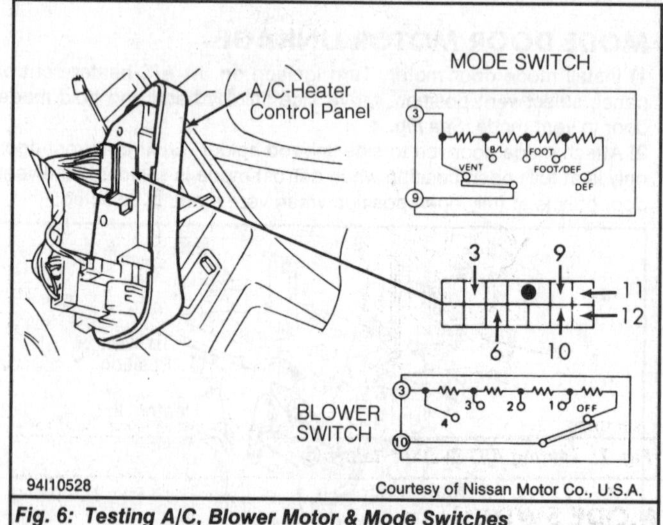
MODE SWITCH
A/C-Heater
Control Panel
3
B/L
FOOT
VENT
FOOT/DEF
DEF
9
3
9
11
12
6
10
3
3
2
1
OFF
4
BLOWER
SWITCH
10
94I10528
Courtesy of Nissan Motor Co., U.S.A.

Fig. 6: Testing A/C, Blower Motor & Mode Switches

BLOWER MOTOR RESISTOR

Disconnect blower motor resistor connector. Check continuity between all terminals of blower motor resistor connector. If there is no continuity between any combination of terminals, replace blower motor resistor.

BLOWER MOTOR SWITCH

Remove A/C-heater control panel. Measure resistance between terminals No. 3 and 10 of A/C-heater control panel connector. *See Fig. 6.* Replace blower motor switch if resistance is not as specified. See BLOWER MOTOR SWITCH RESISTANCE table.

BLOWER MOTOR SWITCH RESISTANCE

Switch Position	[1] Ohms
Off	710
1	1140
2	460
3	270
4	0

[1] - Values are approximate.

LOW-PRESSURE SWITCH

Disconnect low-pressure switch connector. Check continuity between low-pressure switch terminals. See LOW-PRESSURE SWITCH CONTINUITY table. Replace low-pressure switch if continuity is not as specified.

LOW-PRESSURE SWITCH CONTINUITY

Pressure psi (kg/cm²)	Continuity
Decreasing To 28 (2.0)	No
Increasing To 30 (2.1)	Yes

RELAYS

Remove relay. Check continuity between terminals No. 3 and 4. *See Fig. 7.* If there is continuity, replace relay. If there is no continuity, apply battery voltage across terminals No. 1 and 2. Check continuity between terminals No. 3 and 4. If there is no continuity, replace relay.

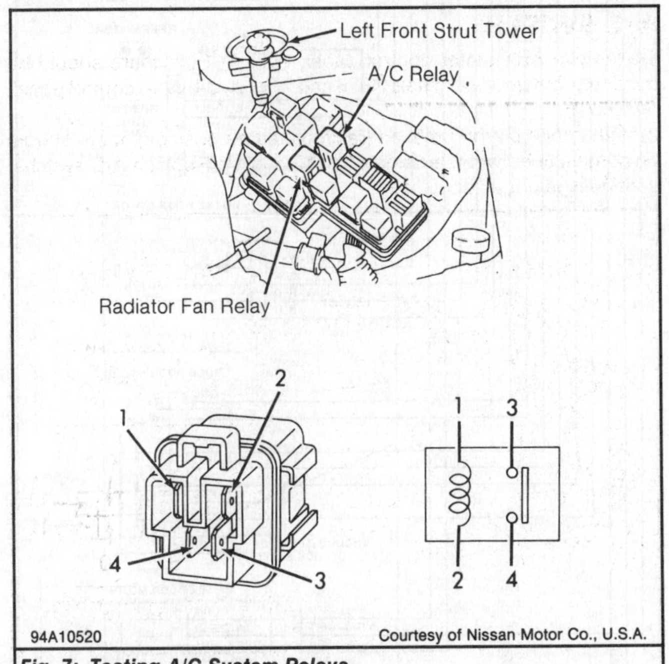

Left Front Strut Tower
A/C Relay
Radiator Fan Relay
1
2
3
4
1
3
2
4
94A10520
Courtesy of Nissan Motor Co., U.S.A.

Fig. 7: Testing A/C System Relays

MODE SWITCH

Remove A/C-heater control panel. Measure resistance between terminals No. 3 and 9 of A/C-heater control panel connector. *See Fig. 6.* Replace mode switch if resistance is not as specified. See MODE SWITCH RESISTANCE table.

MODE SWITCH RESISTANCE

Switch Position	[1] Ohms
Vent	0
Bi-Level	270
Foot	460
Foot/Defrost	1140
Defrost	710

[1] - Values are approximate.

THERMO CONTROL AMPLIFIER

Start engine. Turn A/C on. Measure evaporator outlet air temperature. Backprobe Blue/Black wire terminal of thermo control amplifier connector. *See Fig. 8.* Replace thermo control amplifier if voltage is not as specified. See THERMO CONTROL AMPLIFIER TEST table.

THERMO CONTROL AMPLIFIER TEST

Evaporator Outlet Air Temp. °F (°C)	Volts
Decreasing To 37 (3.0)	[1] About 12
Increasing To 40 (4.5)	[2] 0

[1] - Signalling ECCS to turn off A/C compressor clutch.
[2] - Signalling ECCS to turn on A/C compressor clutch.

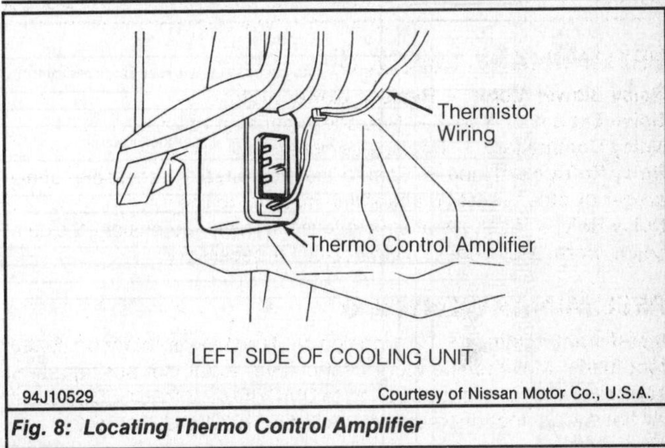

Thermistor Wiring
Thermo Control Amplifier
LEFT SIDE OF COOLING UNIT
94J10529
Courtesy of Nissan Motor Co., U.S.A.

Fig. 8: Locating Thermo Control Amplifier

REMOVAL & INSTALLATION

A/C-HEATING UNIT

Remove and install A/C-heating unit using exploded view as a guide. *See Fig. 9.* For more information, see AUTOMATIC A/C-HEATER SYSTEMS - 300ZX article.

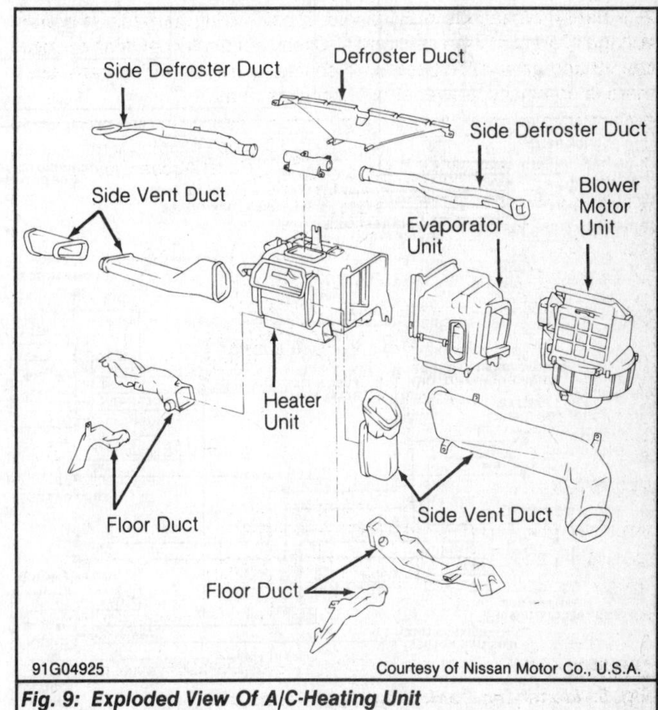

Side Defroster Duct
Defroster Duct
Side Defroster Duct
Side Vent Duct
Evaporator Unit
Blower Motor Unit
Heater Unit
Floor Duct
Side Vent Duct
Floor Duct
91G04925
Courtesy of Nissan Motor Co., U.S.A.

Fig. 9: Exploded View Of A/C-Heating Unit

1993 MANUAL A/C-HEATER SYSTEMS 300ZX (Cont.)

WIRING DIAGRAM

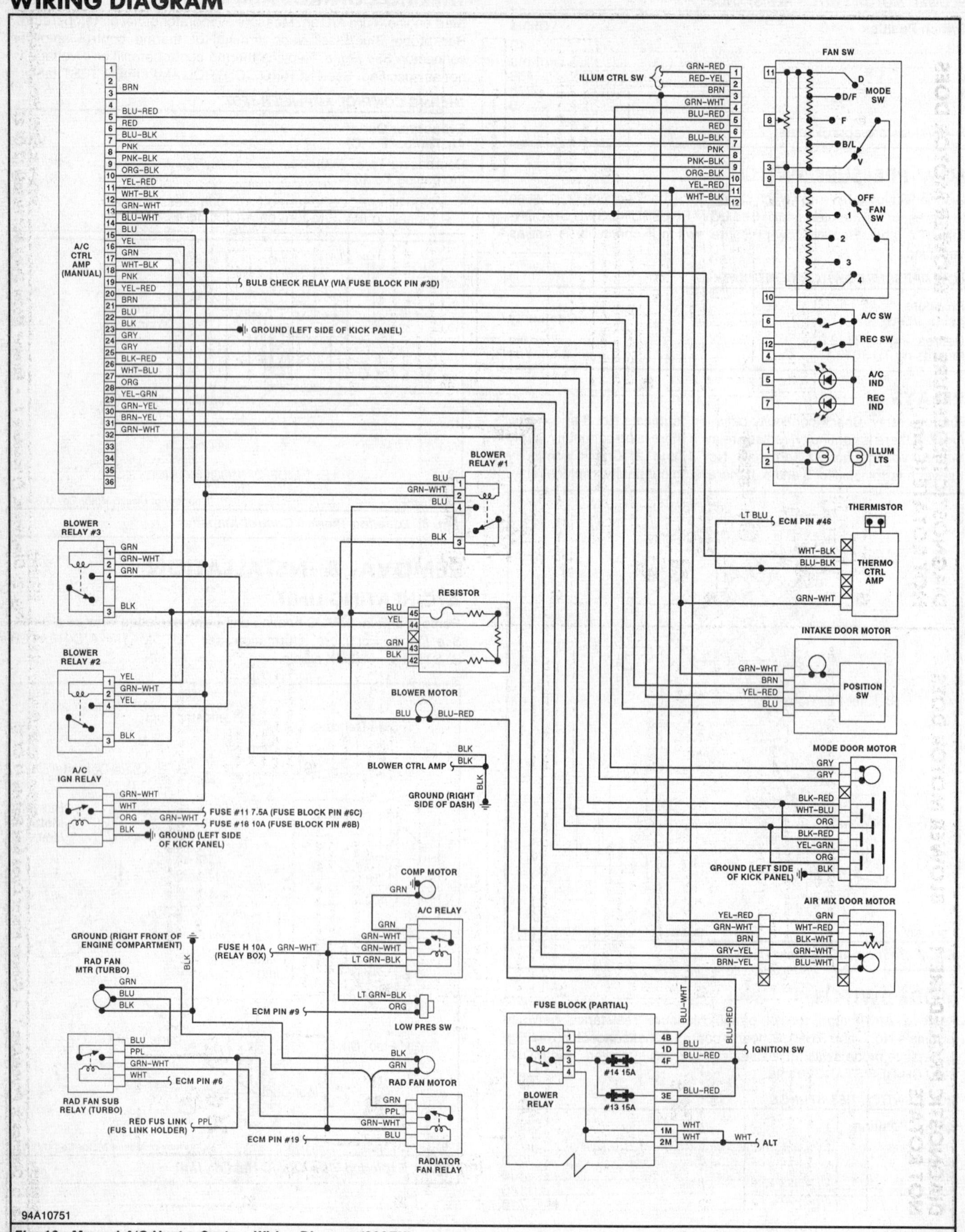
A/C CTRL AMP (MANUAL)
ILLUM CTRL SW
FAN SW
MODE SW
D
D/F
F
B/L
V
OFF
FAN SW
A/C SW
REC SW
A/C IND
REC IND
ILLUM LTS
BULB CHECK RELAY (VIA FUSE BLOCK PIN #3D)
GROUND (LEFT SIDE OF KICK PANEL)
BLOWER RELAY #1
BLOWER RELAY #3
BLOWER RELAY #2
RESISTOR
BLOWER MOTOR
BLOWER CTRL AMP
GROUND (RIGHT SIDE OF DASH)
THERMISTOR
LT BLU
ECM PIN #46
THERMO CTRL AMP
INTAKE DOOR MOTOR
POSITION SW
MODE DOOR MOTOR
GROUND (LEFT SIDE OF KICK PANEL)
AIR MIX DOOR MOTOR
A/C IGN RELAY
FUSE #11 7.5A (FUSE BLOCK PIN #6C)
FUSE #18 10A (FUSE BLOCK PIN #8B)
GROUND (LEFT SIDE OF KICK PANEL)
COMP MOTOR
A/C RELAY
FUSE H 10A (RELAY BOX)
GROUND (RIGHT FRONT OF ENGINE COMPARTMENT)
RAD FAN MTR (TURBO)
ECM PIN #9
LOW PRES SW
RAD FAN SUB RELAY (TURBO)
ECM PIN #6
RAD FAN MOTOR
RED FUS LINK (FUS LINK HOLDER)
ECM PIN #19
RADIATOR FAN RELAY
FUSE BLOCK (PARTIAL)
BLOWER RELAY
#14 15A
#13 15A
IGNITION SW
ALT
94A10751

Fig. 10: Manual A/C-Heater System Wiring Diagram (300ZX)

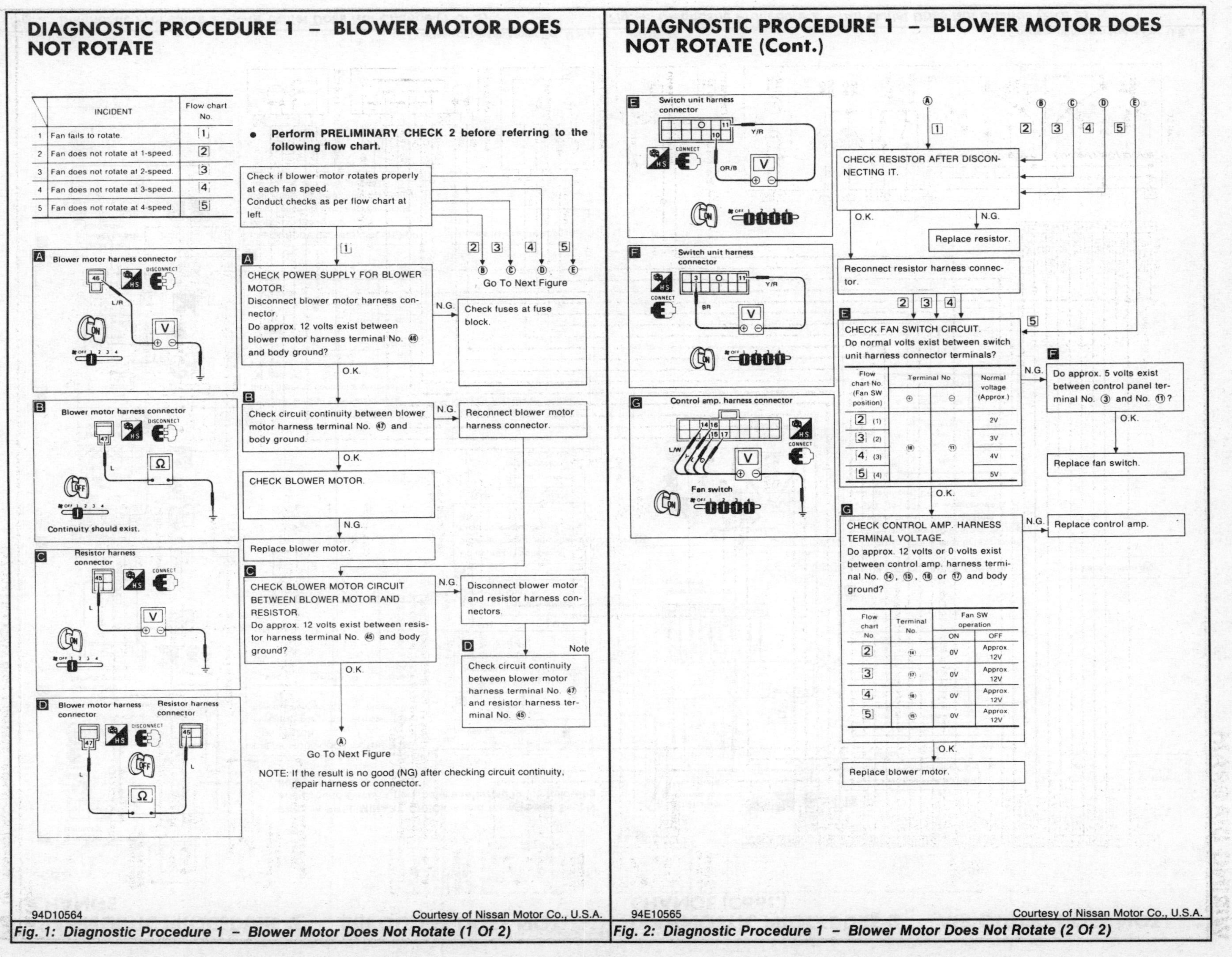
DIAGNOSTIC PROCEDURE 1 – BLOWER MOTOR DOES NOT ROTATE
INCIDENT
Flow chart No.
1 Fan fails to rotate. 1
2 Fan does not rotate at 1-speed. 2
3 Fan does not rotate at 2-speed. 3
4 Fan does not rotate at 3-speed. 4
5 Fan does not rotate at 4-speed. 5
Perform PRELIMINARY CHECK 2 before referring to the following flow chart.
Check if blower motor rotates properly at each fan speed. Conduct checks as per flow chart at left.
Go To Next Figure
A CHECK POWER SUPPLY FOR BLOWER MOTOR. Disconnect blower motor harness connector. Do approx. 12 volts exist between blower motor harness terminal No. 46 and body ground?
N.G.
Check fuses at fuse block.
O.K.
B Check circuit continuity between blower motor harness terminal No. 47 and body ground.
N.G.
Reconnect blower motor harness connector.
O.K.
CHECK BLOWER MOTOR.
N.G.
Replace blower motor.
C CHECK BLOWER MOTOR CIRCUIT BETWEEN BLOWER MOTOR AND RESISTOR. Do approx. 12 volts exist between resistor harness terminal No. 45 and body ground?
N.G.
Disconnect blower motor and resistor harness connectors.
Note
D Check circuit continuity between blower motor harness terminal No. 47 and resistor harness terminal No. 45.
O.K.
Go To Next Figure
NOTE: If the result is no good (NG) after checking circuit continuity, repair harness or connector.
A Blower motor harness connector
B Blower motor harness connector
Continuity should exist.
C Resistor harness connector
D Blower motor harness connector
Resistor harness connector
DISCONNECT
CONNECT
L/R
L
94D10564
Courtesy of Nissan Motor Co., U.S.A.
DIAGNOSTIC PROCEDURE 1 – BLOWER MOTOR DOES NOT ROTATE (Cont.)
E Switch unit harness connector
F Switch unit harness connector
G Control amp. harness connector
Fan switch
Y/R
OR/B
BR
L/W
CHECK RESISTOR AFTER DISCONNECTING IT.
O.K.
N.G.
Replace resistor.
Reconnect resistor harness connector.
E CHECK FAN SWITCH CIRCUIT. Do normal volts exist between switch unit harness connector terminals?
Flow chart No. (Fan SW position) | Terminal No ⊕ | Terminal No ⊖ | Normal voltage (Approx.)
2 (1) | 10 | 11 | 2V
3 (2) | | | 3V
4 (3) | | | 4V
5 (4) | | | 5V
N.G.
F Do approx. 5 volts exist between control panel terminal No. 3 and No. 11?
O.K.
Replace fan switch.
O.K.
G CHECK CONTROL AMP. HARNESS TERMINAL VOLTAGE. Do approx. 12 volts or 0 volts exist between control amp. harness terminal No. 14, 15, 16 or 17 and body ground?
Flow chart No | Terminal No. | Fan SW operation ON | OFF
2 | 14 | 0V | Approx. 12V
3 | 17 | 0V | Approx. 12V
4 | 16 | 0V | Approx. 12V
5 | 15 | 0V | Approx. 12V
N.G.
Replace control amp.
O.K.
Replace blower motor.
94E10565
Courtesy of Nissan Motor Co., U.S.A.

Fig. 1: Diagnostic Procedure 1 – Blower Motor Does Not Rotate (1 Of 2)

Fig. 2: Diagnostic Procedure 1 – Blower Motor Does Not Rotate (2 Of 2)

1993 MANUAL A/C-HEATER SYSTEMS
Trouble Shooting – 300ZX (Cont.)

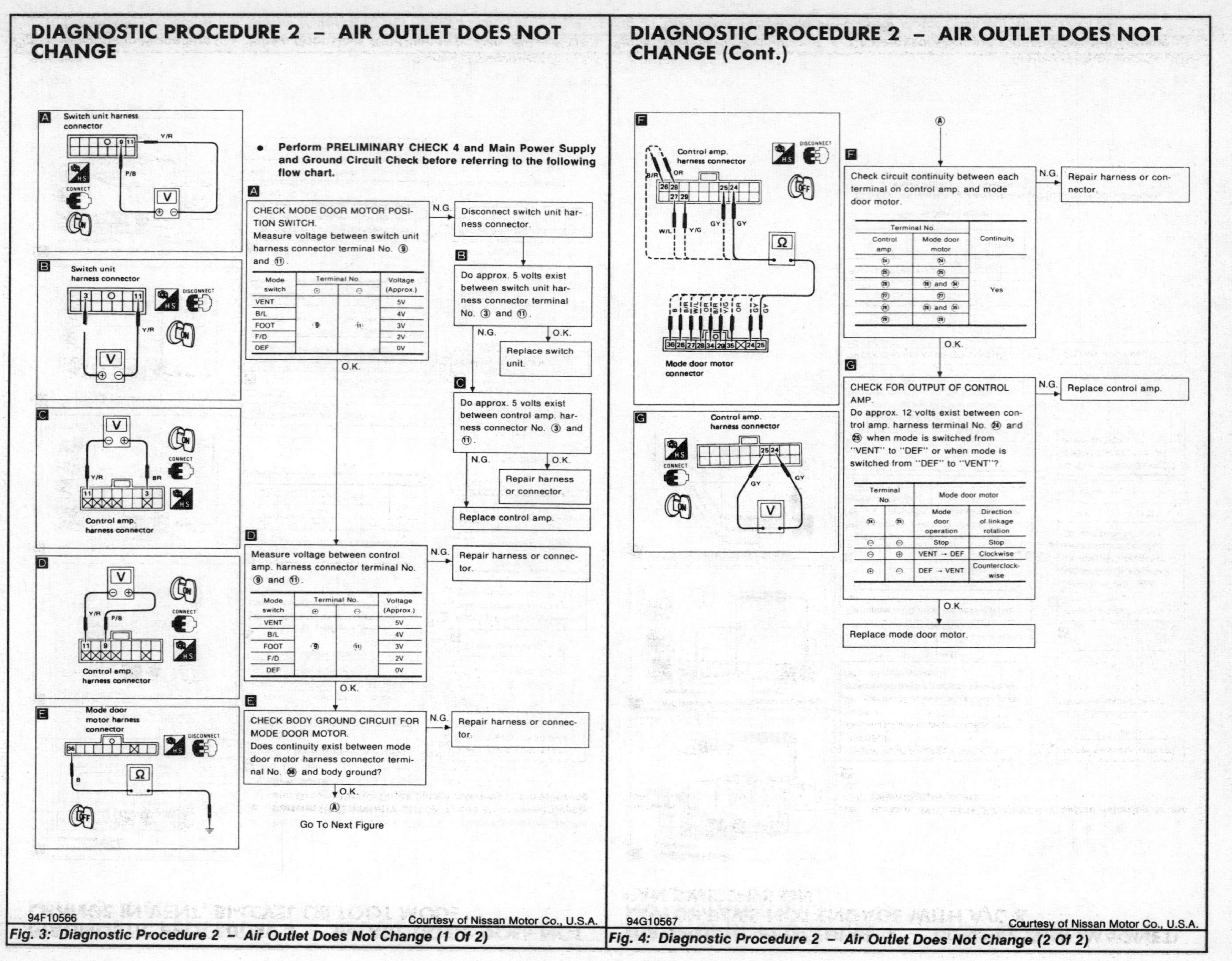
DIAGNOSTIC PROCEDURE 2 – AIR OUTLET DOES NOT CHANGE
A Switch unit harness connector
Y/R
P/B
CONNECT
ON
B Switch unit harness connector
DISCONNECT
Y/R
ON
C
CONNECT
Y/R
BR
Control amp. harness connector
D
Y/R
P/B
CONNECT
Control amp. harness connector
E Mode door motor harness connector
DISCONNECT
B
OFF
• Perform PRELIMINARY CHECK 4 and Main Power Supply and Ground Circuit Check before referring to the following flow chart.
A CHECK MODE DOOR MOTOR POSITION SWITCH.
Measure voltage between switch unit harness connector terminal No. ⑨ and ⑪.
Mode switch | Terminal No. ⊕ | ⊖ | Voltage (Approx.)
VENT | ⑨ | ⑪ | 5V
B/L | | | 4V
FOOT | | | 3V
F/D | | | 2V
DEF | | | 0V
N.G.
Disconnect switch unit harness connector.
B Do approx. 5 volts exist between switch unit harness connector terminal No. ③ and ⑪.
O.K.
Replace switch unit.
N.G.
C Do approx. 5 volts exist between control amp. harness connector No. ③ and ⑪.
O.K.
Repair harness or connector.
N.G.
Replace control amp.
O.K.
D Measure voltage between control amp. harness connector terminal No. ⑨ and ⑪.
Mode switch | Terminal No. ⊕ | ⊖ | Voltage (Approx.)
VENT | ⑨ | ⑪ | 5V
B/L | | | 4V
FOOT | | | 3V
F/D | | | 2V
DEF | | | 0V
N.G.
Repair harness or connector.
O.K.
E CHECK BODY GROUND CIRCUIT FOR MODE DOOR MOTOR.
Does continuity exist between mode door motor harness connector terminal No. ㊱ and body ground?
N.G.
Repair harness or connector.
O.K.
Ⓐ
Go To Next Figure
94F10566
Courtesy of Nissan Motor Co., U.S.A.
DIAGNOSTIC PROCEDURE 2 – AIR OUTLET DOES NOT CHANGE (Cont.)
F Control amp. harness connector
B/R
OR
W/L
Y/G
GY
GY
DISCONNECT
OFF
Mode door motor connector
G Control amp. harness connector
CONNECT
GY
GY
ON
Ⓐ
F Check circuit continuity between each terminal on control amp. and mode door motor.
Terminal No. Control amp. | Mode door motor | Continuity
㉔ | ㉔ | Yes
㉕ | ㉕ |
㉖ | ㉖ and ㉞ |
㉗ | ㉗ |
㉘ | ㉘ and ㉟ |
㉙ | ㉙ |
N.G.
Repair harness or connector.
O.K.
G CHECK FOR OUTPUT OF CONTROL AMP.
Do approx. 12 volts exist between control amp. harness terminal No. ㉔ and ㉕ when mode is switched from "VENT" to "DEF" or when mode is switched from "DEF" to "VENT"?
Terminal No. ㉔ | ㉕ | Mode door motor: Mode door operation | Direction of linkage rotation
⊖ | ⊖ | Stop | Stop
⊖ | ⊕ | VENT → DEF | Clockwise
⊕ | ⊖ | DEF → VENT | Counterclockwise
N.G.
Replace control amp.
O.K.
Replace mode door motor.
94G10567
Courtesy of Nissan Motor Co., U.S.A.

Fig. 3: Diagnostic Procedure 2 – Air Outlet Does Not Change (1 Of 2)

Fig. 4: Diagnostic Procedure 2 – Air Outlet Does Not Change (2 Of 2)

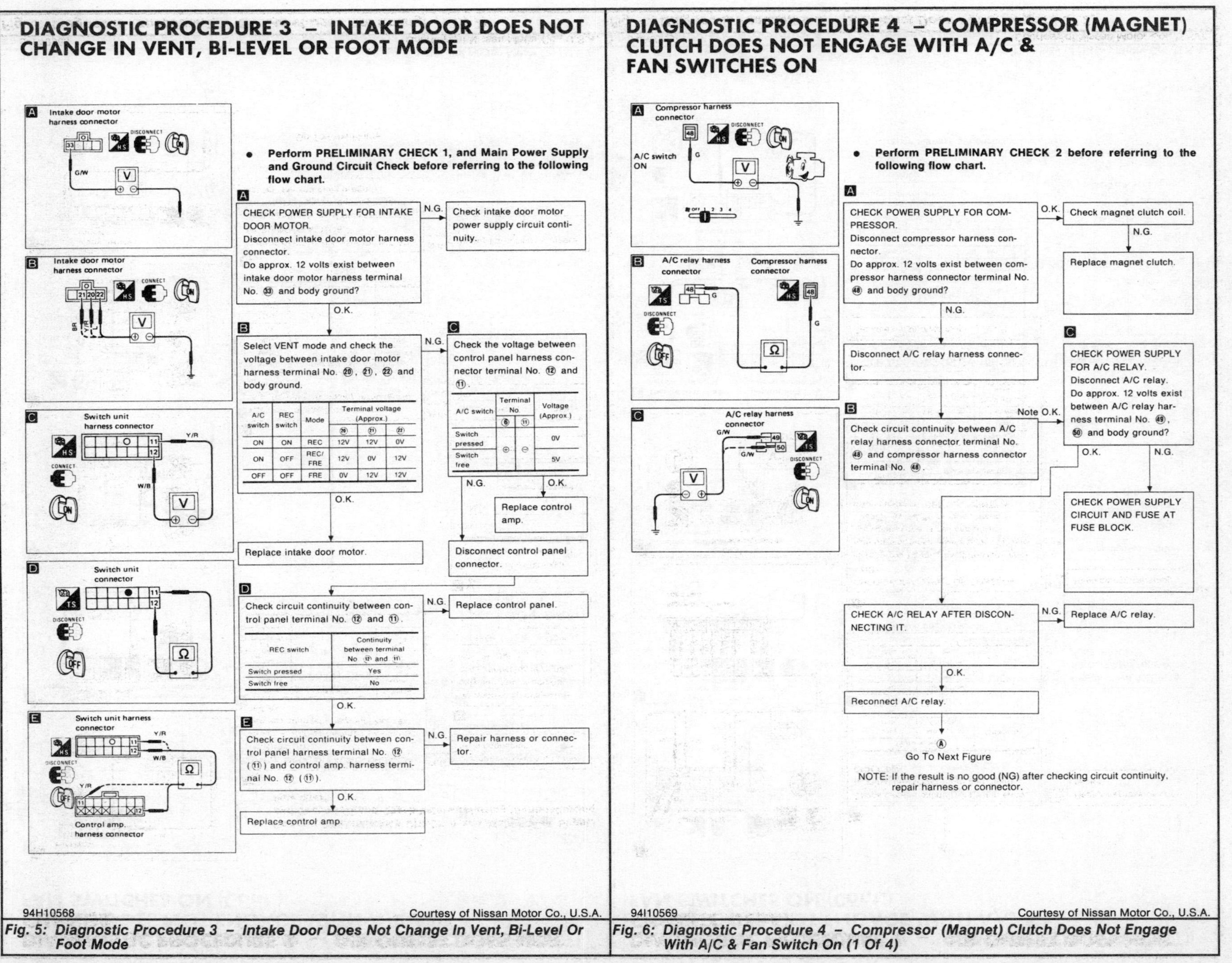

DIAGNOSTIC PROCEDURE 3 – INTAKE DOOR DOES NOT CHANGE IN VENT, BI-LEVEL OR FOOT MODE
A Intake door motor harness connector
DISCONNECT
G/W
B Intake door motor harness connector
CONNECT
BR
C Switch unit harness connector
Y/R
W/B
CONNECT
D Switch unit connector
DISCONNECT
E Switch unit harness connector
Y/R
W/B
DISCONNECT
Control amp. harness connector
• Perform PRELIMINARY CHECK 1, and Main Power Supply and Ground Circuit Check before referring to the following flow chart.
A
CHECK POWER SUPPLY FOR INTAKE DOOR MOTOR.
Disconnect intake door motor harness connector.
Do approx. 12 volts exist between intake door motor harness terminal No. ㉝ and body ground?
N.G.
Check intake door motor power supply circuit continuity.
O.K.
B
Select VENT mode and check the voltage between intake door motor harness terminal No. ⑳, ㉑, ㉒ and body ground.

A/C switch	REC switch	Mode	Terminal voltage (Approx.) ⑳	㉑	㉒
ON	ON	REC	12V	12V	0V
ON	OFF	REC/FRE	12V	0V	12V
OFF	OFF	FRE	0V	12V	12V

N.G.
C
Check the voltage between control panel harness connector terminal No. ⑫ and ⑪.

A/C switch	Terminal No. ⑥	⑪	Voltage (Approx.)
Switch pressed	⊕	⊖	0V
Switch free			5V

O.K.
Replace control amp.
N.G.
Disconnect control panel connector.
O.K.
Replace intake door motor.
D
Check circuit continuity between control panel terminal No. ⑫ and ⑪.

REC switch	Continuity between terminal No ⑫ and ⑪
Switch pressed	Yes
Switch free	No

N.G.
Replace control panel.
O.K.
E
Check circuit continuity between control panel harness terminal No. ⑫ (⑪) and control amp. harness terminal No. ⑫ (⑪).
N.G.
Repair harness or connector.
O.K.
Replace control amp.
94H10568
Courtesy of Nissan Motor Co., U.S.A.

DIAGNOSTIC PROCEDURE 4 – COMPRESSOR (MAGNET) CLUTCH DOES NOT ENGAGE WITH A/C & FAN SWITCHES ON
A Compressor harness connector
A/C switch ON
DISCONNECT
G
OFF 1 2 3 4
B A/C relay harness connector
Compressor harness connector
DISCONNECT
G
C A/C relay harness connector
G/W
DISCONNECT
• Perform PRELIMINARY CHECK 2 before referring to the following flow chart.
A
CHECK POWER SUPPLY FOR COMPRESSOR.
Disconnect compressor harness connector.
Do approx. 12 volts exist between compressor harness connector terminal No. ㊽ and body ground?
O.K.
Check magnet clutch coil.
N.G.
Replace magnet clutch.
N.G.
Disconnect A/C relay harness connector.
B
Check circuit continuity between A/C relay harness connector terminal No. ㊽ and compressor harness connector terminal No. ㊽.
Note O.K.
C
CHECK POWER SUPPLY FOR A/C RELAY.
Disconnect A/C relay.
Do approx. 12 volts exist between A/C relay harness terminal No. ㊾, ㊿ and body ground?
O.K.
N.G.
CHECK POWER SUPPLY CIRCUIT AND FUSE AT FUSE BLOCK.
CHECK A/C RELAY AFTER DISCONNECTING IT.
N.G.
Replace A/C relay.
O.K.
Reconnect A/C relay.
Ⓐ
Go To Next Figure
NOTE: If the result is no good (NG) after checking circuit continuity, repair harness or connector.
94I10569
Courtesy of Nissan Motor Co., U.S.A.

Fig. 5: Diagnostic Procedure 3 – Intake Door Does Not Change In Vent, Bi-Level Or Foot Mode

Fig. 6: Diagnostic Procedure 4 – Compressor (Magnet) Clutch Does Not Engage With A/C & Fan Switch On (1 Of 4)

1993 MANUAL A/C-HEATER SYSTEMS
Trouble Shooting – 300ZX (Cont.)

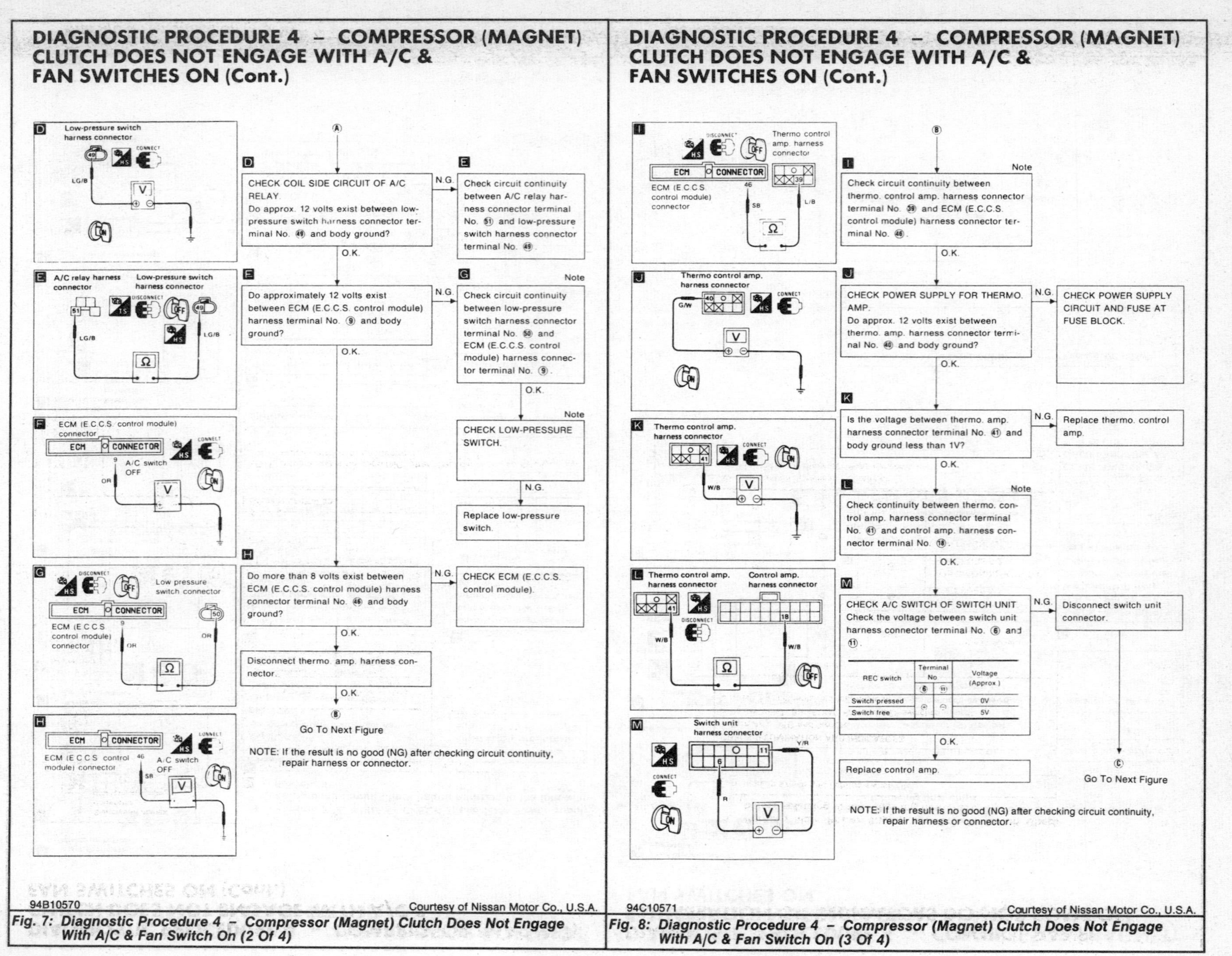
DIAGNOSTIC PROCEDURE 4 – COMPRESSOR (MAGNET) CLUTCH DOES NOT ENGAGE WITH A/C & FAN SWITCHES ON (Cont.)
D Low-pressure switch harness connector
E A/C relay harness connector
Low-pressure switch harness connector
F ECM (E.C.C.S. control module) connector
A/C switch OFF
G ECM (E.C.C.S. control module) connector
Low pressure switch connector
H ECM (E.C.C.S. control module) connector
A/C switch OFF
D CHECK COIL SIDE CIRCUIT OF A/C RELAY. Do approx. 12 volts exist between low-pressure switch harness connector terminal No. 49 and body ground?
E Check circuit continuity between A/C relay harness connector terminal No. 51 and low-pressure switch harness connector terminal No. 49.
F Do approximately 12 volts exist between ECM (E.C.C.S. control module) harness terminal No. 9 and body ground?
G Check circuit continuity between low-pressure switch harness connector terminal No. 50 and ECM (E.C.C.S. control module) harness connector terminal No. 9.
CHECK LOW-PRESSURE SWITCH.
Replace low-pressure switch.
H Do more than 8 volts exist between ECM (E.C.C.S. control module) harness connector terminal No. 46 and body ground?
CHECK ECM (E.C.C.S. control module).
Disconnect thermo. amp. harness connector.
Go To Next Figure
NOTE: If the result is no good (NG) after checking circuit continuity, repair harness or connector.
DIAGNOSTIC PROCEDURE 4 – COMPRESSOR (MAGNET) CLUTCH DOES NOT ENGAGE WITH A/C & FAN SWITCHES ON (Cont.)
I ECM (E.C.C.S. control module) connector
Thermo control amp. harness connector
J Thermo control amp. harness connector
K Thermo control amp. harness connector
L Thermo control amp. harness connector
Control amp. harness connector
M Switch unit harness connector
I Check circuit continuity between thermo. control amp. harness connector terminal No. 39 and ECM (E.C.C.S. control module) harness connector terminal No. 46.
J CHECK POWER SUPPLY FOR THERMO. AMP. Do approx. 12 volts exist between thermo. amp. harness connector terminal No. 40 and body ground?
CHECK POWER SUPPLY CIRCUIT AND FUSE AT FUSE BLOCK.
K Is the voltage between thermo. amp. harness connector terminal No. 41 and body ground less than 1V?
Replace thermo. control amp.
L Check continuity between thermo. control amp. harness connector terminal No. 41 and control amp. harness connector terminal No. 18.
M CHECK A/C SWITCH OF SWITCH UNIT. Check the voltage between switch unit harness connector terminal No. 6 and 11.
REC switch | Terminal No. 6 11 | Voltage (Approx.)
Switch pressed | + – | 0V
Switch free | | 5V
Disconnect switch unit connector.
Replace control amp.
Go To Next Figure
NOTE: If the result is no good (NG) after checking circuit continuity, repair harness or connector.
94B10570
Courtesy of Nissan Motor Co., U.S.A.
94C10571
Courtesy of Nissan Motor Co., U.S.A.

Fig. 7: Diagnostic Procedure 4 – Compressor (Magnet) Clutch Does Not Engage With A/C & Fan Switch On (2 Of 4)

Fig. 8: Diagnostic Procedure 4 – Compressor (Magnet) Clutch Does Not Engage With A/C & Fan Switch On (3 Of 4)

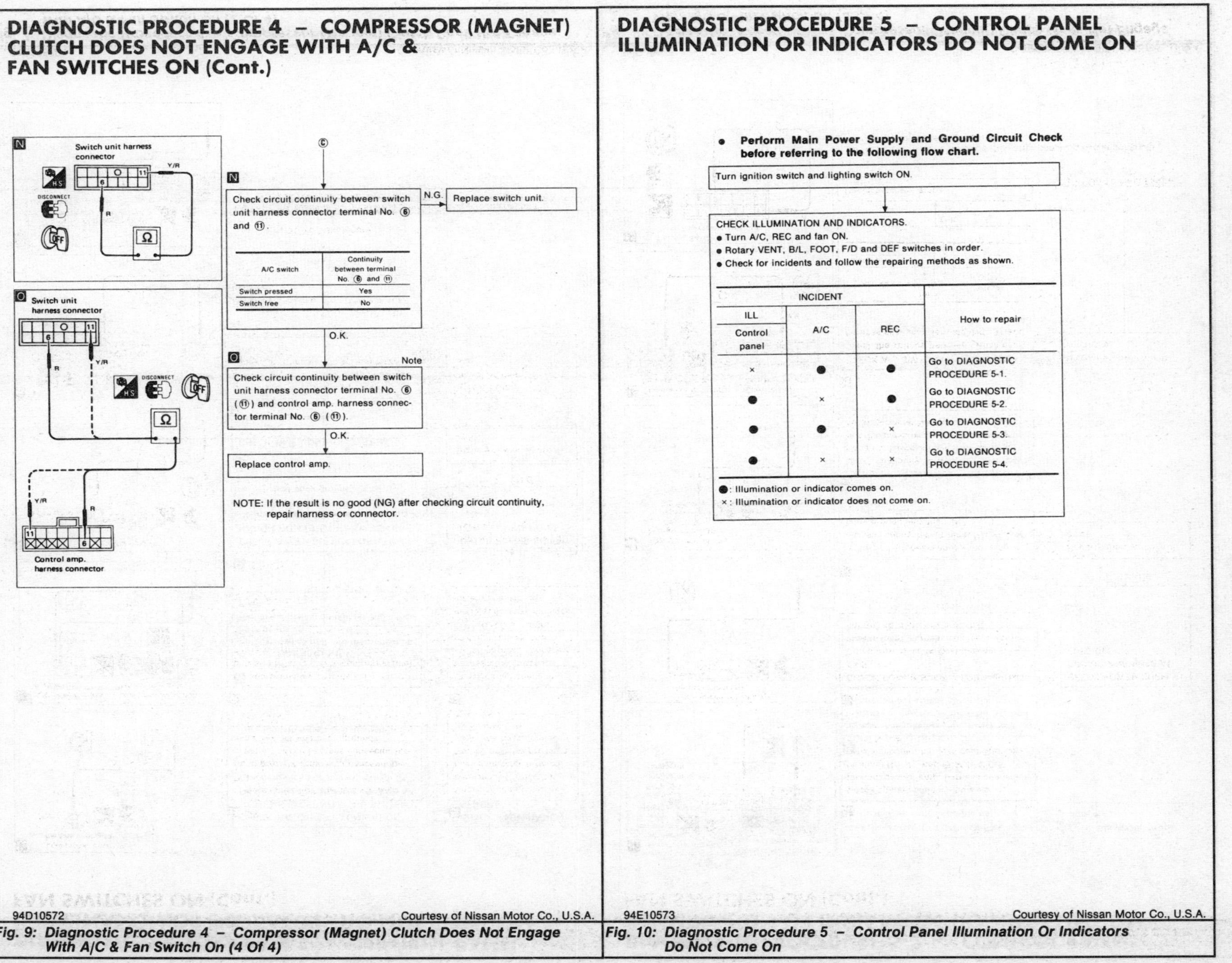

DIAGNOSTIC PROCEDURE 4 – COMPRESSOR (MAGNET) CLUTCH DOES NOT ENGAGE WITH A/C & FAN SWITCHES ON (Cont.)

N
Switch unit harness connector
Y/R
R
6
11
DISCONNECT
OFF
Ω
O
Switch unit harness connector
6
11
R
Y/R
DISCONNECT
OFF
Ω
Y/R
R
11
6
Control amp. harness connector

Ⓒ

N Check circuit continuity between switch unit harness connector terminal No. ⑥ and ⑪.

A/C switch	Continuity between terminal No. ⑥ and ⑪
Switch pressed	Yes
Switch free	No

N.G. → Replace switch unit.

O.K. ↓

O Check circuit continuity between switch unit harness connector terminal No. ⑥ (⑪) and control amp. harness connector terminal No. ⑥ (⑪). Note

O.K. ↓

Replace control amp.

NOTE: If the result is no good (NG) after checking circuit continuity, repair harness or connector.

94D10572 Courtesy of Nissan Motor Co., U.S.A.

Fig. 9: Diagnostic Procedure 4 – Compressor (Magnet) Clutch Does Not Engage With A/C & Fan Switch On (4 Of 4)

DIAGNOSTIC PROCEDURE 5 – CONTROL PANEL ILLUMINATION OR INDICATORS DO NOT COME ON

- **Perform Main Power Supply and Ground Circuit Check before referring to the following flow chart.**

Turn ignition switch and lighting switch ON.

↓

CHECK ILLUMINATION AND INDICATORS.
- Turn A/C, REC and fan ON.
- Rotary VENT, B/L, FOOT, F/D and DEF switches in order.
- Check for incidents and follow the repairing methods as shown.

INCIDENT			How to repair
ILL Control panel	A/C	REC	
×	●	●	Go to DIAGNOSTIC PROCEDURE 5-1.
●	×	●	Go to DIAGNOSTIC PROCEDURE 5-2.
●	●	×	Go to DIAGNOSTIC PROCEDURE 5-3.
●	×	×	Go to DIAGNOSTIC PROCEDURE 5-4.

●: Illumination or indicator comes on.
×: Illumination or indicator does not come on.

94E10573 Courtesy of Nissan Motor Co., U.S.A.

Fig. 10: Diagnostic Procedure 5 – Control Panel Illumination Or Indicators Do Not Come On

1993 MANUAL A/C-HEATER SYSTEMS
Trouble Shooting – 300ZX (Cont.)

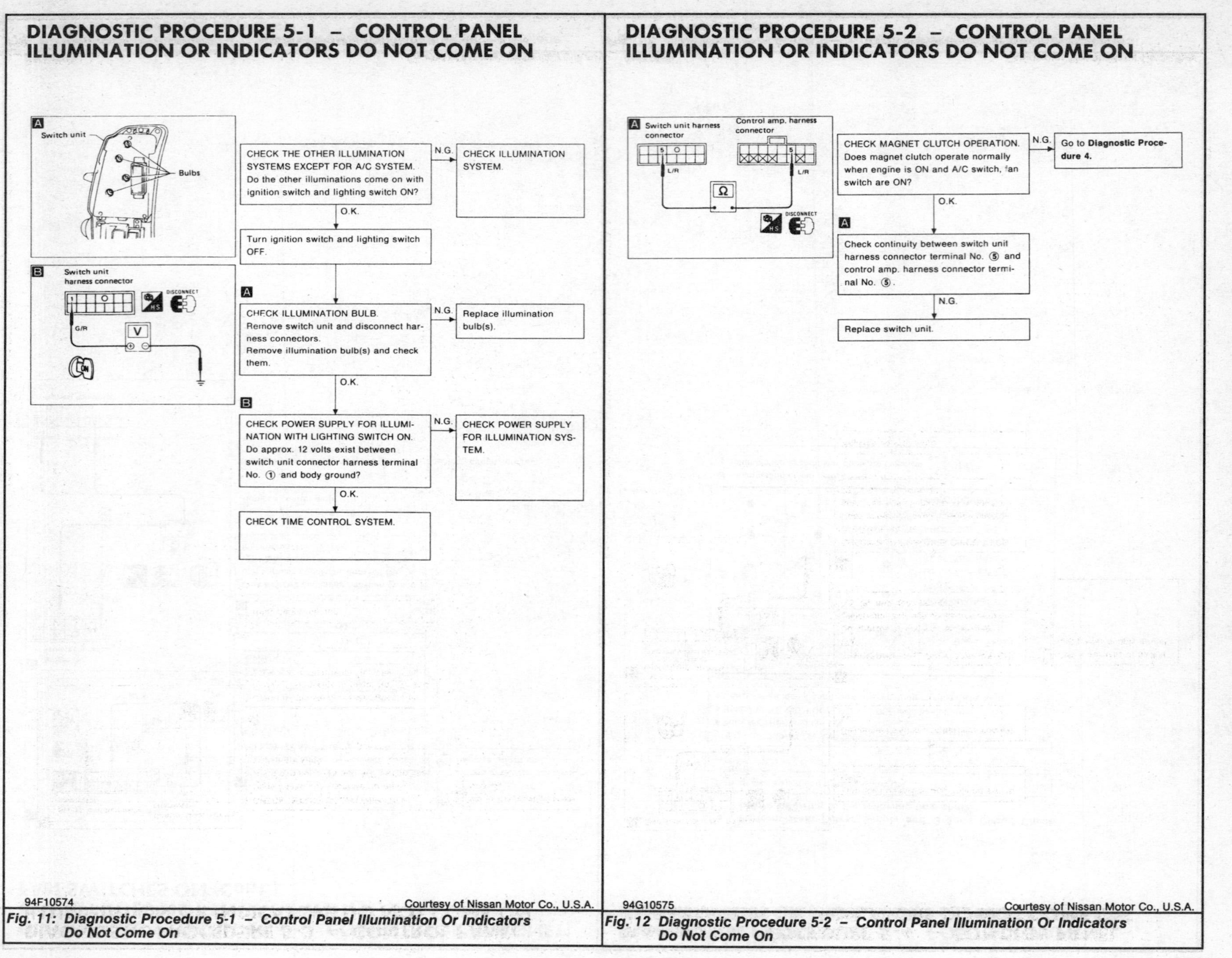
DIAGNOSTIC PROCEDURE 5-1 – CONTROL PANEL ILLUMINATION OR INDICATORS DO NOT COME ON
A
Switch unit
Bulbs
B
Switch unit harness connector
DISCONNECT
G/R
V
CHECK THE OTHER ILLUMINATION SYSTEMS EXCEPT FOR A/C SYSTEM. Do the other illuminations come on with ignition switch and lighting switch ON?
N.G.
CHECK ILLUMINATION SYSTEM.
O.K.
Turn ignition switch and lighting switch OFF.
A
CHFCK ILLUMINATION BULB. Remove switch unit and disconnect harness connectors. Remove illumination bulb(s) and check them.
N.G.
Replace illumination bulb(s).
O.K.
B
CHECK POWER SUPPLY FOR ILLUMINATION WITH LIGHTING SWITCH ON. Do approx. 12 volts exist between switch unit connector harness terminal No. ① and body ground?
N.G.
CHECK POWER SUPPLY FOR ILLUMINATION SYSTEM.
O.K.
CHECK TIME CONTROL SYSTEM.
94F10574
Courtesy of Nissan Motor Co., U.S.A.
DIAGNOSTIC PROCEDURE 5-2 – CONTROL PANEL ILLUMINATION OR INDICATORS DO NOT COME ON
A
Switch unit harness connector
Control amp. harness connector
5
L/R
Ω
DISCONNECT
CHECK MAGNET CLUTCH OPERATION. Does magnet clutch operate normally when engine is ON and A/C switch, fan switch are ON?
N.G.
Go to **Diagnostic Procedure 4.**
O.K.
A
Check continuity between switch unit harness connector terminal No. ⑤ and control amp. harness connector terminal No. ⑤.
N.G.
Replace switch unit.
94G10575
Courtesy of Nissan Motor Co., U.S.A.

Fig. 11: Diagnostic Procedure 5-1 – Control Panel Illumination Or Indicators Do Not Come On

Fig. 12 Diagnostic Procedure 5-2 – Control Panel Illumination Or Indicators Do Not Come On

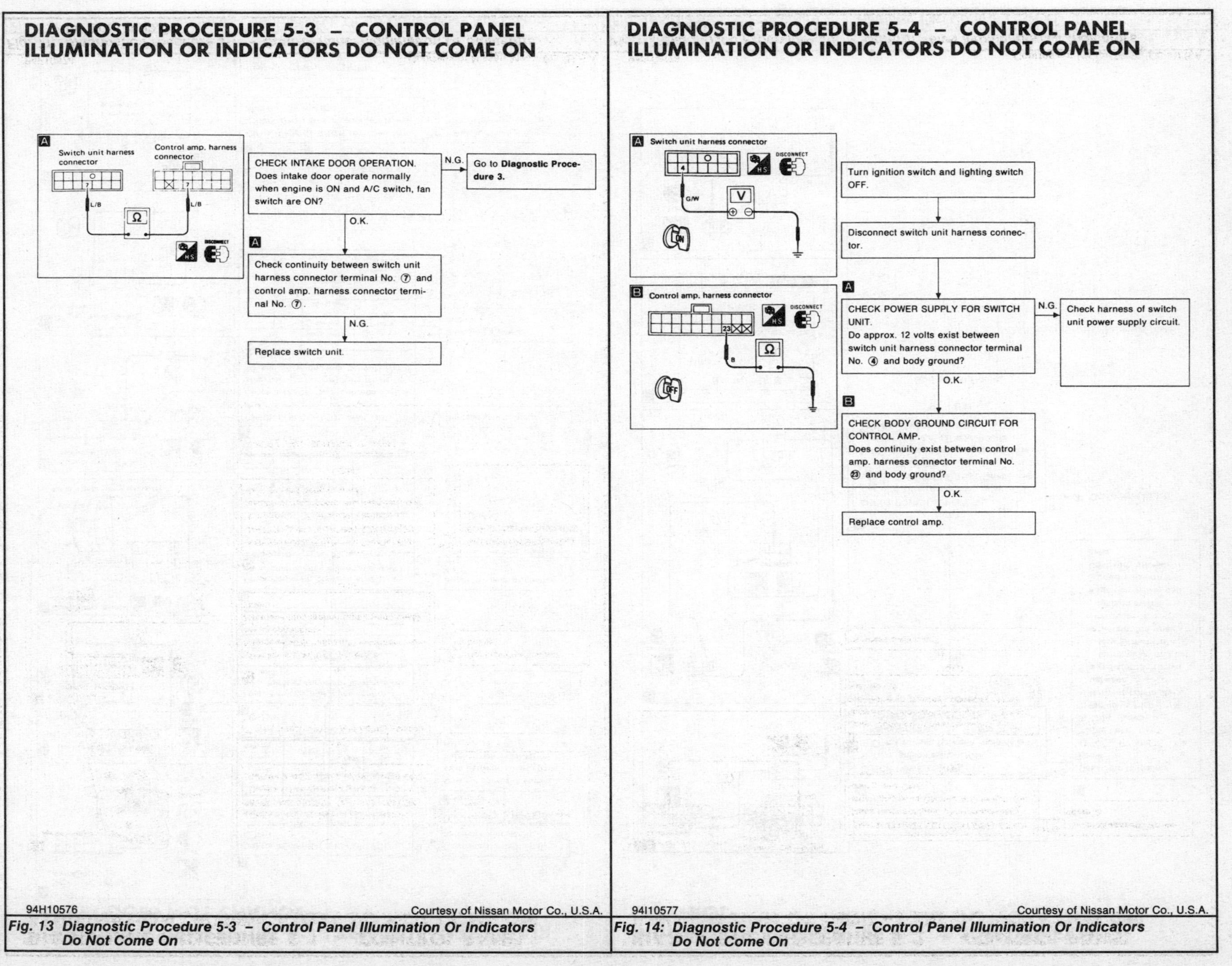
DIAGNOSTIC PROCEDURE 5-3 – CONTROL PANEL ILLUMINATION OR INDICATORS DO NOT COME ON
A
Switch unit harness connector
Control amp. harness connector
L/B
L/B
Ω
DISCONNECT
CHECK INTAKE DOOR OPERATION.
Does intake door operate normally when engine is ON and A/C switch, fan switch are ON?
N.G.
Go to Diagnostic Procedure 3.
O.K.
A
Check continuity between switch unit harness connector terminal No. ⑦ and control amp. harness connector terminal No. ⑦.
N.G.
Replace switch unit.
94H10576
Courtesy of Nissan Motor Co., U.S.A.
DIAGNOSTIC PROCEDURE 5-4 – CONTROL PANEL ILLUMINATION OR INDICATORS DO NOT COME ON
A Switch unit harness connector
G/W
V
DISCONNECT
B Control amp. harness connector
23
B
Ω
DISCONNECT
Turn ignition switch and lighting switch OFF.
Disconnect switch unit harness connector.
A
CHECK POWER SUPPLY FOR SWITCH UNIT.
Do approx. 12 volts exist between switch unit harness connector terminal No. ④ and body ground?
N.G.
Check harness of switch unit power supply circuit.
O.K.
B
CHECK BODY GROUND CIRCUIT FOR CONTROL AMP.
Does continuity exist between control amp. harness connector terminal No. ㉓ and body ground?
O.K.
Replace control amp.
94I10577
Courtesy of Nissan Motor Co., U.S.A.

Fig. 13 Diagnostic Procedure 5-3 – Control Panel Illumination Or Indicators Do Not Come On

Fig. 14: Diagnostic Procedure 5-4 – Control Panel Illumination Or Indicators Do Not Come On

1993 MANUAL A/C-HEATER SYSTEMS
Trouble Shooting – 300ZX (Cont.)

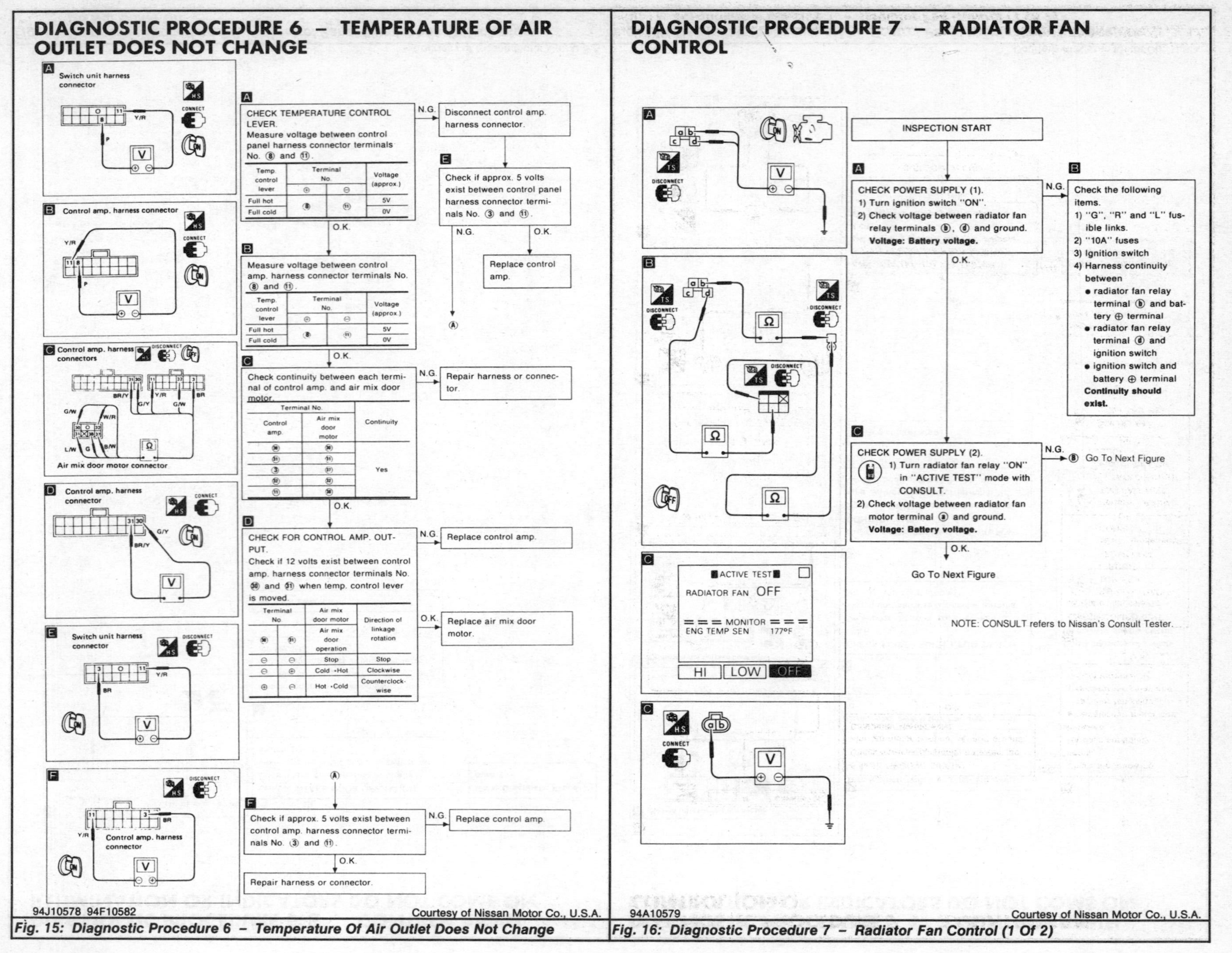
DIAGNOSTIC PROCEDURE 6 – TEMPERATURE OF AIR OUTLET DOES NOT CHANGE
A Switch unit harness connector
B Control amp. harness connector
C Control amp. harness connectors
Air mix door motor connector
D Control amp. harness connector
E Switch unit harness connector
F Control amp. harness connector
A CHECK TEMPERATURE CONTROL LEVER. Measure voltage between control panel harness connector terminals No. ⑧ and ⑪.
Temp. control lever | Terminal No. ⊕ | ⊖ | Voltage (approx.)
Full hot | ⑧ | ⑪ | 5V
Full cold | | | 0V
B Measure voltage between control amp. harness connector terminals No. ⑧ and ⑪.
C Check continuity between each terminal of control amp. and air mix door motor.
Terminal No. Control amp. | Air mix door motor | Continuity
㉚ ㉚, ㉛ ㉛, ③ ㉝, ㉜ ㉜, ⑪ ㉞ | Yes
D CHECK FOR CONTROL AMP. OUTPUT. Check if 12 volts exist between control amp. harness connector terminals No. ㉚ and ㉛ when temp. control lever is moved.
Terminal No. ㉚ ㉛ | Air mix door motor operation | Direction of linkage rotation
⊖ ⊖ | Stop | Stop
⊖ ⊕ | Cold→Hot | Clockwise
⊕ ⊖ | Hot→Cold | Counterclockwise
E Check if approx. 5 volts exist between control panel harness connector terminals No. ③ and ⑪.
F Check if approx. 5 volts exist between control amp. harness connector terminals No. ③ and ⑪.
Disconnect control amp. harness connector.
Replace control amp.
Repair harness or connector.
Replace air mix door motor.
94J10578 94F10582
Courtesy of Nissan Motor Co., U.S.A.
DIAGNOSTIC PROCEDURE 7 – RADIATOR FAN CONTROL
INSPECTION START
A CHECK POWER SUPPLY (1). 1) Turn ignition switch "ON". 2) Check voltage between radiator fan relay terminals ⓑ, ⓓ and ground. Voltage: Battery voltage.
B Check the following items. 1) "G", "R" and "L" fusible links. 2) "10A" fuses 3) Ignition switch 4) Harness continuity between • radiator fan relay terminal ⓑ and battery ⊕ terminal • radiator fan relay terminal ⓓ and ignition switch • ignition switch and battery ⊕ terminal. Continuity should exist.
C CHECK POWER SUPPLY (2). 1) Turn radiator fan relay "ON" in "ACTIVE TEST" mode with CONSULT. 2) Check voltage between radiator fan motor terminal ⓐ and ground. Voltage: Battery voltage.
Go To Next Figure
NOTE: CONSULT refers to Nissan's Consult Tester.
ACTIVE TEST
RADIATOR FAN OFF
MONITOR
ENG TEMP SEN 177°F
HI LOW OFF
94A10579
Courtesy of Nissan Motor Co., U.S.A.

Fig. 15: Diagnostic Procedure 6 – Temperature Of Air Outlet Does Not Change

Fig. 16: Diagnostic Procedure 7 – Radiator Fan Control (1 Of 2)

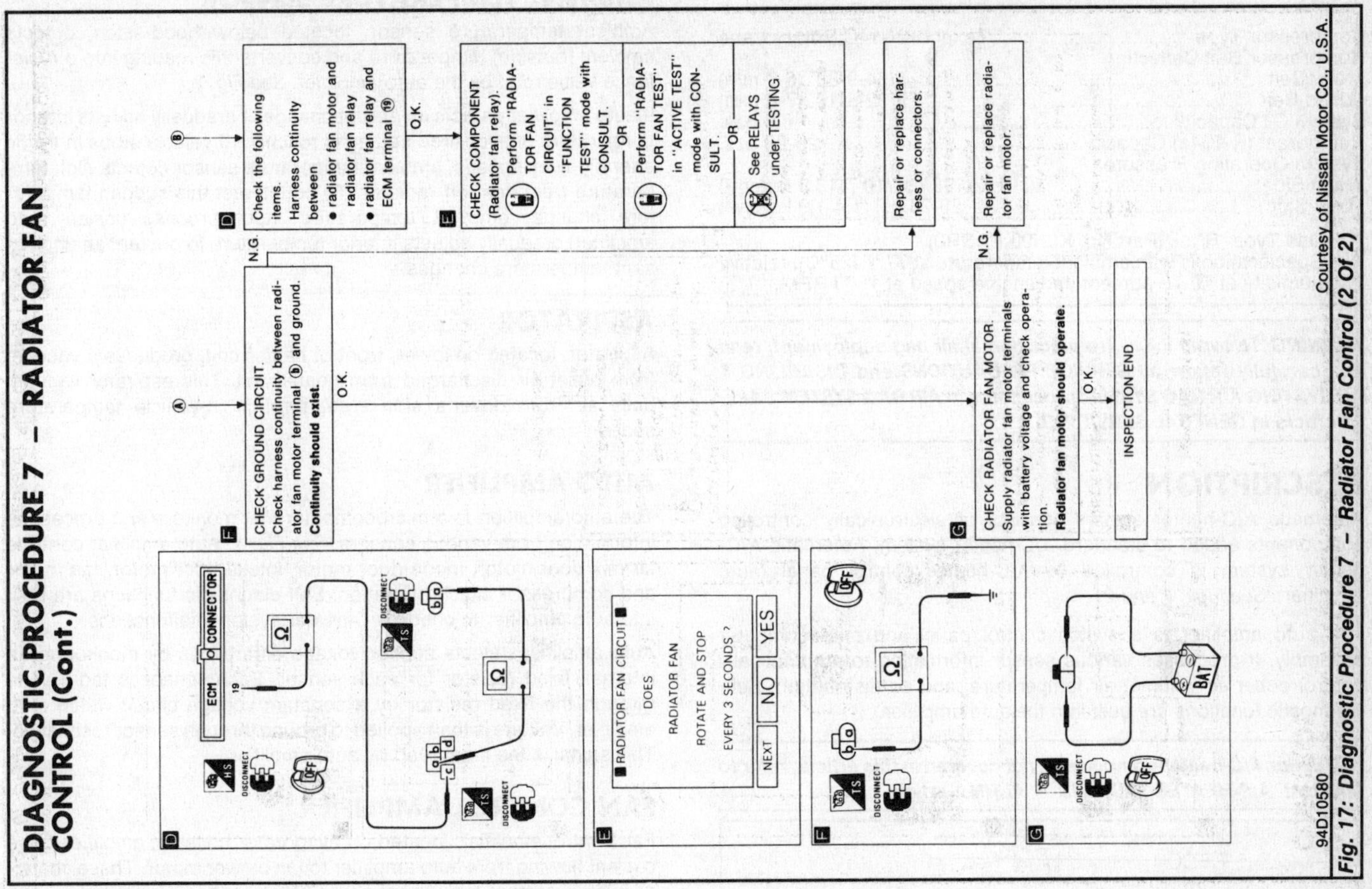

DIAGNOSTIC PROCEDURE 7 – RADIATOR FAN CONTROL (Cont.)
A
B
F
CHECK GROUND CIRCUIT.
Check harness continuity between radiator fan motor terminal b and ground.
Continuity should exist.
N.G.
O.K.
D
Check the following items.
Harness continuity between
• radiator fan motor and radiator fan relay
• radiator fan relay and ECM terminal 19
O.K.
E
CHECK COMPONENT
(Radiator fan relay).
Perform "RADIATOR FAN CIRCUIT" in "FUNCTION TEST" mode with CONSULT.
OR
Perform "RADIATOR FAN TEST" in "ACTIVE TEST" mode with CONSULT.
OR
See RELAYS under TESTING
Repair or replace harness or connectors.
G
CHECK RADIATOR FAN MOTOR.
Supply radiator fan motor terminals with battery voltage and check operation.
Radiator fan motor should operate.
N.G.
Repair or replace radiator fan motor.
O.K.
INSPECTION END
ECM
CONNECTOR
19
DISCONNECT
H.S
T.S
OFF
RADIATOR FAN CIRCUIT
DOES
RADIATOR FAN
ROTATE AND STOP
EVERY 3 SECONDS ?
NEXT
NO
YES
BAT
94D10580
Courtesy of Nissan Motor Co., U.S.A.

Fig. 17: Diagnostic Procedure 7 – Radiator Fan Control (2 Of 2)

1993 AUTOMATIC A/C-HEATER SYSTEMS
Altima

SPECIFICATIONS

Compressor Type .... Zezel DKV-14C Rotary Vane
Compressor Belt Deflection
New Belt .... 5/64-9/32" (6-7 mm)
Used Belt .... 9/32-5/16" (7-8 mm)
System Oil Capacity .... [1] 6.8 ozs.
Refrigerant (R-134a) Capacity .... 25-28 ozs.
System Operating Pressures [2]
High Side .... 152-198 psi (10.7-13.9 kg/cm²)
Low Side .... 20-26 psi (1.4-1.9 kg/cm²)

[1] – Use Type "R" oil (Part No. KLH00-PAGR0).
[2] – Specification is with ambient temperature at 77°F (25°C), relative humidity at 50-70 percent and engine speed at 1500 RPM.

WARNING: To avoid injury from accidental air bag deployment, read and carefully follow all SERVICE PRECAUTIONS and DISABLING & ACTIVATING AIR BAG SYSTEM procedures in AIR BAG SYSTEM SAFETY article in GENERAL SERVICING.

DESCRIPTION

Automatic A/C-heater system consists of electronically controlled components added to standard A/C-heater system. Automatic A/C-heater system is controlled by A/C-heater control panel (auto amplifier). *See Figs. 1 and 2.*

The auto amplifier is a switch control panel and microcomputer assembly. It processes various sensor information to automatically control outlet air volume, air temperature, and air distribution. Self-diagnostic functions are built into the auto amplifier.

NOTE: For A/C-heater components not covered in this article, refer to MANUAL A/C-HEATER SYSTEMS – ALTIMA article.

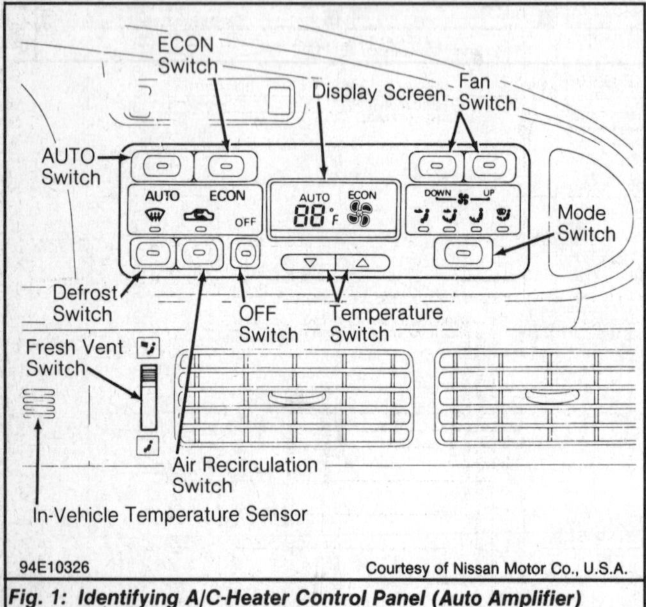
ECON Switch
Display Screen
Fan Switch
AUTO Switch
AUTO
ECON
OFF
88°F
DOWN
UP
Mode Switch
Defrost Switch
OFF Switch
Temperature Switch
Fresh Vent Switch
Air Recirculation Switch
In-Vehicle Temperature Sensor
94E10326
Courtesy of Nissan Motor Co., U.S.A.

Fig. 1: Identifying A/C-Heater Control Panel (Auto Amplifier)

OPERATION

AIR MIX DOOR MOTOR

Air mix door motor is attached to heater unit. Auto amplifier commands air mix door motor to rotate a shaft to move air mix door to a set position/angle. Air mix door position/angle is monitored by Potentiometer Balance Resistor (PBR), located inside air mix door motor. Door position/angle is continuously being fed back to auto amplifier by PBR to allow auto amplifier to move door position/angle for desired temperature.

AMBIENT TEMPERATURE SENSOR

Ambient temperature sensor, located below hood latch, detects ambient (outside) temperature and converts this reading into a resistance value read by the auto amplifier. *See Fig. 2.*

If auto amplifier detects an abrupt change, it gradually adjusts interior temperature until desired setting is reached. If vehicle stops in traffic after highway speeds, ambient temperature sensor detects high temperature from heat off radiator. To counteract this sudden temperature change, ambient temperature input process (inside auto amplifier) gradually adjusts interior temperature to prevent an unpleasant temperature changes.

ASPIRATOR

Aspirator, located on lower, front of heater unit, produces a vacuum from outlet air discharged from heater unit. This aspirator vacuum pulls air from driver's side area, through in-vehicle temperature sensor.

AUTO AMPLIFIER

The auto amplifier, is a microcomputer that monitors and processes information from various sensors. *See Fig. 1.* Auto amplifier controls air mix door motor, mode door motor, intake door motor, fan motor and compressor clutch operation. Self-diagnostic functions are built into auto amplifier to check A/C-heater system malfunctions.

Auto amplifier detects sensor voltage differences by monitoring an internal, fixed resistor for each sensor. Each sensor is fed 5-volts through the fixed resistor by a constant voltage circuit within auto amplifier. Voltage is then applied to ground through sensor resistance. This signal is the input read by auto amplifier.

FAN CONTROL AMPLIFIER

Fan control amplifier, located on evaporator housing, amplifies base current flowing from auto amplifier to fan blower motor. These changes in base current are what changes blower speed. Operating voltage range is from 5-10.5 volts. If auto amplifier senses the need for more than 10.5 volts, high speed relay then applies a direct ground to blower motor for full 12 volts. *See Fig. 2.*

HIGH SPEED RELAY

High speed relay, located on intake unit, receives its signal from auto amplifier to enable blower motor to operate at high speed. *See Fig. 2.*

NOTE: High speed relay may also be referred to as HI relay in TROUBLE SHOOTING charts.

INTAKE DOOR MOTOR

Intake door motor, attached to blower motor unit, is controlled by auto amplifier. *See Fig. 2.* Motor rotation is transferred by a rod and lever to position intake door for correct air intake.

IN-VEHICLE TEMPERATURE SENSOR

In-vehicle temperature sensor is attached to instrument cluster trim panel. *See Fig. 1.* Driver's area air is drawn through sensor by the aspirator. In-vehicle temperature sensor converts temperature variations to a resistance value, monitored by auto amplifier.

MODE DOOR MOTOR

Mode door motor, attached to heater unit, rotates so air is discharged from outlet(s) controlled by auto amplifier. Motor rotation is transferred by a rod and link to position mode door.

POTENTIOMETER BALANCE RESISTOR (PBR)

This variable resistor is built into air mix door motor and converts air mix door position into a resistance value, monitored by auto amplifier.

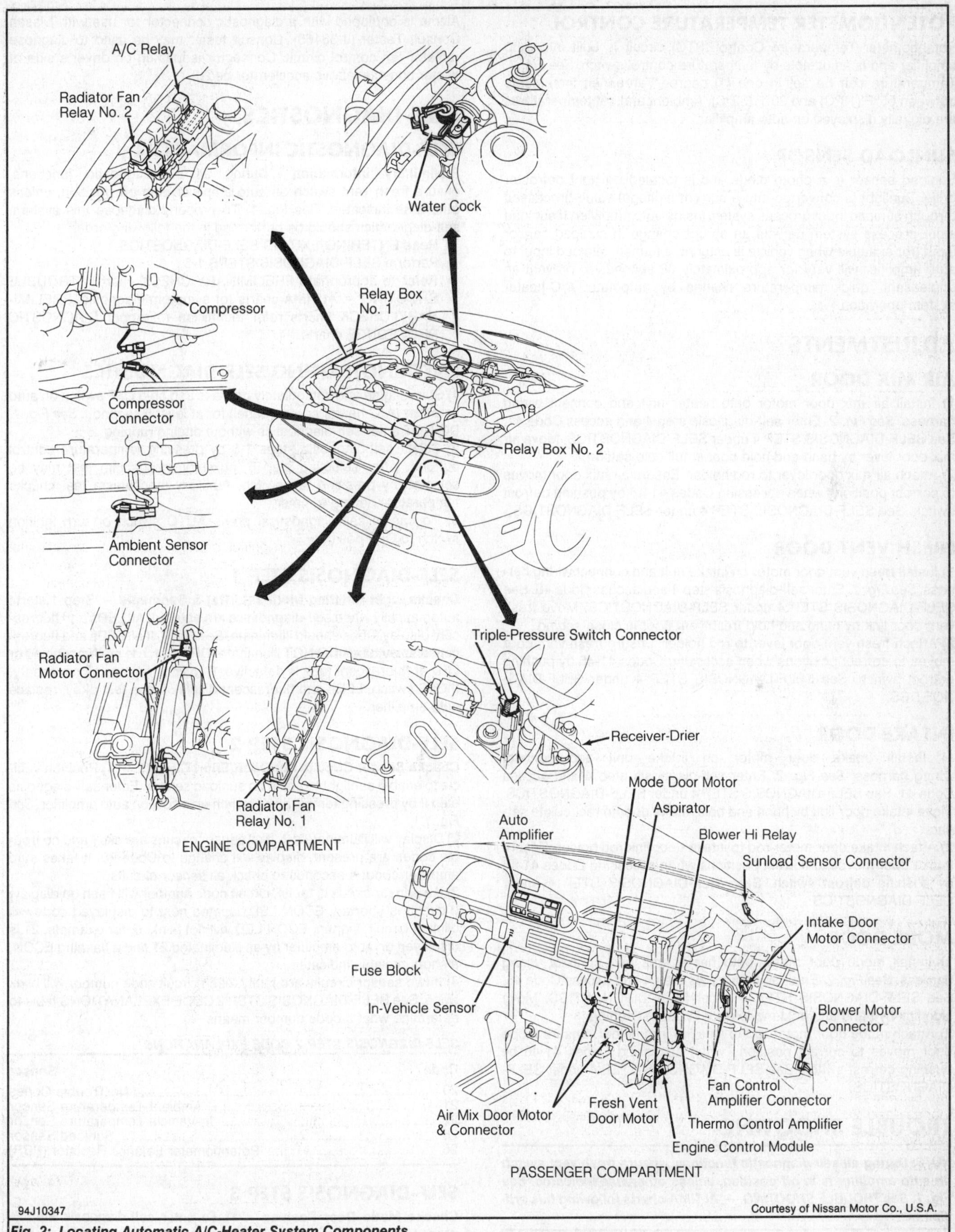
A/C Relay
Radiator Fan Relay No. 2
Water Cock
Relay Box No. 1
Compressor
Compressor Connector
Relay Box No. 2
Ambient Sensor Connector
Triple-Pressure Switch Connector
Radiator Fan Motor Connector
Receiver-Drier
Radiator Fan Relay No. 1
ENGINE COMPARTMENT
Mode Door Motor
Aspirator
Auto Amplifier
Blower Hi Relay
Sunload Sensor Connector
Intake Door Motor Connector
Fuse Block
In-Vehicle Sensor
Blower Motor Connector
Fan Control Amplifier Connector
Fresh Vent Door Motor
Air Mix Door Motor & Connector
Thermo Control Amplifier
Engine Control Module
PASSENGER COMPARTMENT
94J10347
Courtesy of Nissan Motor Co., U.S.A.

Fig. 2: Locating Automatic A/C-Heater System Components

1993 AUTOMATIC A/C-HEATER SYSTEMS
Altima (Cont.)

POTENTIOMETER TEMPERATURE CONTROL

Potentiometer Temperature Control (PTC) circuit is built into auto amplifier and is adjustable by temperature control switch. *See Fig. 1.* Temperature can be set in one (1) degree Fahrenheit increments between 65°F (18°C) and 90°F (32°C). Ambient and set temperatures are digitally displayed on auto amplifier.

SUNLOAD SENSOR

Sunload sensor is a photo diode and is located on right defroster grille. Sunlight is converted into a current (voltage) value processed through sunload input process system inside auto amplifier. If sunload input process system detects an abrupt change in sunload sensor input (for example when vehicle is entering a tunnel), sunload input to auto amplifier will vary for approximately 38 seconds to prevent an unpleasant, quick temperature change by automatic A/C-heater system operation.

ADJUSTMENTS

AIR MIX DOOR

1) Install air mix door motor onto heater unit and connect wiring harness. *See Fig. 2.* Enter self-diagnosis step 4 and access Code 41. See SELF-DIAGNOSIS STEP 4 under SELF-DIAGNOSTICS. Move air mix door lever by hand and hold door in full cold setting.
2) Attach air mix door lever to rod holder. Ensure air mix door moves to correct positions when accessing Codes 41-46 by pushing defrost switch. See SELF-DIAGNOSIS STEP 4 under SELF-DIAGNOSTICS.

FRESH VENT DOOR

1) Install fresh vent door motor on intake unit and connect wiring harness. *See Fig. 2.* Enter self-diagnosis step 4 and access Code 46. See SELF-DIAGNOSIS STEP 4 under SELF-DIAGNOSTICS. Move fresh vent door link by hand and hold fresh vent door in close setting.
2) Attach fresh vent door lever to rod holder. Ensure fresh vent door moves to correct positions when accessing Codes 41-46 by pushing defrost switch. See SELF-DIAGNOSIS STEP 4 under SELF-DIAGNOSTICS.

INTAKE DOOR

1) Install intake door motor on intake unit and connect wiring harness. *See Fig. 2.* Enter self-diagnosis step 4 and access Code 41. See SELF-DIAGNOSIS STEP 4 under SELF-DIAGNOSTICS. Move intake door link by hand and hold intake door in recirculate setting.
2) Attach intake door motor rod to intake door link rod holder. Ensure intake door moves to correct positions when accessing Codes 41-46 by pushing defrost switch. See SELF-DIAGNOSIS STEP 4 under SELF-DIAGNOSTICS.

MODE DOOR

1) Install mode door motor onto heater unit and connect wiring harness. *See Fig. 2.* Enter self-diagnosis step 4 and access Code 46. See SELF-DIAGNOSIS STEP 4 under SELF-DIAGNOSTICS. Move side link by hand and hold mode door in defrost setting.
2) Attach mode door motor rod to side link rod holder. Ensure mode door moves to correct positions when accessing Codes 41-46 by pushing defrost switch. See SELF-DIAGNOSIS STEP 4 under SELF-DIAGNOSTICS.

TROUBLE SHOOTING

***NOTE:** During all self-diagnostic functions, ensure fresh vent switch on auto amplifier is in off position, unless otherwise indicated. See Fig. 1. See TROUBLE SHOOTING - ALTIMA charts following this article.*

Altima is equipped with a diagnostic connector for use with Nissan Consult Tester (J-38465). Consult tester may be used to diagnose radiator fan control circuit. Connector is located on driver's side of center console (above accelerator pedal).

SELF-DIAGNOSTICS

SELF-DIAGNOSTIC INFORMATION

Preliminary Information - During all self-diagnostic functions, ensure fresh vent switch on auto amplifier is in off position, unless otherwise indicated. See Fig. 1. To properly diagnose this system, self-diagnostics should be performed in the following order:

- Read ENTERING/EXITING SELF-DIAGNOSTICS.
- Perform SELF-DIAGNOSIS STEPS 1-5.
- Refer to appropriate PRELIMINARY CHECK chart in TROUBLE SHOOTING - ALTIMA charts for symptom diagnosis. PRELIMINARY CHECK charts refer technician to proper DIAGNOSTIC PROCEDURE charts.

ENTERING/EXITING SELF-DIAGNOSTICS

1) Start engine and immediately depress and hold OFF switch on auto amplifier (A/C-heater control panel) for at least 5 seconds. *See Fig. 1.* DO NOT enter self-diagnostics without engine running.
2) Select self-diagnosis steps 1-5 by pressing temperature control buttons. After selecting step 5, auxiliary mechanism test may be selected by pressing fan switch. Auxiliary mechanism test checks temperature setting trimmer.
3) To cancel self-diagnostics, press AUTO switch or turn ignition switch to OFF position.

SELF-DIAGNOSIS STEP 1

Checks Light Emitting Diodes (LEDs) & Segments - Step 1 starts automatically when self-diagnostics are entered. All LEDs and fluorescent display tubes should illuminate. *See Fig. 1.* If all LEDs and fluorescent display tubes DO NOT illuminate, OFF switch is malfunctioning or LED or fluorescent tube is defective. Repair or replace as necessary. If OFF switch, LEDs and fluorescent display tubes test okay, replace auto amplifier.

SELF-DIAGNOSIS STEP 2

Checks Sensor Circuits For Open/Short Circuits - **1)** Position vehicle to enable sunlight to shine on sunload sensor. Enter self-diagnosis step 2 by pressing temperature switch up arrow on auto amplifier. *See Fig. 1.*
2) Display will illuminate a 2. If all sensor circuits are okay and no trouble codes are present, display will change to Code 20. It takes auto amplifier about 4 seconds to check all sensor circuits.
3) If a sensor circuit is faulty, circuit code number will flash on display. If circuit is shorted, ECON LED, located next to displayed code will blink. If circuit is open, ECON LED will not blink. If, for example, 21 is displayed on auto amplifier by an illuminated 21 and a flashing ECON, a short circuit is indicated.
4) If two sensor circuits are faulty, each circuit code number will blink twice. See SELF-DIAGNOSIS STEP 2 CODE EXPLANATIONS table to determine what a code number means.

SELF-DIAGNOSIS STEP 2 CODE EXPLANATIONS

Code	Sensor
20	No Trouble Codes
21	Ambient Temperature Sensor
22	In-Vehicle Temperature Sensor
25	Sunload Sensor
26	Potentiometer Balance Resistor (PBR)

SELF-DIAGNOSIS STEP 3

Checks Mode Door Position - **1)** To enter self-diagnosis step 3, press temperature switch up arrow on auto amplifier. *See Fig. 1.* Display will illuminate a 3. If all doors are operational, display will change to 30. It takes about 16 seconds to check all mode doors.

1993 AUTOMATIC A/C-HEATER SYSTEMS
Altima (Cont.)

2) If a door is faulty, code number will flash. If two doors are faulty, each code number will blink twice. To determine what a code number means, see SELF-DIAGNOSIS STEP 3 CODE EXPLANATIONS table.

NOTE: If any mode door motor position switch is malfunctioning, mode door motor will also malfunction.

SELF-DIAGNOSIS STEP 3 CODE EXPLANATIONS

Code	Door
30	No Trouble Codes
31	Vent
32	Bi-Level (B/L)
34	[1] Foot/Defrost Mode 1 (F/D 1)
35	[2] Foot/Defrost Mode 2 (F/D 2)
36	Defrost (DEF)

[1] – Foot/defrost mode 1 is used when manual mode is selected on auto amplifier. Mode 1 directs 75 percent air to foot area.
[2] – Foot/defrost mode 2 is used when automatic mode is selected on auto amplifier. Mode 2 directs 50 percent air to foot area.

SELF-DIAGNOSIS STEP 4

Checks Operation Of Each Actuator – 1) Ensure fresh vent switch on auto amplifier is off during tests. To enter self-diagnosis step 4, press temperature switch up arrow on auto amplifier.
2) Display will illuminate Code 41. Each time defrost switch is pressed, display will advance one code number. After Code 46 is reached, numbers go back to Code 41.

SELF-DIAGNOSIS STEP 4 CODE EXPLANATIONS

Application	Door Position
Code 41	
Air Mix Door	Full Cold
Blower Motor	Low [1] (4-5 Volts)
Compressor	On
Fresh Vent Door	Open
Intake Door	Recirculate
Mode Door	Vent
Code 42	
Air Mix Door	Full Cold
Blower Motor	Medium High [1] (9-11 Volts)
Compressor	On
Fresh Vent Door	Open
Intake Door	Recirculate
Mode Door	Bi-Level
Code 43	
Air Mix Door	Full Hot
Blower Motor	Medium Low [1] (7-9 Volts)
Compressor	On
Fresh Vent Door	Closed
Intake Door	20% Fresh
Mode Door	Bi-Level
Code 44	
Air Mix Door	Full Hot
Blower Motor	Medium Low [1] (7-9 Volts)
Compressor	Off
Fresh Vent Door	Closed
Intake Door	Fresh
Mode Door	[2] Foot/Defrost Mode 1
Code 45	
Air Mix Door	Full Hot
Blower Motor	Medium Low [1] (7-9 Volts)
Compressor	Off
Fresh Vent Door	Closed
Intake Door	Fresh
Mode Door	[3] Foot/Defrost Mode 2
Code 46	
Air Mix Door	Full Hot
Blower Motor	High [1] (10-12 Volts)
Compressor	On
Fresh Vent Door	Closed
Intake Door	Fresh
Mode Door	Defrost

[1] – Voltage applied to blower motor for desired speed.
[2] – Foot/defrost mode 1 is used when manual mode is selected on auto amplifier. Mode 1 directs 75 percent air to foot area.
[3] – Foot/defrost mode 2 is used when automatic mode is selected on auto amplifier. Mode 2 directs 50 percent air to foot area.

3) As code numbers advance, auto amplifier commands will change air intake and outlet routes. Ensure doors are switching properly by listening for door operation and/or feeling for air flow from proper outlet(s). See SELF-DIAGNOSIS STEP 4 CODE EXPLANATIONS table to determine proper door positions.

SELF-DIAGNOSIS STEP 5

Checks Temperature Detected By Sensors – 1) To enter self-diagnosis step 5, press temperature switch up arrow on auto amplifier. Display will illuminate a 5. When defrost switch is pressed once, display will show temperature detected by ambient temperature sensor.
2) Press defrost switch again (2nd time), display will show temperature detected by in-vehicle sensor.
3) Press defrost switch again (3rd time), display will return to 5. If temperature shown on display is greatly different from actual temperature, inspect sensor circuit. If sensor circuit is okay, check sensor. See appropriate sensor under TESTING.

AUXILIARY MECHANISM SETTING

Temperature Setting Trimmer – 1) Temperature setting trimmer compensates for small differences between temperature setting on display and actual temperature within a range of 0-12°F (0-6°C).
2) With system in SELF-DIAGNOSIS STEP 5, press fan switch. System is now in auxiliary mode to set trimmer. Each time temperature switch up or down arrow is pressed, temperature display changes in one (1) degree Fahrenheit increments.

NOTE: If battery is disconnected, temperature trimmer setting goes to 0° on both Fahrenheit and Celsius scale and will have to be reset.

TESTING

WARNING: To avoid injury from accidental air bag deployment, read and carefully follow all SERVICE PRECAUTIONS and DISABLING & ACTIVATING AIR BAG SYSTEM procedures in AIR BAG SYSTEM SAFETY article in GENERAL SERVICING.

NOTE: For A/C-heater components not covered in this article, refer to MANUAL A/C-HEATER SYSTEMS – ALTIMA article.

A/C SYSTEM PERFORMANCE

1) Park vehicle out of direct sunlight. Close all doors and open engine hood and windows. Connect A/C pressure gauges to the high and low side pressure ports of system. Disconnect ambient temperature sensor connector.
2) Ambient temperature sensor is located below hood latch. Connect a jumper wire between sensor connector terminals. Determine relative humidity and ambient air temperature.
3) Set temperature control to maximum cold, mode control to vent (face), and recirculation switch to recirculated air position. Turn blower fan switch to highest speed setting. Start and run engine at 1500 RPM.
4) After running A/C for 10 minutes, check high and low side system pressures. Refer to A/C SYSTEM PERFORMANCE TEST table to determine if system is operating within range.

A/C SYSTEM PERFORMANCE TEST

Ambient Air Temp. °F (°C)	High Pressure [1] psi (kg/cm²)	Low Pressure [1] psi (kg/cm²)
68 (20)	121-159 (8.5-11.2)	17.8-23.5 (1.3-1.7)
77 (25)	152-198 (10.7-13.9)	19.9-26.3 (1.4-1.9)
86 (30)	178-235 (12.5-16.5)	22.0-29.2 (1.6-2.1)
95 (35)	182-249 (12.8-17.5)	24.2-33.4 (1.7-2.4)
104 (40)	223-294 (15.7-20.7)	29.2-41.9 (2.1-3.0)

[1] – Specification is with relative humidity at 50-70 percent.

1993 AUTOMATIC A/C-HEATER SYSTEMS
Altima (Cont.)

AMBIENT TEMPERATURE SENSOR

Turn ignition off. Disconnect underhood ambient temperature sensor connector, in front of condenser, near hood latch. *See Fig. 2.* Using an ohmmeter, measure resistance between sensor terminals. See AMBIENT TEMPERATURE SENSOR & IN-VEHICLE TEMPERATURE SENSOR SPECIFICATIONS table.

IN-VEHICLE TEMPERATURE SENSOR

Turn ignition off. Disconnect in-vehicle temperature sensor connector. *See Fig. 2.* Using an ohmmeter, measure resistance between sensor terminals. See AMBIENT TEMPERATURE SENSOR & IN-VEHICLE TEMPERATURE SENSOR SPECIFICATIONS table.

AMBIENT TEMPERATURE SENSOR & IN-VEHICLE TEMPERATURE SENSOR SPECIFICATIONS

Temperature °F (°C)	Resistance (Ohms)
5 (–15)	12,730
14 (–10)	9920
23 (–5)	7800
32 (0)	6190
41 (5)	4950
50 (10)	3990
59 (15)	3240
68 (20)	2650
77 (25)	2190
86 (30)	1810
95 (35)	1510
104 (40)	1270
113 (45)	1070

POTENTIOMETER BALANCE RESISTOR (PBR)

1) Turn ignition on. Backprobe air mix door motor connector with voltmeter and measure voltage between terminals No. 27 (Pink/Blue wire) and No. 33 (Pink wire). *See Fig. 3.* Set temperature switch to coldest setting. With air mix door in full cold position, voltmeter should indicate zero volts.

2) Slowly adjust temperature switch to hottest setting. As air mix door motor moves from full cold to full hot position, voltage should slowly rise to 5 volts. If voltage is not as described, replace air mix door motor.

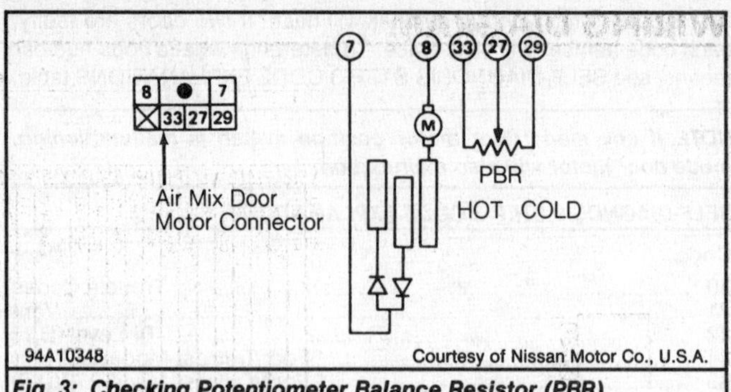
7
8
33
27
29
8
7
33
27
29
M
PBR
HOT COLD
Air Mix Door
Motor Connector
94A10348
Courtesy of Nissan Motor Co., U.S.A.

Fig. 3: Checking Potentiometer Balance Resistor (PBR)

SUNLOAD SENSOR

1) Turn ignition off. Backprobe auto amplifier connector with voltmeter and measure output voltage between terminals No. 26 (Orange wire) and 38 (Black/Yellow wire). To vary voltage reading for testing, apply direct sunlight to sensor, then slowly cover sensor.

2) To measure sunload sensor input to auto amplifier, disconnect sensor from vehicle harness above intake unit. Connect an ammeter between sensor connector terminals. To vary current reading, apply direct sunlight to sensor, then slowly cover sensor. See SUNLOAD SENSOR SPECIFICATIONS table.

SUNLOAD SENSOR SPECIFICATIONS

Input Current (Milliamps)	Output Voltage
0	5.0
.1	4.1
.2	3.1
.3	2.2
.4	1.3
.5	.4

REMOVAL & INSTALLATION

NOTE: For removal of basic A/C-heater system components, see MANUAL A/C-HEATER SYSTEMS – ALTIMA article.

WIRING DIAGRAM

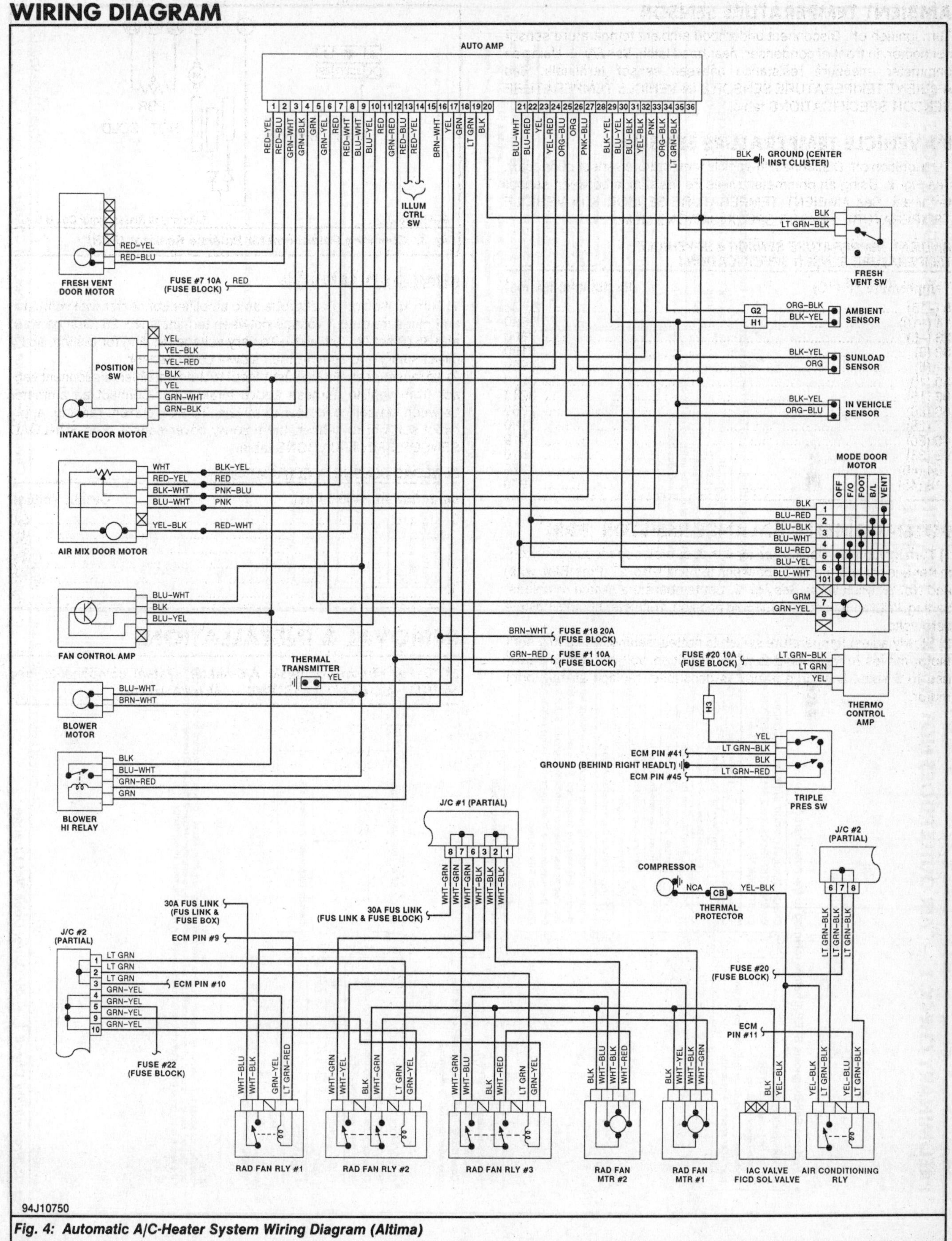
AUTO AMP
ILLUM CTRL SW
FRESH VENT DOOR MOTOR
FUSE #7 10A (FUSE BLOCK)
POSITION SW
INTAKE DOOR MOTOR
AIR MIX DOOR MOTOR
FAN CONTROL AMP
THERMAL TRANSMITTER
BLOWER MOTOR
BLOWER HI RELAY
GROUND (CENTER INST CLUSTER)
FRESH VENT SW
AMBIENT SENSOR
SUNLOAD SENSOR
IN VEHICLE SENSOR
MODE DOOR MOTOR
OFF
F/O
FOOT
B/L
VENT
FUSE #18 20A (FUSE BLOCK)
FUSE #1 10A (FUSE BLOCK)
FUSE #20 10A (FUSE BLOCK)
THERMO CONTROL AMP
ECM PIN #41
GROUND (BEHIND RIGHT HEADLT)
ECM PIN #45
TRIPLE PRES SW
J/C #1 (PARTIAL)
30A FUS LINK (FUS LINK & FUSE BOX)
30A FUS LINK (FUS LINK & FUSE BLOCK)
ECM PIN #9
ECM PIN #10
J/C #2 (PARTIAL)
FUSE #22 (FUSE BLOCK)
COMPRESSOR
NCA
CB
YEL-BLK
THERMAL PROTECTOR
FUSE #20 (FUSE BLOCK)
ECM PIN #11
RAD FAN RLY #1
RAD FAN RLY #2
RAD FAN RLY #3
RAD FAN MTR #2
RAD FAN MTR #1
IAC VALVE FICD SOL VALVE
AIR CONDITIONING RLY
94J10750

Fig. 4: Automatic A/C-Heater System Wiring Diagram (Altima)

1993 AUTOMATIC A/C-HEATER SYSTEMS
Trouble Shooting – Altima

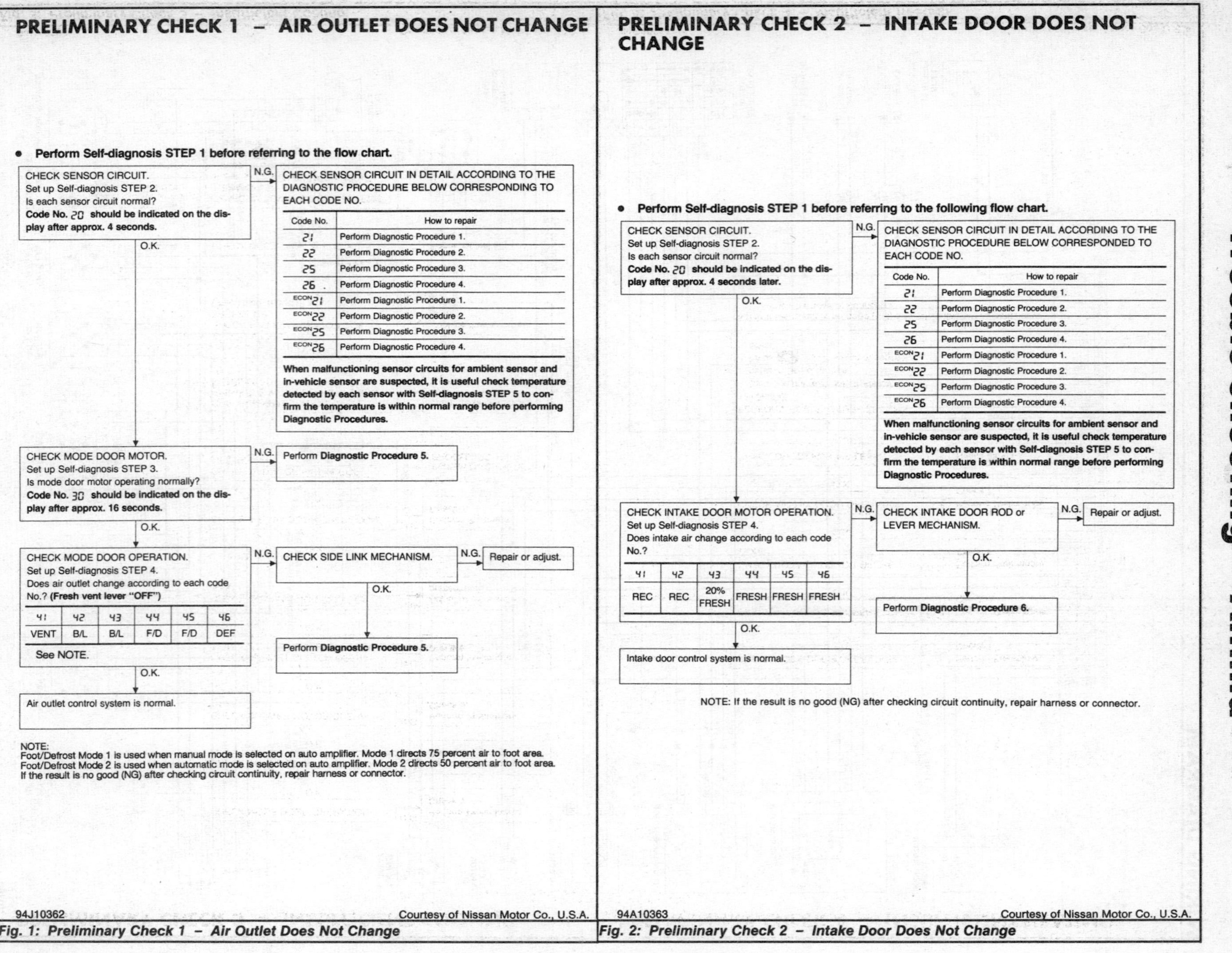
PRELIMINARY CHECK 1 – AIR OUTLET DOES NOT CHANGE
• Perform Self-diagnosis STEP 1 before referring to the flow chart.
CHECK SENSOR CIRCUIT.
Set up Self-diagnosis STEP 2.
Is each sensor circuit normal?
Code No. 20 should be indicated on the display after approx. 4 seconds.
N.G.
CHECK SENSOR CIRCUIT IN DETAIL ACCORDING TO THE DIAGNOSTIC PROCEDURE BELOW CORRESPONDING TO EACH CODE NO.
Code No. | How to repair
21 | Perform Diagnostic Procedure 1.
22 | Perform Diagnostic Procedure 2.
25 | Perform Diagnostic Procedure 3.
26 | Perform Diagnostic Procedure 4.
ECON 21 | Perform Diagnostic Procedure 1.
ECON 22 | Perform Diagnostic Procedure 2.
ECON 25 | Perform Diagnostic Procedure 3.
ECON 26 | Perform Diagnostic Procedure 4.
When malfunctioning sensor circuits for ambient sensor and in-vehicle sensor are suspected, it is useful check temperature detected by each sensor with Self-diagnosis STEP 5 to confirm the temperature is within normal range before performing Diagnostic Procedures.
O.K.
CHECK MODE DOOR MOTOR.
Set up Self-diagnosis STEP 3.
Is mode door motor operating normally?
Code No. 30 should be indicated on the display after approx. 16 seconds.
N.G.
Perform Diagnostic Procedure 5.
O.K.
CHECK MODE DOOR OPERATION.
Set up Self-diagnosis STEP 4.
Does air outlet change according to each code No.? (Fresh vent lever "OFF")
41 | 42 | 43 | 44 | 45 | 46
VENT | B/L | B/L | F/D | F/D | DEF
See NOTE.
N.G.
CHECK SIDE LINK MECHANISM.
N.G.
Repair or adjust.
O.K.
Perform Diagnostic Procedure 5.
O.K.
Air outlet control system is normal.
NOTE:
Foot/Defrost Mode 1 is used when manual mode is selected on auto amplifier. Mode 1 directs 75 percent air to foot area.
Foot/Defrost Mode 2 is used when automatic mode is selected on auto amplifier. Mode 2 directs 50 percent air to foot area.
If the result is no good (NG) after checking circuit continuity, repair harness or connector.
94J10362
Courtesy of Nissan Motor Co., U.S.A.
PRELIMINARY CHECK 2 – INTAKE DOOR DOES NOT CHANGE
• Perform Self-diagnosis STEP 1 before referring to the following flow chart.
CHECK SENSOR CIRCUIT.
Set up Self-diagnosis STEP 2.
Is each sensor circuit normal?
Code No. 20 should be indicated on the display after approx. 4 seconds later.
N.G.
CHECK SENSOR CIRCUIT IN DETAIL ACCORDING TO THE DIAGNOSTIC PROCEDURE BELOW CORRESPONDED TO EACH CODE NO.
Code No. | How to repair
21 | Perform Diagnostic Procedure 1.
22 | Perform Diagnostic Procedure 2.
25 | Perform Diagnostic Procedure 3.
26 | Perform Diagnostic Procedure 4.
ECON 21 | Perform Diagnostic Procedure 1.
ECON 22 | Perform Diagnostic Procedure 2.
ECON 25 | Perform Diagnostic Procedure 3.
ECON 26 | Perform Diagnostic Procedure 4.
When malfunctioning sensor circuits for ambient sensor and in-vehicle sensor are suspected, it is useful check temperature detected by each sensor with Self-diagnosis STEP 5 to confirm the temperature is within normal range before performing Diagnostic Procedures.
O.K.
CHECK INTAKE DOOR MOTOR OPERATION.
Set up Self-diagnosis STEP 4.
Does intake air change according to each code No.?
41 | 42 | 43 | 44 | 45 | 46
REC | REC | 20% FRESH | FRESH | FRESH | FRESH
N.G.
CHECK INTAKE DOOR ROD or LEVER MECHANISM.
N.G.
Repair or adjust.
O.K.
Perform Diagnostic Procedure 6.
O.K.
Intake door control system is normal.
NOTE: If the result is no good (NG) after checking circuit continuity, repair harness or connector.
94A10363
Courtesy of Nissan Motor Co., U.S.A.

Fig. 1: Preliminary Check 1 – Air Outlet Does Not Change

Fig. 2: Preliminary Check 2 – Intake Door Does Not Change

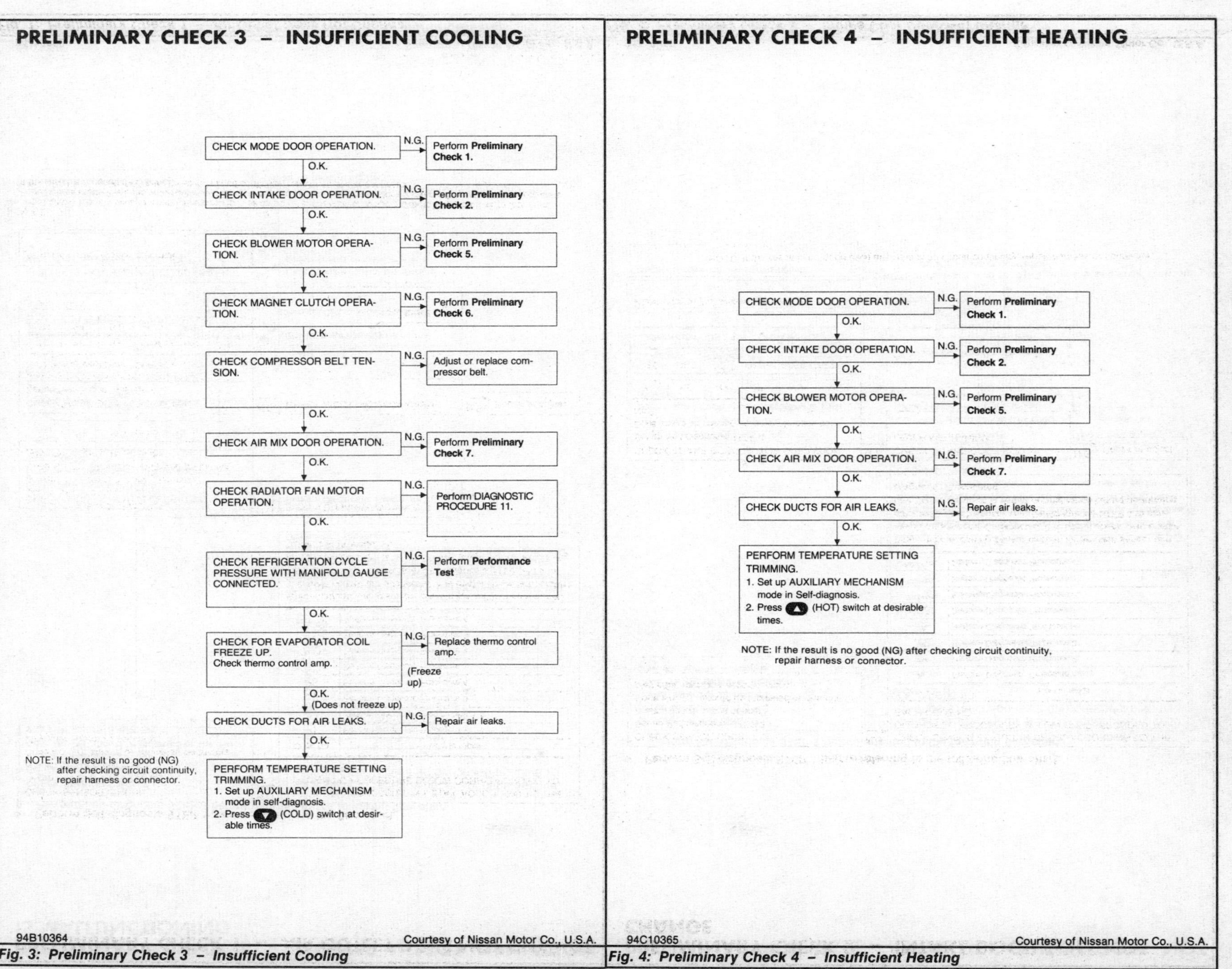
PRELIMINARY CHECK 3 – INSUFFICIENT COOLING
CHECK MODE DOOR OPERATION.
N.G.
Perform Preliminary Check 1.
O.K.
CHECK INTAKE DOOR OPERATION.
N.G.
Perform Preliminary Check 2.
O.K.
CHECK BLOWER MOTOR OPERATION.
N.G.
Perform Preliminary Check 5.
O.K.
CHECK MAGNET CLUTCH OPERATION.
N.G.
Perform Preliminary Check 6.
O.K.
CHECK COMPRESSOR BELT TENSION.
N.G.
Adjust or replace compressor belt.
O.K.
CHECK AIR MIX DOOR OPERATION.
N.G.
Perform Preliminary Check 7.
O.K.
CHECK RADIATOR FAN MOTOR OPERATION.
N.G.
Perform DIAGNOSTIC PROCEDURE 11.
O.K.
CHECK REFRIGERATION CYCLE PRESSURE WITH MANIFOLD GAUGE CONNECTED.
N.G.
Perform Performance Test
O.K.
CHECK FOR EVAPORATOR COIL FREEZE UP. Check thermo control amp.
N.G. (Freeze up)
Replace thermo control amp.
O.K. (Does not freeze up)
CHECK DUCTS FOR AIR LEAKS.
N.G.
Repair air leaks.
O.K.
PERFORM TEMPERATURE SETTING TRIMMING.
1. Set up AUXILIARY MECHANISM mode in self-diagnosis.
2. Press (COLD) switch at desirable times.
NOTE: If the result is no good (NG) after checking circuit continuity, repair harness or connector.
94B10364
Courtesy of Nissan Motor Co., U.S.A.
PRELIMINARY CHECK 4 – INSUFFICIENT HEATING
CHECK MODE DOOR OPERATION.
N.G.
Perform Preliminary Check 1.
O.K.
CHECK INTAKE DOOR OPERATION.
N.G.
Perform Preliminary Check 2.
O.K.
CHECK BLOWER MOTOR OPERATION.
N.G.
Perform Preliminary Check 5.
O.K.
CHECK AIR MIX DOOR OPERATION.
N.G.
Perform Preliminary Check 7.
O.K.
CHECK DUCTS FOR AIR LEAKS.
N.G.
Repair air leaks.
O.K.
PERFORM TEMPERATURE SETTING TRIMMING.
1. Set up AUXILIARY MECHANISM mode in Self-diagnosis.
2. Press (HOT) switch at desirable times.
NOTE: If the result is no good (NG) after checking circuit continuity, repair harness or connector.
94C10365
Courtesy of Nissan Motor Co., U.S.A.

Fig. 3: Preliminary Check 3 – Insufficient Cooling

Fig. 4: Preliminary Check 4 – Insufficient Heating

1993 AUTOMATIC A/C-HEATER SYSTEMS
Trouble Shooting – Altima (Cont.)

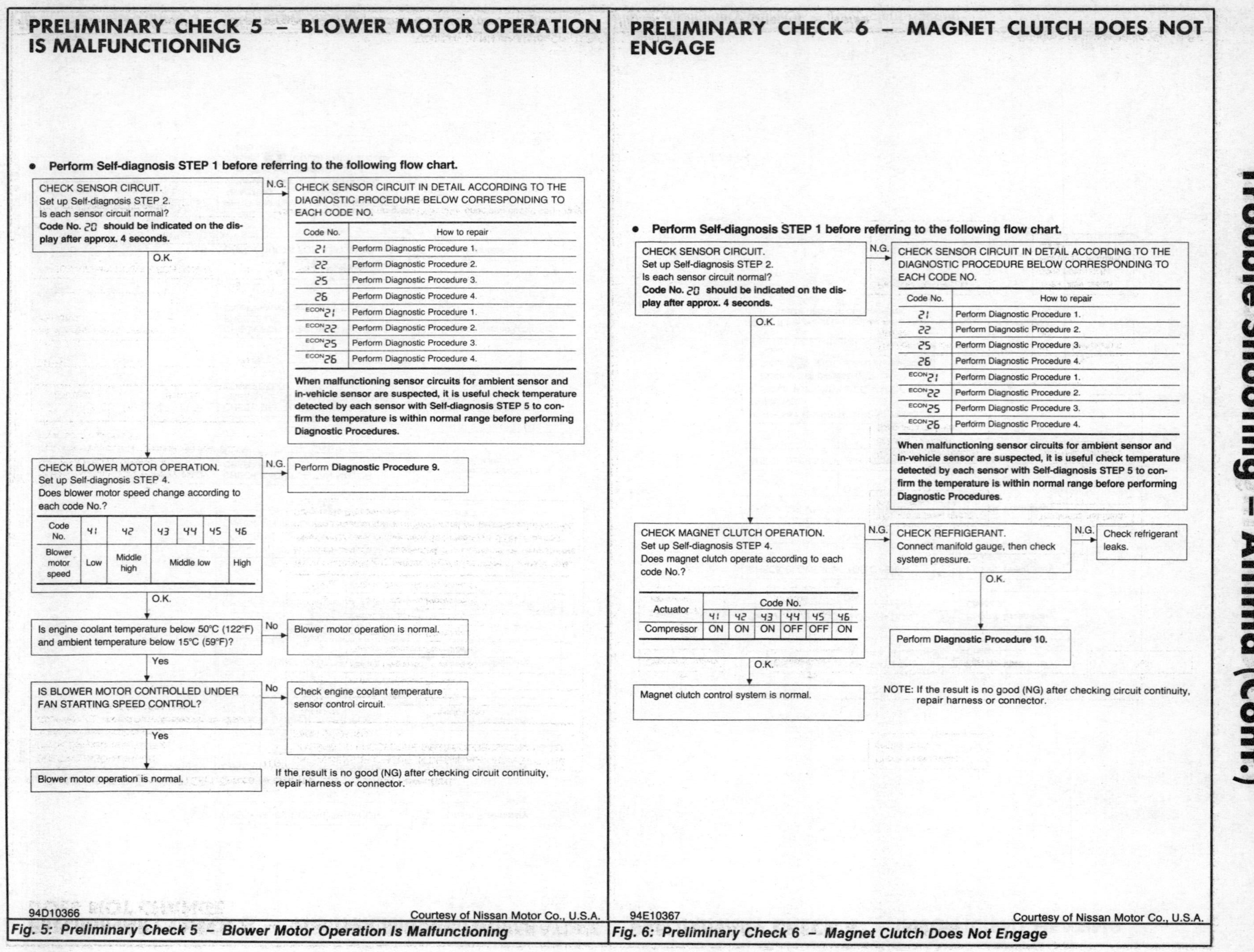
PRELIMINARY CHECK 5 – BLOWER MOTOR OPERATION IS MALFUNCTIONING
• Perform Self-diagnosis STEP 1 before referring to the following flow chart.
CHECK SENSOR CIRCUIT. Set up Self-diagnosis STEP 2. Is each sensor circuit normal? Code No. 20 should be indicated on the display after approx. 4 seconds.
N.G.
CHECK SENSOR CIRCUIT IN DETAIL ACCORDING TO THE DIAGNOSTIC PROCEDURE BELOW CORRESPONDING TO EACH CODE NO.
Code No. | How to repair
21 | Perform Diagnostic Procedure 1.
22 | Perform Diagnostic Procedure 2.
25 | Perform Diagnostic Procedure 3.
26 | Perform Diagnostic Procedure 4.
ECON 21 | Perform Diagnostic Procedure 1.
ECON 22 | Perform Diagnostic Procedure 2.
ECON 25 | Perform Diagnostic Procedure 3.
ECON 26 | Perform Diagnostic Procedure 4.
When malfunctioning sensor circuits for ambient sensor and in-vehicle sensor are suspected, it is useful check temperature detected by each sensor with Self-diagnosis STEP 5 to confirm the temperature is within normal range before performing Diagnostic Procedures.
O.K.
CHECK BLOWER MOTOR OPERATION. Set up Self-diagnosis STEP 4. Does blower motor speed change according to each code No.?
Code No. | 41 | 42 | 43 | 44 | 45 | 46
Blower motor speed | Low | Middle high | Middle low | High
N.G.
Perform Diagnostic Procedure 9.
O.K.
Is engine coolant temperature below 50°C (122°F) and ambient temperature below 15°C (59°F)?
No
Blower motor operation is normal.
Yes
IS BLOWER MOTOR CONTROLLED UNDER FAN STARTING SPEED CONTROL?
No
Check engine coolant temperature sensor control circuit.
Yes
Blower motor operation is normal.
If the result is no good (NG) after checking circuit continuity, repair harness or connector.
94D10366
Courtesy of Nissan Motor Co., U.S.A.
PRELIMINARY CHECK 6 – MAGNET CLUTCH DOES NOT ENGAGE
• Perform Self-diagnosis STEP 1 before referring to the following flow chart.
CHECK SENSOR CIRCUIT. Set up Self-diagnosis STEP 2. Is each sensor circuit normal? Code No. 20 should be indicated on the display after approx. 4 seconds.
N.G.
CHECK SENSOR CIRCUIT IN DETAIL ACCORDING TO THE DIAGNOSTIC PROCEDURE BELOW CORRESPONDING TO EACH CODE NO.
Code No. | How to repair
21 | Perform Diagnostic Procedure 1.
22 | Perform Diagnostic Procedure 2.
25 | Perform Diagnostic Procedure 3.
26 | Perform Diagnostic Procedure 4.
ECON 21 | Perform Diagnostic Procedure 1.
ECON 22 | Perform Diagnostic Procedure 2.
ECON 25 | Perform Diagnostic Procedure 3.
ECON 26 | Perform Diagnostic Procedure 4.
When malfunctioning sensor circuits for ambient sensor and in-vehicle sensor are suspected, it is useful check temperature detected by each sensor with Self-diagnosis STEP 5 to confirm the temperature is within normal range before performing Diagnostic Procedures.
O.K.
CHECK MAGNET CLUTCH OPERATION. Set up Self-diagnosis STEP 4. Does magnet clutch operate according to each code No.?
Actuator | Code No. 41 | 42 | 43 | 44 | 45 | 46
Compressor | ON | ON | ON | OFF | OFF | ON
N.G.
CHECK REFRIGERANT. Connect manifold gauge, then check system pressure.
N.G.
Check refrigerant leaks.
O.K.
Perform Diagnostic Procedure 10.
O.K.
Magnet clutch control system is normal.
NOTE: If the result is no good (NG) after checking circuit continuity, repair harness or connector.
94E10367
Courtesy of Nissan Motor Co., U.S.A.

Fig. 5: Preliminary Check 5 – Blower Motor Operation Is Malfunctioning

Fig. 6: Preliminary Check 6 – Magnet Clutch Does Not Engage

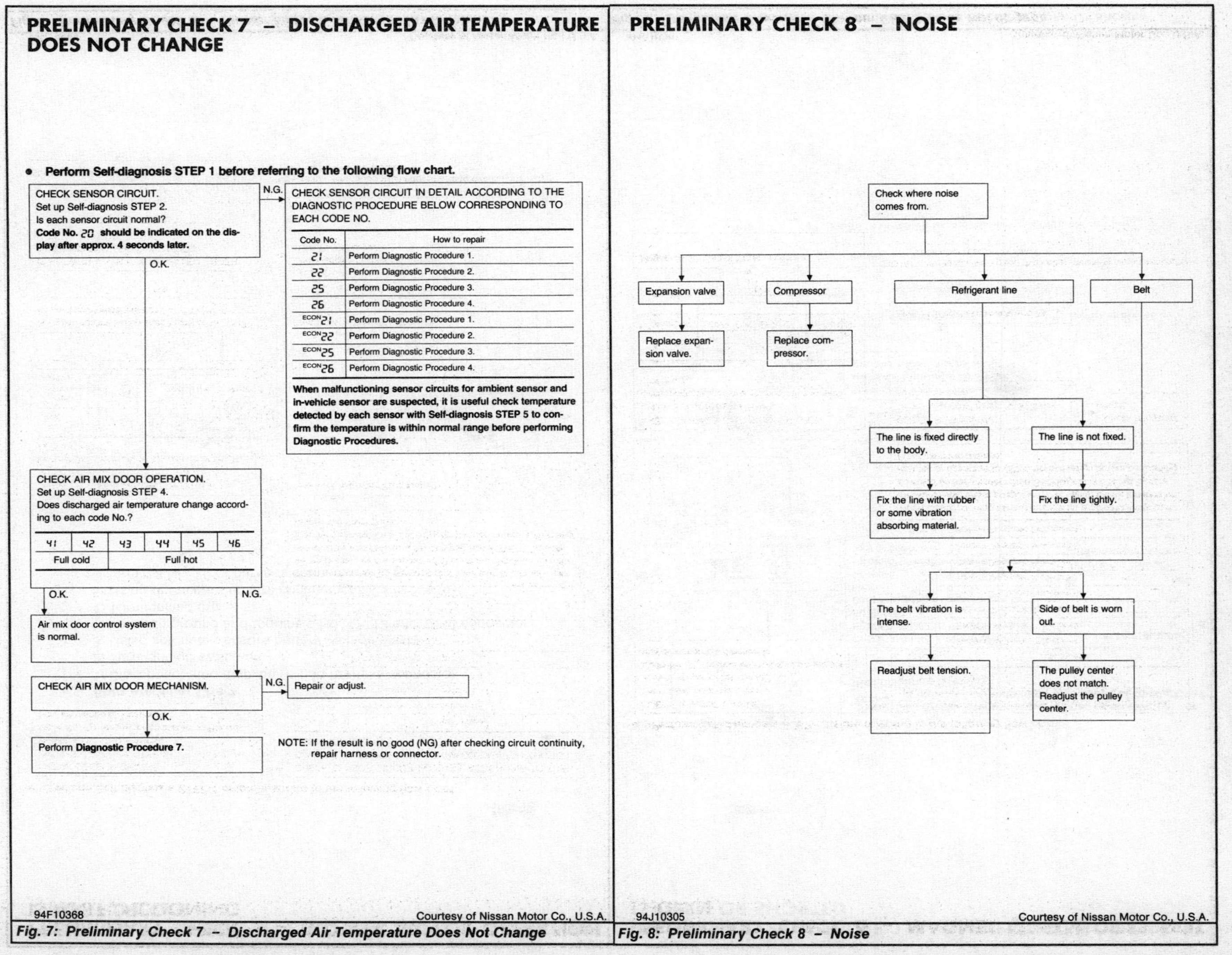

PRELIMINARY CHECK 7 – DISCHARGED AIR TEMPERATURE DOES NOT CHANGE
• Perform Self-diagnosis STEP 1 before referring to the following flow chart.
CHECK SENSOR CIRCUIT. Set up Self-diagnosis STEP 2. Is each sensor circuit normal? Code No. 20 should be indicated on the display after approx. 4 seconds later.
N.G.
CHECK SENSOR CIRCUIT IN DETAIL ACCORDING TO THE DIAGNOSTIC PROCEDURE BELOW CORRESPONDING TO EACH CODE NO.
Code No. | How to repair
21 | Perform Diagnostic Procedure 1.
22 | Perform Diagnostic Procedure 2.
25 | Perform Diagnostic Procedure 3.
26 | Perform Diagnostic Procedure 4.
ECON 21 | Perform Diagnostic Procedure 1.
ECON 22 | Perform Diagnostic Procedure 2.
ECON 25 | Perform Diagnostic Procedure 3.
ECON 26 | Perform Diagnostic Procedure 4.
When malfunctioning sensor circuits for ambient sensor and in-vehicle sensor are suspected, it is useful check temperature detected by each sensor with Self-diagnosis STEP 5 to confirm the temperature is within normal range before performing Diagnostic Procedures.
O.K.
CHECK AIR MIX DOOR OPERATION. Set up Self-diagnosis STEP 4. Does discharged air temperature change according to each code No.?
41 | 42 | 43 | 44 | 45 | 46
Full cold | Full hot
O.K.
Air mix door control system is normal.
N.G.
CHECK AIR MIX DOOR MECHANISM.
N.G.
Repair or adjust.
O.K.
Perform Diagnostic Procedure 7.
NOTE: If the result is no good (NG) after checking circuit continuity, repair harness or connector.
94F10368
Courtesy of Nissan Motor Co., U.S.A.
PRELIMINARY CHECK 8 – NOISE
Check where noise comes from.
Expansion valve
Compressor
Refrigerant line
Belt
Replace expansion valve.
Replace compressor.
The line is fixed directly to the body.
The line is not fixed.
Fix the line with rubber or some vibration absorbing material.
Fix the line tightly.
The belt vibration is intense.
Side of belt is worn out.
Readjust belt tension.
The pulley center does not match. Readjust the pulley center.
94J10305
Courtesy of Nissan Motor Co., U.S.A.

Fig. 7: Preliminary Check 7 – Discharged Air Temperature Does Not Change

Fig. 8: Preliminary Check 8 – Noise

1993 AUTOMATIC A/C-HEATER SYSTEMS
Trouble Shooting – Altima (Cont.)

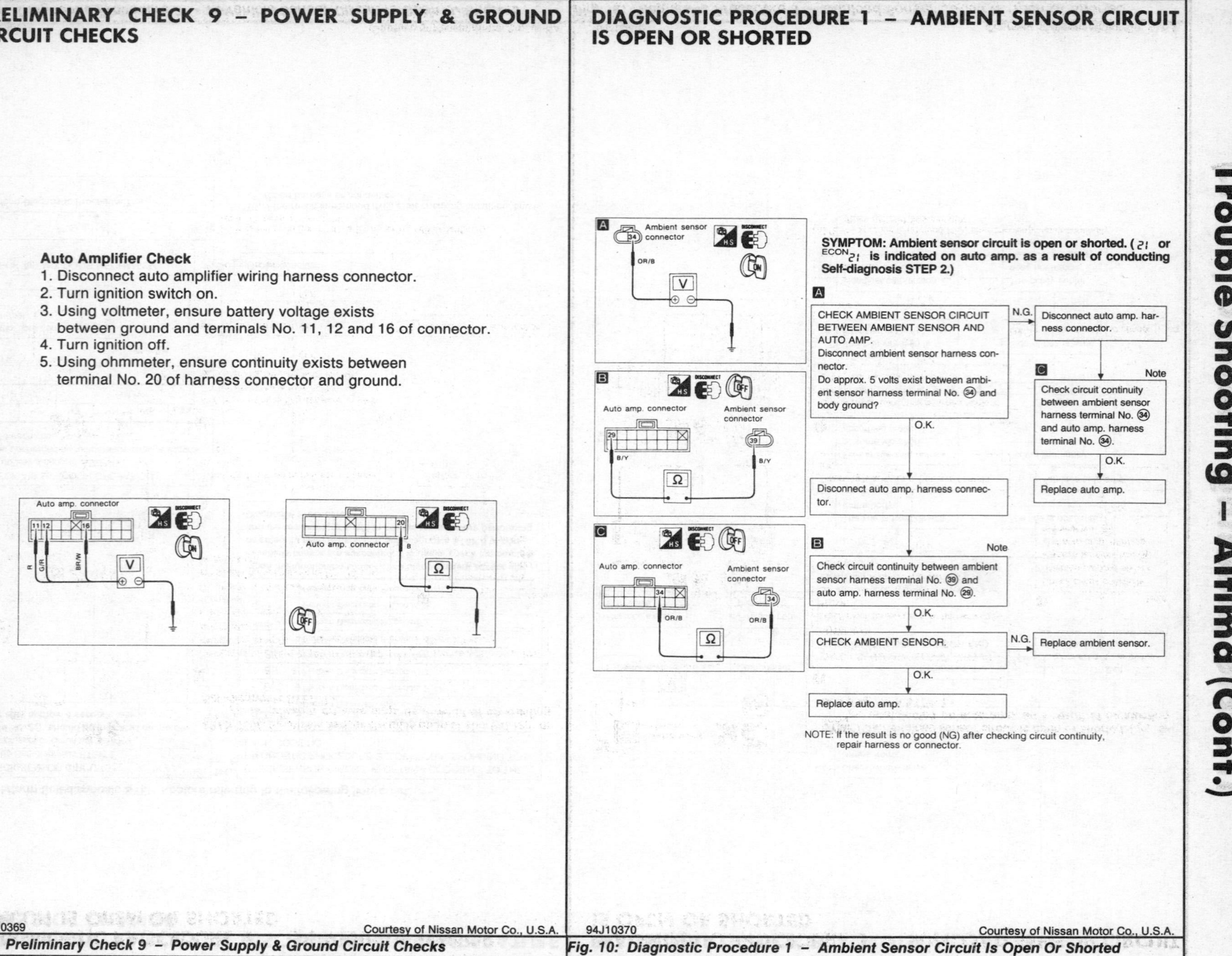
PRELIMINARY CHECK 9 – POWER SUPPLY & GROUND CIRCUIT CHECKS
Auto Amplifier Check
1. Disconnect auto amplifier wiring harness connector.
2. Turn ignition switch on.
3. Using voltmeter, ensure battery voltage exists between ground and terminals No. 11, 12 and 16 of connector.
4. Turn ignition off.
5. Using ohmmeter, ensure continuity exists between terminal No. 20 of harness connector and ground.
Auto amp. connector
11
12
16
R
G/R
BR/W
V
20
B
Ω
94G10369
Courtesy of Nissan Motor Co., U.S.A.
DIAGNOSTIC PROCEDURE 1 – AMBIENT SENSOR CIRCUIT IS OPEN OR SHORTED
A
Ambient sensor connector
34
OR/B
V
B
Auto amp. connector
Ambient sensor connector
29
39
B/Y
Ω
C
Auto amp. connector
Ambient sensor connector
34
OR/B
Ω
SYMPTOM: Ambient sensor circuit is open or shorted. (21 or ECON 21 is indicated on auto amp. as a result of conducting Self-diagnosis STEP 2.)
A
CHECK AMBIENT SENSOR CIRCUIT BETWEEN AMBIENT SENSOR AND AUTO AMP.
Disconnect ambient sensor harness connector.
Do approx. 5 volts exist between ambient sensor harness terminal No. 34 and body ground?
N.G.
Disconnect auto amp. harness connector.
C
Note
Check circuit continuity between ambient sensor harness terminal No. 34 and auto amp. harness terminal No. 34.
O.K.
Replace auto amp.
O.K.
Disconnect auto amp. harness connector.
B
Note
Check circuit continuity between ambient sensor harness terminal No. 39 and auto amp. harness terminal No. 29.
O.K.
CHECK AMBIENT SENSOR.
N.G.
Replace ambient sensor.
O.K.
Replace auto amp.
NOTE: If the result is no good (NG) after checking circuit continuity, repair harness or connector.
94J10370
Courtesy of Nissan Motor Co., U.S.A.

Fig. 9: Preliminary Check 9 – Power Supply & Ground Circuit Checks

Fig. 10: Diagnostic Procedure 1 – Ambient Sensor Circuit Is Open Or Shorted

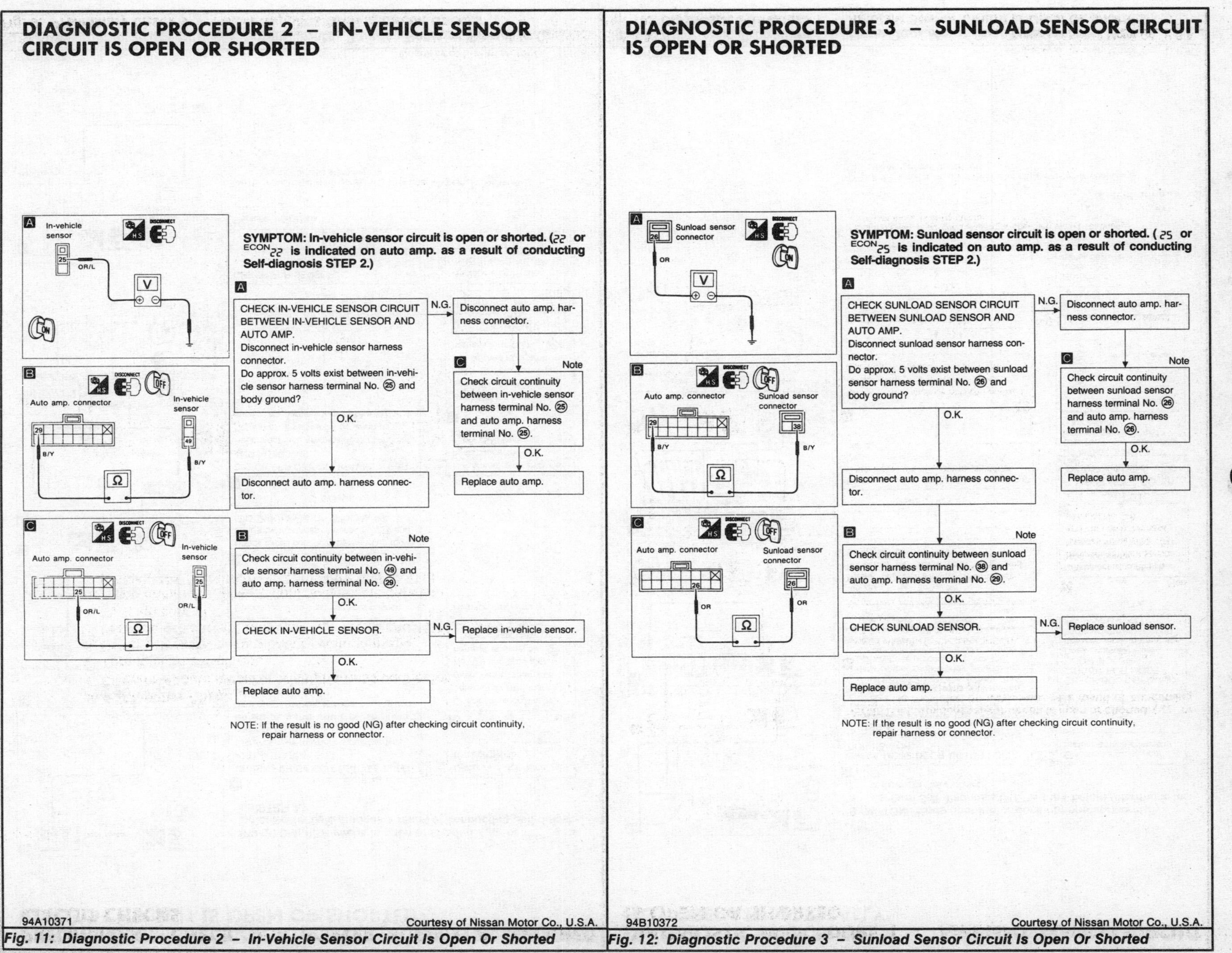
DIAGNOSTIC PROCEDURE 2 – IN-VEHICLE SENSOR CIRCUIT IS OPEN OR SHORTED
A
In-vehicle sensor
25
OR/L
V
B
Auto amp. connector
In-vehicle sensor
29
49
B/Y
Ω
C
Auto amp. connector
In-vehicle sensor
25
OR/L
Ω
SYMPTOM: In-vehicle sensor circuit is open or shorted. (22 or ECON22 is indicated on auto amp. as a result of conducting Self-diagnosis STEP 2.)
A
CHECK IN-VEHICLE SENSOR CIRCUIT BETWEEN IN-VEHICLE SENSOR AND AUTO AMP.
Disconnect in-vehicle sensor harness connector.
Do approx. 5 volts exist between in-vehicle sensor harness terminal No. 25 and body ground?
N.G.
Disconnect auto amp. harness connector.
C
Note
Check circuit continuity between in-vehicle sensor harness terminal No. 25 and auto amp. harness terminal No. 25.
O.K.
Replace auto amp.
O.K.
Disconnect auto amp. harness connector.
B
Note
Check circuit continuity between in-vehicle sensor harness terminal No. 49 and auto amp. harness terminal No. 29.
O.K.
CHECK IN-VEHICLE SENSOR.
N.G.
Replace in-vehicle sensor.
O.K.
Replace auto amp.
NOTE: If the result is no good (NG) after checking circuit continuity, repair harness or connector.
94A10371
Courtesy of Nissan Motor Co., U.S.A.
DIAGNOSTIC PROCEDURE 3 – SUNLOAD SENSOR CIRCUIT IS OPEN OR SHORTED
A
Sunload sensor connector
26
OR
V
B
Auto amp. connector
Sunload sensor connector
29
38
B/Y
Ω
C
Auto amp. connector
Sunload sensor connector
26
OR
Ω
SYMPTOM: Sunload sensor circuit is open or shorted. (25 or ECON25 is indicated on auto amp. as a result of conducting Self-diagnosis STEP 2.)
A
CHECK SUNLOAD SENSOR CIRCUIT BETWEEN SUNLOAD SENSOR AND AUTO AMP.
Disconnect sunload sensor harness connector.
Do approx. 5 volts exist between sunload sensor harness terminal No. 26 and body ground?
N.G.
Disconnect auto amp. harness connector.
C
Note
Check circuit continuity between sunload sensor harness terminal No. 26 and auto amp. harness terminal No. 26.
O.K.
Replace auto amp.
O.K.
Disconnect auto amp. harness connector.
B
Note
Check circuit continuity between sunload sensor harness terminal No. 38 and auto amp. harness terminal No. 29.
O.K.
CHECK SUNLOAD SENSOR.
N.G.
Replace sunload sensor.
O.K.
Replace auto amp.
NOTE: If the result is no good (NG) after checking circuit continuity, repair harness or connector.
94B10372
Courtesy of Nissan Motor Co., U.S.A.

Fig. 11: Diagnostic Procedure 2 – In-Vehicle Sensor Circuit Is Open Or Shorted

Fig. 12: Diagnostic Procedure 3 – Sunload Sensor Circuit Is Open Or Shorted

1993 AUTOMATIC A/C-HEATER SYSTEMS
Trouble Shooting – Altima (Cont.)

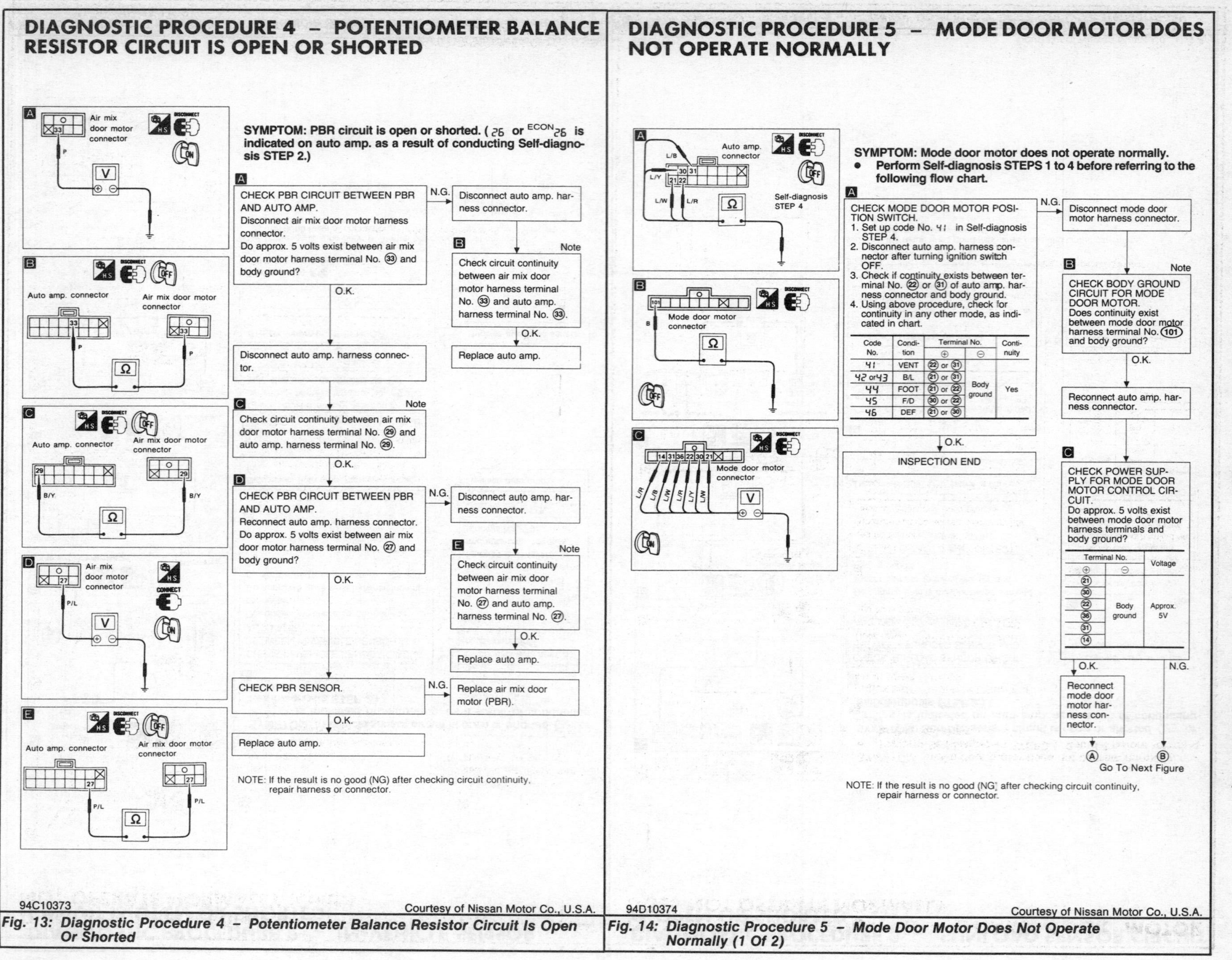
DIAGNOSTIC PROCEDURE 4 – POTENTIOMETER BALANCE RESISTOR CIRCUIT IS OPEN OR SHORTED
SYMPTOM: PBR circuit is open or shorted. (25 or ECON25 is indicated on auto amp. as a result of conducting Self-diagnosis STEP 2.)
A CHECK PBR CIRCUIT BETWEEN PBR AND AUTO AMP. Disconnect air mix door motor harness connector. Do approx. 5 volts exist between air mix door motor harness terminal No. 33 and body ground?
N.G. Disconnect auto amp. harness connector.
B Check circuit continuity between air mix door motor harness terminal No. 33 and auto amp. harness terminal No. 33. Note
O.K. Replace auto amp.
O.K. Disconnect auto amp. harness connector.
C Check circuit continuity between air mix door motor harness terminal No. 29 and auto amp. harness terminal No. 29. Note
O.K.
D CHECK PBR CIRCUIT BETWEEN PBR AND AUTO AMP. Reconnect auto amp. harness connector. Do approx. 5 volts exist between air mix door motor harness terminal No. 27 and body ground?
N.G. Disconnect auto amp. harness connector.
E Check circuit continuity between air mix door motor harness terminal No. 27 and auto amp. harness terminal No. 27. Note
O.K. Replace auto amp.
O.K. CHECK PBR SENSOR.
N.G. Replace air mix door motor (PBR).
O.K. Replace auto amp.
NOTE: If the result is no good (NG) after checking circuit continuity, repair harness or connector.
Air mix door motor connector
Auto amp. connector
DISCONNECT
CONNECT
ON
OFF
HS
94C10373
Courtesy of Nissan Motor Co., U.S.A.
DIAGNOSTIC PROCEDURE 5 – MODE DOOR MOTOR DOES NOT OPERATE NORMALLY
SYMPTOM: Mode door motor does not operate normally.
• Perform Self-diagnosis STEPS 1 to 4 before referring to the following flow chart.
A CHECK MODE DOOR MOTOR POSITION SWITCH.
1. Set up code No. 41 in Self-diagnosis STEP 4.
2. Disconnect auto amp. harness connector after turning ignition switch OFF.
3. Check if continuity exists between terminal No. 22 or 31 of auto amp. harness connector and body ground.
4. Using above procedure, check for continuity in any other mode, as indicated in chart.
Code No. | Condition | Terminal No. ⊕ | Terminal No. ⊖ | Continuity
41 | VENT | 22 or 31 | Body ground | Yes
42 or 43 | B/L | 21 or 31
44 | FOOT | 21 or 22
45 | F/D | 30 or 22
46 | DEF | 21 or 30
O.K. INSPECTION END
N.G. Disconnect mode door motor harness connector.
B CHECK BODY GROUND CIRCUIT FOR MODE DOOR MOTOR. Does continuity exist between mode door motor harness terminal No. 101 and body ground? Note
O.K. Reconnect auto amp. harness connector.
C CHECK POWER SUPPLY FOR MODE DOOR MOTOR CONTROL CIRCUIT. Do approx. 5 volts exist between mode door motor harness terminals and body ground?
Terminal No. ⊕ | Terminal No. ⊖ | Voltage
21, 30, 22, 36, 31, 14 | Body ground | Approx. 5V
O.K. Reconnect mode door motor harness connector. A
N.G. B
Go To Next Figure
NOTE: If the result is no good (NG) after checking circuit continuity, repair harness or connector.
Auto amp. connector
Self-diagnosis STEP 4
Mode door motor connector
L/B
L/Y
L/W
L/R
B
94D10374
Courtesy of Nissan Motor Co., U.S.A.

Fig. 13: Diagnostic Procedure 4 – Potentiometer Balance Resistor Circuit Is Open Or Shorted

Fig. 14: Diagnostic Procedure 5 – Mode Door Motor Does Not Operate Normally (1 Of 2)

1993 AUTOMATIC A/C-HEATER SYSTEMS
Trouble Shooting – Altima (Cont.)

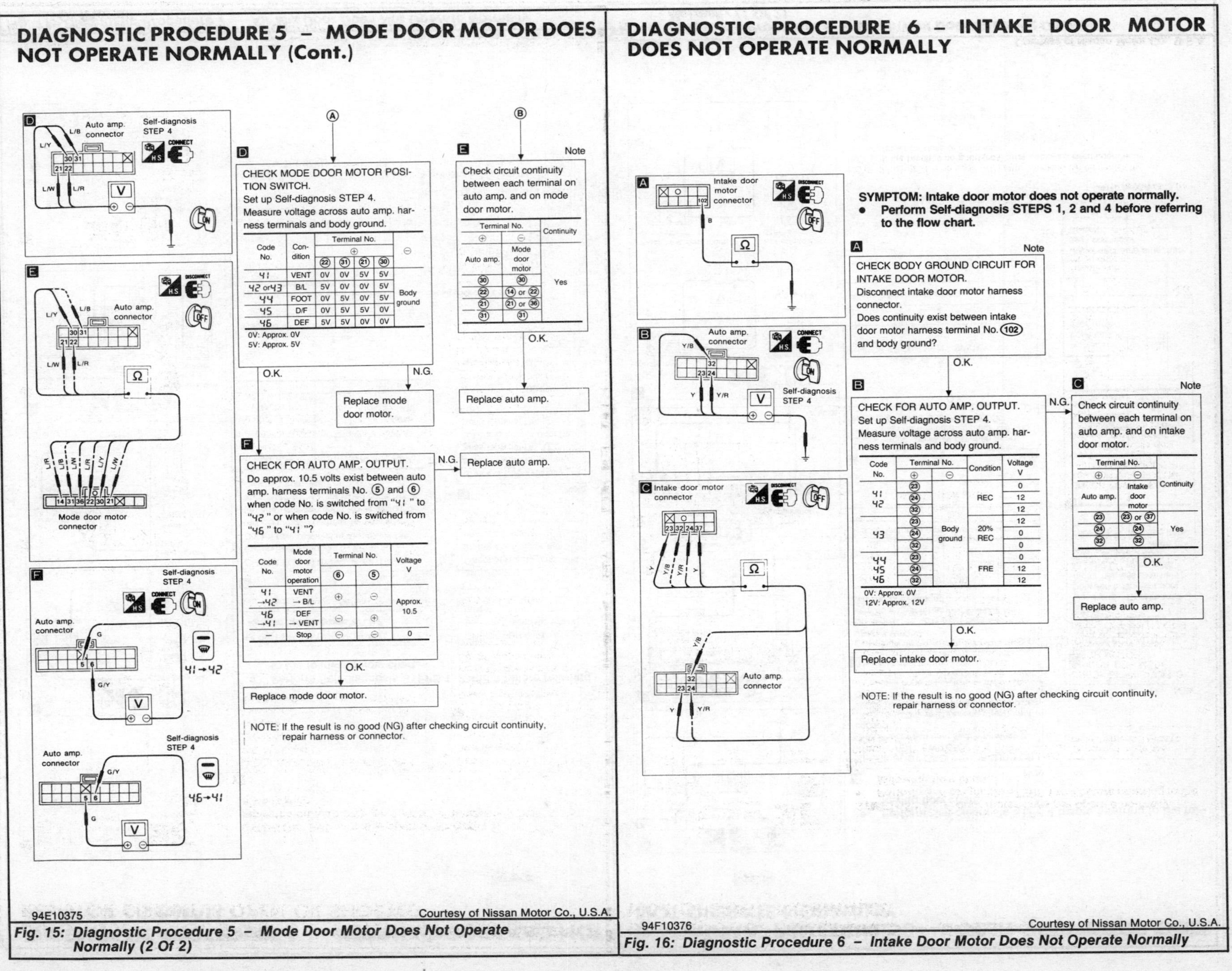
DIAGNOSTIC PROCEDURE 5 – MODE DOOR MOTOR DOES NOT OPERATE NORMALLY (Cont.)
D
Auto amp. connector
Self-diagnosis STEP 4
L/Y
L/B
L/W
L/R
CONNECT
ON
E
Auto amp. connector
DISCONNECT
OFF
Mode door motor connector
F
Self-diagnosis STEP 4
Auto amp. connector
G
G/Y
41→42
46→41
A
D
CHECK MODE DOOR MOTOR POSITION SWITCH.
Set up Self-diagnosis STEP 4.
Measure voltage across auto amp. harness terminals and body ground.
0V: Approx. 0V
5V: Approx. 5V
O.K.
N.G.
Replace mode door motor.
B
E
Note
Check circuit continuity between each terminal on auto amp. and on mode door motor.
O.K.
Replace auto amp.
F
CHECK FOR AUTO AMP. OUTPUT.
Do approx. 10.5 volts exist between auto amp. harness terminals No. 5 and 6 when code No. is switched from "41" to "42" or when code No. is switched from "46" to "41"?
N.G.
Replace auto amp.
O.K.
Replace mode door motor.
NOTE: If the result is no good (NG) after checking circuit continuity, repair harness or connector.
DIAGNOSTIC PROCEDURE 6 – INTAKE DOOR MOTOR DOES NOT OPERATE NORMALLY
A
Intake door motor connector
B
DISCONNECT
OFF
B
Auto amp. connector
Y/B
Y
Y/R
Self-diagnosis STEP 4
CONNECT
ON
C
Intake door motor connector
Auto amp. connector
SYMPTOM: Intake door motor does not operate normally.
• Perform Self-diagnosis STEPS 1, 2 and 4 before referring to the flow chart.
A
Note
CHECK BODY GROUND CIRCUIT FOR INTAKE DOOR MOTOR.
Disconnect intake door motor harness connector.
Does continuity exist between intake door motor harness terminal No. 102 and body ground?
O.K.
B
CHECK FOR AUTO AMP. OUTPUT.
Set up Self-diagnosis STEP 4.
Measure voltage across auto amp. harness terminals and body ground.
0V: Approx. 0V
12V: Approx. 12V
N.G.
O.K.
Replace intake door motor.
C
Note
Check circuit continuity between each terminal on auto amp. and on intake door motor.
O.K.
Replace auto amp.
NOTE: If the result is no good (NG) after checking circuit continuity, repair harness or connector.

Code No.	Condition	Terminal No. ⊕ 22	31	21	30	⊖
41	VENT	0V	0V	5V	5V	Body ground
42 or 43	B/L	5V	0V	0V	5V	
44	FOOT	0V	5V	0V	5V	
45	D/F	0V	5V	5V	0V	
46	DEF	5V	5V	0V	0V	

Terminal No. ⊕ Auto amp.	⊖ Mode door motor	Continuity
30	30	Yes
22	14 or 22	
21	21 or 36	
31	31	

Code No.	Mode door motor operation	Terminal No. 6	5	Voltage V
41 →42	VENT → B/L	⊕	⊖	Approx. 10.5
46 →41	DEF → VENT	⊖	⊕	
–	Stop	⊖	⊖	0

Code No.	Terminal No. ⊕	⊖	Condition	Voltage V
41 42	23	Body ground	REC	0
	24			12
	32			12
43	23		20% REC	12
	24			0
	32			0
44 45 46	23		FRE	0
	24			12
	32			12

Terminal No. ⊕ Auto amp.	⊖ Intake door motor	Continuity
23	23 or 37	Yes
24	24	
32	32	

94E10375 Courtesy of Nissan Motor Co., U.S.A.

Fig. 15: Diagnostic Procedure 5 – Mode Door Motor Does Not Operate Normally (2 Of 2)

94F10376 Courtesy of Nissan Motor Co., U.S.A.

Fig. 16: Diagnostic Procedure 6 – Intake Door Motor Does Not Operate Normally

1993 AUTOMATIC A/C-HEATER SYSTEMS
Trouble Shooting – Altima (Cont.)

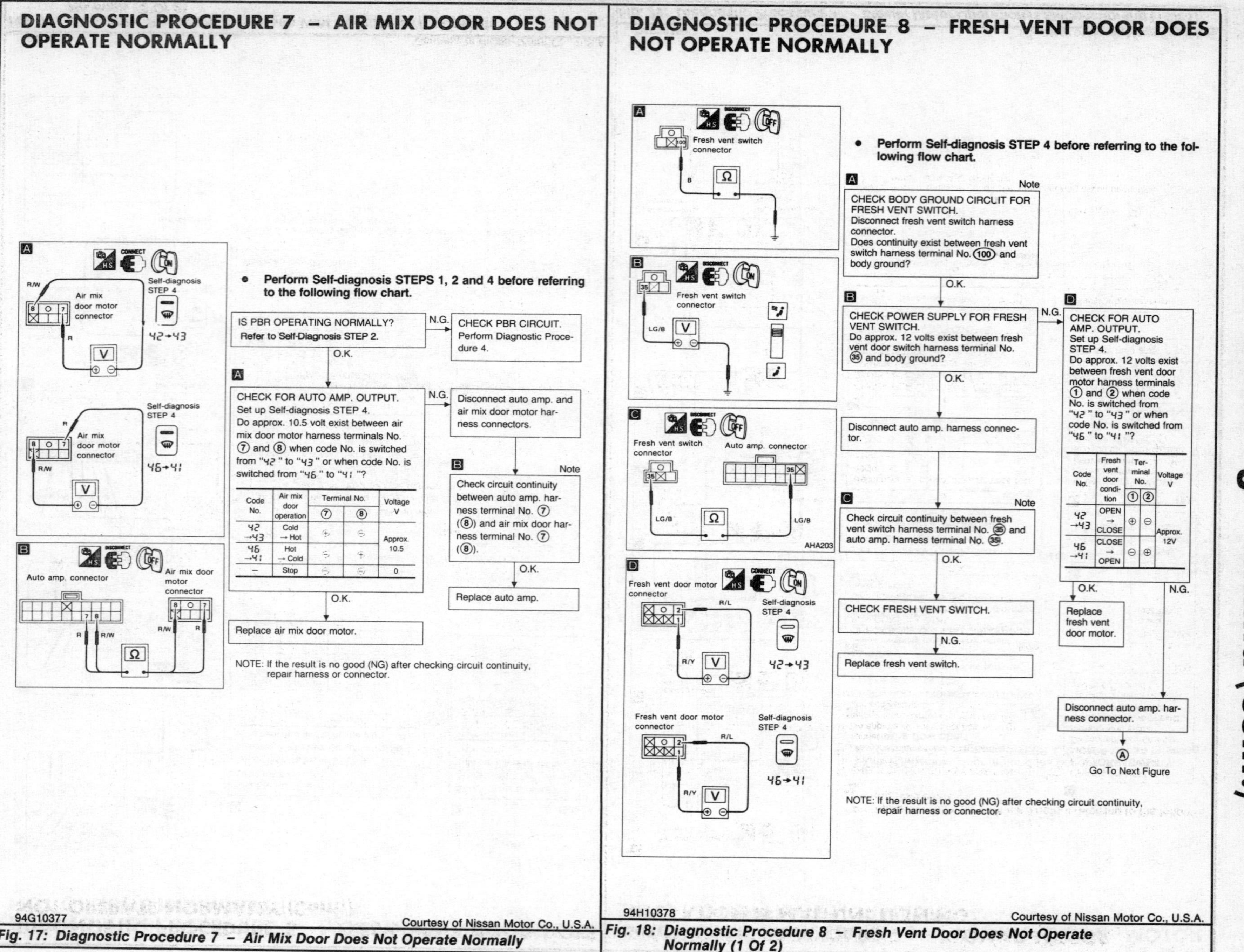
DIAGNOSTIC PROCEDURE 7 – AIR MIX DOOR DOES NOT OPERATE NORMALLY
A
CONNECT
ON
R/W
Air mix door motor connector
Self-diagnosis STEP 4
R
V
42→43
Self-diagnosis STEP 4
R
Air mix door motor connector
R/W
46→41
B
DISCONNECT
OFF
Auto amp. connector
Air mix door motor connector
R
R/W
Ω
• Perform Self-diagnosis STEPS 1, 2 and 4 before referring to the following flow chart.
IS PBR OPERATING NORMALLY? Refer to Self-Diagnosis STEP 2.
N.G.
CHECK PBR CIRCUIT. Perform Diagnostic Procedure 4.
O.K.
A
CHECK FOR AUTO AMP. OUTPUT. Set up Self-diagnosis STEP 4. Do approx. 10.5 volt exist between air mix door motor harness terminals No. ⑦ and ⑧ when code No. is switched from "42" to "43" or when code No. is switched from "46" to "41"?
Code No. | Air mix door operation | Terminal No. ⑦ | Terminal No. ⑧ | Voltage V
42 →43 | Cold → Hot | ⊕ | ⊖ | Approx. 10.5
46 →41 | Hot → Cold | ⊖ | ⊕ |
– | Stop | ⊖ | ⊖ | 0
N.G.
Disconnect auto amp. and air mix door motor harness connectors.
B
Note
Check circuit continuity between auto amp. harness terminal No. ⑦ (⑧) and air mix door harness terminal No. ⑦ (⑧).
O.K.
Replace auto amp.
O.K.
Replace air mix door motor.
NOTE: If the result is no good (NG) after checking circuit continuity, repair harness or connector.
94G10377
Courtesy of Nissan Motor Co., U.S.A.
DIAGNOSTIC PROCEDURE 8 – FRESH VENT DOOR DOES NOT OPERATE NORMALLY
A
DISCONNECT
OFF
Fresh vent switch connector
100
B
Ω
B
DISCONNECT
ON
35
Fresh vent switch connector
LG/B
V
C
DISCONNECT
OFF
Fresh vent switch connector
Auto amp. connector
35
LG/B
Ω
AHA203
D
CONNECT
ON
Fresh vent door motor connector
R/L
Self-diagnosis STEP 4
R/Y
V
42→43
Fresh vent door motor connector
Self-diagnosis STEP 4
R/L
R/Y
46→41
• Perform Self-diagnosis STEP 4 before referring to the following flow chart.
A
Note
CHECK BODY GROUND CIRCLIT FOR FRESH VENT SWITCH. Disconnect fresh vent switch harness connector. Does continuity exist between fresh vent switch harness terminal No. (100) and body ground?
O.K.
B
CHECK POWER SUPPLY FOR FRESH VENT SWITCH. Do approx. 12 volts exist between fresh vent door switch harness terminal No. ㉟ and body ground?
N.G.
D
CHECK FOR AUTO AMP. OUTPUT. Set up Self-diagnosis STEP 4. Do approx. 12 volts exist between fresh vent door motor harness terminals ① and ② when code No. is switched from "42" to "43" or when code No. is switched from "46" to "41"?
Code No. | Fresh vent door condition | Terminal No. ① | Terminal No. ② | Voltage V
42 →43 | OPEN → CLOSE | ⊕ | ⊖ | Approx. 12V
46 →41 | CLOSE → OPEN | ⊖ | ⊕ |
O.K.
Disconnect auto amp. harness connector.
C
Note
Check circuit continuity between fresh vent switch harness terminal No. ㉟ and auto amp. harness terminal No. ㉟.
O.K.
CHECK FRESH VENT SWITCH.
N.G.
Replace fresh vent switch.
O.K.
Replace fresh vent door motor.
N.G.
Disconnect auto amp. harness connector.
Ⓐ
Go To Next Figure
NOTE: If the result is no good (NG) after checking circuit continuity, repair harness or connector.
94H10378
Courtesy of Nissan Motor Co., U.S.A.

Fig. 17: Diagnostic Procedure 7 – Air Mix Door Does Not Operate Normally

Fig. 18: Diagnostic Procedure 8 – Fresh Vent Door Does Not Operate Normally (1 Of 2)

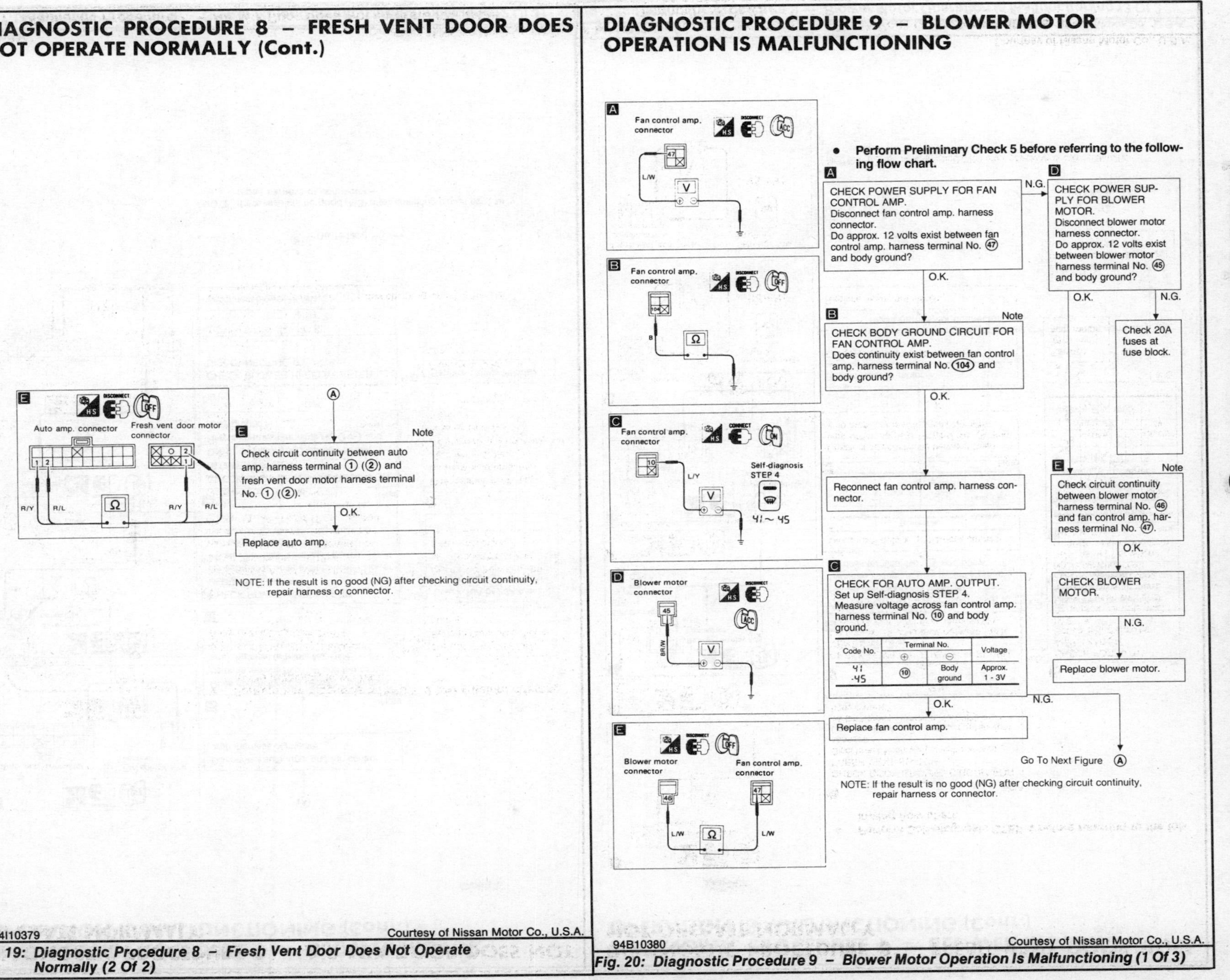
DIAGNOSTIC PROCEDURE 8 – FRESH VENT DOOR DOES NOT OPERATE NORMALLY (Cont.)
E
Auto amp. connector
Fresh vent door motor connector
DISCONNECT
OFF
R/Y
R/L
Ω
Ⓐ
E
Note
Check circuit continuity between auto amp. harness terminal ① (②) and fresh vent door motor harness terminal No. ① (②).
O.K.
Replace auto amp.
NOTE: If the result is no good (NG) after checking circuit continuity, repair harness or connector.
94I10379
Courtesy of Nissan Motor Co., U.S.A.
DIAGNOSTIC PROCEDURE 9 – BLOWER MOTOR OPERATION IS MALFUNCTIONING
A
Fan control amp. connector
DISCONNECT
ACC
47
L/W
V
B
Fan control amp. connector
104
B
Ω
OFF
C
Fan control amp. connector
CONNECT
ON
10
L/Y
V
Self-diagnosis STEP 4
41～45
D
Blower motor connector
45
BR/W
V
ACC
E
Blower motor connector
Fan control amp. connector
46
47
L/W
Ω
• Perform Preliminary Check 5 before referring to the following flow chart.
A
CHECK POWER SUPPLY FOR FAN CONTROL AMP.
Disconnect fan control amp. harness connector.
Do approx. 12 volts exist between fan control amp. harness terminal No. ㊼ and body ground?
N.G.
D
CHECK POWER SUPPLY FOR BLOWER MOTOR.
Disconnect blower motor harness connector.
Do approx. 12 volts exist between blower motor harness terminal No. ㊺ and body ground?
O.K.
N.G.
Check 20A fuses at fuse block.
B
Note
CHECK BODY GROUND CIRCUIT FOR FAN CONTROL AMP.
Does continuity exist between fan control amp. harness terminal No. (104) and body ground?
O.K.
Reconnect fan control amp. harness connector.
E
Note
Check circuit continuity between blower motor harness terminal No. ㊻ and fan control amp. harness terminal No. ㊼.
O.K.
CHECK BLOWER MOTOR.
N.G.
Replace blower motor.
C
CHECK FOR AUTO AMP. OUTPUT.
Set up Self-diagnosis STEP 4.
Measure voltage across fan control amp. harness terminal No. ⑩ and body ground.
Code No. | Terminal No. ⊕ | Terminal No. ⊖ | Voltage
41 -45 | ⑩ | Body ground | Approx. 1 - 3V
O.K.
N.G.
Replace fan control amp.
Go To Next Figure Ⓐ
NOTE: If the result is no good (NG) after checking circuit continuity, repair harness or connector.
94B10380
Courtesy of Nissan Motor Co., U.S.A.

Fig. 19: Diagnostic Procedure 8 – Fresh Vent Door Does Not Operate Normally (2 Of 2)

Fig. 20: Diagnostic Procedure 9 – Blower Motor Operation Is Malfunctioning (1 Of 3)

1993 AUTOMATIC A/C-HEATER SYSTEMS
Trouble Shooting – Altima (Cont.)

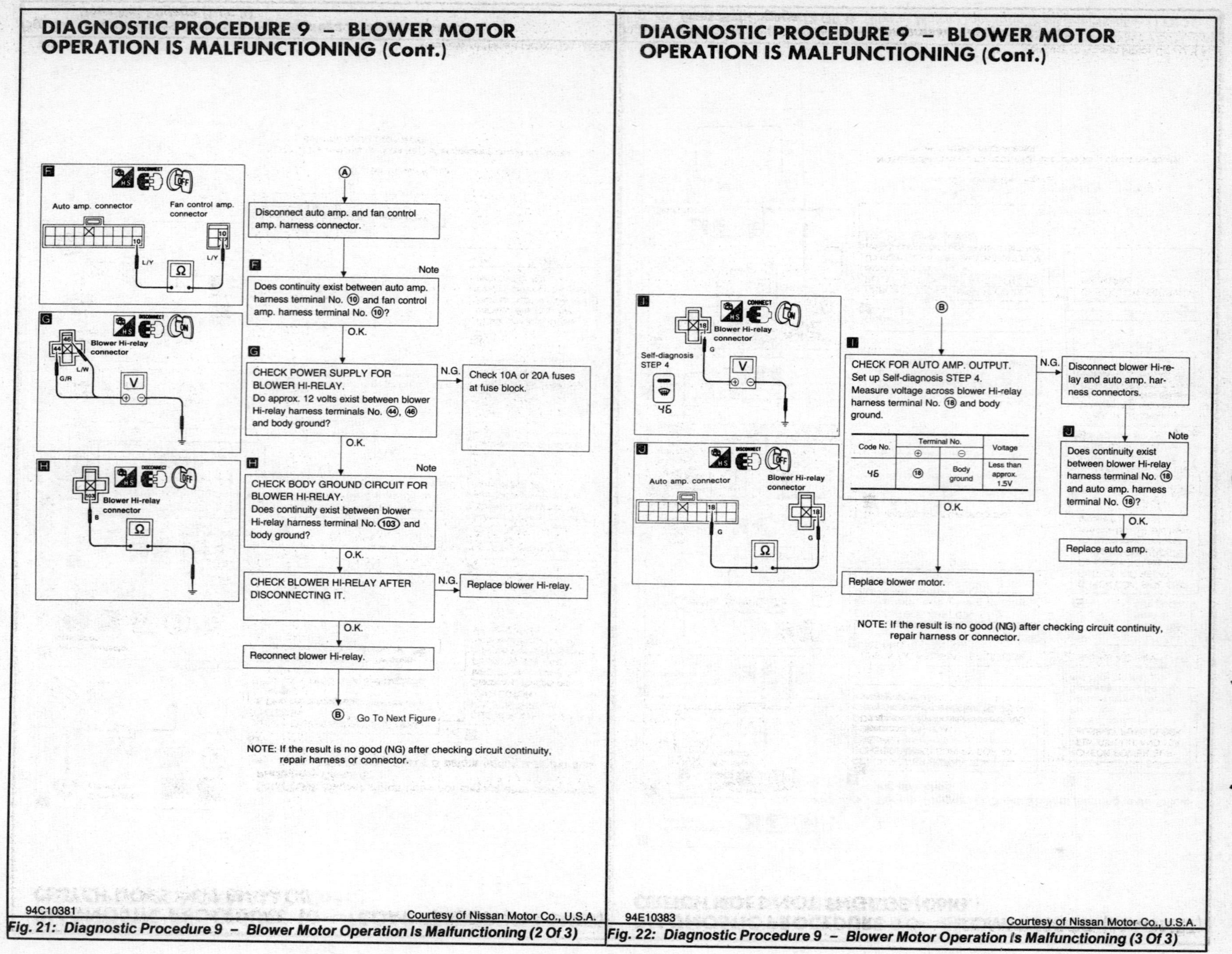
DIAGNOSTIC PROCEDURE 9 – BLOWER MOTOR OPERATION IS MALFUNCTIONING (Cont.)
F
Auto amp. connector
Fan control amp. connector
L/Y
G
Blower Hi-relay connector
L/W
G/R
H
Blower Hi-relay connector
A
Disconnect auto amp. and fan control amp. harness connector.
F
Note
Does continuity exist between auto amp. harness terminal No. (10) and fan control amp. harness terminal No. (10)?
O.K.
G
CHECK POWER SUPPLY FOR BLOWER HI-RELAY.
Do approx. 12 volts exist between blower Hi-relay harness terminals No. (44), (46) and body ground?
N.G.
Check 10A or 20A fuses at fuse block.
O.K.
H
Note
CHECK BODY GROUND CIRCUIT FOR BLOWER HI-RELAY.
Does continuity exist between blower Hi-relay harness terminal No. (103) and body ground?
O.K.
CHECK BLOWER HI-RELAY AFTER DISCONNECTING IT.
N.G.
Replace blower Hi-relay.
O.K.
Reconnect blower Hi-relay.
B Go To Next Figure
NOTE: If the result is no good (NG) after checking circuit continuity, repair harness or connector.
94C10381
Courtesy of Nissan Motor Co., U.S.A.
DIAGNOSTIC PROCEDURE 9 – BLOWER MOTOR OPERATION IS MALFUNCTIONING (Cont.)
I
Blower Hi-relay connector
Self-diagnosis STEP 4
46
J
Auto amp. connector
Blower Hi-relay connector
B
I
CHECK FOR AUTO AMP. OUTPUT.
Set up Self-diagnosis STEP 4.
Measure voltage across blower Hi-relay harness terminal No. (18) and body ground.
Code No. | Terminal No. ⊕ | Terminal No. ⊖ | Voltage
46 | (18) | Body ground | Less than approx. 1.5V
N.G.
Disconnect blower Hi-relay and auto amp. harness connectors.
J
Note
Does continuity exist between blower Hi-relay harness terminal No. (18) and auto amp. harness terminal No. (18)?
O.K.
Replace auto amp.
O.K.
Replace blower motor.
NOTE: If the result is no good (NG) after checking circuit continuity, repair harness or connector.
94E10383
Courtesy of Nissan Motor Co., U.S.A.

Fig. 21: Diagnostic Procedure 9 – Blower Motor Operation Is Malfunctioning (2 Of 3)

Fig. 22: Diagnostic Procedure 9 – Blower Motor Operation Is Malfunctioning (3 Of 3)

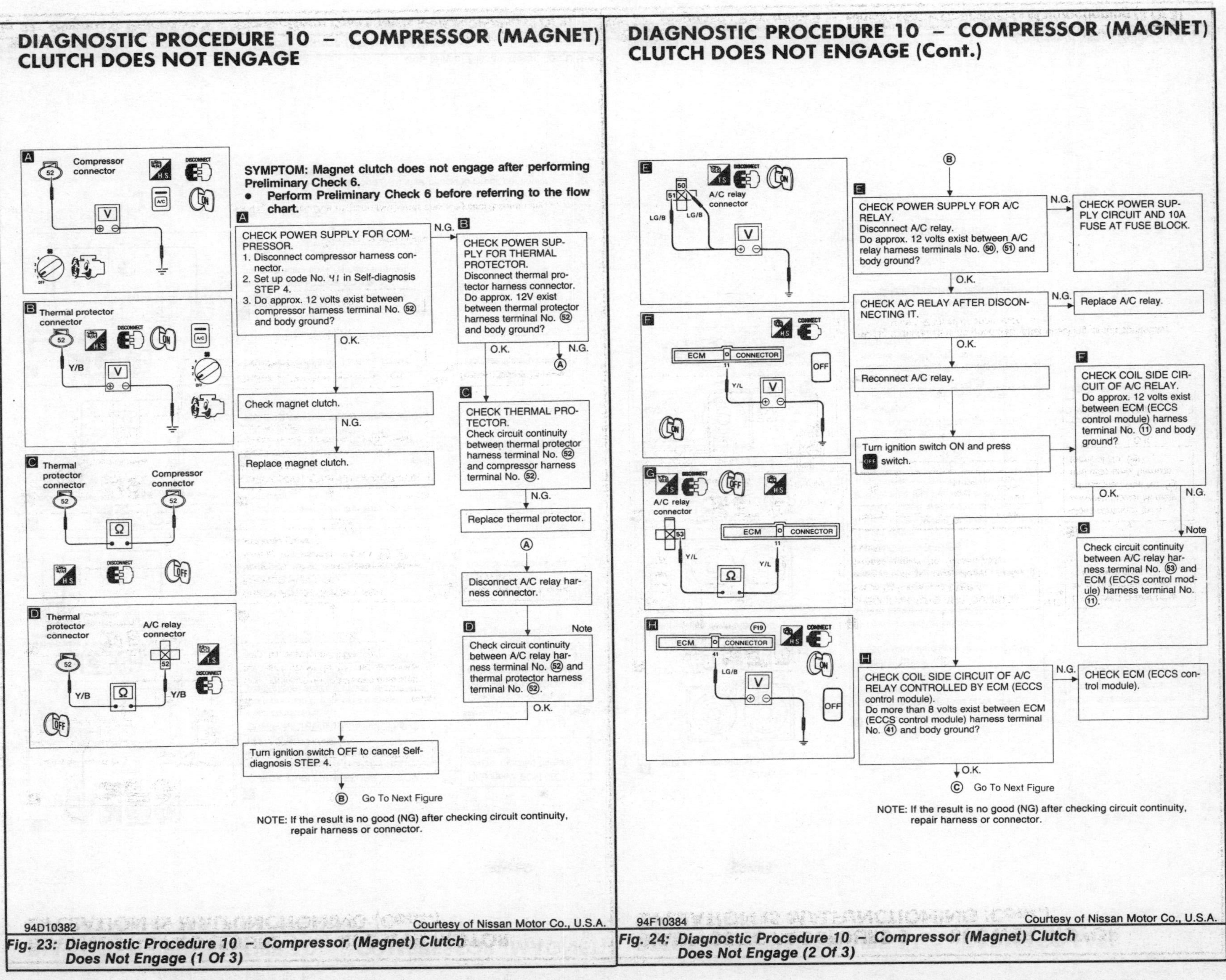
DIAGNOSTIC PROCEDURE 10 – COMPRESSOR (MAGNET) CLUTCH DOES NOT ENGAGE
SYMPTOM: Magnet clutch does not engage after performing Preliminary Check 6.
• Perform Preliminary Check 6 before referring to the flow chart.
A CHECK POWER SUPPLY FOR COMPRESSOR.
1. Disconnect compressor harness connector.
2. Set up code No. 41 in Self-diagnosis STEP 4.
3. Do approx. 12 volts exist between compressor harness terminal No. 52 and body ground?
O.K.
Check magnet clutch.
N.G.
Replace magnet clutch.
N.G.
B CHECK POWER SUPPLY FOR THERMAL PROTECTOR.
Disconnect thermal protector harness connector.
Do approx. 12V exist between thermal protector harness terminal No. 52 and body ground?
O.K.
N.G.
C CHECK THERMAL PROTECTOR.
Check circuit continuity between thermal protector harness terminal No. 52 and compressor harness terminal No. 52.
N.G.
Replace thermal protector.
Disconnect A/C relay harness connector.
Note
D Check circuit continuity between A/C relay harness terminal No. 52 and thermal protector harness terminal No. 52.
O.K.
Turn ignition switch OFF to cancel Self-diagnosis STEP 4.
B Go To Next Figure
NOTE: If the result is no good (NG) after checking circuit continuity, repair harness or connector.
Compressor connector
Thermal protector connector
Y/B
A/C relay connector
94D10382
Courtesy of Nissan Motor Co., U.S.A.
DIAGNOSTIC PROCEDURE 10 – COMPRESSOR (MAGNET) CLUTCH DOES NOT ENGAGE (Cont.)
E CHECK POWER SUPPLY FOR A/C RELAY.
Disconnect A/C relay.
Do approx. 12 volts exist between A/C relay harness terminals No. 50, 51 and body ground?
N.G.
CHECK POWER SUPPLY CIRCUIT AND 10A FUSE AT FUSE BLOCK.
O.K.
CHECK A/C RELAY AFTER DISCONNECTING IT.
N.G.
Replace A/C relay.
O.K.
Reconnect A/C relay.
Turn ignition switch ON and press OFF switch.
F CHECK COIL SIDE CIRCUIT OF A/C RELAY.
Do approx. 12 volts exist between ECM (ECCS control module) harness terminal No. 11 and body ground?
O.K.
N.G.
Note
G Check circuit continuity between A/C relay harness terminal No. 53 and ECM (ECCS control module) harness terminal No. 11.
H CHECK COIL SIDE CIRCUIT OF A/C RELAY CONTROLLED BY ECM (ECCS control module).
Do more than 8 volts exist between ECM (ECCS control module) harness terminal No. 41 and body ground?
N.G.
CHECK ECM (ECCS control module).
O.K.
C Go To Next Figure
NOTE: If the result is no good (NG) after checking circuit continuity, repair harness or connector.
A/C relay connector
LG/B
ECM
CONNECTOR
Y/L
94F10384
Courtesy of Nissan Motor Co., U.S.A.
Fig. 23: Diagnostic Procedure 10 – Compressor (Magnet) Clutch Does Not Engage (1 Of 3)

Fig. 24: Diagnostic Procedure 10 – Compressor (Magnet) Clutch Does Not Engage (2 Of 3)

1993 AUTOMATIC A/C-HEATER SYSTEMS
Trouble Shooting – Altima (Cont.)

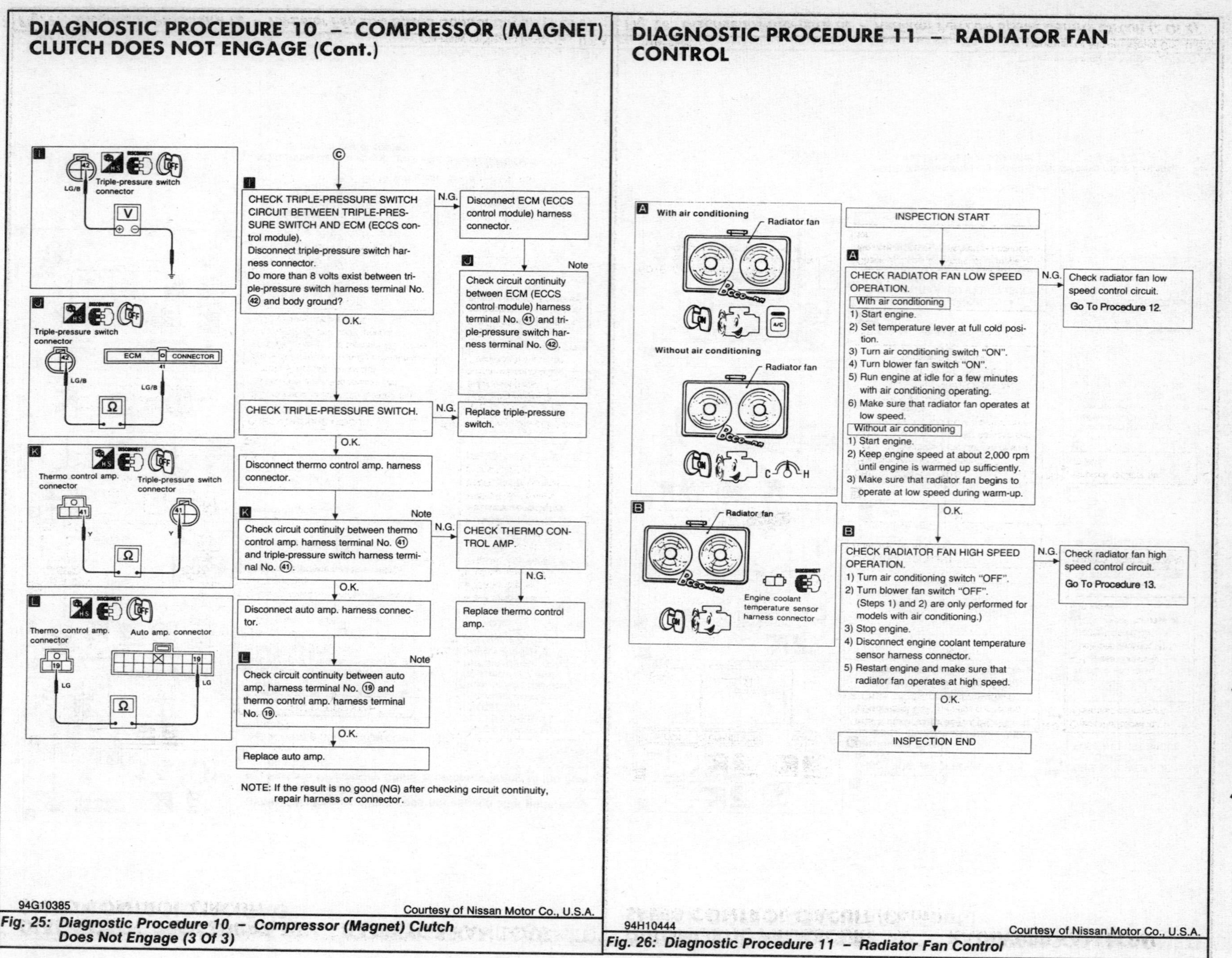
DIAGNOSTIC PROCEDURE 10 – COMPRESSOR (MAGNET) CLUTCH DOES NOT ENGAGE (Cont.)
I
Triple-pressure switch connector
LG/B
V
J
Triple-pressure switch connector
ECM
CONNECTOR
LG/B
Ω
K
Thermo control amp. connector
Triple-pressure switch connector
Y
Ω
L
Thermo control amp. connector
Auto amp. connector
LG
Ω
C
I CHECK TRIPLE-PRESSURE SWITCH CIRCUIT BETWEEN TRIPLE-PRESSURE SWITCH AND ECM (ECCS control module). Disconnect triple-pressure switch harness connector. Do more than 8 volts exist between triple-pressure switch harness terminal No. 42 and body ground?
N.G.
Disconnect ECM (ECCS control module) harness connector.
J Check circuit continuity between ECM (ECCS control module) harness terminal No. 41 and triple-pressure switch harness terminal No. 42.
Note
O.K.
CHECK TRIPLE-PRESSURE SWITCH.
N.G.
Replace triple-pressure switch.
O.K.
Disconnect thermo control amp. harness connector.
K Check circuit continuity between thermo control amp. harness terminal No. 41 and triple-pressure switch harness terminal No. 41.
Note
N.G.
CHECK THERMO CONTROL AMP.
N.G.
Replace thermo control amp.
O.K.
Disconnect auto amp. harness connector.
L Check circuit continuity between auto amp. harness terminal No. 19 and thermo control amp. harness terminal No. 19.
Note
O.K.
Replace auto amp.
NOTE: If the result is no good (NG) after checking circuit continuity, repair harness or connector.
94G10385
Courtesy of Nissan Motor Co., U.S.A.
DIAGNOSTIC PROCEDURE 11 – RADIATOR FAN CONTROL
A With air conditioning
Radiator fan
Without air conditioning
Radiator fan
C H
B
Radiator fan
Engine coolant temperature sensor harness connector
INSPECTION START
A CHECK RADIATOR FAN LOW SPEED OPERATION.
With air conditioning
1) Start engine.
2) Set temperature lever at full cold position.
3) Turn air conditioning switch "ON".
4) Turn blower fan switch "ON".
5) Run engine at idle for a few minutes with air conditioning operating.
6) Make sure that radiator fan operates at low speed.
Without air conditioning
1) Start engine.
2) Keep engine speed at about 2,000 rpm until engine is warmed up sufficiently.
3) Make sure that radiator fan begins to operate at low speed during warm-up.
N.G.
Check radiator fan low speed control circuit.
Go To Procedure 12.
O.K.
B CHECK RADIATOR FAN HIGH SPEED OPERATION.
1) Turn air conditioning switch "OFF".
2) Turn blower fan switch "OFF".
(Steps 1) and 2) are only performed for models with air conditioning.)
3) Stop engine.
4) Disconnect engine coolant temperature sensor harness connector.
5) Restart engine and make sure that radiator fan operates at high speed.
N.G.
Check radiator fan high speed control circuit.
Go To Procedure 13.
O.K.
INSPECTION END
94H10444
Courtesy of Nissan Motor Co., U.S.A.

Fig. 25: Diagnostic Procedure 10 – Compressor (Magnet) Clutch Does Not Engage (3 Of 3)

Fig. 26: Diagnostic Procedure 11 – Radiator Fan Control

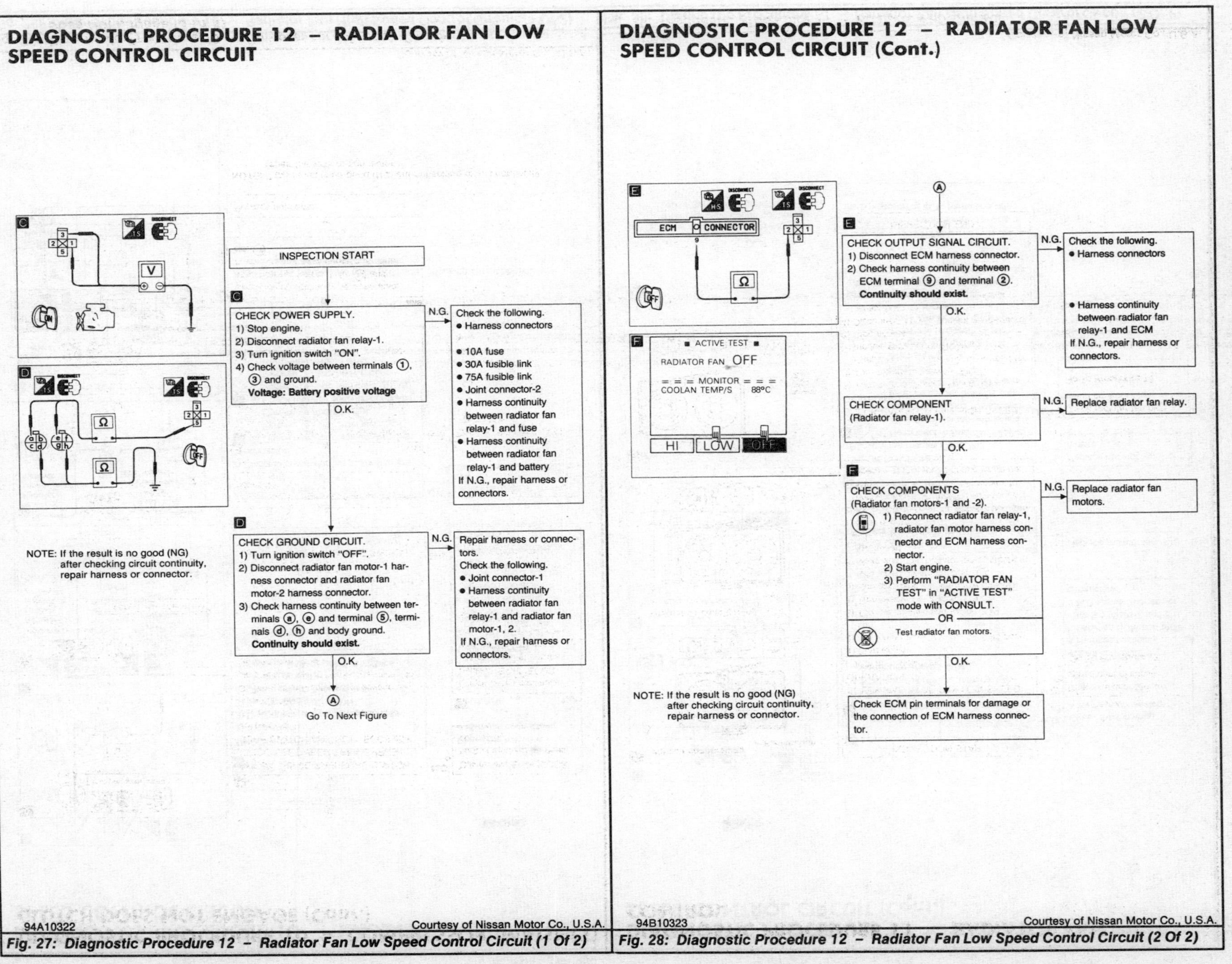
DIAGNOSTIC PROCEDURE 12 – RADIATOR FAN LOW SPEED CONTROL CIRCUIT
INSPECTION START
C
CHECK POWER SUPPLY.
1) Stop engine.
2) Disconnect radiator fan relay-1.
3) Turn ignition switch "ON".
4) Check voltage between terminals ①, ③ and ground.
Voltage: Battery positive voltage
N.G.
Check the following.
• Harness connectors
• 10A fuse
• 30A fusible link
• 75A fusible link
• Joint connector-2
• Harness continuity between radiator fan relay-1 and fuse
• Harness continuity between radiator fan relay-1 and battery
If N.G., repair harness or connectors.
O.K.
D
CHECK GROUND CIRCUIT.
1) Turn ignition switch "OFF".
2) Disconnect radiator fan motor-1 harness connector and radiator fan motor-2 harness connector.
3) Check harness continuity between terminals ⓐ, ⓔ and terminal ⑤, terminals ⓓ, ⓗ and body ground.
Continuity should exist.
N.G.
Repair harness or connectors.
Check the following.
• Joint connector-1
• Harness continuity between radiator fan relay-1 and radiator fan motor-1, 2.
If N.G., repair harness or connectors.
O.K.
Ⓐ
Go To Next Figure
NOTE: If the result is no good (NG) after checking circuit continuity, repair harness or connector.
94A10322
Courtesy of Nissan Motor Co., U.S.A.
DIAGNOSTIC PROCEDURE 12 – RADIATOR FAN LOW SPEED CONTROL CIRCUIT (Cont.)
ECM
CONNECTOR
9
OFF
■ ACTIVE TEST ■
RADIATOR FAN OFF
= = = MONITOR = = =
COOLAN TEMP/S 88°C
HI
LOW
OFF
Ⓐ
E
CHECK OUTPUT SIGNAL CIRCUIT.
1) Disconnect ECM harness connector.
2) Check harness continuity between ECM terminal ⑨ and terminal ②.
Continuity should exist.
N.G.
Check the following.
• Harness connectors
• Harness continuity between radiator fan relay-1 and ECM
If N.G., repair harness or connectors.
O.K.
CHECK COMPONENT
(Radiator fan relay-1).
N.G.
Replace radiator fan relay.
O.K.
F
CHECK COMPONENTS
(Radiator fan motors-1 and -2).
1) Reconnect radiator fan relay-1, radiator fan motor harness connector and ECM harness connector.
2) Start engine.
3) Perform "RADIATOR FAN TEST" in "ACTIVE TEST" mode with CONSULT.
OR
Test radiator fan motors.
N.G.
Replace radiator fan motors.
O.K.
Check ECM pin terminals for damage or the connection of ECM harness connector.
NOTE: If the result is no good (NG) after checking circuit continuity, repair harness or connector.
94B10323
Courtesy of Nissan Motor Co., U.S.A.

Fig. 27: Diagnostic Procedure 12 – Radiator Fan Low Speed Control Circuit (1 Of 2)

Fig. 28: Diagnostic Procedure 12 – Radiator Fan Low Speed Control Circuit (2 Of 2)

1993 AUTOMATIC A/C-HEATER SYSTEMS
Trouble Shooting – Altima (Cont.)

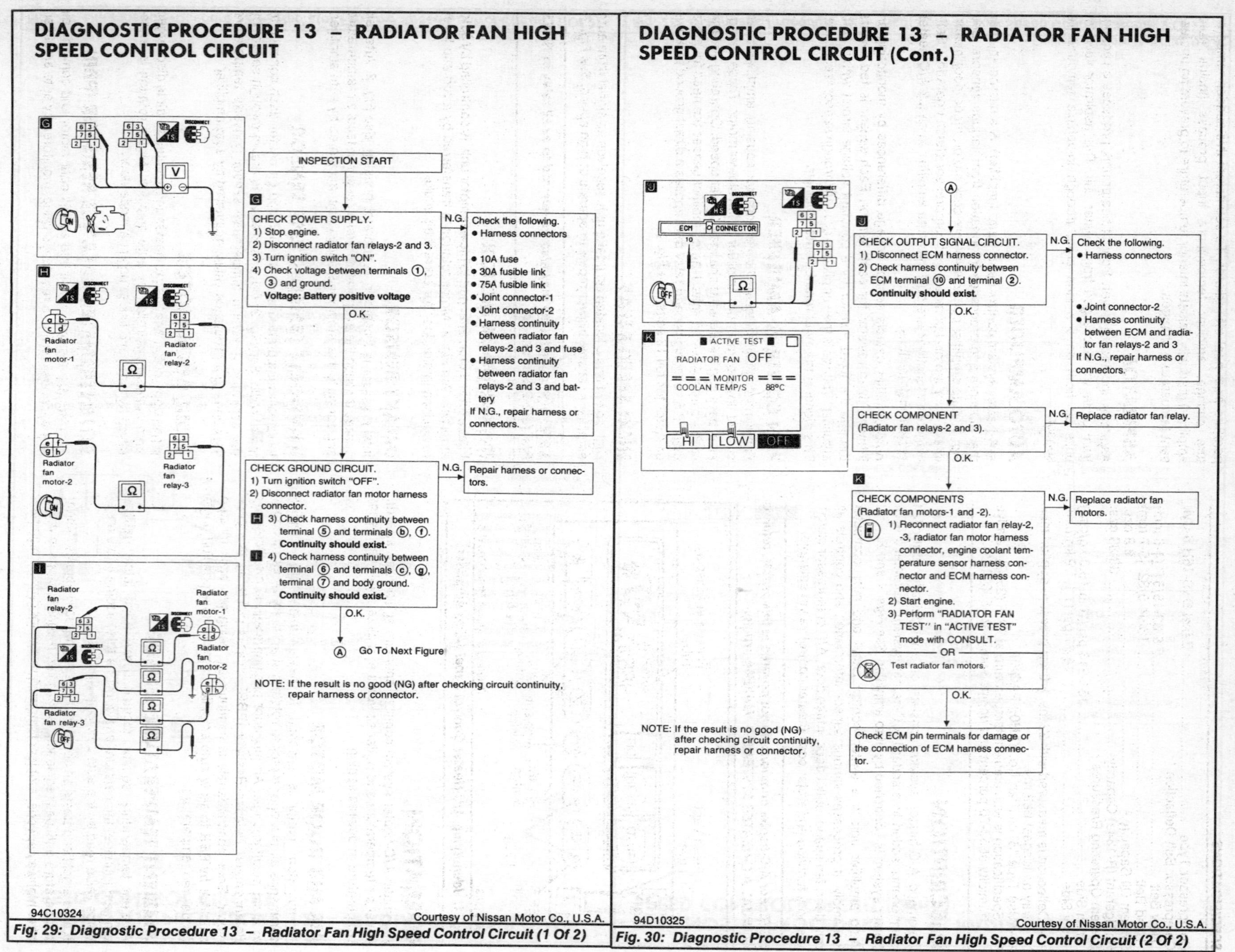
DIAGNOSTIC PROCEDURE 13 – RADIATOR FAN HIGH SPEED CONTROL CIRCUIT
INSPECTION START
G
CHECK POWER SUPPLY.
1) Stop engine.
2) Disconnect radiator fan relays-2 and 3.
3) Turn ignition switch "ON".
4) Check voltage between terminals ①, ③ and ground.
Voltage: Battery positive voltage
N.G.
Check the following.
• Harness connectors
• 10A fuse
• 30A fusible link
• 75A fusible link
• Joint connector-1
• Joint connector-2
• Harness continuity between radiator fan relays-2 and 3 and fuse
• Harness continuity between radiator fan relays-2 and 3 and battery
If N.G., repair harness or connectors.
O.K.
CHECK GROUND CIRCUIT.
1) Turn ignition switch "OFF".
2) Disconnect radiator fan motor harness connector.
H 3) Check harness continuity between terminal ⑤ and terminals ⓑ, ⓕ.
Continuity should exist.
I 4) Check harness continuity between terminal ⑥ and terminals ⓒ, ⓖ, terminal ⑦ and body ground.
Continuity should exist.
N.G.
Repair harness or connectors.
O.K.
Ⓐ Go To Next Figure
NOTE: If the result is no good (NG) after checking circuit continuity, repair harness or connector.
Radiator fan motor-1
Radiator fan relay-2
Radiator fan motor-2
Radiator fan relay-3
94C10324
Courtesy of Nissan Motor Co., U.S.A.
DIAGNOSTIC PROCEDURE 13 – RADIATOR FAN HIGH SPEED CONTROL CIRCUIT (Cont.)
Ⓐ
J
CHECK OUTPUT SIGNAL CIRCUIT.
1) Disconnect ECM harness connector.
2) Check harness continuity between ECM terminal ⑩ and terminal ②.
Continuity should exist.
N.G.
Check the following.
• Harness connectors
• Joint connector-2
• Harness continuity between ECM and radiator fan relays-2 and 3
If N.G., repair harness or connectors.
O.K.
CHECK COMPONENT
(Radiator fan relays-2 and 3).
N.G.
Replace radiator fan relay.
O.K.
K
CHECK COMPONENTS
(Radiator fan motors-1 and -2).
1) Reconnect radiator fan relay-2, -3, radiator fan motor harness connector, engine coolant temperature sensor harness connector and ECM harness connector.
2) Start engine.
3) Perform "RADIATOR FAN TEST" in "ACTIVE TEST" mode with CONSULT.
OR
Test radiator fan motors.
N.G.
Replace radiator fan motors.
O.K.
Check ECM pin terminals for damage or the connection of ECM harness connector.
NOTE: If the result is no good (NG) after checking circuit continuity, repair harness or connector.
ECM
CONNECTOR
10
ACTIVE TEST
RADIATOR FAN OFF
MONITOR
COOLAN TEMP/S 88°C
HI
LOW
OFF
94D10325
Courtesy of Nissan Motor Co., U.S.A.

Fig. 29: Diagnostic Procedure 13 – Radiator Fan High Speed Control Circuit (1 Of 2)

Fig. 30: Diagnostic Procedure 13 – Radiator Fan High Speed Control Circuit (2 Of 2)

1993 AUTOMATIC A/C-HEATER SYSTEMS
Maxima

SPECIFICATIONS

Compressor Type	Zexel DKS-16H 6-Cyl.
Compressor Belt Deflection [1]	
New Belt	5/32-15/64" (4-6 mm)
Used Belt	13/64-9/32" (5-7 mm)
System Oil Capacity [2]	6.8 ozs.
Refrigerant (R-134a) Capacity	30-33 ozs.
System Operating Pressures [3]	
High Side	151-213 psi (10.6-15.0 kg/cm²)
Low Side	16-27 psi (1.1-1.9 kg/cm²)

[1] – Deflection is measured with 22 lbs. (10 kg) pressure applied midway on longest belt run.
[2] – Use Type "S" oil (Part No. KLH00-PAGS0).
[3] – Specification is with ambient temperature at 77°F (25°C), relative humidity at 50-70 percent and engine speed at 1500 RPM.

DESCRIPTION

Automatic A/C-heater system consists of electronically controlled components added to standard A/C-heater system. Automatic A/C-heater system is controlled by auto amplifier. *See Figs. 1 and 2.*

Auto amplifier unit is a switch control panel and microcomputer assembly. It processes various sensor information and controls air mix door, fan speed, outlet door, intake door, A/C compressor clutch, memory function and water cock (heater control valve) solenoid.

NOTE: For A/C-heater components not covered in this article, refer to MANUAL A/C-HEATER SYSTEMS – MAXIMA article.

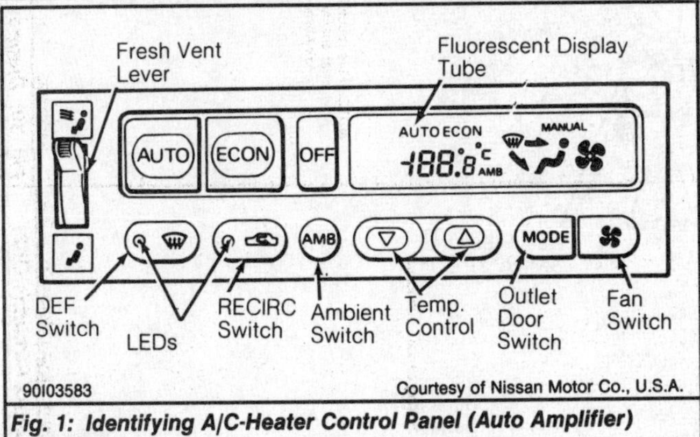
Fresh Vent Lever
Fluorescent Display Tube
AUTO
ECON
OFF
AUTO ECON
MANUAL
AMB
MODE
DEF Switch
LEDs
RECIRC Switch
Ambient Switch
Temp. Control
Outlet Door Switch
Fan Switch
90I03583
Courtesy of Nissan Motor Co., U.S.A.

Fig. 1: Identifying A/C-Heater Control Panel (Auto Amplifier)

OPERATION

Automatic A/C-heater system controls optimum airflow (fan speed), outlet air temperature and outlet air vents to maintain vehicle interior temperature at desired setting.

AIR MIX DOOR MOTOR

Air mix door motor is attached to heater unit. Auto amplifier commands air mix door motor to rotate a shaft to move air mix door to a set position/angle. Air mix door position/angle is monitored by Potentiometer Balance Resistor (PBR), located inside air mix door motor. Door position/angle is continuously being fed back to auto amplifier by PBR to allow auto amplifier to move door position/angle for desired temperature.

AMBIENT TEMPERATURE SENSOR

Ambient temperature sensor, located below hood latch, detects ambient (outside) temperature and converts this reading into a resistance value read by the auto amplifier. *See Fig. 2.*

If auto amplifier detects an abrupt change, it gradually adjusts interior temperature until desired setting is reached. If vehicle stops in traffic after highway speeds, ambient temperature sensor detects high temperature from heat off radiator. To counteract this sudden temperature change, ambient temperature input process (inside auto amplifier) gradually adjusts interior temperature to prevent an unpleasant temperature changes.

ASPIRATOR

Aspirator, located on lower, front of heater unit, produces a vacuum from outlet air discharged from heater unit. This aspirator vacuum pulls air from driver's side area, through in-vehicle temperature sensor.

AUTO AMPLIFIER

A/C-heater system control panel (auto amplifier), is a microcomputer that monitors and processes information from various sensors. *See Fig. 1.* Auto amplifier controls air mix door motor, mode door motor, intake door motor, fan motor and compressor clutch operation. Self-diagnostic functions are built into auto amplifier to check A/C-heater system malfunctions.

Auto amplifier detects sensor voltage differences by monitoring an internal, fixed resistor for each sensor. Each sensor is fed 5-volts through the fixed resistor by a constant voltage circuit within auto amplifier. Voltage is then applied to ground through sensor resistance. This signal is the input read by auto amplifier.

FAN CONTROL AMPLIFIER

Fan control amplifier, located on evaporator housing, amplifies base current flowing from auto amplifier to fan blower motor. These changes in base current are what changes blower speed. Operating voltage range is from 4.5-10.5 volts. If auto amplifier senses the need for more than 10.5 volts, high speed relay then applies a direct ground to blower motor for full 12 volts. *See Fig. 2.*

HIGH SPEED RELAY

High speed relay, located on intake unit, receives its signal from auto amplifier to enable blower motor to operate at high speed. *See Fig. 2.*

NOTE: High speed relay may also be referred to as HI relay in TROUBLE SHOOTING charts.

INTAKE DOOR MOTOR

Intake door motor, attached to blower motor unit, is controlled by auto amplifier. *See Fig. 2.* Motor rotation is transferred by a rod and lever to position intake door for correct air intake.

INTAKE SENSOR

Intake sensor is located in evaporator housing. *See Fig. 2.* After air passes through the evaporator, intake sensor detects air temperature and converts this into a resistance value, monitored by auto amplifier.

IN-VEHICLE TEMPERATURE SENSOR

In-vehicle temperature sensor is located on center dash console, to left of radio. *See Fig. 2.* Driver's area air is drawn through sensor by the aspirator. In-vehicle temperature sensor converts temperature variations to a resistance value, monitored by auto amplifier.

MODE DOOR MOTOR

Mode door motor, attached to heater unit, rotates so air is discharged from outlet(s) controlled by auto amplifier. Motor rotation is transferred by a rod and link to position mode door.

POTENTIOMETER BALANCE RESISTOR (PBR)

This variable resistor is built into air mix door motor and converts air mix door position into a resistance value, monitored by auto amplifier.

1993 AUTOMATIC A/C-HEATER SYSTEMS
Maxima (Cont.)

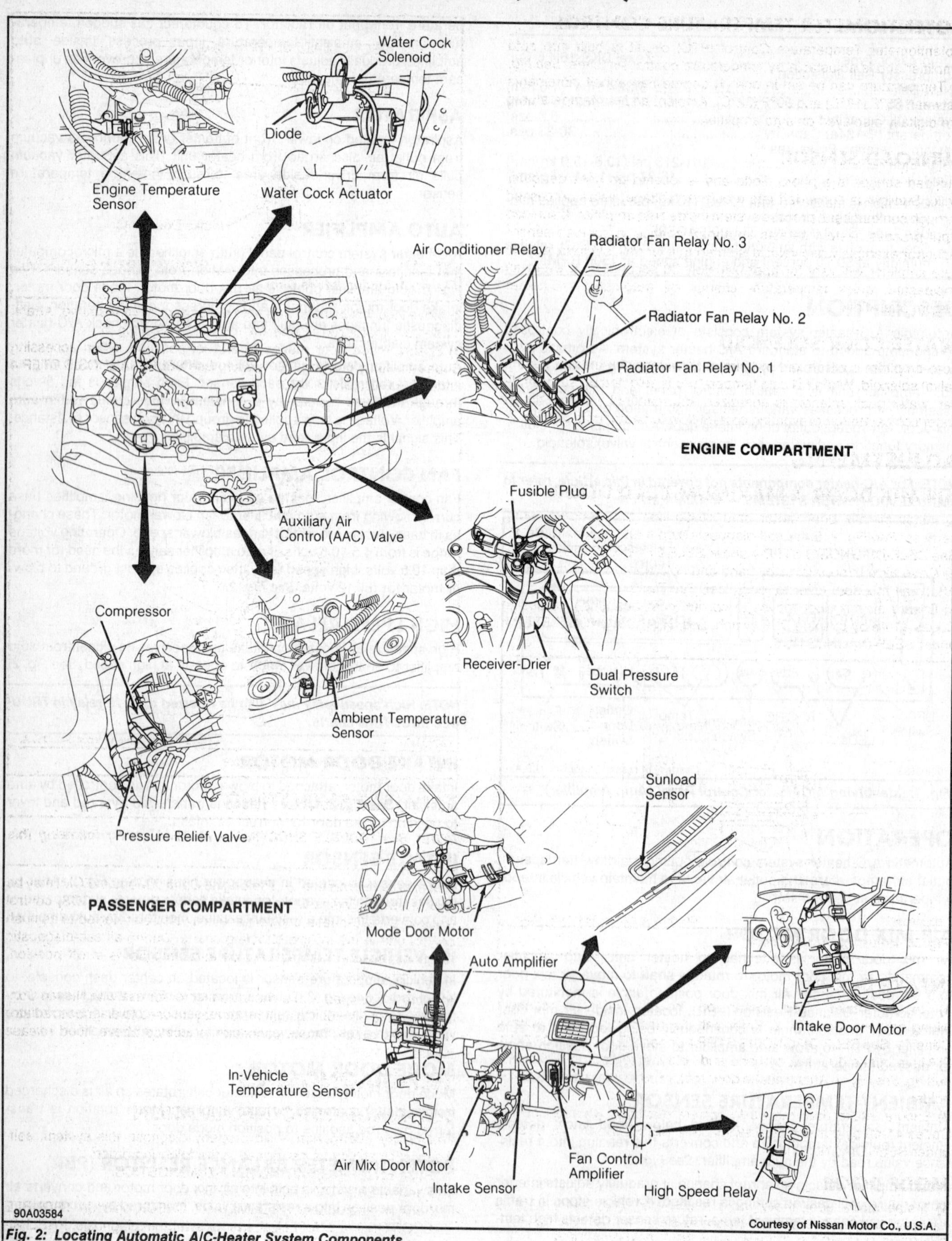
Water Cock Solenoid
Diode
Engine Temperature Sensor
Water Cock Actuator
Air Conditioner Relay
Radiator Fan Relay No. 3
Radiator Fan Relay No. 2
Radiator Fan Relay No. 1
ENGINE COMPARTMENT
Fusible Plug
Auxiliary Air Control (AAC) Valve
Compressor
Receiver-Drier
Dual Pressure Switch
Ambient Temperature Sensor
Sunload Sensor
Pressure Relief Valve
PASSENGER COMPARTMENT
Mode Door Motor
Auto Amplifier
Intake Door Motor
In-Vehicle Temperature Sensor
Air Mix Door Motor
Fan Control Amplifier
Intake Sensor
High Speed Relay
90A03584

Courtesy of Nissan Motor Co., U.S.A.

Fig. 2: Locating Automatic A/C-Heater System Components

POTENTIOMETER TEMPERATURE CONTROL

Potentiometer Temperature Control (PTC) circuit is built into auto amplifier and is adjustable by temperature control switches. *See Fig. 1.* Temperature can be set in one (1) degree Fahrenheit increments between 65°F (18°C) and 90°F (32°C). Ambient and set temperatures are digitally displayed on auto amplifier.

SUNLOAD SENSOR

Sunload sensor is a photo diode and is located on right defroster grille. Sunlight is converted into a current (voltage) value processed through sunload input process system inside auto amplifier. If sunload input process system detects an abrupt change in sunload sensor input (for example when vehicle is entering a tunnel), sunload input to auto amplifier will vary for approximately 38 seconds to prevent an unpleasant, quick temperature change by automatic A/C-heater system operation.

WATER COCK SOLENOID

Auto amplifier controls ground circuit to water cock (heater control valve) solenoid. When full cold temperature is selected on auto amplifier, water cock solenoid is energized and manifold vacuum closes water cock actuator, preventing coolant flow to heater unit. *See Fig. 2.*

ADJUSTMENTS

AIR MIX DOOR & MAXIMUM COLD DOOR

1) Install air mix door motor onto heater unit and connect wiring harness. *See Fig. 2.* Enter self-diagnosis step 4 and access Code 46. See SELF-DIAGNOSIS STEP 4 under SELF-DIAGNOSTICS.
2) Move air mix door lever by hand and hold door in full hot setting. Attach air mix door lever to rod holder. *See Fig. 3.*
3) Ensure air mix door moves to correct positions when accessing Codes 41-46 by pushing DEF switch. See SELF-DIAGNOSIS STEP 4 under SELF-DIAGNOSTICS.

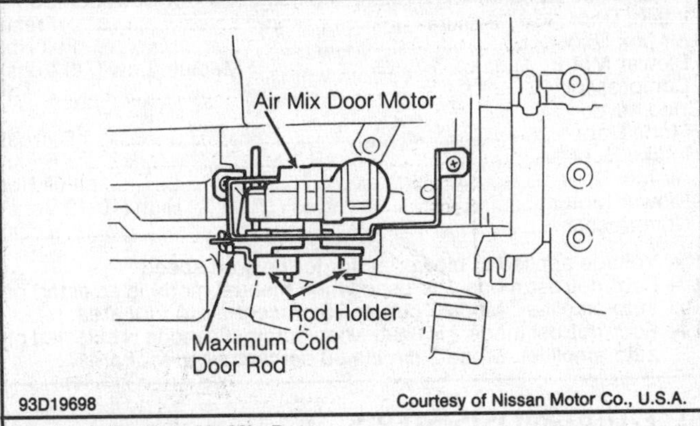
Air Mix Door Motor
Rod Holder
Maximum Cold
Door Rod
93D19698
Courtesy of Nissan Motor Co., U.S.A.
Fig. 3: Adjusting Air Mix Door

INTAKE DOOR

1) Install intake door motor on intake unit and connect wiring harness. *See Fig. 2.* Enter self-diagnosis step 4 and access Code 41. See SELF-DIAGNOSIS STEP 4 under SELF-DIAGNOSTICS.
2) Move intake door link by hand and hold intake door in recirculate setting. *See Fig. 4.* Attach intake door motor rod to intake door link rod holder.
3) Ensure intake door moves to correct positions when accessing Codes 41-46 by pushing DEF switch. See SELF-DIAGNOSIS STEP 4 under SELF-DIAGNOSTICS.

MODE DOOR

1) Install mode door motor onto heater unit and connect wiring harness. *See Fig. 2.* Enter self-diagnosis step 4 and access Code 41. See SELF-DIAGNOSIS STEP 4 under SELF-DIAGNOSTICS.

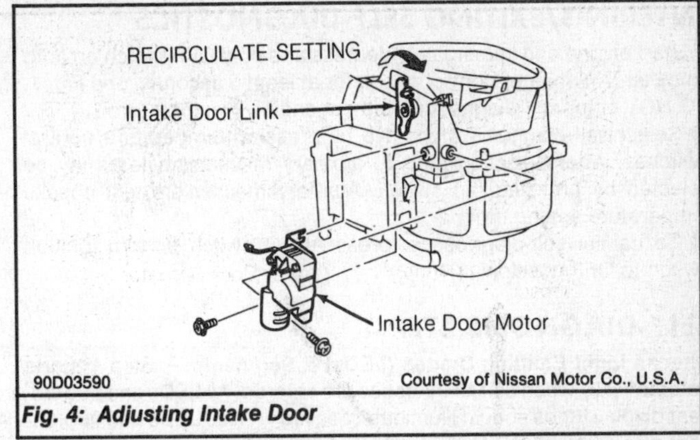
RECIRCULATE SETTING
Intake Door Link
Intake Door Motor
90D03590
Courtesy of Nissan Motor Co., U.S.A.
Fig. 4: Adjusting Intake Door

2) Move side link by hand and hold mode door in vent setting. Attach mode door motor rod to side link rod holder. *See Fig. 5.*
3) Ensure mode door moves to correct positions when accessing Codes 41-46 by pushing DEF switch. See SELF-DIAGNOSIS STEP 4 under SELF-DIAGNOSTICS.

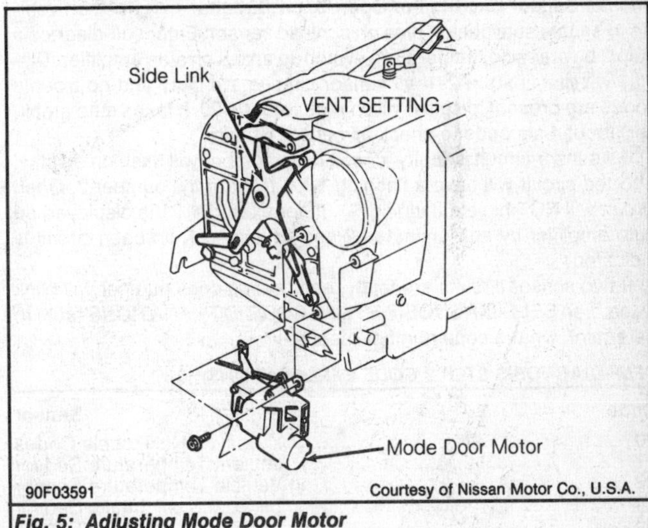
Side Link
VENT SETTING
Mode Door Motor
90F03591
Courtesy of Nissan Motor Co., U.S.A.
Fig. 5: Adjusting Mode Door Motor

TROUBLE SHOOTING

NOTE: See TROUBLE SHOOTING – MAXIMA charts following this article.

Preliminary Information – The Engine Control Module (ECM) may be referred to as Engine Concentrated Control System (ECCS) control unit and the A/C-heater control panel may also be referred to as push control unit in the trouble shooting charts. During all self-diagnostic functions, ensure fresh air vent on auto amplifier is in off position, unless otherwise indicated.

Maxima is equipped with a check connector for use with Nissan Consult Tester (J-38465). Consult tester may be used to diagnose radiator fan control circuit. Check connector is located above hood release handle.

SELF-DIAGNOSTICS

SELF-DIAGNOSTIC INFORMATION

Preliminary Information – To properly diagnose this system, self-diagnostics should be performed in the following order:

- Read ENTERING/EXITING SELF-DIAGNOSTICS.
- Perform SELF-DIAGNOSIS STEPS 1-5.
- Perform appropriate PRELIMINARY CHECK chart in TROUBLE SHOOTING – MAXIMA charts for symptom diagnosis. PRELIMINARY CHECK charts refers technician to proper DIAGNOSTIC PROCEDURE charts.

1993 AUTOMATIC A/C-HEATER SYSTEMS
Maxima (Cont.)

ENTERING/EXITING SELF-DIAGNOSTICS

1) Start engine and immediately depress and hold OFF switch on auto amplifier (A/C-heater control panel) for at least 5 seconds. *See Fig. 1.* DO NOT enter self-diagnostics without engine running.
2) Select self-diagnosis steps 1-5 by pressing temperature control switches. After selecting step 5, auxiliary mechanism test may be selected by pressing fan switch. Auxiliary mechanism test checks temperature setting trimmer.
3) To cancel self-diagnostics, press AUTO switch or turn ignition switch to OFF position.

SELF-DIAGNOSIS STEP 1

Checks Light Emitting Diodes (LEDs) & Segments – Step 1 starts automatically when self-diagnostics are entered. All LEDs and fluorescent display tubes should illuminate. *See Fig. 1.* If all LEDs and fluorescent display tubes DO NOT illuminate, repair or replace as necessary. If LEDs and fluorescent display tubes test okay, replace auto amplifier.

SELF-DIAGNOSIS STEP 2

Checks Sensor Circuits For Open/Short Circuits – **1)** Position vehicle to enable sunlight to shine on sunload sensor. Enter self-diagnosis step 2 by pressing temperature switch up arrow on auto amplifier. Display will illuminate a 2. If all sensor circuits are okay and no trouble codes are present, display will change to Code 20. It takes auto amplifier about 4 seconds to check all sensor circuits.
2) If a sensor circuit is faulty, circuit code number will flash on display. Shorted circuit will have a flashing "–" in front of the number 2. Open circuit will NOT have a flashing "–". If, for example, 21 is displayed on auto amplifier by an illuminated 2 and a flashing 1, an open circuit is indicated.
3) If two sensor circuits are faulty, each circuit code number will blink twice. See SELF-DIAGNOSIS STEP 2 CODE EXPLANATIONS table to determine what a code number means.

SELF-DIAGNOSIS STEP 2 CODE EXPLANATIONS

Code	Sensor
20	No Trouble Codes
21	Ambient Temperature Sensor
22	In-Vehicle Temperature Sensor
24	Intake Sensor
25	Sunload Sensor
26	Potentiometer Balance Resistor (PBR)

SELF-DIAGNOSIS STEP 3

Checks Mode Door Position – **1)** To enter self-diagnosis step 3, press temperature switch up arrow. *See Fig. 1.* Display will illuminate a 3. If all doors are operational, display will change to 30. It takes about 16 seconds to check all mode doors.
2) If a door is faulty, code number will flash. If two doors are faulty, each code number will blink twice. To determine what a code number means, see SELF-DIAGNOSIS STEP 3 CODE EXPLANATIONS table.

NOTE: If any mode door motor position switch is malfunctioning, mode door motor will also malfunction.

SELF-DIAGNOSIS STEP 3 CODE EXPLANATIONS

Code	Door
30	No Trouble Codes
31	Vent
32	Bi-Level (B/L)
33	Bi-Level (B/L)
34 [1]	Foot/Defrost Mode 1 (F/D 1)
35 [2]	Foot/Defrost Mode 2 (F/D 2)
36	Defrost (DEF)

[1] – Foot/defrost mode 1 is used when manual mode is selected on auto amplifier. Mode 1 directs 75 percent air to foot area.
[2] – Foot/defrost mode 2 is used when automatic mode is selected on auto amplifier. Mode 2 directs 50 percent air to foot area.

SELF-DIAGNOSIS STEP 4

Checks Operation Of Each Actuator – **1)** Ensure fresh air lever on auto amplifier is off during tests. To enter self-diagnosis step 4, press temperature switch up arrow. *See Fig. 1.* Display will illuminate Code 41. Each time DEF switch is pressed, display will advance one code number. After Code 46 is reached, numbers go back to Code 41.
2) As code numbers advance, auto amplifier commands will change air intake and outlet routes. Ensure doors are switching properly by listening for door operation and/or feeling for air flow from proper outlet(s). See SELF-DIAGNOSIS STEP 4 CODE EXPLANATIONS table to determine proper door positions.

SELF-DIAGNOSIS STEP 4 CODE EXPLANATIONS

Application	Door Position
Code 41	
Mode Door	Vent
Intake Door	Recirculate
Air Mix Door	Full Cold
Blower Motor	[1] Low (4-5 Volts)
Compressor	On
Code 42	
Mode Door	Bi-Level
Intake Door	Recirculate
Air Mix Door	Full Cold
Blower Motor	[1] Medium High (9-11 Volts)
Compressor	On
Code 43	
Mode Door	Bi-Level
Intake Door	20% Fresh
Air Mix Door	Full Hot
Blower Motor	[1] Medium Low (7-9 Volts)
Compressor	On
Code 44	
Mode Door	[2] Foot/Defrost Mode 1
Intake Door	Fresh
Air Mix Door	Full Hot
Blower Motor	[1] Medium Low (7-9 Volts)
Compressor	Off
Code 45	
Mode Door	[3] Foot/Defrost Mode 2
Intake Door	Fresh
Air Mix Door	Full Hot
Blower Motor	[1] Medium Low (7-9 Volts)
Compressor	Off
Code 46	
Mode Door	Defrost
Intake Door	Fresh
Air Mix Door	Full Hot
Blower Motor	[1] High (10-12 Volts)
Compressor	On

[1] – Voltage applied to blower motor for desired speed.
[2] – Foot/defrost mode 1 is used when manual mode is selected on auto amplifier. Mode 1 directs 75 percent air to foot area.
[3] – Foot/defrost mode 2 is used when automatic mode is selected on auto amplifier. Mode 2 directs 50 percent air to foot area.

SELF-DIAGNOSIS STEP 5

Checks Temperature Detected By Sensors – **1)** To enter self-diagnosis step 5, press temperature switch up arrow. *See Fig. 1.* Display will illuminate a 5. When DEF switch is pressed once, display will show temperature detected by ambient temperature sensor.
2) Press DEF switch again, display will show temperature detected by in-vehicle sensor. Press DEF switch again (3rd time), display will show temperature detected by intake sensor.
3) Press DEF switch again (4th time), display will return to 5. If temperature shown on display is greatly different from actual temperature, inspect sensor circuit. If sensor circuit is okay, check sensor. See appropriate sensor under TESTING.

AUXILIARY MECHANISM SETTING

Temperature Setting Trimmer – **1)** Temperature setting trimmer compensates for small differences between temperature setting on display and actual temperature within a range of 0-12°F (0-6°C).

1993 AUTOMATIC A/C-HEATER SYSTEMS
Maxima (Cont.)

2) With system in SELF-DIAGNOSIS STEP 5, press fan switch. System is now in auxiliary mode to set trimmer. Each time temperature switch up or down arrow is pressed, temperature display changes in one (1) degree Fahrenheit increments.

NOTE:* *If battery is disconnected, temperature trimmer setting goes to 0° on both Fahrenheit and Celsius scale and will have to be reset.

TESTING

A/C SYSTEM PERFORMANCE

1) Park vehicle out of direct sunlight. Close all doors and open engine hood and windows. Connect A/C pressure gauges to the high and low side pressure ports of system. Disconnect ambient temperature sensor connector.

2) Ambient temperature sensor is located near hood latch. Connect a jumper wire between sensor connector terminals. Determine relative humidity and ambient air temperature.

3) Set temperature control to maximum cold, mode control to face vent, and recirculation switch to recirculated air position. Turn blower fan switch to highest position. Start and run engine at 1500 RPM.

4) After running A/C for 10 minutes, check high and low side system pressures. Refer to A/C SYSTEM PERFORMANCE TEST table to determine if system is operating within range.

A/C SYSTEM PERFORMANCE TEST

Ambient Air Temp. °F (°C)	High Pressure [1] psi (kg/cm²)	Low Pressure [1] psi (kg/cm²)
68 (20)	108-164 (7.6-11.5)	10.7-21.3 (.75-1.5)
77 (25)	151-213 (10.6-15.0)	16.0-27.0 (1.1-1.9)
86 (30)	193-262 (13.6-18.4)	20.6-33.4 (1.5-2.3)
95 (35)	236-310 (16.6-21.8)	25.6-39.1 (1.8-2.7)
104 (40)	279-358 (19.6-25.2)	30.0-46.0 (2.1-3.2)

[1] – Specification is with relative humidity at 50-70 percent.

A/C RELAY & RADIATOR FAN RELAY NO. 1

Remove suspected relay from vehicle. *See Fig. 2.* Apply 12 volts to coil side of relay. *See Fig. 6.* Ensure continuity exists between 2 remaining terminals of relay. If continuity does not exist, replace relay.

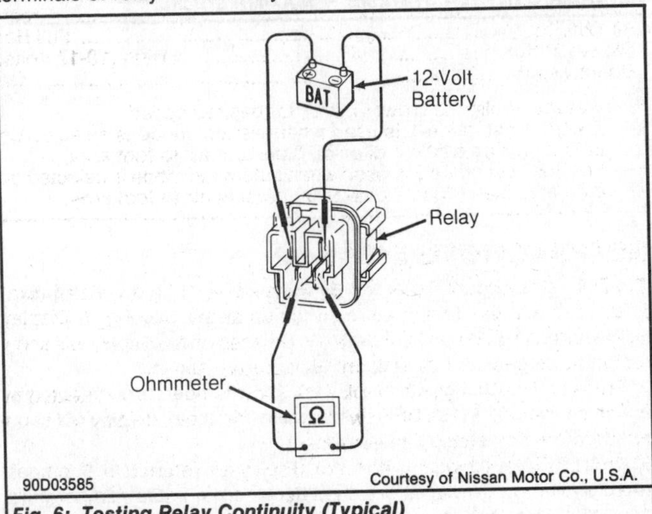
BAT
12-Volt
Battery
Relay
Ohmmeter
Ω
90D03585
Courtesy of Nissan Motor Co., U.S.A.

Fig. 6: Testing Relay Continuity (Typical)

AUTO AMPLIFIER

Power Supply Check – 1) Ensure ignition is off. Disconnect auto amplifier connector. Turn ignition on. Connect a voltmeter between ground and auto amplifier harness terminals No. 1 (Brown/White wire), No. 2 (White/Red wire) and No 3 (Brown/White wire), one at a time. Battery voltage should be present at each terminal.

2) If battery voltage is not present, repair wiring as necessary. If malfunction still exists after following proper trouble shooting procedures and voltage readings are okay, replace auto amplifier.

Ground Circuit Check – Ensure ignition is off. Disconnect auto amplifier connector. Connect an ohmmeter between auto amplifier connector harness terminal No. 8 (Black wire) and ground. Continuity should exist. If continuity does not exist, repair ground circuit as necessary. If malfunction still exists and continuity is okay, replace auto amplifier.

AMBIENT TEMPERATURE SENSOR

Turn ignition off. Disconnect underhood ambient temperature sensor connector, in front of condenser, near hood latch. *See Fig. 2.* Using an ohmmeter, measure resistance between sensor terminals. See AMBIENT TEMPERATURE, IN-VEHICLE TEMPERATURE & INTAKE SENSORS SPECIFICATIONS table.

IN-VEHICLE TEMPERATURE SENSOR

Turn ignition off. Disconnect in-vehicle temperature sensor connector. *See Fig. 2.* Using an ohmmeter, measure resistance between sensor terminals. See AMBIENT TEMPERATURE, IN-VEHICLE TEMPERATURE & INTAKE SENSORS SPECIFICATIONS table.

INTAKE SENSOR

Turn ignition off. Disconnect underdash intake sensor connector. *See Fig. 2.* Using an ohmmeter, measure resistance between harness terminals. See AMBIENT TEMPERATURE, IN-VEHICLE TEMPERATURE & INTAKE SENSORS SPECIFICATIONS table.

AMBIENT TEMPERATURE, IN-VEHICLE TEMPERATURE & INTAKE SENSORS SPECIFICATIONS

Temperature °F (°C)	Resistance (Ohms)
–31 (–35)	38,350
–22 (–30)	28,620
–13 (–25)	21,610
–4 (–20)	16,500
5 (–15)	12,730
14 (–10)	9930
23 (–5)	7800
32 (0)	6190
41 (5)	4950
50 (10)	3990
59 (15)	3240
68 (20)	2650
77 (25)	2190
86 (30)	1810
95 (35)	1510
104 (40)	1270
113 (45)	1070
122 (50)	910
131 (55)	770
140 (60)	660
149 (65)	570

DUAL-PRESSURE SWITCH

Connect A/C manifold gauge set. Start engine and turn A/C system on. Observe high side system pressure. Disconnect pressure switch connector. Dual-pressure switch is located on top of receiver-drier. Using an ohmmeter, check continuity between dual-pressure switch terminals as indicated in DUAL-PRESSURE SWITCH SPECIFICATIONS table. Replace switch if it does not perform as indicated.

DUAL-PRESSURE SWITCH SPECIFICATIONS

Pressure psi (kg/cm²)	System Operation	Continuity
Low Pressure		
Decreasing To 23-28 (1.6-2.0)	Off	No
Increasing To 23-31 (1.6-2.2)	On	Yes
High Pressure		
Increasing To 356-412 (25-29)	Off	No
Decreasing To 57-114 (4.0-8.0)	On	Yes

1993 AUTOMATIC A/C-HEATER SYSTEMS
Maxima (Cont.)

POTENTIOMETER BALANCE RESISTOR (PBR)

1) Turn ignition on. Backprobe air mix door motor connector with voltmeter and measure voltage between terminals No. 16 and 27. *See Fig. 7*. Set temperature control switch to coldest setting. With air mix door in full cold position, voltmeter should indicate zero volts.
2) Slowly adjust temperature control switch to hottest setting. As air mix door motor moves from full cold to full hot position, voltage should slowly rise to 5 volts. If voltage is not as described, replace air mix door motor. PBR is located inside air mix door motor.

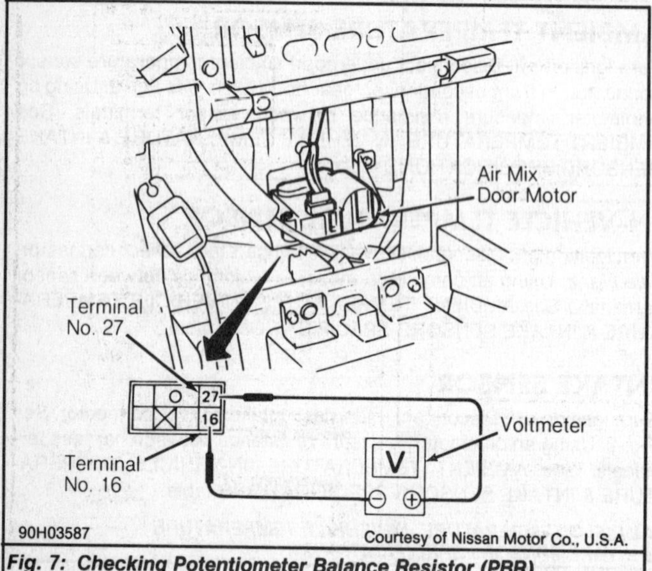
Air Mix
Door Motor
Terminal
No. 27
27
16
Voltmeter
V
Terminal
No. 16
90H03587
Courtesy of Nissan Motor Co., U.S.A.

Fig. 7: Checking Potentiometer Balance Resistor (PBR)

SUNLOAD SENSOR

1) Turn ignition off. Using voltmeter, measure output voltage between auto amplifier connector terminals No. 16 and 35. *See Fig. 8*. To vary voltage reading for testing, apply direct sunlight to sensor, then slowly cover sensor.
2) To measure sunload sensor input to auto amplifier, disconnect sensor from vehicle harness above intake unit. Connect an ammeter between sensor connector terminals. To vary current reading, apply direct sunlight to sensor, then slowly cover sensor. See SUNLOAD SENSOR SPECIFICATIONS table.

SUNLOAD SENSOR SPECIFICATIONS

Input Current (Milliamps)	Output Voltage
0	5.0
.1	4.1
.2	3.1
.3	2.2
.4	1.3
.5	.4

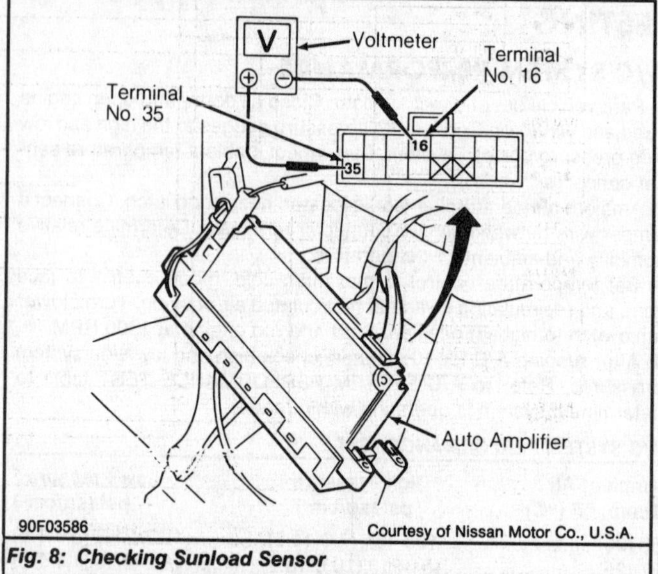
V
Voltmeter
Terminal
No. 16
Terminal
No. 35
16
35
Auto Amplifier
90F03586
Courtesy of Nissan Motor Co., U.S.A.

Fig. 8: Checking Sunload Sensor

WATER COCK SOLENOID

Disconnect water cock solenoid electrical connector. *See Fig. 2*. Using an ohmmeter, check for continuity between solenoid terminals. If continuity is not present, replace solenoid.

REMOVAL & INSTALLATION

NOTE: For removal of basic A/C-heater system components, see MANUAL A/C-HEATER SYSTEMS - MAXIMA article.

1993 AUTOMATIC A/C-HEATER SYSTEMS
Maxima (Cont.)

WIRING DIAGRAM

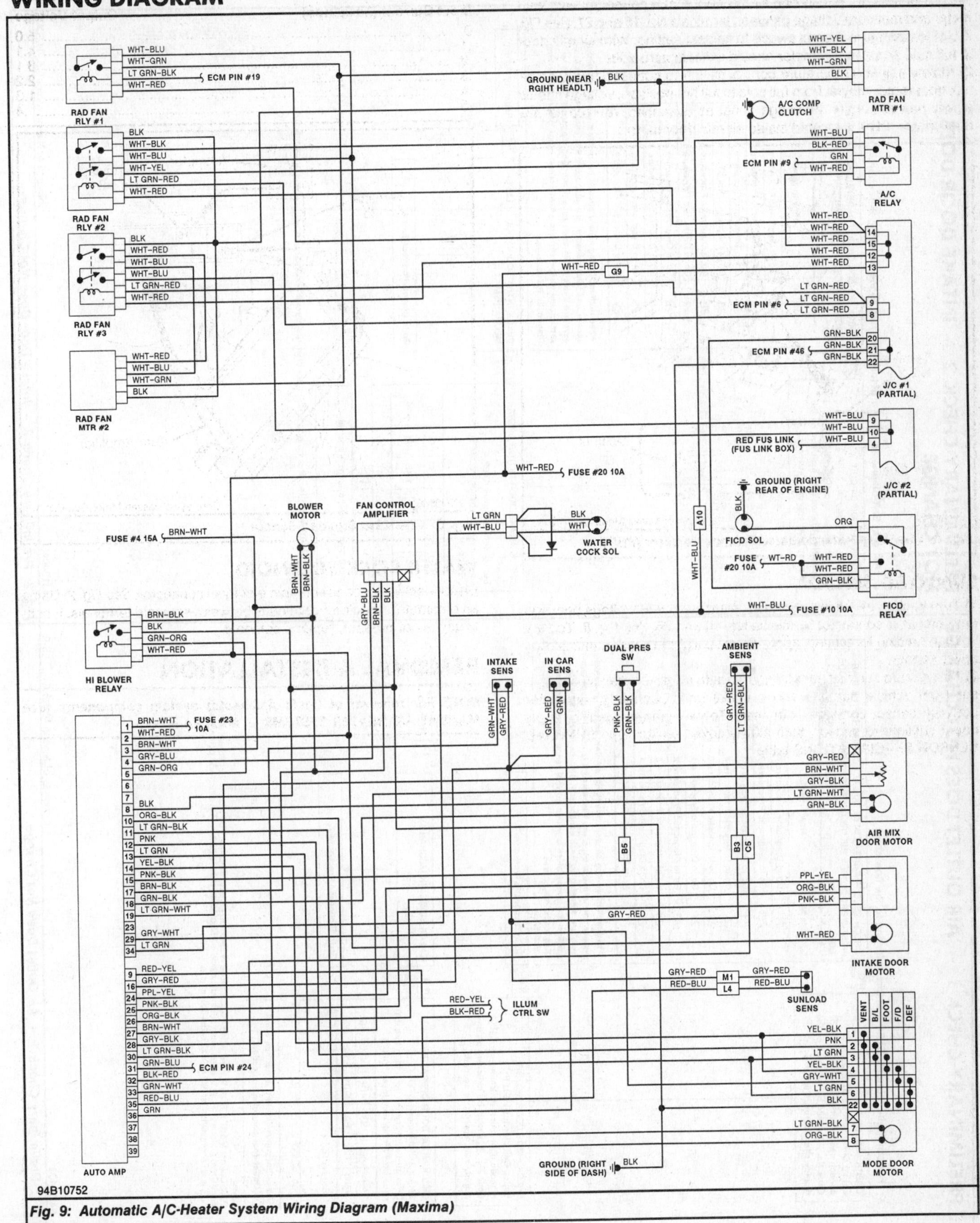

94B10752

Fig. 9: Automatic A/C-Heater System Wiring Diagram (Maxima)

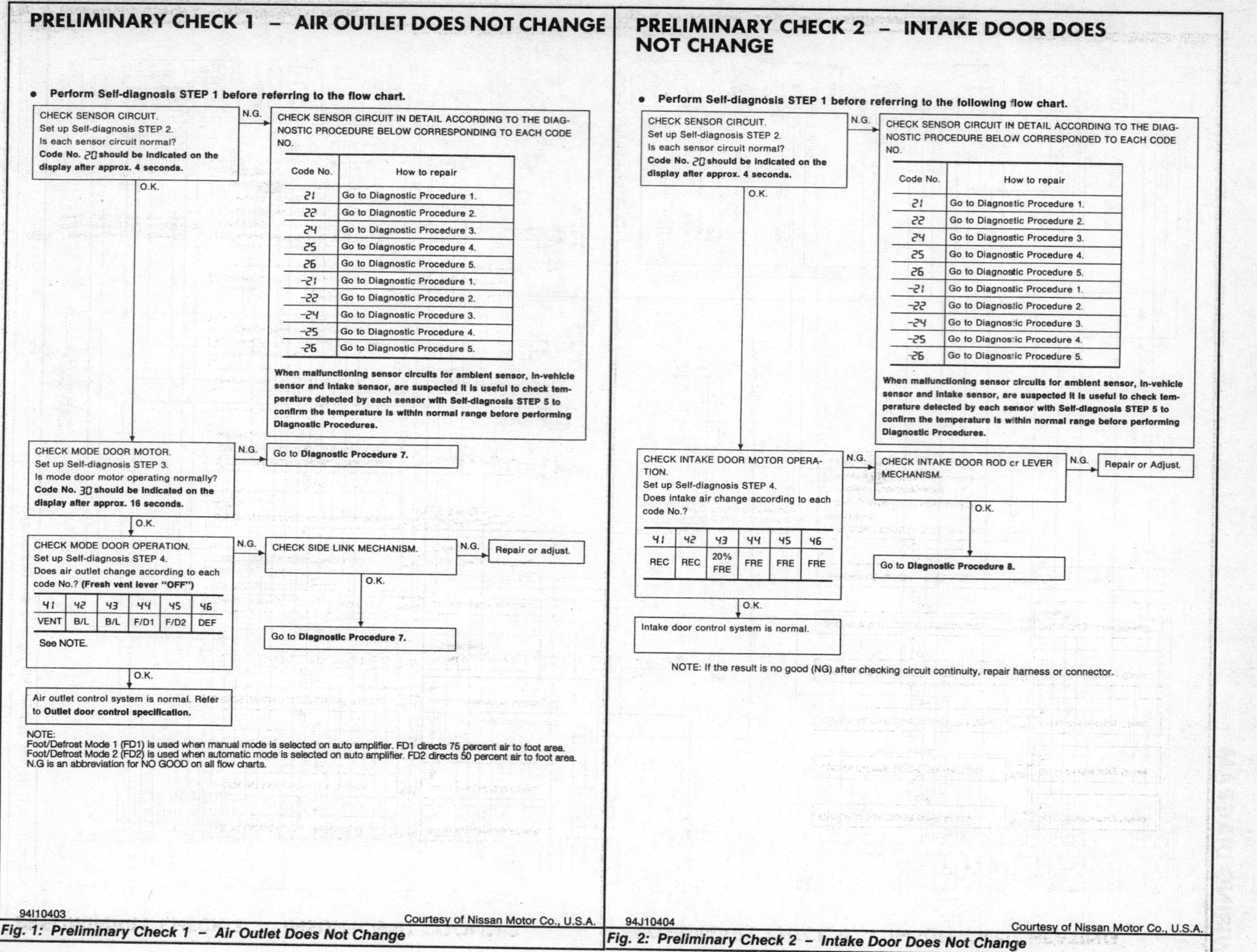
PRELIMINARY CHECK 1 – AIR OUTLET DOES NOT CHANGE
• Perform Self-diagnosis STEP 1 before referring to the flow chart.
CHECK SENSOR CIRCUIT. Set up Self-diagnosis STEP 2. Is each sensor circuit normal? Code No. 20 should be indicated on the display after approx. 4 seconds.
N.G.
CHECK SENSOR CIRCUIT IN DETAIL ACCORDING TO THE DIAGNOSTIC PROCEDURE BELOW CORRESPONDING TO EACH CODE NO.
Code No. | How to repair
21 | Go to Diagnostic Procedure 1.
22 | Go to Diagnostic Procedure 2.
24 | Go to Diagnostic Procedure 3.
25 | Go to Diagnostic Procedure 4.
26 | Go to Diagnostic Procedure 5.
-21 | Go to Diagnostic Procedure 1.
-22 | Go to Diagnostic Procedure 2.
-24 | Go to Diagnostic Procedure 3.
-25 | Go to Diagnostic Procedure 4.
-26 | Go to Diagnostic Procedure 5.
When malfunctioning sensor circuits for ambient sensor, in-vehicle sensor and intake sensor, are suspected it is useful to check temperature detected by each sensor with Self-diagnosis STEP 5 to confirm the temperature is within normal range before performing Diagnostic Procedures.
O.K.
CHECK MODE DOOR MOTOR. Set up Self-diagnosis STEP 3. Is mode door motor operating normally? Code No. 30 should be indicated on the display after approx. 16 seconds.
N.G.
Go to Diagnostic Procedure 7.
O.K.
CHECK MODE DOOR OPERATION. Set up Self-diagnosis STEP 4. Does air outlet change according to each code No.? (Fresh vent lever "OFF")
41 | 42 | 43 | 44 | 45 | 46
VENT | B/L | B/L | F/D1 | F/D2 | DEF
See NOTE.
N.G.
CHECK SIDE LINK MECHANISM.
N.G.
Repair or adjust.
O.K.
Go to Diagnostic Procedure 7.
O.K.
Air outlet control system is normal. Refer to Outlet door control specification.
NOTE:
Foot/Defrost Mode 1 (FD1) is used when manual mode is selected on auto amplifier. FD1 directs 75 percent air to foot area.
Foot/Defrost Mode 2 (FD2) is used when automatic mode is selected on auto amplifier. FD2 directs 50 percent air to foot area.
N.G is an abbreviation for NO GOOD on all flow charts.
94I10403
Courtesy of Nissan Motor Co., U.S.A.
PRELIMINARY CHECK 2 – INTAKE DOOR DOES NOT CHANGE
• Perform Self-diagnosis STEP 1 before referring to the following flow chart.
CHECK SENSOR CIRCUIT. Set up Self-diagnosis STEP 2. Is each sensor circuit normal? Code No. 20 should be indicated on the display after approx. 4 seconds.
N.G.
CHECK SENSOR CIRCUIT IN DETAIL ACCORDING TO THE DIAGNOSTIC PROCEDURE BELOW CORRESPONDED TO EACH CODE NO.
Code No. | How to repair
21 | Go to Diagnostic Procedure 1.
22 | Go to Diagnostic Procedure 2.
24 | Go to Diagnostic Procedure 3.
25 | Go to Diagnostic Procedure 4.
26 | Go to Diagnostic Procedure 5.
-21 | Go to Diagnostic Procedure 1.
-22 | Go to Diagnostic Procedure 2.
-24 | Go to Diagnostic Procedure 3.
-25 | Go to Diagnostic Procedure 4.
-26 | Go to Diagnostic Procedure 5.
When malfunctioning sensor circuits for ambient sensor, in-vehicle sensor and intake sensor, are suspected it is useful to check temperature detected by each sensor with Self-diagnosis STEP 5 to confirm the temperature is within normal range before performing Diagnostic Procedures.
O.K.
CHECK INTAKE DOOR MOTOR OPERATION. Set up Self-diagnosis STEP 4. Does intake air change according to each code No.?
41 | 42 | 43 | 44 | 45 | 46
REC | REC | 20% FRE | FRE | FRE | FRE
N.G.
CHECK INTAKE DOOR ROD or LEVER MECHANISM.
N.G.
Repair or Adjust.
O.K.
Go to Diagnostic Procedure 8.
O.K.
Intake door control system is normal.
NOTE: If the result is no good (NG) after checking circuit continuity, repair harness or connector.
94J10404
Courtesy of Nissan Motor Co., U.S.A.

Fig. 1: Preliminary Check 1 – Air Outlet Does Not Change

Fig. 2: Preliminary Check 2 – Intake Door Does Not Change

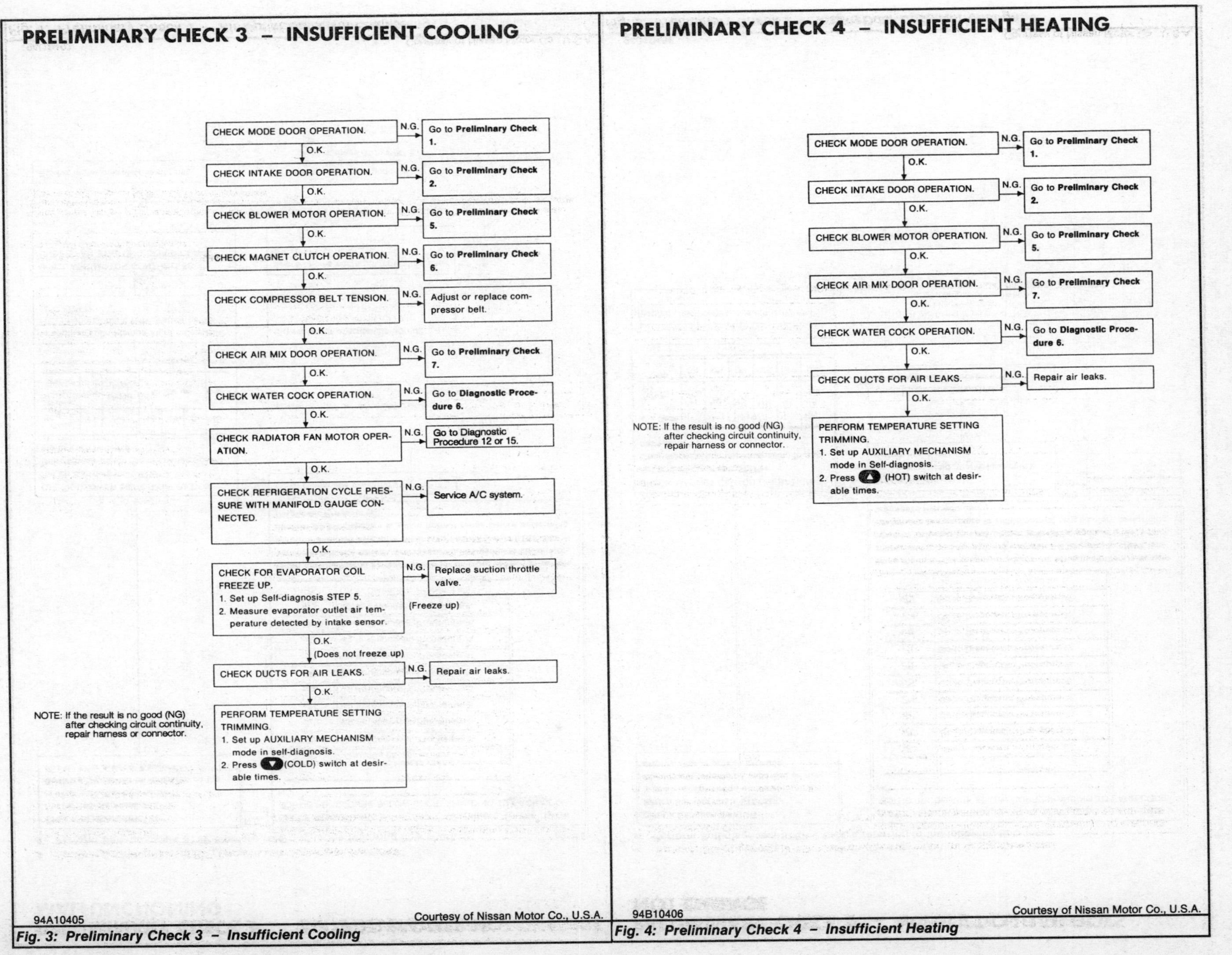
PRELIMINARY CHECK 3 – INSUFFICIENT COOLING
CHECK MODE DOOR OPERATION.
N.G.
Go to Preliminary Check 1.
O.K.
CHECK INTAKE DOOR OPERATION.
N.G.
Go to Preliminary Check 2.
O.K.
CHECK BLOWER MOTOR OPERATION.
N.G.
Go to Preliminary Check 5.
O.K.
CHECK MAGNET CLUTCH OPERATION.
N.G.
Go to Preliminary Check 6.
O.K.
CHECK COMPRESSOR BELT TENSION.
N.G.
Adjust or replace compressor belt.
O.K.
CHECK AIR MIX DOOR OPERATION.
N.G.
Go to Preliminary Check 7.
O.K.
CHECK WATER COCK OPERATION.
N.G.
Go to Diagnostic Procedure 6.
O.K.
CHECK RADIATOR FAN MOTOR OPERATION.
N.G.
Go to Diagnostic Procedure 12 or 15.
O.K.
CHECK REFRIGERATION CYCLE PRESSURE WITH MANIFOLD GAUGE CONNECTED.
N.G.
Service A/C system.
O.K.
CHECK FOR EVAPORATOR COIL FREEZE UP.
1. Set up Self-diagnosis STEP 5.
2. Measure evaporator outlet air temperature detected by intake sensor.
N.G.
(Freeze up)
Replace suction throttle valve.
O.K.
(Does not freeze up)
CHECK DUCTS FOR AIR LEAKS.
N.G.
Repair air leaks.
O.K.
PERFORM TEMPERATURE SETTING TRIMMING.
1. Set up AUXILIARY MECHANISM mode in self-diagnosis.
2. Press (COLD) switch at desirable times.
NOTE: If the result is no good (NG) after checking circuit continuity, repair harness or connector.
94A10405
Courtesy of Nissan Motor Co., U.S.A.
PRELIMINARY CHECK 4 – INSUFFICIENT HEATING
CHECK MODE DOOR OPERATION.
N.G.
Go to Preliminary Check 1.
O.K.
CHECK INTAKE DOOR OPERATION.
N.G.
Go to Preliminary Check 2.
O.K.
CHECK BLOWER MOTOR OPERATION.
N.G.
Go to Preliminary Check 5.
O.K.
CHECK AIR MIX DOOR OPERATION.
N.G.
Go to Preliminary Check 7.
O.K.
CHECK WATER COCK OPERATION.
N.G.
Go to Diagnostic Procedure 6.
O.K.
CHECK DUCTS FOR AIR LEAKS.
N.G.
Repair air leaks.
O.K.
PERFORM TEMPERATURE SETTING TRIMMING.
1. Set up AUXILIARY MECHANISM mode in Self-diagnosis.
2. Press (HOT) switch at desirable times.
NOTE: If the result is no good (NG) after checking circuit continuity, repair harness or connector.
94B10406
Courtesy of Nissan Motor Co., U.S.A.

Fig. 3: Preliminary Check 3 – Insufficient Cooling

Fig. 4: Preliminary Check 4 – Insufficient Heating

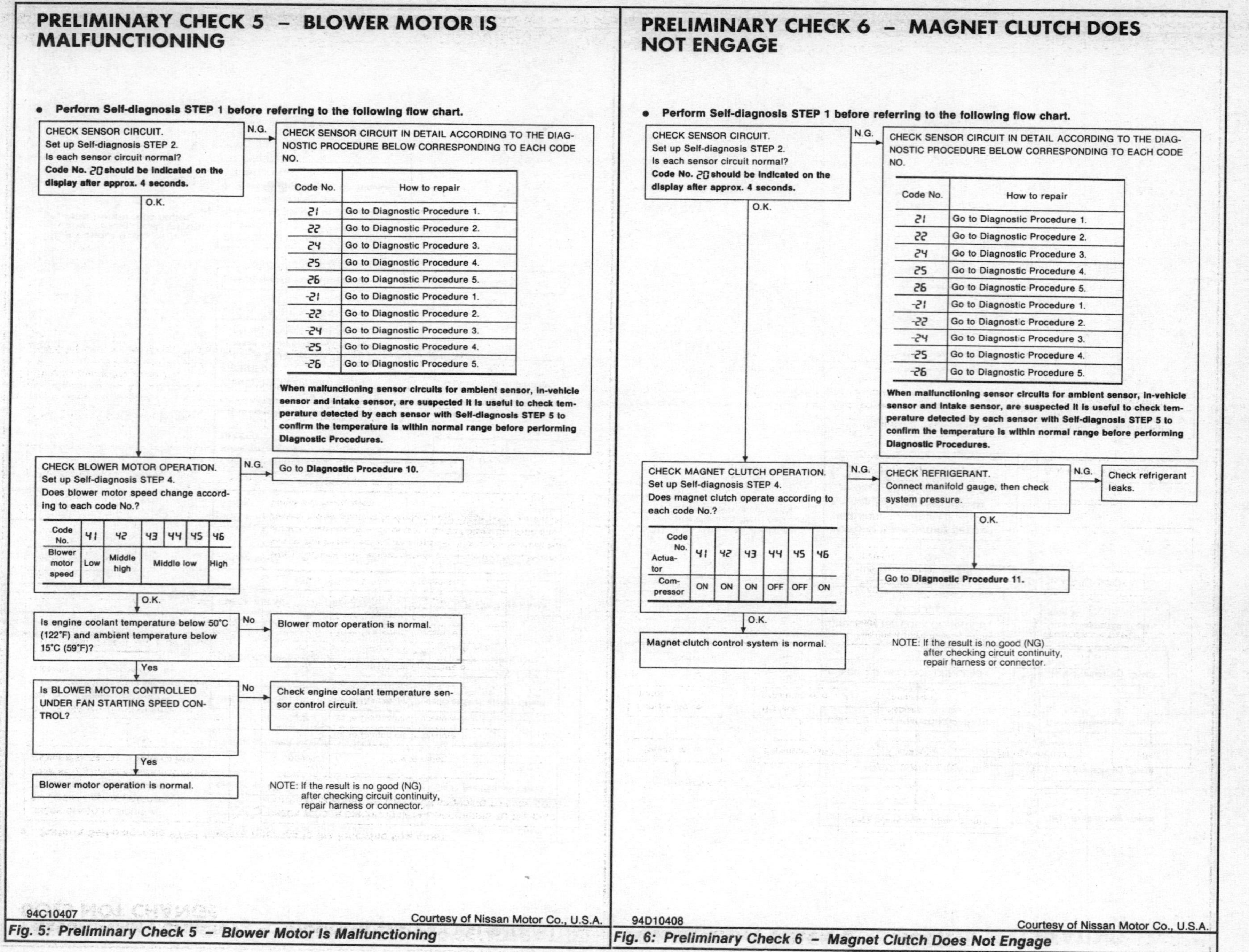
PRELIMINARY CHECK 5 – BLOWER MOTOR IS MALFUNCTIONING
• Perform Self-diagnosis STEP 1 before referring to the following flow chart.
CHECK SENSOR CIRCUIT.
Set up Self-diagnosis STEP 2.
Is each sensor circuit normal?
Code No. 20 should be indicated on the display after approx. 4 seconds.
N.G.
CHECK SENSOR CIRCUIT IN DETAIL ACCORDING TO THE DIAGNOSTIC PROCEDURE BELOW CORRESPONDING TO EACH CODE NO.
Code No. | How to repair
21 | Go to Diagnostic Procedure 1.
22 | Go to Diagnostic Procedure 2.
24 | Go to Diagnostic Procedure 3.
25 | Go to Diagnostic Procedure 4.
26 | Go to Diagnostic Procedure 5.
-21 | Go to Diagnostic Procedure 1.
-22 | Go to Diagnostic Procedure 2.
-24 | Go to Diagnostic Procedure 3.
-25 | Go to Diagnostic Procedure 4.
-26 | Go to Diagnostic Procedure 5.
When malfunctioning sensor circuits for ambient sensor, in-vehicle sensor and intake sensor, are suspected it is useful to check temperature detected by each sensor with Self-diagnosis STEP 5 to confirm the temperature is within normal range before performing Diagnostic Procedures.
O.K.
CHECK BLOWER MOTOR OPERATION.
Set up Self-diagnosis STEP 4.
Does blower motor speed change according to each code No.?
Code No. | 41 | 42 | 43 | 44 | 45 | 46
Blower motor speed | Low | Middle high | Middle low | | | High
N.G.
Go to Diagnostic Procedure 10.
O.K.
Is engine coolant temperature below 50°C (122°F) and ambient temperature below 15°C (59°F)?
No
Blower motor operation is normal.
Yes
Is BLOWER MOTOR CONTROLLED UNDER FAN STARTING SPEED CONTROL?
No
Check engine coolant temperature sensor control circuit.
Yes
Blower motor operation is normal.
NOTE: If the result is no good (NG) after checking circuit continuity, repair harness or connector.
94C10407
Courtesy of Nissan Motor Co., U.S.A.

Fig. 5: Preliminary Check 5 – Blower Motor Is Malfunctioning

PRELIMINARY CHECK 6 – MAGNET CLUTCH DOES NOT ENGAGE
• Perform Self-diagnosis STEP 1 before referring to the following flow chart.
CHECK SENSOR CIRCUIT.
Set up Self-diagnosis STEP 2.
Is each sensor circuit normal?
Code No. 20 should be indicated on the display after approx. 4 seconds.
N.G.
CHECK SENSOR CIRCUIT IN DETAIL ACCORDING TO THE DIAGNOSTIC PROCEDURE BELOW CORRESPONDING TO EACH CODE NO.
Code No. | How to repair
21 | Go to Diagnostic Procedure 1.
22 | Go to Diagnostic Procedure 2.
24 | Go to Diagnostic Procedure 3.
25 | Go to Diagnostic Procedure 4.
26 | Go to Diagnostic Procedure 5.
-21 | Go to Diagnostic Procedure 1.
-22 | Go to Diagnostic Procedure 2.
-24 | Go to Diagnostic Procedure 3.
-25 | Go to Diagnostic Procedure 4.
-26 | Go to Diagnostic Procedure 5.
When malfunctioning sensor circuits for ambient sensor, in-vehicle sensor and intake sensor, are suspected it is useful to check temperature detected by each sensor with Self-diagnosis STEP 5 to confirm the temperature is within normal range before performing Diagnostic Procedures.
O.K.
CHECK MAGNET CLUTCH OPERATION.
Set up Self-diagnosis STEP 4.
Does magnet clutch operate according to each code No.?
Code No. / Actuator | 41 | 42 | 43 | 44 | 45 | 46
Compressor | ON | ON | ON | OFF | OFF | ON
N.G.
CHECK REFRIGERANT.
Connect manifold gauge, then check system pressure.
N.G.
Check refrigerant leaks.
O.K.
Go to Diagnostic Procedure 11.
O.K.
Magnet clutch control system is normal.
NOTE: If the result is no good (NG) after checking circuit continuity, repair harness or connector.
94D10408
Courtesy of Nissan Motor Co., U.S.A.

Fig. 6: Preliminary Check 6 – Magnet Clutch Does Not Engage

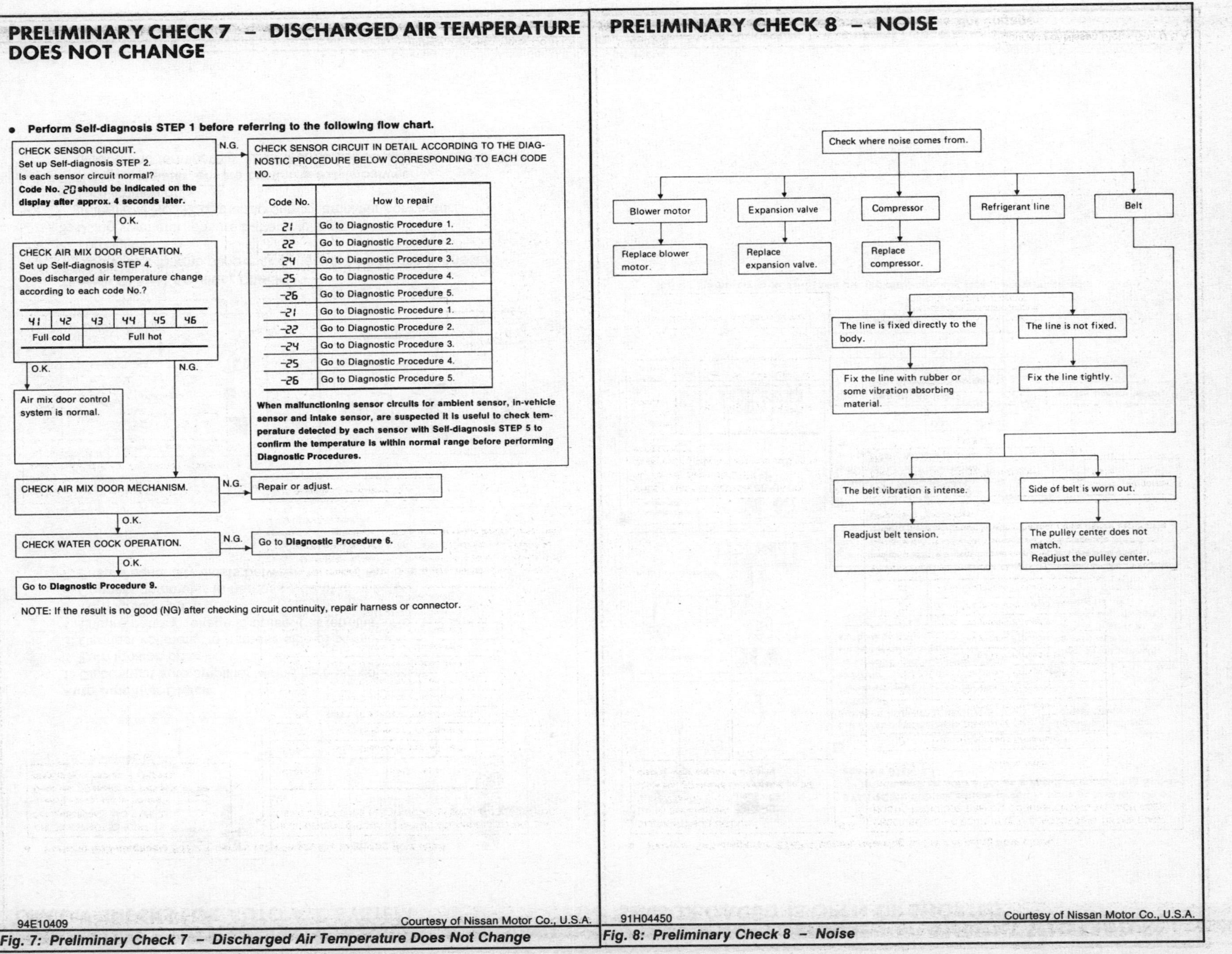

PRELIMINARY CHECK 7 – DISCHARGED AIR TEMPERATURE DOES NOT CHANGE
• Perform Self-diagnosis STEP 1 before referring to the following flow chart.
CHECK SENSOR CIRCUIT. Set up Self-diagnosis STEP 2. Is each sensor circuit normal? Code No. 20 should be indicated on the display after approx. 4 seconds later.
N.G.
CHECK SENSOR CIRCUIT IN DETAIL ACCORDING TO THE DIAGNOSTIC PROCEDURE BELOW CORRESPONDING TO EACH CODE NO.
O.K.
CHECK AIR MIX DOOR OPERATION. Set up Self-diagnosis STEP 4. Does discharged air temperature change according to each code No.?
41 42 43 44 45 46
Full cold
Full hot
O.K.
N.G.
Air mix door control system is normal.
When malfunctioning sensor circuits for ambient sensor, in-vehicle sensor and intake sensor, are suspected it is useful to check temperature detected by each sensor with Self-diagnosis STEP 5 to confirm the temperature is within normal range before performing Diagnostic Procedures.
CHECK AIR MIX DOOR MECHANISM.
N.G.
Repair or adjust.
O.K.
CHECK WATER COCK OPERATION.
N.G.
Go to Diagnostic Procedure 6.
O.K.
Go to Diagnostic Procedure 9.
NOTE: If the result is no good (NG) after checking circuit continuity, repair harness or connector.
94E10409
Courtesy of Nissan Motor Co., U.S.A.
PRELIMINARY CHECK 8 – NOISE
Check where noise comes from.
Blower motor
Expansion valve
Compressor
Refrigerant line
Belt
Replace blower motor.
Replace expansion valve.
Replace compressor.
The line is fixed directly to the body.
The line is not fixed.
Fix the line with rubber or some vibration absorbing material.
Fix the line tightly.
The belt vibration is intense.
Side of belt is worn out.
Readjust belt tension.
The pulley center does not match. Readjust the pulley center.
91H04450
Courtesy of Nissan Motor Co., U.S.A.

Code No.	How to repair
21	Go to Diagnostic Procedure 1.
22	Go to Diagnostic Procedure 2.
24	Go to Diagnostic Procedure 3.
25	Go to Diagnostic Procedure 4.
-26	Go to Diagnostic Procedure 5.
-21	Go to Diagnostic Procedure 1.
-22	Go to Diagnostic Procedure 2.
-24	Go to Diagnostic Procedure 3.
-25	Go to Diagnostic Procedure 4.
-26	Go to Diagnostic Procedure 5.

Fig. 7: Preliminary Check 7 – Discharged Air Temperature Does Not Change

Fig. 8: Preliminary Check 8 – Noise

1993 AUTOMATIC A/C-HEATER SYSTEMS
Trouble Shooting – Maxima (Cont.)

PRELIMINARY CHECK 9 – POWER SUPPLY & GROUND CIRCUIT CHECKS FOR AUTO A/C SYSTEM

Auto Amplifier Check

1. Disconnect auto amplifier wiring harness connector.
2. Turn ignition on.
3. Connect voltmeter to harness side of connector.
4. Ensure battery voltage is present at terminals No. 1, 2 and 3.
5. Turn ignition off.
6. Connect ohmmeter to harness side of connector.
7. Ensure continuity exists between terminal No. 8 and ground.

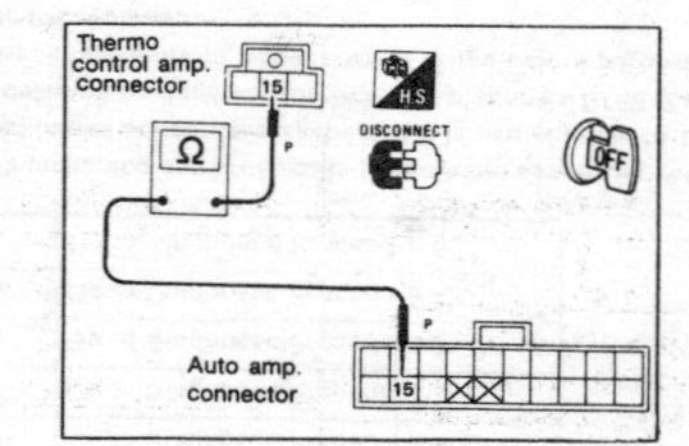
Thermo control amp. connector
W/L
42
V
DISCONNECT

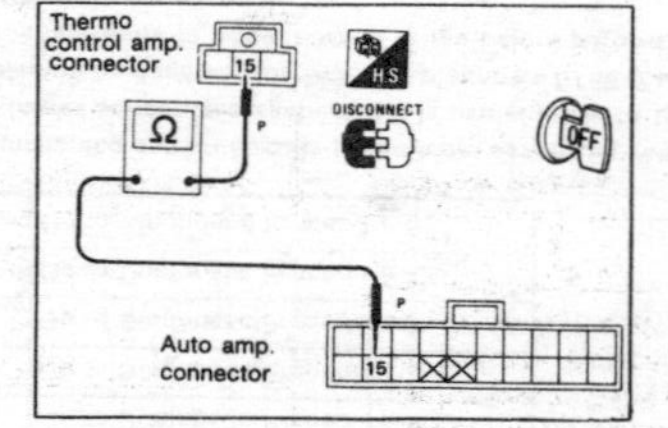
Thermo control amp. connector
15
Ω
Auto amp. connector
DISCONNECT

Thermo Control Amplifier Check

1. Disconnect thermo control amplifier wiring harness connector.
2. Turn ignition on.
3. Using voltmeter, ensure battery voltage is present at terminal No. 42 of thermo control amplifier connector.
4. Turn ignition off.
5. Using ohmmeter, ensure continuity exists between ground and terminal No. 15 of thermo control amplifer connector.

94F10418 Courtesy of Nissan Motor Co., U.S.A.

Fig. 9: Preliminary Check 9 – Power Supply & Ground Circuit Checks For Auto A/C System

DIAGNOSTIC PROCEDURE 1 – AMBIENT TEMPERATURE SENSOR CIRCUIT IS OPEN OR SHORTED

SYMPTOM: Ambient sensor circuit is open or shorted. (2! or -2! is indicated on auto amp. as a result of conducting Self-diagnosis STEP 2.)

A — CHECK AMBIENT SENSOR CIRCUIT BETWEEN AMBIENT SENSOR AND AUTO AMP.
Disconnect ambient sensor harness connector.
Do approx. 5 volts exist between ambient sensor harness terminal No. 30 and body ground.

- N.G. → Disconnect auto amp. harness connector. → C — Check circuit continuity between ambient sensor harness terminal No. 30 and auto amp. harness terminal No. 30. (Note) → O.K. → Replace auto amp.
- O.K. → Disconnect auto amp. harness connector. → B — Check circuit continuity between ambient sensor harness terminal No. 44 and auto amp. harness terminal No. 16. (Note) → O.K. → CHECK AMBIENT SENSOR.
  - N.G. → Replace ambient sensor.
  - O.K. → Replace auto amp.

NOTE: If the result is no good (NG) after checking circuit continuity, repair harness or connector.

94H10410 Courtesy of Nissan Motor Co., U.S.A.

Fig. 10: Diagnostic Procedure 1 – Ambient Temperature Sensor Circuit Is Open Or Shorted

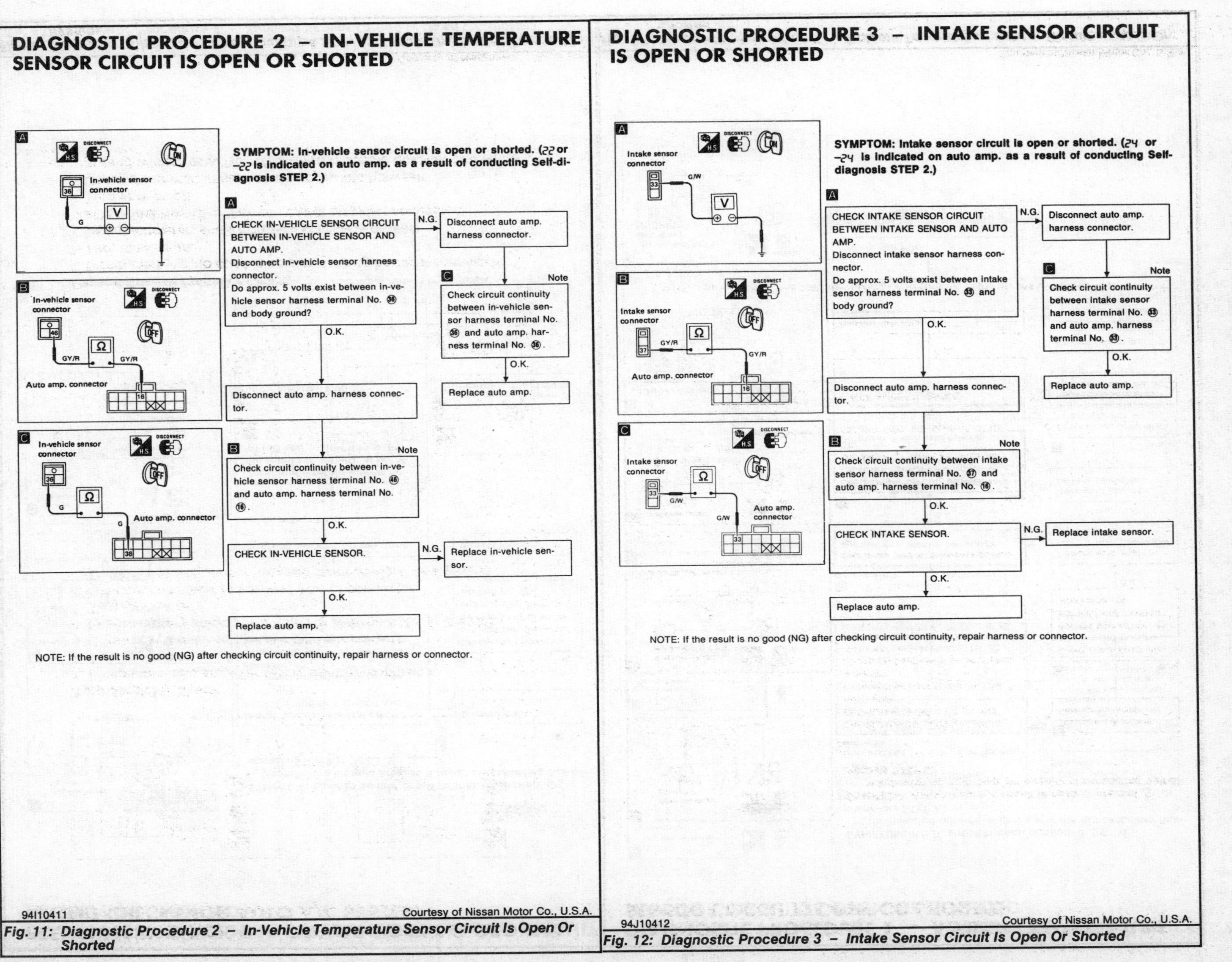
DIAGNOSTIC PROCEDURE 2 – IN-VEHICLE TEMPERATURE SENSOR CIRCUIT IS OPEN OR SHORTED
A
DISCONNECT
H.S
ON
In-vehicle sensor connector
36
G
V
B
In-vehicle sensor connector
DISCONNECT
H.S
OFF
46
GY/R
Ω
GY/R
Auto amp. connector
16
C
In-vehicle sensor connector
DISCONNECT
H.S
OFF
36
Ω
G
Auto amp. connector
G
36
SYMPTOM: In-vehicle sensor circuit is open or shorted. (22 or -22 is indicated on auto amp. as a result of conducting Self-diagnosis STEP 2.)
A
CHECK IN-VEHICLE SENSOR CIRCUIT BETWEEN IN-VEHICLE SENSOR AND AUTO AMP.
Disconnect in-vehicle sensor harness connector.
Do approx. 5 volts exist between in-vehicle sensor harness terminal No. 36 and body ground?
N.G.
Disconnect auto amp. harness connector.
C
Note
Check circuit continuity between in-vehicle sensor harness terminal No. 36 and auto amp. harness terminal No. 36.
O.K.
Replace auto amp.
O.K.
Disconnect auto amp. harness connector.
B
Note
Check circuit continuity between in-vehicle sensor harness terminal No. 46 and auto amp. harness terminal No. 16.
O.K.
CHECK IN-VEHICLE SENSOR.
N.G.
Replace in-vehicle sensor.
O.K.
Replace auto amp.
NOTE: If the result is no good (NG) after checking circuit continuity, repair harness or connector.
94I10411
Courtesy of Nissan Motor Co., U.S.A.
DIAGNOSTIC PROCEDURE 3 – INTAKE SENSOR CIRCUIT IS OPEN OR SHORTED
A
Intake sensor connector
DISCONNECT
H.S
ON
33
G/W
V
B
Intake sensor connector
DISCONNECT
H.S
OFF
37
GY/R
Ω
GY/R
Auto amp. connector
16
C
Intake sensor connector
DISCONNECT
H.S
OFF
33
G/W
Ω
G/W
Auto amp. connector
33
SYMPTOM: Intake sensor circuit is open or shorted. (24 or -24 is indicated on auto amp. as a result of conducting Self-diagnosis STEP 2.)
A
CHECK INTAKE SENSOR CIRCUIT BETWEEN INTAKE SENSOR AND AUTO AMP.
Disconnect intake sensor harness connector.
Do approx. 5 volts exist between intake sensor harness terminal No. 33 and body ground?
N.G.
Disconnect auto amp. harness connector.
C
Note
Check circuit continuity between intake sensor harness terminal No. 33 and auto amp. harness terminal No. 33.
O.K.
Replace auto amp.
O.K.
Disconnect auto amp. harness connector.
B
Note
Check circuit continuity between intake sensor harness terminal No. 37 and auto amp. harness terminal No. 16.
O.K.
CHECK INTAKE SENSOR.
N.G.
Replace intake sensor.
O.K.
Replace auto amp.
NOTE: If the result is no good (NG) after checking circuit continuity, repair harness or connector.
94J10412
Courtesy of Nissan Motor Co., U.S.A.

Fig. 11: Diagnostic Procedure 2 – In-Vehicle Temperature Sensor Circuit Is Open Or Shorted

Fig. 12: Diagnostic Procedure 3 – Intake Sensor Circuit Is Open Or Shorted

1993 AUTOMATIC A/C-HEATER SYSTEMS
Trouble Shooting – Maxima (Cont.)

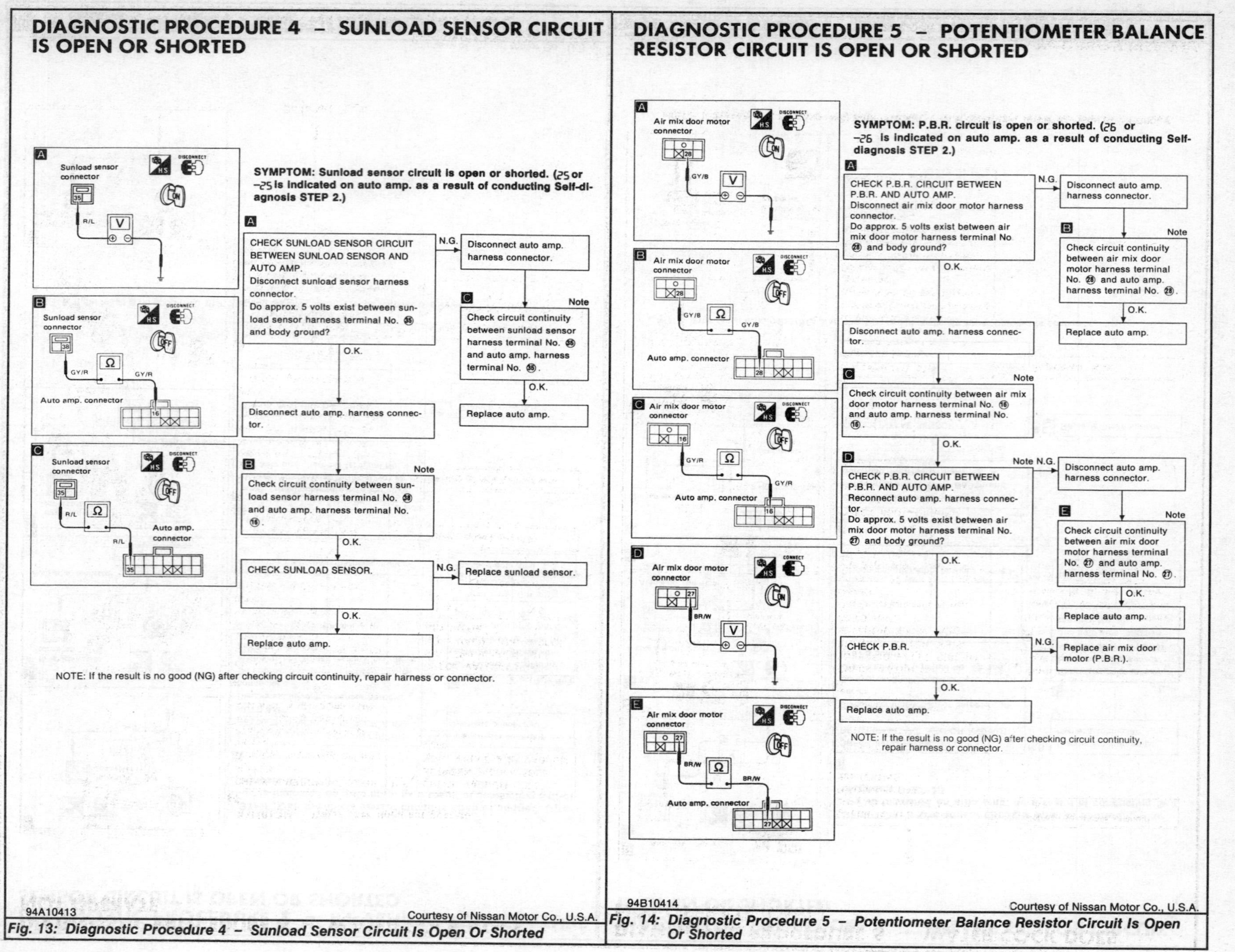
DIAGNOSTIC PROCEDURE 4 – SUNLOAD SENSOR CIRCUIT IS OPEN OR SHORTED
A
Sunload sensor connector
35
R/L
V
DISCONNECT
H.S
ON
B
Sunload sensor connector
38
GY/R
GY/R
Ω
Auto amp. connector
16
OFF
C
Sunload sensor connector
35
R/L
R/L
Ω
Auto amp. connector
35
SYMPTOM: Sunload sensor circuit is open or shorted. (25 or -25 is indicated on auto amp. as a result of conducting Self-diagnosis STEP 2.)
A
CHECK SUNLOAD SENSOR CIRCUIT BETWEEN SUNLOAD SENSOR AND AUTO AMP. Disconnect sunload sensor harness connector. Do approx. 5 volts exist between sunload sensor harness terminal No. (35) and body ground?
N.G.
Disconnect auto amp. harness connector.
C
Note
Check circuit continuity between sunload sensor harness terminal No. (35) and auto amp. harness terminal No. (35).
O.K.
Replace auto amp.
O.K.
Disconnect auto amp. harness connector.
B
Note
Check circuit continuity between sunload sensor harness terminal No. (38) and auto amp. harness terminal No. (16).
O.K.
CHECK SUNLOAD SENSOR.
N.G.
Replace sunload sensor.
O.K.
Replace auto amp.
NOTE: If the result is no good (NG) after checking circuit continuity, repair harness or connector.
94A10413
Courtesy of Nissan Motor Co., U.S.A.
DIAGNOSTIC PROCEDURE 5 – POTENTIOMETER BALANCE RESISTOR CIRCUIT IS OPEN OR SHORTED
A
Air mix door motor connector
28
GY/B
V
DISCONNECT
H.S
ON
B
Air mix door motor connector
28
GY/B
GY/B
Ω
Auto amp. connector
28
OFF
C
Air mix door motor connector
16
GY/R
GY/R
Ω
Auto amp. connector
16
D
Air mix door motor connector
27
BR/W
V
CONNECT
E
Air mix door motor connector
27
BR/W
BR/W
Ω
Auto amp. connector
27
SYMPTOM: P.B.R. circuit is open or shorted. (26 or -26 is indicated on auto amp. as a result of conducting Self-diagnosis STEP 2.)
A
CHECK P.B.R. CIRCUIT BETWEEN P.B.R. AND AUTO AMP. Disconnect air mix door motor harness connector. Do approx. 5 volts exist between air mix door motor harness terminal No (28) and body ground?
N.G.
Disconnect auto amp. harness connector.
B
Note
Check circuit continuity between air mix door motor harness terminal No. (28) and auto amp. harness terminal No. (28).
O.K.
Replace auto amp.
O.K.
Disconnect auto amp. harness connector.
C
Note
Check circuit continuity between air mix door motor harness terminal No. (16) and auto amp. harness terminal No. (16).
O.K.
D
Note
CHECK P.B.R. CIRCUIT BETWEEN P.B.R. AND AUTO AMP. Reconnect auto amp. harness connector. Do approx. 5 volts exist between air mix door motor harness terminal No. (27) and body ground?
N.G.
Disconnect auto amp. harness connector.
E
Note
Check circuit continuity between air mix door motor harness terminal No. (27) and auto amp. harness terminal No. (27).
O.K.
Replace auto amp.
O.K.
CHECK P.B.R.
N.G.
Replace air mix door motor (P.B.R.).
O.K.
Replace auto amp.
NOTE: If the result is no good (NG) after checking circuit continuity, repair harness or connector.
94B10414
Courtesy of Nissan Motor Co., U.S.A.

Fig. 13: Diagnostic Procedure 4 – Sunload Sensor Circuit Is Open Or Shorted

Fig. 14: Diagnostic Procedure 5 – Potentiometer Balance Resistor Circuit Is Open Or Shorted

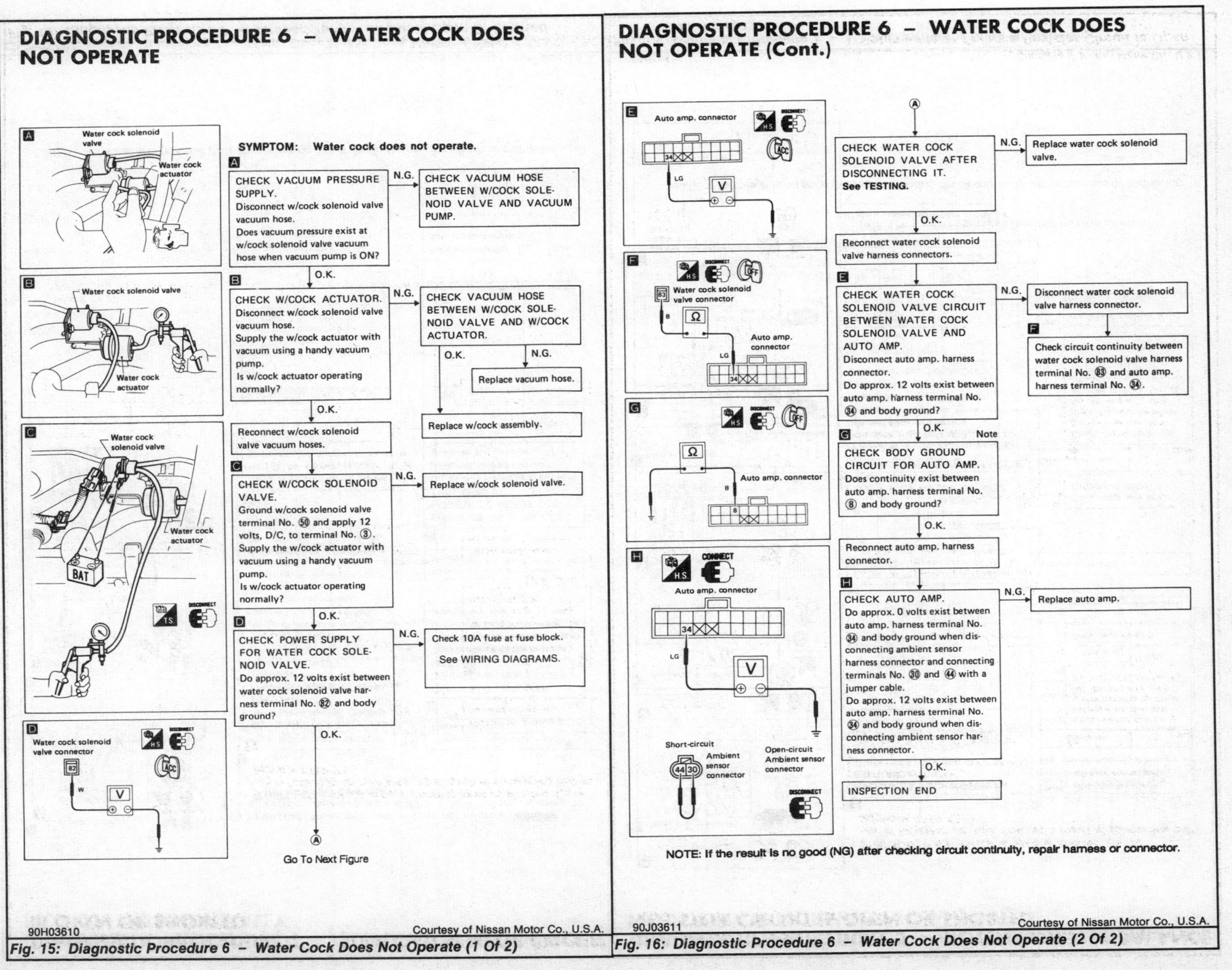
DIAGNOSTIC PROCEDURE 6 – WATER COCK DOES NOT OPERATE
A Water cock solenoid valve
Water cock actuator
B Water cock solenoid valve
Water cock actuator
C Water cock solenoid valve
Water cock actuator
BAT
TS
DISCONNECT
D Water cock solenoid valve connector
82
W
V
HS
DISCONNECT
ACC
SYMPTOM: Water cock does not operate.
A CHECK VACUUM PRESSURE SUPPLY.
Disconnect w/cock solenoid valve vacuum hose.
Does vacuum pressure exist at w/cock solenoid valve vacuum hose when vacuum pump is ON?
N.G.
CHECK VACUUM HOSE BETWEEN W/COCK SOLENOID VALVE AND VACUUM PUMP.
O.K.
B CHECK W/COCK ACTUATOR.
Disconnect w/cock solenoid valve vacuum hose.
Supply the w/cock actuator with vacuum using a handy vacuum pump.
Is w/cock actuator operating normally?
N.G.
CHECK VACUUM HOSE BETWEEN W/COCK SOLENOID VALVE AND W/COCK ACTUATOR.
O.K.
N.G.
Replace vacuum hose.
Replace w/cock assembly.
O.K.
Reconnect w/cock solenoid valve vacuum hoses.
C CHECK W/COCK SOLENOID VALVE.
Ground w/cock solenoid valve terminal No. 50 and apply 12 volts, D/C, to terminal No. 3.
Supply the w/cock actuator with vacuum using a handy vacuum pump.
Is w/cock actuator operating normally?
N.G.
Replace w/cock solenoid valve.
O.K.
D CHECK POWER SUPPLY FOR WATER COCK SOLENOID VALVE.
Do approx. 12 volts exist between water cock solenoid valve harness terminal No. 82 and body ground?
N.G.
Check 10A fuse at fuse block.
See WIRING DIAGRAMS.
O.K.
A
Go To Next Figure
90H03610
Courtesy of Nissan Motor Co., U.S.A.
DIAGNOSTIC PROCEDURE 6 – WATER COCK DOES NOT OPERATE (Cont.)
E Auto amp. connector
34
LG
V
HS
DISCONNECT
ACC
F Water cock solenoid valve connector
83
B
Ω
Auto amp. connector
LG
34
OFF
G Auto amp. connector
Ω
B
8
H CONNECT
Auto amp. connector
34
LG
V
Short-circuit
Ambient sensor connector
44 30
Open-circuit Ambient sensor connector
DISCONNECT
A
CHECK WATER COCK SOLENOID VALVE AFTER DISCONNECTING IT.
See TESTING.
N.G.
Replace water cock solenoid valve.
O.K.
Reconnect water cock solenoid valve harness connectors.
E CHECK WATER COCK SOLENOID VALVE CIRCUIT BETWEEN WATER COCK SOLENOID VALVE AND AUTO AMP.
Disconnect auto amp. harness connector.
Do approx. 12 volts exist between auto amp. harness terminal No. 34 and body ground?
N.G.
Disconnect water cock solenoid valve harness connector.
F Check circuit continuity between water cock solenoid valve harness terminal No. 83 and auto amp. harness terminal No. 34.
O.K.
Note
G CHECK BODY GROUND CIRCUIT FOR AUTO AMP.
Does continuity exist between auto amp. harness terminal No. 8 and body ground?
O.K.
Reconnect auto amp. harness connector.
H CHECK AUTO AMP.
Do approx. 0 volts exist between auto amp. harness terminal No. 34 and body ground when disconnecting ambient sensor harness connector and connecting terminals No. 30 and 44 with a jumper cable.
Do approx. 12 volts exist between auto amp. harness terminal No. 34 and body ground when disconnecting ambient sensor harness connector.
N.G.
Replace auto amp.
O.K.
INSPECTION END
NOTE: If the result is no good (NG) after checking circuit continuity, repair harness or connector.
90J03611
Courtesy of Nissan Motor Co., U.S.A.

Fig. 15: Diagnostic Procedure 6 – Water Cock Does Not Operate (1 Of 2)

Fig. 16: Diagnostic Procedure 6 – Water Cock Does Not Operate (2 Of 2)

1993 AUTOMATIC A/C-HEATER SYSTEMS
Trouble Shooting – Maxima (Cont.)

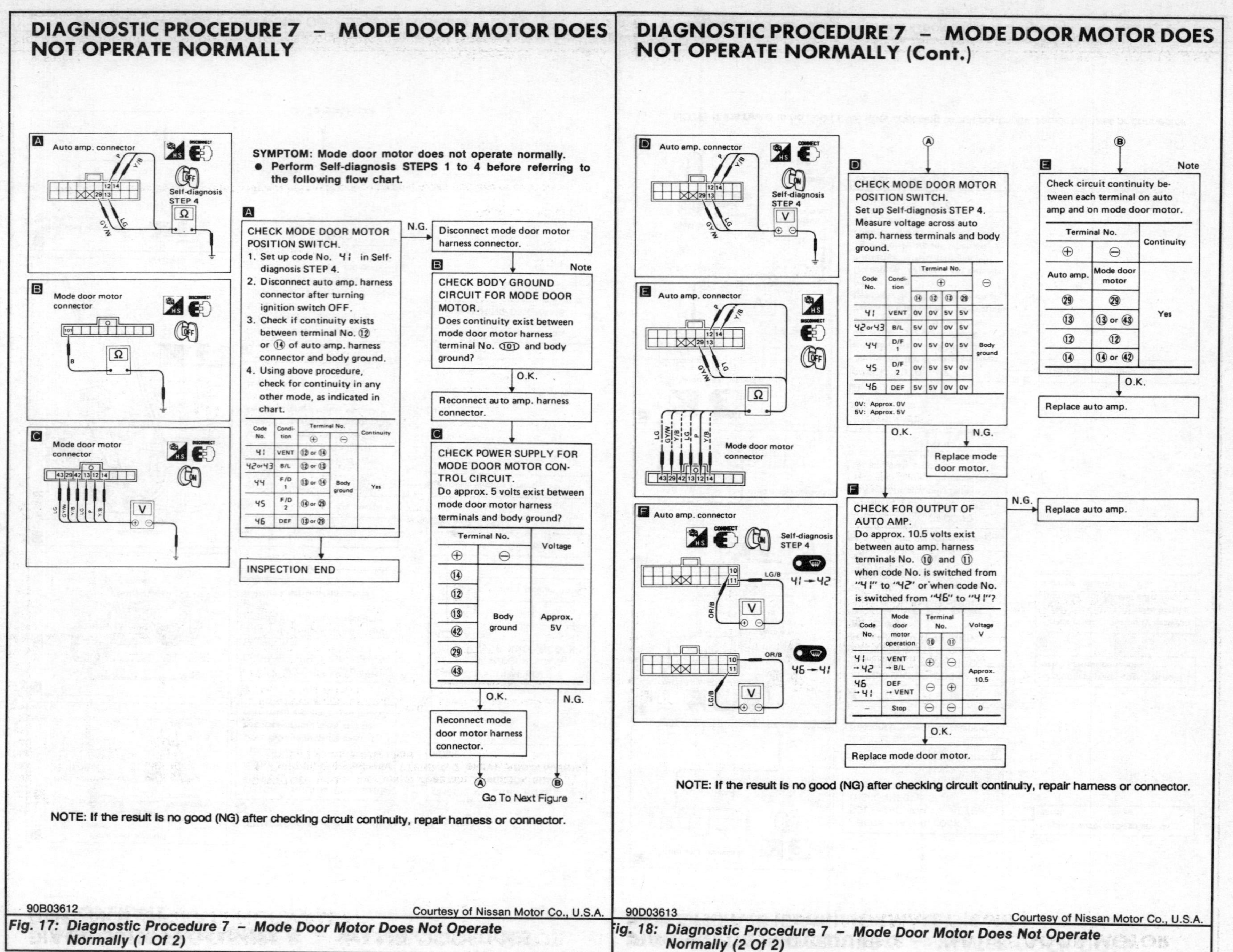
DIAGNOSTIC PROCEDURE 7 – MODE DOOR MOTOR DOES NOT OPERATE NORMALLY
A Auto amp. connector
Self-diagnosis STEP 4
B Mode door motor connector
C Mode door motor connector
SYMPTOM: Mode door motor does not operate normally.
● Perform Self-diagnosis STEPS 1 to 4 before referring to the following flow chart.
A CHECK MODE DOOR MOTOR POSITION SWITCH.
1. Set up code No. 41 in Self-diagnosis STEP 4.
2. Disconnect auto amp. harness connector after turning ignition switch OFF.
3. Check if continuity exists between terminal No. 12 or 14 of auto amp. harness connector and body ground.
4. Using above procedure, check for continuity in any other mode, as indicated in chart.
Code No. | Condition | Terminal No. ⊕ | Terminal No. ⊖ | Continuity
41 | VENT | 12 or 14 | Body ground | Yes
42or43 | B/L | 12 or 13
44 | F/D 1 | 13 or 14
45 | F/D 2 | 14 or 29
46 | DEF | 13 or 29
INSPECTION END
N.G.
Disconnect mode door motor harness connector.
B CHECK BODY GROUND CIRCUIT FOR MODE DOOR MOTOR.
Does continuity exist between mode door motor harness terminal No. 101 and body ground?
Note
O.K.
Reconnect auto amp. harness connector.
C CHECK POWER SUPPLY FOR MODE DOOR MOTOR CONTROL CIRCUIT.
Do approx. 5 volts exist between mode door motor harness terminals and body ground?
Terminal No. ⊕ | Terminal No. ⊖ | Voltage
14, 12, 13, 42, 29, 43 | Body ground | Approx. 5V
O.K.
N.G.
Reconnect mode door motor harness connector.
Go To Next Figure
NOTE: If the result is no good (NG) after checking circuit continuity, repair harness or connector.
90B03612
Courtesy of Nissan Motor Co., U.S.A.
DIAGNOSTIC PROCEDURE 7 – MODE DOOR MOTOR DOES NOT OPERATE NORMALLY (Cont.)
D Auto amp. connector
Self-diagnosis STEP 4
E Auto amp. connector
Mode door motor connector
F Auto amp. connector
Self-diagnosis STEP 4
41 → 42
46 → 41
D CHECK MODE DOOR MOTOR POSITION SWITCH.
Set up Self-diagnosis STEP 4.
Measure voltage across auto amp. harness terminals and body ground.
Code No. | Condition | 14 | 12 | 13 | 29 | ⊖
41 | VENT | 0V | 0V | 5V | 5V | Body ground
42or43 | B/L | 5V | 0V | 0V | 5V
44 | D/F 1 | 0V | 5V | 0V | 5V
45 | D/F 2 | 0V | 5V | 5V | 0V
46 | DEF | 5V | 5V | 0V | 0V
0V: Approx. 0V
5V: Approx. 5V
O.K.
N.G.
Replace mode door motor.
E Check circuit continuity between each terminal on auto amp and on mode door motor.
Note
Auto amp. ⊕ | Mode door motor ⊖ | Continuity
29 | 29 | Yes
13 | 13 or 43
12 | 12
14 | 14 or 42
O.K.
Replace auto amp.
F CHECK FOR OUTPUT OF AUTO AMP.
Do approx. 10.5 volts exist between auto amp. harness terminals No. 10 and 11 when code No. is switched from "41" to "42" or when code No. is switched from "46" to "41"?
Code No. | Mode door motor operation | 10 | 11 | Voltage V
41 → 42 | VENT → B/L | ⊕ | ⊖ | Approx. 10.5
46 → 41 | DEF → VENT | ⊖ | ⊕
– | Stop | ⊖ | ⊖ | 0
N.G.
Replace auto amp.
O.K.
Replace mode door motor.
NOTE: If the result is no good (NG) after checking circuit continuity, repair harness or connector.
90D03613
Courtesy of Nissan Motor Co., U.S.A.

Fig. 17: Diagnostic Procedure 7 – Mode Door Motor Does Not Operate Normally (1 Of 2)

Fig. 18: Diagnostic Procedure 7 – Mode Door Motor Does Not Operate Normally (2 Of 2)

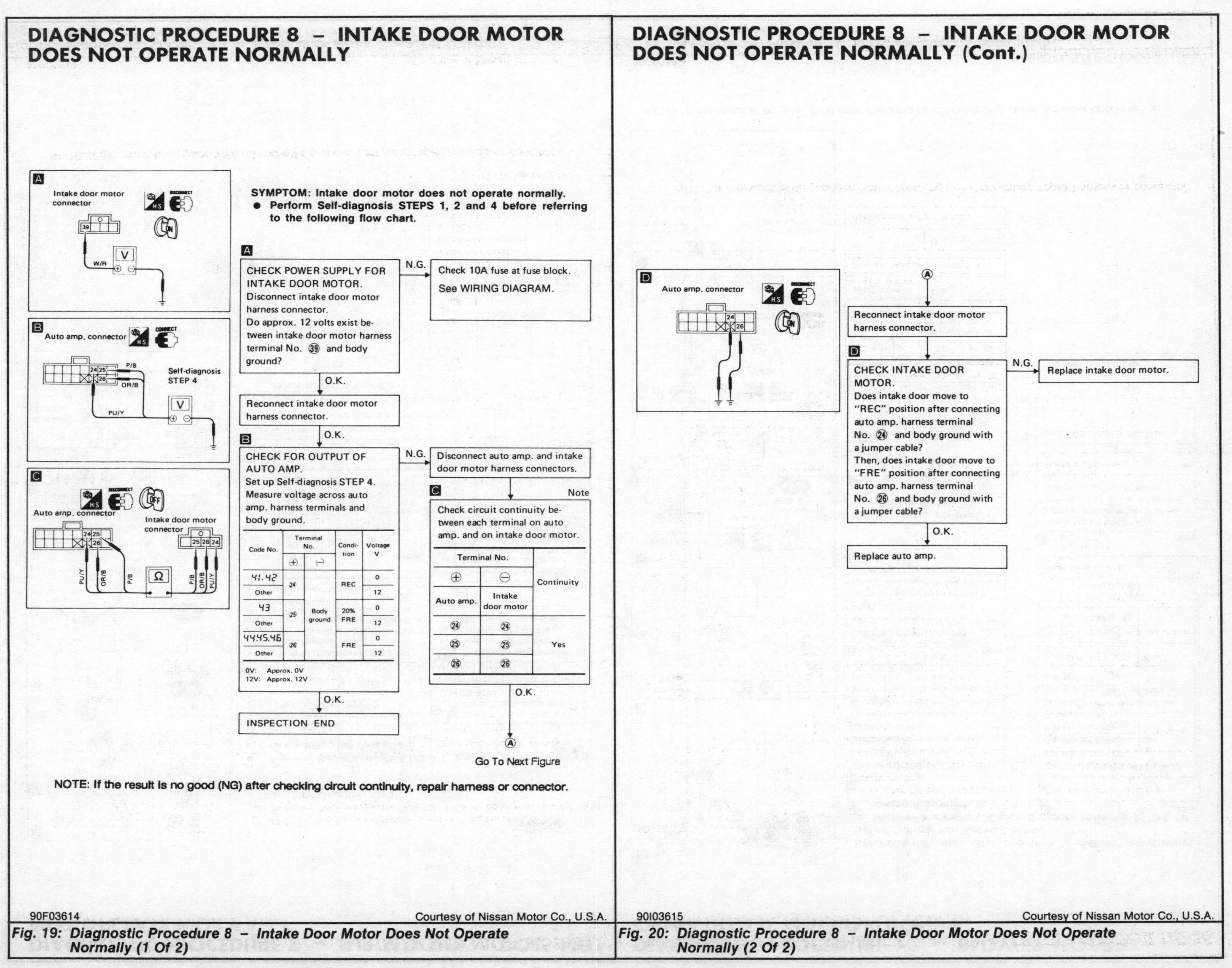

DIAGNOSTIC PROCEDURE 8 – INTAKE DOOR MOTOR DOES NOT OPERATE NORMALLY
A
Intake door motor connector
39
W/R
V
B
Auto amp. connector
24 25 26
P/B
OR/B
PU/Y
Self-diagnosis STEP 4
V
C
Auto amp. connector
Intake door motor connector
25 26 24
PU/Y
OR/B
P/B
Ω
SYMPTOM: Intake door motor does not operate normally.
• Perform Self-diagnosis STEPS 1, 2 and 4 before referring to the following flow chart.
A
CHECK POWER SUPPLY FOR INTAKE DOOR MOTOR.
Disconnect intake door motor harness connector.
Do approx. 12 volts exist between intake door motor harness terminal No. 39 and body ground?
N.G.
Check 10A fuse at fuse block.
See WIRING DIAGRAM.
O.K.
Reconnect intake door motor harness connector.
O.K.
B
CHECK FOR OUTPUT OF AUTO AMP.
Set up Self-diagnosis STEP 4.
Measure voltage across auto amp. harness terminals and body ground.
Code No. | Terminal No. ⊕ | Terminal No. ⊖ | Condition | Voltage V
41, 42 | 24 | Body ground | REC | 0
Other | | | | 12
43 | 25 | | 20% FRE | 0
Other | | | | 12
44, 45, 46 | 26 | | FRE | 0
Other | | | | 12
0V: Approx. 0V
12V: Approx. 12V
N.G.
Disconnect auto amp. and intake door motor harness connectors.
C
Note
Check circuit continuity between each terminal on auto amp. and on intake door motor.
Terminal No. ⊕ Auto amp. | Terminal No. ⊖ Intake door motor | Continuity
24 | 24 | Yes
25 | 25 |
26 | 26 |
O.K.
INSPECTION END
O.K.
A
Go To Next Figure
NOTE: If the result is no good (NG) after checking circuit continuity, repair harness or connector.
90F03614
Courtesy of Nissan Motor Co., U.S.A.
DIAGNOSTIC PROCEDURE 8 – INTAKE DOOR MOTOR DOES NOT OPERATE NORMALLY (Cont.)
D
Auto amp. connector
24
26
A
Reconnect intake door motor harness connector.
D
CHECK INTAKE DOOR MOTOR.
Does intake door move to "REC" position after connecting auto amp. harness terminal No. 24 and body ground with a jumper cable?
Then, does intake door move to "FRE" position after connecting auto amp. harness terminal No. 26 and body ground with a jumper cable?
N.G.
Replace intake door motor.
O.K.
Replace auto amp.
90I03615
Courtesy of Nissan Motor Co., U.S.A.

Fig. 19: Diagnostic Procedure 8 – Intake Door Motor Does Not Operate Normally (1 Of 2)

Fig. 20: Diagnostic Procedure 8 – Intake Door Motor Does Not Operate Normally (2 Of 2)

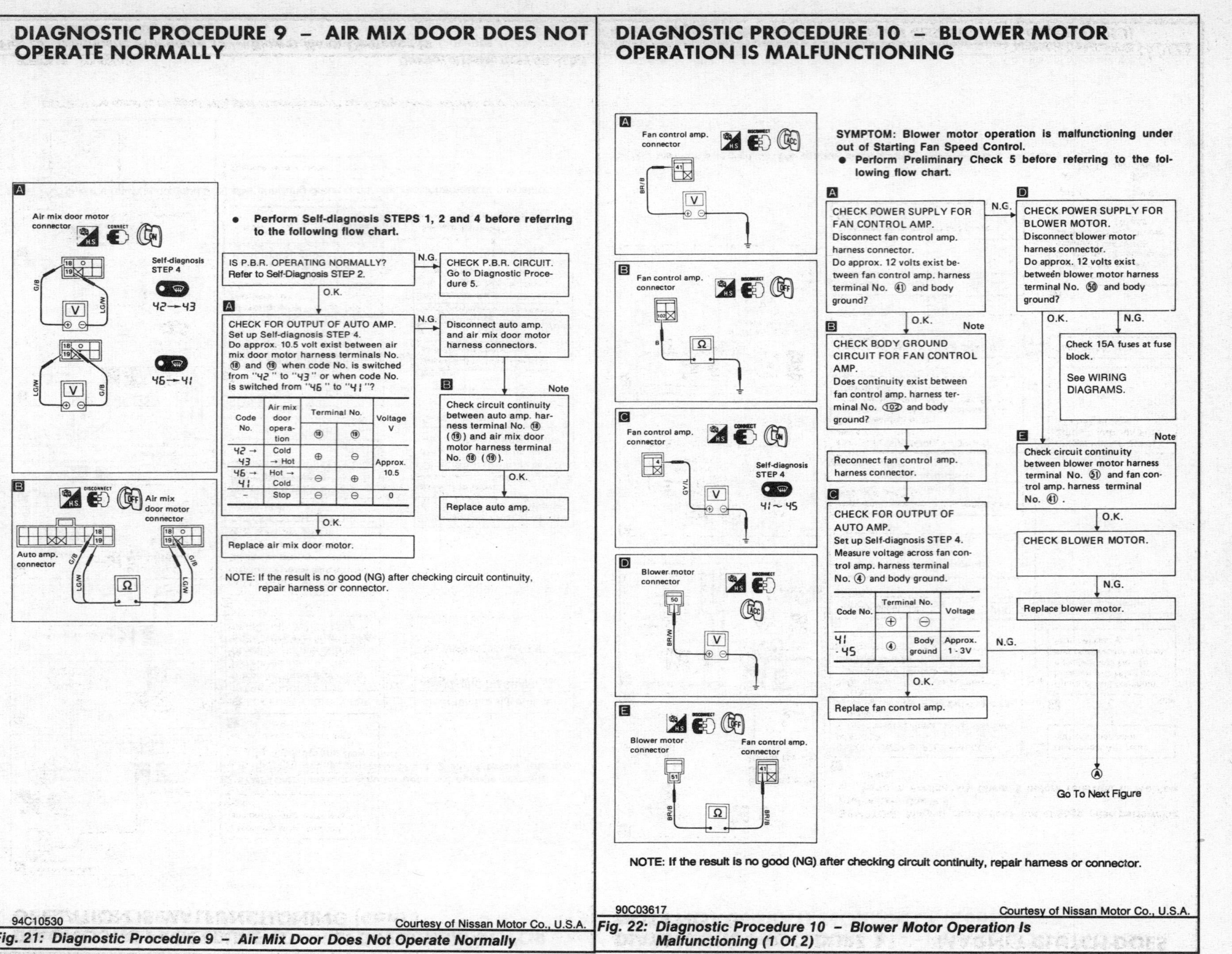

DIAGNOSTIC PROCEDURE 9 – AIR MIX DOOR DOES NOT OPERATE NORMALLY

A
Air mix door motor connector
CONNECT
18
19
G/B
LG/W
V
Self-diagnosis STEP 4
42→43
46→41
B
DISCONNECT
Air mix door motor connector
Auto amp. connector
18
19
G/B
LG/W
Ω

- Perform Self-diagnosis STEPS 1, 2 and 4 before referring to the following flow chart.

IS P.B.R. OPERATING NORMALLY? Refer to Self-Diagnosis STEP 2.

N.G. → CHECK P.B.R. CIRCUIT. Go to Diagnostic Procedure 5.

O.K. ↓

A CHECK FOR OUTPUT OF AUTO AMP. Set up Self-diagnosis STEP 4. Do approx. 10.5 volt exist between air mix door motor harness terminals No. ⑱ and ⑲ when code No. is switched from "42" to "43" or when code No. is switched from "46" to "41"?

Code No.	Air mix door operation	Terminal No. ⑱	Terminal No. ⑲	Voltage V
42 → 43	Cold → Hot	⊕	⊖	Approx. 10.5
46 → 41	Hot → Cold	⊖	⊕	Approx. 10.5
–	Stop	⊖	⊖	0

N.G. → Disconnect auto amp. and air mix door motor harness connectors. ↓ B Check circuit continuity between auto amp. harness terminal No. ⑱ (⑲) and air mix door motor harness terminal No. ⑱ (⑲). (Note) → O.K. → Replace auto amp.

O.K. → Replace air mix door motor.

NOTE: If the result is no good (NG) after checking circuit continuity, repair harness or connector.

94C10530 Courtesy of Nissan Motor Co., U.S.A.

Fig. 21: Diagnostic Procedure 9 – Air Mix Door Does Not Operate Normally

DIAGNOSTIC PROCEDURE 10 – BLOWER MOTOR OPERATION IS MALFUNCTIONING

A
Fan control amp. connector
41
BR/B
V
B
Fan control amp. connector
102
B
Ω
C
Fan control amp. connector
CONNECT
4
GY/L
V
Self-diagnosis STEP 4
41~45
D
Blower motor connector
50
BR/W
V
E
DISCONNECT
Blower motor connector
Fan control amp. connector
51
41
BR/B
Ω

SYMPTOM: Blower motor operation is malfunctioning under out of Starting Fan Speed Control.

- Perform Preliminary Check 5 before referring to the following flow chart.

A CHECK POWER SUPPLY FOR FAN CONTROL AMP. Disconnect fan control amp. harness connector. Do approx. 12 volts exist between fan control amp. harness terminal No. ㊶ and body ground?

N.G. → D CHECK POWER SUPPLY FOR BLOWER MOTOR. Disconnect blower motor harness connector. Do approx. 12 volts exist between blower motor harness terminal No. ㊿ and body ground?

- N.G. → Check 15A fuses at fuse block. See WIRING DIAGRAMS.
- O.K. → E Check circuit continuity between blower motor harness terminal No. (51) and fan control amp. harness terminal No. ㊶. (Note) → O.K. → CHECK BLOWER MOTOR. → N.G. → Replace blower motor.

O.K. ↓ (Note)

B CHECK BODY GROUND CIRCUIT FOR FAN CONTROL AMP. Does continuity exist between fan control amp. harness terminal No. (102) and body ground?

↓

Reconnect fan control amp. harness connector.

↓

C CHECK FOR OUTPUT OF AUTO AMP. Set up Self-diagnosis STEP 4. Measure voltage across fan control amp. harness terminal No. ④ and body ground.

Code No.	Terminal No. ⊕	Terminal No. ⊖	Voltage
41 - 45	④	Body ground	Approx. 1 - 3V

O.K. → Replace fan control amp.

N.G. → Ⓐ Go To Next Figure

NOTE: If the result is no good (NG) after checking circuit continuity, repair harness or connector.

90C03617 Courtesy of Nissan Motor Co., U.S.A.

Fig. 22: Diagnostic Procedure 10 – Blower Motor Operation Is Malfunctioning (1 Of 2)

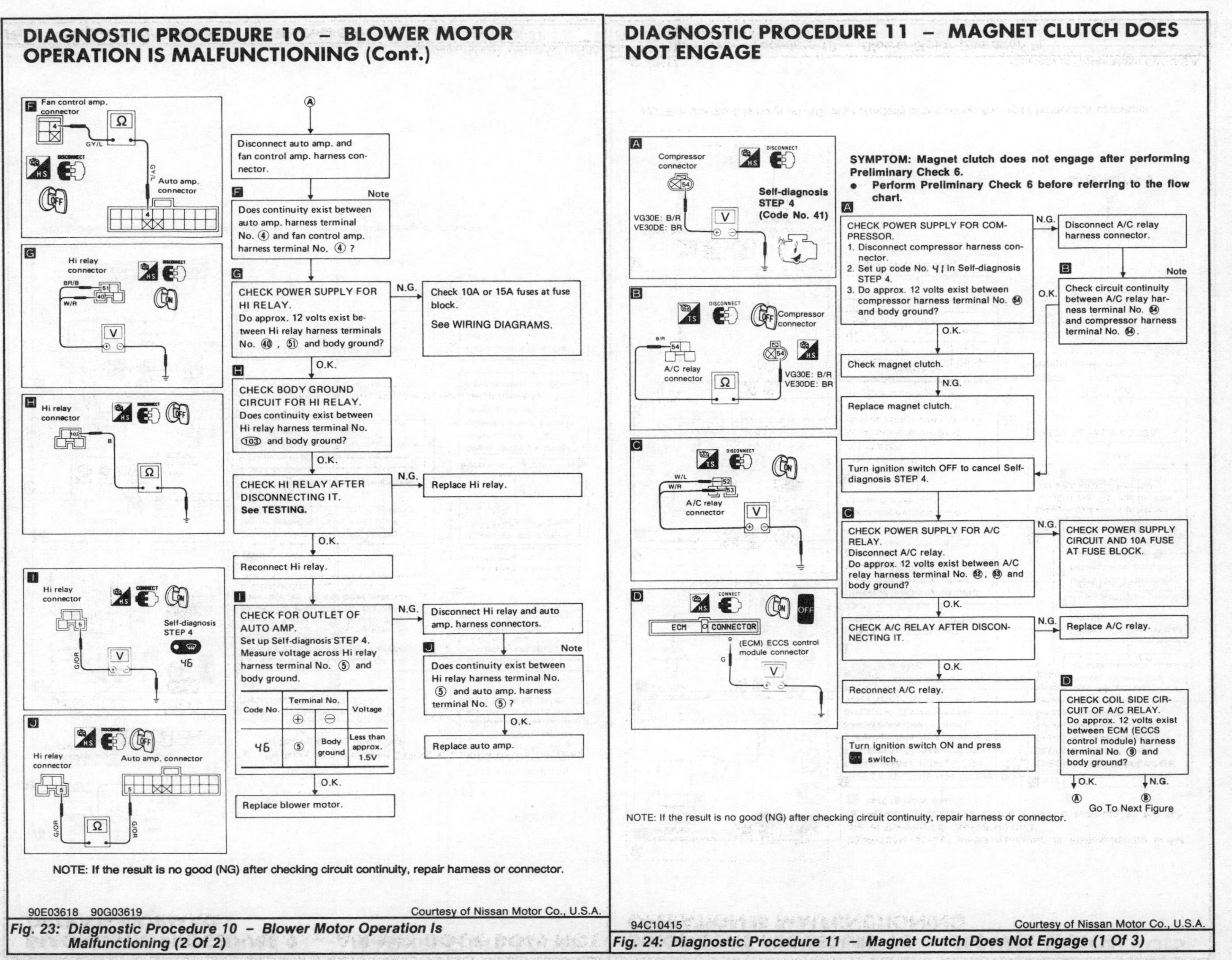

DIAGNOSTIC PROCEDURE 10 – BLOWER MOTOR OPERATION IS MALFUNCTIONING (Cont.)
F Fan control amp. connector
GY/L
Auto amp. connector
G Hi relay connector
BR/B
W/R
H Hi relay connector
I Hi relay connector
Self-diagnosis STEP 4
46
G/OR
J Hi relay connector
Auto amp. connector
G/OR
A
Disconnect auto amp. and fan control amp. harness connector.
F Note
Does continuity exist between auto amp. harness terminal No. ④ and fan control amp. harness terminal No. ④ ?
G
CHECK POWER SUPPLY FOR HI RELAY. Do approx. 12 volts exist between Hi relay harness terminals No. ⑩ , ⑤① and body ground?
N.G.
Check 10A or 15A fuses at fuse block. See WIRING DIAGRAMS.
O.K.
H
CHECK BODY GROUND CIRCUIT FOR HI RELAY. Does continuity exist between Hi relay harness terminal No. ⑩③ and body ground?
O.K.
CHECK HI RELAY AFTER DISCONNECTING IT. See TESTING.
N.G.
Replace Hi relay.
O.K.
Reconnect Hi relay.
I
CHECK FOR OUTLET OF AUTO AMP. Set up Self-diagnosis STEP 4. Measure voltage across Hi relay harness terminal No. ⑤ and body ground.
Code No. | Terminal No. ⊕ | ⊖ | Voltage
46 | ⑤ | Body ground | Less than approx. 1.5V
N.G.
Disconnect Hi relay and auto amp. harness connectors.
J Note
Does continuity exist between Hi relay harness terminal No. ⑤ and auto amp. harness terminal No. ⑤ ?
O.K.
Replace auto amp.
O.K.
Replace blower motor.
NOTE: If the result is no good (NG) after checking circuit continuity, repair harness or connector.
90E03618 90G03619
Courtesy of Nissan Motor Co., U.S.A.
DIAGNOSTIC PROCEDURE 11 – MAGNET CLUTCH DOES NOT ENGAGE
A Compressor connector
VG30E: B/R
VE30DE: BR
Self-diagnosis STEP 4 (Code No. 41)
B A/C relay connector
Compressor connector
VG30E: B/R
VE30DE: BR
C A/C relay connector
W/L
W/R
D ECM CONNECTOR
(ECM) ECCS control module connector
SYMPTOM: Magnet clutch does not engage after performing Preliminary Check 6.
• Perform Preliminary Check 6 before referring to the flow chart.
A
CHECK POWER SUPPLY FOR COMPRESSOR.
1. Disconnect compressor harness connector.
2. Set up code No. 41 in Self-diagnosis STEP 4.
3. Do approx. 12 volts exist between compressor harness terminal No. ⑤④ and body ground?
N.G.
Disconnect A/C relay harness connector.
B Note
Check circuit continuity between A/C relay harness terminal No. ⑤④ and compressor harness terminal No. ⑤④.
O.K.
O.K.
Check magnet clutch.
N.G.
Replace magnet clutch.
Turn ignition switch OFF to cancel Self-diagnosis STEP 4.
C
CHECK POWER SUPPLY FOR A/C RELAY. Disconnect A/C relay. Do approx. 12 volts exist between A/C relay harness terminal No. ⑤②, ⑤③ and body ground?
N.G.
CHECK POWER SUPPLY CIRCUIT AND 10A FUSE AT FUSE BLOCK.
O.K.
CHECK A/C RELAY AFTER DISCONNECTING IT.
N.G.
Replace A/C relay.
O.K.
Reconnect A/C relay.
Turn ignition switch ON and press switch.
D
CHECK COIL SIDE CIRCUIT OF A/C RELAY. Do approx. 12 volts exist between ECM (ECCS control module) harness terminal No. ⑨ and body ground?
O.K. A
N.G. B
Go To Next Figure
NOTE: If the result is no good (NG) after checking circuit continuity, repair harness or connector.
94C10415
Courtesy of Nissan Motor Co., U.S.A.

Fig. 23: Diagnostic Procedure 10 – Blower Motor Operation Is Malfunctioning (2 Of 2)

Fig. 24: Diagnostic Procedure 11 – Magnet Clutch Does Not Engage (1 Of 3)

1993 AUTOMATIC A/C-HEATER SYSTEMS
Trouble Shooting – Maxima (Cont.)

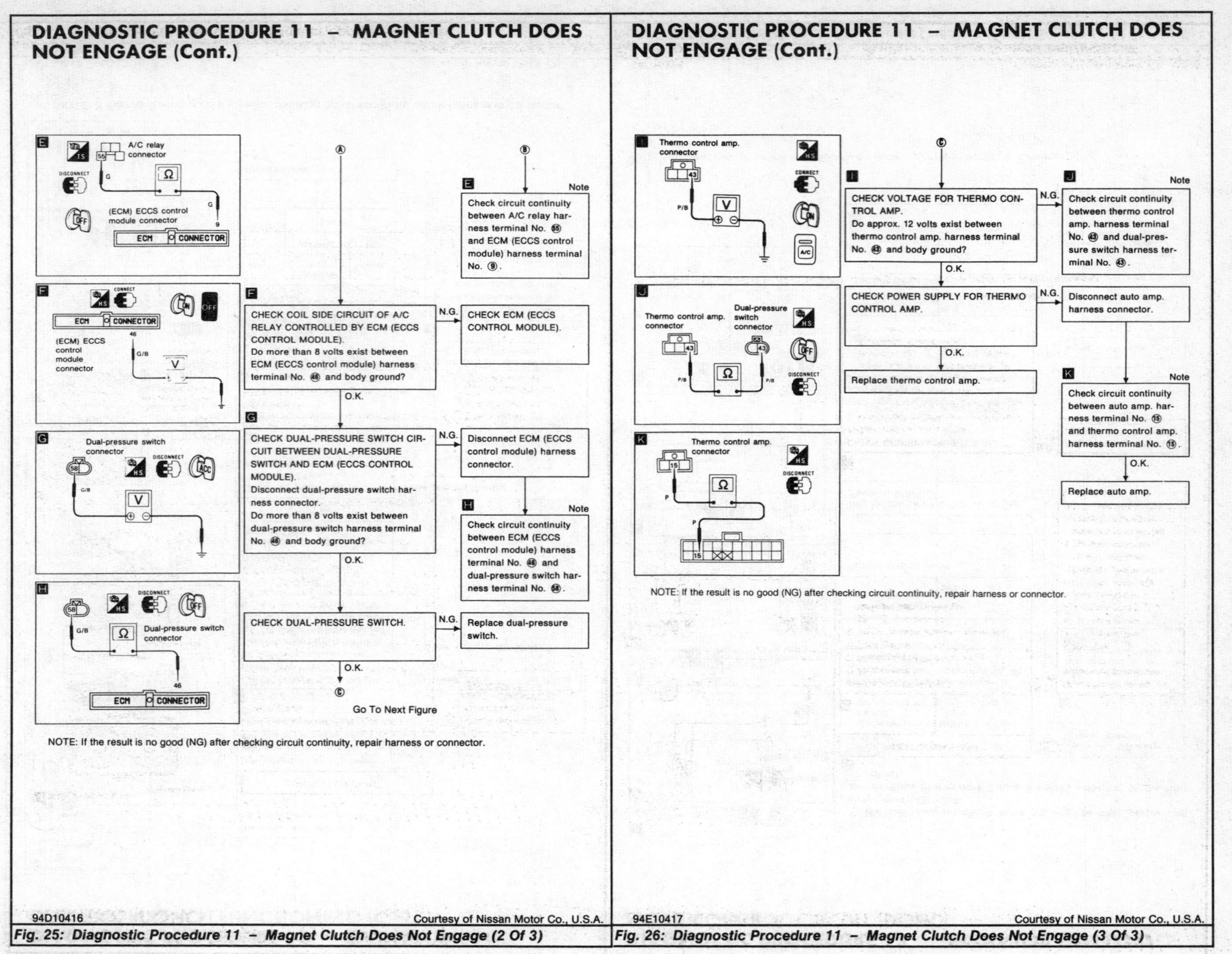
DIAGNOSTIC PROCEDURE 11 – MAGNET CLUTCH DOES NOT ENGAGE (Cont.)
E
A/C relay connector
DISCONNECT
(ECM) ECCS control module connector
ECM CONNECTOR
F
CONNECT
ECM CONNECTOR
(ECM) ECCS control module connector
G
Dual-pressure switch connector
DISCONNECT
H
DISCONNECT
Dual-pressure switch connector
ECM CONNECTOR
E
Check circuit continuity between A/C relay harness terminal No. 55 and ECM (ECCS control module) harness terminal No. 9.
Note
F
CHECK COIL SIDE CIRCUIT OF A/C RELAY CONTROLLED BY ECM (ECCS CONTROL MODULE).
Do more than 8 volts exist between ECM (ECCS control module) harness terminal No. 46 and body ground?
N.G.
CHECK ECM (ECCS CONTROL MODULE).
O.K.
G
CHECK DUAL-PRESSURE SWITCH CIRCUIT BETWEEN DUAL-PRESSURE SWITCH AND ECM (ECCS CONTROL MODULE).
Disconnect dual-pressure switch harness connector.
Do more than 8 volts exist between dual-pressure switch harness terminal No. 46 and body ground?
N.G.
Disconnect ECM (ECCS control module) harness connector.
H
Check circuit continuity between ECM (ECCS control module) harness terminal No. 46 and dual-pressure switch harness terminal No. 58.
Note
O.K.
CHECK DUAL-PRESSURE SWITCH.
N.G.
Replace dual-pressure switch.
O.K.
Go To Next Figure
NOTE: If the result is no good (NG) after checking circuit continuity, repair harness or connector.
94D10416
Courtesy of Nissan Motor Co., U.S.A.

Fig. 25: Diagnostic Procedure 11 – Magnet Clutch Does Not Engage (2 Of 3)

DIAGNOSTIC PROCEDURE 11 – MAGNET CLUTCH DOES NOT ENGAGE (Cont.)
I
Thermo control amp. connector
CONNECT
J
Thermo control amp. connector
Dual-pressure switch connector
DISCONNECT
K
Thermo control amp. connector
DISCONNECT
I
CHECK VOLTAGE FOR THERMO CONTROL AMP.
Do approx. 12 volts exist between thermo control amp. harness terminal No. 43 and body ground?
N.G.
J
Check circuit continuity between thermo control amp. harness terminal No. 43 and dual-pressure switch harness terminal No. 43.
Note
O.K.
CHECK POWER SUPPLY FOR THERMO CONTROL AMP.
N.G.
Disconnect auto amp. harness connector.
O.K.
Replace thermo control amp.
K
Check circuit continuity between auto amp. harness terminal No. 15 and thermo control amp. harness terminal No. 15.
Note
O.K.
Replace auto amp.
NOTE: If the result is no good (NG) after checking circuit continuity, repair harness or connector.
94E10417
Courtesy of Nissan Motor Co., U.S.A.

Fig. 26: Diagnostic Procedure 11 – Magnet Clutch Does Not Engage (3 Of 3)

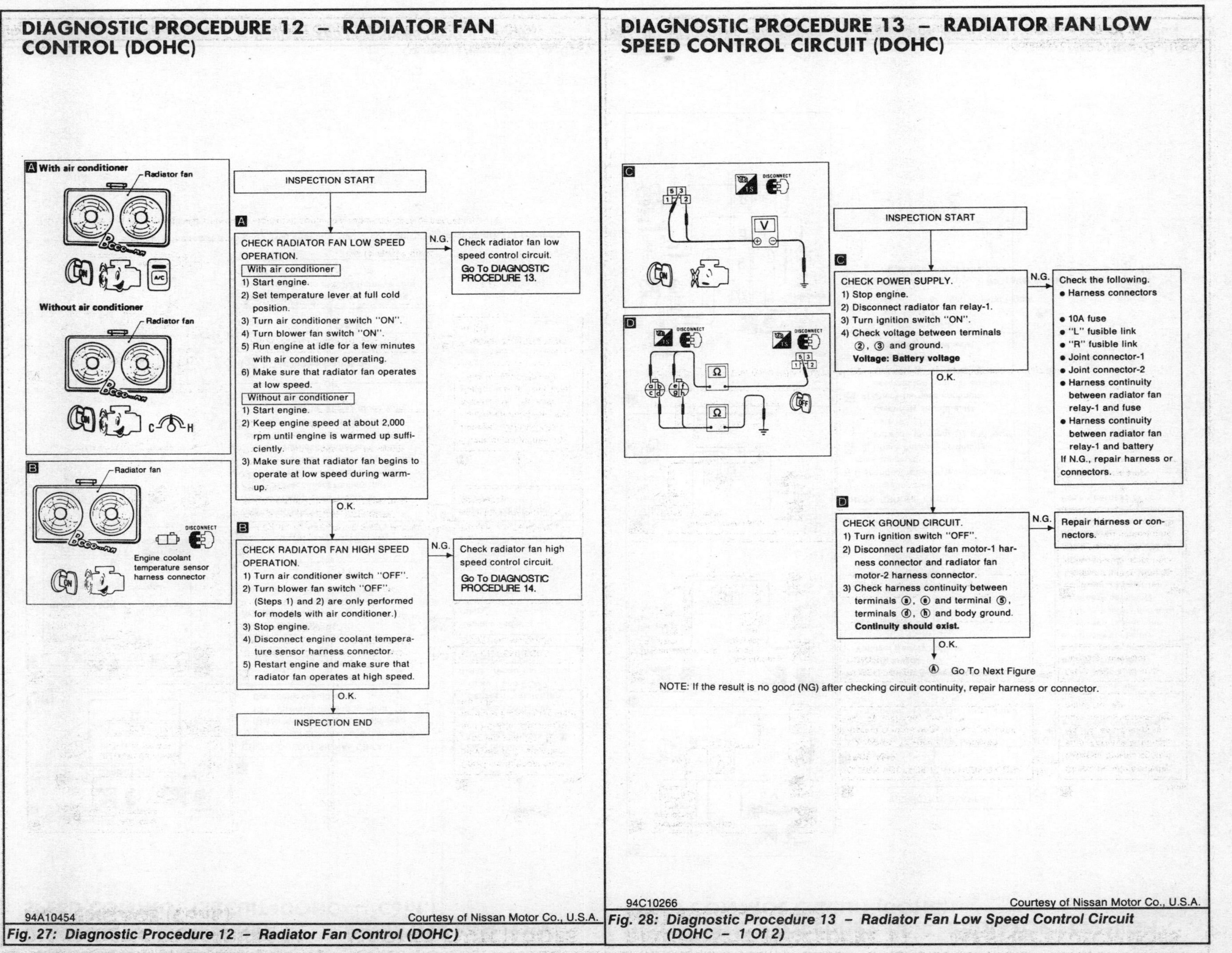
DIAGNOSTIC PROCEDURE 12 – RADIATOR FAN CONTROL (DOHC)
A With air conditioner
Radiator fan
Without air conditioner
Radiator fan
B
Radiator fan
DISCONNECT
Engine coolant temperature sensor harness connector
INSPECTION START
A
CHECK RADIATOR FAN LOW SPEED OPERATION.
With air conditioner
1) Start engine.
2) Set temperature lever at full cold position.
3) Turn air conditioner switch "ON".
4) Turn blower fan switch "ON".
5) Run engine at idle for a few minutes with air conditioner operating.
6) Make sure that radiator fan operates at low speed.
Without air conditioner
1) Start engine.
2) Keep engine speed at about 2,000 rpm until engine is warmed up sufficiently.
3) Make sure that radiator fan begins to operate at low speed during warm-up.
N.G.
Check radiator fan low speed control circuit.
Go To DIAGNOSTIC PROCEDURE 13.
O.K.
B
CHECK RADIATOR FAN HIGH SPEED OPERATION.
1) Turn air conditioner switch "OFF".
2) Turn blower fan switch "OFF".
(Steps 1) and 2) are only performed for models with air conditioner.)
3) Stop engine.
4) Disconnect engine coolant temperature sensor harness connector.
5) Restart engine and make sure that radiator fan operates at high speed.
N.G.
Check radiator fan high speed control circuit.
Go To DIAGNOSTIC PROCEDURE 14.
O.K.
INSPECTION END
94A10454
Courtesy of Nissan Motor Co., U.S.A.
DIAGNOSTIC PROCEDURE 13 – RADIATOR FAN LOW SPEED CONTROL CIRCUIT (DOHC)
C
DISCONNECT
D
DISCONNECT
DISCONNECT
INSPECTION START
C
CHECK POWER SUPPLY.
1) Stop engine.
2) Disconnect radiator fan relay-1.
3) Turn ignition switch "ON".
4) Check voltage between terminals ②, ③ and ground.
Voltage: Battery voltage
N.G.
Check the following.
• Harness connectors
• 10A fuse
• "L" fusible link
• "R" fusible link
• Joint connector-1
• Joint connector-2
• Harness continuity between radiator fan relay-1 and fuse
• Harness continuity between radiator fan relay-1 and battery
If N.G., repair harness or connectors.
O.K.
D
CHECK GROUND CIRCUIT.
1) Turn ignition switch "OFF".
2) Disconnect radiator fan motor-1 harness connector and radiator fan motor-2 harness connector.
3) Check harness continuity between terminals ⓐ, ⓔ and terminal ⑤, terminals ⓓ, ⓑ and body ground.
Continuity should exist.
N.G.
Repair harness or connectors.
O.K.
Ⓐ Go To Next Figure
NOTE: If the result is no good (NG) after checking circuit continuity, repair harness or connector.
94C10266
Courtesy of Nissan Motor Co., U.S.A.

Fig. 27: Diagnostic Procedure 12 – Radiator Fan Control (DOHC)

Fig. 28: Diagnostic Procedure 13 – Radiator Fan Low Speed Control Circuit (DOHC – 1 Of 2)

1993 MANUAL A/C-HEATER SYSTEMS
Trouble Shooting – Maxima (Cont.)

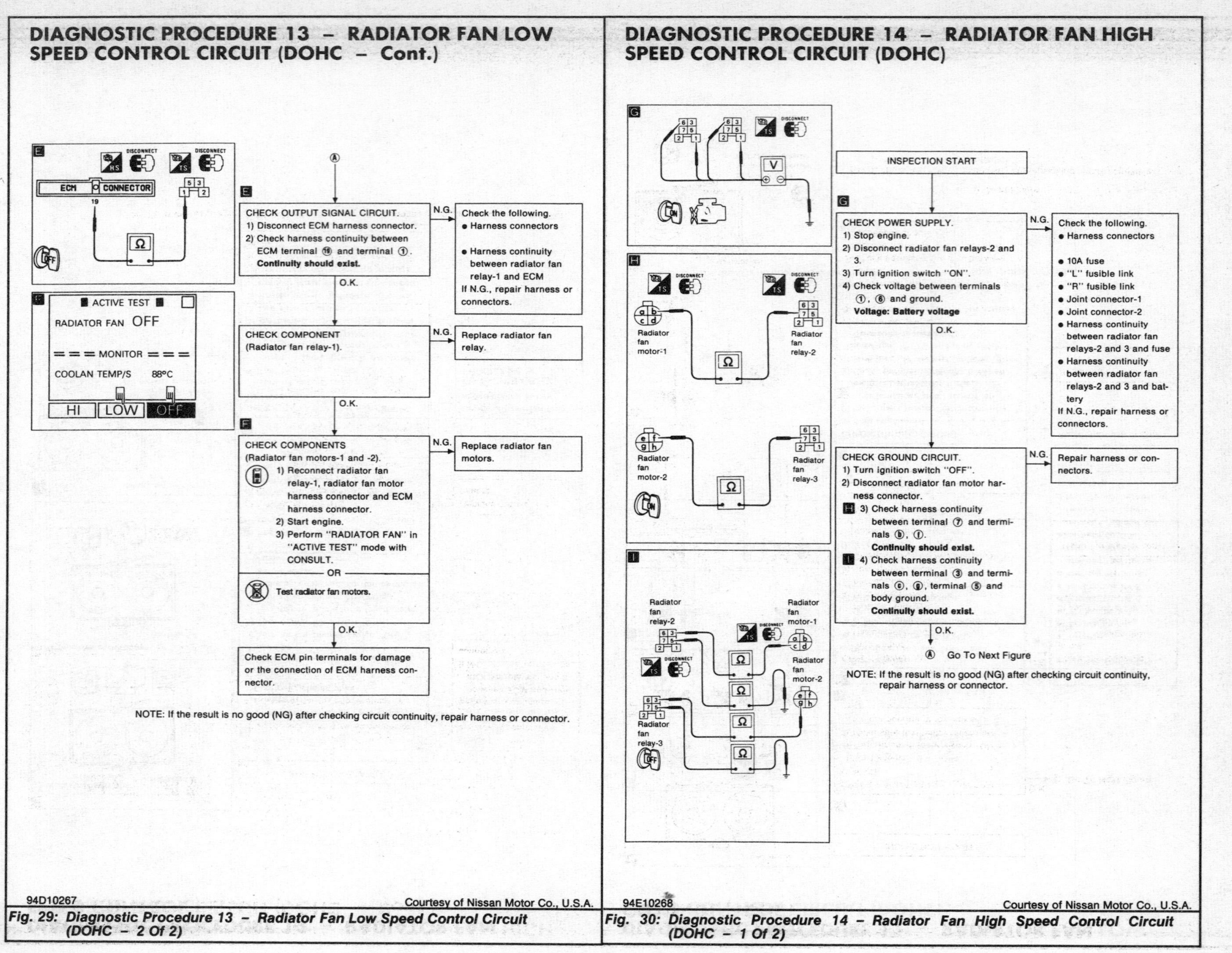
DIAGNOSTIC PROCEDURE 13 – RADIATOR FAN LOW SPEED CONTROL CIRCUIT (DOHC – Cont.)
E
DISCONNECT
HS
TS
ECM
CONNECTOR
19
5 3
1 2
Ω
OFF
F
ACTIVE TEST
RADIATOR FAN OFF
=== MONITOR ===
COOLAN TEMP/S 88°C
HI
LOW
OFF
Ⓐ
E
CHECK OUTPUT SIGNAL CIRCUIT.
1) Disconnect ECM harness connector.
2) Check harness continuity between ECM terminal ⑲ and terminal ①.
Continuity should exist.
N.G.
Check the following.
• Harness connectors
• Harness continuity between radiator fan relay-1 and ECM
If N.G., repair harness or connectors.
O.K.
CHECK COMPONENT
(Radiator fan relay-1).
N.G.
Replace radiator fan relay.
O.K.
F
CHECK COMPONENTS
(Radiator fan motors-1 and -2).
1) Reconnect radiator fan relay-1, radiator fan motor harness connector and ECM harness connector.
2) Start engine.
3) Perform "RADIATOR FAN" in "ACTIVE TEST" mode with CONSULT.
OR
Test radiator fan motors.
N.G.
Replace radiator fan motors.
O.K.
Check ECM pin terminals for damage or the connection of ECM harness connector.
NOTE: If the result is no good (NG) after checking circuit continuity, repair harness or connector.
94D10267
Courtesy of Nissan Motor Co., U.S.A.
DIAGNOSTIC PROCEDURE 14 – RADIATOR FAN HIGH SPEED CONTROL CIRCUIT (DOHC)
G
6 3
7 5
2 1
DISCONNECT
TS
V
ON
H
Radiator fan motor-1
Radiator fan relay-2
Ω
Radiator fan motor-2
Radiator fan relay-3
I
Radiator fan relay-2
Radiator fan motor-1
Radiator fan motor-2
Radiator fan relay-3
INSPECTION START
G
CHECK POWER SUPPLY.
1) Stop engine.
2) Disconnect radiator fan relays-2 and 3.
3) Turn ignition switch "ON".
4) Check voltage between terminals ①, ⑥ and ground.
Voltage: Battery voltage
N.G.
Check the following.
• Harness connectors
• 10A fuse
• "L" fusible link
• "R" fusible link
• Joint connector-1
• Joint connector-2
• Harness continuity between radiator fan relays-2 and 3 and fuse
• Harness continuity between radiator fan relays-2 and 3 and battery
If N.G., repair harness or connectors.
O.K.
CHECK GROUND CIRCUIT.
1) Turn ignition switch "OFF".
2) Disconnect radiator fan motor harness connector.
H 3) Check harness continuity between terminal ⑦ and terminals ⓑ, ⓕ.
Continuity should exist.
I 4) Check harness continuity between terminal ③ and terminals ⓔ, ⓖ, terminal ⑤ and body ground.
Continuity should exist.
N.G.
Repair harness or connectors.
O.K.
Ⓐ Go To Next Figure
NOTE: If the result is no good (NG) after checking circuit continuity, repair harness or connector.
94E10268
Courtesy of Nissan Motor Co., U.S.A.

Fig. 29: Diagnostic Procedure 13 – Radiator Fan Low Speed Control Circuit (DOHC – 2 Of 2)

Fig. 30: Diagnostic Procedure 14 – Radiator Fan High Speed Control Circuit (DOHC – 1 Of 2)

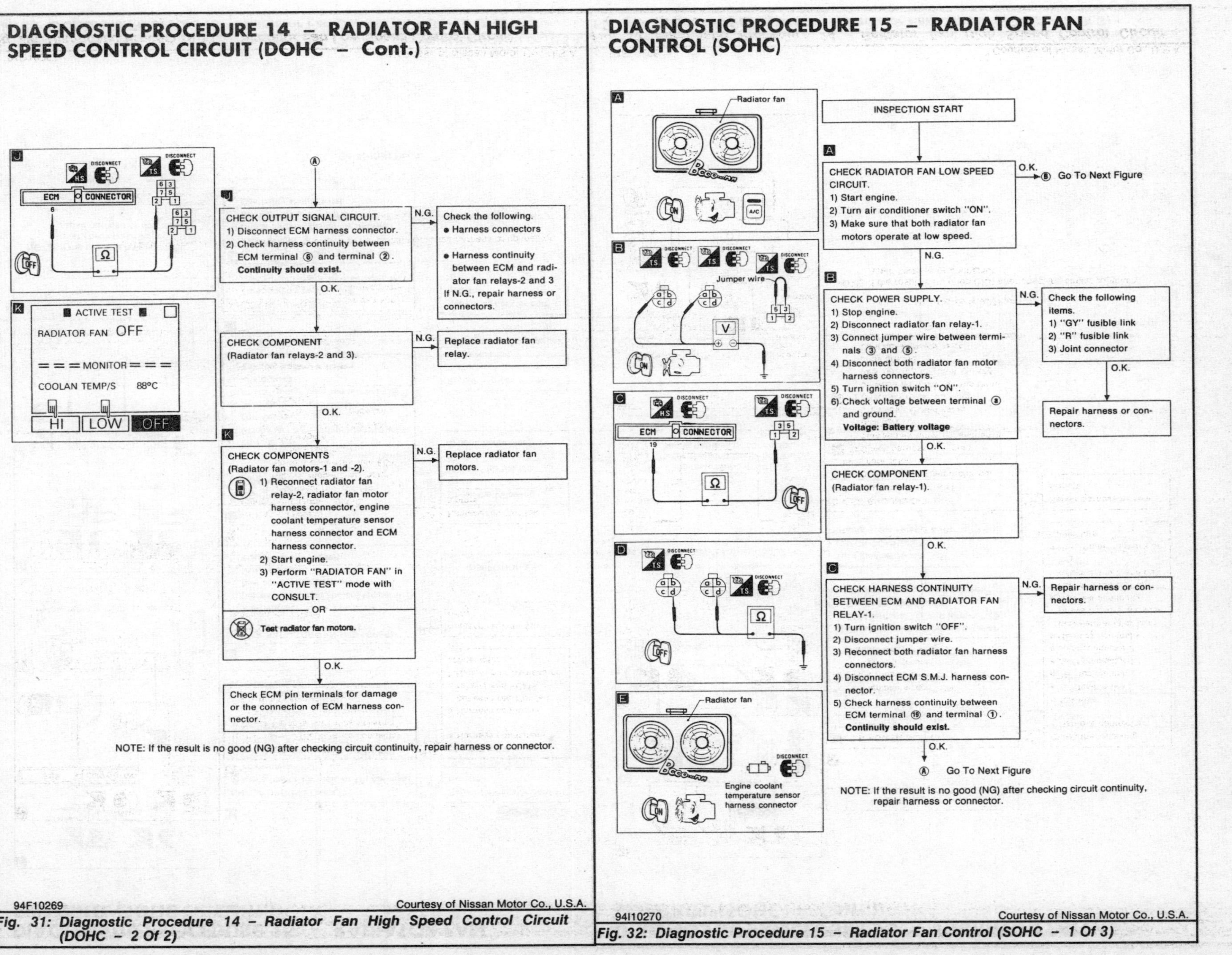
DIAGNOSTIC PROCEDURE 14 – RADIATOR FAN HIGH SPEED CONTROL CIRCUIT (DOHC – Cont.)
J
ECM
CONNECTOR
6
Ω
OFF
K
ACTIVE TEST
RADIATOR FAN OFF
=== MONITOR ===
COOLAN TEMP/S 88°C
HI
LOW
OFF
Ⓐ
J
CHECK OUTPUT SIGNAL CIRCUIT.
1) Disconnect ECM harness connector.
2) Check harness continuity between ECM terminal ⑥ and terminal ②.
Continuity should exist.
N.G.
Check the following.
• Harness connectors
• Harness continuity between ECM and radiator fan relays-2 and 3
If N.G., repair harness or connectors.
O.K.
CHECK COMPONENT
(Radiator fan relays-2 and 3).
N.G.
Replace radiator fan relay.
O.K.
K
CHECK COMPONENTS
(Radiator fan motors-1 and -2).
1) Reconnect radiator fan relay-2, radiator fan motor harness connector, engine coolant temperature sensor harness connector and ECM harness connector.
2) Start engine.
3) Perform "RADIATOR FAN" in "ACTIVE TEST" mode with CONSULT.
OR
Test radiator fan motors.
N.G.
Replace radiator fan motors.
O.K.
Check ECM pin terminals for damage or the connection of ECM harness connector.
NOTE: If the result is no good (NG) after checking circuit continuity, repair harness or connector.
94F10269
Courtesy of Nissan Motor Co., U.S.A.
DIAGNOSTIC PROCEDURE 15 – RADIATOR FAN CONTROL (SOHC)
A
Radiator fan
ON
A/C
B
Jumper wire
V
ON
C
ECM
CONNECTOR
19
Ω
OFF
D
Ω
OFF
E
Radiator fan
Engine coolant temperature sensor harness connector
ON
INSPECTION START
A
CHECK RADIATOR FAN LOW SPEED CIRCUIT.
1) Start engine.
2) Turn air conditioner switch "ON".
3) Make sure that both radiator fan motors operate at low speed.
O.K.
Ⓑ Go To Next Figure
N.G.
B
CHECK POWER SUPPLY.
1) Stop engine.
2) Disconnect radiator fan relay-1.
3) Connect jumper wire between terminals ③ and ⑤.
4) Disconnect both radiator fan motor harness connectors.
5) Turn ignition switch "ON".
6) Check voltage between terminal ⓐ and ground.
Voltage: Battery voltage
N.G.
Check the following items.
1) "GY" fusible link
2) "R" fusible link
3) Joint connector
O.K.
Repair harness or connectors.
O.K.
CHECK COMPONENT
(Radiator fan relay-1).
O.K.
C
CHECK HARNESS CONTINUITY BETWEEN ECM AND RADIATOR FAN RELAY-1.
1) Turn ignition switch "OFF".
2) Disconnect jumper wire.
3) Reconnect both radiator fan harness connectors.
4) Disconnect ECM S.M.J. harness connector.
5) Check harness continuity between ECM terminal ⑲ and terminal ①.
Continuity should exist.
N.G.
Repair harness or connectors.
O.K.
Ⓐ Go To Next Figure
NOTE: If the result is no good (NG) after checking circuit continuity, repair harness or connector.
94I10270
Courtesy of Nissan Motor Co., U.S.A.

Fig. 31: Diagnostic Procedure 14 – Radiator Fan High Speed Control Circuit (DOHC – 2 Of 2)

Fig. 32: Diagnostic Procedure 15 – Radiator Fan Control (SOHC – 1 Of 3)

1993 MANUAL A/C-HEATER SYSTEMS
Trouble Shooting – Maxima (Cont.)

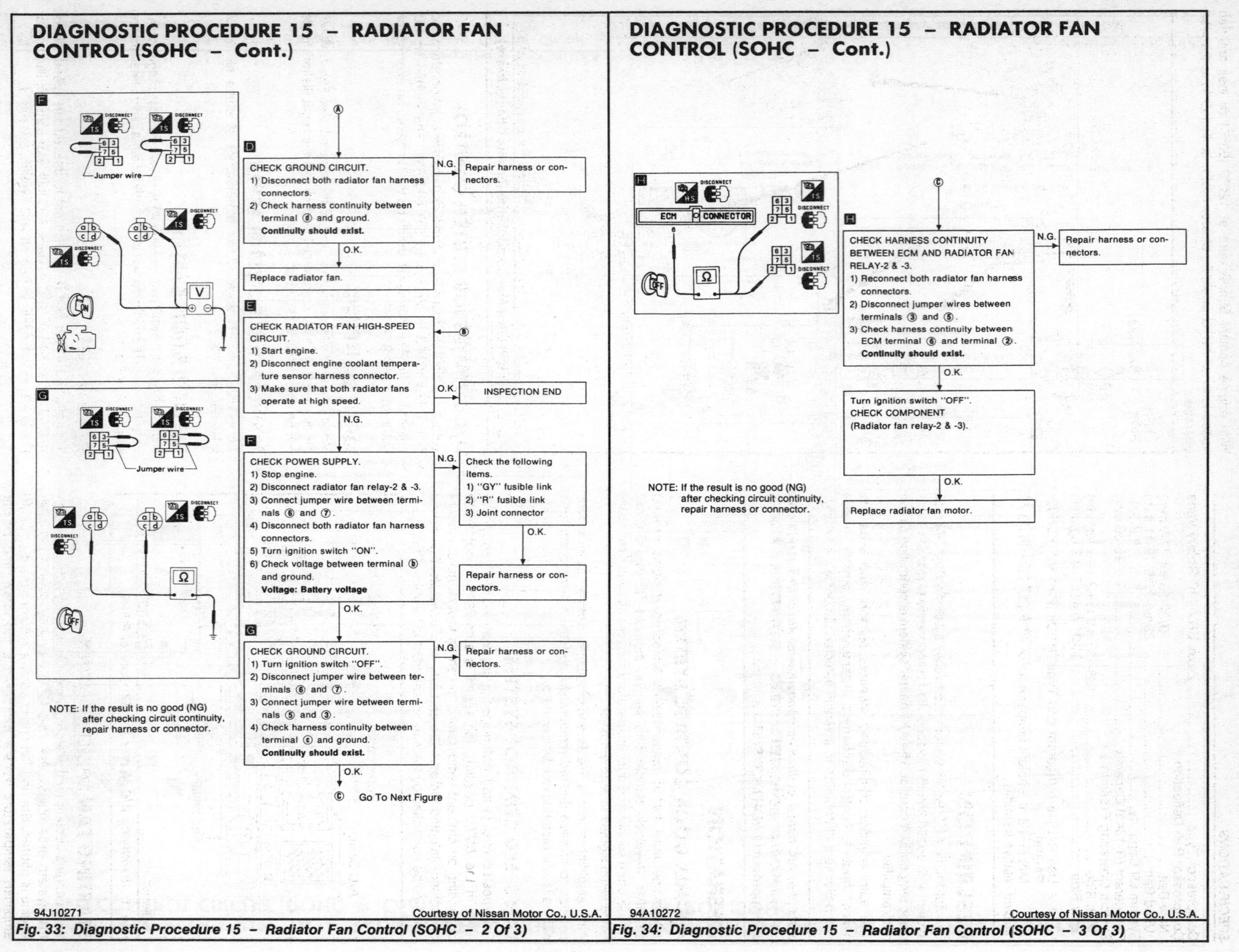
DIAGNOSTIC PROCEDURE 15 – RADIATOR FAN CONTROL (SOHC – Cont.)
F
DISCONNECT
TS
Jumper wire
V
G
Jumper wire
Ω
NOTE: If the result is no good (NG) after checking circuit continuity, repair harness or connector.
Ⓐ
D
CHECK GROUND CIRCUIT.
1) Disconnect both radiator fan harness connectors.
2) Check harness continuity between terminal ⓓ and ground.
Continuity should exist.
N.G.
Repair harness or connectors.
O.K.
Replace radiator fan.
E
CHECK RADIATOR FAN HIGH-SPEED CIRCUIT.
1) Start engine.
2) Disconnect engine coolant temperature sensor harness connector.
3) Make sure that both radiator fans operate at high speed.
Ⓑ
O.K.
INSPECTION END
N.G.
F
CHECK POWER SUPPLY.
1) Stop engine.
2) Disconnect radiator fan relay-2 & -3.
3) Connect jumper wire between terminals ⑥ and ⑦.
4) Disconnect both radiator fan harness connectors.
5) Turn ignition switch "ON".
6) Check voltage between terminal ⓑ and ground.
Voltage: Battery voltage
N.G.
Check the following items.
1) "GY" fusible link
2) "R" fusible link
3) Joint connector
O.K.
Repair harness or connectors.
O.K.
G
CHECK GROUND CIRCUIT.
1) Turn ignition switch "OFF".
2) Disconnect jumper wire between terminals ⑥ and ⑦.
3) Connect jumper wire between terminals ⑤ and ③.
4) Check harness continuity between terminal ⓒ and ground.
Continuity should exist.
N.G.
Repair harness or connectors.
O.K.
Ⓒ Go To Next Figure
94J10271
Courtesy of Nissan Motor Co., U.S.A.
DIAGNOSTIC PROCEDURE 15 – RADIATOR FAN CONTROL (SOHC – Cont.)
H
DISCONNECT
HS
TS
ECM
CONNECTOR
Ω
NOTE: If the result is no good (NG) after checking circuit continuity, repair harness or connector.
Ⓒ
H
CHECK HARNESS CONTINUITY BETWEEN ECM AND RADIATOR FAN RELAY-2 & -3.
1) Reconnect both radiator fan harness connectors.
2) Disconnect jumper wires between terminals ③ and ⑤.
3) Check harness continuity between ECM terminal ⑥ and terminal ②.
Continuity should exist.
N.G.
Repair harness or connectors.
O.K.
Turn ignition switch "OFF".
CHECK COMPONENT
(Radiator fan relay-2 & -3).
O.K.
Replace radiator fan motor.
94A10272
Courtesy of Nissan Motor Co., U.S.A.

Fig. 33: Diagnostic Procedure 15 – Radiator Fan Control (SOHC – 2 Of 3)

Fig. 34: Diagnostic Procedure 15 – Radiator Fan Control (SOHC – 3 Of 3)

SPECIFICATIONS

Compressor Type .... Zexel DKV-14C Rotary Vane
Compressor Belt Deflection
New Belt .... 9/32-23/64" (7-9 mm)
Used Belt .... 23/64-7/16" (9-11 mm)
System Oil Capacity .... 6.8 ozs.
Refrigerant (R-134a) Capacity [1] .... 26-30 ozs.
System Operating Pressures [2]
High Side .... 188-232 psi (13.2-16.3 kg/cm²)
Low Side .... 24-31 psi (1.7-2.2 kg/cm²)

[2] – [1] – Use R-134a refrigerant and Type "R" Oil (Part No. KLH00-PAGR0).
Measured at ambient temperature of 77°F (25°C), with 50-70 percent relative humidity.

DESCRIPTION

The automatic A/C-heater system is basically a standard A/C-heater system with added electronic-controlled components to provide automatic temperature control. The A/C-heater system is controlled by the auto amplifier.

The auto amplifier continuously monitors sensors and uses the sensor inputs to control discharged air temperature, airflow volume and outlet vent distribution to maintain selected temperature setting.

NOTE: For A/C-heater system components not described in this article, see MANUAL A/C-HEATER SYSTEMS – PATHFINDER & PICKUP and appropriate HEATER SYSTEMS articles.

OPERATION

AIR-MIX DOOR CONTROL SYSTEM

The temperature switch inputs desired temperature signal to auto amplifier. In-vehicle temperature sensor, sunload sensor, ambient temperature sensor and duct temperature sensors all input their resistance value signals to auto amplifier.

Auto amplifier monitors inputs and calculates desired air-mix door position to achieve desired temperature setting. It takes about one minute to stabilize duct air temperature.

FAN SPEED CONTROL SYSTEM

Fan speed control system determines airflow volume. With fan control lever in the AUTO position, fan speed is automatically controlled depending on ambient temperature, in-vehicle temperature, amount of sunload, selected temperature and A/C switch signals. Fan speed can also be controlled by manual operation of fan switch. *See Fig. 1.*

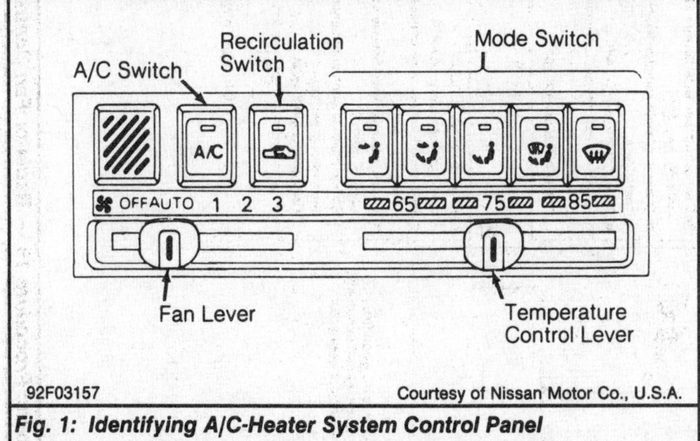

Recirculation Switch
Mode Switch
A/C Switch
A/C
OFF AUTO 1 2 3
65
75
85
Fan Lever
Temperature Control Lever
92F03157
Courtesy of Nissan Motor Co., U.S.A.

Fig. 1: Identifying A/C-Heater System Control Panel

STARTING FAN SPEED CONTROL

When engine coolant temperature is low, the starting fan speed control system prevents excess cold air from being discharged after engine is started. Starting fan speed control system consists of auto amplifier, temperature sensor microswitch, fan relays and blower motor.

With engine coolant temperature at 122°F (50°C) or less and fan speed lever at AUTO position, blower motor is limited to low-speed operation.

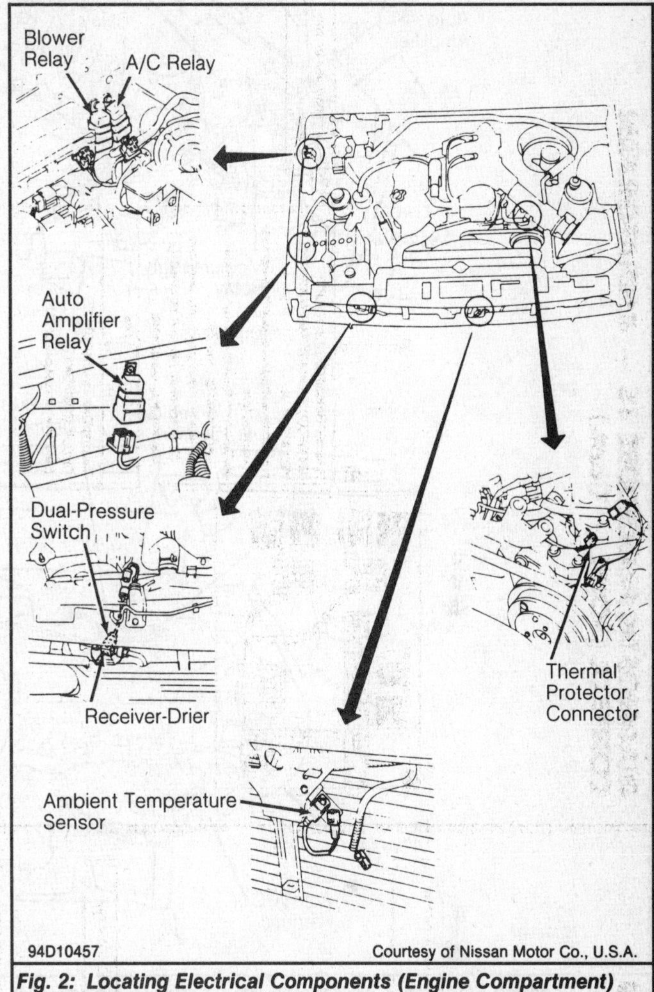

Blower Relay
A/C Relay
Auto Amplifier Relay
Dual-Pressure Switch
Receiver-Drier
Thermal Protector Connector
Ambient Temperature Sensor
94D10457
Courtesy of Nissan Motor Co., U.S.A.

Fig. 2: Locating Electrical Components (Engine Compartment)

A/C COMPRESSOR CLUTCH CONTROL

With A/C switch on, thermistor monitors evaporator temperature and sends information to thermo control amplifier. The thermo control amplifier controls compressor clutch operation based on information received. *See Fig. 3.*

MODE SWITCHES

Mode switches allow outlet air flow to be selected. *See Fig. 1.* When mode switch is set to defrost or foot/defrost, the recirculation mode will be automatically canceled.

TEMPERATURE CONTROL LEVER

Temperature control lever allows temperature of outlet air to be adjusted. *See Fig. 1.*

RECIRCULATION SWITCH

With recirculation switch off, outside air is drawn into passenger compartment. With recirculation switch on, interior air is recirculated inside vehicle. *See Fig. 1.*

A/C SWITCH

With engine running and fan switch set to desired fan speed, press A/C switch to turn on A/C system. A/C indicator light will illuminate. Press A/C switch again to turn off A/C system. *See Fig. 1.*

1993 AUTOMATIC A/C-HEATER SYSTEMS
Pathfinder (Cont.)

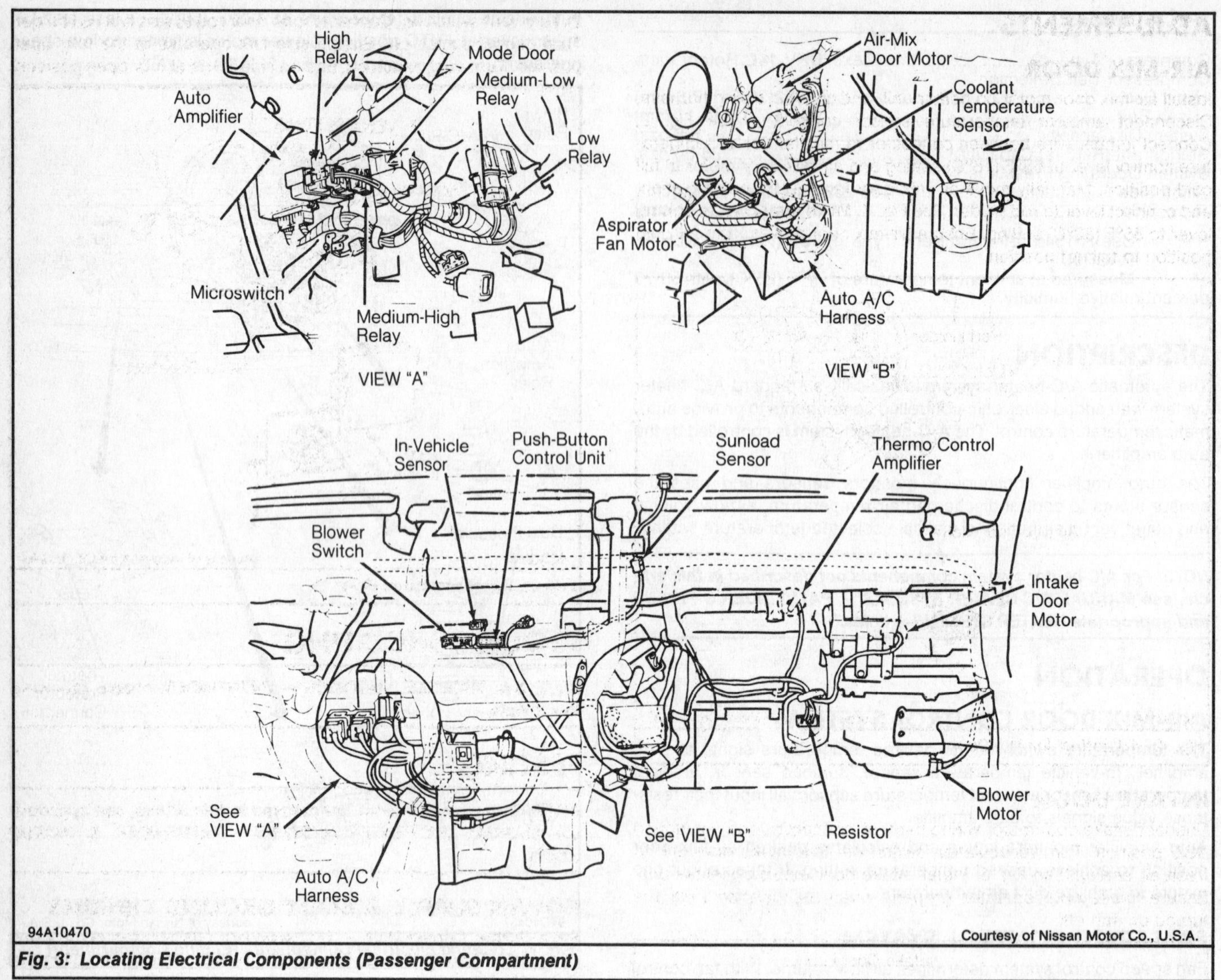
High Relay
Mode Door
Medium-Low Relay
Auto Amplifier
Low Relay
Microswitch
Medium-High Relay
VIEW "A"
Air-Mix Door Motor
Coolant Temperature Sensor
Aspirator Fan Motor
Auto A/C Harness
VIEW "B"
In-Vehicle Sensor
Push-Button Control Unit
Sunload Sensor
Thermo Control Amplifier
Blower Switch
Intake Door Motor
Blower Motor
See VIEW "A"
See VIEW "B"
Resistor
Auto A/C Harness
94A10470
Courtesy of Nissan Motor Co., U.S.A.

Fig. 3: Locating Electrical Components (Passenger Compartment)

ADJUSTMENTS

AIR-MIX DOOR

Install air-mix door motor on heater unit, and connect wiring harness. Disconnect ambient temperature sensor connector. *See Fig. 2.* Connect jumper wire between connector terminals. Set air temperature control lever at 65°F (18°C) setting and air-mix door motor at full cold position. Manually move air-mix door lever to full cold position, and connect lever to rod holder. *See Fig. 4.* Move temperature control lever to 85°F (32°C) setting. Ensure air-mix door moves from full cold position to full hot position.

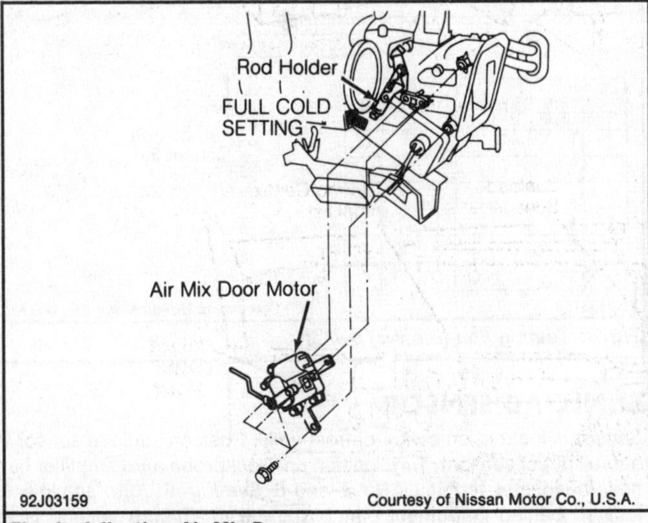
Rod Holder
FULL COLD SETTING
Air Mix Door Motor
92J03159
Courtesy of Nissan Motor Co., U.S.A.

Fig. 4: Adjusting Air Mix Door

INTAKE DOOR

Connect intake door motor wiring harness connector. Turn ignition to ACC position. Turn recirculation switch off. Set intake door link to fresh air setting. *See Fig. 5.* Install intake door motor on intake unit. Ensure intake door operates properly when recirculation switch is turned on and off.

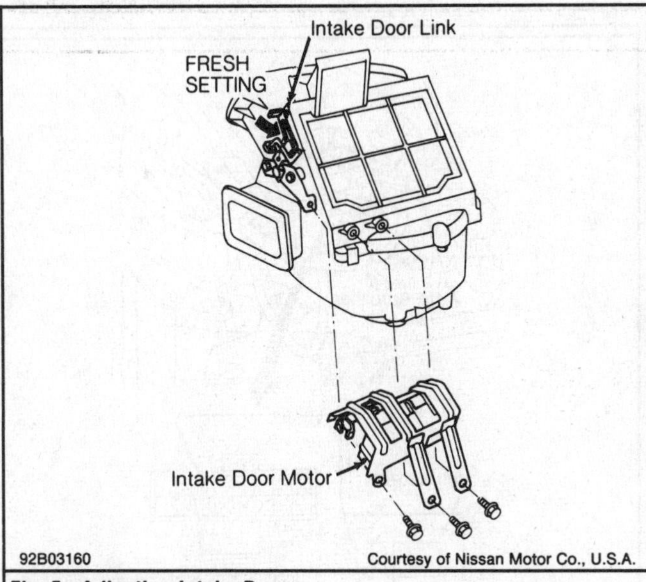
Intake Door Link
FRESH SETTING
Intake Door Motor
92B03160
Courtesy of Nissan Motor Co., U.S.A.

Fig. 5: Adjusting Intake Door

MODE DOOR

1) Remove auto amplifier and relay bracket. *See Figs. 1 and 3.* Manually move side link, and hold mode door in vent position. Install mode door motor on heater unit, and connect wiring harness. *See Fig. 6.* Turn ignition on.

2) Turn vent switch on. Connect mode door rod to side link rod holder. Turn defrost switch on. Ensure side link operates at the fully open position. Turn vent switch on. Ensure side link is at fully open position.

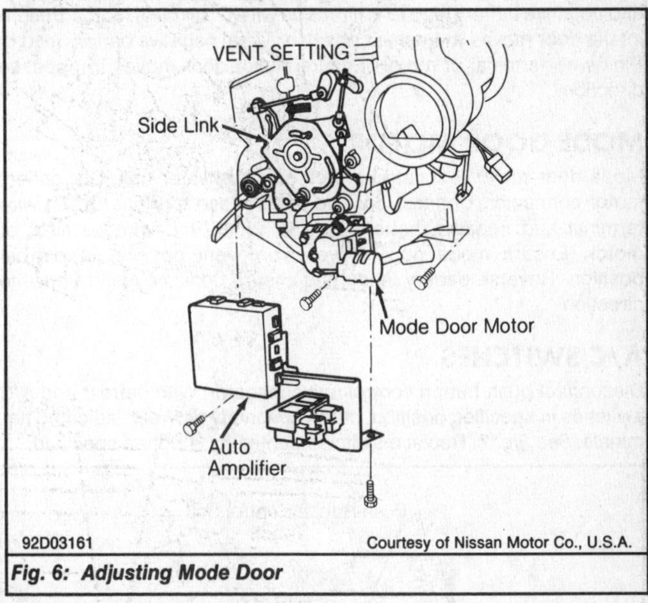
VENT SETTING
Side Link
Mode Door Motor
Auto Amplifier
92D03161
Courtesy of Nissan Motor Co., U.S.A.

Fig. 6: Adjusting Mode Door

TROUBLE SHOOTING

NOTE: See TROUBLE SHOOTING - PATHFINDER charts following this article.

TESTING

NOTE: For test procedures not covered in this article, see appropriate MANUAL A/C-HEATER SYSTEMS - PATHFINDER & PICKUP article.

POWER SUPPLY & BODY GROUND CIRCUITS

Push-Button Control Unit - 1) Disconnect push-button control unit connector. Turn ignition switch to ACC position. Measure voltage at Green/White wire terminal of connector. If 12 volts is present, go to next step. If not, repair open Green/White wire.

2) Turn ignition switch to ON position. Check continuity between Black wire terminal of connector and body ground. Ensure continuity exists. If there is no continuity, repair open Black wire.

Auto Amplifier - 1) Disconnect auto amplifier connector. Turn ignition switch to ON position. Measure voltage at White/Black wire terminal of connector. If 12 volts is present, go to next step. If not, repair open White/Black wire.

2) Turn ignition off. Check continuity between Black/Pink wire terminal of connector and body ground. Ensure continuity exists. If there is no continuity, repair open Black/Pink wire.

Thermo Control Amplifier - 1) Disconnect thermo control amplifier connector. Turn ignition on. Measure voltage at Green/Blue wire terminal of thermo control amplifier harness connector. If 12 volts is present, go to next step. If not, repair open Green/Blue wire.

2) Turn ignition off. Turn blower fan switch and A/C switch on. Check continuity between Green/Black wire terminal of connector and body ground. Ensure continuity exists. If there is no continuity, repair open Green/Black wire.

AIR-MIX DOOR MOTOR

Air-mix door motor is attached to heater unit. Disconnect motor connector. Connect positive battery lead to Orange/Black wire terminal and negative battery lead to Orange/Blue wire terminal of motor. Ensure air-mix door moves from cold position to hot position. Reverse battery leads and ensure door moves in opposite direction.

1993 AUTOMATIC A/C-HEATER SYSTEMS
Pathfinder (Cont.)

INTAKE DOOR MOTOR

Motor is installed on the intake unit. Disconnect Intake door motor connector. Connect positive battery lead to Green/White wire terminal and negative battery lead to White/Blue wire terminal of motor. Ensure intake door moves to fresh air position. Move negative battery lead to Pink wire terminal of motor. Ensure intake door moves in opposite direction.

MODE DOOR MOTOR

Mode door motor is located on left side of heater unit. Disconnect motor connector. Connect positive battery lead to White/Green wire terminal and negative battery lead to White/Red wire terminal of motor. Ensure mode door moves from vent position to defrost position. Reverse battery leads and ensure door moves in opposite direction.

A/C SWITCHES

Disconnect push-button control unit connector. With defrost and A/C switches in specified position, check continuity between indicated terminals. *See Fig. 7.* Replace switch if continuity is not as specified.

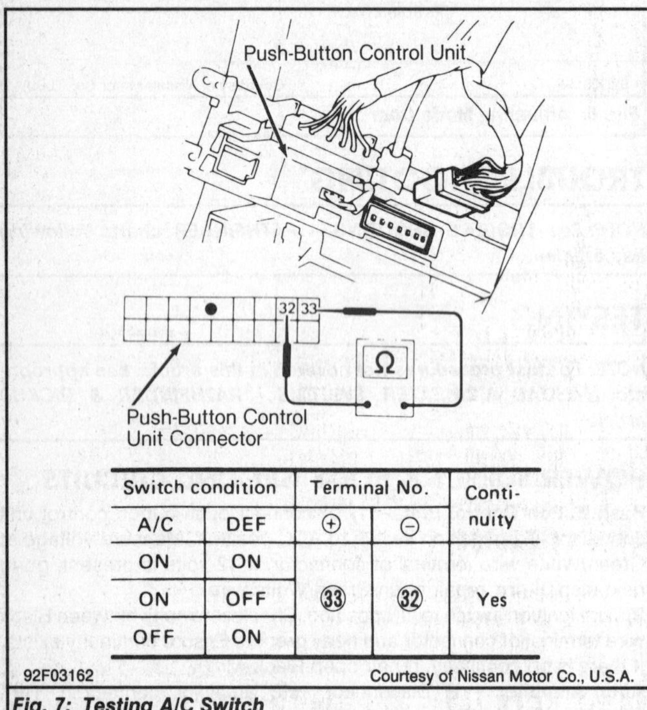
Push-Button Control Unit
32
33
Ω
Push-Button Control Unit Connector
92F03162
Courtesy of Nissan Motor Co., U.S.A.

Switch condition		Terminal No.		Conti-nuity
A/C	DEF	⊕	⊖	
ON	ON			
ON	OFF	33	32	Yes
OFF	ON			

Fig. 7: Testing A/C Switch

FAN (BLOWER) SWITCH

Disconnect fan (blower) switch connector. Check continuity between indicated terminals with fan switch in specified position. *See Fig. 8.* Replace switch if continuity is not as specified.

MICROSWITCH

Microswitch is installed around side link of heater unit. Microswitch operates link in response to mode switch position. Disconnect microswitch connector. Check continuity between indicated terminals with mode switch at specified position. Replace microswitch if continuity is not as specified. See MICROSWITCH CONTINUITY TEST table.

MICROSWITCH CONTINUITY TEST

Mode Switch Position	Continuity Between Terminals (Wire Color)
Vent	Brown/White & Red
Bi-Level	Brown/White & Yellow/Red
Foot	Brown/White & Yellow/Red
Foot/Defrost	Brown/White & Yellow/Red
Defrost	Brown/White & Red

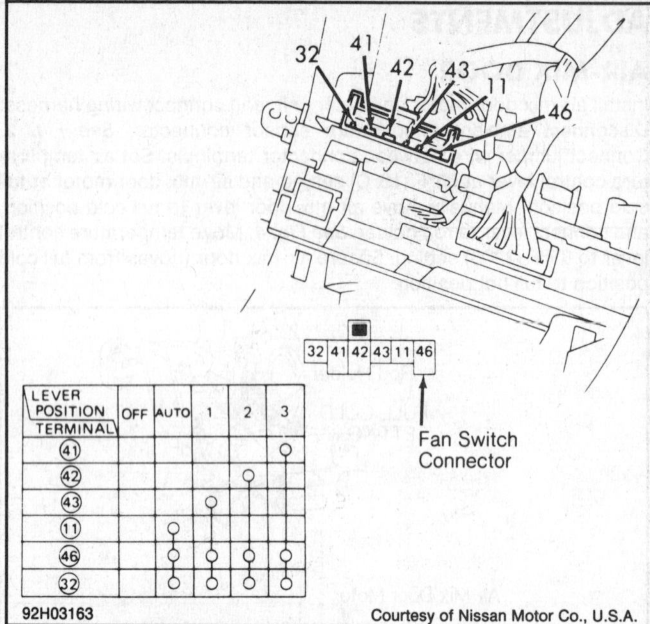
32
41
42
43
11
46
32 41 42 43 11 46
Fan Switch Connector
92H03163
Courtesy of Nissan Motor Co., U.S.A.

LEVER POSITION / TERMINAL	OFF	AUTO	1	2	3
41					○
42				○	
43			○		
11		○			
46		○	○	○	○
32		○	○	○	○

Fig. 8: Testing Fan (Blower) Switch

SUNLOAD SENSOR

Sensor is located on center defrost grille. Position sunload sensor to get full direct sunlight. Turn ignition on. Backprobe auto amplifier harness connector terminals No. 5 and 6. *See Fig. 9.* Auto amplifier is located behind instrument panel. *See Fig. 3.* Ensure voltage is as specified. See SUNLOAD SENSOR table.

SUNLOAD SENSOR

Input Current (Milliamps)	Output Voltage
0	5
0.1	4
0.2	3
0.3	2
0.4	1
0.5	0

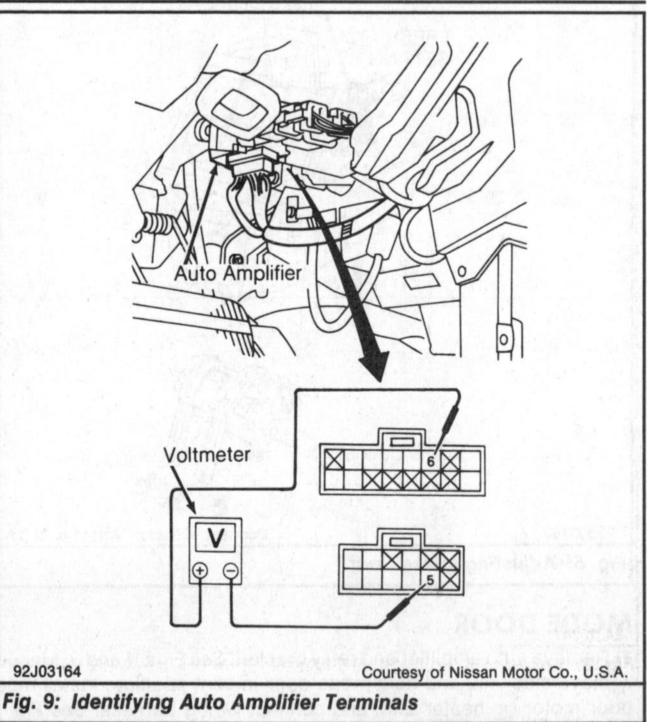
Auto Amplifier
Voltmeter
V
6
5
92J03164
Courtesy of Nissan Motor Co., U.S.A.

Fig. 9: Identifying Auto Amplifier Terminals

IN-VEHICLE TEMPERATURE SENSOR

The in-vehicle temperature sensor is attached to left side of A/C-heater control unit. Disconnect sensor harness connector. Measure resistance between sensor terminals. Replace sensor if resistance is not as specified. See IN-VEHICLE TEMPERATURE SENSOR RESISTANCE table.

IN-VEHICLE TEMPERATURE SENSOR RESISTANCE

Temperature °F (°C)	Ohms
32 (0)	6190
41 (5)	4950
50 (10)	3990
59 (15)	3240
68 (20)	2650
77 (25)	2190
86 (30)	1810
95 (35)	1510
104 (40)	1270

AMBIENT TEMPERATURE SENSOR

Ambient temperature sensor is located on hood lock stay. *See Fig. 2.* Disconnect sensor harness connector. Measure resistance between sensor terminals. Replace sensor if resistance is not as specified. See AMBIENT TEMPERATURE SENSOR RESISTANCE table.

AMBIENT TEMPERATURE SENSOR RESISTANCE

Temperature °F (°C)	Ohms
32 (0)	3260
50 (10)	1980
68 (20)	1250
77 (25)	1000
86 (30)	810
104 (40)	540

COOLANT TEMPERATURE SENSOR

Sensor is attached to heater unit and is in contact with heater core. *See Fig. 3.* Disconnect sensor harness connector. Measure resistance between sensor terminals. See COOLANT TEMPERATURE SENSOR RESISTANCE table. Replace sensor if resistance is not as specified.

COOLANT TEMPERATURE SENSOR RESISTANCE

Temperature °F (°C)	Ohms
32 (0)	3990
50 (10)	2540
68 (20)	1670
86 (30)	1120
104 (40)	780
122 (50)	550
140 (60)	400
158 (70)	290
176 (80)	220

REMOVAL & INSTALLATION

NOTE: See MANUAL A/C-HEATER SYSTEMS – PATHFINDER & PICK-UP and appropriate HEATER SYSTEMS articles.

1993 AUTOMATIC A/C-HEATER SYSTEMS Pathfinder (Cont.)

WIRING DIAGRAM

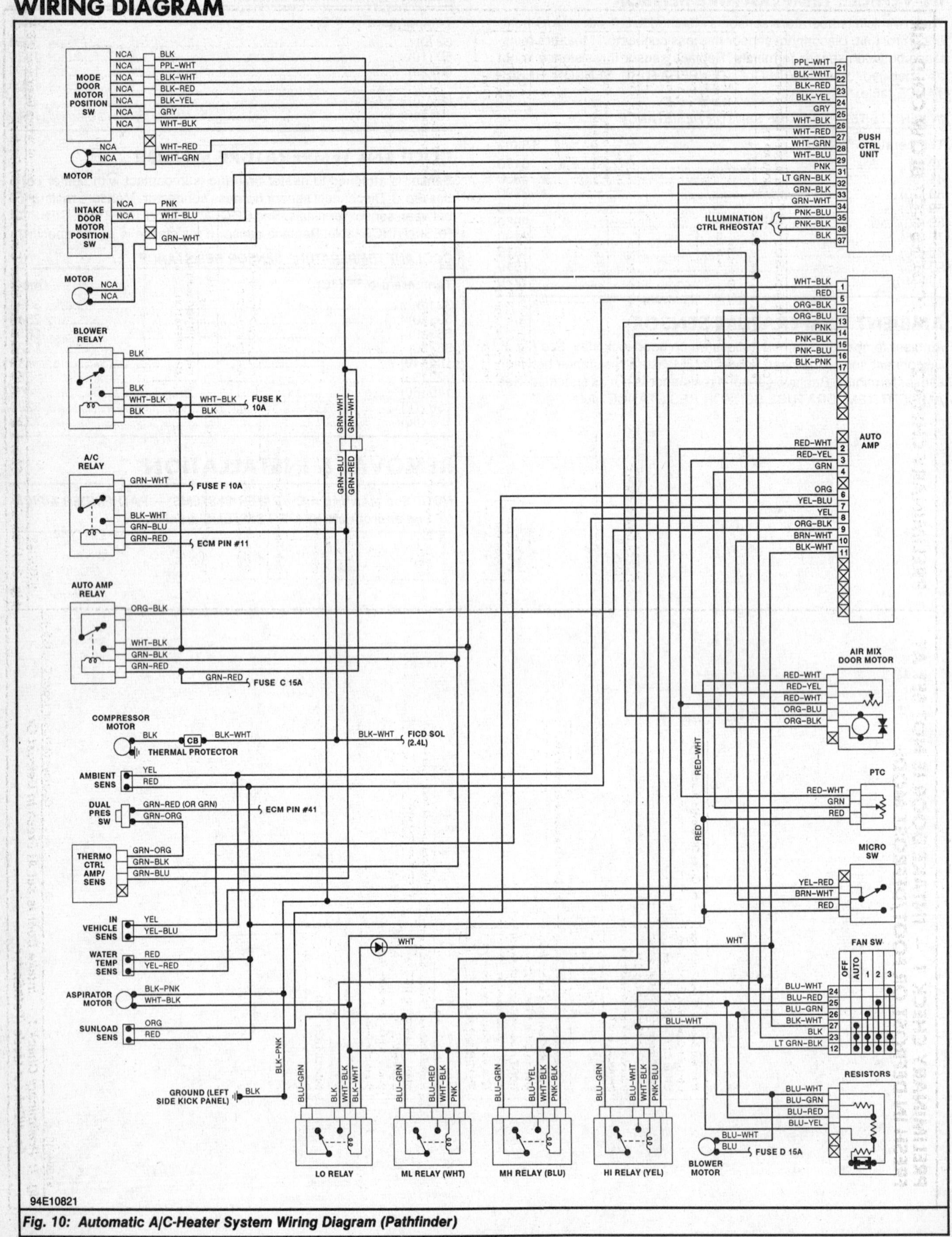
MODE DOOR MOTOR POSITION SW
NCA
BLK
PPL-WHT
BLK-WHT
BLK-RED
BLK-YEL
GRY
WHT-BLK
WHT-RED
WHT-GRN
MOTOR
INTAKE DOOR MOTOR POSITION SW
PNK
WHT-BLU
GRN-WHT
BLOWER RELAY
FUSE K 10A
A/C RELAY
FUSE F 10A
BLK-WHT
GRN-BLU
GRN-RED
ECM PIN #11
AUTO AMP RELAY
ORG-BLK
GRN-BLK
FUSE C 15A
COMPRESSOR MOTOR
CB
THERMAL PROTECTOR
FICD SOL (2.4L)
AMBIENT SENS
YEL
RED
DUAL PRES SW
GRN-RED (OR GRN)
GRN-ORG
ECM PIN #41
THERMO CTRL AMP/ SENS
IN VEHICLE SENS
YEL-BLU
WATER TEMP SENS
YEL-RED
ASPIRATOR MOTOR
BLK-PNK
SUNLOAD SENS
ORG
GROUND (LEFT SIDE KICK PANEL)
LO RELAY
ML RELAY (WHT)
MH RELAY (BLU)
HI RELAY (YEL)
BLOWER MOTOR
BLU-WHT
BLU
FUSE D 15A
PUSH CTRL UNIT
WHT-GRN
WHT-BLU
LT GRN-BLK
ILLUMINATION CTRL RHEOSTAT
PNK-BLU
PNK-BLK
AUTO AMP
ORG-BLU
RED-WHT
RED-YEL
GRN
YEL-BLU
BRN-WHT
AIR MIX DOOR MOTOR
PTC
MICRO SW
YEL-RED
FAN SW
OFF
AUTO
BLU-RED
BLU-GRN
RESISTORS
BLU-YEL
WHT
94E10821

Fig. 10: Automatic A/C-Heater System Wiring Diagram (Pathfinder)

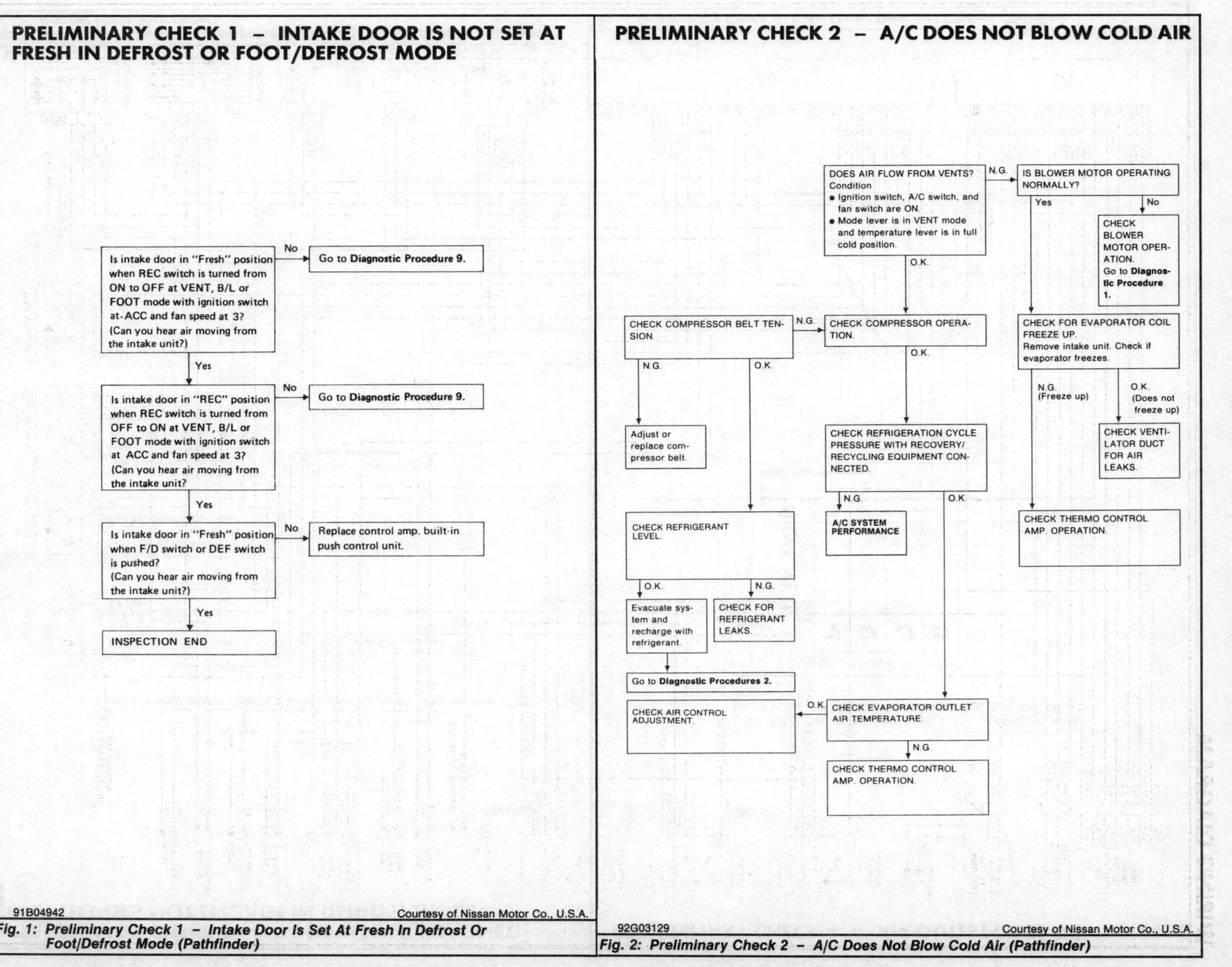
PRELIMINARY CHECK 1 – INTAKE DOOR IS NOT SET AT FRESH IN DEFROST OR FOOT/DEFROST MODE
Is intake door in "Fresh" position when REC switch is turned from ON to OFF at VENT, B/L or FOOT mode with ignition switch at-ACC and fan speed at 3? (Can you hear air moving from the intake unit?)
No
Go to Diagnostic Procedure 9.
Yes
Is intake door in "REC" position when REC switch is turned from OFF to ON at VENT, B/L or FOOT mode with ignition switch at ACC and fan speed at 3? (Can you hear air moving from the intake unit?)
No
Go to Diagnostic Procedure 9.
Yes
Is intake door in "Fresh" position when F/D switch or DEF switch is pushed? (Can you hear air moving from the intake unit?)
No
Replace control amp. built-in push control unit.
Yes
INSPECTION END
91B04942
Courtesy of Nissan Motor Co., U.S.A.
PRELIMINARY CHECK 2 – A/C DOES NOT BLOW COLD AIR
DOES AIR FLOW FROM VENTS? Condition
• Ignition switch, A/C switch, and fan switch are ON.
• Mode lever is in VENT mode and temperature lever is in full cold position.
N.G.
IS BLOWER MOTOR OPERATING NORMALLY?
Yes
No
CHECK BLOWER MOTOR OPERATION. Go to Diagnostic Procedure 1.
O.K.
CHECK COMPRESSOR BELT TENSION.
N.G.
CHECK COMPRESSOR OPERATION.
CHECK FOR EVAPORATOR COIL FREEZE UP. Remove intake unit. Check if evaporator freezes.
N.G.
O.K.
Adjust or replace compressor belt.
O.K.
CHECK REFRIGERATION CYCLE PRESSURE WITH RECOVERY/ RECYCLING EQUIPMENT CONNECTED.
N.G. (Freeze up)
O.K. (Does not freeze up)
CHECK VENTILATOR DUCT FOR AIR LEAKS.
N.G.
O.K.
CHECK REFRIGERANT LEVEL.
A/C SYSTEM PERFORMANCE
CHECK THERMO CONTROL AMP. OPERATION.
O.K.
N.G.
Evacuate system and recharge with refrigerant.
CHECK FOR REFRIGERANT LEAKS.
Go to Diagnostic Procedures 2.
CHECK AIR CONTROL ADJUSTMENT.
O.K.
CHECK EVAPORATOR OUTLET AIR TEMPERATURE.
N.G.
CHECK THERMO CONTROL AMP. OPERATION.
92G03129
Courtesy of Nissan Motor Co., U.S.A.

Fig. 1: Preliminary Check 1 – Intake Door Is Set At Fresh In Defrost Or Foot/Defrost Mode (Pathfinder)

Fig. 2: Preliminary Check 2 – A/C Does Not Blow Cold Air (Pathfinder)

1993 AUTOMATIC A/C-HEATER SYSTEMS
Trouble Shooting – Pathfinder (Cont.)

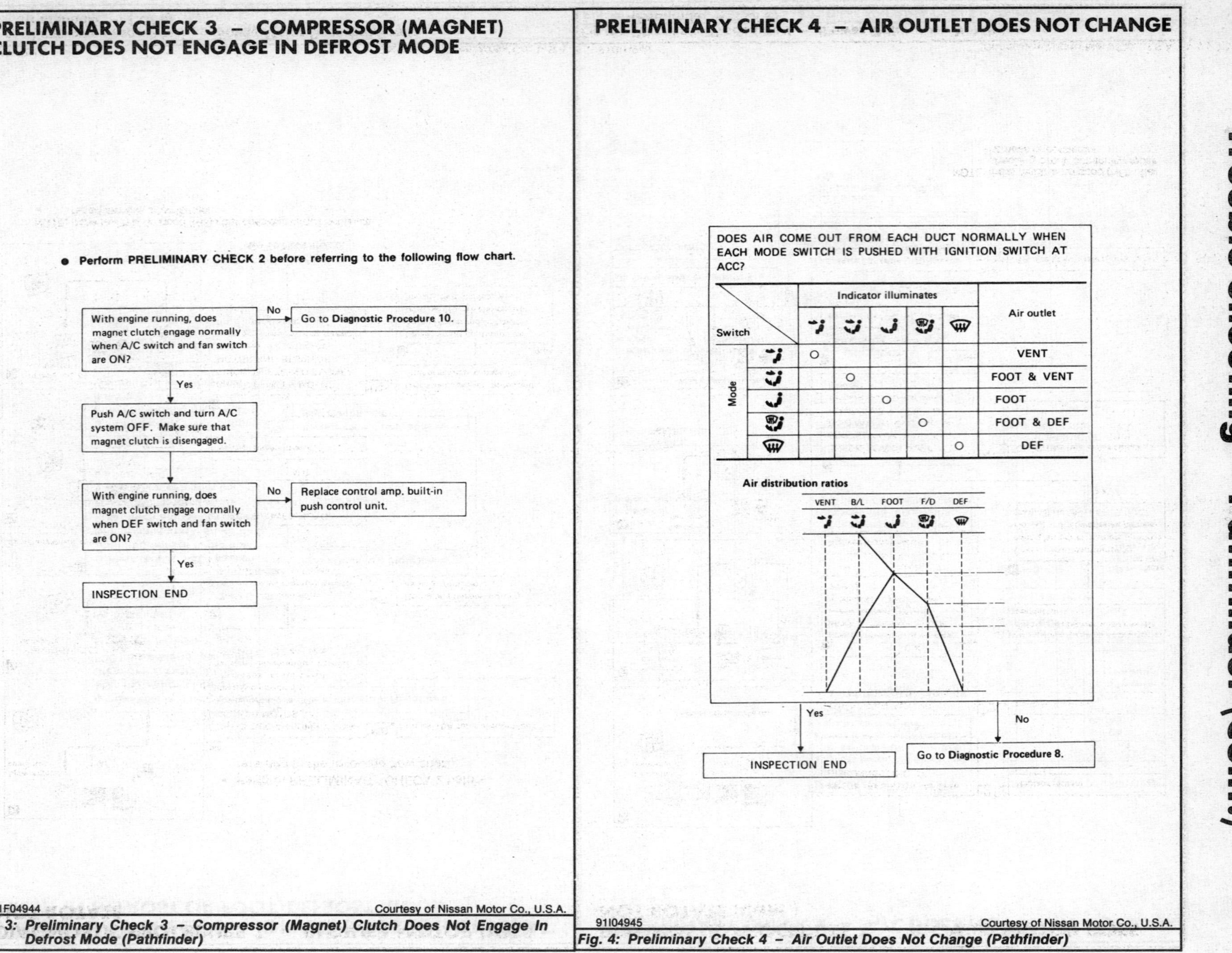
PRELIMINARY CHECK 3 – COMPRESSOR (MAGNET) CLUTCH DOES NOT ENGAGE IN DEFROST MODE
• Perform PRELIMINARY CHECK 2 before referring to the following flow chart.
With engine running, does magnet clutch engage normally when A/C switch and fan switch are ON?
No
Go to Diagnostic Procedure 10.
Yes
Push A/C switch and turn A/C system OFF. Make sure that magnet clutch is disengaged.
With engine running, does magnet clutch engage normally when DEF switch and fan switch are ON?
No
Replace control amp. built-in push control unit.
Yes
INSPECTION END
91F04944
Courtesy of Nissan Motor Co., U.S.A.
PRELIMINARY CHECK 4 – AIR OUTLET DOES NOT CHANGE
DOES AIR COME OUT FROM EACH DUCT NORMALLY WHEN EACH MODE SWITCH IS PUSHED WITH IGNITION SWITCH AT ACC?
Indicator illuminates
Switch
Mode
Air outlet
O
VENT
O
FOOT & VENT
O
FOOT
O
FOOT & DEF
O
DEF
Air distribution ratios
VENT
B/L
FOOT
F/D
DEF
Yes
No
INSPECTION END
Go to Diagnostic Procedure 8.
91I04945
Courtesy of Nissan Motor Co., U.S.A.

Fig. 3: Preliminary Check 3 – Compressor (Magnet) Clutch Does Not Engage In Defrost Mode (Pathfinder)

Fig. 4: Preliminary Check 4 – Air Outlet Does Not Change (Pathfinder)

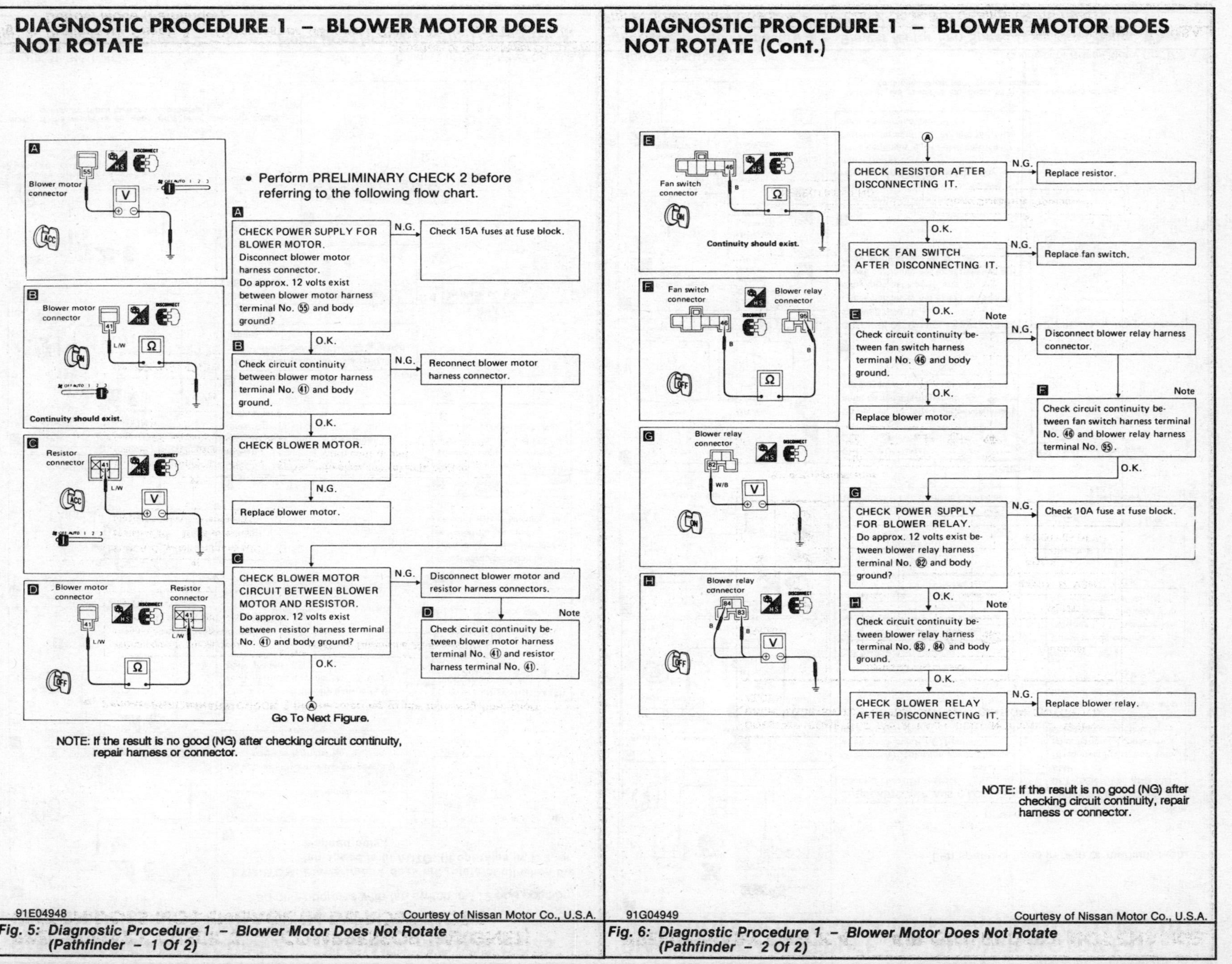
DIAGNOSTIC PROCEDURE 1 – BLOWER MOTOR DOES NOT ROTATE
• Perform PRELIMINARY CHECK 2 before referring to the following flow chart.
A
CHECK POWER SUPPLY FOR BLOWER MOTOR. Disconnect blower motor harness connector. Do approx. 12 volts exist between blower motor harness terminal No. 55 and body ground?
N.G.
Check 15A fuses at fuse block.
O.K.
B
Check circuit continuity between blower motor harness terminal No. 41 and body ground.
N.G.
Reconnect blower motor harness connector.
O.K.
CHECK BLOWER MOTOR.
N.G.
Replace blower motor.
C
CHECK BLOWER MOTOR CIRCUIT BETWEEN BLOWER MOTOR AND RESISTOR. Do approx. 12 volts exist between resistor harness terminal No. 41 and body ground?
N.G.
Disconnect blower motor and resistor harness connectors.
D
Note
Check circuit continuity between blower motor harness terminal No. 41 and resistor harness terminal No. 41.
O.K.
A
Go To Next Figure.
Blower motor connector
55
Resistor connector
41
L/W
Continuity should exist.
NOTE: If the result is no good (NG) after checking circuit continuity, repair harness or connector.
91E04948
Courtesy of Nissan Motor Co., U.S.A.
DIAGNOSTIC PROCEDURE 1 – BLOWER MOTOR DOES NOT ROTATE (Cont.)
A
CHECK RESISTOR AFTER DISCONNECTING IT.
N.G.
Replace resistor.
O.K.
CHECK FAN SWITCH AFTER DISCONNECTING IT.
N.G.
Replace fan switch.
O.K.
E
Note
Check circuit continuity between fan switch harness terminal No. 46 and body ground.
N.G.
Disconnect blower relay harness connector.
F
Note
Check circuit continuity between fan switch harness terminal No. 46 and blower relay harness terminal No. 95.
O.K.
Replace blower motor.
O.K.
G
CHECK POWER SUPPLY FOR BLOWER RELAY. Do approx. 12 volts exist between blower relay harness terminal No. 82 and body ground?
N.G.
Check 10A fuse at fuse block.
O.K.
H
Note
Check circuit continuity between blower relay harness terminal No. 83, 84 and body ground.
O.K.
CHECK BLOWER RELAY AFTER DISCONNECTING IT.
N.G.
Replace blower relay.
Fan switch connector
46
Blower relay connector
95
82
83
84
B
W/B
NOTE: If the result is no good (NG) after checking circuit continuity, repair harness or connector.
91G04949
Courtesy of Nissan Motor Co., U.S.A.

Fig. 5: Diagnostic Procedure 1 – Blower Motor Does Not Rotate (Pathfinder – 1 Of 2)

Fig. 6: Diagnostic Procedure 1 – Blower Motor Does Not Rotate (Pathfinder – 2 Of 2)

1993 AUTOMATIC A/C-HEATER SYSTEMS
Trouble Shooting – Pathfinder (Cont.)

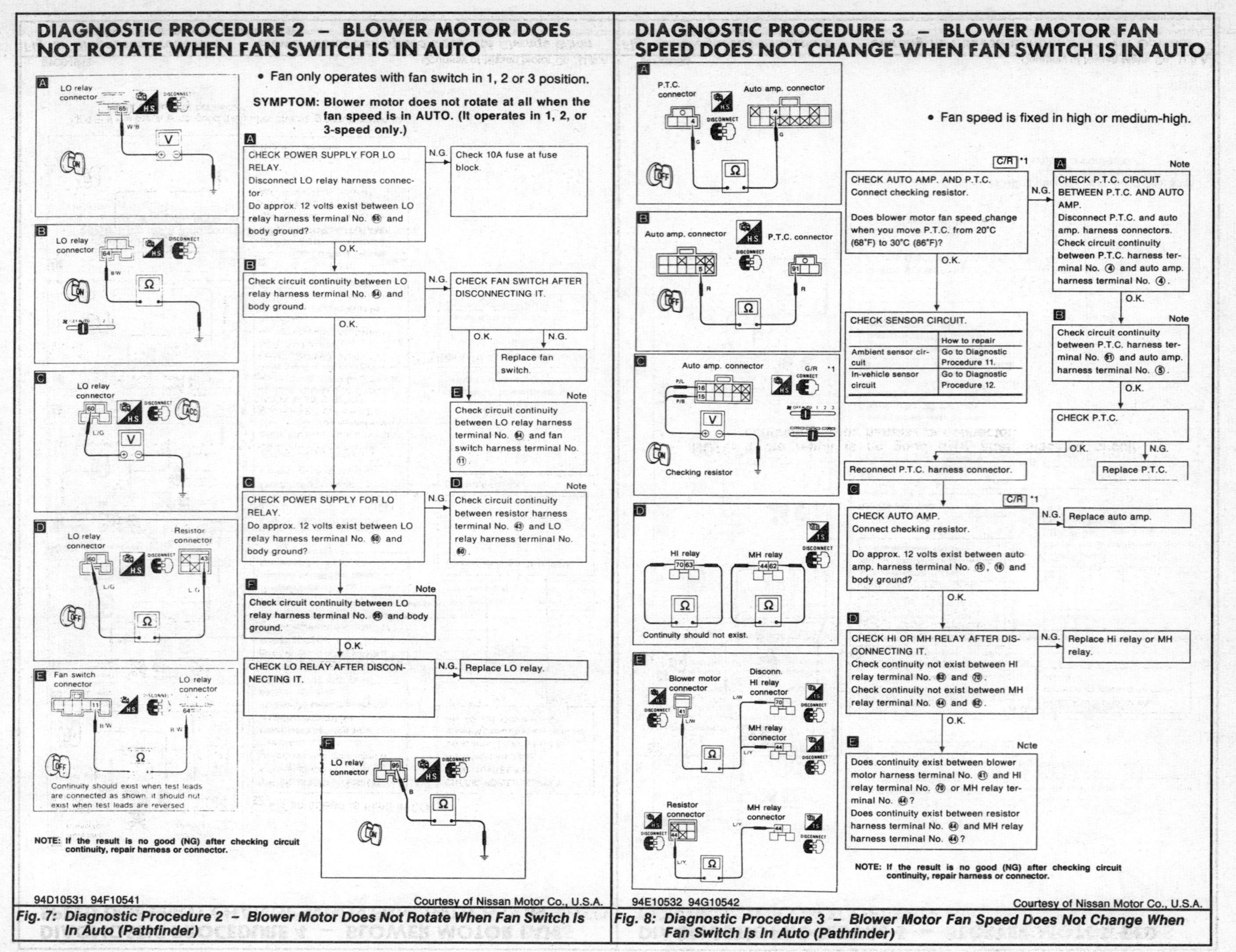
DIAGNOSTIC PROCEDURE 2 – BLOWER MOTOR DOES NOT ROTATE WHEN FAN SWITCH IS IN AUTO
• Fan only operates with fan switch in 1, 2 or 3 position.
SYMPTOM: Blower motor does not rotate at all when the fan speed is in AUTO. (It operates in 1, 2, or 3-speed only.)
A CHECK POWER SUPPLY FOR LO RELAY. Disconnect LO relay harness connector. Do approx. 12 volts exist between LO relay harness terminal No. 65 and body ground?
N.G. Check 10A fuse at fuse block.
O.K.
B Check circuit continuity between LO relay harness terminal No. 64 and body ground.
N.G. CHECK FAN SWITCH AFTER DISCONNECTING IT.
O.K.
N.G. Replace fan switch.
O.K.
E Note Check circuit continuity between LO relay harness terminal No. 64 and fan switch harness terminal No. 11.
C CHECK POWER SUPPLY FOR LO RELAY. Do approx. 12 volts exist between LO relay harness terminal No. 60 and body ground?
N.G.
D Note Check circuit continuity between resistor harness terminal No. 43 and LO relay harness terminal No. 60.
F Note Check circuit continuity between LO relay harness terminal No. 95 and body ground.
O.K.
CHECK LO RELAY AFTER DISCONNECTING IT.
N.G. Replace LO relay.
A LO relay connector 65 W/B V DISCONNECT H.S ON
B LO relay connector 64 B/W Ω DISCONNECT H.S ON
C LO relay connector 60 L/G V DISCONNECT H.S ACC
D LO relay connector 60 L/G Resistor connector 43 L/G Ω DISCONNECT H.S OFF
E Fan switch connector 11 LO relay connector 64 B/W R/W Ω DISCONNECT H.S OFF
Continuity should exist when test leads are connected as shown. It should not exist when test leads are reversed.
F LO relay connector 95 B Ω DISCONNECT H.S ON
NOTE: If the result is no good (NG) after checking circuit continuity, repair harness or connector.
94D10531 94F10541
Courtesy of Nissan Motor Co., U.S.A.
DIAGNOSTIC PROCEDURE 3 – BLOWER MOTOR FAN SPEED DOES NOT CHANGE WHEN FAN SWITCH IS IN AUTO
• Fan speed is fixed in high or medium-high.
C/R *1
CHECK AUTO AMP. AND P.T.C. Connect checking resistor. Does blower motor fan speed change when you move P.T.C. from 20°C (68°F) to 30°C (86°F)?
N.G.
A Note CHECK P.T.C. CIRCUIT BETWEEN P.T.C. AND AUTO AMP. Disconnect P.T.C. and auto amp. harness connectors. Check circuit continuity between P.T.C. harness terminal No. 4 and auto amp. harness terminal No. 4.
O.K.
B Note Check circuit continuity between P.T.C. harness terminal No. 91 and auto amp. harness terminal No. 5.
O.K.
CHECK P.T.C.
O.K. N.G.
Replace P.T.C.
O.K.
CHECK SENSOR CIRCUIT.
	How to repair
Ambient sensor circuit	Go to Diagnostic Procedure 11.
In-vehicle sensor circuit	Go to Diagnostic Procedure 12.
Reconnect P.T.C. harness connector.
C C/R *1 CHECK AUTO AMP. Connect checking resistor. Do approx. 12 volts exist between auto amp. harness terminal No. 15, 16 and body ground?
N.G. Replace auto amp.
O.K.
D CHECK HI OR MH RELAY AFTER DISCONNECTING IT. Check continuity not exist between HI relay terminal No. 63 and 70. Check continuity not exist between MH relay terminal No. 44 and 62.
N.G. Replace Hi relay or MH relay.
O.K.
E Note Does continuity exist between blower motor harness terminal No. 41 and HI relay terminal No. 70 or MH relay terminal No. 44? Does continuity exist between resistor harness terminal No. 44 and MH relay harness terminal No. 44?
A P.T.C. connector 4 G Auto amp. connector 4 G Ω DISCONNECT H.S OFF
B Auto amp. connector 5 R P.T.C. connector 91 R Ω DISCONNECT H.S OFF
C Auto amp. connector 16 15 P/L P/B V G/R *1 CONNECT H.S ON Checking resistor
D HI relay 70 63 MH relay 44 62 Ω DISCONNECT T.S Continuity should not exist.
E Blower motor connector 41 L/W Disconn. HI relay connector 70 MH relay connector 44 L/Y Resistor connector 44 MH relay connector 44 Ω DISCONNECT H.S T.S
NOTE: If the result is no good (NG) after checking circuit continuity, repair harness or connector.
94E10532 94G10542
Courtesy of Nissan Motor Co., U.S.A.

Fig. 7: Diagnostic Procedure 2 – Blower Motor Does Not Rotate When Fan Switch Is In Auto (Pathfinder)

Fig. 8: Diagnostic Procedure 3 – Blower Motor Fan Speed Does Not Change When Fan Switch Is In Auto (Pathfinder)

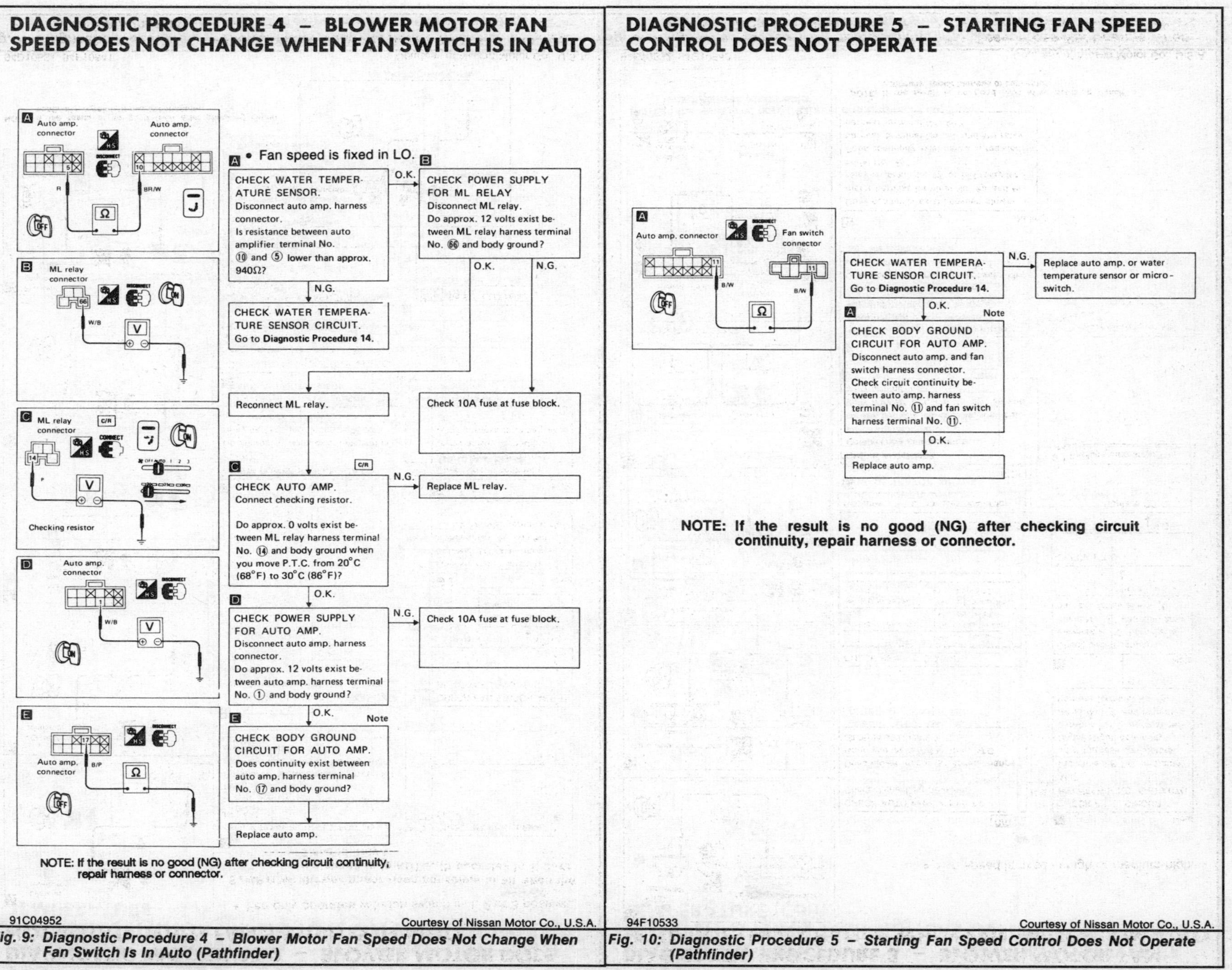
DIAGNOSTIC PROCEDURE 4 – BLOWER MOTOR FAN SPEED DOES NOT CHANGE WHEN FAN SWITCH IS IN AUTO
A Auto amp. connector
Auto amp. connector
R
BR/W
B ML relay connector
W/B
C ML relay connector
C/R
Checking resistor
D Auto amp. connector
W/B
E Auto amp. connector
B/P
A • Fan speed is fixed in LO.
CHECK WATER TEMPERATURE SENSOR.
Disconnect auto amp. harness connector.
Is resistance between auto amplifier terminal No. ⑩ and ⑤ lower than approx. 940Ω?
O.K.
N.G.
B CHECK POWER SUPPLY FOR ML RELAY
Disconnect ML relay.
Do approx. 12 volts exist between ML relay harness terminal No. 66 and body ground?
O.K.
N.G.
CHECK WATER TEMPERATURE SENSOR CIRCUIT.
Go to Diagnostic Procedure 14.
Reconnect ML relay.
Check 10A fuse at fuse block.
C CHECK AUTO AMP.
Connect checking resistor.
Do approx. 0 volts exist between ML relay harness terminal No. ⑭ and body ground when you move P.T.C. from 20°C (68°F) to 30°C (86°F)?
N.G.
Replace ML relay.
O.K.
D CHECK POWER SUPPLY FOR AUTO AMP.
Disconnect auto amp. harness connector.
Do approx. 12 volts exist between auto amp. harness terminal No. ① and body ground?
N.G.
Check 10A fuse at fuse block.
O.K.
Note
E CHECK BODY GROUND CIRCUIT FOR AUTO AMP.
Does continuity exist between auto amp. harness terminal No. ⑰ and body ground?
Replace auto amp.
NOTE: If the result is no good (NG) after checking circuit continuity, repair harness or connector.
91C04952
Courtesy of Nissan Motor Co., U.S.A.
DIAGNOSTIC PROCEDURE 5 – STARTING FAN SPEED CONTROL DOES NOT OPERATE
A Auto amp. connector
Fan switch connector
B/W
B/W
CHECK WATER TEMPERATURE SENSOR CIRCUIT.
Go to Diagnostic Procedure 14.
N.G.
Replace auto amp. or water temperature sensor or micro-switch.
O.K.
Note
A CHECK BODY GROUND CIRCUIT FOR AUTO AMP.
Disconnect auto amp. and fan switch harness connector.
Check circuit continuity between auto amp. harness terminal No. ⑪ and fan switch harness terminal No. ⑪.
O.K.
Replace auto amp.
NOTE: If the result is no good (NG) after checking circuit continuity, repair harness or connector.
94F10533
Courtesy of Nissan Motor Co., U.S.A.

Fig. 9: Diagnostic Procedure 4 – Blower Motor Fan Speed Does Not Change When Fan Switch Is In Auto (Pathfinder)

Fig. 10: Diagnostic Procedure 5 – Starting Fan Speed Control Does Not Operate (Pathfinder)

1993 AUTOMATIC A/C-HEATER SYSTEMS
Trouble Shooting – Pathfinder (Cont.)

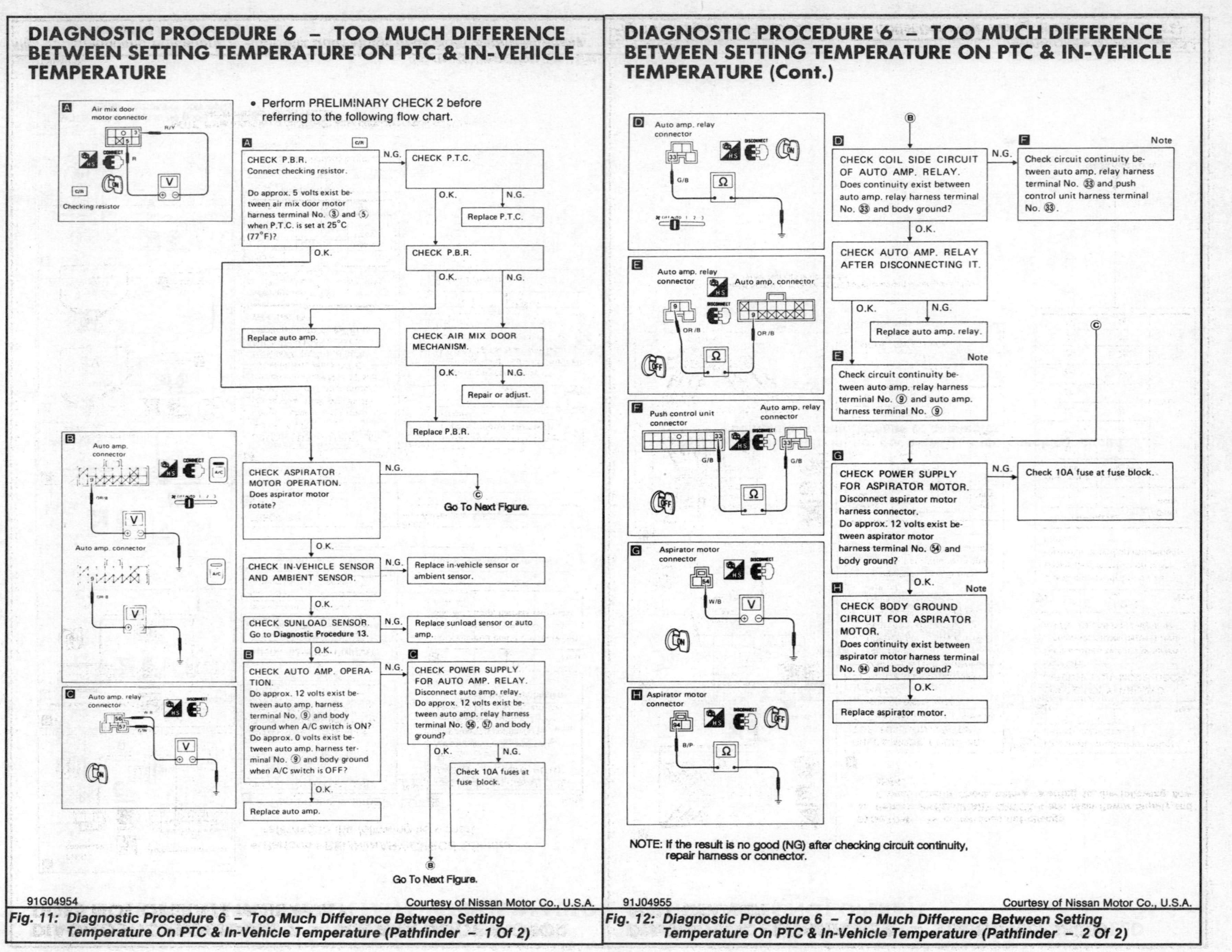
DIAGNOSTIC PROCEDURE 6 – TOO MUCH DIFFERENCE BETWEEN SETTING TEMPERATURE ON PTC & IN-VEHICLE TEMPERATURE
• Perform PRELIMINARY CHECK 2 before referring to the following flow chart.
A Air mix door motor connector
Checking resistor
A CHECK P.B.R. Connect checking resistor. Do approx. 5 volts exist between air mix door motor harness terminal No. ③ and ⑤ when P.T.C. is set at 25°C (77°F)?
N.G.
CHECK P.T.C.
O.K.
N.G.
Replace P.T.C.
CHECK P.B.R.
O.K.
N.G.
Replace auto amp.
CHECK AIR MIX DOOR MECHANISM.
Repair or adjust.
Replace P.B.R.
B Auto amp. connector
Auto amp. connector
CHECK ASPIRATOR MOTOR OPERATION. Does aspirator motor rotate?
Go To Next Figure.
CHECK IN-VEHICLE SENSOR AND AMBIENT SENSOR.
Replace in-vehicle sensor or ambient sensor.
CHECK SUNLOAD SENSOR. Go to Diagnostic Procedure 13.
Replace sunload sensor or auto amp.
C Auto amp. relay connector
B CHECK AUTO AMP. OPERATION. Do approx. 12 volts exist between auto amp. harness terminal No. ⑨ and body ground when A/C switch is ON? Do approx. 0 volts exist between auto amp. harness terminal No. ⑨ and body ground when A/C switch is OFF?
C CHECK POWER SUPPLY FOR AUTO AMP. RELAY. Disconnect auto amp. relay. Do approx. 12 volts exist between auto amp. relay harness terminal No. ㊿, ㊿ and body ground?
Check 10A fuses at fuse block.
Replace auto amp.
Go To Next Figure.
91G04954
Courtesy of Nissan Motor Co., U.S.A.
DIAGNOSTIC PROCEDURE 6 – TOO MUCH DIFFERENCE BETWEEN SETTING TEMPERATURE ON PTC & IN-VEHICLE TEMPERATURE (Cont.)
D Auto amp. relay connector
E Auto amp. relay connector
Auto amp. connector
F Push control unit connector
Auto amp. relay connector
G Aspirator motor connector
H Aspirator motor connector
D CHECK COIL SIDE CIRCUIT OF AUTO AMP. RELAY. Does continuity exist between auto amp. relay harness terminal No. ㉝ and body ground?
F Note
Check circuit continuity between auto amp. relay harness terminal No. ㉝ and push control unit harness terminal No. ㉝.
CHECK AUTO AMP. RELAY AFTER DISCONNECTING IT.
Replace auto amp. relay.
E Note
Check circuit continuity between auto amp. relay harness terminal No. ⑨ and auto amp. harness terminal No. ⑨
G CHECK POWER SUPPLY FOR ASPIRATOR MOTOR. Disconnect aspirator motor harness connector. Do approx. 12 volts exist between aspirator motor harness terminal No. 54 and body ground?
Check 10A fuse at fuse block.
H Note
CHECK BODY GROUND CIRCUIT FOR ASPIRATOR MOTOR. Does continuity exist between aspirator motor harness terminal No. 94 and body ground?
Replace aspirator motor.
NOTE: If the result is no good (NG) after checking circuit continuity, repair harness or connector.
91J04955
Courtesy of Nissan Motor Co., U.S.A.

Fig. 11: Diagnostic Procedure 6 – Too Much Difference Between Setting Temperature On PTC & In-Vehicle Temperature (Pathfinder – 1 Of 2)

Fig. 12: Diagnostic Procedure 6 – Too Much Difference Between Setting Temperature On PTC & In-Vehicle Temperature (Pathfinder – 2 Of 2)

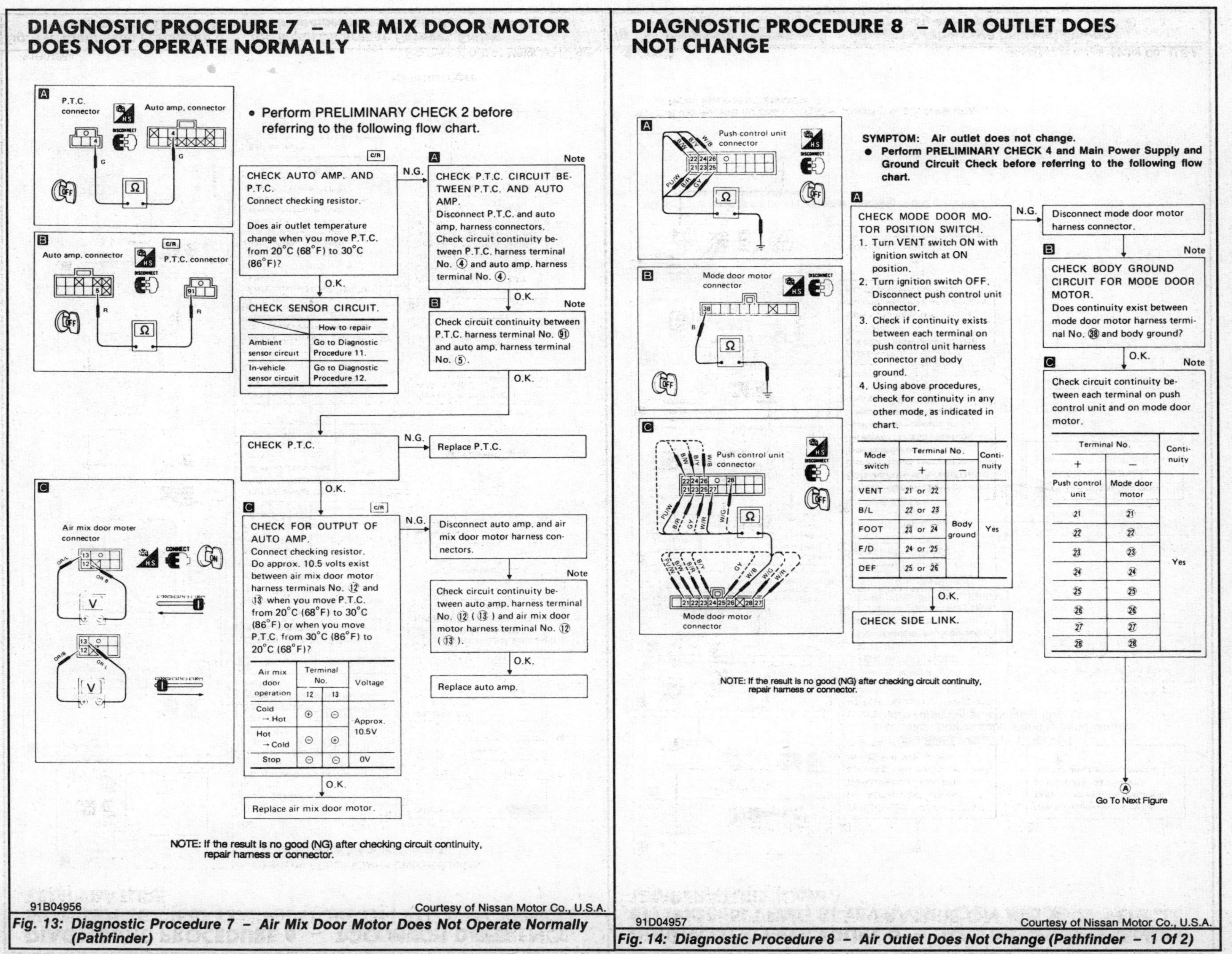

DIAGNOSTIC PROCEDURE 7 – AIR MIX DOOR MOTOR DOES NOT OPERATE NORMALLY
A
P.T.C. connector
Auto amp. connector
B
Auto amp. connector
P.T.C. connector
C
Air mix door moter connector
• Perform PRELIMINARY CHECK 2 before referring to the following flow chart.
CHECK AUTO AMP. AND P.T.C.
Connect checking resistor.
Does air outlet temperature change when you move P.T.C. from 20°C (68°F) to 30°C (86°F)?
N.G.
A Note
CHECK P.T.C. CIRCUIT BETWEEN P.T.C. AND AUTO AMP.
Disconnect P.T.C. and auto amp. harness connectors.
Check circuit continuity between P.T.C. harness terminal No. ④ and auto amp. harness terminal No. ④.
O.K.
B Note
Check circuit continuity between P.T.C. harness terminal No. 91 and auto amp. harness terminal No. ⑤.
O.K.
CHECK SENSOR CIRCUIT.
CHECK P.T.C.
N.G.
Replace P.T.C.
O.K.
C
CHECK FOR OUTPUT OF AUTO AMP.
Connect checking resistor.
Do approx. 10.5 volts exist between air mix door motor harness terminals No. ⑫ and ⑬ when you move P.T.C. from 20°C (68°F) to 30°C (86°F) or when you move P.T.C. from 30°C (86°F) to 20°C (68°F)?
N.G.
Disconnect auto amp. and air mix door motor harness connectors.
Note
Check circuit continuity between auto amp. harness terminal No. ⑫ (⑬) and air mix door motor harness terminal No. ⑫ (⑬).
O.K.
Replace auto amp.
O.K.
Replace air mix door motor.
NOTE: If the result is no good (NG) after checking circuit continuity, repair harness or connector.
91B04956
Courtesy of Nissan Motor Co., U.S.A.
DIAGNOSTIC PROCEDURE 8 – AIR OUTLET DOES NOT CHANGE
A
Push control unit connector
B
Mode door motor connector
C
Push control unit connector
Mode door motor connector
SYMPTOM: Air outlet does not change.
• Perform PRELIMINARY CHECK 4 and Main Power Supply and Ground Circuit Check before referring to the following flow chart.
A
CHECK MODE DOOR MOTOR POSITION SWITCH.
1. Turn VENT switch ON with ignition switch at ON position.
2. Turn ignition switch OFF. Disconnect push control unit connector.
3. Check if continuity exists between each terminal on push control unit harness connector and body ground.
4. Using above procedures, check for continuity in any other mode, as indicated in chart.
N.G.
Disconnect mode door motor harness connector.
B Note
CHECK BODY GROUND CIRCUIT FOR MODE DOOR MOTOR.
Does continuity exist between mode door motor harness terminal No. 38 and body ground?
O.K.
C Note
Check circuit continuity between each terminal on push control unit and on mode door motor.
O.K.
CHECK SIDE LINK.
Ⓐ Go To Next Figure
NOTE: If the result is no good (NG) after checking circuit continuity, repair harness or connector.
91D04957
Courtesy of Nissan Motor Co., U.S.A.

	How to repair
Ambient sensor circuit	Go to Diagnostic Procedure 11.
In-vehicle sensor circuit	Go to Diagnostic Procedure 12.

Air mix door operation	Terminal No. 12	Terminal No. 13	Voltage
Cold → Hot	⊕	⊖	Approx. 10.5V
Hot → Cold	⊖	⊕	
Stop	⊖	⊖	0V

Mode switch	Terminal No. +	Terminal No. –	Continuity
VENT	21 or 22	Body ground	Yes
B/L	22 or 23		
FOOT	23 or 24		
F/D	24 or 25		
DEF	25 or 26		

Terminal No. + Push control unit	Terminal No. – Mode door motor	Continuity
21	21	Yes
22	22	
23	23	
24	24	
25	25	
26	26	
27	27	
28	28	

Fig. 13: Diagnostic Procedure 7 – Air Mix Door Motor Does Not Operate Normally (Pathfinder)

Fig. 14: Diagnostic Procedure 8 – Air Outlet Does Not Change (Pathfinder – 1 Of 2)

1993 AUTOMATIC A/C-HEATER SYSTEMS
Trouble Shooting – Pathfinder (Cont.)

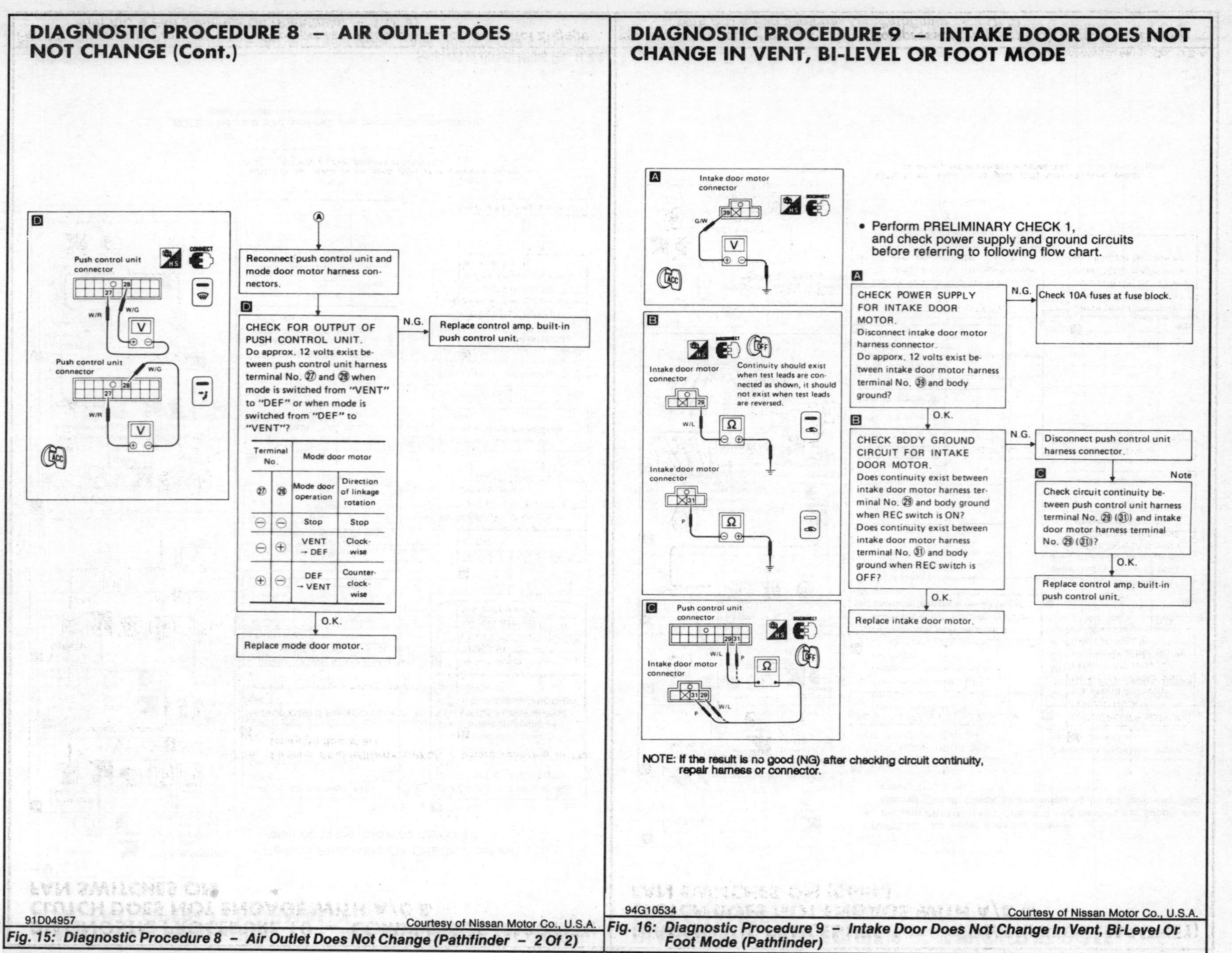
DIAGNOSTIC PROCEDURE 8 – AIR OUTLET DOES NOT CHANGE (Cont.)
D
Push control unit connector
27
28
W/R
W/G
V
Push control unit connector
ACC
A
Reconnect push control unit and mode door motor harness connectors.
D
CHECK FOR OUTPUT OF PUSH CONTROL UNIT.
Do approx. 12 volts exist between push control unit harness terminal No. 27 and 28 when mode is switched from "VENT" to "DEF" or when mode is switched from "DEF" to "VENT"?
Terminal No.
Mode door motor
Mode door operation
Direction of linkage rotation
Stop
VENT → DEF
Clock-wise
DEF → VENT
Counter-clockwise
N.G.
Replace control amp. built-in push control unit.
O.K.
Replace mode door motor.
91D04957
Courtesy of Nissan Motor Co., U.S.A.
DIAGNOSTIC PROCEDURE 9 – INTAKE DOOR DOES NOT CHANGE IN VENT, BI-LEVEL OR FOOT MODE
A
Intake door motor connector
39
G/W
V
ACC
B
Intake door motor connector
Continuity should exist when test leads are connected as shown, it should not exist when test leads are reversed.
29
W/L
Ω
OFF
31
P
C
Push control unit connector
29 31
W/L
P
Intake door motor connector
31 29
• Perform PRELIMINARY CHECK 1, and check power supply and ground circuits before referring to following flow chart.
A
CHECK POWER SUPPLY FOR INTAKE DOOR MOTOR.
Disconnect intake door motor harness connector.
Do apporx. 12 volts exist between intake door motor harness terminal No. 39 and body ground?
N.G.
Check 10A fuses at fuse block.
O.K.
B
CHECK BODY GROUND CIRCUIT FOR INTAKE DOOR MOTOR.
Does continuity exist between intake door motor harness terminal No. 29 and body ground when REC switch is ON?
Does continuity exist between intake door motor harness terminal No. 31 and body ground when REC switch is OFF?
N.G.
Disconnect push control unit harness connector.
C
Note
Check circuit continuity between push control unit harness terminal No. 29 (31) and intake door motor harness terminal No. 29 (31)?
O.K.
Replace control amp. built-in push control unit.
O.K.
Replace intake door motor.
NOTE: If the result is no good (NG) after checking circuit continuity, repair harness or connector.
94G10534
Courtesy of Nissan Motor Co., U.S.A.

Fig. 15: Diagnostic Procedure 8 – Air Outlet Does Not Change (Pathfinder – 2 Of 2)

Fig. 16: Diagnostic Procedure 9 – Intake Door Does Not Change In Vent, Bi-Level Or Foot Mode (Pathfinder)

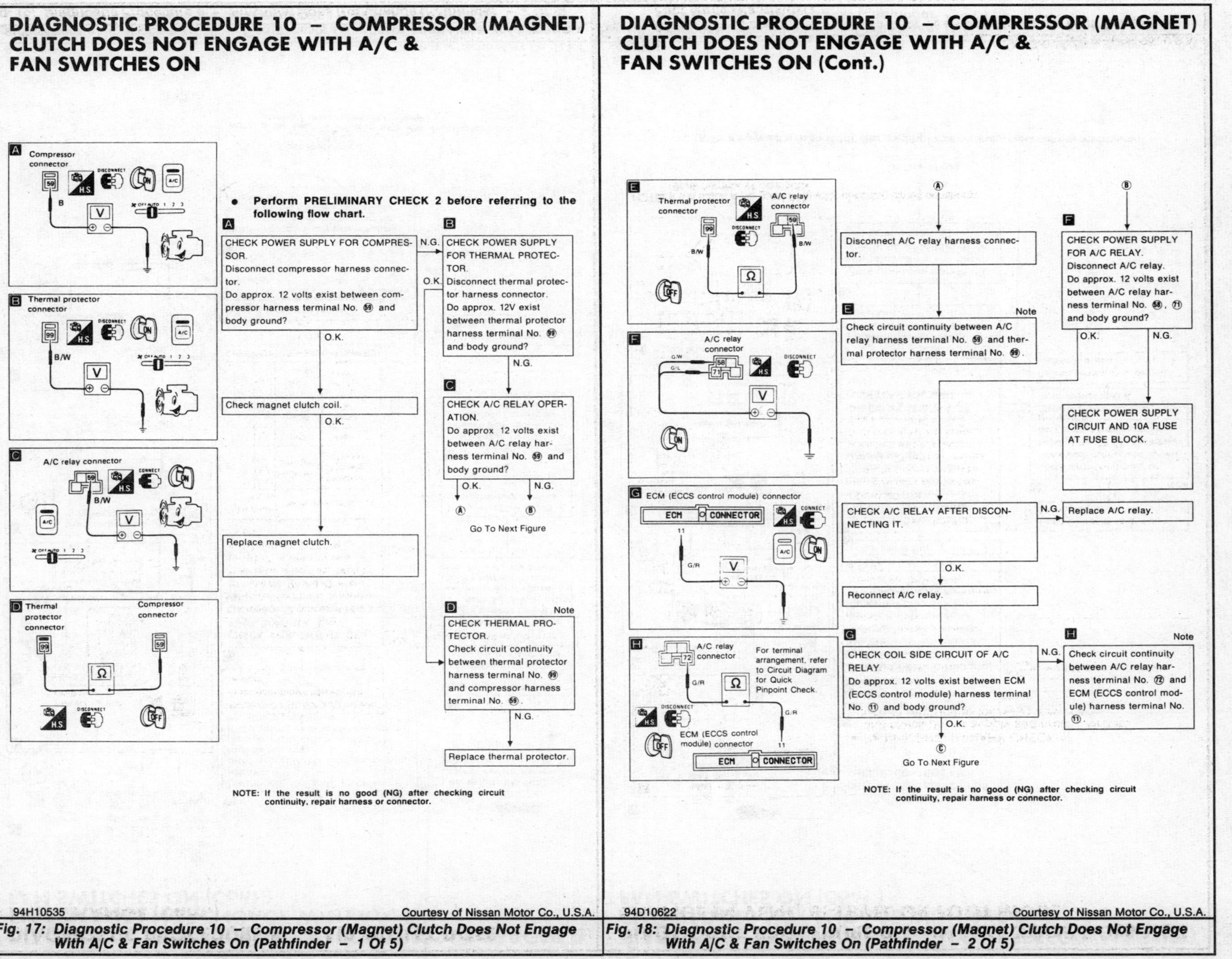
DIAGNOSTIC PROCEDURE 10 – COMPRESSOR (MAGNET) CLUTCH DOES NOT ENGAGE WITH A/C & FAN SWITCHES ON
A Compressor connector
B Thermal protector connector
C A/C relay connector
D Thermal protector connector
Compressor connector
• Perform PRELIMINARY CHECK 2 before referring to the following flow chart.
A CHECK POWER SUPPLY FOR COMPRESSOR.
Disconnect compressor harness connector.
Do approx. 12 volts exist between compressor harness terminal No. 59 and body ground?
N.G.
O.K.
Check magnet clutch coil.
O.K.
Replace magnet clutch.
B CHECK POWER SUPPLY FOR THERMAL PROTECTOR.
Disconnect thermal protector harness connector.
Do approx. 12V exist between thermal protector harness terminal No. 99 and body ground?
N.G.
O.K.
C CHECK A/C RELAY OPERATION.
Do approx 12 volts exist between A/C relay harness terminal No. 59 and body ground?
O.K.
N.G.
A
B
Go To Next Figure
D CHECK THERMAL PROTECTOR.
Note
Check circuit continuity between thermal protector harness terminal No. 99 and compressor harness terminal No. 59.
N.G.
Replace thermal protector.
NOTE: If the result is no good (NG) after checking circuit continuity, repair harness or connector.
94H10535
Courtesy of Nissan Motor Co., U.S.A.
DIAGNOSTIC PROCEDURE 10 – COMPRESSOR (MAGNET) CLUTCH DOES NOT ENGAGE WITH A/C & FAN SWITCHES ON (Cont.)
E Thermal protector connector
A/C relay connector
F A/C relay connector
G ECM (ECCS control module) connector
H A/C relay connector
For terminal arrangement, refer to Circuit Diagram for Quick Pinpoint Check.
ECM (ECCS control module) connector
A
Disconnect A/C relay harness connector.
E Check circuit continuity between A/C relay harness terminal No. 59 and thermal protector harness terminal No. 99.
Note
CHECK A/C RELAY AFTER DISCONNECTING IT.
N.G.
O.K.
Reconnect A/C relay.
G CHECK COIL SIDE CIRCUIT OF A/C RELAY
Do approx. 12 volts exist between ECM (ECCS control module) harness terminal No. 11 and body ground?
N.G.
O.K.
C
Go To Next Figure
B
F CHECK POWER SUPPLY FOR A/C RELAY.
Disconnect A/C relay.
Do approx. 12 volts exist between A/C relay harness terminal No. 58, 71 and body ground?
O.K.
N.G.
CHECK POWER SUPPLY CIRCUIT AND 10A FUSE AT FUSE BLOCK.
Replace A/C relay.
H Check circuit continuity between A/C relay harness terminal No. 72 and ECM (ECCS control module) harness terminal No. 11.
Note
NOTE: If the result is no good (NG) after checking circuit continuity, repair harness or connector.
94D10622
Courtesy of Nissan Motor Co., U.S.A.

Fig. 17: Diagnostic Procedure 10 – Compressor (Magnet) Clutch Does Not Engage With A/C & Fan Switches On (Pathfinder – 1 Of 5)

Fig. 18: Diagnostic Procedure 10 – Compressor (Magnet) Clutch Does Not Engage With A/C & Fan Switches On (Pathfinder – 2 Of 5)

1993 AUTOMATIC A/C-HEATER SYSTEMS
Trouble Shooting – Pathfinder (Cont.)

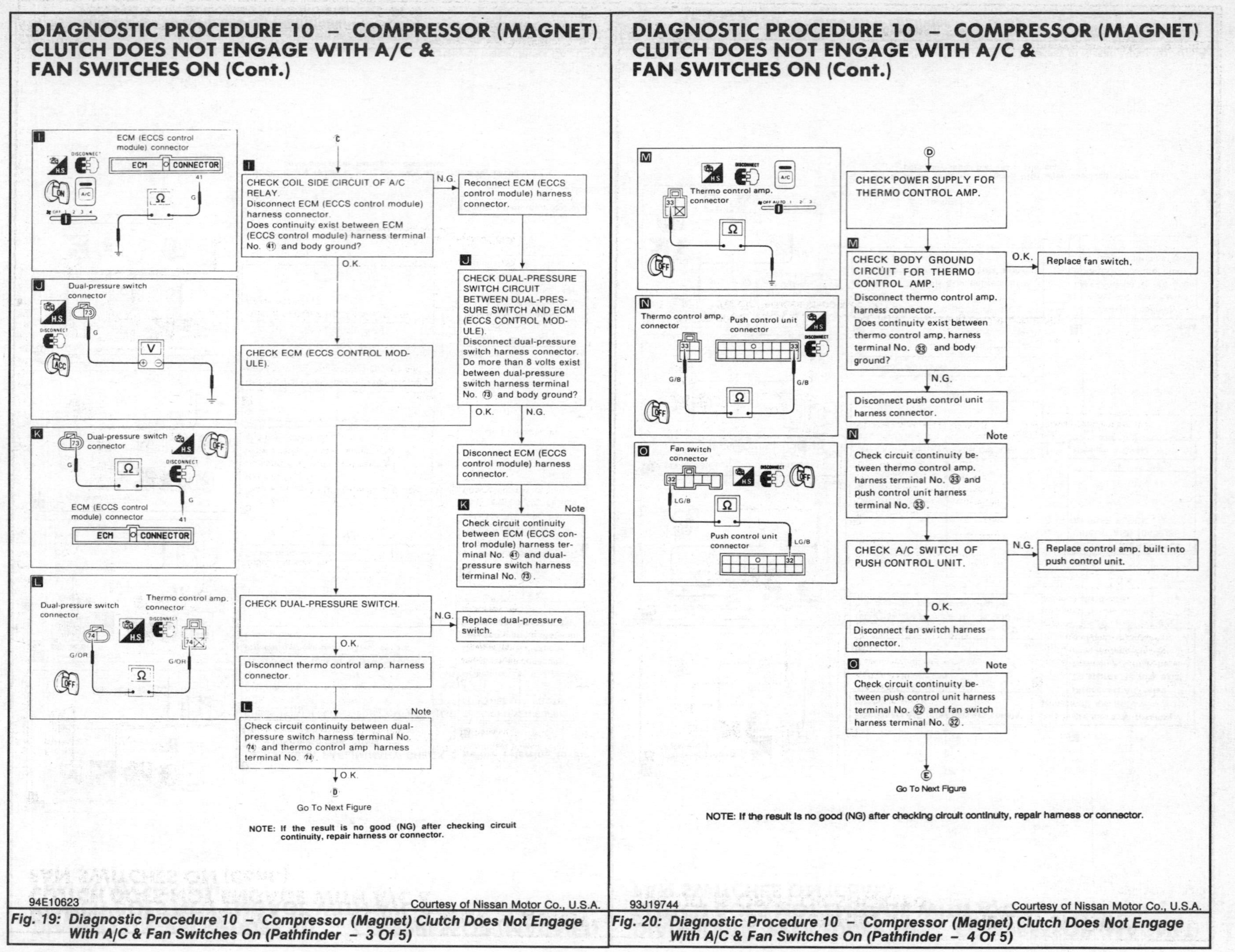
DIAGNOSTIC PROCEDURE 10 – COMPRESSOR (MAGNET) CLUTCH DOES NOT ENGAGE WITH A/C & FAN SWITCHES ON (Cont.)
I
ECM (ECCS control module) connector
ECM CONNECTOR
41
G
C
CHECK COIL SIDE CIRCUIT OF A/C RELAY.
Disconnect ECM (ECCS control module) harness connector.
Does continuity exist between ECM (ECCS control module) harness terminal No. 41 and body ground?
N.G.
Reconnect ECM (ECCS control module) harness connector.
O.K.
CHECK ECM (ECCS CONTROL MODULE).
J
Dual-pressure switch connector
73
G
V
J
CHECK DUAL-PRESSURE SWITCH CIRCUIT BETWEEN DUAL-PRESSURE SWITCH AND ECM (ECCS CONTROL MODULE).
Disconnect dual-pressure switch harness connector.
Do more than 8 volts exist between dual-pressure switch harness terminal No. 73 and body ground?
O.K.
N.G.
Disconnect ECM (ECCS control module) harness connector.
K
Dual-pressure switch connector
73
G
ECM (ECCS control module) connector
ECM CONNECTOR
41
K
Note
Check circuit continuity between ECM (ECCS control module) harness terminal No. 41 and dual-pressure switch harness terminal No. 73.
L
Dual-pressure switch connector
Thermo control amp. connector
74
G/OR
CHECK DUAL-PRESSURE SWITCH.
N.G.
Replace dual-pressure switch.
O.K.
Disconnect thermo control amp. harness connector.
L
Note
Check circuit continuity between dual-pressure switch harness terminal No. 74 and thermo control amp harness terminal No. 74.
O.K.
D
Go To Next Figure
NOTE: If the result is no good (NG) after checking circuit continuity, repair harness or connector.
94E10623
Courtesy of Nissan Motor Co., U.S.A.
DIAGNOSTIC PROCEDURE 10 – COMPRESSOR (MAGNET) CLUTCH DOES NOT ENGAGE WITH A/C & FAN SWITCHES ON (Cont.)
M
Thermo control amp. connector
33
D
CHECK POWER SUPPLY FOR THERMO CONTROL AMP.
M
CHECK BODY GROUND CIRCUIT FOR THERMO CONTROL AMP.
Disconnect thermo control amp. harness connector.
Does continuity exist between thermo control amp. harness terminal No. 33 and body ground?
O.K.
Replace fan switch.
N.G.
Disconnect push control unit harness connector.
N
Thermo control amp. connector
Push control unit connector
33
G/B
N
Note
Check circuit continuity between thermo control amp. harness terminal No. 33 and push control unit harness terminal No. 33.
O
Fan switch connector
32
LG/B
Push control unit connector
CHECK A/C SWITCH OF PUSH CONTROL UNIT.
N.G.
Replace control amp. built into push control unit.
O.K.
Disconnect fan switch harness connector.
O
Note
Check circuit continuity between push control unit harness terminal No. 32 and fan switch harness terminal No. 32.
E
Go To Next Figure
NOTE: If the result is no good (NG) after checking circuit continuity, repair harness or connector.
93J19744
Courtesy of Nissan Motor Co., U.S.A.

Fig. 19: Diagnostic Procedure 10 – Compressor (Magnet) Clutch Does Not Engage With A/C & Fan Switches On (Pathfinder – 3 Of 5)

Fig. 20: Diagnostic Procedure 10 – Compressor (Magnet) Clutch Does Not Engage With A/C & Fan Switches On (Pathfinder – 4 Of 5)

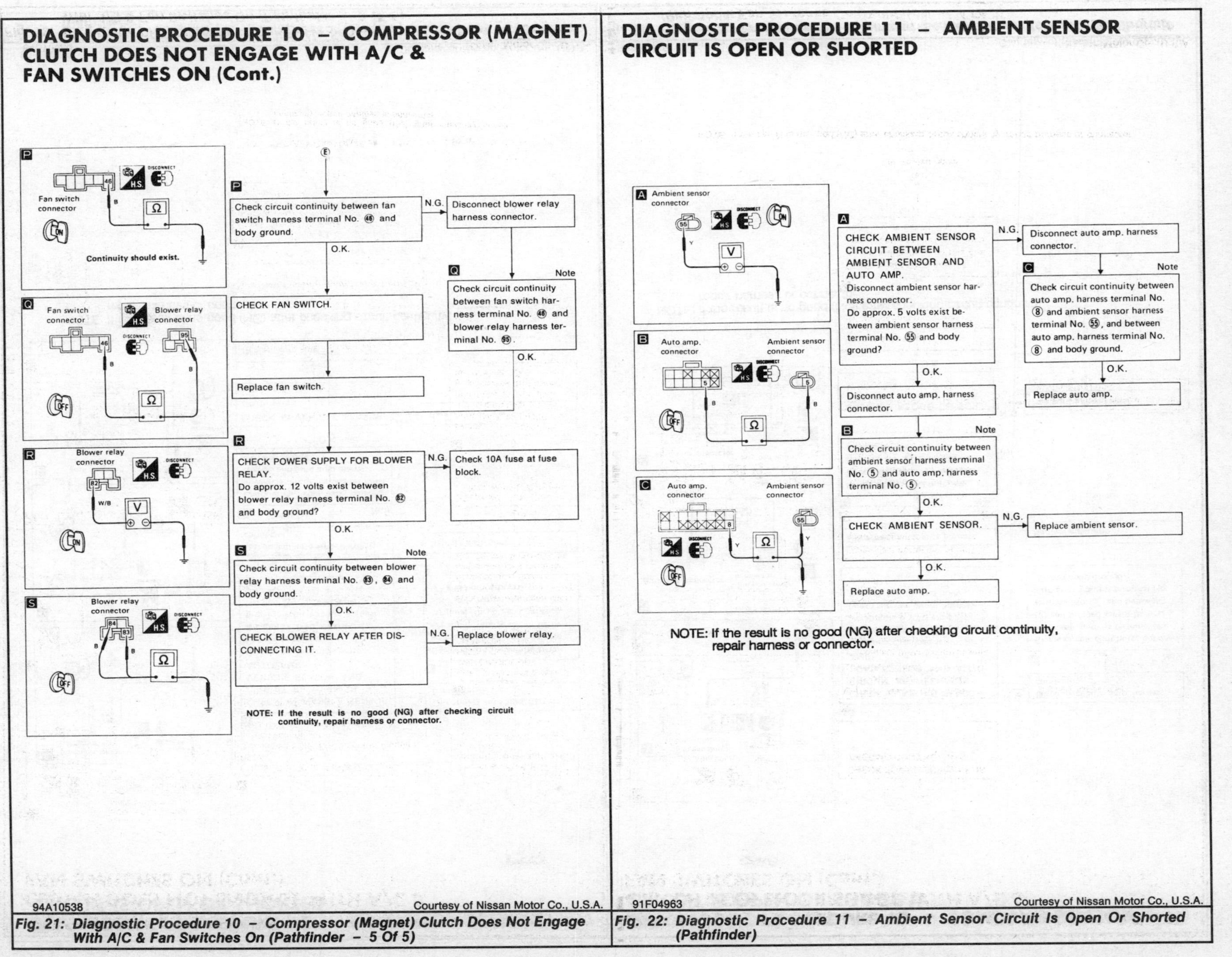
DIAGNOSTIC PROCEDURE 10 – COMPRESSOR (MAGNET) CLUTCH DOES NOT ENGAGE WITH A/C & FAN SWITCHES ON (Cont.)
P
Fan switch connector
Continuity should exist.
Q
Fan switch connector
Blower relay connector
R
Blower relay connector
S
Blower relay connector
E
P
Check circuit continuity between fan switch harness terminal No. 46 and body ground.
N.G.
Disconnect blower relay harness connector.
O.K.
CHECK FAN SWITCH.
Replace fan switch.
Q
Note
Check circuit continuity between fan switch harness terminal No. 46 and blower relay harness terminal No. 95.
O.K.
R
CHECK POWER SUPPLY FOR BLOWER RELAY.
Do approx. 12 volts exist between blower relay harness terminal No. 82 and body ground?
N.G.
Check 10A fuse at fuse block.
O.K.
S
Note
Check circuit continuity between blower relay harness terminal No. 83, 84 and body ground.
O.K.
CHECK BLOWER RELAY AFTER DISCONNECTING IT.
N.G.
Replace blower relay.
NOTE: If the result is no good (NG) after checking circuit continuity, repair harness or connector.
94A10538
Courtesy of Nissan Motor Co., U.S.A.
DIAGNOSTIC PROCEDURE 11 – AMBIENT SENSOR CIRCUIT IS OPEN OR SHORTED
A
Ambient sensor connector
B
Auto amp. connector
Ambient sensor connector
C
Auto amp. connector
Ambient sensor connector
A
CHECK AMBIENT SENSOR CIRCUIT BETWEEN AMBIENT SENSOR AND AUTO AMP.
Disconnect ambient sensor harness connector.
Do approx. 5 volts exist between ambient sensor harness terminal No. 55 and body ground?
N.G.
Disconnect auto amp. harness connector.
C
Note
Check circuit continuity between auto amp. harness terminal No. 8 and ambient sensor harness terminal No. 55, and between auto amp. harness terminal No. 8 and body ground.
O.K.
Replace auto amp.
O.K.
Disconnect auto amp. harness connector.
B
Note
Check circuit continuity between ambient sensor harness terminal No. 5 and auto amp. harness terminal No. 5.
O.K.
CHECK AMBIENT SENSOR.
N.G.
Replace ambient sensor.
O.K.
Replace auto amp.
NOTE: If the result is no good (NG) after checking circuit continuity, repair harness or connector.
91F04963
Courtesy of Nissan Motor Co., U.S.A.

Fig. 21: Diagnostic Procedure 10 – Compressor (Magnet) Clutch Does Not Engage With A/C & Fan Switches On (Pathfinder – 5 Of 5)

Fig. 22: Diagnostic Procedure 11 – Ambient Sensor Circuit Is Open Or Shorted (Pathfinder)

1993 AUTOMATIC A/C-HEATER SYSTEMS
Trouble Shooting – Pathfinder (Cont.)

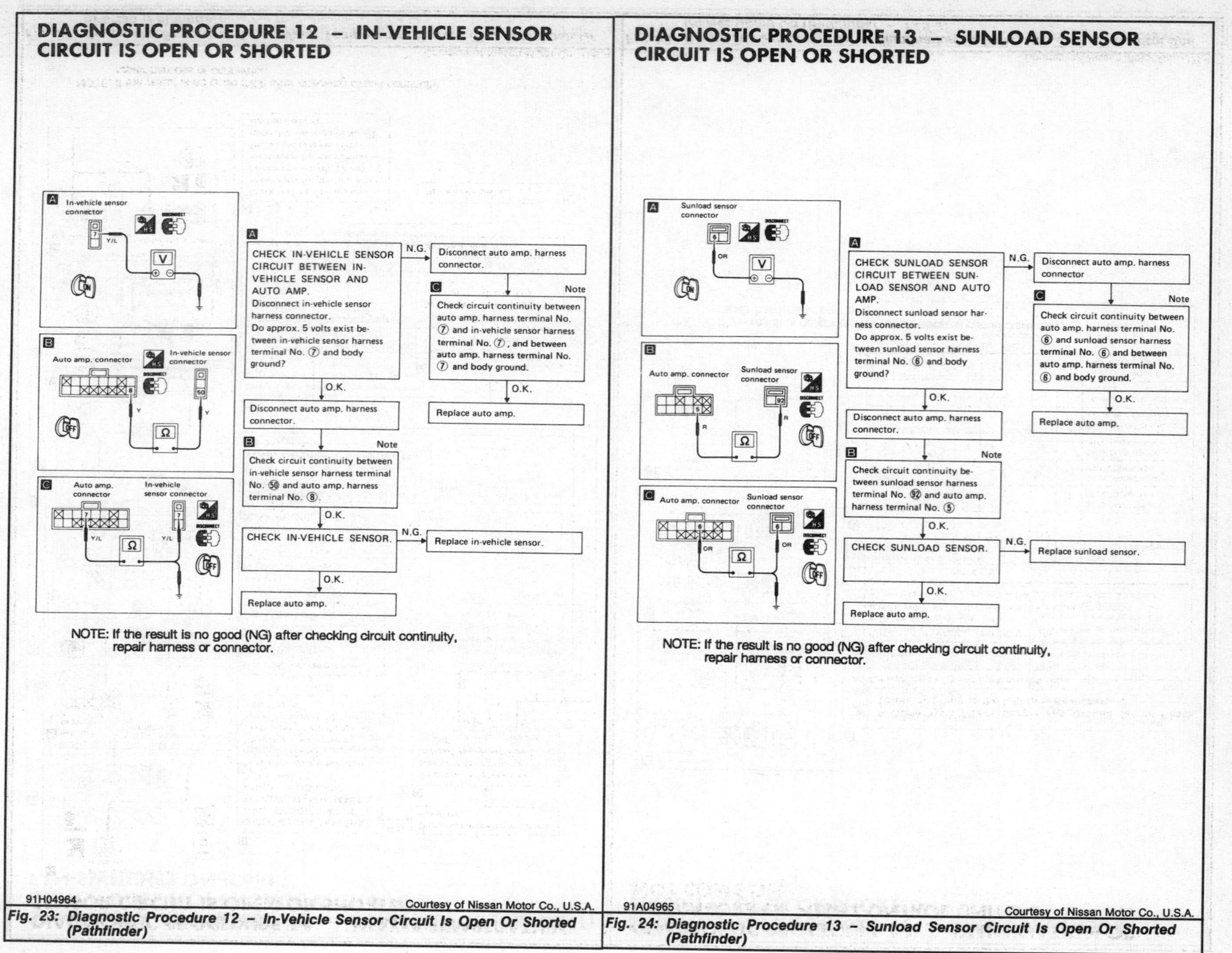
DIAGNOSTIC PROCEDURE 12 – IN-VEHICLE SENSOR CIRCUIT IS OPEN OR SHORTED
A In-vehicle sensor connector
B Auto amp. connector
In-vehicle sensor connector
C Auto amp. connector
In-vehicle sensor connector
A CHECK IN-VEHICLE SENSOR CIRCUIT BETWEEN IN-VEHICLE SENSOR AND AUTO AMP. Disconnect in-vehicle sensor harness connector. Do approx. 5 volts exist between in-vehicle sensor harness terminal No. ⑦ and body ground?
N.G.
Disconnect auto amp. harness connector.
C Check circuit continuity between auto amp. harness terminal No. ⑦ and in-vehicle sensor harness terminal No. ⑦, and between auto amp. harness terminal No. ⑦ and body ground.
Note
O.K.
Replace auto amp.
O.K.
Disconnect auto amp. harness connector.
B Check circuit continuity between in-vehicle sensor harness terminal No. ㊿ and auto amp. harness terminal No. ⑧.
Note
O.K.
CHECK IN-VEHICLE SENSOR.
N.G.
Replace in-vehicle sensor.
O.K.
Replace auto amp.
NOTE: If the result is no good (NG) after checking circuit continuity, repair harness or connector.
91H04964
Courtesy of Nissan Motor Co., U.S.A.
DIAGNOSTIC PROCEDURE 13 – SUNLOAD SENSOR CIRCUIT IS OPEN OR SHORTED
A Sunload sensor connector
B Auto amp. connector
Sunload sensor connector
C Auto amp. connector
Sunload sensor connector
A CHECK SUNLOAD SENSOR CIRCUIT BETWEEN SUNLOAD SENSOR AND AUTO AMP. Disconnect sunload sensor harness connector. Do approx. 5 volts exist between sunload sensor harness terminal No. ⑥ and body ground?
N.G.
Disconnect auto amp. harness connector
C Check circuit continuity between auto amp. harness terminal No. ⑥ and sunload sensor harness terminal No. ⑥ and between auto amp. harness terminal No. ⑥ and body ground.
Note
O.K.
Replace auto amp.
O.K.
Disconnect auto amp. harness connector.
B Check circuit continuity between sunload sensor harness terminal No. ㊷ and auto amp. harness terminal No. ⑤
Note
O.K.
CHECK SUNLOAD SENSOR.
N.G.
Replace sunload sensor.
O.K.
Replace auto amp.
NOTE: If the result is no good (NG) after checking circuit continuity, repair harness or connector.
91A04965
Courtesy of Nissan Motor Co., U.S.A.

Fig. 23: Diagnostic Procedure 12 – In-Vehicle Sensor Circuit Is Open Or Shorted (Pathfinder)

Fig. 24: Diagnostic Procedure 13 – Sunload Sensor Circuit Is Open Or Shorted (Pathfinder)

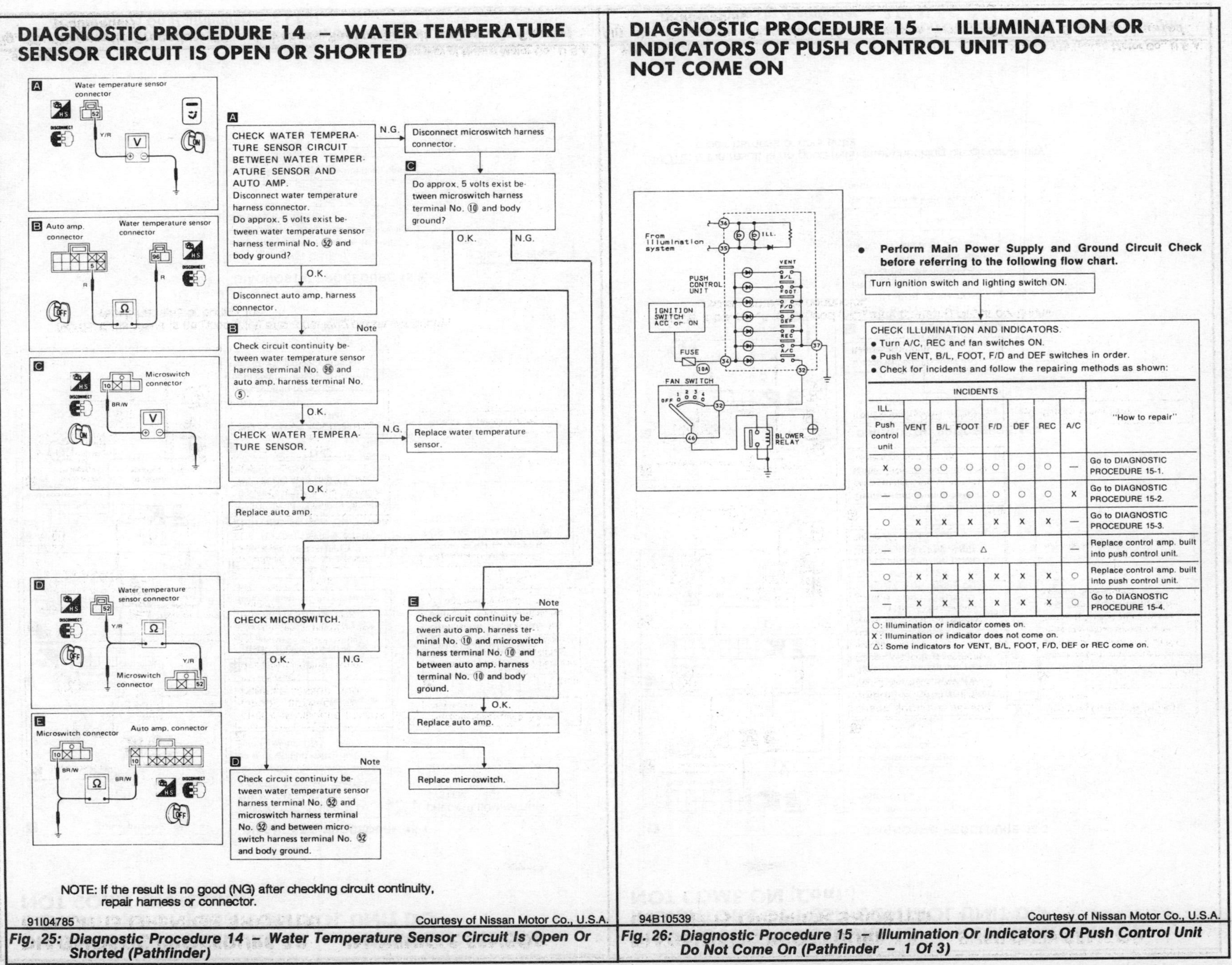
DIAGNOSTIC PROCEDURE 14 – WATER TEMPERATURE SENSOR CIRCUIT IS OPEN OR SHORTED
A Water temperature sensor connector
52
Y/R
V
ON
B Auto amp. connector
Water temperature sensor connector
96
5
R
Ω
OFF
C Microswitch connector
10
BR/W
V
ON
D Water temperature sensor connector
52
Y/R
Ω
OFF
Microswitch connector
52
E Microswitch connector
Auto amp. connector
10
BR/W
Ω
OFF
A CHECK WATER TEMPERATURE SENSOR CIRCUIT BETWEEN WATER TEMPERATURE SENSOR AND AUTO AMP. Disconnect water temperature harness connector. Do approx. 5 volts exist between water temperature sensor harness terminal No. 52 and body ground?
N.G.
Disconnect microswitch harness connector.
C Do approx. 5 volts exist between microswitch harness terminal No. 10 and body ground?
O.K.
N.G.
O.K.
Disconnect auto amp. harness connector.
B Check circuit continuity between water temperature sensor harness terminal No. 96 and auto amp. harness terminal No. 5.
Note
O.K.
CHECK WATER TEMPERATURE SENSOR.
N.G.
Replace water temperature sensor.
O.K.
Replace auto amp.
CHECK MICROSWITCH.
O.K.
N.G.
D Check circuit continuity between water temperature sensor harness terminal No. 52 and microswitch harness terminal No. 52 and between microswitch harness terminal No. 52 and body ground.
Note
E Check circuit continuity between auto amp. harness terminal No. 10 and microswitch harness terminal No. 10 and between auto amp. harness terminal No. 10 and body ground.
Note
O.K.
Replace auto amp.
Replace microswitch.
NOTE: If the result is no good (NG) after checking circuit continuity, repair harness or connector.
91I04785
Courtesy of Nissan Motor Co., U.S.A.
DIAGNOSTIC PROCEDURE 15 – ILLUMINATION OR INDICATORS OF PUSH CONTROL UNIT DO NOT COME ON
From illumination system
36
35
ILL.
PUSH CONTROL UNIT
VENT
B/L
FOOT
F/D
DEF
REC
A/C
IGNITION SWITCH ACC or ON
FUSE
10A
34
37
32
FAN SWITCH
OFF 1 2 3 4
46
BLOWER RELAY
• Perform Main Power Supply and Ground Circuit Check before referring to the following flow chart.
Turn ignition switch and lighting switch ON.
CHECK ILLUMINATION AND INDICATORS.
• Turn A/C, REC and fan switches ON.
• Push VENT, B/L, FOOT, F/D and DEF switches in order.
• Check for incidents and follow the repairing methods as shown:
○: Illumination or indicator comes on.
X: Illumination or indicator does not come on.
Δ: Some indicators for VENT, B/L, FOOT, F/D, DEF or REC come on.
94B10539
Courtesy of Nissan Motor Co., U.S.A.

INCIDENTS								
ILL. Push control unit	VENT	B/L	FOOT	F/D	DEF	REC	A/C	"How to repair"
X	○	○	○	○	○	○	—	Go to DIAGNOSTIC PROCEDURE 15-1.
—	○	○	○	○	○	○	X	Go to DIAGNOSTIC PROCEDURE 15-2.
○	X	X	X	X	X	X	—	Go to DIAGNOSTIC PROCEDURE 15-3.
—				Δ				Replace control amp. built into push control unit.
○	X	X	X	X	X	X	○	Replace control amp. built into push control unit.
—	X	X	X	X	X	X	○	Go to DIAGNOSTIC PROCEDURE 15-4.

Fig. 25: Diagnostic Procedure 14 – Water Temperature Sensor Circuit Is Open Or Shorted (Pathfinder)

Fig. 26: Diagnostic Procedure 15 – Illumination Or Indicators Of Push Control Unit Do Not Come On (Pathfinder – 1 Of 3)

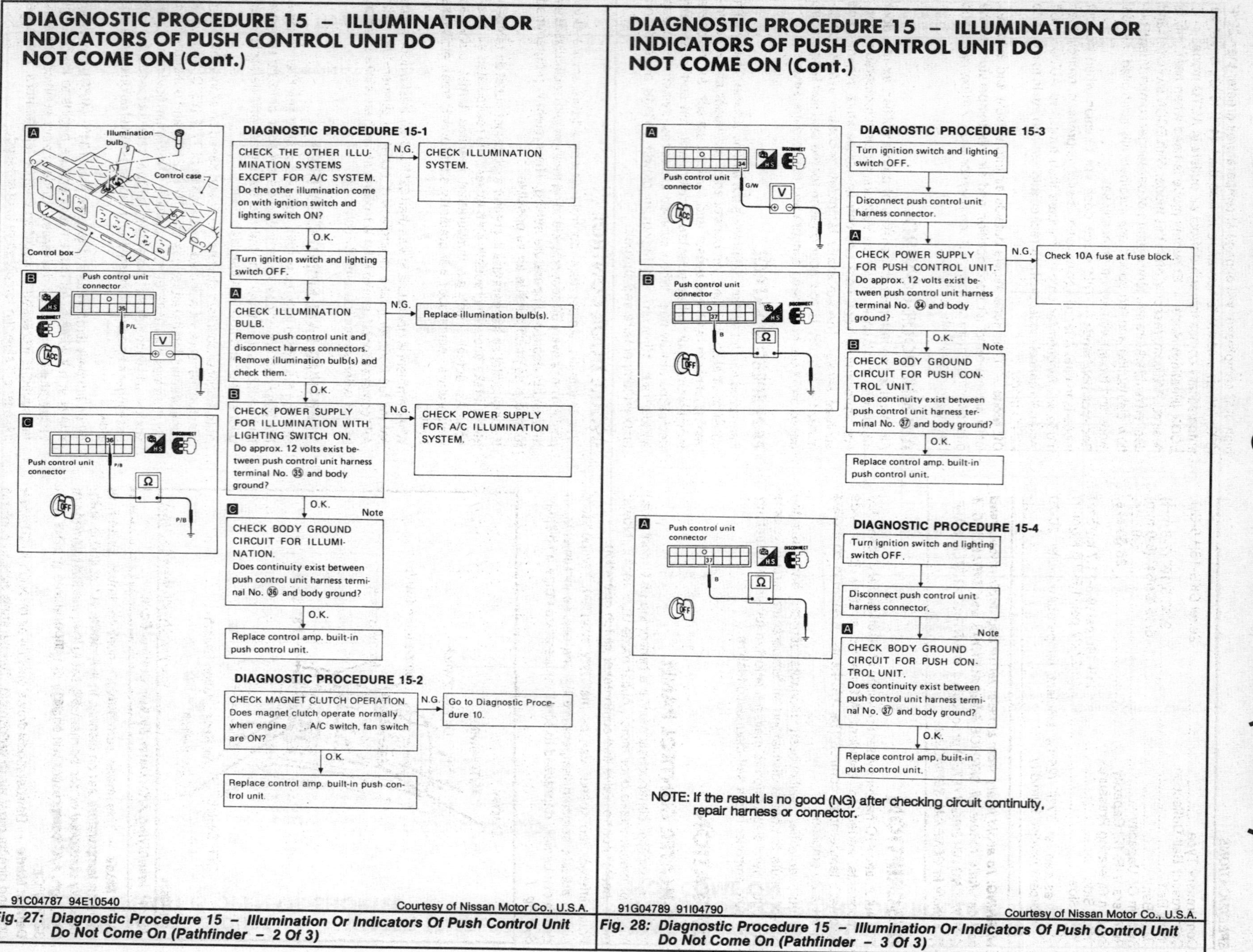
DIAGNOSTIC PROCEDURE 15 – ILLUMINATION OR INDICATORS OF PUSH CONTROL UNIT DO NOT COME ON (Cont.)
A
Illumination bulb
Control case
Control box
B
Push control unit connector
35
P/L
V
C
Push control unit connector
36
P/B
Ω
DIAGNOSTIC PROCEDURE 15-1
CHECK THE OTHER ILLUMINATION SYSTEMS EXCEPT FOR A/C SYSTEM. Do the other illumination come on with ignition switch and lighting switch ON?
N.G.
CHECK ILLUMINATION SYSTEM.
O.K.
Turn ignition switch and lighting switch OFF.
A
CHECK ILLUMINATION BULB. Remove push control unit and disconnect harness connectors. Remove illumination bulb(s) and check them.
N.G.
Replace illumination bulb(s).
O.K.
B
CHECK POWER SUPPLY FOR ILLUMINATION WITH LIGHTING SWITCH ON. Do approx. 12 volts exist between push control unit harness terminal No. 35 and body ground?
N.G.
CHECK POWER SUPPLY FOR A/C ILLUMINATION SYSTEM.
O.K.
Note
C
CHECK BODY GROUND CIRCUIT FOR ILLUMINATION. Does continuity exist between push control unit harness terminal No. 36 and body ground?
O.K.
Replace control amp. built-in push control unit.
DIAGNOSTIC PROCEDURE 15-2
CHECK MAGNET CLUTCH OPERATION. Does magnet clutch operate normally when engine , A/C switch, fan switch are ON?
N.G.
Go to Diagnostic Procedure 10.
O.K.
Replace control amp. built-in push control unit.
91C04787 94E10540
Courtesy of Nissan Motor Co., U.S.A.
DIAGNOSTIC PROCEDURE 15 – ILLUMINATION OR INDICATORS OF PUSH CONTROL UNIT DO NOT COME ON (Cont.)
A
Push control unit connector
34
G/W
V
B
Push control unit connector
37
B
Ω
DIAGNOSTIC PROCEDURE 15-3
Turn ignition switch and lighting switch OFF.
Disconnect push control unit harness connector.
A
CHECK POWER SUPPLY FOR PUSH CONTROL UNIT. Do approx. 12 volts exist between push control unit harness terminal No. 34 and body ground?
N.G.
Check 10A fuse at fuse block.
O.K.
Note
B
CHECK BODY GROUND CIRCUIT FOR PUSH CONTROL UNIT. Does continuity exist between push control unit harness terminal No. 37 and body ground?
O.K.
Replace control amp. built-in push control unit.
A
Push control unit connector
37
B
Ω
DIAGNOSTIC PROCEDURE 15-4
Turn ignition switch and lighting switch OFF.
Disconnect push control unit harness connector.
Note
A
CHECK BODY GROUND CIRCUIT FOR PUSH CONTROL UNIT. Does continuity exist between push control unit harness terminal No. 37 and body ground?
O.K.
Replace control amp. built-in push control unit.
NOTE: If the result is no good (NG) after checking circuit continuity, repair harness or connector.
91G04789 91I04790
Courtesy of Nissan Motor Co., U.S.A.

Fig. 27: *Diagnostic Procedure 15 – Illumination Or Indicators Of Push Control Unit Do Not Come On (Pathfinder – 2 Of 3)*

Fig. 28: *Diagnostic Procedure 15 – Illumination Or Indicators Of Push Control Unit Do Not Come On (Pathfinder – 3 Of 3)*

1993 AUTOMATIC A/C-HEATER SYSTEMS
300ZX

SPECIFICATIONS

Compressor Type .... Zexel DKS-16H 6-Cyl.
Compressor Belt Deflection
New Belt .... 9/32-5/16" (7-8 mm)
Use Belt .... 5/16-23/64" (8-9 mm)
System Oil Capacity .... 6.8 ozs.
Refrigerant (R-12) Capacity .... 26-30 ozs.
System Operating Pressures [1]
High Side .... 118-166 psi (8.3-11.7 kg/cm²)
Low Side .... 27-37 psi (1.9-2.6 kg/cm²)

1 - Measured at 77°F (25°C) ambient temperature, with 50-70 percent relative humidity.

WARNING: To avoid injury from accidental air bag deployment, read and carefully follow all SERVICE PRECAUTIONS and DISABLING & ACTIVATING AIR BAG SYSTEM procedures in AIR BAG SYSTEM SAFETY article in GENERAL SERVICING.

DESCRIPTION

The automatic A/C-heater system consists of electronically controlled components added to standard A/C-heater system to provide automatic temperature control. The A/C-heater system is controlled by the auto amplifier.

The auto amplifier continuously monitors sensors and uses the sensor inputs to control discharged air temperature, airflow volume and outlet vent distribution to maintain selected temperature setting. The auto amplifier has a self-diagnostic feature.

OPERATION

A/C-HEATER CONTROL PANEL

The auto amplifier continuously monitors sensor inputs to control air mix door motor, intake door motor, outlet mode door motor, blower motor, heater control valve and compressor clutch operation.

Four different fan speeds can be manually selected. Temperature switch adjusts selected temperature by one-degree increments, or switch can be held depressed to scroll temperature range on display. *See Fig. 1.*

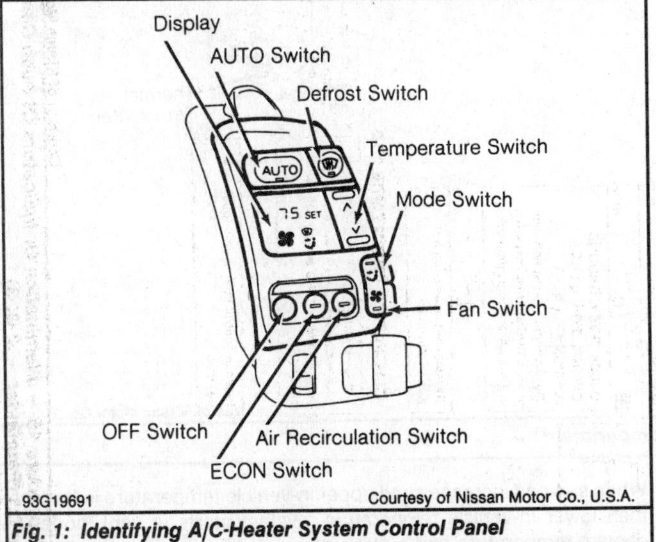
Display
AUTO Switch
Defrost Switch
Temperature Switch
Mode Switch
Fan Switch
OFF Switch
Air Recirculation Switch
ECON Switch
AUTO
75 SET
93G19691
Courtesy of Nissan Motor Co., U.S.A.

Fig. 1: Identifying A/C-Heater System Control Panel

AUTO Mode - This mode automatically controls entire system to maintain temperature set on display. In this mode, fan speed is automatically controlled or can be manually set to low, medium 1, medium 2 or high. A/C compressor will engage at temperatures greater than 32°F (0°C).

Defrost Mode - Defrost mode draws outside air through A/C-heater unit and directs most air to windshield. Temperature setting controls defrost heat. Fan speed can be set to low, medium 1, medium 2 or high. A/C compressor will engage at temperatures greater than 32°F (0°C). When ambient temperature is less than 41°F (5°C), outlet air automatically comes through defrost air outlets in AUTO mode.

ECON (Heating) Mode - Economy mode is used when heat only is desired. A/C compressor is off in this mode. With ECON switch on and desired temperature set, temperature of passenger compartment, airflow distribution and fan speed are automatically controlled. Airflow mode and fan speed may be manually set.

Recirculation Mode - This mode does not function when defrost mode is in use. After air recirculation switch is pressed, recirculation mode will function for only 10 minutes then switch to AUTO or off mode. To cancel mode, push air recirculation switch again to return to AUTO mode.

Off Mode - This mode allows outside air into vehicle and automatically adjusts outlet air door position and air mix temperature to the desired temperature setting. A/C compressor is off. Airflow mode and fan speed may be manually set.

AIR MIX DOOR CONTROL

Air mix door control system consists of auto amplifier, air mix door motor, upper and lower in-vehicle sensors, ambient temperature sensor, various duct (vent, floor and defrost) temperature sensors, and sunload sensor. The automatic temperature control system determines the optimum air mix door position for the selected temperature based on inputs from these sensors and temperature switch.

FAN SPEED CONTROL

Fan speed control system determines the airflow volume. The system consists of auto amplifier, fan control amplifier, upper and lower in-vehicle sensors, ambient sensor and sunload sensor. As in-vehicle temperature approaches selected temperature, fan control system decreases airflow rate. When sunload increases, system increases airflow rate. Minimum and maximum blower voltage depends on ambient temperature and sunload.

INTAKE DOOR CONTROL

The automatic temperature control system adjusts intake door position once every 30 seconds, blending fresh air with recirculated air to maintain desired temperature setting. The system is programmed to take in as much outside air as possible.

If actual outlet air temperature is greater than target outlet air temperature, intake door will gradually shift toward the recirculated air position. As actual outlet air temperature reaches target outlet air temperature, intake door will gradually shift toward fresh air intake setting.

When ambient temperature is less than 68°F (20°C), intake door will be set for full fresh air intake regardless of outlet air temperature. With A/C compressor off, intake door will be set at fresh air intake position, except when air recirculation switch is on.

STARTING FAN SPEED CONTROL

Starting fan speed control system consists of auto amplifier, fan control amplifier, upper and lower in-vehicle sensors, ambient temperature sensor, sunload sensor, thermal transmitter and defroster, vent duct sensor and floor duct sensor.

Auto amplifier operates starting fan speed based on all in-vehicle temperature sensors. At selected temperature of 77°F (25°C), with upper compartment temperature less than 70°F (21°C) and outlet duct temperature less than 95°F (30°C), fan starts at minimum flow rate. As discharge air temperature increases, airflow rate increases to bring passenger compartment temperature to target level as quickly as possible.

When ambient temperature is greater than 104°F (40°C), fan airflow rate is at full volume. As interior temperature begins to reach target temperature, fan speed decreases. Under heavy sunload condition, fan speed is increased to maintain interior temperature. Fan speed increases if selected temperature is decreased.

1993 AUTOMATIC A/C-HEATER SYSTEMS
300ZX (Cont.)

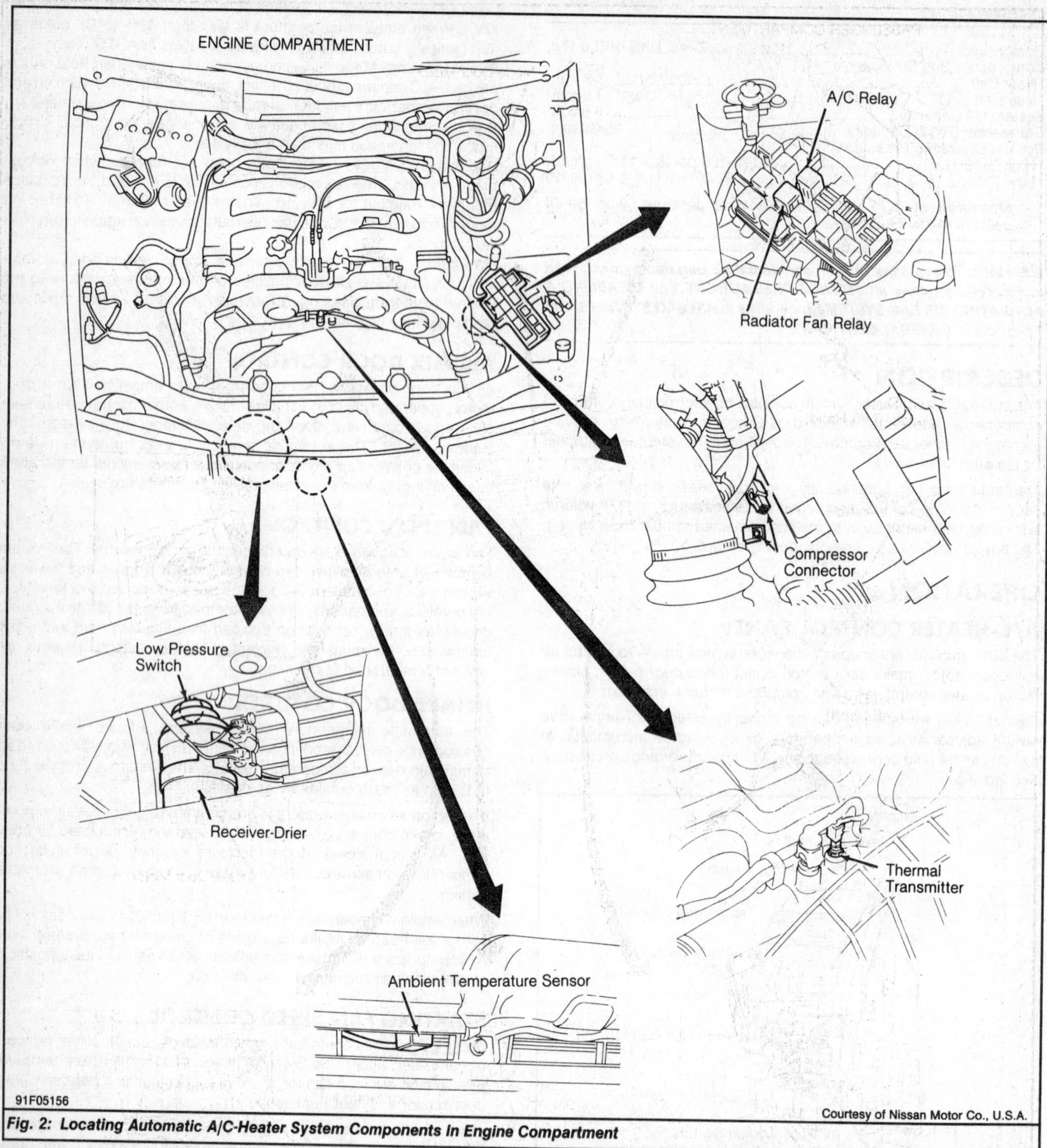
ENGINE COMPARTMENT
A/C Relay
Radiator Fan Relay
Compressor
Connector
Low Pressure
Switch
Receiver-Drier
Thermal
Transmitter
Ambient Temperature Sensor
91F05156
Courtesy of Nissan Motor Co., U.S.A.

Fig. 2: Locating Automatic A/C-Heater System Components In Engine Compartment

OUTLET DOOR CONTROL

The automatic temperature control system regulates airflow distribution to various outlets (vent, defrost and floor) based on amount of sunload, ambient temperature and selected temperature.

At selected temperature of 77°F (25°C), with upper compartment temperature less than 70°F (21°C) and outlet duct temperature less than 75°F (24°C), fan starts at minimum flow rate in defrost mode. When defrost duct temperature exceeds 75°F (24°C), air outlet mode changes from defrost to foot/defrost mode. When floor duct temperature exceeds 102°F (39°C), system goes into full AUTO mode.

When sunload increases and upper in-vehicle temperature is far more than lower in-vehicle temperature, system starts in vent mode. As coolant temperature and outlet air temperature increase, system will go into full AUTO mode.

HEATER (WATER) CONTROL VALVE

Heater control valve is cable connected to air mix doors. When air mix doors are at full cold position, heater valve is closed. When air mix doors are at full hot position, heater valve is open. Heater valve position corresponds to opening angle of air mix doors.

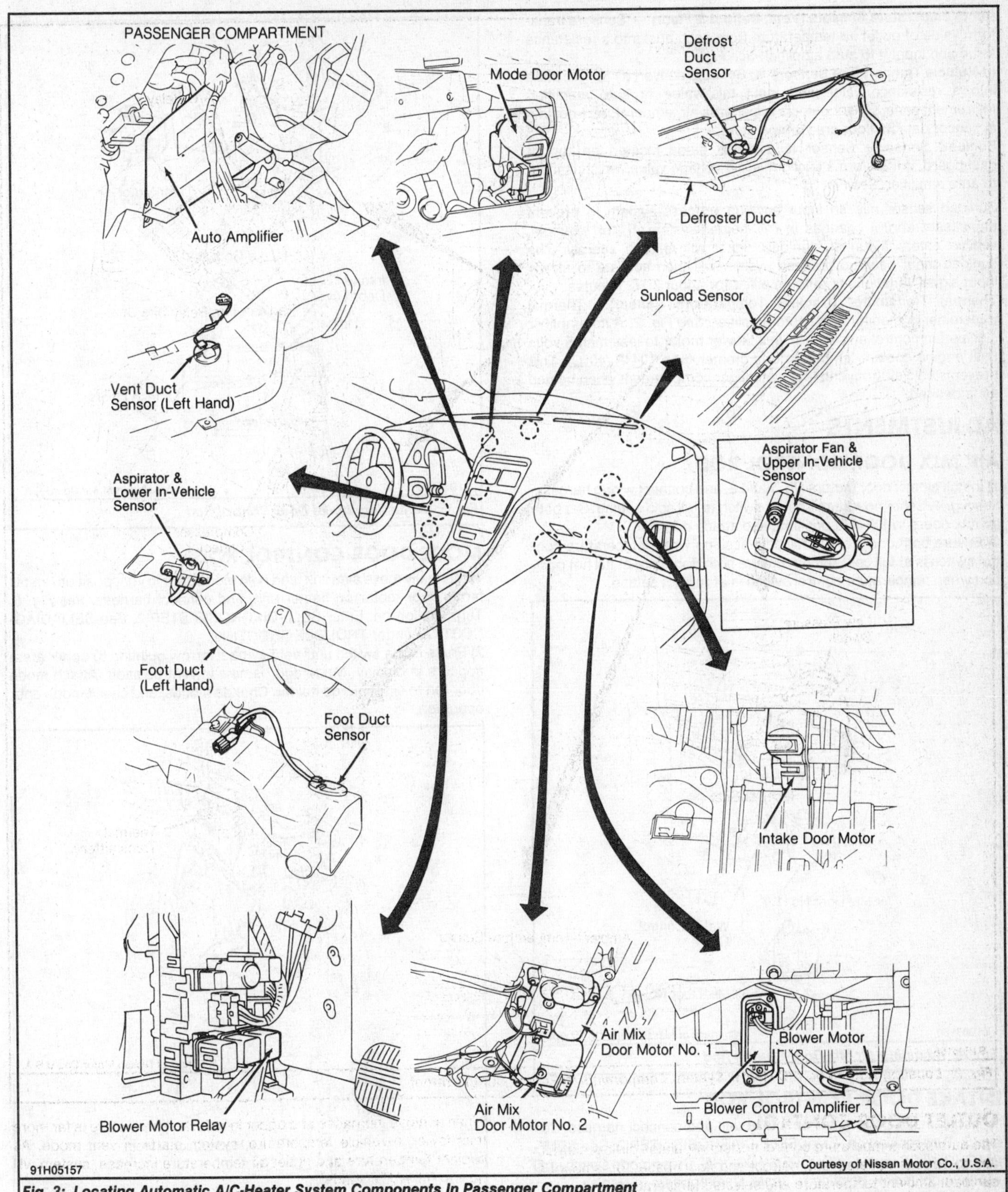
PASSENGER COMPARTMENT
Mode Door Motor
Defrost
Duct
Sensor
Defroster Duct
Auto Amplifier
Sunload Sensor
Vent Duct
Sensor (Left Hand)
Aspirator Fan &
Upper In-Vehicle
Sensor
Aspirator &
Lower In-Vehicle
Sensor
Foot Duct
(Left Hand)
Foot Duct
Sensor
Intake Door Motor
Air Mix
Door Motor No. 1
Blower Motor
Blower Control Amplifier
Blower Motor Relay
Air Mix
Door Motor No. 2
Courtesy of Nissan Motor Co., U.S.A.
91H05157

Fig. 3: Locating Automatic A/C-Heater System Components In Passenger Compartment

SENSORS

Ambient Temperature Sensor – Sensor transforms ambient air temperature into a resistance value and inputs it to auto amplifier. Sensor is located behind lower front grille. *See Fig. 2.*

Ambient temperature sensor has an input back-up process system to prevent unpleasant abrupt changes in A/C-heater system. If, for example, vehicle comes to a stop after high-speed cruising, ambient temperature sensor will signal a sharp rise in temperature. Ambient temperature input back-up process system will activate to slowly increase in-vehicle air temperature .11°F (.06°C) every 12 seconds.

1993 AUTOMATIC A/C-HEATER SYSTEMS 300ZX (Cont.)

Duct Temperature Sensors (Vent, Defrost & Floor) – Sensors transform value of outlet air temperature from each duct into a resistance value and input it to auto amplifier. *See Fig. 3.*

In-Vehicle Temperature Sensors – Sensors convert air temperature into a resistance value and input this value to auto amplifier. Instrument panel sensor detects upper area air temperature. Foot level sensor detects floor area temperature.

Sunload Sensor – Sensor is a photo diode located on top of dashboard. It transforms sunlight into a voltage value, which is input to auto amplifier. *See Fig. 3.*

Sunload sensor has an input back-up process system to prevent unpleasant abrupt changes in A/C-heater system. If, for example, vehicle enters a tunnel, sunload signal will change sharply. The sunload input back-up process system will then activate to slowly input signal variations to auto amplifier for about 2 1/2 minutes.

Thermal Transmitter (Coolant Temperature Sensor) – Thermal transmitter is monitored by auto amplifier. *See Fig. 2.* Auto amplifier signals fan control amplifier to limit blower motor to less than 5 volts until engine coolant temperature is greater than 104°F (40°C). This prevents cold air from entering passenger compartment when heated air is desired.

ADJUSTMENTS

AIR MIX DOOR CONTROL ROD

1) Install air mix door motors No. 1 and 2, and connect wiring harness. *See Fig. 4.* Set temperature control switch to full cold setting. Set both air mix doors to full cold position, and attach door rod.

2) Ensure both doors are at full cold position when temperature control switch is at full cold setting. Ensure both doors are at full hot position when temperature control switch is at full hot setting.

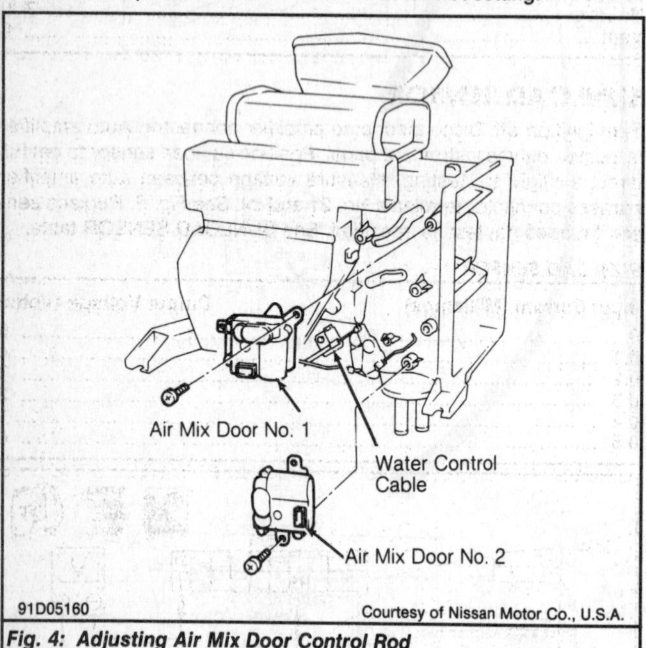
Air Mix Door No. 1
Water Control Cable
Air Mix Door No. 2
91D05160
Courtesy of Nissan Motor Co., U.S.A.

Fig. 4: Adjusting Air Mix Door Control Rod

INTAKE DOOR CONTROL ROD

1) Install intake door motor on intake unit and connect harness. *See Fig. 5.* Turn ignition on. Enter SELF-DIAGNOSIS STEP 2. See SELF-DIAGNOSTICS under TROUBLE SHOOTING. Press mode switch until vent symbol (arrow pointing to upper area) appears in display.

2) Intake door is now in recirculated air position. Install intake door lever. Set intake door rod in recirculated air position, and attach rod to holder. Change modes, and check intake door operation.

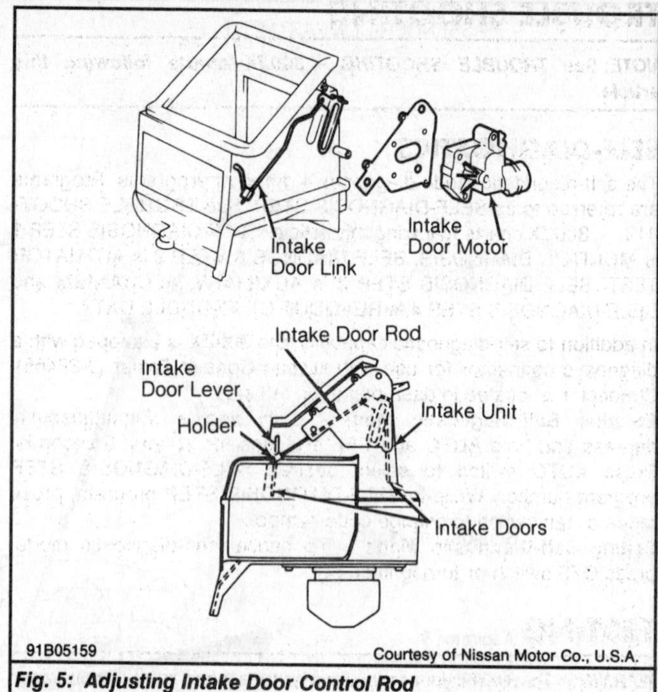
Intake Door Link
Intake Door Motor
Intake Door Rod
Intake Door Lever
Holder
Intake Unit
Intake Doors
91B05159
Courtesy of Nissan Motor Co., U.S.A.

Fig. 5: Adjusting Intake Door Control Rod

MODE DOOR CONTROL ROD

1) Manually move side link, and hold mode door in vent position. Install mode door motor on heater unit, and connect harness. *See Fig. 6.* Turn ignition on. Enter SELF-DIAGNOSIS STEP 2. See SELF-DIAGNOSTICS under TROUBLE SHOOTING.

2) Press mode switch until vent symbol (arrow pointing to upper area) appears in display. Mode door is now in vent position. Attach mode door rod to side link rod holder. Change modes, and check mode door operation.

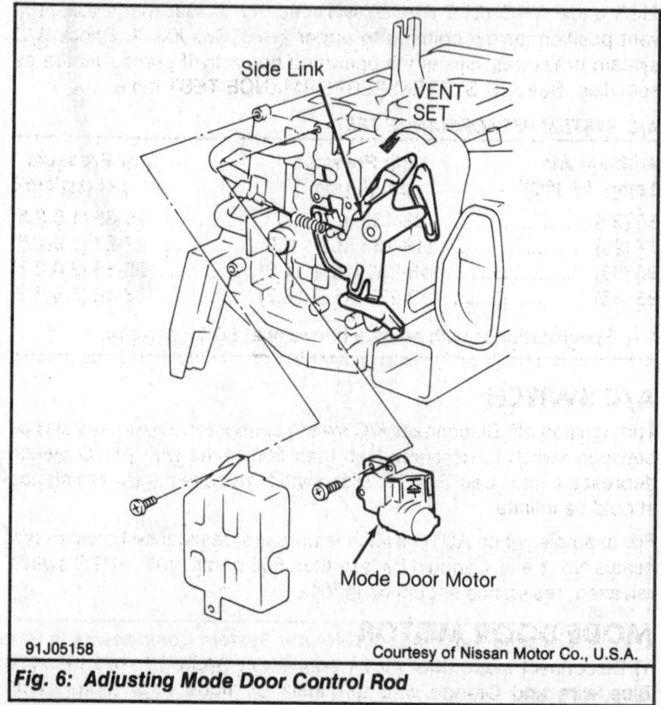
Side Link
VENT SET
Mode Door Motor
91J05158
Courtesy of Nissan Motor Co., U.S.A.

Fig. 6: Adjusting Mode Door Control Rod

HEATER (WATER) CONTROL VALVE CABLE

Clamp cable at full closed position when air mix door No. 2 is at full cold position. Ensure cable is at full open position when air mix door No. 2 is at full hot position.

TROUBLE SHOOTING

NOTE: See TROUBLE SHOOTING - 300ZX charts following this article.

SELF-DIAGNOSTICS

The self-diagnostic mode diagnoses 4 different programs. Programs are referred to as SELF-DIAGNOSIS STEP. See TROUBLE SHOOTING - 300ZX charts following this article. SELF-DIAGNOSIS STEP 1 is MONITOR DIAGNOSIS. SELF-DIAGNOSIS STEP 2 is ACTUATOR TEST. SELF-DIAGNOSIS STEP 3 is AUXILIARY MECHANISM and SELF-DIAGNOSIS STEP 4 is READOUT OF TROUBLE DATA.

In addition to self-diagnostic capability, the 300ZX is equipped with a diagnostic connector for use with Nissan Consult Tester (J-38465). Connector is located in dash panel, on left side.

Entering Self-Diagnostic Mode - Start engine. Simultaneously depress and hold AUTO and OFF switches for at least 5 seconds. Press AUTO switch to select desired SELF-DIAGNOSIS STEP program number. While in SELF-DIAGNOSIS STEP program, press mode or fan switch to change code symbol.

Exiting Self-Diagnostic Mode - To cancel self-diagnostic mode, press OFF switch or turn ignition off.

TESTING

WARNING: To avoid injury from accidental air bag deployment, read and carefully follow all SERVICE PRECAUTIONS and DISABLING & ACTIVATING AIR BAG SYSTEM procedures in AIR BAG SYSTEM SAFETY article in GENERAL SERVICING.

NOTE: For test procedures not covered in this article, see MANUAL A/C-HEATER SYSTEMS - 300ZX article.

A/C SYSTEM PERFORMANCE

Park vehicle out of direct sunlight. Close all doors. Open engine hood and windows. Enter SELF-DIAGNOSIS STEP 2. See SELF-DIAGNOSTICS under TROUBLE SHOOTING. *See Fig. 2.* Set mode switch in vent position (arrow pointing to upper area). *See Fig. 1.* Check A/C system pressures. System is operating correctly if pressures are as specified. See A/C SYSTEM PERFORMANCE TEST table.

A/C SYSTEM PERFORMANCE TEST

Ambient Air Temp. °F (°C)	High Pressure [1] psi (kg/cm²)	Low Pressure [1] psi (kg/cm²)
68 (20)	88-132 (6.2-9.3)	26-36 (1.8-2.5)
77 (25)	118-166 (8.3-11.7)	27-37 (1.9-2.6)
86 (30)	148-203 (10.4-14.3)	28-38 (2.0-2.7)
95 (35)	179-237 (12.6-16.7)	33-46 (2.3-3.2)

[1] - Specification is with relative humidity at 50-70 percent.

A/C SWITCH

Turn ignition off. Disconnect A/C switch connector. Ensure resistance between switch terminals is less than 500 ohms with AUTO switch depressed (on). *See Fig. 7.* With switch released (off), resistance should be infinite.

For example, when AUTO switch is pressed, resistance between terminals No. 1 and 4 should be less than 500 ohms. With AUTO switch released, resistance should be infinite.

MODE DOOR MOTOR

1) Disconnect mode door motor connector. Apply 12 volts between Blue wire and Orange wire terminals of mode door motor. With positive battery lead connected to Orange wire terminal and negative battery lead to Blue wire terminal, mode door should move from defrost to vent position. Reverse battery leads, and ensure door moves in opposite direction.

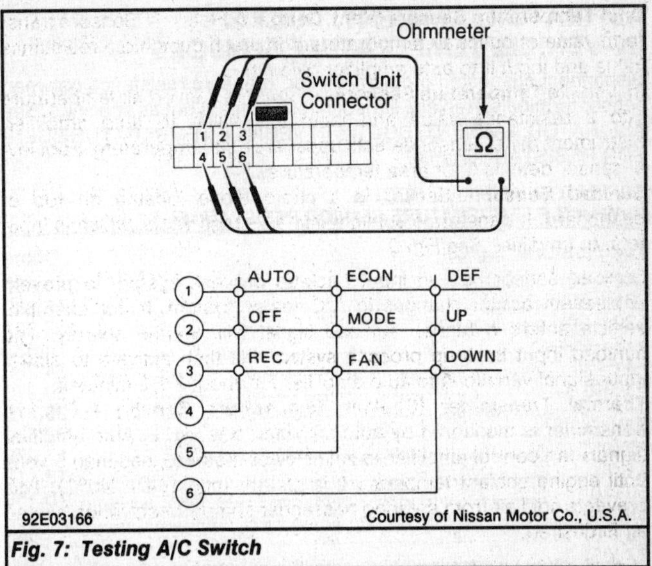
Ohmmeter
Switch Unit
Connector
1 2 3
4 5 6
Ω
AUTO
ECON
DEF
OFF
MODE
UP
REC
FAN
DOWN
1
2
3
4
5
6
92E03166
Courtesy of Nissan Motor Co., U.S.A.

Fig. 7: Testing A/C Switch

2) Check resistance between Red/Blue wire and Light Blue wire terminals of Potentiometer Balance Resistor (PBR). Replace PBR if resistance is not as specified. See MODE DOOR MOTOR PBR RESISTANCE table.

MODE DOOR MOTOR PBR RESISTANCE

Mode Door Position	Ohms
Defrost	3000
Foot/Defrost	1600
Bi-Level	700
Vent	0

SUNLOAD SENSOR

Turn ignition off. Disconnect auto amplifier connector. Auto amplifier is located behind instrument panel. Position sunload sensor to get full direct sunlight for testing. Measure voltage between auto amplifier harness connector terminals No. 21 and 24. *See Fig. 8.* Replace sensor if it does not test as specified. See SUNLOAD SENSOR table.

SUNLOAD SENSOR

Input Current (Milliamps)	Output Voltage (Volts)
0	5
0.1	4
0.2	3
0.3	2
0.4	1
0.5	0

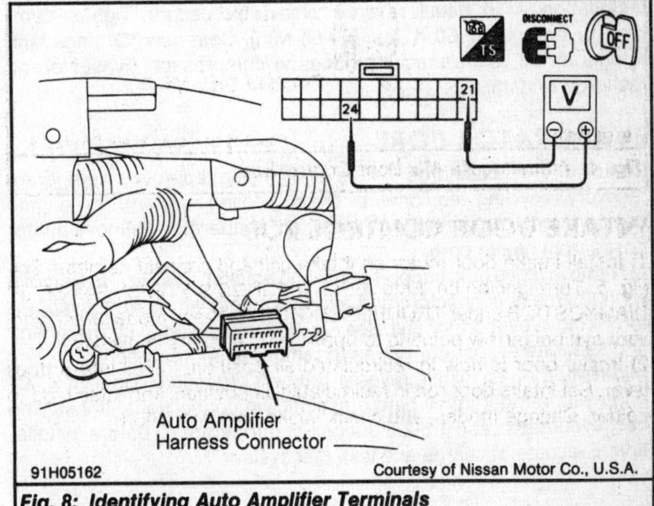
DISCONNECT
TS
OFF
24
21
V
Auto Amplifier
Harness Connector
91H05162
Courtesy of Nissan Motor Co., U.S.A.

Fig. 8: Identifying Auto Amplifier Terminals

1993 AUTOMATIC A/C-HEATER SYSTEMS 300ZX (Cont.)

ASPIRATOR, AMBIENT, DUCT & IN-VEHICLE TEMPERATURE SENSORS

Disconnect suspected problem sensor. Measure resistance between sensor terminals. Replace sensor if resistance is not as specified. See ASPIRATOR, AMBIENT, DUCT & IN-VEHICLE TEMPERATURE SENSOR RESISTANCE table.

ASPIRATOR, AMBIENT, DUCT & IN-VEHICLE TEMPERATURE SENSOR RESISTANCE

Temperature °F (°C)	Ohms
-40 (-40)	210,550
-31 (-35)	146,860
-22 (-30)	103,907
-13 (-25)	74,630
-4 (-20)	54,280
5 (-15)	39,970
14 (-10)	29,770
23 (-5)	22,430
32 (0)	17,070
41 (5)	13,110
50 (10)	10,180
59 (15)	7960
68 (20)	6290
77 (25)	5000
86 (30)	4010
95 (35)	3240
104 (40)	2630
113 (45)	2150
122 (50)	1770
131 (55)	1470
140 (60)	1220
149 (65)	1020
158 (70)	860
167 (75)	730
176 (80)	620

REMOVAL & INSTALLATION

WARNING: To avoid injury from accidental air bag deployment, read and carefully follow all SERVICE PRECAUTIONS and DISABLING & ACTIVATING AIR BAG SYSTEM procedures in AIR BAG SYSTEM SAFETY article in GENERAL SERVICING.

A/C COMPRESSOR

Removal - 1) Disconnect negative battery cable. Discharge A/C system using approved refrigerant recovery/recycling equipment. Remove engine undercover. Remove low pressure tube, front stabilizer bar and clamps. Loosen idler pulley nut and adjusting bolt. Remove idler pulley.

2) Remove necessary air pipes and hoses. Remove nuts to separate high- and low-pressure flexible hoses from compressor. Disconnect electrical connectors. Remove compressor bolts and compressor.

Installation - To install, reverse removal procedure. Tighten compressor bolts to 37-50 ft. lbs. (50-68 N.m). Coat new "O" rings with refrigerant oil when attaching hoses to compressor. Evacuate and recharge system.

EVAPORATOR CORE

Removal - 1) Discharge A/C system using approved refrigerant recovery/recycling equipment. Drain cooling system. In engine compartment, disconnect A/C lines from evaporator. Remove heater hoses from heater core.

2) Remove glove box, support panel and bracket. *See Fig. 10.* Remove wiring harness connectors and air inlet/outlet clamps from evaporator. Remove evaporator unit. *See Fig. 9.* Remove spring clip retainers, and separate evaporator halves to remove evaporator core.

Installation - To install, reverse removal procedure. Coat new "O" rings with refrigerant oil before assembling connections. If installing new evaporator, add 1.5-2.5 ounces of refrigerant oil before installation. Evacuate, recharge and leak test system.

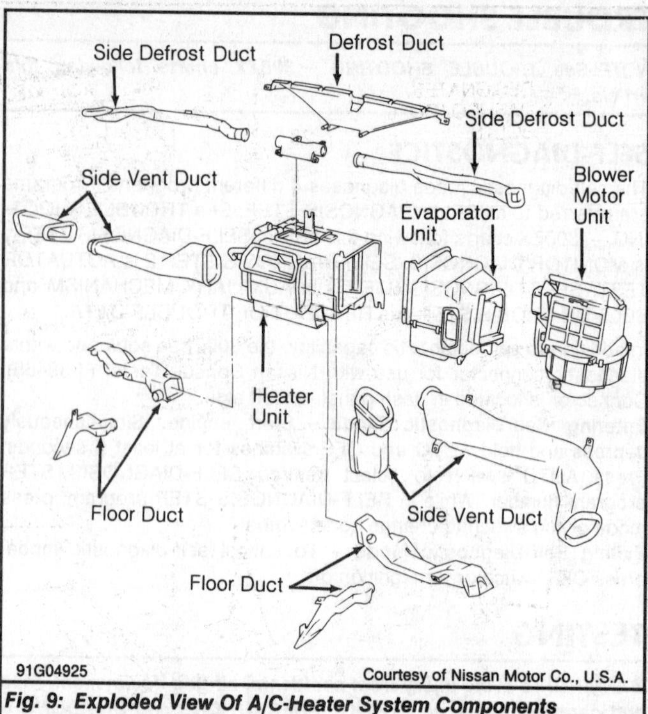
Side Defrost Duct
Defrost Duct
Side Defrost Duct
Side Vent Duct
Blower Motor Unit
Evaporator Unit
Heater Unit
Floor Duct
Side Vent Duct
Floor Duct
91G04925
Courtesy of Nissan Motor Co., U.S.A.

Fig. 9: Exploded View Of A/C-Heater System Components

HEATER CORE

Removal & Installation - 1) Remove radio faceplate by removing narrow plastic strip above radio and both end caps of top vent outlet. *See Fig. 10.* Remove faceplate screws located behind strip and top vent end caps. Bottom of faceplate is held by clips; pull or pry faceplate outward to remove.

2) Remove center console screws located inside ashtray and below A/C-heater control panel. Remove console by pulling front upward to remove rear pawls from rear console. Remove both center section side covers.

3) Remove right defrost grille first; use flat-blade screwdriver through grille slats to release metal clips. Remove left defrost grille in same manner. Remove dashboard bolts from inside of defrost duct, noting location of bolts.

4) Remove steering column covers and driver-side instrument panel undercover. Remove steering column support bracket bolts and lower steering column. Remove screw on bottom of switch panel housing, and pull bottom of switch panel out and downward to release top pawl hooks. Note location, and disconnect wiring harness. Remove switch panel housing screws.

5) Remove instrument cluster bezel housing-to-instrument cluster hood screws. Remove instrument cluster hood. Pull instrument cluster bezel housing outward to disconnect housing from bottom clips. Remove instrument cluster retainer and instrument cluster, noting location of harness connectors. Using flat-blade screwdriver, cover tip with cloth and then pry off dashboard side outlet vents.

6) Remove dashboard bolts behind side outlet vents, in center rear of instrument cluster recessed area, inside defrost ducts, at bottom of center section and on each side of steering column. *See Fig. 10.* Pull dashboard top corners upward and outward to disengage fastening clips.

7) Pull dashboard outward enough to disconnect cables and wiring harness from heater. Disconnect all air ducts, and remove heater unit. Remove spring clip retainers, and separate heater case halves to remove heater core. To install, reverse removal procedure.

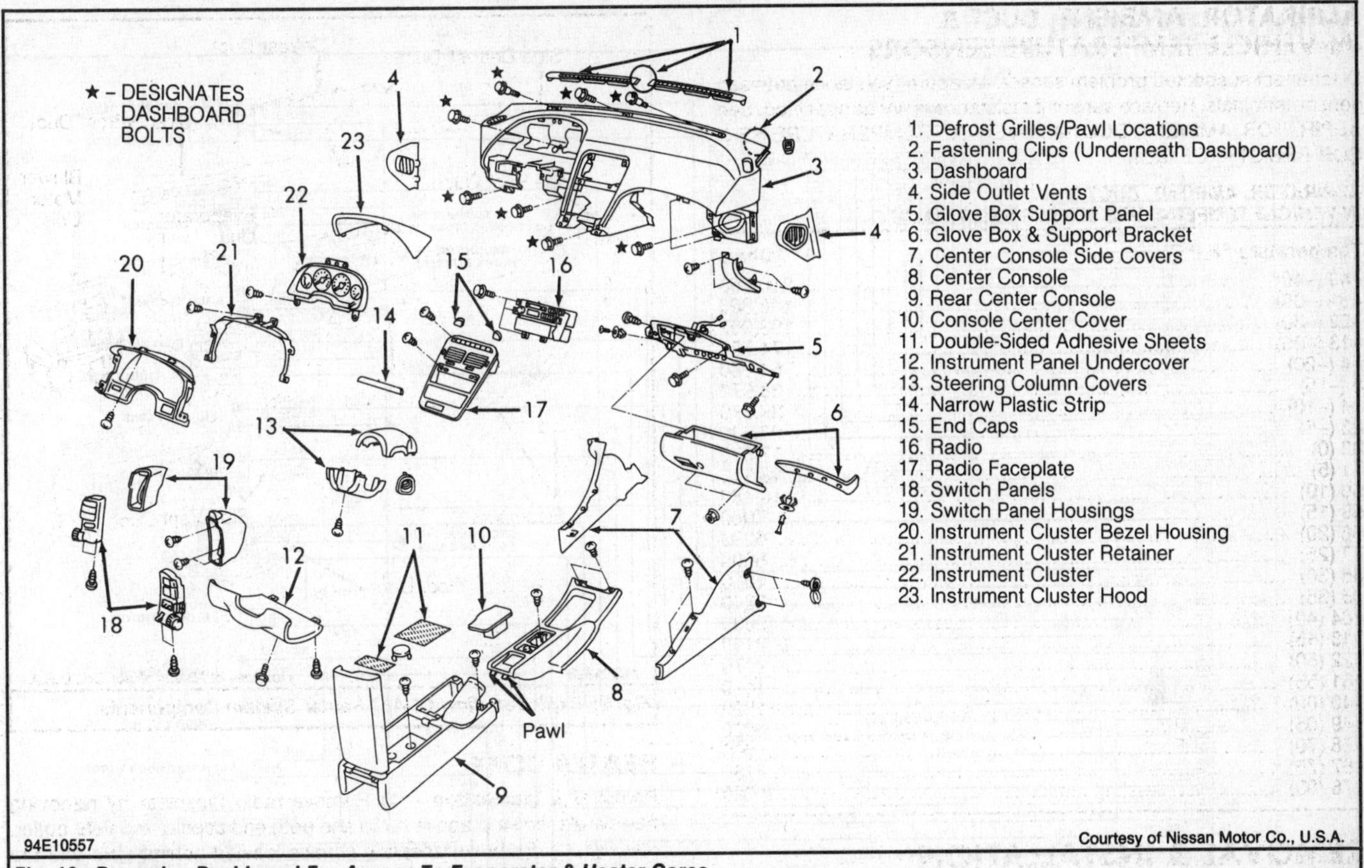
★ - DESIGNATES DASHBOARD BOLTS
1. Defrost Grilles/Pawl Locations
2. Fastening Clips (Underneath Dashboard)
3. Dashboard
4. Side Outlet Vents
5. Glove Box Support Panel
6. Glove Box & Support Bracket
7. Center Console Side Covers
8. Center Console
9. Rear Center Console
10. Console Center Cover
11. Double-Sided Adhesive Sheets
12. Instrument Panel Undercover
13. Steering Column Covers
14. Narrow Plastic Strip
15. End Caps
16. Radio
17. Radio Faceplate
18. Switch Panels
19. Switch Panel Housings
20. Instrument Cluster Bezel Housing
21. Instrument Cluster Retainer
22. Instrument Cluster
23. Instrument Cluster Hood
Pawl
94E10557
Courtesy of Nissan Motor Co., U.S.A.

Fig. 10: Removing Dashboard For Access To Evaporator & Heater Cores

CONDENSER

Removal - Drain engine coolant. Discharge A/C system using approved refrigerant recovery/recycling equipment. Disconnect radiator hoses and wiring harness. Remove radiator cooling fan, shroud assembly and radiator. Remove front grille. Disconnect refrigerant lines from condenser and receiver-drier. Remove condenser.

Installation - To install, reverse removal procedure. Coat new "O" rings with refrigerant oil before assembling connections. If installing new condenser, add 1.0-1.7 ounces of refrigerant oil before installation. Evacuate, recharge and leak test system.

RECEIVER-DRIER

Removal - Discharge A/C system using approved refrigerant recovery/recycling equipment. Remove front grille to access receiver-drier. Disconnect low pressure switch connector. *See Fig. 2.* Disconnect A/C lines from receiver-drier, and plug openings. Remove screws and receiver-drier.

Installation - To install, reverse removal procedure. Coat new "O" rings with refrigerant oil before assembling connections. If installing new receiver-drier, add 0.5-0.8 ounce of refrigerant oil before installation. Evacuate, recharge and leak test system.

TORQUE SPECIFICATIONS

TORQUE SPECIFICATIONS

Application	Ft. Lbs. (N.m)
Refrigerant Line Connections	15-21 (20-29)
Refrigerant Pipe Fittings	
Compressor	11-14 (15-19)
Condenser	11-18 (15-25)
Evaporator Outlet	15-21 (20-29)
Receiver-Drier Inlet	11-18 (15-25)
	INCH Lbs. (N.m)
Refrigerant Pipe Fittings	
Evaporator Inlet	89-180 (10-20)
Receiver-Drier Outlet	89-180 (10-20)

1993 AUTOMATIC A/C-HEATER SYSTEMS 300ZX (Cont.)

WIRING DIAGRAM

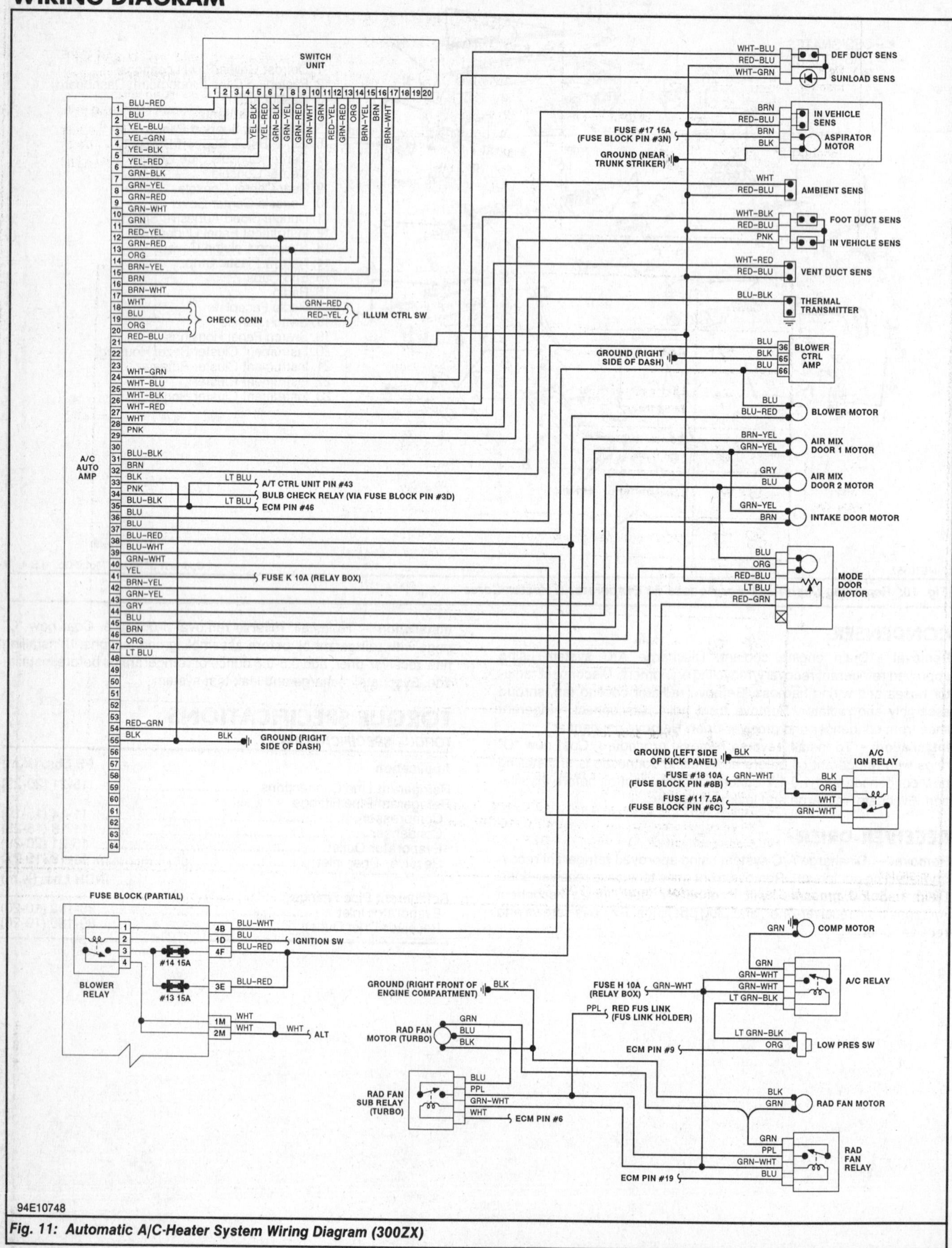
SWITCH UNIT
A/C AUTO AMP
BLU-RED
BLU
YEL-BLU
YEL-GRN
YEL-BLK
YEL-RED
GRN-BLK
GRN-YEL
GRN-RED
GRN-WHT
GRN
RED-YEL
ORG
BRN-YEL
BRN
BRN-WHT
WHT
RED-BLU
CHECK CONN
ILLUM CTRL SW
WHT-GRN
WHT-BLU
WHT-BLK
WHT-RED
PNK
BLU-BLK
BLK
LT BLU
A/T CTRL UNIT PIN #43
BULB CHECK RELAY (VIA FUSE BLOCK PIN #3D)
ECM PIN #46
BLU-WHT
YEL
GRY
FUSE K 10A (RELAY BOX)
RED-GRN
GROUND (RIGHT SIDE OF DASH)
DEF DUCT SENS
SUNLOAD SENS
IN VEHICLE SENS
ASPIRATOR MOTOR
FUSE #17 15A (FUSE BLOCK PIN #3N)
GROUND (NEAR TRUNK STRIKER)
AMBIENT SENS
FOOT DUCT SENS
IN VEHICLE SENS
VENT DUCT SENS
THERMAL TRANSMITTER
BLOWER CTRL AMP
BLOWER MOTOR
AIR MIX DOOR 1 MOTOR
AIR MIX DOOR 2 MOTOR
INTAKE DOOR MOTOR
MODE DOOR MOTOR
GROUND (LEFT SIDE OF KICK PANEL)
FUSE #18 10A (FUSE BLOCK PIN #8B)
FUSE #11 7.5A (FUSE BLOCK PIN #6C)
A/C IGN RELAY
FUSE BLOCK (PARTIAL)
BLOWER RELAY
#14 15A
#13 15A
IGNITION SW
ALT
COMP MOTOR
A/C RELAY
LT GRN-BLK
GROUND (RIGHT FRONT OF ENGINE COMPARTMENT)
FUSE H 10A (RELAY BOX)
PPL
RED FUS LINK (FUS LINK HOLDER)
RAD FAN MOTOR (TURBO)
LOW PRES SW
ECM PIN #9
RAD FAN SUB RELAY (TURBO)
ECM PIN #6
RAD FAN MOTOR
RAD FAN RELAY
ECM PIN #19
94E10748

Fig. 11: Automatic A/C-Heater System Wiring Diagram (300ZX)

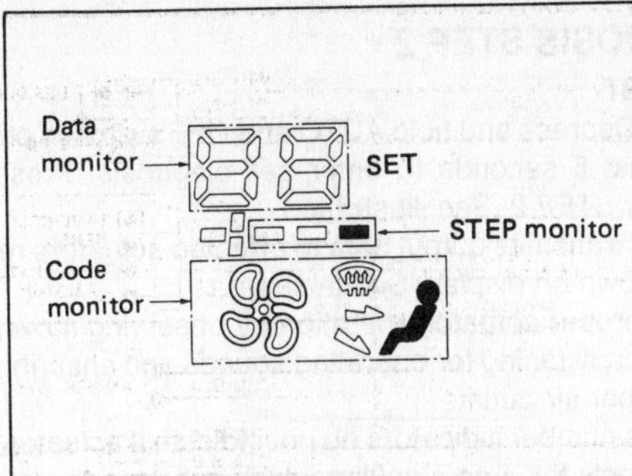
Data monitor
SET
STEP monitor
Code monitor

SELF-DIAGNOSIS STEP 1

MONITOR DIAGNOSIS

1) Start engine. Simultaneously depress and hold AUTO and OFF switches on control panel for at least 5 seconds to enter self-diagnosis. Display will show that STEP 1 has begun. See illustration.

2) Pressing fan switch or mode switch changes code symbol and corresponding data in display. If temperature data shown in display differs greatly from actual temperature reading, check sensor circuit for fault, and check sensor resistances. See TESTING in AUTOMATIC A/C-HEATER SYSTEMS - 300ZX article.

Press FAN SW. ↑

Press MODE SW. ↓

Code	Item	Unit	Code	Item	Unit
	Ambient temperature	°C (°F)		Internal data	–
	Upper compartment temperature	°C (°F)		Internal data	–
	Lower compartment temperature	°C (°F)		Internal data	–
	DEF outlet air temperature	°C (°F)		Internal data	–
	VENT outlet air temperature	°C (°F)		Internal data	–
	FOOT outlet air temperature	°C (°F)		Internal data	–
	Sunload	*1		Difference between upper and lower target temperatures	°C (°F)
	Water temperature *3	°C (°F)		Internal data	–
	Mode door voltage*4	*2			

*1: One tenth of the value in kcal/h·m² unit
*2: Ten times of the value in V
*3: When coolant temperature is below 40°C (104°F), indicates 20°C (68°F)
When coolant temperature is avove 40°C (104°F), indicates 80°C (176°F)
*4: Mode door voltage: 0 = VENT, 5 = DEF

92G03167

Courtesy of Nissan Motor Co., U.S.A.

Fig. 1: Self-Diagnosis Step 1 – Monitor Diagnosis (300ZX)

1993 AUTOMATIC A/C-HEATER SYSTEMS
Trouble Shooting – 300ZX (Cont.)

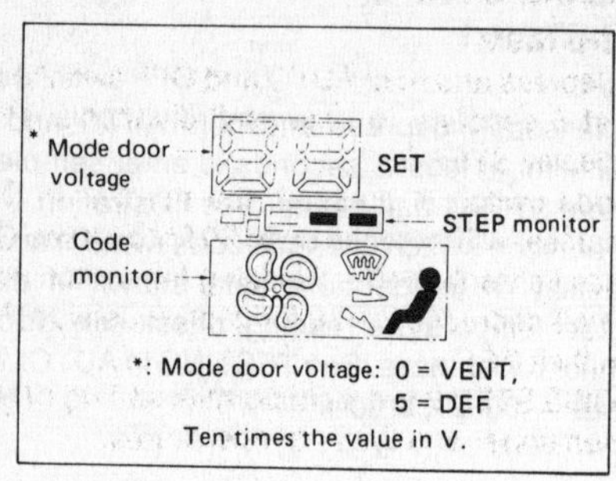
* Mode door voltage
SET
STEP monitor
Code monitor
*: Mode door voltage: 0 = VENT, 5 = DEF
Ten times the value in V.

Press MODE SW. →

Actuator \ Display				
Mode door	DEF	D/FOOT	B/L	VENT
Intake door	FRE	FRE	50% FRE	REC
Air mix door	Full Hot	Full Hot	30°C (86°F)	Full Cold
Compressor	OFF	OFF	ON	ON

Operating condition of each actuator cannot be checked by indicators.

SELF-DIAGNOSIS STEP 2

ACTUATOR TEST

1) Start engine. Depress and hold AUTO and OFF switches on control panel for at least 5 seconds to enter self-diagnosis. Press AUTO switch to display STEP 2. See illustration.

2) Auto amplifier transmits output data to affected actuators related to code symbol shown on display. See tables.

3) Check for improper actuator operation by observing movement of actuator and door, listening for operating sounds and ensuring airflow comes from proper air outlets.

4) Code and data number indicators do not indicate if actuator is operating. Numbers only tell auto amplifier which actuator operation is to be energized.

5) Each operating condition can be set by pressing fan or mode switch. See tables. It may take as long as one minute for outlet temperatures and airflow rates to stabilize.

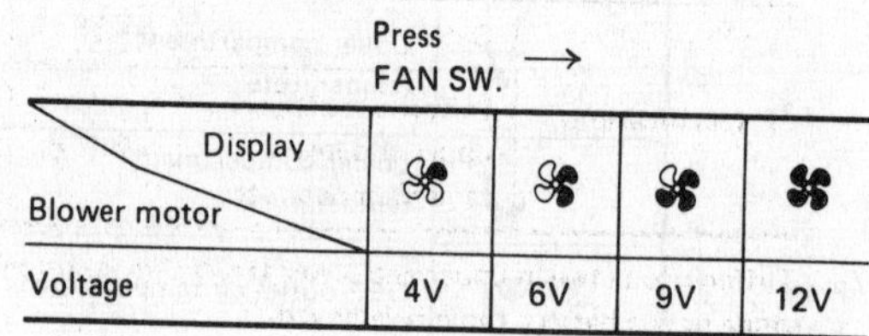

Press FAN SW. →

Blower motor \ Display				
Voltage	4V	6V	9V	12V

92I03168

Courtesy of Nissan Motor Co., U.S.A.

Fig. 2: Self-Diagnosis Step 2 – Actuator Test (300ZX)

1993 AUTOMATIC A/C-HEATER SYSTEMS
Trouble Shooting – 300ZX (Cont.)

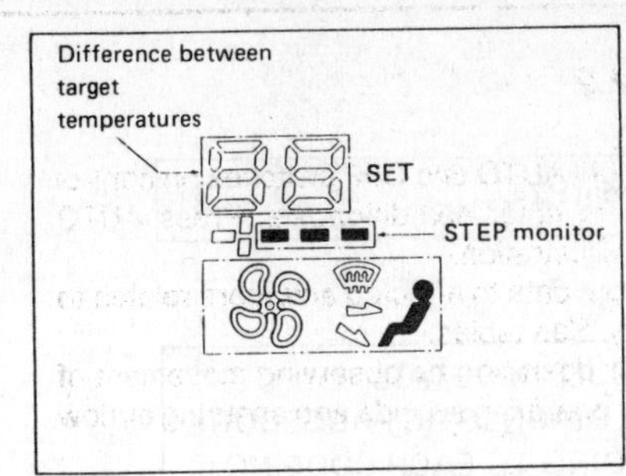
Difference between target temperatures
SET
STEP monitor

SELF-DIAGNOSIS STEP 3

AUXILIARY MECHANISM

1) Start engine. Depress and hold AUTO and OFF switches on control panel for at least 5 seconds to enter self-diagnosis. Press AUTO switch twice to display STEP 3.

2) Each time mode switch is pressed, the number in SET section advances. This number will increase up to 20 for degrees Celsius (°C), and 36 for degrees Fahrenheit (°F). Pressing fan switch will decrease number. Number will decrease to -20 for degree Celsius (°C), and -36 for degree Fahrenheit (°F).

3) SELF-DIAGNOSIS STEP 3 program permits setting of temperature difference between upper and lower temperatures.

← Press FAN SW. Press MODE SW. →

°C specifications	Data	-20	----	-1	0	1	----	20
	Difference between upper and lower target temperatures	-2.0°C	----	-1°C	0°C	0.1°C	----	2.0°C
°F specifications	Data	-36	----	-2	0	2°C	----	36
	Difference between upper and lower target temperatures	-3.6°F	----	-0.2°F	0°F	0.2°F	----	3.6°F

Difference between upper and lower target temperatures changed in the preceding procedure is kept until the next change is done or the battery cable is removed.

Courtesy of Nissan Motor Co., U.S.A.

94G10583

Fig. 3: Self-Diagnosis Step 3 – Auxiliary Mechanism (300ZX)

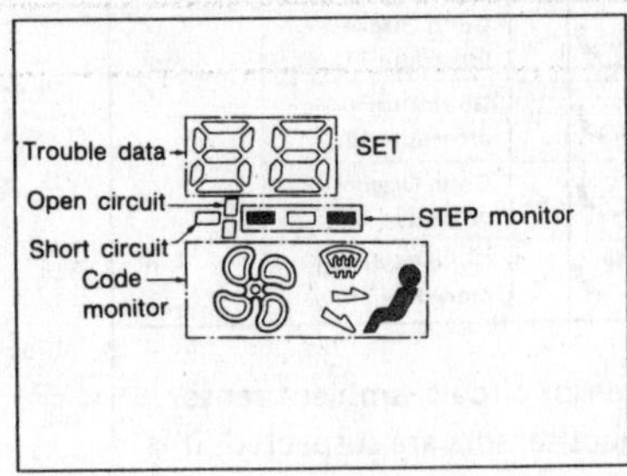
Trouble data
SET
Open circuit
STEP monitor
Short circuit
Code monitor

SELF-DIAGNOSIS STEP 4

READOUT OF TROUBLE DATA

1) Start engine. Depress and hold AUTO and OFF switches on control panel for at least 5 seconds to enter self-diagnosis. Press AUTO switch 3 times to display STEP 4.

2) Each time fan or mode switch is pressed, code monitor changes, and data or status of each sensor appears in data monitor. The data number refers to degrees Celsius, and number in parenthesis refers to degrees Fahrenheit.

3) If sensor becomes inoperative, number of engine starts since last problem was detected appears in SET section. An open circuit is indicated by a vertical rectangle, and short circuit is indicated by a horizontal rectangle.

Conditions for open or short circuit

Code	Sensor	Open circuit	Short circuit
	Ambient sensor	Less than -70°C (-94°F)	Greater than 141°C (286°F)
	Room upper sensor	Less than -38°C (-36°F)	Greater than 141°C (286°F)
	Room lower sensor	Less than -38°C (-36°F)	Greater than 141°C (286°F)
	DEF duct sensor	Less than -38°C (-36°F)	Greater than 141°C (286°F)
	VENT duct sensor	Less than -38°C (-36°F)	Greater than 141°C (286°F)
	Foot duct sensor	Less than -38°C (-36°F)	Greater than 141°C (286°F)
	Sunloaded sensor	Open circuit can not be detected by self-diagnosis.	Greater than 1.784 kW (1,534 kcal/h, 6,087 BTU/h) /m² [0.1657 kW (142.51 kcal/h, 565.5 BTU/h)/sq ft]

Courtesy of Nissan Motor Co., U.S.A.

94H10584

Fig. 4: Self-Diagnosis Step 4 – Readout Of Trouble Data (300ZX)

1993 AUTOMATIC A/C-HEATER SYSTEMS
Trouble Shooting – 300ZX (Cont.)

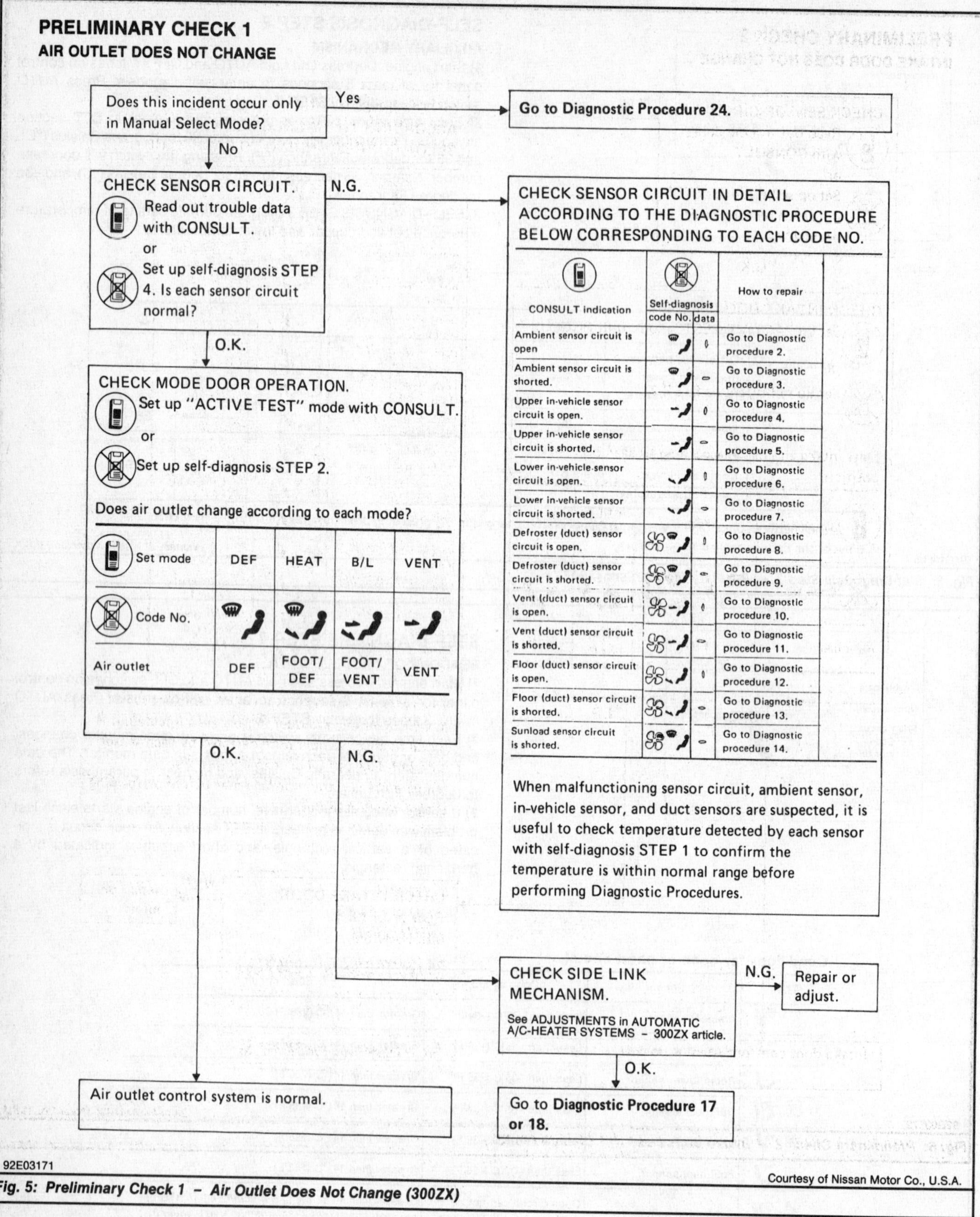
PRELIMINARY CHECK 1
AIR OUTLET DOES NOT CHANGE
Does this incident occur only in Manual Select Mode?
Yes
Go to Diagnostic Procedure 24.
No
CHECK SENSOR CIRCUIT.
Read out trouble data with CONSULT.
or
Set up self-diagnosis STEP 4. Is each sensor circuit normal?
N.G.
CHECK SENSOR CIRCUIT IN DETAIL ACCORDING TO THE DIAGNOSTIC PROCEDURE BELOW CORRESPONDING TO EACH CODE NO.
CONSULT indication
Self-diagnosis
code No.
data
How to repair
Ambient sensor circuit is open
Go to Diagnostic procedure 2.
Ambient sensor circuit is shorted.
Go to Diagnostic procedure 3.
Upper in-vehicle sensor circuit is open.
Go to Diagnostic procedure 4.
Upper in-vehicle sensor circuit is shorted.
Go to Diagnostic procedure 5.
Lower in-vehicle sensor circuit is open.
Go to Diagnostic procedure 6.
Lower in-vehicle sensor circuit is shorted.
Go to Diagnostic procedure 7.
Defroster (duct) sensor circuit is open.
Go to Diagnostic procedure 8.
Defroster (duct) sensor circuit is shorted.
Go to Diagnostic procedure 9.
Vent (duct) sensor circuit is open.
Go to Diagnostic procedure 10.
Vent (duct) sensor circuit is shorted.
Go to Diagnostic procedure 11.
Floor (duct) sensor circuit is open.
Go to Diagnostic procedure 12.
Floor (duct) sensor circuit is shorted.
Go to Diagnostic procedure 13.
Sunload sensor circuit is shorted.
Go to Diagnostic procedure 14.
When malfunctioning sensor circuit, ambient sensor, in-vehicle sensor, and duct sensors are suspected, it is useful to check temperature detected by each sensor with self-diagnosis STEP 1 to confirm the temperature is within normal range before performing Diagnostic Procedures.
O.K.
CHECK MODE DOOR OPERATION.
Set up "ACTIVE TEST" mode with CONSULT.
or
Set up self-diagnosis STEP 2.
Does air outlet change according to each mode?
Set mode
DEF
HEAT
B/L
VENT
Code No.
Air outlet
DEF
FOOT/ DEF
FOOT/ VENT
VENT
O.K.
N.G.
CHECK SIDE LINK MECHANISM.
See ADJUSTMENTS in AUTOMATIC A/C-HEATER SYSTEMS – 300ZX article.
N.G.
Repair or adjust.
O.K.
Go to Diagnostic Procedure 17 or 18.
Air outlet control system is normal.
92E03171
Courtesy of Nissan Motor Co., U.S.A.

Fig. 5: Preliminary Check 1 – Air Outlet Does Not Change (300ZX)

1993 AUTOMATIC A/C-HEATER SYSTEMS
Trouble Shooting – 300ZX (Cont.)

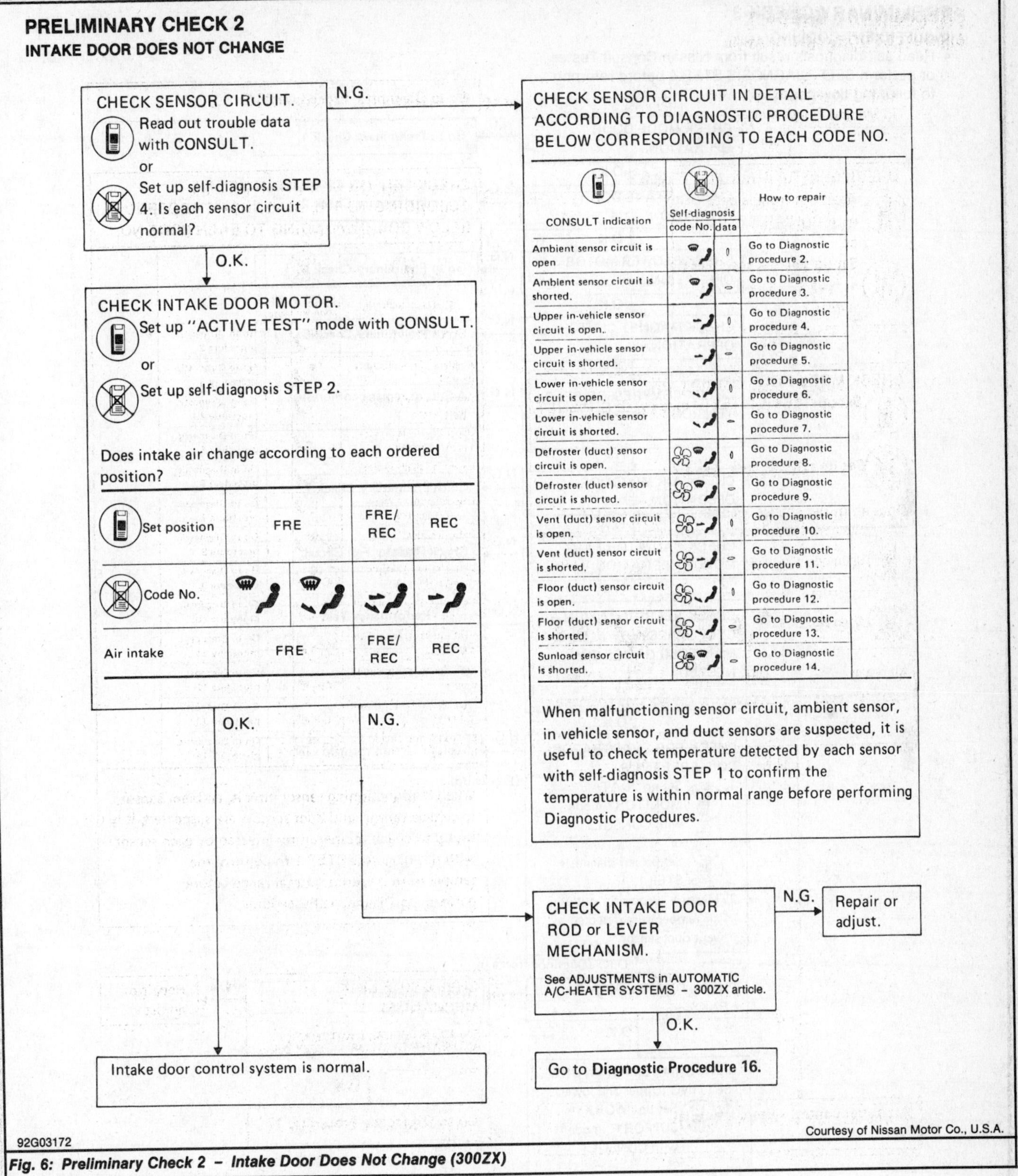
PRELIMINARY CHECK 2
INTAKE DOOR DOES NOT CHANGE
CHECK SENSOR CIRCUIT.
Read out trouble data with CONSULT.
or
Set up self-diagnosis STEP 4. Is each sensor circuit normal?
N.G.
O.K.
CHECK SENSOR CIRCUIT IN DETAIL ACCORDING TO DIAGNOSTIC PROCEDURE BELOW CORRESPONDING TO EACH CODE NO.
CONSULT indication
Self-diagnosis
code No.
data
How to repair
Ambient sensor circuit is open
Go to Diagnostic procedure 2.
Ambient sensor circuit is shorted.
Go to Diagnostic procedure 3.
Upper in-vehicle sensor circuit is open.
Go to Diagnostic procedure 4.
Upper in-vehicle sensor circuit is shorted.
Go to Diagnostic procedure 5.
Lower in-vehicle sensor circuit is open.
Go to Diagnostic procedure 6.
Lower in-vehicle sensor circuit is shorted.
Go to Diagnostic procedure 7.
Defroster (duct) sensor circuit is open.
Go to Diagnostic procedure 8.
Defroster (duct) sensor circuit is shorted.
Go to Diagnostic procedure 9.
Vent (duct) sensor circuit is open.
Go to Diagnostic procedure 10.
Vent (duct) sensor circuit is shorted.
Go to Diagnostic procedure 11.
Floor (duct) sensor circuit is open.
Go to Diagnostic procedure 12.
Floor (duct) sensor circuit is shorted.
Go to Diagnostic procedure 13.
Sunload sensor circuit is shorted.
Go to Diagnostic procedure 14.
When malfunctioning sensor circuit, ambient sensor, in vehicle sensor, and duct sensors are suspected, it is useful to check temperature detected by each sensor with self-diagnosis STEP 1 to confirm the temperature is within normal range before performing Diagnostic Procedures.
CHECK INTAKE DOOR MOTOR.
Set up "ACTIVE TEST" mode with CONSULT.
or
Set up self-diagnosis STEP 2.
Does intake air change according to each ordered position?
Set position
FRE
FRE/REC
REC
Code No.
Air intake
FRE
FRE/REC
REC
O.K.
N.G.
CHECK INTAKE DOOR ROD or LEVER MECHANISM.
See ADJUSTMENTS in AUTOMATIC A/C-HEATER SYSTEMS – 300ZX article.
N.G.
Repair or adjust.
O.K.
Intake door control system is normal.
Go to Diagnostic Procedure 16.
92G03172
Courtesy of Nissan Motor Co., U.S.A.

Fig. 6: Preliminary Check 2 – Intake Door Does Not Change (300ZX)

1993 AUTOMATIC A/C-HEATER SYSTEMS
Trouble Shooting – 300ZX (Cont.)

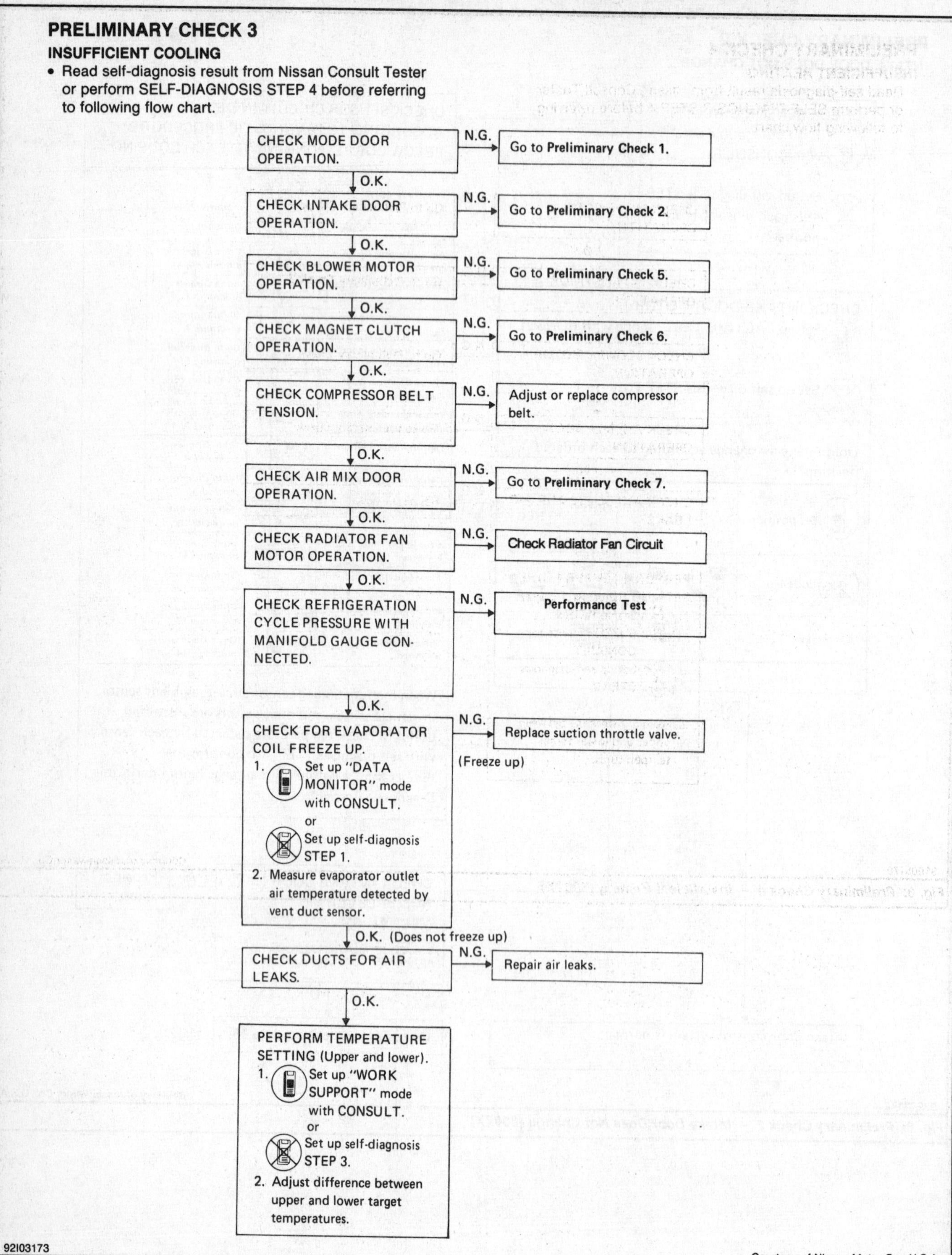
PRELIMINARY CHECK 3
INSUFFICIENT COOLING
• Read self-diagnosis result from Nissan Consult Tester or perform SELF-DIAGNOSIS STEP 4 before referring to following flow chart.
CHECK MODE DOOR OPERATION.
N.G.
Go to Preliminary Check 1.
O.K.
CHECK INTAKE DOOR OPERATION.
N.G.
Go to Preliminary Check 2.
O.K.
CHECK BLOWER MOTOR OPERATION.
N.G.
Go to Preliminary Check 5.
O.K.
CHECK MAGNET CLUTCH OPERATION.
N.G.
Go to Preliminary Check 6.
O.K.
CHECK COMPRESSOR BELT TENSION.
N.G.
Adjust or replace compressor belt.
O.K.
CHECK AIR MIX DOOR OPERATION.
N.G.
Go to Preliminary Check 7.
O.K.
CHECK RADIATOR FAN MOTOR OPERATION.
N.G.
Check Radiator Fan Circuit
O.K.
CHECK REFRIGERATION CYCLE PRESSURE WITH MANIFOLD GAUGE CONNECTED.
N.G.
Performance Test
O.K.
CHECK FOR EVAPORATOR COIL FREEZE UP.
1. Set up "DATA MONITOR" mode with CONSULT.
or
Set up self-diagnosis STEP 1.
2. Measure evaporator outlet air temperature detected by vent duct sensor.
N.G.
(Freeze up)
Replace suction throttle valve.
O.K. (Does not freeze up)
CHECK DUCTS FOR AIR LEAKS.
N.G.
Repair air leaks.
O.K.
PERFORM TEMPERATURE SETTING (Upper and lower).
1. Set up "WORK SUPPORT" mode with CONSULT.
or
Set up self-diagnosis STEP 3.
2. Adjust difference between upper and lower target temperatures.
92I03173

Courtesy of Nissan Motor Co., U.S.A.

Fig. 7: Preliminary Check 3 – Insufficient Cooling (300ZX)

1993 AUTOMATIC A/C-HEATER SYSTEMS
Trouble Shooting – 300ZX (Cont.)

PRELIMINARY CHECK 4

INSUFFICIENT HEATING

- Read self-diagnosis result from Nissan Consult Tester or perform SELF-DIAGNOSIS STEP 4 before referring to following flow chart.

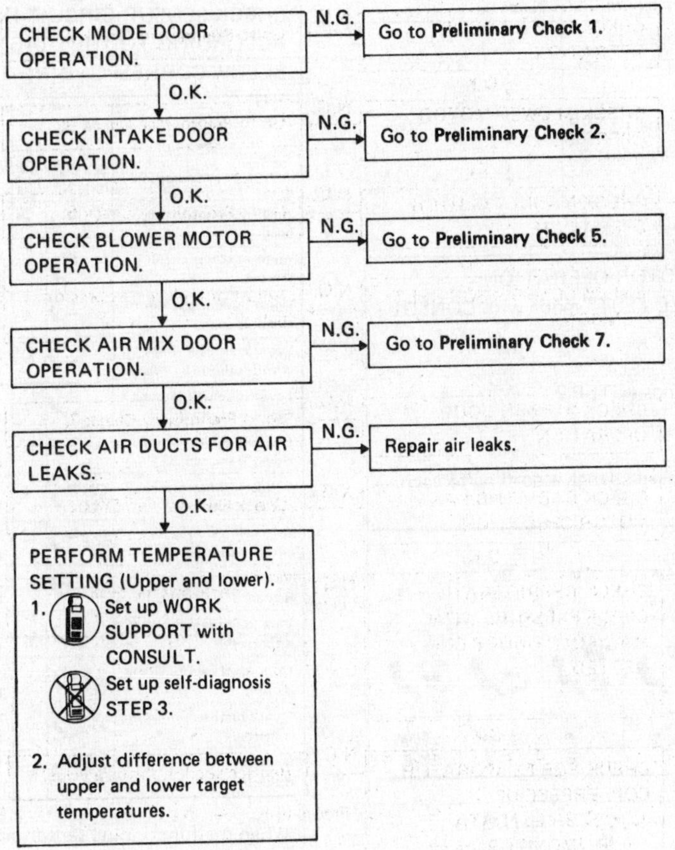
CHECK MODE DOOR OPERATION.
N.G.
Go to Preliminary Check 1.
O.K.
CHECK INTAKE DOOR OPERATION.
N.G.
Go to Preliminary Check 2.
O.K.
CHECK BLOWER MOTOR OPERATION.
N.G.
Go to Preliminary Check 5.
O.K.
CHECK AIR MIX DOOR OPERATION.
N.G.
Go to Preliminary Check 7.
O.K.
CHECK AIR DUCTS FOR AIR LEAKS.
N.G.
Repair air leaks.
O.K.
PERFORM TEMPERATURE SETTING (Upper and lower).
1. Set up WORK SUPPORT with CONSULT.
Set up self-diagnosis STEP 3.
2. Adjust difference between upper and lower target temperatures.

91E05170

Courtesy of Nissan Motor Co., U.S.A.

Fig. 8: Preliminary Check 4 – Insufficient Heating (300ZX)

1993 AUTOMATIC A/C-HEATER SYSTEMS
Trouble Shooting – 300ZX (Cont.)

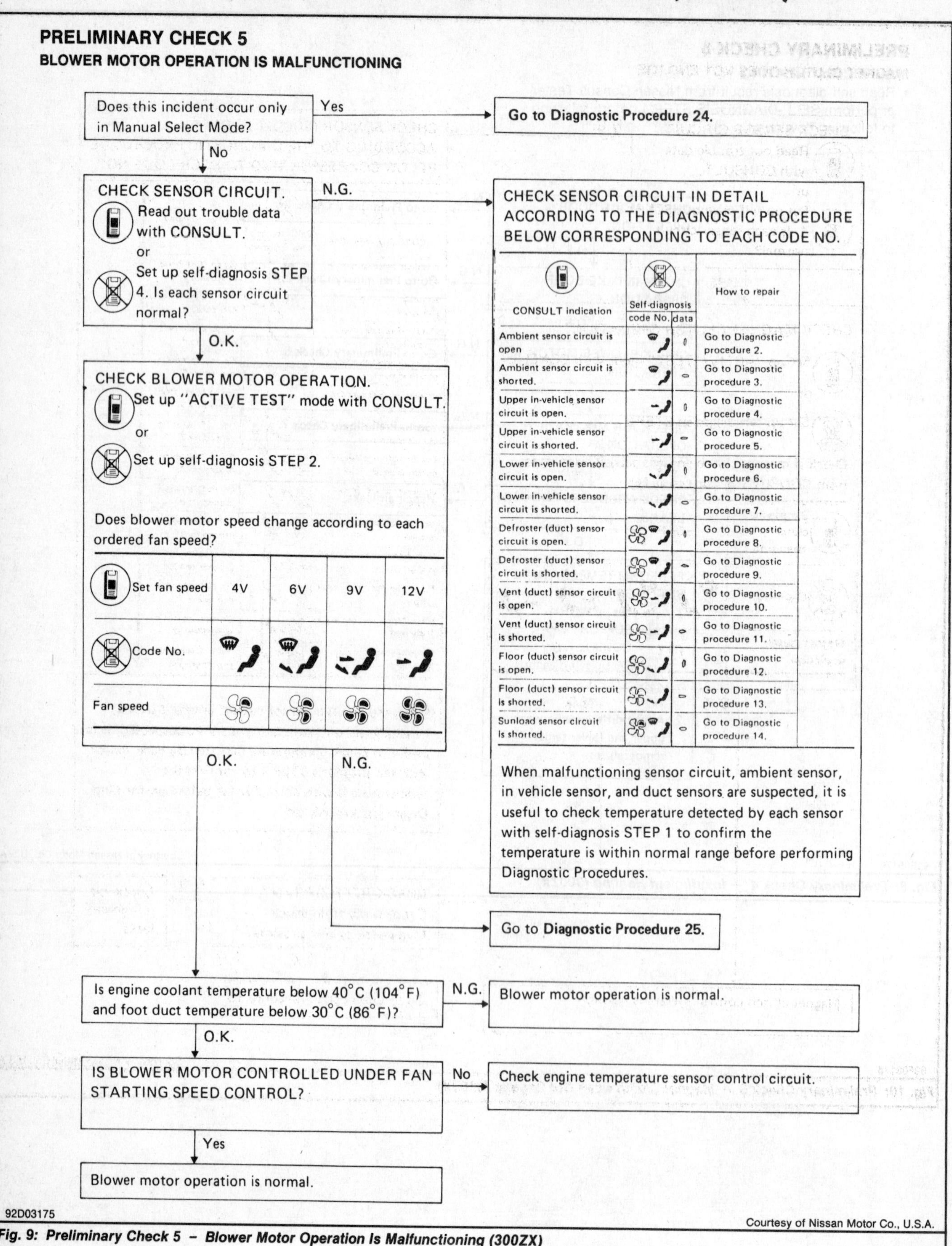
PRELIMINARY CHECK 5
BLOWER MOTOR OPERATION IS MALFUNCTIONING
Does this incident occur only in Manual Select Mode?
Yes
Go to Diagnostic Procedure 24.
No
CHECK SENSOR CIRCUIT.
Read out trouble data with CONSULT.
or
Set up self-diagnosis STEP 4. Is each sensor circuit normal?
N.G.
CHECK SENSOR CIRCUIT IN DETAIL ACCORDING TO THE DIAGNOSTIC PROCEDURE BELOW CORRESPONDING TO EACH CODE NO.
O.K.
CHECK BLOWER MOTOR OPERATION.
Set up "ACTIVE TEST" mode with CONSULT.
or
Set up self-diagnosis STEP 2.
Does blower motor speed change according to each ordered fan speed?
Set fan speed
4V
6V
9V
12V
Code No.
Fan speed
O.K.
N.G.
When malfunctioning sensor circuit, ambient sensor, in vehicle sensor, and duct sensors are suspected, it is useful to check temperature detected by each sensor with self-diagnosis STEP 1 to confirm the temperature is within normal range before performing Diagnostic Procedures.
Go to Diagnostic Procedure 25.
Is engine coolant temperature below 40°C (104°F) and foot duct temperature below 30°C (86°F)?
N.G.
Blower motor operation is normal.
O.K.
IS BLOWER MOTOR CONTROLLED UNDER FAN STARTING SPEED CONTROL?
No
Check engine temperature sensor control circuit.
Yes
Blower motor operation is normal.
92D03175
Courtesy of Nissan Motor Co., U.S.A.

CONSULT indication	Self-diagnosis code No.	Self-diagnosis data	How to repair
Ambient sensor circuit is open		0	Go to Diagnostic procedure 2.
Ambient sensor circuit is shorted.		–	Go to Diagnostic procedure 3.
Upper in-vehicle sensor circuit is open.		0	Go to Diagnostic procedure 4.
Upper in-vehicle sensor circuit is shorted.		–	Go to Diagnostic procedure 5.
Lower in-vehicle sensor circuit is open.		0	Go to Diagnostic procedure 6.
Lower in-vehicle sensor circuit is shorted.		–	Go to Diagnostic procedure 7.
Defroster (duct) sensor circuit is open.		0	Go to Diagnostic procedure 8.
Defroster (duct) sensor circuit is shorted.		–	Go to Diagnostic procedure 9.
Vent (duct) sensor circuit is open.		0	Go to Diagnostic procedure 10.
Vent (duct) sensor circuit is shorted.		–	Go to Diagnostic procedure 11.
Floor (duct) sensor circuit is open.		0	Go to Diagnostic procedure 12.
Floor (duct) sensor circuit is shorted.		–	Go to Diagnostic procedure 13.
Sunload sensor circuit is shorted.		–	Go to Diagnostic procedure 14.

Fig. 9: Preliminary Check 5 – Blower Motor Operation Is Malfunctioning (300ZX)

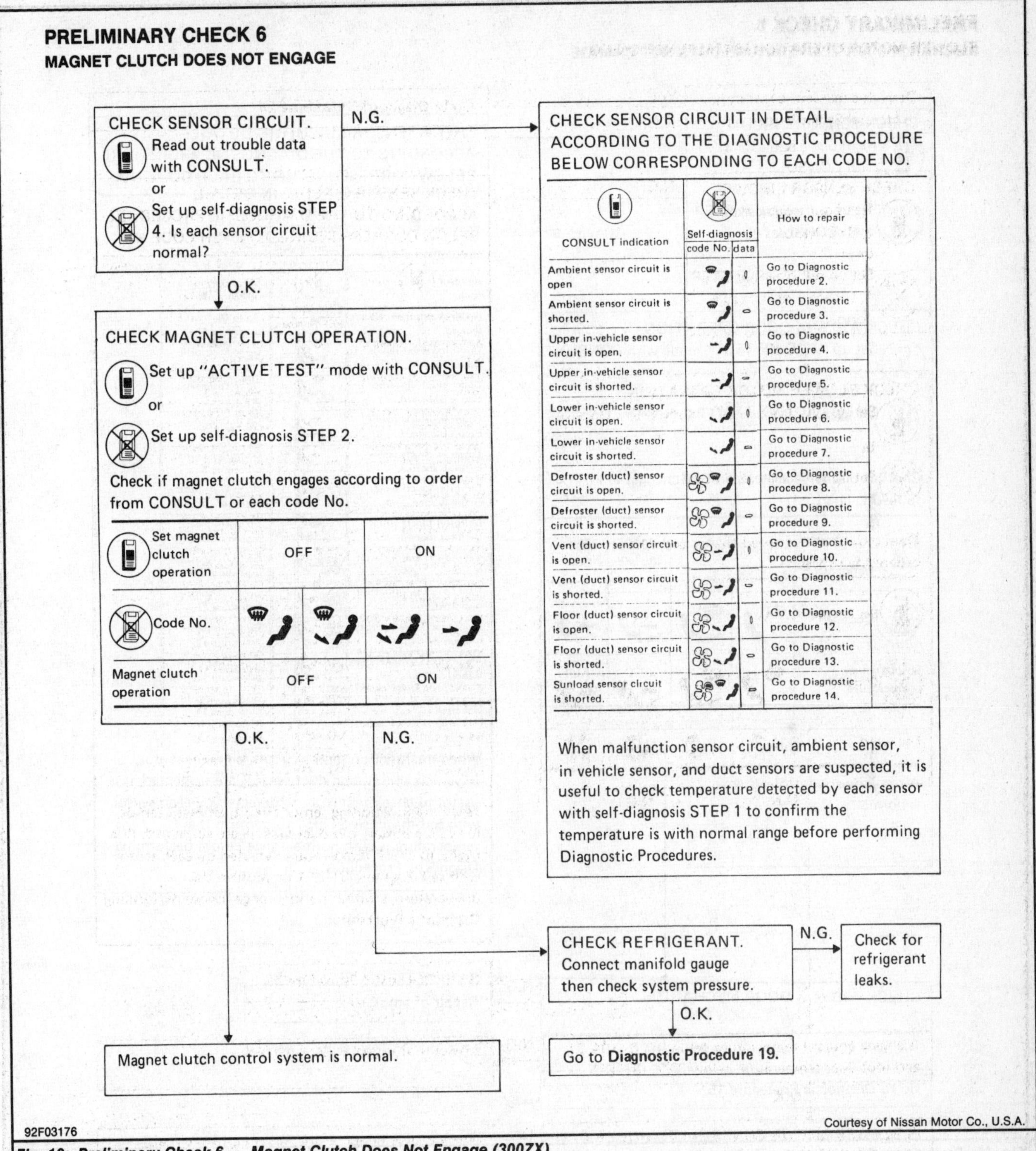
PRELIMINARY CHECK 6
MAGNET CLUTCH DOES NOT ENGAGE
CHECK SENSOR CIRCUIT.
Read out trouble data with CONSULT.
or
Set up self-diagnosis STEP 4. Is each sensor circuit normal?
N.G.
O.K.
CHECK SENSOR CIRCUIT IN DETAIL ACCORDING TO THE DIAGNOSTIC PROCEDURE BELOW CORRESPONDING TO EACH CODE NO.
CONSULT indication
Self-diagnosis
code No.
data
How to repair
Ambient sensor circuit is open
Go to Diagnostic procedure 2.
Ambient sensor circuit is shorted.
Go to Diagnostic procedure 3.
Upper in-vehicle sensor circuit is open.
Go to Diagnostic procedure 4.
Upper in-vehicle sensor circuit is shorted.
Go to Diagnostic procedure 5.
Lower in-vehicle sensor circuit is open.
Go to Diagnostic procedure 6.
Lower in-vehicle sensor circuit is shorted.
Go to Diagnostic procedure 7.
Defroster (duct) sensor circuit is open.
Go to Diagnostic procedure 8.
Defroster (duct) sensor circuit is shorted.
Go to Diagnostic procedure 9.
Vent (duct) sensor circuit is open.
Go to Diagnostic procedure 10.
Vent (duct) sensor circuit is shorted.
Go to Diagnostic procedure 11.
Floor (duct) sensor circuit is open.
Go to Diagnostic procedure 12.
Floor (duct) sensor circuit is shorted.
Go to Diagnostic procedure 13.
Sunload sensor circuit is shorted.
Go to Diagnostic procedure 14.
When malfunction sensor circuit, ambient sensor, in vehicle sensor, and duct sensors are suspected, it is useful to check temperature detected by each sensor with self-diagnosis STEP 1 to confirm the temperature is with normal range before performing Diagnostic Procedures.
CHECK MAGNET CLUTCH OPERATION.
Set up "ACTIVE TEST" mode with CONSULT.
or
Set up self-diagnosis STEP 2.
Check if magnet clutch engages according to order from CONSULT or each code No.
Set magnet clutch operation
OFF
ON
Code No.
Magnet clutch operation
OFF
ON
O.K.
N.G.
CHECK REFRIGERANT.
Connect manifold gauge then check system pressure.
N.G.
Check for refrigerant leaks.
O.K.
Go to Diagnostic Procedure 19.
Magnet clutch control system is normal.
92F03176
Courtesy of Nissan Motor Co., U.S.A.

Fig. 10: Preliminary Check 6 – Magnet Clutch Does Not Engage (300ZX)

1993 AUTOMATIC A/C-HEATER SYSTEMS
Trouble Shooting – 300ZX (Cont.)

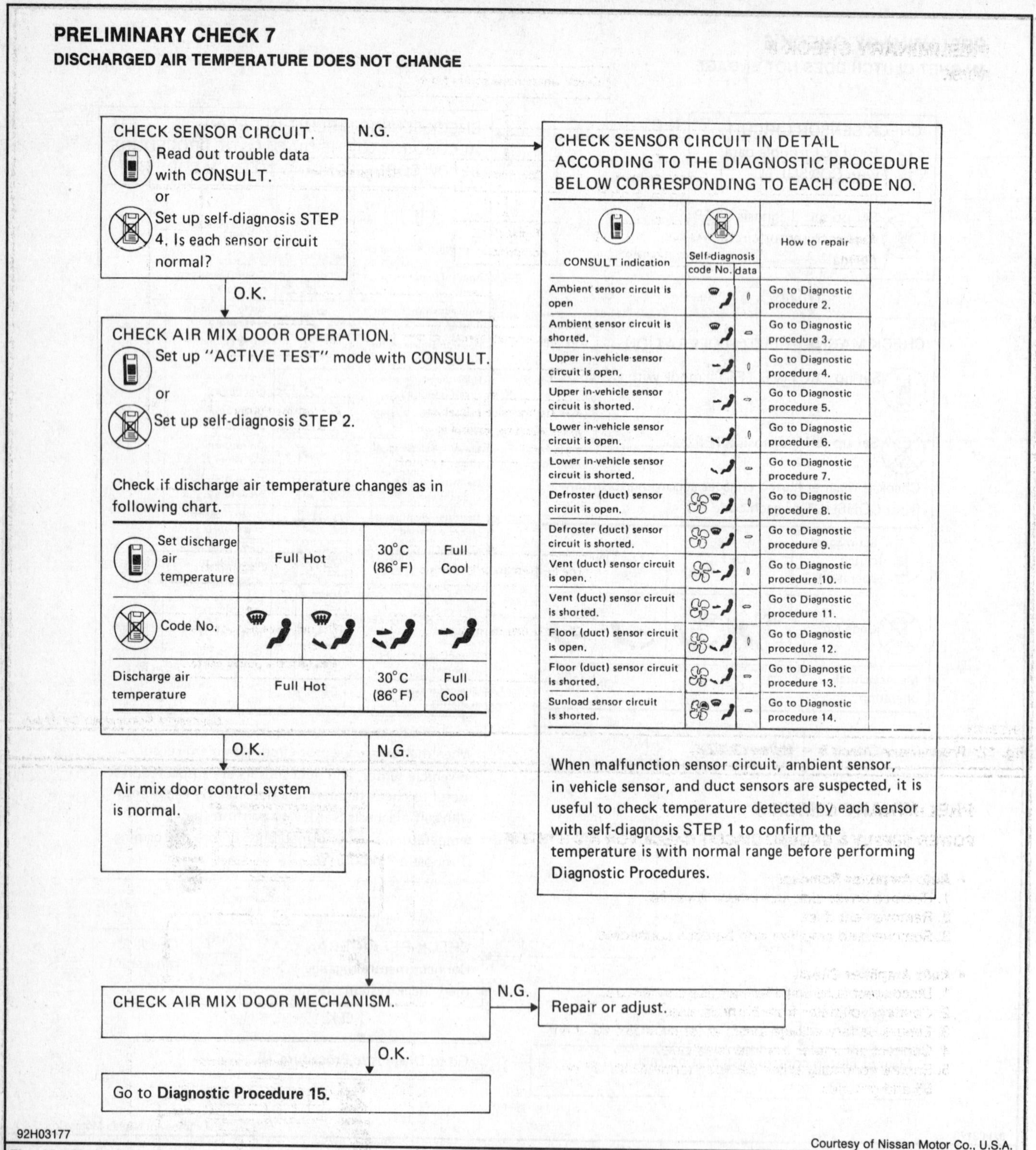

PRELIMINARY CHECK 7

DISCHARGED AIR TEMPERATURE DOES NOT CHANGE

CHECK SENSOR CIRCUIT.
Read out trouble data with CONSULT.
or
Set up self-diagnosis STEP 4. Is each sensor circuit normal?

N.G. → CHECK SENSOR CIRCUIT IN DETAIL ACCORDING TO THE DIAGNOSTIC PROCEDURE BELOW CORRESPONDING TO EACH CODE NO.

CONSULT indication	Self-diagnosis code No.	Self-diagnosis data	How to repair
Ambient sensor circuit is open			Go to Diagnostic procedure 2.
Ambient sensor circuit is shorted.			Go to Diagnostic procedure 3.
Upper in-vehicle sensor circuit is open.			Go to Diagnostic procedure 4.
Upper in-vehicle sensor circuit is shorted.			Go to Diagnostic procedure 5.
Lower in-vehicle sensor circuit is open.			Go to Diagnostic procedure 6.
Lower in-vehicle sensor circuit is shorted.			Go to Diagnostic procedure 7.
Defroster (duct) sensor circuit is open.			Go to Diagnostic procedure 8.
Defroster (duct) sensor circuit is shorted.			Go to Diagnostic procedure 9.
Vent (duct) sensor circuit is open.			Go to Diagnostic procedure 10.
Vent (duct) sensor circuit is shorted.			Go to Diagnostic procedure 11.
Floor (duct) sensor circuit is open.			Go to Diagnostic procedure 12.
Floor (duct) sensor circuit is shorted.			Go to Diagnostic procedure 13.
Sunload sensor circuit is shorted.			Go to Diagnostic procedure 14.

When malfunction sensor circuit, ambient sensor, in vehicle sensor, and duct sensors are suspected, it is useful to check temperature detected by each sensor with self-diagnosis STEP 1 to confirm the temperature is with normal range before performing Diagnostic Procedures.

O.K. ↓

CHECK AIR MIX DOOR OPERATION.
Set up "ACTIVE TEST" mode with CONSULT.
or
Set up self-diagnosis STEP 2.

Check if discharge air temperature changes as in following chart.

Set discharge air temperature	Full Hot		30°C (86°F)	Full Cool
Code No.				
Discharge air temperature	Full Hot		30°C (86°F)	Full Cool

O.K. → Air mix door control system is normal.

N.G. ↓

CHECK AIR MIX DOOR MECHANISM.

N.G. → Repair or adjust.

O.K. ↓

Go to **Diagnostic Procedure 15.**

92H03177

Courtesy of Nissan Motor Co., U.S.A.

Fig. 11: Preliminary Check 7 – Discharged Air Temperature Does Not Change (300ZX)

PRELIMINARY CHECK 8

NOISE

Check where noise comes from.

Blower motor → Replace blower motor.

Expansion valve → Replace expansion valve.

Compressor → Replace compressor.

Refrigerant line

- The line is fixed directly to the body. → Fix the line with rubber or some vibration absorbing material.
- The line is not fixed. → Fix the line tightly.

Belt

- The belt vibration is intense. → Readjust belt tension.
- Side of belt is worn out. → The pulley center does not match. Readjust the pulley center.

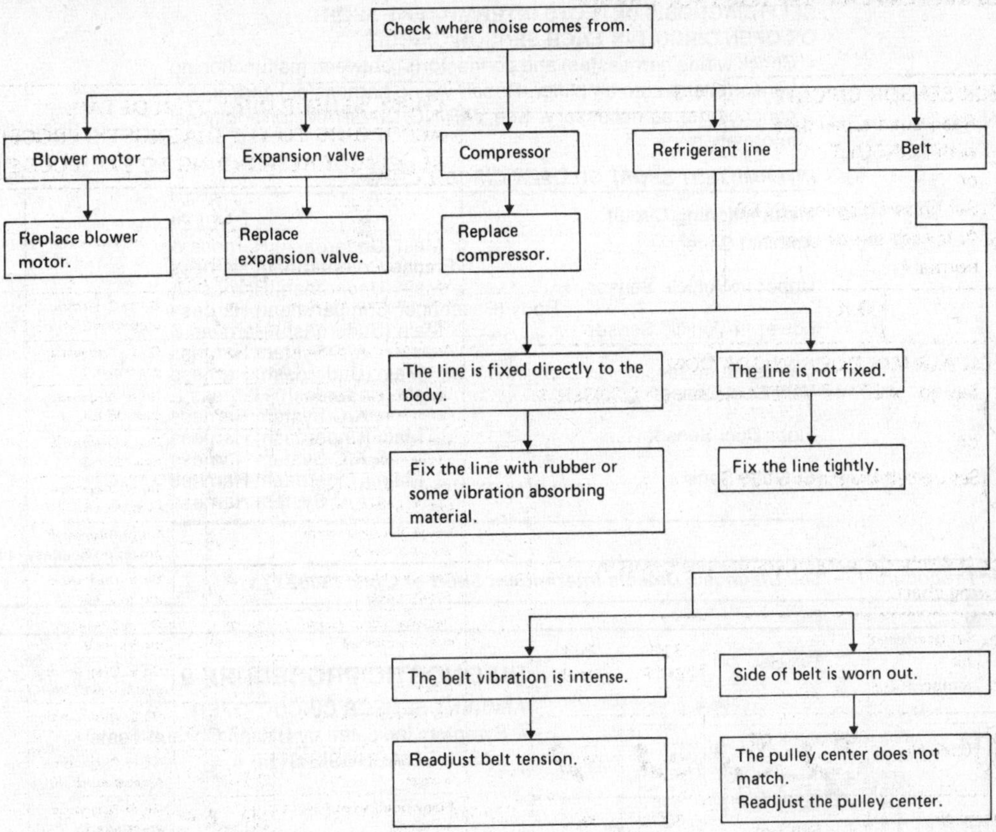

91C05174

Courtesy of Nissan Motor Co., U.S.A.

Fig. 12: Preliminary Check 8 – Noise (300ZX)

PRELIMINARY CHECK 9

POWER SUPPLY & GROUND CIRCUIT CHECK FOR A/C SYSTEM

- **Auto Amplifier Removal**
  1. Remove driver-side instrument lower lid.
  2. Remove vent duct.
  3. Remove auto amplifier with harness connected.

- **Auto Amplifier Check**
  1. Disconnect auto amplifier harness connectors.
  2. Connect voltmeter from harness side.
  3. Ensure battery voltage exists at terminal No. 40 or 41.
  4. Connect ohmmeter from harness side.
  5. Ensure continuity exists between terminal No. 33 or 55 and ground.

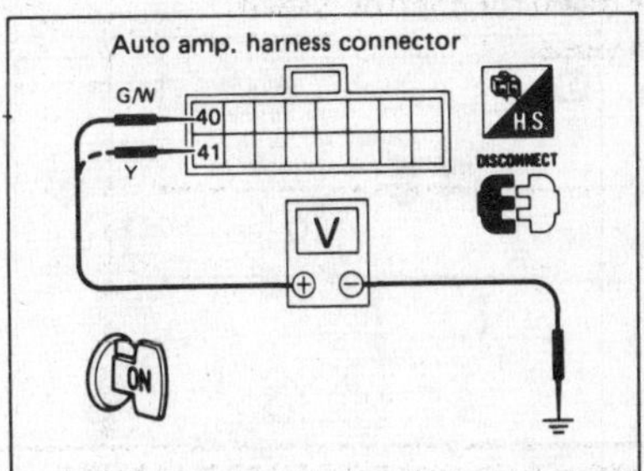
Auto amp. harness connector
G/W
40
41
Y
V
H S
DISCONNECT
ON

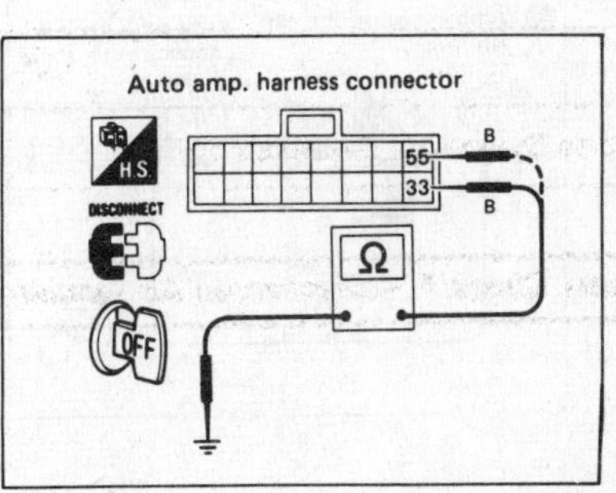
Auto amp. harness connector
56
33
B
B
Ω
H S
DISCONNECT
OFF

93G19683

Courtesy of Nissan Motor Co., U.S.A.

Fig. 13: Preliminary Check 9 – Power Supply Circuit Check For A/C System (300ZX)

1993 AUTOMATIC A/C-HEATER SYSTEMS
Trouble Shooting – 300ZX (Cont.)

DIAGNOSTIC PROCEDURE 1

SELF-DIAGNOSIS DETECTS INTERMITTENT SHORT OR OPEN CIRCUIT IN EACH SENSOR CIRCUIT

- Check wiring harness(es) and connector(s) between malfunctioning sensor(s) and auto amplifier. Repair wiring harness(es) and/or connector(s) as necessary. See WIRING DIAGRAM for additional information.

INTERMITTENT SHORT OR OPEN CIRCUIT CHECK

Malfunctioning Circuit	Check
Ambient Sensor	Main (Underdash) Harness & Engine Compartment Harness
Upper In-Vehicle Sensor	Main (Underdash) Harness & Body (Passenger Compartment) Harness
Lower In-Vehicle Sensor	Main (Underdash) Harness & A/C System Harness
Defrost Duct Sensor	Main (Underdash) Harness
Vent Duct Sensor	Main (Underdash) Harness & A/C System Harness
Floor Duct Sensor	Main (Underdash) Harness & A/C System Harness
Sunload Sensor	Main (Underdash) Harness & A/C System Harness

91H05176

Courtesy of Nissan Motor Co., U.S.A.

Fig. 14: Diagnostic Procedure 1 – Self-Diagnosis Detects Intermittent Short or Open (300ZX)

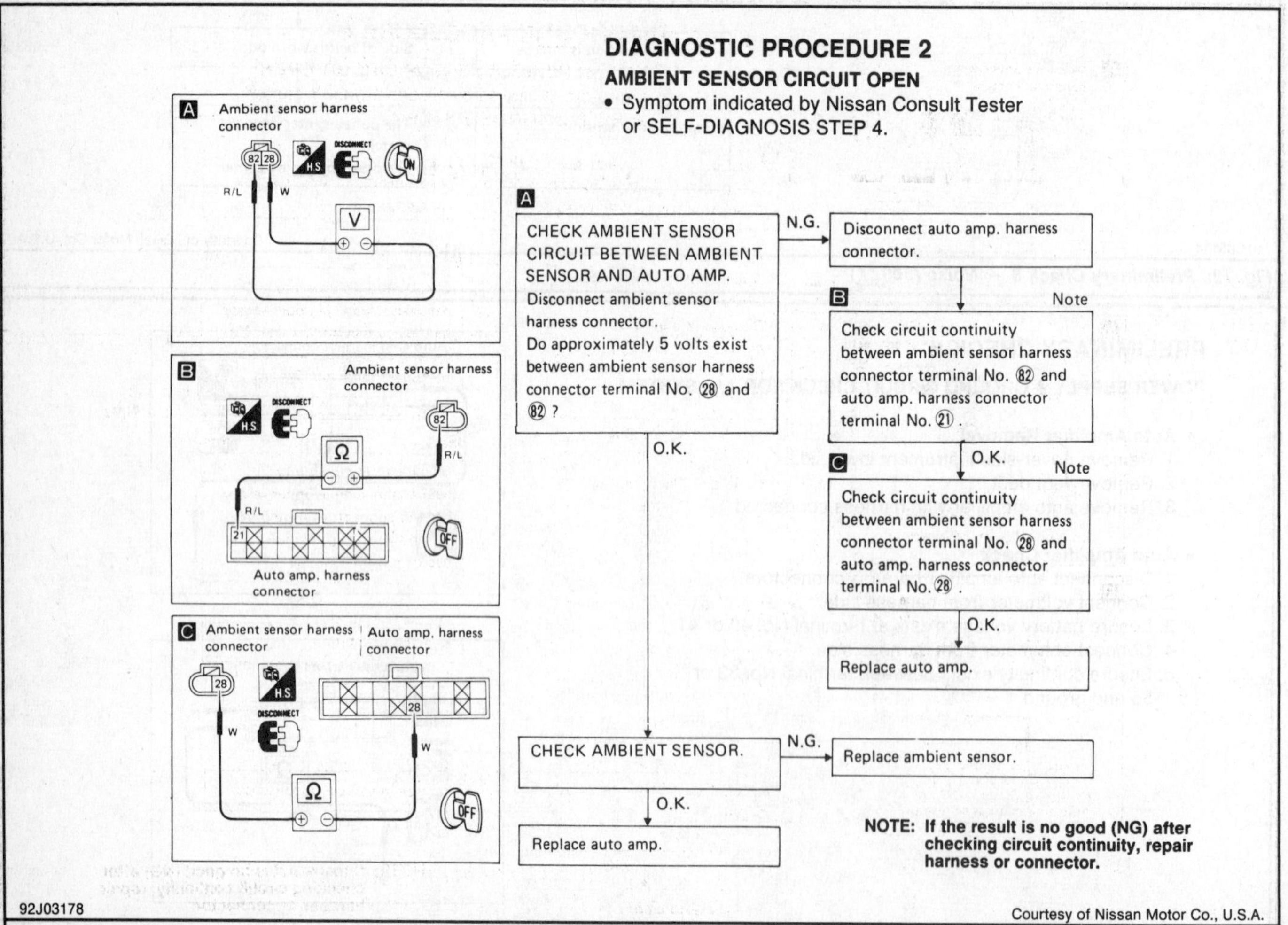
DIAGNOSTIC PROCEDURE 2
AMBIENT SENSOR CIRCUIT OPEN
• Symptom indicated by Nissan Consult Tester or SELF-DIAGNOSIS STEP 4.
A Ambient sensor harness connector
82 28
R/L
W
DISCONNECT
ON
V
B Ambient sensor harness connector
DISCONNECT
82
R/L
Ω
R/L
21
OFF
Auto amp. harness connector
C Ambient sensor harness connector
Auto amp. harness connector
28
DISCONNECT
W
28
W
Ω
OFF
A
CHECK AMBIENT SENSOR CIRCUIT BETWEEN AMBIENT SENSOR AND AUTO AMP.
Disconnect ambient sensor harness connector.
Do approximately 5 volts exist between ambient sensor harness connector terminal No. 28 and 82 ?
N.G.
Disconnect auto amp. harness connector.
B Note
Check circuit continuity between ambient sensor harness connector terminal No. 82 and auto amp. harness connector terminal No. 21 .
O.K.
C Note
Check circuit continuity between ambient sensor harness connector terminal No. 28 and auto amp. harness connector terminal No. 28 .
O.K.
Replace auto amp.
O.K.
CHECK AMBIENT SENSOR.
N.G.
Replace ambient sensor.
O.K.
Replace auto amp.
NOTE: If the result is no good (NG) after checking circuit continuity, repair harness or connector.
92J03178
Courtesy of Nissan Motor Co., U.S.A.

Fig. 15: Diagnostic Procedure 2 – Ambient Sensor Circuit Open (300ZX)

1993 AUTOMATIC A/C-HEATER SYSTEMS
Trouble Shooting – 300ZX (Cont.)

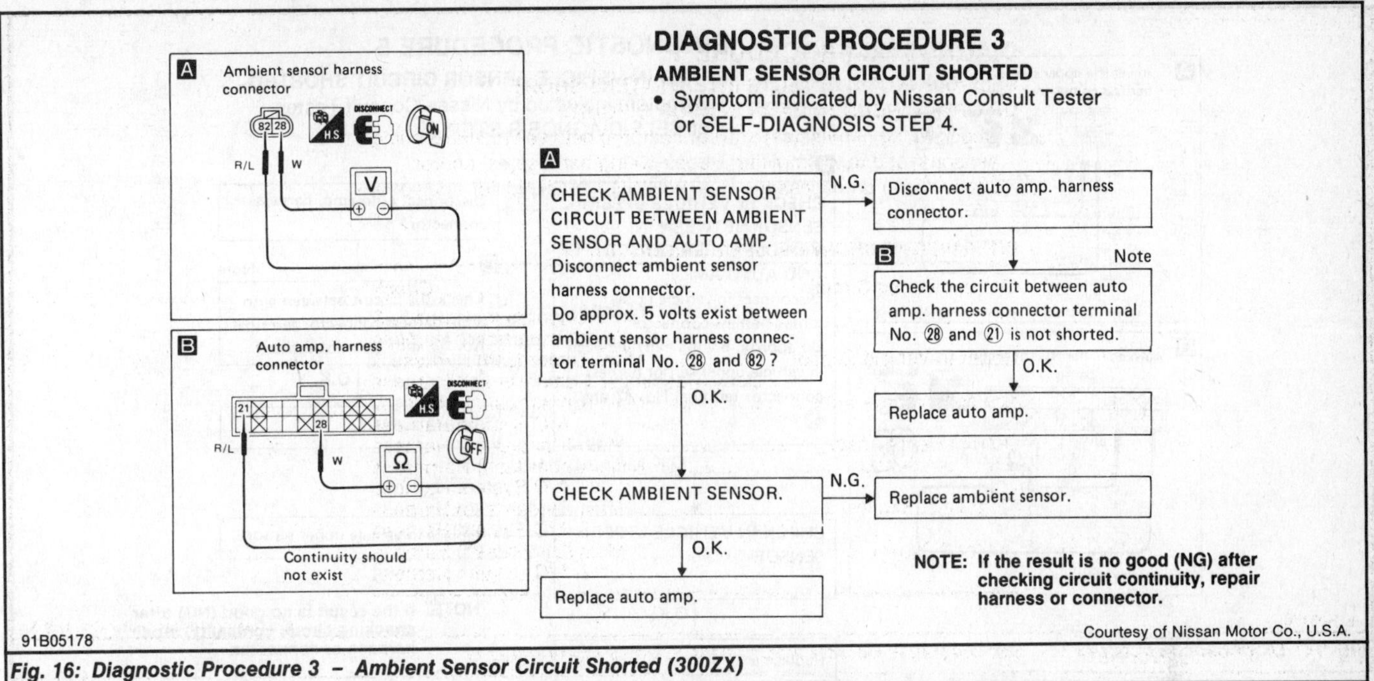
A Ambient sensor harness connector
82 28
R/L
W
V
DISCONNECT
ON
B Auto amp. harness connector
21
28
R/L
W
Ω
DISCONNECT
OFF
Continuity should not exist
DIAGNOSTIC PROCEDURE 3
AMBIENT SENSOR CIRCUIT SHORTED
• Symptom indicated by Nissan Consult Tester or SELF-DIAGNOSIS STEP 4.
A
CHECK AMBIENT SENSOR CIRCUIT BETWEEN AMBIENT SENSOR AND AUTO AMP.
Disconnect ambient sensor harness connector.
Do approx. 5 volts exist between ambient sensor harness connector terminal No. 28 and 82 ?
N.G.
Disconnect auto amp. harness connector.
B
Note
Check the circuit between auto amp. harness connector terminal No. 28 and 21 is not shorted.
O.K.
Replace auto amp.
O.K.
CHECK AMBIENT SENSOR.
N.G.
Replace ambient sensor.
O.K.
Replace auto amp.
NOTE: If the result is no good (NG) after checking circuit continuity, repair harness or connector.
91B05178
Courtesy of Nissan Motor Co., U.S.A.

Fig. 16: Diagnostic Procedure 3 – Ambient Sensor Circuit Shorted (300ZX)

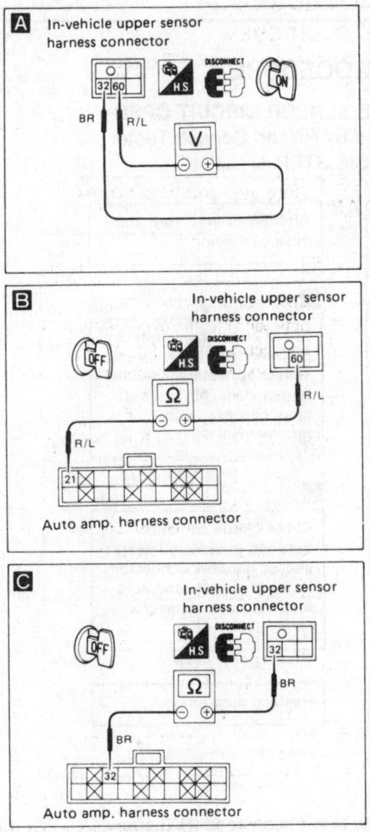

A In-vehicle upper sensor harness connector (32, 60; BR, R/L; V; DISCONNECT; ON)

B In-vehicle upper sensor harness connector (60; R/L; Ω; DISCONNECT; OFF) – Auto amp. harness connector (21; R/L)

C In-vehicle upper sensor harness connector (32; BR; Ω; DISCONNECT; OFF) – Auto amp. harness connector (32; BR)

DIAGNOSTIC PROCEDURE 4

UPPER IN-VEHICLE SENSOR CIRCUIT OPEN

• Symptom indicated by Nissan Consult Tester or SELF-DIAGNOSIS STEP 4.

A CHECK IN-VEHICLE UPPER SENSOR CIRCUIT BETWEEN IN-VEHICLE UPPER SENSOR AND AUTO AMP.
Disconnect in-vehicle upper sensor harness connector.
Do approximately 5 volts exist between in-vehicle upper sensor harness connector terminal No. 32 and 60 ?

- N.G. → Disconnect auto amp. harness connector.
  - **B** Note: Check circuit continuity between in-vehicle upper sensor harness connector terminal No. 60 and auto amp. harness connector terminal No. 21 .
  - O.K. → **C** Note: Check circuit continuity between in-vehicle upper sensor harness connector terminal No. 32 and auto amp. harness connector terminal No. 32 .
  - O.K. → Replace auto amp.
- O.K. → CHECK IN-VEHICLE UPPER SENSOR.
  - N.G. → Replace in-vehicle upper sensor.
  - O.K. → Replace auto amp.

NOTE: If the result is no good (NG) after checking circuit continuity, repair harness or connector.

92B03179

Courtesy of Nissan Motor Co., U.S.A.

Fig. 17: Diagnostic Procedure 4 – Upper In-Vehicle Sensor Circuit Open (300ZX)

1993 AUTOMATIC A/C-HEATER SYSTEMS
Trouble Shooting – 300ZX (Cont.)

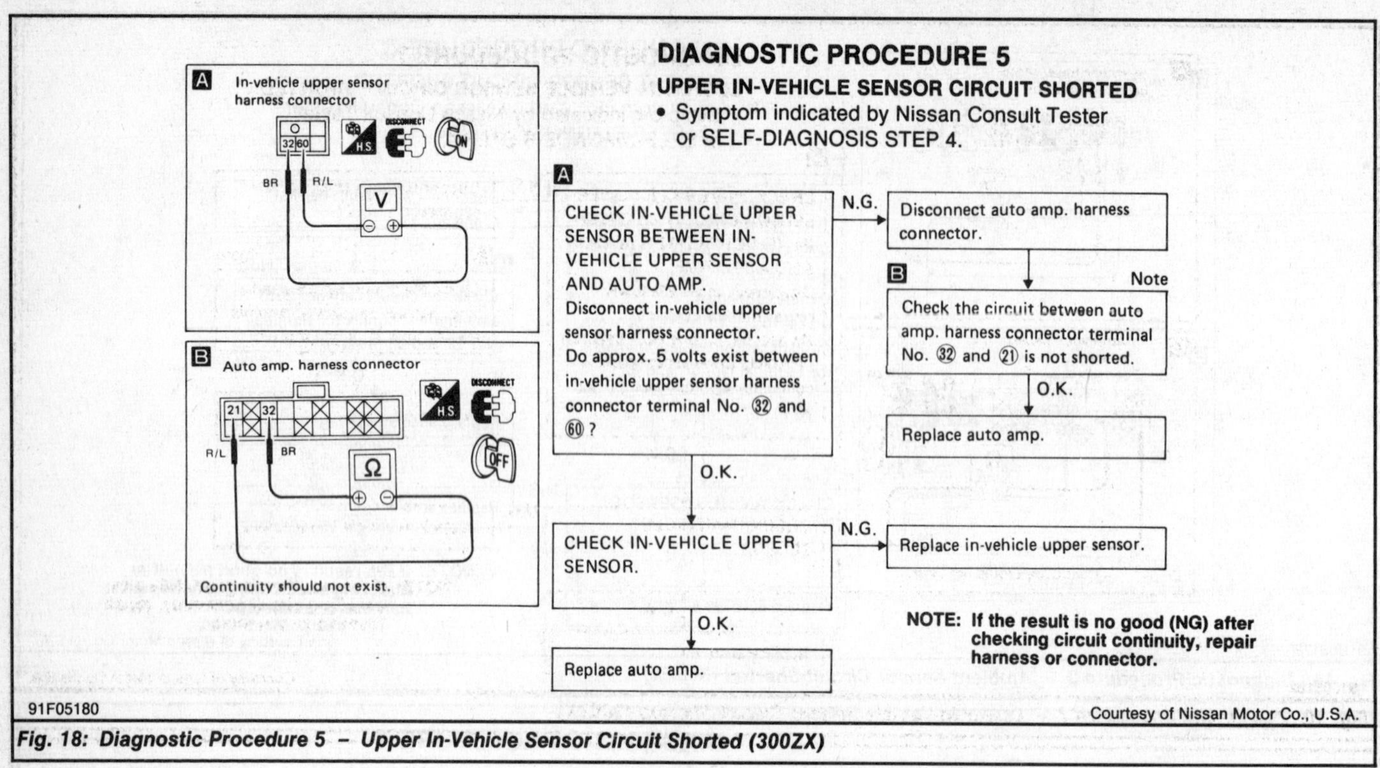
DIAGNOSTIC PROCEDURE 5
UPPER IN-VEHICLE SENSOR CIRCUIT SHORTED
• Symptom indicated by Nissan Consult Tester or SELF-DIAGNOSIS STEP 4.
A In-vehicle upper sensor harness connector
32 60
H.S.
DISCONNECT
ON
BR
R/L
V
B Auto amp. harness connector
21 32
DISCONNECT
OFF
R/L
BR
Ω
Continuity should not exist.
A
CHECK IN-VEHICLE UPPER SENSOR BETWEEN IN-VEHICLE UPPER SENSOR AND AUTO AMP.
Disconnect in-vehicle upper sensor harness connector.
Do approx. 5 volts exist between in-vehicle upper sensor harness connector terminal No. 32 and 60 ?
N.G.
Disconnect auto amp. harness connector.
B
Note
Check the circuit between auto amp. harness connector terminal No. 32 and 21 is not shorted.
O.K.
Replace auto amp.
O.K.
CHECK IN-VEHICLE UPPER SENSOR.
N.G.
Replace in-vehicle upper sensor.
O.K.
Replace auto amp.
NOTE: If the result is no good (NG) after checking circuit continuity, repair harness or connector.
91F05180
Courtesy of Nissan Motor Co., U.S.A.

Fig. 18: Diagnostic Procedure 5 – Upper In-Vehicle Sensor Circuit Shorted (300ZX)

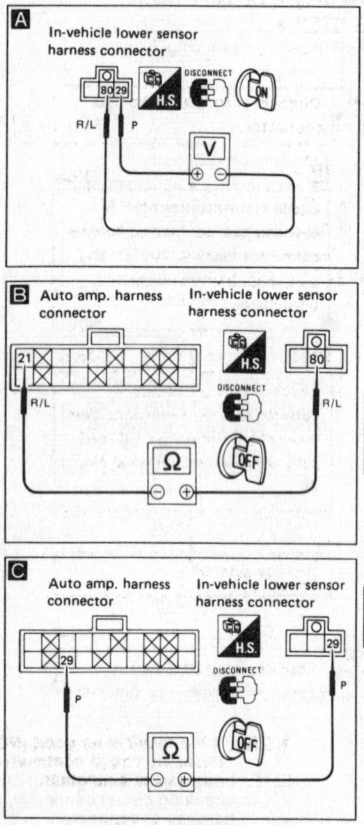

DIAGNOSTIC PROCEDURE 6

LOWER IN-VEHICLE SENSOR CIRCUIT OPEN

• Symptom indicated by Nissan Consult Tester or SELF-DIAGNOSIS STEP 4.

A In-vehicle lower sensor harness connector

80 29 H.S. DISCONNECT ON

R/L P

V

B Auto amp. harness connector — In-vehicle lower sensor harness connector

21 H.S. 80 DISCONNECT OFF

R/L R/L

Ω

C Auto amp. harness connector — In-vehicle lower sensor harness connector

29 H.S. 29 DISCONNECT OFF

P P

Ω

A

CHECK IN-VEHICLE LOWER SENSOR CIRCUIT BETWEEN IN-VEHICLE LOWER SENSOR AND AUTO AMP.
Disconnect in-vehicle lower sensor harness connector.
Do approx. 5 volts exist between in-vehicle lower sensor harness connector terminal No. 29 and 80 ?

N.G. → Disconnect auto amp. harness connector.

B Note

Check circuit continuity between in-vehicle lower sensor harness connector terminal No. 80 and auto amp. harness connector terminal No. 21.

O.K.

C Note

Check circuit continuity between in-vehicle lower sensor harness connector terminal No. 29 and auto amp. harness connector terminal No. 29.

O.K.

Replace auto amp.

O.K.

CHECK IN-VEHICLE LOWER SENSOR.

O.K. → Replace auto amp.

N.G. → Replace in-vehicle lower sensor.

NOTE: If the result is no good (NG) after checking circuit continuity, repair harness or connector.

94G10625

Courtesy of Nissan Motor Co., U.S.A.

Fig. 19: Diagnostic Procedure 6 – Lower In-Vehicle Sensor Circuit Open (300ZX)

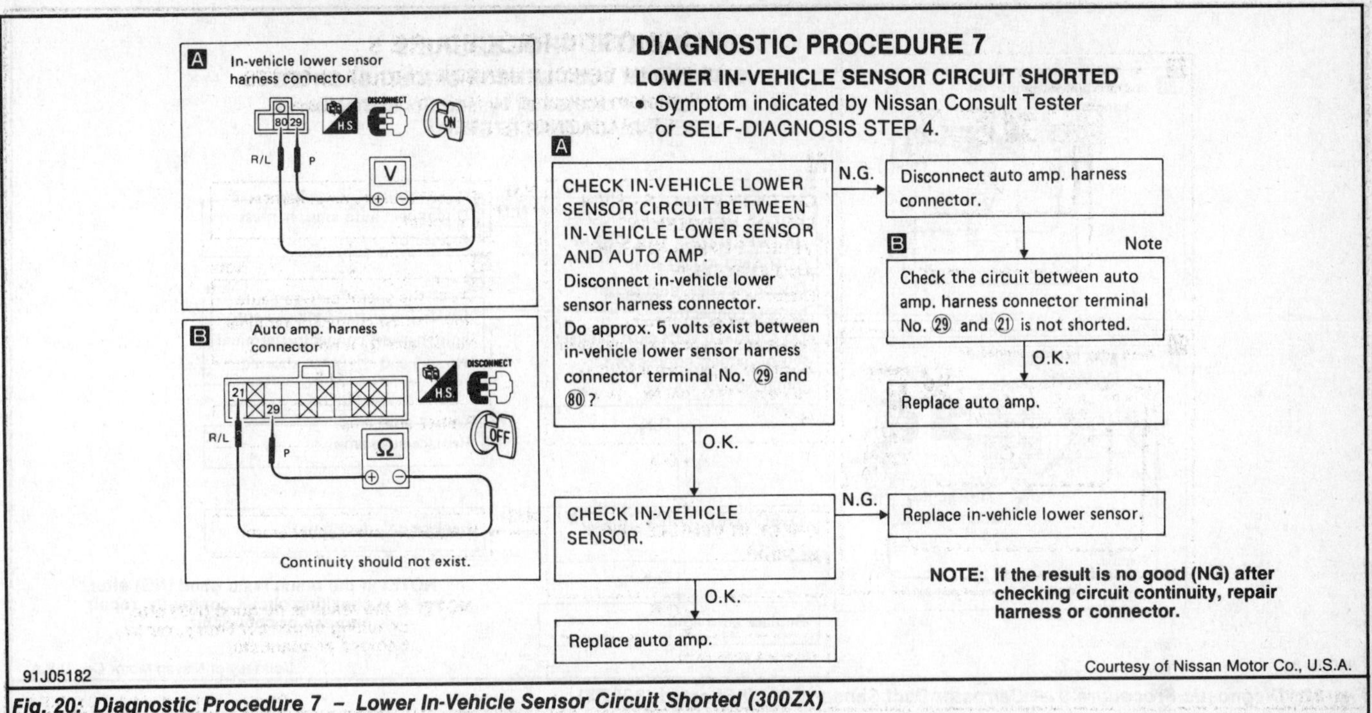

DIAGNOSTIC PROCEDURE 7
LOWER IN-VEHICLE SENSOR CIRCUIT SHORTED
• Symptom indicated by Nissan Consult Tester or SELF-DIAGNOSIS STEP 4.
A In-vehicle lower sensor harness connector
80 29
R/L
P
DISCONNECT
H.S
ON
V
B Auto amp. harness connector
21
29
R/L
P
DISCONNECT
H.S
OFF
Ω
Continuity should not exist.
A
CHECK IN-VEHICLE LOWER SENSOR CIRCUIT BETWEEN IN-VEHICLE LOWER SENSOR AND AUTO AMP.
Disconnect in-vehicle lower sensor harness connector.
Do approx. 5 volts exist between in-vehicle lower sensor harness connector terminal No. 29 and 80 ?
N.G.
Disconnect auto amp. harness connector.
B
Note
Check the circuit between auto amp. harness connector terminal No. 29 and 21 is not shorted.
O.K.
Replace auto amp.
O.K.
CHECK IN-VEHICLE SENSOR.
N.G.
Replace in-vehicle lower sensor.
O.K.
Replace auto amp.
NOTE: If the result is no good (NG) after checking circuit continuity, repair harness or connector.
Courtesy of Nissan Motor Co., U.S.A.
91J05182

Fig. 20: Diagnostic Procedure 7 – Lower In-Vehicle Sensor Circuit Shorted (300ZX)

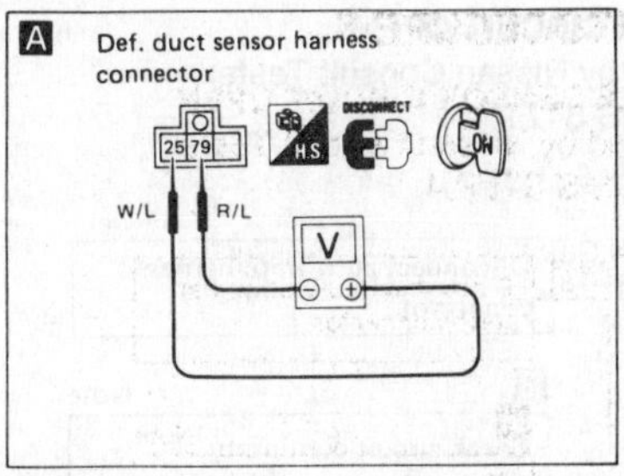

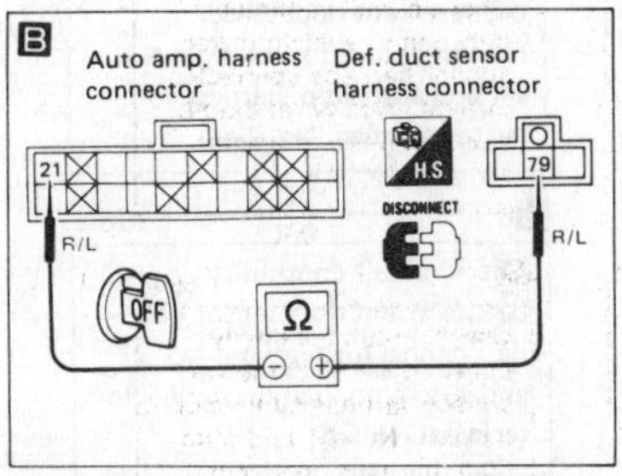

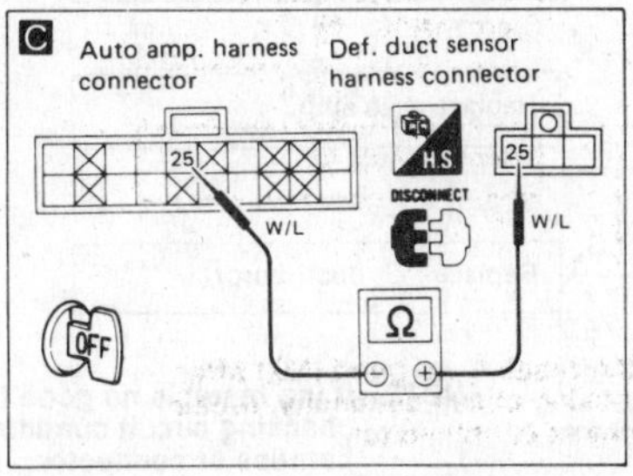

DIAGNOSTIC PROCEDURE 8

DEFROSTER DUCT SENSOR CIRCUIT OPEN

- Symptom indicated by Nissan Consult Tester or SELF-DIAGNOSIS STEP 4.

A Def. duct sensor harness connector
25 79
W/L
R/L
DISCONNECT
H.S
ON
V

B Auto amp. harness connector
Def. duct sensor harness connector
21
79
R/L
R/L
H.S
DISCONNECT
OFF
Ω

C Auto amp. harness connector
Def. duct sensor harness connector
25
25
W/L
W/L
H.S
DISCONNECT
OFF
Ω

A

CHECK DEF. DUCT SENSOR CIRCUIT BETWEEN DEF. DUCT SENSOR AND AUTO AMP.
Disconnect def. duct sensor harness connector.
Do approximately 5 volts exist between def. duct sensor harness connector terminal No. 25 and 79 ?

N.G. → Disconnect auto amp. harness connector.

B Note

Check circuit continuity between def. duct sensor harness connector terminal No. 79 and auto amp. harness connector terminal No. 21.

O.K.

C Note

Check circuit continuity between def. duct sensor harness connector terminal No. 25 and auto amp. harness terminal No. 25.

O.K.

Replace auto amp.

O.K.

CHECK DEF. DUCT SENSOR.

N.G. → Replace def. duct sensor.

O.K.

Replace auto amp.

NOTE: If the result is no good (NG) after checking circuit continuity, repair harness or connector.

92D03180

Courtesy of Nissan Motor Co., U.S.A.

Fig. 21: Diagnostic Procedure 8 – Defroster Duct Sensor Circuit Open (300ZX)

1993 AUTOMATIC A/C-HEATER SYSTEMS
Trouble Shooting – 300ZX (Cont.)

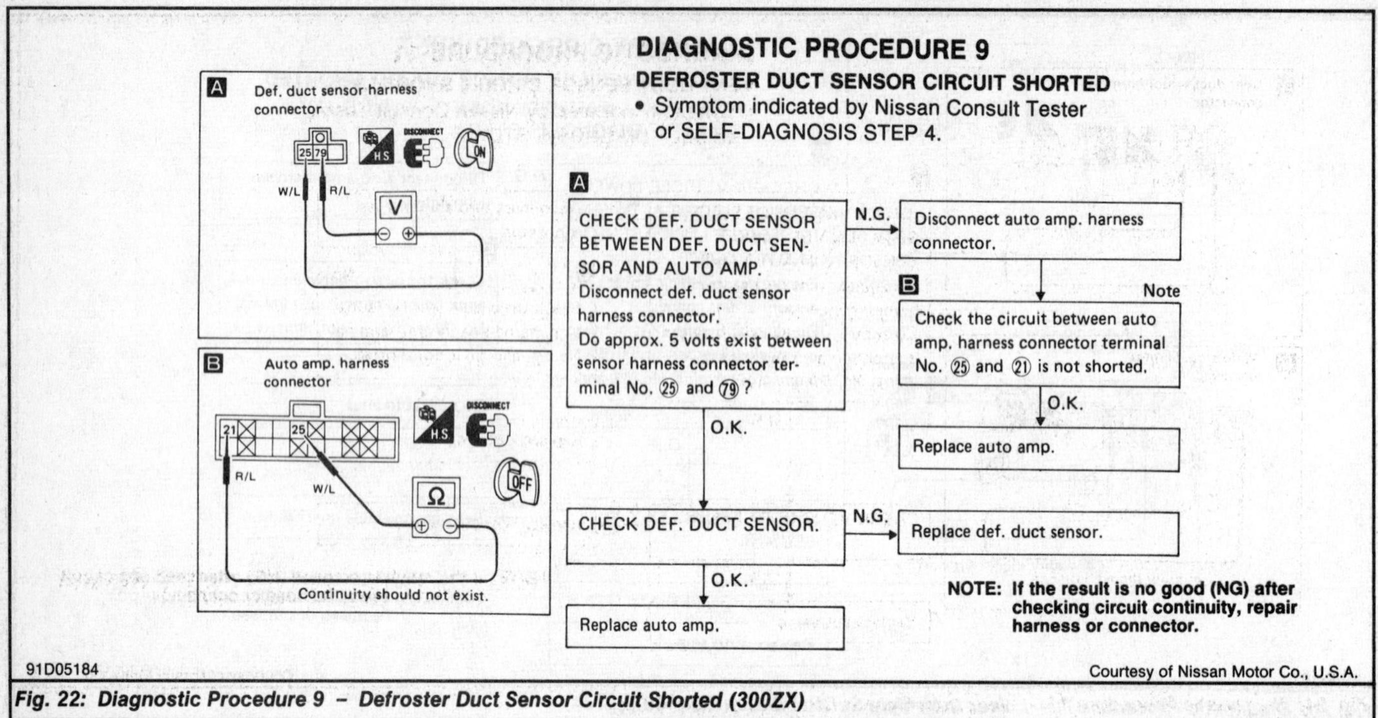
DIAGNOSTIC PROCEDURE 9
DEFROSTER DUCT SENSOR CIRCUIT SHORTED
• Symptom indicated by Nissan Consult Tester or SELF-DIAGNOSIS STEP 4.
A
Def. duct sensor harness connector
25 79
W/L
R/L
V
DISCONNECT
ON
B
Auto amp. harness connector
21
25
R/L
W/L
Ω
DISCONNECT
OFF
Continuity should not exist.
A
CHECK DEF. DUCT SENSOR BETWEEN DEF. DUCT SENSOR AND AUTO AMP.
Disconnect def. duct sensor harness connector.
Do approx. 5 volts exist between sensor harness connector terminal No. 25 and 79?
N.G.
Disconnect auto amp. harness connector.
B
Note
Check the circuit between auto amp. harness connector terminal No. 25 and 21 is not shorted.
O.K.
Replace auto amp.
O.K.
CHECK DEF. DUCT SENSOR.
N.G.
Replace def. duct sensor.
O.K.
Replace auto amp.
NOTE: If the result is no good (NG) after checking circuit continuity, repair harness or connector.
91D05184
Courtesy of Nissan Motor Co., U.S.A.

Fig. 22: Diagnostic Procedure 9 – Defroster Duct Sensor Circuit Shorted (300ZX)

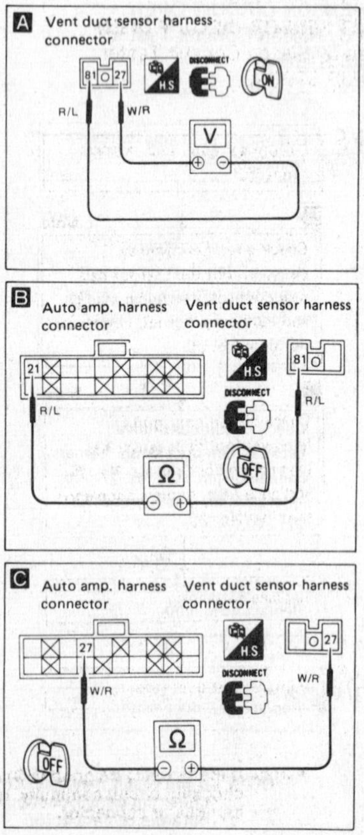

DIAGNOSTIC PROCEDURE 10

VENT DUCT SENSOR CIRCUIT OPEN

- Symptom indicated by Nissan Consult Tester or SELF-DIAGNOSIS STEP 4.

A – Vent duct sensor harness connector (81, 27; R/L, W/R; V; DISCONNECT; ON)

B – Auto amp. harness connector / Vent duct sensor harness connector (21, 81; R/L; Ω; DISCONNECT; OFF)

C – Auto amp. harness connector / Vent duct sensor harness connector (27, 27; W/R; Ω; DISCONNECT; OFF)

A: CHECK VENT DUCT SENSOR CIRCUIT BETWEEN VENT DUCT SENSOR AND AUTO AMP.
Disconnect vent duct sensor harness connector.
Do approximately 5 volts exist between vent duct sensor harness connector terminal No. 27 and 81 ?

- N.G. → Disconnect auto amp. harness connector.
  - B (Note): Check circuit continuity between vent duct sensor harness connector terminal No. 81 and auto amp. harness connector terminal No. 21 .
  - O.K. → C (Note): Check circuit continuity between vent duct sensor harness connector terminal No. 27 and auto amp. harness connector terminal No. 27 .
  - O.K. → Replace auto amp.
- O.K. → CHECK VENT DUCT SENSOR.
  - N.G. → Replace duct sensor.
  - O.K. → Replace auto amp.

NOTE: If the result is no good (NG) after checking circuit continuity, repair harness or connector.

92F03181

Courtesy of Nissan Motor Co., U.S.A.

Fig. 23: Diagnostic Procedure 10 – Vent Duct Sensor Circuit Open (300ZX)

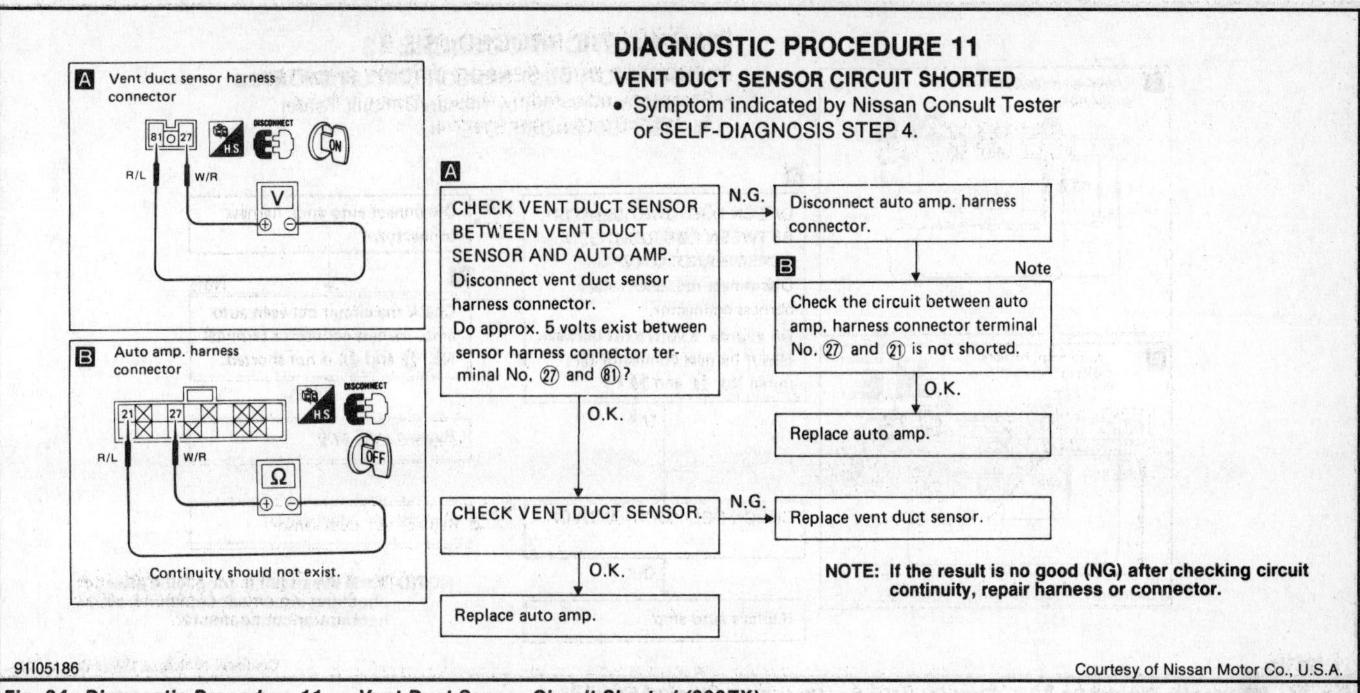
DIAGNOSTIC PROCEDURE 11
VENT DUCT SENSOR CIRCUIT SHORTED
• Symptom indicated by Nissan Consult Tester or SELF-DIAGNOSIS STEP 4.
A Vent duct sensor harness connector
81 27
R/L
W/R
V
DISCONNECT
ON
B Auto amp. harness connector
21 27
R/L
W/R
Ω
OFF
Continuity should not exist.
A
CHECK VENT DUCT SENSOR BETWEEN VENT DUCT SENSOR AND AUTO AMP.
Disconnect vent duct sensor harness connector.
Do approx. 5 volts exist between sensor harness connector terminal No. 27 and 81?
N.G.
Disconnect auto amp. harness connector.
B
Note
Check the circuit between auto amp. harness connector terminal No. 27 and 21 is not shorted.
O.K.
Replace auto amp.
O.K.
CHECK VENT DUCT SENSOR.
N.G.
Replace vent duct sensor.
O.K.
Replace auto amp.
NOTE: If the result is no good (NG) after checking circuit continuity, repair harness or connector.
91I05186
Courtesy of Nissan Motor Co., U.S.A.

Fig. 24: Diagnostic Procedure 11 – Vent Duct Sensor Circuit Shorted (300ZX)

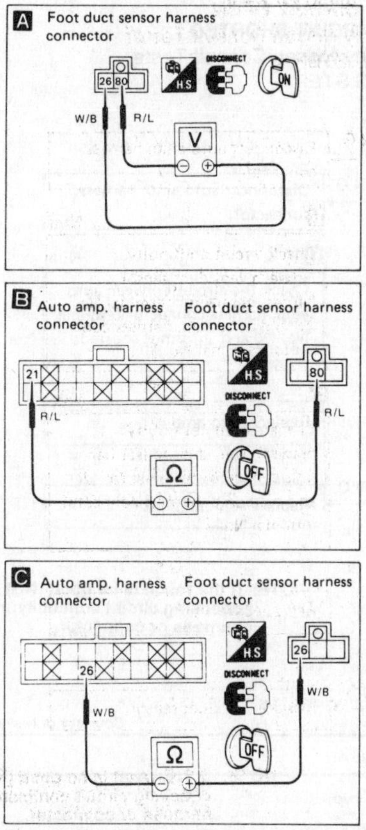

DIAGNOSTIC PROCEDURE 12

FLOOR (FOOT) DUCT SENSOR CIRCUIT OPEN

• Symptom indicated by Nissan Consult Tester or SELF-DIAGNOSIS STEP 4.

A Foot duct sensor harness connector
26 80
W/B
R/L
V
DISCONNECT
ON

B Auto amp. harness connector
Foot duct sensor harness connector
21
80
R/L
R/L
Ω
OFF

C Auto amp. harness connector
Foot duct sensor harness connector
26
26
W/B
W/B
Ω
OFF

A

CHECK FOOT DUCT SENSOR CIRCUIT BETWEEN FOOT DUCT SENSOR AND AUTO AMP.
Disconnect foot duct sensor harness connector.
Do approximately 5 volts exist between foot duct sensor harness connector terminal No. 26 and 80?

N.G. → Disconnect auto amp. harness connector.

B (Note) Check circuit continuity between foot duct sensor harness connector terminal No. 80 and auto amp. harness connector terminal No. 21.

O.K. ↓

C (Note) Check circuit continuity between foot duct sensor harness connector terminal No. 26 and auto amp. harness connector terminal No. 26.

O.K. ↓

Replace auto amp.

O.K. ↓

CHECK FOOT DUCT SENSOR.

N.G. → Replace foot duct sensor.

O.K. ↓

Replace auto amp.

NOTE: If the result is no good (NG) after checking circuit continuity, repair harness or connector.

92H03182

Courtesy of Nissan Motor Co., U.S.A.

Fig. 25: Diagnostic Procedure 12 – Foot Duct Sensor Circuit Open (300ZX)

1993 AUTOMATIC A/C-HEATER SYSTEMS
Trouble Shooting – 300ZX (Cont.)

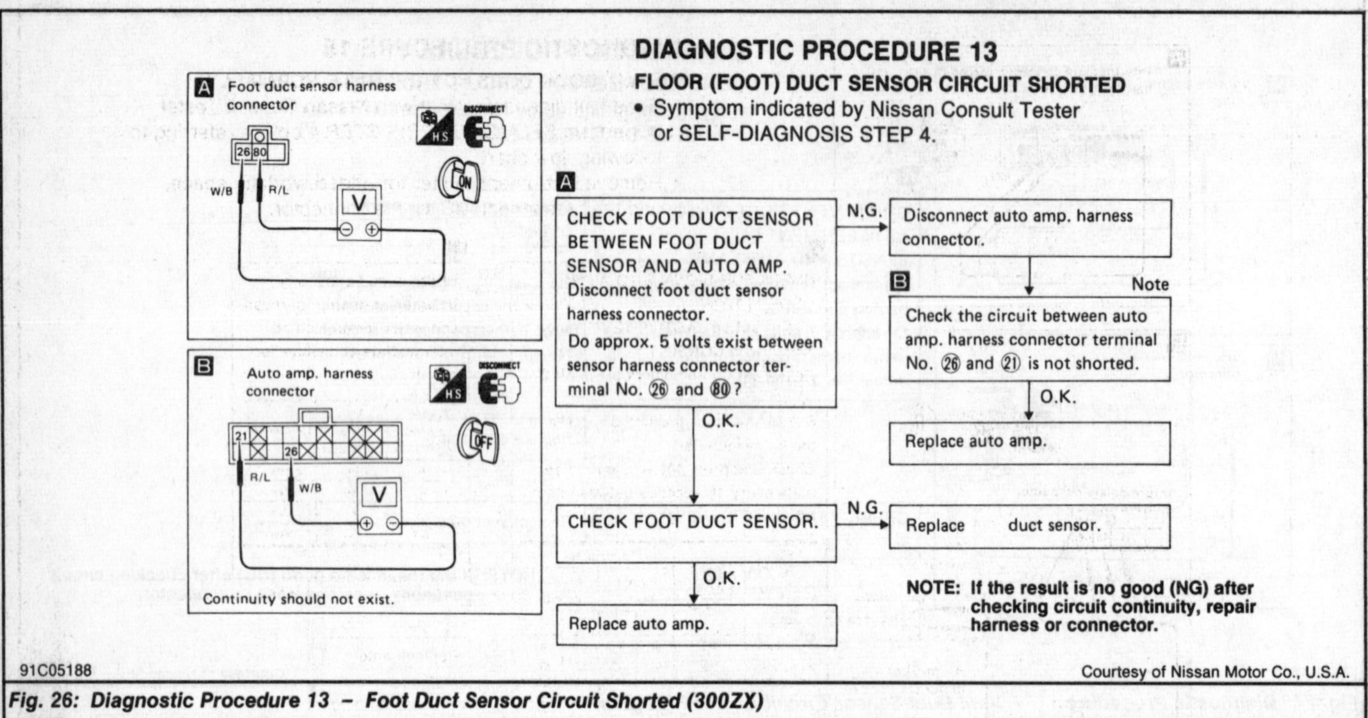
DIAGNOSTIC PROCEDURE 13
FLOOR (FOOT) DUCT SENSOR CIRCUIT SHORTED
• Symptom indicated by Nissan Consult Tester or SELF-DIAGNOSIS STEP 4.
A Foot duct sensor harness connector
26 80
W/B
R/L
V
B Auto amp. harness connector
21
26
R/L
W/B
V
Continuity should not exist.
A
CHECK FOOT DUCT SENSOR BETWEEN FOOT DUCT SENSOR AND AUTO AMP.
Disconnect foot duct sensor harness connector.
Do approx. 5 volts exist between sensor harness connector terminal No. 26 and 80?
N.G.
Disconnect auto amp. harness connector.
B
Note
Check the circuit between auto amp. harness connector terminal No. 26 and 21 is not shorted.
O.K.
Replace auto amp.
O.K.
CHECK FOOT DUCT SENSOR.
N.G.
Replace duct sensor.
O.K.
Replace auto amp.
NOTE: If the result is no good (NG) after checking circuit continuity, repair harness or connector.
91C05188
Courtesy of Nissan Motor Co., U.S.A.

Fig. 26: Diagnostic Procedure 13 – Foot Duct Sensor Circuit Shorted (300ZX)

DIAGNOSTIC PROCEDURE 14

SUNLOAD SENSOR CIRCUIT SHORTED

- Symptom indicated by Nissan Consult Tester or SELF-DIAGNOSIS STEP 4.

A Sunload sensor harness connector

24 78

V

B Auto amp. harness connector

21

24

R/L

W/G

Ω

Continuity should not exist.

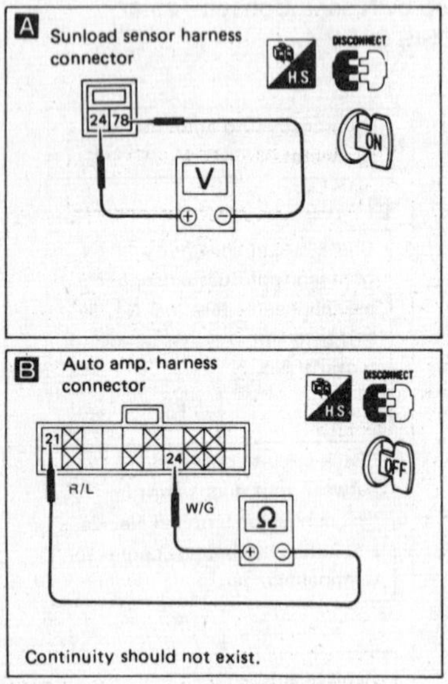

A

CHECK SUNLOAD SENSOR BETWEEN SUNLOAD SENSOR AND AUTO AMP.
Disconnect sunload sensor harness connector.
Do approx. 5 volts exist between sunload sensor harness connector terminal No. 24 and 78?

N.G. → Disconnect auto amp. harness connector.

B Note

Check the circuit between auto amp. harness connector terminal No. 24 and 21 is not shorted.

O.K. → Replace auto amp.

O.K. → CHECK SUNLOAD SENSOR.

N.G. → Replace sunload sensor.

O.K. → Replace auto amp.

NOTE: If the result is no good (NG) after checking circuit continuity, repair harness or connector.

91E05189

Courtesy of Nissan Motor Co., U.S.A.

Fig. 27: Diagnostic Procedure 14 – Sunload Sensor Circuit Shorted (300ZX)

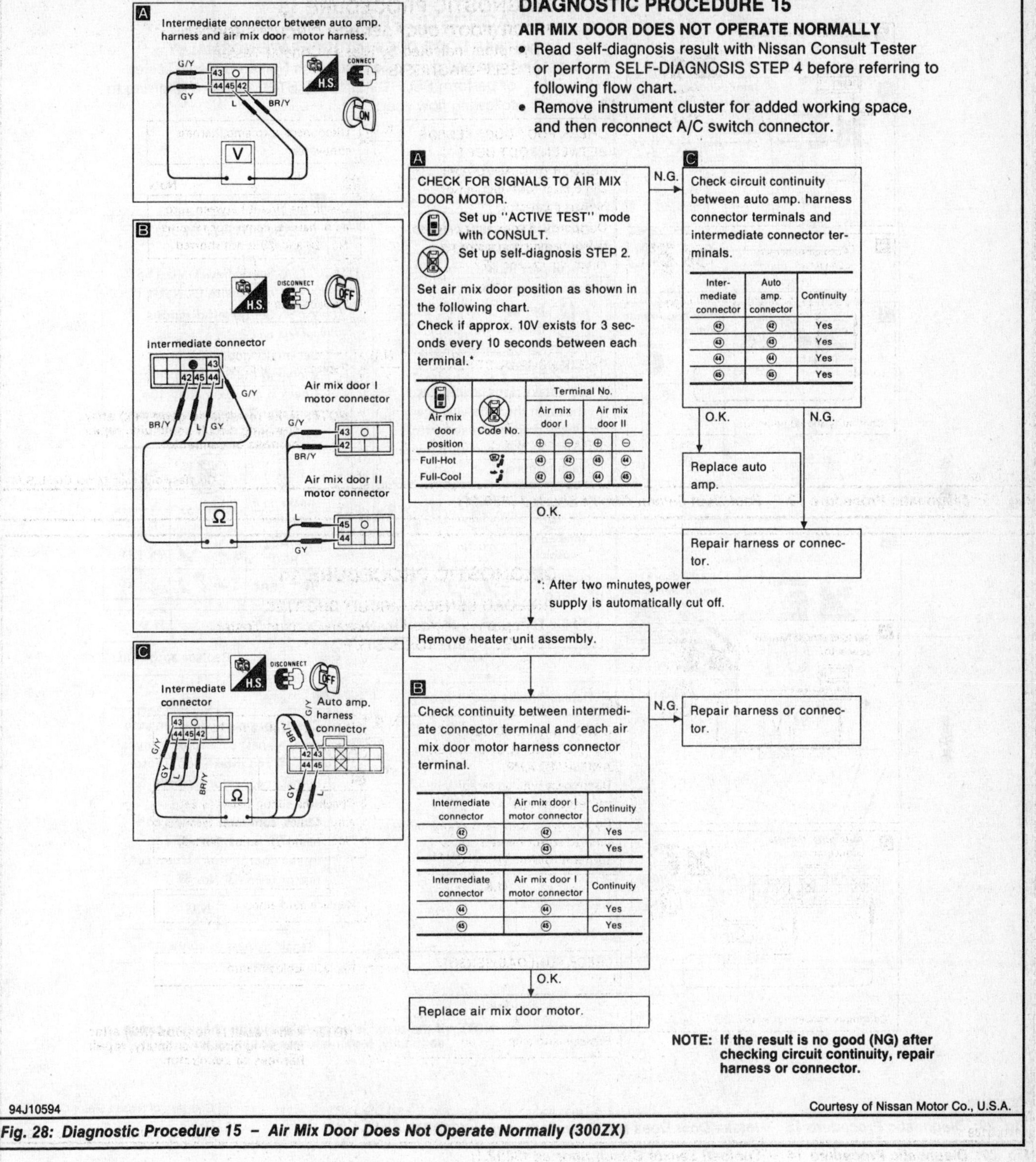

A
Intermediate connector between auto amp. harness and air mix door motor harness.
G/Y
43
44 45 42
GY
L
BR/Y
H.S.
CONNECT
ON
V
B
H.S.
DISCONNECT
OFF
Intermediate connector
43
42 45 44
G/Y
BR/Y
L
GY
Air mix door I motor connector
G/Y
43
42
BR/Y
Air mix door II motor connector
Ω
L
45
44
GY
C
H.S.
DISCONNECT
OFF
Intermediate connector
43
44 45 42
G/Y
GY
L
BR/Y
Ω
Auto amp. harness connector
G/Y
BR/Y
42 43
44 45
GY
L
DIAGNOSTIC PROCEDURE 15
AIR MIX DOOR DOES NOT OPERATE NORMALLY
• Read self-diagnosis result with Nissan Consult Tester or perform SELF-DIAGNOSIS STEP 4 before referring to following flow chart.
• Remove instrument cluster for added working space, and then reconnect A/C switch connector.
A
CHECK FOR SIGNALS TO AIR MIX DOOR MOTOR.
Set up "ACTIVE TEST" mode with CONSULT.
Set up self-diagnosis STEP 2.
Set air mix door position as shown in the following chart.
Check if approx. 10V exists for 3 seconds every 10 seconds between each terminal.*
Air mix door position	Code No.	Air mix door I ⊕	Air mix door I ⊖	Air mix door II ⊕	Air mix door II ⊖
Full-Hot		43	42	45	44
Full-Cool		42	43	44	45
N.G.
C
Check circuit continuity between auto amp. harness connector terminals and intermediate connector terminals.
Intermediate connector	Auto amp. connector	Continuity
42	42	Yes
43	43	Yes
44	44	Yes
45	45	Yes
O.K.
N.G.
Replace auto amp.
Repair harness or connector.
O.K.
*: After two minutes, power supply is automatically cut off.
Remove heater unit assembly.
B
Check continuity between intermediate connector terminal and each air mix door motor harness connector terminal.
Intermediate connector	Air mix door I motor connector	Continuity
42	42	Yes
43	43	Yes
Intermediate connector	Air mix door I motor connector	Continuity
44	44	Yes
45	45	Yes
N.G.
Repair harness or connector.
O.K.
Replace air mix door motor.
NOTE: If the result is no good (NG) after checking circuit continuity, repair harness or connector.
94J10594
Courtesy of Nissan Motor Co., U.S.A.

Fig. 28: Diagnostic Procedure 15 – Air Mix Door Does Not Operate Normally (300ZX)

1993 AUTOMATIC A/C-HEATER SYSTEMS
Trouble Shooting – 300ZX (Cont.)

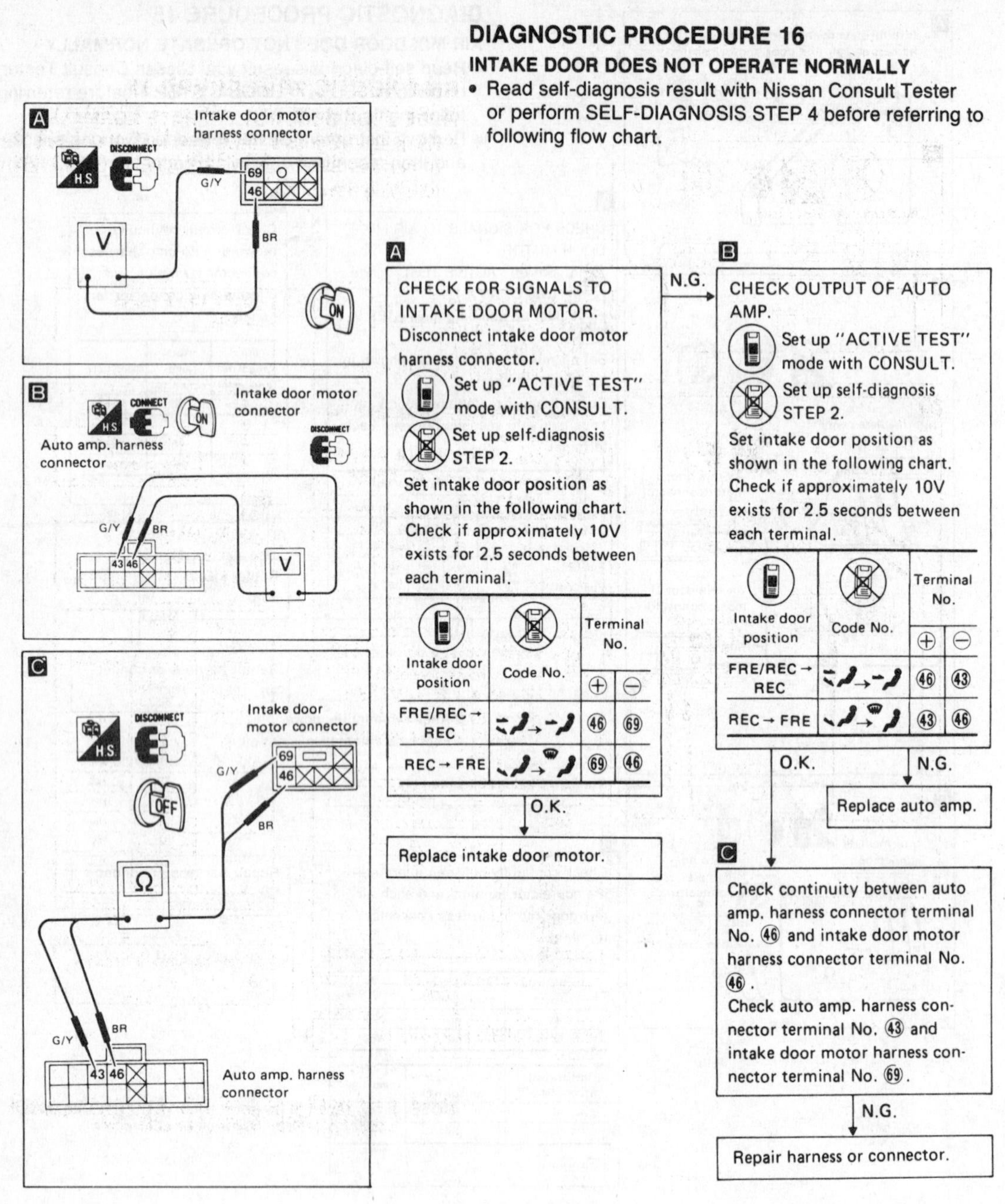
DIAGNOSTIC PROCEDURE 16
INTAKE DOOR DOES NOT OPERATE NORMALLY
• Read self-diagnosis result with Nissan Consult Tester or perform SELF-DIAGNOSIS STEP 4 before referring to following flow chart.
A
Intake door motor harness connector
DISCONNECT
H.S.
G/Y
69
46
BR
V
ON
B
CONNECT
H.S.
ON
Intake door motor connector
DISCONNECT
Auto amp. harness connector
G/Y
BR
43 46
V
C
DISCONNECT
H.S.
Intake door motor connector
69
46
G/Y
BR
OFF
Ω
G/Y
BR
43 46
Auto amp. harness connector
A
CHECK FOR SIGNALS TO INTAKE DOOR MOTOR.
Disconnect intake door motor harness connector.
Set up "ACTIVE TEST" mode with CONSULT.
Set up self-diagnosis STEP 2.
Set intake door position as shown in the following chart.
Check if approximately 10V exists for 2.5 seconds between each terminal.
Intake door position
Code No.
Terminal No.
⊕ ⊖
FRE/REC → REC 46 69
REC → FRE 69 46
N.G.
O.K.
Replace intake door motor.
B
CHECK OUTPUT OF AUTO AMP.
Set up "ACTIVE TEST" mode with CONSULT.
Set up self-diagnosis STEP 2.
Set intake door position as shown in the following chart.
Check if approximately 10V exists for 2.5 seconds between each terminal.
Intake door position
Code No.
Terminal No.
⊕ ⊖
FRE/REC → REC 46 43
REC → FRE 43 46
O.K.
N.G.
Replace auto amp.
C
Check continuity between auto amp. harness connector terminal No. 46 and intake door motor harness connector terminal No. 46.
Check auto amp. harness connector terminal No. 43 and intake door motor harness connector terminal No. 69.
N.G.
Repair harness or connector.
NOTE: If the result is no good (NG) after checking circuit continuity, repair harness or connector.
92J03183
Courtesy of Nissan Motor Co., U.S.A.

Fig. 29: Diagnostic Procedure 16 – Intake Door Does Not Operate Normally (300ZX)

DIAGNOSTIC PROCEDURE 17

MODE DOOR DOES NOT OPERATE NORMALLY

- Read self-diagnosis result with Nissan Consult Tester or perform SELF-DIAGNOSIS STEP 4 before referring to following flow chart.

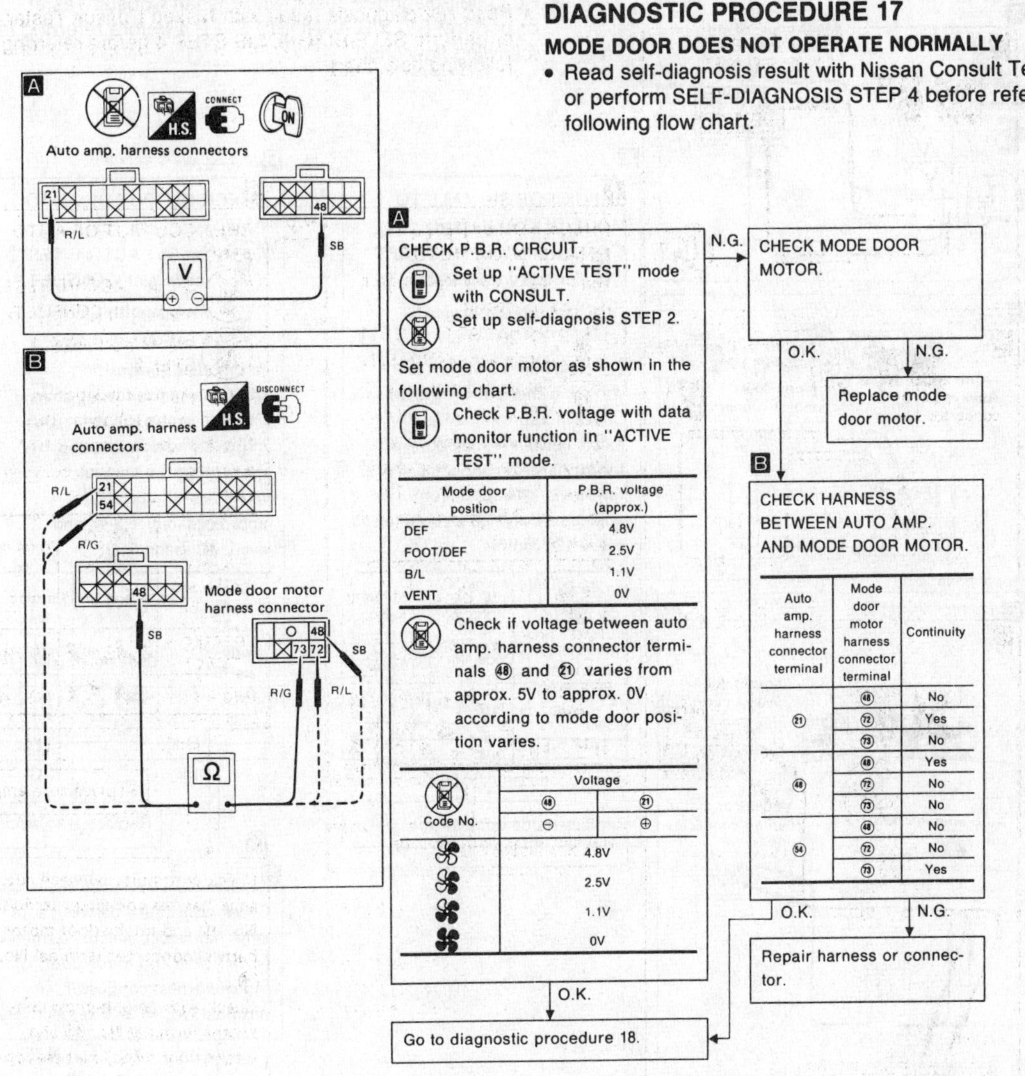

A
CONNECT
H.S.
ON
Auto amp. harness connectors
21
48
R/L
SB
V
B
DISCONNECT
H.S.
Auto amp. harness connectors
R/L
21
54
R/G
48
SB
Mode door motor harness connector
48
73
72
SB
R/G
R/L
Ω
A
CHECK P.B.R. CIRCUIT.
Set up "ACTIVE TEST" mode with CONSULT.
Set up self-diagnosis STEP 2.
Set mode door motor as shown in the following chart.
Check P.B.R. voltage with data monitor function in "ACTIVE TEST" mode.
Check if voltage between auto amp. harness connector terminals ⑱ and ㉑ varies from approx. 5V to approx. 0V according to mode door position varies.
N.G.
CHECK MODE DOOR MOTOR.
O.K.
N.G.
Replace mode door motor.
B
CHECK HARNESS BETWEEN AUTO AMP. AND MODE DOOR MOTOR.
O.K.
N.G.
Repair harness or connector.
O.K.
Go to diagnostic procedure 18.

Mode door position	P.B.R. voltage (approx.)
DEF	4.8V
FOOT/DEF	2.5V
B/L	1.1V
VENT	0V

Code No.	Voltage ⑱ ⊖ – ㉑ ⊕
(mode symbol)	4.8V
(mode symbol)	2.5V
(mode symbol)	1.1V
(mode symbol)	0V

Auto amp. harness connector terminal	Mode door motor harness connector terminal	Continuity
㉑	⑱	No
	㊲ 72	Yes
	73	No
⑱	⑱	Yes
	72	No
	73	No
54	⑱	No
	72	No
	73	Yes

NOTE: If the result is no good (NG) after checking circuit continuity, repair harness or connector.

92B03184

Courtesy of Nissan Motor Co., U.S.A.

Fig. 30: Diagnostic Procedure 17 – Mode Door Does Not Operate Normally (300ZX)

1993 AUTOMATIC A/C-HEATER SYSTEMS
Trouble Shooting – 300ZX (Cont.)

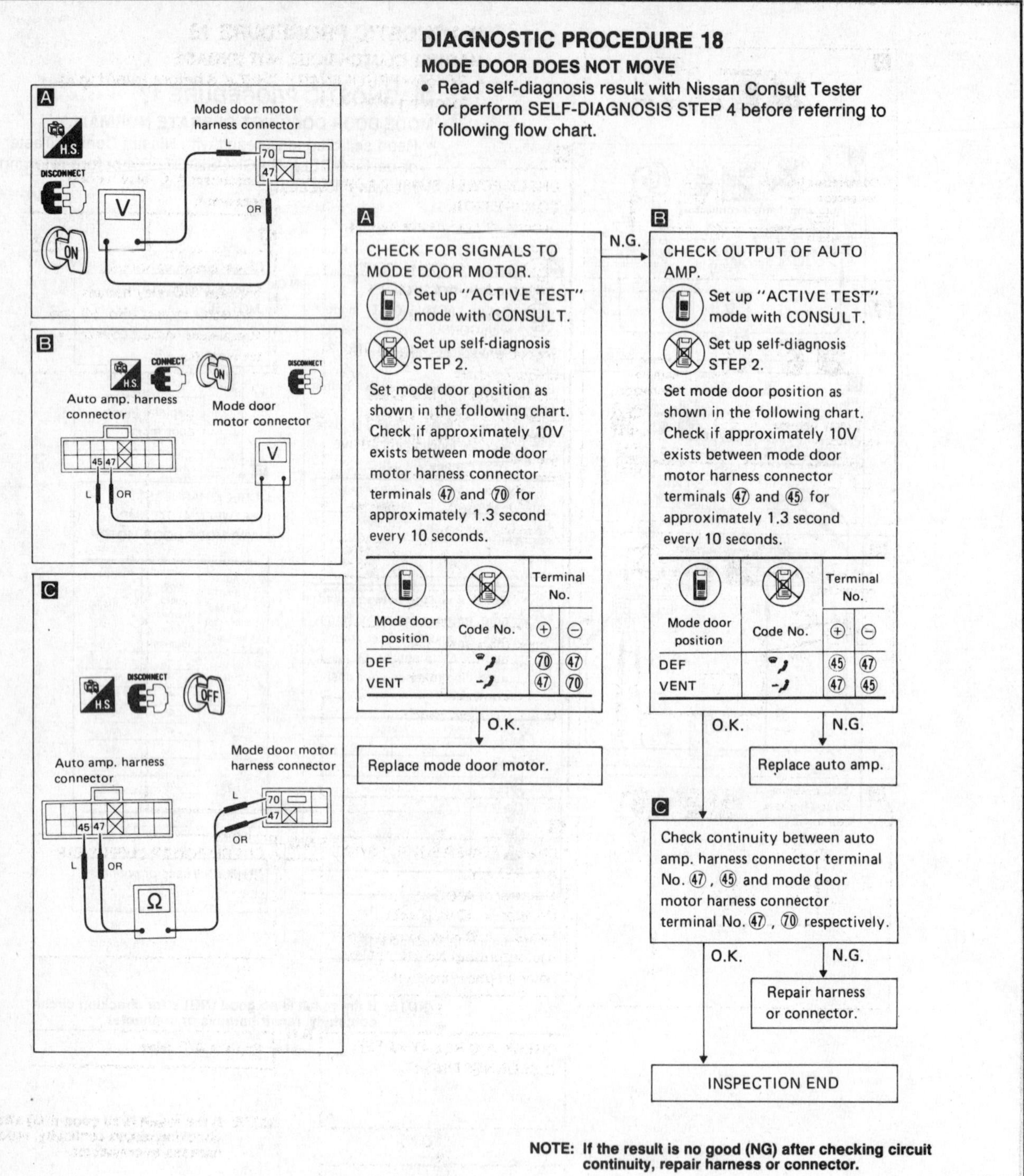
DIAGNOSTIC PROCEDURE 18
MODE DOOR DOES NOT MOVE
• Read self-diagnosis result with Nissan Consult Tester or perform SELF-DIAGNOSIS STEP 4 before referring to following flow chart.
A
Mode door motor harness connector
H.S.
DISCONNECT
ON
V
L
OR
70
47
B
H.S.
CONNECT
ON
DISCONNECT
Auto amp. harness connector
Mode door motor connector
45
47
L
OR
V
C
H.S.
DISCONNECT
OFF
Auto amp. harness connector
Mode door motor harness connector
L
OR
70
47
45
47
Ω
A
CHECK FOR SIGNALS TO MODE DOOR MOTOR.
Set up "ACTIVE TEST" mode with CONSULT.
Set up self-diagnosis STEP 2.
Set mode door position as shown in the following chart. Check if approximately 10V exists between mode door motor harness connector terminals ㊼ and ⑦⓪ for approximately 1.3 second every 10 seconds.
Mode door position | Code No. | Terminal No. ⊕ ⊖
DEF | ⑦⓪ ㊼
VENT | ㊼ ⑦⓪
O.K.
Replace mode door motor.
N.G.
B
CHECK OUTPUT OF AUTO AMP.
Set up "ACTIVE TEST" mode with CONSULT.
Set up self-diagnosis STEP 2.
Set mode door position as shown in the following chart. Check if approximately 10V exists between mode door motor harness connector terminals ㊼ and ㊺ for approximately 1.3 second every 10 seconds.
Mode door position | Code No. | Terminal No. ⊕ ⊖
DEF | ㊺ ㊼
VENT | ㊼ ㊺
O.K.
N.G.
Replace auto amp.
C
Check continuity between auto amp. harness connector terminal No. ㊼, ㊺ and mode door motor harness connector terminal No. ㊼, ⑦⓪ respectively.
O.K.
N.G.
Repair harness or connector.
INSPECTION END
NOTE: If the result is no good (NG) after checking circuit continuity, repair harness or connector.
92E03185
Courtesy of Nissan Motor Co., U.S.A.

Fig. 31: Diagnostic Procedure 18 – Mode Door Does Not Move (300ZX)

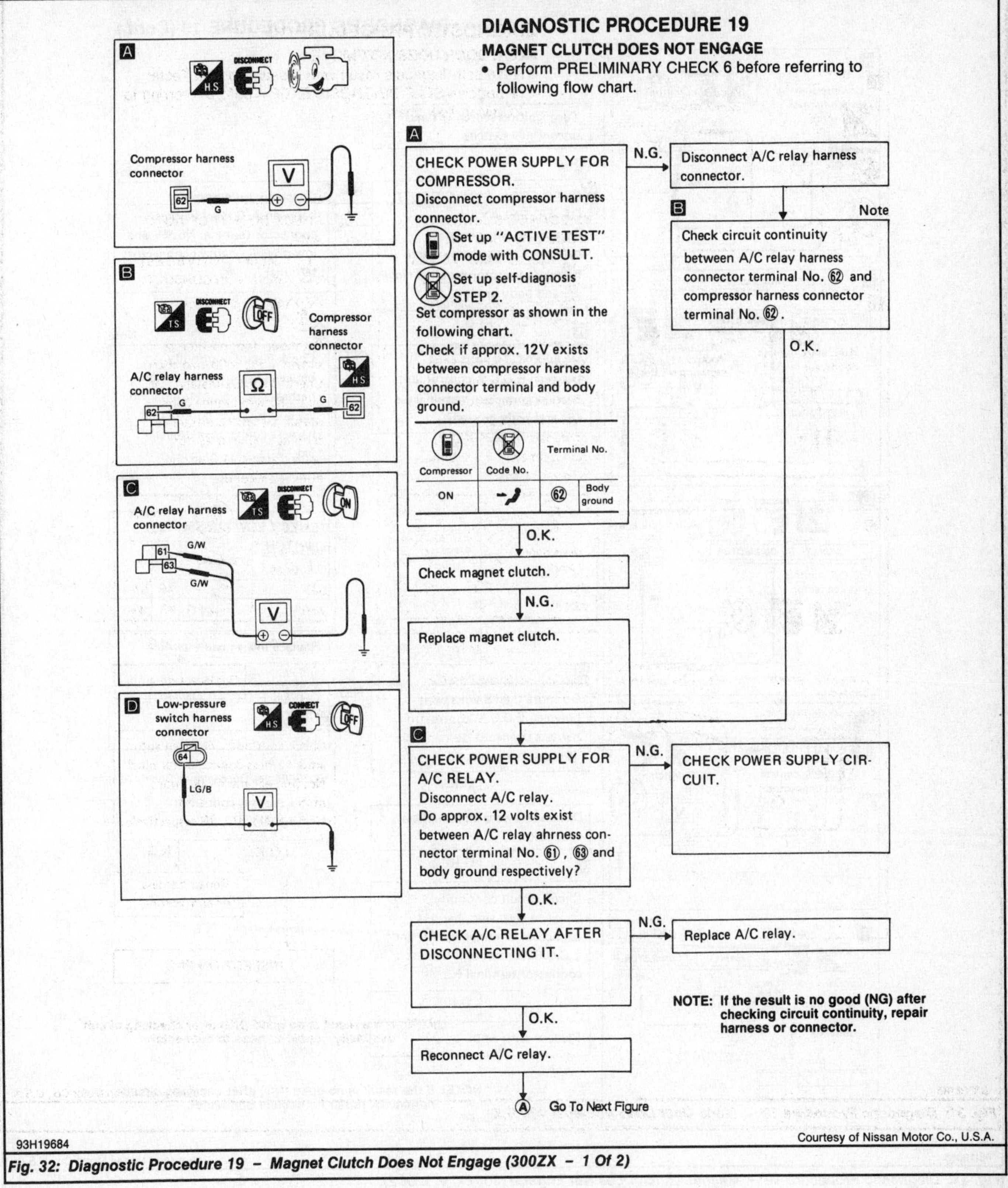

DIAGNOSTIC PROCEDURE 19
MAGNET CLUTCH DOES NOT ENGAGE
• Perform PRELIMINARY CHECK 6 before referring to following flow chart.
A
CHECK POWER SUPPLY FOR COMPRESSOR.
Disconnect compressor harness connector.
Set up "ACTIVE TEST" mode with CONSULT.
Set up self-diagnosis STEP 2.
Set compressor as shown in the following chart.
Check if approx. 12V exists between compressor harness connector terminal and body ground.
Compressor
Code No.
Terminal No.
ON
62
Body ground
N.G.
Disconnect A/C relay harness connector.
B
Note
Check circuit continuity between A/C relay harness connector terminal No. 62 and compressor harness connector terminal No. 62.
O.K.
O.K.
Check magnet clutch.
N.G.
Replace magnet clutch.
C
CHECK POWER SUPPLY FOR A/C RELAY.
Disconnect A/C relay.
Do approx. 12 volts exist between A/C relay ahrness connector terminal No. 61, 63 and body ground respectively?
N.G.
CHECK POWER SUPPLY CIRCUIT.
O.K.
CHECK A/C RELAY AFTER DISCONNECTING IT.
N.G.
Replace A/C relay.
O.K.
Reconnect A/C relay.
A Go To Next Figure
NOTE: If the result is no good (NG) after checking circuit continuity, repair harness or connector.
A
DISCONNECT
H S
Compressor harness connector
62
G
V
B
DISCONNECT
T S
OFF
Compressor harness connector
A/C relay harness connector
H S
Ω
62
G
C
A/C relay harness connector
DISCONNECT
T S
ON
61
63
G/W
V
D
Low-pressure switch harness connector
CONNECT
H S
OFF
64
LG/B
V
93H19684
Courtesy of Nissan Motor Co., U.S.A.

Fig. 32: Diagnostic Procedure 19 – Magnet Clutch Does Not Engage (300ZX – 1 Of 2)

1993 AUTOMATIC A/C-HEATER SYSTEMS
Trouble Shooting – 300ZX (Cont.)

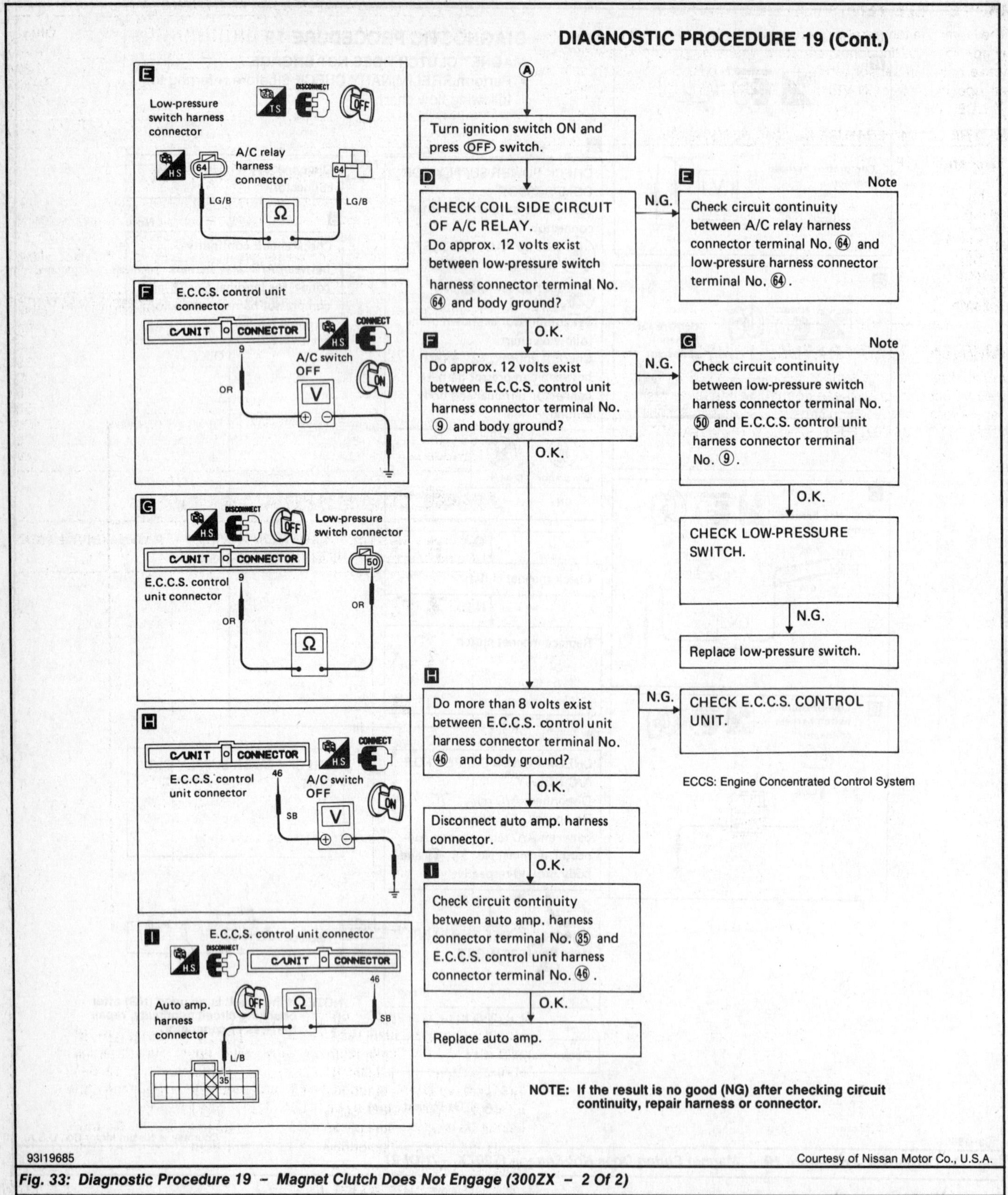
DIAGNOSTIC PROCEDURE 19 (Cont.)
E
Low-pressure switch harness connector
DISCONNECT
A/C relay harness connector
64
LG/B
F
E.C.C.S. control unit connector
C/UNIT CONNECTOR
CONNECT
9
A/C switch OFF
OR
V
G
DISCONNECT
Low-pressure switch connector
E.C.C.S. control unit connector
50
OR
H
E.C.C.S. control unit connector
46
A/C switch OFF
SB
I
E.C.C.S. control unit connector
Auto amp. harness connector
L/B
35
A
Turn ignition switch ON and press OFF switch.
D
CHECK COIL SIDE CIRCUIT OF A/C RELAY.
Do approx. 12 volts exist between low-pressure switch harness connector terminal No. 64 and body ground?
N.G.
E Note
Check circuit continuity between A/C relay harness connector terminal No. 64 and low-pressure harness connector terminal No. 64.
O.K.
F
Do approx. 12 volts exist between E.C.C.S. control unit harness connector terminal No. 9 and body ground?
N.G.
G Note
Check circuit continuity between low-pressure switch harness connector terminal No. 50 and E.C.C.S. control unit harness connector terminal No. 9.
O.K.
CHECK LOW-PRESSURE SWITCH.
N.G.
Replace low-pressure switch.
H
Do more than 8 volts exist between E.C.C.S. control unit harness connector terminal No. 46 and body ground?
N.G.
CHECK E.C.C.S. CONTROL UNIT.
ECCS: Engine Concentrated Control System
O.K.
Disconnect auto amp. harness connector.
I
Check circuit continuity between auto amp. harness connector terminal No. 35 and E.C.C.S. control unit harness connector terminal No. 46.
Replace auto amp.
NOTE: If the result is no good (NG) after checking circuit continuity, repair harness or connector.
93I19685
Courtesy of Nissan Motor Co., U.S.A.

Fig. 33: Diagnostic Procedure 19 – Magnet Clutch Does Not Engage (300ZX – 2 Of 2)

1993 AUTOMATIC A/C-HEATER SYSTEMS
Trouble Shooting – 300ZX (Cont.)

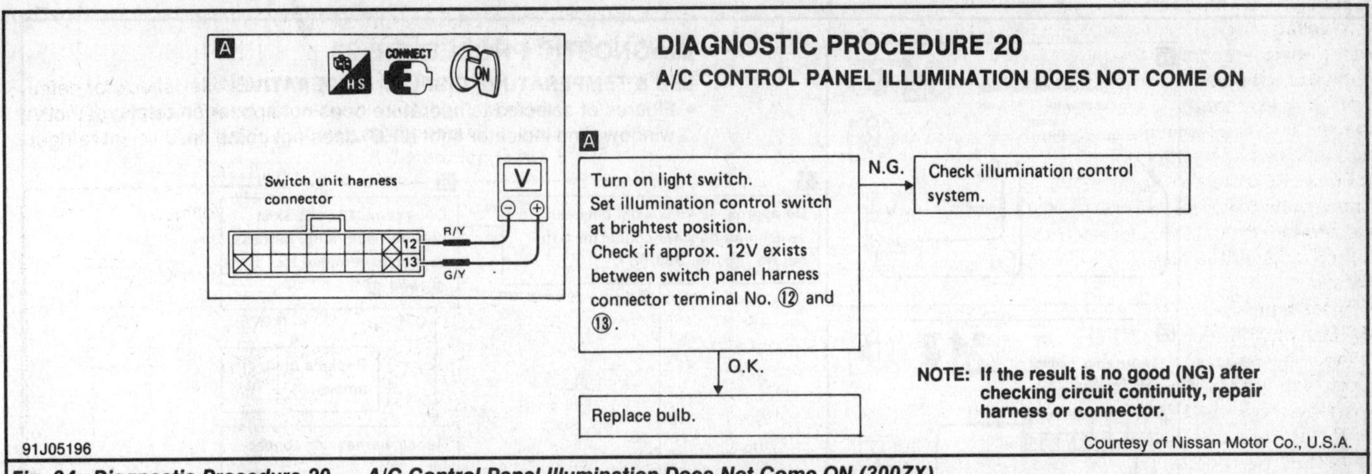
A
CONNECT
H S
ON
Switch unit harness connector
V
12
13
R/Y
G/Y
DIAGNOSTIC PROCEDURE 20
A/C CONTROL PANEL ILLUMINATION DOES NOT COME ON
A
Turn on light switch. Set illumination control switch at brightest position. Check if approx. 12V exists between switch panel harness connector terminal No. ⑫ and ⑬.
N.G.
Check illumination control system.
O.K.
Replace bulb.
NOTE: If the result is no good (NG) after checking circuit continuity, repair harness or connector.
91J05196
Courtesy of Nissan Motor Co., U.S.A.

Fig. 34: Diagnostic Procedure 20 – A/C Control Panel Illumination Does Not Come ON (300ZX)

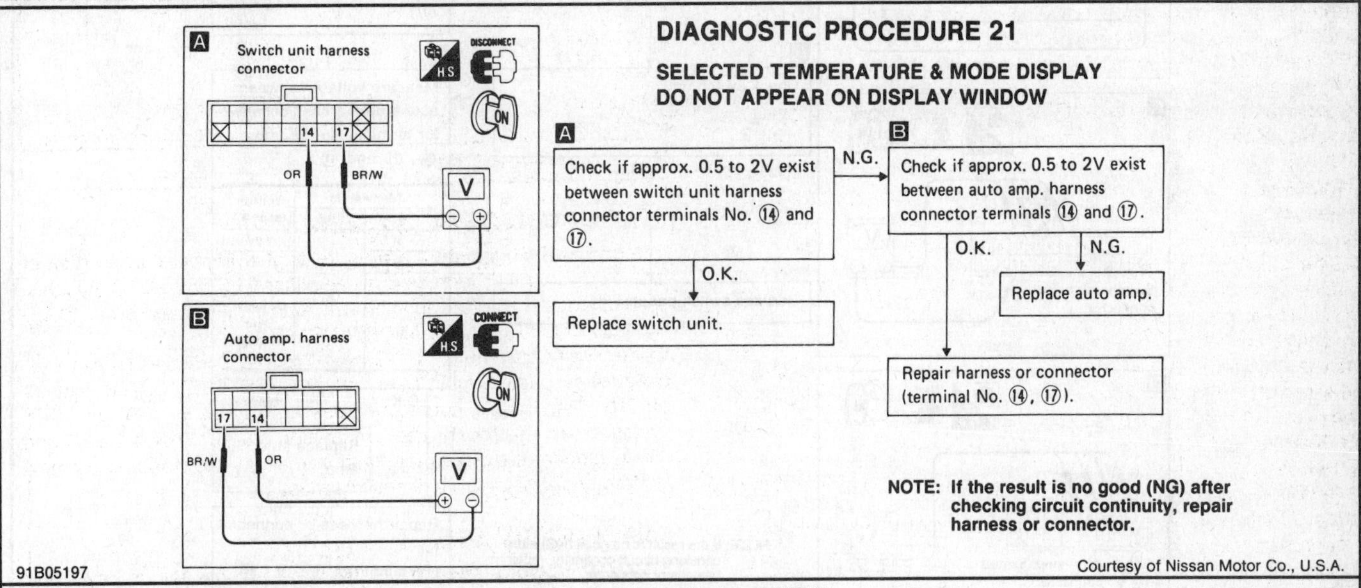
A
Switch unit harness connector
DISCONNECT
H S
ON
14
17
OR
BR/W
V
B
Auto amp. harness connector
CONNECT
17
14
BR/W
OR
DIAGNOSTIC PROCEDURE 21
SELECTED TEMPERATURE & MODE DISPLAY DO NOT APPEAR ON DISPLAY WINDOW
A
Check if approx. 0.5 to 2V exist between switch unit harness connector terminals No. ⑭ and ⑰.
N.G.
B
Check if approx. 0.5 to 2V exist between auto amp. harness connector terminals ⑭ and ⑰.
O.K.
Replace switch unit.
O.K.
N.G.
Replace auto amp.
Repair harness or connector (terminal No. ⑭, ⑰).
NOTE: If the result is no good (NG) after checking circuit continuity, repair harness or connector.
91B05197
Courtesy of Nissan Motor Co., U.S.A.

Fig. 35: Diagnostic Procedure 21 – Temperatures Do Not Appear In Display (300ZX)

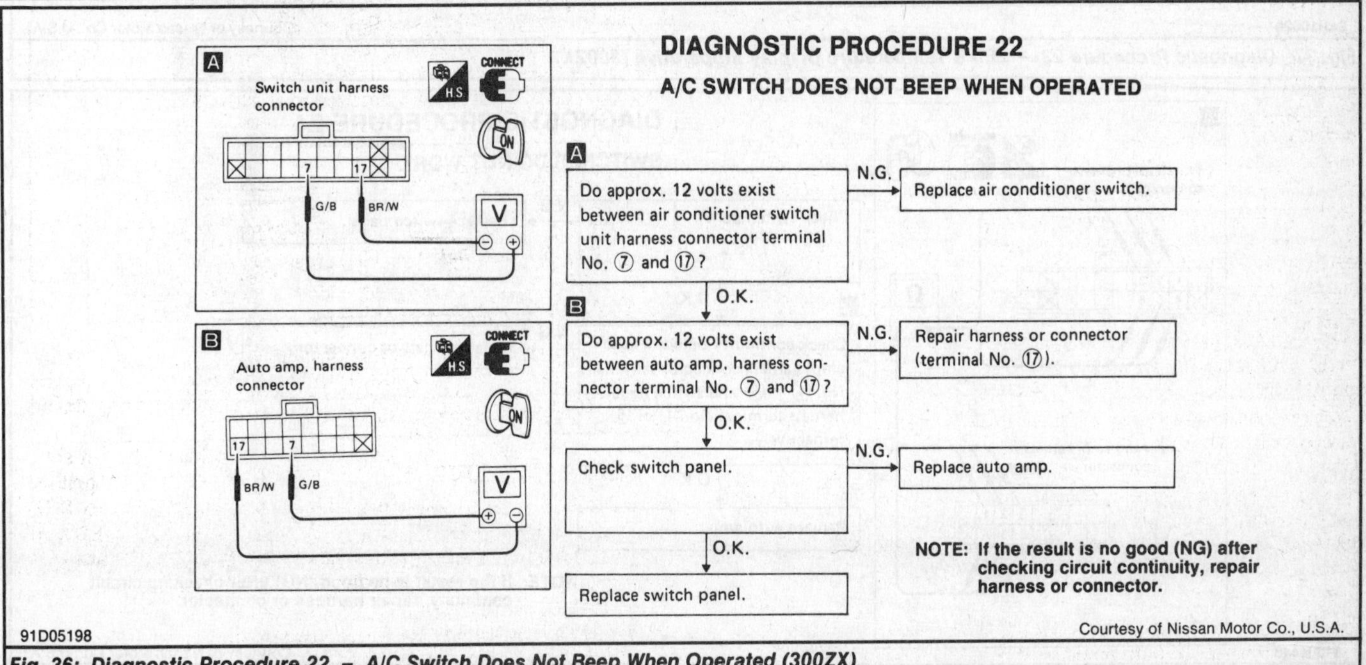
A
Switch unit harness connector
CONNECT
H S
ON
7
17
G/B
BR/W
V
B
Auto amp. harness connector
17
7
BR/W
G/B
DIAGNOSTIC PROCEDURE 22
A/C SWITCH DOES NOT BEEP WHEN OPERATED
A
Do approx. 12 volts exist between air conditioner switch unit harness connector terminal No. ⑦ and ⑰?
N.G.
Replace air conditioner switch.
O.K.
B
Do approx. 12 volts exist between auto amp. harness connector terminal No. ⑦ and ⑰?
N.G.
Repair harness or connector (terminal No. ⑰).
O.K.
Check switch panel.
N.G.
Replace auto amp.
O.K.
Replace switch panel.
NOTE: If the result is no good (NG) after checking circuit continuity, repair harness or connector.
91D05198
Courtesy of Nissan Motor Co., U.S.A.

Fig. 36: Diagnostic Procedure 22 – A/C Switch Does Not Beep When Operated (300ZX)

1993 AUTOMATIC A/C-HEATER SYSTEMS
Trouble Shooting – 300ZX (Cont.)

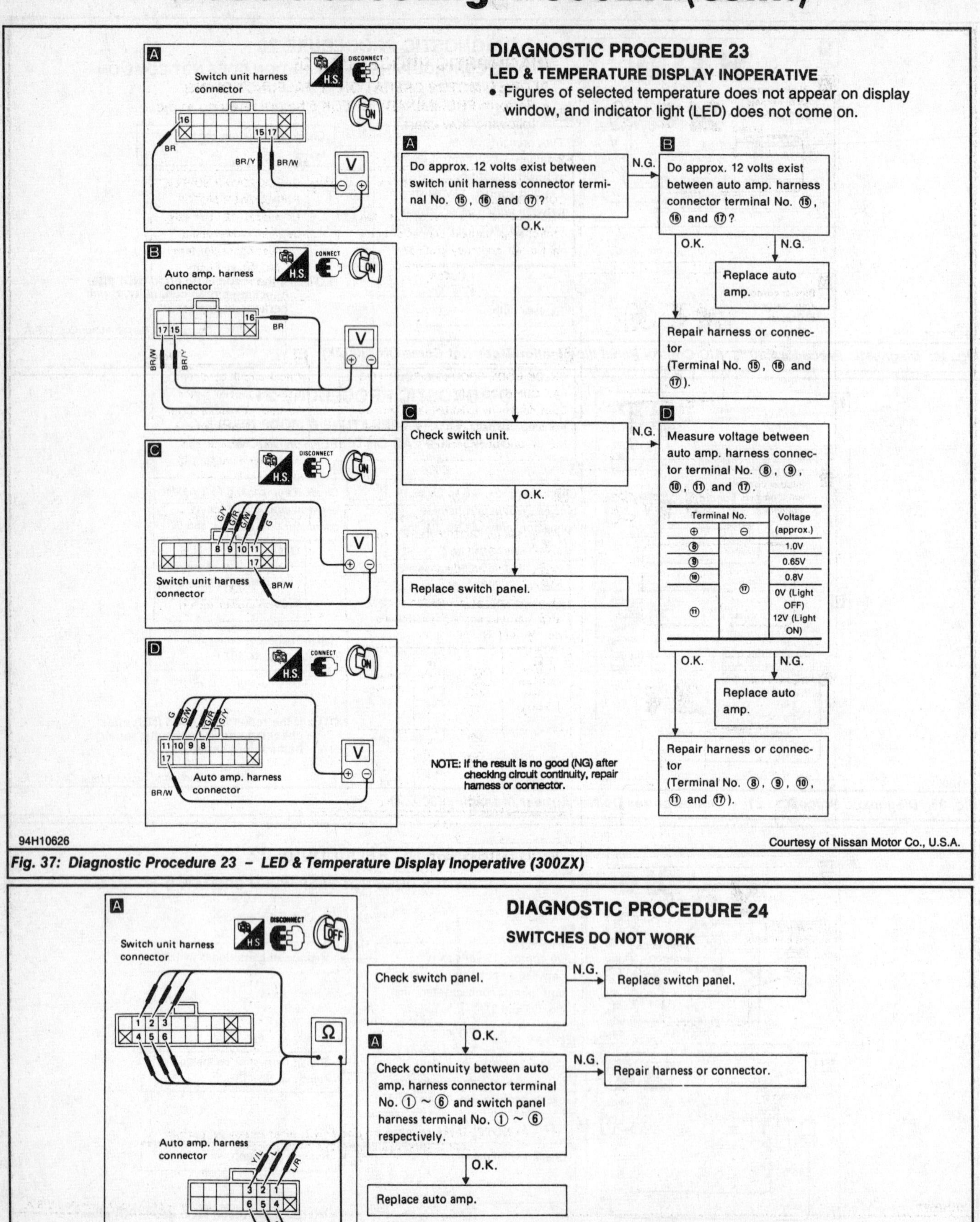
DIAGNOSTIC PROCEDURE 23
LED & TEMPERATURE DISPLAY INOPERATIVE
• Figures of selected temperature does not appear on display window, and indicator light (LED) does not come on.
A
Switch unit harness connector
DISCONNECT
H.S.
ON
16
15 17
BR
BR/Y
BR/W
V
A
Do approx. 12 volts exist between switch unit harness connector terminal No. ⑮, ⑯ and ⑰?
N.G.
O.K.
B
Do approx. 12 volts exist between auto amp. harness connector terminal No. ⑮, ⑯ and ⑰?
O.K.
N.G.
Replace auto amp.
Repair harness or connector (Terminal No. ⑮, ⑯ and ⑰).
B
Auto amp. harness connector
CONNECT
H.S.
ON
16
17 15
BR
BR/W
BR/Y
V
C
Check switch unit.
N.G.
O.K.
Replace switch panel.
D
Measure voltage between auto amp. harness connector terminal No. ⑧, ⑨, ⑩, ⑪ and ⑰.
C
DISCONNECT
H.S.
ON
G/Y
G/R
G/W
G
8 9 10 11
17
Switch unit harness connector
BR/W
V
D
CONNECT
H.S.
ON
G
G/W
G/R
G/Y
11 10 9 8
17
Auto amp. harness connector
BR/W
V
NOTE: If the result is no good (NG) after checking circuit continuity, repair harness or connector.
O.K.
N.G.
Replace auto amp.
Repair harness or connector (Terminal No. ⑧, ⑨, ⑩, ⑪ and ⑰).
94H10626
Courtesy of Nissan Motor Co., U.S.A.

Terminal No. ⊕	Terminal No. ⊖	Voltage (approx.)
⑧	⑰	1.0V
⑨	⑰	0.65V
⑩	⑰	0.8V
⑪	⑰	0V (Light OFF) 12V (Light ON)

Fig. 37: Diagnostic Procedure 23 – LED & Temperature Display Inoperative (300ZX)

DIAGNOSTIC PROCEDURE 24
SWITCHES DO NOT WORK
A
Switch unit harness connector
DISCONNECT
H.S.
OFF
1 2 3
4 5 6
Ω
Auto amp. harness connector
Y/L
L
L/R
3 2 1
6 5 4
Y/R
Y/B
L/Y
Check switch panel.
N.G.
Replace switch panel.
O.K.
A
Check continuity between auto amp. harness connector terminal No. ① ~ ⑥ and switch panel harness terminal No. ① ~ ⑥ respectively.
N.G.
Repair harness or connector.
O.K.
Replace auto amp.
NOTE: If the result is no good (NG) after checking circuit continuity, repair harness or connector.
91J04446
Courtesy of Nissan Motor Co., U.S.A.

Fig. 38: Diagnostic Procedure 24 – Switches Do Not Work (300ZX)

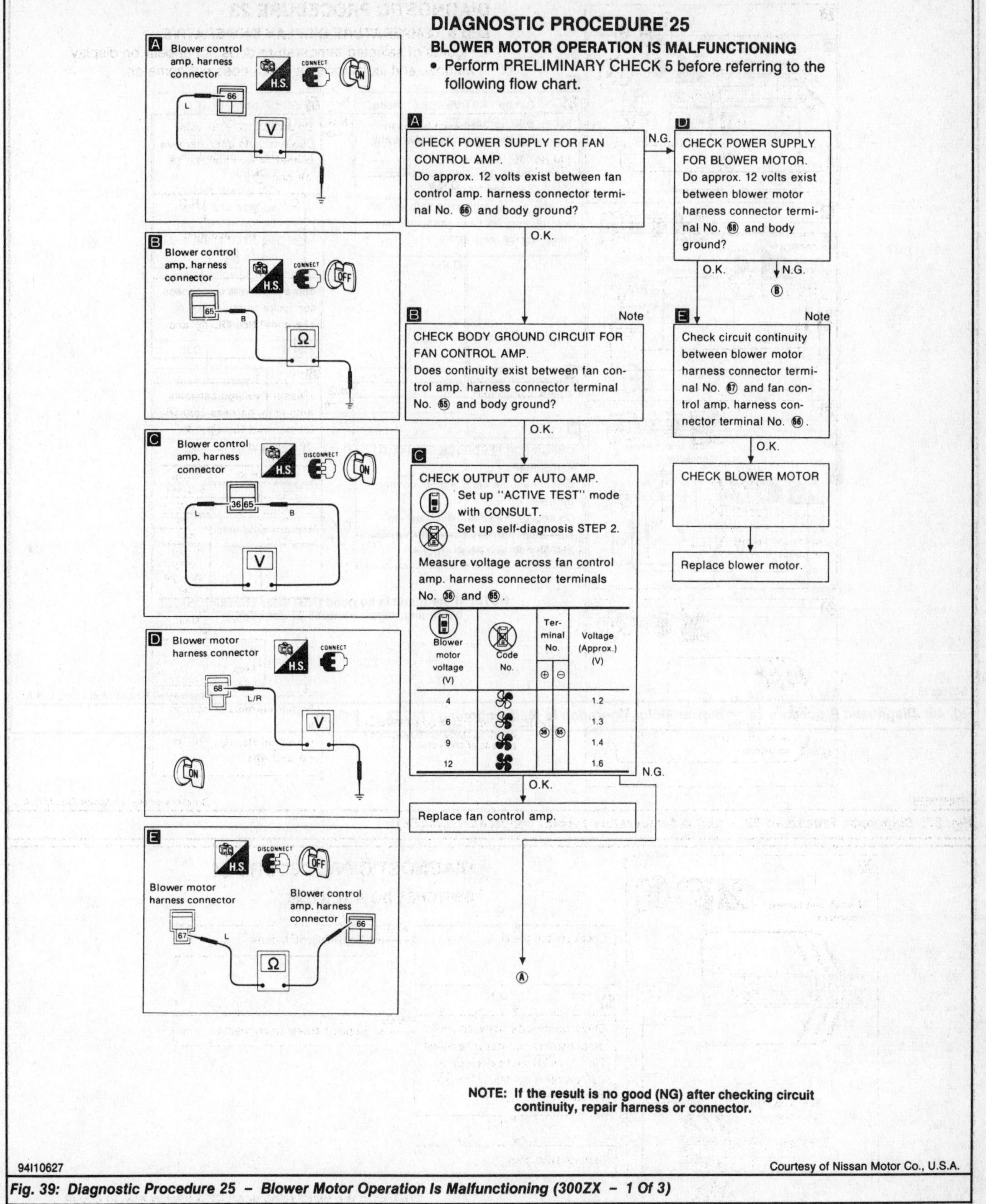
DIAGNOSTIC PROCEDURE 25
BLOWER MOTOR OPERATION IS MALFUNCTIONING
• Perform PRELIMINARY CHECK 5 before referring to the following flow chart.
A Blower control amp. harness connector
CONNECT
ON
66
L
V
A CHECK POWER SUPPLY FOR FAN CONTROL AMP. Do approx. 12 volts exist between fan control amp. harness connector terminal No. 66 and body ground?
N.G.
D CHECK POWER SUPPLY FOR BLOWER MOTOR. Do approx. 12 volts exist between blower motor harness connector terminal No. 68 and body ground?
O.K.
N.G.
B
B Blower control amp. harness connector
CONNECT
OFF
65
B
Ω
B CHECK BODY GROUND CIRCUIT FOR FAN CONTROL AMP. Does continuity exist between fan control amp. harness connector terminal No. 65 and body ground?
Note
E Check circuit continuity between blower motor harness connector terminal No. 67 and fan control amp. harness connector terminal No. 66.
CHECK BLOWER MOTOR
Replace blower motor.
C Blower control amp. harness connector
DISCONNECT
36 65
C CHECK OUTPUT OF AUTO AMP.
Set up "ACTIVE TEST" mode with CONSULT.
Set up self-diagnosis STEP 2.
Measure voltage across fan control amp. harness connector terminals No. 36 and 65.
Blower motor voltage (V)
Code No.
Terminal No.
Voltage (Approx.) (V)
4
6
9
12
1.2
1.3
1.4
1.6
D Blower motor harness connector
68
L/R
Replace fan control amp.
E Blower motor harness connector
Blower control amp. harness connector
67
A
NOTE: If the result is no good (NG) after checking circuit continuity, repair harness or connector.
94I10627
Courtesy of Nissan Motor Co., U.S.A.

Fig. 39: Diagnostic Procedure 25 – Blower Motor Operation Is Malfunctioning (300ZX – 1 Of 3)

1993 AUTOMATIC A/C-HEATER SYSTEMS
Trouble Shooting – 300ZX (Cont.)

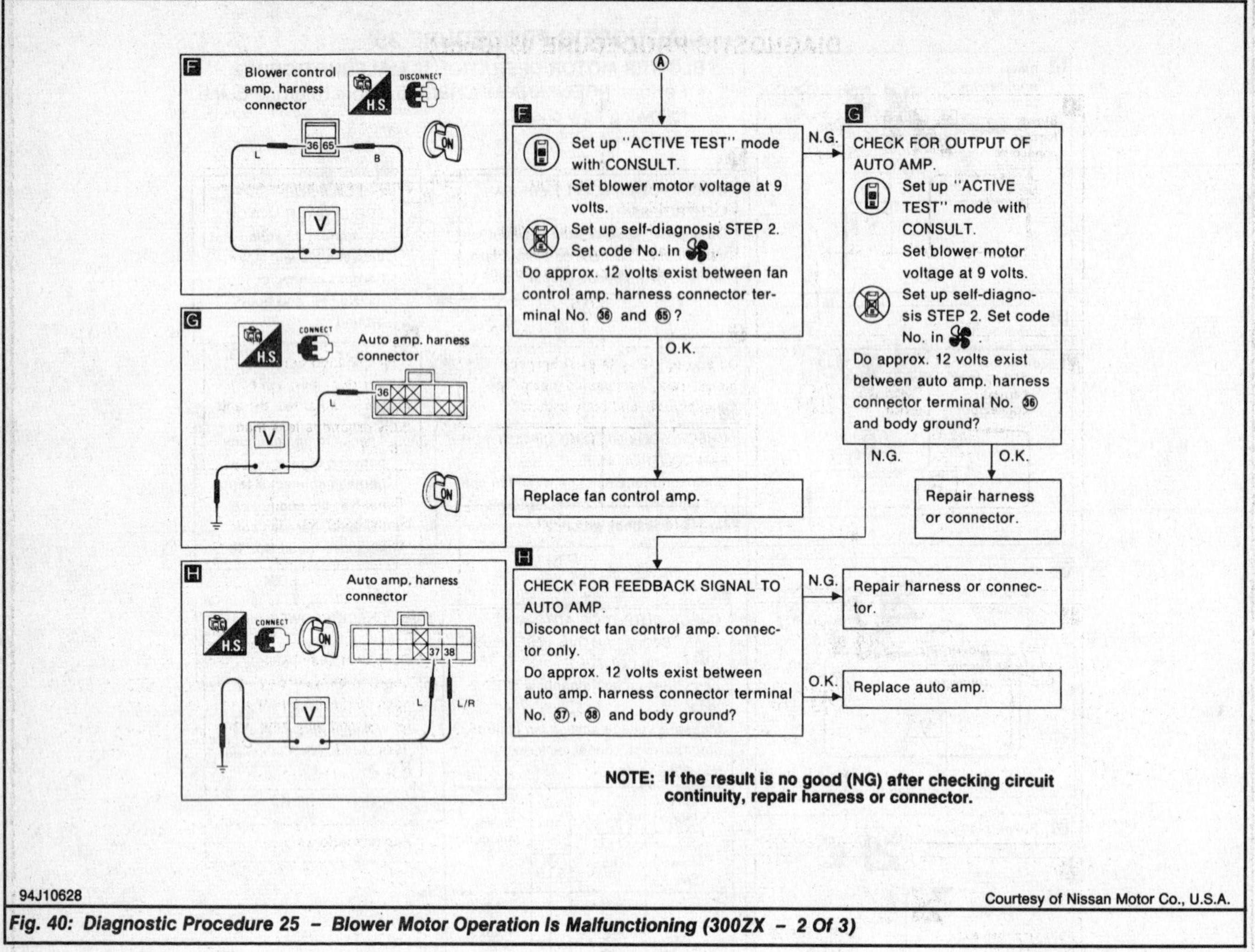
F
Blower control amp. harness connector
DISCONNECT
H.S.
ON
36 65
L
B
V
G
CONNECT
Auto amp. harness connector
36
L
V
ON
H
Auto amp. harness connector
CONNECT
ON
37 38
L
L/R
V
Ⓐ
F
Set up "ACTIVE TEST" mode with CONSULT.
Set blower motor voltage at 9 volts.
Set up self-diagnosis STEP 2.
Set code No. in
Do approx. 12 volts exist between fan control amp. harness connector terminal No. 36 and 65?
N.G.
G
CHECK FOR OUTPUT OF AUTO AMP.
Set up "ACTIVE TEST" mode with CONSULT.
Set blower motor voltage at 9 volts.
Set up self-diagnosis STEP 2. Set code No. in
Do approx. 12 volts exist between auto amp. harness connector terminal No. 36 and body ground?
O.K.
Replace fan control amp.
N.G.
O.K.
Repair harness or connector.
H
CHECK FOR FEEDBACK SIGNAL TO AUTO AMP.
Disconnect fan control amp. connector only.
Do approx. 12 volts exist between auto amp. harness connector terminal No. 37, 38 and body ground?
N.G.
Repair harness or connector.
O.K.
Replace auto amp.
NOTE: If the result is no good (NG) after checking circuit continuity, repair harness or connector.
94J10628
Courtesy of Nissan Motor Co., U.S.A.

Fig. 40: Diagnostic Procedure 25 – Blower Motor Operation Is Malfunctioning (300ZX – 2 Of 3)

1993 AUTOMATIC A/C-HEATER SYSTEMS
Trouble Shooting – 300ZX (Cont.)

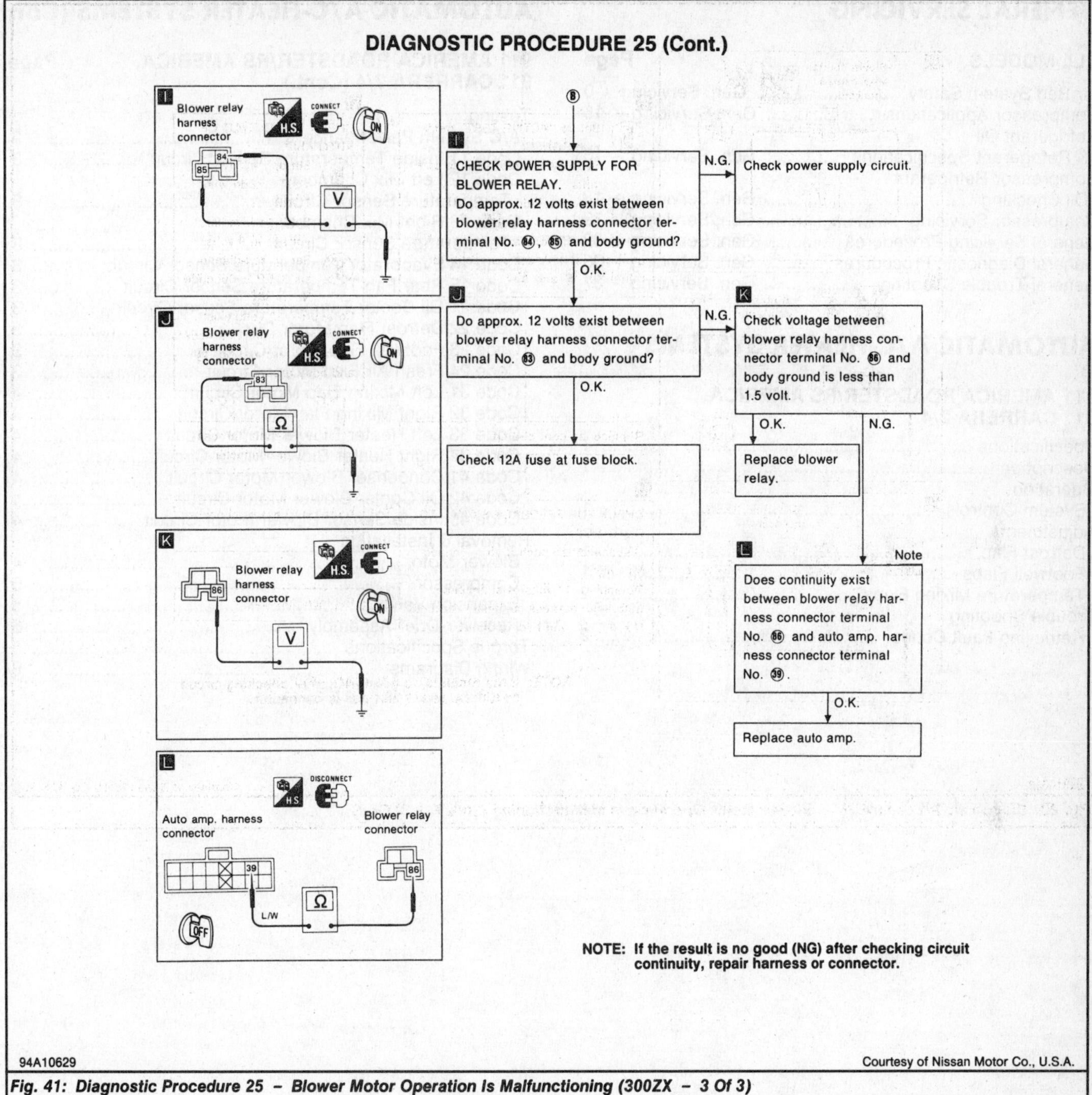
DIAGNOSTIC PROCEDURE 25 (Cont.)
I
Blower relay harness connector
H.S.
CONNECT
ON
84
85
V
8
I
CHECK POWER SUPPLY FOR BLOWER RELAY.
Do approx. 12 volts exist between blower relay harness connector terminal No. 84, 85 and body ground?
N.G.
Check power supply circuit.
O.K.
J
Blower relay harness connector
H.S.
CONNECT
ON
83
Ω
J
Do approx. 12 volts exist between blower relay harness connector terminal No. 83 and body ground?
N.G.
K
Check voltage between blower relay harness connector terminal No. 86 and body ground is less than 1.5 volt.
O.K.
Check 12A fuse at fuse block.
O.K.
Replace blower relay.
N.G.
K
Blower relay harness connector
H.S.
CONNECT
ON
86
V
L
Note
Does continuity exist between blower relay harness connector terminal No. 86 and auto amp. harness connector terminal No. 39.
O.K.
Replace auto amp.
L
H.S.
DISCONNECT
Auto amp. harness connector
Blower relay connector
39
86
Ω
L/W
OFF
NOTE: If the result is no good (NG) after checking circuit continuity, repair harness or connector.
94A10629
Courtesy of Nissan Motor Co., U.S.A.

Fig. 41: Diagnostic Procedure 25 – Blower Motor Operation Is Malfunctioning (300ZX – 3 Of 3)

1993 PORSCHE CONTENTS

GENERAL SERVICING

AUTOMATIC A/C-HEATER SYSTEMS

AUTOMATIC A/C-HEATER SYSTEMS (Cont.

1993 AUTOMATIC A/C-HEATER SYSTEMS
911

911 America Roadster/RS America, 911 Carrera 2/4

NOTE: This article does not apply to 911 Turbo.

SPECIFICATIONS

Compressor Type	Nippondenso 10-Cyl.
Compressor Belt Deflection [1]	13/64-25/64" (5-10 mm)
Refrigerant (R-134a) Capacity [2]	29.5 ozs.
System Oil Capacity	4.6 ozs.
System Operating Pressures [3]	
Low Side	9-15 psi (0.6-1 kg/cm²)
High Side	174-218 psi (12-15 kg/cm²)

[1] – With light pressure applied to center of belt.
[2] – Use R-134a refrigerant and Nippondenso ND8 refrigerant oil.
[3] – Specifications are with ambient temperature at about 77°F (25°C).

WARNING: To avoid injury from accidental air bag deployment, read and carefully follow all SERVICE PRECAUTIONS and DISABLING & ACTIVATING AIR BAG SYSTEM procedures in AIR BAG SYSTEM SAFETY article in GENERAL SERVICING.

DESCRIPTION

The A/C-heater system consists of A/C-heater control unit (regulator), air distribution housing with 2 infinitely controlled, front-mounted A/C-heater blowers, blower final stage, air distribution flaps and flap drive motors, temperature sensor, compressor, and evaporator (located between dashboard and fuel tank). The automatic A/C-heater system regulates interior temperature by means of temperature sensors and temperature control knob.

OPERATION

SYSTEM CONTROLS

A/C Switch – With engine running, push A/C switch to operate the air conditioner. Indicator light will come on, and A/C compressor will be switched on by a magnetic clutch.

Air Recirculation Switch – Pressing air recirculation switch will stop fresh air intake and recirculate inside air. Automatic temperature control will continue to operate. Pressing button a second time will resume fresh air circulation.

Defrost Button – Pressing defrost button will activate automatic defrost mode. This mode has priority over other modes (including indicator lights of previously operated buttons). Fan will be switched to maximum speed, and entire air volume supplied to the defrost nozzles. Pressing button a second time will resume mode selected before defrost was activated.

Temperature Control Knob – Temperature of passenger compartment is regulated by temperature control knob. Temperature selected is kept constant by temperature sensors. Temperature selection ranges from 64-86°F (18-30°C), but selected temperature cannot be less than outside temperature.

Air Distribution Slide Controls – The top slide control operates a cable that controls defrost (windshield) and face (fresh air) outlets. The bottom slide control operates a cable that controls footwell heating outlets.

Blower Control Knob – Blower motors are operated by a 5-speed rotary fan switch. In "0" position, fan runs at minimum speed.

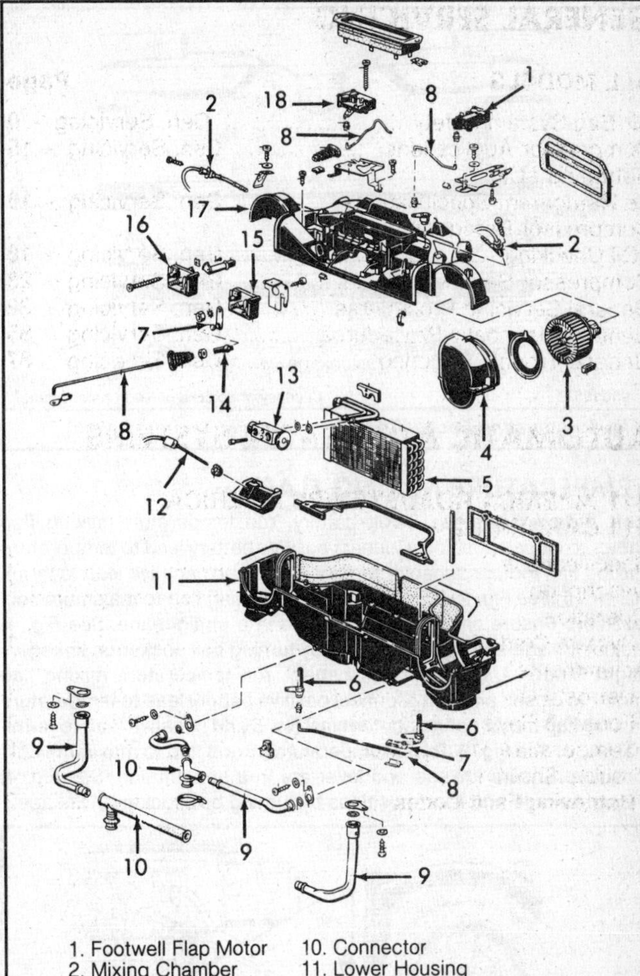
1
2
8
18
8
17
16
15
2
7
13
8
14
3
4
5
12
11
6
6
9
10
7
8
9
10
9
1. Footwell Flap Motor
2. Mixing Chamber Temperature Sensor
3. Blower Motor
4. Housing Cover
5. Evaporator
6. Drive
7. Lever
8. Linkage
9. Water Drain Pipe
10. Connector
11. Lower Housing
12. Evaporator Temperature Sensor
13. Expansion Valve
14. Ball Socket
15. Temperature Mixing Flap Motor
16. Defrost Flap Motor
17. Upper Housing
18. Fresh Air Flap Motor
93E19574
Courtesy of Porsche of North America, Inc.

Fig. 1: Exploded View Of A/C-Heater System

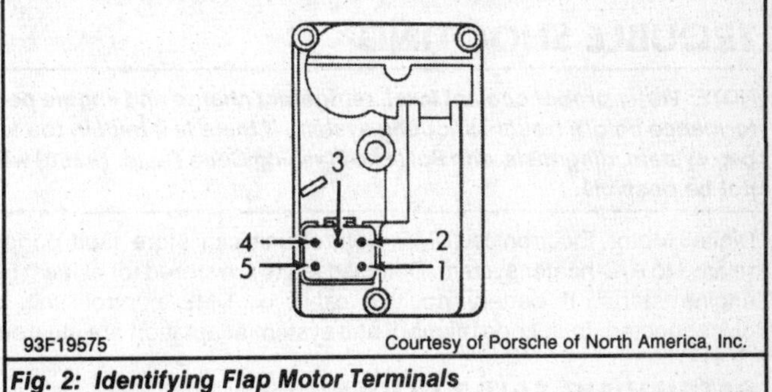
3
4
5
2
1
93F19575
Courtesy of Porsche of North America, Inc.

Fig. 2: Identifying Flap Motor Terminals

ADJUSTMENTS

DEFROST FLAP

Disconnect drive from joint on defrost flap motor. *See Fig. 1*. Using a 12-volt battery, run defrost flap motor to closed position. Connect positive battery lead to defrost flap motor connector terminal No. 4 and negative lead to terminal No. 5. *See Fig. 2*. Push defrost flap to closed position. Disconnect jumper wires, and connect drive to joint on flap motor.

FOOTWELL FLAPS

Disconnect linkage from footwell flap lever. *See Fig. 3*. Using a 12-volt battery, run footwell flap motor to closed position. Connect positive battery lead to footwell flap motor connector terminal No. 5 and negative lead to terminal No. 4. *See Fig. 2*. Push footwell flaps to closed position. Disconnect jumper wires, and connect linkage to footwell flap lever.

1993 AUTOMATIC A/C-HEATER SYSTEMS
911 (Cont.)

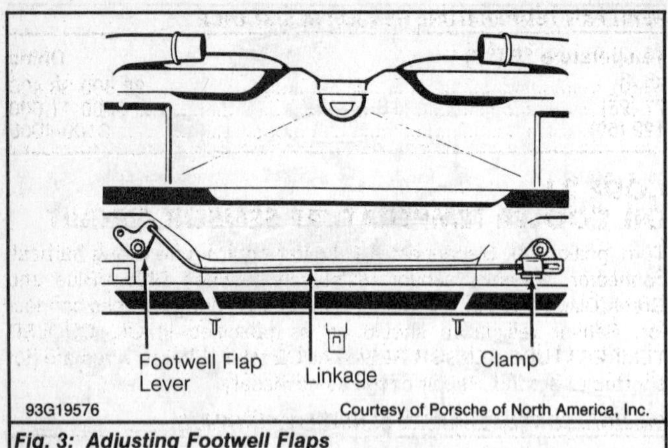
Footwell Flap
Lever
Linkage
Clamp
93G19576
Courtesy of Porsche of North America, Inc.

Fig. 3: Adjusting Footwell Flaps

TEMPERATURE MIXING FLAPS

Left Side – Using a 12-volt battery, run temperature mixing flap motor to closed position. Connect positive battery lead to temperature mixing flap motor connector terminal No. 4 and negative lead to terminal No. 5. *See Fig. 2.* Press temperature mixing flap to maximum cold position. Ensure linkage and lever are in a straight line. *See Fig. 4.* Adjust linkage and lever positions by turning ball socket on linkage.

Right Side – Using a 12-volt battery, run temperature mixing flap motor to closed position. Connect positive battery lead to temperature mixing flap motor connector terminal No. 5 and negative lead to terminal No. 4. *See Fig. 2.* Press temperature mixing flap to maximum cold position. Ensure linkage and lever are in a straight line. *See Fig. 4.* Adjust linkage and lever positions by turning ball socket on linkage.

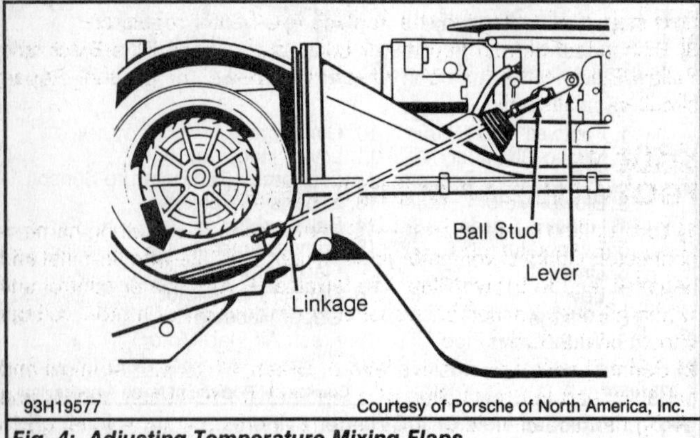
Ball Stud
Lever
Linkage
93H19577
Courtesy of Porsche of North America, Inc.

Fig. 4: Adjusting Temperature Mixing Flaps

TROUBLE SHOOTING

NOTE: Verify proper coolant level, refrigerant charge and engine performance before trouble shooting system. If there is a fault in the air bag system, diagnosis with Porsche Flashing Code Tester (9268) will not be possible.

Digital Motor Electronics (DME) control unit can store fault codes related to A/C-heater system. Detected faults are stored for at least 50 engine starts. If battery positive cable or DME control unit is disconnected, fault code memory and system adaptation are cleared.

RETRIEVING FAULT CODES

1) Ensure transmission is in Park or Neutral, and ignition is off. Connect Porsche System Tester (9288), or Porsche Flashing Code Tester (9268) and Adapter Leads (9268/2 and 9288/1) to 19-pin diagnostic connector. Diagnostic connector is located underneath a cover, in front passenger-side footwell.

2) If using system tester, turn tester on and follow instructions displayed. In addition to reading fault memory, tester can activate a number of components.

3) If using flashing code tester and adapter leads, 4-digit fault codes will be flashed by tester. First digit of A/C-heater fault codes will always be an 8. Second digit will be either a 1 or 2. Number 1 indicates fault was present during last vehicle operation, and number 2 indicates fault was not present when vehicle was last operated. Third and fourth digits identify affected circuit and probable cause or defect. See FAULT CODE IDENTIFICATION table. After retrieving fault code, perform appropriate repair. See TESTING.

FAULT CODE IDENTIFICATION

Fault Codes [1]	Affected Circuit
11	Inside Temperature Sensor
12	Left Mix Chamber Temp. Sensor
13	Right Mix Chamber Temp. Sensor
14	Evaporator Temp. Sensor
15	Rear Fan Temperature Sensor
21	Oil Cooler Temperature Sensor
22	Defrost Flap Motor
23	Footwell Flap Motor
24	Fresh Air Flap Motor
31	Left Mixing Flap Motor
32	Right Mixing Flap Motor
33	Left Heater Blower Motor
34	Right Heater Blower Motor
41	Condenser Blower Motor
42	Oil Cooler Blower Motor
43 & 46 [2]	Rear Blower Motor (Stage 1)
44 & 47 [2]	Rear Blower Motor (Stage 2)
45	Inside Sensor Blower Motor

[1] – Fault codes are displayed as 4-digit numbers. First 2 digits (not shown) indicate when fault was last present. See step **3)** of RETRIEVING FAULT CODES.

[2] – Rear blower motors are only used on 911 Turbo. If Codes 46 and 47 are set on other models, check jumper wire used in A/C-heater control unit connector. These codes will cause left blower motor to operate at a reduced speed while heater is on.

TESTING

WARNING: To avoid injury from accidental air bag deployment, read and carefully follow all SERVICE PRECAUTIONS and DISABLING & ACTIVATING AIR BAG SYSTEM procedures in AIR BAG SYSTEM SAFETY article in GENERAL SERVICING.

A/C SYSTEM PERFORMANCE

1) Park vehicle out of direct sunlight. Ensure condenser is clean. Close sunroof, doors and windows. Turn temperature control knob to maximum cooling position. Put air distribution slide controls against right stops (opened). Turn blower control knob to maximum speed. Open all dash outlets.

2) Measure outside air temperature. Connect manifold gauge set to A/C service valves. Insert thermometer in center vent. Start and run engine at 2000 RPM. Turn air conditioner on.

3) After 2 minutes, check reading on thermometer in center vent. See A/C SYSTEM PERFORMANCE SPECIFICATIONS table. Check high and low pressure readings. See A/C SYSTEM HIGH SIDE PRESSURE SPECIFICATIONS and A/C SYSTEM LOW SIDE PRESSURE SPECIFICATIONS tables.

4) If readings are not as specified, ensure temperature mixing flaps are completely closed. Adjust if necessary. Ensure condenser fan operates in second speed when high side pressure reaches approximately 276 psi (19 kg/cm²).

A/C SYSTEM PERFORMANCE SPECIFICATIONS

Ambient Temperature °F (°C)	Outlet Air Temperature °F (°C)
68 (20)	45.5-51 (7.5-10.5)
77 (25)	45.5-52 (8-11)
86 (30)	49-54.5 (9.5-12.5)
95 (35)	52-57 (11-14)
104 (40)	54.5-60 (12.5-15.5)

1993 AUTOMATIC A/C-HEATER SYSTEMS 911 (Cont.)

A/C SYSTEM HIGH SIDE PRESSURE SPECIFICATIONS

Ambient Temp. °F (°C)	Pressure psi (kg/cm²)
68 (20)	145-189 (10-13 kg/cm²)
77 (25)	174-218 (12-15 kg/cm²)
86 (30)	225-268 (16-19 kg/cm²)
95 (35)	254-297 (18-21 kg/cm²)
104 (40)	268-312 (19-22 kg/cm²)

A/C SYSTEM LOW SIDE PRESSURE SPECIFICATIONS

Ambient Temp. °F (°C)	Pressure psi (kg/cm²)
68 (20)	6-12 (0.4-0.8 kg/cm²)
77 (25)	9-15 (0.6-1 kg/cm²)
86 (30)	9-15 (0.6-1 kg/cm²)
95 (35)	12-17 (0.8-1.2 kg/cm²)
104 (40)	13-19 (0.9-1.3 kg/cm²)

CODE 11
INSIDE TEMPERATURE SENSOR CIRCUIT

Replace A/C-heater control unit.

CODE 12
LEFT MIX CHAMBER TEMPERATURE SENSOR CIRCUIT

Turn ignition off. Disconnect A/C-heater control unit wiring harness connector. Measure sensor resistance between Brown/Blue and Red/Black wire at A/C-heater control unit wiring harness connector. Sensor resistance should be as specified in MIXING CHAMBER TEMPERATURE SENSOR RESISTANCE table. Ensure wires are not shorted to ground. Repair circuit as necessary.

MIXING CHAMBER TEMPERATURE SENSOR RESISTANCE

Temperature °F (°C)	Ohms
32 (0)	30,600-34,700
77 (25)	9500-10,500
122 (50)	3400-3800

CODE 13
RIGHT MIX CHAMBER TEMPERATURE SENSOR CIRCUIT

Turn ignition off. Disconnect A/C-heater control unit wiring harness connector. Measure sensor resistance between Brown/Blue and Red/Yellow wires at A/C-heater control unit wiring harness connector. Sensor resistance should be as specified in MIXING CHAMBER TEMPERATURE SENSOR RESISTANCE table. Ensure wires are not shorted to ground. Repair circuit as necessary.

CODE 14
EVAPORATOR TEMPERATURE SENSOR CIRCUIT

Turn ignition off. Disconnect A/C-heater control unit wiring harness connector. Measure sensor resistance between Brown/Blue and White/Black wires at A/C-heater control unit wiring harness connector. Sensor resistance should be as specified in EVAPORATOR TEMPERATURE SENSOR RESISTANCE table. Ensure wires are not shorted to ground. Repair circuit as necessary.

EVAPORATOR TEMPERATURE SENSOR RESISTANCE

Temperature °F (°C)	Ohms
32 (0)	8800-9200
77 (25)	2600-2900

CODE 15
REAR FAN TEMPERATURE SENSOR CIRCUIT

Turn ignition off. Disconnect A/C-heater control unit wiring harness connector. Measure sensor resistance between Brown/Blue and Blue/Green wires at A/C-heater control unit wiring harness connector. Sensor resistance should be as specified in REAR FAN TEMPERATURE SENSOR RESISTANCE table. Ensure wires are not shorted to ground. Repair circuit as necessary.

REAR FAN TEMPERATURE SENSOR RESISTANCE

Temperature °F (°C)	Ohms
32 (0)	28,800-36,400
77 (25)	9000-11,000
122 (50)	3100-4000

CODE 21
OIL COOLER TEMPERATURE SENSOR CIRCUIT

Turn ignition off. Disconnect A/C-heater control unit wiring harness connector. Measure sensor resistance between Brown/Blue and Green/Black wires at A/C-heater control unit wiring harness connector. Sensor resistance should be as specified in OIL COOLER TEMPERATURE SENSOR RESISTANCE table. Ensure wires are not shorted to ground. Repair circuit as necessary.

OIL COOLER TEMPERATURE SENSOR RESISTANCE

Temperature °F (°C)	Ohms
140 (60)	3600-4000
185 (85)	1400-1600
212 (100)	900-1000

CODE 22
DEFROST FLAP MOTOR CIRCUIT

1) Turn ignition on. Backprobe A/C-heater control unit wiring harness connector. Connect voltmeter positive lead to Black wire terminal and negative lead to Brown/Blue wire terminal at A/C-heater control unit wiring harness connector. Depending on position of motor, voltage should be 0.2-5 volts.

2) Connect voltmeter positive lead to Green/White wire terminal and negative lead to Brown/Blue wire terminal at A/C-heater control unit wiring harness connector. If voltage is approximately 5 volts, go to next step. If no voltage exists, replace A/C-heater regulator.

3) Disconnect defrost flap motor connector. Check Blue/Black and Yellow/Black wires for open or short to power or ground. Repair circuit as necessary.

CODE 23
FOOTWELL FLAP MOTOR CIRCUIT

1) Turn ignition on. Backprobe A/C-heater control unit wiring harness connector. Connect voltmeter positive lead to White wire terminal and negative lead to Brown/Blue wire terminal at A/C-heater control unit wiring harness connector. Depending on position of motor, voltage should be 0.2-5 volts.

2) Connect voltmeter positive lead to Green/White wire terminal and negative lead to Brown/Blue wire terminal at A/C-heater control unit wiring harness connector. If voltage is approximately 5 volts, go to next step. If no voltage exists, replace A/C-heater regulator.

3) Disconnect defrost flap motor connector. Check Blue/White and Yellow/White wires for open or short to power or ground. Repair circuit as necessary.

CODE 24
FRESH AIR FLAP MOTOR CIRCUIT

1) Turn ignition on. Backprobe A/C-heater control unit wiring harness connector. Connect voltmeter positive lead to Red wire terminal and negative lead to Brown/Blue wire terminal at A/C-heater control unit wiring harness connector. Depending on position of motor, voltage should be 0.2-5 volts.

2) Connect voltmeter positive lead to Green/White wire terminal and negative lead to Brown/Blue wire terminal at A/C-heater control unit wiring harness connector. If voltage is approximately 5 volts, go to next step. If no voltage exists, replace A/C-heater regulator.

3) Disconnect defrost flap motor connector. Check Blue/Red and Yellow/Red wires for open or short to power or ground. Repair circuit as necessary.

1993 AUTOMATIC A/C-HEATER SYSTEMS
911 (Cont.)

CODE 31
LEFT MIXING FLAP MOTOR CIRCUIT

1) Turn ignition on. Backprobe A/C-heater control unit wiring harness connector. Connect voltmeter positive lead to Green wire terminal and negative lead to Brown/Blue wire terminal at A/C-heater control unit wiring harness connector. Depending on position of motor, voltage should be 0.2-5 volts.
2) Connect voltmeter positive lead to Green/White wire terminal and negative lead to Brown/Blue wire terminal at A/C-heater control unit wiring harness connector. If voltage is approximately 5 volts, go to next step. If no voltage exists, replace A/C-heater regulator.
3) Disconnect defrost flap motor connector. Check Blue/Green and Yellow/Green wires for open or short to power or ground. Repair circuit as necessary.

CODE 32
RIGHT MIXING FLAP MOTOR CIRCUIT

1) Turn ignition on. Backprobe A/C-heater control unit wiring harness connector. Connect voltmeter positive lead to Gray wire terminal and negative lead to Brown/Blue wire terminal at A/C-heater control unit wiring harness connector. Depending on position of motor, voltage should be 0.2-5 volts.
2) Connect voltmeter positive lead to Green/White wire terminal and negative lead to Brown/Blue wire terminal at A/C-heater control unit wiring harness connector. If voltage is approximately 5 volts, go to next step. If no voltage exists, replace A/C-heater regulator.
3) Disconnect defrost flap motor connector. Check Blue/Gray and Yellow/Gray wires for open or short to power or ground. Repair circuit as necessary.

CODE 33
LEFT HEATER BLOWER MOTOR CIRCUIT

Ensure blower final stage is properly secured to aluminum cooling panel. Check for seized motor. Repair as necessary.

NOTE: Rear blower motors are only used on 911 Turbo. If Codes 46 and 47 are set on other models, check jumper wire used in A/C-heater control unit connector. These codes will cause left blower motor to operate at a reduced speed while heater is on.

CODE 34
RIGHT HEATER BLOWER MOTOR CIRCUIT

Ensure blower final stage is properly secured to aluminum cooling panel. Check for seized motor. Repair as necessary.

CODE 41
CONDENSER BLOWER MOTOR CIRCUIT

1) Turn ignition on. Disconnect blower motor relay connector (located in right rear corner of luggage compartment). Measure voltage at Red wire terminals of condenser blower relay. If voltage exists at both terminals, go to next step. If there is no voltage, check Red wire between terminals or Red wire to fuse block.
2) Connect a jumper wire between terminal No. 30 (Red wire) and No. 87 (Green/White wire) at condenser blower relay. See WIRING DIAGRAMS. If motor runs, go to next step. If motor does not run, replace condenser blower motor.
3) Check Green/White wire between condenser blower relay and condenser blower motor for open or short to ground. Check for open Green/White wire between condenser blower motor and A/C-heater control unit wiring harness connector. Repair circuit as necessary.

CODE 42
OIL COOLER BLOWER MOTOR CIRCUIT

1) Turn ignition on. Disconnect oil cooler relay connector (located in right rear corner of luggage compartment). Measure voltage at Red wire terminals of oil cooler relay. If voltage exists at both terminals, go to next step. If there is no voltage, check Red wire between terminals or back to fuse block.
2) Connect a jumper wire between terminal No. 30 (Red wire) and No. 87 (Green/Blue wire) at oil cooler relay. See WIRING DIAGRAMS. If motor runs, go to next step. If motor does not run, replace oil cooler blower motor.
3) Check Green/Blue wire between oil cooler relay and oil cooler blower motor for open or short to ground. Check for open Green/Blue wire between oil cooler blower motor and A/C-heater control unit wiring harness connector. Repair circuit as necessary.

CODE 45
INSIDE SENSOR BLOWER MOTOR CIRCUIT

Inside sensor is an integral part of A/C control panel. Check voltage at plug receptacle. Voltage should be approximately 12 volts. If voltage is not as specified, check for seized motor. Repair as necessary.

REMOVAL & INSTALLATION

WARNING: To avoid injury from accidental air bag deployment, read and carefully follow all SERVICE PRECAUTIONS and DISABLING & ACTIVATING AIR BAG SYSTEM procedures in AIR BAG SYSTEM SAFETY article in GENERAL SERVICING.

BLOWER MOTOR

Removal & Installation – 1) Disconnect negative battery cable. Remove 2 A/C-heater cover screws and washers. Disconnect harness connector from relay box. Remove wire harness cover, and set relay box aside. Disconnect harness connector from blower motor final stage. Remove firewall. Remove blower motor cover.
2) To remove right side blower motor, disconnect harness connector at blower motor. Remove connector from holder, and go to next step. To remove left side blower motor, discharge A/C system using approved refrigerant recovery/recycling equipment. Disconnect A/C lines at back of blower motor from inside vehicle. Remove expansion tank from blower motor, and go to next step.
3) Release blower motor cover clamps, and remove cover. Remove 2 hidden screws (if equipped) between blower motor and blower wheel. *See Fig. 5.* Install Puller "A" (9512-A) on blower shaft and turn clockwise. Ensure openings in blower wheel align with openings in housing. Slide Puller "B" (9512-B) over puller "A", and install Wing Nut "C" (9512-C). *See Fig. 6.* Tighten wing nut until blower motor disengages, and remove connectors.
4) To install, reverse removal procedures. Ensure blower motor is engaged. Ensure blower wheel turns easily and connecting wires are not pinched.

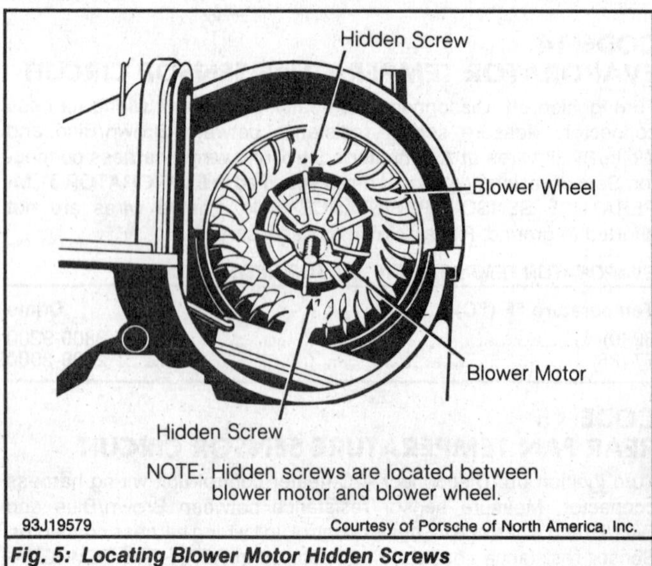
Hidden Screw
Blower Wheel
Blower Motor
Hidden Screw
NOTE: Hidden screws are located between blower motor and blower wheel.
93J19579
Courtesy of Porsche of North America, Inc.

Fig. 5: Locating Blower Motor Hidden Screws

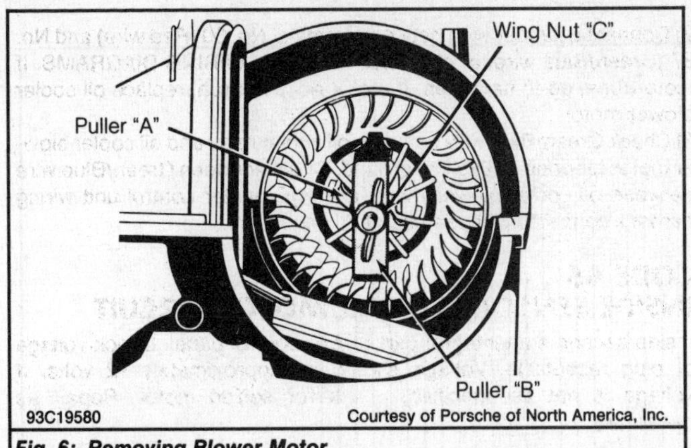
Wing Nut "C"
Puller "A"
Puller "B"
93C19580
Courtesy of Porsche of North America, Inc.

Fig. 6: Removing Blower Motor

COMPRESSOR

CAUTION: New compressors may be under pressure. Unscrew caps slowly to allow air to escape. Remove caps only after all air has escaped.

Removal & Installation – Discharge A/C system using approved refrigerant recovery/recycling equipment. Disconnect and plug A/C hoses. Disconnect wiring connector. Loosen but DO NOT remove compressor plate bolts. Loosen compressor belt by unscrewing tensioner bolt lock nut. Remove tensioner bolt, and push compressor to the left to remove compressor belt. Remove compressor plate bolts, and remove compressor. To install, reverse removal procedure.

EXPANSION VALVE

Removal & Installation – Discharge A/C system using approved refrigerant recovery/recycling equipment. Disconnect A/C lines. Remove insulating tape from expansion valve. Remove capillary tube holder. Remove A/C line and pressure switch from expansion valve. Remove expansion valve nut from evaporator, and remove expansion valve. To install, reverse removal procedure. Recharge A/C system.

RECEIVER-DRIER ASSEMBLY

Removal & Installation – Discharge A/C system using approved refrigerant recovery/recycling equipment. Disconnect A/C lines. Open hose clamps completely, and remove receiver-drier assembly. To install, reverse removal procedure. Recharge A/C system.

TORQUE SPECIFICATIONS

TORQUE SPECIFICATIONS

Application	Ft. Lbs. (N.m)
Compressor Bolts	21 (28)
Refrigerant Hoses	
16-mm Diameter	10-15 (14-20)
19-mm Diameter	15-21 (20-28)
22-mm Diameter	21-27 (29-37)
	INCH Lbs. (N.m)
Blower Motor Fan Nut	22 (2.5)
Expansion Valve	
5-mm Bolt	53 (6)
6-mm Bolt	80 (9)

1993 AUTOMATIC A/C-HEATER SYSTEMS
911 (Cont.)

WIRING DIAGRAMS

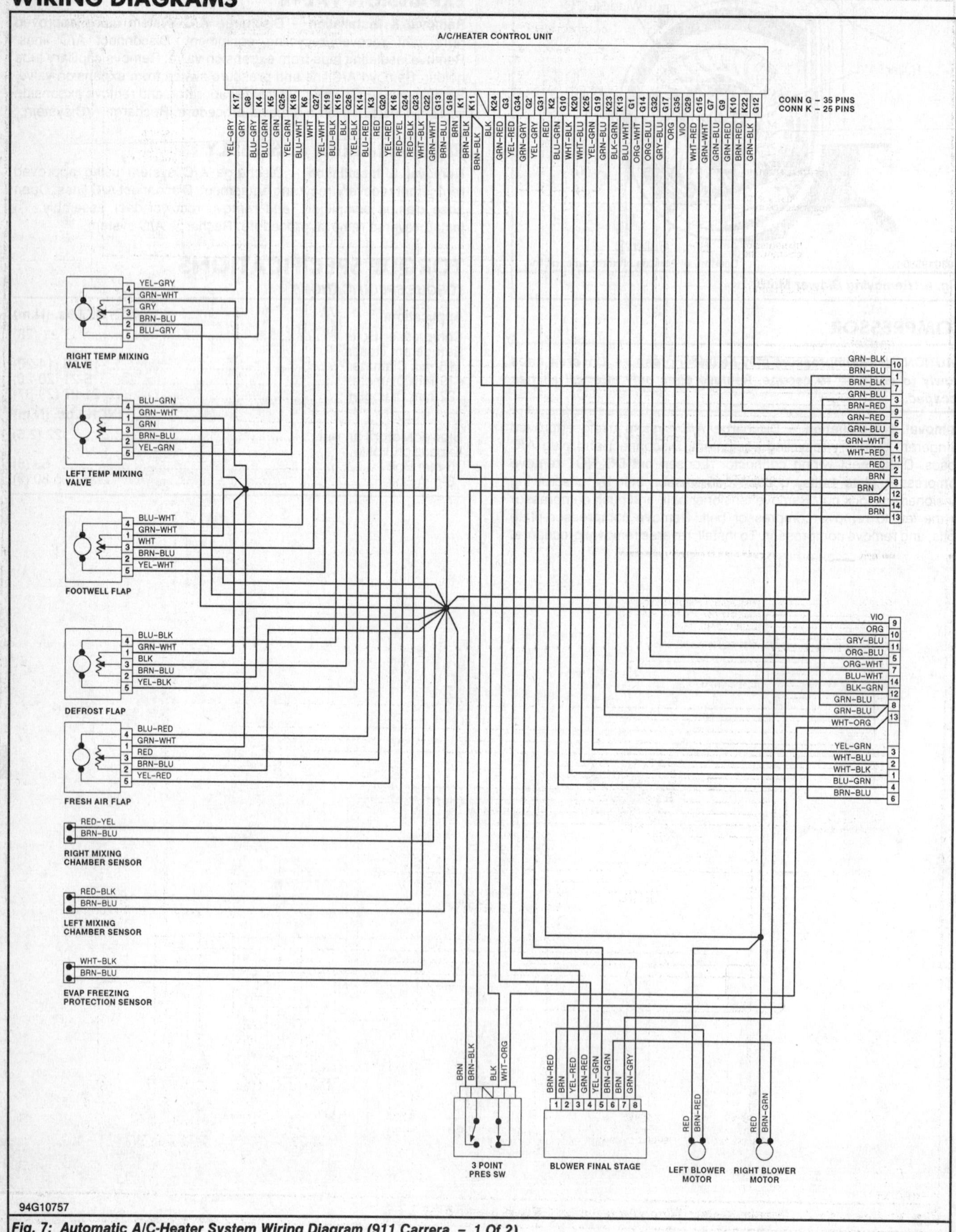
A/C/HEATER CONTROL UNIT
CONN G – 35 PINS
CONN K – 25 PINS
RIGHT TEMP MIXING VALVE
LEFT TEMP MIXING VALVE
FOOTWELL FLAP
DEFROST FLAP
FRESH AIR FLAP
RIGHT MIXING CHAMBER SENSOR
LEFT MIXING CHAMBER SENSOR
EVAP FREEZING PROTECTION SENSOR
3 POINT PRES SW
BLOWER FINAL STAGE
LEFT BLOWER MOTOR
RIGHT BLOWER MOTOR
94G10757

Fig. 7: Automatic A/C-Heater System Wiring Diagram (911 Carrera – 1 Of 2)

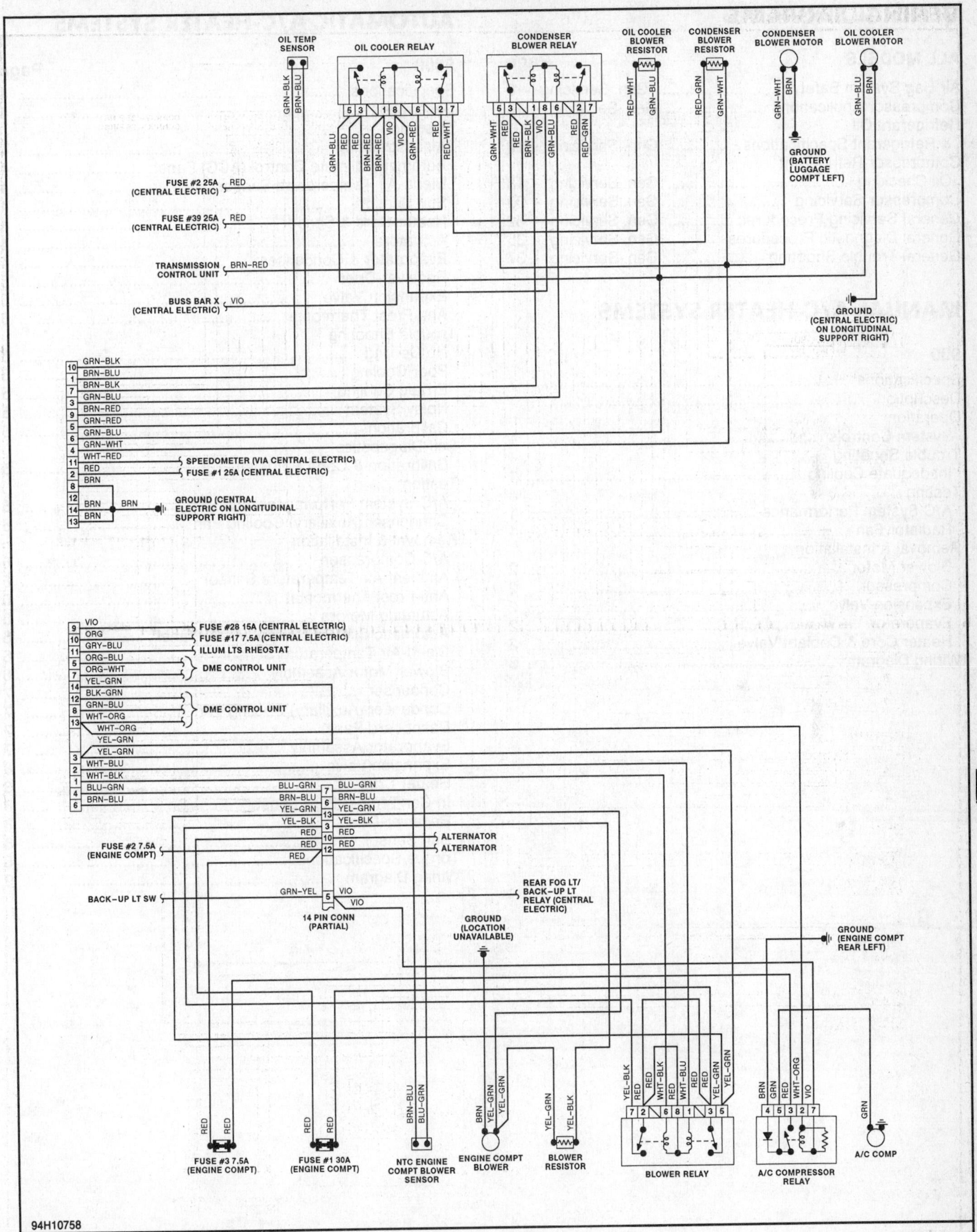

1993 AUTOMATIC A/C-HEATER SYSTEMS 911 (Cont.)

OIL TEMP SENSOR
OIL COOLER RELAY
CONDENSER BLOWER RELAY
OIL COOLER BLOWER RESISTOR
CONDENSER BLOWER RESISTOR
CONDENSER BLOWER MOTOR
OIL COOLER BLOWER MOTOR
GRN-BLK
BRN-BLU
GRN-BLU
RED
BRN-RED
VIO
GRN-RED
RED-WHT
GRN-WHT
BRN-BLK
RED-GRN
GRN-WHT
BRN
GROUND (BATTERY LUGGAGE COMPT LEFT)
FUSE #2 25A (CENTRAL ELECTRIC)
FUSE #39 25A (CENTRAL ELECTRIC)
TRANSMISSION CONTROL UNIT
BUSS BAR X (CENTRAL ELECTRIC)
GROUND (CENTRAL ELECTRIC) ON LONGITUDINAL SUPPORT RIGHT)
SPEEDOMETER (VIA CENTRAL ELECTRIC)
FUSE #1 25A (CENTRAL ELECTRIC)
GROUND (CENTRAL ELECTRIC ON LONGITUDINAL SUPPORT RIGHT)

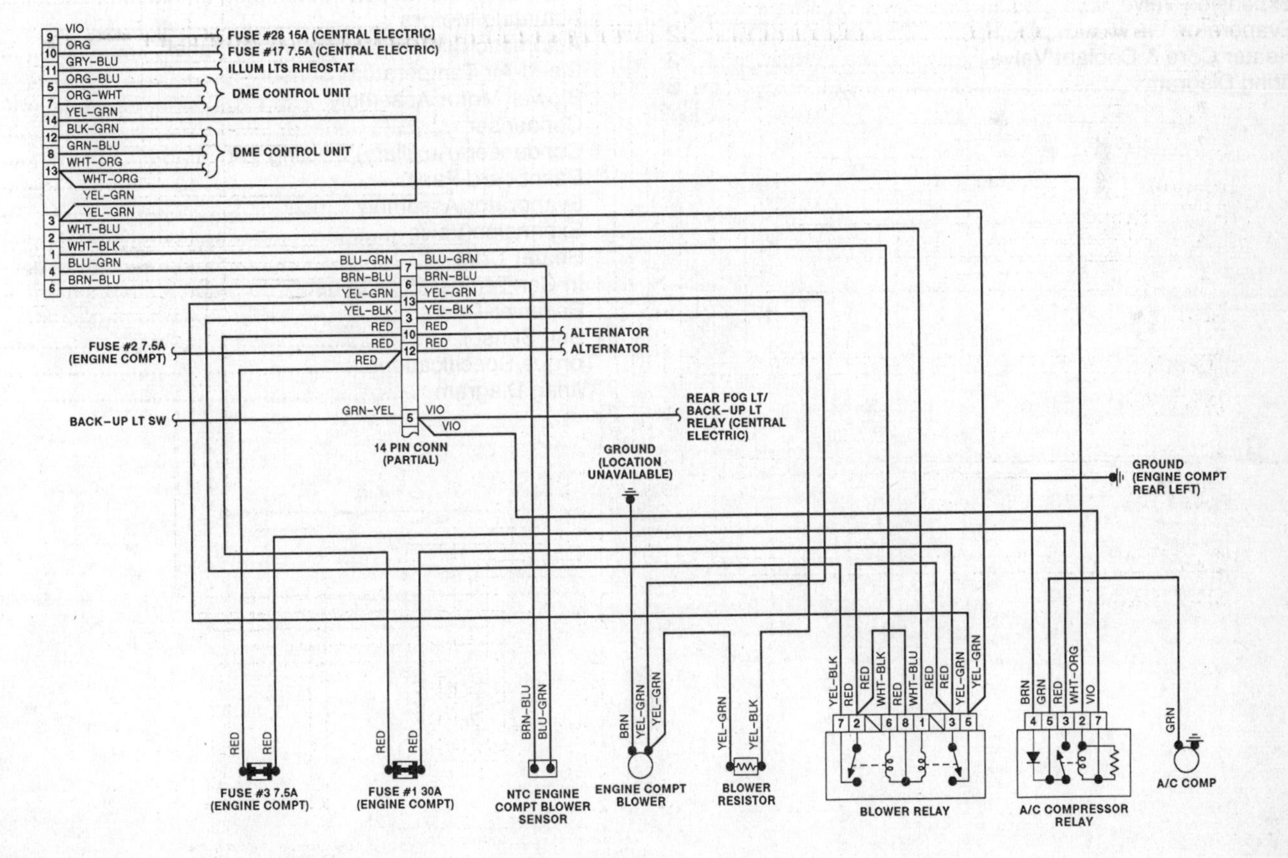
VIO
ORG
GRY-BLU
ORG-BLU
ORG-WHT
YEL-GRN
BLK-GRN
GRN-BLU
WHT-ORG
FUSE #28 15A (CENTRAL ELECTRIC)
FUSE #17 7.5A (CENTRAL ELECTRIC)
ILLUM LTS RHEOSTAT
DME CONTROL UNIT
DME CONTROL UNIT
WHT-ORG
YEL-GRN
YEL-GRN
WHT-BLU
WHT-BLK
BLU-GRN
BRN-BLU
YEL-BLK
RED
ALTERNATOR
ALTERNATOR
FUSE #2 7.5A (ENGINE COMPT)
BACK-UP LT SW
GRN-YEL
VIO
14 PIN CONN (PARTIAL)
REAR FOG LT/ BACK-UP LT RELAY (CENTRAL ELECTRIC)
GROUND (LOCATION UNAVAILABLE)
GROUND (ENGINE COMPT REAR LEFT)
FUSE #3 7.5A (ENGINE COMPT)
FUSE #1 30A (ENGINE COMPT)
NTC ENGINE COMPT BLOWER SENSOR
ENGINE COMPT BLOWER
BLOWER RESISTOR
BLOWER RELAY
A/C COMPRESSOR RELAY
A/C COMP
94H10758

Fig. 8: Automatic A/C-Heater System Wiring Diagram (911 Carrera – 2 Of 2)

1993 SAAB CONTENTS

GENERAL SERVICING

ALL MODELS **Page**

MANUAL A/C-HEATER SYSTEMS

900

AUTOMATIC A/C-HEATER SYSTEMS

9000 **Page**

1993 MANUAL A/C-HEATER SYSTEMS 900

SPECIFICATIONS

Compressor Type	Sanden 5-Cyl.
Compressor Belt Deflection [1]	13/64" (4.7 mm)
System Oil Capacity	5.9 ozs.
Refrigerant (R-12) Capacity	34-36 ozs.
System Operating Pressures [2]	
High Side	149-220 psi (10.5-15.5 kg/cm²)
Low Side	21-28 psi (1.5-2.0 kg/cm²)

[1] – Deflection is with 10 lbs. (4.5 kg) pressure applied midway on longest belt run.
[2] – Specification is with ambient temperature at about 80°F (27°C).

WARNING: To avoid injury from accidental air bag deployment, read and carefully follow all SERVICE PRECAUTIONS and DISABLING & ACTIVATING AIR BAG SYSTEM procedures in AIR BAG SYSTEM SAFETY article in GENERAL SERVICING.

CAUTION: When battery is disconnected, radio will go into anti-theft protection mode. Obtain radio anti-theft protection code from owner prior to servicing vehicle.

DESCRIPTION

This is a cycling clutch flow-through system. System controls are located in center of instrument panel. *See Figs. 1 and 2.* All incoming air enters at right hood louver, through filter and A/C evaporator, and then through heater core. Air from interior is exhausted through outlets in luggage compartment.

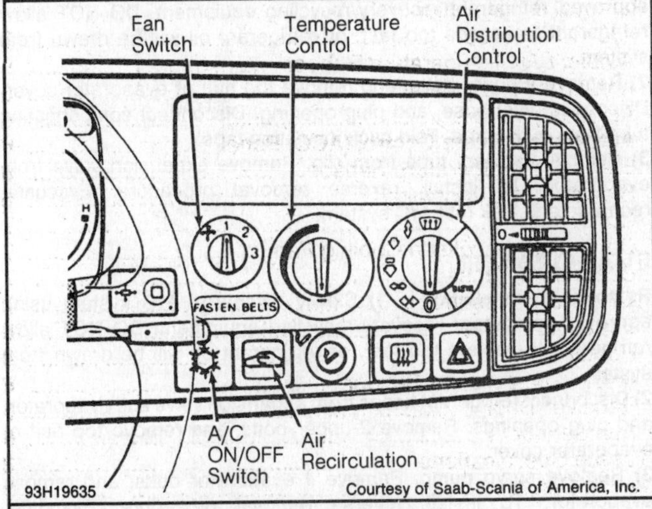
Fan Switch
Temperature Control
Air Distribution Control
FASTEN BELTS
A/C ON/OFF Switch
Air Recirculation
93H19635
Courtesy of Saab-Scania of America, Inc.

Fig. 1: Identifying A/C-Heater Control Panel

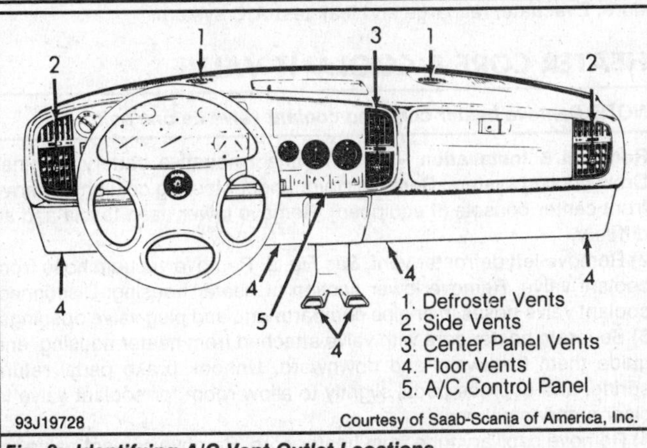
1
2
3
1
2
4
4
4
4
5
4
1. Defroster Vents
2. Side Vents
3. Center Panel Vents
4. Floor Vents
5. A/C Control Panel
93J19728
Courtesy of Saab-Scania of America, Inc.

Fig. 2: Identifying A/C Vent Outlet Locations

OPERATION

SYSTEM CONTROLS

NOTE: Refer to A/C-heater control panel illustration to identify selection controls (buttons, knobs and switches). See Fig. 1.

A/C Switch – Push switch to engage A/C compressor. Compressor will not engage with ambient temperature less than 38°F (3°C).
Air Recirculation Switch – Use this switch when maximum cooling is required. Switch closes fresh air intake, and opens recirculation flap.
Air Distribution Control Knob – Control knob selects distribution of incoming air. Going clockwise from 6 o'clock position , air distribution positions of control knob are as follows: Off (fresh air intake closed, fan off), Max Vent (automatic recirculation, fan on third speed), Panel Vent, Floor and Vent, Floor, Bi-Level and Defrost.
Fan Switch – Fan switch is off when air distribution control is in "O" position. With air distribution control in maximum vent position, blower automatically runs in third speed. In other air distribution positions, rotary fan switch has 3 positions.
Temperature Control Knob – Control knob regulates heat added to air by controlling flow of coolant through heater core.

ADJUSTMENTS

NOTE: All control doors are vacuum operated and are not adjustable.

TROUBLE SHOOTING

INADEQUATE COOLING

Ensure temperature and air distribution control knobs are correctly set. Verify that condenser, located in front of cooling system radiator, is not clogged. Check A/C compressor belt for damage, wear or looseness. Check fuses for fan and A/C compressor.

TESTING

NOTE: Additional testing information is not available from manufacturer.

A/C SYSTEM PERFORMANCE

1) Park vehicle out of direct sunlight. Install A/C gauge set. Start engine and allow it to idle at 1500 RPM. Set A/C controls to recirculate air, panel (vent) mode, full cold, and A/C button on.
2) Set blower fan on third speed and close doors and windows. Insert thermometer in side vent. *See Fig 2.* Operate system for 20 minutes to allow system to stabilize. Measure temperature. Temperature must be approximately 50°F (10°C) at center vent, with high side and low side pressures within specification. See SPECIFICATIONS table at beginning of article.

RADIATOR FAN

Power comes from fuse box through a relay controlled by an A/C coolant temperature switch. At about 198°F (92°C) switch will close, A/C compressor relay will energize and power will be supplied to radiator fan. When A/C is on, power is supplied to radiator fan through radiator fan relay. *See Fig. 3.*
Fan Motor – Turn ignition on. Remove rubber cover from radiator fan switch located on lower left side of radiator. Using a jumper wire, connect 2 terminals on radiator fan switch. Motor should run.
Fan Switch – **1)** Check fuses to ensure power supply. Check power supply to radiator fan and A/C compressor relay. *See Fig 3.* Check operation of radiator fan relay and radiator fan by connecting a jumper across A/C coolant temperature switch.
2) Bring engine to normal operating temperature and check performance of temperature switch. Check all connectors, cable harnesses and ground connections.

1993 MANUAL A/C-HEATER SYSTEMS
900 (Cont.)

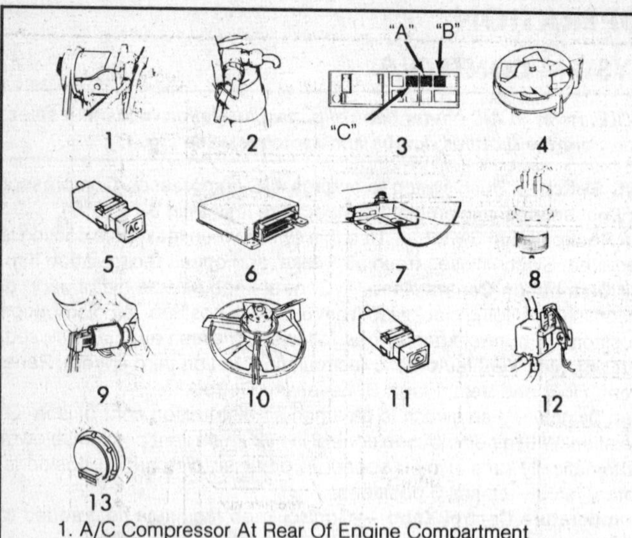
"A"
"B"
"C"
1
2
3
4
5
6
7
8
9
10
11
12
13
1. A/C Compressor At Rear Of Engine Compartment
2. A/C Radiator Fan Pressure Switch On Receiver/Drier
3. Relay Box On Left Fender Well
A. Radiator Fan Relay
B. A/C Compressor Relay
C. A/C Radiator Fan Relay
4. A/C Radiator Fan On Left Side Of Radiator
5. A/C Switch In Center Of Fascia
6. Control Unit LH/CU14 System Under Right Side Fascia
7. Clutch Cycling Thermostat Under Right Side Fascia
8. A/C Coolant Temperature Switch On Radiator Inlet Hose
9. Idle Speed Solenoid On Throttle Housing
10. Radiator Fan Motor At Front Of Engine Compartment
11. A/C Recirculation Switch At Fascia Center
12. Recirculation Valve Under Right Side Fascia
13. Throttle Angle Transmitter LH System On Throttle Housing
93A19638
Courtesy of Saab-Scania of America, Inc.

Fig. 3: Identifying A/C Components

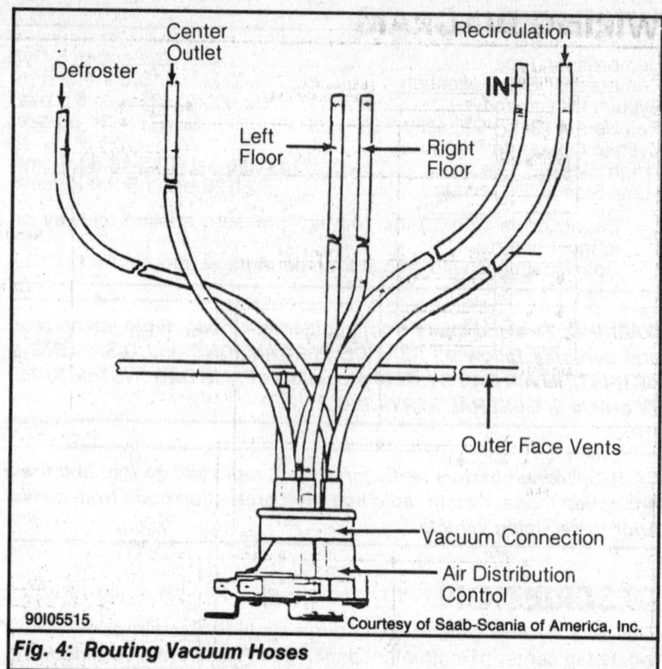
Center
Outlet
Recirculation
Defroster
IN
Left
Floor
Right
Floor
Outer Face Vents
Vacuum Connection
Air Distribution
Control
90I05515
Courtesy of Saab-Scania of America, Inc.

Fig. 4: Routing Vacuum Hoses

REMOVAL & INSTALLATION

WARNING: To avoid injury from accidental air bag deployment, read and carefully follow all SERVICE PRECAUTIONS and DISABLING & ACTIVATING AIR BAG SYSTEM procedures in AIR BAG SYSTEM SAFETY article in GENERAL SERVICING.

NOTE: Whenever system is exposed to atmosphere, entire system must be evacuated, recharged and tested for proper operation. Always use NEW "O" rings.

BLOWER MOTOR

Removal – 1) Disconnect negative battery terminal. Remove steering wheel and both speaker/defroster vents. Remove 4 instrument panel screws. Tilt panel toward rear, and disconnect electrical connections and vacuum hoses from air distribution control. Remove instrument panel.

2) Remove upper dash fascia screws. Remove dash fascia screws under glove box. Lift off dash fascia. Disconnect electrical connections from blower motor, and remove right side defroster damper housing screws. Remove fan motor screws, and lift out motor.

Installation – To install, reverse removal procedure. Ensure electrical wiring or vacuum hoses are not pinched. Ensure vacuum hoses are routed properly. *See Fig. 4.*

COMPRESSOR

Removal & Installation – 1) Slowly discharge A/C system using approved refrigerant recovery/recycling equipment. DO NOT allow refrigerant to escape too fast, or refrigerant oil will be drawn from system.

2) Loosen adjusting link, and remove belt. Remove refrigerant hoses from compressor, and plug openings. Disconnect wire connectors. Remove 4 compressor bolts, and remove compressor. To install, reverse removal procedure.

EXPANSION VALVE

Removal & Installation – 1) Slowly discharge A/C system using approved refrigerant recovery/recycling equipment. DO NOT allow refrigerant to escape too fast, or refrigerant oil will be drawn from system.

2) Remove 2 upper bolts, and remove top half of evaporator cover. Disconnect inlet hose, and plug opening. Disconnect compensating tube from outlet pipe. Fold back insulation tape.

3) Remove capillary tube from clip. Remove expansion valve from evaporator. To install, reverse removal procedure. Evacuate, recharge and leak test A/C system.

EVAPORATOR

Removal & Installation – 1) Slowly discharge A/C system using approved refrigerant recovery/recycling equipment. DO NOT allow refrigerant to escape too fast, or refrigerant oil will be drawn from system.

2) Disconnect refrigerant hoses from expansion valve and evaporator, and plug openings. Remove 2 upper bolts, and remove top half of evaporator cover.

3) Remove servo pump. Remove 4 evaporator bolts, and remove evaporator. To install, reverse removal procedure. Evacuate, recharge and leak test A/C system. To install, reverse removal procedure. Evacuate, recharge and leak test A/C system.

HEATER CORE & COOLANT VALVE

NOTE: Remove heater core and coolant valve as one unit.

Removal & Installation – 1) Disconnect negative battery terminal. Drain cooling system. Remove cover under steering column. Remove front center console (if equipped). Remove lower dash fascia and air diffuser.

2) Remove left defroster vent. *See Fig. 2.* Remove vacuum hose from coolant valve. Remove lower section of heater housing. Disconnect coolant valve hoses in engine compartment, and plug valve openings.

3) Separate heater core with valve attached from heater housing, and guide them backward and downward. Unhook brake pedal return spring, and depress pedal slightly to allow room for coolant valve to clear steering column.

4) Remove capillary tube from heater core. Remove coolant-valve-to-heater core screws. To install, reverse removal procedure. Fill and pressure check cooling system.

1993 MANUAL A/C-HEATER SYSTEMS 900 (Cont.)

WIRING DIAGRAM

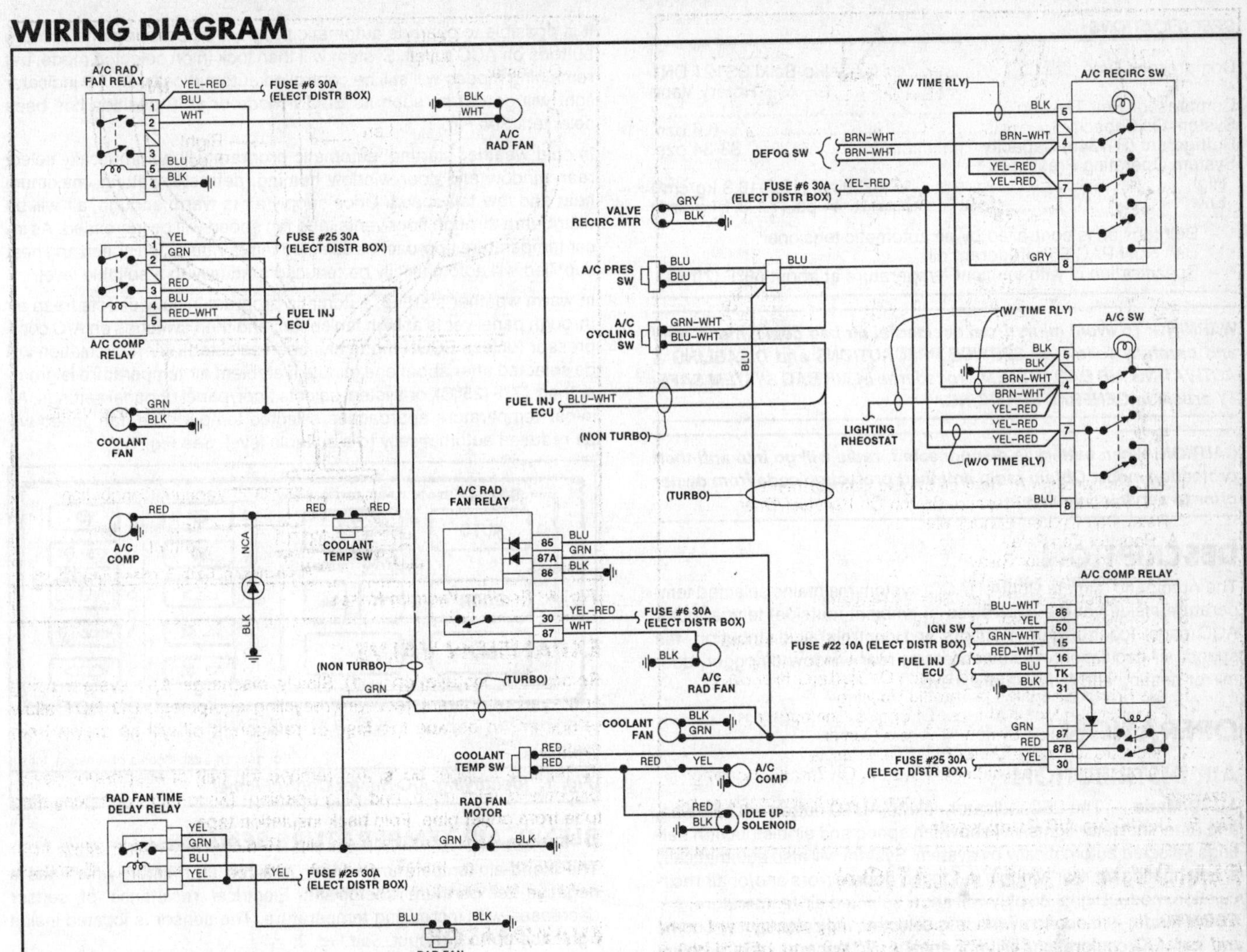
A/C RAD FAN RELAY
YEL-RED
FUSE #6 30A (ELECT DISTR BOX)
BLU
WHT
BLU
BLK
A/C RAD FAN
YEL
GRN
RED
BLU
RED-WHT
FUSE #25 30A (ELECT DISTR BOX)
FUEL INJ ECU
A/C COMP RELAY
GRN
BLK
COOLANT FAN
RED
A/C COMP
NCA
BLK
COOLANT TEMP SW
A/C RAD FAN RELAY
85
87A
86
30
87
FUSE #6 30A (ELECT DISTR BOX)
(NON TURBO)
(TURBO)
A/C RAD FAN
COOLANT FAN
COOLANT TEMP SW
A/C COMP
IDLE UP SOLENOID
RAD FAN TIME DELAY RELAY
RAD FAN MOTOR
FUSE #25 30A (ELECT DISTR BOX)
RAD FAN TEMP SW
VALVE RECIRC MTR
GRY
A/C PRES SW
A/C CYCLING SW
GRN-WHT
BLU-WHT
FUEL INJ ECU
(NON TURBO)
(TURBO)
(W/ TIME RLY)
A/C RECIRC SW
DEFOG SW
BRN-WHT
FUSE #6 30A (ELECT DISTR BOX)
(W/ TIME RLY)
A/C SW
LIGHTING RHEOSTAT
(W/O TIME RLY)
A/C COMP RELAY
IGN SW
FUSE #22 10A (ELECT DISTR BOX)
FUEL INJ ECU
50
15
16
TK
31
87B
94I10759

Fig. 5: Manual A/C-Heater System Wiring Diagram (900)

1993 AUTOMATIC A/C-HEATER SYSTEMS
9000

SPECIFICATIONS

Compressor Type	Seiko-Seiki SS121 DN1 Rotary Vane
Compressor Belt Tension	[1]
System Oil Capacity [2]	6.6 ozs.
Refrigerant (R-134a) Capacity	33-34 ozs.
System Operating Pressures [3]	
High	174-239 psi (12.2-16.8 kg/cm²)
Low	15-44 psi (1.1-3.1 kg/cm²)

[1] – Belt tension is controlled by an automatic tensioner.
[2] – Use SUN PAG 56 refrigerant oil.
[3] – Specification is with ambient temperature at about 68°F (20°C).

WARNING: To avoid injury from accidental air bag deployment, read and carefully follow all SERVICE PRECAUTIONS and DISABLING & ACTIVATING AIR BAG SYSTEM procedures in AIR BAG SYSTEM SAFETY article in GENERAL SERVICING.

CAUTION: When battery is disconnected, radio will go into anti-theft protection mode. Obtain radio anti-theft protection code from owner prior to servicing vehicle.

DESCRIPTION

The Automatic Climate Control (ACC) system maintains selected temperature inside vehicle regardless of ambient (outside) temperature. ACC panel (control unit) monitors and controls air distribution, fan speed, air circulation, A/C compressor, rear window defogger, door mirror heating and temperature valve.

OPERATION

AIR DISTRIBUTION

AUTO Mode – The LED indicator next to AUTO button will come on, and other indicator lights will show fan speed and air distribution settings selected automatically by system. System will also automatically select heating for rear window defogger, door mirrors and/or air recirculation mode. Digital display will show selected air temperature.

ECON Mode – If economy mode is selected, indicator light will come on, and A/C compressor will not engage. If temperature of ambient (outside) air exceeds 81°F (27°C), air circulation will also be selected. All other functions will operate in automatic mode.

Defrost Mode – In this mode, air is directed through defroster vents. A slight air leakage will occur through floor vents. When this button is pressed, rear window defogger and door mirror heating elements will be switched on, in addition to functions selected automatically by system.

Heating for rear window defogger and door mirrors will be switched on automatically if system selects defrost mode when in automatic mode. Heating will be switched off automatically after 10-11 minutes. Heating element can be switched off sooner by pressing defrost button. Fans in the rear doors are controlled automatically and run at the same speed as main fan. The fans can also be switched on manually.

Recirculated Air Mode – Depressing recirculated air button will cause indicator light to come on, and air within passenger compartment will be recirculated. Air recirculation is controlled automatically, but can also be selected or cancelled manually. Air recirculation does not change quality of air significantly.

Floor Air Mode – Mode allows maximum flow of air through all floor vents and a small amount of air through defroster vents.

Bi-Lev Air Mode – In this mode, air flows through panel vents and front and rear floor vents. A small amount of air will also be directed through defroster vents.

Vent Mode – In this mode, all panel vents are fully open.

AUTOMATIC CLIMATE CONTROL (ACC) PANEL

ACC panel (control unit) receives information from 4 sensors and push-button settings. When vehicle is started, system will be switched on automatically, and temperature will be brought up or down to selected temperature.

It is possible to override automatic program by pressing one or more buttons on ACC panel. System will then lock in on selected mode, but remaining modes will still be controlled automatically. AUTO indicator light will go out as soon as ECON mode or OFF position has been selected. *See Fig. 1.*

In cold weather starting, automatic program will automatically select rear window and door window heating, defroster setting, maximum heat and low fan speed. Once supply air is warm enough, air will be distributed through floor vents, and fan speed will be increased. As in-car temperature approaches selected temperature, fan speed and heat supplied will automatically be reduced gradually to a suitable level.

In warm weather starting, automatic program initially directs fresh air through panel vents at high fan speed, and then switches on A/C compressor (unless ECON mode has been selected). Air recirculation will be selected after about one minute if ambient air temperature is greater than 77°F (25°C), or system selects floor/panel or panel settings. As in-car temperature approaches selected temperature, fan speed will be reduced automatically to a suitable level. *See Fig. 1.*

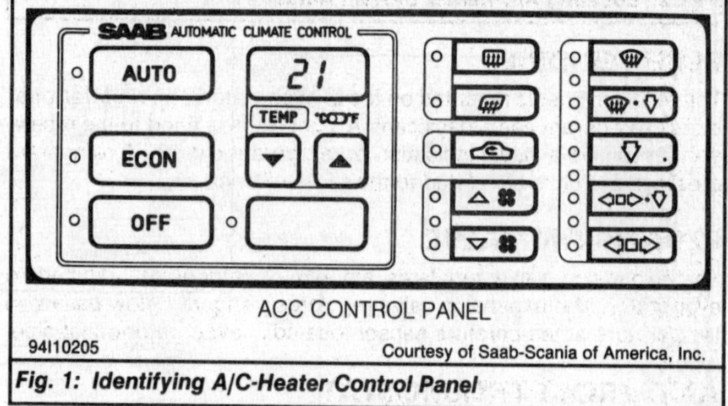
SAAB AUTOMATIC CLIMATE CONTROL
AUTO
ECON
OFF
21
TEMP
°C/°F
ACC CONTROL PANEL
94I10205
Courtesy of Saab-Scania of America, Inc.

Fig. 1: Identifying A/C-Heater Control Panel

BLEND-AIR TEMPERATURE SENSOR

The blend-air temperature sensor is a rod thermistor, which has a negative temperature coefficient. Electrical resistance of sensor decreases with increasing temperature. The sensor is located inside right side defroster duct. *See Fig. 2.*

SUN SENSOR

The sun sensor, located on top of dashboard panel, is a photo diode that transforms sunlight into a voltage signal. The ACC control unit computes angle of the sun relative to car, altitude and intensity of sun. Based on information received from this sensor, ACC control unit varies fan speed depending on whether vehicle's interior is exposed to direct sunlight or shadows.

HEATER CORE & SENSOR

The heater core is located at bottom of A/C-heater assembly. Since no heater control valve is used in this system, the heater core is always warm. A heater core sensor is used to sense temperature of air leaving heater core.

ACTUATORS

The temperature valve, air distribution valve and air recirculation valve are all operated by electrical actuators (stepper motors). *See Fig. 2.* Settings of respective valves are controlled by ACC unit. If a motor has been replaced, ACC system must be recalibrated. See CALIBRATION & CODE RETRIEVAL under SELF-DIAGNOSTICS.

EVAPORATOR & CONDENSER

The fin-type evaporator is fitted with a refrigerant manifold. The condenser is made of aluminum, and cooling tubes are arranged in a serpentine configuration. A mechanical safety valve is fitted in the hose running from condenser outlet. If system pressure rises to more than 483 psi (34 kg/cm²), the valve opens. The valve closes as soon as pressure falls to 435 psi (30.5 kg/cm²).

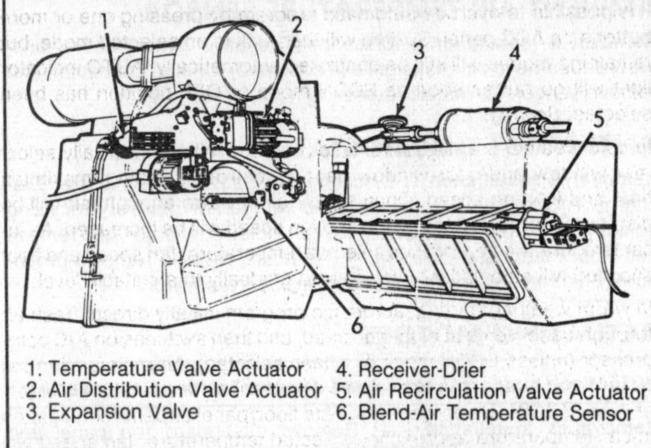
1
2
3
4
5
6
1. Temperature Valve Actuator
2. Air Distribution Valve Actuator
3. Expansion Valve
4. Receiver-Drier
5. Air Recirculation Valve Actuator
6. Blend-Air Temperature Sensor
90D03533
Courtesy of Saab-Scania of America, Inc.

Fig. 2: Locating A/C-Heater System Actuators

RECEIVER-DRIER

The receiver-drier is mounted on top of evaporator. The receiver-drier stores refrigerant and a desiccant. A sight glass is fitted to the receiver-drier to give a visual indication of refrigerant charge. A refrigerant pressure switch is also fitted to the receiver-drier.

EXPANSION VALVE

The expansion valve regulates amount of refrigerant admitted to evaporator. The expansion valve regulates refrigerant flow based on temperature at temperature sensor located in evaporator outlet pipe.

ANTI-FROST THERMOSTAT

The anti-frost thermostat is fitted on top of evaporator. Its function is to prevent formation of frost or ice on evaporator cooling fins. A capillary tube is fitted between evaporator fins to monitor temperature.

If evaporator temperature falls to 34-38°F (.9-3.1°C), the thermostat will break power supply to A/C compressor. Once evaporator temperature reaches 35-40°F (1.9-4.1°C), A/C compressor will again be engaged.

TROUBLE SHOOTING

NOTE: Components listed indicate most likely cause(s) of trouble. Possible causes are not listed in any order of probability.

NO COOLING

Check components listed, and repair or replace as necessary: A/C fuse; wiring harness and connectors; fan motor; A/C belt; anti-frost thermostat; expansion valve; leak in system; blockage in hose or component; low refrigerant charge.

POOR COOLING

Check components listed, and repair or replace as necessary: fan motor; A/C belt; blockage in air ducts; A/C compressor; inlet air filter; low refrigerant charge; expansion valve tube; receiver blockage; moisture in system; air in system.

ERRATIC COOLING

Check components listed, and repair or replace as necessary: fan motor; A/C compressor clutch; moisture in system; frosting on air side of evaporator; anti-frost thermostat; expansion valve tube coil.

NOISY SYSTEM

Check components listed, and repair or replace as necessary: A/C compressor clutch; fan motor; A/C belt; A/C compressor; low refrigerant charge; excessive moisture in system.

SELF-DIAGNOSTICS

The self-diagnostic function detects abnormal conditions of A/C control unit, related sensors and wirings. Self-diagnostic function includes an automatic control back-up, which provides substitute value in case of system failure.

CALIBRATION & CODE RETRIEVAL

NOTE: All stored code(s) will be deleted after calibration cycle. If using ISAT diagnostic tester, follow tester manufacturer's instructions.

1) Calibrate Automatic Climate Control (ACC) system after replacing valve motor, control panel or battery. Calibration is also required if battery has been disconnected for at least 30 seconds, if battery has been discharged, or if battery voltage exceeds 16 volts.
2) To calibrate ACC system, simultaneously press AUTO and vent buttons on ACC panel. The ISAT diagnostic tester can also be used to calibrate system. Calibration and auto-testing will take about 30 seconds.
3) After initiating calibration mode, the LED next to vent button will illuminate for about 7 seconds, indicating calibration is taking place. After 7 seconds, the light will climb up through the LEDs to the defrost button.
4) The lights on ACC panel will flash once, indicating that calibration and auto-testing have started. A "0" will be shown on display panel if no faults are detected within the first 15 seconds of test cycle.
5) If fault(s) is detected (1-5), the number of faults found, not the actual fault code, will be indicated on the display. The ISAT diagnostic tester must be used to access fault code(s). Diagnostic connector is located under right front seat, protected by a plastic cover. Follow tester manufacturer's instructions. For fault codes and description, see SELF-DIAGNOSTIC FAULT CODES table.
6) At the end of first 15-second period, selected temperature will be shown on the display, and ACC will select appropriate settings. Auto-testing will continue to run for another 15 seconds.
7) At end of the 30-second cycle, it is possible to access the number of faults again, if any, by pressing AUTO and OFF buttons. *See Fig. 1.* The number of fault(s) will then be displayed for about 5 seconds. If no faults are present, system will revert to selected temperature.

SELF-DIAGNOSTIC FAULT CODES [1]

Fault Code	Component/Circuit
B1343	Sun Sensor
B1347	Mixed Air Sensor
B1348	Mixed Air Sensor
B1352	Interior Temperature Sensor
B1353	Interior Temperature Sensor
B1355	Power Supply For Vent Motor & Interior Temperature Sensor
B1360	Keyboard
B1493	A/C System
B1498	Electrically Heated Rear Window
B1515	Sensors
B1605	Control Module
B1675	Air Distribution Flap Motor
B1676	Recirculation Flap Motor
B1677	Heater Flap Motor
B2402	Air Distribution Flap Stepper Motor
B2403	Air Distribution Flap Stepper Motor
B2404	Air Distribution Flap Stepper Motor
B2405	Air Distribution Flap Stepper Motor
B2406	Air Distribution Flap Stepper Motor
B2413	Recirculation Flap Motor
B2414	Recirculation Flap Motor
B2422	Fan Test Voltage
B2423	Fan Test Voltage
B2426	Fan Control Voltage
B2427	Fan Control Voltage
B2428	Fan Control Voltage
B2492	Air Distribution Flap Stepper Motor
B2493	Air Distribution Flap Stepper Motor
B2494	Air Distribution Flap Stepper Motor
B2495	Air Distribution Flap Stepper Motor
B2496	Air Distribution Flap Stepper Motor

[1] – Codes can only be retrieved with ISAT diagnostic tester.

1993 AUTOMATIC A/C-HEATER SYSTEMS 9000 (Cont.)

TESTING

NOTE: Additional testing information is not available from manufacturer.

A/C SYSTEM PERFORMANCE

1) Attach manifold gauge set to A/C system. Insert thermometer in center vent of dash panel. Close all passenger compartment doors. Press blower button on ACC control panel to select highest blower motor speed.

2) Set temperature setting to LO (shown on digital display). Manually select air recirculation mode, and press VENT button. Ensure engine is fully warmed and running at 1500-2000 RPM. Compare manifold gauge set/thermometer readings with values in A/C SYSTEM PERFORMANCE SPECIFICATIONS table.

A/C SYSTEM PERFORMANCE SPECIFICATIONS

Application	Specification
Ambient Temperature	68°F (20°C)
Center Vent Temperature	43-50°F (6-10°C)
System Operating Pressures	
Cut-In Pressures	
High	174 psi (12.2 kg/cm²)
Low	44 psi (3.1 kg/cm²)
Cut-Out Pressures	
High	239 psi (16.8 kg/cm²)
Low	15 psi (1.1 kg/cm²)

CONDENSER (AUXILIARY) COOLING FAN

Power comes from fuse box through a relay controlled by an A/C coolant temperature switch. At about 198°F (92°C) switch will close, A/C compressor relay will energize and power will be supplied to radiator fan. When A/C is on, power is supplied to fan through fan relay.

Fan Motor – Turn ignition on. Remove rubber cover from fan switch located on lower left side of radiator. Using a jumper wire, connect 2 terminals on fan switch. Motor should run.

Fan Switch – **1)** Check fuses to ensure power supply. Check power supply to fan and A/C compressor relay. Check operation of fan relay and fan by connecting a jumper across A/C coolant temperature switch.

2) Bring engine to normal operating temperature and check performance of temperature switch. Check all connectors, cable harnesses and ground connections.

REMOVAL & INSTALLATION

WARNING: To avoid injury from accidental air bag deployment, read and carefully follow all SERVICE PRECAUTIONS and DISABLING & ACTIVATING AIR BAG SYSTEM procedures in AIR BAG SYSTEM SAFETY article in GENERAL SERVICING.

NOTE: Before working on any ACC component, wait at least 30 seconds after turning off ignition switch, to give system time to reset valve motors and store any fault codes.

A/C COMPRESSOR

Removal – **1)** Disconnect negative battery cable. Discharge A/C system using approved refrigerant recovery/recycling equipment. Bend aside power steering fluid reservoir. Disconnect and plug hoses from A/C compressor. Disconnect compressor clutch electrical lead. Remove plastic cover from right headlight.

2) Loosen belt tensioner pulley nuts. Remove A/C compressor belt. Remove belt tensioner pulley from compressor, and allow it to rest underneath coolant expansion tank hose. Remove A/C compressor bolts. Carefully remove compressor from vehicle.

Installation – To install, reverse removal procedure. Tighten compressor bolts to 15-19 ft. lbs. (20-25 N.m). Tighten A/C hoses to 53-80 INCH lbs (6-9 N.m). Recharge A/C system. Check A/C-heater system for proper operation.

AMBIENT AIR TEMPERATURE SENSOR

Removal & Installation – Disconnect negative battery cable. Unscrew and remove air intake grille (if equipped). Unplug connector, and remove sensor. To install, reverse removal procedure.

ANTI-FROST THERMOSTAT

Removal & Installation – Disconnect negative battery cable. Discharge A/C system using approved refrigerant recovery/recycling equipment. Remove evaporator cover. Unplug connector, and remove anti-frost thermostat. *See Fig. 4*. To install, reverse removal procedure. Ensure capillary tube bottoms inside evaporator.

ACTUATING MOTORS

NOTE: Each motor is a sealed unit. Replace motor as an assembly.

Removal & Installation – **1)** Remove dashboard top panel and speaker grilles. See DASHBOARD PANEL. Remove glove box, and drop fuse/relay panel forward. Remove right side air duct. Remove right side defroster duct.

2) Remove retaining clip, and disconnect control cable from actuator lever. Disconnect actuator motor and sensor connector. Remove sensor and sensor bracket as an assembly. Remove actuator motor mounting screws. Remove actuating motor assembly. To install, reverse removal procedure.

AUTOMATIC CLIMATE CONTROL (ACC) PANEL

Removal & Installation – **1)** Disconnect negative battery cable. Remove ashtray. Insert screwdriver into ashtray opening, and release tabs securing ashtray trim panel. Remove ashtray trim panel.

2) Reach through ashtray opening, and push out ACC panel. Disconnect ACC panel connector and ground lead. Cut wiring harness tie strap, and remove ACC panel. To install, reverse removal procedure.

BLEND-AIR TEMPERATURE SENSOR

Removal & Installation – Disconnect negative battery cable. Remove glove box, and allow fuse/relay block to drop forward. Unplug sensor connector. Push connector through actuating motor bracket. Remove sensor. To install, reverse removal procedure. *See Figs. 2 and 3.*

BLOWER MOTOR ASSEMBLY

Removal & Installation – **1)** Disconnect negative battery cable. Remove wiper arms and hood. Remove covers from windshield wiper motor and evaporator. Unplug fan control unit connector.

2) Remove seal from false bulkhead panel, and lift out signal converter. Remove false bulkhead panel. Remove bolts, and place electronic ignition control unit aside. Remove 4 screws and lead-through panel from false bulkhead.

3) Cut wiring harness tie strap. Unplug connectors, and remove complete wiper assembly. Drain cooling system. Remove rubber grommets for coolant hoses. Disconnect quick-release couplings for coolant hoses at heater core.

4) Remove screws, and push vacuum pump for cruise control system aside. Remove evaporator screws and clips for refrigerant hoses. Remove lock washer, and disconnect cable from temperature valve.

5) Remove engine bracket from right rear corner of engine compartment. Remove nut from rear engine mount. Attach engine sling to rear lift hook on engine, and carefully tilt engine forward.

6) Carefully lift evaporator, and remove complete blower motor assembly by releasing clips (on either side) and twisting assembly diagonally upward. Remove 4 clips and screws holding assembly together. Separate assembly, and remove screw securing blower motor. *See Fig. 3*.

7) To install, reverse removal procedure. Hook top edge of blower motor assembly over A/C-heater unit, and press unit into place. Ensure clips engage properly. Ensure seal and drain pipe from evaporator are correctly positioned.

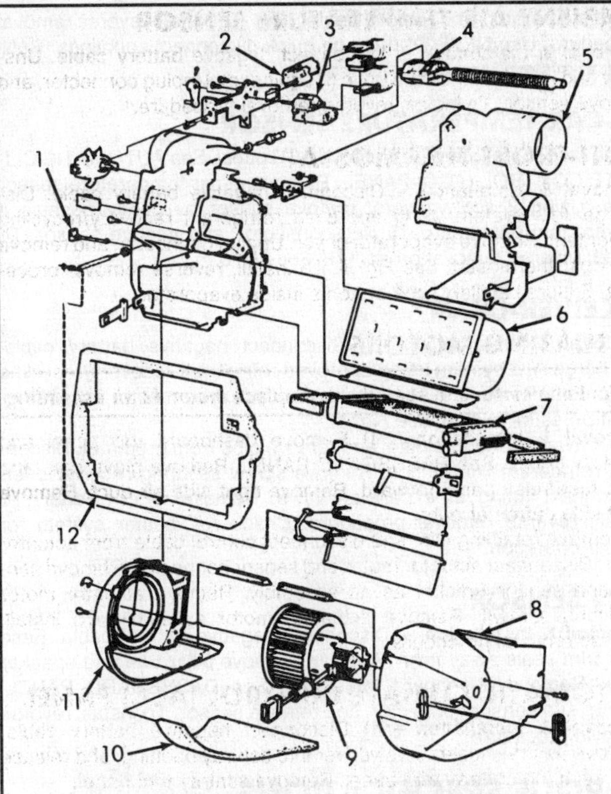
1. Blend-Air Temperature Sensor
2. Temperature Valve Actuator
3. Air Distribution Actuator
4. In-Car Temperature Sensor
5. Heater Housing
6. Air Deflector Housing
7. Heater Core
8. Blower Motor Housing
9. Blower Motor
10. Insulation
11. Blower Motor Housing
12. Seal
90I03535
Courtesy of Saab-Scania of America, Inc.

Fig. 3: Exploded View Of Blower Motor Assembly

CONDENSER

Removal & Installation – Discharge A/C system using approved refrigerant recovery/recycling equipment. Remove front spoiler and grille. Disconnect condenser fittings, and cap all openings. Remove condenser (auxiliary) cooling fan, if equipped. Remove bolts from beneath condenser, and carefully remove condenser from underneath. To install, reverse removal procedure. Check A/C-heater system for proper operation.

CONDENSER (AUXILIARY) COOLING FAN

Removal & Installation – **1)** Remove front spoiler and grille. Remove top bolts from radiator support bars. Remove center bolts from bottom of radiator crossmember.

2) Loosen headlight cluster screw, and ease out light fixture. Remove headlights. Remove bracket and ignition coil assembly. Remove bolts for radiator and cooler assembly.

3) Remove end bolts from top of radiator crossmember. Carefully remove top radiator crossmember without damaging paint. Remove nut and 2 bolts securing condenser cooling fan, and remove fan. To install, reverse removal procedure.

DASHBOARD PANEL

Removal & Installation – Remove "A" pillar trim panel. Remove speaker grilles and mounting screws from dashboard top panel. Unhook dashboard panel from steel cable. Unplug sun sensor electrical connector. Note sun sensor position, and remove sun sensor from dashboard. To install, reverse removal procedure. Ensure top dashboard panel is hooked to steel cable.

EVAPORATOR ASSEMBLY

Removal – **1)** Disconnect negative battery cable. Remove hood and wiper arms. Discharge A/C system using approved refrigerant recovery/recycling equipment. Remove covers from windshield wiper motor and evaporator.

2) Remove seal from false bulkhead panel, and lift out signal converter. Remove false bulkhead panel and top stay for oil filler pipe. Remove engine bracket from right rear corner of engine compartment.

3) Remove nut from rear engine mount. Attach engine sling to rear lift hook on engine, and carefully tilt engine forward. Loosen fittings on inlet side of receiver-drier and outlet side of evaporator.

4) Remove grommet from firewall, and remove power steering fluid reservoir. Position reservoir and pipes out of way. Remove cruise control vacuum pump. Unplug connectors for fan control unit, air recirculation valve actuator (servomotor), anti-frost thermostat and refrigerant pressure switch on receiver-drier.

5) Remove screw securing evaporator assembly. Carefully move evaporator assembly toward center of vehicle lift assembly. With evaporator assembly on bench, remove fresh air filter. *See Fig. 4.*

6) Remove screw securing receiver-drier, and disconnect fitting between receiver-drier and expansion valve. Remove insulation to enable clips securing sensor probe to be removed.

7) Disconnect capillary tube and expansion valve. Remove anti-frost thermostat. Remove air recirculation valve actuator. Cut through gasket on evaporator case flange. Release fasteners, separate case halves, and remove evaporator core.

Installation – **1)** To install, reverse removal procedure. Ensure evaporator core is placed in inner grooves of evaporator case; outer grooves are for fresh air filter.

2) Ensure anti-frost thermostat is fully seated. Ensure expansion valve capillary tube makes good contact with evaporator discharge pipe. Wrap insulation around capillary tube. *See Fig. 5.* Check A/C-heater system for proper operation.

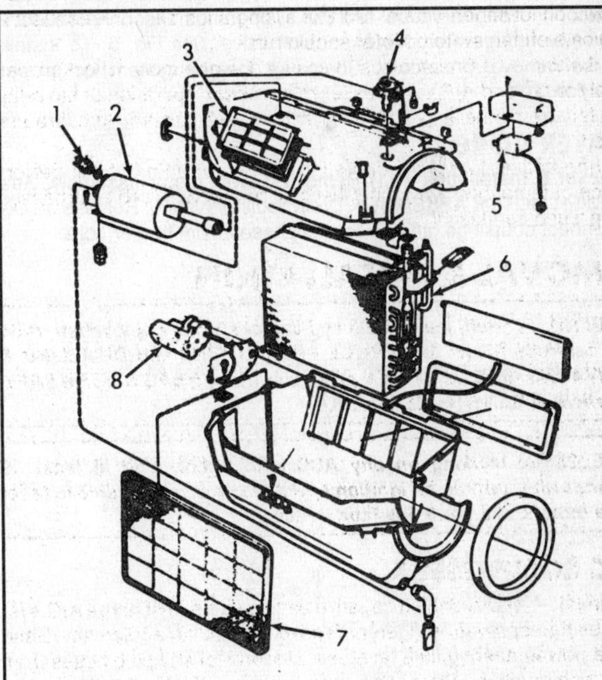
1. Refrigerant Pressure Switch
2. Receiver-Drier
3. Filter
4. Expansion Valve
5. Anti-Frost Thermostat
6. Evaporator Core
7. Fresh Air Filter
8. Air Recirculation Valve Actuator
90A03536
Courtesy of Saab-Scania of America, Inc.

Fig. 4: Exploded View Of Evaporator Assembly

1993 AUTOMATIC A/C-HEATER SYSTEMS 9000 (Cont.)

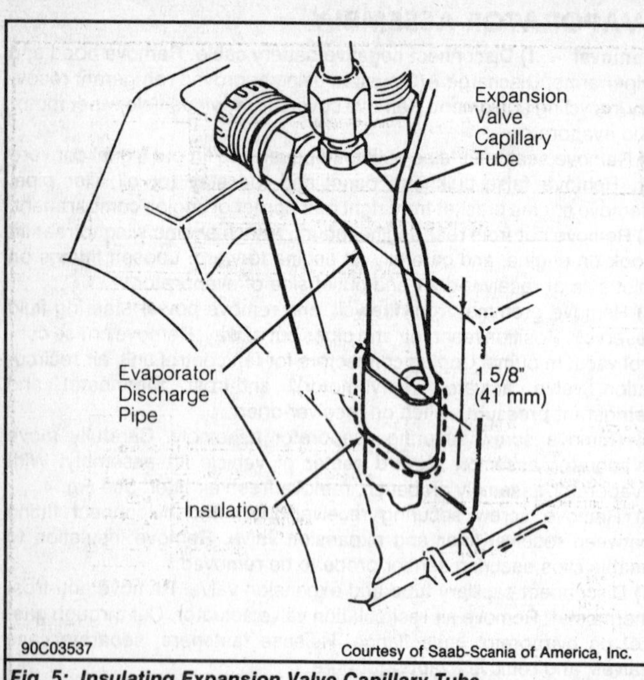
Expansion Valve Capillary Tube
Evaporator Discharge Pipe
1 5/8" (41 mm)
Insulation
90C03537
Courtesy of Saab-Scania of America, Inc.

Fig. 5: Insulating Expansion Valve Capillary Tube

EXPANSION VALVE

Removal & Installation – 1) Disconnect negative battery cable. Discharge A/C system using approved refrigerant recovery/recycling equipment. Remove evaporator cover. Remove false bulkhead panel from engine compartment. Remove insulation and clip.

2) Disconnect capillary tube, and cap all openings. Disconnect expansion valve fittings. Remove expansion valve. *See Fig. 5*. To install, reverse removal procedure. Check A/C-heater system for proper operation.

HEATER CORE

Removal & Installation – 1) Remove blower motor assembly. See BLOWER MOTOR ASSEMBLY. Drain cooling system. Release quick-disconnect couplings, and disconnect hoses from heater core.

2) Lift evaporator, and remove heater core. To install, reverse removal procedure. Use NEW "O" rings on quick-disconnect couplings. Refill cooling system, and check for leaks.

IN-CAR TEMPERATURE SENSOR

Removal & Installation – Remove ACC panel. See AUTOMATIC CLIMATE CONTROL (ACC) PANEL. Remove in-car temperature sensor grille. Using 2 screwdrivers, remove sensor by gently pushing it forward into dashboard. Unplug connector, and remove sensor. To install, reverse removal procedure. *See Fig. 3.*

RECEIVER-DRIER

Removal & Installation – 1) Disconnect negative battery cable. Discharge A/C system using approved refrigerant recovery/recycling equipment. Remove evaporator cover. Unplug connector from refrigerant pressure switch. *See Fig. 4*.

2) Pull away rubber molding, and remove pipe from grommet. Disconnect refrigerant line fittings. Remove screw securing receiver-drier. Disconnect fitting at expansion valve. Remove receiver-drier. To install, reverse removal procedure. Check A/C-heater system for proper operation.

SUN SENSOR

Removal & Installation – Disconnect negative battery cable. Ease door trim seals away from "A" pillar. Remove pillar trim and speaker grille. Remove dashboard top panel. See DASHBOARD PANEL. Unplug sun sensor connector, and remove sensor. To install, reverse removal procedure.

TORQUE SPECIFICATIONS

TORQUE SPECIFICATIONS

Application	Ft. Lbs. (N.m)
A/C Compressor Mounting Bolt	15-19 (20-25)
Receiver-Drier Hoses	13-19 (18-25)
	INCH Lbs. (N.m)
Expansion Valve (Evaporator)	27-53 (3-6)
Safety Valve	97-115 (11-13)

1993 AUTOMATIC A/C-HEATER SYSTEMS 9000 (Cont.)

WIRING DIAGRAM

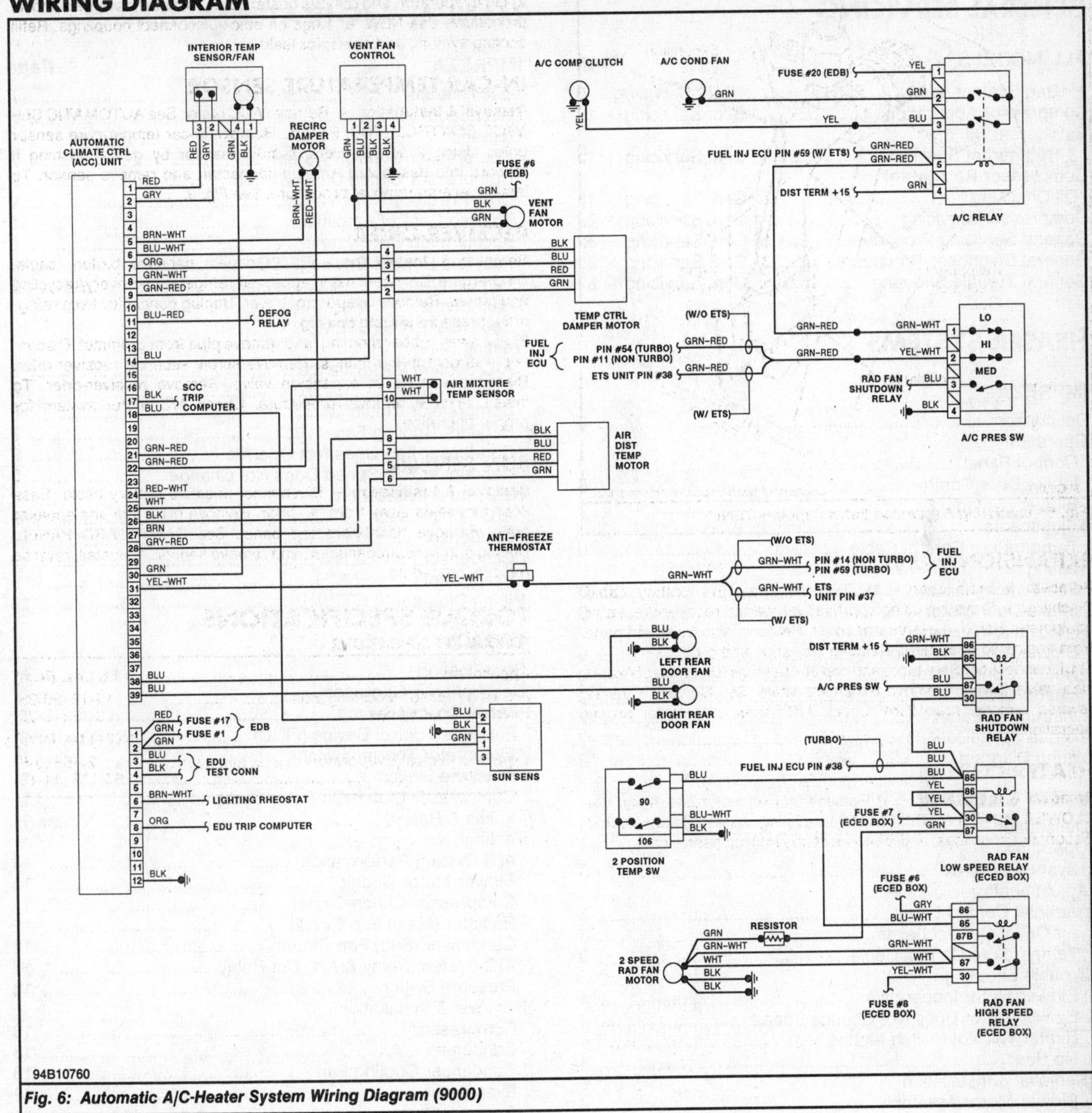
INTERIOR TEMP SENSOR/FAN
VENT FAN CONTROL
A/C COMP CLUTCH
A/C COND FAN
FUSE #20 (EDB)
A/C RELAY
AUTOMATIC CLIMATE CTRL (ACC) UNIT
RECIRC DAMPER MOTOR
FUSE #6 (EDB)
VENT FAN MOTOR
FUEL INJ ECU PIN #59 (W/ ETS)
DIST TERM +15
DEFOG RELAY
TEMP CTRL DAMPER MOTOR
FUEL INJ ECU
PIN #54 (TURBO)
PIN #11 (NON TURBO)
ETS UNIT PIN #38
(W/O ETS)
(W/ ETS)
RAD FAN SHUTDOWN RELAY
A/C PRES SW
AIR MIXTURE TEMP SENSOR
SCC TRIP COMPUTER
AIR DIST TEMP MOTOR
ANTI-FREEZE THERMOSTAT
PIN #14 (NON TURBO)
PIN #59 (TURBO)
ETS UNIT PIN #37
LEFT REAR DOOR FAN
RIGHT REAR DOOR FAN
FUSE #17
FUSE #1
EDB
EDU TEST CONN
SUN SENS
LIGHTING RHEOSTAT
EDU TRIP COMPUTER
(TURBO)
FUEL INJ ECU PIN #38
2 POSITION TEMP SW
FUSE #7 (ECED BOX)
RAD FAN LOW SPEED RELAY (ECED BOX)
FUSE #6 (ECED BOX)
RESISTOR
2 SPEED RAD FAN MOTOR
FUSE #8 (ECED BOX)
RAD FAN HIGH SPEED RELAY (ECED BOX)
94B10760

Fig. 6: Automatic A/C-Heater System Wiring Diagram (9000)

1993 SUBARU CONTENTS

GENERAL SERVICING

ALL MODELS

HEATER SYSTEMS

IMPREZA

JUSTY & LEGACY

MANUAL A/C-HEATER SYSTEMS

IMPREZA

LEGACY

1993 SUBARU CONTENTS (Cont.)

MANUAL A/C-HEATER SYSTEMS (Cont.)

AUTOMATIC A/C-HEATER SYSTEMS

1993 HEATER SYSTEMS
Impreza

DESCRIPTION

System delivers outside air into passenger compartment through center and side ventilator grilles when blower fan is operated. The heating and ventilating system consists of mode doors, an air mix door, intake door and blower motor. Vehicle is also equipped with front side window defroster and rear heater duct.

***WARNING:** To avoid injury from accidental air bag deployment, read carefully follow all SERVICE PRECAUTIONS and DISABLING & ACTIVATING AIR BAG SYSTEM procedures in AIR BAG SYSTEM SAFETY article in GENERAL SERVICING.*

OPERATION

CONTROL PANEL

Air Flow Control Dial – When dial is placed in REC position, it allows air to flow through instrument panel outlets and interior air is recirculated. When dial is placed in VENT position, it allows air to flow through instrument panel outlets.

When dial is placed in BI.LEV position air flows through instrument panel outlets and foot outlets. With dial in HEAT position, air flows through foot outlets and some through windshield defroster outlets.

With dial in HEAT defrost position, air flows through windshield defroster outlets and foot outlets. With dial in defrost position, air flows through windshield defroster outlets.

Temperature Control Dial – This dial regulates hot air flow from heater, over a range, from Blue area to Red area.

Fan Control Dial – Fan operates only when ignition switch is turned to ON position. Fan control dial is used to select 4 fan speeds.

INTAKE DOOR CONTROL

Intake door motor is located on upper part of intake unit. It opens and closes intake door with a rod and a link. When MAX A/C switch is on (REC position on heater control panel), the ground circuit of intake door motor is switched to terminal No. 2 from terminal No. 1. Motor starts to rotate as position switch contacts built into it are set to current flow position. Contacts turn along with motor. When they reach non-contact flow position, motor will stop. Motor always turns in same direction.

BLOWER SYSTEM

Blower relay is controlled by turning ignition on and off. When ignition is turned on and fan switch is operated from 1st to 4th speed, electric current from battery goes through blower motor, resistor, fan switch and ground. Resistor is switched by position of fan switch and controls blower motor speed from 1st to 4th speed.

ADJUSTMENTS

TEMPERATURE CONTROL CABLE

Place temperature control switch to full cold and mode selector switch to MAX A/C position (REC position on heater control panel). Install control cable to lever. While pushing outer cable, secure control cable with clip. *See Fig. 1.*

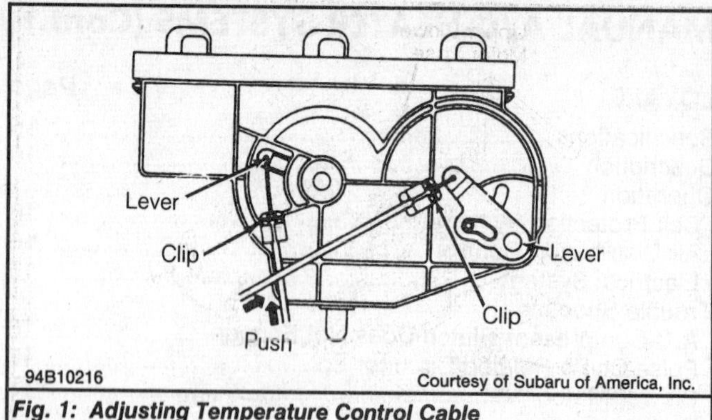
Lever
Clip
Push
Lever
Clip
94B10216
Courtesy of Subaru of America, Inc.

Fig. 1: Adjusting Temperature Control Cable

TESTING

FAN SWITCH

Check continuity between terminals at each switch position. See FAN SWITCH CONTINUITY TEST table.

FAN SWITCH CONTINUITY TEST

Fan Switch Position	Continuity Between Terminal No.
Low	1, 2 & 6
Medium-Low	1, 3 & 6
Medium-High	1, 4 & 6
High	1, 5 & 6

INTAKE DOOR MOTOR

Disconnect intake door motor. Using jumper wires, apply voltage to terminal No. 3. Ground terminal No. 2. Intake door motor should move to fresh air position. Leaving jumper wires connected to terminal No. 3, ground terminal No. 1. Intake door motor should move to recirculated air position. *See Fig. 2.*

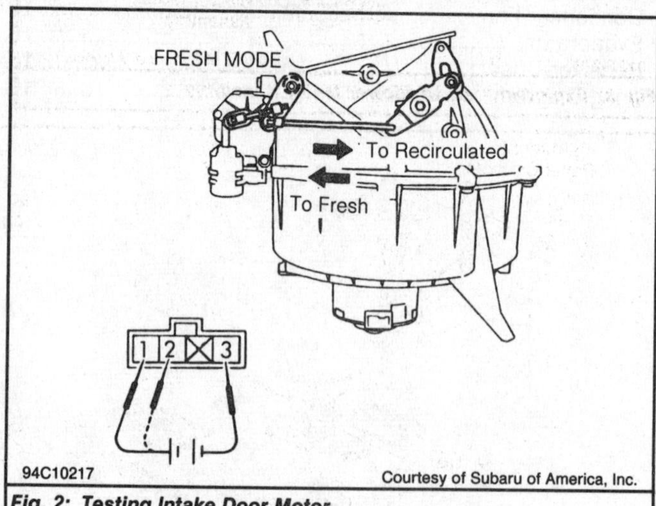
FRESH MODE
To Recirculated
To Fresh
1
2
3
94C10217
Courtesy of Subaru of America, Inc.

Fig. 2: Testing Intake Door Motor

REMOVAL & INSTALLATION

***WARNING:** To avoid injury from accidental air bag deployment, read carefully follow all SERVICE PRECAUTIONS and DISABLING & ACTIVATING AIR BAG SYSTEM procedures in AIR BAG SYSTEM SAFETY article in GENERAL SERVICING.*

BLOWER MOTOR ASSEMBLY

Removal & Installation – Disconnect battery ground cable. Remove glove box. Disconnect blower motor harness connector. Disconnect aspirator pipe. Remove blower motor screws. Remove blower motor assembly. *See Fig. 3.* To install, reverse removal procedure.

HEATER CONTROL PANEL

Removal & Installation – Disconnect battery ground cable. Set temperature control switch to full cold position and mode selector switch to defrost position. Remove temperature control cable and mode door control cable from heater unit. Remove center panel. Remove heater control panel. To install, reverse removal procedure.

HEATER UNIT

Removal & Installation – **1)** Disconnect battery ground cable. Drain coolant from radiator by removing drain plug. Disconnect temperature control cable and mode door control cable from heater unit.

1993 HEATER SYSTEMS
Impreza (Cont.)

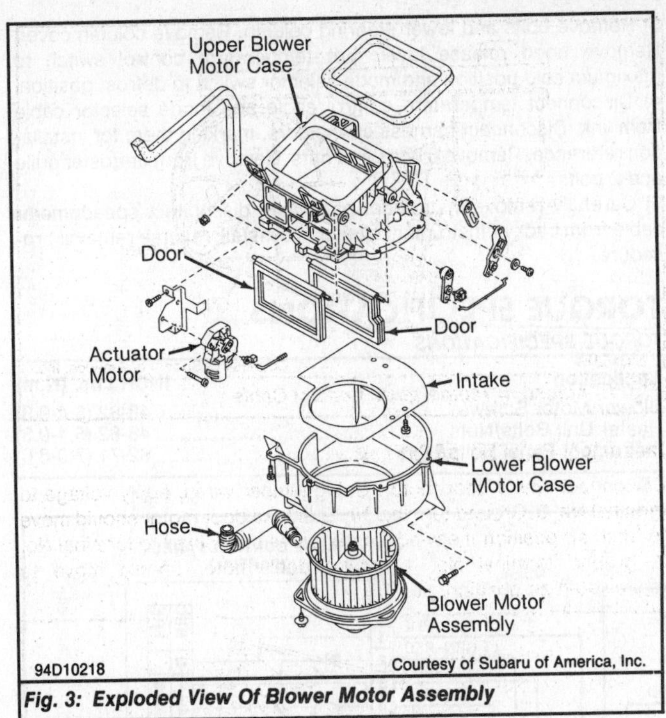
Upper Blower
Motor Case
Door
Door
Actuator
Motor
Intake
Lower Blower
Motor Case
Hose
Blower Motor
Assembly
94D10218
Courtesy of Subaru of America, Inc.

Fig. 3: Exploded View Of Blower Motor Assembly

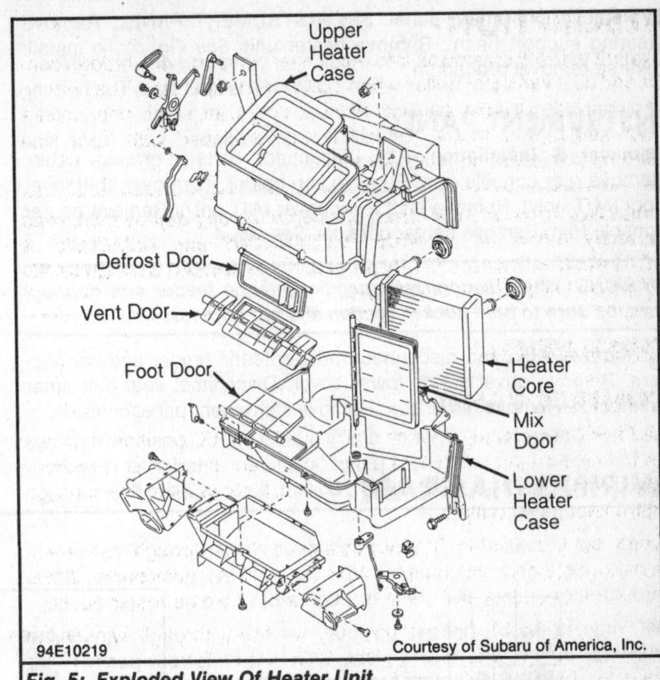
Upper
Heater
Case
Defrost Door
Vent Door
Foot Door
Heater
Core
Mix
Door
Lower
Heater
Case
94E10219
Courtesy of Subaru of America, Inc.

Fig. 5: Exploded View Of Heater Unit

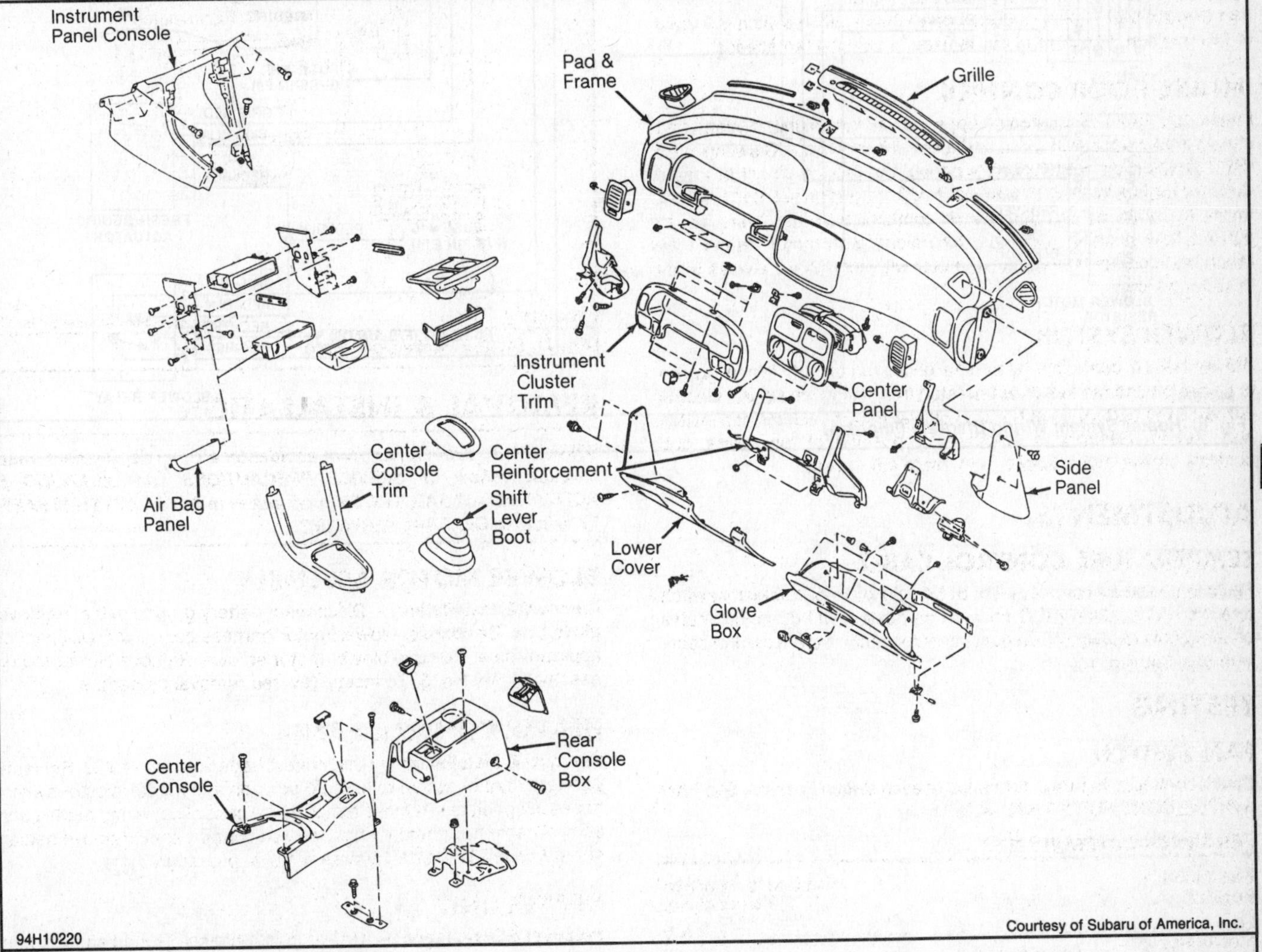

Instrument
Panel Console
Pad &
Frame
Grille
Instrument
Cluster
Trim
Center
Panel
Center
Console
Trim
Center
Reinforcement
Air Bag
Panel
Shift
Lever
Boot
Side
Panel
Lower
Cover
Glove
Box
Rear
Console
Box
Center
Console
94H10220
Courtesy of Subaru of America, Inc.

Fig. 4: Exploded View Of Instrument Panel

1993 HEATER SYSTEMS
Impreza (Cont.)

2) Remove instrument panel. See INSTRUMENT PANEL. Remove steering support beam. Remove heater unit. *See Fig. 5*. To install, reverse removal procedure.

INSTRUMENT PANEL

Removal & Installation - 1) Disconnect battery ground cable. Remove rear console box. Remove cup holder. Turn over shift lever boot (M/T only). Remove shift lever cover (A/T only). Remove center console trim. Remove center console. *See Fig. 4*.

WARNING: When disconnecting radio antenna feeder and connectors, be sure to hold socket section and not harness.

2) Remove radio and disconnect radio antenna feeder and connectors. Remove driver's side lower cover. Disconnect seat belt timer connector. Remove glove box. Remove instrument panel console.

3) Remove bolts and lower steering column. Remove column cover. Remove hood release lever. Set temperature control switch to maximum cold position and mode selector switch to defrost position.

4) Disconnect temperature control cable and mode selector cable from link. Disconnect harness connectors, marking them for installation reference. Remove 6 bolts and nuts. Remove front defroster grille and 2 bolts.

5) Carefully remove instrument panel and disconnect speedometer cable from back of instrument cluster. To install, reverse removal procedure.

TORQUE SPECIFICATIONS

TORQUE SPECIFICATIONS

Application	INCH Lbs. (N.m)
Blower Motor Screws	48-82 (5.4-9.3)
Heater Unit Bolts/Nuts	48-82 (5.4-9.3)
Instrument Panel Bolts/Nuts	62-71 (7.0-8.0)

WIRING DIAGRAM

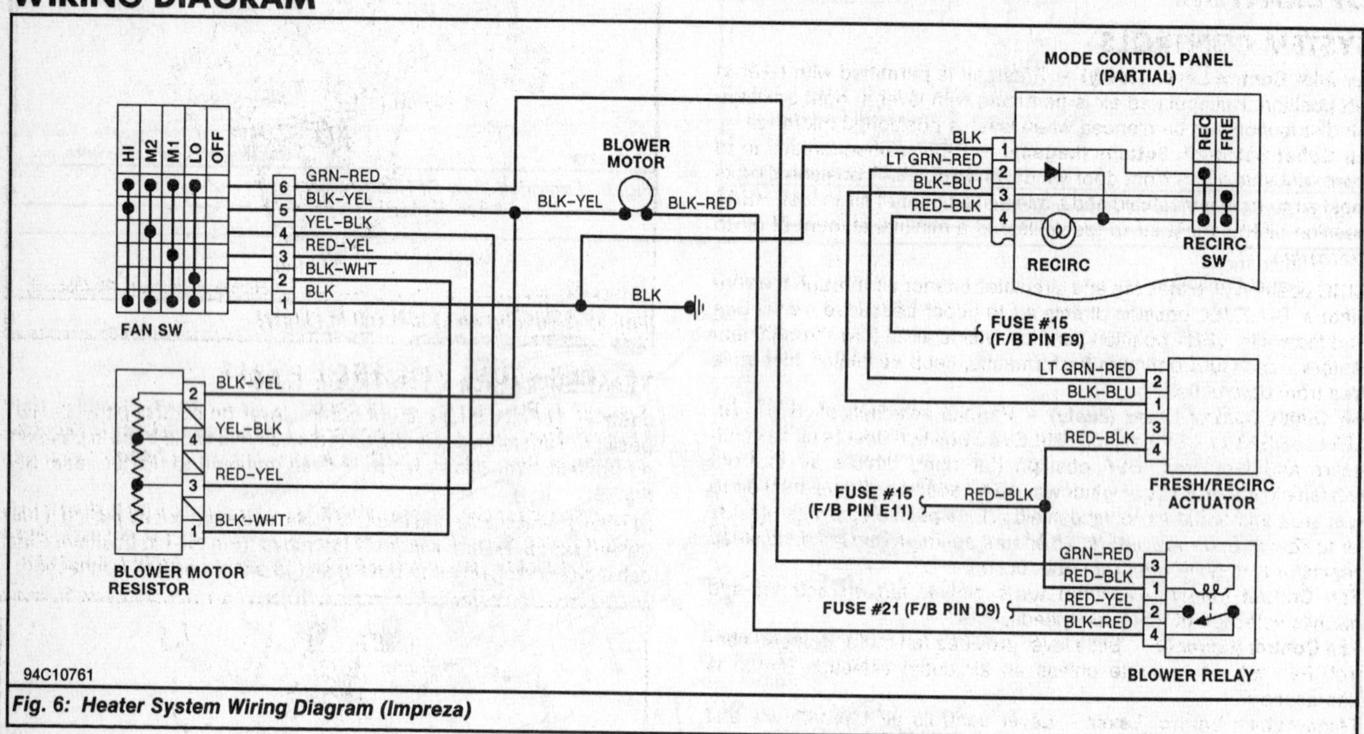
HI
M2
M1
LO
OFF
FAN SW
GRN-RED
BLK-YEL
YEL-BLK
RED-YEL
BLK-WHT
BLK
BLOWER MOTOR
BLK-YEL
BLK-RED
BLK
MODE CONTROL PANEL (PARTIAL)
LT GRN-RED
BLK-BLU
RED-BLK
REC
FRE
RECIRC
RECIRC SW
FUSE #15 (F/B PIN F9)
BLOWER MOTOR RESISTOR
YEL-BLK
RED-YEL
BLK-WHT
FRESH/RECIRC ACTUATOR
FUSE #15 (F/B PIN E11)
FUSE #21 (F/B PIN D9)
BLK-RED
BLOWER RELAY
94C10761

Fig. 6: Heater System Wiring Diagram (Impreza)

1993 HEATER SYSTEMS
Justy & Legacy

DESCRIPTION

The system delivers outside air or recirculated air to the passenger compartment. Airflow selection distributes airflow to desired outlets. The temperature control lever regulates the temperature of delivered air. The fan switch regulates blower motor speed.

The heating and ventilating system consists of control panel, heater unit, blower assembly, heater ducts and hoses. On Justy, all control panel functions are controlled by sliding levers. Legacy uses push-button air outlet selection switches and a sliding temperature control lever.

WARNING: To avoid injury from accidental air bag deployment, read and carefully follow all SERVICE PRECAUTIONS and DISABLING & ACTIVATING AIR BAG SYSTEM procedures in AIR BAG SYSTEM SAFETY article in GENERAL SERVICING.

OPERATION

SYSTEM CONTROLS

Air Inlet Control Lever (Justy) – Fresh air is permitted with lever in left position. Recirculated air is permitted with lever in right position. Air distribution can be blended when lever is positioned midrange.

Air Outlet Selection Buttons (Legacy) – DEF position directs air to front windshield and front door windows. DEF/HEAT position directs most air to front windshield and a minimal amount of air to feet. HEAT position directs most air to footwells and a minimal amount of air to defrosters.

CIRC position operates fan and circulates interior air through the ventilators. BI-LEVEL position directs air to upper body-level ventilators and footwells. VENT position permits outside air to flow through ventilators. To ensure optimum performance, keep ventilator inlet grille free from obstruction.

Air Outlet Control Lever (Justy) – Permits selection of VENT, BI-LEVEL, HEAT or DEF position. BI-LEVEL position directs air to ventilators and feet area. DEF position (far right) directs air to front windshield and front door windows. HEAT position directs most air to feet area and some air to windshield. VENT position permits outside air to flow through ventilators. To ensure optimum performance, keep ventilator inlet grille free from obstruction.

Fan Control (Justy) – Control turns blower fan on and off and permits selection of 3 blower speeds.

Fan Control (Legacy) – Slide lever provides fan motor 4-speed control. Fan will not operate unless an air outlet selection button is depressed.

Temperature Control Lever – Lever controls air temperature and can be set at any position between COLD and HOT. With control lever in COLD position, air is directed around heater core. With lever in HOT position, air is directed through heater core. With lever positioned at various intervals between the extremes of HOT and COLD, intermediate blend-air temperatures are obtained.

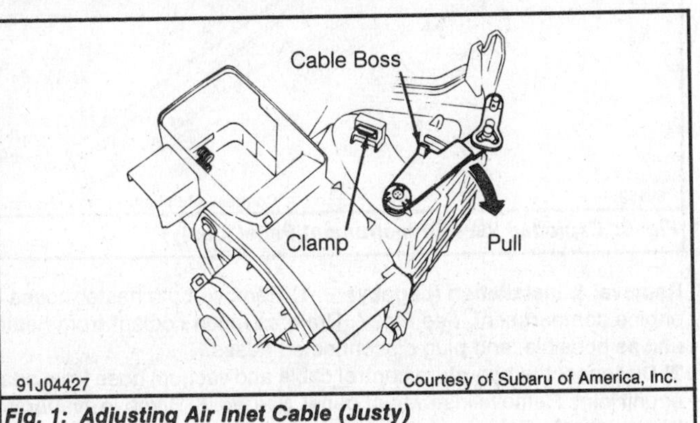
Cable Boss
Clamp
Pull
91J04427
Courtesy of Subaru of America, Inc.

Fig. 1: Adjusting Air Inlet Cable (Justy)

ADJUSTMENTS

AIR INLET CONTROL LEVER

Justy – Place air inlet control lever to far left (recirculation) position. Adjust inside/outside shutter to open to blower chamber. Pull cable out and attach it to lever boss. Hold cable in position while attaching it to clamp. *See Fig. 1.*

AIR OUTLET CONTROL LEVER

Justy – **1)** Place air outlet control lever in VENT position. Turn mode link downward so clamp boss is positioned furthest from clamp, which is flush-mounted to heater case. *See Fig. 2.*

2) Hook mode cable ring in cable boss. Secure mode cable ring by pulling cable toward clamp. Ensure mode link does not move from lowest position. Push cable connection ring into boss once more to ensure proper connection.

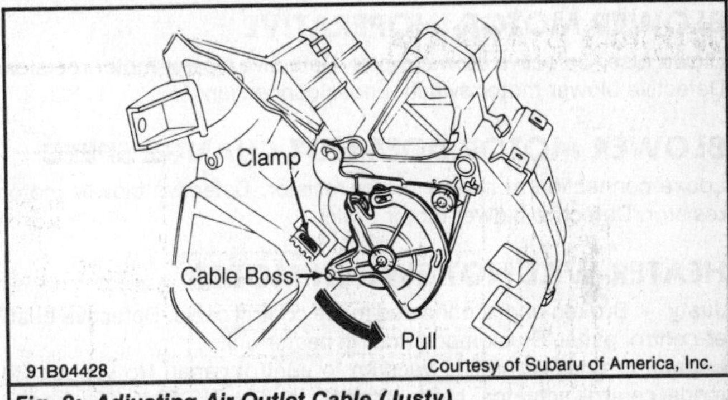
Clamp
Cable Boss
Pull
91B04428
Courtesy of Subaru of America, Inc.

Fig. 2: Adjusting Air Outlet Cable (Justy)

TEMPERATURE CONTROL CABLE

Justy – **1)** Place temperature control lever on control panel in HOT position. Turn air-mix link downward so air mix cable boss is positioned furthest from clamp, which is flush-mounted to heater case. *See Fig. 3.*

2) Hook air-mix cable ring in cable boss, and secure it by pulling it fully toward clamp. Ensure link does not move from lowest position. Push cable connection ring into boss again to ensure proper connection.

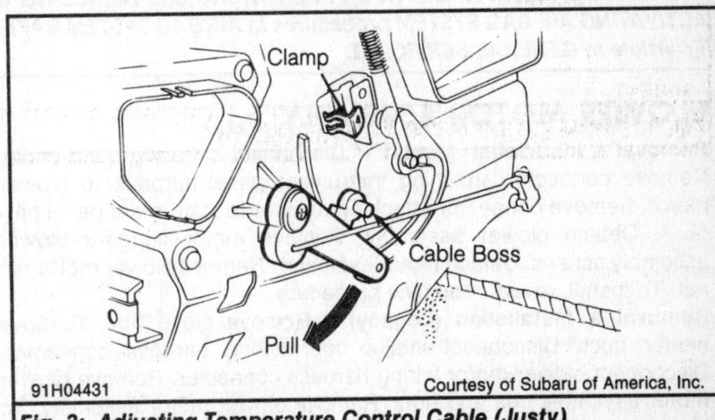
Clamp
Cable Boss
Pull
91H04431
Courtesy of Subaru of America, Inc.

Fig. 3: Adjusting Temperature Control Cable (Justy)

Legacy – **1)** To adjust cable at control panel, loosen temperature control cable clamp. Set temperature lever to COLD position. Pull outer cable away from lever while tightening cable. *See Fig. 4.*

2) To adjust cable at heater unit, loosen temperature control cable clamp. Set temperature lever to COLD position. Pull outer cable away from lever while tightening cable.

1993 HEATER SYSTEMS
Justy & Legacy (Cont.)

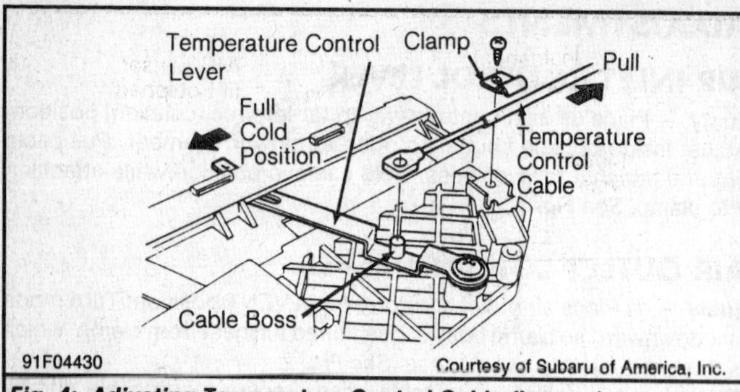
Temperature Control Lever
Clamp
Pull
Full Cold Position
Temperature Control Cable
Cable Boss
91F04430
Courtesy of Subaru of America, Inc.

Fig. 4: Adjusting Temperature Control Cable (Legacy)

TROUBLE SHOOTING

BLOWER MOTOR INOPERATIVE

Blown fuse. Defective blower motor. Defective blower motor resistor. Defective blower motor switch. Loose connections.

BLOWER MOTOR DOES NOT CHANGE SPEED

Loose connection at blower motor resistor. Defective blower motor resistor. Defective blower motor switch.

HEATER WILL NOT SWITCH MODES

Justy – Broken or disconnected mode control cable. Defective heater control panel. Stuck mode door in heater unit.

Legacy – Loss of engine vacuum to control panel. No vacuum to mode control actuator. Mode control door stuck. Defective heater control panel.

NO HEAT

Broken or disconnected temperature control lever. Low engine coolant level. Plugged heater core.

REMOVAL & INSTALLATION

WARNING: To avoid injury from accidental air bag deployment, read and carefully follow all SERVICE PRECAUTIONS and DISABLING & ACTIVATING AIR BAG SYSTEM procedures in AIR BAG SYSTEM SAFETY article in GENERAL SERVICING.

BLOWER MOTOR ASSEMBLY

Removal & Installation (Justy) – Disconnect battery ground cable. Remove connector attaching instrument panel harness to blower motor. Remove connector attaching resistor to instrument panel harness. Detach blower assembly. Remove motor flange-to-blower assembly screws. Detach motor assembly. Remove blower motor fan nut. To install, reverse removal procedure.

Removal & Installation (Legacy) – Remove glove box. Remove heater duct. Disconnect intake door wiring harness connector. Disconnect blower motor wiring harness connector. Remove blower motor assembly bolt and nuts. Remove blower motor assembly. To install, reverse removal procedure.

CONTROL PANEL

Removal & Installation (Justy) – **1)** Remove mode, temperature control, inside-outside air control and fan switch levers by pulling knobs away from levers. Remove center pocket. Reaching through hole in center pocket, push A/C indicator panel from its back (if equipped).

2) On radio-equipped vehicles, pull knobs at both ends and remove dress nut to remove plate. Loosen center panel screw, and remove center panel. Remove heater control panel screw. Pull heater control panel outward. Disconnect air inlet, air outlet and temperature control cables. Disconnect fan switch connector. To install, reverse removal procedure.

Removal & Installation (Legacy) – Remove temperature control cable from heater unit. Remove instrument cluster meter visor. *See Fig. 8.* Remove control panel wiring harness connector. Remove heater control unit from instrument panel front trim.

HEATER UNIT

Removal & Installation (Justy) – **1)** Disconnect battery ground cable. Drain coolant from radiator by removing drain plug. Remove outlet and inlet heater hoses by loosening hose clamp screws. Pull off right and left defroster ducts from defroster nozzles.

2) Pull ducts from heater unit. Disconnect wires between fan switch and blower motor. Disconnect temperature control cable and air outlet cable from heater unit. Remove bolt attaching heater unit to instrument panel.

3) Open glove box, and pull glove box stopper clip toward inside. Turn glove box door fully downward. Disconnect air inlet control cable from blower assembly. Remove instrument panel. *See Fig. 5.* Remove heater unit bolts and blower motor assembly bolts.

4) Remove heater unit. *See Fig. 6.* Avoid spilling residual coolant in heater core on passenger compartment floor. Carefully remove heater unit through body hole to prevent damage to heater pipe. To install, reverse removal procedure.

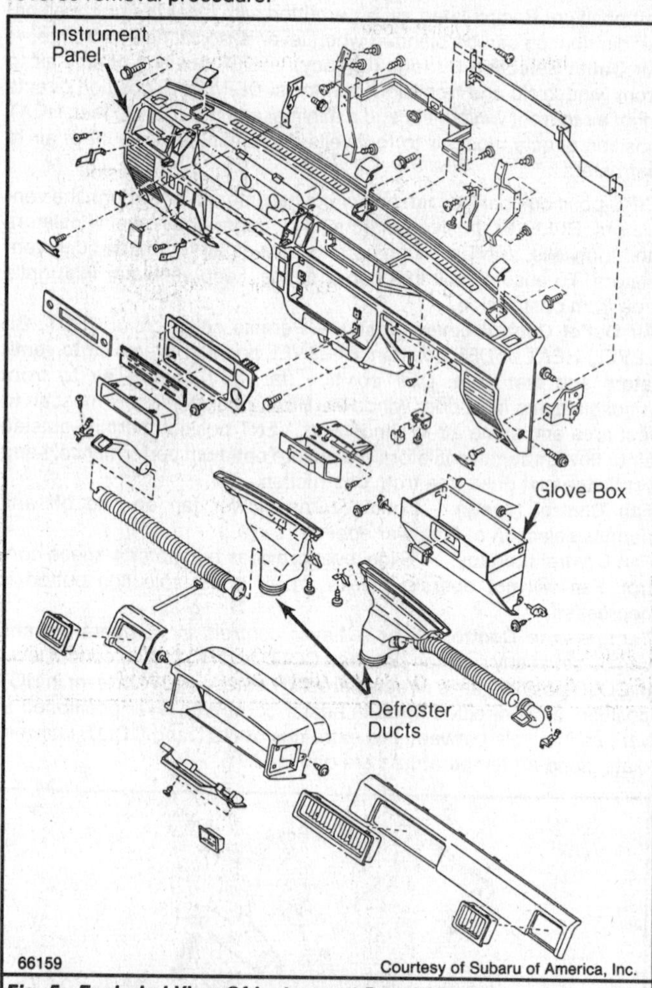
Instrument Panel
Glove Box
Defroster Ducts
66159
Courtesy of Subaru of America, Inc.

Fig. 5: Exploded View Of Instrument Panel (Justy)

Removal & Installation (Legacy) – **1)** Remove both heater hoses in engine compartment. *See Fig. 7.* Drain as much coolant from heater unit as possible, and plug disconnected hoses.

2) Disconnect temperature control cable and vacuum hose from heater unit joint. Remove instrument panel. *See Fig. 8.* Remove evaporator (if equipped). Remove heater unit. *See Fig. 7.* To install, reverse removal procedure.

1993 HEATER SYSTEMS
Justy & Legacy (Cont.)

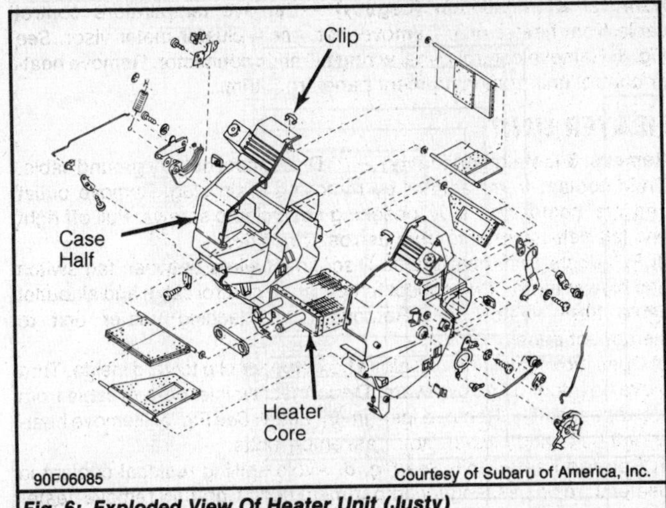
Clip
Case
Half
Heater
Core
90F06085
Courtesy of Subaru of America, Inc.

Fig. 6: Exploded View Of Heater Unit (Justy)

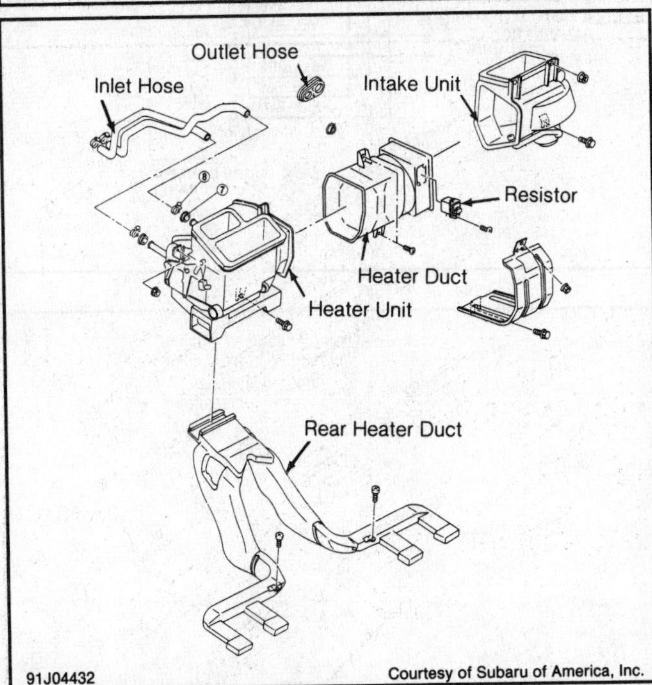
Outlet Hose
Inlet Hose
Intake Unit
Resistor
Heater Duct
Heater Unit
Rear Heater Duct
91J04432
Courtesy of Subaru of America, Inc.

Fig. 7: Exploded View Of Heater Unit & Ducts (Legacy)

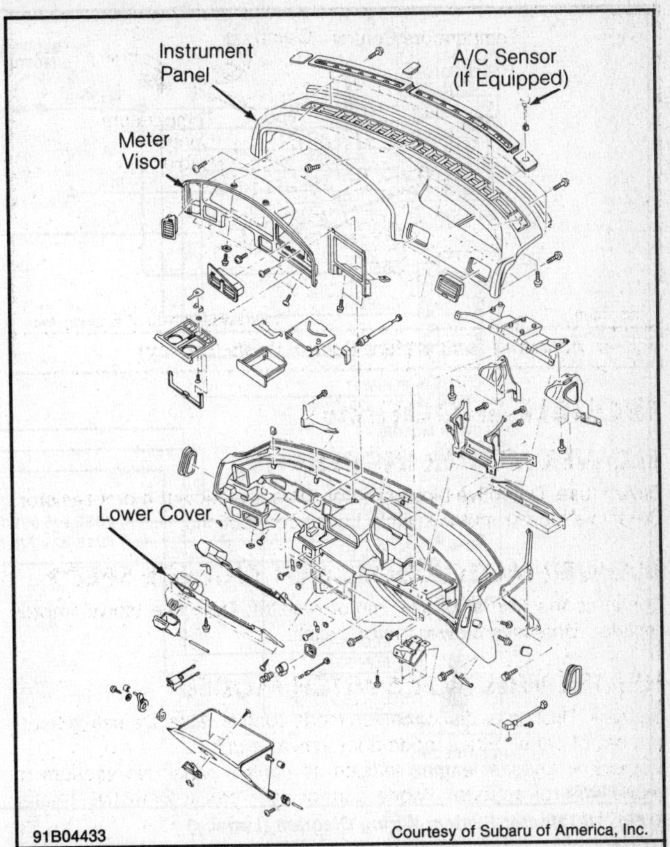

Instrument
Panel
A/C Sensor
(If Equipped)
Meter
Visor
Lower Cover
91B04433
Courtesy of Subaru of America, Inc.

Fig. 8: Exploded View Of Instrument Panel (Legacy)

WIRING DIAGRAMS

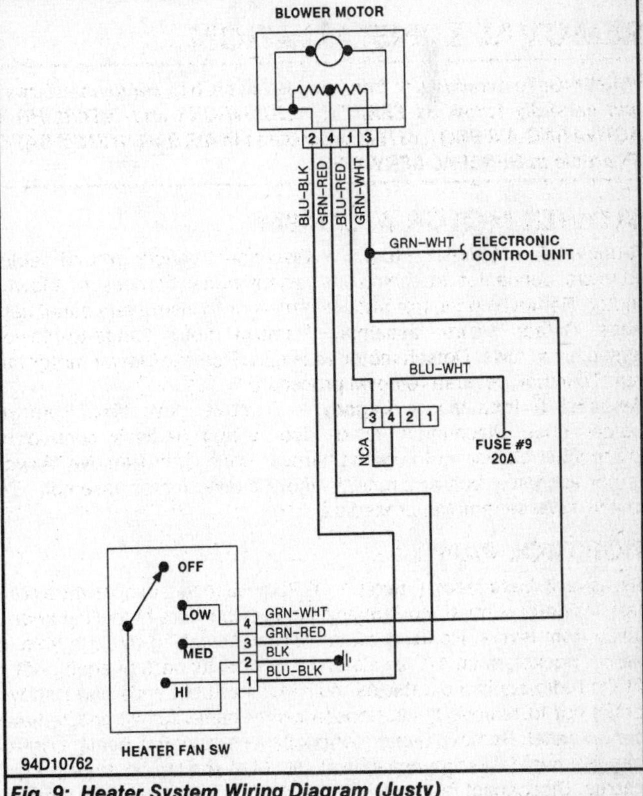
BLOWER MOTOR
2 4 1 3
BLU-BLK
GRN-RED
BLU-RED
GRN-WHT
GRN-WHT
ELECTRONIC
CONTROL UNIT
BLU-WHT
3 4 2 1
NCA
FUSE #9
20A
OFF
LOW
MED
HI
4
3
2
1
GRN-WHT
GRN-RED
BLK
BLU-BLK
HEATER FAN SW
94D10762

Fig. 9: Heater System Wiring Diagram (Justy)

1993 HEATER SYSTEMS
Justy & Legacy (Cont.)

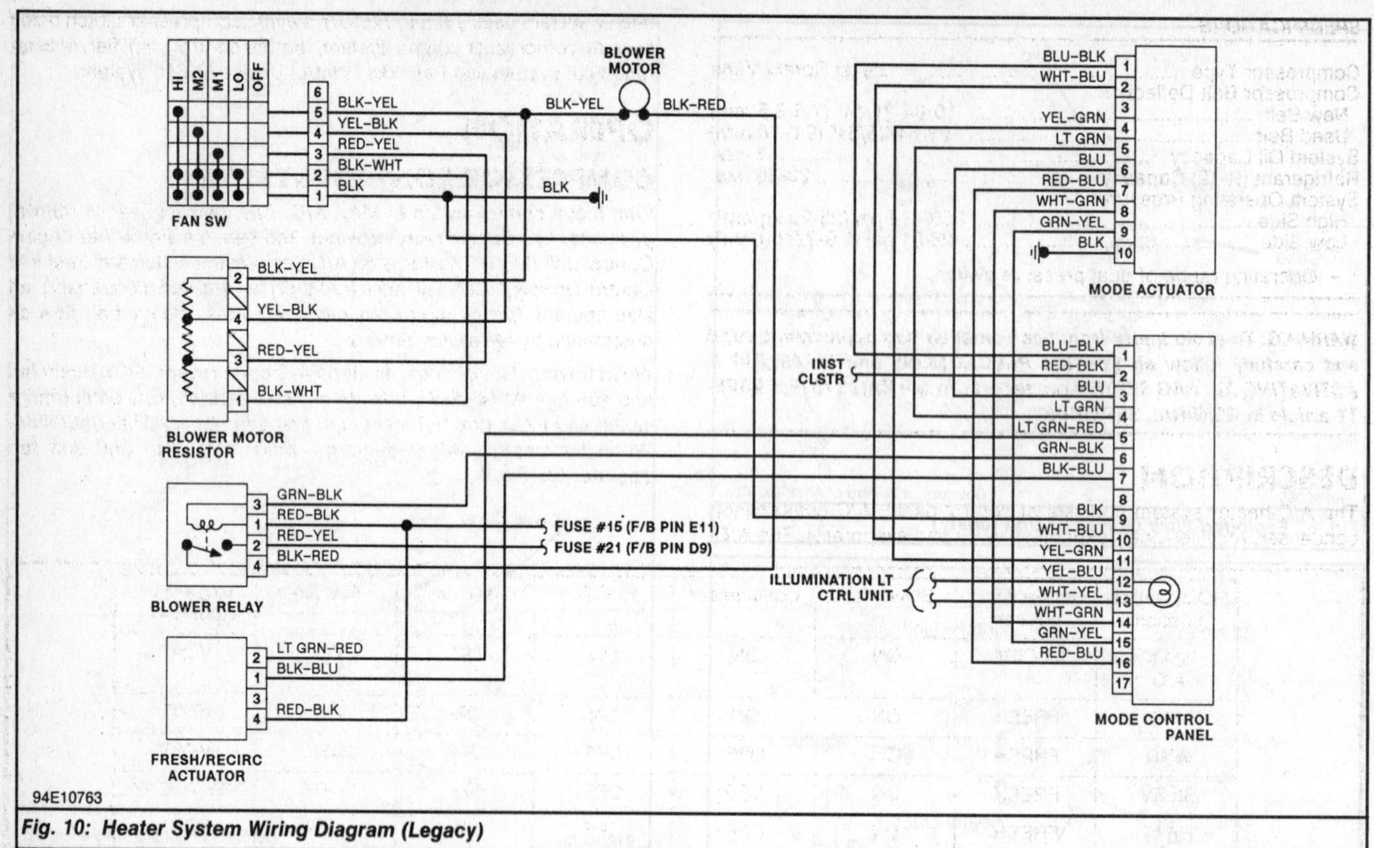
FAN SW
HI
M2
M1
LO
OFF
BLK-YEL
YEL-BLK
RED-YEL
BLK-WHT
BLK
BLOWER MOTOR
BLK-YEL
BLK-RED
BLK
BLOWER MOTOR RESISTOR
BLK-YEL
YEL-BLK
RED-YEL
BLK-WHT
BLOWER RELAY
GRN-BLK
RED-BLK
RED-YEL
BLK-RED
FUSE #15 (F/B PIN E11)
FUSE #21 (F/B PIN D9)
FRESH/RECIRC ACTUATOR
LT GRN-RED
BLK-BLU
RED-BLK
MODE ACTUATOR
BLU-BLK
WHT-BLU
YEL-GRN
LT GRN
BLU
RED-BLU
WHT-GRN
GRN-YEL
BLK
INST CLSTR
ILLUMINATION LT CTRL UNIT
MODE CONTROL PANEL
BLU-BLK
RED-BLK
BLU
LT GRN
LT GRN-RED
GRN-BLK
BLK-BLU
BLK
WHT-BLU
YEL-GRN
YEL-BLU
WHT-YEL
WHT-GRN
GRN-YEL
RED-BLU
94E10763

Fig. 10: Heater System Wiring Diagram (Legacy)

1993 MANUAL A/C-HEATER SYSTEMS
Impreza

SPECIFICATIONS

Compressor Type .... Zexel Rotary Vane
Compressor Belt Deflection
New Belt .... 19/64-21/64" (7.5-8.5 mm)
Used Belt .... 23/64-25/64" (9.0-10 mm)
System Oil Capacity .... 6.1 ozs.
Refrigerant (R-12) Capacity .... 23-26 ozs.
System Operating Pressures [1]
High Side .... 356-412 psi (25-29 kg/cm²)
Low Side .... 26-31 psi (1.9-2.2 kg/cm²)

[1] – Operating range of dual pressure switch.

WARNING: To avoid injury from accidental air bag deployment, read and carefully follow all SERVICE PRECAUTIONS and DISABLING & ACTIVATING AIR BAG SYSTEM procedures in AIR BAG SYSTEM SAFETY article in GENERAL SERVICING.

DESCRIPTION

The A/C-heater system consists of control panel, A/C compressor, condenser, receiver-drier, expansion valve and evaporator. The A/C-heater system uses a dual-pressure switch, compressor clutch delay system, compressor control system, thermo control amplifier, acceleration cut system and Fast Idle Control Device (FICD) system.

OPERATION

COMPRESSOR CONTROL SYSTEM

With mode control switch in MAX A/C, A/C, defrost/heat or defrost positions, A/C system relay activates and sends a signal into Engine Control Unit (ECU). This turns on A/C compressor clutch and Fast Idle Control Device (FICD). The main (radiator) fan and sub (condenser) fan also operate. Blower motor relay also operates, to direct air flow as determined by fan switch position.

When thermostat activates, its stops A/C compressor, FICD, main fan and sub fan. When dual pressure switch operates, A/C compressor clutch and FICD stop but main man and sub fan continue operating. When fan control switch operates, both main man and sub fan operate. *See Fig. 1.*

MODE switch position	Intake door position	Blower fan	Compressor	F.I.C.D.	Main fan	Sub fan	Mode door position
MAX A/C	RECIRC	ON	ON	ON	ON	ON	VENT
A/C	FRESH	ON	ON	ON	ON	ON	VENT
VENT	FRESH	ON	OFF	OFF	OFF	OFF	VENT
BILEV	FRESH	ON	OFF	OFF	OFF	OFF	VENT/HEAT
HEAT	FRESH	ON	OFF	OFF	OFF	OFF	HEAT
DEF HEAT	FRESH	ON	ON	ON	ON	ON	DEF/HEAT
DEF	FRESH	ON	ON	ON	ON	ON	DEF

94B10257

Courtesy of Subaru of America, Inc.

Fig. 1: Manual A/C-Heater System Operation

Water temperature	Compressor clutch	Vehicle speed	EGI relay output		Fan function	
			Fan 1	Fan 2	Main	Sub
○	ON	○	○	○	Hi	Hi
		×	○	○	Hi	Hi
	OFF	○	○	○	Hi	Hi
		×	○	×	Low	Low
×	ON	○	○	○	Hi	Hi
		×	○	×	Low	Low
	OFF	○	×	×	OFF	OFF
		×	×	×	OFF	OFF
○ / × 89 (192.2) 95 (203) °C (°F)	*	○ / × 10 (50) 20 (68) km/h (mph)	○: Output available ×: No output available		–	–

*: ① The blower switch is in the ON state.
② The Hi/Lo switch is inactive.
③ The thermo control amplifier is inactive.
④ The A/C switch is in the ON state.
"ON" when the conditions ① through ④ are satisfied

94C10258

Courtesy of Subaru of America, Inc.

Fig. 2: Manual A/C-Heater Fan Control Switch Operation

1993 MANUAL A/C-HEATER SYSTEMS
Impreza (Cont.)

COMPRESSOR CLUTCH DELAY SYSTEM

When A/C system relay operates, a signal is sent into Engine Control Unit (ECU). The ECU then activates the A/C cut relay. Maximum A/C compressor clutch "on" delay occurs 0.8 seconds after A/C cut relay activates.

DUAL-PRESSURE SWITCH

Dual-pressure switch is located in high-pressure line. Switch consists of a diaphragm, diaphragm springs, pin and 2 contact points. One contact point activates when internal pressure is low or too high. The other contact point controls operation of sub (condenser) fan.

THERMO CONTROL AMPLIFIER

When temperature of evaporator fin drops close to 36°F (2°C), the thermo control amplifier disconnects A/C compressor clutch circuit to prevent evaporator freeze up. As evaporator is cooled, thermistor (located on evaporator fins) interrupts the base current of thermo control amplifier. This de-energizes A/C relay coil, which disconnects A/C compressor clutch circuit.

ACCELERATION CUT SYSTEM

On and off operation of A/C switch is transmitted to Engine Control Unit (ECU). The A/C cut relay breaks current flow to A/C compressor, when a full-throttle signal is received by the ECU. Disengaging A/C compressor clutch during acceleration prevents poor acceleration performance.

FAST IDLE CONTROL DEVICE

The Fast Idle Control Device (FICD), in actuality a by-pass air control solenoid, increases engine idle speed when A/C compressor is turned on. Engine Control Unit (ECU) activates the by-pass air control solenoid. This solenoid controls the amount of by-pass air flowing through throttle body. This is in relation to signal emitted from A/C switch so that proper idle speed specified for each engine load is achieved.

FAN CONTROL

Main (radiator) fan and sub (condenser) fan are switched between 2 stages, high and low, according to operating modes. *See Fig. 2*.

ADJUSTMENTS

NOTE: For adjustments see HEATER SYSTEMS - IMPREZA article.

TESTING

WARNING: To avoid injury from accidental air bag deployment, read and carefully follow all SERVICE PRECAUTIONS and DISABLING & ACTIVATING AIR BAG SYSTEM procedures in AIR BAG SYSTEM SAFETY article in GENERAL SERVICING.

A/C SYSTEM PERFORMANCE

1) Park vehicle out of direct sunlight and any wind. Close all doors, open front windows and hood. Start and run engine at 1500 RPM. Set A/C controls to recirculated air, maximum cold, and blower speed to 4th position. Turn A/C system on.

2) Operate system for 10 minutes to allow system to stabilize. Insert thermometer in center grille. Condenser intake air temperature is measured 3 feet in front and in line with center of condenser. High side and low side pressures must be within specification. See SPECIFICATIONS table.

BLOWER MOTOR

1) Turn ignition on. Place mode switch in MAX A/C or A/C position. If blower motor does not operate, check two 15-amp fuses for blower relay. If a fuse is blown, check Red/Yellow wire and Red/Black wire for a short to ground. Repair wire(s) as necessary. If fuses are okay, go to next step.

2) Ground either Black/Yellow, Yellow/Black, Red/Yellow, or Black/White wire at fan switch. If blower operates, check resistor connection. If no problem is found, replace resistor.

3) If blower does not operate, check for voltage on Black/Red wire. If voltage is present, check wire connection. If no problem is found, replace blower motor. If voltage is not present, go to next step.

4) Check voltage on Red/Yellow wire. If voltage is present, check wire connection. If no problem is found, replace blower motor relay. If voltage is not present, check connector and fuse holder. Repair or replace parts as necessary.

COMPRESSOR CLUTCH

1) Turn ignition on. Place mode switch in MAX A/C or A/C position. If A/C compressor clutch is not engaged, check both 10-amp fuses for A/C system. If a fuse is blown, check wiring harness between A/C fuse (10-amp) and compressor clutch for a short to ground. Repair wire(s) as necessary. If fuses are okay, go to next step.

2) Check battery voltage at A/C relay Brown/Red wire with relay connected. If there is no voltage, repair open Brown/Red wire. If voltage is present, check battery voltage at A/C relay Red/White wire with relay connected. If there is no voltage, go to step **9)**. If voltage is present, go to next step.

3) Check battery voltage at thermal switch Red/White wire. If there is no voltage, repair open Red/White wire. If voltage is present, check voltage at thermal switch Red/Green wire. If there is no voltage, repair open Red/Green wire. If there is voltage, go to next step.

4) Check battery voltage at A/C cut relay Green/Red wire. If there is no voltage, repair open Green/Red wire. If voltage is present, check voltage at A/C cut relay Yellow/Green wire. If there is no voltage, go to step **6)**. If voltage is present, go to next step.

5) Check battery voltage at compressor clutch Yellow/Green wire. If there is no voltage, repair open Yellow/Green wire. If voltage is present, replace A/C compressor clutch.

6) Check voltage at A/C cut relay Brown/Red wire. If there is no voltage, repair open Brown/Red wire. If voltage is present, check if Engine Control Unit (ECU) A/C signal (Green) wire is shorted to ground. If there is no short to ground, go to step **8)**. If there is a short to ground, go to next step.

7) Check if A/C cut relay Blue wire is shorted to ground. If there is a short to ground, replace A/C cut relay. If there is not a short to ground, repair Blue wire.

8) Check for battery voltage at ECU A/C signal (Green) wire. If there is no voltage at ECU A/C signal wire, repair Green wire. If voltage is present at ECU A/C signal wire, replace ECU.

9) If there was no voltage present at A/C relay Red/White wire with relay connected, check if there is voltage present at A/C relay Black/White wire. If there is no voltage, repair Black/White wire. If voltage is present, go to next step.

10) Check for battery voltage at A/C relay Black/White wire. If voltage is present, go to step **12)**. If there is no voltage, check for voltage at A/C switch Black/White wire. If voltage is present, repair Black/White wire.

11) If there is no voltage, check for battery voltage at A/C switch Red/Black wire. If voltage is present, replace A/C switch. If there is no voltage, repair Red/Black wire.

12) Check if A/C relay Brown/Yellow wire is shorted to ground. If there is a short to ground, replace A/C relay. If there is no short to ground, check if continuity exists between A/C relay Brown/Yellow wire and dual-pressure switch Brown/Yellow wire. If there is no continuity, repair Brown/Yellow wire. If there is continuity, go to next step.

13) Check if pressure in high-pressure line is 30-384 psi (2.1-27 kg/cm²). If pressure is within this range, replace dual-pressure switch. If pressure is not within this range, check continuity of Green wire between pressure switch and evaporator thermo switch. If there is no continuity, repair Green wire. If continuity does exist, go to next step.

14) Check for battery voltage at evaporator thermo switch Red/Black wire. If there is no voltage, repair Red/Black wire. If voltage is present, check if evaporator thermo switch Brown/White wire is grounded. If wire is not grounded, repair Brown/White wire. If wire is grounded, replace evaporator thermo switch.

1993 MANUAL A/C-HEATER SYSTEMS
Impreza (Cont.)

RADIATOR COOLING FAN

1) If main (radiator) cooling fan does not operate, check 20-amp fuse for radiator cooling fan and 10-amp fuse for A/C system. If a fuse is blown, repair short circuit and replace fuse. If fuses are okay, go to next step.
2) Check if voltage is present at fan motor connector Light Green/ Black wire. If there is no voltage, go to next step. If voltage is present, check if fan motor connector Black wire is grounded. If Black wire is grounded, replace fan motor. If Black wire is not grounded, repair Black (ground) wire.
3) Check if voltage is present at main fan relay Yellow/Red wire. If voltage is present, repair Yellow/Red wire. If there is no voltage, check if voltage is present at main fan relay wiring harness (bus bar).
4) If there is no voltage, repair wiring harness (bus bar). If voltage is present, check if main fan relay Red/White wire is grounded. If wire is grounded, replace main fan relay. If wire is not grounded, go to next step.
5) Check if voltage is present at Engine Control Unit (ECU) wiring harness Red/Blue wire. If voltage is present, replace ECU. If there is no voltage, repair Red/Blue wire.

CONDENSER FAN DOES NOT OPERATE

1) If sub (condenser) fan does not operate, check 20-amp fuse for condenser fan. If fuse is blown, repair short circuit and replace fuse. If fuse is okay, check if voltage is present at sub fan motor connector Yellow/Green wire. If there is no voltage, go to step **3)**.
2) If voltage is present, check if fan motor connector Black wire is grounded. If wire is grounded, replace sub fan motor. If wire is not grounded, repair Black (ground) wire.
3) Check if voltage is present sub (condenser) fan relay White/Blue wire. If there is no voltage, repair White/Blue wire. If voltage is present, check if voltage present at condenser fan relay White wire. If voltage is present, go to next step. If there is no voltage, repair White wire.
4) Check if condenser fan relay White/Red wire is grounded. If wire is grounded, replace condenser fan relay. If wire is not grounded, repair White/Red wire.

CONDENSER FAN SPEED DOES NOT CHANGE

1) If sub (condenser) fan speed does not increase when coolant temperature is 203°F (95°C) or more, go to step **3)**. If condenser fan speed does not decrease when coolant temperature is 192°F (89°C) or less, check if fan control switch Green/Red wire is grounded. If wire is grounded, replace Engine Control Unit (ECU).
2) If fan control switch Green/Red wire is not grounded, check if condenser fan Green/Red wire is shorted to ground. If wire is not shorted to ground, replace sub (condenser) fan relay. If wire is shorted to ground, repair Green/Red wire.
3) Check if battery voltage is present at condenser fan White/Blue wire. If voltage is present, replace connector or condenser fan motor. If there is no voltage, go to next step.
4) Check if battery voltage is present at sub (condenser) fan relay White/Blue wire. If there is no voltage, repair White Blue wire. If voltage is present, go to next step.
5) Check if battery voltage is present at condenser fan relay White wire. If there is no voltage, repair White wire. If voltage is present, check if fan control switch Green/Red wire is grounded.
6) If wire is not grounded, replace Engine Control Unit (ECU). If wire is grounded, check if condenser fan Green/Red wire is grounded. If wire is grounded, replace relay. If wire is not grounded, repair Green/Red wire.

REMOVAL & INSTALLATION

WARNING: To avoid injury from accidental air bag deployment, read and carefully follow all SERVICE PRECAUTIONS and DISABLING & ACTIVATING AIR BAG SYSTEM procedures in AIR BAG SYSTEM SAFETY article in GENERAL SERVICING.

A/C COMPRESSOR

Removal – 1) Disconnect negative battery cable. Discharge A/C system using approved refrigerant recovery/recycling equipment. Remove low-pressure and high-pressure hoses. Remove compressor belt and generator belt covers.
2) Remove generator and compressor belts. Disconnect generator and compressor wiring harnesses. Remove A/C compressor bracket and A/C compressor. Remove A/C compressor from bracket.
Installation – To install, reverse removal procedure. Tighten compressor bolts to 18-25 ft. lbs. (24-34 N.m).

CONDENSER

Removal – 1) Disconnect negative battery cable. Discharge A/C system using approved refrigerant recovery/recycling equipment. Remove front grille. Remove radiator bracket.
2) Disconnect high-pressure hose and high-pressure pipe from condenser. Remove two bolts which secure condenser. Lift condenser out through space between radiator and radiator panel.
Installation – To install, reverse removal procedure. If installing a new condenser, add 1.5 ounces of refrigerant oil to condenser.

CONDENSER FAN

Removal & Installation – Disconnect negative battery cable. Disconnect wiring harness from condenser fan motor. Remove right-hand radiator bracket. Remove condenser fan bolt from radiator. Remove condenser fan. To install, reverse removal procedure.

EVAPORATOR

Removal & Installation – 1) Disconnect negative battery cable. Discharge A/C system using approved refrigerant recovery/recycling equipment. Disconnect discharge pipe, suction pipe, and grommets from engine compartment side of firewall.
2) Remove glove box. Disconnect wiring harness from evaporator. Disconnect drain hose. Remove evaporator mounting bolt and nut. *See Fig. 3.* To install, reverse removal procedure. If installing a new evaporator, add 2.8 ounces of refrigerant oil to evaporator.

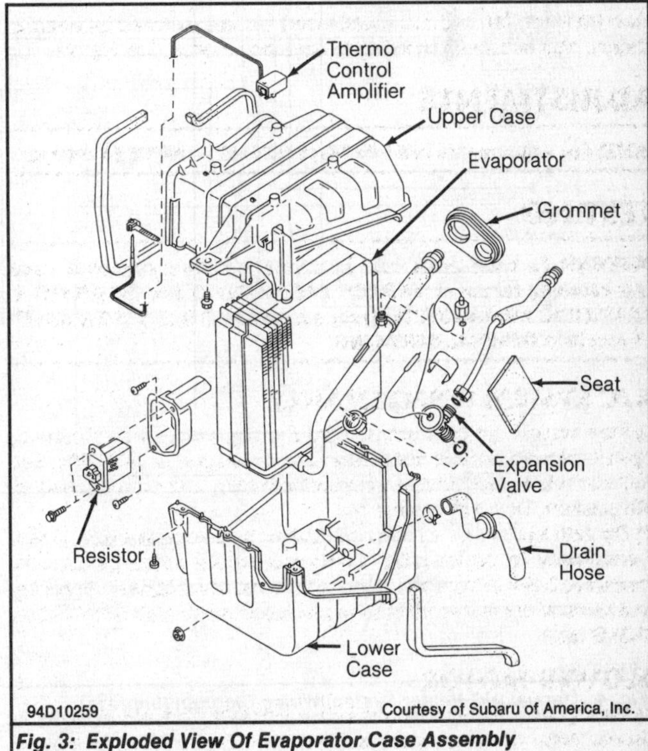
Thermo
Control
Amplifier
Upper Case
Evaporator
Grommet
Seat
Expansion
Valve
Resistor
Drain
Hose
Lower
Case
94D10259
Courtesy of Subaru of America, Inc.

Fig. 3: Exploded View Of Evaporator Case Assembly

1993 MANUAL A/C-HEATER SYSTEMS
Impreza (Cont.)

WIRING DIAGRAM

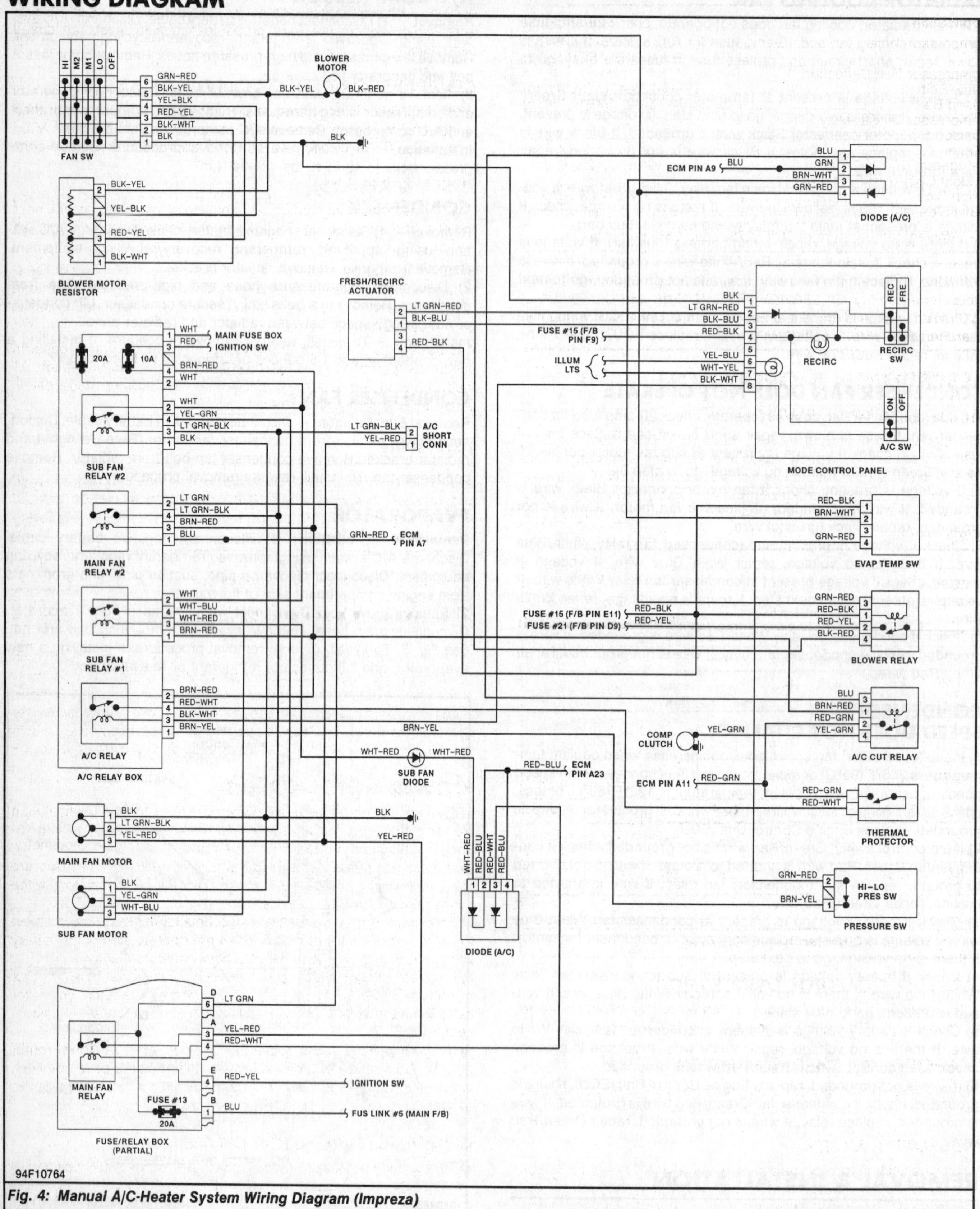
FAN SW
HI
M2
M1
LO
OFF
GRN-RED
BLK-YEL
YEL-BLK
RED-YEL
BLK-WHT
BLK
BLOWER MOTOR
BLK-RED
BLOWER MOTOR RESISTOR
FRESH/RECIRC ACTUATOR
LT GRN-RED
BLK-BLU
RED-BLK
MAIN FUSE BOX
IGNITION SW
20A
10A
WHT
RED
BRN-RED
YEL-GRN
LT GRN-BLK
SUB FAN RELAY #2
A/C SHORT CONN
LT GRN
BLU
ECM PIN A7
MAIN FAN RELAY #2
WHT-BLU
WHT-RED
SUB FAN RELAY #1
RED-WHT
BRN-YEL
A/C RELAY
A/C RELAY BOX
SUB FAN DIODE
MAIN FAN MOTOR
YEL-RED
SUB FAN MOTOR
ECM PIN A23
RED-BLU
RED-WHT
DIODE (A/C)
MAIN FAN RELAY
FUSE #13
IGNITION SW
FUS LINK #5 (MAIN F/B)
FUSE/RELAY BOX (PARTIAL)
ECM PIN A9
GRN
BRN-WHT
FUSE #15 (F/B PIN F9)
ILLUM LTS
YEL-BLU
WHT-YEL
REC
FRE
RECIRC
RECIRC SW
ON
OFF
A/C SW
MODE CONTROL PANEL
EVAP TEMP SW
FUSE #15 (F/B PIN E11)
FUSE #21 (F/B PIN D9)
BLOWER RELAY
COMP CLUTCH
RED-GRN
A/C CUT RELAY
ECM PIN A11
THERMAL PROTECTOR
HI-LO PRES SW
PRESSURE SW
94F10764

Fig. 4: Manual A/C-Heater System Wiring Diagram (Impreza)

SPECIFICATIONS

Application	Specification
Compressor Type	Calsonic V5-15C 5-Cyl. Zexel DKS-15CH 5-Cyl.
Compressor Belt Deflection	
New Belt	19/64-23/64" (7.0-9.0 mm)
Used Belt	23/64-13/32" (9.0-10.0 mm)
Compressor Oil Capacity	
Calsonic	3.2 ozs.
Zexel	2.4 ozs.
Refrigerant (R-12) Capacity	29-32 ozs.
System Operating Pressures [1]	
High Side	149-203 psi (10.5-14.3 kg/cm²)
Low Side	24-37 psi (1.7-2.6 kg/cm²)

[1] – Ambient temperature of 80°F (27°C) and 65% humidity.

WARNING: To avoid injury from accidental air bag deployment, read and carefully follow all SERVICE PRECAUTIONS and DISABLING & ACTIVATING AIR BAG SYSTEM procedures in AIR BAG SYSTEM SAFETY article in GENERAL SERVICING.

DESCRIPTION & OPERATION

MODE CONTROL SWITCH

With mode control switch in A/C, MAX A/C, DEF/HEAT or DEF (defrost) position, A/C switch closes and A/C relay is energized. *See Fig. 1.* A signal is then sent to Electronic Control Unit (ECU). ECU activates the A/C cut relay, energizing the compressor clutch, Fast Idle Control Device (FICD), radiator (main) fan, condenser (sub) fan and blower motor.

MODE switch position	Intake door position	Blower fan	Compressor	F.I.C.D.	Main fan	Sub fan	Mode door position
OFF	FRESH	OFF	OFF	OFF	OFF	OFF	HEAT
MAX A/C	RE-CIRC	ON	ON	ON	ON	ON	VENT
A/C	FRESH	ON	ON	ON	ON	ON	VENT
VENT	FRESH	ON	OFF	OFF	OFF	OFF	VENT
BILEV	FRESH	ON	OFF	OFF	OFF	OFF	VENT/HEAT
HEAT	FRESH	ON	OFF	OFF	OFF	OFF	HEAT
DEF HEAT	FRESH	ON	ON	ON	ON	ON	DEF/HEAT
DEF	FRESH	ON	ON	ON	ON	ON	DEF

91H04836 Courtesy of Subaru of America, Inc.

Fig. 1: Manual A/C-Heater System Operation

FAST IDLE CONTROL DEVICE (FICD)

FICD is mounted on throttle body. Solenoid opens throttle plate to increase engine RPM at idle during A/C compressor operation.

EVAPORATOR THERMOSWITCH

This switch senses evaporator temperature and shuts off compressor clutch, FICD, and radiator and condenser fans.

PRESSURE SWITCH

Pressure switch is located on top of receiver-drier. Pressure switch consists of the high/low pressure switch and fan switch. If high-side system pressure exceeds maximum level or drops to minimum level, high/low portion of pressure switch stops operation of compressor clutch and FICD, but radiator and condenser fans continue to operate.

When high-side system pressure exceeds maximum level, fan switch portion of pressure switch increases speed of radiator and condenser fans. When system pressure drops to minimum level, fan speed decreases.

COMPRESSOR CLUTCH ON DELAY SYSTEM

When A/C relay is energized, a signal is sent to ECU, which then judges engine operating conditions and activates A/C cut relay. Maximum clutch ON delay occurs 0.8 second after A/C cut relay activates.

FUSES & RELAYS

The A/C cut relay is located under right side of instrument panel, near top of evaporator. *See Fig. 3.* Blower motor relay is located under left end of instrument panel.

All other A/C system relays (A/C relay, condenser fan relay, condenser fan water temperature relay and radiator fan relay) are located in relay/fuse panel. Relay/fuse panel is mounted to left inner fender in engine compartment.

A/C system uses 10-amp and 20-amp fuses in relay/fuse panel in engine compartment. Fuse No. 15 (10-amp) and fuses No. 20 and 21 (both 15-amp) are located in passenger compartment fuse panel, under left end of instrument panel.

TESTING

WARNING: To avoid injury from accidental air bag deployment, read and carefully follow all SERVICE PRECAUTIONS and DISABLING & ACTIVATING AIR BAG SYSTEM procedures in AIR BAG SYSTEM SAFETY article in GENERAL SERVICING.

A/C SYSTEM PERFORMANCE

1) Park vehicle out of direct sunlight and wind. Start and run engine at 1500 RPM. Vehicle doors should be closed, front windows open, hood open and A/C on.

2) Set A/C control to maximum cold position. Set blower/fan on high speed. Operate system for 10 minutes to allow system to stabilize.

3) Measure evaporator intake air temperature at recirculation door, evaporator discharge air temperature at center grille, and condenser intake air temperature. Ensure low and high side pressures are within specifications. See SPECIFICATIONS table at beginning of article.

BLOWER MOTOR CIRCUIT

1) Turn ignition on. Place mode switch in A/C or MAX A/C position. If blower motor does not operate, check fuses No. 20 and 21 (both 15-amp) in passenger compartment fuse panel.

2) If fuses are blown, repair short circuit as necessary. If fuses are okay, individually ground each wire terminal at blower motor switch connector (except Black wire terminal).

3) If blower operates, repair harness connector at blower motor resistor or replace resistor. If blower does not operate, check for battery voltage at Brown wire terminal of blower motor connector.

4) If battery voltage exists, repair harness connector at blower motor or replace blower motor. If battery voltage does not exist, check for battery voltage at Red/Yellow wire terminal of blower motor relay connector.

5) If battery voltage exists, repair harness connector at blower motor relay or replace blower motor relay. If battery voltage does not exist, check connector and fuse holder. Repair or replace parts as necessary.

COMPRESSOR CLUTCH CIRCUIT

1) Turn ignition on. Place mode switch in A/C or MAX A/C position. If clutch does not engage, check both 10-amp A/C fuses in passenger compartment fuse panel.

2) If either or both fuses are blown, repair short circuit(s) as necessary. If fuses are okay, check for battery voltage on Brown/Red wire terminal of A/C relay (relay connected).

1993 MANUAL A/C-HEATER SYSTEMS
Legacy (Cont.)

3) If battery voltage does not exist, repair wiring harness. If battery voltage exists, check for battery voltage at Red/White wire terminal of A/C relay connector (relay disconnected). If battery voltage does not exist, go to step **7)**.
4) If battery voltage exists, disconnect A/C cut relay. Check for battery voltage between Blue/Red wire terminal and Yellow/Green wire terminal of A/C cut relay connector.
5) If battery voltage does not exist, repair wiring harness. If battery voltage exists, check for battery voltage at Brown/Red wire terminal of A/C cut relay connector (relay connected). If battery voltage does not exist, A/C cut relay or ECU is faulty.
6) If battery voltage exists, check for battery voltage at Blue/Red wire terminal of compressor connector. If battery voltage does not exist, repair wiring harness. If battery voltage exists, replace compressor clutch.
7) Check for battery voltage at Brown/Yellow wire terminal of A/C relay connector. If battery voltage exists, go to step **9)**. If battery voltage does not exist, check for continuity between Red/Blue wire terminal and Black wire terminal of high/low pressure switch connector.
8) If continuity exists, repair wiring harness. If continuity does not exist, check pressure in high-pressure line. If pressure is 28-384 psi (2.0-27.0 kg/cm²), replace high/low pressure switch. If pressure is not 28-384 psi (2.0-27.0 kg/cm²), repair cause of abnormal pressure.
9) Check for continuity between ground and Green/Red wire terminal of A/C relay connector. If there is continuity, replace A/C relay. If there is no continuity, check for continuity between ground and Brown/White wire terminal of evaporator thermoswitch connector.
10) If there is continuity, repair wiring harness. If there is no continuity, check for continuity between ground and Red/Black wire terminal of evaporator thermoswitch connector.
11) If there is no continuity, replace mode switch or repair wiring harness. If there is continuity, check for battery voltage at Red/Black wire terminal of evaporator thermoswitch connector. If there is continuity, replace evaporator thermoswitch. If there is no continuity, repair power supply to thermoswitch.

RADIATOR (MAIN) FAN CIRCUIT

1) Check fuse No. 13 (20-amp) in passenger compartment fuse panel and A/C fuse (10-amp) in relay/fuse panel in engine compartment. If either or both fuses are blown, repair short circuit(s) as necessary.
2) If fuses are okay, check for battery voltage at Yellow/Red wire terminal of radiator (main) fan motor connector. If no voltage exists at Yellow/Red wire terminal, go to step **4)**.
3) If battery voltage exists at Yellow/Red wire terminal, check continuity between ground and Black wire terminal of main fan motor connector. If continuity exists, replace main fan motor. If continuity does not exist, repair wiring harness.
4) Check for battery voltage at Yellow/Red wire terminal of main fan relay connector. If battery voltage exists, repair wiring harness. If no voltage exists, check for battery voltage at Blue wire terminal of main fan relay connector.
5) If battery voltage does not exist at Blue wire terminal, repair wiring harness. If battery voltage exists, check continuity between ground and Red/Blue wire terminal of main fan relay connector. If there is continuity, replace main fan relay. If there is no continuity, check continuity between ground and Brown/White wire terminal of evaporator thermoswitch connector.
6) If there is continuity, repair wiring harness. If there is no continuity, check continuity between ground and Red/Blue wire terminal of evaporator thermoswitch connector. If there is no continuity, replace mode switch or repair wiring harness.
7) If there is continuity, check for battery voltage at Red/Black wire terminal of evaporator thermoswitch connector. If battery voltage exists, replace evaporator thermoswitch. If battery voltage does not exist, repair power supply to evaporator thermoswitch.

CONDENSER (SUB) FAN CIRCUIT

Condenser Fan Does Not Operate – 1) Check A/C fuse (20-amp) in relay/fuse panel in engine compartment. If fuse is blown, repair short circuit as necessary.
2) If fuse is okay, check for battery voltage at Yellow/Green wire terminal of condenser fan motor connector. If battery voltage does not exist at Yellow/Green wire terminal, go to step **4)**.
3) If battery voltage exists, check continuity between ground and Black wire terminal of condenser fan motor connector. If continuity exists, replace condenser fan motor. If continuity does not exist, repair wiring harness.
4) Check for battery voltage at Yellow/Green wire terminal of condenser fan relay connector. If battery voltage exists, repair wiring harness. If battery voltage does not exist, check for battery voltage at White wire terminal of condenser fan relay connector. If battery voltage exists, go to step **6)**.
5) If battery voltage does not exist, check for battery voltage at Light Green/Blue wire terminal of radiator (main) fan relay connector. If battery voltage exists, repair wiring harness. If battery voltage does not exist, perform RADIATOR (MAIN) FAN CIRCUIT test.
6) Check for continuity between ground and Black wire at condenser fan relay connector. If there is continuity, replace condenser fan relay. If there is no continuity, repair wiring harness.
Condenser Fan Speed Does Not Increase When High Pressure Is At Least 256 psi (18 kg/cm²) – 1) Check for battery voltage at Yellow/Green wire terminal of condenser fan motor connector. If battery voltage exists, repair fan motor connector or replace fan motor.
2) If battery voltage does not exist, check for battery voltage at Yellow/Green wire terminal of condenser fan relay connector. If battery voltage does not exist, repair wiring harness. If battery voltage exists, check for battery voltage at Brown/Red wire terminal of pressure switch connector.
3) If battery voltage exists, repair wiring harness or replace condenser fan relay. If battery voltage does not exist, repair wiring harness or replace pressure switch.
Condenser Fan Speed Does Not Decrease When High Pressure Is At Least 156 psi (11 kg/cm²) – Check for battery voltage at Red/Blue wire terminal of pressure switch connector. If battery voltage exists, replace pressure switch. If battery voltage does not exist, replace condenser fan relay.

A/C SYSTEM RELAY & A/C CUT RELAY

1) Remove relay. Measure resistance between terminals No. 3 and 4. *See Fig. 2 or 3*. On A/C cut relay, resistance should be 120 ohms. On A/C system relay, resistance should be 100 ohms.
2) On all relays, check continuity between terminals No. 1 and 2. Continuity should not be present. Replace relay if continuity is present.
3) Apply battery voltage to terminal No. 3 and ground terminal No. 4. Continuity between terminals No. 1 and 2 should now be present. Replace relay if continuity is not present.

NOTE: Blower motor relay testing procedures are not available from manufacturer.

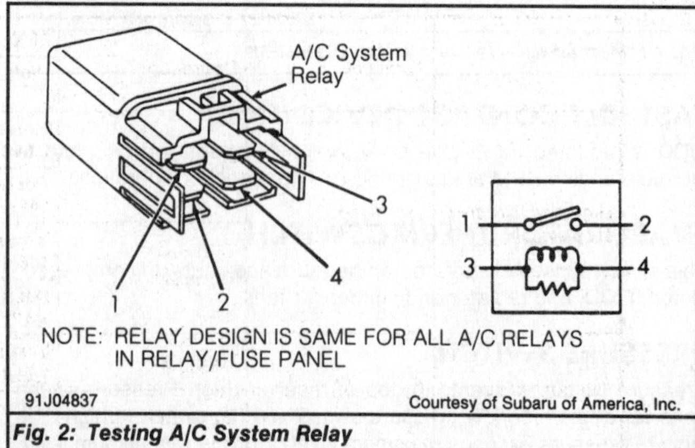
A/C System Relay
3
4
1
2
1
2
3
4
NOTE: RELAY DESIGN IS SAME FOR ALL A/C RELAYS IN RELAY/FUSE PANEL
91J04837
Courtesy of Subaru of America, Inc.

Fig. 2: Testing A/C System Relay

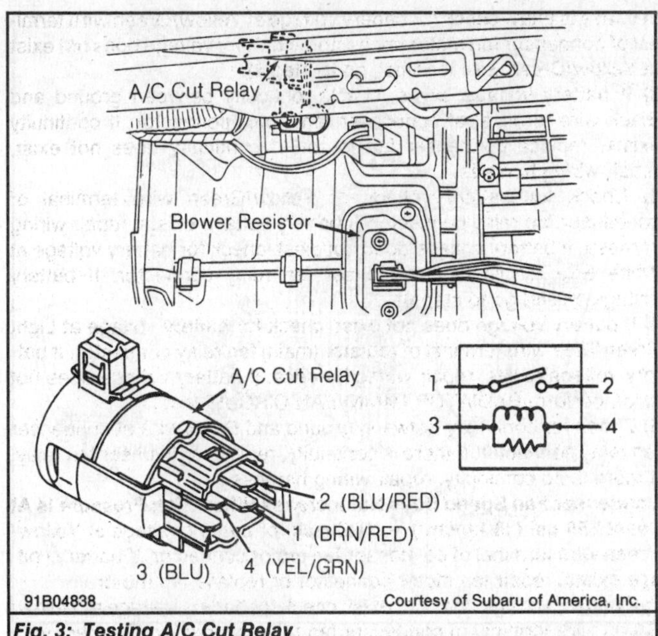

A/C Cut Relay
Blower Resistor
A/C Cut Relay
1
2
3
4
2 (BLU/RED)
1 (BRN/RED)
3 (BLU)
4 (YEL/GRN)

91B04838 Courtesy of Subaru of America, Inc.

Fig. 3: Testing A/C Cut Relay

PRESSURE SWITCH

Disconnect harness connector from pressure switch. *See Fig. 4.* Check continuity between specified terminals of pressure switch connector. *See Fig. 5.* If switch does not operate as specified under pressure conditions specified, replace switch.

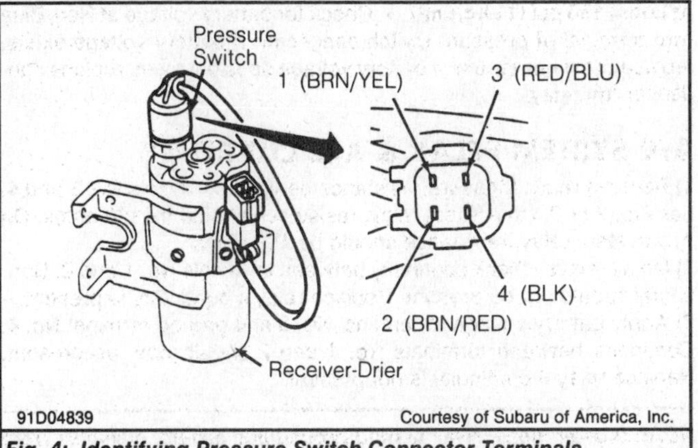

Pressure Switch
1 (BRN/YEL)
3 (RED/BLU)
4 (BLK)
2 (BRN/RED)
Receiver-Drier

91D04839 Courtesy of Subaru of America, Inc.

Fig. 4: Identifying Pressure Switch Connector Terminals

REMOVAL & INSTALLATION

WARNING: To avoid injury from accidental air bag deployment, read and carefully follow all SERVICE PRECAUTIONS and DISABLING & ACTIVATING AIR BAG SYSTEM procedures in AIR BAG SYSTEM SAFETY article in GENERAL SERVICING.

COMPRESSOR

Removal & Installation – 1) Disconnect negative battery cable. Discharge A/C system using approved refrigerant recovery/recycling equipment. Disconnect low and high pressure hoses. Remove belt covers from compressor and alternator. Remove alternator belt. Remove compressor belt.

2) Remove cooling fan assembly. Disconnect electrical connectors from alternator and compressor as necessary. Remove compressor bracket bolts, and remove compressor. To install, reverse removal procedure. Evacuate and charge system.

CONDENSER

Removal & Installation – Disconnect negative battery cable. Remove front grille and radiator support bracket. Discharge A/C system using approved refrigerant recovery/recycling equipment. Disconnect A/C lines from condenser. Remove condenser bolts and condenser. To install, reverse removal procedure. Evacuate and charge system.

CONDENSER COOLING FAN

Removal & Installation – Disconnect negative battery cable. Disconnect motor wiring connector. Loosen bolts at bottom of condenser fan shroud. Remove bolts from top of condenser fan shroud. Remove condenser fan assembly. To install, reverse removal procedure.

EVAPORATOR

Removal – Disconnect negative battery cable. Discharge A/C system using approved refrigerant recovery/recycling equipment. Disconnect lines from evaporator in engine compartment. Remove glove box. Remove glove box support bracket. Disconnect electrical connectors from evaporator. Remove evaporator bolts, nuts and evaporator. *See Fig. 6 or 7.*

Installation – To install, reverse removal procedure. Ensure evaporator sensing tube fits into evaporator near 4th vertical fin and approximately 1.18" (30 mm) from top of evaporator. Evacuate and charge system.

	Terminal	Operation	ZEXEL High pressure side line-pressure kPa (kg/cm^2, psi)	CALSONIC High pressure side line-pressure kPa (kg/cm^2, psi)
High and low pressure switch	③ — ④	Turns OFF	Increasing to 2,648± 196 (27.0± 2, 384± 28)	Increasing to 2,648± 196 (27± 2, 384± 28)
			Decreasing to 196± 20 (2.0± 0.2, 28.4± 2.8)	Decreasing to 196± 34.3 (2.0± 0.35, 28.4± 5.0)
		Turns ON	Increasing to 206± 29 (2.1± 0.3, 30± 4)	Increasing to 210.9± 34.3 (2.15± 0.35, 30.6± 5.0)
			Decreasing to $1,471^{+196}_{-98}$ (15^{+2}_{-1}, 213^{+28}_{-14})	Decreasing to 2,059± 196 (21± 2, 299± 28)
Fan control switch	① — ②	Turns ON	Increasing to 1,569± 127 (16± 1.3, 228± 18)	Increasing to 1,471± 98 (15± 1.0, 213± 14)
		Turns OFF	Decreasing to 1,275± 147 (13± 1.5, 185± 21)	Decreasing to 1,079± 98 (11± 1, 156± 14)

93J19603 Courtesy of Subaru of America, Inc.

Fig. 5: Testing Pressure Switch Operation

1993 MANUAL A/C-HEATER SYSTEMS
Legacy (Cont.)

RECEIVER-DRIER

Removal & Installation – Disconnect negative battery cable. Disconnect pressure switch connector from pressure switch. *See Fig. 4*. Discharge A/C system using approved refrigerant recovery/recycling equipment. Disconnect lines from receiver-drier. Remove bolts and receiver-drier. To install, reverse removal procedure. Evacuate and charge system.

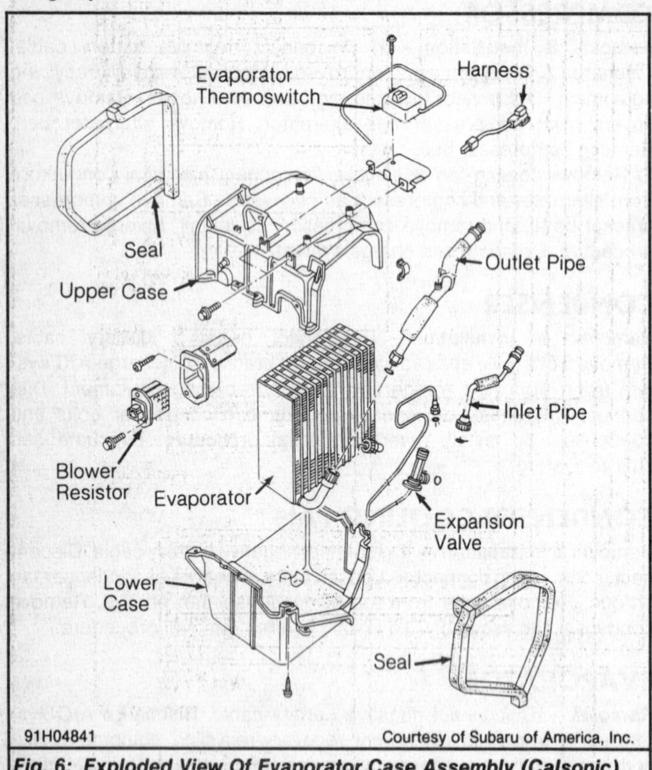
Evaporator Thermoswitch
Harness
Seal
Upper Case
Outlet Pipe
Inlet Pipe
Blower Resistor
Evaporator
Expansion Valve
Lower Case
Seal
91H04841
Courtesy of Subaru of America, Inc.

Fig. 6: Exploded View Of Evaporator Case Assembly (Calsonic)

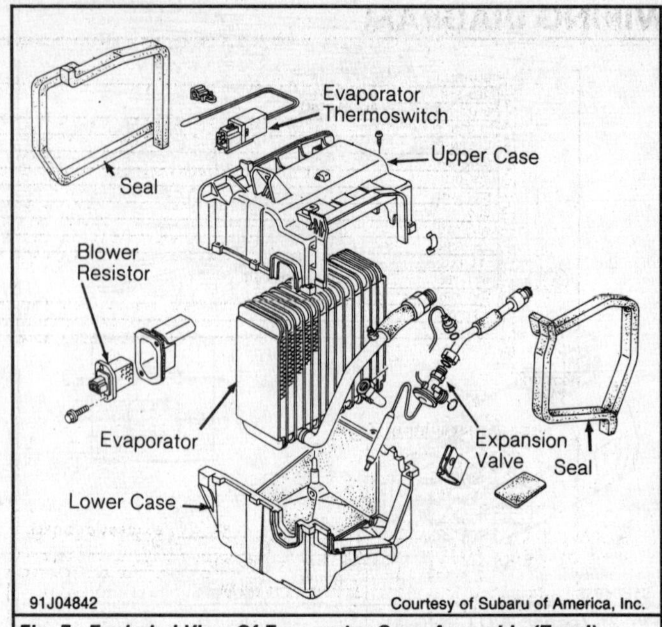
Evaporator Thermoswitch
Seal
Upper Case
Blower Resistor
Evaporator
Expansion Valve
Seal
Lower Case
91J04842
Courtesy of Subaru of America, Inc.

Fig. 7: Exploded View Of Evaporator Case Assembly (Zexel)

WIRING DIAGRAM

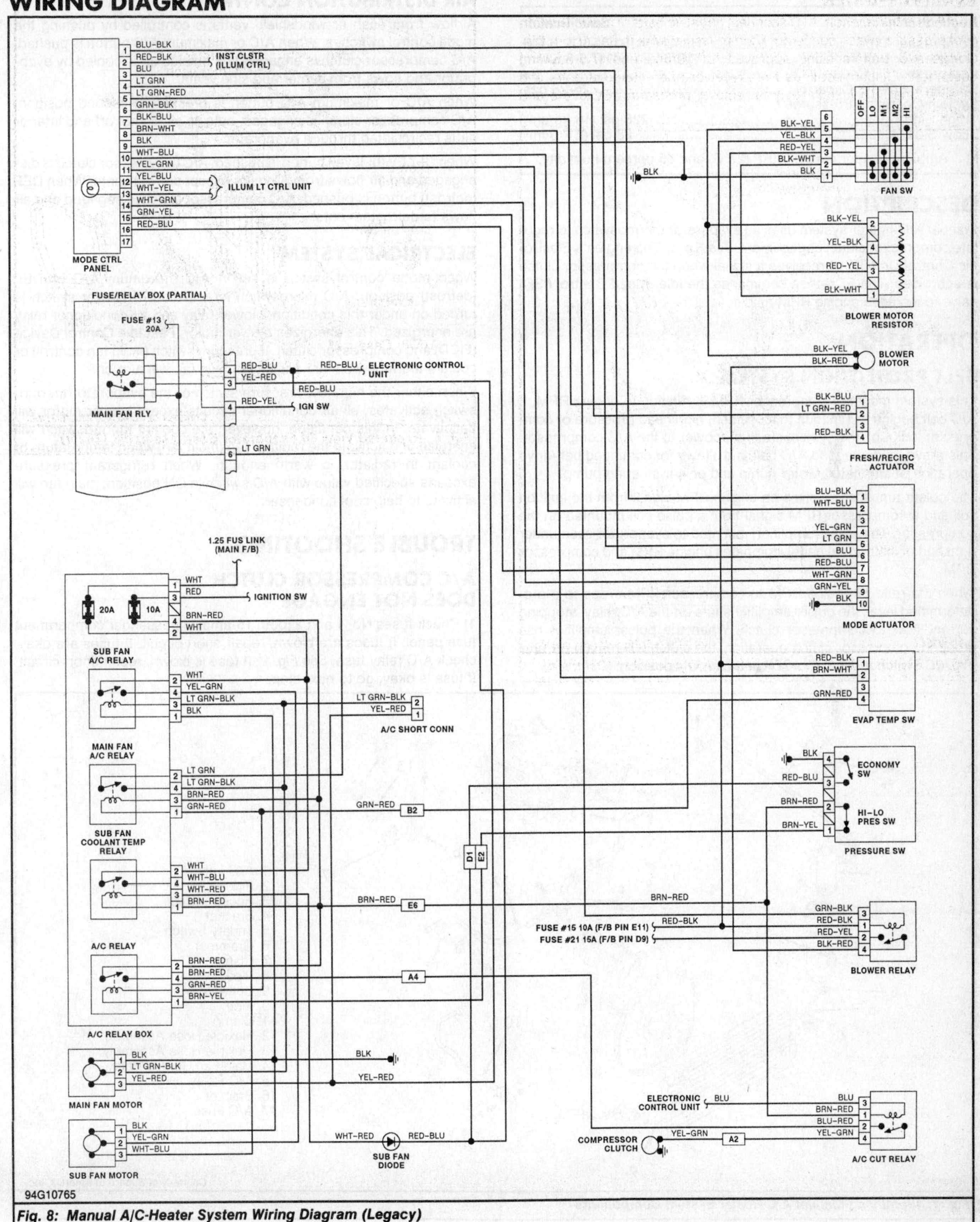
INST CLSTR (ILLUM CTRL)
ILLUM LT CTRL UNIT
MODE CTRL PANEL
FUSE/RELAY BOX (PARTIAL)
FUSE #13 20A
ELECTRONIC CONTROL UNIT
IGN SW
MAIN FAN RLY
1.25 FUS LINK (MAIN F/B)
IGNITION SW
SUB FAN A/C RELAY
A/C SHORT CONN
MAIN FAN A/C RELAY
SUB FAN COOLANT TEMP RELAY
A/C RELAY
A/C RELAY BOX
MAIN FAN MOTOR
SUB FAN MOTOR
SUB FAN DIODE
FAN SW
OFF
LO
M1
M2
HI
BLOWER MOTOR RESISTOR
BLOWER MOTOR
FRESH/RECIRC ACTUATOR
MODE ACTUATOR
EVAP TEMP SW
ECONOMY SW
HI-LO PRES SW
PRESSURE SW
FUSE #15 10A (F/B PIN E11)
FUSE #21 15A (F/B PIN D9)
BLOWER RELAY
ELECTRONIC CONTROL UNIT
COMPRESSOR CLUTCH
A/C CUT RELAY
94G10765

Fig. 8: Manual A/C-Heater System Wiring Diagram (Legacy)

1993 MANUAL A/C-HEATER SYSTEMS
Loyale

SPECIFICATIONS

Application	Specification
Compressor Type	Hitachi MJS170-5DP 6-Cyl.
Compressor Belt Tension	19/64-21/64" (7.5-8.5 mm)
Compressor Oil Capacity	2.4
Refrigerant (R-12) Capacity	26-28 ozs.
System Operating Pressures [1]	
High Side	228 psi (16 kg/cm^2)
Low Side	28 psi (2 kg/cm^2)

[1] – Ambient temperature of 80°F (27°C) and 65 percent humidity.

DESCRIPTION

Manual A/C-heater system uses an evaporator thermoswitch to regulate compressor clutch engagement. *See Fig. 1.* The engine's Electronic Control Unit (ECU) receives a signal when the compressor clutch is energized. The ECU then commands the Idle Speed Control (ISC) valve to increase engine RPM at idle.

OPERATION

BELT PROTECTION SYSTEM

This system monitors compressor RPM in relation to engine RPM. If A/C belt begins to slip (due to loose belt, high head pressure or compressor lock-up), the system shuts off power to the A/C compressor. This prevents damage to A/C belt and allows for continued belt-drive operation of alternator, water pump and power steering pump.

The pulser amplifier receives an engine RPM signal from the ignition coil and a compressor RPM signal from a pulse coil mounted on the compressor. The pulser amplifier, mounted to evaporator case under right end of instrument panel, compares engine RPM and compressor RPM.

When the ratio of engine RPM to compressor RPM drops to a predetermined level, the pulser amplifier shuts off the A/C relay, stopping current flow to compressor clutch. When the pulser amplifier has stopped compressor clutch operation, the clutch will remain off until the A/C switch is turned to OFF and then ON position.

AIR DISTRIBUTION CONTROL

Airflow from dash or windshield vents is controlled by pushing the mode control switches. When A/C or maximum A/C button is pushed, A/C compressor clutch is engaged and outside air is cooled by evaporator and flows from center and side vents.

When A/C or maximum A/C button is pressed to second position, A/C compressor clutch is engaged, outside air is shut off and interior air is recirculated through evaporator.

When BI-LEV (bi-level) button is pushed, A/C compressor clutch is disengaged and air flows from all vents except defrost vents. When DEF (defrost) button is pushed, A/C compressor clutch is engaged and air flows to defroster vents.

ELECTRICAL SYSTEM

When mode control switch is set in A/C, maximum A/C or DEF (defrost) position, A/C microswitch is activated. If blower switch is turned on under this condition, blower relay and air conditioner relay are energized. This energizes blower motor, Fast Idle Control Device (FICD) and compressor clutch. If pressure switch (main fan control) or coolant thermoswitch are activated, main fan will turn on.

When either the high-low pressure switch or the evaporator thermoswitch activates, all air conditioner circuits except blower motor will deactivate. In this condition, however, the coolant thermoswitch will energize and activate the radiator fan (main fan) when temperature of coolant in radiator is warm enough. When refrigerant pressure exceeds specified value with A/C switch in ON position, main fan will activate to help cool condenser.

TROUBLE SHOOTING

A/C COMPRESSOR CLUTCH DOES NOT ENGAGE

1) Check fuses No. 1 and 2 (both 15-amp) in passenger compartment fuse panel. If fuses are blown, repair short circuit. If fuses are okay, check A/C relay fuse. *See Fig. 2.* If fuse is blown, repair short circuit. If fuse is okay, go to next step.

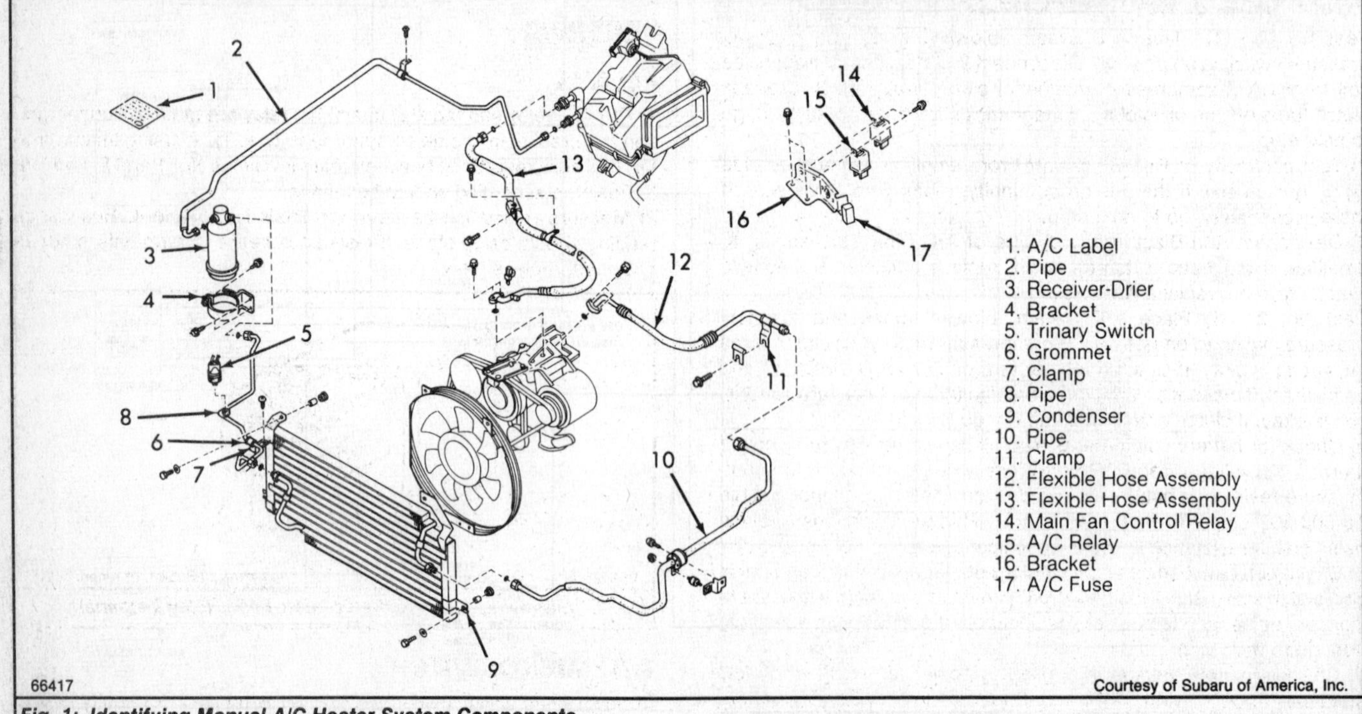
1
2
3
4
5
6
7
8
9
10
11
12
13
14
15
16
17
1. A/C Label
2. Pipe
3. Receiver-Drier
4. Bracket
5. Trinary Switch
6. Grommet
7. Clamp
8. Pipe
9. Condenser
10. Pipe
11. Clamp
12. Flexible Hose Assembly
13. Flexible Hose Assembly
14. Main Fan Control Relay
15. A/C Relay
16. Bracket
17. A/C Fuse
66417
Courtesy of Subaru of America, Inc.

Fig. 1: Identifying Manual A/C-Heater System Components

1993 MANUAL A/C-HEATER SYSTEMS
Loyale (Cont.)

2) Using a voltmeter, check for voltage at Blue/Yellow wire terminal of A/C relay connector. If battery voltage does not exist, go to next step. If battery voltage exists, check compressor (magnetic) clutch wire connection and compressor ground. Repair connection or ground if necessary. If connection and ground are okay, replace compressor clutch.
3) Check for voltage at Red/Black wire terminal of A/C relay connector. If battery voltage exists, replace A/C relay. If battery voltage does not exist, connect jumper wire between ground and Red/Black wire terminal of A/C relay connector.
4) If A/C compressor clutch does not engage, replace A/C relay. If compressor clutch engages, connect jumper wire between Green/White and Red wires at pulser amplifier connector. If clutch engages, replace pulse coil or pulser amplifier.
5) If clutch does not engage, connect jumper wire between ground and Red/White wire terminal of evaporator thermoswitch. If clutch engages, repair ground circuit of mode control switch. If clutch does not engage, replace evaporator thermoswitch.

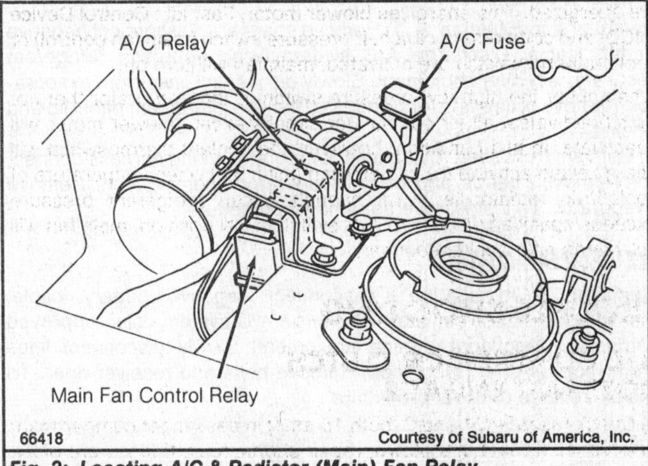
A/C Relay
A/C Fuse
Main Fan Control Relay
66418
Courtesy of Subaru of America, Inc.

Fig. 2: Locating A/C & Radiator (Main) Fan Relay

PULSE COIL & RELATED CIRCUITS

Test No. 1 - 1) Place A/C switch, blower switch and high/low pressure switch in on position. Disconnect 2-pin connector from pulse coil to check if compressor (magnetic) clutch turns off. If magnetic clutch turns off, circuit is okay. If magnetic clutch does not turn off, go to next step.
2) Test continuity of Red/Black wire from amplifier to negative side (-) of ignition coil. If there is no continuity, repair Red/Black wire. If there is continuity, go to next step.
3) Disconnect Red/Black (ground) wire of A/C relay coil, leading to amplifier. If magnetic clutch turns off, replace amplifier. If magnetic clutch stays on, replace A/C relay.
Test No. 2 - 1) Place A/C switch, blower switch and high/low pressure switch to on position. If compressor (magnetic) clutch turns on, circuit is okay. If clutch does not turn on, turn A/C switch off and on to check if magnetic clutch turns on. If magnetic clutch turns on, circuit is okay. If clutch does not come on, go to next step.
2) Check for battery voltage at Green/White wire of A/C relay coil. If there is no voltage, repair Green/White wire. If voltage is present, measure resistance between pulse coil terminals. Resistance should be 600-800 ohms. If resistance is not within specifications, replace pulse coil. If resistance is within specifications, go to next step.
3) Check gap between pawl (protrusion) of magnetic clutch and pulse coil (clutch side). Gap should be 1/64" (4 mm). If gap is not within specification, adjust gap to correct specification. If gap is within specification, go to next step.
4) Check if battery voltage is applied to power terminal (+) of A/C amplifier (through wiring from high/low pressure switch). If battery voltage is present, replace A/C amplifier. If battery voltage is not present, repair wiring or switch.

BLOWER MOTOR

1) If blower motor does not operate, check two 15-amp fuses for blower relay. If fuse is blown, repair short circuit in Blue/Red wire or Red/Yellow wire and replace fuse. If fuses are okay, go to next step.
2) Ground either Blue (4-speed), Blue/Black (3-speed), Blue/Yellow (2-speed) or Blue/White (1-speed) wire to blower switch. If blower motor does not run, go to next step. If blower motor runs, check ground circuit and wire connections. If no problem is found, replace blower switch.
3) Ground blower motor Blue wire. If blower motor does not run, go to next step. If blower motor runs, check connection of blower motor resistor. If no problem is found, replace blower motor resistor.
4) Connect 12-volt test light to Green/White wire leading to blower motor. If test light does not come on, go to next step. If test light comes on, check Green/White wire connection. If no problem is found, replace blower motor.
5) Connect 12-volt test light to Blue/Red wire leading to blower motor relay. If test light comes on, check Blue/Red wire connection. If no problem is found, replace blower motor relay. If test light does not come on, check connector and fuse holder. Repair or replace parts as necessary.

RADIATOR FAN

1) If radiator (main) fan does not operate, check 15-amp fuse for radiator fan. If fuse is blown, repair short in cooling fan motor circuit and replace fuse. If fuse is okay, go to next step.
2) Connect 12-volt test light between radiator fan motor Blue/Red wire and ground. If test light does not come on, check for an open Blue/Red wire. If test light comes on, go to next step.
3) Turn A/C switch off. Connect 12-volt test light between fan control relay Yellow/White wire and ground. If test light comes on, go to next step. If test light does not come on, check wire connections. If no problem is found, replace radiator (main) fan.
4) Turn A/C switch off, and disconnect pressure switch and fan relay. Connect 12-volt test light between A/C relay Blue/Yellow wire and ground. If test light comes on, check A/C relay connector. If connector is okay, replace A/C relay. If test light does not come on, check wire connection. If no problem is found, replace fan control relay.

TESTING

RELAYS

1) The A/C relay and radiator (main) fan relay are mounted under ignition coil bracket in engine compartment. *See Fig. 2.* Using an ohmmeter, measure resistance between relay terminals No. 1 and 2. *See Fig. 3.* Resistance reading should be infinite.
2) Measure resistance between terminals No. 3 and 4. Resistance reading should be 80 ohms. If resistance between terminals is not as specified, replace relay.

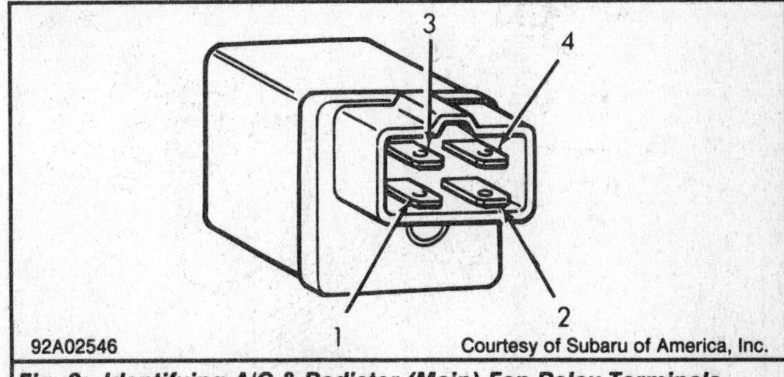
3
4
1
2
92A02546
Courtesy of Subaru of America, Inc.

Fig. 3: Identifying A/C & Radiator (Main) Fan Relay Terminals

A/C MICROSWITCH

Connect ohmmeter between A/C switch terminals. Continuity should not exist with control button released. Continuity should exist when control button is pushed. Replace A/C switch if it does not test as specified.

1993 MANUAL A/C-HEATER SYSTEMS
Loyale (Cont.)

A/C PULSER AMPLIFIER

Testing procedures for pulser amplifier are not available from manufacturer. Functional description of pulser amplifier is available. *See Fig. 4.*

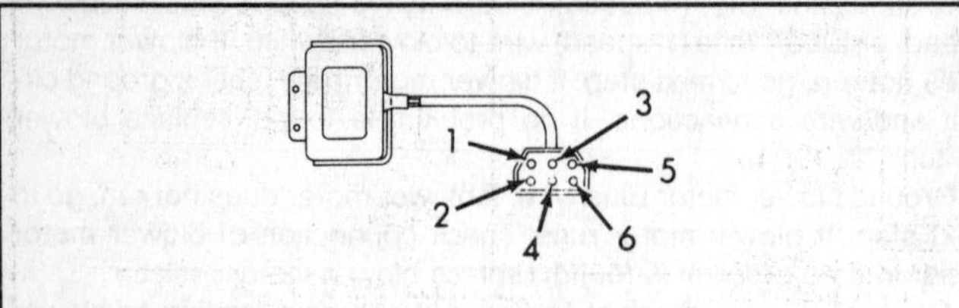
3
1
5
2
4
6

Terminal			Description
No.	Cable color	Destination	
1	RY (MT) RB (AT)	Power supply	Supplies current to the pulser amplifier through the air conditioner switch and trinary (low-pressure) switch for the purpose of activating accessories.
2	Y	Ignition coil (–)	Transmits engine rpms to the pulser amplifier in pulse form.
3	R	Pulse sensor (–)	Transmits compressor rpms to the pulser amplifier for comparison with ignition pulses.
4	GW	Pulse sensor (+)	When compressor rpms drop below 75 to 80% of engine rpms, the RG's grounding circuit will open.
5	RG	Magnetic clutch drive relay coil	When the thermostat activates to close the ground circuit with the air conditioner switch "ON", the clutch will engage. When compressor is locked, the thermostat activates to open the ground circuit, disengaging the clutch.
6	RB	Ground	The thermostat opens and closes the ground circuit, depending on the temperature of the evaporator.

105655 Courtesy of Subaru of America, Inc.

Fig. 4: Identifying Functions Of Pulser Amplifier Terminals

REMOVAL & INSTALLATION

COMPRESSOR

Removal & Installation – 1) Disconnect negative battery cable. Remove spare tire. Remove pulser amplifier and fan shroud. Discharge A/C system using approved refrigerant recovery/recycling equipment. Remove and plug low and high pressure hoses. Remove alternator belt.

2) Remove upper compressor bracket mounting. Remove cooling fan assembly. Remove idler pulley assembly. Remove compressor and lower bracket as a unit. To install, reverse removal procedure.

CONDENSER

Removal & Installation – Disconnect negative battery cable. Remove front grille. Remove lower stay. Discharge A/C system using approved refrigerant recovery/recycling equipment. Remove A/C lines from condenser. Remove condenser bolts and condenser. To install, reverse removal procedure.

CONDENSER FAN

Removal & Installation – Disconnect condenser fan motor wiring harness connector. Remove shroud bolts and shroud. Remove condenser fan bolts and fan. Remove wiring from shroud. Remove fan motor bolts and motor. To install, reverse removal procedure.

EVAPORATOR

Removal & Installation – 1) Remove spare tire. Disconnect negative battery cable. Discharge A/C system using approved refrigerant recovery/recycling equipment. Slowly disconnect lines from evaporator. Remove grommets for all hoses. Remove instrument panel lid and pocket.

2) Remove front shelf. Disconnect evaporator wiring harness connector. Remove 2 bands, and loosen evaporator mounting bolts. Remove evaporator. To install, reverse removal procedure.

RECEIVER-DRIER

Removal & Installation – Disconnect negative battery cable. Remove fuel vapor canister. Discharge A/C system using approved refrigerant recovery/recycling equipment. Slowly disconnect lines from receiver-drier. Plug lines. Remove bolts and receiver-drier. To install, reverse removal procedure.

WIRING DIAGRAM

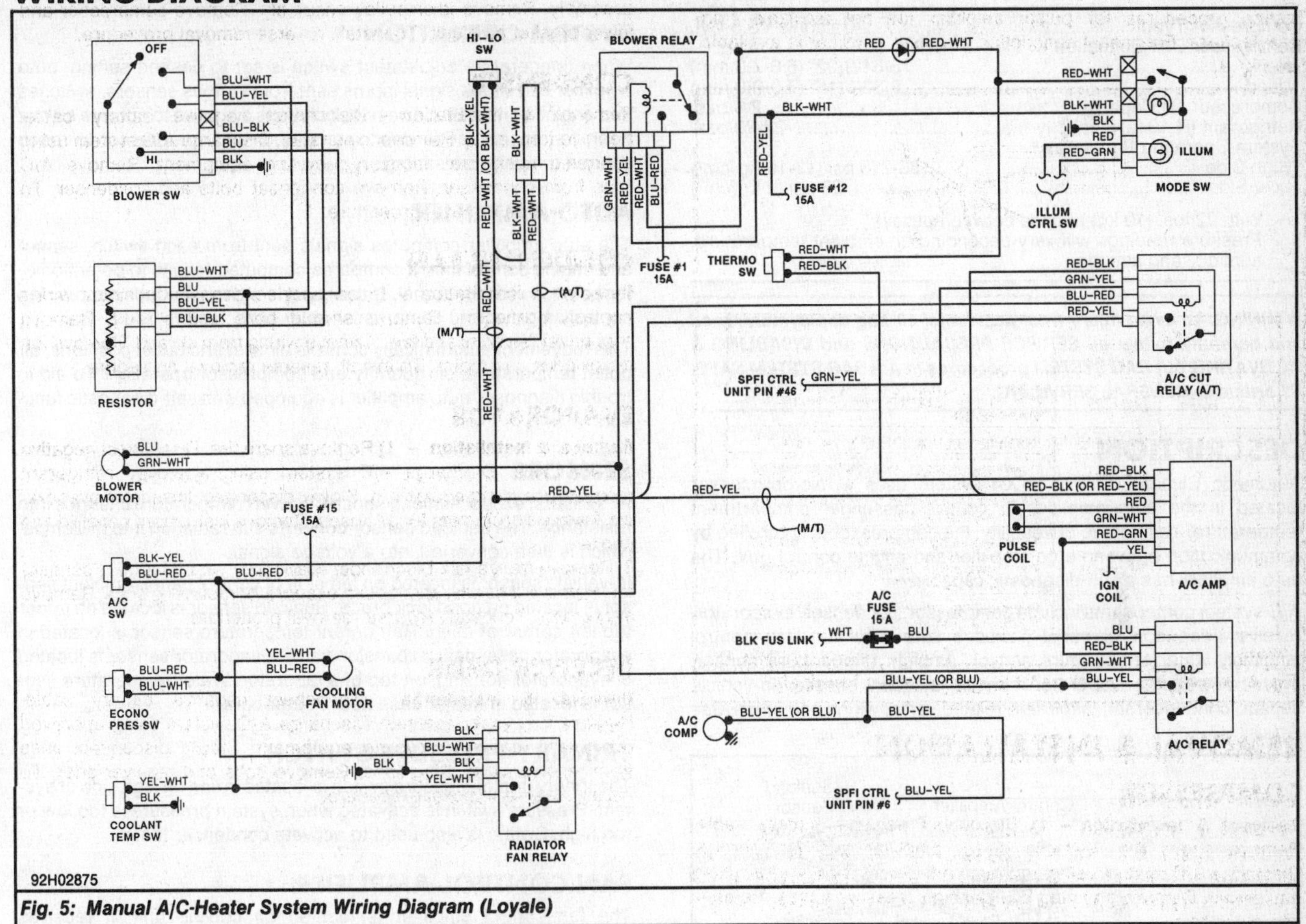
OFF
HI
BLOWER SW
BLU-WHT
BLU-YEL
BLU-BLK
BLU
BLK
HI-LO SW
BLOWER RELAY
RED
RED-WHT
BLK-WHT
RED-GRN
ILLUM
MODE SW
ILLUM CTRL SW
FUSE #12 15A
FUSE #1 15A
THERMO SW
RED-BLK
GRN-YEL
BLU-RED
RED-YEL
A/C CUT RELAY (A/T)
RESISTOR
SPFI CTRL UNIT PIN #46
BLOWER MOTOR
GRN-WHT
(A/T)
(M/T)
FUSE #15 15A
BLK-YEL
A/C SW
RED-BLK (OR RED-YEL)
PULSE COIL
IGN COIL
A/C AMP
YEL
A/C FUSE 15 A
BLK FUS LINK
WHT
A/C RELAY
BLU-YEL (OR BLU)
BLU-YEL
A/C COMP
YEL-WHT
COOLING FAN MOTOR
ECONO PRES SW
COOLANT TEMP SW
RADIATOR FAN RELAY
SPFI CTRL UNIT PIN #6
BLK-WHT (OR BLK-WHT)
92H02875

Fig. 5: Manual A/C-Heater System Wiring Diagram (Loyale)

1993 AUTOMATIC A/C-HEATER SYSTEMS SVX

SPECIFICATIONS

Compressor Type	Calsonic V5 5-Cyl.
Compressor Belt Deflection [1]	
New	15/64-9/32" (6.0-7.0 mm)
Used	9/32-5/16" (7.0-8.0 mm)
Compressor Oil Capacity	2.4 ozs.
Refrigerant (R-134a) Capacity	22-23 ozs.
System Operating Pressures [2]	
High Side	185-213 psi (13-15 kg/cm²)
Low Side	28 psi (2 kg/cm²)

[1] - With 22 lbs. (10 kg) applied between pulleys.
[2] - Pressure readings will vary depending on ambient temperature, humidity and altitude.

WARNING: To avoid injury from accidental air bag deployment, read and carefully follow all SERVICE PRECAUTIONS and DISABLING & ACTIVATING AIR BAG SYSTEM procedures in AIR BAG SYSTEM SAFETY article in GENERAL SERVICING.

DESCRIPTION

Automatic Climate Control (ACC) system uses a microprocessor located in the auto amplifier to control passenger compartment temperature. To improve driveability, the compressor is controlled by communication between auto amplifier and engine control unit. The auto amplifier has a self-diagnostic capability.

A/C system components include compressor, condenser, evaporator, receiver-drier, control panel (includes auto amplifier), fan control amplifier, water temperature sensor, ambient temperature sensor, pressure switch, evaporator sensor, sunload sensor, in-vehicle sensor, condenser fan, aspirator, related vents, wiring and fuses. *See Fig. 1.*

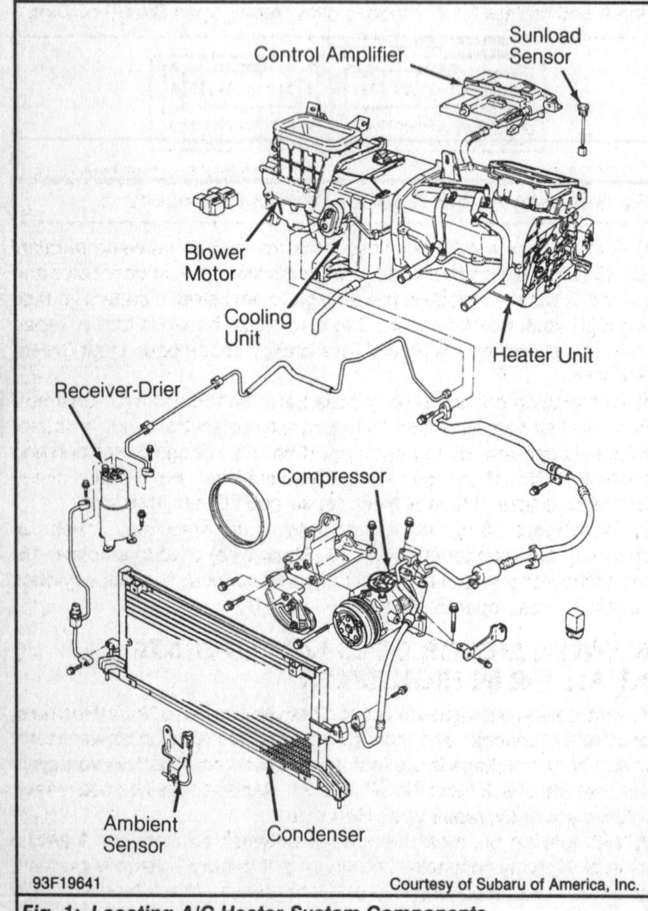
Control Amplifier
Sunload Sensor
Blower Motor
Cooling Unit
Heater Unit
Receiver-Drier
Compressor
Ambient Sensor
Condenser
93F19641
Courtesy of Subaru of America, Inc.

Fig. 1: Locating A/C-Heater System Components

OPERATION

SYSTEM OPERATION

When temperature adjustment switch is set to desired setting, auto amplifier calculates signal inputs sent from various sensors, switches and engine control unit. These calculations are used to operate air mix door, fan speed, mode door, intake door and compressor to reach desired temperature setting.

AUTO AMPLIFIER

The auto amplifier computes signals sent from each switch, sensor and engine control unit. It compares computed results to potentiometer balance resistor signal. It then sends signals to door motors, fan control amplifier and compressor solenoid actuator.

This movement automatically controls air inlet and outlet positions, air outlet temperature, air quantity and compressor operation. To aid in trouble diagnosis, auto amplifier is equipped with self-diagnostic function.

SENSORS

All sensors, except sunload sensor, convert temperature changes into resistance. The sunload sensor converts sun radiation into milliamps, which is then converted into a voltage signal.

In-vehicle sensor is located on left side of control panel. Ambient sensor is located on hood lock brace. Sunload sensor is located on upper top left corner of dash. Refrigerant temperature sensor is located in evaporator case, near expansion valve. Evaporator sensor is located in evaporator housing, on top of evaporator. Water temperature sensor is located in heater case near heater core.

TRINARY PRESSURE SWITCH

The trinary (triple) pressure switch is located in line on high side of system. Pressure switch is activated when system pressure is too low or too high. Switch is also used to activate condenser fan.

FAN CONTROL AMPLIFIER

The fan control amplifier is located on cooling unit. It receives reference current from auto amplifier and controls voltage sent to blower motor.

RELAYS

Max Hi Relay - The max hi (maximum high speed) relay is located on blower motor unit. It is turned on and off by auto amplifier. When max hi relay is turned on, blower motor operates at high speed.

Off Relay - The off relay is located on blower motor unit. When a control panel function is selected, auto amplifier turns off relay on. When off relay is on, power is sent to fan control amplifier for blower motor operation. When off relay is off, power is disconnected from fan control amplifier.

A/C Relay - The A/C relay is in relay box on left side of engine compartment. A/C relay controls compressor clutch operation.

INTAKE DOOR MOTOR

The intake door motor is on the right upper side of blower motor case. It opens and closes the intake air door. Intake motor rotates in one direction only. When CIRC (recirculated air) switch is off and compressor is off, intake door is in fresh air position. When CIRC (recirculated air) switch is on and compressor is on, intake door is positioned in fresh, 20 percent fresh or recirculating position.

AIR MIX DOOR MOTOR

The air mix door is located on bottom of heater unit. The air mix door motor rotates in both directions. A Potentiometric Balance Resistor (PBR) is built into mix door motor. The PBR registers air mix door position and sends signal back to auto amplifier. Along with other inputs, auto amplifier then adjusts air mix door position for temperature adjustment.

MODE DOOR MOTOR

The mode door motor is located on left side of heater unit. Mode door motor actuates defrost door, vent door and heat doors. Mode door motor rotates in both directions. When AUTO position is selected on control panel, auto amplifier uses evaporator sensor and other inputs to drive mode door to vent, defrost or heat position.

FAHRENHEIT/CELSIUS SELECTION

Control panel temperature reading can be displayed in either degrees Fahrenheit (°F) or Celsius (°C). To display temperature in Fahrenheit, the connector located behind left front kick panel must connected. *See Fig. 2.* Disconnect connector to display temperature in degrees Celsius.

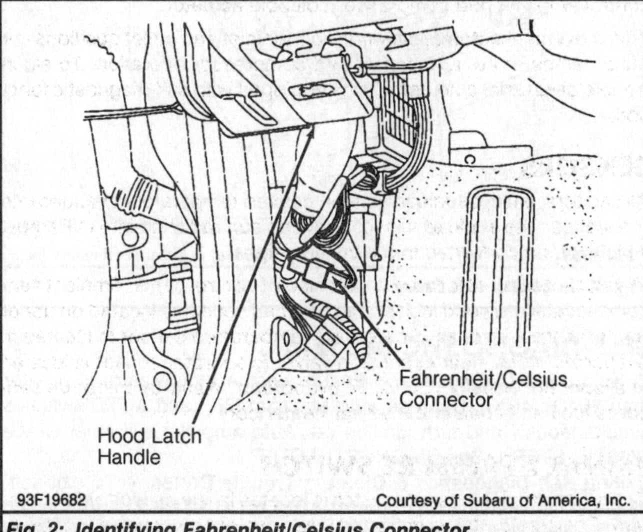
Fahrenheit/Celsius
Connector
Hood Latch
Handle
93F19682
Courtesy of Subaru of America, Inc.

Fig. 2: Identifying Fahrenheit/Celsius Connector

TROUBLE SHOOTING

PRELIMINARY INSPECTION

Power Supply – Measure battery voltage and specific gravity. Battery voltage must be a minimum of 12 volts and specific gravity must be greater than 1.260. Check condition of A/C, heater and other fuses. Check wiring harness and connectors.

Refrigerant – Check amount of refrigerant through sight glass.

Control Panel Linkage – Check linkage operation of mode door, air mix door and air intake door.

BASIC CHECKS

NOTE: If any BASIC CHECKS fail to function as described, proceed to SELF-DIAGNOSTIC SYSTEM.

Off Mode – With OFF switch in off position, control panel LED and temperature display should go off. Airflow should stop. Air outlet should be in heat position. Air inlet should be in fresh air position. Compressor should be off.

AUTO Mode (Temperature Set At 65°F) – With AUTO switch in on position, AUTO switch LED and temperature display should be on. Outlet air should be cool and coming from front vents. Airflow should be high and automatically controlled. Inlet air and compressor are automatically controlled.

AUTO Mode (Temperature Gradually Changed From 65°F To 85°F) – AUTO switch LED should be on. Outlet air should change from cool to hot. Outlet air should move from front vents to bi-level to heater vents. Airflow and inlet air are automatically controlled. Compressor is off.

AUTO Mode (Temperature Set At 85°F) – AUTO switch LED should be on. Outlet air should be hot and coming from heater vents. Airflow should be high and automatically controlled. Inlet air is fresh and automatically controlled. Compressor is automatically controlled.

ECON Mode (Temperature Set Between 65-85°F) – With ECON switch in on position, ECON switch LED and temperature display should be on. Air temperature, airflow and outlet air location are automatically controlled. Inlet air is fresh and compressor is off.

DEF (Defrost) Mode (Temperature Set Between 65-85°F) – With defrost switch in on position, DEF switch LED and temperature display should be on. Air temperature and airflow are automatically controlled. Inlet air is fresh and compressor is off. Outlet air should come from defrost vents.

VENT Mode – With VENT switch in on position, VENT switch LED should be on. Temperature display should go off. In-vehicle air temperature should be the same as outside temperature. Airflow should be fixed at medium speed. Inlet air is fresh and compressor is off. Outlet air should come from front vents.

CIRC (Recirculated Air) Mode – With CIRC switch in on position, CIRC switch LED should be on. Inlet air is set to recirculate for 10 minutes, then inlet air door will move to fresh position. CIRC LED will go off.

OUT-TEMP (Outside Temperature) Display Function – With OUT-TEMP switch in on position, ambient temperature flashes on temperature display panel. Set temperature reappears on temperature display panel.

A/C SYSTEM OR SELF-DIAGNOSTICS INOPERATIVE

1) Remove auto amplifier to access connectors. See AUTO AMPLIFIER under REMOVAL & INSTALLATION. Leave auto amplifier connected. With ignition off, measure voltage between terminal No. 1 (Blue/Red wire) of auto amplifier 16-pin connector and ground. *See Fig. 3.*

2) If battery voltage is present, go to next step. If battery voltage is not present, check fuse No. 25 in fuse block. If fuse is blown, repair short circuit and replace fuse. If fuse is okay, repair open Blue/Red wire.

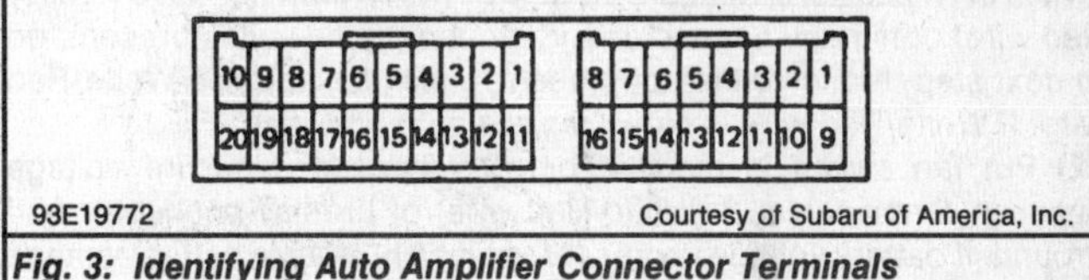
10 9 8 7 6 5 4 3 2 1
20 19 18 17 16 15 14 13 12 11
8 7 6 5 4 3 2 1
16 15 14 13 12 11 10 9
93E19772
Courtesy of Subaru of America, Inc.

Fig. 3: Identifying Auto Amplifier Connector Terminals

3) With ignition in ACC position, measure voltage between terminal No. 18 (Light Green/Red wire) of auto amplifier 20-pin connector and ground. If battery voltage is present, go to next step. If battery voltage is not present, check fuse No. 3 in fuse block. If fuse is blown, repair short circuit and replace fuse. If fuse is okay, repair open Light Green/Red wire.

4) With ignition on, measure voltage between terminal No. 2 (Green/Red wire) of auto amplifier 16-pin connector and ground. If battery voltage is present, go to next step. If battery voltage is not present, check fuse No. 15 in fuse block. If fuse is blown, repair short circuit and replace fuse. If fuse is okay, repair open Green/Red wire.

5) Disconnect 16-pin connector from auto amplifier. Check for continuity between terminal No. 16 (Black wire) of auto amplifier 16-pin connector and ground. Continuity should exist. If continuity does not exist, repair open Black wire.

BLOWER MOTOR DOES NOT OPERATE AT ALL OR IN HIGH SPEED

1) With ignition off, measure voltage between terminal No. 2 (Red wire) of off relay connector and ground. Off relay is located on blower motor unit. If battery voltage is present, go to next step. If battery voltage is not present, check fuses No. 20 and 21. Replace fuses as necessary. If fuses are okay, repair open Red wire.

2) With ignition on, measure voltage between terminal No. 1 (White wire) of off relay connector and ground. If battery voltage is present, go to next step. If battery voltage is not present, check fuse No. 15. If fuse is blown, repair short circuit and replace fuse. If fuse is okay, repair open White wire.

3) Turn ignition and A/C control panel OFF switch to on position. Measure voltage between terminal No. 3 (Blue wire) of off relay connector and ground. If battery voltage is present, go to next step. If battery voltage is not present, check for open Blue wire between terminal No. 3 of off relay connector and terminal No. 12 of auto amplifier 16-pin connector. Repair wiring as necessary. If Blue wire is okay, replace auto amplifier and retest.
4) Put AUTO switch in on position and fan switch in HI position. Measure voltage between terminal No. 3 (Blue wire) of off relay connector and ground. If approximately one volt is present, go to next step. If approximately one volt is not present, replace auto amplifier and retest.
5) Disconnect 2-pin blower motor connector. Turn ignition on. Put AUTO switch in on position and fan switch in HI position. Measure voltage between terminal No. 1 (Red/Black wire) of blower motor connector and ground. If battery voltage is present, go to step **7)**.
6) If battery voltage is not present, check Red/Black wire between terminal No. 1 of blower motor connector and terminal No. 4 of off relay connector. Repair wiring as necessary. If Red/Black wire is okay, replace off relay.
7) Remove glove box and disconnect fan control amplifier connector. Fan control amplifier is located on cooling unit. With ignition on and AUTO switch in on position, put fan switch in LO or medium position.
8) Measure voltage between terminal No. 2 (Black/Red wire) of hi relay connector and ground. If battery voltage is not present, check for open Black/Red wire. If Black/Red wire is okay, replace blower motor.
9) If battery voltage is present, measure voltage between terminal No. 1 (White wire) of hi relay connector and ground. If battery voltage is not present, repair open White wire. If voltage is present, disconnect hi relay connector.
10) Check for continuity between terminal No. 4 (Black wire) of hi relay connector and ground. If no continuity exists, repair open Black wire. If continuity exists, reconnect hi relay connector and go to next step.
11) Ensure ignition is on. Put AUTO switch in on position. Put fan switch in HI position. Measure voltage between terminal No. 3 (White/Red wire) of hi relay connector and ground. If one volt is present, go to next step. If one volt is not present, check for an open White/Red wire. If White/Red wire is okay, replace auto amplifier.
12) Put fan switch in medium or LOW speeds. Measure voltage between terminal No. 3 (White/Red wire) of hi relay connector and ground. If battery voltage is present, replace hi relay. If battery voltage is not present, replace auto amplifier.

BLOWER MOTOR OPERATES AT HIGH SPEED ONLY

1) Remove glove box. Disconnect fan control amplifier 3-pin connector. Turn ignition on. Put AUTO switch in on position and fan switch in HI position. Measure voltage between terminal No. 2 (Black/Red wire) of fan control amplifier connector and ground.
2) If one volt is not present, check for open Black/Red wire. Repair wiring as necessary. If one volt is present, put fan switch in LO or medium position. Measure voltage between terminal No. 2 (Black/Red wire) of fan control amplifier connector and ground.
3) If battery voltage is not present, check for open Black/Red wire. Repair wiring as necessary. If battery voltage is present, reconnect fan control amplifier connector. With ignition on, put AUTO switch in on position and fan switch in HI position.
4) Measure voltage between terminal No. 1 (Light Green wire) of fan control amplifier connector and ground. Voltage should not be present. If voltage is present, check for faulty harness and repair as necessary. If harness is okay, replace auto amplifier. If voltage is not present, put fan switch in LO or medium position.
5) Measure voltage between terminal No. 1 (Light Green wire) of fan control amplifier connector and ground. If 1-2 volts are not present, check for faulty harness and repair as necessary. If harness is okay, replace auto amplifier. If 1-2 volts are present, disconnect fan control amplifier connector.
6) Check for continuity between terminal No. 4 (Black wire) of fan control amplifier connector and ground. If continuity does not exist, check for open Black wire. Repair wiring as necessary. If continuity exists, replace fan control amplifier.

COMPRESSOR CLUTCH DOES NOT TURN ON OR OFF

Check for blown A/C fuse. *See Fig. 4.* If fuse is okay check for defective trinary (triple) pressure switch, faulty A/C relay, defective multipoint injection Electronic Control Unit (ECU), insufficient refrigerant or faulty wiring harness.

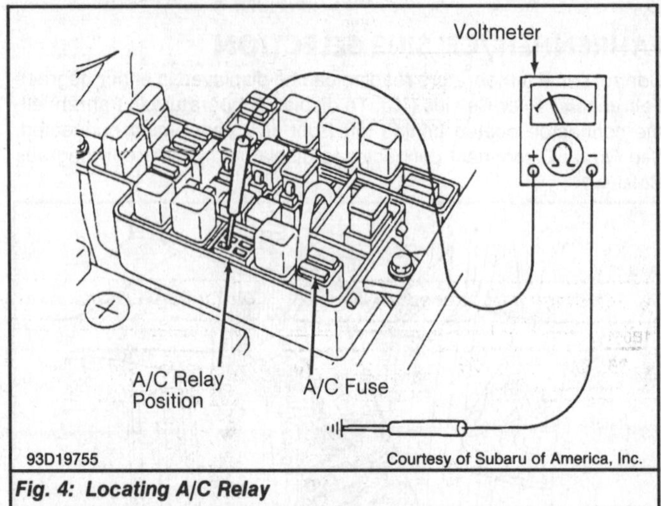
Voltmeter
A/C Relay
Position
A/C Fuse
93D19755
Courtesy of Subaru of America, Inc.

Fig. 4: Locating A/C Relay

SELF-DIAGNOSTIC SYSTEM

Entering Self-Diagnostics – Ensure engine temperature is greater than 104°F (40°C). Depress auto amplifier OFF and AUTO switches simultaneously and turn ignition on. Auto amplifier will enter DIAGNOSTIC STEP 1. See DIAGNOSTIC STEP 1.
Exiting Self-Diagnostics & Clearing Trouble Codes – To exit self-diagnostics, system must be in DIAGNOSTIC STEP 2. Turn ignition off. To clear trouble codes, depress auto amplifier OFF and DEF switches simultaneously and turn ignition on. AUTO switch LED and –88 in temperature display will flash 3 times. All trouble codes are now cleared and system will exit self-diagnostics.

DIAGNOSTIC STEP 1

Display Indicator Inspection – **1)** Indicator lights should be on and temperature display should indicate –88 (all segments on). *See Fig. 5.*
2) If indicators are not on, or temperature display does not indicate –88, check auto amplifier power supply and ground circuits. See A/C SYSTEM OR SELF-DIAGNOSTICS INOPERATIVE. If indicator lights and temperature display segments are okay, after approximately 9 seconds, self-diagnostics will proceed to DIAGNOSTIC STEP 2.

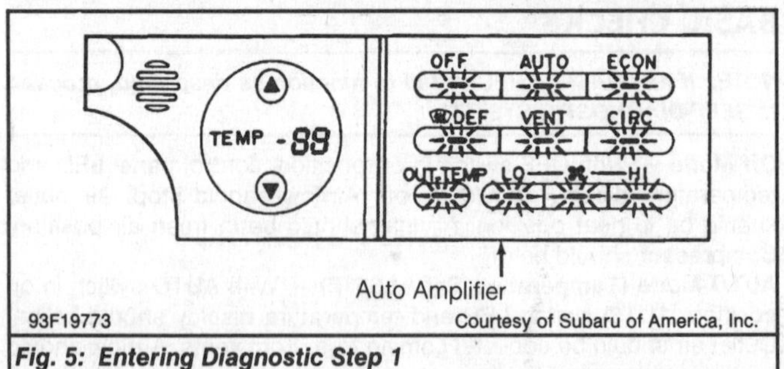
OFF
AUTO
ECON
DEF
VENT
CIRC
TEMP -88
OUT.TEMP
LO
HI
Auto Amplifier
93F19773
Courtesy of Subaru of America, Inc.

Fig. 5: Entering Diagnostic Step 1

DIAGNOSTIC STEP 2

Sensor Circuit & Door Motor Inspection – **1)** If a malfunction has occurred in a monitored circuit, temperature display will indicate a trouble code. If monitored circuits are functioning properly, temperature display will show "00" indicating no system malfunctions. See SENSOR CIRCUIT TROUBLE CODES table.
2) If a trouble code is indicated, proceed to appropriate code testing procedure under TESTING. If all sensors are okay (Code 00 displayed), depress AUTO switch to proceed to DIAGNOSTIC STEP 3

or depress DEF for a minimum of 4 seconds to proceed to DIAGNOSTIC STEP 4. Diagnostic step 3 checks A/C output components. Diagnostic step 4 is used to adjust display temperature.

SENSOR CIRCUIT TROUBLE CODES [1]

Code No.	Diagnosis
00	No Malfunctions
11/21	Open/Short In In-Vehicle Sensor Circuit
12/22	Open/Short In Ambient Sensor Circuit
13/23	Open/Short In Sunload Sensor Circuit
14/24	Open/Short In Evaporator Sensor Circuit
15/25	Open/Short In Refrigerant Temp. Sensor Circuit
16/26	Open/Short In Water Temp. Sensor Circuit
31	Faulty Air Mix Door Motor Circuit
32	Faulty Mode Door Motor Circuit
33	Faulty Air Mix Door Motor Circuit
34	Faulty Mode Door Motor Circuit
35	Faulty Intake Door Motor Circuit

1 – If malfunction is currently occurring, code will be circled in the display.

DIAGNOSTIC STEP 3

Actuator Inspection – 1) Temperature display should read 41. Check compressor and blower operation and positioning of mode door motor, intake door motor and air mix door motor. See ACTUATOR OPERATION SPECIFICATIONS table.

2) To advance to next code, press DEF switch. Ensure all actuators operate as specified. If any actuators do not function as specified, test appropriate circuit under TESTING.

ACTUATOR OPERATION SPECIFICATIONS

Actuator	Test Results
Code 41	
Mode Door	Defrost
Intake Door	Fresh/Recirculation
Air Mix Door	Full Hot
Blower Motor	5 Volts
Compressor	On
Compressor Solenoid	Zero Amps
Code 42	
Mode Door	Heat
Intake Door	Fresh
Air Mix Door	Full Hot
Blower Motor	7 Volts
Compressor	On
Compressor Solenoid	.65 Amps
Code 43	
Mode Door	Bi-Level
Intake Door	Fresh
Air Mix Door	50% Hot
Blower Motor	11 Volts
Compressor	Off
Compressor Solenoid	Zero Amps
Code 44	
Mode Door	Vent
Intake Door	Fresh
Air Mix Door	Full Cold
Blower Motor	Fan High
Compressor	Off
Compressor Solenoid	Zero Amps
Code 45	
Mode Door	Vent
Intake Door	Recirculation
Air Mix Door	Full Cold
Blower Motor	Fan High
Compressor	Off
Compressor Solenoid	Zero Amps

DIAGNOSTIC STEP 4

Display Temperature Correction – 1) This procedure is used to adjust display temperature when small differences between temperature setting and actual temperature felt by passengers exist.

2) Once DIAGNOSTIC STEP 4 has been activated, temperature display will show one of the following. A "10" indicates that temperature has previously been adjusted to read a higher temperature.

3) A "00" indicates that temperature display has previously been adjusted to read a lower temperature. A "05" indicates that temperature has not been previously adjusted and is at the standard (default) position.

4) Press temperature LO or HI switches as necessary to adjust temperature display. Each time LO or HI switch is pressed, temperature setting will change. If vehicle battery is disconnected, temperature setting will default to standard position.

TESTING

WARNING: To avoid injury from accidental air bag deployment, read and carefully follow all SERVICE PRECAUTIONS and DISABLING & ACTIVATING AIR BAG SYSTEM procedures in AIR BAG SYSTEM SAFETY article in GENERAL SERVICING.

A/C SYSTEM PERFORMANCE

Connect manifold gauge set. Open all windows. Start and run engine at 1500-1700 RPM. Place blower fan on high speed. Press temperature control button and set temperature at 65°F (18°C). Ensure reading is within specifications. See SPECIFICATIONS table at beginning of article.

A/C AUTO AMPLIFIER PIN VOLTAGE TEST

Remove A/C amplifier to gain access to connectors. See AUTO AMPLIFIER under REMOVAL & INSTALLATION. With wiring harness connected to A/C amplifier, ensure voltages are as specified. Connect voltmeter between specified terminal(s) and/or ground.

See A/C AUTO AMPLIFIER PIN VOLTAGE TEST (16-PIN CONNECTOR) and A/C AUTO AMPLIFIER PIN VOLTAGE TEST (20-PIN CONNECTOR) tables. If voltage is not as specified, check appropriate circuit and input/output device. Repair or replace as necessary. If circuit and input/output device are okay, replace A/C amplifier.

A/C AUTO AMPLIFIER PIN VOLTAGE TEST (16-PIN CONNECTOR)

Circuit & Test Condition	Voltage
A/C Relay	
Terminal No. 12 (Brown Wire) To Ground	[1] Battery
Air Mix Door Motor (PBR)	
Terminal No. 5 (Green/Black Wire) To Terminal No. 6 (Green/Yellow Wire)	[2] Battery
Auto Amplifier Ground Circuit	
Terminal No. 16 (Black Wire) To Ground	Zero
Hi Relay	
Terminal No. 12 (Yellow/Green Wire) To Ground	[3] Battery
Ignition Power Supply	
Terminal No. 2 (Green/Red Wire) To Ground	
Ignition On	Battery
Engine Running	13-14
Memory Back-Up (Battery Voltage)	
Terminal No. 1 (Blue/Red Wire) To Ground	[4] 13-14
Mode Door Motor	
Terminal No. 3 (Green/Red Wire) To Terminal No. 4 (Light Green/Black Wire)	[3] Battery
Off Relay	
Terminal No. 12 (Blue/Black Wire) To Ground	[4] Battery

1 – Ignition and A/C switches on.
2 – With ignition on, voltmeter positive lead at terminal No. 5 and negative lead at terminal No. 6 and temperature set at 65°F (18°C). Battery voltage should also be present with voltmeter positive lead at terminal No. 6 and negative lead at terminal No. 5 and temperature set at 85°F (32°C).
3 – With ignition on.
4 – Voltage specified is with engine running.
5 – With ignition on, voltmeter positive lead at terminal No. 3 and negative lead at terminal No. 4 and VENT switch depressed. Battery voltage should also be present with voltmeter positive lead at terminal No. 4 and negative lead at terminal No. 3 and DEF switch depressed.

1993 AUTOMATIC A/C-HEATER SYSTEMS SVX (Cont.)

A/C AUTO AMPLIFIER PIN VOLTAGE TEST (20-PIN CONNECTOR)

Circuit & Test Condition	Voltage
Accessory Power Supply	
Terminal No. 18 (Light Green/Red Wire) To Ground	
Engine Cranking	Zero
Engine Running	Battery
Air Mix Door Motor (PBR)	
Terminal No. 14 (Black/White Wire) To Terminal No. 11 (Green/Black Wire)	[1] About .5
Ambient Sensor	
Terminal No. 2 (White/Green Wire) To Terminal No. 11 (Green/Black Wire)	[2] About 5
Evaporator Sensor	
Terminal No. 3 (Black/Yellow Wire) To Terminal No. 11 (Green/Black Wire)	[2] About 5
Illumination Control Signal	
Terminal No. 10 (Red Wire) To Ground	[3] Battery
Mode Door Motor (Fresh Voltage)	
Terminal No. 7 (Green/White Wire) To Terminal No. 11 (Green/Black Wire)	[4] Battery
Mode Door Motor (PBR)	
Terminal No. 15 (Light Green/Black Wire) To Terminal No. 11 (Green/Black Wire)	[5] About 4.5
Mode Door Motor (REC Voltage)	
Terminal No. 5 (Green Wire) To Terminal No. 11 (Green/Black Wire)	[6] Battery
Refrigerant Temperature Sensor	
Terminal No. 4 (Yellow/Blue Wire) To Terminal No. 11 (Green/Black Wire)	[2] About 5
Sensor Ground Circuit	
Terminal No. 11 (Green/Black Wire) To Ground	Zero
Sunload Sensor	
Terminal No. 13 (White/Blue Wire) To Terminal No. 11 (Green/Black Wire)	[2] About 5
Sensor Voltage	
Terminal No. 1 (Blue/Red Wire) To Ground	[7] Zero
Water Temperature Sensor	
Terminal No. 12 (Blue/White Wire) To Terminal No. 11 (Green/Black Wire)	[2] About 5

[1] – With temperature set at 65°F (18°C) and AUTO switch on. Voltage reading of 4.5 volts with temperature set at 85°F (29°C).
[2] – With ignition on and sensor connector disconnected.
[3] – With ignition and light switches on.
[4] – With ignition and DEF switches on.
[5] – With ignition and VENT switches on. Voltage reading should be .5 volt with ignition and DEF switches on.
[6] – With ignition and CIRC switches on.
[7] – With ignition on, voltage reading should be 5 volts.

CODE 11/21, IN-VEHICLE TEMPERATURE SENSOR CIRCUIT

In-Vehicle Sensor Resistance – 1) Turn ignition off. Remove auto amplifier. See AUTO AMPLIFIER under REMOVAL & INSTALLATION. Disconnect in-vehicle temperature sensor 2-pin connector. *See Fig. 6*. Check resistance between sensor connector terminals. See IN-VEHICLE TEMPERATURE SENSOR RESISTANCE SPECIFICATIONS table.

2) If resistance reading is not as specified, replace sensor. If resistance reading is okay, turn ignition on. Measure voltage available to in-vehicle sensor. If approximately 5 volts is not available to sensor, check wiring harness between in-vehicle sensor and auto amplifier.

3) Repair wiring harness as necessary. If wiring harness is okay, replace auto amplifier. If approximately 5 volts is available to sensor, an intermittent problem may exist. Ensure auto amplifier connectors are properly connected to auto amplifier.

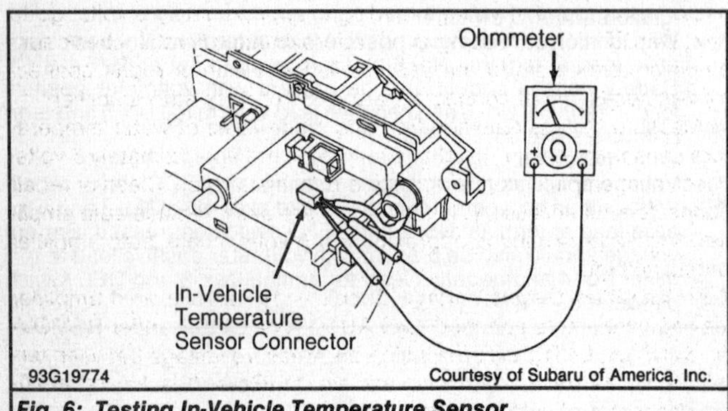
Ohmmeter
In-Vehicle
Temperature
Sensor Connector
93G19774
Courtesy of Subaru of America, Inc.

Fig. 6: Testing In-Vehicle Temperature Sensor

IN-VEHICLE TEMPERATURE SENSOR RESISTANCE SPECIFICATIONS

Temperature °F (°C)	Ohms
-4 (-20)	16,500
32 (0)	9930
50 (10)	6000
68 (20)	3750
77 (25)	3000
86 (30)	2420
104 (40)	1060

CODE 12/22, AMBIENT TEMPERATURE SENSOR CIRCUIT

Ambient Temperature Sensor Resistance – 1) Turn ignition off. Disconnect ambient temperature sensor 2-pin connector. Sensor is located on hood lock brace.

2) Check resistance between sensor connector terminals. If resistance reading is not as specified, replace sensor. See AMBIENT TEMPERATURE SENSOR RESISTANCE SPECIFICATIONS table. If resistance reading is okay, check ambient temperature sensor harness.

AMBIENT TEMPERATURE SENSOR RESISTANCE SPECIFICATIONS

Temperature °F (°C)	Ohms
-4 (-20)	16,500
32 (0)	9930
50 (10)	6000
68 (20)	3750
77 (25)	3000
86 (30)	2420
104 (40)	1060

Ambient Temperature Sensor Harness Check – 1) Turn ignition on. Measure voltage between terminal No. 2 (White/Green wire) of ambient temperature sensor connector and ground. If voltage reading is approximately 5 volts, go to next step. If voltage reading is not approximately 5 volts, check auto amplifier connectors for proper installation. If connectors are okay, replace auto amplifier.

2) Measure voltage between terminals No. 1 (Green/Black wire) and No. 2 (White/Green wire) of ambient temperature sensor connector. If voltage reading is not approximately 5 volts, check auto amplifier connectors for proper installation. Clean or repair connectors as necessary. If connectors are okay, replace auto amplifier. If voltage reading is approximately 5 volts, check auto amplifier output voltage.

Auto Amplifier Output Voltage Check – 1) Remove auto amplifier leaving connectors attached. See AUTO AMPLIFIER under REMOVAL & INSTALLATION. Disconnect ambient sensor connector. Turn ignition on. Measure voltage between terminals No. 2 (White/Green wire) and No. 11 (Green/Black wire) of auto amplifier 16-pin connector. *See Fig. 3*.

2) If voltage is approximately 5 volts, check and repair wiring harness as necessary. If voltage is not approximately 5 volts, check wiring harness between ambient sensor and auto amplifier. Repair wiring harness as necessary. If wiring is okay, replace auto amplifier.

CODE 13/23, SUNLOAD SENSOR CIRCUIT

Auto Amplifier Output Voltage Check – 1) Turn ignition off. Remove auto amplifier leaving connectors attached. See AUTO AMPLIFIER under REMOVAL & INSTALLATION. Place cover over sunload sensor to block sunlight. Sensor is located on top left corner of dash. Measure voltage between terminal No. 11 (Green/Black wire) and terminal No. 13 (White/Black wire) of 20-pin auto amplifier connector. *See Fig. 3*.

2) If approximately 5 volts is present, go to next step. If approximately 5 volts is not present, check 20-pin auto amplifier connector for proper installation. Clean or repair connector as necessary. If connector is okay, replace auto amplifier.

NOTE: If sunlight is not available, use a 100-watt light bulb to simulate sunlight in the following step.

3) Remove cover from sunload sensor and allow sunlight to shine on sensor. Measure voltage between terminals No. 11 (Green/Black wire) and No. 13 (White/Black wire) of auto amplifier 20-pin connector. If voltage is approximately 3 volts, sensor circuit is okay. Replace auto amplifier.

4) If voltage is not approximately 3 volts, check wiring harness between auto amplifier and sunload sensor. Repair wiring harness as necessary and retest. If wiring harness is okay, replace sensor.

CODE 14/24, EVAPORATOR TEMPERATURE SENSOR CIRCUIT

Evaporator Temperature Sensor Resistance – 1) Turn ignition off. Remove glove box. Disconnect evaporator temperature sensor 2-pin connector. Sensor is located below blower motor unit.

2) Check resistance between Yellow/Red and Green/White wires of evaporator sensor connector. If resistance reading is not as specified, replace sensor. See EVAPORATOR TEMPERATURE SENSOR RESISTANCE SPECIFICATIONS table. If resistance is okay, check evaporator temperature sensor harness.

EVAPORATOR TEMPERATURE SENSOR RESISTANCE SPECIFICATIONS

Temperature °F (°C)	Ohms
32 (0)	6190
50 (10)	4010
68 (20)	2670
77 (25)	2200
86 (30)	1830
104 (40)	1280

Evaporator Temperature Sensor Harness Check – 1) Turn ignition on. Measure voltage between Yellow/Red wire of evaporator temperature sensor connector and ground. If voltage reading is approximately 5 volts, go to next step. If voltage reading is not approximately 5 volts, check auto amplifier connectors for proper installation. Clean or repair connectors as necessary. If connectors are okay, replace auto amplifier.

2) Measure voltage between Yellow/Red and Green/White wires of evaporator temperature sensor connector. If voltage reading is not approximately 5 volts, check auto amplifier connectors for proper installation. If connectors are okay, replace auto amplifier. If voltage reading is approximately 5 volts, check auto amplifier output voltage.

Auto Amplifier Output Voltage Check – 1) Remove auto amplifier leaving connectors attached. See AUTO AMPLIFIER under REMOVAL & INSTALLATION. Turn ignition on. Measure voltage between terminals No. 3 (Black/Yellow wire) and No. 11 (Green/Black wire) of auto amplifier 20-pin connector.

2) If voltage reading is approximately 5 volts, an intermittent problem may exist. Ensure auto amplifier connectors are properly connected to auto amplifier. If voltage reading is not approximately 5 volts, check auto amplifier 20-pin connector for proper installation. Clean or repair connector as necessary and retest. If connector is okay, replace auto amplifier.

CODE 15/25, REFRIGERANT TEMPERATURE SENSOR CIRCUIT

Refrigerant Temperature Sensor Resistance – 1) Turn ignition off. Remove glove box. Disconnect refrigerant temperature sensor 2-pin connector. Sensor is located below blower motor unit.

2) Check resistance between Brown/White and Green/Black wires of refrigerant sensor connector. If resistance reading is not as specified, replace sensor. See REFRIGERANT TEMPERATURE SENSOR RESISTANCE SPECIFICATIONS table. If resistance is okay, check refrigerant temperature sensor harness.

REFRIGERANT TEMPERATURE SENSOR RESISTANCE SPECIFICATIONS

Temperature °F (°C)	Ohms
32 (0)	6190
50 (10)	4010
68 (20)	2670
77 (25)	2200
86 (30)	1830
104 (40)	1280

Refrigerant Temperature Sensor Harness Check – 1) Turn ignition on. Measure voltage between Brown/White wire of refrigerant temperature sensor connector and ground. If voltage reading is approximately 5 volts, go to next step. If voltage reading is not approximately 5 volts, check auto amplifier connectors for proper installation. If connectors are okay, replace auto amplifier.

2) Measure voltage between Brown/White and Green/White wires of refrigerant temperature sensor connector. If voltage reading is not approximately 5 volts, check auto amplifier connectors for proper installation. Clean or repair connectors as necessary. If connectors are okay, replace auto amplifier. If voltage reading is approximately 5 volts, check auto amplifier output voltage.

Auto Amplifier Output Voltage Check – 1) Remove auto amplifier leaving connectors attached. See AUTO AMPLIFIER under REMOVAL & INSTALLATION. Turn ignition on. Measure voltage between terminals No. 4 (Yellow/Blue wire) and No. 11 (Green/Black wire) of auto amplifier 20-pin connector.

2) If voltage reading is approximately 5 volts, an intermittent problem may exist. Ensure auto amplifier connectors are properly connected to auto amplifier. If voltage reading is not approximately 5 volts, check auto amplifier 20-pin connector for proper installation. Clean or repair connector as necessary and retest. If connector is okay, replace auto amplifier.

CODE 16/26, WATER TEMPERATURE SENSOR CIRCUIT

Water Temperature Sensor Resistance – 1) Turn ignition off. Remove glove box. Disconnect water temperature sensor 2-pin connector. Sensor is located in heater case, near heater core.

2) Check resistance between Red and White wires of water sensor connector. If resistance reading is not as specified, replace sensor. See WATER TEMPERATURE SENSOR RESISTANCE SPECIFICATIONS table. If resistance is okay, check water temperature sensor harness.

WATER TEMPERATURE SENSOR RESISTANCE SPECIFICATIONS

Temperature °F (°C)	Ohms
32 (0)	6190
50 (10)	4010
68 (20)	2670
77 (25)	2200
86 (30)	1830
104 (40)	1280

Water Temperature Sensor Harness Check – 1) Turn ignition on. Measure voltage between Red wire of water temperature sensor connector and ground. If voltage reading is approximately 5 volts, go to next step. If voltage reading is not approximately 5 volts, check auto amplifier connectors for proper installation. Clean or repair connectors as necessary. If connectors are okay, replace auto amplifier.

2) Measure voltage between Red and White wires of water temperature sensor connector. If voltage reading is not approximately 5 volts, check auto amplifier connectors for proper installation. Clean or repair connectors as necessary. If connectors are okay, replace auto amplifier. If voltage reading is approximately 5 volts, check auto amplifier output voltage.

Auto Amplifier Output Voltage Check – 1) Remove auto amplifier leaving connectors attached. See AUTO AMPLIFIER under REMOVAL & INSTALLATION. Turn ignition on. Measure voltage between terminals No. 12 (Blue/White wire) and No. 11 (Green/Black wire) at 20-pin connector of auto amplifier.

1993 AUTOMATIC A/C-HEATER SYSTEMS SVX (Cont.)

2) If voltage reading is approximately 5 volts, an intermittent problem may exist. Ensure auto amplifier connectors are properly connected to auto amplifier. If voltage reading is not approximately 5 volts, check auto amplifier 20-pin connector for proper installation. Clean or repair connector as necessary and retest. If connector is okay, replace auto amplifier.

CODE 31, AIR MIX DOOR MOTOR CIRCUIT

1) Remove auto amplifier leaving connectors attached. See AUTO AMPLIFIER under REMOVAL & INSTALLATION. Enter DIAGNOSTIC STEP 3. See ENTERING SELF-DIAGNOSTICS under SELF-DIAGNOSTIC SYSTEM.
2) Measure voltage between terminals No. 14 (Black/White wire) and No. 11 (Green/Black wire) of auto amplifier 20-pin connector. With temperature display at 41 or 42, voltage reading should be 4.5 volts.
3) Depress DEF switch to advance to next temperature display. With temperature display at 43, voltage reading should be 2.5 volts. With temperature display at 44 or 45, voltage reading should be .5 volt.
4) If voltage readings are okay, perform procedures under CODE 33 AIR MIX DOOR MOTOR CIRCUIT. If voltage readings are not as specified, check auto amplifier output voltage.
Auto Amplifier Output Voltage Check – 1) Disconnect air mix door motor 7-pin (5 wire) connector. Connector is located near cooling unit. Turn ignition on. Measure voltage between terminals No. 1 (Blue/White wire) and No. 11 (Green/Black wire) of auto amplifier 20-pin connector.
2) If voltage reading is not approximately 5 volts, check auto amplifier connectors for proper installation. Clean or repair connectors as necessary. If connectors are okay, replace auto amplifier. If voltage reading is approximately 5 volts, check air mix door motor wiring harness.
Air Mix Door Motor Wiring Harness Check – 1) Disconnect auto amplifier connectors. With air mix door motor connector disconnected, measure resistance between terminal No. 1 (Blue/White wire) of auto amplifier 20-pin connector and terminal No. 3 (Blue wire) of air mix door motor connector. Resistance should be zero ohms.
2) Measure resistance between terminal No. 14 (Black/White wire) of auto amplifier 20-pin connector and terminal No. 6 (Brown wire) of air mix door motor connector. Resistance should be zero ohms.
3) Measure resistance between terminal No. 11 (Green/Black wire) of auto amplifier 20-pin connector and terminal No. 2 (White wire) of air mix door motor connector. Resistance should be zero ohms.
4) If resistance readings are not as specified, check auto amplifier connectors for proper installation. Clean or repair connectors as necessary. If connectors are okay, replace auto amplifier. If resistance readings are okay, go to next step.
5) Measure resistance between ground and terminals No. 11 (Green/Black wire), No. 14 (Black/White wire), and No. 3 (Blue wire) of auto amplifier 20-pin connector. Resistance readings should be infinite. If resistance readings are not as specified, check and repair wiring harness as necessary. If resistance readings are okay, replace air mix door motor.

CODE 32, MODE DOOR MOTOR CIRCUIT

Potentiometric Balance Resistor (PBR) Check – 1) Remove auto amplifier leaving connectors attached. See AUTO AMPLIFIER under REMOVAL & INSTALLATION. Enter DIAGNOSTIC STEP 3. See ENTERING SELF-DIAGNOSTICS under SELF-DIAGNOSTIC SYSTEM.
2) Measure voltage between terminals No. 15 (Light Green/Black wire) and No. 11 (Green/Black wire) of auto amplifier 20-pin connector. With temperature display at 41, voltage reading should be .5 volt. With temperature display at 44, voltage reading should be 4.5 volts.
3) If voltage readings are okay, perform procedures under CODE 34 MODE DOOR MOTOR CIRCUIT. If voltage readings are not as specified, check auto amplifier output voltage.
Auto Amplifier Output Voltage Check – 1) Disconnect mode door motor 7-pin (5 wire) connector. Connector is located on left side of heater unit. Turn ignition on. Measure voltage between terminals No. 1 (Blue/Red wire) and No. 11 (Green/Black wire) of 20-pin connector.
2) If voltage reading is not approximately 5 volts, check auto amplifier connectors for proper installation. Clean or repair connectors as necessary. If connectors are okay, replace auto amplifier. If voltage reading is approximately 5 volts, check mode door motor wiring harness.
Mode Door Motor Wiring Harness Check – 1) Disconnect auto amplifier connectors. With mode door motor connector disconnected, measure resistance between terminal No. 1 (Blue/White wire) of auto amplifier 20-pin connector and terminal No. 3 (Blue wire) of air mix door motor connector. Resistance should be zero ohms.
2) Measure resistance between terminal No. 14 (Black/White wire) of auto amplifier 20-pin connector and terminal No. 6 (Brown wire) of air mix door motor connector. Resistance should be zero ohms.
3) Measure resistance between terminal No. 11 (Green/Black wire) of auto amplifier 20-pin connector and terminal No. 2 (White wire) of air mix door motor connector. Resistance should be zero ohms.
4) If resistance readings are not as specified, check auto amplifier connectors for proper installation. Clean or repair connectors as necessary. If connectors are okay, replace auto amplifier. If resistance readings are okay, go to next step.
5) Measure resistance between ground and terminals No. 11 (Green/Black wire), No. 14 (Black/White wire), and No. 3 (Blue wire) of auto amplifier 20-pin connector. Resistance readings should be infinite. If resistance readings are not as specified, check and repair wiring harness as necessary. If resistance readings are okay, replace air mix door motor.

CODE 33, AIR MIX DOOR MOTOR CIRCUIT

Auto Amplifier Output Voltage Check – 1) Remove auto amplifier leaving connectors attached. See AUTO AMPLIFIER under REMOVAL & INSTALLATION. Enter DIAGNOSTIC STEP 3. See ENTERING SELF-DIAGNOSTICS under SELF-DIAGNOSTIC SYSTEM.
2) Using an analog voltmeter, connect voltmeter positive lead to terminal No. 6 (Green/Yellow wire) and negative lead to terminal No. 5 (Green/Black wire) of auto amplifier 16-pin connector. Observe voltmeter and change temperature display from No. 45 to 41. Voltage reading should fluctuate between zero and 5 volts.

NOTE:* *Voltage is only displayed when air mix door motor is operating.

3) Reverse voltmeter leads and change temperature display from No. 42 to 44. Voltage reading should fluctuate between zero and 5 volts. If voltage readings are not as specified, check auto amplifier connectors for proper installation. Clean or repair connectors as necessary. If connectors are okay, replace auto amplifier. If voltage readings are okay, check air mix door motor wiring harness.
Air Mix Door Motor Wiring Harness Check – 1) Disconnect auto amplifier and air mix door motor connectors. Measure resistance between terminal No. 6 (Green/Yellow wire) of auto amplifier 16-pin connector and terminal No. 5 (Green/Black wire) of air mix door motor connector. Resistance should be zero ohms.
2) Measure resistance between terminal No. 5 (Green/Black wire) of auto amplifier 16-pin connector and terminal No. 7 (Yellow wire) of air mix door motor connector. Resistance should be zero ohms. If resistance is not as specified, check and repair wiring harness as necessary. If resistance is okay, go to next step.
3) Measure resistance between ground and terminals No. 6 (Green/Yellow wire) and No. 5 (Green/Black wire) of auto amplifier 16-pin connector. Resistance readings should be infinite. If resistance readings are not as specified, check and repair wiring harness as necessary. If resistance readings are okay, replace air mix door motor.

CODE 34, MODE DOOR MOTOR CIRCUIT

Auto Amplifier Output Voltage Check – 1) Remove glove box. Remove auto amplifier leaving connectors attached. See AUTO

AMPLIFIER under REMOVAL & INSTALLATION. Enter DIAGNOSTIC STEP 3. See ENTERING SELF-DIAGNOSTICS under SELF-DIAGNOSTIC SYSTEM.

2) Using an analog voltmeter, connect voltmeter positive lead to terminal No. 3 (Green/Red wire) and negative lead to terminal No. 4 (Light Green/Black wire) of auto amplifier 16-pin connector. Observe voltmeter and change temperature display from No. 41 to 45. Voltage reading should fluctuate between zero and 5 volts.

NOTE: Voltage is only displayed when mode door motor is operating.

3) Reverse voltmeter leads and change set display from No. 45 to 41. Voltage reading should fluctuate between zero and 5 volts. If voltage readings are not as specified, check auto amplifier connectors for proper installation.

4) Clean or repair connectors as necessary. If connectors are okay, replace auto amplifier. If voltage readings are okay, check mode door motor wiring harness.

Mode Door Motor Wiring Harness Check – 1) Disconnect auto amplifier and mode door motor connectors. Measure resistance between terminal No. 3 (Green/Red wire) of auto amplifier 16-pin connector and terminal No. 5 (Red/White wire) of mode door motor connector. Resistance should be zero ohms.

2) Measure resistance between terminal No. 4 (Light Green/Black wire) of auto amplifier 16-pin connector and terminal No. 7 (White/Red wire) of mode door motor connector. Resistance should be zero ohms. If resistance is not as specified, check and repair wiring harness as necessary. If resistance is okay, go to next step.

3) Measure resistance between ground and terminals No. 3 (Green/Red wire) and No. 4 (Light Green/Black wire) of auto amplifier 16-pin connector. Resistance readings should be infinite. If resistance readings are not as specified, check and repair wiring harness as necessary. If resistance readings are okay, replace mode door motor.

CODE 35, INTAKE MODE DOOR MOTOR CIRCUIT

Intake Door Motor Voltage Check – 1) Remove glove box. Disconnect intake door motor 7-pin (6 wire) connector. Connector is located on right side of blower motor unit. Turn ignition on. Measure voltage between terminal No. 4 (White wire) and ground.

2) If battery voltage is not present, check fuse No. 15 in fuse block. If fuse is blown, repair short circuit and replace fuse. If fuse is okay, check and repair wiring harness as necessary. If battery voltage is present, check intake door motor.

Intake Door Motor Check – 1) Remove auto amplifier, leaving connectors attached. See AUTO AMPLIFIER under REMOVAL & INSTALLATION. Enter DIAGNOSTIC STEP 3. See ENTERING SELF-DIAGNOSTICS under SELF-DIAGNOSTIC SYSTEM.

2) Wait approximately 10 seconds. Measure voltage between terminal No. 5 (Green wire) of auto amplifier 20-pin connector and ground. With temperature display at 45, voltage reading should be approximately 5 volts. With temperature display at any number other than 45, voltage reading should be zero volts.

3) Measure voltage between terminal No. 6 (Green/Yellow wire) of auto amplifier 20-pin connector and ground. With temperature display at 41, voltage reading should be approximately 5 volts. With temperature display at any number other than 41, voltage reading should be zero volts.

4) Measure voltage between terminal No. 7 (Green/White wire) of auto amplifier 20-pin connector and ground. With temperature display at 42, 43 or 44, voltage reading should be approximately 5 volts. With temperature display at 41 or 45, voltage reading should be zero volts.

5) If voltage readings are not as specified, check auto amplifier connectors for proper installation. Clean or repair connectors as necessary. If connectors are okay, replace auto amplifier. If voltage readings are okay, check intake door motor wiring harness.

Intake Door Motor Wiring Harness Check – 1) Disconnect auto amplifier connectors. With intake door motor connector disconnected, measure resistance between terminal No. 5 (Green/wire) at 20-pin connector of auto amplifier and terminal No. 6 (Green/Yellow wire) of intake door motor connector. Resistance should be zero ohms.

2) Measure resistance between terminal No. 6 (Green/Yellow wire) at 20-pin connector of auto amplifier and terminal No. 3 (Black/Yellow wire) of intake door motor connector. Resistance should be zero ohms.

3) Measure resistance between terminal No. 7 (Green/White wire) of auto amplifier 20-pin connector and terminal No. 2 (White/Green wire) of intake door motor connector. Resistance should be zero ohms.

4) Measure resistance between terminal No. 11 (Green/Black wire) of auto amplifier 20-pin connector and terminal No. 1 (Blue/White wire) of intake door motor connector. Resistance should be zero ohms.

5) If resistance readings are not as specified, check auto amplifier connectors for proper installation. Clean or repair connectors as necessary. If connectors are okay, replace auto amplifier. If resistance readings are okay, go to next step.

6) Measure resistance between terminal No. 5 (Green wire), No. 6 (Green/Yellow wire), No. 7 (Green/White wire), and No. 11 (Green/Black wire) of auto amplifier 20-pin connector and ground. Resistance readings should be infinite. If resistance readings are not as specified, check and repair wiring harness as necessary. If resistance readings are okay, replace intake door motor.

REMOVAL & INSTALLATION

WARNING: To avoid injury from accidental air bag deployment, read and carefully follow all SERVICE PRECAUTIONS and DISABLING & ACTIVATING AIR BAG SYSTEM procedures in AIR BAG SYSTEM SAFETY article in GENERAL SERVICING.

AUTO AMPLIFIER

Removal & Installation – Remove instrument cluster cover. *See Fig. 7.* Remove center grille. Remove auto amplifier screws. Disconnect aspirator duct from auto amplifier. Remove auto amplifier from dashboard. To install, reverse removal procedure. Ensure no clearance exists between components.

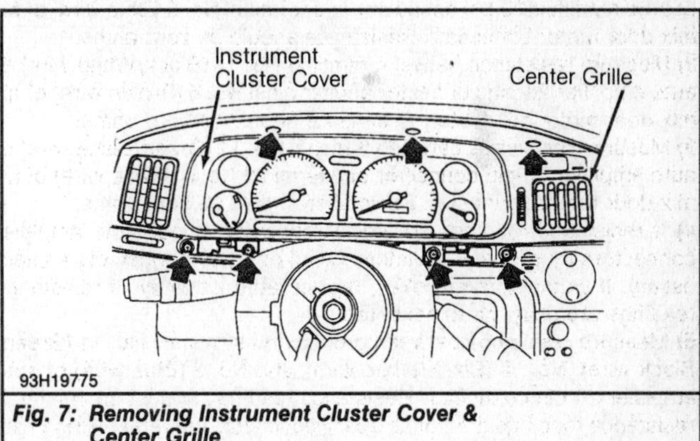

Instrument Cluster Cover
Center Grille
93H19775

Fig. 7: Removing Instrument Cluster Cover & Center Grille

A/C COMPRESSOR

Removal – 1) Disconnect negative battery cable. Discharge A/C system using approved refrigerant recovery/recycling equipment. Remove belt cover. Remove alternator and A/C compressor belt.

2) Disconnect low-pressure and high-pressure hoses from compressor. Remove alternator and A/C compressor connectors. Remove lower compressor bracket. Remove compressor.

Installation – To install, reverse removal procedure. Tighten compressor bolts to 23-29 ft. lbs. (31-39 N.m). Evacuate and charge A/C system. Check A/C system for proper operation.

CONDENSER

Removal – 1) Disconnect negative battery cable. Discharge A/C system using approved refrigerant recovery/recycling equipment. Disconnect radiator fan connectors. Remove front grille. Remove upper radiator bracket. Disconnect pipe and hose connections from condenser. Remove radiator fans.

1993 AUTOMATIC A/C-HEATER SYSTEMS SVX (Cont.)

2) Disconnect cooling hose located under radiator fan shroud. Position fuel evaporation canister out of way. Disconnect trinary (triple) pressure switch connector. Raise and support vehicle.
3) Remove splash shield from underneath vehicle. Remove 2 bolts securing oil cooler to condenser. Lower vehicle. Remove condenser bolts. Move radiator forward and remove condenser.
Installation – To install, reverse removal procedure. Ensure guide on lower side of condenser is inserted into hole in radiator panel. Evacuate and charge A/C system. Check A/C system for proper operation.

EVAPORATOR

Removal – **1)** Disconnect negative battery cable. Discharge A/C system using approved refrigerant recovery/recycling equipment. Disconnect low and high-pressure hoses from evaporator.
2) Remove glove box. Disconnect fan control amplifier connector. *See Fig. 8.* Remove time control unit. Time control unit is located above fan amplifier. Disconnect cooling unit drain hose. Remove cooling unit bolts.
3) Remove cooling unit. Remove refrigerant temperature and evaporator sensors from cooling unit. Remove clamps holding cooling unit upper and lower housings. Separate cooling unit housing. Remove evaporator. *See Fig. 8*
Installation – To install, reverse removal procedure. Evacuate and charge A/C system. Check A/C system for proper operation.

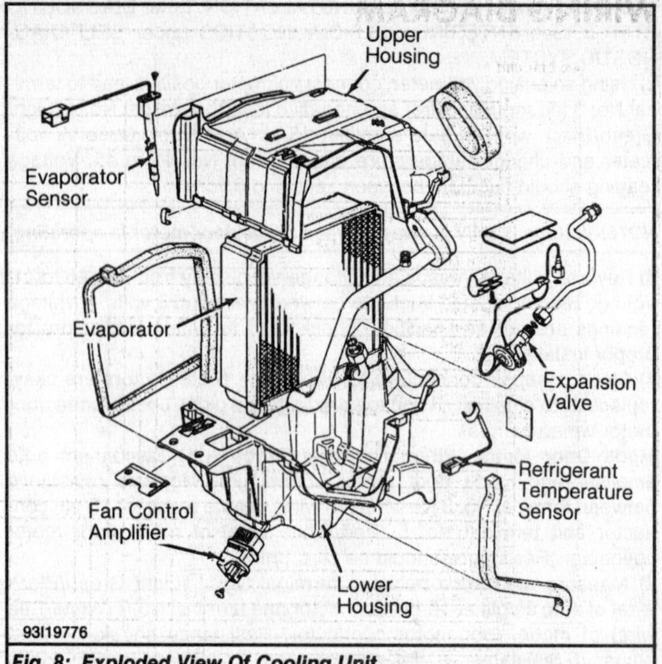
Upper
Housing
Evaporator
Sensor
Evaporator
Expansion
Valve
Refrigerant
Temperature
Sensor
Fan Control
Amplifier
Lower
Housing
93I19776

Fig. 8: Exploded View Of Cooling Unit

WIRING DIAGRAM

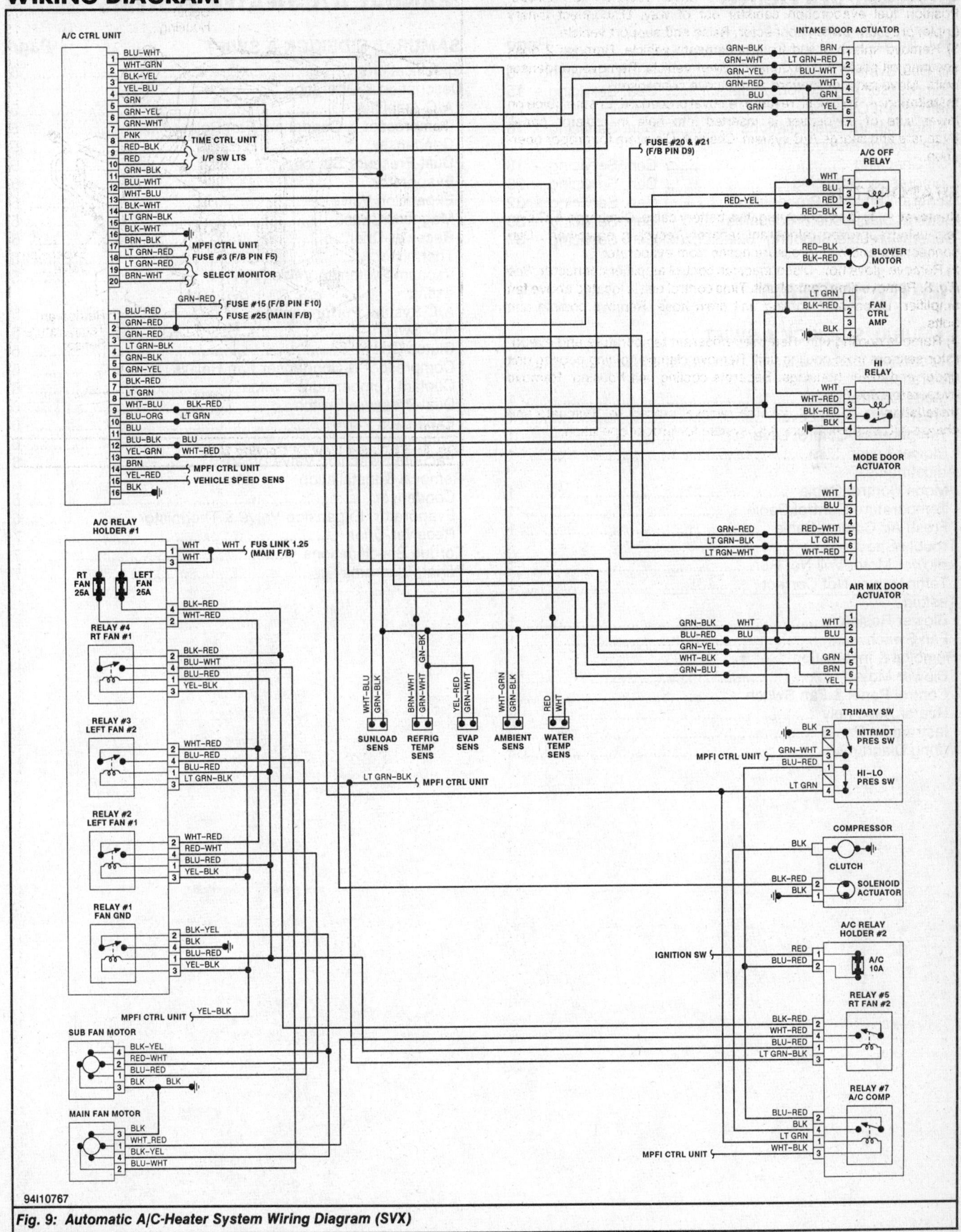
A/C CTRL UNIT
BLU-WHT
WHT-GRN
BLK-YEL
YEL-BLU
GRN
GRN-YEL
GRN-WHT
PNK
RED-BLK
RED
GRN-BLK
BLU-WHT
WHT-BLU
BLK-WHT
LT GRN-BLK
BLK-WHT
BRN-BLK
LT GRN-RED
LT GRN-RED
BRN-WHT
TIME CTRL UNIT
I/P SW LTS
MPFI CTRL UNIT
FUSE #3 (F/B PIN F5)
SELECT MONITOR
GRN-RED
FUSE #15 (F/B PIN F10)
FUSE #25 (MAIN F/B)
BLU-RED
GRN-RED
GRN-RED
LT GRN-BLK
GRN-BLK
GRN-YEL
BLK-RED
LT GRN
WHT-BLU
BLU-ORG
BLU
BLU-BLK
YEL-GRN
BRN
YEL-RED
BLK
BLK-RED
LT GRN
WHT-RED
MPFI CTRL UNIT
VEHICLE SPEED SENS
A/C RELAY HOLDER #1
WHT
FUS LINK 1.25 (MAIN F/B)
RT FAN 25A
LEFT FAN 25A
RELAY #4 RT FAN #1
RELAY #3 LEFT FAN #2
RELAY #2 LEFT FAN #1
RELAY #1 FAN GND
BLU-WHT
YEL-BLK
BLK-YEL
BLK
MPFI CTRL UNIT
SUB FAN MOTOR
RED-WHT
MAIN FAN MOTOR
WHT_RED
SUNLOAD SENS
REFRIG TEMP SENS
EVAP SENS
AMBIENT SENS
WATER TEMP SENS
BRN-WHT
GRN-WHT
GN-BK
YEL-RED
WHT-GRN
LT GRN-BLK
MPFI CTRL UNIT
FUSE #20 & #21 (F/B PIN D9)
INTAKE DOOR ACTUATOR
LT GRN-RED
RED-YEL
A/C OFF RELAY
BLOWER MOTOR
FAN CTRL AMP
HI RELAY
MODE DOOR ACTUATOR
LT RGN-WHT
AIR MIX DOOR ACTUATOR
WHT-BLK
GRN-BLU
TRINARY SW
INTRMDT PRES SW
HI-LO PRES SW
COMPRESSOR
CLUTCH
SOLENOID ACTUATOR
A/C RELAY HOLDER #2
IGNITION SW
A/C 10A
RELAY #5 RT FAN #2
RELAY #7 A/C COMP
94I10767

Fig. 9: Automatic A/C-Heater System Wiring Diagram (SVX)

1993 SUZUKI CONTENTS

GENERAL SERVICING

HEATER SYSTEMS

MANUAL A/C-HEATER SYSTEMS

1993 HEATER SYSTEMS
Samurai, Sidekick & Swift

DESCRIPTION

The flow-through heater system allows ram air to constantly be forced into the vehicle. The air is heated by engine coolant passing through the heater core and blown into the passenger compartment by the blower motor.

OPERATION

MODE CONTROL LEVER

The mode control lever controls the flow of air into the vehicle. When control lever is in the ventilation position, air is discharged from the center and side outlets of the instrument panel. When lever is in the bi-level position, warmed air is discharged from the floor outlets and cooler air is discharged from center and side outlets (when temperature control lever is in maximum heating or cooling position, all outlets will discharge air at chosen temperature).

When mode control lever is in heater position, heated air is discharged from the floor outlets only. In heater and defrost position, heated air is discharged from floor outlets and windshield and side defroster outlets. When lever is in the defrost position, heated air is discharged from the windshield and side defroster outlets.

FRESH AIR CONTROL LEVER

The fresh air control lever allows either fresh or recirculated air into the passenger compartment.

TEMPERATURE CONTROL LEVER

The temperature control lever mechanically controls flow of engine coolant entering the heater core, thus regulating the temperature of air entering passenger compartment.

BLOWER LEVER

The blower lever controls fan speed. When lever is in OFF position, ram air will continue to enter the passenger compartment.

ADJUSTMENTS

MODE CONTROL CABLE

Move control lever to ventilation position. Put outer cable into control lever cable guide. Clamp control cable securely. Push mode control door lever to fully open position. This will put cable in proper position.

TEMPERATURE CONTROL CABLE

Move control lever to maximum cooling position. Push temperature control door lever fully in counterclockwise direction. This will adjust cable to proper position.

FRESH AIR CONTROL CABLE

Move control lever to fresh air position. Push fresh air control door lever fully clockwise. This will adjust cable to proper position.

TROUBLE SHOOTING

BLOWER MOTOR WILL NOT RUN

Check fuse. Check blower motor resistor for damage. Check blower motor and blower motor resistor continuity. See BLOWER RESISTOR under TESTING.

TEMPERATURE NOT CORRECT

Control cable is broken or binding. Check cables, and adjust them as necessary. Air damper is broken. Repair air damper. Air ducts are restricted. Repair ducts as necessary. Heater core is leaking or clogged. Replace heater core. Heater hoses are leaking or clogged. Replace heater hoses.

TESTING

BLOWER RESISTOR

Samurai – Blower resistor is located on left side of heater case. Disconnect resistor. Using ohmmeter, check continuity between Blue/White and Blue wire terminals. If resistance is not indicated, replace blower resistor.

Sidekick & Swift – **1)** Blower resistor is mounted in front lower blower motor housing. Disconnect wiring harness from resistor. Terminal identification numbers are molded into resistor block.

2) On Sidekick, check resistance between terminals "H" and "LO". Resistance should be about 1.8 ohms. Check resistance between terminals "H" and "M1". Resistance should be about one ohm. Check resistance between terminals "H" and "M2". Resistance should be about 0.5 ohm. If resistance is not as specified, replace blower motor resistor.

3) On Swift, check for continuity between terminals "H" and "LO", between terminals "H" and "M1", and between terminals "H" and "M2". Continuity should exist. If continuity is not as specified, replace blower motor resistor.

FAN SWITCH

Check continuity between fan switch terminals. See FAN SWITCH CONTINUITY table.

FAN SWITCH CONTINUITY

Switch Position	Continuity Between Terminals
Samurai	
I	Light Green & Blue/White
II	Light Green, Blue/White & Blue/Yellow
III	Light Green, Blue/White & Blue
Sidekick & Swift	
I	Light Green & Pink/Black
II	Light Green, Pink/Black & Pink/Blue
III	Light Green, Pink/Black & Pink/Green
IV	Light Green, Pink/Black & Pink

REMOVAL & INSTALLATION

BLOWER MOTOR

Removal & Installation (Samurai) – For removal and installation procedure, see HEATER ASSEMBLY.

Removal & Installation (Sidekick) – Disconnect negative battery cable. Remove glove box and support. Remove blower motor electrical connector. Disconnect fresh air control cable from blower motor case. *See Fig. 1.* Remove blower motor screws and blower motor from case. To install, reverse removal procedure.

Removal & Installation (Swift) – Disconnect negative battery cable. Disconnect electrical connector from blower motor resistor. *See Fig. 2.* Remove fresh air control cable from blower case. Remove glove box upper panel and bolts. Remove blower motor. To install, reverse removal procedure.

CONTROL PANEL & FAN SWITCH

Removal & Installation (Samurai) – **1)** Remove instrument panel. See INSTRUMENT PANEL. Remove control panel screws and control panel.

2) Disconnect electrical connector from control panel fan switch. Remove switch, and check continuity. See FAN SWITCH under TESTING. To install, reverse removal procedure. Ensure all control levers operate smoothly. If control levers do not operate smoothly, adjust cable clamp positions as necessary.

Removal & Installation (Sidekick & Swift) – **1)** On Swift, remove console box. Remove ashtray, ashtray upper plate, and cigarette lighter. On all models, pull off control lever knobs. Remove heater control lever garnish. Remove heater control lever panel.

2) Remove glove box. Remove heater control lever screws. Disconnect electrical connector from control panel fan switch. Remove switch, and check continuity. See FAN SWITCH under TESTING.

1993 HEATER SYSTEMS
Samurai, Sidekick & Swift (Cont.)

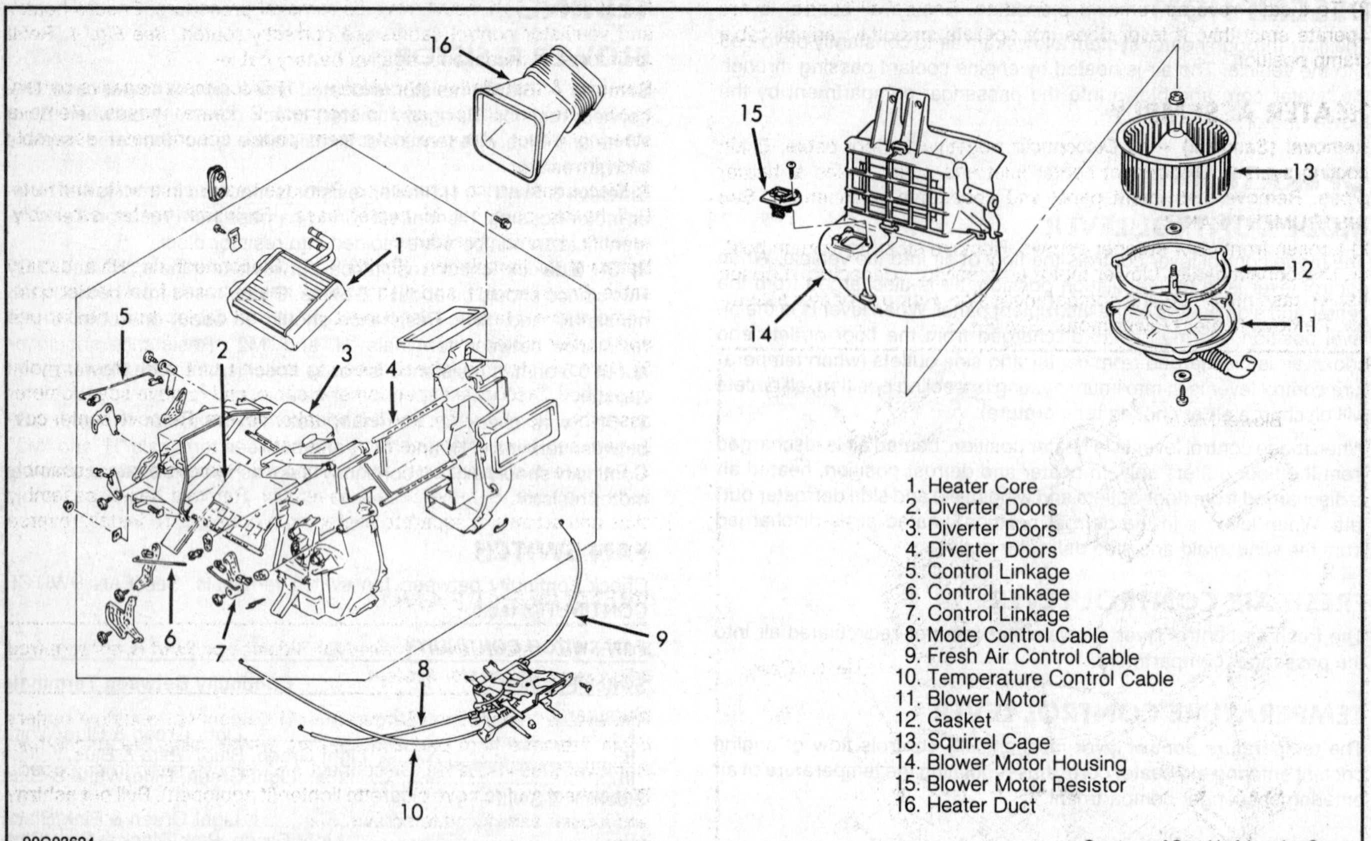

1. Heater Core
2. Diverter Doors
3. Diverter Doors
4. Diverter Doors
5. Control Linkage
6. Control Linkage
7. Control Linkage
8. Mode Control Cable
9. Fresh Air Control Cable
10. Temperature Control Cable
11. Blower Motor
12. Gasket
13. Squirrel Cage
14. Blower Motor Housing
15. Blower Motor Resistor
16. Heater Duct

90G03624

Courtesy of Suzuki of America Corp.

Fig. 1: Identifying Heater & Blower Motor Components (Sidekick)

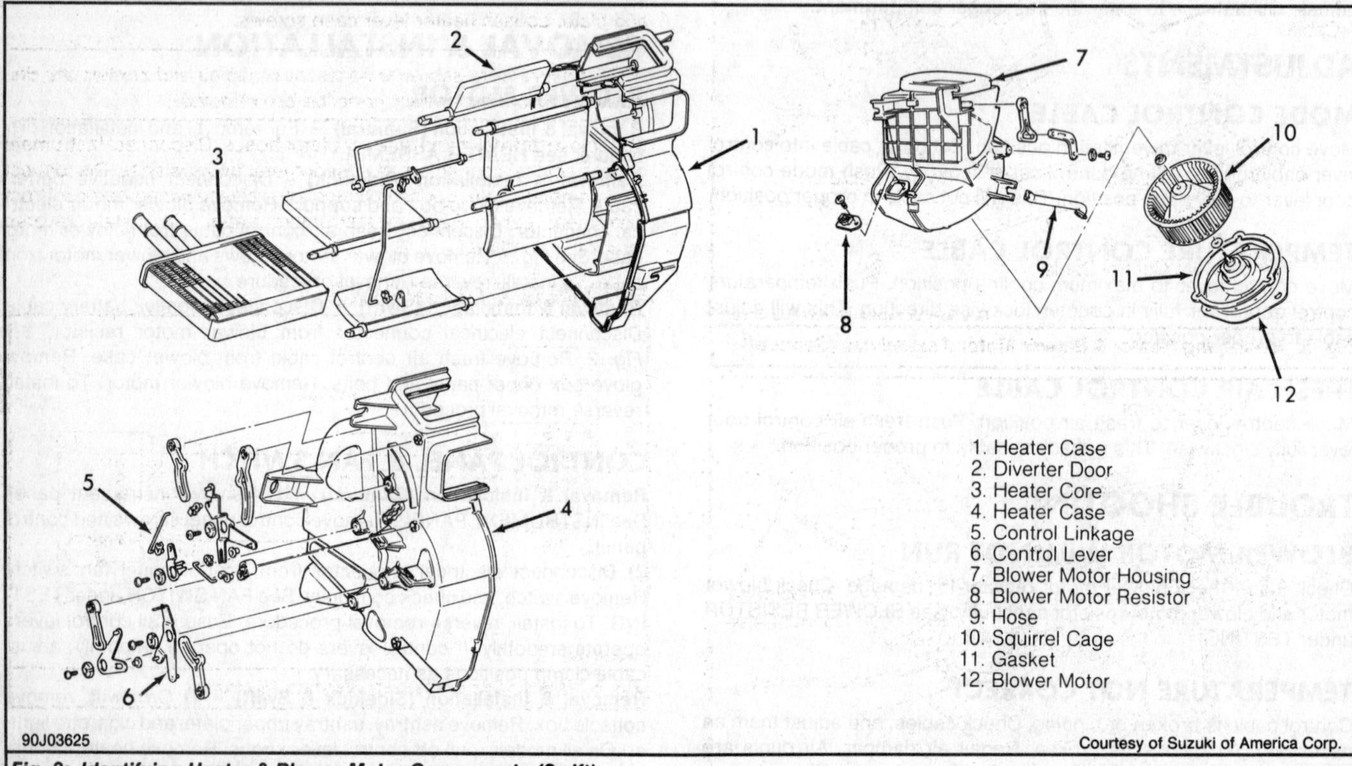
1. Heater Case
2. Diverter Door
3. Heater Core
4. Heater Case
5. Control Linkage
6. Control Lever
7. Blower Motor Housing
8. Blower Motor Resistor
9. Hose
10. Squirrel Cage
11. Gasket
12. Blower Motor
90J03625
Courtesy of Suzuki of America Corp.

Fig. 2: Identifying Heater & Blower Motor Components (Swift)

1993 HEATER SYSTEMS
Samurai, Sidekick & Swift (Cont.)

3) To install, reverse removal procedure. Ensure all control levers operate smoothly. If lever does not operate smoothly, adjust cable clamp position.

HEATER ASSEMBLY

Removal (Samurai) – 1) Disconnect negative battery cable. Drain cooling system. Disconnect heater inlet and outlet hoses at heater pipes. Remove instrument panel and speedometer assembly. See INSTRUMENT PANEL.

2) Loosen front door stopper screws. Remove steering column holder. Disconnect heater blower motor and resistor connectors. Loosen heater case nut on engine compartment side. Remove heater assembly. Remove heater blower motor. *See Fig. 3.*

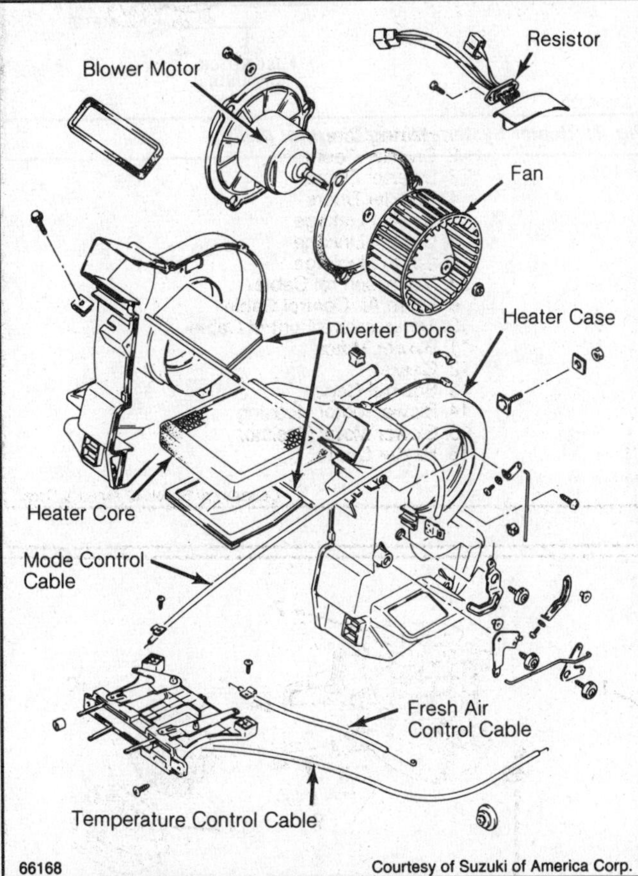
Resistor
Blower Motor
Fan
Heater Case
Diverter Doors
Heater Core
Mode Control Cable
Fresh Air Control Cable
Temperature Control Cable
66168
Courtesy of Suzuki of America Corp.

Fig. 3: Identifying Heater & Blower Motor Assemblies (Samurai)

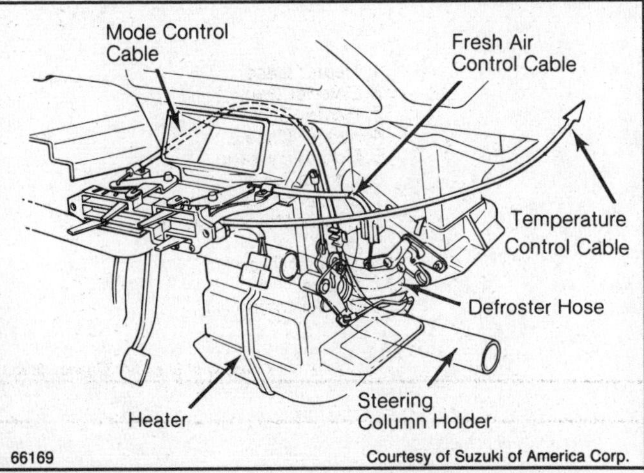
Mode Control Cable
Fresh Air Control Cable
Temperature Control Cable
Defroster Hose
Heater
Steering Column Holder
66169
Courtesy of Suzuki of America Corp.

Fig. 4: Checking Heater & Ventilator Control Cable Routing (Samurai)

Installation – To install, reverse removal procedure. Ensure heater and ventilator control cables are correctly routed. *See Fig. 4.* Refill radiator, and reconnect negative battery cable.

Removal & Installation (Sidekick) – 1) Disconnect negative battery cable. Drain radiator, and disconnect 2 heater hoses. Remove steering wheel. Remove instrument panel, speedometer assembly and glove box.

2) Disconnect wiring connectors. Remove heater case bolts and nuts. Pull heater core out of heater case. To install heater assembly, reverse removal procedure.

Removal & Installation (Swift) – 1) Disconnect negative battery cable. Drain radiator, and disconnect 2 heater hoses from heater core. Remove console box. Disconnect wires and cables from heater unit and blower motor unit.

2) Remove steering wheel, steering column unit and steering joint upper bolt. Disconnect speedometer cable, and remove speedometer assembly. Remove right and left speaker covers. Remove center cover garnish. Remove engine hood opener.

3) Remove dashboard bolts and dashboard. Remove heater assembly bolts and nuts. Remove heater assembly. Remove heater assembly clips and screws to separate heater from housing. To install, reverse removal procedure.

INSTRUMENT PANEL

NOTE: Instrument panel removal for Sidekick or Swift is not required when servicing heater system.

Removal & Installation (Samurai) – 1) Disconnect negative battery cable. Remove horn pad and steering wheel using Steering Wheel Remover (09944-38210). Disconnect and remove radio (if equipped). Disconnect and remove cigarette lighter (if equipped). Pull out ashtray and loosen ashtray plate screws.

2) Disconnect front hood opening cable from lock assembly. Loosen glove box screw and hood opening cable lock nut on back side of glove box. Disconnect cables from control levers. Pull out lever knobs and plate. Loosen heater lever case screws.

NOTE: Ensure all hoses, wire harnesses, cables and screws are disconnected from instrument panel before removal.

3) Remove defroster and side ventilator hoses. Disconnect instrument panel electrical connectors at speedometer and switches. Disconnect speedometer cable. Loosen clamps and release wiring harness from instrument panel. Remove instrument panel. To install, reverse removal procedure.

WIRING DIAGRAMS

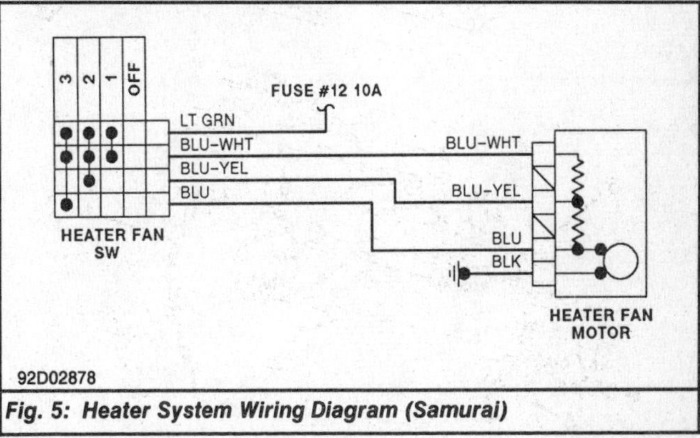
3
2
1
OFF
FUSE #12 10A
LT GRN
BLU-WHT
BLU-YEL
BLU
HEATER FAN SW
BLU-WHT
BLU-YEL
BLU
BLK
HEATER FAN MOTOR
92D02878

Fig. 5: Heater System Wiring Diagram (Samurai)

1993 HEATER SYSTEMS
Samurai, Sidekick & Swift (Cont.)

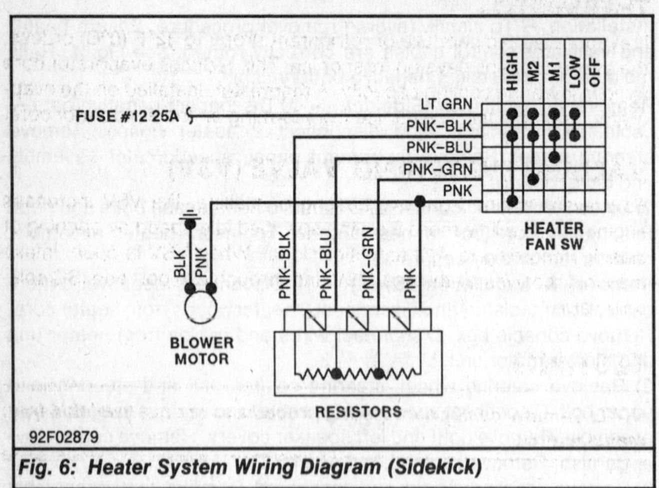
FUSE #12 25A
LT GRN
PNK-BLK
PNK-BLU
PNK-GRN
PNK
HIGH
M2
M1
LOW
OFF
HEATER
FAN SW
BLK
PNK
BLOWER
MOTOR
PNK-BLK
PNK-BLU
PNK-GRN
PNK
RESISTORS
92F02879

Fig. 6: Heater System Wiring Diagram (Sidekick)

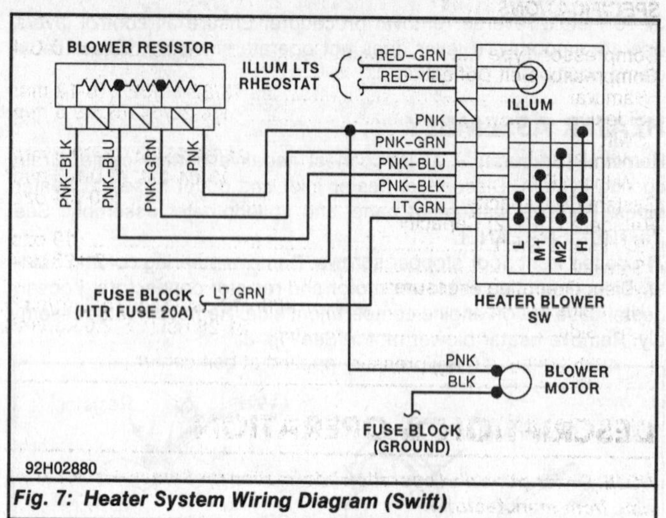
BLOWER RESISTOR
ILLUM LTS
RHEOSTAT
RED-GRN
RED-YEL
ILLUM
PNK-BLK
PNK-BLU
PNK-GRN
PNK
PNK
PNK-GRN
PNK-BLU
PNK-BLK
LT GRN
L
M1
M2
H
HEATER BLOWER
SW
FUSE BLOCK
(IITR FUSE 20A)
LT GRN
PNK
BLK
BLOWER
MOTOR
FUSE BLOCK
(GROUND)
92H02880

Fig. 7: Heater System Wiring Diagram (Swift)

1993 MANUAL A/C-HEATER SYSTEMS
Samurai, Sidekick & Swift

SPECIFICATIONS

Compressor Type	Nippondenso 10-Cyl.
Compressor Belt Deflection [1]	
Samurai	13/32-15/32" (10-12 mm)
Sidekick	1/4-23/64" (6.5-9.0 mm)
Swift	
With P/S	21/64-25/64" (8-10.5 mm)
Without P/S	13/64-1/4" (5.0-6.5 mm)
System Oil Capacity	2.0-3.4 ozs.
Refrigerant (R-12) Capacity	
Samurai & Swift	18 ozs.
Sidekick	21-23 ozs.
System Operating Pressures	
High Side	206-213 psi (14.5-15.0 kg/cm²)
Low Side	21-28 psi (1.5-2.0 kg/cm²)

[1] – With 22 lbs. (10 kg) pressure applied at belt center.

DESCRIPTION & OPERATION

NOTE: Description and operation information for Samurai is not available from manufacturer.

A/C AMPLIFIER

The A/C amplifier (located on lower evaporator case) controls operation of the Vacuum Switching Valve (VSV), A/C compressor clutch and condenser fan motor based on signals from different sensors.

COMPRESSOR & CONDENSER FAN RELAYS

Relays operate condenser fan motor and magnetic clutch on A/C compressor. Fan motor operates as long as the A/C compressor is under operation.

CONDENSER

The condenser assembly, located in front of the radiator, consists of coils and cooling fins. Air passing through the condenser cools the high pressure refrigerant vapor, causing it to condense into liquid.

DUAL-PRESSURE SWITCH

The dual-pressure switch stops A/C compressor operation when refrigerant pressure drops or reaches too great a level. Switch is installed on the high pressure line, behind receiver-drier.

EVAPORATOR

The evaporator cools and dehumidifies the air before it enters the vehicle. Heat in the air passing through the evaporator core is lost to the cooler surface of the core, thereby cooling and conditioning the air. As the air loses its heat to the evaporator core surface, any moisture (humidity) in the air condenses on the outside surface of the evaporator core and is drained off as water.

EXPANSION VALVE

High pressure liquid refrigerant enters the expansion valve through inlet screen and passes through the valve seat and orifice. Upon passing through the orifice, the high pressure liquid becomes a low pressure liquid. The low pressure liquid leaves the expansion valve, flowing into the evaporator core, where it absorbs heat and changes to a low pressure vapor.

MAGNETIC CLUTCH

A/C switch, coolant temperature switch and dual-pressure switch control magnetic clutch on A/C compressor. When engine is running, magnetic clutch allows compressor to run according to signals sent by A/C amplifier.

RECEIVER-DRIER

Receiver-drier temporarily stores condensed liquid refrigerant. It also removes dirt and moisture in refrigerant by means of a filter and desiccant bag. A sight glass, installed on top of receiver-drier, indicates refrigerant flow.

THERMISTOR

If evaporative temperature of refrigerant drops to 32°F (0°C) or less, the evaporator fins develop frost or ice. This reduces evaporator core airflow, lowering cooling capacity. A thermistor, installed on the evaporator, prevents this frost or ice from forming on the evaporator core.

VACUUM SWITCHING VALVE (VSV)

To prevent engine from overheating or stalling, the VSV increases engine speed a little more than the specified idle speed by opening or closing according to A/C amplifier signal, When VSV is open, intake manifold receives air through VSV and through idle port and ISC solenoid valve.

TESTING

NOTE: Samurai component testing procedures are not available from manufacturer.

A/C SYSTEM PERFORMANCE

1) Connect manifold gauge set to A/C compressor service fittings. Start engine and allow it to idle at 2000 RPM. Turn A/C on. Set blower lever to maximum speed, and temperature lever to cool position. Open all windows and doors.
2) Insert dry bulb thermometer in cool air outlet. Thermometer should read 77-95°F (25-35°C). High pressure gauge reading should be 200-220 psi (14-15.5 kg/cm²).

A/C SWITCH

Sidekick & Swift – 1) Disconnect negative battery cable. Remove A/C-heater control knob and panel to access A/C switch. Disconnect A/C switch electrical connector.
2) With A/C switch off, continuity should not be present between any terminals. With A/C switch on, continuity should exist between Blue and Pink/Black wire terminals. If continuity is not as specified, replace A/C switch.

CLUTCH COIL

Sidekick & Swift – If compressor clutch is oil-soaked, check front shaft seal for leak. Replace shaft seal if necessary. Check pulley bearing for roughness and noise. Replace bearing if necessary. Ensure clutch coil resistance is 3.0-3.4 ohms at 77°F (25°C). If resistance is not as specified, replace clutch coil.

COMPRESSOR & CONDENSER FAN RELAYS

Sidekick & Swift – 1) Disconnect negative battery cable. Disconnect relay electrical connectors, and remove relay. Apply battery voltage to relay terminals No. 1 and 2. *See Fig. 1.*

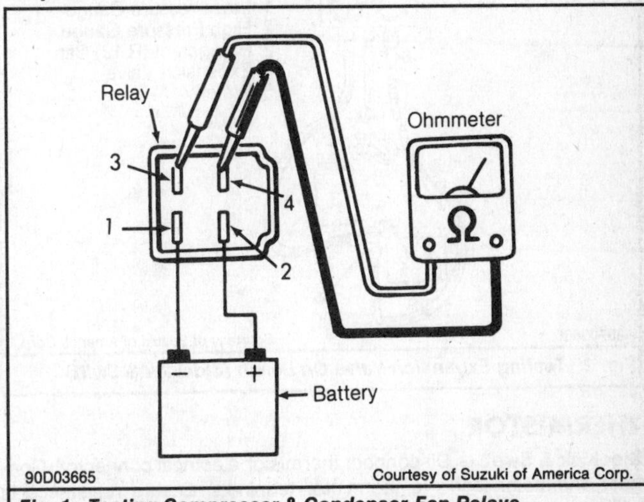
Relay
Ohmmeter
3
4
1
2
Ω
–
+
Battery
90D03665
Courtesy of Suzuki of America Corp.

Fig. 1: Testing Compressor & Condenser Fan Relays (Sidekick & Swift)

1993 MANUAL A/C-HEATER SYSTEMS
Samurai, Sidekick & Swift (Cont.)

2) Attach ohmmeter leads to relay terminals No. 3 and 4. Continuity should be present with battery voltage applied. If continuity is not present, replace relay.

COOLANT TEMPERATURE SWITCH

Sidekick & Swift – Heat temperature switch in boiling water until temperature reaches 235°F (113°C) on Sidekick or 226°F (108°C) on Swift. Continuity should exist between switch terminal and switch body. If continuity does not exist, replace coolant temperature switch.

DUAL-PRESSURE SWITCH

Sidekick & Swift – **1)** Connect manifold gauge set to A/C service ports. Start engine, and turn A/C on. Ensure system pressure is normal. Disconnect dual-pressure switch electrical connector.
2) Connect ohmmeter probes to switch terminals. If pressure is 30 psi (2.1 kg/cm²) or less, low pressure switch should not show continuity. If pressure is 383 psi (26.9 kg/cm²) or more, high pressure switch should not show continuity. If continuity is not as specified, replace dual-pressure switch.

EXPANSION VALVE

Sidekick & Swift (On-Vehicle Testing) – **1)** Connect manifold gauge set to compressor. Run engine at fast idle with A/C on. Ensure low pressure gauge shows a reading of 7-71 psi (0.5-5.0 kg/cm²).
2) If reading is less than 7 psi (0.5 kg/cm²), check expansion valve and receiver-drier. Replace components as necessary. If reading is more than 71 psi (5.0 kg/cm²), tighten remote bulb holder or replace expansion valve.
Sidekick & Swift (Bench Testing) – **1)** Connect manifold gauge set to expansion valve. Connect manifold gauge charge hose to R-12 source. *See Fig. 2.* Ensure manifold gauge set valves are closed. Put expansion valve bulb in container of water with thermometer.
2) Slowly open high side of manifold gauge set to 70 psi (4.9 kg/cm²). Read low side pressure. Pressure should correspond to bulb temperature as indicated in EXPANSION VALVE PRESSURE table. If pressure values are incorrect, replace expansion valve.

EXPANSION VALVE PRESSURE

Temperature °F (°C)	psi (kg/cm²)
32 (0)	20-28 (1.5-2.0)
50 (10)	32-42 (2.2-2.8)
75 (24)	62-72 (4.1-4.5)

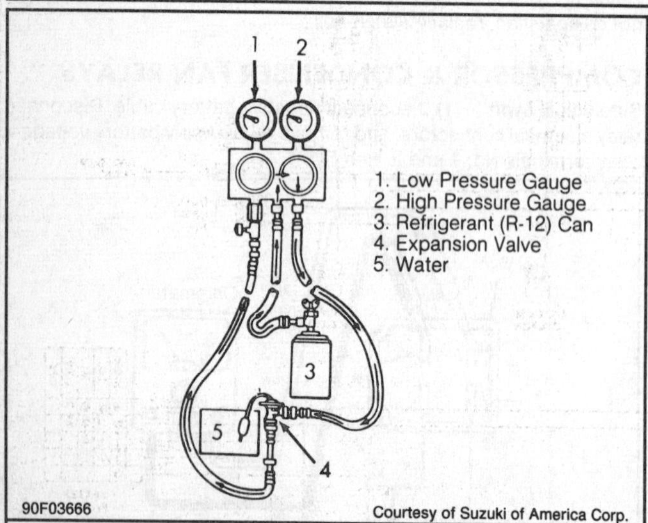
1
2
3
4
5
1. Low Pressure Gauge
2. High Pressure Gauge
3. Refrigerant (R-12) Can
4. Expansion Valve
5. Water
90F03666
Courtesy of Suzuki of America Corp.
Fig. 2: Testing Expansion Valve On Bench (Sidekick & Swift)

THERMISTOR

Sidekick & Swift – Disconnect thermistor electrical connector. Connect ohmmeter leads to thermistor terminals. Ensure resistance is within specifications. See THERMISTOR RESISTANCE table. If continuity is not as specified, replace thermistor.

THERMISTOR RESISTANCE

Temperature °F (°C)	[1] Ohms
32 (0)	4200-5000
50 (10)	2800-3200
70 (20)	1800-2000

[1] – Resistance values are approximate.

VACUUM SWITCHING VALVE (VSV)

Swift – **1)** Disconnect vacuum hose and connector from VSV. Check VSV solenoid by applying battery voltage to valve terminals. Air should flow from port "A" to port "B". *See Fig. 3.*
2) Using an ohmmeter, check continuity between VSV body and each valve terminal. Continuity should not be present. Connect ohmmeter leads to VSV terminals. Ohmmeter reading should be 24-30 ohms. Replace VSV if readings are not as specified.

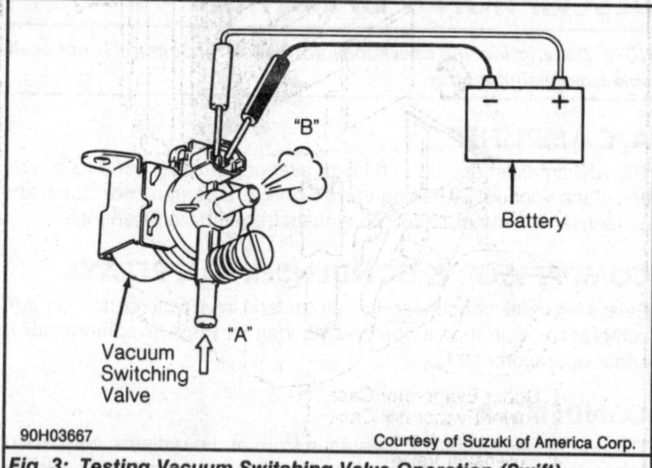
"B"
–
+
Battery
"A"
Vacuum
Switching
Valve
90H03667
Courtesy of Suzuki of America Corp.
Fig. 3: Testing Vacuum Switching Valve Operation (Swift)

REMOVAL & INSTALLATION

NOTE: For removal and installation procedures not covered in this article, see appropriate HEATER SYSTEMS article.

CONDENSER

Removal & Installation – **1)** Discharge A/C system using approved refrigerant recovery/recycling equipment. On Samurai and Sidekick, remove front grille. On Swift, remove front bumper.
2) On all models, disconnect refrigerant hose(s) from condenser fittings. On Samurai and Sidekick, remove condenser fan and condenser. Plug hoses to prevent contamination.
3) On Swift, disconnect and plug receiver-drier outlet pipe above condenser cooling fan. Remove hood latch and lock assembly. Disconnect fan motor wiring harness. Remove condenser, cooling fan and receiver-drier as an assembly. Remove cooling fan and receiver-drier from condenser.
4) On all models, reverse removal procedure to install. When installing a new condenser on Sidekick and Swift, add 0.7-1 ounce of refrigerant oil. Evacuate and recharge system, and check it for leaks.

EVAPORATOR, EXPANSION VALVE & THERMISTOR

Removal & Installation – **1)** Disconnect negative battery cable. Discharge A/C system using approved refrigerant recovery/recycling equipment. On Swift, disconnect blower motor and blower motor resistor wires. Disconnect fresh air control cable from blower motor housing.
2) On Sidekick and Swift, remove glove box. Remove blower motor unit. On Swift, disconnect A/C amplifier and thermistor wires. *See Fig. 4.* On all models, disconnect refrigerant lines and remove evaporator unit.

1993 MANUAL A/C-HEATER SYSTEMS
Samurai, Sidekick & Swift (Cont.)

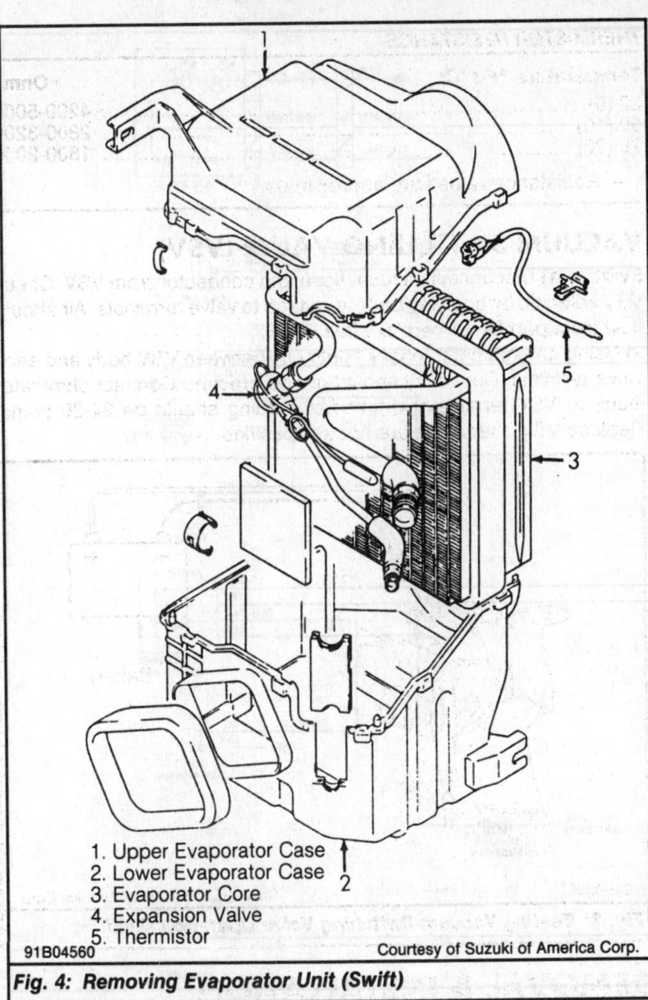
1
4
5
3
2
1. Upper Evaporator Case
2. Lower Evaporator Case
3. Evaporator Core
4. Expansion Valve
5. Thermistor
91B04560
Courtesy of Suzuki of America Corp.

Fig. 4: Removing Evaporator Unit (Swift)

3) Remove clamps, and separate evaporator housing. Remove evaporator core, expansion valve or thermistor as required. To install, reverse removal procedure. Evacuate and recharge system, and check it for leaks.

RECEIVER-DRIER

Removal & Installation – 1) Discharge A/C system using approved refrigerant recovery/recycling equipment. Disconnect liquid lines from inlet and outlet fittings. Remove receiver-drier from holder.

2) To install, reverse removal procedure. When installing a new receiver/drier on Sidekick and Swift, add 0.4 ounce of refrigerant oil. Evacuate and recharge system, and check it for leaks.

TORQUE SPECIFICATIONS

TORQUE SPECIFICATIONS

Application	Ft. Lbs. (N.m)
Compressor Bolts	
8-mm	18-22 (25-30)
10-mm	30-37 (40-50)
Refrigerant Hoses	
8-mm	10.1 (13.7)
13-mm	16.6 (22.5)
16-mm	23.8 (32.3)
	INCH Lbs. (N.m)
Coolant Temperature Switch	106 (12)

WIRING DIAGRAMS

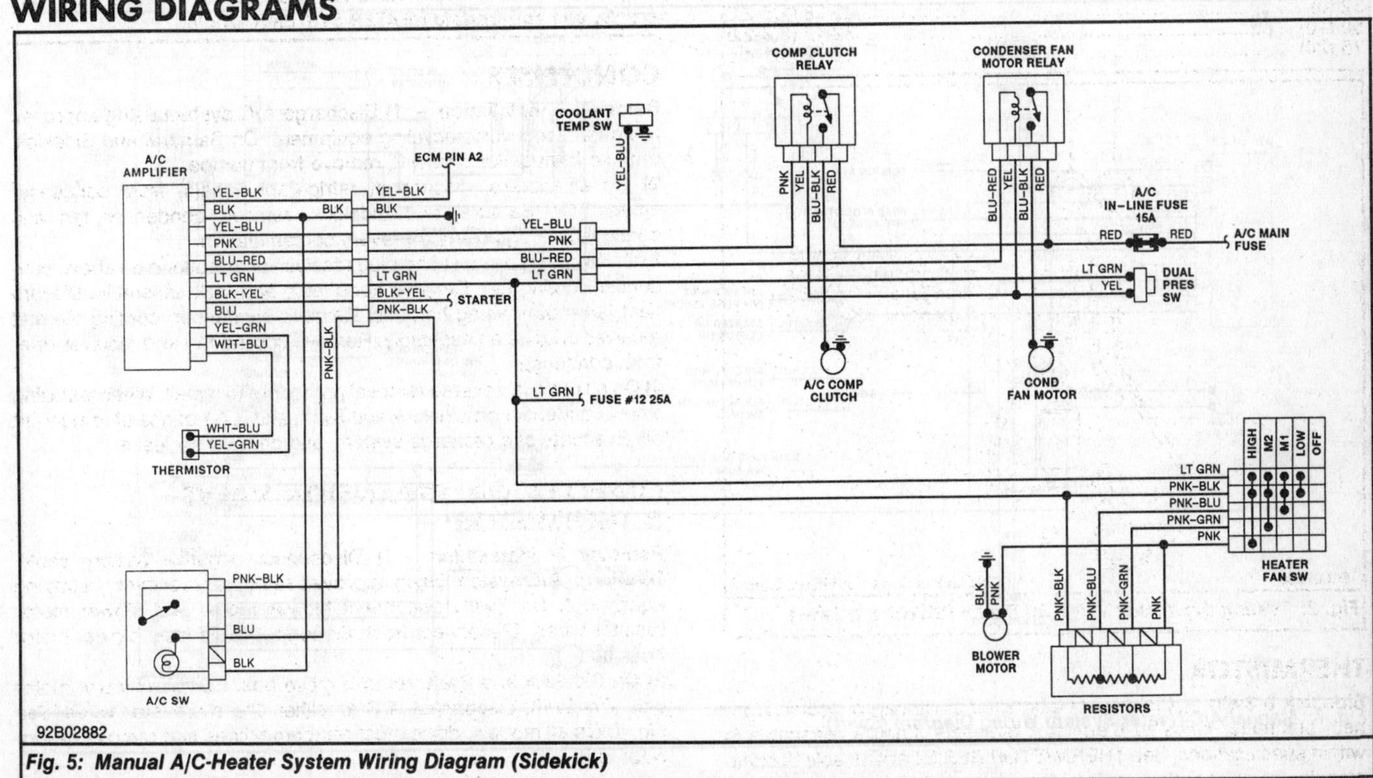
COMP CLUTCH RELAY
CONDENSER FAN MOTOR RELAY
COOLANT TEMP SW
ECM PIN A2
A/C AMPLIFIER
YEL-BLK
BLK
YEL-BLU
PNK
BLU-RED
LT GRN
BLK-YEL
BLU
YEL-GRN
WHT-BLU
STARTER
PNK-BLK
RED
A/C IN-LINE FUSE 15A
A/C MAIN FUSE
DUAL PRES SW
YEL
A/C COMP CLUTCH
COND FAN MOTOR
FUSE #12 25A
THERMISTOR
HIGH
M2
M1
LOW
OFF
PNK-BLU
PNK-GRN
HEATER FAN SW
BLOWER MOTOR
RESISTORS
A/C SW
92B02882

Fig. 5: Manual A/C-Heater System Wiring Diagram (Sidekick)

1993 MANUAL A/C-HEATER SYSTEMS
Samurai, Sidekick & Swift (Cont.)

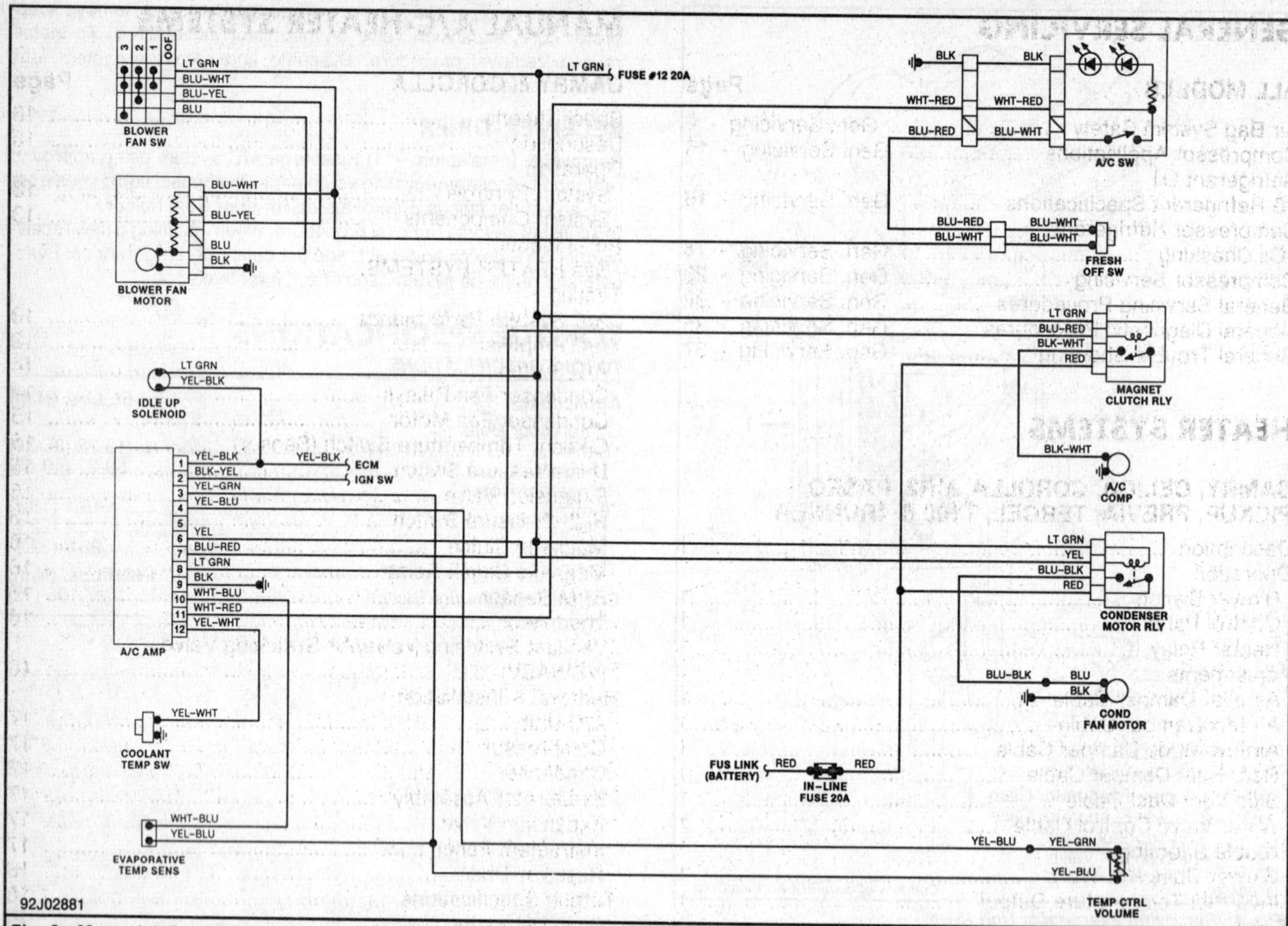

92J02881

Fig. 6: Manual A/C-Heater System Wiring Diagram (Samurai)

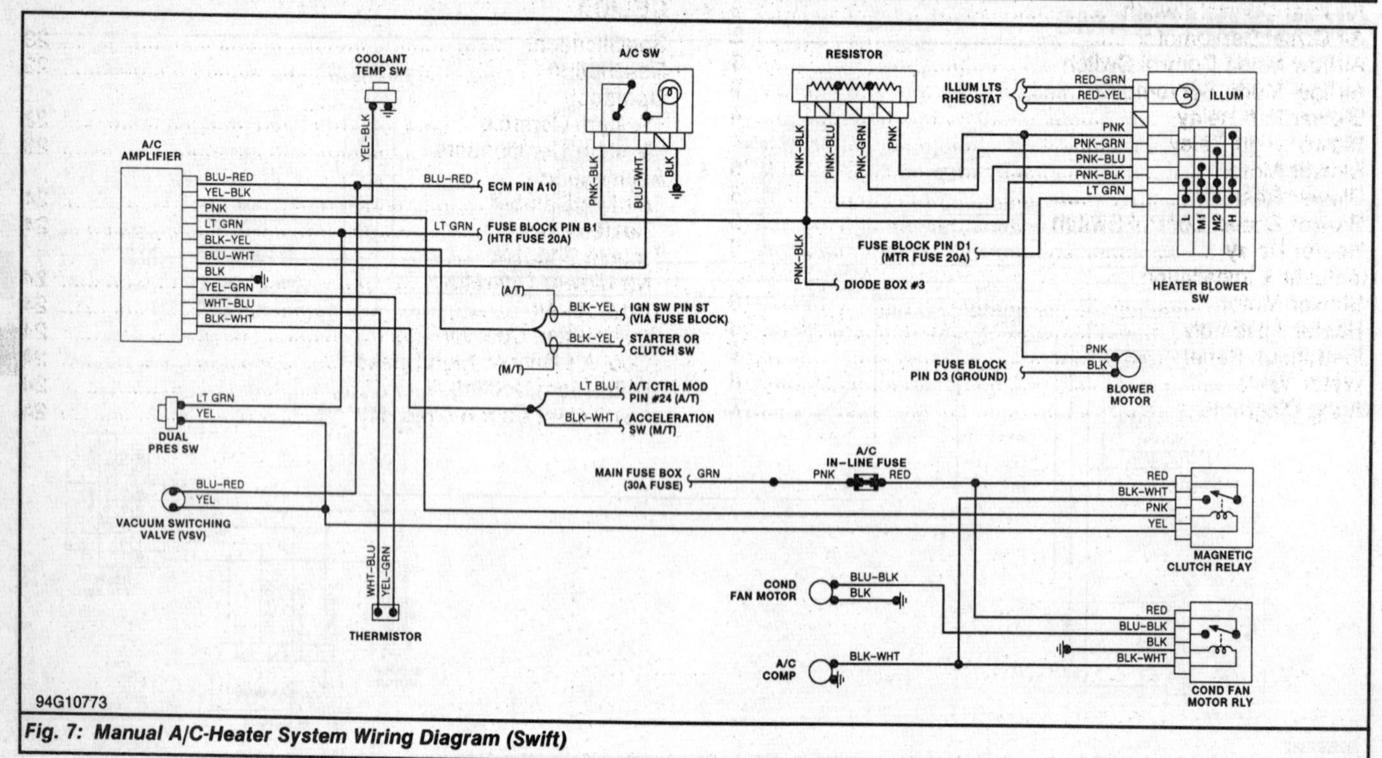
COOLANT TEMP SW
A/C SW
RESISTOR
ILLUM LTS RHEOSTAT
ILLUM
A/C AMPLIFIER
BLU-RED
YEL-BLK
PNK
LT GRN
BLK-YEL
BLU-WHT
BLK
YEL-GRN
WHT-BLU
BLK-WHT
ECM PIN A10
FUSE BLOCK PIN B1 (HTR FUSE 20A)
FUSE BLOCK PIN D1 (MTR FUSE 20A)
DIODE BOX #3
HEATER BLOWER SW
(A/T)
(M/T)
IGN SW PIN ST (VIA FUSE BLOCK)
STARTER OR CLUTCH SW
A/T CTRL MOD PIN #24 (A/T)
ACCELERATION SW (M/T)
FUSE BLOCK PIN D3 (GROUND)
BLOWER MOTOR
DUAL PRES SW
VACUUM SWITCHING VALVE (VSV)
MAIN FUSE BOX (30A FUSE)
A/C IN-LINE FUSE
MAGNETIC CLUTCH RELAY
COND FAN MOTOR
A/C COMP
THERMISTOR
COND FAN MOTOR RLY
94G10773

Fig. 7: Manual A/C-Heater System Wiring Diagram (Swift)

1993 TOYOTA CONTENTS

GENERAL SERVICING

ALL MODELS

HEATER SYSTEMS

CAMRY, CELICA, COROLLA, MR2, PASEO, PICKUP, PREVIA, TERCEL, T100 & 4RUNNER

MANUAL A/C-HEATER SYSTEMS

CAMRY & COROLLA

CELICA

1993 TOYOTA CONTENTS (Cont.)

MANUAL A/C-HEATER SYSTEMS (Cont.)

CELICA (Cont.)

LAND CRUISER, PICKUP & 4RUNNER

MANUAL A/C-HEATER SYSTEMS (Cont.)

MR2

PASEO & TERCEL

1993 TOYOTA CONTENTS (Cont.)

MANUAL A/C-HEATER SYSTEMS (Cont.)

PASEO & TERCEL (Cont.)

PREVIA

MANUAL A/C-HEATER SYSTEMS (Cont.)

T100

AUTOMATIC A/C-HEATER SYSTEMS

CELICA

1993 TOYOTA CONTENTS (Cont.)

AUTOMATIC A/C-HEATER SYSTEMS (Cont.)

SUPRA

AUTOMATIC A/C-HEATER SYSTEMS (Cont.)

SUPRA (Cont.)

1993 HEATER SYSTEMS
Except Land Cruiser & Supra

Camry, Celica, Corolla, MR2, Paseo, Pickup, Previa, Tercel, T100, 4Runner

DESCRIPTION

Heater assembly consists of heater core, control panel, blower motor, control cables (electric servomotors on push button-controlled models) and air ducts. The 4Runner is equipped with a dual-heater system with separate controls for front and rear; rear heater blower motor, temperature control and blower switch are located in the console, between front seats. On all other models, all components are located under instrument panel.

WARNING: To avoid injury from accidental air bag deployment, read and carefully follow all SERVICE PRECAUTIONS and DISABLING & ACTIVATING AIR BAG SYSTEM procedures in AIR BAG SYSTEM SAFETY article in GENERAL SERVICING.

CAUTION: When battery is disconnected, radio will go into anti-theft protection mode. Obtain radio anti-theft protection code from owner prior to servicing vehicle.

OPERATION

BLOWER SWITCH

Switch controls blower motor speed through blower resistor. Switch is operated by control lever, dial knob or push button.

CONTROL PANEL

Lever-Controlled Models – Temperature and mode levers are cable-connected to heater coolant valve and air doors. All models have a fresh/recirculation lever to provide choice of outside air entry or inside air recirculation.

Push Button-Controlled Models – Air inlet (fresh/recirculation), mode control and air mix are controlled by electric servomotors. Temperature selection is controlled by slide lever or rotating dial knob.

HEATER RELAY

A heater (or main) relay in heater circuit controls current flow through system. See WIRING DIAGRAMS. For location of heater relay, see HEATER RELAY LOCATION table.

HEATER RELAY LOCATION

Models	Location
Camry	Relay/Fuse Block, Behind Right Kick Panel
Celica	Relay/Fuse Block, Behind Right Kick Panel
Corolla	Relay/Fuse Block, Behind Right Kick Panel
MR2	Relay Block, Front Right Of Luggage Compartment
Paseo & Tercel	Relay Block, Behind Right Side Of Glove Box
Pickup & 4Runner	Relay/Fuse Block, Above Glove Box
Previa	Relay/Fuse Block, Center Of Instrument Panel
T100	Relay Block, Front Right Side Of Engine Compartment

ADJUSTMENTS

AIR INLET DAMPER CABLE

Lever-Controlled Models – Set air inlet damper and control lever to fresh air position. Remove cable retaining clip, and ensure damper and cable are in full fresh position. Attach control cable using retaining clip, and check operation of air intake damper.

AIR MIX DAMPER CABLE

Lever-Controlled Models (Except Pickup, Previa & 4Runner) – Set air door lever to warm position, and remove cable retaining clip. Ensure cable and damper are in full cool position. Install cable retaining clip. Check air mix damper operation.

Push Button-Controlled Models (Pickup, Previa & 4Runner) – Set air door lever to cool position, and remove cable retaining clip. Ensure cable and damper are in full cool position. Install cable retaining clip. Check air mix damper operation.

AIRFLOW MODE DAMPER CABLE

Lever-Controlled Models (Except Previa & 4Runner) – Set control lever to defrost position. Remove cable retaining clip. Ensure airflow mode damper and cable are in full defrost position. Install cable retaining clip.

Lever-Controlled Models (Previa & 4Runner) – Set control lever to vent position. Remove cable retaining clip. Ensure airflow mode damper and cable are in full vent position. Install cable retaining clip.

REAR HEAT DAMPER CABLE

Previa – Set control lever to rear heat position. Remove cable retaining clip. Ensure rear heat damper and cable are in full rear heat position. Install cable retaining clip.

SIDE VENT DUCT CABLE

Previa – Set control lever to vent position. Remove cable retaining clip. Ensure side vent, duct and cable are in full vent position. Install cable retaining clip.

WATER VALVE CONTROL CABLE

Lever-Controlled Models (Except Pickup, Previa & 4Runner) – Set control lever to warm position. Remove cable retaining clip. Ensure water valve control cable is in full warm position. Install cable retaining clip.

Lever-Controlled Models (Pickup, Previa & 4Runner) – Set control lever to cool position. Remove cable retaining clip. Ensure water valve control cable is in full cool position. Install cable retaining clip.

TROUBLE SHOOTING

BLOWER DOES NOT WORK

Check for open circuit breaker (some models), blown heater fuse and faulty heater relay. Also check for heater blower switch, heater blower resistor, heater blower motor, wiring or ground circuit fault.

INCORRECT TEMPERATURE OUTPUT

Lever-Controlled Models – Check for control cables broken or out of adjustment, heater hoses leaking or clogged and faulty water pump. Also check for broken air dampers, faulty servomotor (some models), clogged air ducts, leaking or clogged heater core and faulty heater control unit.

TESTING

WARNING: To avoid injury from accidental air bag deployment, read and carefully follow all SERVICE PRECAUTIONS and DISABLING & ACTIVATING AIR BAG SYSTEM procedures in AIR BAG SYSTEM SAFETY article in GENERAL SERVICING.

AIR INLET CONTROL SERVOMOTOR

Camry (Push Button Type) – **1)** Disconnect air inlet control servomotor wiring harness connector. Ground terminal No. 2, and apply battery voltage to terminal No. 1. *See Fig. 1*. Ensure arm rotates smoothly to fresh (full counterclockwise) position.

2) Ground terminal No. 3, and apply battery voltage to terminal No. 1. Ensure arm rotates smoothly to recirculation (full clockwise) position. If operation is not as specified, replace servomotor.

Celica – **1)** Disconnect air inlet control servomotor wiring harness connector. Ground terminal No. 3, and apply battery voltage to terminal No. 1. *See Fig. 2*. Ensure arm rotates smoothly to fresh (full counterclockwise) position.

1993 HEATER SYSTEMS
Except Land Cruiser & Supra (Cont.)

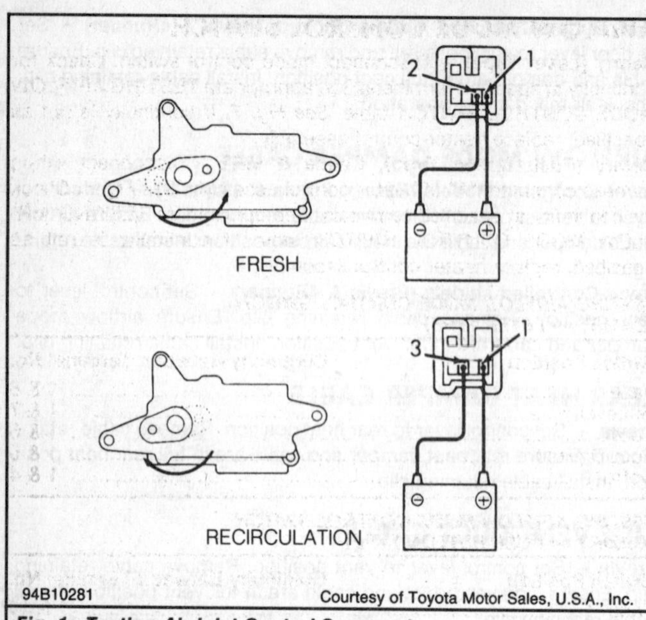
2
1
FRESH
3
1
RECIRCULATION
94B10281
Courtesy of Toyota Motor Sales, U.S.A., Inc.

Fig. 1: Testing Air Inlet Control Servomotor (Camry - Push Button Type)

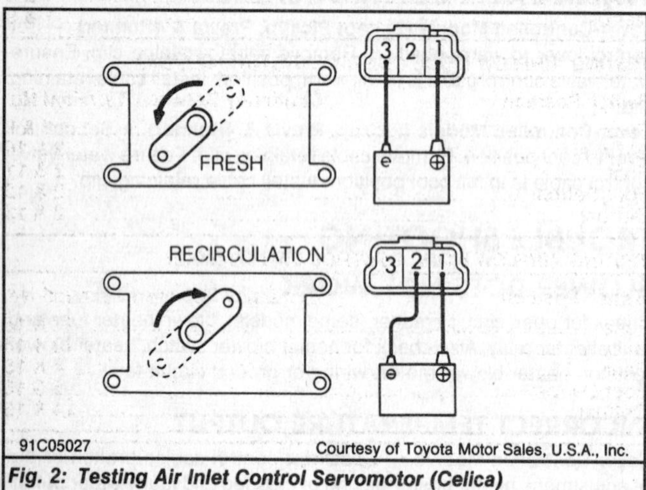
3 2 1
FRESH
RECIRCULATION
3 2
91C05027
Courtesy of Toyota Motor Sales, U.S.A., Inc.

Fig. 2: Testing Air Inlet Control Servomotor (Celica)

2) Ground terminal No. 2, and apply battery voltage to terminal No. 1. Ensure arm rotates smoothly to recirculation (full clockwise) position. If operation is not as specified, replace servomotor.

MR2 - 1) Disconnect air inlet control servomotor wiring harness connector. Ground terminal No. 4, and apply battery voltage to terminal No. 3. *See Fig. 3.* Ensure arm rotates smoothly to fresh (full counterclockwise) position.

2) Ground terminal No. 4, and apply battery voltage to terminal No. 1. Ensure arm rotates smoothly to recirculation (full clockwise) position. If operation is not as specified, replace servomotor.

AIR INLET CONTROL SWITCH

Camry (Push Button Type) - 1) Disconnect wiring harness connector "A" of heater control assembly. *See Fig. 4.* With recirculation button depressed, ensure continuity exists between terminals No. 1 and 5.

2) With fresh button depressed, continuity should exist between terminals No. 1 and 6. If continuity is not as specified, replace heater control assembly.

Celica - 1) Disconnect wiring harness connector "A" of heater control assembly. *See Fig. 4.* With recirculation button depressed, continuity should exist between terminals No. 2 and 7.

2) With fresh button depressed, continuity should exist between terminals No. 2 and 8. Switch contains diodes. Before deciding switch is

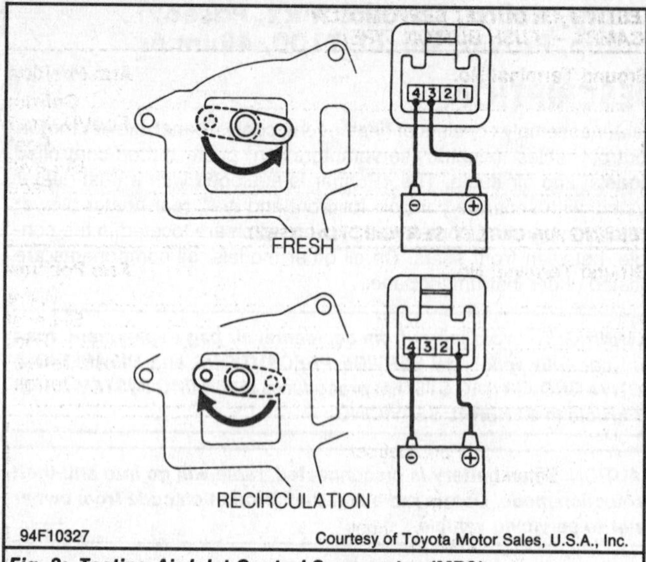
4 3 2 1
FRESH
4 3 2 1
RECIRCULATION
94F10327
Courtesy of Toyota Motor Sales, U.S.A., Inc.

Fig. 3: Testing Air Inlet Control Servomotor (MR2)

faulty, check for continuity in both directions. If continuity is not as specified, replace heater control assembly.

MR2 - 1) Disconnect wiring harness connector "A" of heater control assembly. *See Fig. 4.* With recirculation button depressed, continuity should exist between terminals No. 9 and 15. With fresh button depressed, continuity should exist between terminals No. 1 and 15.

2) If continuity is not as specified, replace heater control assembly. Switch contains diodes. Before deciding switch is faulty, check for continuity in both directions. If continuity is not as specified, replace heater control assembly.

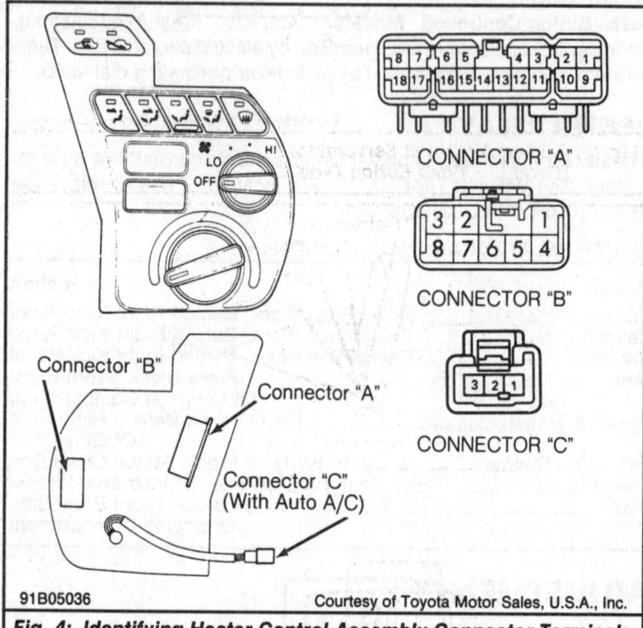
LO
HI
OFF
8 7 6 5 4 3 2 1
18 17 16 15 14 13 12 11 10 9
CONNECTOR "A"
3 2 1
8 7 6 5 4
CONNECTOR "B"
3 2 1
CONNECTOR "C"
Connector "B"
Connector "A"
Connector "C"
(With Auto A/C)
91B05036
Courtesy of Toyota Motor Sales, U.S.A., Inc.

Fig. 4: Identifying Heater Control Assembly Connector Terminals (Celica Shown; Camry & MR2 Are Similar)

AIR OUTLET SERVOMOTOR

Camry (Push Button Type) & MR2 - 1) Disconnect air outlet servomotor wiring harness connector. Ground terminal No. 7. Apply battery voltage to terminal No. 6. *See Figs. 5 and 6.*

2) Ground each specified terminal and ensure arm rotates smoothly to correct position. See appropriate TESTING AIR OUTLET SERVOMOTOR table.

TESTING AIR OUTLET SERVOMOTOR (CAMRY - PUSH BUTTON TYPE)

Ground Terminal No.	Arm Position
1	Defrost
2	Foot/Defrost
3	Foot
4	Bi-Level
5	Face

TESTING AIR OUTLET SERVOMOTOR (MR2)

Ground Terminal No.	Arm Position
1	Vent
2	Bi-Level
3	Foot
4	Foot/Defrost
5	Defrost

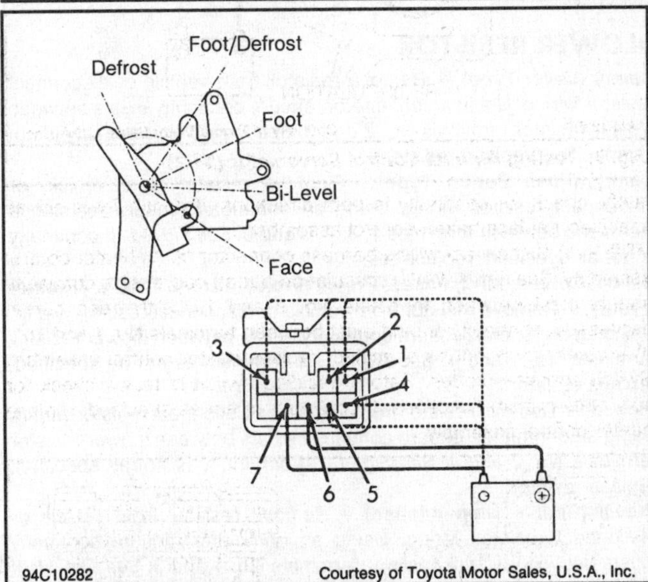

Foot/Defrost
Defrost
Foot
Bi-Level
Face
3
2
1
4
7
6
5
94C10282
Courtesy of Toyota Motor Sales, U.S.A., Inc.

Fig. 5: Testing Air Outlet Servomotor (Camry - Push Button Type)

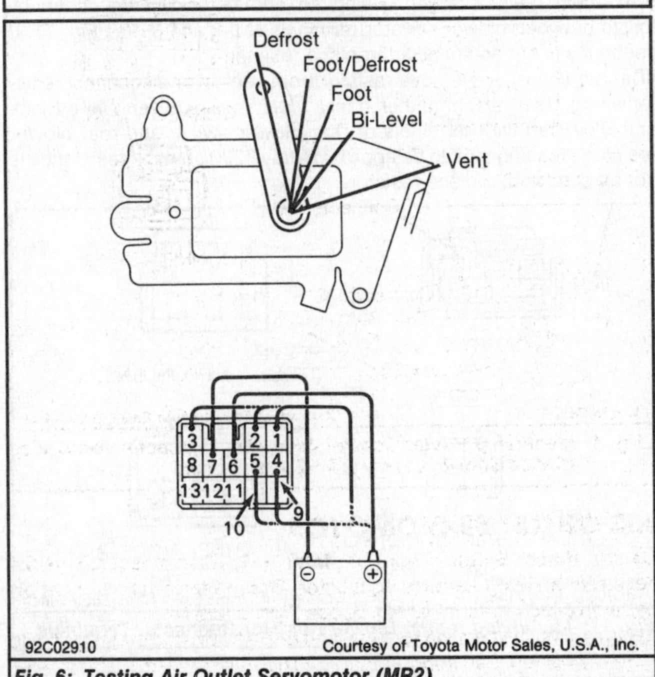

Defrost
Foot/Defrost
Foot
Bi-Level
Vent
3
2
1
8
7
6
5
4
13
12
11
9
10
92C02910
Courtesy of Toyota Motor Sales, U.S.A., Inc.

Fig. 6: Testing Air Outlet Servomotor (MR2)

AIRFLOW MODE CONTROL SWITCH

Camry (Lever Type) - Disconnect mode control switch. Check for continuity at specified terminals. See appropriate TESTING AIRFLOW MODE CONTROL SWITCH table. *See Fig. 7.* If continuity is not as specified, replace heater control assembly.

Camry (Push Button Type), Celica & MR2 - Disconnect wiring harness connector "A" of heater control assembly. *See Fig. 4.* Check for continuity at specified terminals. See appropriate TESTING AIRFLOW MODE CONTROL SWITCH table. If continuity is not as specified, replace heater control assembly.

TESTING AIRFLOW MODE CONTROL SWITCH (CAMRY - LEVER TYPE)

Switch Position	Continuity Between Terminal No.
Face	1 & 8
Bi-Level	1 & 7
Foot	1 & 6
Foot/Defrost	1 & 5
Defrost	1 & 4

TESTING AIRFLOW MODE CONTROL SWITCH (CAMRY - PUSH BUTTON TYPE)

Switch Position	Continuity Between Terminal No.
Face	1 & 11
Bi-Level	1 & 3
Foot	1 & 10
Foot/Defrost	1 & 2
Defrost	1 & 9

TESTING AIRFLOW MODE CONTROL SWITCH (CELICA)

Switch Position	Continuity Between Terminal No.
Face	2 & 9
Bi-Level	2 & 10
Foot	2 & 11
Foot/Defrost	2 & 12
Defrost	2 & 13

TESTING AIRFLOW MODE CONTROL SWITCH (MR2)

Switch Position	Continuity Between Terminal No.
Face	12 & 15
Bi-Level	13 & 15
Foot	4 & 15
Foot/Defrost	5 & 15
Defrost	14 & 15

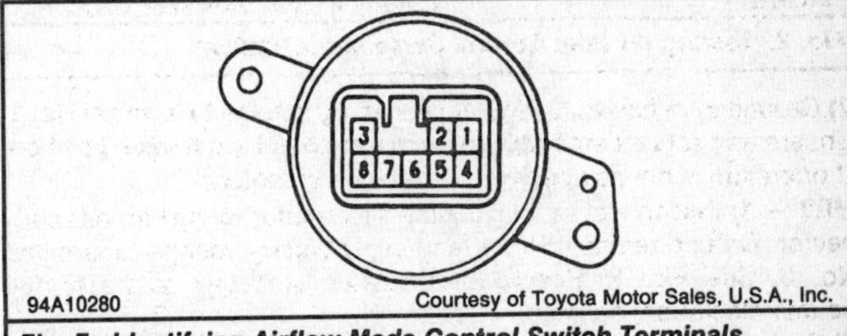

3
2
1
8
7
6
5
4
94A10280
Courtesy of Toyota Motor Sales, U.S.A., Inc.

Fig. 7: Identifying Airflow Mode Control Switch Terminals (Camry - Lever Type)

AIRFLOW MODE SERVOMOTOR

Celica - Disconnect servomotor connector. Ground terminal No. 6, and apply battery voltage to terminal No. 5. *See Fig. 8.* Ground each specified terminals, and ensure arm rotates smoothly to correct position. See TESTING AIRFLOW MODE SERVOMOTOR (CELICA) table. Replace servomotor if operation is not as specified.

TESTING AIRFLOW MODE SERVOMOTOR (CELICA)

Ground Terminal No.	Arm Position
1	Vent
2	Bi-Level
3	Foot 2
4	Foot/Defrost
7	Defrost
8	Foot 1

1993 HEATER SYSTEMS
Except Land Cruiser & Supra (Cont.)

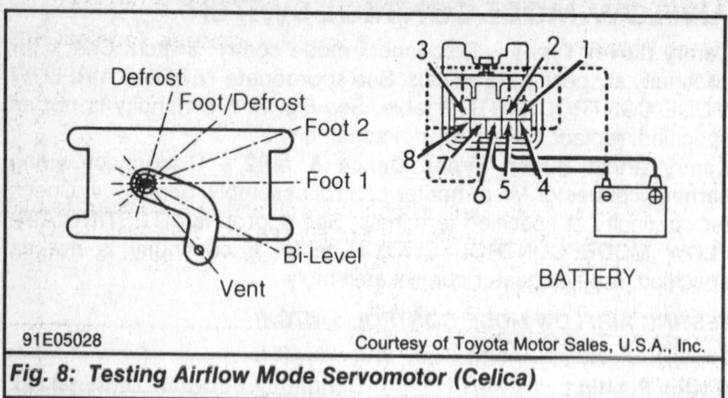
Defrost
Foot/Defrost
Foot 2
Foot 1
Bi-Level
Vent
BATTERY
3
2
1
8
7
6
5
4
91E05028
Courtesy of Toyota Motor Sales, U.S.A., Inc.

Fig. 8: Testing Airflow Mode Servomotor (Celica)

BLOWER FAN RELAY

Celica – Disconnect wiring harness connector. Test blower fan relay as specified. See TESTING BLOWER FAN RELAY table. *See Fig. 9.* If continuity is not as specified, replace relay.

TESTING BLOWER FAN RELAY

Apply Battery Voltage Between Terminal No.	[1] Continuity Should Exist Between Terminal No.
5 & 6	1 & 3
5 & 7	3 & 4
5 & 8	2 & 3

[1] – When battery voltage is not applied, constant continuity is present between terminals No. 5 and 6, 5 and 7, and 5 and 8.

MR2 – Disconnect negative battery cable. Remove blower fan relay. Using an ohmmeter, ensure continuity exists between terminals No. 1 and 2 and between terminals No. 3 and 4. *See Fig. 10.* If continuity is not as specified, replace relay.

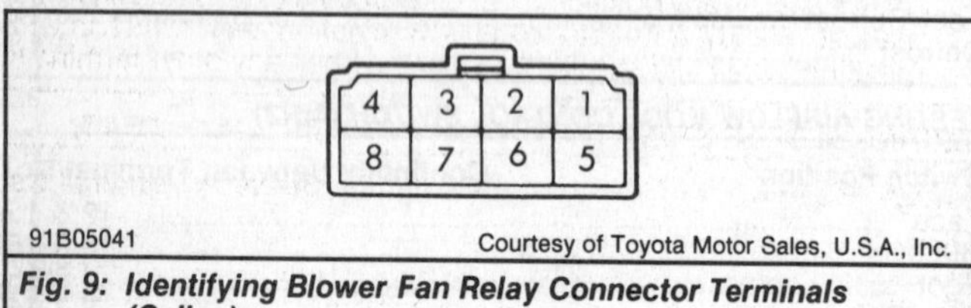
4
3
2
1
8
7
6
5
91B05041
Courtesy of Toyota Motor Sales, U.S.A., Inc.

Fig. 9: Identifying Blower Fan Relay Connector Terminals (Celica)

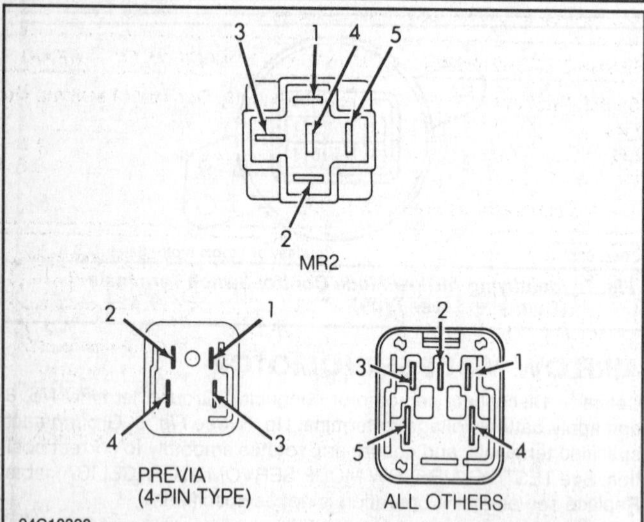
3
1
4
5
2
MR2
2
1
4
3
PREVIA
(4-PIN TYPE)
2
3
1
5
4
ALL OTHERS
94G10328
94H10329 94A10330
Courtesy of Toyota Motor Sales, U.S.A., Inc.

Fig. 10: Identifying Blower Fan Relay (MR2), Blower High Relay (Previa) & Heater Relay Connector Terminals (All Models)

BLOWER HIGH RELAY

Previa – **1)** Disconnect negative battery cable. Remove blower high relay (located in fuse/relay block at center of instrument panel). Using an ohmmeter, ensure continuity exists between blower high relay terminals No. 1 and 3, and between terminals No. 2 and 4. *See Fig. 10.* Ensure continuity does not exist between terminals No. 4 and 5. If continuity is not as specified, replace relay.

2) Ground terminal No. 3, and apply battery voltage to terminal No. 1. Ensure continuity exists between terminals No. 4 and 5. If continuity is not as specified, replace relay.

BLOWER MOTOR

Disconnect blower motor wiring harness connector. Apply battery voltage to motor side of connector. Motor should operate smoothly. If motor operation is not smooth, replace motor.

BLOWER RESISTOR

Camry (Lever Type) – Remove resistor from vehicle or disconnect resistor wiring. Using an ohmmeter, ensure continuity exists between blower resistor terminals No. 2 and 3. *See Fig. 11.* If continuity is not as specified, replace resistor.

Camry (Push Button Type) – Remove resistor from vehicle or disconnect resistor wiring. Using an ohmmeter, ensure resistance increases between terminals 1, 3, 2, 6 and 5. *See Fig. 11.* If continuity is not as specified, replace resistor.

Celica, Corolla, MR2, Paseo, Previa (Front), Tercel, T100 & 4Runner (Front) – Remove resistor from vehicle or disconnect resistor wiring. Using an ohmmeter, ensure continuity exists between blower resistor terminals No. 1 and 4. *See Fig. 11.* If continuity is not as specified, replace resistor.

Pickup – Remove resistor from vehicle or disconnect resistor wiring. Using an ohmmeter, ensure continuity exists between blower resistor terminals No. 2 and 4. *See Fig. 11.* If continuity is not as specified, replace resistor.

Previa (Rear – Nippondenso) – Remove resistor from vehicle or disconnect resistor wiring. Using an ohmmeter, ensure continuity exists between blower resistor terminals No. 1 and 3. *See Fig. 11.* If continuity is not as specified, replace resistor.

Previa (Rear – Panasonic) – Remove resistor from vehicle or disconnect resistor wiring. Using an ohmmeter, ensure continuity exists between blower resistor terminals No. 2 and 3. *See Fig. 11.* If continuity is not as specified, replace resistor.

4Runner (Rear) – Remove resistor from vehicle or disconnect resistor wiring. Using an ohmmeter, check resistance between White/Black and Blue/Red wire terminals of rear blower switch and rear blower resistor. Reading should be approximately 3200 ohms. If resistance is not as specified, replace resistor.

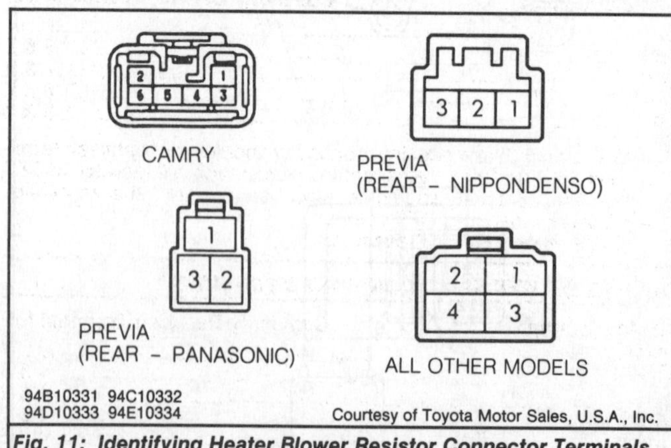
2
1
6
5
4
3
CAMRY
3
2
1
PREVIA
(REAR – NIPPONDENSO)
1
3
2
PREVIA
(REAR – PANASONIC)
2
1
4
3
ALL OTHER MODELS
94B10331 94C10332
94D10333 94E10334
Courtesy of Toyota Motor Sales, U.S.A., Inc.

Fig. 11: Identifying Heater Blower Resistor Connector Terminals

BLOWER SPEED CONTROL SWITCH

Camry & Celica – Disconnect wiring harness connector "B" of heater control panel. Using an ohmmeter, check continuity between specified

1993 HEATER SYSTEMS
Except Land Cruiser & Supra (Cont.)

terminals and switch positions. *See Fig. 4*. See appropriate TESTING BLOWER SPEED CONTROL SWITCH table. If continuity is not as specified, replace blower switch.

Except Camry & Celica – Disconnect blower speed control switch wiring harness connector. Using an ohmmeter, check continuity between specified terminals and switch positions. See appropriate TESTING BLOWER SPEED CONTROL SWITCH table. *See Fig. 12*. If continuity is not as specified, replace blower switch.

TESTING BLOWER SPEED CONTROL SWITCH (CAMRY – LEVER TYPE)

Switch Position	[1] Continuity Between Terminal No.
OFF	[1]
LO	1 & 3
(□) [2]	1, 3 & 4
(□) [3]	1, 3 & 8
HI	1, 3 & 5

[1] – With switch in any position, continuity should exist between terminals No. 6 and 7 for heater control illumination. With switch in OFF position, continuity should not exist between any other terminals.
[2] – Square (□) closest to LO position.
[3] – Square (□) closest to HI position.

TESTING BLOWER SPEED CONTROL SWITCH (CAMRY – PUSH BUTTON TYPE)

Switch Position	[1] Continuity Between Terminal No.
OFF	[1]
(□)	5 & 7
(□□)	2 & 4; 5 & 7
(□□□)	2, 4, 5 & 7
(□□□□)	1 & 2; 5 & 7
(□□□□□)	1 & 2; 4, 5 & 7
(□□□□□□)	1 & 4; 5 & 7
(□□□□□□□)	1, 4, 5 & 7

[1] – With switch in any position, continuity should exist between terminals No. 6 and 8 for heater control illumination. With switch in OFF position, continuity should not exist between any other terminals.

TESTING BLOWER SPEED CONTROL SWITCH (CELICA)

Switch Position	Continuity Between Terminal No.
OFF	[1]
LO	1, 3 & 7
(□) [2]	2, 3 & 6
(□) [3]	2, 3 & 4
HI	2, 3 & 5

[1] – No continuity.
[2] – Square (□) closest to LO position.
[3] – Square (□) closest to HI position.

TESTING BLOWER SPEED CONTROL SWITCH (COROLLA)

Switch Position	[1] Continuity Between Terminal No.
OFF	[1]
(•) [2]	3 & 7
(••)	3, 7 & 8
(•••) [3]	3, 6 & 7
HI	3, 5 & 7

[1] – With switch in any position, continuity should exist between terminals No. 1 and 2 for heater control illumination. With switch in OFF position, continuity should not exist between any other terminals.
[2] – Circle (•) closest to OFF position.
[3] – Circle (•) closest to HI position.

TESTING BLOWER SPEED CONTROL SWITCH (MR2)

Switch Position	Continuity Between Terminal No.
OFF	[1]
LO	4 & 6
(■)	1, 4 & 6
(■■)	2, 4 & 6
HI	3, 4 & 6

[1] – No continuity between terminals.

TESTING BLOWER SPEED CONTROL SWITCH (PASEO & TERCEL)

Switch Position	[1] Continuity Between Terminal No.
OFF	[1]
LO	2 & 5
(•) [2]	1, 2 & 5
(•) [3]	2, 5 & 7
HI	2, 3 & 5

[1] – With switch in any position, continuity should exist between terminals No. 6 and 8 for heater control illumination. With switch in OFF position, continuity should not exist between any other terminals.
[2] – Circle (•) closest to LO position.
[3] – Circle (•) closest to HI position.

TESTING BLOWER SPEED CONTROL SWITCH (PICKUP, T100 & 4RUNNER – FRONT)

Switch Position	[1] Continuity Between Terminal No.
OFF	[1]
LO	5 & 6
(•) [2]	1, 5 & 6
(•) [3]	2, 5 & 6
HI	5, 6 & 8

[1] – With switch in any position, continuity should exist between terminals No. 3 and 4 for heater control illumination. With switch in OFF position, continuity should not exist between any other terminals.
[2] – Circle (•) closest to LO position.
[3] – Circle (•) closest to HI position.

TESTING BLOWER SPEED CONTROL SWITCH (PREVIA – FRONT)

Switch Position	[1] Continuity Between Terminal No.
OFF	[1]
LO	5 & 6
(■)	1, 5 & 6
(■■)	2, 5 & 6
HI	5, 6 & 8

[1] – With switch in any position, continuity should exist between terminals No. 3 and 4 for heater control illumination. With switch in OFF position, continuity should not exist between any other terminals.

TESTING BLOWER SPEED CONTROL SWITCH (PREVIA – REAR)

Switch Position	Continuity Between Terminal No.
OFF	[1]
LO	3 & 4
(■)	1, 3 & 4
HI	2, 3 & 4

[1] – No continuity between terminals.

TESTING BLOWER SPEED CONTROL SWITCH (4RUNNER – REAR)

Switch Position	Continuity Between Terminal No.
OFF	[1]
LO	1 & 4
HI	1, 2 & 4

[1] – No continuity between terminals.

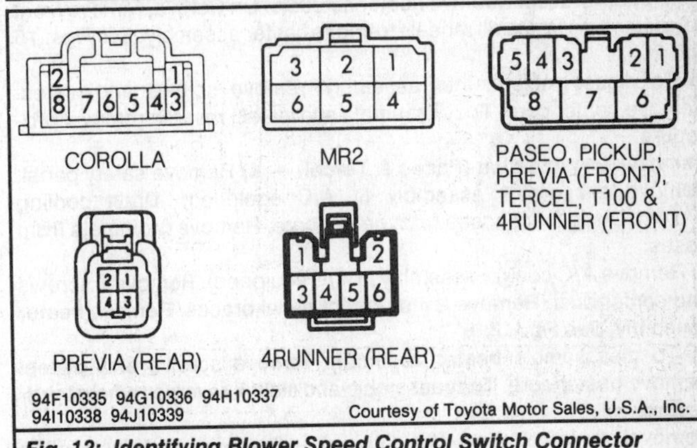
2
1
8 7 6 5 4 3
COROLLA
3 2 1
6 5 4
MR2
5 4 3
2 1
8 7 6
PASEO, PICKUP, PREVIA (FRONT), TERCEL, T100 & 4RUNNER (FRONT)
2 1
4 3
PREVIA (REAR)
1 2
3 4 5 6
4RUNNER (REAR)
94F10335 94G10336 94H10337
94I10338 94J10339
Courtesy of Toyota Motor Sales, U.S.A., Inc.

Fig. 12: Identifying Blower Speed Control Switch Connector Terminals (Except Camry & Celica)

1993 HEATER SYSTEMS
Except Land Cruiser & Supra (Cont.)

HEATER RELAY

Except MR2 & Previa (4-Pin Type) – 1) Disconnect negative battery cable. Remove heater relay. Using an ohmmeter, ensure continuity exists between heater relay terminals No. 1 and 3, and between terminals No. 2 and 4. *See Fig. 10.* Ensure continuity does not exist between terminals No. 4 and 5. If continuity is not as specified, replace relay.
2) Ground terminal No. 3, and apply battery voltage to terminal No. 1. Ensure continuity exists between terminals No. 4 and 5. If continuity is not as specified, replace relay.
MR2 – 1) Disconnect negative battery cable. Remove relay. Using an ohmmeter, ensure continuity exists between heater relay terminals No. 1 and 2 and between terminals No. 3 and 4. *See Fig. 10.* If continuity is not as specified, replace relay.
2) Ground terminal No. 2, and apply battery voltage to terminal No. 1. Ensure continuity exists between terminals No. 3 and 5. If continuity is not as specified, replace relay.
Previa (4-Pin Type) – 1) Disconnect negative battery cable. Remove relay. Using an ohmmeter, ensure continuity exists between heater relay terminals No. 1 and 3. *See Fig. 10.* If continuity is not as specified, replace relay.
2) Ground terminal No. 3, and apply battery voltage to terminal No. 1. Ensure continuity exists between terminals No. 2 and 4. If continuity is not as specified, replace relay.

REMOVAL & INSTALLATION

WARNING: To avoid injury from accidental air bag deployment, read and carefully follow all SERVICE PRECAUTIONS and DISABLING & ACTIVATING AIR BAG SYSTEM procedures in AIR BAG SYSTEM SAFETY article in GENERAL SERVICING.

BLOWER MOTOR

Removal & Installation (Corolla & T100) – Disconnect negative battery cable. Remove glove box, if necessary. Disconnect blower motor and resistor connectors. Remove 3 screws and blower motor. To install, reverse removal procedure. *See Figs. 15 and 20.*
Removal & Installation (Paseo & Tercel) – Disconnect negative battery cable. Remove A/C amplifier (located under glove box). Disconnect blower motor connector. Remove 3 screws and blower motor. To install, reverse removal procedure. *See Fig. 17.*
Removal & Installation (All Others) – Removal and installation procedures are not available from manufacturer. Exploded views of heater systems are provided. *See Figs. 13, 14, 16, 18, 19 and 21.*

HEATER ASSEMBLY

Removal & Installation (Corolla & T100) – 1) Remove evaporator assembly (if A/C equipped). Drain cooling system. Disconnect hoses from heater core. Remove grommets from hoses. Remove instrument panel. See INSTRUMENT PANEL.
2) Disconnect control cables from heater assembly. Remove 2 instrument panel braces. Remove heater air ducts. On Corolla, remove front defroster nozzle. On all models, remove heater assembly. *See Figs. 15 and 20.*
3) To disassemble heater assembly, remove screws and plates. Remove heater core. To reassemble and install, reverse removal procedure.
Removal & Installation (Paseo & Tercel) – 1) Remove safety panel. Remove evaporator assembly (if A/C equipped). Drain cooling system. Disconnect hoses from heater core. Remove grommets from hoses.
2) Remove A/C control assembly (if A/C equipped). Remove 3 screws and center duct. Remove 2 instrument panel braces. Remove heater assembly. *See Fig. 17.*
3) To disassemble heater assembly, remove screws and plates. Remove heater core. To reassemble and install, reverse removal procedure.
Removal & Installation (All Others) – Removal and installation procedures are not available from manufacturer. Exploded views of heater systems are provided. *See Figs. 13, 14, 16, 18, 19 and 21.*

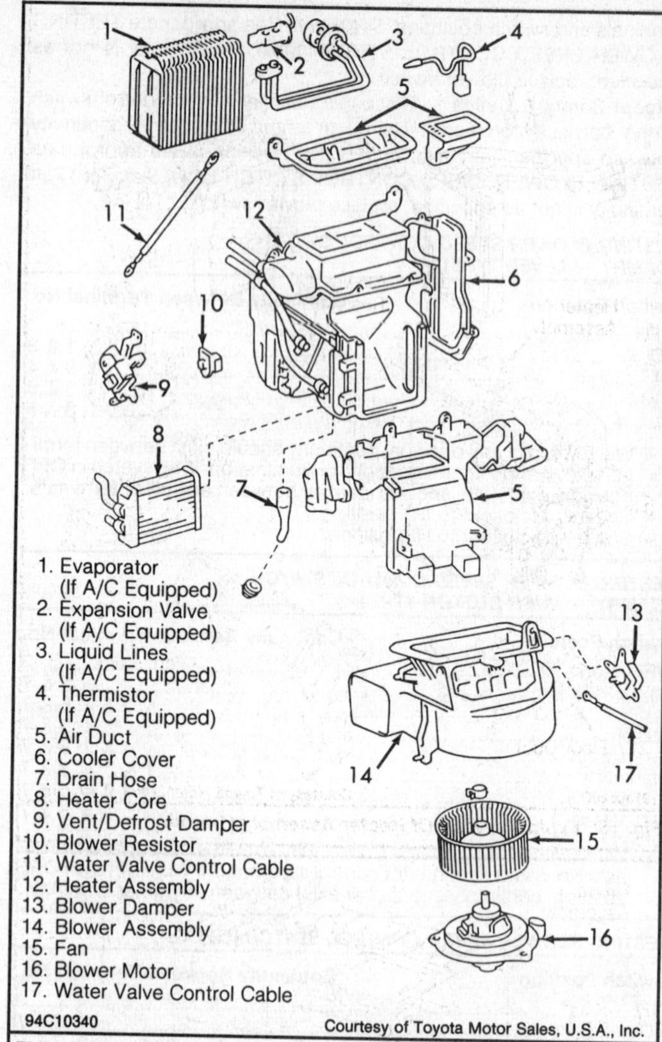
1. Evaporator (If A/C Equipped)
2. Expansion Valve (If A/C Equipped)
3. Liquid Lines (If A/C Equipped)
4. Thermistor (If A/C Equipped)
5. Air Duct
6. Cooler Cover
7. Drain Hose
8. Heater Core
9. Vent/Defrost Damper
10. Blower Resistor
11. Water Valve Control Cable
12. Heater Assembly
13. Blower Damper
14. Blower Assembly
15. Fan
16. Blower Motor
17. Water Valve Control Cable
94C10340
Courtesy of Toyota Motor Sales, U.S.A., Inc.

Fig. 13: Exploded View Of Heater Assembly (Camry)

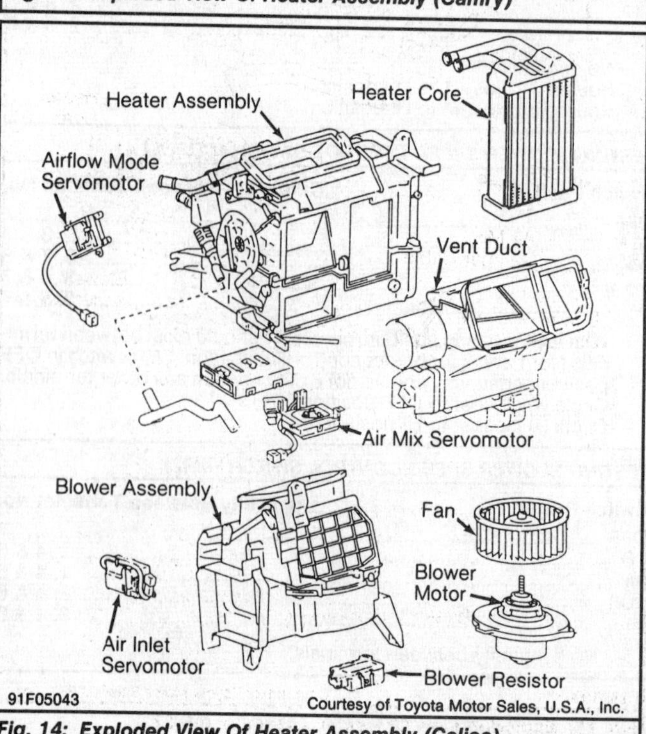
Heater Assembly
Heater Core
Airflow Mode Servomotor
Vent Duct
Air Mix Servomotor
Blower Assembly
Fan
Blower Motor
Air Inlet Servomotor
Blower Resistor
91F05043
Courtesy of Toyota Motor Sales, U.S.A., Inc.

Fig. 14: Exploded View Of Heater Assembly (Celica)

1993 HEATER SYSTEMS
Except Land Cruiser & Supra (Cont.)

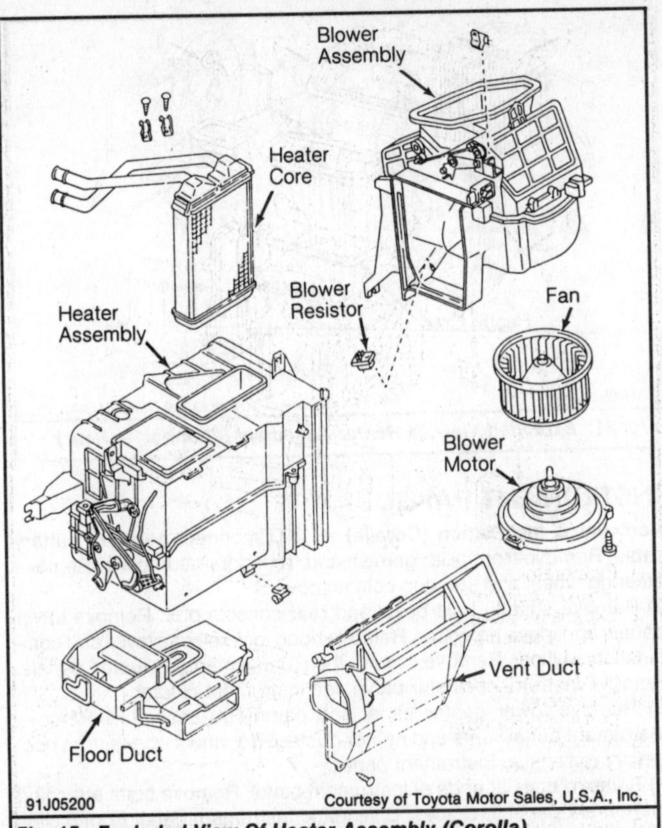
Blower
Assembly
Heater
Core
Heater
Assembly
Blower
Resistor
Fan
Blower
Motor
Vent Duct
Floor Duct
91J05200
Courtesy of Toyota Motor Sales, U.S.A., Inc.

Fig. 15: Exploded View Of Heater Assembly (Corolla)

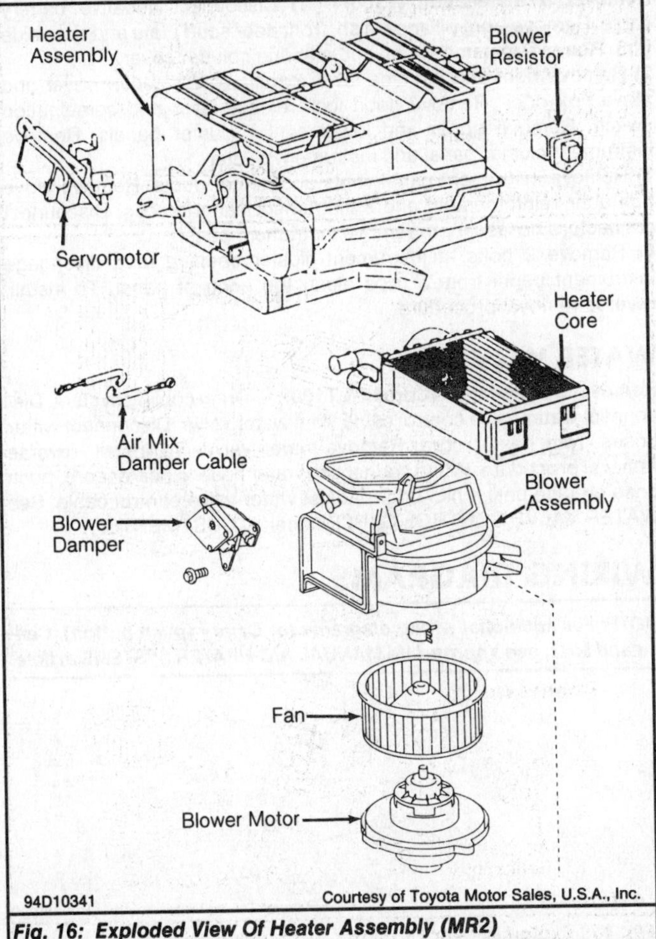
Heater
Assembly
Blower
Resistor
Servomotor
Heater
Core
Air Mix
Damper Cable
Blower
Damper
Blower
Assembly
Fan
Blower Motor
94D10341
Courtesy of Toyota Motor Sales, U.S.A., Inc.

Fig. 16: Exploded View Of Heater Assembly (MR2)

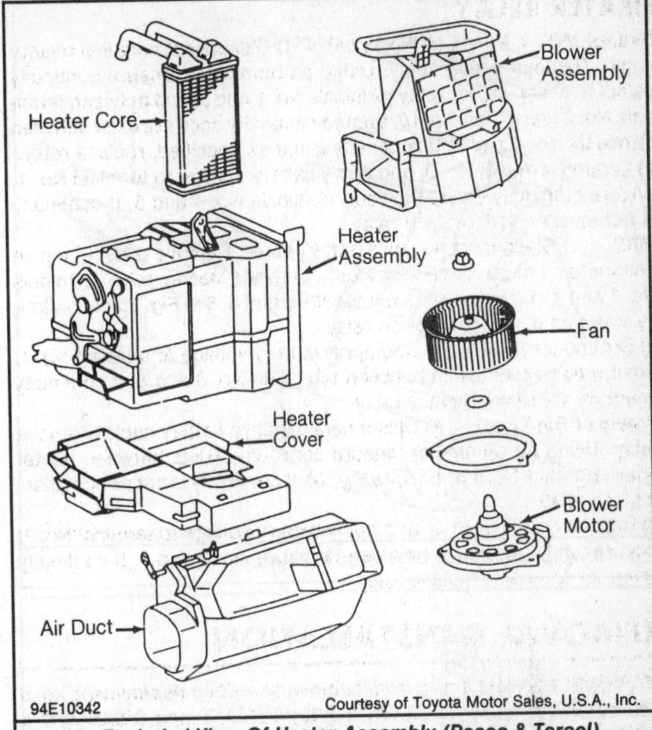
Blower
Assembly
Heater Core
Heater
Assembly
Fan
Heater
Cover
Blower
Motor
Air Duct
94E10342
Courtesy of Toyota Motor Sales, U.S.A., Inc.

Fig. 17: Exploded View Of Heater Assembly (Paseo & Tercel)

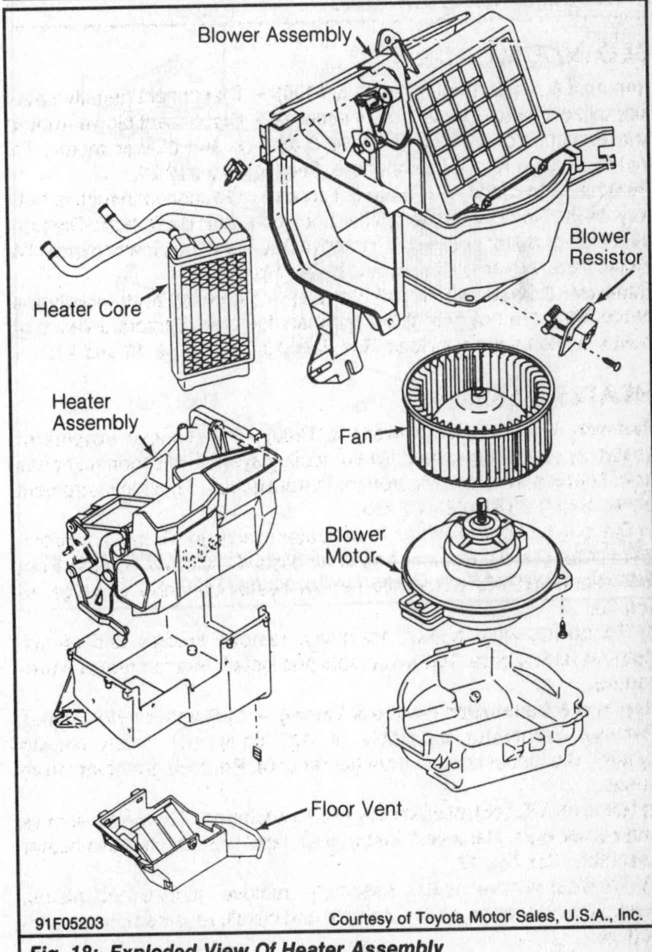
Blower Assembly
Blower
Resistor
Heater Core
Heater
Assembly
Fan
Blower
Motor
Floor Vent
91F05203
Courtesy of Toyota Motor Sales, U.S.A., Inc.

Fig. 18: Exploded View Of Heater Assembly (Pickup & 4Runner – Front)

1993 HEATER SYSTEMS
Except Land Cruiser & Supra (Cont.)

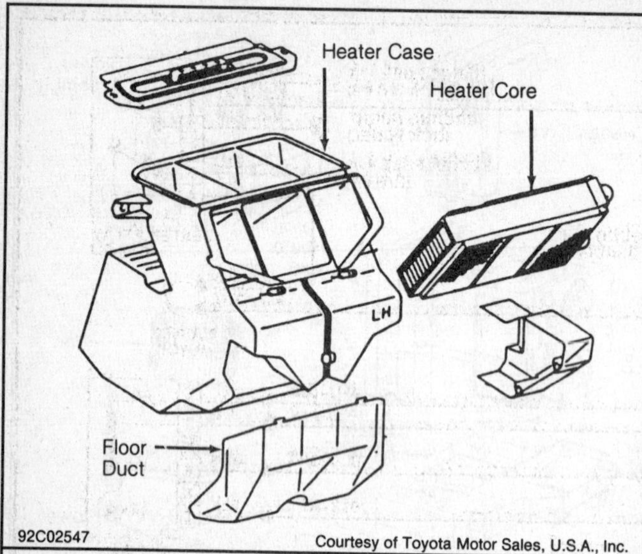
Heater Case
Heater Core
LH
Floor Duct
92C02547
Courtesy of Toyota Motor Sales, U.S.A., Inc.

Fig. 19: Exploded View Of Heater Assembly (Previa)

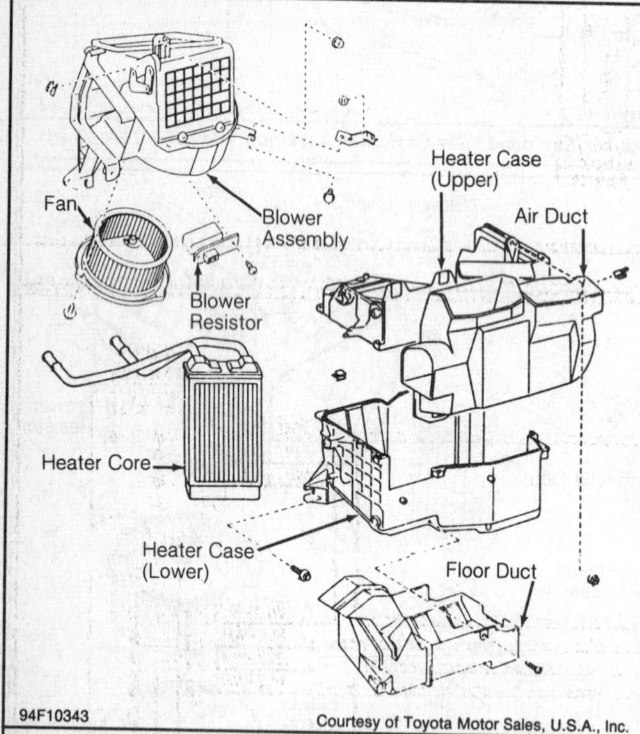
Heater Case (Upper)
Fan
Blower Assembly
Air Duct
Blower Resistor
Heater Core
Heater Case (Lower)
Floor Duct
94F10343
Courtesy of Toyota Motor Sales, U.S.A., Inc.

Fig. 20: Exploded View Of Heater Assembly (T100)

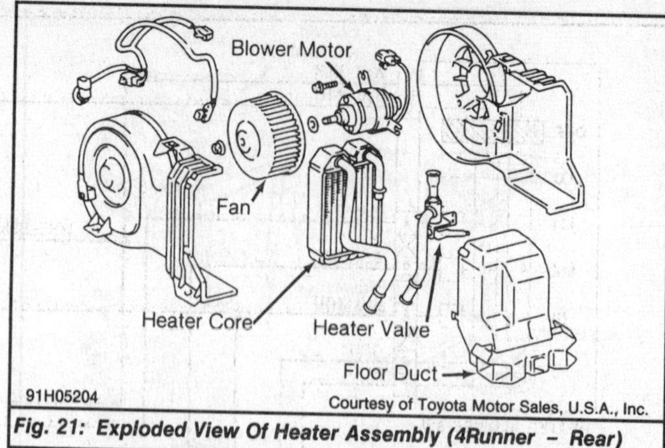
Blower Motor
Fan
Heater Core
Heater Valve
Floor Duct
91H05204
Courtesy of Toyota Motor Sales, U.S.A., Inc.

Fig. 21: Exploded View Of Heater Assembly (4Runner – Rear)

INSTRUMENT PANEL

Removal & Installation (Corolla) – 1) Disconnect negative battery cable. Remove front pillar garnish and front door scuff plate. Remove steering wheel and steering column cover.

2) Remove shifting hole bezel and rear console box. Remove lower panels and glove box door. Remove hood lock release lever and combination switch. Remove lower, then upper center cluster panels. Remove instrument cluster panel and instrument cluster.

3) Remove lower center panel and panel sub assembly. Remove instrument panel vents and heater ducts. Disconnect connectors necessary to remove instrument panel.

4) Remove bolts at ends of instrument panel. Remove bolts attaching instrument panel to braces. Disengage instrument panel from 5 clips along top edge of panel. To install, reverse removal procedure.

Removal & Installation (T100) – 1) Disconnect negative battery cable. Remove front pillar garnish, front door scuff plate and cowl side trim. Remove steering wheel and steering column cover.

2) Remove right and left side lower panels, lower center cover and glove box door. Remove hood lock release lever and combination switch. Remove upper and lower center cluster panels. Remove instrument cluster panel and instrument cluster.

3) Remove instrument panel vents and heater ducts. Remove glove box door reinforcement and 2 instrument panel braces. Disconnect connectors necessary to remove instrument panel.

4) Remove 2 bolts at instrument cluster opening, and disengage instrument panel from 5 clips along top edge of panel. To install, reverse removal procedure.

WATER VALVE

Removal & Installation (Corolla & T100) – Drain cooling system. Disconnect water valve control cable from water valve. Disconnect water hoses from heater core. Remove water valve. To install, reverse removal procedure. When connecting water hose to heater core, push hose on pipe until it hits ridge. Adjust water valve control cable. See WATER VALVE CONTROL CABLE under ADJUSTMENTS.

WIRING DIAGRAMS

NOTE: For additional wiring diagrams for Camry (push button), Celica and MR2, see appropriate MANUAL A/C-HEATER SYSTEMS article.

1993 HEATER SYSTEMS
Except Land Cruiser & Supra (Cont.)

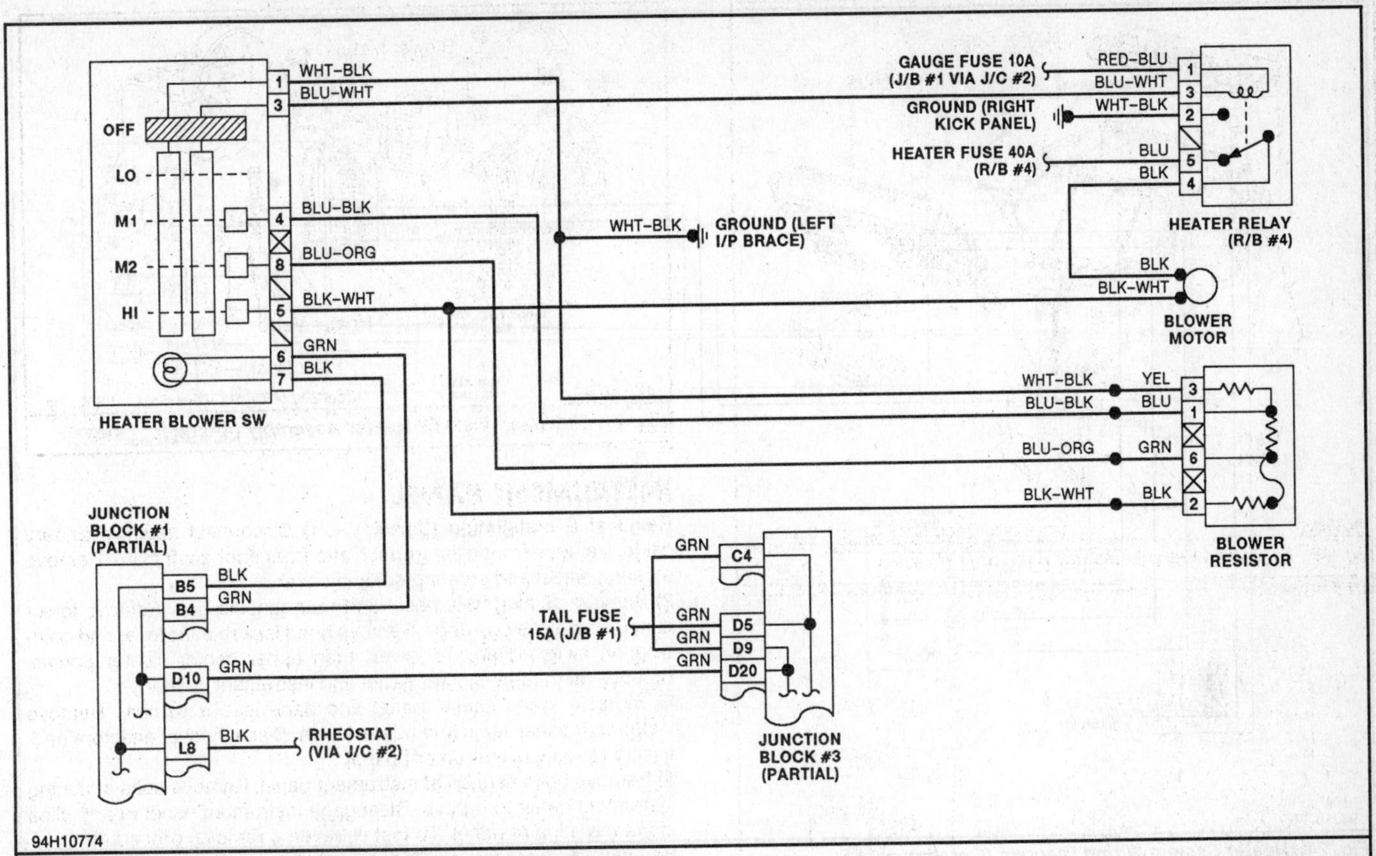

WHT-BLK
BLU-WHT
OFF
LO
M1
M2
HI
BLU-BLK
BLU-ORG
BLK-WHT
GRN
BLK
HEATER BLOWER SW
GAUGE FUSE 10A (J/B #1 VIA J/C #2)
GROUND (RIGHT KICK PANEL)
HEATER FUSE 40A (R/B #4)
RED-BLU
BLU-WHT
WHT-BLK
BLU
BLK
HEATER RELAY (R/B #4)
WHT-BLK
GROUND (LEFT I/P BRACE)
BLK
BLK-WHT
BLOWER MOTOR
WHT-BLK
YEL
BLU-BLK
BLU
BLU-ORG
GRN
BLK-WHT
BLK
BLOWER RESISTOR
JUNCTION BLOCK #1 (PARTIAL)
B5
B4
D10
L8
BLK
GRN
GRN
BLK
RHEOSTAT (VIA J/C #2)
GRN
C4
TAIL FUSE 15A (J/B #1)
GRN
GRN
GRN
D5
D9
D20
JUNCTION BLOCK #3 (PARTIAL)
94H10774

Fig. 22: Heater System Wiring Diagram (Camry – Lever Type)

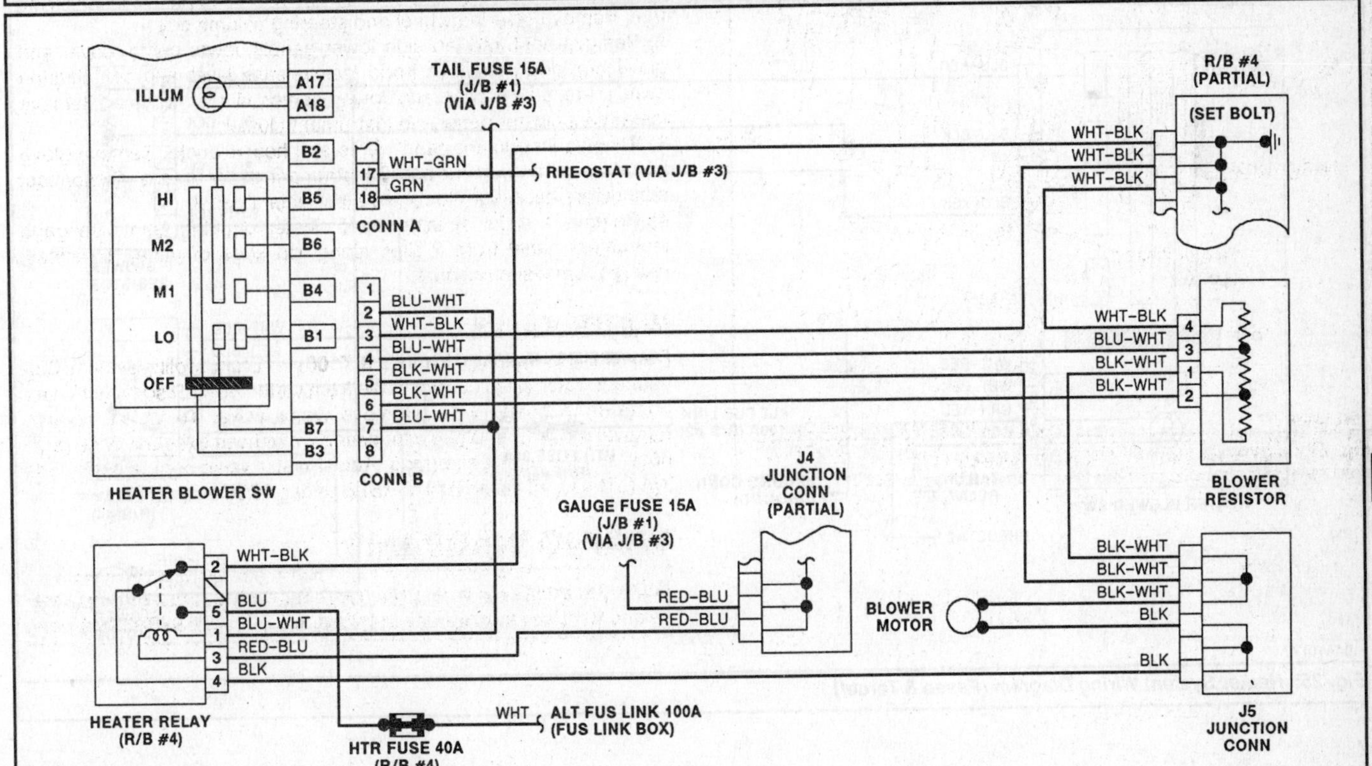

ILLUM
A17
A18
B2
HI
B5
M2
B6
M1
B4
LO
B1
OFF
B7
B3
HEATER BLOWER SW
TAIL FUSE 15A (J/B #1) (VIA J/B #3)
WHT-GRN
GRN
RHEOSTAT (VIA J/B #3)
CONN A
BLU-WHT
WHT-BLK
BLU-WHT
BLK-WHT
BLK-WHT
BLU-WHT
CONN B
R/B #4 (PARTIAL)
(SET BOLT)
WHT-BLK
WHT-BLK
WHT-BLK
WHT-BLK
BLU-WHT
BLK-WHT
BLK-WHT
BLOWER RESISTOR
HEATER RELAY (R/B #4)
WHT-BLK
BLU
BLU-WHT
RED-BLU
BLK
GAUGE FUSE 15A (J/B #1) (VIA J/B #3)
RED-BLU
RED-BLU
J4 JUNCTION CONN (PARTIAL)
BLOWER MOTOR
BLK-WHT
BLK-WHT
BLK-WHT
BLK
BLK
J5 JUNCTION CONN
HTR FUSE 40A (R/B #4)
WHT
ALT FUS LINK 100A (FUS LINK BOX)
94I10775

Fig. 23: Heater System Wiring Diagram (Celica)

1993 HEATER SYSTEMS
Except Land Cruiser & Supra (Cont.)

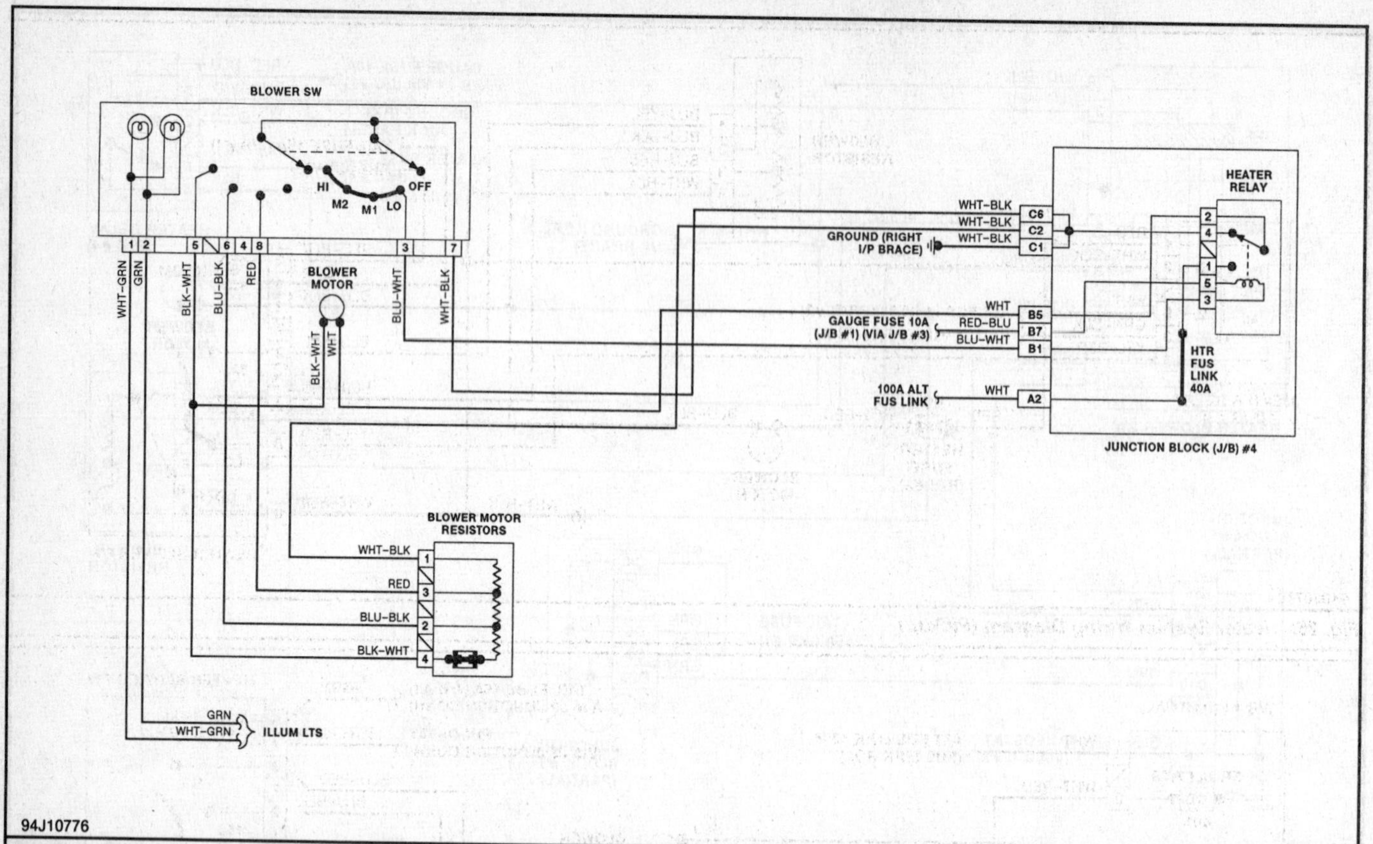

BLOWER SW
HI
M2
M1
LO
OFF
1 2 5 6 4 8 3 7
WHT-GRN
GRN
BLK-WHT
BLU-BLK
RED
BLOWER MOTOR
BLK-WHT
WHT
BLU-WHT
WHT-BLK
WHT-BLK C6
WHT-BLK C2
GROUND (RIGHT I/P BRACE) WHT-BLK C1
WHT B5
GAUGE FUSE 10A (J/B #1) (VIA J/B #3) RED-BLU B7
BLU-WHT B1
100A ALT FUS LINK WHT A2
HEATER RELAY
2 4 1 5 3
HTR FUS LINK 40A
JUNCTION BLOCK (J/B) #4
BLOWER MOTOR RESISTORS
WHT-BLK 1
RED 3
BLU-BLK 2
BLK-WHT 4
GRN
WHT-GRN
ILLUM LTS

94J10776

Fig. 24: Heater System Wiring Diagram (Corolla)

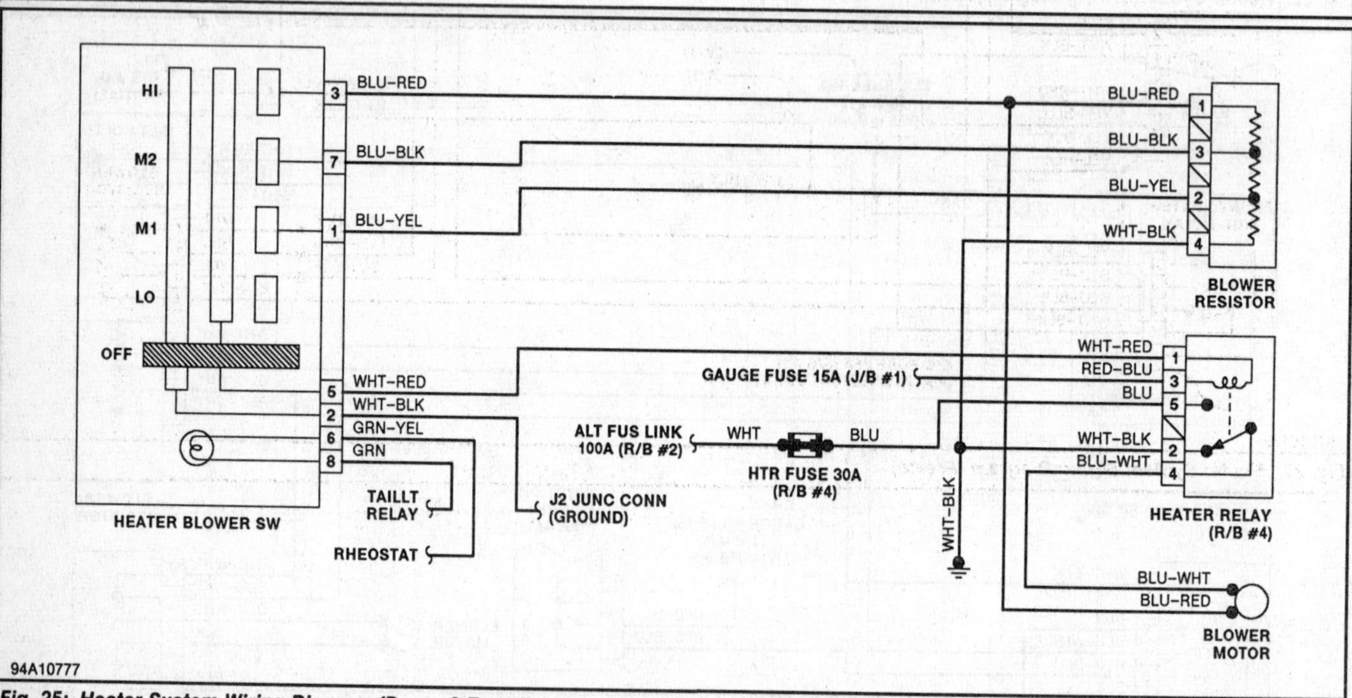
HI
M2
M1
LO
OFF
3 BLU-RED
7 BLU-BLK
1 BLU-YEL
5 WHT-RED
2 WHT-BLK
6 GRN-YEL
8 GRN
HEATER BLOWER SW
TAILLT RELAY
RHEOSTAT
J2 JUNC CONN (GROUND)
ALT FUS LINK 100A (R/B #2)
WHT
BLU
HTR FUSE 30A (R/B #4)
GAUGE FUSE 15A (J/B #1)
WHT-BLK
BLU-RED 1
BLU-BLK 3
BLU-YEL 2
WHT-BLK 4
BLOWER RESISTOR
WHT-RED 1
RED-BLU 3
BLU 5
WHT-BLK 2
BLU-WHT 4
HEATER RELAY (R/B #4)
BLU-WHT
BLU-RED
BLOWER MOTOR
94A10777

Fig. 25: Heater System Wiring Diagram (Paseo & Tercel)

1993 HEATER SYSTEMS
Except Land Cruiser & Supra (Cont.)

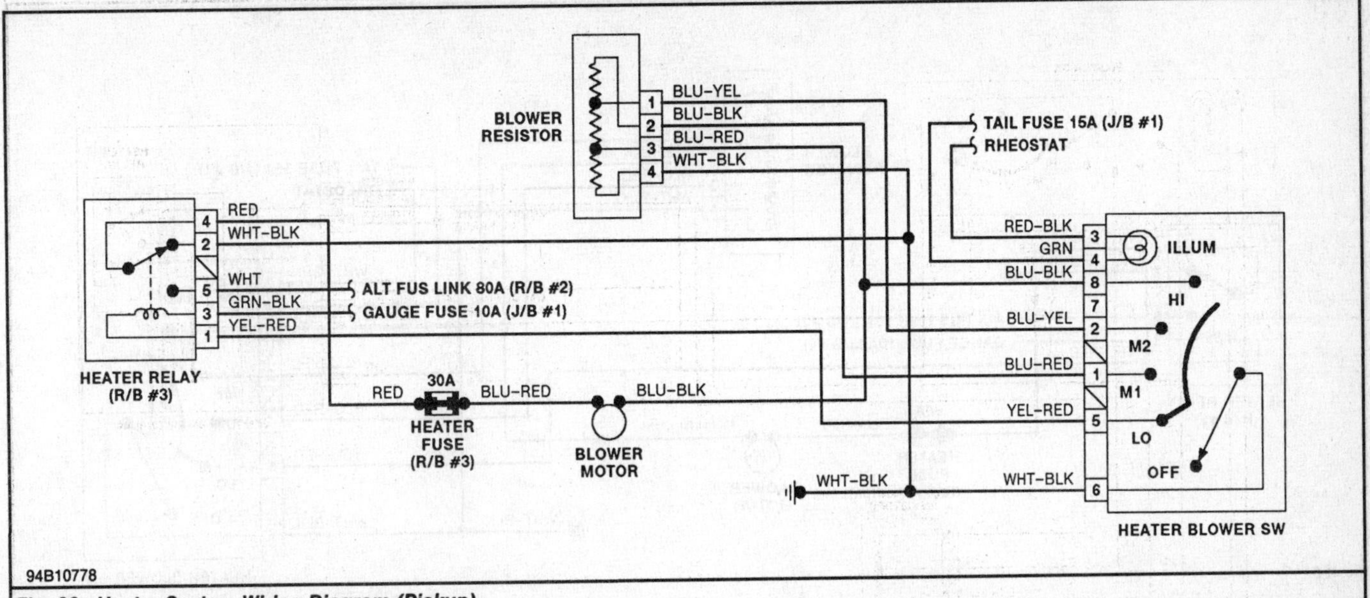
BLOWER
RESISTOR
1
2
3
4
BLU-YEL
BLU-BLK
BLU-RED
WHT-BLK
TAIL FUSE 15A (J/B #1)
RHEOSTAT
RED
WHT-BLK
WHT
GRN-BLK
YEL-RED
ALT FUS LINK 80A (R/B #2)
GAUGE FUSE 10A (J/B #1)
HEATER RELAY
(R/B #3)
RED
30A
HEATER
FUSE
(R/B #3)
BLU-RED
BLU-BLK
BLOWER
MOTOR
RED-BLK
GRN
BLU-BLK
BLU-YEL
BLU-RED
YEL-RED
WHT-BLK
WHT-BLK
ILLUM
HI
M2
M1
LO
OFF
HEATER BLOWER SW
94B10778

Fig. 26: Heater System Wiring Diagram (Pickup)

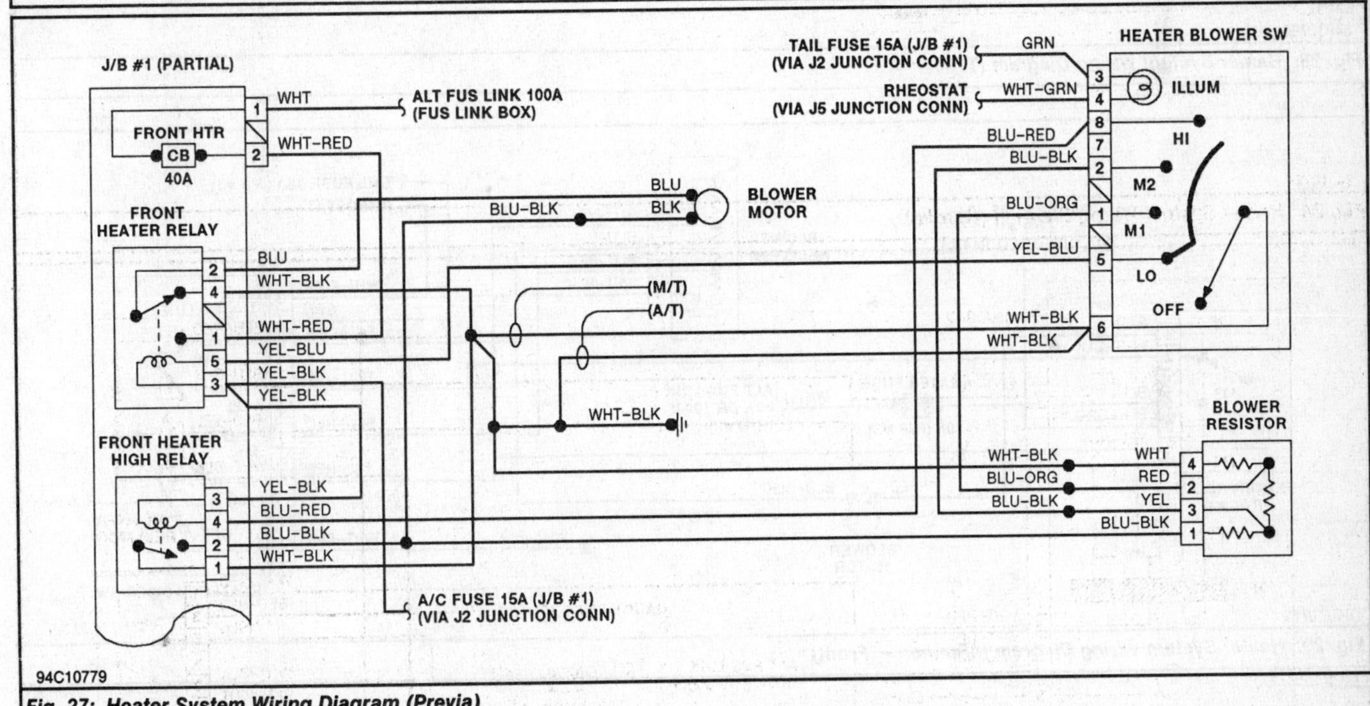
J/B #1 (PARTIAL)
FRONT HTR
CB
40A
WHT
WHT-RED
ALT FUS LINK 100A
(FUS LINK BOX)
TAIL FUSE 15A (J/B #1)
(VIA J2 JUNCTION CONN)
RHEOSTAT
(VIA J5 JUNCTION CONN)
GRN
WHT-GRN
HEATER BLOWER SW
ILLUM
BLU-RED
BLU-BLK
BLU-ORG
YEL-BLU
HI
M2
M1
LO
OFF
WHT-BLK
WHT-BLK
FRONT
HEATER RELAY
BLU
BLK
BLU-BLK
BLOWER
MOTOR
BLU
WHT-BLK
WHT-RED
YEL-BLU
YEL-BLK
YEL-BLK
(M/T)
(A/T)
WHT-BLK
FRONT HEATER
HIGH RELAY
YEL-BLK
BLU-RED
BLU-BLK
WHT-BLK
A/C FUSE 15A (J/B #1)
(VIA J2 JUNCTION CONN)
BLOWER
RESISTOR
WHT-BLK
BLU-ORG
BLU-BLK
WHT
RED
YEL
BLU-BLK
94C10779

Fig. 27: Heater System Wiring Diagram (Previa)

1993 HEATER SYSTEMS
Except Land Cruiser & Supra (Cont.)

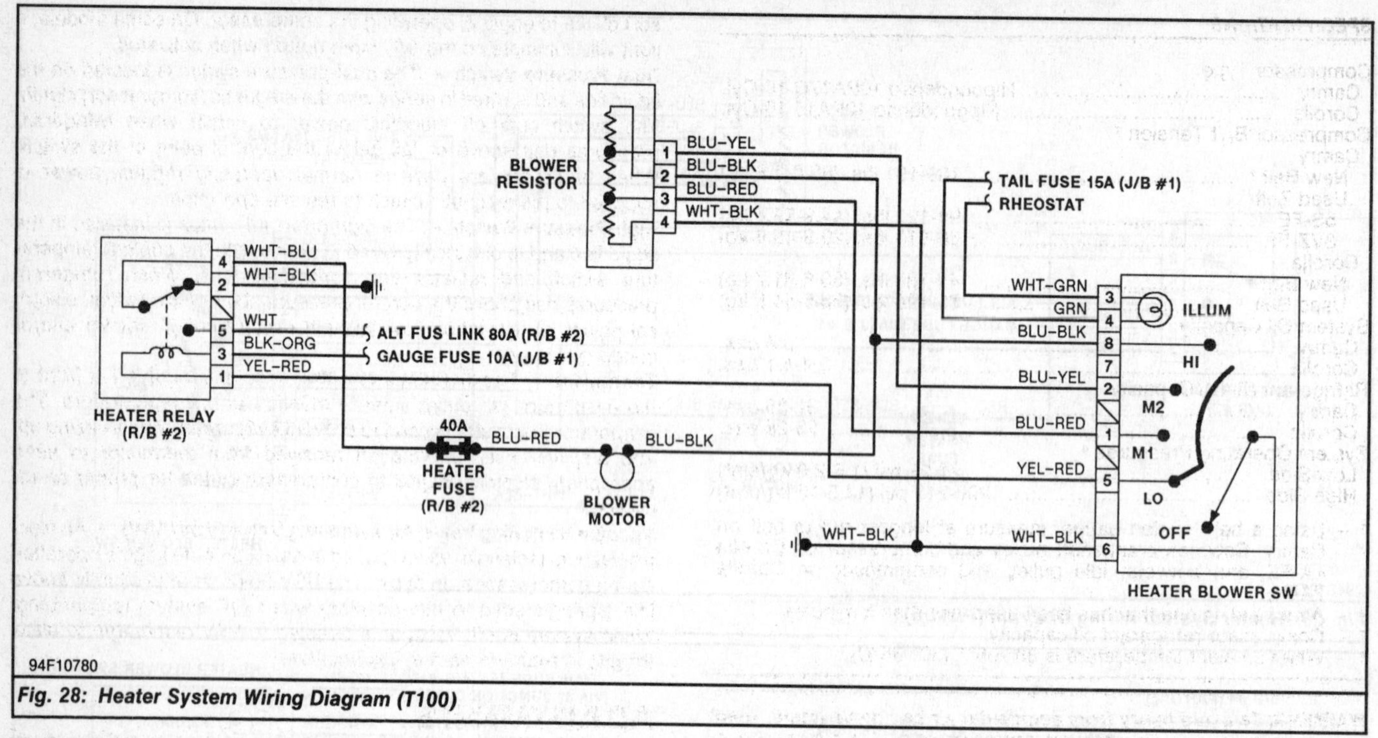
BLOWER RESISTOR
1
2
3
4
BLU-YEL
BLU-BLK
BLU-RED
WHT-BLK
TAIL FUSE 15A (J/B #1)
RHEOSTAT
WHT-BLU
WHT-BLK
WHT
BLK-ORG
YEL-RED
ALT FUS LINK 80A (R/B #2)
GAUGE FUSE 10A (J/B #1)
HEATER RELAY (R/B #2)
40A
HEATER FUSE (R/B #2)
BLU-RED
BLU-BLK
BLOWER MOTOR
WHT-GRN
GRN
BLU-BLK
BLU-YEL
BLU-RED
YEL-RED
WHT-BLK
ILLUM
HI
M2
M1
LO
OFF
HEATER BLOWER SW
94F10780

Fig. 28: Heater System Wiring Diagram (T100)

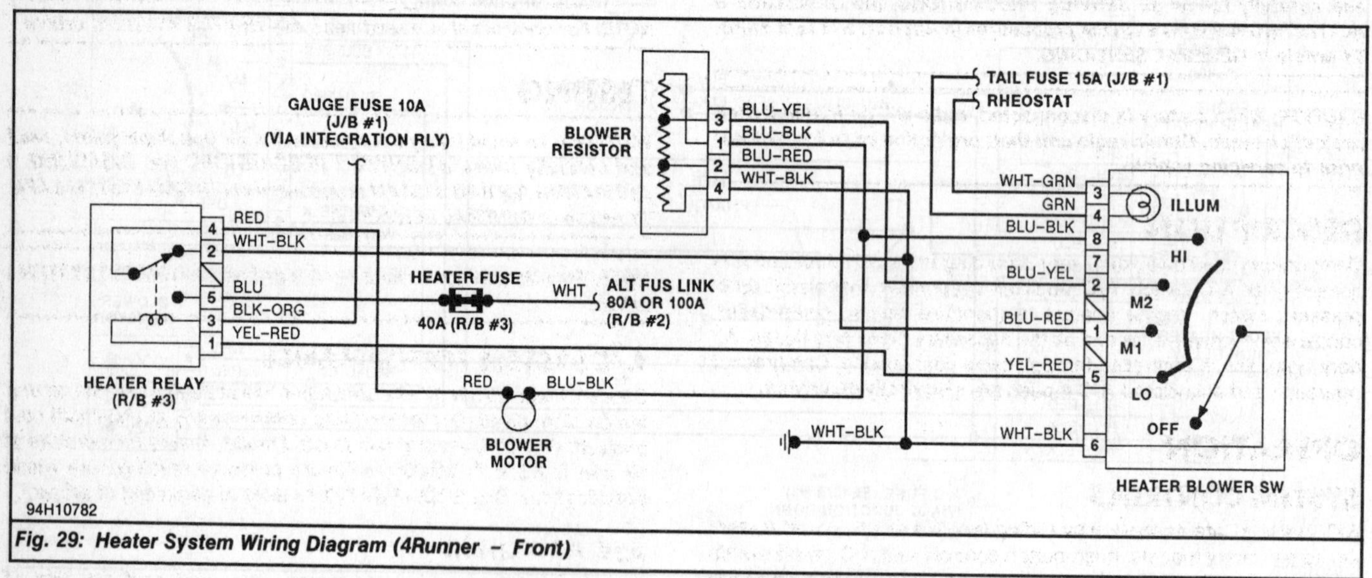
GAUGE FUSE 10A (J/B #1) (VIA INTEGRATION RLY)
BLOWER RESISTOR
BLU-YEL
BLU-BLK
BLU-RED
WHT-BLK
TAIL FUSE 15A (J/B #1)
RHEOSTAT
RED
WHT-BLK
BLU
BLK-ORG
YEL-RED
HEATER FUSE
40A (R/B #3)
WHT
ALT FUS LINK 80A OR 100A (R/B #2)
HEATER RELAY (R/B #3)
RED
BLU-BLK
BLOWER MOTOR
WHT-GRN
GRN
BLU-BLK
BLU-YEL
BLU-RED
YEL-RED
WHT-BLK
ILLUM
HI
M2
M1
LO
OFF
HEATER BLOWER SW
94H10782

Fig. 29: Heater System Wiring Diagram (4Runner – Front)

1993 MANUAL A/C-HEATER SYSTEMS
Camry & Corolla

SPECIFICATIONS

Compressor Type	
Camry	Nippondenso 10PA17C 10-Cyl.
Corolla	Nippondenso 10PA15 10-Cyl.
Compressor Belt Tension [1]	
Camry	
New Belt [2]	139-191 lbs. (63.0-8.6 kg)
Used Belt	
5S-FE	99-121 lbs. (44.9-59.4 kg)
3VZ-FE	66-110 lbs. (29.9-49.9 kg)
Corolla	
New Belt [2]	140-180 lbs. (63.6-81.7 kg)
Used Belt	80-120 lbs. (36.3-54.5 kg)
System Oil Capacity	
Camry	[3] 3.5 ozs.
Corolla	3.4-4.1 ozs.
Refrigerant (R-12) Capacity	
Camry	32-35 ozs.
Corolla	25-28 ozs.
System Operating Pressures [4]	
Low Side	21-28 psi (1.5-2.0 kg/cm²)
High Side	206-213 psi (14.5-15 kg/cm²)

[1] – Using a belt tension gauge, measure at longest run of belt on Camry. Between crankshaft pulley and compressor on Corolla 4A-FE, and between idle pulley and compressor on Corolla 7A-FE.
[2] – A new belt is one that has been used less than 5 minutes.
[3] – Compressor refrigerant oil capacity.
[4] – When ambient temperature is 86°-95°F (30°-35°C).

WARNING: To avoid injury from accidental air bag deployment, read and carefully follow all SERVICE PRECAUTIONS and DISABLING & ACTIVATING AIR BAG SYSTEM procedures in AIR BAG SYSTEM SAFETY article in GENERAL SERVICING.

CAUTION: When battery is disconnected, radio will go into anti-theft protection mode. Obtain radio anti-theft protection code from owner prior to servicing vehicle.

DESCRIPTION

Components used on system vary according to model. Most systems consist of an A/C switch, A/C amplifier, evaporator, thermistor, dual-pressure switch, engine coolant temperature switch, compressor, condenser, receiver-drier and all the necessary pipes and hoses. Air door operation is controlled through cable connections. Compressor operation and associated A/C modes are electrically controlled.

OPERATION

SYSTEM CONTROLS

A/C functions are controlled by sliding levers and A/C on-off switch. On some Camry models, push-button controls and A/C on-off switch are used. On all models, A/C controls operate air supply selection (fresh or recirculated air), mode and temperature selection, and blower speeds.

Temperature control lever operates the blend air door in A/C-heater unit. This mixes both cooled and heated air so the desirable air temperature can be obtained. The system will provide cooled air when A/C switch is on and blower motor is in any position except OFF. The temperature control lever should be in the far left (maximum cooling) side of temperature selection scale when maximum A/C operation is desired.

SYSTEM COMPONENTS

NOTE: A/C systems components may vary according to model. A/C systems may not use all of the components listed.

A/C Switch – When A/C switch is pushed, A/C will operate if the blower motor control lever or push button is in any position except OFF. When activated, the A/C switch allows the magnetic (compressor) clutch to engage, operating the compressor. On some models, a light will illuminate on the A/C push button when activated.

Dual-Pressure Switch – The dual-pressure switch is located on the liquid line and is wired in series with the magnetic (compressor) clutch. The switch cuts off electrical power to clutch when refrigerant pressures rise above or fall below the control point of the switch. When pressures are back in normal operating ranges, power is supplied to the magnetic clutch to resume operation.

High-Pressure Switch – The high-pressure switch is installed in the liquid line and is electrically wired in series with the coolant temperature switch and radiator and condenser fans. When refrigerant pressures rise above the control pressure point of the switch, electrical power is allowed to flow through circuit turning radiator and/or condenser fan on.

Thermistor – The thermistor is a thermocouple mounted in front of the evaporator (air outlet side) to monitor airflow temperature. The evaporator thermistor is used to prevent evaporator from freezing up. The amplifier uses information received from thermistor to send appropriate electrical signal to compressor clutch for proper on-off cycling.

Vacuum Switching Valve/Air Switching Valve (VSV/ASV) – An electro-vacuum (solenoid) valve is used to assist smooth engine operation during compressor's on cycle. The VSV holds throttle slightly above idle (spring-loaded to this position) when A/C system is operating. When system is off, vacuum is directed to VSV diaphragm to allow throttle to return to normal idle position.

ADJUSTMENTS

NOTE: For control cable adjustment, see HEATER SYSTEMS article.

TESTING

WARNING: To avoid injury from accidental air bag deployment, read and carefully follow all SERVICE PRECAUTIONS and DISABLING & ACTIVATING AIR BAG SYSTEM procedures in AIR BAG SYSTEM SAFETY article in GENERAL SERVICING.

NOTE: For information not found in this article, see HEATER SYSTEMS article.

A/C SYSTEM PERFORMANCE

Connect manifold gauge set. Let engine idle at 2000 RPM. Set blower fan on high speed. Set temperature control switch at maximum cool position. With airflow set in recirculated mode, ensure temperature at air inlet is 86-95°F (30-35°C). Ensure pressure readings are within specifications. See SPECIFICATIONS table at beginning of article.

A/C AMPLIFIER

Disconnect A/C amplifier connector. Test wire harness side of connector. *See Fig. 1.* On Camry, A/C amplifier is located behind

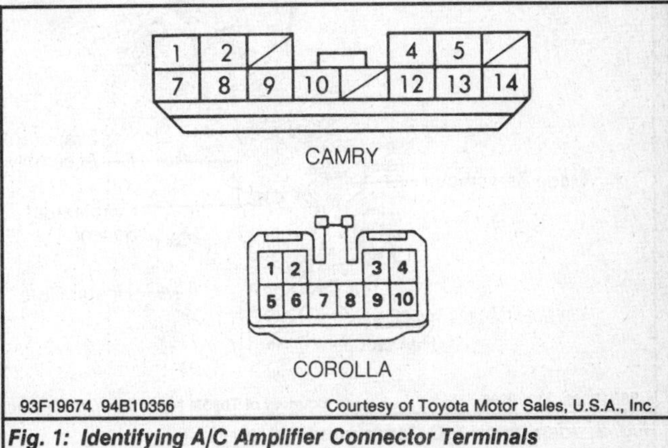
1
2
4
5
7
8
9
10
12
13
14
CAMRY
1
2
3
4
5
6
7
8
9
10
COROLLA
93F19674 94B10356
Courtesy of Toyota Motor Sales, U.S.A., Inc.

Fig. 1: Identifying A/C Amplifier Connector Terminals

1993 MANUAL A/C-HEATER SYSTEMS
Camry & Corolla (Cont.)

A/C AMPLIFIER CIRCUIT TEST (CAMRY)

Terminals [1]	Specification
5 & Ground	Continuity
12 & Ground	
A/C Switch On	Battery Voltage
A/C Switch Off	No Voltage
2 & Ground	
A/C Switch On	Battery Voltage
A/C Switch Off	No Voltage
10 & Ground	
A/C Switch On	Battery Voltage
A/C Switch Off	No Voltage
8 & Ground	
A/C Switch On	Battery Voltage
A/C Switch Off	No Voltage
4 & Ground	
Start Engine	About 10-14 Volts
Stop Engine	No Voltage
9 & 13 [2]	About 1500 Ohms
13 & 14 [3]	About 115 Ohms

[1] - Ensure ignition switch is on (if required), temperature control lever is at the maximum cool position, and blower switch is in HI position.
[2] - Test with air temperature at 77°F (25°C).
[3] - Test with air temperature at 68°F (20°C).

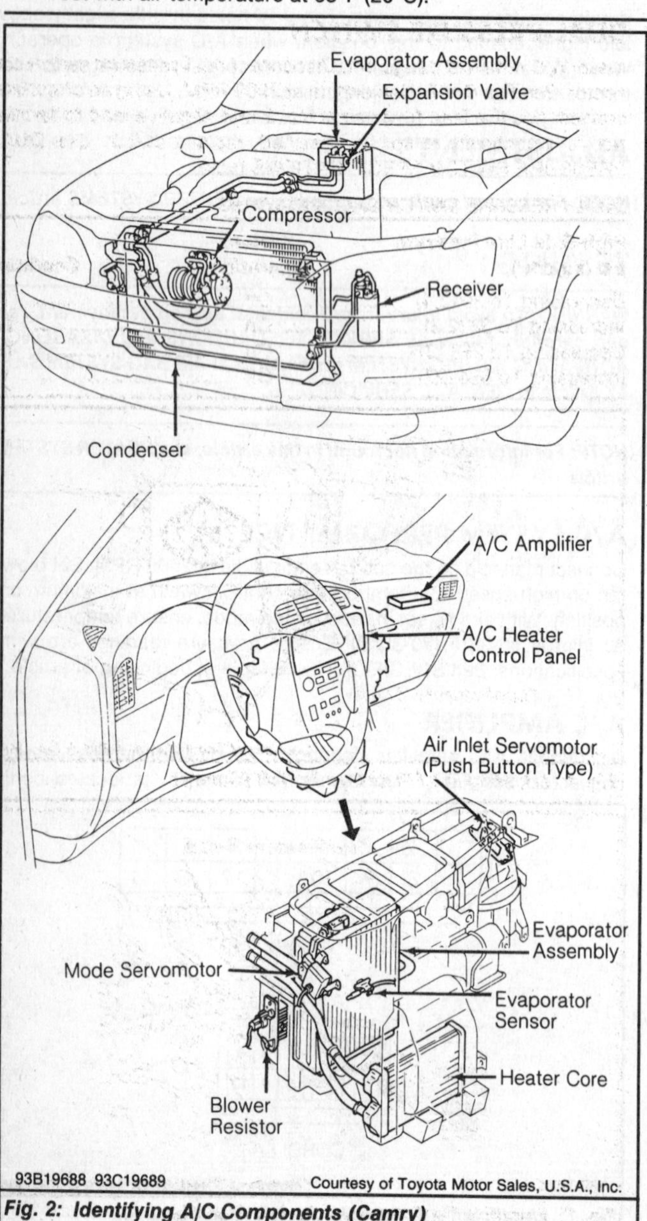
Evaporator Assembly
Expansion Valve
Compressor
Receiver
Condenser
A/C Amplifier
A/C Heater
Control Panel
Air Inlet Servomotor
(Push Button Type)
Evaporator
Assembly
Mode Servomotor
Evaporator
Sensor
Heater Core
Blower
Resistor
93B19688 93C19689
Courtesy of Toyota Motor Sales, U.S.A., Inc.

Fig. 2: Identifying A/C Components (Camry)

instrument panel, above glove box. *See Fig. 2.* On Corolla, A/C amplifier is located on top of A/C cooling unit (evaporator housing). Test circuit as indicated. See appropriate A/C AMPLIFIER CIRCUIT TEST table. If circuit does not test as specified, repair or replace as necessary.

A/C AMPLIFIER CIRCUIT TEST (COROLLA)

Terminals [1]	Specification
4 & Ground	Continuity
1 & Ground	
Ignition Switch On	About 10-14 Volts
5 & Ground	
A/C Switch On	About 10-14 Volts
7 & Ground	
A/C Switch On	Less Than 1 Volt
9 & Ground	
Magnetic Clutch On	0 Volts
8 & Ground	
Magnetic Clutch On	Less Than 1 Volt
4 & 10 [2]	About 1500 Ohms

[1] - Ensure ignition switch is on (if required), temperature control lever is at the maximum cool position, and blower switch is on.
[2] - Test with air temperature at 77°F (25°C).

A/C SWITCH

Disconnect negative battery cable. Remove A/C switch, and disconnect wire harness connector. On some models, it may be necessary to remove A/C control panel to remove switch. Check continuity at specified terminals. See A/C SWITCH CONTINUITY table. *See Fig. 3.* Replace switch if continuity is not as specified. Most A/C switches have one-way diodes; check continuity in both directions before replacing any component.

A/C SWITCH CONTINUITY

Switch Position	Continuity Between Terminals
Camry	
Off	[1]
On	7 & 8
Corolla	
Off	[2]
On	5 & 6

[1] - No continuity with switch in the OFF position.
[2] - With switch in either position, continuity should exist between terminals No. 1 and 3 for A/C switch illumination. When switch is not depressed, continuity should not exist between any other terminals.

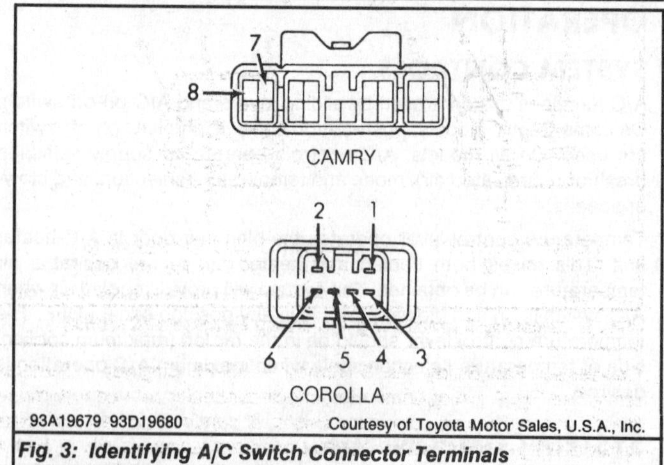
7
8
CAMRY
2
1
6
5
4
3
COROLLA
93A19679 93D19680
Courtesy of Toyota Motor Sales, U.S.A., Inc.

Fig. 3: Identifying A/C Switch Connector Terminals

CONDENSER FAN RELAYS

Condenser Fan Relay No. 2 (Camry - 5S-FE Engine) - 1) Remove relay. *See Fig. 4.* Using ohmmeter, check continuity between terminals No. 3 and 5, and between terminals No. 1 and 4. Ensure continuity exists. If continuity does not exist, replace relay.

2) Apply battery voltage between terminals No. 1 and 4. Ensure continuity exists between terminals No. 2 and 3. If continuity does not exist, replace relay.

Condenser Fan Relay No. 2 (Corolla) – 1) Remove relay. *See Fig. 5.* Using ohmmeter, check continuity between terminals No. 1 and 2, and between terminals No. 3 and 4. Ensure continuity exists. If continuity does not exist, replace relay.

2) Apply battery voltage between terminals No. 1 and 2. Ensure continuity exists between terminals No. 3 and 5. If continuity does not exist, replace relay.

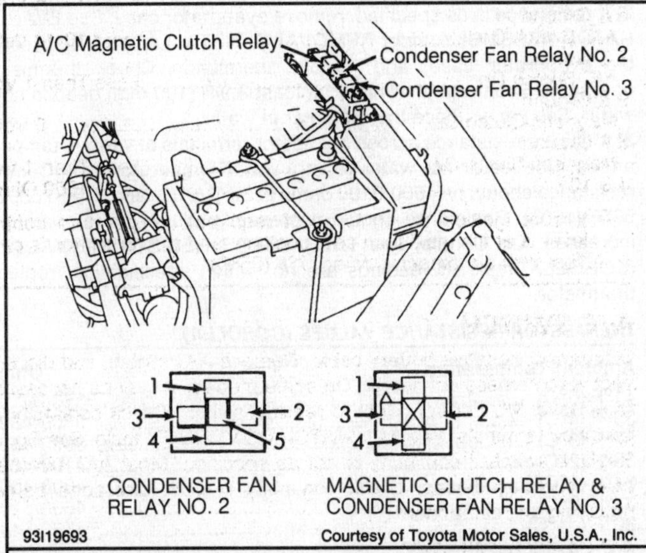

A/C Magnetic Clutch Relay
Condenser Fan Relay No. 2
Condenser Fan Relay No. 3
1
2
3
4
5
CONDENSER FAN RELAY NO. 2
MAGNETIC CLUTCH RELAY & CONDENSER FAN RELAY NO. 3
93I19693
Courtesy of Toyota Motor Sales, U.S.A., Inc.

Fig. 4: Locating & Identifying A/C Relay Terminals (Camry)

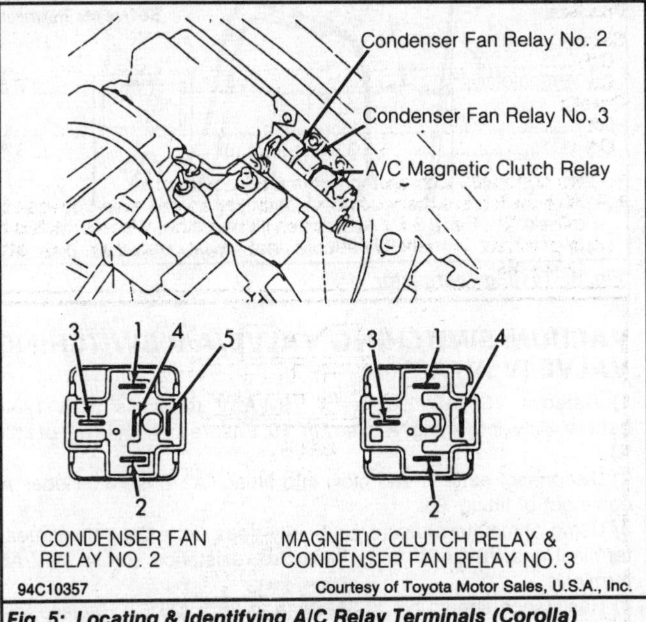

Condenser Fan Relay No. 2
Condenser Fan Relay No. 3
A/C Magnetic Clutch Relay
3
1
4
5
2
CONDENSER FAN RELAY NO. 2
MAGNETIC CLUTCH RELAY & CONDENSER FAN RELAY NO. 3
94C10357
Courtesy of Toyota Motor Sales, U.S.A., Inc.

Fig. 5: Locating & Identifying A/C Relay Terminals (Corolla)

Condenser Fan Relay No. 3 (Camry – 5S-FE Engine) – Remove relay. *See Fig. 4.* Using ohmmeter, check continuity between terminals No. 1 and 4. Ensure continuity exists. If continuity does not exist, replace relay. Apply battery voltage between terminals No. 1 and 4. Ensure continuity exists between terminals No. 2 and 3. If continuity does not exist, replace relay.

Condenser Fan Relay No. 3 (Corolla) – Remove relay. *See Fig. 5.* Using ohmmeter, check continuity between terminals No. 1 and 2. Ensure continuity exists. If continuity does not exist, replace relay. Apply battery voltage between terminals No. 1 and 2. Ensure continuity exists between terminals No. 3 and 4. If continuity does not exist, replace relay.

CONDENSER FAN MOTOR

Disconnect 2-pin fan motor connector. Apply battery voltage to fan motor side of connector. Fan motor should rotate smoothly and current draw should be 5.7-7.7 amps. If motor does not test as specified, replace condenser fan motor.

COOLANT TEMPERATURE SWITCH (SENSOR)

Camry (3VZ-FE) – Remove coolant temperature switch, located in thermostat housing behind right side of radiator. Place switch and a thermometer in a pan of water. Heat the water to more than 176°F (80°C). Using ohmmeter, check resistance between switch terminals. Resistance should be 1480-1580 ohms. If resistance is not as specified, replace switch.

Camry (5S-FE) & Corolla – 1) Remove coolant temperature switch, located at right front of cooling fan on Camry, and near distributor on Corolla. Place switch and a thermometer in a pan of water. Heat the water to more than 199°F (93°C). Using ohmmeter, check for continuity between switch terminals. No continuity should exist.

2) Cool water to less than 181°F (83°C). Ensure continuity exists between switch terminals. If continuity is not as specified, replace switch.

DUAL-PRESSURE SWITCH

Install A/C manifold gauge set. Disconnect dual-pressure switch connector. *See Fig. 6 or 7.* Run engine at 2000 RPM. Using an ohmmeter, connect positive lead to terminal No. 2 and negative lead to terminal No. 1. If continuity is not as specified, replace switch. See DUAL-PRESSURE SWITCH SPECIFICATIONS table.

DUAL-PRESSURE SWITCH SPECIFICATIONS

High-Side Line Pressure psi (kg/cm²)	System Operation	Continuity
Decreasing To 30 (2.1)	Off	No
Increasing To 33 (2.3)	On	Yes
Decreasing To 299 (21)	On	Yes
Increasing To 384 (27)	Off	No

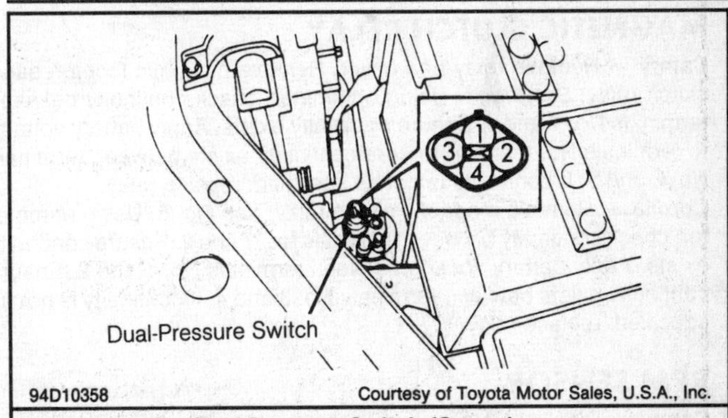

1
2
3
4
Dual-Pressure Switch
94D10358
Courtesy of Toyota Motor Sales, U.S.A., Inc.

Fig. 6: Locating Dual-Pressure Switch (Camry)

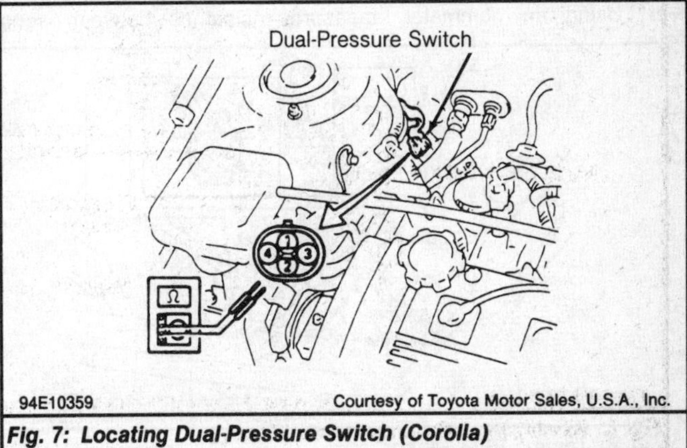

Dual-Pressure Switch
94E10359
Courtesy of Toyota Motor Sales, U.S.A., Inc.

Fig. 7: Locating Dual-Pressure Switch (Corolla)

1993 MANUAL A/C-HEATER SYSTEMS
Camry & Corolla (Cont.)

EXPANSION VALVE

Install manifold gauge set. Run engine at 2000 RPM for 5 minutes. Ensure high pressure reading is 185-213 psi (13-15 kg/cm²). Ensure low pressure reading is not zero psi. If low pressure reading is zero psi, no temperature difference will be felt at receiver-drier inlet and outlet sides. If readings are not as specified, replace expansion valve.

HIGH-PRESSURE SWITCH

Camry - 1) Install manifold gauge set. Remove high-pressure switch. High-pressure switch is integral with dual-pressure switch. Run engine at 2000 RPM. Using ohmmeter, connect positive lead to terminal No. 2 and negative lead to terminal No. 3.

2) When refrigerant pressure reaches 220 psi (15.5 kg/cm²), pressure switch will open, and current to A/C magnetic (compressor) clutch will be interrupted. When high-side pressure drops back to 178 psi (12.5 kg/cm²), switch will close, and current to A/C magnetic clutch will be restored. If switch does not function as specified, replace switch.

Corolla - 1) Install manifold gauge set. Remove high-pressure switch. High-pressure switch is integral with dual-pressure switch. Run engine at 2000 RPM. Using ohmmeter, connect positive lead to terminal No. 3 and negative lead to terminal No. 4.

2) When refrigerant pressure reaches 192 psi (13.5 kg/cm²), pressure switch will open, and current to A/C magnetic clutch will be interrupted. When high-side pressure drops back to 142 psi (10 kg/cm²), switch will close, and current to A/C magnetic clutch will be restored. If switch does not function as specified, replace switch.

MAGNETIC CLUTCH

1) Inspect pressure plate and rotor for signs of oil contamination. Check clutch bearing for noisy operation and grease leakage. If abnormal noise is heard near compressor when A/C is off, replace magnetic (compressor) clutch.

2) Disconnect magnetic clutch connector. Connect battery positive lead to connector terminal and negative lead to ground. Magnetic clutch should be energized. If operation is not as specified, replace magnetic clutch.

MAGNETIC CLUTCH RELAY

Camry - Remove relay box cover. Remove magnetic (compressor) clutch relay. *See Fig. 4*. Using ohmmeter, check continuity between terminals No. 1 and 4. Ensure continuity exists. Apply battery voltage to terminals No. 1 and 4. Ensure continuity exists between terminals No. 2 and 3. If continuity is not as specified, replace relay.

Corolla - Remove magnetic clutch relay. *See Fig. 5*. Using ohmmeter, check continuity between terminals No. 1 and 2. Ensure continuity exists. Apply battery voltage between terminals No. 1 and 2. Ensure continuity exists between terminals No. 3 and 4. If continuity is not as specified, replace relay.

RPM SENSOR

Camry - Disconnect negative battery cable. Disconnect wire harness connector. Sensor is located on A/C compressor discharge cover. Using an ohmmeter, measure resistance between sensor terminals No. 1 and 2. *See Fig. 8*. With air temperature at 68°F (20°C), resistance should be 100-130 ohms. If resistance is not as specified, replace sensor.

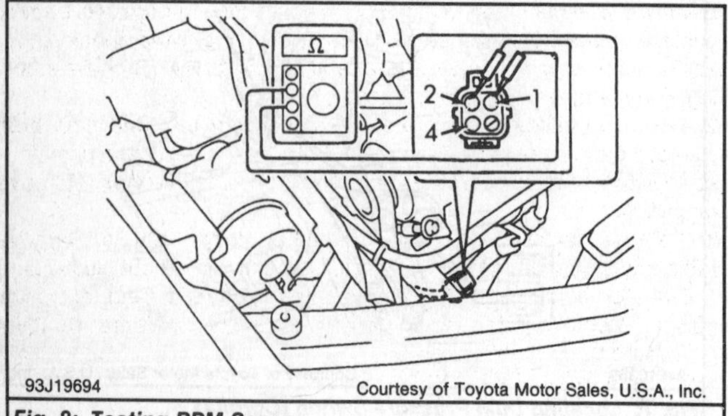
Ω
2
1
4
93J19694
Courtesy of Toyota Motor Sales, U.S.A., Inc.

Fig. 8: Testing RPM Sensor

THERMISTOR

1) Disconnect negative battery cable. Remove lower trim panel and glove box. Check thermistor installed operation. Using an ohmmeter, measure resistance between thermistor terminals. Resistance should be 1500 ohms at 77 °F (25 °C). If resistance is not as specified, replace thermistor.

2) If resistance is as specified, remove evaporator case. See EVAPORATOR ASSEMBLY under REMOVAL & INSTALLATION. Disassemble evaporator case, and remove thermistor. Check thermistor operation. Submerge thermistor at least 3.94" (100 mm) deep in cold water. *See Fig. 9*. Place thermometer in water.

3) Measure resistance across connector terminals at various temperatures. Use ice or hot water to vary water temperature. On Camry, resistance should be 4600-5100 ohms at 32°F (0°C), and 2100-2600 at 59°F (15°C). Resistance should decrease gradually as temperature increases. On Corolla, see THERMISTOR RESISTANCE VALUES (COROLLA) table. If readings are not within specification, replace thermistor.

THERMISTOR RESISTANCE VALUES (COROLLA)

Ambient Temperature	Ohms
41°F (5°C)	3500-4100
39°F (4°C)	3800-4300
37°F (3°C)	3900-4500
36°F (2°C)	4100-4800
34°F (1°C)	4300-4900
32°F (0°C)	4500-5200
30°F (-1°C)	4700-5400

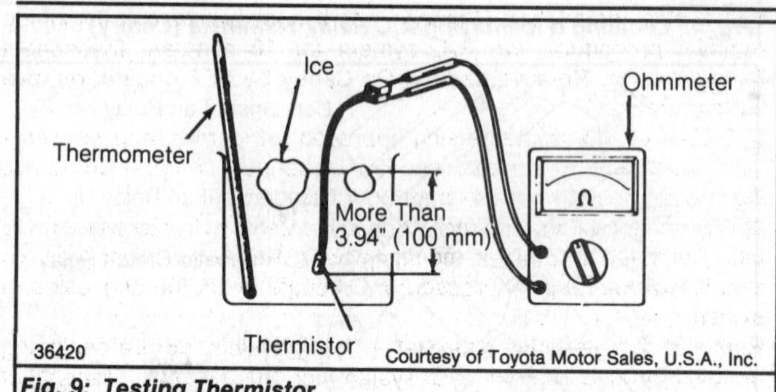
Ice
Ohmmeter
Thermometer
Ω
More Than
3.94" (100 mm)
Thermistor
36420
Courtesy of Toyota Motor Sales, U.S.A., Inc.

Fig. 9: Testing Thermistor

VACUUM SWITCHING VALVE/AIR SWITCHING VALVE (VSV/ASV)

1) Remove VSV/ASV. Connect VSV/ASV terminals to a 12-volt battery. Blow into fitting "A". *See Fig. 10*. Ensure air comes out of fitting "B".

2) Disconnect battery, and blow into fitting "A". Ensure air does not come out of fitting "B".

3) Using ohmmeter, ensure continuity does not exist between each terminal and VSV/ASV body. Measure resistance across VSV/ASV terminals.

4) Resistance should be 30-34 ohms at 68°F (20°C). Replace VSV/ASV if it does not test as specified.

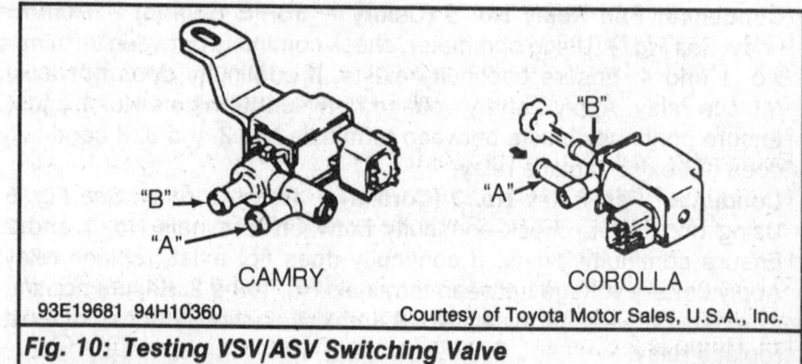
"B"
"A"
"B"
"A"
CAMRY
COROLLA
93E19681 94H10360
Courtesy of Toyota Motor Sales, U.S.A., Inc.

Fig. 10: Testing VSV/ASV Switching Valve

REMOVAL & INSTALLATION

WARNING: To avoid injury from accidental air bag deployment, read and carefully follow all SERVICE PRECAUTIONS and DISABLING & ACTIVATING AIR BAG SYSTEM procedures in AIR BAG SYSTEM SAFETY article in GENERAL SERVICING.

NOTE: For information not found in this article, see HEATER SYSTEMS article.

A/C UNIT

Removal & Installation (Camry) – 1) Disconnect negative battery cable. Discharge A/C system using approved refrigerant recovery/ recycling equipment. Disconnect water valve control cable from water valve. Disconnect hoses from heater core. Remove instrument panel and reinforcement. See INSTRUMENT PANEL.

2) Remove glove box, ECU and ECU bracket. Remove 2 screws and blower unit connector bracket. Disconnect blower unit connector and air inlet damper control cable. Remove blower unit.

3) Disconnect tubes from block joint. Remove rear air ducts and heater protector. Remove 3 nuts and A/C unit. To install, reverse removal procedure. Evacuate, recharge and leak test A/C system.

Removal & Installation (Corolla) – 1) Disconnect negative battery cable. Discharge A/C system using approved refrigerant recovery/ recycling equipment. Disconnect and plug A/C unit hoses.

2) Remove front door scuff plate. Remove glove box. Disconnect electrical connectors. Remove A/C unit. To install, reverse removal procedure. Evacuate, recharge and leak test A/C system.

COMPRESSOR

Removal & Installation (Camry) – 1) If possible, before beginning removal procedure, run A/C system for 10 minutes. Disconnect battery cables. Remove battery. On Camry 3VZ-FE engine, remove battery bracket.

2) Discharge A/C system using approved refrigerant recovery/recycling equipment. Remove cooling fan. Disconnect compressor hoses. Cap hose ends to keep moisture out of system.

3) Disconnect magnetic clutch connector. Remove compressor drive belt. Remove compressor mounting bolts. Remove compressor. To install, reverse removal procedure. Evacuate, recharge and leak test system.

Removal & Installation (Corolla) – 1) If possible, before beginning removal procedure, run A/C system for 10 minutes. Disconnect negative battery cable. Discharge A/C system using approved refrigerant recovery/recycling equipment.

2) Remove washer reserve tank. Loosen idle pulley lock nut and drive belt. Disconnect wiring harness and hoses from compressor. Cap hose ends to keep moisture out of system. Remove compressor.

3) To install, reverse removal procedure. Evacuate, recharge and leak test system.

CONDENSER

Removal & Installation (Camry) – 1) Discharge A/C system using approved refrigerant recovery/recycling equipment. Disconnect battery cables, and remove battery. Remove upper cover and bracket (if equipped). On 3VZ-FE engines, remove cooling fan.

2) On all models, remove 2 bolts and 2 upper supports. Disconnect and cap liquid lines from condenser. Remove headlights. Remove 2 bolts and condenser.

3) To install, reverse removal procedure. If installing new condenser, add 1.2 ounces of refrigerant oil. Evacuate, recharge and leak test system.

Removal & Installation (Corolla) – 1) Discharge A/C system using approved refrigerant recovery/recycling equipment. Disconnect battery cables, and remove battery. Remove radiator grille, horn, hood lock and center brace.

2) Remove radiator reserve tank and bracket. Disconnect and cap liquid lines from condenser. Disconnect wiring harness from condenser fan. Remove 2 clips and condenser fan. Remove oxygen sensor.

3) Disconnect and cap discharge hose from condenser. Remove radiator support brackets. Remove condenser. To install, reverse removal procedure. If installing new condenser, add 1.4-1.7 ounces of refrigerant oil. Evacuate, recharge and leak test system.

EVAPORATOR ASSEMBLY

Removal & Installation (Camry) – 1) Disconnect negative battery cable. Discharge A/C system using approved refrigerant recovery/ recycling equipment. Remove glove box, ECU and ECU bracket. Remove 2 screws and blower unit connector bracket.

2) Remove blower unit connector. Disconnect air inlet damper control cable. Remove blower unit. Remove 2 liquid and suction tube bolts. Remove 8 screws and evaporator cover. Remove evaporator.

3) To install, reverse removal procedure. If installing a new evaporator, add 1.6 ounces of compressor oil. Evacuate, recharge and leak test A/C system.

Removal & Installation (Corolla) – 1) Disconnect negative battery cable. Discharge A/C system using approved refrigerant recovery/ recycling equipment. Remove A/C unit. See A/C UNIT.

2) Disconnect A/C wiring harness from thermistor. Remove thermistor connector from upper case. Remove 3 clips and 4 screws. Separate upper and lower cases from evaporator core. Remove blower resistor from upper case.

3) Remove thermistor and expansion valve. Remove hoses to evaporator. To install, reverse removal procedure. If installing a new evaporator, add 1.4-1.7 ounces of compressor oil to compressor. Evacuate, recharge and leak test A/C system.

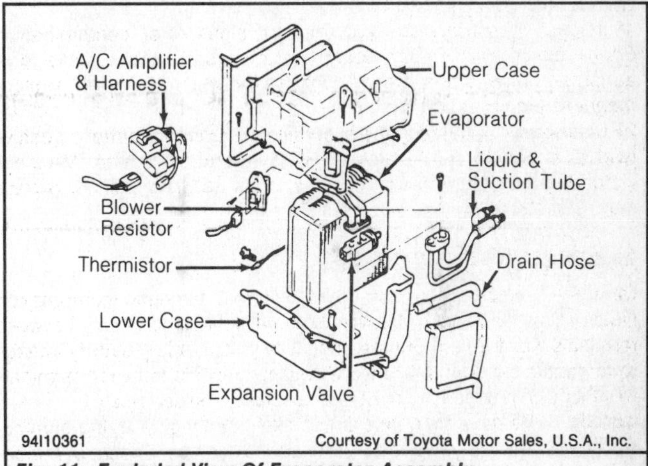
A/C Amplifier & Harness
Upper Case
Evaporator
Liquid & Suction Tube
Blower Resistor
Thermistor
Drain Hose
Lower Case
Expansion Valve
94I10361
Courtesy of Toyota Motor Sales, U.S.A., Inc.

Fig. 11: Exploded View Of Evaporator Assembly (Corolla Shown; Camry Is Similar)

EXPANSION VALVE

Removal & Installation – Evaporator must be disassembled in order to remove expansion valve. See EVAPORATOR ASSEMBLY.

INSTRUMENT PANEL

Removal & Installation (Camry) – 1) Disconnect negative battery cable. Remove front pillar garnish, inside scuff plate and opening cover. Remove hood lock release lever and cowl side trim. Remove steering wheel and steering column cover.

2) Remove console upper panel, rear console box and coin box. Remove instrument panel lower pad. Remove 4 screws and combination switch. Remove lower panels and front console box. Remove glove box.

3) Remove center cluster and instrument cluster panels. Remove radio and instrument panel registers. Remove instrument cluster and A/C-heater control panel. Remove right side duct and defroster nozzle. Remove instrument panel. To install, reverse removal procedure.

1993 MANUAL A/C-HEATER SYSTEMS
Camry & Corolla (Cont.)

RECEIVER-DRIER

Removal – Discharge A/C system using approved refrigerant recovery/recycling equipment. Disconnect negative battery cable. On Corolla, remove radiator grille and horn. On all models, remove liquid lines from receiver-drier. Plug all openings. Remove mounting bolts and receiver-drier.

Installation – To install, reverse removal procedure. On Camry, add 0.7 ounce of refrigerant oil to receiver-drier. On Corolla, add 0.5 ounce of refrigerant oil to receiver-drier. Evacuate, recharge and leak test system.

TORQUE SPECIFICATIONS

TORQUE SPECIFICATIONS

Application	Ft. Lbs. (N.m)
A/C Compressor Bolt	18 (25)
A/C Compressor Bracket Bolt/Nut	35 (47)
Oxygen Sensor	15 (20)
	INCH Lbs. (N.m)
Dual-Pressure Switch Bolt	89 (10)
Expansion Valve (Fittings)	48 (5.4)
Magnetic Clutch Pressure Plate Bolt	124 (14)
Receiver-Drier Bolt/Nut	48 (5.4)
Refrigerant Hoses	
Compressor	[1]
Condenser	
Camry	89 (10)
Corolla	
High Pressure (Discharge) Hose	89 (10)
Low Pressure (Suction) Hose	124 (14)
Evaporator	
Camry	89 (10)
Corolla	
High Pressure (Discharge) Hose	124 (14)
Low Pressure (Suction) Hose	[2]
Receiver-Drier	
Camry	89 (10)
Corolla	48 (5.4)

[1] – Tighten to 18 ft. lbs. (25 N.m).
[2] – Tighten to 24 ft. lbs. (32 N.m).

WIRING DIAGRAMS

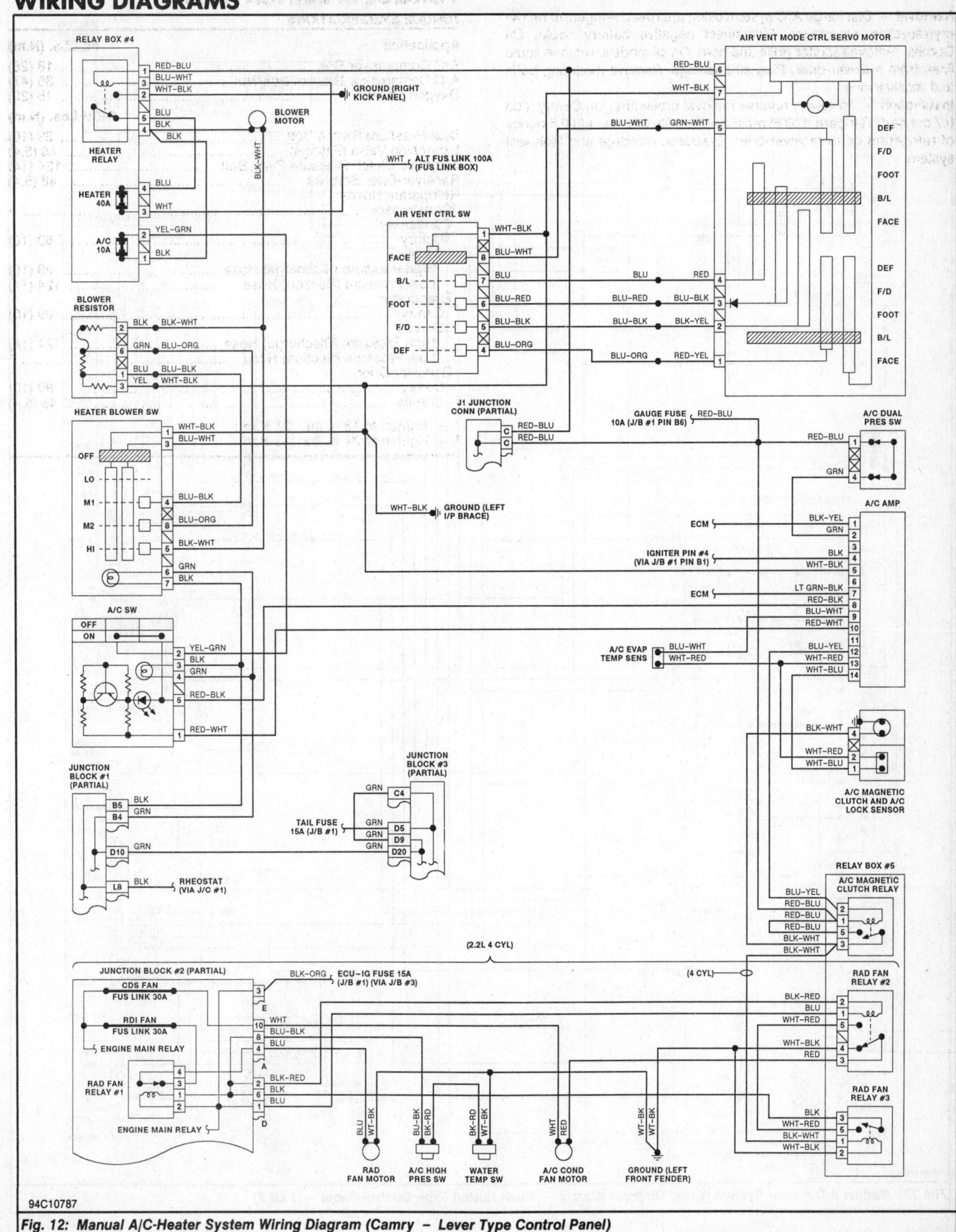
RELAY BOX #4
HEATER RELAY
HEATER 40A
A/C 10A
BLOWER MOTOR
GROUND (RIGHT KICK PANEL)
ALT FUS LINK 100A (FUS LINK BOX)
AIR VENT CTRL SW
BLOWER RESISTOR
HEATER BLOWER SW
A/C SW
JUNCTION BLOCK #1 (PARTIAL)
RHEOSTAT (VIA J/C #1)
JUNCTION BLOCK #3 (PARTIAL)
TAIL FUSE 15A (J/B #1)
J1 JUNCTION CONN (PARTIAL)
GROUND (LEFT I/P BRACE)
AIR VENT MODE CTRL SERVO MOTOR
GAUGE FUSE 10A (J/B #1 PIN B6)
A/C DUAL PRES SW
A/C AMP
ECM
IGNITER PIN #4 (VIA J/B #1 PIN B1)
A/C EVAP TEMP SENS
A/C MAGNETIC CLUTCH AND A/C LOCK SENSOR
RELAY BOX #5
A/C MAGNETIC CLUTCH RELAY
(2.2L 4 CYL)
(4 CYL)
JUNCTION BLOCK #2 (PARTIAL)
CDS FAN FUS LINK 30A
RDI FAN FUS LINK 30A
ENGINE MAIN RELAY
RAD FAN RELAY #1
ECU-IG FUSE 15A (J/B #1) (VIA J/B #3)
RAD FAN RELAY #2
RAD FAN RELAY #3
RAD FAN MOTOR
A/C HIGH PRES SW
WATER TEMP SW
A/C COND FAN MOTOR
GROUND (LEFT FRONT FENDER)
94C10787

Fig. 12: Manual A/C-Heater System Wiring Diagram (Camry – Lever Type Control Panel)

1993 MANUAL A/C-HEATER SYSTEMS
Camry & Corolla (Cont.)

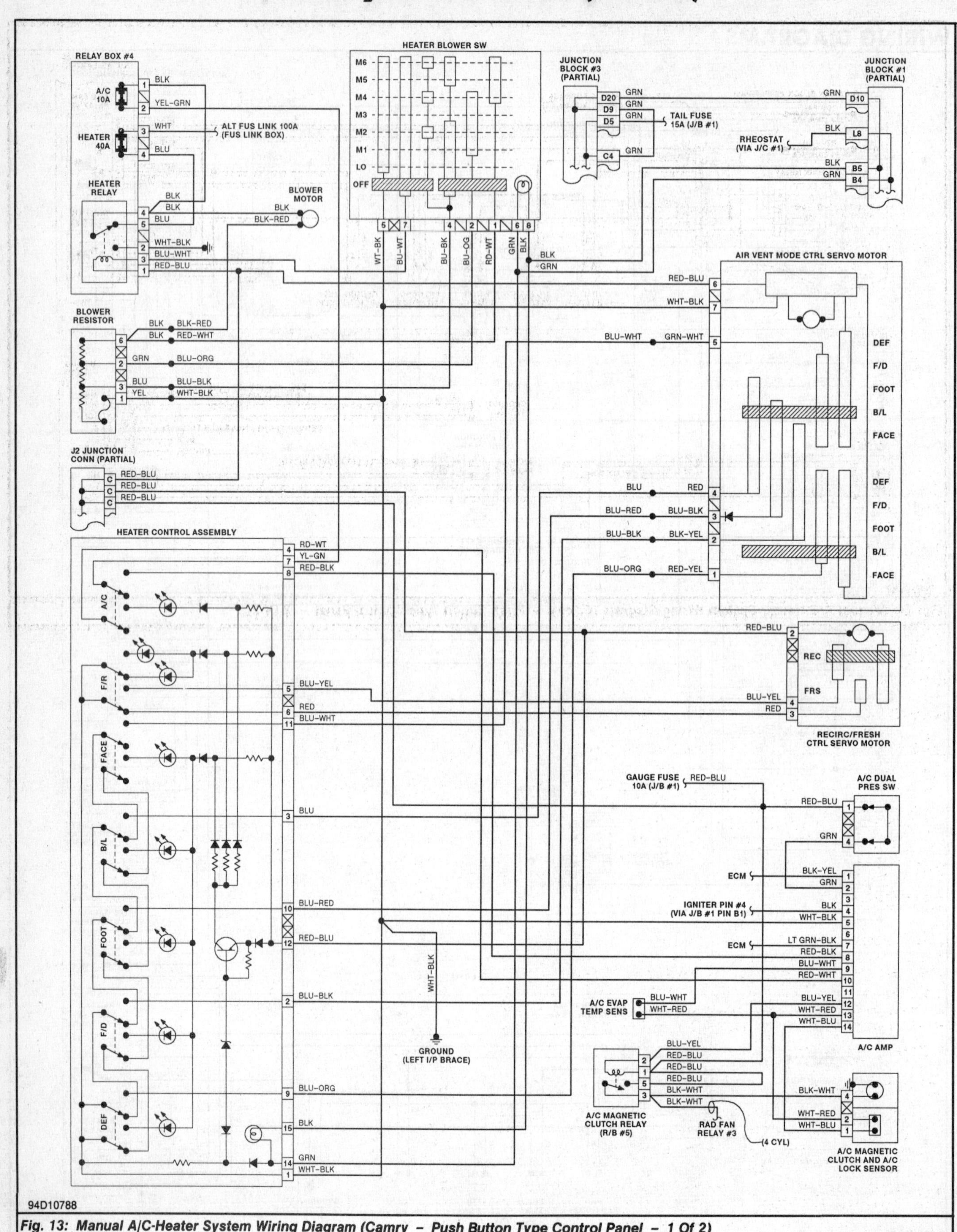

RELAY BOX #4
A/C 10A
HEATER 40A
HEATER RELAY
ALT FUS LINK 100A (FUS LINK BOX)
BLOWER MOTOR
HEATER BLOWER SW
M6
M5
M4
M3
M2
M1
LO
OFF
JUNCTION BLOCK #3 (PARTIAL)
D20
D9
D5
C4
TAIL FUSE 15A (J/B #1)
JUNCTION BLOCK #1 (PARTIAL)
D10
L8
B5
B4
RHEOSTAT (VIA J/C #1)
BLOWER RESISTOR
AIR VENT MODE CTRL SERVO MOTOR
DEF
F/D
FOOT
B/L
FACE
J2 JUNCTION CONN (PARTIAL)
HEATER CONTROL ASSEMBLY
A/C
F/R
REC
FRS
RECIRC/FRESH CTRL SERVO MOTOR
GAUGE FUSE 10A (J/B #1)
A/C DUAL PRES SW
ECM
IGNITER PIN #4 (VIA J/B #1 PIN B1)
A/C EVAP TEMP SENS
A/C AMP
GROUND (LEFT I/P BRACE)
A/C MAGNETIC CLUTCH RELAY (R/B #5)
RAD FAN RELAY #3
(4 CYL)
A/C MAGNETIC CLUTCH AND A/C LOCK SENSOR
94D10788

Fig. 13: Manual A/C-Heater System Wiring Diagram (Camry – Push Button Type Control Panel – 1 Of 2)

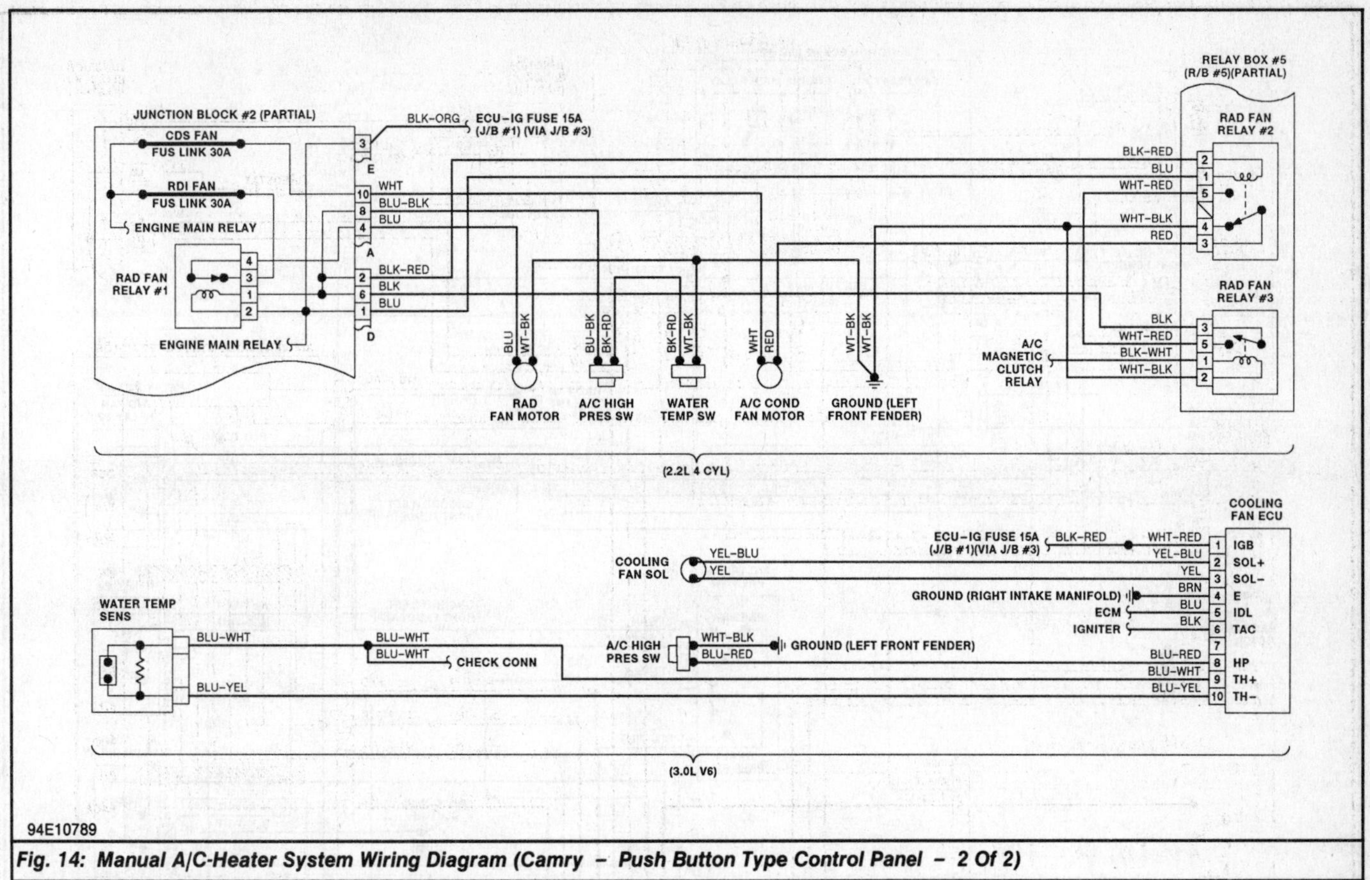

RELAY BOX #5
(R/B #5)(PARTIAL)
JUNCTION BLOCK #2 (PARTIAL)
BLK-ORG
ECU-IG FUSE 15A
(J/B #1) (VIA J/B #3)
CDS FAN
FUS LINK 30A
RDI FAN
FUS LINK 30A
ENGINE MAIN RELAY
RAD FAN
RELAY #1
ENGINE MAIN RELAY
WHT
BLU-BLK
BLU
BLK-RED
BLK
BLU
RAD FAN
RELAY #2
BLK-RED
BLU
WHT-RED
WHT-BLK
RED
RAD FAN
RELAY #3
BLK
WHT-RED
BLK-WHT
WHT-BLK
A/C
MAGNETIC
CLUTCH
RELAY
BLU
WT-BK
BU-BK
BK-RD
BK-RD
WT-BK
WHT
RED
WT-BK
WT-BK
RAD
FAN MOTOR
A/C HIGH
PRES SW
WATER
TEMP SW
A/C COND
FAN MOTOR
GROUND (LEFT
FRONT FENDER)
(2.2L 4 CYL)
COOLING
FAN ECU
ECU-IG FUSE 15A
(J/B #1)(VIA J/B #3)
BLK-RED
WHT-RED
YEL-BLU
YEL
BRN
BLU
BLK
BLU-RED
BLU-WHT
BLU-YEL
IGB
SOL+
SOL-
E
IDL
TAC
HP
TH+
TH-
COOLING
FAN SOL
YEL-BLU
YEL
GROUND (RIGHT INTAKE MANIFOLD)
ECM
IGNITER
WATER TEMP
SENS
BLU-WHT
BLU-WHT
BLU-WHT
CHECK CONN
BLU-YEL
A/C HIGH
PRES SW
WHT-BLK
BLU-RED
GROUND (LEFT FRONT FENDER)
(3.0L V6)
94E10789

Fig. 14: Manual A/C-Heater System Wiring Diagram (Camry – Push Button Type Control Panel – 2 Of 2)

1993 MANUAL A/C-HEATER SYSTEMS
Camry & Corolla (Cont.)

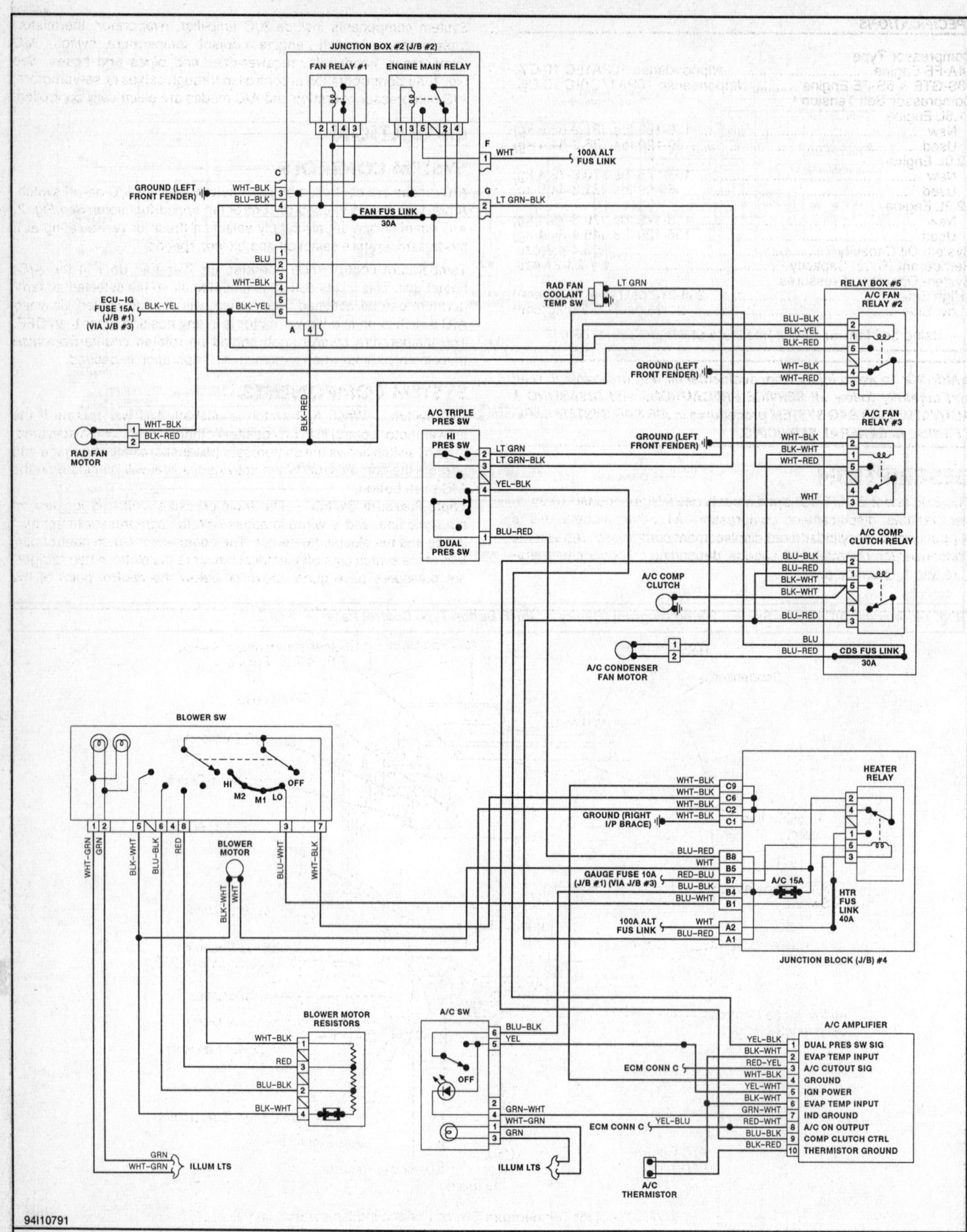
JUNCTION BOX #2 (J/B #2)
FAN RELAY #1
ENGINE MAIN RELAY
100A ALT FUS LINK
WHT
LT GRN-BLK
GROUND (LEFT FRONT FENDER)
WHT-BLK
BLU-BLK
FAN FUS LINK 30A
BLU
ECU-IG FUSE 15A (J/B #1) (VIA J/B #3)
BLK-YEL
RAD FAN COOLANT TEMP SW
LT GRN
RELAY BOX #5
A/C FAN RELAY #2
BLK-RED
WHT-RED
A/C FAN RELAY #3
BLK-WHT
RAD FAN MOTOR
A/C TRIPLE PRES SW
HI PRES SW
YEL-BLK
BLU-RED
DUAL PRES SW
A/C COMP CLUTCH RELAY
A/C COMP CLUTCH
CDS FUS LINK 30A
A/C CONDENSER FAN MOTOR
BLOWER SW
HI
M2
M1
LO
OFF
BLOWER MOTOR
WHT-GRN
GRN
BLK-WHT
RED
BLU-WHT
HEATER RELAY
GROUND (RIGHT I/P BRACE)
GAUGE FUSE 10A (J/B #1) (VIA J/B #3)
RED-BLU
A/C 15A
HTR FUS LINK 40A
JUNCTION BLOCK (J/B) #4
BLOWER MOTOR RESISTORS
A/C SW
A/C AMPLIFIER
DUAL PRES SW SIG
EVAP TEMP INPUT
A/C CUTOUT SIG
GROUND
IGN POWER
EVAP TEMP INPUT
IND GROUND
A/C ON OUTPUT
COMP CLUTCH CTRL
THERMISTOR GROUND
ECM CONN C
YEL-BLU
GRN-WHT
ILLUM LTS
A/C THERMISTOR
94I10791

Fig. 15: Manual A/C-Heater System Wiring Diagram (Corolla)

SPECIFICATIONS

Compressor Type
 4A-FE Engine .... Nippondenso 10PA15C 10-Cyl.
 3S-GTE & 5S-FE Engine .... Nippondenso 10PA17C/VC 10-Cyl.
Compressor Belt Tension [1]
 1.6L Engine
  New .... 135-185 lbs. (61.2-83.9 kg)
  Used .... 80-120 lbs. (36.2-54.4 kg)
 2.0L Engine
  New .... 155-175 lbs. (70.3-79.4 kg)
  Used .... 69-99 lbs. (31.3-44.9 kg)
 2.2L Engine
  New .... 155-175 lbs. (70.3-79.4 kg)
  Used .... 100-120 lbs. (45.4-54.4 kg)
System Oil Capacity .... 3.4-4.7 ozs.
Refrigerant (R-12) Capacity .... 24-27 ozs.
System Operating Pressures
 High Side .... 206-213 psi (14.5-15 kg/cm²)
 Low Side .... 21-28 psi (1.5-2.0 kg/cm²)

[1] – Using belt tension gauge, measure at longest run of belt.

WARNING: To avoid injury from accidental air bag deployment, read and carefully follow all SERVICE PRECAUTIONS and DISABLING & ACTIVATING AIR BAG SYSTEM procedures in AIR BAG SYSTEM SAFETY article in GENERAL SERVICING.

DESCRIPTION

The 2.0L and 2.2L A/T equipped models use a Nippondenso 10-cylinder variable displacement compressor. All other models use a Nippondenso 10-cylinder fixed displacement compressor. An electric condenser fan operates at 2 speeds, depending on coolant temperature and A/C switch position.

System components include A/C amplifier, evaporator, thermistor, triple-pressure switch, engine coolant temperature switch, A/C compressor, condenser, receiver-drier and pipes and hoses. *See Fig. 1.* Air door operation is controlled through cables or servomotors. A/C compressor operation and A/C modes are electrically controlled.

OPERATION

SYSTEM CONTROLS

A/C modes are controlled by push buttons and an A/C on-off switch. A dial type switch is used to control fan speed functions. *See Fig. 2.* A/C controls operate air supply selection (fresh or recirculating air), mode, temperature selection and blower speeds.

Temperature control knob operates the blend-air door in the A/C-heater unit. This mixes cooled and heated air so the selected air temperature can be obtained. The system will provide cooled air when A/C switch is on and blower motor is in any position other than OFF. The temperature control knob should be rotated counterclockwise (maximum cooling) when maximum A/C operation is desired.

SYSTEM COMPONENTS

A/C Switch – When A/C switch is pushed, A/C will operate if the blower motor control is in any position other than off. When activated, the A/C switch allows the compressor (magnetic) clutch to engage and operate the compressor. When activated, a light will illuminate on the A/C push button.

Triple-Pressure Switch – The triple-pressure switch is located on the liquid line, and is wired in series with the compressor (magnetic) clutch and the electric fan motor. The compressor clutch control portion of the switch cuts off electrical power to the clutch when refrigerant pressures have gone above or below the control point of the

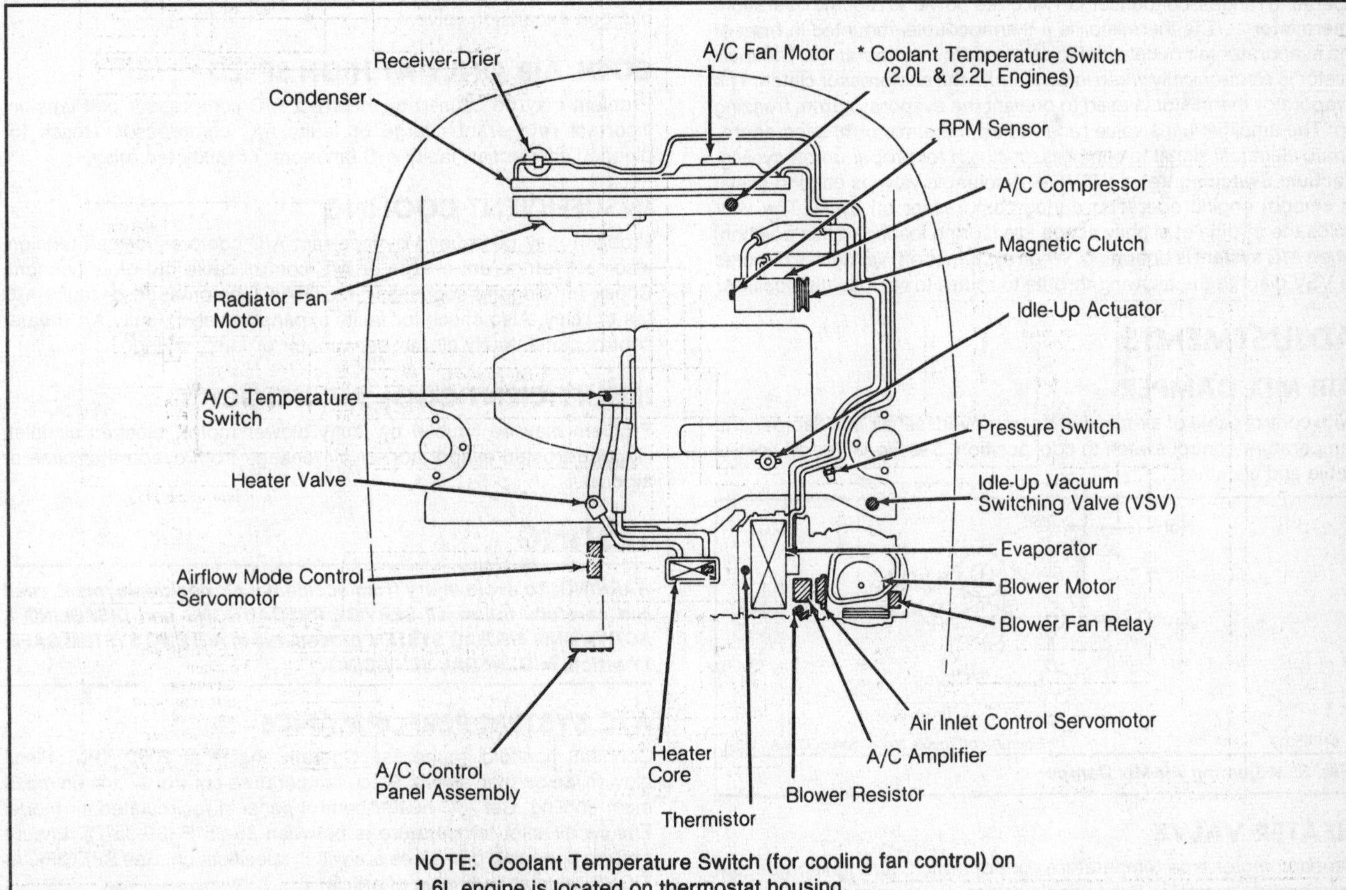

Receiver-Drier
A/C Fan Motor
* Coolant Temperature Switch (2.0L & 2.2L Engines)
Condenser
RPM Sensor
A/C Compressor
Magnetic Clutch
Radiator Fan Motor
Idle-Up Actuator
A/C Temperature Switch
Pressure Switch
Heater Valve
Idle-Up Vacuum Switching Valve (VSV)
Evaporator
Airflow Mode Control Servomotor
Blower Motor
Blower Fan Relay
Air Inlet Control Servomotor
Heater Core
A/C Amplifier
A/C Control Panel Assembly
Blower Resistor
Thermistor
NOTE: Coolant Temperature Switch (for cooling fan control) on 1.6L engine is located on thermostat housing.
93I19610
Courtesy of Toyota Motor Sales, U.S.A., Inc.

Fig. 1: Identifying Manual A/C-Heater System Components

1993 MANUAL A/C-HEATER SYSTEMS
Celica (Cont.)

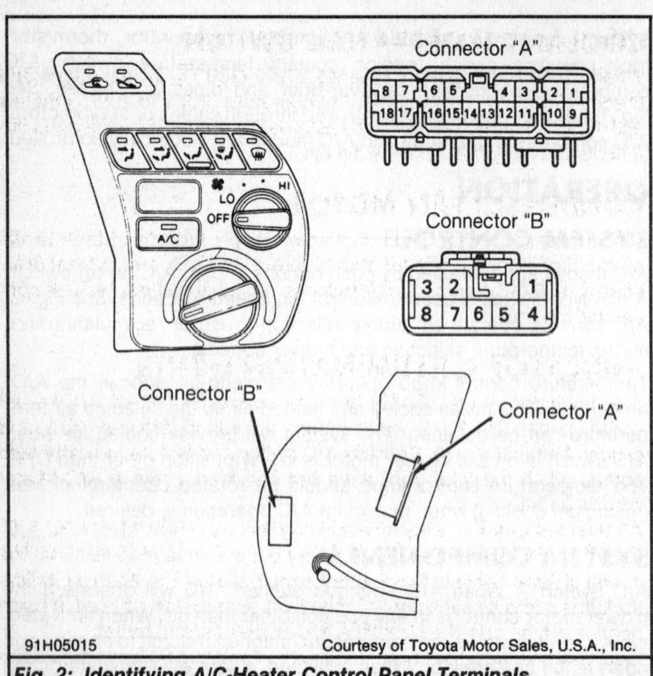
Connector "A"
8 7 6 5 4 3 2 1
18 17 16 15 14 13 12 11 10 9
LO
HI
OFF
A/C
Connector "B"
3 2 1
8 7 6 5 4
Connector "B"
Connector "A"

91H05015 Courtesy of Toyota Motor Sales, U.S.A., Inc.

Fig. 2: Identifying A/C-Heater Control Panel Terminals

switch. When pressures have returned to normal operating ranges, compressor clutch receives power to resume operation.

The fan control portion of the switch cuts off electrical power to the condenser fan motor when refrigerant pressures have gone above the control point of the switch. When pressures have returned to normal operating ranges, condenser fan receives power to resume operation.

Thermistor – The thermistor is a thermocouple, mounted in front of the evaporator (air outlet side) to sense airflow temperature. The thermistor is electronically wired in series with the compressor clutch. The evaporator thermistor is used to prevent the evaporator from freezing up. The amplifier uses value received from thermistor to send appropriate electrical signal to compressor clutch for proper on-off cycling.

Vacuum Switching Valve (VSV) – A solenoid valve is used to assist in smooth engine operation during compressor on cycle. The VSV holds the throttle at slightly above idle (spring loaded to this position) when A/C system is operating. When system is off, vacuum is directed to VSV diaphragm, allowing throttle to return to normal idle position.

ADJUSTMENTS

AIR MIX DAMPER

With control cable of air mix damper removed, set air mix damper and temperature control switch to cool position. *See Fig. 3*. Install control cable and clamp.

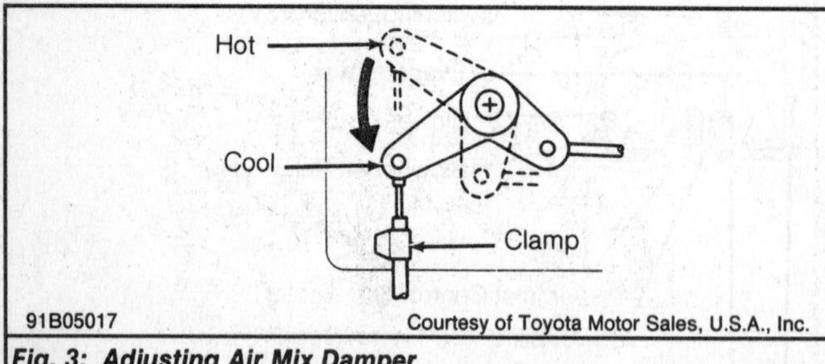
Hot
Cool
Clamp

91B05017 Courtesy of Toyota Motor Sales, U.S.A., Inc.

Fig. 3: Adjusting Air Mix Damper

HEATER VALVE

On servomotor type temperature control switch, turn ignition on, set temperature control switch to cool position, and turn blower motor on. Set heater valve and temperature control switch to cool position. *See Fig. 4*. Install control cable and clamp.

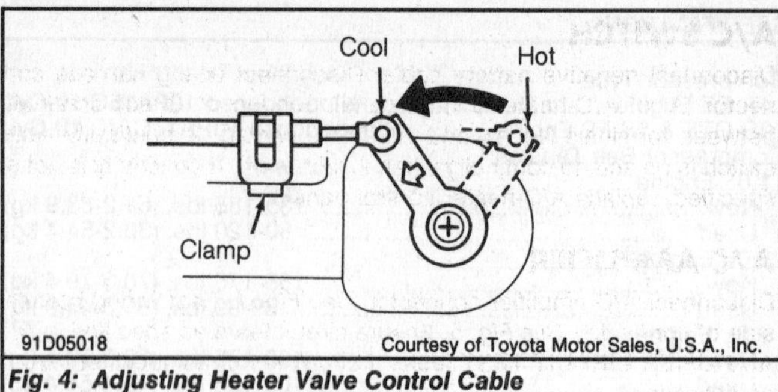
Cool
Hot
Clamp

91D05018 Courtesy of Toyota Motor Sales, U.S.A., Inc.

Fig. 4: Adjusting Heater Valve Control Cable

TROUBLE SHOOTING

NO BLOWER OPERATION

Problem may be due to blown fuses, faulty heater relay, or faulty blower motor or resistor. Also check for faulty blower fan relay or blower switch, faulty A/C-heater control panel, faulty wiring or bad ground.

NO COOL AIR

Problem may be due to blown fuses, incorrect refrigerant charge, incorrect A/C compressor belt tension, faulty compressor (magnetic) clutch relay, or faulty pressure switch or A/C compressor. Check for plugged receiver-drier, condenser, expansion valve or evaporator. Also check for faulty A/C-heater control panel, faulty thermistor or A/C amplifier, faulty wiring or bad ground.

INTERMITTENT COOL AIR

Problem may be caused by incorrect A/C compressor belt tension, incorrect refrigerant charge or faulty compressor clutch. Check for plugged expansion valve.

COOL AIR ONLY AT HIGH SPEED

Problem may be caused by incorrect A/C compressor belt tension, incorrect refrigerant charge or faulty A/C compressor. Check for plugged condenser, faulty A/C fan motor or faulty fan relay.

INSUFFICIENT COOLING

Problem may be caused by incorrect A/C compressor belt tension, incorrect refrigerant charge or A/C control cable out of adjustment. Check for clogged condenser, faulty A/C compressor, or faulty A/C fan or relay. Also check for faulty expansion valve, faulty A/C-heater control panel, faulty air mix servomotor or faulty wiring.

INSUFFICIENT COOL AIR VELOCITY

Problem may be caused by faulty blower motor, blocked air inlet, clogged/frosted evaporator, or air leakage from evaporator case or air duct.

TESTING

WARNING: To avoid injury from accidental air bag deployment, read and carefully follow all SERVICE PRECAUTIONS and DISABLING & ACTIVATING AIR BAG SYSTEM procedures in AIR BAG SYSTEM SAFETY article in GENERAL SERVICING.

A/C SYSTEM PERFORMANCE

Connect manifold gauge set. Operate engine at 2000 RPM. Place blower fan on high speed. Place temperature control switch on maximum cooling. Set A/C-heater control panel in recirculated air mode. Ensure air inlet temperature is between 86-95°F (30-35°C). Ensure system operating pressures are within specification. See SPECIFICATIONS table at beginning of article.

A/C SWITCH

Disconnect negative battery cable. Disconnect wiring harness connector "A" of A/C-heater control panel. *See Fig. 2.* Check continuity between terminals No. 14 and 16. There should be continuity when switch is on and no continuity when switch is off. If continuity is not as specified, replace A/C-heater control panel.

A/C AMPLIFIER

Disconnect A/C amplifier connector. *See Fig. 1.* Test wiring harness side of connector. *See Fig. 5.* Ensure circuit tests as specified in A/C AMPLIFIER CIRCUIT TEST table. If circuit is not as specified, repair as necessary.

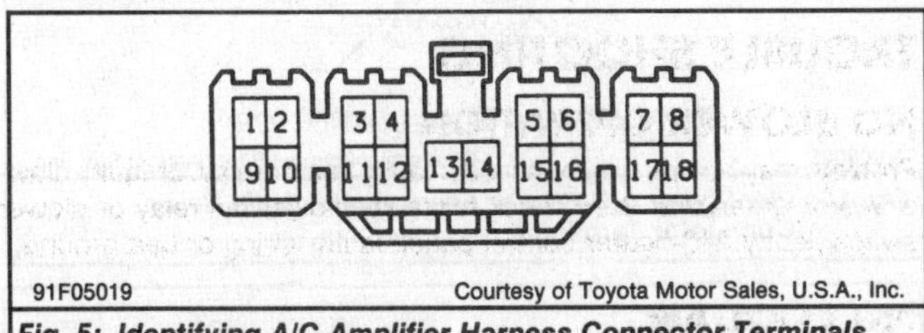
1 2
3 4
5 6
7 8
9 10
11 12
13 14
15 16
17 18
91F05019
Courtesy of Toyota Motor Sales, U.S.A., Inc.

Fig. 5: Identifying A/C Amplifier Harness Connector Terminals

A/C AMPLIFIER CIRCUIT TEST

Terminal No. & Test Condition [1]	Specification
2 & Ground [2]	
Coolant Temp. Less Than 203°F (95°C)	Continuity
Coolant Temp. Greater Than 212°F (100°C)	No Continuity
15 & Ground	Continuity
10 & Ground	
3S-GTE (2.0L)	No Continuity
5S-FE (2.2L)	Continuity
5 & Ground [2]	Approx. 12 Ohms
9 & 14	Approx. 115 Ohms
16 & 14	
Air Temp. @ 77°F (25°C)	Approx. 15,000 Ohms
1 & Ground	
A/C Switch On	Voltage
A/C Switch Off	No Voltage
3 & Ground	
A/C Switch On	Battery Voltage
A/C Switch Off	No Voltage
6 & Ground	Battery Voltage
8 & Ground	Battery Voltage
13 & Ground	Battery Voltage
18 & Ground	
Start Engine	Approx. 10-14 Volts
Stop Engine	No Voltage

[1] - Basic test condition: ignition on, temperature control in maximum cool position and blower switch on HI position.
[2] - Models with variable displacement compressor only.

BLOWER MOTOR

Disconnect wiring harness connector. Apply battery voltage to motor connector. *See Fig. 6.* Motor should operate smoothly. If motor does not operate smoothly, replace motor.

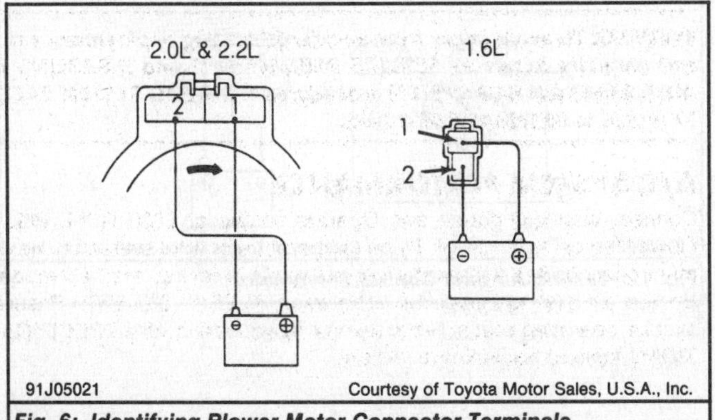
2.0L & 2.2L
1.6L
2
1
1
2
91J05021
Courtesy of Toyota Motor Sales, U.S.A., Inc.

Fig. 6: Identifying Blower Motor Connector Terminals

COOLANT TEMPERATURE SWITCH

When coolant temperature reaches 212°F (100°C), switch opens and breaks continuity. When coolant temperature drops to approximately 203°F (95°C), switch closes and restores continuity. If switch does not function as specified, replace switch.

CONDENSER FAN MOTOR

Disconnect fan motor 2-pin connector. Apply battery voltage to fan motor connector. Fan motor should rotate smoothly and current draw should be 6.0-7.4 amps. If operation is not as specified, replace condenser fan motor.

INDICATOR & ILLUMINATION LIGHTS

A/C Indicator – Disconnect harness connector "A" of A/C-heater control panel. *See Fig. 2.* Apply battery voltage to terminal No. 1, and ground terminal No. 15. Depress A/C switch and ensure indicator light comes on. If indicator light does not come on, replace A/C-heater control panel.

Air Inlet Indicator – Disconnect wiring harness connector "A" of A/C-heater control panel. *See Fig. 2.* Apply battery voltage to terminal No. 1, and ground terminal No. 2. Ensure recirculated and fresh air indicator lights come on each time air inlet control switch is pressed. If operation is not as specified, replace A/C-heater control panel.

Illumination Light Operation – Disconnect wiring harness connector "A" of A/C-heater control panel. *See Fig. 2.* Apply battery voltage to terminal No. 18, and ground terminal No. 17. Illumination light should come on. If illumination light does not come on, remove and check bulb.

Indicator Light Dimming Operation – Disconnect wiring harness connector "A" of A/C-heater control panel. *See Fig. 2.* Apply battery voltage to terminal No. 1, and ground terminal No. 2. Apply battery voltage to terminal No. 3. Indicator lights should dim. If operation is not as specified, replace A/C-heater control panel.

Mode Indicator – Disconnect wiring harness connector "A" of A/C-heater control panel. *See Fig. 2.* Apply battery voltage to terminal No. 1, and ground terminal No. 2. Press each mode button and ensure proper indicator light comes on. If any light fails to come on, replace A/C-heater control panel.

MAGNETIC CLUTCH

1) Inspect pressure plate and rotor for oil contamination. Check clutch bearing for noisy operation and grease leakage. Using an ohmmeter, measure resistance of stator coil between compressor connector terminal No. 1 and ground. *See Fig. 7.*

2) Resistance should be 3.4-3.8 ohms at 68°F (20°C). If reading is not as specified, replace stator coil. Apply 12 volts to coil side of A/C compressor connector. If clutch does not energize, replace stator coil.

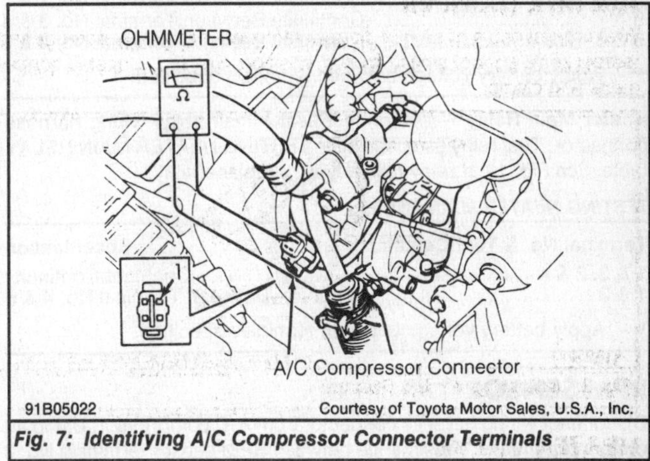
OHMMETER
Ω
1
A/C Compressor Connector
91B05022
Courtesy of Toyota Motor Sales, U.S.A., Inc.

Fig. 7: Identifying A/C Compressor Connector Terminals

RELAYS

Magnetic Clutch Relay – Remove relay. Using an ohmmeter, ensure continuity exists between terminals No. 1 and 2. *See Fig. 8.* Apply battery voltage to terminals No. 1 and 2. Continuity should exist between terminals No. 3 and 4. If continuity is not as specified, replace relay.

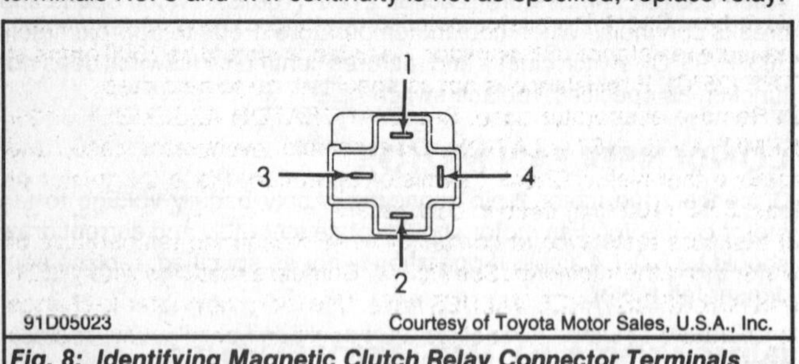
1
3
4
2
91D05023
Courtesy of Toyota Motor Sales, U.S.A., Inc.

Fig. 8: Identifying Magnetic Clutch Relay Connector Terminals

Fan Relay No. 1 – Remove relay. Using ohmmeter, ensure continuity exists between terminals No. 1 and 2 and terminals No. 3 and 4. *See Fig. 9*. Apply battery voltage between terminals No. 1 and 2. Continuity should not exist between terminals No. 3 and 4. If continuity is not as specified, replace relay.

Fan Relay No. 2 – Remove relay. Using ohmmeter, check continuity between terminals No. 1 and 2 and terminals No. 3 and 4. *See Fig. 9*. If continuity does not exist, replace relay. Apply battery voltage between terminals No. 1 and 2. Check continuity between terminals No. 3 and 5. If continuity does not exist, replace relay.

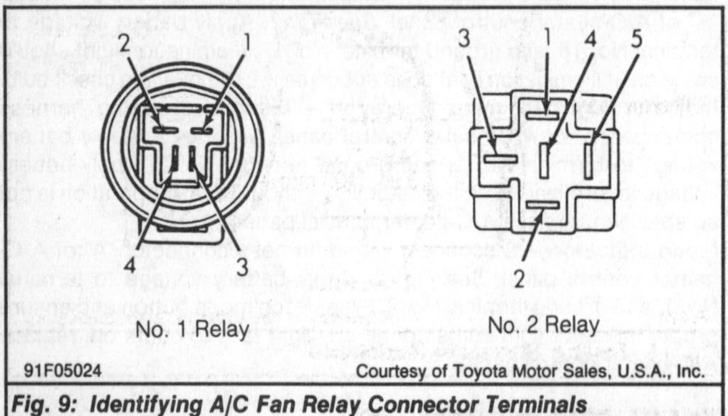
2
1
4
3
No. 1 Relay
3
1
4
5
2
No. 2 Relay
91F05024
Courtesy of Toyota Motor Sales, U.S.A., Inc.

Fig. 9: Identifying A/C Fan Relay Connector Terminals

Blower Fan Relay – Disconnect blower fan relay wiring harness connector. Test relay as specified in TESTING BLOWER FAN RELAY table. *See Fig. 10*. If relay fails any test, replace relay.

TESTING BLOWER FAN RELAY

Terminal No. & Test Condition	Specification
5 & 6, 5 & 7, 5 & 8	Constant Continuity
5 & 6 [1]	Continuity Between Terminal No. 1 & 3
5 & 7 [1]	Continuity Between Terminal No. 3 & 4
5 & 8 [1]	Continuity Between Terminal No. 2 & 3

[1] – Apply battery voltage between terminals specified.

Heater Main Relay – Disconnect heater main relay wiring harness connector. Test relay as specified in TESTING HEATER MAIN RELAY table. *See Fig. 10*. If relay fails any test, replace relay.

TESTING HEATER MAIN RELAY

Terminal No. & Test Condition	Specification
1 & 3, 2 & 4	Constant Continuity
1 & 3 [1]	Continuity Between Terminal No. 4 & 5

[1] – Apply battery voltage between terminals specified.

RPM SENSOR

Disconnect wiring harness connector from A/C compressor. Using an ohmmeter, measure resistance between RPM sensor terminals No. 2 and 3. *See Fig. 11*. Resistance should be 100-130 ohms at 68°F (20°C). If resistance is not within specification, replace RPM sensor.

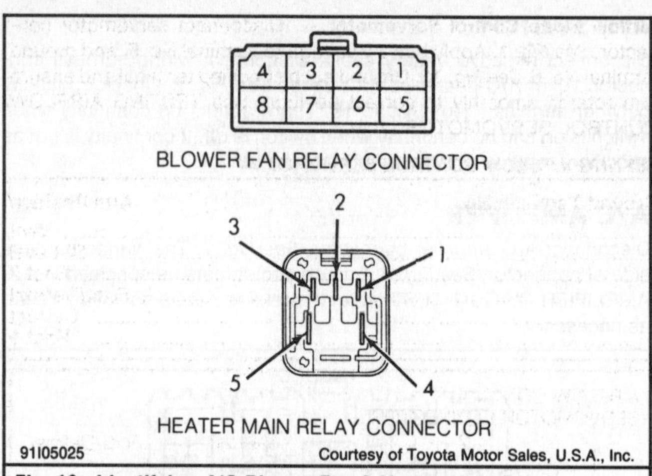
4
3
2
1
8
7
6
5
BLOWER FAN RELAY CONNECTOR
2
3
1
5
4
HEATER MAIN RELAY CONNECTOR
91I05025
Courtesy of Toyota Motor Sales, U.S.A., Inc.

Fig. 10: Identifying A/C Blower Fan & Heater Main Relay Connector Terminals

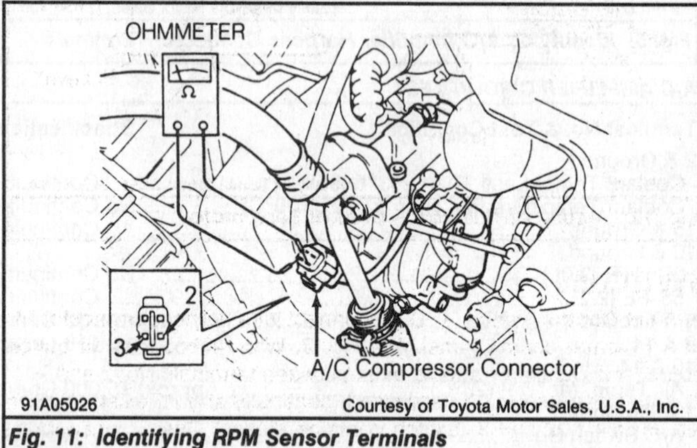
OHMMETER
2
3
A/C Compressor Connector
91A05026
Courtesy of Toyota Motor Sales, U.S.A., Inc.

Fig. 11: Identifying RPM Sensor Terminals

SERVOMOTORS

Air Inlet Control Servomotor – **1)** Disconnect servomotor connector. *See Fig. 1*. Apply battery voltage to terminal No. 1, and ground terminal No. 3. *See Fig. 12*. Ensure arm rotates smoothly to fresh air side.

2) Apply battery voltage to terminal No. 1, and ground terminal No. 2. *See Fig. 12*. Ensure arm rotates smoothly to recirculated air side. If operation is not as specified, replace servomotor.

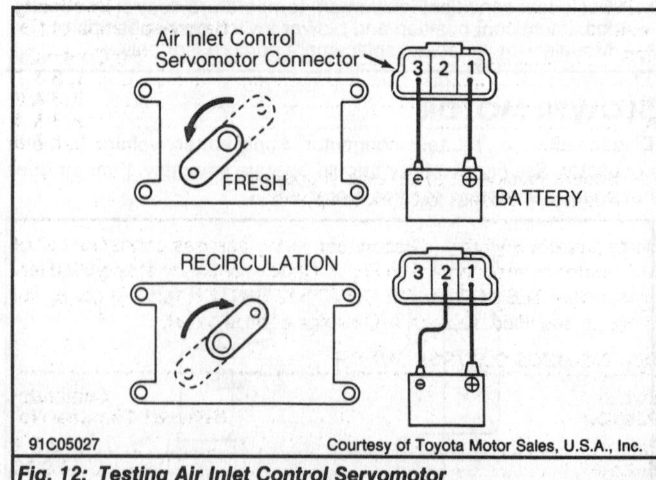
Air Inlet Control
Servomotor Connector
3
2
1
FRESH
BATTERY
RECIRCULATION
3
2
1
91C05027
Courtesy of Toyota Motor Sales, U.S.A., Inc.

Fig. 12: Testing Air Inlet Control Servomotor

Airflow Mode Control Servomotor - Disconnect servomotor connector. *See Fig. 1*. Apply battery voltage to terminal No. 5, and ground terminal No. 6. *See Fig. 13*. Ground each specified terminal and ensure arm rotates smoothly to correct position. See TESTING AIRFLOW CONTROL SERVOMOTOR table.

TESTING AIRFLOW CONTROL SERVOMOTOR

Ground Terminal No.	Arm Position
1	Vent
2	Bi-Level
3	Foot 2
4	Foot/Defrost
7	Defrost
8	Foot 1

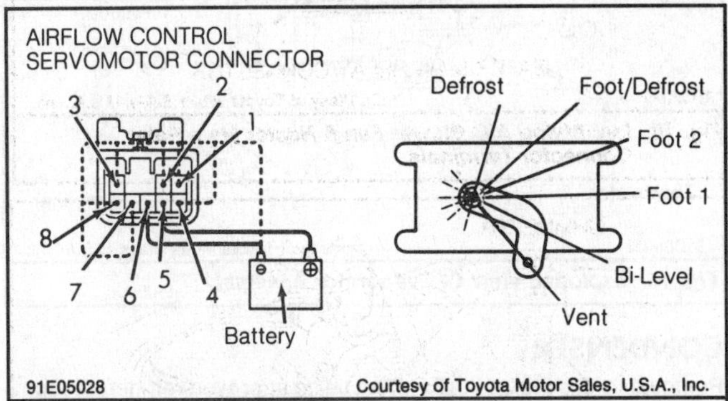

AIRFLOW CONTROL
SERVOMOTOR CONNECTOR
1
2
3
4
5
6
7
8
Battery
Defrost
Foot/Defrost
Foot 2
Foot 1
Bi-Level
Vent
91E05028

Courtesy of Toyota Motor Sales, U.S.A., Inc.

Fig. 13: Testing Airflow Mode Control Servomotor

SWITCHES

Air Inlet Control Switch - 1) Disconnect wire harness connector "A" of A/C-heater control panel. *See Fig. 2*. With recirculated air button depressed, continuity should exist between terminals No. 2 and 7.

2) With fresh air button depressed, continuity should exist between terminals No. 2 and 8. Switch contains diodes. Check continuity in both directions before assuming switch is faulty. Continuity should exist in one direction only. If continuity does not exist or exists in both directions, replace A/C-heater control panel.

Blower Speed Control Switch - Disconnect wire harness connector "B" of A/C-heater control panel. *See Fig. 2*. Check continuity at specified terminals. See TESTING BLOWER SPEED CONTROL SWITCH table. If continuity is not as specified, replace A/C-heater control panel.

TESTING BLOWER SPEED CONTROL SWITCH

Switch Position	Continuity Between Terminal No.
OFF	No Continuity
LO	1, 3 & 7
(■) [1]	2, 3 & 6
(■) [2]	2, 3 & 4
HI	2, 3 & 5

[1] - Square (■) closest to LO switch position.
[2] - Square (■) closest to HI switch position.

Mode Control Switch - Disconnect wiring harness connector "A" of A/C-heater control panel. *See Fig. 2*. Check continuity at specified terminals. See TESTING MODE CONTROL SWITCH table. If continuity is not as specified, replace A/C-heater control panel.

TESTING MODE CONTROL SWITCH

Switch Position	Continuity Between Terminal No.
Face	2 & 9
Bi-Level	2 & 10
Foot	2 & 11
Foot/Defrost	2 & 12
Defrost	2 & 13

THERMISTOR

1) Disconnect negative battery cable. Remove lower trim panel and glove box. Check thermistor installed operation. Using an ohmmeter, measure resistance of thermistor. Resistance should be 1500 ohms at 77°F (25°C). If resistance is not as specified, go to next step.

2) Remove evaporator case. See EVAPORATOR ASSEMBLY under REMOVAL & INSTALLATION. Disassemble evaporator case, and remove thermistor. Check thermistor operation. Place thermistor at least 3.94" (100 mm) deep in cold water.

3) Measure resistance at connector while measuring temperature of water using thermometer. *See Fig. 14*. Compare readings with THERMISTOR RESISTANCE VALUES table. Use ice or hot water to change temperature of water. If readings are not within specification, replace thermistor.

THERMISTOR RESISTANCE VALUES

Temperature °F (°C)	Ohms
41 (5)	3500-4100
39 (4)	3800-4300
37 (3)	3900-4500
36 (2)	4100-4800
34 (1)	4300-4900
32 (0)	4500-5200
30 (-1)	4700-5400

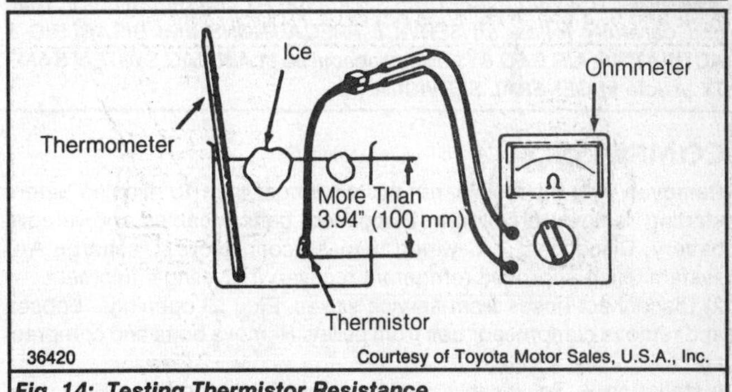

Ice
Ohmmeter
Thermometer
More Than
3.94" (100 mm)
Thermistor
36420

Courtesy of Toyota Motor Sales, U.S.A., Inc.

Fig. 14: Testing Thermistor Resistance

TRIPLE-PRESSURE SWITCH

Magnetic Clutch Control - 1) Install A/C manifold gauges. Start engine, turn A/C on and observe gauge readings. If low side pressure is less than 30 psi (2.1 kg/cm²), system pressure is too low and pressure switch (terminals No. 3 and 4) should be open and clutch disengaged.

2) If low side pressure is greater than 33 psi (2.4 kg/cm²), switch should be closed and clutch engaged. If pressure drops below 33 psi (2.4 kg/cm²), switch will open and disengage clutch.

3) During system operation, switch opens and disengages clutch if high side pressure becomes greater than 384 psi (27 kg/cm²). Switch remains open until high side pressure drops to less than 299 psi (21 kg/cm²). If switch does not operate as specified, replace switch. If switch is okay, proceed to ELECTRIC FAN CONTROL.

Electric Fan Control - If high side pressure becomes greater than 220 psi (15.5 kg/cm²), switch closes and condenser fan operates at high speed. When pressure drops to approximately 178 psi (12.5 kg/cm²), switch opens (terminals No. 1 and 2) and condenser fan returns to low speed operation. If switch does not function as specified, replace switch.

VACUUM SWITCHING VALVE (VSV)

1) Remove vacuum connections from fittings "A" and "B" on VSV. *See Fig. 15*. Connect VSV terminal connector to battery. Blow air through fitting "A". Air should pass from fitting "A" out through fitting "B". Air should not be felt at "C" (atmospheric port).

2) Disconnect battery from VSV terminal connector. Blow air through fitting "A". Air should pass from fitting "A" out through "C" (atmospheric port). Air should not come out of fitting "B".

1993 MANUAL A/C-HEATER SYSTEMS
Celica (Cont.)

3) Use ohmmeter to check for short between each terminal and VSV body. Also check resistance between terminals. Reading should be 38-43 ohms at 68°F (20°C).

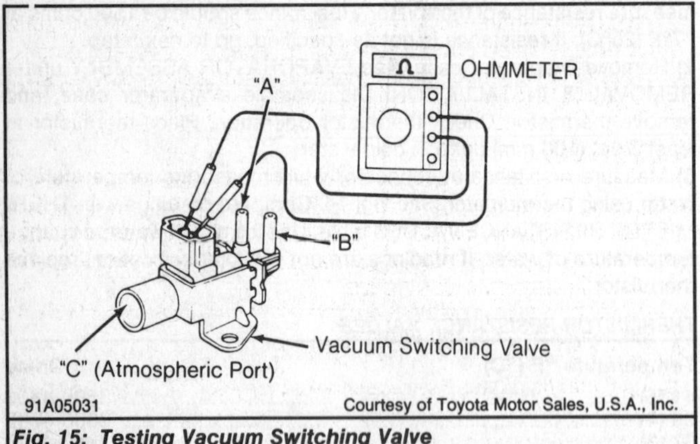
OHMMETER
"A"
"B"
"C" (Atmospheric Port)
Vacuum Switching Valve
91A05031
Courtesy of Toyota Motor Sales, U.S.A., Inc.

Fig. 15: Testing Vacuum Switching Valve

REMOVAL & INSTALLATION

WARNING: To avoid injury from accidental air bag deployment, read and carefully follow all SERVICE PRECAUTIONS and DISABLING & ACTIVATING AIR BAG SYSTEM procedures in AIR BAG SYSTEM SAFETY article in GENERAL SERVICING.

COMPRESSOR

Removal – **1)** If possible, run system longer than 10 minutes before starting removal procedure. Disconnect battery cables and remove battery. Disconnect A/C wiring harness connectors. Discharge A/C system using approved refrigerant recovery/recycling equipment.

2) Disconnect hoses from service valves. Plug all openings. Loosen and remove compressor belt from pulley. Remove bolts and compressor.

Installation – To install, reverse removal procedure. Evacuate, recharge and leak test system.

EVAPORATOR ASSEMBLY

Removal – Disconnect negative battery cable. Discharge A/C system using approved refrigerant recovery/recycling equipment. Disconnect inlet and outlet lines and grommets from evaporator. Plug openings. Disconnect electrical leads from evaporator. Remove glove box and reinforcement. Remove nuts, bolts and evaporator assembly.

Disassembly – Release spring clips holding covers together. *See Fig. 16.* Remove any screws at case joints. Separate upper and lower cases from evaporator core. Remove thermistor with holder. Remove heat insulator from outlet tube. Remove high side (inlet) line from expansion valve, and remove expansion valve.

Reassembly & Installation – To reassemble and install evaporator assembly, reverse disassembly and removal procedures. If installing new evaporator core, add 1.4-1.7 ounces of refrigerant oil to core before installing. Evacuate, recharge and leak test system.

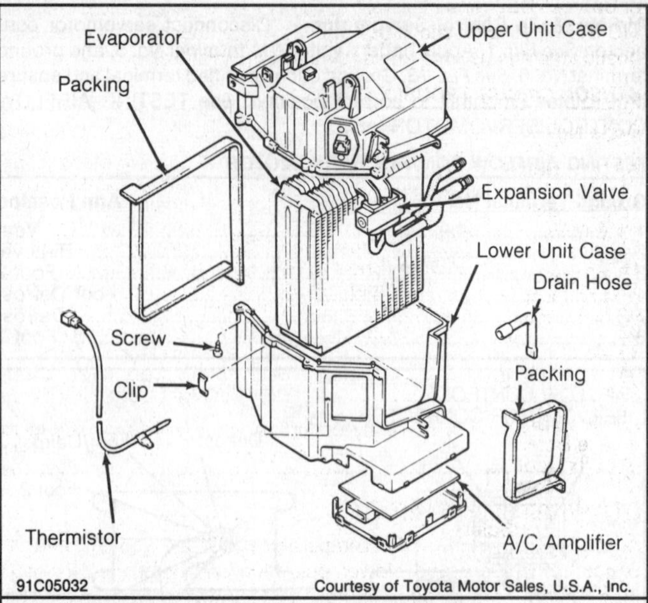
Evaporator
Upper Unit Case
Packing
Expansion Valve
Lower Unit Case
Drain Hose
Screw
Packing
Clip
Thermistor
A/C Amplifier
91C05032
Courtesy of Toyota Motor Sales, U.S.A., Inc.

Fig. 16: Exploded View Of Evaporator Assembly

CONDENSER

Removal – Discharge A/C system using approved refrigerant recovery/recycling equipment. Remove lower engine cover. Remove grille and hood lock brace. Remove horns. Detach lines from condenser. Plug all openings. Remove bolts and condenser.

Installation – To install, reverse removal procedure. If installing new condenser, add 1.4-1.7 ounces of refrigeration oil before installing. Evacuate, recharge and leak test system.

RECEIVER-DRIER

Removal – Discharge A/C system using approved refrigerant recovery/recycling equipment. Remove lines from receiver-drier. Plug all openings. Remove bolts and receiver-drier.

Installation – To install, reverse removal procedure. Add 0.7 ounce of refrigerant oil. Evacuate, recharge and leak test system.

TORQUE SPECIFICATIONS

TORQUE SPECIFICATIONS

Application	Ft. Lbs. (N.m)
A/C Compressor	18 (25)
A/C Compressor Bracket (1.6L)	35 (47)
Condenser	
Discharge Hose	17 (23)
Liquid Tube	10 (14)
Evaporator Suction Tube	24 (32)
	INCH Lbs. (N.m)
Evaporator Liquid Tube	115 (13)
Expansion Valve Allen Bolt	48 (5.4)
Receiver-Drier	115 (13)

WIRING DIAGRAMS

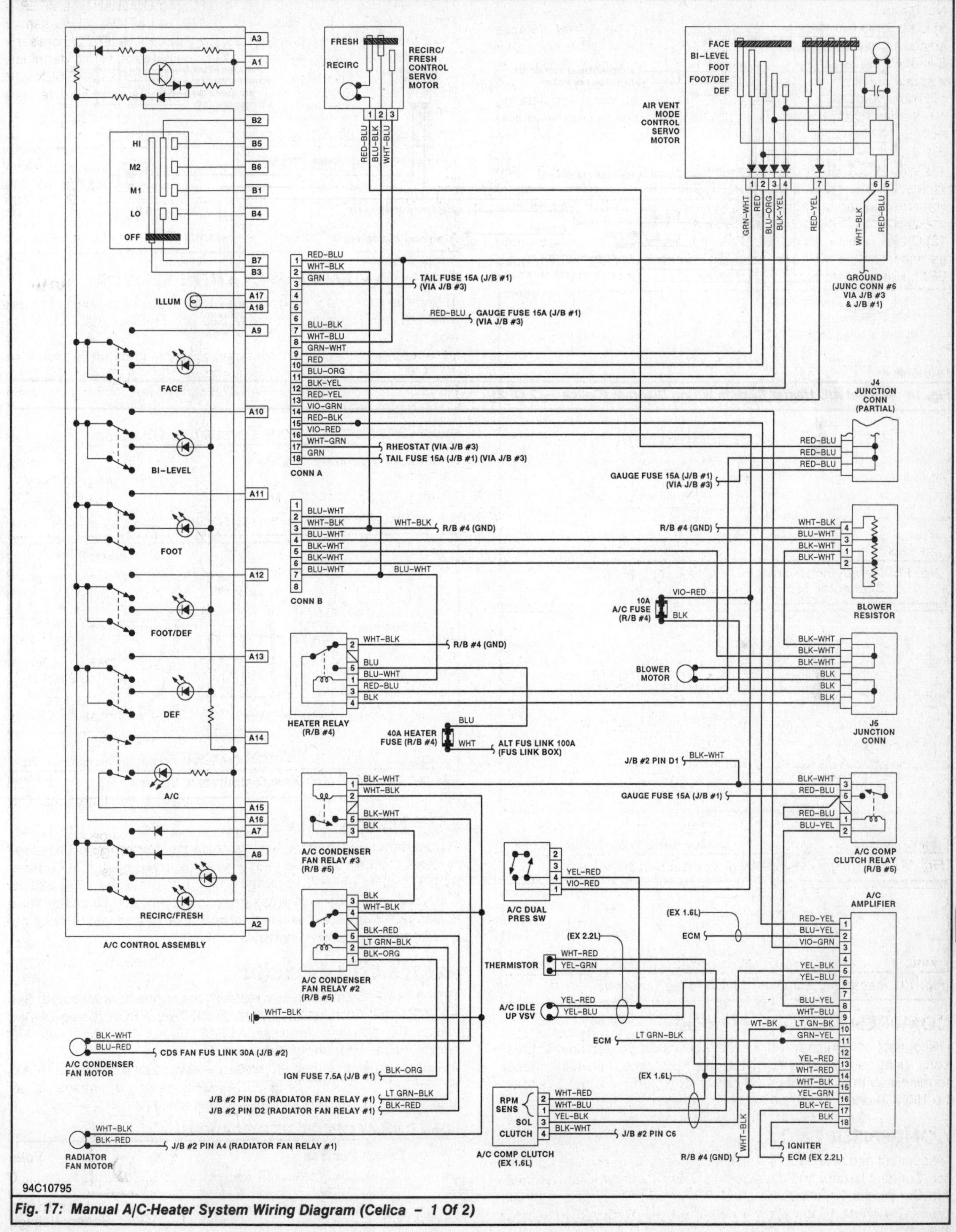
A/C CONTROL ASSEMBLY
RECIRC/FRESH CONTROL SERVO MOTOR
AIR VENT MODE CONTROL SERVO MOTOR
CONN A
CONN B
TAIL FUSE 15A (J/B #1) (VIA J/B #3)
GAUGE FUSE 15A (J/B #1) (VIA J/B #3)
RHEOSTAT (VIA J/B #3)
R/B #4 (GND)
J4 JUNCTION CONN (PARTIAL)
BLOWER RESISTOR
10A A/C FUSE (R/B #4)
BLOWER MOTOR
J5 JUNCTION CONN
HEATER RELAY (R/B #4)
40A HEATER FUSE (R/B #4)
ALT FUS LINK 100A (FUS LINK BOX)
A/C CONDENSER FAN RELAY #3 (R/B #5)
A/C CONDENSER FAN RELAY #2 (R/B #5)
A/C COMP CLUTCH RELAY (R/B #5)
A/C DUAL PRES SW
A/C AMPLIFIER
THERMISTOR
A/C IDLE UP VSV
ECM
A/C CONDENSER FAN MOTOR
CDS FAN FUS LINK 30A (J/B #2)
IGN FUSE 7.5A (J/B #1)
J/B #2 PIN D5 (RADIATOR FAN RELAY #1)
J/B #2 PIN D2 (RADIATOR FAN RELAY #1)
RADIATOR FAN MOTOR
J/B #2 PIN A4 (RADIATOR FAN RELAY #1)
A/C COMP CLUTCH (EX 1.6L)
J/B #2 PIN C6
IGNITER
ECM (EX 2.2L)
GROUND (JUNC CONN #6 VIA J/B #3 & J/B #1)
94C10795

Fig. 17: Manual A/C-Heater System Wiring Diagram (Celica – 1 Of 2)

1993 MANUAL A/C-HEATER SYSTEMS
Celica (Cont.)

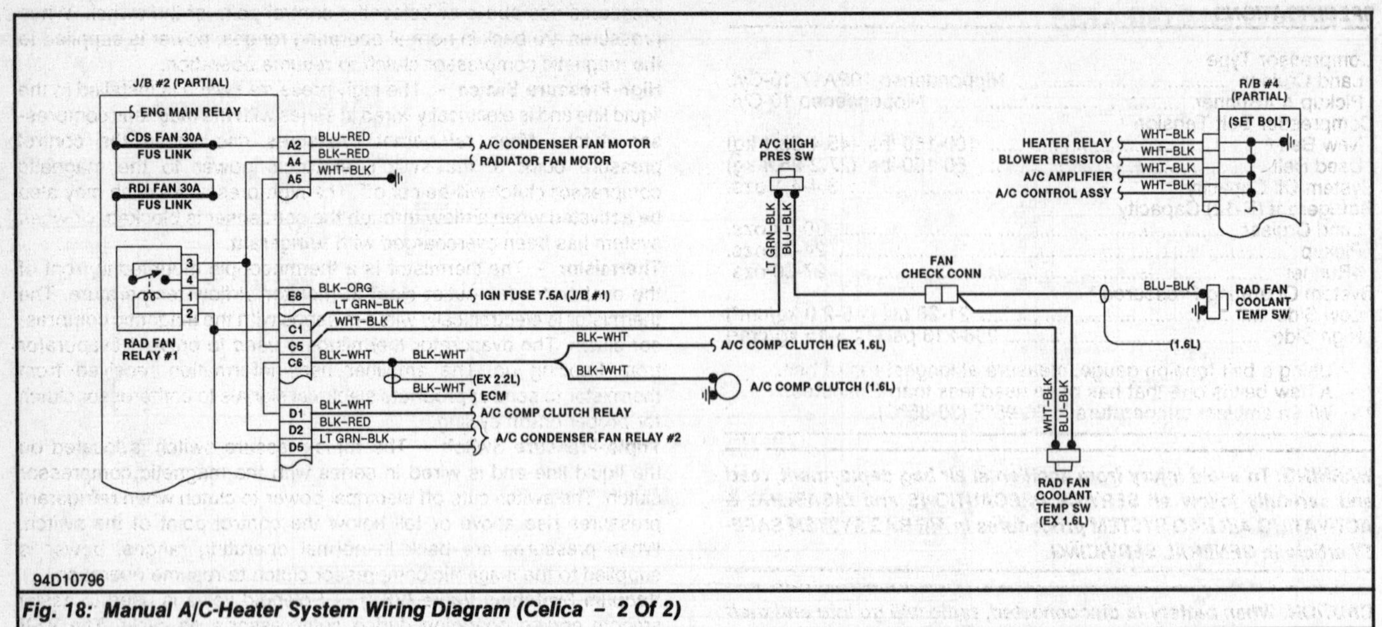
J/B #2 (PARTIAL)
ENG MAIN RELAY
CDS FAN 30A
FUS LINK
RDI FAN 30A
FUS LINK
A2
A4
A5
BLU-RED
BLK-RED
WHT-BLK
A/C CONDENSER FAN MOTOR
RADIATOR FAN MOTOR
3
4
1
2
RAD FAN
RELAY #1
E8
C1
C5
C6
BLK-ORG
LT GRN-BLK
WHT-BLK
BLK-WHT
IGN FUSE 7.5A (J/B #1)
BLK-WHT
A/C COMP CLUTCH (EX 1.6L)
BLK-WHT
BLK-WHT
(EX 2.2L)
ECM
A/C COMP CLUTCH (1.6L)
D1
D2
D5
BLK-WHT
BLK-RED
LT GRN-BLK
A/C COMP CLUTCH RELAY
A/C CONDENSER FAN RELAY #2
A/C HIGH
PRES SW
LT GRN-BLK
BLU-BLK
FAN
CHECK CONN
BLU-BLK
RAD FAN
COOLANT
TEMP SW
(1.6L)
WHT-BLK
BLU-BLK
RAD FAN
COOLANT
TEMP SW
(EX 1.6L)
R/B #4
(PARTIAL)
(SET BOLT)
HEATER RELAY
BLOWER RESISTOR
A/C AMPLIFIER
A/C CONTROL ASSY
WHT-BLK
WHT-BLK
WHT-BLK
WHT-BLK
94D10796

Fig. 18: Manual A/C-Heater System Wiring Diagram (Celica – 2 Of 2)

1993 MANUAL A/C-HEATER SYSTEMS
Land Cruiser, Pickup & 4Runner

SPECIFICATIONS

Compressor Type	
Land Cruiser	Nippondenso 10PA17 10-Cyl.
Pickup & 4Runner	Nippondenso 10-Cyl.
Compressor Belt Tension [1]	
New Belt [2]	100-150 lbs. (45.4-68.1 kg)
Used Belt	60-100 lbs. (27.2-25.4 kg)
System Oil Capacity	3.4-4.1 ozs.
Refrigerant (R-12) Capacity	
Land Cruiser	30-34 ozs.
Pickup	24-29 ozs.
4Runner	27-30 ozs.
System Operating Pressures [3]	
Low Side	21-28 psi (1.5-2.0 kg/cm²)
High Side	206-213 psi (14.5-15 kg/cm²)

[1] – Using a belt tension gauge, measure at longest run of belt.
[2] – A new belt is one that has been used less than 5 minutes.
[3] – When ambient temperature is 86-95°F (30-35°C).

WARNING: To avoid injury from accidental air bag deployment, read and carefully follow all SERVICE PRECAUTIONS and DISABLING & ACTIVATING AIR BAG SYSTEM procedures in AIR BAG SYSTEM SAFETY article in GENERAL SERVICING.

CAUTION: When battery is disconnected, radio will go into anti-theft protection mode. Obtain radio anti-theft protection code from owner prior to servicing vehicle.

DESCRIPTION

Slight variations exist among the various manual A/C-heater systems used. Nippondenso 10-cylinder compressors are used. Compressors only operate in the normal operating temperatures and pressures set for each model. An electric condenser fan operates at 2 speeds, depending on coolant temperature and A/C switch position.

System components used vary depending on model. Most systems consist of a fan switch, A/C amplifier, evaporator, thermistor, dual-pressure (high and low) switch, engine coolant temperature switch, compressor, condenser, receiver-drier and all the necessary pipes and hoses. Air door operation is controlled through cable connections. Compressor operation and associated A/C modes are electrically controlled.

OPERATION

SYSTEM CONTROLS

The A/C functions are controlled by sliding levers and A/C on-off switch. A/C controls operate air supply selection (fresh or recirculating air), mode and temperature selection, and blower speeds. Temperature control lever operates blend air door in A/C-heater unit, to mix both cooled and heated air so the desired air temperature can be obtained. The system will provide cooled air when A/C switch is in the ON position and blower motor is in any position except OFF. The temperature control lever should be in the far left (maximum cooling) side of temperature selection scale when maximum A/C operation is desired.

SYSTEM COMPONENTS

NOTE: Components within A/C systems may vary according to model. A/C systems may not use all system components listed.

A/C Switch – When A/C switch is pushed, A/C will operate if the blower motor control lever or push button is in any position except OFF. When activated, the A/C switch allows the magnetic compressor clutch to engage, operating the compressor. On some models, a light will illuminate on the A/C push button when activated.

Dual-Pressure Switch – The dual-pressure switch is located on the liquid line and is wired in series with the magnetic compressor clutch. The switch cuts off electrical power to clutch when refrigerant pressures rise above or below the control point of the switch. When pressures are back in normal operating ranges, power is supplied to the magnetic compressor clutch to resume operation.

High-Pressure Switch – The high-pressure switch is installed in the liquid line and is electrically wired in series with the magnetic compressor clutch. When refrigerant pressures rise above the control pressure point of the switch, electrical power to the magnetic compressor clutch will be cut off. The high-pressure switch may also be activated when airflow through the condenser is blocked, or when system has been overcharged with refrigerant.

Thermistor – The thermistor is a thermocouple mounted in front of the evaporator (air outlet side) to monitor airflow temperature. The thermistor is electronically wired in series with the magnetic compressor clutch. The evaporator thermistor is used to prevent evaporator from freezing up. The amplifier uses information received from thermistor to send appropriate electrical signals to compressor clutch for proper on-off cycling.

Triple-Pressure Switch – The triple-pressure switch is located on the liquid line and is wired in series with the magnetic compressor clutch. The switch cuts off electrical power to clutch when refrigerant pressures rise above or fall below the control point of the switch. When pressures are back in normal operating ranges, power is supplied to the magnetic compressor clutch to resume operation.

Vacuum Switching Valve (VSV) – Solenoid valve is used to assist smooth engine operation during compressor's on cycle. The VSV holds throttle slightly above idle (spring-loaded to this position) when A/C system is operating. When system is off, vacuum is directed to VSV diaphragm to allow throttle to return to normal idle position.

ADJUSTMENTS

NOTE: For control cable adjustment, see appropriate HEATER SYSTEMS article.

TROUBLE SHOOTING

A/C SWITCH FLASHES

Check for slipping A/C drive belt, faulty A/C amplifier or faulty RPM sensor (models with power steering only).

COMPRESSOR DOES NOT ROTATE PROPERLY

Check for loose or broken A/C drive belt. Check for faulty compressor or faulty expansion valve. Check refrigerant system for leak.

COOL AIR ONLY AT HIGH SPEED

Check for clogged condenser. Check for slipping A/C drive belt. Check for faulty A/C compressor. Check for incorrect refrigerant charge. Check for air in refrigerant system.

COOLING BLOWER DOES NOT OPERATE

Check for blown fuse. Check for faulty heater main relay or faulty blower motor. Check for faulty circuit breaker, blower resistor or blower switch. Check for faulty wiring or bad ground.

INSUFFICIENT COOL AIR VELOCITY

Check for faulty blower motor. Check for blocked air inlet. Check for clogged or frosted evaporator. Check for air leakage from evaporator case or air duct. Check for faulty A/C amplifier.

INSUFFICIENT COOLING

Check for incorrect refrigerant charge. Check for slipping A/C drive belt. Check for clogged condenser. Check for faulty magnetic clutch, A/C compressor, expansion valve, thermistor or A/C amplifier. Check for excessive air or compressor oil in system. Check for plugged receiver-drier. Check if heater valve is out of adjustment.

1993 MANUAL A/C-HEATER SYSTEMS
Land Cruiser, Pickup & 4Runner (Cont.)

INTERMITTENT COOL AIR

Check magnetic clutch for slipping. Check for faulty expansion valve. Check for excessive moisture in refrigerant system. Check for faulty revolution detecting sensor or faulty A/C amplifier. Check for faulty wiring or bad ground.

MAGNETIC CLUTCH DOES NOT ENGAGE

Check for blown fusible link or A/C fuse. Check for faulty magnetic clutch relay or magnetic clutch. Check for faulty A/C switch, thermistor, A/C amplifier or pressure switch. Check for faulty wiring or bad ground. Check for incorrect refrigerant charge.

TESTING

WARNING: To avoid injury from accidental air bag deployment, read and carefully follow all SERVICE PRECAUTIONS and DISABLING & ACTIVATING AIR BAG SYSTEM procedures in AIR BAG SYSTEM SAFETY article in GENERAL SERVICING.

A/C SYSTEM PERFORMANCE

1) Park vehicle out of direct sunlight. Install manifold gauge set and turn A/C controls to recirculated air position, with inlet air temperature at 86-95°F (30-35°C). Start engine and allow it to run at 2000 RPM.
2) Set blower/fan on high speed and temperature control switch set to maximum cool. Verify high side and low side pressures are within specification. See SPECIFICATIONS table at beginning of article.

A/C AMPLIFIER

Disconnect A/C amplifier connector. A/C amplifier is located either on top or bottom of A/C cooling unit (evaporator housing). Test wire harness side of connector. *See Fig. 1*. Ensure circuit tests as specified in appropriate A/C AMPLIFIER CIRCUIT TEST table. If circuits do not test as specified, repair as necessary.

A/C AMPLIFIER CIRCUIT TEST (LAND CRUISER)

Terminal No. & Test Condition [1]	Specification
6 & Ground	Continuity
8 & 9	Continuity
2 & 6	
A/C Switch ON	Battery Voltage
A/C Switch OFF	No Voltage
3 & 6	
A/C Switch ON	Battery Voltage
A/C Switch OFF	No Voltage
5 & 6	
Start Engine	About 10-14 Volts
Stop Engine	No Voltage
9 & 6	[2] 1500 Ohms

[1] - Ensure ignition switch is on, temperature control lever is at the maximum cool position, and blower switch is on HI position.
[2] - Test with air temperature at 77°F (25°C).

A/C AMPLIFIER CIRCUIT TEST (PICKUP & 4RUNNER)

Terminal No. & Test Condition [1]	Specification
2 & 5	Continuity
8 & Ground	Continuity
3 & 8	
A/C Switch ON	Battery Voltage
A/C Switch OFF	Battery Voltage
4 & 8	
A/C Switch ON	Battery Voltage
A/C Switch OFF	No Voltage
6 & 8	
Start Engine	About 10-14 Volts
Stop Engine	No Voltage
8 & 9	
A/C Switch ON	Battery Voltage
A/C Switch OFF	Battery Voltage
5 & 8	[2] About 1500 Ohms
7 & 8	
Pickup	Continuity
4Runner	About 3.6 Ohms

[1] - Ensure ignition switch is on, temperature control lever is at the maximum cool position, and blower switch is on HI position.
[2] - Test with air temperature at 77°F (25°C).

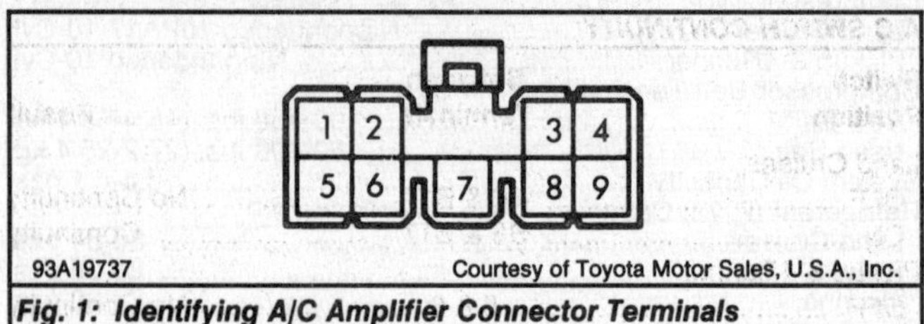
1
2
3
4
5
6
7
8
9
93A19737
Courtesy of Toyota Motor Sales, U.S.A., Inc.

Fig. 1: Identifying A/C Amplifier Connector Terminals

A/C-CUT RELAY

Pickup (4WD - 3VZ-E With A/T) - Remove relay. Relay is located on right side of A/C cooling unit. Check continuity between terminals No. 1 and 3. *See Figs. 2 and 3*. Ensure continuity exists. If continuity does not exist, replace relay. Apply battery voltage between terminals No. 1 and 3. Check continuity between terminals No. 2 and 4. Ensure continuity exists. If continuity does not exist, replace relay.

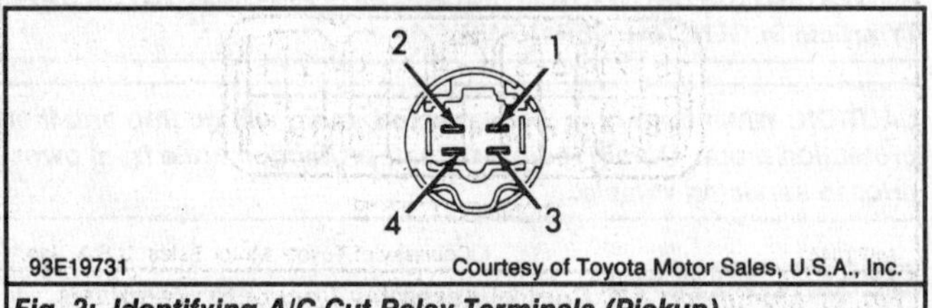
2
1
4
3
93E19731
Courtesy of Toyota Motor Sales, U.S.A., Inc.

Fig. 2: Identifying A/C-Cut Relay Terminals (Pickup)

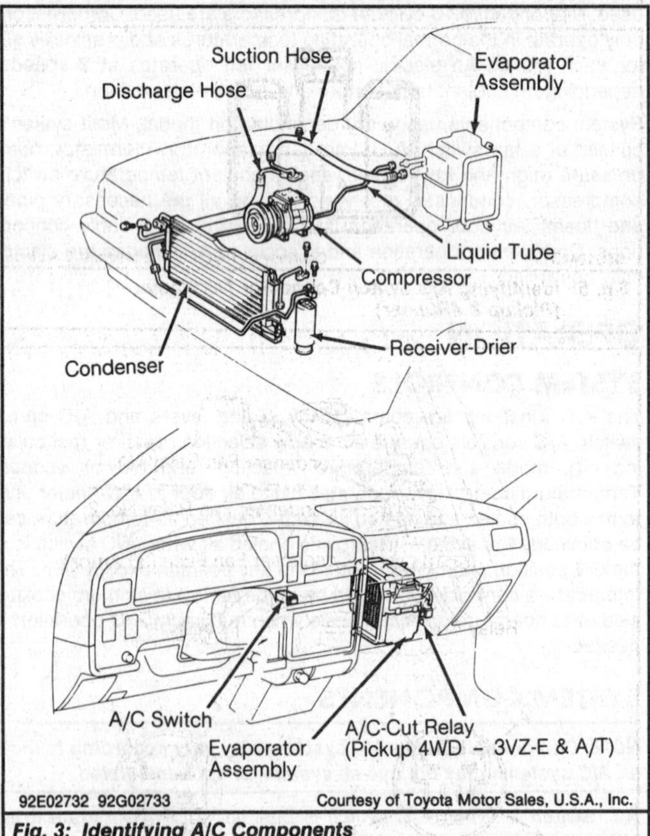
Suction Hose
Evaporator Assembly
Discharge Hose
Liquid Tube
Compressor
Receiver-Drier
Condenser
A/C Switch
A/C-Cut Relay (Pickup 4WD - 3VZ-E & A/T)
Evaporator Assembly
92E02732 92G02733
Courtesy of Toyota Motor Sales, U.S.A., Inc.

Fig. 3: Identifying A/C Components (Pickup Shown; 4Runner Is Similar)

A/C SWITCH

Disconnect negative battery cable. Remove glove box, A/C switch, and disconnect wire harness connector. On some models, it may be necessary to remove A/C control panel to remove switch. Check continuity at specified terminals. See A/C SWITCH CONTINUITY table.

1993 MANUAL A/C-HEATER SYSTEMS
Land Cruiser, Pickup & 4Runner (Cont.)

See Figs. 4 and 5. Most A/C switches have one-way diodes; check continuity in both directions before replacing any component.

A/C SWITCH CONTINUITY

Switch Position	Between Terminals	Result
Land Cruiser		
OFF	B6 & B17	No Continuity
ON	B6 & B17	Continuity
Pickup & 4Runner		
OFF	5 & 6	No Continuity
ON	5 & 6	Continuity

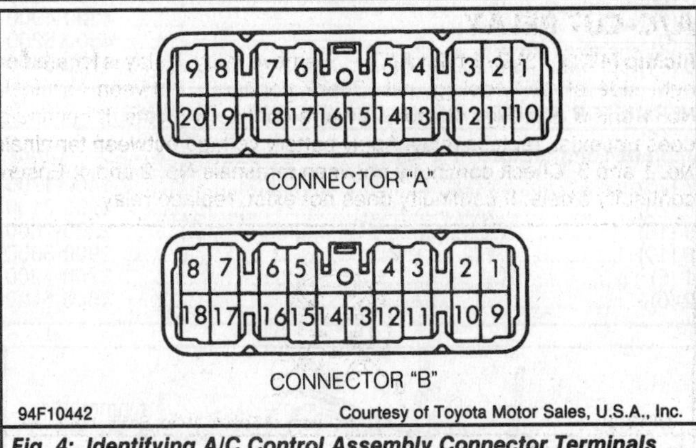
9 8 7 6 5 4 3 2 1
20 19 18 17 16 15 14 13 12 11 10
CONNECTOR "A"
8 7 6 5 4 3 2 1
18 17 16 15 14 13 12 11 10 9
CONNECTOR "B"
94F10442
Courtesy of Toyota Motor Sales, U.S.A., Inc.

Fig. 4: Identifying A/C Control Assembly Connector Terminals (Land Cruiser)

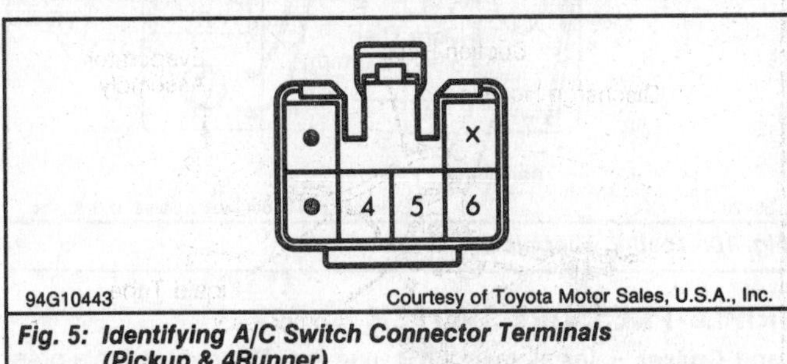
X
4 5 6
94G10443
Courtesy of Toyota Motor Sales, U.S.A., Inc.

Fig. 5: Identifying A/C Switch Connector Terminals (Pickup & 4Runner)

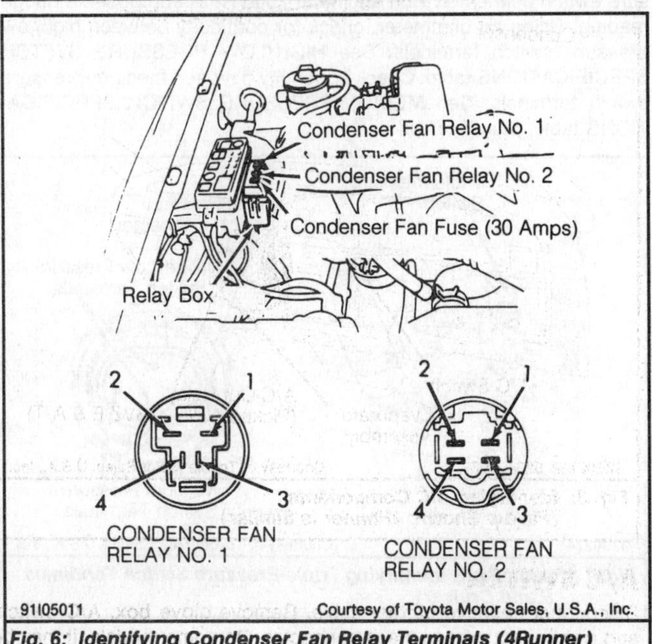
Condenser Fan Relay No. 1
Condenser Fan Relay No. 2
Condenser Fan Fuse (30 Amps)
Relay Box
2
1
4
3
CONDENSER FAN RELAY NO. 1
CONDENSER FAN RELAY NO. 2
91I05011
Courtesy of Toyota Motor Sales, U.S.A., Inc.

Fig. 6: Identifying Condenser Fan Relay Terminals (4Runner)

CONDENSER FAN MOTOR

4Runner – Disconnect 2-pin fan motor connector. Apply battery voltage to fan motor side of connector. Fan motor should rotate smoothly and current draw should be 7.3-8.7 amps. If operation is not as specified, replace condenser fan motor.

CONDENSER FAN RELAY

4Runner (Condenser Fan Relay No. 1) – Remove relay. Using ohmmeter, check continuity between terminals No. 1 and 2, and between terminals No. 3 and 4. *See Fig. 6.* Ensure continuity exists. If continuity does not exist, replace relay. Apply battery voltage between terminals No. 1 and 2. Check continuity between terminals No. 3 and 4. Continuity should not exist. If continuity exists, replace relay.

4Runner (Condenser Fan Relay No. 2) – Remove relay. Using ohmmeter, check continuity between terminals No. 1 and 3. *See Fig. 6.* Continuity should exist. If continuity does not exist, replace relay. Apply battery voltage between terminals No. 1 and 3. Check continuity between terminals No. 2 and 4. If continuity exists, relay is okay. If continuity is not present, replace relay.

DUAL-PRESSURE SWITCH

Pickup & 4Runner – Disconnect negative battery cable. Install manifold gauge set. Remove glove box. Disconnect dual-pressure switch connector. *See Fig. 7 or 8.* Check switch operation. See DUAL-PRESSURE SWITCH TEST table. Replace switch if it does not function as specified.

DUAL-PRESSURE SWITCH TEST

Pressure psi (kg/cm²)	System Operation	[1] Continuity
Decreasing To 30 (2.1) [2]	Off	No
Increasing To 33 (2.3) [3]	On	Yes
Decreasing To 299 (21)	On	Yes
Increasing To 384 (27)	Off	No

[1] – On Pickup, check between Red/Green wire and Black/Yellow wire terminals. On 4Runner, check between Yellow/Green wire and White/Black wire terminals.

[2] – On Pickup, low side pressure decreases to 38 psi (2.7 kg/cm²).

[3] – On Pickup, low side pressure increases to 42 psi (3.0 kg/cm²).

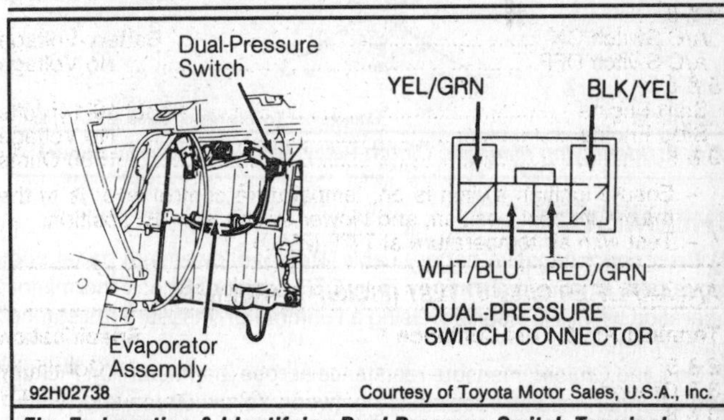
Dual-Pressure Switch
YEL/GRN
BLK/YEL
WHT/BLU
RED/GRN
DUAL-PRESSURE SWITCH CONNECTOR
Evaporator Assembly
92H02738
Courtesy of Toyota Motor Sales, U.S.A., Inc.

Fig. 7: Locating & Identifying Dual-Pressure Switch Terminals (Pickup)

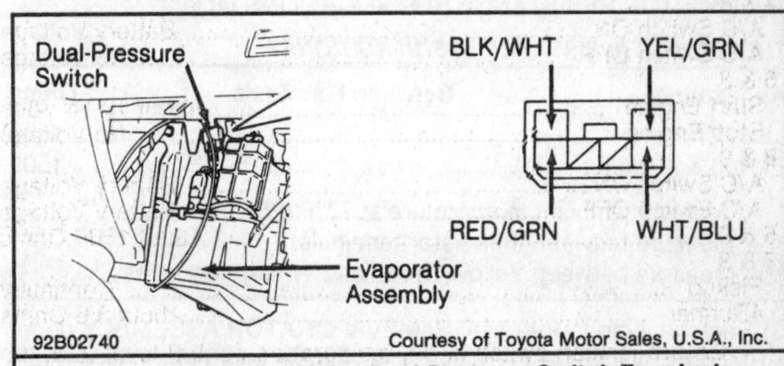
Dual-Pressure Switch
BLK/WHT
YEL/GRN
RED/GRN
WHT/BLU
Evaporator Assembly
92B02740
Courtesy of Toyota Motor Sales, U.S.A., Inc.

Fig. 8: Locating & Identifying Dual-Pressure Switch Terminals (4Runner)

1993 MANUAL A/C-HEATER SYSTEMS
Land Cruiser, Pickup & 4Runner (Cont.)

HIGH-PRESSURE SWITCH

4Runner – 1) Pressure switch is located near receiver-drier. Disconnect negative battery cable. Install manifold gauge set, and check pressure readings. Disconnect pressure switch connector. Using an ohmmeter, check high-pressure switch operation. Check continuity between connector terminals as pressure changes.

2) Ensure continuity does not exist between switch connector terminals when refrigerant pressure reaches 220 psi (15.5 kg/cm²). When high-pressure switch opens, current to magnetic clutch will be interrupted. Ensure continuity exists when high-side pressure drops to 178 psi (12.5 kg/cm²). When high-pressure switch closes, current to magnetic clutch will be restored. If switch does not function as specified, replace switch.

MAGNETIC CLUTCH

Land Cruiser – Inspect pressure plate and rotor for signs of oil contamination. Check clutch bearing for noisy operation and grease leakage. Connect battery voltage to magnetic clutch connector. Connect negative battery lead to ground. Ensure magnetic clutch is energized. If magnetic clutch is not energized, replace magnetic clutch.

Pickup & 4Runner – Inspect pressure plate and rotor for signs of oil contamination. Check clutch bearing for noisy operation and grease leakage. Using an ohmmeter, measure resistance of stator coil between clutch and ground. Resistance should be 3.4-3.8 ohms at 68°F (20°C). If reading is not within specification, replace coil. Apply battery voltage to magnetic clutch connector terminal. Ensure magnetic clutch is energized. If magnetic clutch is not energized, replace stator coil.

MAGNETIC CLUTCH RELAY

Land Cruiser – Remove magnetic clutch relay. Using ohmmeter, check continuity between terminals No. 1 and 2. *See Fig. 9.* Ensure continuity exists. Apply battery voltage between terminals No. 1 and 2. Ensure continuity exists between terminals No. 3 and 4. If continuity is not as specified, replace relay.

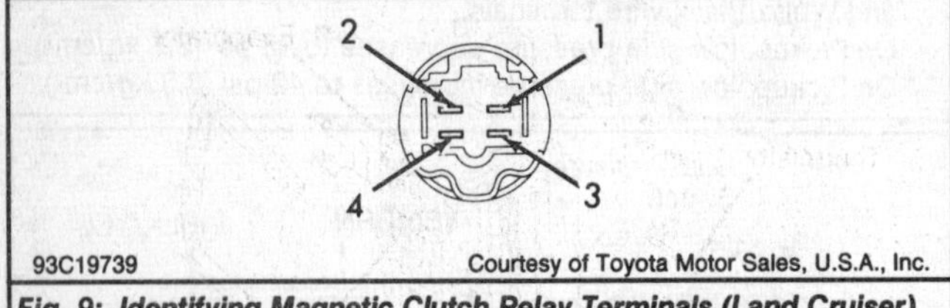
2
1
4
3
93C19739
Courtesy of Toyota Motor Sales, U.S.A., Inc.

Fig. 9: Identifying Magnetic Clutch Relay Terminals (Land Cruiser)

THERMISTOR

1) Disconnect negative battery cable. Remove lower trim panel and glove box. Ensure ignition key is in OFF position. Check thermistor operation while it is installed. Using an ohmmeter, measure resistance of thermistor.

2) On Land Cruiser, measure resistance across thermistor. On Pickup and 4Runner, measure resistance between Yellow/Green and White/Blue wires. On all models, if resistance is not within specification, replace thermistor. If resistance is as specified, go to next step. See THERMISTOR RESISTANCE SPECIFICATIONS table.

THERMISTOR RESISTANCE SPECIFICATIONS

Application	Between Terminals	[1] Ohms
Land Cruiser	[2]	1500
Pickup & 4Runner	[3]	1500

[1] – Test with ambient temperature at 77°F (25°C)
[2] – Measure between thermistor terminals.
[3] – Measure between Yellow/Green and White/Blue wires.

3) Remove evaporator case. See EVAPORATOR ASSEMBLY under REMOVAL & INSTALLATION. Disassemble evaporator case, and remove thermistor. Check thermistor operation. Submerge thermistor at least 3.94" deep in cold water. *See Fig. 10.* Place thermometer in water.

4) Measure resistance of thermistor at various temperatures. Use ice or hot water to vary water temperature. If readings are not within specification, replace thermistor. See appropriate THERMISTOR RESISTANCE VALUES table.

THERMISTOR RESISTANCE VALUES (LAND CRUISER)

Ambient Temperature °F (°C)	Ohms
41 (5)	3500-4100
39 (4)	3800-4300
37 (3)	3900-4500
36 (2)	4100-4800
34 (1)	4300-4900
32 (0)	4500-5200
30 (–1)	4700-5400

THERMISTOR RESISTANCE VALUES (PICKUP & 4RUNNER)

Ambient Temperature °F (°C)	Ohms
77 (25)	1400-1700
68 (20)	1700-2100
59 (15)	2200-2600
50 (10)	2900-3300
41 (5)	3700-4200
32 (0)	4600-5100

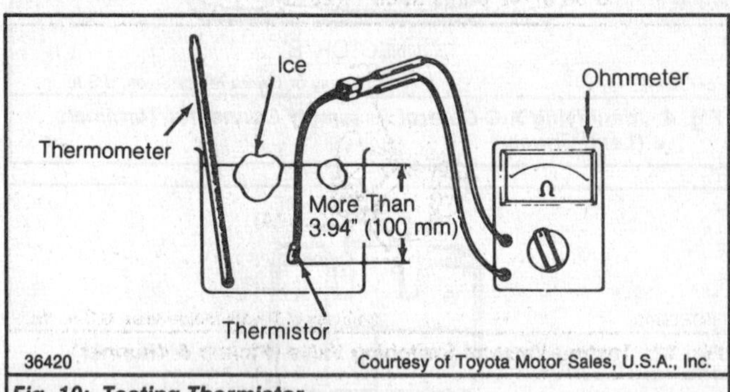
Ice
Ohmmeter
Thermometer
More Than
3.94" (100 mm)
Thermistor
36420
Courtesy of Toyota Motor Sales, U.S.A., Inc.

Fig. 10: Testing Thermistor

TRIPLE-PRESSURE SWITCH

Land Cruiser – Install manifold gauge set. Disconnect triple-pressure switch connector. Run engine at 2000 RPM and observe gauge reading. Using an ohmmeter, check for continuity between high/low pressure switch terminals. See HIGH/LOW PRESSURE SWITCH SPECIFICATIONS table. Check continuity between medium-pressure switch terminals. See MEDIUM-PRESSURE SWITCH SPECIFICATIONS table. *See Fig. 11.*

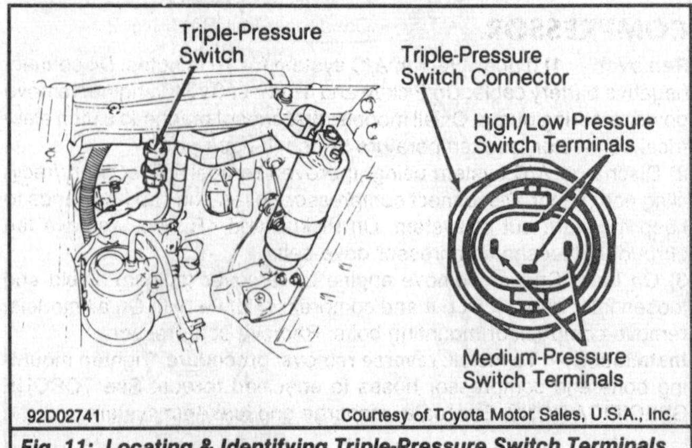
Triple-Pressure
Switch
Triple-Pressure
Switch Connector
High/Low Pressure
Switch Terminals
Medium-Pressure
Switch Terminals
92D02741
Courtesy of Toyota Motor Sales, U.S.A., Inc.

Fig. 11: Locating & Identifying Triple-Pressure Switch Terminals (Land Cruiser)

HIGH/LOW PRESSURE SWITCH SPECIFICATIONS

Pressure psi (kg/cm²)	System Operation	Continuity
Increasing To 30 (2.1)	Off	No
Decreasing To 33 (2.3)	On	Yes
Decreasing To 327 (23)	On	Yes
Increasing To 412 (29)	Off	No

MEDIUM-PRESSURE SWITCH SPECIFICATIONS

Pressure psi (kg/cm²)	System Operation	Continuity
Increasing To 156 (11.0)	On	Yes
Decreasing To 192 (13.4)	Off	No

VACUUM SWITCHING VALVE (VSV)

Pickup & 4Runner - 1) Remove VSV. Connect battery voltage to VSV terminals. Blow into fitting "A". *See Fig. 12.* Ensure air comes out of fitting "B" but does not come out of fitting "C".

2) Disconnect battery. Blow into fitting "B". Ensure air comes out of fitting "C" and does not come out of fitting "A".

3) Using an ohmmeter, ensure continuity does not exist between each terminal and VSV body. Measure resistance at both terminals. Resistance should be 37-42 ohms at 68°F (20°C).

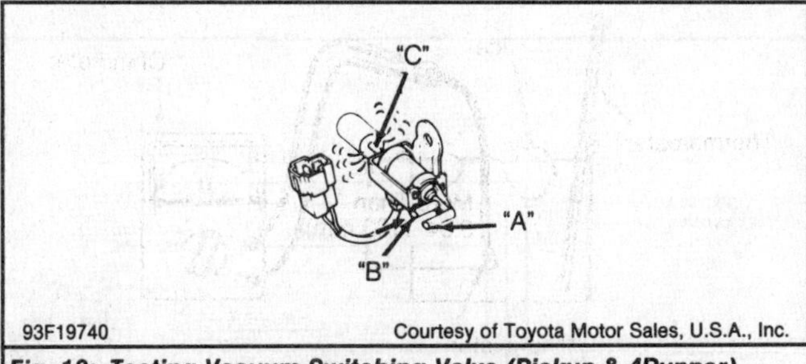
"C"
"A"
"B"
93F19740
Courtesy of Toyota Motor Sales, U.S.A., Inc.

Fig. 12: Testing Vacuum Switching Valve (Pickup & 4Runner)

REMOVAL & INSTALLATION

WARNING: To avoid injury from accidental air bag deployment, read and carefully follow all SERVICE PRECAUTIONS and DISABLING & ACTIVATING AIR BAG SYSTEM procedures in AIR BAG SYSTEM SAFETY article in GENERAL SERVICING.

NOTE: For removal and installation procedures of heater components, see appropriate HEATER SYSTEMS article.

COMPRESSOR

Removal - 1) If possible, run A/C system for 10 minutes. Disconnect negative battery cable. On Pickup and 4Runner 3VZ-E engine, remove power steering pump. On all models, disconnect magnetic clutch electrical connector, and temperature switch (if equipped).

2) Discharge A/C system using approved refrigerant recovery/recycling equipment. Disconnect compressor hoses and cap hose ends to keep moisture out of system. On Pickup and 4Runner, remove fan shroud and loosen compressor drive belt.

3) On Land Cruiser, remove engine undercover (splash) shield and loosen idler pulley lock nut and compressor drive belt. On all models, remove compressor mounting bolts. Remove compressor.

Installation - To install, reverse removal procedure. Tighten mounting bolts and compressor hoses to specified torque. See TORQUE SPECIFICATIONS. Evacuate, recharge and leak test system.

CONDENSER

Removal - 1) Discharge A/C system using approved refrigerant recovery/recycling equipment. Disconnect negative battery cable. On Pickup and 4Runner, remove clearance lights, grille, and hood lock brace. On Pickup, remove radiator fan and condenser fan.

2) On all models, disconnect A/C lines from condenser. Plug all openings. On 4Runner, remove condenser fan motor. Remove mounting bolts and condenser.

Installation - To install, reverse removal procedure. Tighten mounting bolts and condenser hoses to specified torque. See TORQUE SPECIFICATIONS. If installing new condenser, add 1.4-1.7 ounces of refrigerant oil before installing. Evacuate, recharge and leak test system.

EVAPORATOR ASSEMBLY

Removal - 1) Disconnect negative battery cable. Discharge A/C system using approved refrigerant recovery/recycling equipment. Disconnect inlet lines, outlet lines and grommets from evaporator. Plug openings.

2) Disconnect electrical leads from evaporator. Remove glove box and lower trim panel. Remove side air duct. Remove nuts, bolts and evaporator assembly.

Disassembly - 1) Release spring clips holding covers together. Remove any screws at case joints. Separate upper and lower cases from evaporator core. Remove thermistor together with holder. *See Fig. 13.*

2) Remove heat insulator from outlet tube. Remove high-side (inlet) line from expansion valve, and remove expansion valve. Remove pressure switch (if equipped).

Reassembly & Installation - To reassemble and install evaporator assembly, reverse disassembly and removal procedures. If installing new evaporator core, add 1.4-1.7 ounces of refrigerant oil to core before installing. Evacuate, recharge and leak test system.

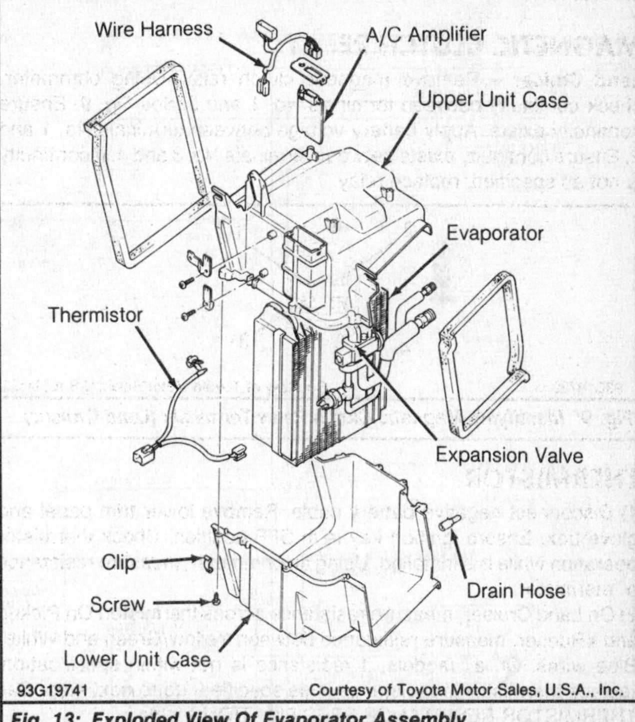
Wire Harness
A/C Amplifier
Upper Unit Case
Evaporator
Thermistor
Expansion Valve
Clip
Drain Hose
Screw
Lower Unit Case
93G19741
Courtesy of Toyota Motor Sales, U.S.A., Inc.

Fig. 13: Exploded View Of Evaporator Assembly (4Runner Shown; Land Cruiser & Pickup Are Similar)

EXPANSION VALVE

Removal & Installation - Evaporator must be removed in order to remove expansion valve. See EVAPORATOR ASSEMBLY under REMOVAL & INSTALLATION.

RECEIVER-DRIER

Removal - Discharge A/C system using approved refrigerant recovery/recycling equipment. Disconnect negative battery cable. Remove reserve tank, clearance lights and front grille. Remove A/C lines from

1993 MANUAL A/C-HEATER SYSTEMS
Land Cruiser, Pickup & 4Runner (Cont.)

receiver-drier. Plug all openings. Remove mounting bolts and receiver-drier.

Installation – To install, reverse removal procedure. Add 0.7 ounce of refrigerant oil if installing a new receiver-drier. Evacuate, recharge and leak test system.

TORQUE SPECIFICATIONS

TORQUE SPECIFICATIONS

Application	Ft. Lbs. (N.m)
A/C Compressor Bolts	18 (25)
A/C Compressor Belt	
Idler Pulley Bolt	
Land Cruiser & Pickup	27 (37)
4Runner	29 (39)
Compressor Bracket Bolts	
Land Cruiser	27 (37)
Pickup & 4Runner	
M/T	27 (37)
A/T	35 (47)
Compressor Stay	18 (25)
Compressor-To-Bracket Bolts	18 (25)
Condenser Bolts	
Land Cruiser & Pickup	10 (13)
4Runner	13 (18)

TORQUE SPECIFICATIONS (Cont.)

Application	Ft. Lbs. (N.m)
Refrigerant Hoses	
Compressor	18 (25)
Condenser	
Land Cruiser	10 (13)
Pickup	
High Pressure (Discharge)	14 (19)
Low Pressure (Suction)	[1]
4Runner	
Condenser-To-Receiver	[1]
Condenser-To-Tube Nut	7 (10)
High Pressure Discharge	10 (13)
Low Pressure (Suction)	10 (13)
Evaporator	
Land Cruiser	[1]
Pickup	
High Pressure (Discharge)	10 (13)
Low Pressure (Suction)	24 (32)
4Runner	10 (13)
Receiver-Drier	[1]
	INCH Lbs. (N.m)
Dual-Pressure Switch Bolt	89 (10)
Expansion Valve (Fittings)	48 (5.4)
Receiver-Drier Bolt/Nut	48 (5.4)

[1] – Torque specification is 48 INCH lbs. (5.4 N.m)

WIRING DIAGRAMS

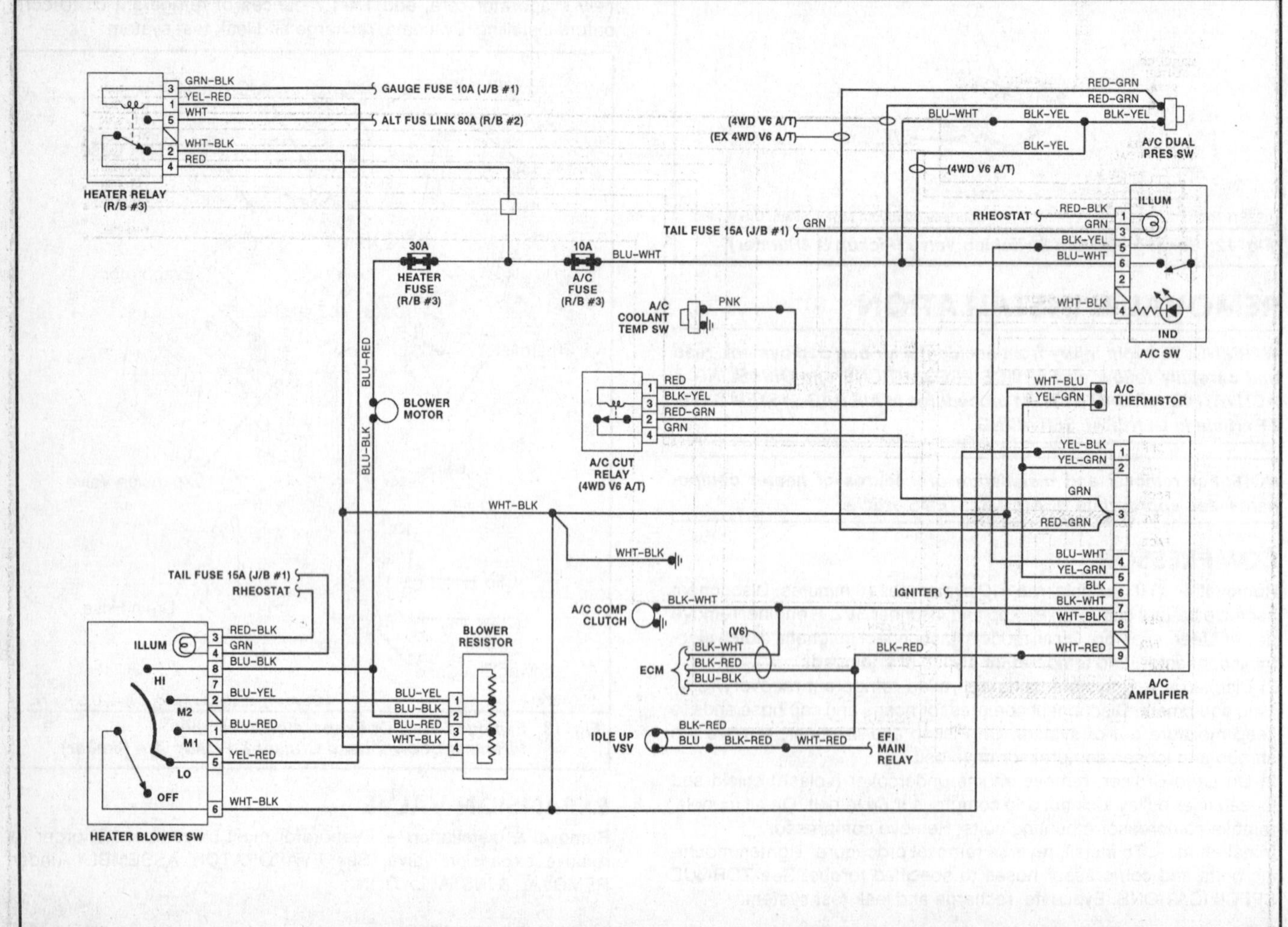
HEATER RELAY (R/B #3)
GRN-BLK
YEL-RED
WHT
WHT-BLK
RED
GAUGE FUSE 10A (J/B #1)
ALT FUS LINK 80A (R/B #2)
30A HEATER FUSE (R/B #3)
10A A/C FUSE (R/B #3)
BLU-WHT
BLU-RED
BLU-BLK
BLOWER MOTOR
WHT-BLK
(4WD V6 A/T)
(EX 4WD V6 A/T)
RED-GRN
BLK-YEL
A/C DUAL PRES SW
TAIL FUSE 15A (J/B #1)
RHEOSTAT
RED-BLK
GRN
ILLUM
IND
A/C SW
A/C COOLANT TEMP SW
PNK
A/C CUT RELAY (4WD V6 A/T)
WHT-BLU
YEL-GRN
A/C THERMISTOR
YEL-BLK
IGNITER
BLK
BLK-WHT
WHT-RED
A/C AMPLIFIER
A/C COMP CLUTCH
(V6)
ECM
BLK-RED
BLU-BLK
IDLE UP VSV
BLU
EFI MAIN RELAY
BLOWER RESISTOR
BLU-YEL
YEL-RED
HI
M2
M1
LO
OFF
HEATER BLOWER SW
94J10784

Fig. 14: Manual A/C-Heater System Wiring Diagram (Pickup)

1993 MANUAL A/C-HEATER SYSTEMS
Land Cruiser, Pickup & 4Runner (Cont.)

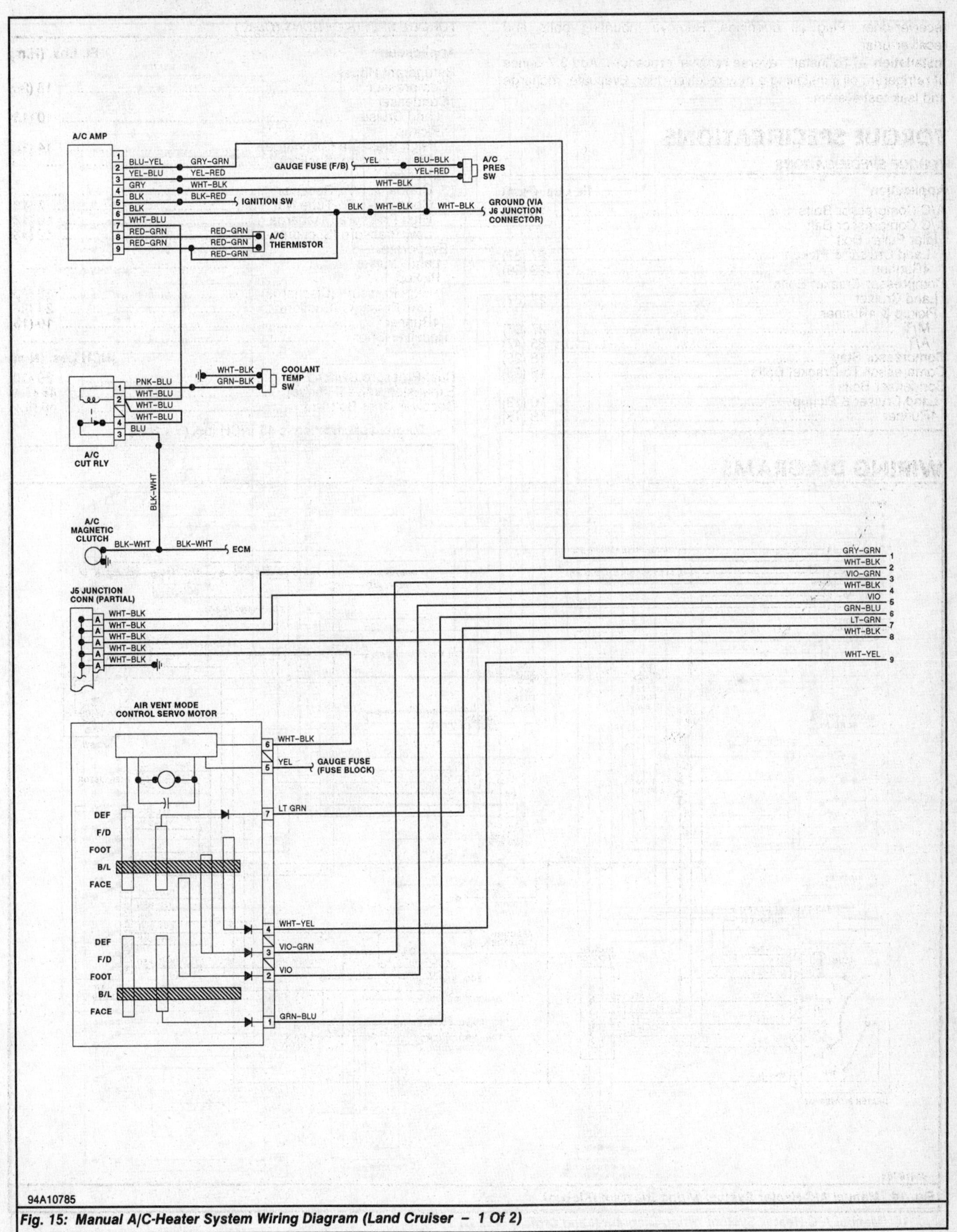
A/C AMP
BLU-YEL
YEL-BLU
GRY
BLK
BLK
WHT-BLU
RED-GRN
RED-GRN
GRY-GRN
YEL-RED
WHT-BLK
BLK-RED
IGNITION SW
GAUGE FUSE (F/B)
YEL
BLU-BLK
YEL-RED
A/C PRES SW
BLK
WHT-BLK
GROUND (VIA J6 JUNCTION CONNECTOR)
RED-GRN
A/C THERMISTOR
COOLANT TEMP SW
PNK-BLU
GRN-BLK
BLU
A/C CUT RLY
BLK-WHT
A/C MAGNETIC CLUTCH
ECM
J5 JUNCTION CONN (PARTIAL)
AIR VENT MODE CONTROL SERVO MOTOR
GAUGE FUSE (FUSE BLOCK)
LT GRN
DEF
F/D
FOOT
B/L
FACE
WHT-YEL
VIO-GRN
VIO
GRN-BLU
GRY-GRN
LT-GRN
94A10785

Fig. 15: Manual A/C-Heater System Wiring Diagram (Land Cruiser – 1 Of 2)

1993 MANUAL A/C-HEATER SYSTEMS
Land Cruiser, Pickup & 4Runner (Cont.)

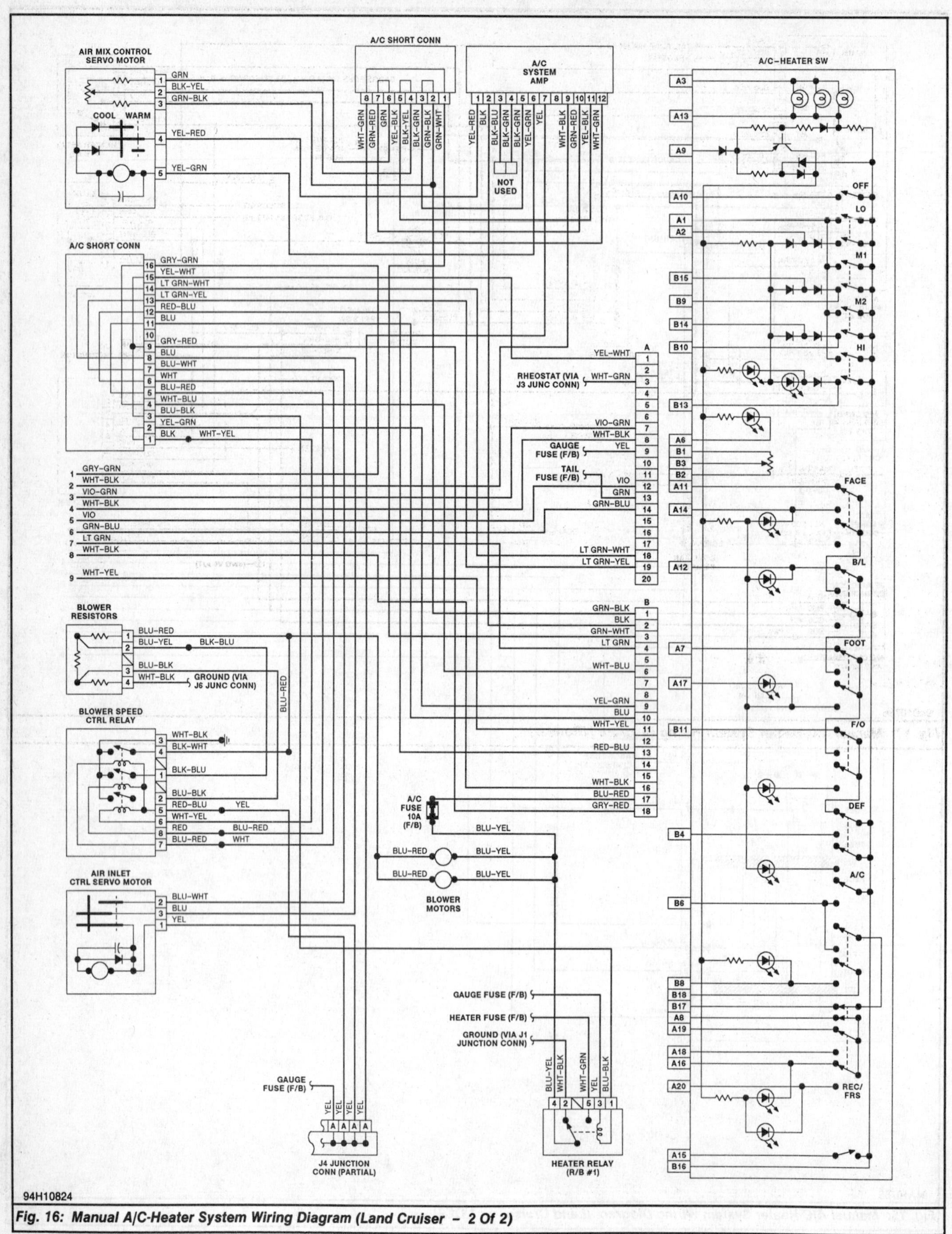
A/C SHORT CONN
AIR MIX CONTROL SERVO MOTOR
A/C SYSTEM AMP
A/C-HEATER SW
COOL
WARM
NOT USED
A/C SHORT CONN
RHEOSTAT (VIA J3 JUNC CONN)
GAUGE FUSE (F/B)
TAIL FUSE (F/B)
BLOWER RESISTORS
GROUND (VIA J6 JUNC CONN)
BLOWER SPEED CTRL RELAY
A/C FUSE 10A (F/B)
BLOWER MOTORS
AIR INLET CTRL SERVO MOTOR
GAUGE FUSE (F/B)
HEATER FUSE (F/B)
GROUND (VIA J1 JUNCTION CONN)
J4 JUNCTION CONN (PARTIAL)
HEATER RELAY (R/B #1)
OFF
LO
M1
M2
HI
FACE
B/L
FOOT
F/O
DEF
A/C
REC/FRS
94H10824

Fig. 16: Manual A/C-Heater System Wiring Diagram (Land Cruiser – 2 Of 2)

1993 MANUAL A/C-HEATER SYSTEMS
Land Cruiser, Pickup & 4Runner (Cont.)

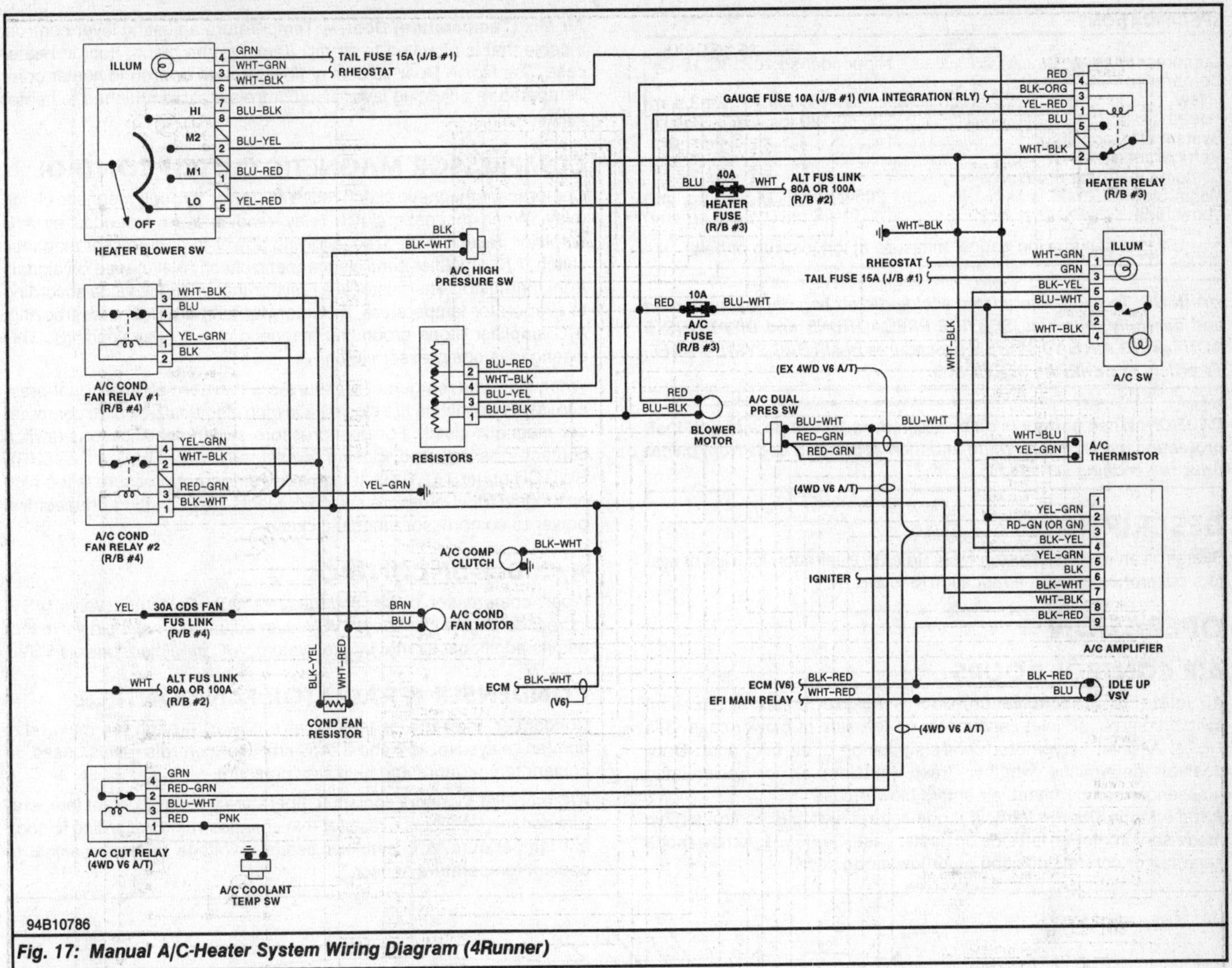
ILLUM
GRN
WHT-GRN
WHT-BLK
TAIL FUSE 15A (J/B #1)
RHEOSTAT
HI
M2
M1
LO
OFF
BLU-BLK
BLU-YEL
BLU-RED
YEL-RED
HEATER BLOWER SW
BLK
BLK-WHT
A/C HIGH PRESSURE SW
YEL-GRN
A/C COND FAN RELAY #1 (R/B #4)
RESISTORS
RED-GRN
A/C COND FAN RELAY #2 (R/B #4)
A/C COMP CLUTCH
YEL
30A CDS FAN FUS LINK (R/B #4)
BRN
BLU
A/C COND FAN MOTOR
WHT
ALT FUS LINK 80A OR 100A (R/B #2)
BLK-YEL
WHT-RED
COND FAN RESISTOR
ECM
(V6)
A/C CUT RELAY (4WD V6 A/T)
PNK
A/C COOLANT TEMP SW
94B10786
GAUGE FUSE 10A (J/B #1) (VIA INTEGRATION RLY)
RED
BLK-ORG
YEL-RED
HEATER RELAY (R/B #3)
40A
HEATER FUSE (R/B #3)
10A
A/C FUSE (R/B #3)
BLU-WHT
A/C SW
(EX 4WD V6 A/T)
BLOWER MOTOR
A/C DUAL PRES SW
WHT-BLU
A/C THERMISTOR
(4WD V6 A/T)
RD-GN (OR GN)
IGNITER
A/C AMPLIFIER
BLK-RED
ECM (V6)
EFI MAIN RELAY
IDLE UP VSV

Fig. 17: Manual A/C-Heater System Wiring Diagram (4Runner)

1993 MANUAL A/C-HEATER SYSTEMS
MR2

SPECIFICATIONS

Compressor Type .... Nippondenso 10P13C 10-Cyl.
Compressor Belt Tension [1]
New .... 135-185 lbs. (61.2-83.9 kg)
Used .... 80-120 lbs. (36.3-54.4 kg)
System Oil Capacity .... 3.4-4.1 ozs.
Refrigerant (R-12) Capacity .... 28-32 ozs.
System Operating Pressures
High Side .... 206-213 psi (14.5-15 kg/cm²)
Low Side .... 21-28 psi (1.5-2.0 kg/cm²)

[1] – Using a belt tension gauge, measure at longest run of belt.

WARNING: To avoid injury from accidental air bag deployment, read and carefully follow all SERVICE PRECAUTIONS and DISABLING & ACTIVATING AIR BAG SYSTEM procedures in AIR BAG SYSTEM SAFETY article in GENERAL SERVICING.

CAUTION: When battery is disconnected, radio will go into anti-theft protection mode. Obtain radio anti-theft protection code from owner prior to servicing vehicle.

DESCRIPTION

System is an expansion valve type. Refer to illustration for a list of system components and their location. *See Fig. 1.*

OPERATION

AIR CONTROL DOORS

Air Inlet (Fresh/Recirculation) Door – Air inlet (fresh/recirculation) switch controls air inlet servomotor on left side of blower case. *See Fig. 4*. Air inlet servomotor controls position of air inlet door. Door position determines whether fresh (outside) air or recirculated (passenger compartment) air enters blower case.

Airflow Mode Door – Airflow mode control switches control airflow mode servomotor on left side on heater case. *See Fig. 4*. Airflow mode servomotor controls position of airflow mode door.

Air Mix (Temperature) Door – Temperature adjusting lever controls a cable that is attached to air mix (temperature blend) door in heater case. *See Fig. 4.* Door adjusts airflow through or around heater core. Temperature adjusting lever also controls a cable attached to heater valve.

COMPRESSOR MAGNETIC CLUTCH CONTROL

Compressor magnetic clutch receives power through magnetic clutch relay. When magnetic clutch relay windings are grounded by A/C amplifier, relay is energized, allowing power to compressor magnetic clutch. A/C amplifier controls magnetic clutch relay based on signals from thermistor. Thermistor is a resistor that changes value according to evaporator temperature. If evaporator temperature nears freezing, A/C amplifier stops grounding magnetic clutch relay windings. This disengages compressor clutch.

When high side refrigerant pressure is within normal range, dual-pressure switch contacts are closed, allowing electrical power to compressor magnetic clutch. For dual-pressure switch specifications (switch contact opening and closing pressures), see DUAL-PRESSURE SWITCH under TESTING. If high side refrigerant pressure is too high or too low, dual-pressure switch contacts open, cutting off electrical power to compressor magnetic clutch.

A/C IDLE-UP CONTROL

When compressor clutch engages, Vacuum Switching Valve (VSV) increases engine idle speed. VSV is an adjustable solenoid valve that admits additional air into intake system. A/C amplifier controls VSV.

CONDENSER & RADIATOR FAN CONTROL

Condenser and radiator fans receive power through fan main relay and fan relays No. 1, 2 and 3. A/C amplifier controls relays based on coolant temperature and high side pressure.

A/C amplifier monitors coolant temperature through coolant temperature sensor. Sensor is a resistor that changes value according to coolant temperature. A/C amplifier sends a voltage reference signal to coolant temperature sensor.

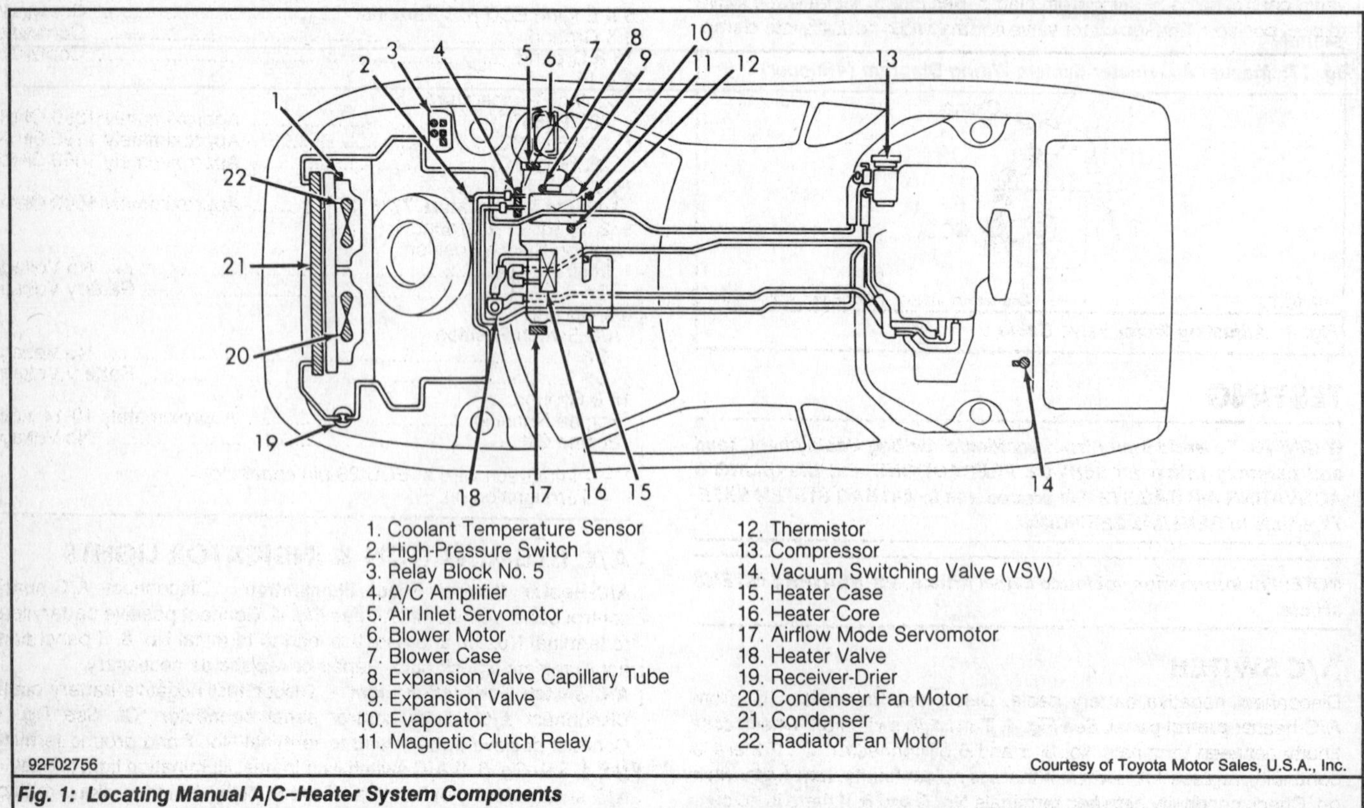
1
2
3
4
5
6
7
8
9
10
11
12
13
14
15
16
17
18
19
20
21
22
1. Coolant Temperature Sensor
2. High-Pressure Switch
3. Relay Block No. 5
4. A/C Amplifier
5. Air Inlet Servomotor
6. Blower Motor
7. Blower Case
8. Expansion Valve Capillary Tube
9. Expansion Valve
10. Evaporator
11. Magnetic Clutch Relay
12. Thermistor
13. Compressor
14. Vacuum Switching Valve (VSV)
15. Heater Case
16. Heater Core
17. Airflow Mode Servomotor
18. Heater Valve
19. Receiver-Drier
20. Condenser Fan Motor
21. Condenser
22. Radiator Fan Motor
92F02756
Courtesy of Toyota Motor Sales, U.S.A., Inc.

Fig. 1: Locating Manual A/C–Heater System Components

1993 MANUAL A/C-HEATER SYSTEMS MR2 (Cont.)

A/C amplifier monitors high side pressure through high-pressure switch. If refrigerant pressure exceeds 192 psi (13.5 kg/cm²), high-pressure switch contacts close. When refrigerant pressure decreases to 156 psi (11 kg/cm²), high-pressure switch contacts open.

ADJUSTMENTS

AIR MIX DAMPER CONTROL CABLE

Move temperature adjusting lever to cool position. Release air mix damper control cable housing from clamp. *See Fig. 2.* Move air mix door to cool position. Engage air mix control cable housing into clamp.

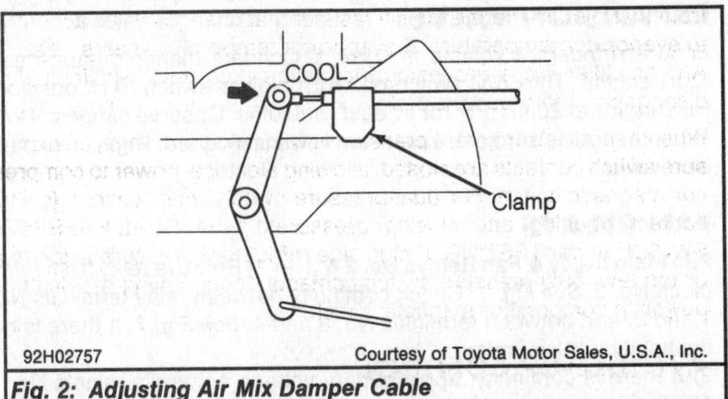
COOL
Clamp
92H02757
Courtesy of Toyota Motor Sales, U.S.A., Inc.

Fig. 2: Adjusting Air Mix Damper Cable

VACUUM SWITCHING VALVE (VSV) IDLE SPEED

Warm engine. Shift to Neutral position. Turn A/C on. Turn blower switch to high speed. Fully open driver-side window. With compressor clutch engaged, if engine idles at 900-1000 RPM, idle speed is correct. With compressor clutch engaged, if engine does not idle at 900-1000 RPM, turn VSV idle speed adjusting screw until idle is as specified. *See Fig. 12.* DO NOT force adjusting screw while turning.

WATER VALVE CONTROL CABLE

Move temperature adjusting lever to cool position. Release water valve control cable housing from clamp. *See Fig. 3.* Move water valve to cool position. Engage water valve control cable housing into clamp.

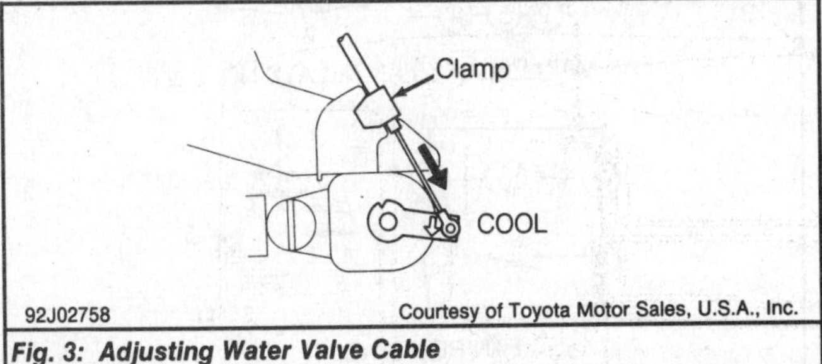
Clamp
COOL
92J02758
Courtesy of Toyota Motor Sales, U.S.A., Inc.

Fig. 3: Adjusting Water Valve Cable

TESTING

WARNING: To avoid injury from accidental air bag deployment, read and carefully follow all SERVICE PRECAUTIONS and DISABLING & ACTIVATING AIR BAG SYSTEM procedures in AIR BAG SYSTEM SAFETY article in GENERAL SERVICING.

NOTE: For information not found in this article, see HEATER SYSTEMS article.

A/C SWITCH

Disconnect negative battery cable. Disconnect connector "C" from A/C-heater control panel. *See Fig. 4.* Turn A/C switch off. Check continuity between terminals No. 3, 5 and 6 of connector "C". If there is continuity, replace A/C switch. If there is no continuity, turn A/C switch on. Check continuity between terminals No. 5 and 6. If there is no continuity, replace A/C switch. If there is continuity, A/C switch is okay.

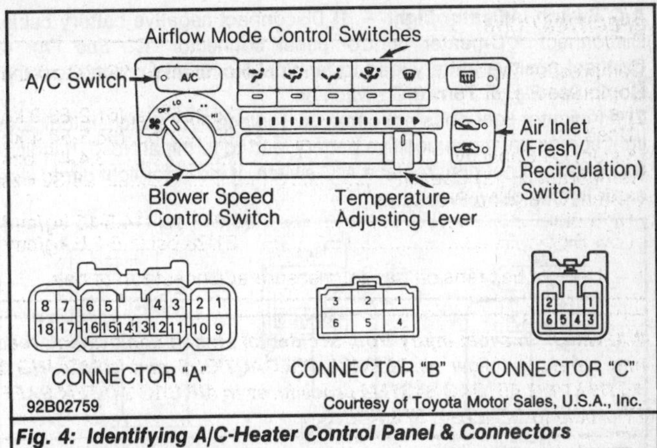
Airflow Mode Control Switches
A/C Switch
A/C
Air Inlet (Fresh/ Recirculation) Switch
Blower Speed Control Switch
Temperature Adjusting Lever
8 7 6 5 4 3 2 1
18 17 16 15 14 13 12 11 10 9
3 2 1
6 5 4
2 1
6 5 4 3
CONNECTOR "A"
CONNECTOR "B"
CONNECTOR "C"
92B02759
Courtesy of Toyota Motor Sales, U.S.A., Inc.

Fig. 4: Identifying A/C-Heater Control Panel & Connectors

A/C AMPLIFIER CIRCUITS

Disconnect A/C amplifier connector. Set temperature control lever to maximum cool position, and blower fan speed switch to HI position. Check continuity, resistance and voltage at harness side of A/C amplifier connector. *See Fig. 5.* Ensure circuits test as specified in A/C AMPLIFIER CIRCUIT TEST table. Turn ignition off when checking continuity and resistance. If circuit is faulty, repair as necessary.

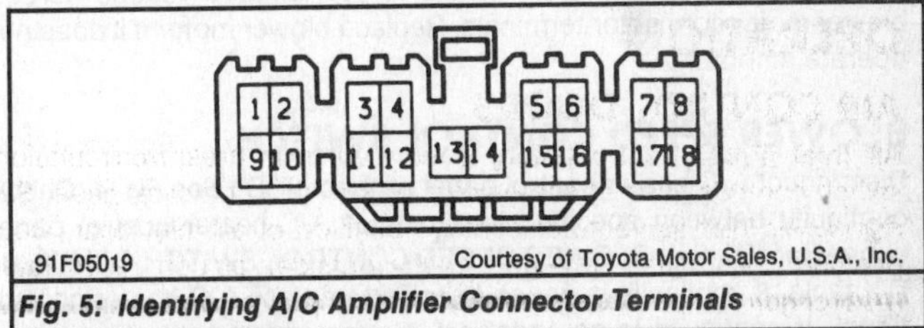
1 2 3 4 5 6 7 8
9 10 11 12 13 14 15 16 17 18
91F05019
Courtesy of Toyota Motor Sales, U.S.A., Inc.

Fig. 5: Identifying A/C Amplifier Connector Terminals

A/C AMPLIFIER CIRCUIT TEST

Terminals & Test Condition	Specification
8 & Engine ECU A/C Terminal [1]	Continuity
3 & Ground	Continuity
13 & Ground	Continuity
9 & 15	
Coolant Temperature	
185°F (85°C)	Approximately 1350 Ohms
194°F (90°C)	Approximately 1190 Ohms
203°F (95°C)	Approximately 1050 Ohms
14 & 17	
Ambient Temperature 77°F (25°C)	Approximately 1500 Ohms
1, 2, 7, 10, 11 & Ground	
Ignition Switch Position	
Lock Or ACC	No Voltage
On	Battery Voltage
6 & Ground [2]	
A/C Switch Position	
Off	No Voltage
On	Battery Voltage
18 & Ground	
Engine Running	Approximately 10-14 Volts
Engine Off	No Voltage

[1] – Pink/Green wire at ECU 26-pin connector.
[2] – Turn ignition on.

A/C ILLUMINATION & INDICATOR LIGHTS

A/C-Heater Control Panel Illumination – Disconnect A/C-heater control panel connector "A". *See Fig. 4.* Connect positive battery lead to terminal No. 18, and negative lead to terminal No. 8. If panel does not illuminate, check bulb. Repair or replace as necessary.

A/C Switch Illumination Light – Disconnect negative battery cable. Disconnect A/C-heater control panel connector "C". *See Fig. 4.* Connect positive battery lead to terminal No. 1 and ground terminal No. 4. *See Fig. 6.* If A/C switch illuminates, illumination light is okay. If A/C switch does not illuminate, check bulb. If bulb is okay, replace A/C switch.

1993 MANUAL A/C-HEATER SYSTEMS
MR2 (Cont.)

A/C Switch Indicator Light – 1) Disconnect negative battery cable. Disconnect A/C-heater control panel connector "C". *See Fig. 4.* Connect positive battery lead to terminal No. 5, and ground terminal No. 2. *See Fig. 6.* Turn A/C switch on.

2) If indicator light does not come on, replace A/C switch. If indicator light comes on, move positive battery lead to terminal No. 3. If indicator light does not dim, replace A/C switch. If indicator light dims, indicator light is okay.

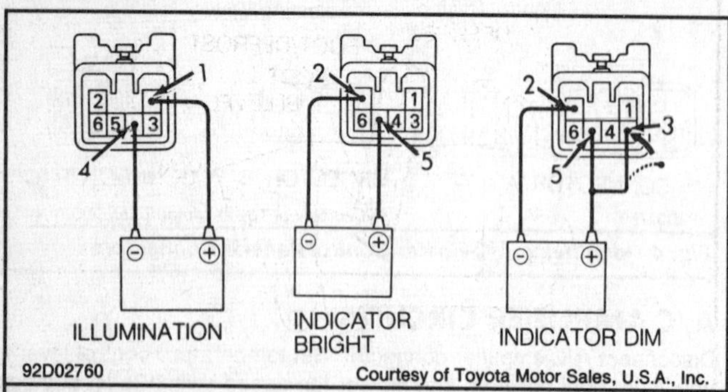
ILLUMINATION
INDICATOR BRIGHT
INDICATOR DIM
92D02760
Courtesy of Toyota Motor Sales, U.S.A., Inc.

Fig. 6: Testing A/C Switch Illumination & Indicator Lights

BLOWER MOTOR

Disconnect blower motor connector. Apply battery voltage across blower motor connector terminals. Replace blower motor if it does not operate smoothly.

BLOWER SPEED CONTROL SWITCH

Disconnect A/C-heater control panel connector "B". *See Fig. 4.* Check continuity between specified terminals of A/C-heater control panel connector "B". See BLOWER SPEED CONTROL SWITCH CONTINUITY table. If continuity is not as specified, replace A/C-heater control panel. If continuity is as specified, blower speed control switch is okay.

BLOWER SPEED CONTROL SWITCH CONTINUITY

Switch Position	Continuity Between Terminals
OFF	No Continuity
LO	4 & 6
(■)	1, 4 & 6
(■ ■)	2, 4 & 6
HI	3, 4 & 6

CONDENSER FAN MOTOR

Disconnect condenser fan motor connector. Apply battery voltage across condenser fan motor connector terminals. Replace condenser fan motor if it does not operate.

COOLANT TEMPERATURE SENSOR

Disconnect coolant temperature sensor connector. Measure resistance across sensor connector terminals. See COOLANT TEMPERATURE SENSOR RESISTANCE SPECIFICATIONS table. If resistance is not as specified, replace coolant temperature sensor.

COOLANT TEMPERATURE SENSOR RESISTANCE SPECIFICATIONS

Coolant Temperature °F (°C)	Ohms
185 (85)	Approximately 1350
194 (90)	Approximately 1190
203 (95)	Approximately 1050

DUAL-PRESSURE SWITCH

Remove dual-pressure switch connector, located behind glove box. Connect manifold gauge set. Start engine. Turn A/C on. Observe high side pressure readings. Check continuity across dual-pressure switch connector terminals. See DUAL-PRESSURE SWITCH SPECIFICATIONS table. If continuity is not as specified, replace dual-pressure switch. If continuity is as specified, dual-pressure switch is okay.

DUAL-PRESSURE SWITCH SPECIFICATIONS

Condition	Continuity
Pressure Increasing	
To 33 psi (2.4 kg/cm²)	Yes
To 412 psi (29 kg/cm²)	No
Pressure Decreasing	
To 30 psi (2.1 kg/cm²)	No
To 327 psi (23 kg/cm²)	Yes

EXPANSION VALVE

Ensure refrigerant volume is correct. Connect manifold gauge set. Start engine. Turn A/C switch on. Turn blower switch to HI position. Run engine at 2000 RPM for at least 5 minutes. Observe gauges. If low side pressure is zero psi, expansion valve is clogged. Replace expansion valve.

FAN RELAYS

Fan Main Relay & Fan Relays No. 2 & 3 – 1) Remove relay from relay block No. 5. *See Fig. 1.* Check continuity between relay terminals No. 1 and 2, and between terminals No. 3 and 4. *See Fig. 7.* If there is no continuity, replace relay.

2) If there is continuity, apply battery voltage across terminals No. 1 and 2. Check continuity between terminals No. 3 and 5. If there is continuity, relay is okay. If there is no continuity, replace relay.

Fan Relay No. 1 – Remove relay from relay block No. 5. *See Fig. 1.* Check continuity between relay terminals No. 3 and 5. *See Fig. 7.* If there is continuity, replace relay. If there is no continuity, apply battery voltage across terminals No. 1 and 2. Check continuity between terminals No. 3 and 5. If there is continuity, relay is okay. If there is no continuity, replace relay.

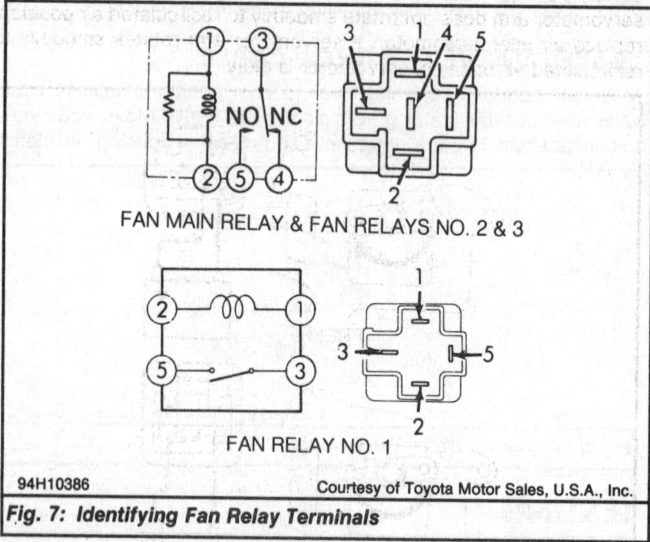
NO NC
FAN MAIN RELAY & FAN RELAYS NO. 2 & 3
FAN RELAY NO. 1
94H10386
Courtesy of Toyota Motor Sales, U.S.A., Inc.

Fig. 7: Identifying Fan Relay Terminals

HIGH-PRESSURE SWITCH

1) Remove high-pressure switch connector. *See Fig. 1.* Connect manifold gauge set. Start engine. Turn A/C on. Observe high side pressure readings.

2) Check continuity across high-pressure switch connector terminals. See HIGH-PRESSURE SWITCH SPECIFICATIONS table. If continuity is not as specified, replace high-pressure switch. If continuity is as specified, high-pressure switch is okay.

HIGH-PRESSURE SWITCH SPECIFICATIONS

Condition	Continuity
Pressure Increasing To 192 psi (13.5 kg/cm²)	Yes
Pressure Decreasing To 156 psi (11 kg/cm²)	No

MAGNETIC CLUTCH

Disconnect magnetic (compressor) clutch connector. Connect positive battery lead to magnetic clutch connector, and negative lead to ground. If clutch engages, magnetic clutch is okay. If clutch does not engage, check clutch air gap. If air gap is okay, replace magnetic clutch.

MAGNETIC CLUTCH RELAY

Remove magnetic (compressor) clutch relay. Check continuity between relay terminals No. 2 and 4. *See Fig. 8.* If there is continuity, replace relay. If there is no continuity, apply battery voltage across terminals No. 1 and 3. Check continuity between terminals No. 2 and 4. If there is continuity, relay is okay. If there is no continuity, replace relay.

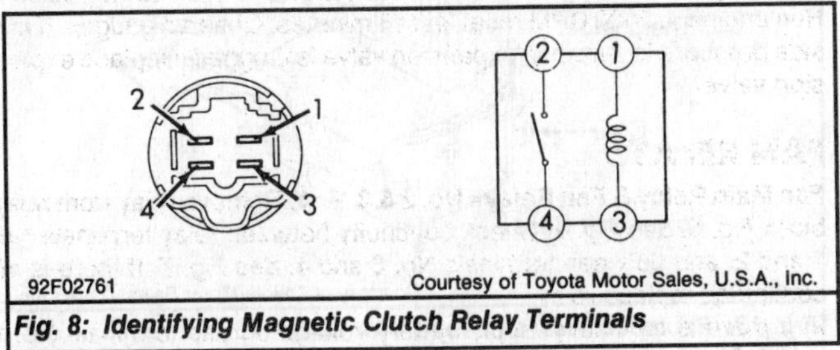
2
1
4
3
92F02761
Courtesy of Toyota Motor Sales, U.S.A., Inc.

Fig. 8: Identifying Magnetic Clutch Relay Terminals

SERVOMOTORS

Air Inlet Servomotor – 1) Disconnect air inlet servomotor connector. Connect positive battery lead to terminal No. 3, and ground terminal No. 4 of air inlet servomotor connector. *See Fig. 9.* If servomotor arm does not rotate smoothly to fresh air position, replace servomotor.
2) If servomotor arm rotates smoothly to fresh air position, connect battery positive lead to terminal No. 1, and ground terminal No. 4. If servomotor arm does not rotate smoothly to recirculated air position, replace air inlet servomotor. If servomotor arm rotates smoothly to recirculated air position, servomotor is okay.

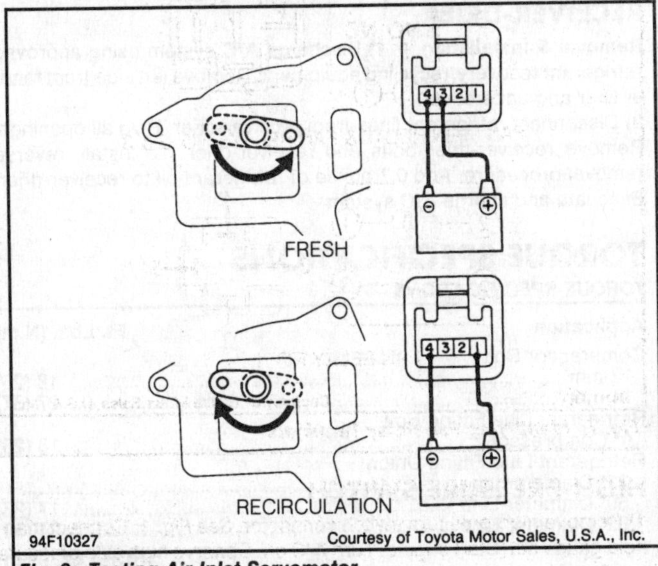
4 3 2 1
FRESH
4 3 2 1
RECIRCULATION
94F10327
Courtesy of Toyota Motor Sales, U.S.A., Inc.

Fig. 9: Testing Air Inlet Servomotor

Airflow Mode Servomotor – 1) Disconnect airflow mode servomotor connector. Connect positive battery lead to terminal No. 6, and ground terminal No. 7 of airflow mode servomotor connector. *See Fig. 10.* Leave battery leads connected throughout test.
2) Connect positive battery lead to each specified terminal of airflow mode servomotor connector. See TESTING AIRFLOW MODE SERVOMOTOR table. If servomotor arm does not rotate smoothly to specified position, replace airflow mode servomotor. If servomotor arm rotates smoothly to specified position, servomotor is okay.

TESTING AIRFLOW MODE SERVOMOTOR

Terminal No.	Arm Position
1	Vent
2	Bi-Level
3	Foot
4	Foot/Defrost
5	Defrost

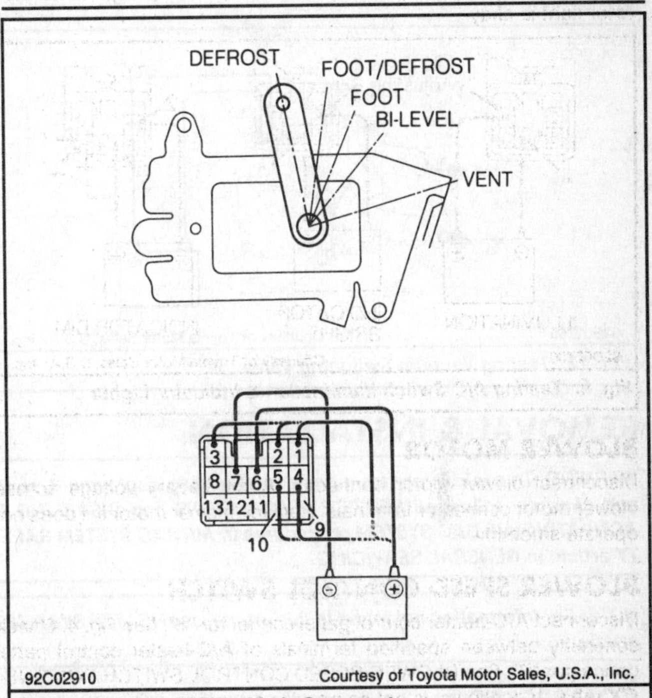
DEFROST
FOOT/DEFROST
FOOT
BI-LEVEL
VENT
3
2 1
8 7 6 5 4
13 12 11
9
10
92C02910
Courtesy of Toyota Motor Sales, U.S.A., Inc.

Fig. 10: Testing Airflow Mode Servomotor

THERMISTOR

Remove thermistor. Place thermistor in at least 3.94" (100 mm) of ice water. *See Fig. 11.* Use ice or hot water to change water temperature. With water at specified temperature, measure resistance across thermistor connector terminals. See THERMISTOR RESISTANCE SPECIFICATIONS table. If resistance is not as specified, replace thermistor.

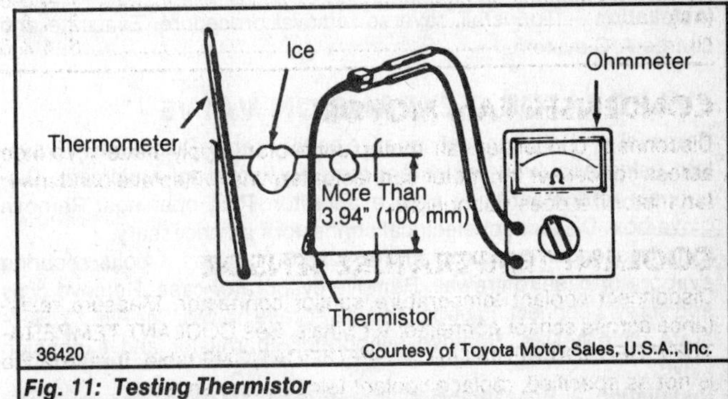
Ice
Ohmmeter
Thermometer
More Than
3.94" (100 mm)
Thermistor
36420
Courtesy of Toyota Motor Sales, U.S.A., Inc.

Fig. 11: Testing Thermistor

THERMISTOR RESISTANCE SPECIFICATIONS

Water Temperature °F (°C)	Ohms
30 (–1)	4700-5400
32 (0)	4500-5200
34 (1)	4300-4900
36 (2)	4000-4700
38 (3)	3800-4400
40 (4)	3700-4200

1993 MANUAL A/C-HEATER SYSTEMS
MR2 (Cont.)

VACUUM SWITCHING VALVE (VSV)

Disconnect vacuum hoses from VSV fittings. Apply battery voltage across VSV connector terminals. *See Fig. 12.* Blow air through fitting "A". If air does not come out of fitting "B", replace VSV. If air comes out of fitting "B", disconnect battery leads from VSV. Blow air through fitting "A". If air comes out of fitting "B", replace VSV. If air does not come out of fitting "B", VSV is okay.

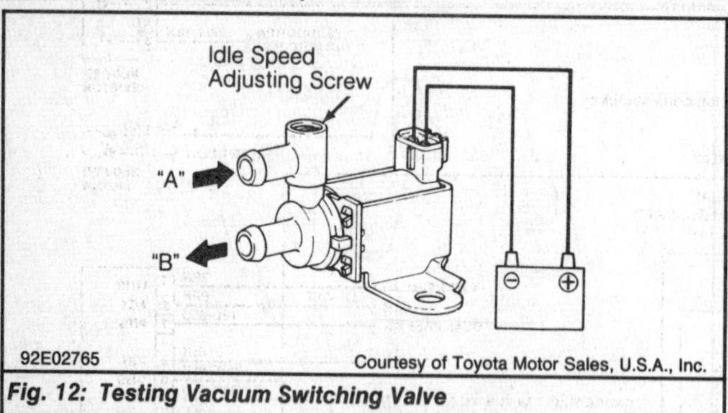
Idle Speed
Adjusting Screw
"A"
"B"
92E02765
Courtesy of Toyota Motor Sales, U.S.A., Inc.

Fig. 12: Testing Vacuum Switching Valve

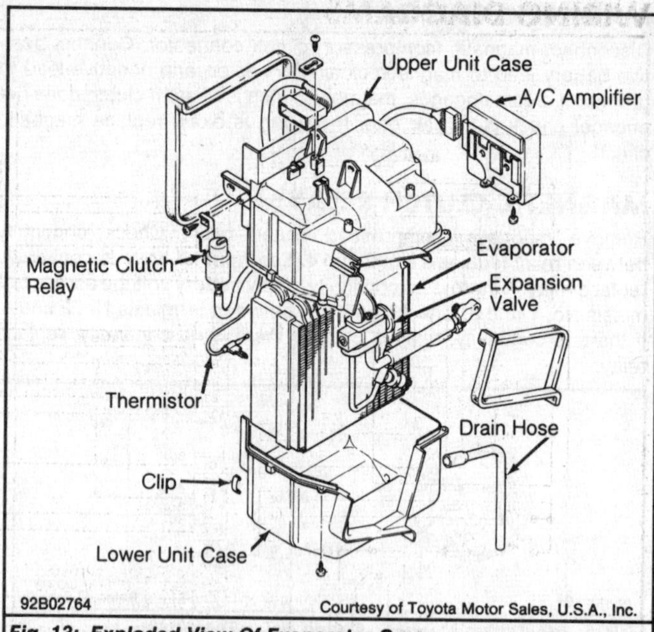
Upper Unit Case
A/C Amplifier
Evaporator
Magnetic Clutch
Relay
Expansion
Valve
Thermistor
Drain Hose
Clip
Lower Unit Case
92B02764
Courtesy of Toyota Motor Sales, U.S.A., Inc.

Fig. 13: Exploded View Of Evaporator Case

REMOVAL & INSTALLATION

WARNING: To avoid injury from accidental air bag deployment, read and carefully follow all SERVICE PRECAUTIONS and DISABLING & ACTIVATING AIR BAG SYSTEM procedures in AIR BAG SYSTEM SAFETY article in GENERAL SERVICING.

NOTE: For information not found in this article, see HEATER SYSTEMS article.

COMPRESSOR

Removal – 1) Run engine at idle with A/C on for at least 10 minutes (if possible). Stop engine. Disconnect negative battery cable. Remove engine undercover. Disconnect compressor magnetic clutch connector. Discharge A/C system using approved refrigerant recovery/recycling equipment.

2) Disconnect refrigerant hoses from compressor. Plug all openings. Loosen drive belt. Remove drive belt idler pulley bracket. Remove bolts and compressor.

Installation – To install, reverse removal procedure. Evacuate and charge A/C system.

EVAPORATOR & EXPANSION VALVE

Removal – 1) Disconnect negative battery cable. Discharge A/C system using approved refrigerant recovery/recycling equipment. Disconnect refrigerant lines from evaporator. Plug openings. Remove glove box. Disconnect electrical connectors as necessary.

2) In passenger compartment, remove 3 nuts and 4 bolts securing evaporator case to firewall. Remove evaporator case. Remove clips and screws connecting upper and lower case halves. *See Fig. 13.* Separate case halves. Remove evaporator, thermistor and expansion valve.

Installation – Reassemble evaporator case. Install evaporator case in reverse order of removal. If installing new evaporator core, add 1.4-1.7 ounces of refrigerant oil to evaporator core before installing. Evacuate and charge A/C system.

CONDENSER

Removal – Discharge A/C system using approved refrigerant recovery/recycling equipment. Remove cover from top of condenser in front luggage compartment. Remove condenser upper brackets. Disconnect refrigerant lines from condenser. Plug all openings. Remove condenser bolts and condenser.

Installation – To install, reverse removal procedure. If installing new condenser, add 1.4-1.7 ounces of refrigerant oil to condenser before installing. Evacuate and charge A/C system.

RECEIVER-DRIER

Removal & Installation – 1) Discharge A/C system using approved refrigerant recovery/recycling equipment. Remove left side front fender liner and undercover.

2) Disconnect refrigerant lines from receiver-drier. Plug all openings. Remove receiver-drier bolts and receiver-drier. To install, reverse removal procedure. Add 0.7 ounce of refrigerant oil to receiver-drier. Evacuate and charge A/C system.

TORQUE SPECIFICATIONS

TORQUE SPECIFICATIONS

Application	Ft. Lbs. (N.m)
Compressor Bolt	
12-mm	18 (25)
14-mm	27 (37)
Refrigerant Line Fitting Bolt	
At Compressor	18 (25)
Refrigerant Line Fitting Union	
.31" Diameter Line	[1]
.50" Diameter Line	17 (23)
.62" Diameter Line	24 (32)
	INCH Lbs. (N.m)
Refrigerant Line Fitting Bolt	
At Condenser	106 (12)
At Receiver-Drier	48 (5.4)

[1] – Tighten to 124 INCH lbs. (14 N.m).

1993 MANUAL A/C-HEATER SYSTEMS MR2 (Cont.)

WIRING DIAGRAMS

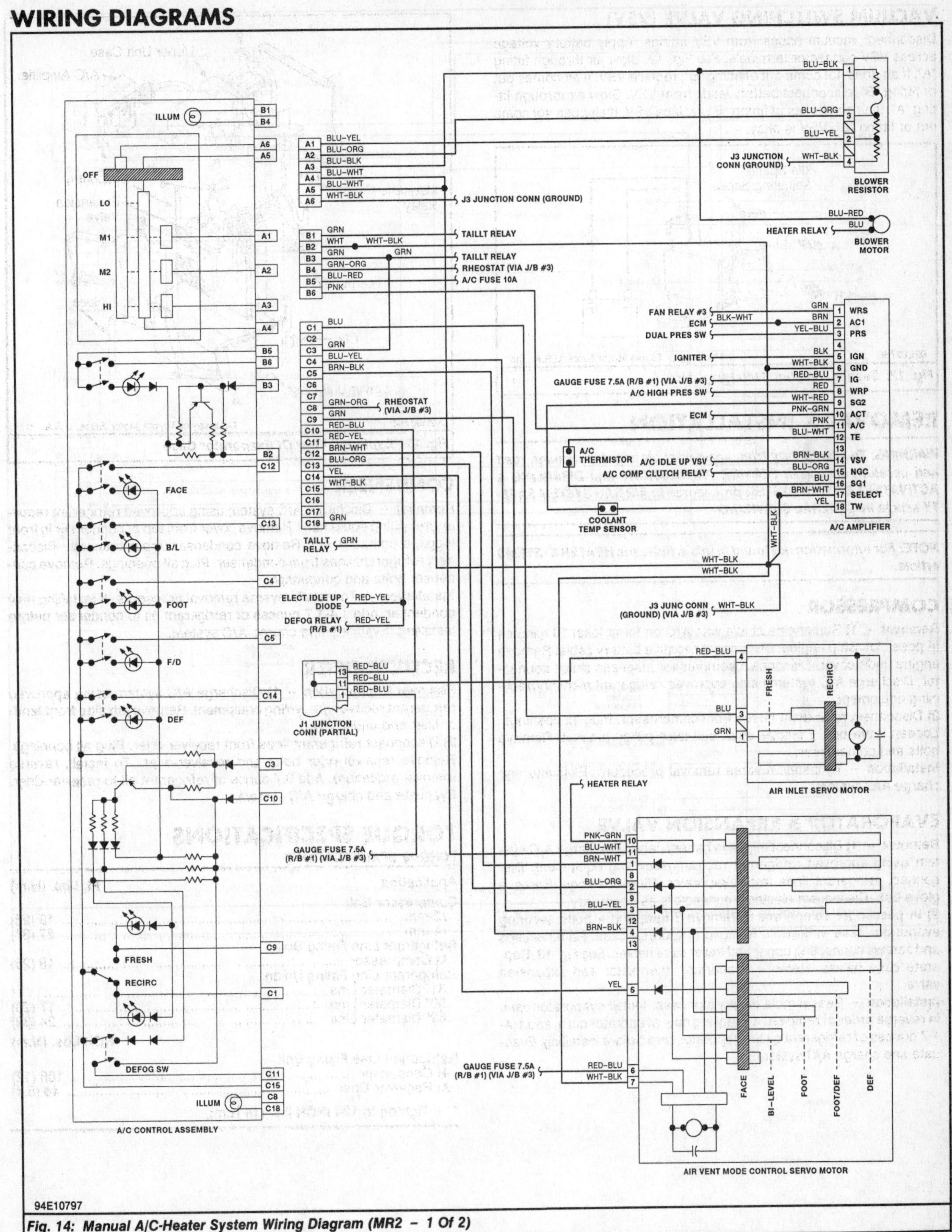
ILLUM
OFF
LO
M1
M2
HI
FACE
B/L
FOOT
F/D
DEF
FRESH
RECIRC
DEFOG SW
ILLUM
A/C CONTROL ASSEMBLY
BLU-YEL
BLU-ORG
BLU-BLK
BLU-WHT
BLU-WHT
WHT-BLK
J3 JUNCTION CONN (GROUND)
GRN
WHT
WHT-BLK
GRN
GRN
GRN-ORG
BLU-RED
PNK
TAILLT RELAY
TAILLT RELAY
RHEOSTAT (VIA J/B #3)
A/C FUSE 10A
BLU
GRN
BLU-YEL
BRN-BLK
GRN-ORG
GRN
RHEOSTAT (VIA J/B #3)
RED-BLU
RED-YEL
BRN-WHT
BLU-ORG
YEL
WHT-BLK
GRN
TAILLT RELAY
ELECT IDLE UP DIODE
DEFOG RELAY (R/B #1)
RED-YEL
RED-YEL
RED-BLU
RED-BLU
RED-BLU
J1 JUNCTION CONN (PARTIAL)
GAUGE FUSE 7.5A (R/B #1) (VIA J/B #3)
BLU-BLK
BLU-ORG
BLU-YEL
WHT-BLK
J3 JUNCTION CONN (GROUND)
BLOWER RESISTOR
BLU-RED
BLU
HEATER RELAY
BLOWER MOTOR
FAN RELAY #3
ECM
DUAL PRES SW
IGNITER
GAUGE FUSE 7.5A (R/B #1) (VIA J/B #3)
A/C HIGH PRES SW
ECM
A/C THERMISTOR
A/C IDLE UP VSV
A/C COMP CLUTCH RELAY
COOLANT TEMP SENSOR
GRN
BLK-WHT
BRN
YEL-BLU
BLK
WHT-BLK
RED-BLU
RED
WHT-RED
PNK-GRN
PNK
BLU-WHT
BRN-BLK
BLU-ORG
BLU
BRN-WHT
YEL
WRS
AC1
PRS
IGN
GND
IG
WRP
SG2
ACT
A/C
TE
VSV
NGC
SG1
SELECT
TW
A/C AMPLIFIER
WHT-BLK
WHT-BLK
WHT-BLK
J3 JUNC CONN (GROUND) (VIA J/B #3)
WHT-BLK
RED-BLU
BLU
GRN
FRESH
RECIRC
AIR INLET SERVO MOTOR
HEATER RELAY
PNK-GRN
BLU-WHT
BRN-WHT
BLU-ORG
BLU-YEL
BRN-BLK
YEL
GAUGE FUSE 7.5A (R/B #1) (VIA J/B #3)
RED-BLU
WHT-BLK
FACE
BI-LEVEL
FOOT
FOOT/DEF
DEF
AIR VENT MODE CONTROL SERVO MOTOR
94E10797

Fig. 14: Manual A/C-Heater System Wiring Diagram (MR2 – 1 Of 2)

1993 MANUAL A/C-HEATER SYSTEMS
MR2 (Cont.)

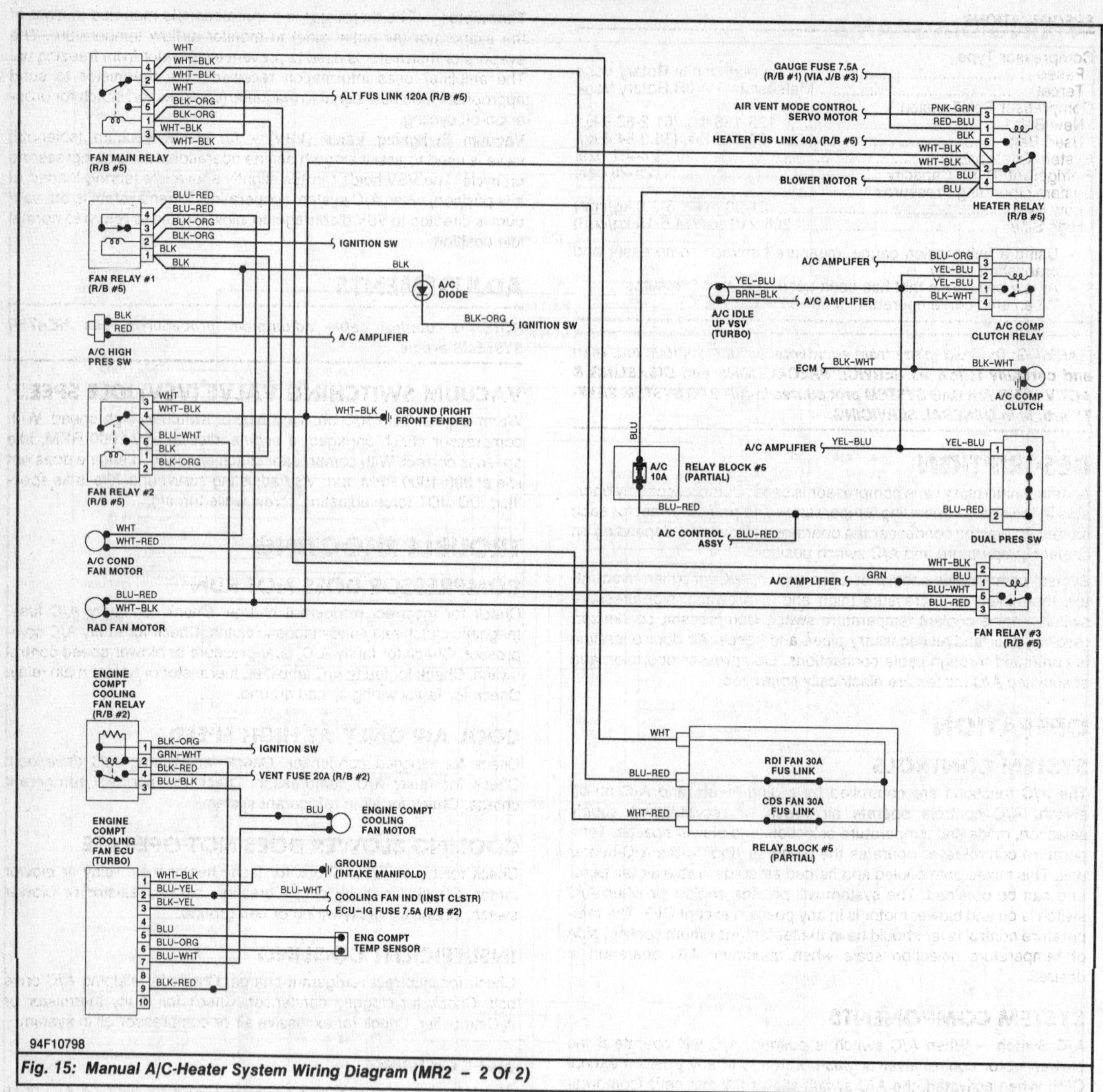
WHT
WHT-BLK
WHT-BLK
WHT
BLK-ORG
BLK-ORG
WHT-BLK
WHT-BLK
ALT FUS LINK 120A (R/B #5)
FAN MAIN RELAY
(R/B #5)
BLU-RED
BLU-RED
BLK-ORG
BLK-ORG
BLK
BLK
IGNITION SW
FAN RELAY #1
(R/B #5)
BLK
A/C
DIODE
BLK-ORG
IGNITION SW
BLK
RED
A/C AMPLIFIER
A/C HIGH
PRES SW
WHT
WHT-BLK
WHT-BLK
GROUND (RIGHT
FRONT FENDER)
BLU-WHT
BLK
BLK-ORG
FAN RELAY #2
(R/B #5)
WHT
WHT-RED
A/C COND
FAN MOTOR
BLU-RED
WHT-BLK
RAD FAN MOTOR
ENGINE
COMPT
COOLING
FAN RELAY
(R/B #2)
BLK-ORG
GRN-WHT
BLK-RED
BLU-BLK
IGNITION SW
VENT FUSE 20A (R/B #2)
BLU
ENGINE COMPT
COOLING
FAN MOTOR
ENGINE
COMPT
COOLING
FAN ECU
(TURBO)
GROUND
(INTAKE MANIFOLD)
WHT-BLK
BLU-YEL
BLK-YEL
BLU-WHT
COOLING FAN IND (INST CLSTR)
ECU-IG FUSE 7.5A (R/B #2)
BLU
BLU-ORG
BLU-WHT
ENG COMPT
TEMP SENSOR
BLK-RED
94F10798
GAUGE FUSE 7.5A
(R/B #1) (VIA J/B #3)
AIR VENT MODE CONTROL
SERVO MOTOR
PNK-GRN
RED-BLU
BLK
HEATER FUS LINK 40A (R/B #5)
WHT-BLK
WHT-BLK
BLU
BLOWER MOTOR
BLU
HEATER RELAY
(R/B #5)
A/C AMPLIFIER
BLU-ORG
YEL-BLU
YEL-BLU
BLK-WHT
YEL-BLU
BRN-BLK
A/C AMPLIFIER
A/C IDLE
UP VSV
(TURBO)
A/C COMP
CLUTCH RELAY
ECM
BLK-WHT
BLK-WHT
A/C COMP
CLUTCH
A/C AMPLIFIER
YEL-BLU
YEL-BLU
BLU
A/C
10A
RELAY BLOCK #5
(PARTIAL)
BLU-RED
BLU-RED
DUAL PRES SW
A/C CONTROL
ASSY
BLU-RED
WHT-BLK
BLU
A/C AMPLIFIER
GRN
BLU-WHT
BLU-RED
FAN RELAY #3
(R/B #5)
WHT
BLU-RED
RDI FAN 30A
FUS LINK
WHT-RED
CDS FAN 30A
FUS LINK
RELAY BLOCK #5
(PARTIAL)

Fig. 15: Manual A/C-Heater System Wiring Diagram (MR2 - 2 Of 2)

1993 MANUAL A/C-HEATER SYSTEMS
Paseo & Tercel

SPECIFICATIONS

Compressor Type
- Paseo .... Matsushita Rotary Vane
- Tercel .... Matsushita TV10B Rotary Vane

Compressor Belt Tension [1]
- New Belt [2] .... 135-185 lbs. (61.2-83.9 kg)
- Used Belt .... 80-120 lbs. (36.3-54.4 kg)

System Oil Capacity .... 3.4-4.1 ozs.
Refrigerant (R-12) Capacity .... 25-28 ozs.
System Operating Pressures [3]
- Low Side .... 21-28 psi (1.5-2.0 kg/cm²)
- High Side .... 206-213 psi (14.5-15 kg/cm²)

[1] – Using a belt tension gauge, measure between compressor and crankshaft pulley.
[2] – A new belt is one that has been used less than 5 minutes.
[3] – When ambient temperature is 86°-95°F (30°-35°C).

WARNING: To avoid injury from accidental air bag deployment, read and carefully follow all SERVICE PRECAUTIONS and DISABLING & ACTIVATING AIR BAG SYSTEM procedures in AIR BAG SYSTEM SAFETY article in GENERAL SERVICING.

DESCRIPTION

A Matsushita rotary vane compressor is used. Compressor only operates in the normal operating temperatures and pressures set for each model. An electric condenser fan operates at 2 speeds, depending on coolant temperature and A/C switch position.

System components consist of a fan switch, A/C amplifier, evaporator, thermistor, dual-pressure (high and low) switch, high-pressure switch, engine coolant temperature switch, compressor, condenser, receiver-drier and all necessary pipes and hoses. Air door operation is controlled through cable connections. Compressor operation and associated A/C modes are electrically controlled.

OPERATION

SYSTEM CONTROLS

The A/C functions are controlled by sliding levers and A/C on-off switch. A/C controls operate air (fresh or recirculating) supply selection, mode and temperature selection, and blower speeds. Temperature control lever operates the blend air door in the A/C-heater unit. This mixes both cooled and heated air so desirable air temperature can be obtained. The system will provide cooled air when A/C switch is on and blower motor is in any position except OFF. The temperature control lever should be in the far left (maximum cooling) side of temperature selection scale when maximum A/C operation is desired.

SYSTEM COMPONENTS

A/C Switch – When A/C switch is pushed, A/C will operate if the blower motor control lever or push button is in any position except OFF. When activated, the A/C switch allows the magnetic (compressor) clutch to engage, operating the compressor. A light will illuminate on the A/C push button when activated.

Dual-Pressure Switch – The dual-pressure switch is located on the liquid line and is wired in series with the magnetic (compressor) clutch. The switch cuts off electrical power to clutch when refrigerant pressures rise above or below the control point of the switch. When pressures are back in normal operating ranges, power is supplied to the magnetic clutch to resume operation.

High-Pressure Switch – The high-pressure switch is installed in the liquid line and is electrically wired in series with the coolant temperature switch and radiator and condenser fans. When refrigerant pressures rise above the control pressure point of the switch, electrical power to the magnetic (compressor) clutch will be cut off. The high-pressure switch may also be activated when airflow through the condenser is blocked, or when system has been overcharged with refrigerant.

Thermistor – The thermistor is a thermocouple mounted in front of the evaporator (air outlet side) to monitor airflow temperature. The evaporator thermistor is used to prevent evaporator from freezing up. The amplifier uses information received from thermistor to send appropriate electrical signal to magnetic (compressor) clutch for proper on-off cycling.

Vacuum Switching Valve (VSV) – An electro-vacuum (solenoid) valve is used to assist smooth engine operation during compressor's on cycle. The VSV holds throttle slightly above idle (spring-loaded to this position) when A/C system is operating. When system is off, vacuum is directed to VSV diaphragm to allow throttle to return to normal idle position.

ADJUSTMENTS

NOTE: For control cable adjustment procedures, see HEATER SYSTEMS article.

VACUUM SWITCHING VALVE (VSV) IDLE SPEED

Warm engine. Turn A/C on. Turn blower switch to high speed. With compressor clutch engaged, if engine idles at 900-1000 RPM, idle speed is correct. With compressor clutch engaged, if engine does not idle at 900-1000 RPM, turn VSV adjusting screw until idle is as specified. DO NOT force adjusting screw while turning.

TROUBLE SHOOTING

COMPRESSOR DOES NOT RUN

Check for incorrect refrigerant charge. Check for faulty A/C fuse, magnetic clutch relay and magnetic clutch. Check for faulty A/C compressor. Check for faulty A/C, dual-pressure or blower speed control switch. Check for faulty A/C amplifier, thermistor or heater main relay. Check for faulty wiring or bad ground.

COOL AIR ONLY AT HIGH SPEED

Check for clogged condenser. Check for slipping A/C drive belt. Check for faulty A/C compressor. Check for incorrect refrigerant charge. Check for air in refrigerant system.

COOLING BLOWER DOES NOT OPERATE

Check for blown fuse. Check for faulty heater main relay or blower motor. Check for faulty circuit breaker, blower resistor or blower switch. Check for faulty wiring or bad ground.

INSUFFICIENT COOLING

Check for incorrect refrigerant charge. Check for slipping A/C drive belt. Check for clogged condenser. Check for faulty thermistor or A/C amplifier. Check for excessive air or compressor oil in system.

NO COOLING

Check for incorrect refrigerant charge. Check for slipping A/C drive belt. Check for faulty magnetic (compressor) clutch or compressor. Check compressor control circuit.

TESTING

WARNING: To avoid injury from accidental air bag deployment, read and carefully follow all SERVICE PRECAUTIONS and DISABLING & ACTIVATING AIR BAG SYSTEM procedures in AIR BAG SYSTEM SAFETY article in GENERAL SERVICING.

NOTE: For information not found in this article, see HEATER SYSTEMS article.

1993 MANUAL A/C-HEATER SYSTEMS
Paseo & Tercel (Cont.)

A/C SYSTEM PERFORMANCE

Connect manifold gauge set. Let engine idle at 2000 RPM. Set blower fan on high speed. Set temperature control switch at maximum cool position. With airflow set in recirculated mode, ensure temperature at air inlet is 86-95°F (30-35°C). Ensure pressure readings are within specifications. See SPECIFICATIONS table at beginning of article.

A/C AMPLIFIER

Disconnect A/C amplifier connector. A/C amplifier is located on bottom of A/C cooling unit (evaporator housing). Turn ignition on (as required). Slide temperature control lever to maximum cool position. Turn blower switch on. Test wire harness side of connector. *See Fig. 1*. Ensure circuit tests as specified in A/C AMPLIFIER CIRCUIT TEST table. If circuit does not test as specified, repair as necessary.

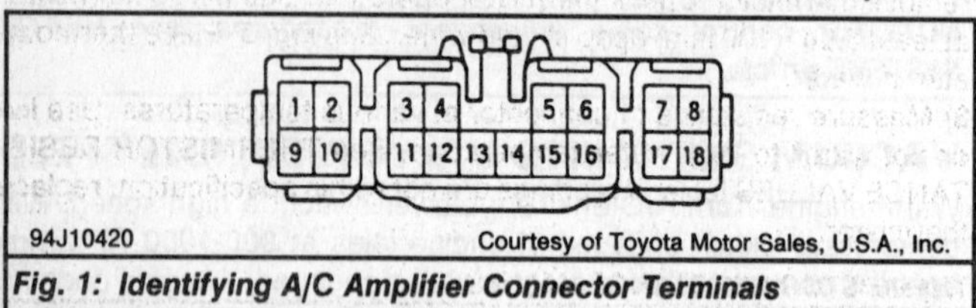
1 2 3 4 5 6 7 8
9 10 11 12 13 14 15 16 17 18
94J10420
Courtesy of Toyota Motor Sales, U.S.A., Inc.

Fig. 1: Identifying A/C Amplifier Connector Terminals

A/C AMPLIFIER CIRCUIT TEST

Terminals & Test Condition	Specification
1 & Ground	
Engine Running	About 10-14 Volts
Engine Off	No Voltage
8 & Ground	
A/C Switch On	Battery Voltage
A/C Switch Off	No Voltage
7 & Ground	
Blower Switch On	Battery Voltage
Blower Switch Off	No Voltage
2 & 13	[1] 1500 Ohms
9 & 13	About 240 Ohms
5 & 7	Continuity
12 & Ground	Continuity

[1] – Test with air temperature at 77°F (25°C).

A/C SWITCH

Disconnect negative battery cable. Remove A/C switch, and disconnect wire harness connector. Check continuity at specified terminals. See A/C SWITCH CONTINUITY table. *See Fig. 2*. If continuity is not as specified, replace A/C switch.

A/C SWITCH CONTINUITY

Switch Position	Continuity Between Terminals
Off	[1]
On	4 & 5; 4 & 6

[1] – With switch in any position, continuity should exist between terminal No. 1 and 3 for A/C switch illumination. With switch in the off position, continuity should not exist between any other terminals.

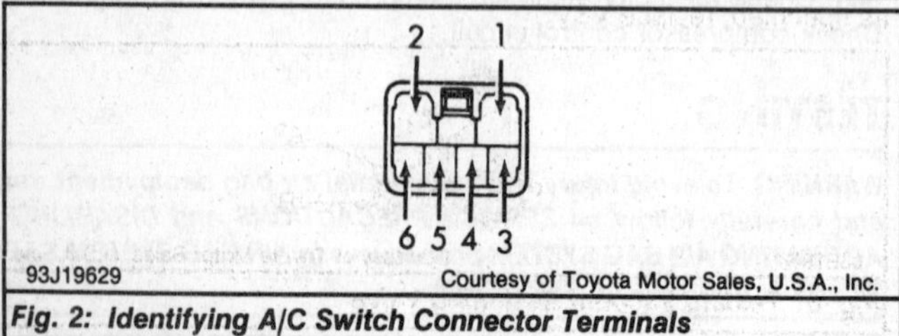
2 1
6 5 4 3
93J19629
Courtesy of Toyota Motor Sales, U.S.A., Inc.

Fig. 2: Identifying A/C Switch Connector Terminals

BLOWER MOTOR

Disconnect blower motor connector. Apply battery voltage across blower motor connector terminals. Replace blower motor if it does not operate smoothly.

CONDENSER FAN MOTOR

Disconnect 2-pin fan motor connector. Apply battery voltage to fan motor side of connector. Fan motor should rotate smoothly, and current draw should be 8-11 amps. If operation is not as specified, replace condenser fan motor.

CONDENSER FAN RELAY

Condenser Fan Relay No. 2 – Remove condenser fan relay. *See Fig. 3*. Using an ohmmeter, check continuity between terminals No. 1 and 3, and between terminals No. 2 and 4. Ensure continuity exists. Apply battery voltage between terminals No. 1 and 3. Ensure continuity exists between terminals No. 4 and 5. If continuity is not as specified, replace relay.

Condenser Fan Relay No. 3 – Remove relay. *See Fig. 3*. Using an ohmmeter, check continuity between terminals No. 1 and 3. Ensure continuity exists. Apply battery voltage between terminals No. 1 and 3. Ensure continuity exists between terminals No. 2 and 4. If continuity is not as specified, replace relay.

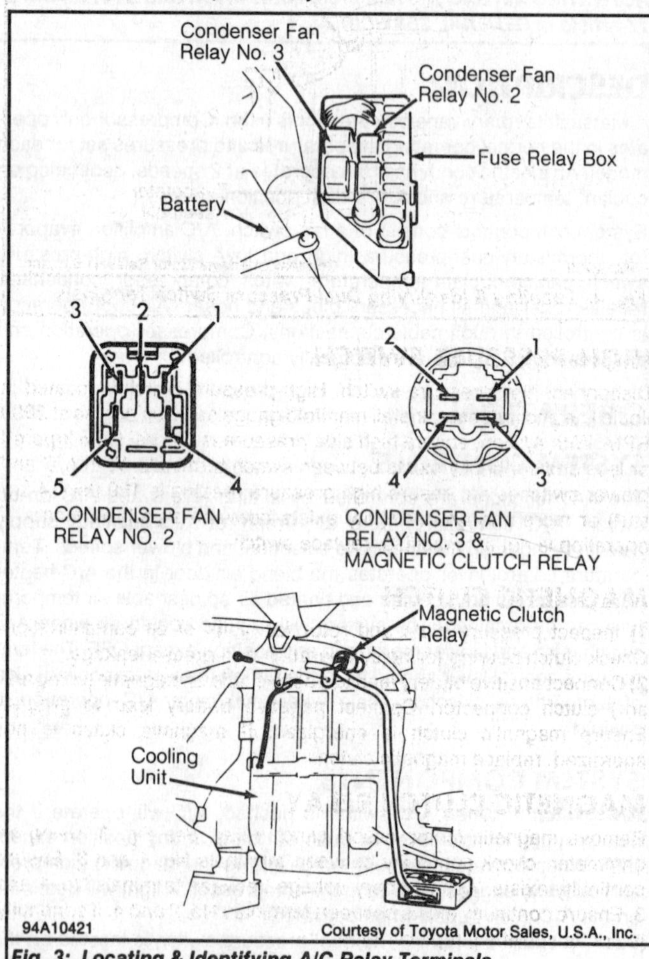
Condenser Fan Relay No. 3
Condenser Fan Relay No. 2
Fuse Relay Box
Battery
3 2 1
5 4
CONDENSER FAN RELAY NO. 2
2 1
4 3
CONDENSER FAN RELAY NO. 3 & MAGNETIC CLUTCH RELAY
Magnetic Clutch Relay
Cooling Unit
94A10421
Courtesy of Toyota Motor Sales, U.S.A., Inc.

Fig. 3: Locating & Identifying A/C Relay Terminals

COOLANT TEMPERATURE SWITCH

Remove coolant temperature switch. Switch is located on A/C compressor discharge cover. Place switch in a pan of engine oil. Using an ohmmeter, check for continuity at specified temperatures. See COOLANT TEMPERATURE SWITCH SPECIFICATIONS table. If continuity is not as specified, replace switch.

COOLANT TEMPERATURE SWITCH SPECIFICATIONS

Engine Oil Temperature	Continuity
248°F (120°C)	Yes
356°F (180°C)	No

EXPANSION VALVE

1) Ensure refrigerant volume is correct. Connect manifold gauge set. Start engine. Turn A/C switch on. Turn blower switch to HI position. Run engine at 2000 RPM for at least 5 minutes. Observe gauges.
2) If low side pressure is zero psi when high pressure reading is 185-213 psi (13-15 kg/cm²), expansion valve is clogged. Replace expansion valve.

DUAL-PRESSURE SWITCH

Install A/C manifold gauge set. Disconnect dual-pressure switch connector. Dual-pressure switch is located near or on evaporator. *See Fig. 4.* Using an ohmmeter, check for continuity between dual-pressure switch terminals. With high pressure readings of 30-386 psi (2.1-27.0 kg/cm²), continuity should be present. If continuity is not as specified, replace dual-pressure switch.

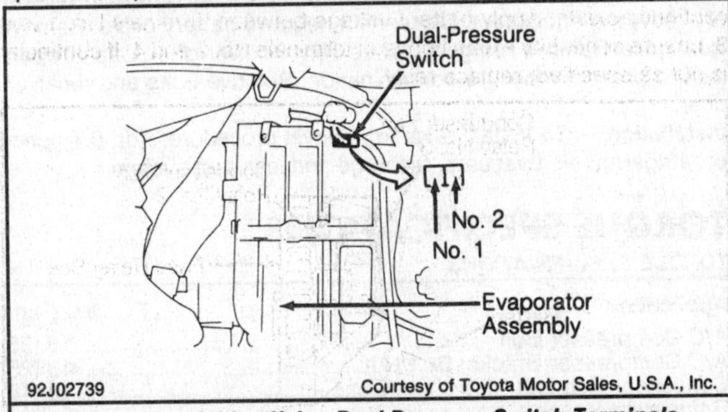

Dual-Pressure Switch
No. 2
No. 1
Evaporator Assembly
92J02739
Courtesy of Toyota Motor Sales, U.S.A., Inc.

Fig. 4: Locating & Identifying Dual-Pressure Switch Terminals

HIGH-PRESSURE SWITCH

Disconnect high-pressure switch. High-pressure switch is located in liquid line at condenser. Install manifold gauge set. Run engine at 2000 RPM. With A/C off, ensure high side pressure is 164 psi (11.5 kg/cm²) or less and continuity exists between switch terminals. With A/C and blower switches on, ensure high pressure reading is 199 psi (14 kg/cm²) or more and no continuity exists between switch terminals. If operation is not as specified, replace switch.

MAGNETIC CLUTCH

1) Inspect pressure plate and rotor for signs of oil contamination. Check clutch bearing for noisy operation and grease leakage.
2) Connect positive battery lead to positive side of magnetic (compressor) clutch connector. Connect negative battery lead to ground. Ensure magnetic clutch is energized. If magnetic clutch is not energized, replace magnetic clutch.

MAGNETIC CLUTCH RELAY

Remove magnetic (compressor) clutch relay. *See Fig. 3.* Using an ohmmeter, check continuity between terminals No. 1 and 3. Ensure continuity exists. Apply battery voltage between terminals No. 1 and 3. Ensure continuity exists between terminals No. 2 and 4. If continuity is not as specified, replace relay.

RPM SENSOR

Disconnect wire harness connector. Sensor is located on A/C compressor discharge cover. Using an ohmmeter, measure resistance between sensor terminals. If resistance is not within specification, replace sensor. See RPM SENSOR RESISTANCE SPECIFICATIONS table.

RPM SENSOR RESISTANCE SPECIFICATIONS

Ambient Temperature	Ohms
68°F (20°C)	160-320

THERMISTOR

1) Disconnect negative battery cable. Remove lower trim panel and glove box. Check thermistor installed operation. Thermistor is mounted in front of evaporator. Turn ignition off. Using an ohmmeter, measure resistance between thermistor terminals. If resistance is not within specification, go to next step. See THERMISTOR RESISTANCE SPECIFICATIONS table.

THERMISTOR RESISTANCE SPECIFICATIONS

Ambient Temperature	Between Terminals	Ohms
77°F (25°C)	1 & 2	1500

2) Remove evaporator case. See EVAPORATOR ASSEMBLY under REMOVAL & INSTALLATION. Disassemble evaporator case, and remove thermistor. Check thermistor operation. Submerge thermistor at least 3.94" (100 mm) deep in cold water. *See Fig. 5.* Place thermometer in water.
3) Measure resistance of connector at various temperatures. Use ice or hot water to vary water temperature. See THERMISTOR RESISTANCE VALUES table. If readings are not within specification, replace thermistor.

THERMISTOR RESISTANCE VALUES

Ambient Temperature	Ohms
41°F (5°C)	3500-4100
39°F (4°C)	3800-4300
37°F (3°C)	3900-4500
36°F (2°C)	4100-4800
34°F (1°C)	4300-4900
32°F (0°C)	4500-5200
30°F (-1°C)	4700-5400

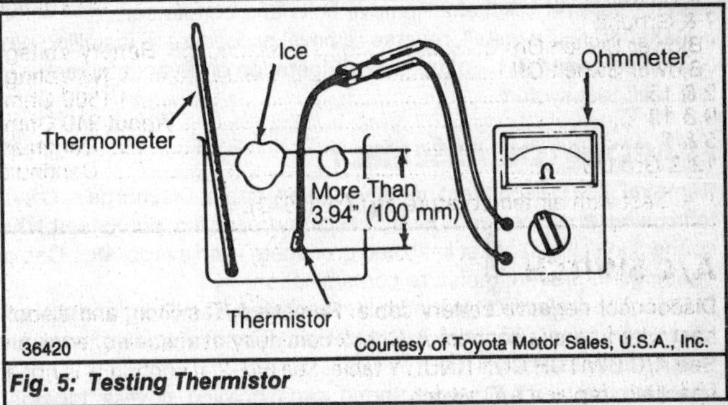

Ice
Ohmmeter
Thermometer
More Than 3.94" (100 mm)
Thermistor
36420
Courtesy of Toyota Motor Sales, U.S.A., Inc.

Fig. 5: Testing Thermistor

VACUUM SWITCHING VALVE (VSV)

1) Remove VSV. Connect VSV terminals to 12-volt battery. Blow into fitting "A". *See Fig. 6.* Ensure air comes out of fitting "B". Disconnect battery, and blow into fitting "A". Ensure air does not comes out of fitting "B".
2) Using an ohmmeter, ensure continuity does not exist between each terminal and VSV body. Measure resistance between terminals. Resistance should be 30-34 ohms at 68°F (20°C). If readings are not as specified, replace VSV.

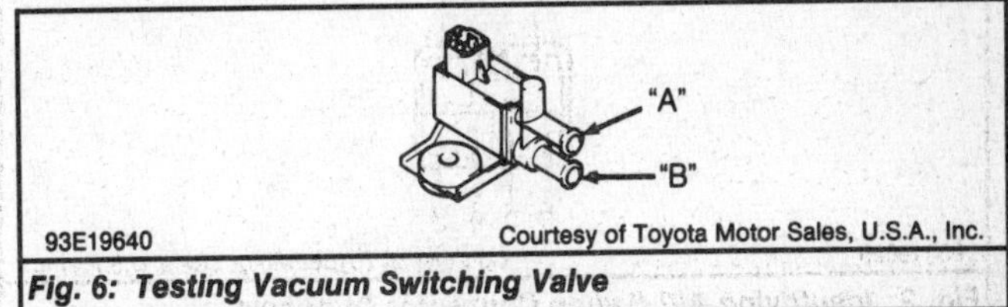

"A"
"B"
93E19640
Courtesy of Toyota Motor Sales, U.S.A., Inc.

Fig. 6: Testing Vacuum Switching Valve

1993 MANUAL A/C-HEATER SYSTEMS
Paseo & Tercel (Cont.)

REMOVAL & INSTALLATION

WARNING: To avoid injury from accidental air bag deployment, read and carefully follow all SERVICE PRECAUTIONS and DISABLING & ACTIVATING AIR BAG SYSTEM procedures in AIR BAG SYSTEM SAFETY article in GENERAL SERVICING.

NOTE: For information not found in this article, see HEATER SYSTEMS article.

COMPRESSOR

Removal - **1)** If possible, before beginning removal procedure, run A/C system for 10 minutes. Disconnect negative battery cable. Discharge A/C system using approved refrigerant recovery/recycling equipment. Remove engine undercover (splash) shield. Disconnect magnetic clutch electrical connector.

2) Disconnect compressor hoses. Cap hose ends to keep moisture out of system. Loosen compressor drive belt. Remove compressor bolts. Remove compressor.

Installation - To install, reverse removal procedure. Evacuate, recharge and leak test system.

CONDENSER

Removal - **1)** Discharge A/C system using approved refrigerant recovery/recycling equipment. Disconnect negative battery cable. Remove front grille, hood lock and center brace. Remove horn. Remove condenser fan.

2) Disconnect refrigerant lines from condenser. Cap all openings to prevent moisture contamination. Remove receiver-drier. Remove radiator support brackets. Remove bolts and condenser.

Installation - To install, reverse removal procedure. If installing new condenser, add 1.4-1.7 ounces of refrigeration oil. Evacuate, recharge and leak test system.

EVAPORATOR ASSEMBLY

Removal - **1)** Disconnect negative battery cable. Discharge A/C system using approved refrigerant recovery/recycling equipment. Disconnect inlet lines, outlet lines and grommets from evaporator. Cap all openings to prevent moisture contamination.

2) Disconnect electrical leads from evaporator. Remove glove box and lower trim panel. Remove A/C amplifier. Remove screws, nuts and evaporator assembly.

Disassembly - **1)** Release spring clips holding covers together. Remove any screws at case joints. Separate upper and lower cases from evaporator core. Remove thermistor together with holder.

2) Remove dual-pressure switch. Remove high-side (inlet) line from expansion valve, and remove expansion valve. Remove pressure switch (if equipped).

Reassembly & Installation - To reassemble and install evaporator assembly, reverse disassembly and removal procedures. If installing new evaporator core, add 1.4-1.7 ounces of refrigerant oil to core before installing. Evacuate, recharge and leak test system.

EXPANSION VALVE

Removal & Installation - Evaporator must be removed in order to remove expansion valve. See EVAPORATOR ASSEMBLY under REMOVAL & INSTALLATION.

RECEIVER-DRIER

Removal - Discharge A/C system using approved refrigerant recovery/recycling equipment. Disconnect negative battery cable. Remove front grille. Remove refrigerant lines from receiver-drier. Cap all openings to prevent moisture contamination. Remove bolts and receiver-drier.

Installation - To install, reverse removal procedure. Add 0.7 ounce of refrigerant oil. Evacuate, recharge and leak test system.

TORQUE SPECIFICATIONS

TORQUE SPECIFICATIONS

Application	Ft. Lbs. (N.m)
A/C Compressor Bolt	18 (25)
A/C Compressor Bracket Bolt/Nut	18 (25)
Condenser Bolt/Nut	13 (18)
Refrigerant Hoses	
Compressor	18 (25)
Condenser	
Paseo	13 (18)
Tercel	[1]
Evaporator	
High Pressure (Discharge) Hose	[2]
Low Pressure (Suction) Hose	24 (33)
	INCH Lbs. (N.m)
Dual-Pressure Switch Bolt	89 (10)
Expansion Valve (Fittings)	48 (5.4)
Magnetic Clutch Pressure Plate Bolt	124 (14)
Receiver-Drier Bolt/Nut	48 (5.4)
RPM Sensor Bolt	97 (11)

[1] - Tighten to 115 INCH lbs. (13 N.m).
[2] - Tighten to 124 INCH lbs. (14 N.m).

WIRING DIAGRAMS

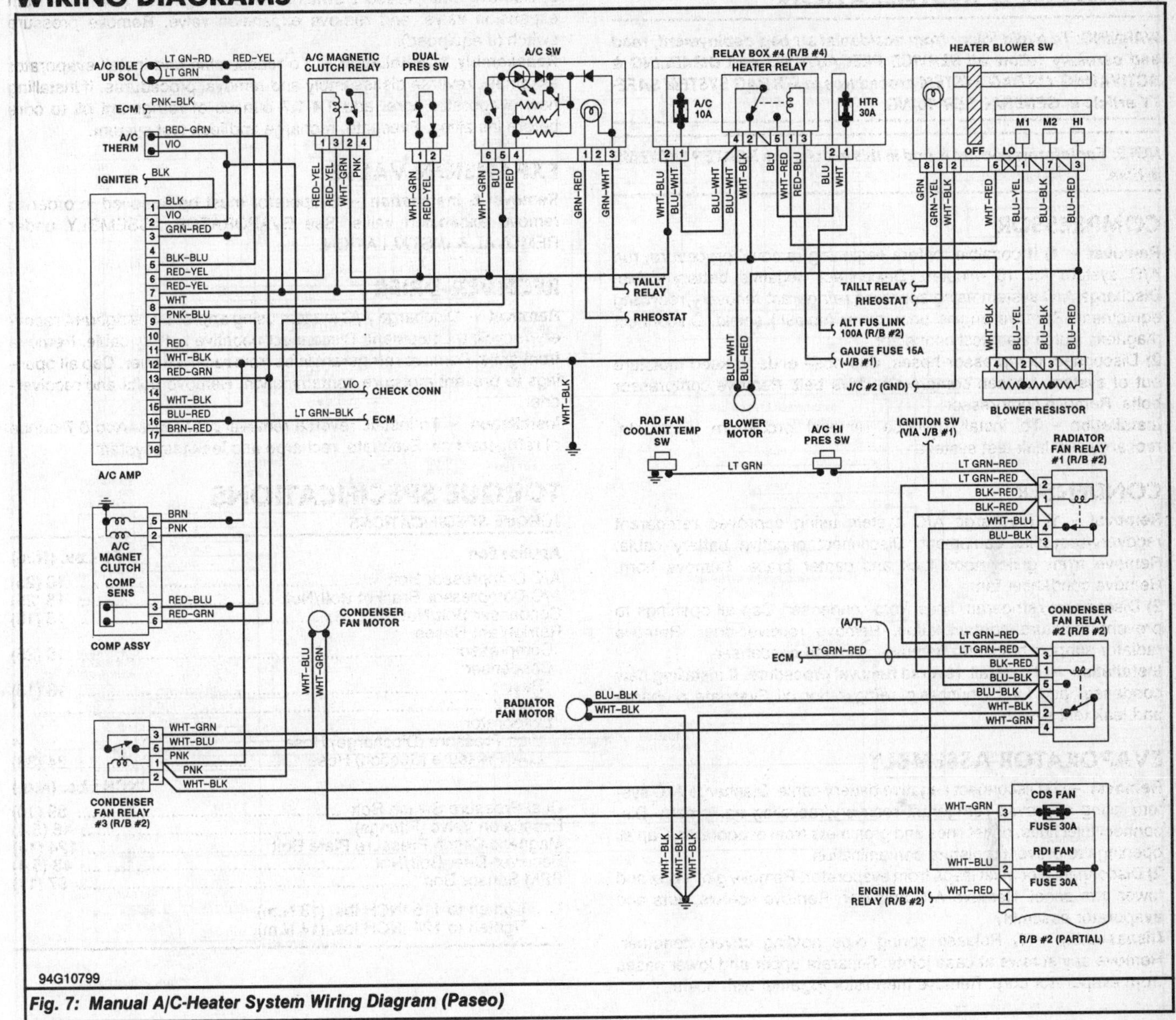
A/C IDLE UP SOL
ECM
A/C THERM
IGNITER
A/C AMP
A/C MAGNETIC CLUTCH RELAY
DUAL PRES SW
A/C SW
RELAY BOX #4 (R/B #4)
HEATER RELAY
A/C 10A
HTR 30A
HEATER BLOWER SW
OFF
LO
M1
M2
HI
TAILLT RELAY
RHEOSTAT
ALT FUS LINK 100A (R/B #2)
GAUGE FUSE 15A (J/B #1)
J/C #2 (GND)
CHECK CONN
BLOWER RESISTOR
RAD FAN COOLANT TEMP SW
BLOWER MOTOR
A/C HI PRES SW
IGNITION SW (VIA J/B #1)
RADIATOR FAN RELAY #1 (R/B #2)
A/C MAGNET CLUTCH
COMP SENS
COMP ASSY
CONDENSER FAN MOTOR
CONDENSER FAN RELAY #2 (R/B #2)
RADIATOR FAN MOTOR
CONDENSER FAN RELAY #3 (R/B #2)
CDS FAN FUSE 30A
RDI FAN FUSE 30A
ENGINE MAIN RELAY (R/B #2)
R/B #2 (PARTIAL)
94G10799

Fig. 7: Manual A/C-Heater System Wiring Diagram (Paseo)

1993 MANUAL A/C-HEATER SYSTEMS
Paseo & Tercel (Cont.)

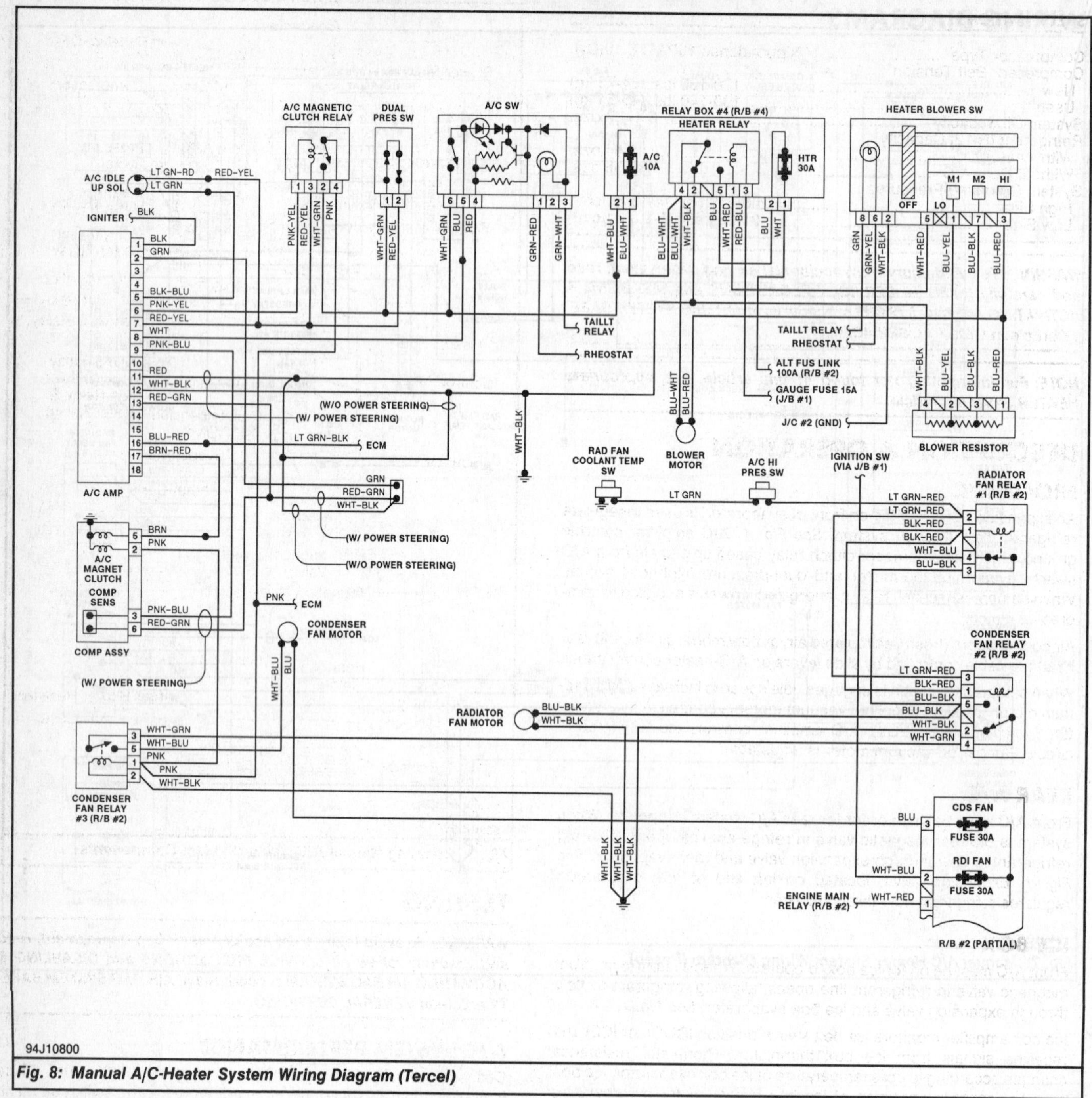
A/C MAGNETIC CLUTCH RELAY
DUAL PRES SW
A/C SW
RELAY BOX #4 (R/B #4)
HEATER RELAY
HEATER BLOWER SW
A/C IDLE UP SOL
IGNITER
A/C AMP
A/C 10A
HTR 30A
OFF
LO
M1
M2
HI
TAILLT RELAY
RHEOSTAT
ALT FUS LINK 100A (R/B #2)
GAUGE FUSE 15A (J/B #1)
J/C #2 (GND)
BLOWER RESISTOR
(W/O POWER STEERING)
(W/ POWER STEERING)
ECM
RAD FAN COOLANT TEMP SW
BLOWER MOTOR
A/C HI PRES SW
IGNITION SW (VIA J/B #1)
RADIATOR FAN RELAY #1 (R/B #2)
A/C MAGNET CLUTCH
COMP SENS
COMP ASSY
CONDENSER FAN MOTOR
CONDENSER FAN RELAY #2 (R/B #2)
RADIATOR FAN MOTOR
CONDENSER FAN RELAY #3 (R/B #2)
CDS FAN FUSE 30A
RDI FAN FUSE 30A
ENGINE MAIN RELAY (R/B #2)
R/B #2 (PARTIAL)
94J10800

Fig. 8: Manual A/C-Heater System Wiring Diagram (Tercel)

1993 MANUAL A/C-HEATER SYSTEMS
Previa

SPECIFICATIONS

Compressor Type	Nippondenso 10PA17E 10-Cyl.
Compressor Belt Tension	
New	120-160 lbs. (54-73 kg)
Used	100-140 lbs. (45-64 kg)
System Oil Capacity	3.4-4.7 ozs.
Refrigerant (R-12) Capacity	
With Rear A/C	41-44 ozs.
Without Rear A/C	32-35 ozs.
System Operating Pressures	
High Side	206-213 psi (14-15 kg/cm²)
Low Side	21-28 psi (1.5-2.0 kg/cm²)

***WARNING:* To avoid injury from accidental air bag deployment, read and carefully follow all SERVICE PRECAUTIONS and DISABLING & ACTIVATING AIR BAG SYSTEM procedures in AIR BAG SYSTEM SAFETY article in GENERAL SERVICING.**

***NOTE:* For information not found in this article, see appropriate HEATER SYSTEMS article.**

DESCRIPTION & OPERATION

FRONT A/C

An expansion valve, located on front of evaporator, is used to regulate refrigerant flow through system. *See Fig. 1*. A/C amplifier controls ground circuit of compressor clutch relay based on signals from A/C switch, evaporator thermistor and dual-pressure (high/low) switch. When compressor clutch relay is energized, power is supplied to compressor clutch.

Air control doors (fresh/recirculated air, airflow mode, air mix and rear heat) are cable controlled by slide levers on A/C-heater control panel.

When compressor clutch is engaged, idle speed is increased by a vacuum motor. Vacuum supply to vacuum motor is controlled by a Vacuum Switching Valve (VSV). A/C amplifier controls the VSV ground circuit. Plunger on vacuum motor is adjustable.

REAR A/C

Front A/C must be on in order for rear A/C system to operate. When system is on, rear magnetic valve in refrigerant line opens, allowing refrigerant to flow through expansion valve and rear evaporator. *See Fig. 1*. Expansion valve, located on left end of rear evaporator, regulates refrigerant flow through system.

ICE BOX

Front A/C must be on for ice box to operate. When system is on, front magnetic valve in refrigerant line opens, allowing refrigerant to flow through expansion valve and ice box evaporator. *See Fig. 1*.

Ice box amplifier monitors ice box switch position (COOL or ICE) and receives signals from ice box thermistor. Thermistor resistance changes according to core temperature of ice box evaporator. Ice box amplifier controls operation of ice box blower motor by grounding motor circuit. When ice box amplifier signals the A/C amplifier, the A/C amplifier turns on the front magnetic valve.

ADJUSTMENTS

DOOR CONTROL CABLES

Rear Heat – Set control lever to REAR HEAT position. Disconnect rear heat door control cable housing from retaining clip (leave cable wire connected to door lever). Move door lever fully in the cable-retracted direction. Connect cable housing to retaining clip.

Side Vents – Set control lever to VENT position. Disconnect side vent door control cable housing from retaining clip (leave cable wire connected to door lever). Move door lever fully in the cable-extended direction. Connect cable housing to retaining clip.

All Other Positions – See appropriate HEATER SYSTEMS article.

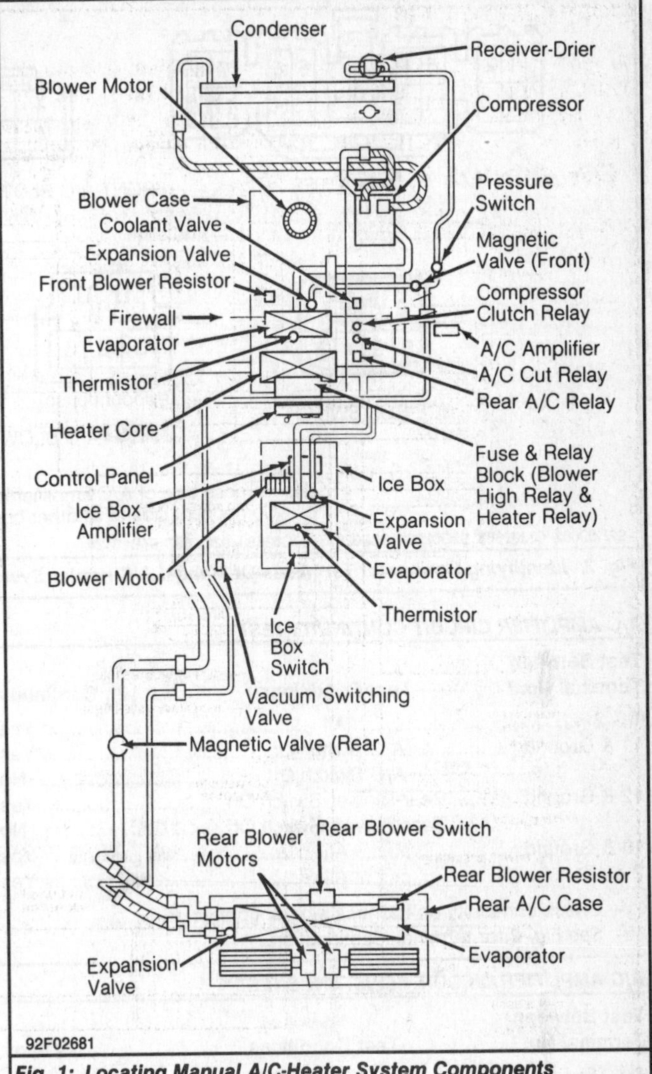
Condenser
Receiver-Drier
Blower Motor
Compressor
Pressure Switch
Blower Case
Coolant Valve
Magnetic Valve (Front)
Expansion Valve
Front Blower Resistor
Compressor Clutch Relay
Firewall
Evaporator
A/C Amplifier
A/C Cut Relay
Thermistor
Rear A/C Relay
Heater Core
Fuse & Relay Block (Blower High Relay & Heater Relay)
Control Panel
Ice Box
Ice Box Amplifier
Expansion Valve
Blower Motor
Evaporator
Thermistor
Ice Box Switch
Vacuum Switching Valve
Magnetic Valve (Rear)
Rear Blower Motors
Rear Blower Switch
Rear Blower Resistor
Rear A/C Case
Evaporator
Expansion Valve
92F02681

Fig. 1: Locating Manual A/C-Heater System Components

TESTING

***WARNING:* To avoid injury from accidental air bag deployment, read and carefully follow all SERVICE PRECAUTIONS and DISABLING & ACTIVATING AIR BAG SYSTEM procedures in AIR BAG SYSTEM SAFETY article in GENERAL SERVICING.**

A/C SYSTEM PERFORMANCE

Connect manifold gauge set. Operate engine at 2000 RPM. Place blower fan on high speed. Place temperature control switch on maximum cooling and air intake lever on recirculated air position.. Ensure system operating pressures are within specifications. See SPECIFICATIONS table at beginning of article.

A/C AMPLIFIER CIRCUIT

1) Disconnect A/C amplifier connector. Check continuity as indicated in A/C AMPLIFIER CIRCUIT CONTINUITY TEST table. If continuity is as specified, go to next step. If continuity is not as specified, repair appropriate circuit.

2) Check resistance as indicated in A/C AMPLIFIER CIRCUIT RESISTANCE TEST table. If resistance is as specified, go to next step. If resistance is not as specified, repair appropriate circuit.

3) Check voltage as indicated in A/C AMPLIFIER CIRCUIT VOLTAGE TEST table. If voltage is not as specified, repair appropriate circuit. If voltage is as specified, replace A/C amplifier.

1993 MANUAL A/C-HEATER SYSTEMS
Previa (Cont.)

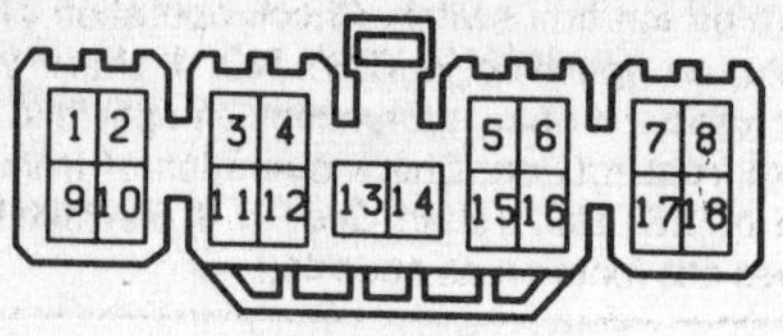
A/C AMPLIFIER

FRONT A/C BLOWER RESISTOR

FRONT A/C SWITCH

ICE BOX AMPLIFIER

ICE BOX SWITCH

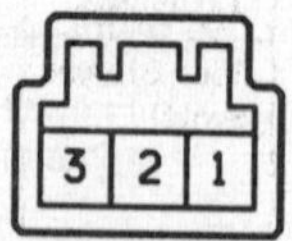
(Nippondenso)

(Panasonic)

REAR A/C BLOWER RESISTOR

REAR A/C BLOWER SWITCH

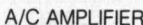

NOTE: Harness side of A/C amplifier connector and ice box amplifier connector is shown. Component side of all other connectors is shown.

92H02682 92J02683 92B02684 92E02685 92G02686 92I02687 94D10424

Courtesy of Toyota Motor Sales, U.S.A., Inc.

Fig. 2: Identifying Connector Terminals Of Manual A/C-Heater System Components (Except Relays)

A/C AMPLIFIER CIRCUIT CONTINUITY TEST [1]

Test Between Terminal No. [2]	Test Conditions	Continuity
1 & 2	All	Yes
11 & Ground	A/C Switch On	Yes
	A/C Switch Off	No
12 & Ground	Rear Blower Switch On	Yes
	Rear Blower Switch Off	No
13 & Ground	All	Yes
2 & 17	All	Yes

[1] – Check continuity on harness side of connector.
[2] – *See Fig. 2* for terminal identification.

A/C AMPLIFIER CIRCUIT RESISTANCE TEST [1]

Test Between Terminal No. [2]	Test Conditions	Ohms
1 & 15	All	About 1500
3 & 7	All	About 60
4 & 8	All	About 20

[1] – Check resistance on harness side of connector.
[2] – *See Fig. 2* for terminal identification.

A/C AMPLIFIER CIRCUIT VOLTAGE TEST [1]

Test Between Terminal No. [2]	Test Conditions	Volts
4 & Ground	LOCK, ACC Or START	0
	Ignition On	Battery
5 & Ground	LOCK, ACC Or START	0
	Ignition On	Battery
6 & Ground	LOCK, ACC Or START	0
	Ignition On	Battery
12 & Ground	Engine On	Battery
	Engine Off	0

[1] – Check voltage on harness side of connector.
[2] – *See Fig. 2* for terminal identification.

BLOWER RESISTOR

Front A/C – Check continuity between terminals No. 1, 2, 3 and 4 of blower resistor connector. *See Fig. 2.* Replace blower resistor if there is no continuity between any combination of terminals.

Rear A/C – Check continuity between terminals No. 1, 2 and 3 of blower resistor connector. *See Fig. 2.* Replace blower resistor if there is no continuity between any combination of terminals.

DUAL-PRESSURE SWITCH

Connect manifold gauge set. Disconnect dual-pressure switch connector. Turn A/C on. Check continuity between switch dual-pressure switch terminals. See DUAL-PRESSURE SWITCH CONTINUITY TEST table. Replace switch if it does not test as specified.

DUAL-PRESSURE SWITCH CONTINUITY TEST

Condition	Continuity
Low Pressure Increasing To 33 psi (2.3 kg/cm²)	Yes
Decreasing To 30 psi (2.1 kg/cm²)	No
High Pressure	
Decreasing To 299 psi (21.0 kg/cm²)	Yes
Increasing To 384 psi (27.0 kg/cm²)	No

FRONT A/C SWITCH

Check continuity as indicated in FRONT A/C SWITCH CONTINUITY TEST table. Ensure continuity exists between appropriate terminals. Replace switch if continuity is not as specified.

FRONT A/C SWITCH CONTINUITY TEST

Switch Position	Continuity Between [1] Terminal No.
Off	1, 3 & 5; 4 & 5
On	1, 3, 5 & 6; 4, 5 & 6

[1] – *See Fig. 2* for terminal identification.

IDLE-UP SYSTEM (VACUUM SWITCHING VALVE)

1) Warm engine. Turn A/C on. Turn blower switch to high speed. Ensure compressor clutch is engaged. If engine idles at 900-1000 RPM, idle-up system is okay. If engine does not idle at 900-1000 RPM, check vacuum motor plunger on throttle body. If vacuum motor plunger is extended, rotate vacuum motor plunger until idle is as specified.

2) If vacuum motor plunger is not extended, apply vacuum to vacuum motor. If plunger does not extend, replace vacuum motor. If plunger extends, disconnect vacuum hoses and electrical connector from Vacuum Switching Valve (VSV).

3) Connect battery source across VSV terminals. *See Fig. 3.* Blow air through pipe "A". Air should exit through pipe "B" but not through filter "C".

4) Disconnect battery source. Blow air through pipe "A". Air should exit through filter "C" but not through pipe "B". Replace VSV if it does not operate as specified. Using an ohmmeter, measure resistance between VSV terminals. If resistance is not 30-34 ohms at 68°F (20°C), replace VSV.

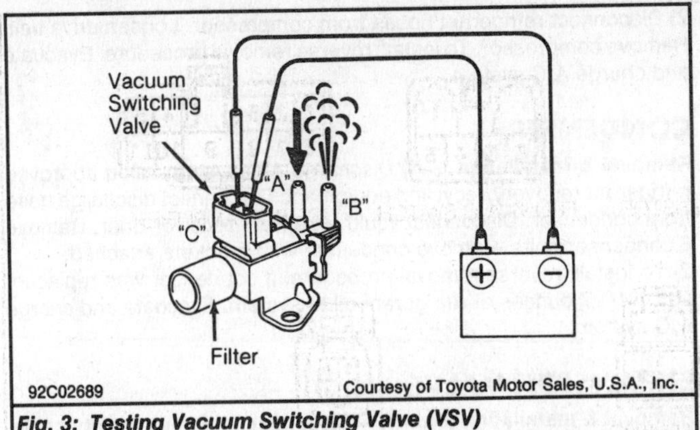
Vacuum
Switching
Valve
"A"
"B"
"C"
Filter
92C02689
Courtesy of Toyota Motor Sales, U.S.A., Inc.

Fig. 3: Testing Vacuum Switching Valve (VSV)

ICE BOX AMPLIFIER CIRCUIT

1) Check resistance as indicated in ICE BOX AMPLIFIER CIRCUIT RESISTANCE TEST table. If resistance is as specified, go to next step. If resistance is not as specified, repair appropriate circuit.

2) Check voltage as indicated in ICE BOX AMPLIFIER CIRCUIT VOLTAGE TEST table. If voltage is not as specified, repair appropriate circuit. If voltage is as specified, replace ice box amplifier.

ICE BOX AMPLIFIER CIRCUIT RESISTANCE TEST [1]

Test Between Terminal No. [2]	Test Conditions	Ohms
2 & Ground	All	About 13,000
4 & Ground	All	0 (Continuity)
7 & 11	32°F (0°C) [3]	About 4900
	59°F (15°C) [3]	About 2300

[1] – Check resistance on harness side of connector.
[2] – *See Fig. 2* for terminal identification.
[3] – Ice box evaporator core temperature.

ICE BOX AMPLIFIER CIRCUIT VOLTAGE TEST [1]

Test Between Terminal No. [2]	Test Conditions	Volts
1 & Ground	OFF [3]	0
	COOL [3]	Battery
5 & Ground	LOCK Or ACC	0
	Ignition On	Battery
8 & Ground	LOCK Or ACC	0
	Ignition On	Battery

[1] – Check voltage on harness side of connector.
[2] – *See Fig. 2* for terminal identification.
[3] – With ignition on and ice box switch in this position.

ICE BOX SWITCH

Check continuity of switch as indicated in ICE BOX SWITCH CONTINUITY TEST table. Ensure continuity exists between appropriate terminals. Replace switch if continuity is not as specified.

ICE BOX SWITCH CONTINUITY TEST

Switch Position	Continuity Between [1] Terminal No.
OFF	None
COOL	3 & 5

[1] – *See Fig. 2* for terminal identification.

MAGNETIC VALVES

NOTE: Front valve is used on vehicles with ice box. Rear valve is used on vehicles with rear A/C.

Test No. 1 – Turn off ice box switch. Check operation of magnetic valve (front or rear) as specified in TEST NO. 1 chart. *See Fig. 4.* Replace magnetic valve if it does not function as specified.

Test No. 2 – Turn front A/C on. Check operation of front magnetic valve as specified in TEST NO. 2 chart. *See Fig. 4.* Replace front magnetic valve if it does not function as specified.

Device \ Condition		1	2	3	4
A/C Switch	Front	ON	ON	OFF	OFF
Rear Blower Switch	Rear	ON	OFF	ON	OFF
Magnetic Valve	ON / OFF; 2°C (35.6°F) 3°C (37.4°F); Air Temp. in Cooling Unit				
	Front	ON	ON	OFF	OFF
	Rear	ON	OFF	OFF	OFF
Compressor Magnetic Clutch		ON	ON	OFF	OFF

TEST NO. 1

Condition		1	2
Magnetic Valve		ON	OFF
Cool/Ice Box Switch	ICE Mode	15 sec.	60 sec.
	COOL Mode	10 sec.	120 sec.
Refrigerator		Operate	Non-operate

TEST NO. 2

92E02690 Courtesy of Toyota Motor Sales, U.S.A., Inc.

Fig. 4: Magnetic Valve Operation Charts

REAR A/C BLOWER SWITCH

Check continuity as indicated in REAR A/C BLOWER SWITCH CONTINUITY TEST table. Ensure continuity exists between appropriate terminals. *See Fig. 2.* Replace switch if continuity is not as specified.

REAR A/C BLOWER SWITCH CONTINUITY TEST

Application & Switch Position	Continuity Between [1] Terminal No.
Off	None
Low	3 & 4
Medium	1, 3 & 4
High	2, 3 & 4

[1] – *See Fig. 2* for terminal identification.

RELAYS

A/C-Cut Relay – Apply battery voltage across relay terminals No. 3 and 4. *See Fig. 5.* Ensure continuity exists between terminals No. 1 and 2.

Blower High Relay, Heater Relay (5-Pin) & Rear A/C Relay – Ensure continuity exists between relay terminals No. 2 and 4. *See Fig. 5.* Apply battery voltage across terminals No. 1 and 3. Ensure continuity exists between terminals No. 4 and 5.

Compressor Clutch Relay – Apply battery voltage across relay terminals No. 1 and 3. *See Fig. 5.* Ensure continuity exists between terminals No. 2 and 4.

Heater Relay (4-Pin) – Apply battery voltage across relay terminals No. 1 and 2. *See Fig. 5.* Ensure continuity exists between terminals No. 3 and 4.

1993 MANUAL A/C-HEATER SYSTEMS
Previa (Cont.)

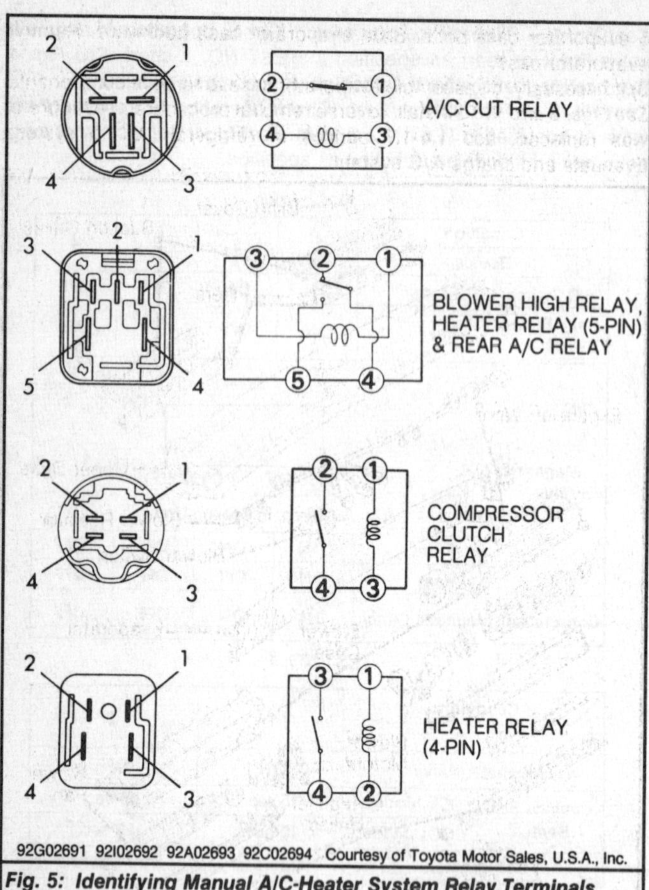
A/C-CUT RELAY
BLOWER HIGH RELAY, HEATER RELAY (5-PIN) & REAR A/C RELAY
COMPRESSOR CLUTCH RELAY
HEATER RELAY (4-PIN)
92G02691 92I02692 92A02693 92C02694 Courtesy of Toyota Motor Sales, U.S.A., Inc.

Fig. 5: Identifying Manual A/C-Heater System Relay Terminals

THERMISTOR

Front A/C & Ice Box – Remove thermistor and immerse in ice cold water. Measure resistance across thermistor terminals. See FRONT A/C & ICE BOX THERMISTOR RESISTANCE SPECIFICATIONS table. If resistance is not within specification, replace thermistor. If resistance is within specification, thermistor is okay.

FRONT A/C & ICE BOX THERMISTOR RESISTANCE SPECIFICATIONS

Water Temperature °F (°C)	Ohms
30 (–1)	4800-5400
32 (0)	4500-5200
34 (1)	4300-5000
36 (2)	4100-4800
38 (3)	3900-4500
40 (4)	3700-4300

REMOVAL & INSTALLATION

WARNING: To avoid injury from accidental air bag deployment, read and carefully follow all SERVICE PRECAUTIONS and DISABLING & ACTIVATING AIR BAG SYSTEM procedures in AIR BAG SYSTEM SAFETY article in GENERAL SERVICING.

NOTE: For removal and installation procedures not covered in this article, see appropriate HEATER SYSTEMS article.

COMPRESSOR

Removal & Installation – **1)** Operate engine at idle with A/C on for 10 minutes. Stop engine. Disconnect negative battery cable. Disconnect compressor clutch wire. Discharge A/C system using approved refrigerant recovery/recycling equipment.

2) Disconnect refrigerant hoses from compressor. Loosen drive belt. Remove compressor. To install, reverse removal procedure. Evacuate and charge A/C system.

CONDENSER

Removal & Installation – **1)** Discharge A/C system using approved refrigerant recovery/recycling equipment. Disconnect discharge hose from condenser. Disconnect liquid tube from receiver-drier. Remove 6 condenser bolts. Remove condenser with brackets attached.

2) To install, reverse removal procedure. If condenser was replaced, add 1.4-1.7 ounces of refrigerant oil to system. Evacuate and charge A/C system.

EXPANSION VALVE

Removal & Installation (Front) – Disconnect negative battery cable. Discharge A/C system using approved refrigerant recovery/recycling equipment. Remove air duct and blower motor from engine compartment. Disconnect refrigerant lines from expansion valve flange. *See Fig. 6.* Remove expansion valve. To install, reverse removal procedure. Evacuate and charge A/C system.

Removal & Installation (Rear) – Disconnect negative battery cable. Discharge A/C system using approved refrigerant recovery/recycling equipment. If necessary, remove components from evaporator case to remove expansion valve. *See Figs. 8 and 9.* To install, reverse removal procedure. Evacuate and charge A/C system.

FRONT EVAPORATOR

Removal & Installation – **1)** Disconnect negative battery cable. Discharge A/C system using approved refrigerant recovery/recycling equipment. Remove air duct and blower motor from engine compartment.

2) Disconnect electrical connectors. Disconnect refrigerant lines from expansion valve flange. *See Fig. 6.* Remove 2 nuts, one bolt and cover. Remove evaporator.

3) To install, reverse removal procedure. If evaporator was replaced, add 1.4-1.7 ounces of refrigerant oil to system. Evacuate and charge A/C system.

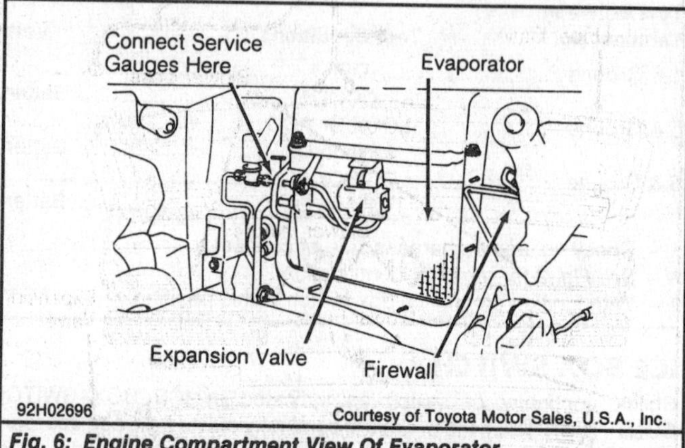
Connect Service Gauges Here
Evaporator
Expansion Valve
Firewall
92H02696
Courtesy of Toyota Motor Sales, U.S.A., Inc.

Fig. 6: Engine Compartment View Of Evaporator (Air Duct & Blower Motor Removed)

ICE BOX

Removal & Installation – **1)** Disconnect negative battery cable. Remove ice box side covers. Disconnect electrical connectors. Discharge A/C system using approved refrigerant recovery/recycling equipment. Disconnect refrigerant lines from ice box evaporator.

2) Remove 6 ice box nuts. Remove ice box. If necessary, disassemble ice box to remove components. *See Fig. 7.* To install, reverse removal procedure. Evacuate and charge A/C system.

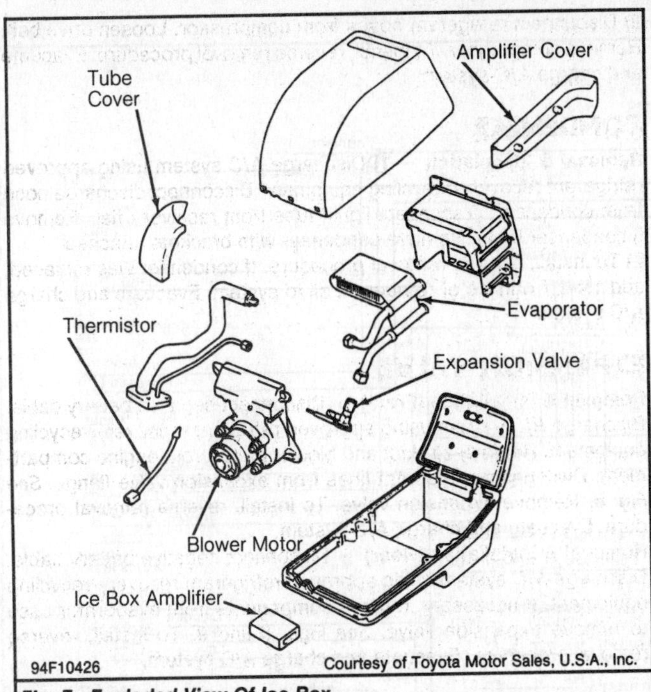

Amplifier Cover
Tube Cover
Thermistor
Evaporator
Expansion Valve
Blower Motor
Ice Box Amplifier
94F10426
Courtesy of Toyota Motor Sales, U.S.A., Inc.

Fig. 7: Exploded View Of Ice Box

REAR EVAPORATOR CASE

Removal & Installation – 1) Disconnect negative battery cable. Discharge A/C system using approved refrigerant recovery/recycling equipment. Remove center cover. Remove tube fitting covers on ends of case. Disconnect refrigerant lines from evaporator.

2) Disconnect right and left drain hoses. Disconnect electrical connectors. Remove blind covers concealing evaporator case bolts. Remove 5 evaporator case bolts. Slide evaporator case backward. Remove evaporator case.

3) If necessary, disassemble evaporator case to remove components. *See Figs. 8 and 9*. To install, reverse removal procedure. If evaporator was replaced, add 1.4-1.7 ounces of refrigerant oil to system. Evacuate and charge A/C system.

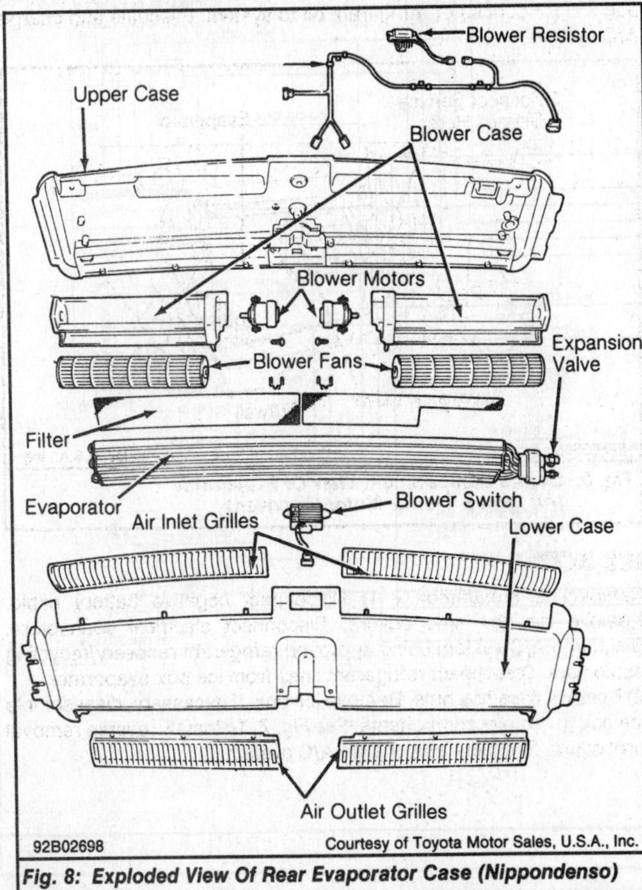

Blower Resistor
Upper Case
Blower Case
Blower Motors
Expansion Valve
Blower Fans
Filter
Evaporator
Blower Switch
Air Inlet Grilles
Lower Case
Air Outlet Grilles
92B02698
Courtesy of Toyota Motor Sales, U.S.A., Inc.

Fig. 8: Exploded View Of Rear Evaporator Case (Nippondenso)

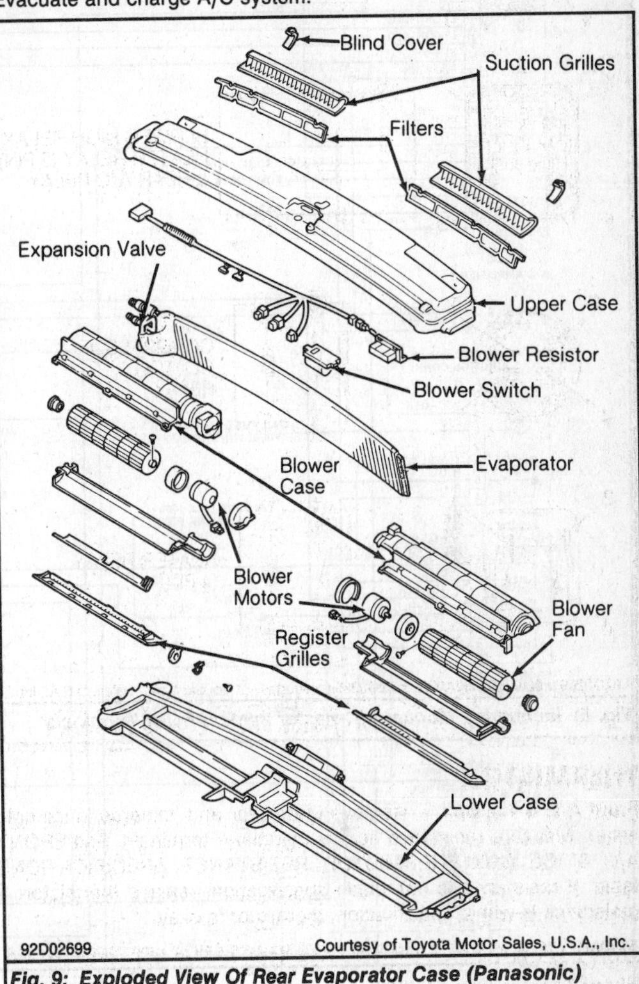

Blind Cover
Suction Grilles
Filters
Expansion Valve
Upper Case
Blower Resistor
Blower Switch
Blower Case
Evaporator
Blower Motors
Blower Fan
Register Grilles
Lower Case
92D02699
Courtesy of Toyota Motor Sales, U.S.A., Inc.

Fig. 9: Exploded View Of Rear Evaporator Case (Panasonic)

RECEIVER-DRIER

Removal & Installation – 1) Discharge A/C system using approved refrigerant recovery/recycling equipment. Disconnect refrigerant lines from receiver-drier. Remove receiver-drier from holder.

2) To install, reverse removal procedure. If receiver-drier was replaced, add .7 ounce of refrigerant oil to system. Evacuate and charge A/C system.

TORQUE SPECIFICATIONS

TORQUE SPECIFICATIONS

Application	Ft. Lbs. (N.m)
Refrigerant Line Fitting Bolt Or Union	
At Compressor	13 (18)
At Condenser	10 (14)
At Ice Box	
Suction	17 (23)
Discharge	10 (14)
At Rear Evaporator	
Suction	16-18 (21-25)
Discharge	9-11 (13-15)
At Receiver-Drier	10 (14)
	INCH Lbs. (N.m)
Refrigerant Line Fitting Bolt	
At Front Evaporator	69 (7.8)

1993 MANUAL A/C-HEATER SYSTEMS
Previa (Cont.)

WIRING DIAGRAM

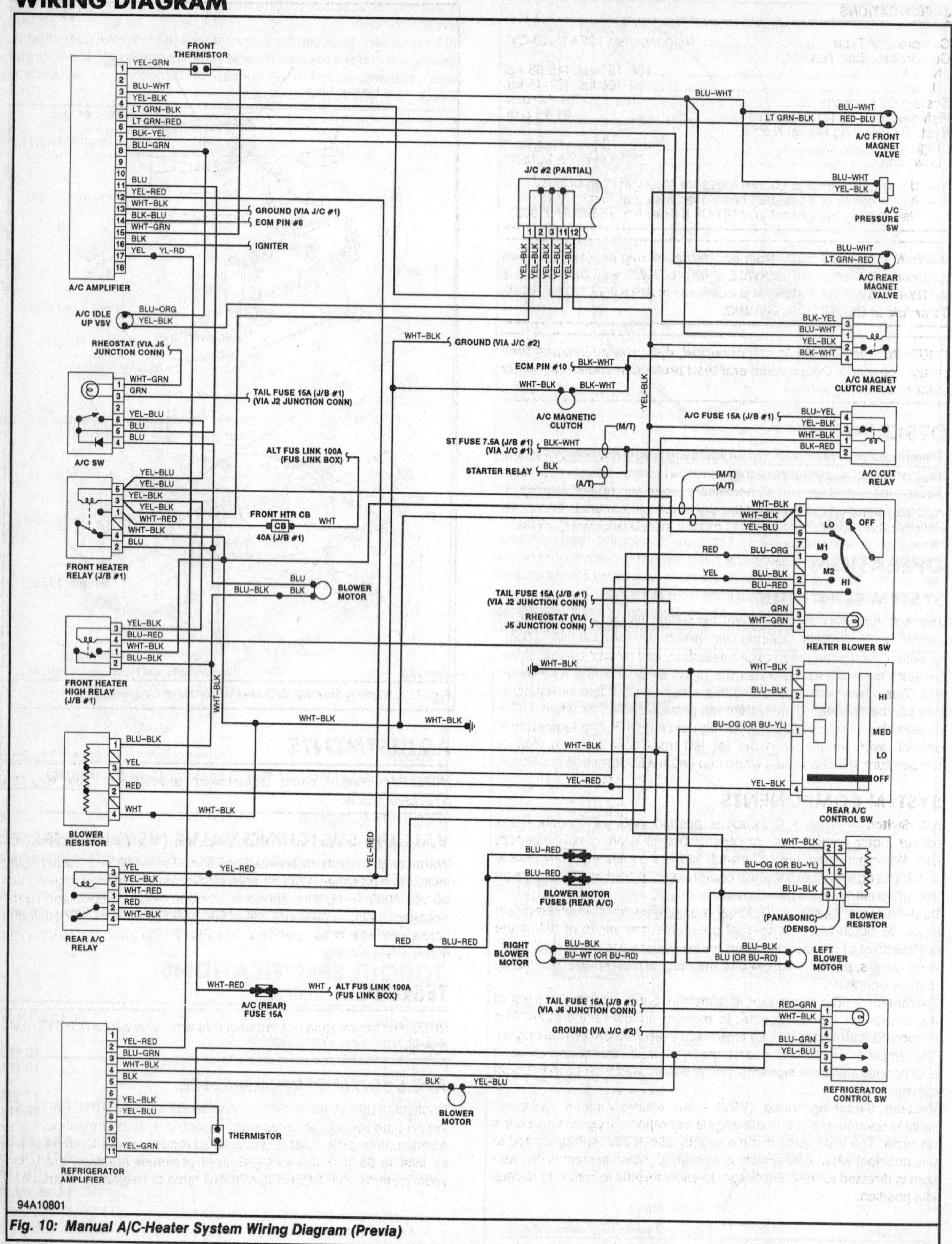
FRONT THERMISTOR
YEL-GRN
BLU-WHT
YEL-BLK
LT GRN-BLK
LT GRN-RED
BLK-YEL
BLU-GRN
BLU
YEL-RED
WHT-BLK
BLK-BLU
WHT-GRN
BLK
YEL
YL-RD
GROUND (VIA J/C #1)
ECM PIN #6
IGNITER
A/C AMPLIFIER
A/C IDLE UP VSV
BLU-ORG
RHEOSTAT (VIA J5 JUNCTION CONN)
TAIL FUSE 15A (J/B #1) (VIA J2 JUNCTION CONN)
A/C SW
ALT FUS LINK 100A (FUS LINK BOX)
FRONT HTR CB
40A (J/B #1)
WHT
FRONT HEATER RELAY (J/B #1)
BLOWER MOTOR
FRONT HEATER HIGH RELAY (J/B #1)
BLOWER RESISTOR
REAR A/C RELAY
A/C (REAR) FUSE 15A
REFRIGERATOR AMPLIFIER
THERMISTOR
94A10801
J/C #2 (PARTIAL)
GROUND (VIA J/C #2)
ECM PIN #10
A/C MAGNETIC CLUTCH
ST FUSE 7.5A (J/B #1) (VIA J/C #1)
STARTER RELAY
(M/T)
(A/T)
A/C FRONT MAGNET VALVE
A/C PRESSURE SW
A/C REAR MAGNET VALVE
A/C MAGNET CLUTCH RELAY
A/C FUSE 15A (J/B #1)
A/C CUT RELAY
HEATER BLOWER SW
OFF
LO
M1
M2
HI
REAR A/C CONTROL SW
MED
BU-OG (OR BU-YL)
BLOWER MOTOR FUSES (REAR A/C)
(PANASONIC)
(DENSO)
RIGHT BLOWER MOTOR
LEFT BLOWER MOTOR
BU-WT (OR BU-RD)
BLU (OR BU-RD)
TAIL FUSE 15A (J/B #1) (VIA J6 JUNCTION CONN)
RED-GRN
REFRIGERATOR CONTROL SW

Fig. 10: Manual A/C-Heater System Wiring Diagram (Previa)

1993 MANUAL A/C-HEATER SYSTEMS
T100

SPECIFICATIONS

Compressor Type .... Nippondenso 10PA15 10-Cyl.
Compressor Belt Tension [1]
New [2] .... 100-150 lbs. (45-68 kg)
Used .... 60-100 lbs. (27-45 kg)
System Oil Capacity .... 3.4-4.1 ozs.
Refrigerant (R-134a) Capacity [3] .... 21-25 ozs.
System Operating Pressures
High Side .... 199-228 (14-16 kg/cm²)
Low Side .... 21-36 (1.5-2.5 kg/cm²)

[1] – Using a belt tension gauge, measure at longest run of belt.
[2] – A new belt is one that has been used less than 5 minutes.
[3] – Use R-134a refrigerant and ND-Oil 8 (Part No. 38899-PR7-003).

WARNING: To avoid injury from accidental air bag deployment, read and carefully follow all SERVICE PRECAUTIONS and DISABLING & ACTIVATING AIR BAG SYSTEM procedures in AIR BAG SYSTEM SAFETY article in GENERAL SERVICING.

CAUTION: When battery is disconnected, radio will go into anti-theft protection mode. Obtain radio anti-theft protection code from owner prior to servicing vehicle.

DESCRIPTION

System components consist of an A/C switch, A/C amplifier, evaporator, thermistor, dual-pressure (high and low) switch, compressor, condenser, receiver-drier and all necessary pipes and hoses. *See Fig. 1.* Air door operation is controlled through cable connections. Compressor operation and associated A/C modes are electrically controlled.

OPERATION

SYSTEM CONTROLS

The A/C functions are controlled by sliding levers and A/C on-off switch. A/C controls operate air (fresh or recirculated) supply selection, mode and temperature selection, and blower speeds. Temperature control lever operates the blend air door in the A/C-heater unit. This mixes both cooled and heated air so desirable air temperature can be obtained. The system will provide cooled air when A/C is on and blower motor is in any position except OFF. The temperature control lever should be in the far left (maximum cooling) side of temperature selection scale when maximum A/C operation is desired.

SYSTEM COMPONENTS

A/C Switch – When A/C switch is pushed, A/C will operate if the blower motor control lever or push button is in any position except OFF. When activated, the A/C switch allows the magnetic compressor clutch to engage, operating the compressor. A light will illuminate on the A/C push button when activated.

Dual-Pressure Switch – The dual-pressure switch cuts off electrical power to clutch when refrigerant pressures rise above or below the control point of the switch. When pressures are back in normal operating ranges, power is supplied to the magnetic compressor clutch to resume operation.

Thermistor – The thermistor is a thermocouple mounted in front of the evaporator (air outlet side) to monitor airflow temperature. The evaporator thermistor is used to prevent evaporator from freezing up. The amplifier uses information received from thermistor to send appropriate electrical signal to compressor clutch for proper on-off cycling.

Vacuum Switching Valve (VSV) – An electro-vacuum (solenoid) valve is used to assist smooth engine operation during compressor's on cycle. The VSV holds throttle slightly above idle (spring-loaded to this position) when A/C system is operating. When system is off, vacuum is directed to VSV diaphragm to allow throttle to return to normal idle position.

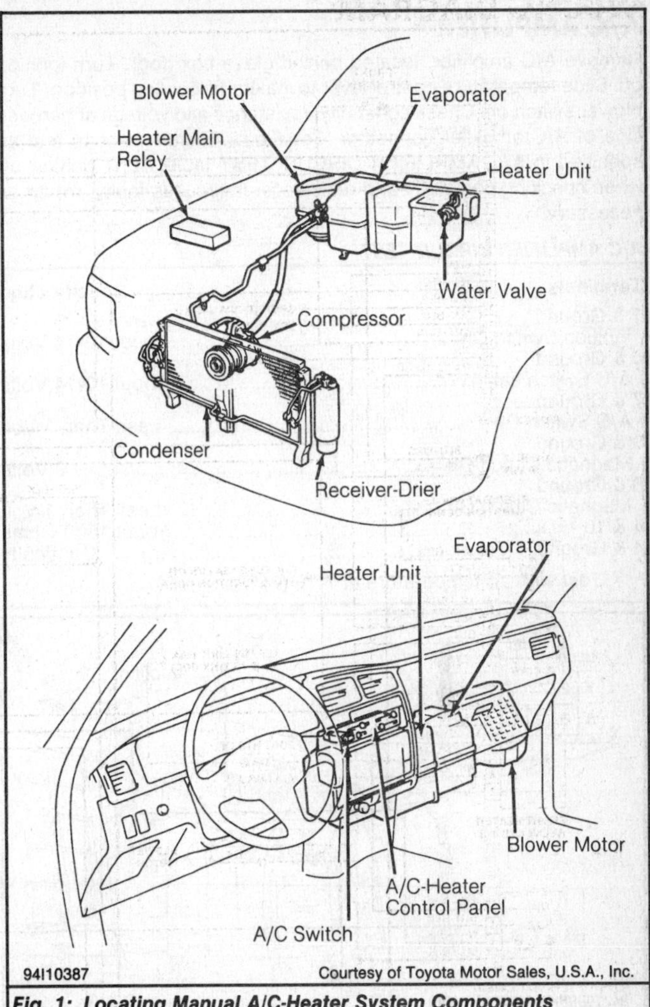
Blower Motor
Evaporator
Heater Main Relay
Heater Unit
Water Valve
Compressor
Condenser
Receiver-Drier
Evaporator
Heater Unit
Blower Motor
A/C-Heater Control Panel
A/C Switch
94I10387
Courtesy of Toyota Motor Sales, U.S.A., Inc.

Fig. 1: Locating Manual A/C-Heater System Components

ADJUSTMENTS

NOTE: For control cable adjustment procedures, see HEATER SYSTEMS article.

VACUUM SWITCHING VALVE (VSV) IDLE SPEED

Warm engine. Shift to Neutral position. Turn A/C on. Turn blower switch to high speed. With compressor clutch engaged, if engine idles at 900-1000 RPM, idle speed is correct. With compressor clutch engaged, if engine does not idle at 900-1000 RPM, turn VSV adjusting screw until idle is as specified. *See Fig. 6.* DO NOT force adjusting screw while turning.

TESTING

NOTE: For information not found in this article, see HEATER SYSTEMS article.

A/C SYSTEM PERFORMANCE

Connect manifold gauge set. Let engine idle at 2000 RPM. Set blower fan on high speed. Set temperature control switch at maximum cool position. With airflow set in recirculated mode, ensure temperature at air inlet is 86-95°F (30-35°C). Ensure pressure readings are within specifications. See SPECIFICATIONS table at beginning of article.

1993 MANUAL A/C-HEATER SYSTEMS
T100 (Cont.)

A/C AMPLIFIER

Remove A/C amplifier, located behind glove box door. Turn ignition on. Slide temperature control lever to maximum cooling position. Turn blower switch on. Check continuity, resistance and voltage at harness side of A/C amplifier connector. *See Fig. 2.* Ensure circuits test as specified in A/C AMPLIFIER CIRCUIT TEST table. Turn ignition off when checking continuity and resistance. If circuit is faulty, repair as necessary.

A/C AMPLIFIER CIRCUIT TEST

Terminals	Specification
1 & Ground	
Ignition Switch On	About 10-14 Volts
5 & Ground	
A/C Switch On	About 10-14 Volts
7 & Ground	
A/C Switch On	Less Than 1 Volt
9 & Ground	
Magnetic Clutch On	0 Volts
8 & Ground	
Magnetic Clutch On	Less Than 1 Volt
4 & 10 [1]	About 1500 Ohms
4 & Ground	Continuity

[1] – Test with air temperature at 77°F (25°C).

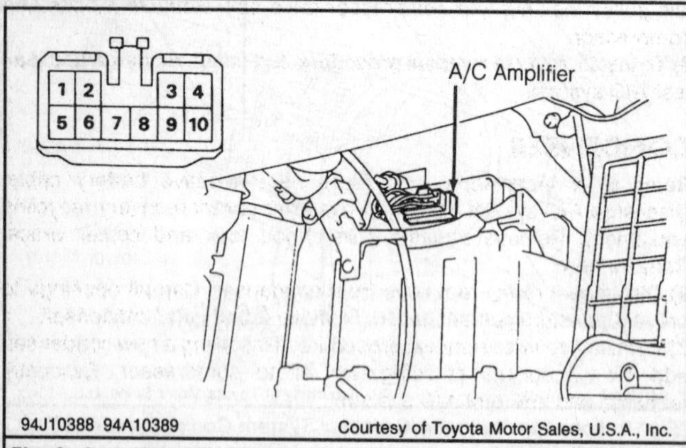
1 2 3 4
5 6 7 8 9 10
A/C Amplifier
94J10388 94A10389
Courtesy of Toyota Motor Sales, U.S.A., Inc.

Fig. 2: Locating A/C Amplifier & Identifying Connector Terminals

A/C SWITCH

Remove A/C switch from A/C-heater control panel. Check continuity between specified terminals. See A/C SWITCH CONTINUITY table. *See Fig. 3.* If continuity is not as specified, replace switch.

A/C SWITCH CONTINUITY

Switch Position	Continuity Between Terminals
Off	[1]
On	4 & 5; 4 & 6

[1] – With switch in either position, continuity should exist between terminals No. 1 and 3 for A/C switch illumination. When switch is not depressed, continuity should not exist between any other terminals.

BLOWER MOTOR

Disconnect blower motor connector. Apply battery voltage across blower motor connector terminals. Replace blower motor if it does not operate smoothly.

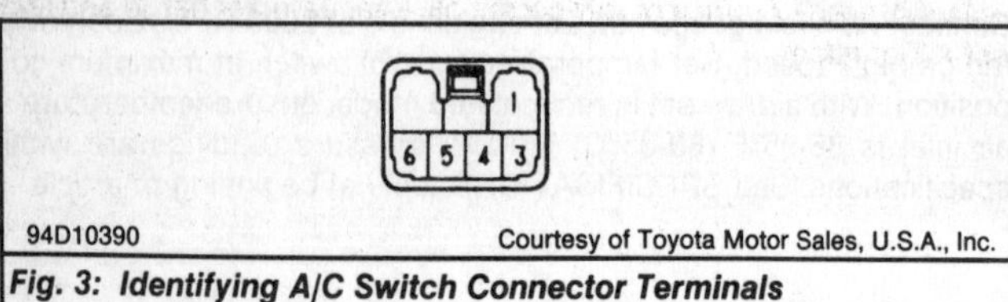
1
6 5 4 3
94D10390
Courtesy of Toyota Motor Sales, U.S.A., Inc.

Fig. 3: Identifying A/C Switch Connector Terminals

DUAL-PRESSURE SWITCH

Install manifold gauge set. Remove 2 screws and glove box door. Disconnect dual-pressure switch connector. *See Fig. 4.* Run engine at 2000 RPM. Connect ohmmeter between switch terminals No. 3 and 4. If continuity is not as specified, replace switch. See DUAL-PRESSURE SWITCH TEST table.

DUAL-PRESSURE SWITCH TEST

High-Side Line Pressure psi (kg/cm²)	System Operation	Continuity
Decreasing To 28 (2.0)	Off	No
Increasing To 33 (2.3)	On	Yes
Decreasing To 370 (26)	On	Yes
Increasing To 455 (32)	Off	No

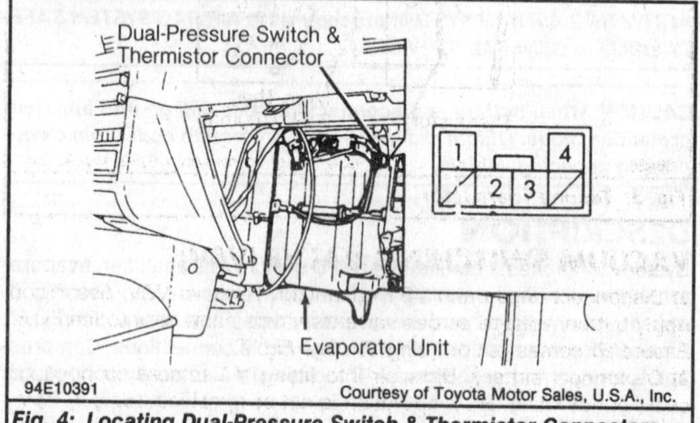
Dual-Pressure Switch &
Thermistor Connector
1 4
2 3
Evaporator Unit
94E10391
Courtesy of Toyota Motor Sales, U.S.A., Inc.

Fig. 4: Locating Dual-Pressure Switch & Thermistor Connectors

EXPANSION VALVE

1) Ensure refrigerant volume is correct. Connect manifold gauge set. Start engine. Turn A/C switch on. Turn blower switch to high speed. Run engine at 2000 RPM for at least 5 minutes. Observe gauges.
2) If low side pressure is zero psi when high pressure reading is 185-213 psi (13-15 kg/cm²), expansion valve is clogged. Replace expansion valve.

MAGNETIC CLUTCH

1) Inspect pressure plate and rotor for signs of oil contamination. Check clutch bearing for noisy operation and grease leakage. If abnormal noise is heard near compressor when A/C is off, replace magnetic (compressor) clutch.
2) Disconnect magnetic clutch connector. Connect battery positive lead to connector terminal, and negative lead to ground. Magnetic clutch should engage. If operation is not as specified, replace magnetic clutch.

THERMISTOR

1) Disconnect negative battery cable. Remove glove box door, and disconnect thermistor connector. *See Fig. 4.* Check resistance between terminals No. 1 and 2. With ambient temperature of 77°F (25°C), resistance should be 1500 ohms. If resistance is not as specified, replace thermistor.
2) If resistance is as specified, remove thermistor. See EVAPORATOR, EXPANSION VALVE & THERMISTOR under REMOVAL & INSTALLATION. Submerge thermistor at least 3.94" (100 mm) deep in cold water. *See Fig. 5.* Place thermometer in water.
3) Measure resistance across connector terminals at various temperatures. Use ice or hot water to vary water temperature. See THERMISTOR RESISTANCE VALUES table. If readings are not within specification, replace thermistor.

1993 MANUAL A/C-HEATER SYSTEMS T100 (Cont.)

THERMISTOR RESISTANCE VALUES

Ambient Temperature	Ohms
32°F (0°C)	4600-5200
41°F (5°C)	3700-4200
50°F (10°C)	2800-3300
59°F (15°C)	2200-2600
68°F (20°C)	1700-2100
77°F (25°C)	1300-1700

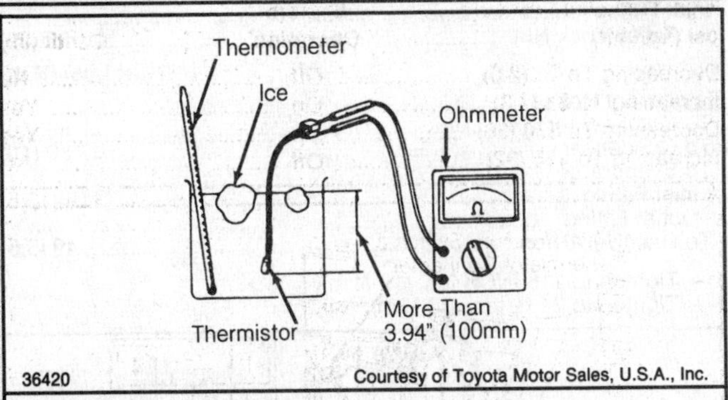
Thermometer
Ice
Ohmmeter
Thermistor
More Than
3.94" (100mm)
36420
Courtesy of Toyota Motor Sales, U.S.A., Inc.

Fig. 5: Testing Thermistor

VACUUM SWITCHING VALVE (VSV)

1) Disconnect hoses and VSV connector. Remove VSV. *See Fig. 6.* Apply battery voltage across valve terminals. Blow air into fitting "A". Ensure air comes out of fitting "B". *See Fig. 7.*

2) Disconnect battery. Blow air into fitting "A". Ensure air does not come out of fitting "B". If operation is not as specified, replace VSV.

3) If operation is as specified, use an ohmmeter to check for continuity between each terminal and ground. No continuity should exist. Check resistance between terminals. With ambient temperature of 68°F (20°C), resistance should be 30-34 ohms. If readings are not as specified, replace VSV.

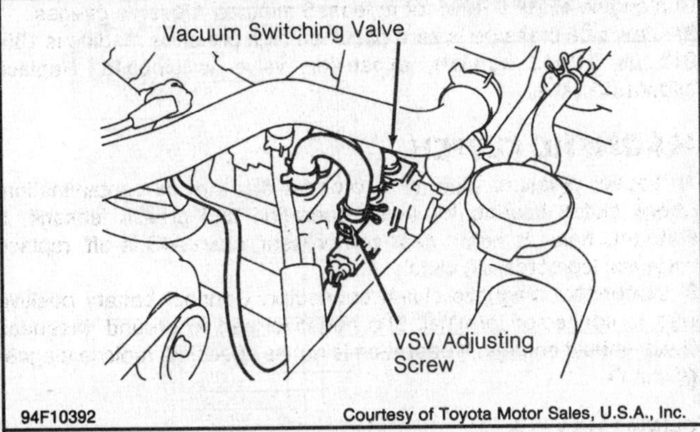
Vacuum Switching Valve
VSV Adjusting
Screw
94F10392
Courtesy of Toyota Motor Sales, U.S.A., Inc.

Fig. 6: Locating Vacuum Switching Valve

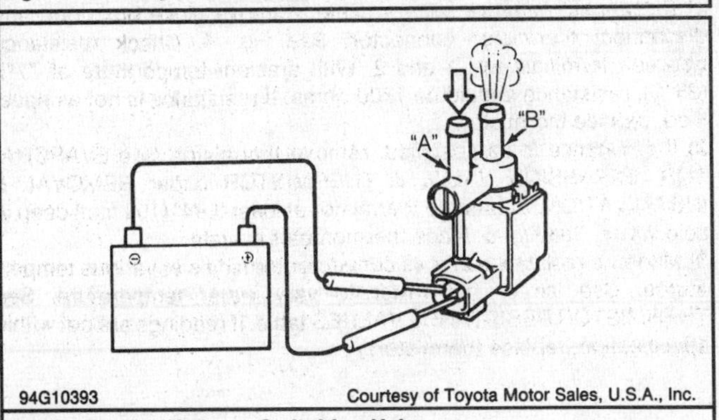
"A"
"B"
94G10393
Courtesy of Toyota Motor Sales, U.S.A., Inc.

Fig. 7: Testing Vacuum Switching Valve

REMOVAL & INSTALLATION

NOTE: For information not found in this article, see HEATER SYSTEMS article.

A/C UNIT

Removal & Installation – 1) Disconnect negative battery cable. Discharge A/C system using approved refrigerant recovery/recycling equipment. Disconnect refrigerant lines from A/C unit. Remove grommets from refrigerant lines. Remove drain pipe grommet.

2) Remove 2 screws and glove box door. Remove instrument panel lower center cover and glove box reinforcement. Remove A/C unit. To install, reverse removal procedure. Evacuate, recharge and leak test A/C system.

COMPRESSOR

Removal & Installation – 1) If possible, turn A/C on and idle engine for about 10 minutes. Stop engine. Disconnect negative battery cable. Discharge A/C system using approved refrigerant recovery/recycling equipment. Disconnect magnetic (compressor) clutch connector.

2) Disconnect refrigerant hoses from compressor. Cap all openings to prevent moisture contamination. Remove engine undercover. Loosen idle pulley lock nut and compressor drive belt. Remove 4 bolts and compressor.

3) To install, reverse removal procedure. Evacuate, recharge and leak test A/C system.

CONDENSER

Removal & Installation – 1) Disconnect negative battery cable. Discharge A/C system using approved refrigerant recovery/recycling equipment. Remove radiator grille, hood lock and center brace. Remove horn.

2) Disconnect refrigerant lines from condenser. Cap all openings to prevent moisture contamination. Remove 2 bolts and condenser.

3) To install, reverse removal procedure. If installing a new condenser, add 1.4-1.7 ounces of refrigerant oil to compressor. Evacuate, recharge and leak test A/C system.

EVAPORATOR, EXPANSION VALVE & THERMISTOR

Removal & Installation – 1) Disconnect negative battery cable. Discharge A/C system using approved refrigerant recovery/recycling equipment. Remove A/C unit. See A/C UNIT.

2) Disconnect wiring harness to A/C unit. Remove 4 clips and 4 screws, and remove evaporator upper case. Remove thermistor and holder. Remove evaporator lower case. *See Fig. 8.* Disconnect liquid line from inlet fitting of expansion valve. Remove packing and heat sensing tube from evaporator suction tube. Remove expansion valve.

3) To install, reverse removal procedure. Ensure tube fitting "O" rings are positioned correctly. If evaporator was replaced, add 1.4-1.7 ounces of refrigerant oil. Evacuate, recharge and leak test A/C system.

RECEIVER-DRIER

Removal & Installation – 1) Discharge A/C system using approved refrigerant recovery/recycling equipment. Remove radiator grille. Remove refrigerant hoses from receiver-drier. Cap all openings to prevent moisture contamination. Remove receiver-drier.

2) To install, reverse removal procedure. If receiver-drier was replaced, add 0.7 ounce of refrigerant oil. Evacuate, recharge and leak test A/C system.

1993 MANUAL A/C-HEATER SYSTEMS
T100 (Cont.)

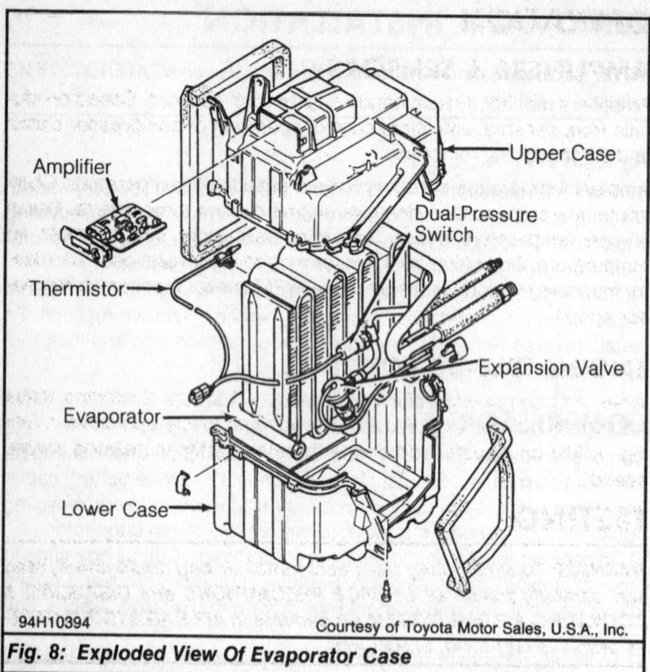
Amplifier
Upper Case
Dual-Pressure Switch
Thermistor
Expansion Valve
Evaporator
Lower Case

94H10394 Courtesy of Toyota Motor Sales, U.S.A., Inc.

Fig. 8: Exploded View Of Evaporator Case

TORQUE SPECIFICATIONS

TORQUE SPECIFICATIONS

Application	Ft. Lbs. (N.m)
Compressor-To-	
Compressor Bracket Bolts	18 (25)
Compressor Bracket-To-Engine Bolts	34 (47)
Expansion Valve	
To Evaporator Inlet Fitting	16 (22)
Inlet Fitting	[1]
Idle Pulley Lock Nut	29 (39)
	INCH Lbs. (N.m)
Refrigerant Hoses	
To Compressor	89 (10)
To Condenser	89 (10)
To Evaporator	
Inlet Fitting	119 (13.5)
Outlet Fitting	[2]
To Receiver-Drier	49 (5.5)

[1] – Tighten to 115 INCH lbs. (13 N.m).
[2] – Tighten to 24 ft. lbs. (33 N.m).

WIRING DIAGRAM

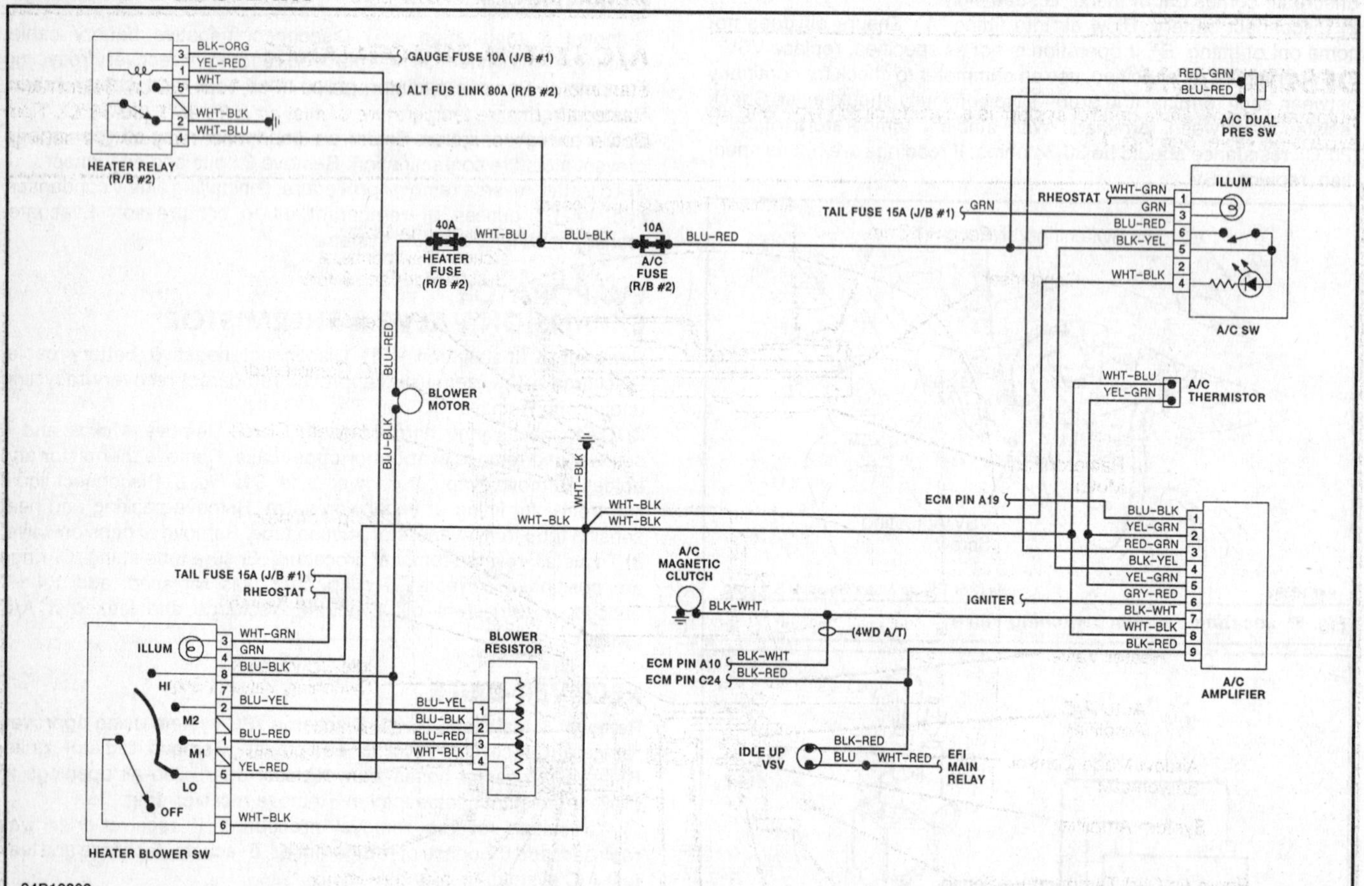

94B10802 Courtesy of Toyota Motor Sales, U.S.A., Inc.

Fig. 9: Manual A/C-Heater System Wiring Diagram (T100)

1993 AUTOMATIC A/C-HEATER SYSTEMS
Celica

SPECIFICATIONS

Compressor Type
- 1.6L .... Nippondenso 10PA15C 10-Cyl.
- 2.0L & 2.2L .... Nippondenso 10PA17C/VC 10-Cyl.

Compressor Belt Tension [1]
- 1.6L
  - New .... 135-185 Lbs. (61.2-83.9 kg)
  - Used .... 80-120 Lbs. (36.3-54.4 kg)
- 2.0L
  - New .... 155-175 Lbs. (70.3-79.4 kg)
  - Used .... 69-99 Lbs. (31.3-44.9 kg)
- 2.2L
  - New .... 155-175 Lbs. (70.3-79.4 kg)
  - Used .... 100-120 Lbs. (45.4-54.4 kg)

System Oil Capacity .... 3.4-4.1 ozs.
Refrigerant (R-12) Capacity .... 24-27 ozs.
System Operating Pressures [2]
- High Side .... 206-213 psi (14.5-15.0 kg/cm²)
- Low Side .... 21-28 psi (1.5-2.0 kg/cm²)

[1] – Using a belt tension gauge, measure at longest run of belt.
[2] – Specification is with ambient temperature at 86-95°F (30-35°C) and engine speed at 2000 RPM.

WARNING: To avoid injury from accidental air bag deployment, read and carefully follow all SERVICE PRECAUTIONS and DISABLING & ACTIVATING AIR BAG SYSTEM procedures in AIR BAG SYSTEM SAFETY article in GENERAL SERVICING.

CAUTION: When battery is disconnected, radio will go into anti-theft protection mode. Obtain radio anti-theft protection code from owner prior to servicing vehicle.

DESCRIPTION

Automatic temperature control system is a cycling clutch type with an expansion valve. *See Fig. 1.*

OPERATION

AMPLIFIERS & SENSORS

Amplifiers monitor system conditions through sensors. Based on signals from sensors, amplifiers control operation of compressor clutch and air control servomotors.

Ambient temperature sensor monitors outside air temperature. Coolant temperature sensor monitors engine coolant temperature. Room (in-car) temperature sensor monitors passenger compartment air temperature. Solar (sunload) sensor monitors sunlight load. Thermistor monitors evaporator temperature. RPM sensor monitors compressor speed.

ENGINE IDLE-UP CONTROL

When A/C compressor clutch is engaged, Vacuum Switching Valve (VSV) solenoid is energized, allowing vacuum to idle-up actuator. *See Fig. 1.* Idle-up actuator rod opens throttle slightly, increasing engine speed.

TESTING

WARNING: To avoid injury from accidental air bag deployment, read and carefully follow all SERVICE PRECAUTIONS and DISABLING & ACTIVATING AIR BAG SYSTEM procedures in AIR BAG SYSTEM SAFETY article in GENERAL SERVICING.

NOTE: For testing of components not listed in this article, see MANUAL A/C-HEATER SYSTEMS – CELICA article.

A/C SYSTEM PERFORMANCE

Start engine and allow it to idle at 2000 RPM. Turn A/C on. Select recirculated air. Ensure temperature of inlet air is 86-95°F (30-35°C). Turn blower to highest speed. Select maximum cool temperature setting.

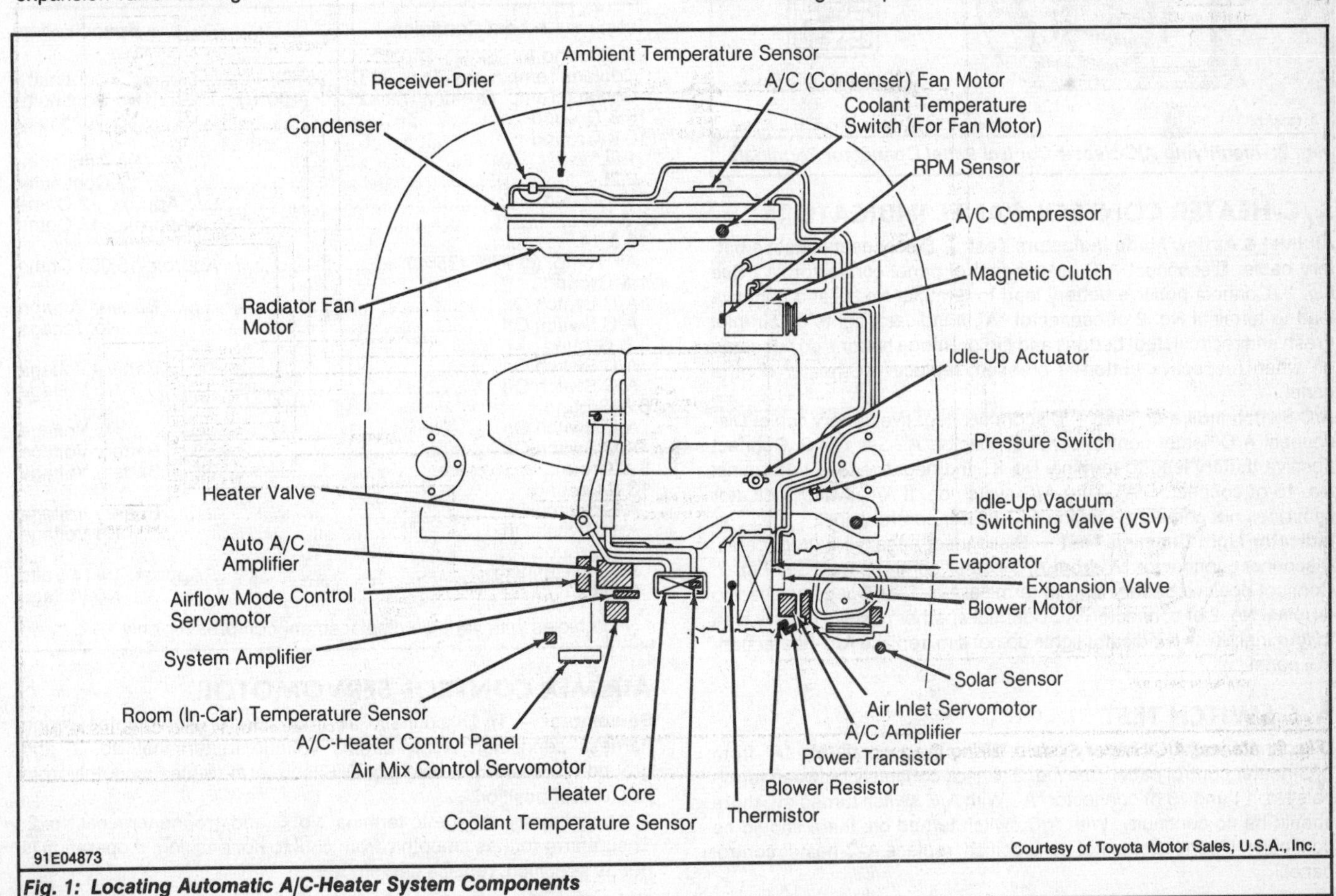
Ambient Temperature Sensor
Receiver-Drier
A/C (Condenser) Fan Motor
Coolant Temperature Switch (For Fan Motor)
Condenser
RPM Sensor
A/C Compressor
Magnetic Clutch
Radiator Fan Motor
Idle-Up Actuator
Pressure Switch
Heater Valve
Idle-Up Vacuum Switching Valve (VSV)
Auto A/C Amplifier
Evaporator
Expansion Valve
Airflow Mode Control Servomotor
Blower Motor
System Amplifier
Solar Sensor
Air Inlet Servomotor
Room (In-Car) Temperature Sensor
A/C Amplifier
A/C-Heater Control Panel
Power Transistor
Air Mix Control Servomotor
Blower Resistor
Heater Core
Thermistor
Coolant Temperature Sensor
91E04873
Courtesy of Toyota Motor Sales, U.S.A., Inc.

Fig. 1: Locating Automatic A/C-Heater System Components

1993 AUTOMATIC A/C-HEATER SYSTEMS
Celica (Cont.)

Allow several minutes for system to stabilize. Ensure high side and low side pressures are within specification. See SPECIFICATIONS table at beginning of article.

A/C COMPRESSOR CLUTCH TEST

1) Ensure compressor clutch pressure plate, rotor and bearings are okay, and air gap is .002-.006" (.05-.15 mm). Disconnect compressor connector. Check resistance between Black/White wire terminal of compressor connector and compressor body (ground).
2) If resistance is not 3.4-3.8 ohms at 68°F (20°C), replace clutch coil. If resistance is as specified, connect positive battery lead to Black/White wire terminal, and negative lead to compressor body (ground). Clutch is okay if it engages. Replace clutch if it does not engage.

A/C-HEATER CONTROL PANEL ILLUMINATION

Disconnect negative battery cable. Disconnect A/C-heater control panel connector "A". *See Fig. 2.* Connect positive battery lead to terminal No. 18, and negative lead to terminal No. 17 of connector "A". If illumination lights do not come on, check bulbs. If bulbs are okay, replace A/C-heater control panel.

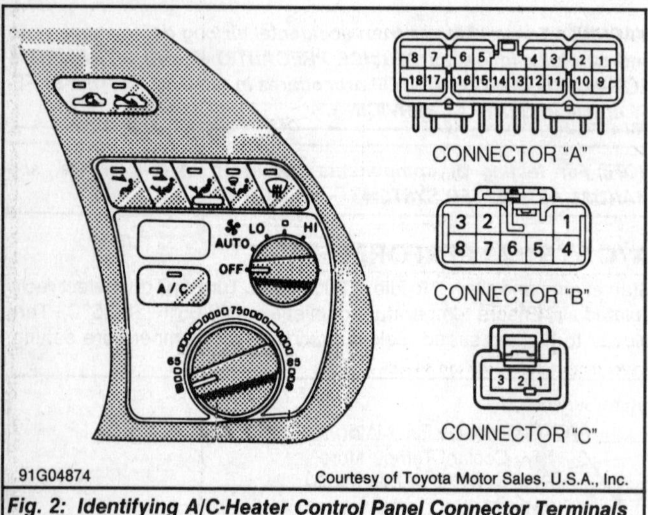
8 7 6 5 4 3 2 1
18 17 16 15 14 13 12 11 10 9
CONNECTOR "A"
3 2 1
8 7 6 5 4
CONNECTOR "B"
3 2 1
CONNECTOR "C"
AUTO
LO
HI
OFF
A/C
91G04874
Courtesy of Toyota Motor Sales, U.S.A., Inc.

Fig. 2: Identifying A/C-Heater Control Panel Connector Terminals

A/C-HEATER CONTROL PANEL INDICATORS

Air Inlet & Airflow Mode Indicators Test – Disconnect negative battery cable. Disconnect A/C-heater control panel connector "A". *See Fig. 2.* Connect positive battery lead to terminal No. 1, and negative lead to terminal No. 2 of connector "A". If indicator lights on air inlet (fresh and recirculated) buttons and airflow mode buttons do not come on when respective button is pressed, replace A/C-heater control panel.

A/C Switch Indicator Test – Disconnect negative battery cable. Disconnect A/C-heater control panel connector "A". *See Fig. 2.* Connect positive battery lead to terminal No. 1, and negative lead to terminal No. 15 of connector "A". Turn A/C switch on. If A/C switch indicator light does not come on, replace A/C-heater control panel.

Indicator Light Dimming Test – Disconnect negative battery cable. Disconnect connector "A" from A/C-heater control panel. *See Fig. 2.* Connect positive battery lead to terminal No. 1, and negative lead to terminal No. 2 of connector "A". Connect another positive battery lead to terminal No. 3. If indicator lights do not dim, replace A/C-heater control panel.

A/C SWITCH TEST

Disconnect negative battery cable. Disconnect connector "A" from A/C-heater control panel. *See Fig. 2.* Check continuity between terminals No. 14 and 16 of connector "A". With A/C switch turned off, there should be no continuity. With A/C switch turned on, there should be continuity. If continuity is not as specified, replace A/C-heater control panel.

AIR INLET SWITCHES TEST

NOTE:* *Air inlet switches contain diodes. Check continuity in both directions (polarity) before assuming switch is faulty.

Disconnect connector "A" from A/C-heater control panel. *See Fig. 2.* With recirculated air button pressed, continuity should exist between terminals No. 2 and 7 of connector "A". With fresh air button pressed, continuity should exist between terminals No. 2 and 8. If continuity is not as specified, replace A/C-heater control panel.

AIRFLOW MODE CONTROL SWITCHES TEST

Disconnect connector "A" from A/C-heater control panel. *See Fig. 2.* Check continuity between specified terminals of connector "A". See AIRFLOW MODE CONTROL SWITCHES CONTINUITY TEST table. If continuity is not as specified, replace A/C-heater control panel.

AIRFLOW MODE CONTROL SWITCHES CONTINUITY TEST

Switch Position	Continuity Between Terminal No.
Face	2 & 9
Bi-Level	2 & 10
Foot	2 & 11
Foot/Defrost	2 & 12
Defrost	2 & 13

A/C AMPLIFIER CIRCUIT TEST

Disconnect A/C amplifier connector. Turn ignition on. Turn temperature control dial to maximum cool position. Turn blower switch to HI position. At harness side of A/C amplifier connector, check continuity, resistance and voltage at specified terminals. See A/C AMPLIFIER CIRCUIT TEST table. *See Fig. 4.* If continuity, resistance or voltage is not as specified, repair appropriate circuit.

A/C AMPLIFIER CIRCUIT TEST

Terminals & Test Condition	Specification
2 & Ground [1]	
Coolant Temp. Less Than 203°F (95°C)	Continuity
Coolant Temp. Greater Than 212°F (100°C)	No Continuity
15 & Ground	Continuity
10 & Ground	
1.6L	No Continuity
2.2L	Continuity
5 & Ground [1]	Approx. 12 Ohms
9 & 14	Approx. 115 Ohms
16 & 14	
Air Temp. @ 77°F (25°C)	Approx. 15,000 Ohms
1 & Ground	
A/C Switch On	Battery Voltage
A/C Switch Off	No Voltage
3 & Ground	
A/C Switch On	Battery Voltage
A/C Switch Off	No Voltage
6 & Ground	
A/C Switch On	No Voltage
A/C Switch Off	Battery Voltage
8 & Ground	Battery Voltage
13 & Ground	
A/C Switch On	Battery Voltage
A/C Switch Off	No Voltage
18 & Ground	
Engine Running	Approx. 10-14 Volts
Engine Off	No Voltage

[1] – Vehicles with variable displacement compressor only.

AIR MIX CONTROL SERVOMOTOR

Servomotor – **1)** Disconnect air mix control servomotor wiring harness connector. Apply battery voltage to terminal No. 2, and ground terminal No. 6. *See Fig. 5.* Ensure arm rotates smoothly from hot to cool position.
2) Apply battery voltage to terminal No. 6, and ground terminal No. 2. Ensure arm rotates smoothly from cool to hot position. If operation is not as specified, replace servomotor.

1993 AUTOMATIC A/C-HEATER SYSTEMS
Celica (Cont.)

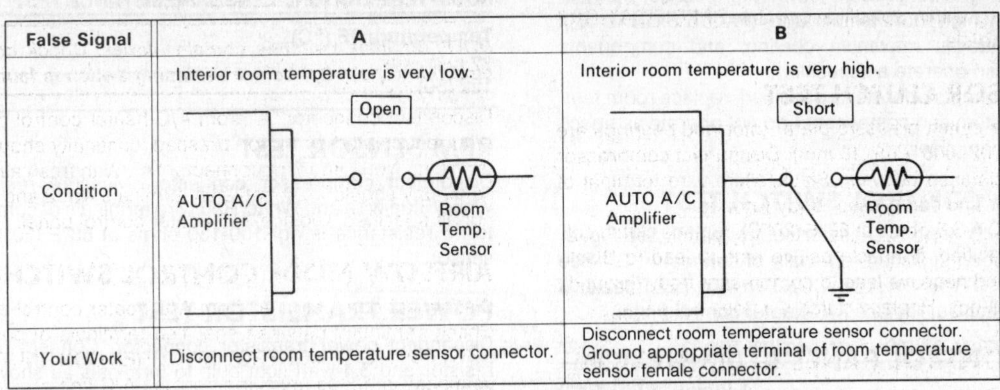

False Signal	A	B
Condition	Interior room temperature is very low.	Interior room temperature is very high.
Your Work	Disconnect room temperature sensor connector.	Disconnect room temperature sensor connector. Ground appropriate terminal of room temperature sensor female connector.

Open
AUTO A/C Amplifier
Room Temp. Sensor
Short
AUTO A/C Amplifier
Room Temp. Sensor

System Main Parts	False Signal	Motion			
Air Mix Control Servomotor	A	Air mix control servo motor shaft moves towards max-hot side.			
	B	Air mix control servo motor shaft moves towards max-cool side.			
Airflow Mode Control Servomotor		Airflow Mode Door Position			
		VENT	BI-LEVEL	HEAT	DEF
	A	Close	Close	Open	Close
	B	Open	Close	Close	Close

System Main Parts	False Signal	Motion
Blower Motor	A	Blower motor rotates at high speed.
	B	
Heater Water Valve	A	OPEN
	B	CLOSE
Air Inlet Control Servomotor	FRE Switch ON	Fresh air is ventilated.
	REC Switch ON	Recirculated air is ventilated.

93D19771 Courtesy of Toyota Motor Sales, U.S.A., Inc.

Fig. 3: Testing Auto A/C Amplifier

WIRING HARNESS CONNECTOR

1 2 3 4 5 6 7 8
9 10 11 12 13 14 15 16 17 18

66631 Courtesy of Toyota Motor Sales, U.S.A., Inc.

Fig. 4: Identifying A/C Amplifier Connector Terminals

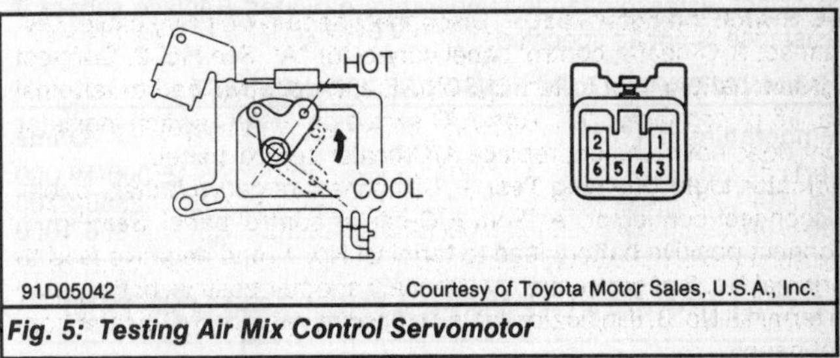

HOT
COOL
2 1
6 5 4 3

91D05042 Courtesy of Toyota Motor Sales, U.S.A., Inc.

Fig. 5: Testing Air Mix Control Servomotor

Position Sensor – Measure resistance between terminals No. 1 and 3. *See Fig. 5.* Reading should be about 6000 ohms. Set arm to cool position. While rotating arm to hot position, measure resistance between terminals No. 1 and 4. Resistance should decrease from about 4800 ohms to 1200 ohms. If readings are not as specified, replace air mix control servomotor.

AUTO A/C AMPLIFIER TEST

1) Set temperature control dial to 77°F (25°C). Disconnect room temperature sensor connector. This simulates very low room temperature (FALSE SIGNAL "A"). *See Fig. 3.* System should operate at maximum heating, and components indicated in chart should operate as specified.

1993 AUTOMATIC A/C-HEATER SYSTEMS
Celica (Cont.)

2) Ground appropriate terminal of room temperature sensor connector. This simulates very high room temperature (FALSE SIGNAL "B"). System should operate at maximum cooling, and components indicated in chart should operate as specified.
3) If system and components operate as specified, replace room temperature sensor. If system and components do not operate as specified, replace auto A/C amplifier.

BLOWER SPEED CONTROL SWITCH TEST

Disconnect connector "B" from A/C-heater control panel. *See Fig. 2.* Check continuity between specified terminals of connector "B". See BLOWER SPEED CONTROL SWITCH CONTINUITY TEST table. If continuity is not as specified, replace A/C-heater control panel.

BLOWER SPEED CONTROL SWITCH CONTINUITY TEST

Switch Position	Continuity Between Terminal No.
OFF	None
AUTO	1, 3 & 7
LO	2, 3 & 6
■	2, 3 & 4
HI	2, 3 & 5

TEMPERATURE CONTROL DIAL TEST

1) Disconnect connector "C" from A/C-heater control panel. *See Fig. 2.* Measure resistance between terminals No. 2 and 3 of connector "C". Resistance should be approximately 3000 ohms.
2) Measure resistance between terminals No. 1 and 3 while rotating temperature control dial from cool position to hot position. If resistance does not vary from zero to about 3000 ohms, replace A/C-heater control panel.

AMBIENT TEMPERATURE SENSOR TEST

Disconnect electrical connector from ambient temperature sensor, located at front grille, near horns. Check resistance across ambient temperature sensor terminals. If resistance is not as specified, replace sensor. See AMBIENT TEMPERATURE SENSOR RESISTANCE TEST table.

AMBIENT TEMPERATURE SENSOR RESISTANCE TEST

Temperature °F (°C)	Ohms
77 (25)	1700
122 (50)	620

COOLANT TEMPERATURE SENSOR TEST

Remove coolant temperature sensor. Submerge sensing portion of sensor in container of water. Monitor water temperature with thermometer, and measure resistance between sensor terminals. See COOLANT TEMPERATURE SENSOR RESISTANCE TEST table. Use ice or hot water to change temperature of water. Replace sensor if resistance is not as specified.

COOLANT TEMPERATURE SENSOR RESISTANCE TEST

Temperature °F (°C)	Ohms
34 (1)	15,000-19,000
104 (40)	2500-2700
158 (70)	800-1000

ROOM (IN-CAR) TEMPERATURE SENSOR TEST

***NOTE:** If room temperature sensor circuit is open, system will operate at maximum heating. If circuit is shorted, system will operate at maximum cooling.*

Disconnect electrical connector from room temperature sensor, located under driver knee bolster. Measure resistance across sensor terminals. If resistance is not as specified, replace sensor. See ROOM TEMPERATURE SENSOR RESISTANCE TEST table.

ROOM TEMPERATURE SENSOR RESISTANCE TEST

Temperature °F (°C)	Ohms
77 (25)	1700
122 (50)	620

RPM SENSOR TEST

Disconnect compressor connector. Measure resistance between White/Blue wire and White/Red wire terminals of compressor connector. If resistance is not 100-130 ohms at 68°F (20°C), replace RPM sensor.

POWER TRANSISTOR TEST

Disconnect power transistor connector. Connect battery, 120-ohm resistor and 3.4-watt light bulb to terminals as shown. *See Fig. 5.* If light bulb does not come on, replace power transistor.

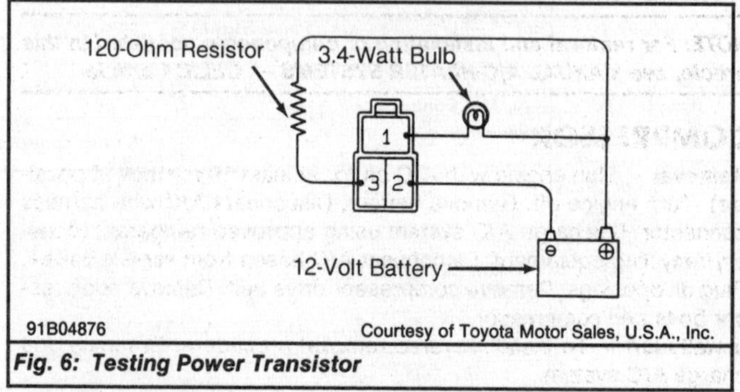
120-Ohm Resistor
3.4-Watt Bulb
1
3
2
12-Volt Battery
91B04876
Courtesy of Toyota Motor Sales, U.S.A., Inc.

Fig. 6: Testing Power Transistor

SOLAR (SUNLOAD) SENSOR TEST

Disconnect solar sensor connector. Check continuity across solar sensor terminals. If there is no continuity, replace solar sensor.

SYSTEM AMPLIFIER TEST

1) Disconnect system amplifier connector. Turn ignition on. Turn temperature control dial to maximum cool position. At system amplifier connector, check continuity and voltage at specified terminals. See SYSTEM AMPLIFIER TEST (PART 1 OF 2) table. *See Fig. 7.*

SYSTEM AMPLIFIER TEST (PART 1 OF 2)

Terminal No.	Specified Value
1 & 6	Continuity
9 & Ground	Continuity
7 & Ground	Battery Voltage

2) If continuity and voltage are not as specified, repair appropriate circuit. If continuity and voltage are as specified, turn off ignition. Reconnect system amplifier connector. Start engine. Turn A/C on. Turn blower switch to HI position.
3) Set temperature dial in appropriate position, and check voltage at specified terminals of system amplifier connector (backprobe terminals). See SYSTEM AMPLIFIER TEST (PART 2 OF 2) table. If voltage is as specified, system amplifier is okay. If voltage is not as specified, replace system amplifier.

SYSTEM AMPLIFIER TEST (PART 2 OF 2)

Terminals & Test Condition	Specification
3 & Ground	
Maximum Hot	Approximately Zero Volts
Maximum Cool	[1] Approximately 5 Volts
4 & Ground	
Maximum Hot	[1] Approximately 5 Volts
Maximum Cool	Approximately Zero Volts

[1] – When temperature control dial is turned, reading may drop to zero volts and then slowly return to 5 volts.

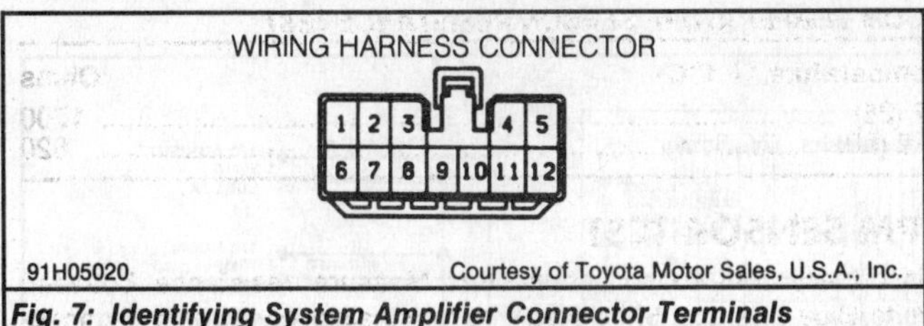

WIRING HARNESS CONNECTOR
1 2 3 4 5
6 7 8 9 10 11 12
91H05020
Courtesy of Toyota Motor Sales, U.S.A., Inc.

Fig. 7: Identifying System Amplifier Connector Terminals

REMOVAL & INSTALLATION

WARNING: To avoid injury from accidental air bag deployment, read and carefully follow all SERVICE PRECAUTIONS and DISABLING & ACTIVATING AIR BAG SYSTEM procedures in AIR BAG SYSTEM SAFETY article in GENERAL SERVICING.

NOTE: For removal and installation of components not listed in this article, see MANUAL A/C-HEATER SYSTEMS - CELICA article.

COMPRESSOR

Removal - Run engine with A/C on for at least 10 minutes (if possible). Turn engine off. Remove battery. Disconnect A/C wire harness connector. Discharge A/C system using approved refrigerant recovery/recycling equipment. Disconnect A/C hoses from service valves. Plug all openings. Remove compressor drive belt. Remove compressor bolts and compressor.

Installation - To install, reverse removal procedure. Evacuate and charge A/C system.

EVAPORATOR, EXPANSION VALVE & THERMISTOR

Removal - **1)** Disconnect negative battery cable. Discharge A/C system using approved refrigerant recovery/recycling equipment. Disconnect inlet and outlet lines and grommets from evaporator at engine compartment firewall. Plug openings.

2) Disconnect electrical connectors from evaporator case as necessary. Remove glove box and reinforcement. In passenger compartment, remove 3 nuts and 4 bolts securing evaporator case to firewall. Remove evaporator case.

Disassembly - Remove evaporator case clips and screws. *See Fig. 8.* Separate evaporator case halves. Remove thermistor, evaporator and expansion valve.

Reassembly & Installation - To reassemble and install evaporator assembly, reverse disassembly and removal procedures. If installing new evaporator core, add 1.4-1.7 ounces of refrigerant oil to system. Evacuate and charge A/C system.

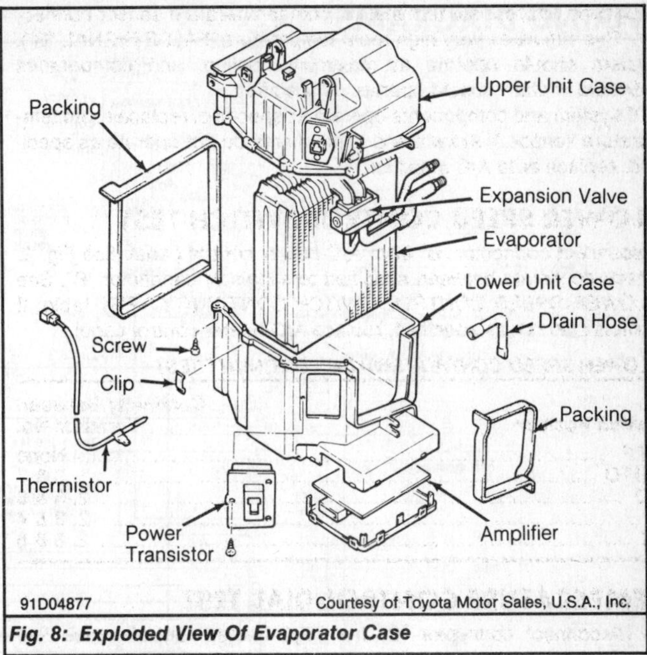

Packing
Upper Unit Case
Expansion Valve
Evaporator
Lower Unit Case
Drain Hose
Screw
Clip
Packing
Thermistor
Power Transistor
Amplifier
91D04877
Courtesy of Toyota Motor Sales, U.S.A., Inc.

Fig. 8: Exploded View Of Evaporator Case

CONDENSER

Removal - Discharge A/C system using approved refrigerant recovery/recycling equipment. Remove lower engine cover. Remove grille and hood lock brace. Remove horns. Disconnect A/C lines from condenser. Plug all openings. Remove mounting bolts and condenser.

Installation - To install, reverse removal procedure. If installing new condenser, add 1.4-1.7 ounces of refrigeration oil to system. Evacuate and charge A/C system.

RECEIVER-DRIER

Removal - Discharge A/C system using approved refrigerant recovery/recycling equipment. Disconnect A/C hoses from receiver-drier. Plug all openings. Remove receiver-drier bolts and receiver-drier.

Installation - To install, reverse removal procedure. Add 0.7 ounce of refrigerant oil to system. Evacuate and charge A/C system.

TORQUE SPECIFICATIONS

TORQUE SPECIFICATIONS

Application	Ft. Lbs. (N.m)
Compressor Bolts	
1.6L	18 (24)
2.0L & 2.2L	25 (34)
Refrigerant Hose Fitting	
At Compressor	18 (24)
At Condenser	
Liquid Line	10 (14)
Discharge Line	17 (23)
At Evaporator	
Liquid Line	10 (14)
Suction Line	24 (32)
At Receiver-Drier	10 (14)

WIRING DIAGRAMS

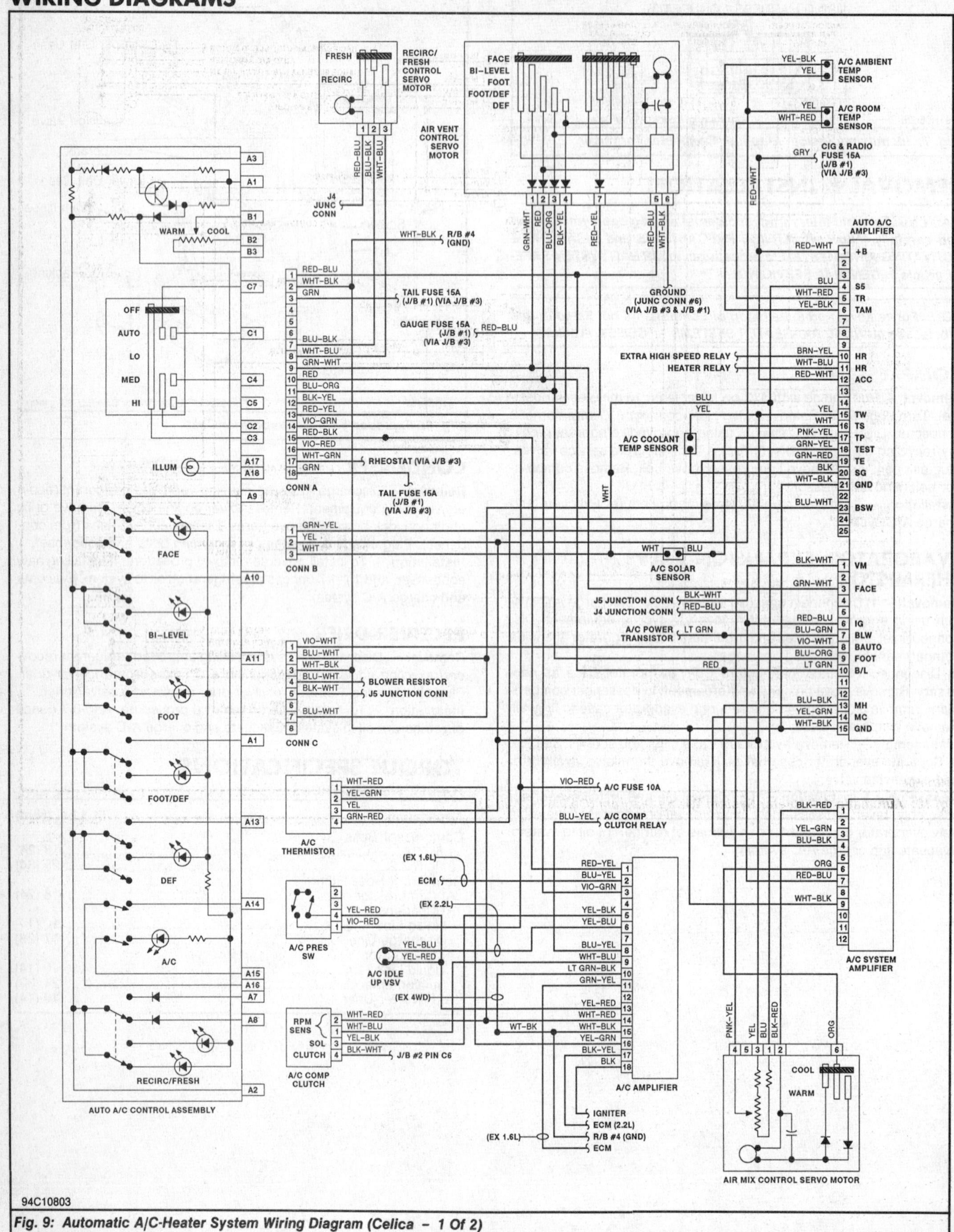
FRESH
RECIRC
RECIRC/ FRESH CONTROL SERVO MOTOR
FACE
BI-LEVEL
FOOT
FOOT/DEF
DEF
AIR VENT CONTROL SERVO MOTOR
A/C AMBIENT TEMP SENSOR
A/C ROOM TEMP SENSOR
CIG & RADIO FUSE 15A (J/B #1) (VIA J/B #3)
J4 JUNC CONN
R/B #4 (GND)
TAIL FUSE 15A (J/B #1) (VIA J/B #3)
GAUGE FUSE 15A (J/B #1) (VIA J/B #3)
GROUND (JUNC CONN #6) (VIA J/B #3 & J/B #1)
AUTO A/C AMPLIFIER
EXTRA HIGH SPEED RELAY
HEATER RELAY
A/C COOLANT TEMP SENSOR
RHEOSTAT (VIA J/B #3)
CONN A
ILLUM
WARM
COOL
OFF
AUTO
LO
MED
HI
A/C SOLAR SENSOR
CONN B
J5 JUNCTION CONN
J4 JUNCTION CONN
A/C POWER TRANSISTOR
BLOWER RESISTOR
J5 JUNCTION CONN
CONN C
A/C FUSE 10A
A/C COMP CLUTCH RELAY
A/C THERMISTOR
ECM
(EX 1.6L)
(EX 2.2L)
(EX 4WD)
A/C PRES SW
A/C IDLE UP VSV
RPM SENS
SOL CLUTCH
A/C COMP CLUTCH
J/B #2 PIN C6
A/C AMPLIFIER
A/C SYSTEM AMPLIFIER
IGNITER
ECM (2.2L)
R/B #4 (GND)
ECM
(EX 1.6L)
AIR MIX CONTROL SERVO MOTOR
AUTO A/C CONTROL ASSEMBLY
FACE
BI-LEVEL
FOOT
FOOT/DEF
DEF
A/C
RECIRC/FRESH
94C10803

Fig. 9: Automatic A/C-Heater System Wiring Diagram (Celica – 1 Of 2)

1993 AUTOMATIC A/C-HEATER SYSTEMS
Celica (Cont.)

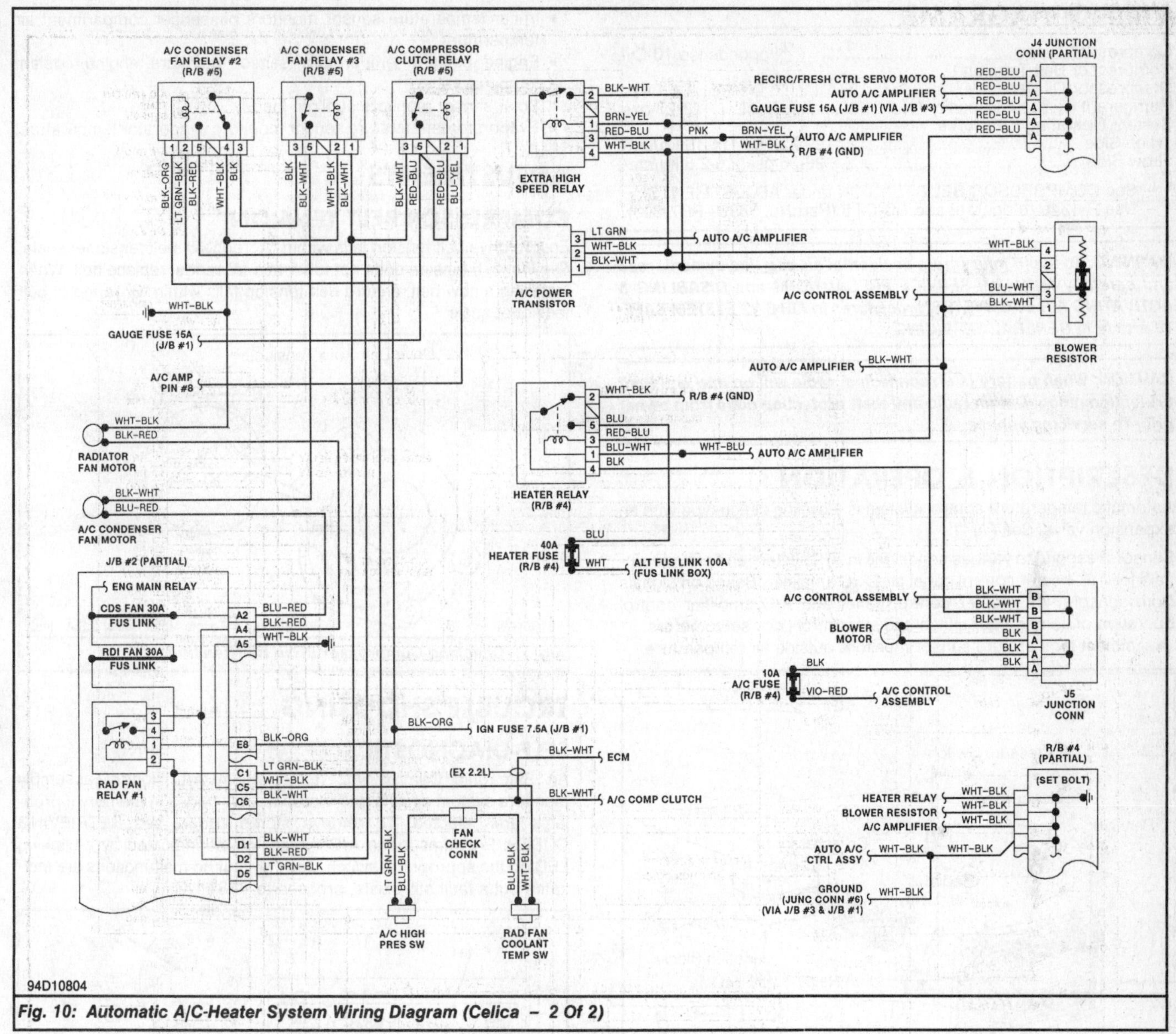
A/C CONDENSER FAN RELAY #2 (R/B #5)
A/C CONDENSER FAN RELAY #3 (R/B #5)
A/C COMPRESSOR CLUTCH RELAY (R/B #5)
EXTRA HIGH SPEED RELAY
BLK-WHT
BRN-YEL
RED-BLU
WHT-BLK
PNK
AUTO A/C AMPLIFIER
R/B #4 (GND)
J4 JUNCTION CONN (PARTIAL)
RECIRC/FRESH CTRL SERVO MOTOR
AUTO A/C AMPLIFIER
GAUGE FUSE 15A (J/B #1) (VIA J/B #3)
RED-BLU
BLK-ORG
LT GRN-BLK
BLK-RED
WHT-BLK
BLK
BLK-WHT
WHT-BLK
RED-BLU
BLU-YEL
A/C POWER TRANSISTOR
LT GRN
AUTO A/C AMPLIFIER
A/C CONTROL ASSEMBLY
BLU-WHT
BLOWER RESISTOR
GAUGE FUSE 15A (J/B #1)
A/C AMP PIN #8
RADIATOR FAN MOTOR
A/C CONDENSER FAN MOTOR
BLU-RED
HEATER RELAY (R/B #4)
BLU
WHT-BLU
40A HEATER FUSE (R/B #4)
WHT
ALT FUS LINK 100A (FUS LINK BOX)
J/B #2 (PARTIAL)
ENG MAIN RELAY
CDS FAN 30A FUS LINK
RDI FAN 30A FUS LINK
RAD FAN RELAY #1
BLOWER MOTOR
10A A/C FUSE (R/B #4)
VIO-RED
A/C CONTROL ASSEMBLY
J5 JUNCTION CONN
IGN FUSE 7.5A (J/B #1)
ECM
(EX 2.2L)
A/C COMP CLUTCH
FAN CHECK CONN
A/C HIGH PRES SW
RAD FAN COOLANT TEMP SW
R/B #4 (PARTIAL)
(SET BOLT)
HEATER RELAY
BLOWER RESISTOR
A/C AMPLIFIER
AUTO A/C CTRL ASSY
GROUND (JUNC CONN #6) (VIA J/B #3 & J/B #1)
94D10804

Fig. 10: Automatic A/C-Heater System Wiring Diagram (Celica – 2 Of 2)

1993 AUTOMATIC A/C-HEATER SYSTEMS
Supra

SPECIFICATIONS

Compressor Type .... Nippondenso 10-Cyl.
Compressor Belt Tension [1]
Compressor Oil Capacity .... 4.1 ozs.
Refrigerant (R-134a) Capacity [2] .... 23-27 ozs.
System Operating Pressures
High Side .... 199-228 psi (14-16 kg/cm²)
Low Side .... 28-36 psi (2.0-2.5 kg/cm²)

[1] – See COMPRESSOR BELT TENSION under ADJUSTMENTS.
[2] – Use R-134a refrigerant and ND-Oil 8 (Part No. 38899-PR7-003).

WARNING: To avoid injury from accidental air bag deployment, read and carefully follow all SERVICE PRECAUTIONS and DISABLING & ACTIVATING AIR BAG SYSTEM procedures in AIR BAG SYSTEM SAFETY article in GENERAL SERVICING.

CAUTION: When battery is disconnected, radio will go into anti-theft protection mode. Obtain radio anti-theft protection code from owner prior to servicing vehicle.

DESCRIPTION & OPERATION

Automatic temperature control system is a cycling clutch type with an expansion valve. *See Fig. 1.*

Sensors respond to various conditions in A/C system and provide signals for A/C-heater control panel and A/C amplifier. Based on signals from sensors, A/C-heater control panel and A/C amplifier control operation of compressor clutch and air control door servomotors.

- Ambient temperature sensor monitors outside air temperature.

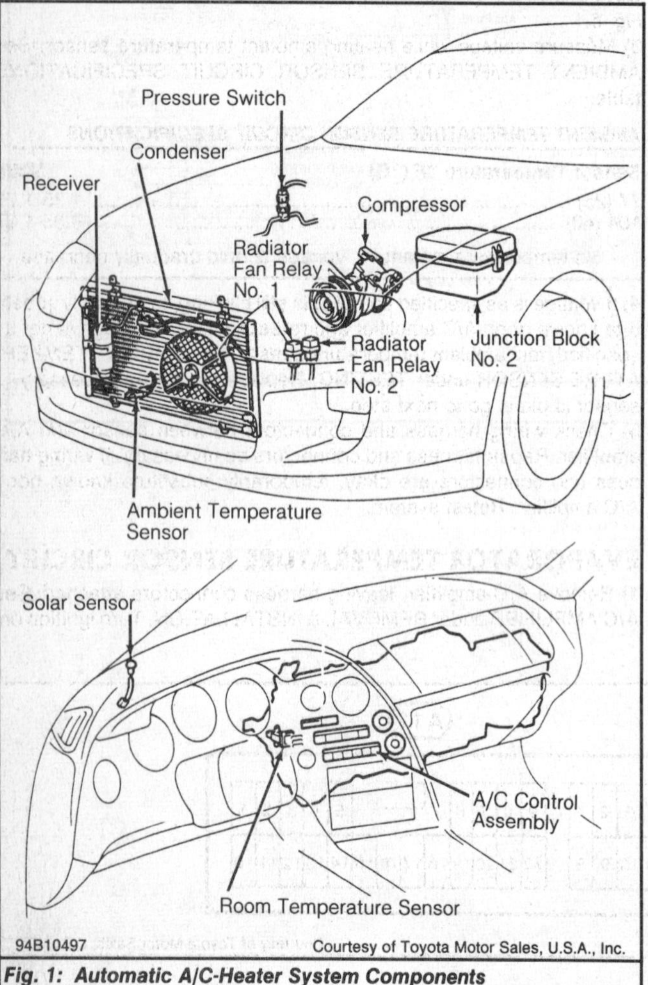
Pressure Switch
Condenser
Receiver
Compressor
Radiator
Fan Relay
No. 1
Radiator
Fan Relay
No. 2
Junction Block
No. 2
Ambient Temperature
Sensor
Solar Sensor
A/C Control
Assembly
Room Temperature Sensor
94B10497
Courtesy of Toyota Motor Sales, U.S.A., Inc.

Fig. 1: Automatic A/C-Heater System Components

- In-car temperature sensor monitors passenger compartment air temperature.
- Engine coolant temperature sensor monitors engine coolant temperature.
- Solar sensor monitors sunlight load.
- Evaporator temperature sensor monitors evaporator temperature.

ADJUSTMENTS

COMPRESSOR BELT TENSION

Ensure drive belt tension falls within "A" range of belt tensioner scale. *See Fig. 2.* If tension does not fall within "A" range, replace belt. When installing a new belt, ensure belt tension falls within "B" range of belt tensioner scale.

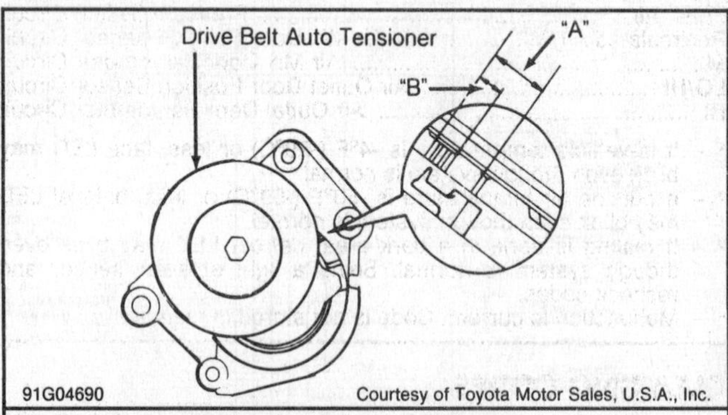
Drive Belt Auto Tensioner
"A"
"B"
91G04690
Courtesy of Toyota Motor Sales, U.S.A., Inc.

Fig. 2: Checking Compressor Drive Belt Tension

TROUBLE SHOOTING

SELF-DIAGNOSTICS

An Electronic Control Unit (ECU) within A/C control assembly monitors system circuits and stores trouble codes in memory if problems are detected. To retrieve stored codes, see RETRIEVING CODES. Problems in the A/C system will be indicated by a blinking LED on the appropriate switch. *See Fig. 3.* If no malfunctions are indicated but a fault still exists, proceed to TESTING.

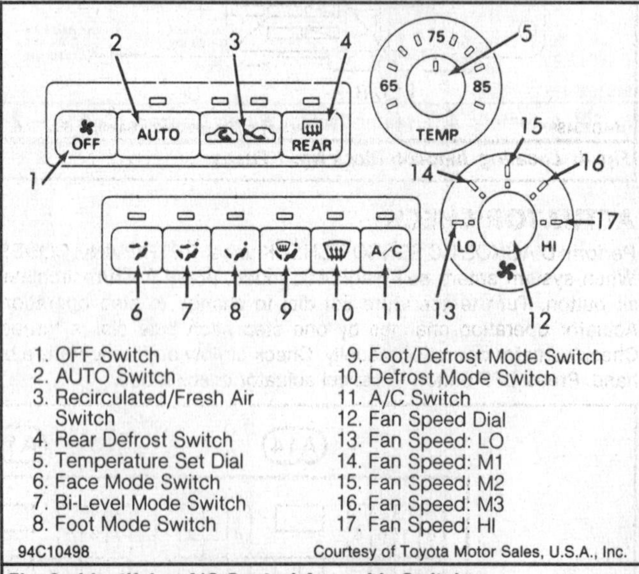
OFF
AUTO
REAR
65
75
85
TEMP
A/C
LO
HI
1. OFF Switch
2. AUTO Switch
3. Recirculated/Fresh Air Switch
4. Rear Defrost Switch
5. Temperature Set Dial
6. Face Mode Switch
7. Bi-Level Mode Switch
8. Foot Mode Switch
9. Foot/Defrost Mode Switch
10. Defrost Mode Switch
11. A/C Switch
12. Fan Speed Dial
13. Fan Speed: LO
14. Fan Speed: M1
15. Fan Speed: M2
16. Fan Speed: M3
17. Fan Speed: HI
94C10498
Courtesy of Toyota Motor Sales, U.S.A., Inc.

Fig. 3: Identifying A/C Control Assembly Switches

RETRIEVING CODES

Diagnostic Sensor Check – 1) Press and hold AUTO and recirculated air buttons. *See Fig. 3.* Turn ignition on. All indicators will flash 4 times at one-second intervals. Press OFF button to cancel indicator check.

2) After indicator check is complete, system will enter self-diagnostic mode. Stored trouble codes will cause LED on appropriate switch to blink. See DIAGNOSTIC CODE IDENTIFICATION table.

3) To slow rate of display, press rear defogger switch to change display to step operation. Each time REAR defrost switch is pressed, display changes by one step.

DIAGNOSTIC CODE IDENTIFICATION

Blinking LED	Diagnosis
AUTO	Normal
Face [1]	Room Temperature Sensor Circuit
Bi-Level [2]	Ambient Temperature Sensor Circuit
Foot	Evaporator Temperature Sensor Circuit
Foot/Defrost	Coolant Temperature Sensor Circuit
Defrost [3]	Solar Sensor Circuit
A/C [4]	Compressor Lock Sensor Circuit
Fresh Air [4]	Pressure Switch Circuit
Recirculated Air/M2	Air Mix Door Position Sensor Circuit
M2	Air Mix Door Servomotor Circuit
LO/HI	Air Outlet Door Position Sensor Circuit
HI	Air Outlet Door Servomotor Circuit

1 - If in-vehicle temperature is -4°F (-20°C) or less, face LED may blink even though system is normal.
2 - If outside air temperature is -58°F (-50°C) or less, bi-level LED may blink even though system is normal.
3 - If testing is done in a dark area, defrost LED may blink even though system is normal. Shine a light at solar sensor and recheck codes.
4 - Malfunction is current. Code is not stored in memory.

CLEARING CODES

1) Remove ECU-B fuse from junction block No. 1 (located behind left kick panel). *See Fig. 4.* Wait at least 10 seconds before installing fuse. Perform RETRIEVING CODES procedure. Ensure only normal code is displayed.

2) Another method of clearing codes is to press REAR defrost switch and A/C switch simultaneously during sensor check mode.

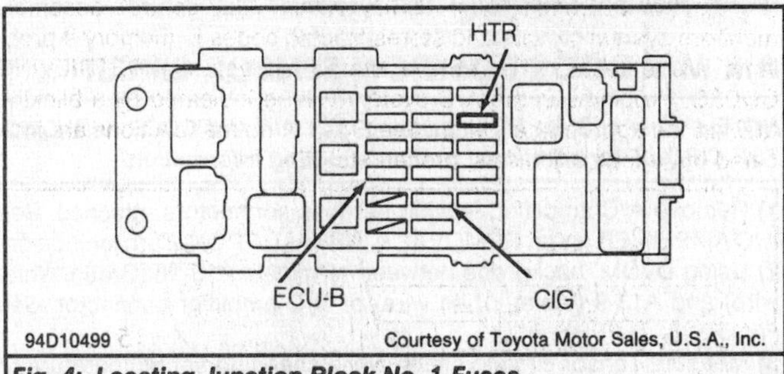
HTR
ECU-B
CIG
94D10499
Courtesy of Toyota Motor Sales, U.S.A., Inc.

Fig. 4: Locating Junction Block No. 1 Fuses

ACTUATOR CHECK

Perform DIAGNOSTIC SENSOR CHECK under RETRIEVING CODES. When system enters self-diagnostic mode, press fresh/recirculated air button. Turn temperature set dial to change to step operation. Actuator operation changes by one step each time dial is turned. Check actuator operation visually. Check airflow and temperature by hand. Press OFF button to cancel actuator check mode.

ROOM TEMPERATURE SENSOR CIRCUIT

1) Remove A/C amplifier, leaving harness connectors attached. See A/C AMPLIFIER under REMOVAL & INSTALLATION. Turn ignition on.

2) Using DVOM, backprobe between terminals A13-5 (Yellow/Blue wire) and A13-9 (Violet/White wire) of A/C amplifier connector. *See Fig. 5.*

3) Measure voltage while heating in-vehicle temperature sensor. See ROOM TEMPERATURE SENSOR CIRCUIT SPECIFICATIONS table.

ROOM TEMPERATURE SENSOR CIRCUIT SPECIFICATIONS

Sensor Temperature °F (°C)	[1] Volts
77 (25)	1.8-2.2
104 (40)	1.2-1.6

1 - As temperature increases, voltage should gradually decrease.

4) If voltage is as specified and LED is still blinking, temporarily substitute known good A/C amplifier and retest system. If voltage is not as specified, test room temperature sensor. See ROOM TEMPERATURE SENSOR under TESTING. Replace sensor as necessary. If sensor is okay, go to next step.

5) Check wiring harness and connectors between sensor and A/C amplifier. Repair harness and connectors as necessary. If wiring harness and connectors are okay, temporarily substitute known good A/C amplifier. Retest system.

AMBIENT TEMPERATURE SENSOR CIRCUIT

1) Remove A/C amplifier, leaving harness connectors attached. See A/C AMPLIFIER under REMOVAL & INSTALLATION. Turn ignition on.

2) Using DVOM, backprobe between terminals A13-6 (Pink/Black wire) and A13-9 (Violet/White wire) of A/C amplifier connector. *See Fig. 5.*

3) Measure voltage while heating ambient temperature sensor. See AMBIENT TEMPERATURE SENSOR CIRCUIT SPECIFICATIONS table.

AMBIENT TEMPERATURE SENSOR CIRCUIT SPECIFICATIONS

Sensor Temperature °F (°C)	[1] Volts
77 (25)	1.35-1.75
104 (40)	0.85-1.25

1 - As temperature increases, voltage should gradually decrease.

4) If voltage is as specified and LED is still blinking, temporarily substitute known good A/C amplifier and retest system. If voltage is not as specified, test ambient temperature sensor. See AMBIENT TEMPERATURE SENSOR under TESTING. Replace sensor as necessary. If sensor is okay, go to next step.

5) Check wiring harness and connectors between sensor and A/C amplifier. Repair harness and connectors as necessary. If wiring harness and connectors are okay, temporarily substitute known good A/C amplifier. Retest system.

EVAPORATOR TEMPERATURE SENSOR CIRCUIT

1) Remove A/C amplifier, leaving harness connectors attached. See A/C AMPLIFIER under REMOVAL & INSTALLATION. Turn ignition on.

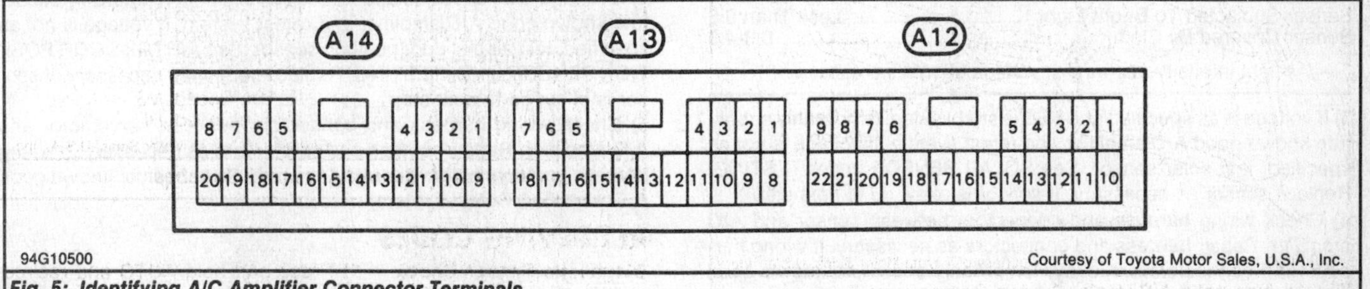
A14
A13
A12
8 7 6 5 4 3 2 1
20 19 18 17 16 15 14 13 12 11 10 9
7 6 5 4 3 2 1
18 17 16 15 14 13 12 11 10 9 8
9 8 7 6 5 4 3 2 1
22 21 20 19 18 17 16 15 14 13 12 11 10
94G10500
Courtesy of Toyota Motor Sales, U.S.A., Inc.

Fig. 5: Identifying A/C Amplifier Connector Terminals

2) Using DVOM, backprobe between terminals A13-7 (Blue/Yellow wire) and A13-9 (Violet/White wire) of A/C amplifier connector. *See Fig. 5.*

3) Measure voltage at specified temperatures. See EVAPORATOR TEMPERATURE SENSOR CIRCUIT SPECIFICATIONS table.

EVAPORATOR TEMPERATURE SENSOR CIRCUIT SPECIFICATIONS

Sensor Temperature °F (°C)	[1] Volts
32 (0)	2.0-2.4
59 (15)	1.4-1.8

[1] – As temperature increases, voltage should gradually decrease.

4) If voltage is as specified and LED is still blinking, temporarily substitute known good A/C amplifier and retest system. If voltage is not as specified, test evaporator temperature sensor. See EVAPORATOR TEMPERATURE SENSOR under TESTING. Replace sensor as necessary. If sensor is okay, go to next step.

5) Check wiring harness and connectors between sensor and A/C amplifier. Repair harness and connectors as necessary. If wiring harness and connectors are okay, temporarily substitute known good A/C amplifier. Retest system.

COOLANT TEMPERATURE SENSOR CIRCUIT

1) Remove A/C amplifier, leaving harness connectors attached. See A/C AMPLIFIER under REMOVAL & INSTALLATION. Turn ignition on.

2) Using a DVOM, backprobe between terminals A13-16 (Light Green/Red wire) and A13-9 (Violet/White wire) of A/C amplifier connector. *See Fig. 5.* Measure voltage at specified temperatures. See COOLANT TEMPERATURE SENSOR CIRCUIT SPECIFICATIONS table.

COOLANT TEMPERATURE SENSOR CIRCUIT SPECIFICATIONS

Sensor Temperature °F (°C)	[1] Volts
32 (0)	2.8-3.2
104 (40)	1.8-2.2
158 (70)	1.3-1.5

[1] – As temperature increases, voltage should gradually decrease.

3) If voltage is as specified and LED is still blinking, temporarily substitute known good A/C amplifier and retest system. If voltage is not as specified, test coolant temperature sensor. See COOLANT TEMPERATURE SENSOR under TESTING. Replace sensor as necessary. If sensor is okay, go to next step.

4) Check wiring harness and connectors between sensor and A/C amplifier. Repair harness and connectors as necessary. If wiring harness and connectors are okay, temporarily substitute known good A/C amplifier. Retest system.

SOLAR SENSOR CIRCUIT

1) Remove A/C amplifier, leaving harness connectors attached. See A/C AMPLIFIER under REMOVAL & INSTALLATION. Turn ignition on.

2) Using DVOM, backprobe between terminals A13-2 (Brown/White wire) and A13-9 (Violet/White wire) of A/C amplifier connector. *See Fig. 5.* Measure voltage under specified conditions. See SOLAR SENSOR CIRCUIT SPECIFICATIONS table.

SOLAR SENSOR CIRCUIT SPECIFICATIONS

Condition	[1] Volts
Sensor Subjected To Bright Light	Less Than 0.8
Sensor Covered By Cloth	0.8-4.3

[1] – As light intensity decreases, voltage should increase.

3) If voltage is as specified and LED is still blinking, temporarily substitute known good A/C amplifier and retest system. If voltage is not as specified, test solar sensor. See SOLAR SENSOR under TESTING. Replace sensor as necessary. If sensor is okay, go to next step.

4) Check wiring harness and connectors between sensor and A/C amplifier. Repair harness and connectors as necessary. If wiring harness and connectors are okay, temporarily substitute known good A/C amplifier. Retest system.

COMPRESSOR LOCK SENSOR CIRCUIT

NOTE: When replacing drive belt, new belt tension should be in range "B" on tensioner scale. See Fig. 2.

1) Ensure drive belt fits properly on compressor pulley. If tension is not in range "A" on scale, replace belt. *See Fig. 2.* If tension is okay, go to next step.

2) Start engine. Turn blower and A/C on. Observe compressor. If compressor locks during operation, repair compressor. If compressor does not lock during operation, check compressor lock sensor. See COMPRESSOR LOCK SENSOR under TESTING. Replace sensor as necessary. If sensor is okay, go to next step.

3) Check wiring harness and connectors between sensor and A/C amplifier. Repair harness and connectors as necessary. If wiring harness and connectors are okay, temporarily substitute known good A/C amplifier. Retest system.

PRESSURE SWITCH CIRCUIT

1) Remove A/C amplifier, leaving harness connectors attached. See A/C AMPLIFIER under REMOVAL & INSTALLATION. Install manifold gauge set.

2) Turn ignition on. Using DVOM, backprobe A/C amplifier connector between terminal A13-14 (Blue/Yellow wire) and ground. *See Fig. 5.*

3) Start engine. Turn blower and A/C on. Battery voltage should be present with low side pressure less than 28 psi (2.0 kg/cm²). Voltage should be present with high side pressure more than 455 psi (32 kg/cm²). If voltage is as specified, temporarily substitute known good A/C amplifier and retest system.

4) If voltage is not as specified, test pressure switch. See PRESSURE SWITCH under TESTING. Replace pressure switch as necessary. If switch is okay, go to next step.

5) Check wiring harness and connectors between pressure switch and A/C amplifier. Repair harness and connectors as necessary. If wiring harness and connectors are okay, temporarily substitute known good A/C amplifier. Retest system.

AIR MIX DOOR POSITION SENSOR CIRCUIT

NOTE: If only LED for M2 is blinking, see AIR MIX DOOR SERVOMOTOR CIRCUIT for additional trouble shooting information.

1) Remove A/C amplifier, leaving harness connectors attached. See A/C AMPLIFIER under REMOVAL & INSTALLATION. Turn ignition on.

2) Using DVOM, backprobe between terminals A13-18 (Green/White wire) and A13-9 (Violet/White wire) of A/C amplifier connector. *See Fig. 5.*

3) Measure sensor circuit voltage while changing set temperature to activate air mix door. See AIR MIX DOOR POSITION SENSOR CIRCUIT SPECIFICATIONS table.

AIR MIX DOOR POSITION SENSOR CIRCUIT SPECIFICATIONS

Set Temperature	[1] Volts
Maximum Cool	3.5-4.5
Maximum Hot	0.5-1.5

[1] – As set temperature increases, voltage should gradually decrease.

4) If voltage is as specified and LED is still blinking, temporarily substitute known good A/C amplifier and retest system. If voltage is not as specified, test air mix door position sensor. See AIR MIX DOOR POSITION SENSOR under TESTING. Replace sensor as necessary. If sensor is okay, go to next step.

5) Check wiring harness and connectors between servomotor and A/C amplifier. Repair harness and connectors as necessary. If wiring harness and connectors are okay, temporarily substitute known good A/C amplifier. Retest system.

AIR MIX DOOR SERVOMOTOR CIRCUIT

NOTE: See AIR MIX DOOR POSITION SENSOR CIRCUIT for additional trouble shooting information.

1) Warm engine to normal operating temperature. Perform RETRIEVING CODES. After system enters self-diagnostic mode, perform ACTUATOR CHECK. Turn temperature set dial to enter step mode. Air mix door operation should be as specified. See AIR MIX DOOR AIRFLOW table.
2) If air mix door functions as specified, no problem is indicated at this time. If air mix door does not function as specified, test air mix door servomotor. See AIR MIX DOOR SERVOMOTOR under TESTING. Replace air mix door servomotor as necessary. If servomotor is okay, go to next step.
3) Check wiring harness and connectors between servomotor and A/C amplifier. Repair harness and connectors as necessary. If wiring harness and connectors are okay, substitute known good A/C amplifier. Retest system.

AIR MIX DOOR AIRFLOW

Set Temperature	Air Mix Door	Airflow
Less Than 20	Fully Closed	Cool Air
20-23	Half Open	Blend (Cool/Hot) Air
More Than 23	Fully Open	Hot Air

AIR OUTLET DOOR POSITION SENSOR CIRCUIT

NOTE: If only LED for HI is blinking, see AIR OUTLET DOOR SERVOMOTOR CIRCUIT for additional trouble shooting information.

1) Remove A/C amplifier, leaving harness connectors attached. See A/C AMPLIFIER under REMOVAL & INSTALLATION. Turn ignition on.
2) Using DVOM, backprobe between terminals A14-10 (Light Green wire) and A13-9 (Violet/White wire) of A/C amplifier connector. *See Fig. 5.*
3) Measure sensor circuit voltage while changing mode switch to activate air outlet door. See AIR OUTLET DOOR POSITION SENSOR CIRCUIT SPECIFICATIONS table.

AIR OUTLET DOOR POSITION SENSOR CIRCUIT SPECIFICATIONS

Mode Switch	[1] Volts
Face	3.5-4.5
Defrost	0.5-1.5

[1] - As air outlet servomotor is moved from face to defrost position, voltage should gradually decrease.

4) If voltage is as specified and LED is still blinking, temporarily substitute known good A/C amplifier and retest system. If voltage is not as specified, test air outlet door position sensor. See AIR OUTLET DOOR POSITION SENSOR under TESTING. Replace sensor as necessary. If sensor is okay, go to next step.
5) Check wiring harness and connectors between servomotor and A/C amplifier. Repair harness and connectors as necessary. If wiring harness and connectors are okay, substitute known good A/C amplifier. Retest system.

AIR OUTLET DOOR SERVOMOTOR CIRCUIT

NOTE: See AIR OUTLET DOOR POSITION SENSOR CIRCUIT for additional trouble shooting information.

1) Warm engine to normal operating temperature. Perform RETRIEVING CODES. After system enters self-diagnostic mode, perform ACTUATOR CHECK. Turn temperature set dial to enter step mode. Air outlet door operation should be as specified. See AIR OUTLET DOOR AIRFLOW table.
2) If air outlet door functions as specified, no problem is indicated at this time. If air outlet door does not function as specified, test air outlet door servomotor. See AIR OUTLET DOOR SERVOMOTOR under TESTING. Replace air outlet door servomotor as necessary. If servomotor is okay, go to next step.
3) Check wiring harness and connectors between servomotor and A/C amplifier. Repair harness and connectors as necessary. If wiring harness and connectors are okay, substitute known good A/C amplifier. Retest system.

AIR OUTLET DOOR AIRFLOW

Set Temperature	Airflow
Less Than 20	Face
20-23	Bi-Level
23-27	Foot
27-30	Foot/Defrost
More Than 30	Defrost

TESTING

WARNING: To avoid injury from accidental air bag deployment, read and carefully follow all SERVICE PRECAUTIONS and DISABLING & ACTIVATING AIR BAG SYSTEM procedures in AIR BAG SYSTEM SAFETY article in GENERAL SERVICING.

A/C SYSTEM PERFORMANCE

Connect manifold gauge set. Operate engine at 1500 RPM. Set blower fan on high speed. Set temperature control switch at maximum cool position. With airflow set in recirculated air mode, ensure temperature at air inlet is 86-95°F (30-35°C). Ensure system operating pressures are within specifications. See SPECIFICATIONS table at beginning of article.

A/C CONTROL ASSEMBLY

1) Push each switch and turn fan speed dial on A/C control assembly. Ensure each LED lights when appropriate switch is operated. If operation is as specified, A/C control assembly is okay. If some LEDs do not light, go to next step. If no LEDs light, check IG (ignition) switch circuit. See IG POWER SOURCE CIRCUIT under TESTING.
2) Disconnect A/C control assembly connector. Check for voltage between terminal of LED being tested and terminal H12-9 (White/Black wire). *See Fig. 6.*
3) With switch on, there should be less than one volt. With switch off, there should be 10-14 volts. If voltage is not as specified, go to next step. If voltage is as specified, repair or replace A/C control assembly.
4) Check for continuity in harness and connector between A/C control panel and A/C amplifier. If there is continuity, go to next step. If there is no continuity, repair or replace harness or connector as necessary.
5) Remove A/C control assembly. Disconnect all electrical connectors. Test for continuity between indicated terminals. See SWITCH TERMINAL IDENTIFICATION table. With switch pressed, continuity should exist. When switch is off, no continuity should exist.
6) If continuity is not as specified, substitute known good A/C control assembly. Retest system. If continuity is as specified, substitute known good A/C amplifier. Retest system.

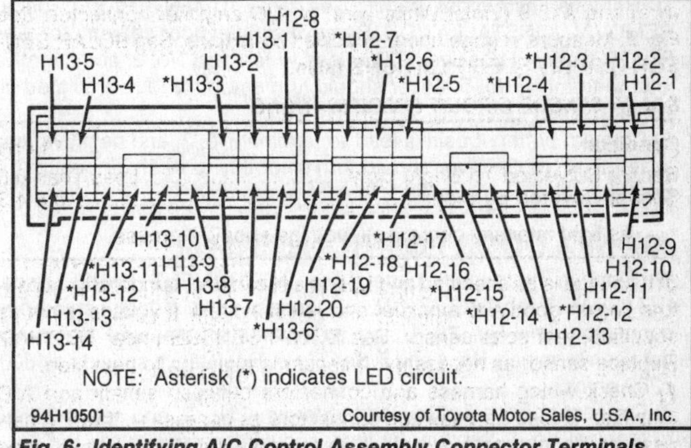
H12-8
H13-1
*H12-7
H13-5
H13-2
*H12-6
*H12-3
H12-2
H13-4
*H13-3
*H12-5
*H12-4
H12-1
H13-10
*H12-17
H12-9
*H13-11
H13-9
*H12-18
H12-16
H12-10
*H13-12
H13-8
H12-19
*H12-15
H12-11
H13-13
H13-7
H12-20
*H12-14
*H12-12
H13-14
*H13-6
H12-13
NOTE: Asterisk (*) indicates LED circuit.
94H10501
Courtesy of Toyota Motor Sales, U.S.A., Inc.
Fig. 6: Identifying A/C Control Assembly Connector Terminals

SWITCH TERMINAL IDENTIFICATION

Switch	Between Terminal No.
OFF	H12-16 & H13-7
Fresh/Recirculated Air	H12-16 & H13-2
Defrost	H12-16 & H12-13
Foot	H13-1 & H13-7
Foot/Defrost	H13-1 & H13-2
A/C	H13-1 & H12-13
REAR Defrost	H13-10 & H13-7
Face	H13-10 & H13-2
Fan Speed Dial [1]	H13-10 & H12-13
AUTO	H13-9 & H13-7
Bi-Level	H13-9 & H13-2
Fan Speed Dial [2]	H13-9 & H12-13

[1] – Turn fan speed dial counterclockwise.
[2] – Turn fan speed dial clockwise.

ACC POWER SOURCE CIRCUIT

1) Remove A/C amplifier, leaving harness connectors attached. See A/C AMPLIFIER under REMOVAL & INSTALLATION. Turn ignition switch to ACC position. Using DVOM, backprobe terminal A12-20 (Blue/Red wire) of A/C amplifier connector and ground. *See Fig. 5*.
2) If battery voltage is present, no problem is indicated at this time. If battery voltage is not present, check CIG fuse in junction block No. 1 (located under left kick panel). *See Fig. 4*. If fuse is okay, check wiring harness between A/C amplifier and battery. Repair wiring as necessary. If fuse is blown, check for short circuit and replace fuse.

AIR INLET DOOR SERVOMOTOR CIRCUIT

1) Warm engine to normal operating temperature. Perform RETRIEVING CODES. After system enters self-diagnostic mode, perform ACTUATOR CHECK. Turn temperature set dial to enter step mode. Air inlet door operation should be as specified. See AIR INLET DOOR AIRFLOW table.
2) If air inlet door functions as specified, no problem is indicated at this time. If air inlet door does not function as specified, test air inlet door servomotor. See AIR INLET DOOR SERVOMOTOR under TESTING. Replace air inlet door servomotor as necessary. If servomotor is okay, go to next step.
3) Check wiring harness and connectors between servomotor and A/C amplifier. Repair harness and connectors as necessary. If wiring harness and connectors are okay, substitute known good A/C amplifier. Retest system.

AIR INLET DOOR AIRFLOW

Set Temperature	Door Position
Less Than 20	Recirculated Air
20-23	Fresh/Recirculated Air
More Than 23	Fresh Air

AIR INLET DOOR SERVOMOTOR

1) Remove instrument panel. See INSTRUMENT PANEL under REMOVAL & INSTALLATION. Remove air inlet door servomotor. *See Fig. 19*. Connect positive battery lead to terminal No. 2, and negative lead to terminal No. 5. Lever should turn smoothly to recirculated air position. *See Fig. 7*.
2) Connect battery positive lead to terminal No. 2, and negative lead to terminal No. 3. Lever should turn smoothly to fresh air position. If operation is not as specified, replace servomotor.

AIR MIX DOOR POSITION SENSOR

1) Remove instrument panel. See INSTRUMENT PANEL under REMOVAL & INSTALLATION. Disconnect air mix door servomotor connector. *See Fig. 19*. Using an ohmmeter, measure resistance between terminals No. 4 and 5. *See Fig. 8*. Resistance should be 4800-7200 ohms.
2) Connect positive battery lead to terminal No. 2, and negative lead to terminal No. 1. Servomotor lever should turn smoothly to hot position. Reverse battery leads. Lever should turn smoothly to cool position.

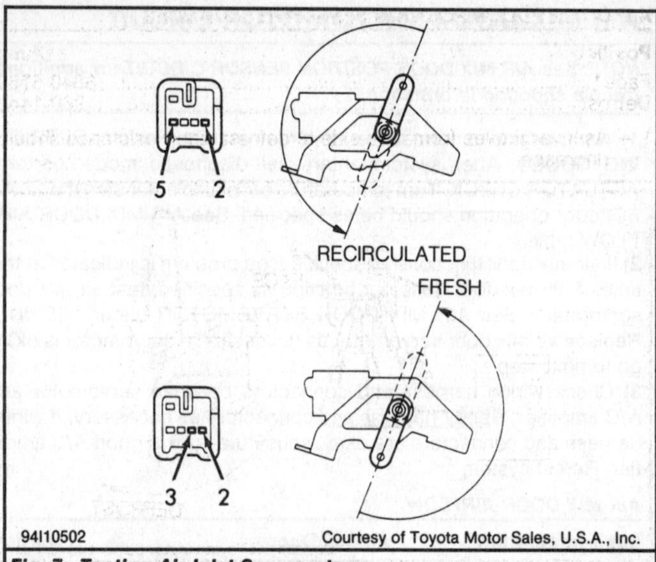
5
2
RECIRCULATED
FRESH
3
2
94I10502
Courtesy of Toyota Motor Sales, U.S.A., Inc.

Fig. 7: Testing Air Inlet Servomotor

3) While operating servomotor in this manner, measure resistance between terminals No. 3 and 5. See AIR MIX DOOR POSITION SENSOR RESISTANCES table. If resistances are not as specified, replace sensor.

AIR MIX DOOR POSITION SENSOR RESISTANCES

Position	[1] Ohms
Maximum Cool	3840-5760
Maximum Hot	960-1440

[1] – As lever moves from cool side to hot side, resistance should decrease.

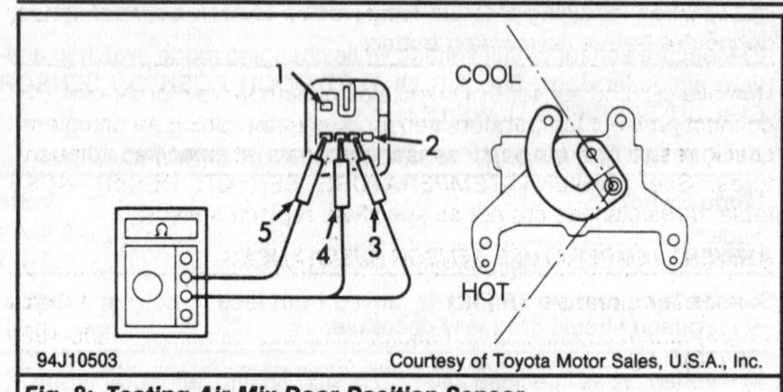
1
COOL
2
5
4
3
HOT
Ω
94J10503
Courtesy of Toyota Motor Sales, U.S.A., Inc.

Fig. 8: Testing Air Mix Door Position Sensor

AIR MIX DOOR SERVOMOTOR

Remove air mix door servomotor. *See Fig. 19*. Connect positive battery lead to terminal No. 2, and negative lead to terminal No. 1. Lever should turn smoothly to hot position. *See Fig. 8*. Reverse battery leads. Lever should turn smoothly to cool position. If operation is not as specified, replace servomotor.

AIR OUTLET DOOR POSITION SENSOR

1) Remove instrument panel. See INSTRUMENT PANEL under REMOVAL & INSTALLATION. Disconnect air outlet door servomotor connector. *See Fig. 19*. Using an ohmmeter, measure resistance between terminals No. 4 and 5. *See Fig. 9*. Resistance should be 4700-7200 ohms.
2) Connect positive battery lead to terminal No. 1, and negative lead to terminal No. 2. Servomotor lever should turn smoothly to face position. Reverse battery leads. Lever should turn smoothly to defrost position.
3) While operating servomotor in this manner, measure resistance between terminals No. 3 and 5. See AIR OUTLET DOOR POSITION SENSOR RESISTANCES table. If resistances are not as specified, replace sensor.

AIR OUTLET DOOR POSITION SENSOR RESISTANCES

Position	[1] Ohms
Face	3840-5760
Defrost	960-1440

[1] - As lever moves from face side to defrost side, resistance should decrease.

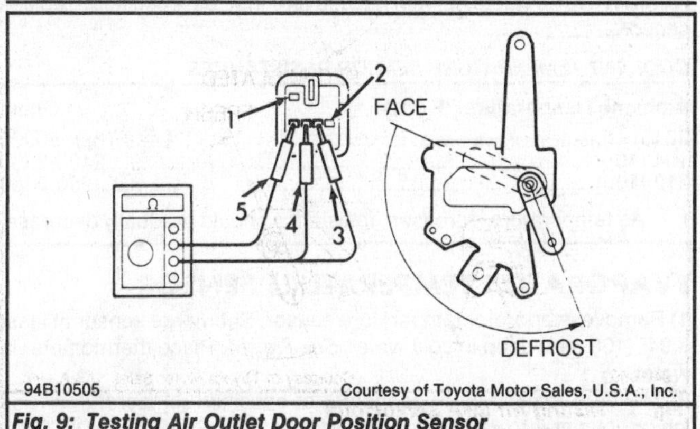

1
2
FACE
5
4
3
DEFROST
94B10505
Courtesy of Toyota Motor Sales, U.S.A., Inc.

Fig. 9: Testing Air Outlet Door Position Sensor

AIR OUTLET DOOR SERVOMOTOR

Remove instrument panel. See INSTRUMENT PANEL under REMOVAL & INSTALLATION. Remove air outlet door servomotor. *See Fig. 19.* Connect positive battery lead to terminal No. 1, and negative lead to terminal No. 2. Lever should turn smoothly to face position. *See Fig. 9.* Reverse battery leads. Lever should turn smoothly to defrost position. If operation is not as specified, replace servomotor.

AMBIENT TEMPERATURE SENSOR

NOTE: When installing ambient temperature sensor, connect sensor connector before connecting battery.

Remove clip and sensor from right side of bumper reinforcement. Disconnect ambient temperature sensor connector. Using an ohmmeter, check resistance between sensor terminals at specified temperatures. See AMBIENT TEMPERATURE SENSOR RESISTANCES table. If resistances are not as specified, replace sensor.

AMBIENT TEMPERATURE SENSOR RESISTANCES

Sensor Temperature °F (°C)	[1] Ohms
77 (25)	1600-1800
122 (50)	500-700

[1] - As temperature increases, resistance should gradually decrease.

BACK-UP POWER SOURCE CIRCUIT

1) Remove A/C amplifier, leaving harness connectors attached. See A/C AMPLIFIER under REMOVAL & INSTALLATION. Turn ignition on. Using DVOM, backprobe terminal A14-7 (White/Red wire) of A/C amplifier connector and ground. *See Fig. 5.*

2) If battery voltage is present, no problem is indicated at this time. If battery voltage is not present, check ECU-B fuse in junction block No. 1 (located behind left kick panel). *See Fig. 4.* If fuse is okay, check wiring harness between A/C amplifier and battery. Repair wiring as necessary. If fuse is blown, check for short circuit and replace fuse.

BLOWER MOTOR CIRCUIT

1) Remove A/C amplifier, leaving harness connectors attached. See A/C AMPLIFIER under REMOVAL & INSTALLATION. Turn ignition and blower motor on. Using DVOM, backprobe terminal A14-15 (Blue wire) of A/C amplifier connector and ground. *See Fig. 5.*

2) If 1-3 volts are present, no problem is indicated at this time. If 1-3 volts are not present, go to next step. Remove blower motor. See BLOWER MOTOR under REMOVAL & INSTALLATION. Connect positive battery lead to terminal No. 2 (Black wire), and negative lead to terminal No. 1 (Brown wire).

3) Blower motor should operate smoothly. If blower motor does not operate smoothly, replace blower motor. If blower motor operates smoothly, go to next step.

4) Disconnect blower motor control relay, leaving harness connectors attached. Turn ignition and blower motor on. Test specified terminals as indicated. See BLOWER MOTOR CONTROL RELAY SPECIFICATIONS table. *See Fig. 10.* If readings are not as specified, replace relay. If readings are as specified, repair or replace wiring or harness.

BLOWER MOTOR CONTROL RELAY SPECIFICATIONS

Terminals	Specification
GND & Ground	Continuity
+B & Ground	Battery Voltage
M+ & Ground	Battery Voltage
M+ & M-	Battery Voltage
SI & Ground	1-3 Volts

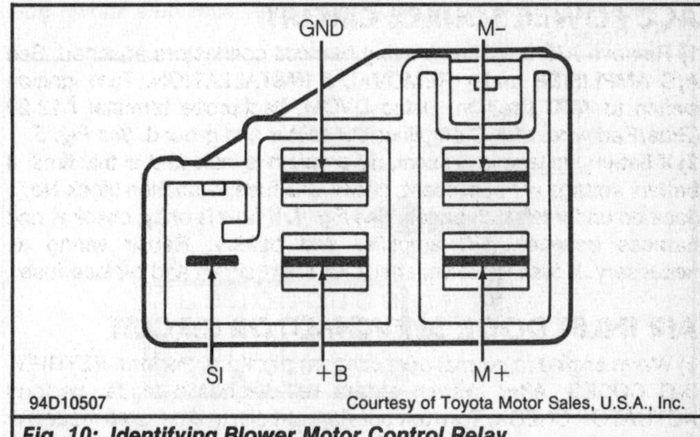

GND
M-
SI
+B
M+
94D10507
Courtesy of Toyota Motor Sales, U.S.A., Inc.

Fig. 10: Identifying Blower Motor Control Relay Connector Terminals

COMPRESSOR CIRCUIT

1) Remove A/C amplifier, leaving harness connectors attached. Start engine. Using DVOM, backprobe between terminal A12-7 (Blue wire) of A/C amplifier connector and ground. *See Fig. 5.*

2) Turn A/C on. When magnetic clutch is engaged, voltmeter should indicate 10-14 volts. Turn A/C off. Voltmeter should indicate less than one volt. If compressor circuit voltage is as specified, go to next step. If compressor circuit voltage is not as specified, go to step **5)**.

3) Disconnect magnetic clutch connector. Apply battery voltage to magnetic clutch connector terminal No. 4. Connect negative lead to ground. If magnetic clutch does not engage, repair or replace magnetic clutch.

4) If magnetic clutch engages, check wiring harness and connectors between magnetic clutch relay and A/C amplifier. Repair harness and connectors as necessary. If wiring harness and connectors are okay, go to next step.

5) Start engine. Using DVOM, backprobe between terminal A14-6 (Blue/Red wire) of A/C amplifier connector and ground. Turn A/C on. When magnetic clutch is engaged, voltmeter should indicate less than one volt. Turn A/C off. Voltmeter should indicate 10-14 volts. If voltage is as specified, go to step **8)**. If voltage is not as specified, go to next step.

6) Remove Electronic Control Module (ECM), leaving harness connectors attached. Turn ignition and A/C on. Measure voltage between A/C terminal (Blue/Red wire) of ECM connector and ground. *See Fig. 11.* When magnetic clutch is engaged, there should be less than one volt. When magnetic clutch is not engaged, there should be 4-6 volts. If voltage is as specified, go to next step. If voltage is not as specified, temporarily substitute known good ECM. Retest system.

7) Check wiring harness and connectors between A/C amplifier and ECM. Repair harness and connectors as necessary. If wiring harness and connectors are okay, temporarily substitute known good A/C amplifier. Retest system.

8) Remove magnetic clutch relay from junction block No. 2, located in left side of engine compartment. *See Fig. 12.* Check continuity

1993 AUTOMATIC A/C-HEATER SYSTEMS
Supra (Cont.)

between relay terminals. Continuity should exist between terminals No. 1 and 2. *See Fig. 13*. Continuity should not exist between terminals No. 3 and 5.

9) Connect positive battery lead to relay terminal No. 1, and negative lead to terminal No. 2. Continuity should exist between terminals No. 3 and 5. If continuity is not as specified, replace magnetic clutch relay. If continuity is as specified, go to next step.

10) Remove ECM, leaving harness connectors attached. Turn ignition on. Set fan to any speed. Using DVOM, backprobe between terminal ACMG (White/Green wire) of ECM connector and ground. *See Fig. 11*.

11) With A/C system on, voltmeter should indicate about 1.3 volts. With A/C system off, voltage should be between 1.3 volts and battery voltage. If voltage is not as specified, go to next step. If voltage is as specified, no problem is indicated at this time.

12) Check wiring between ECM and battery. Repair or replace wiring as necessary. If wiring is okay, temporarily substitute known good ECM. Retest system.

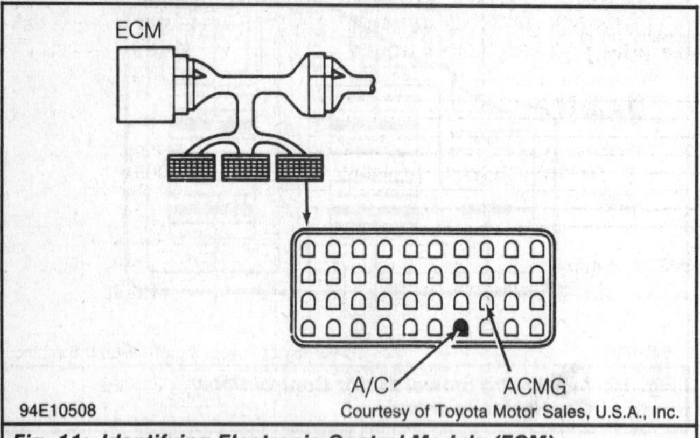
ECM
A/C
ACMG

94E10508 Courtesy of Toyota Motor Sales, U.S.A., Inc.

Fig. 11: Identifying Electronic Control Module (ECM) Connector Terminals

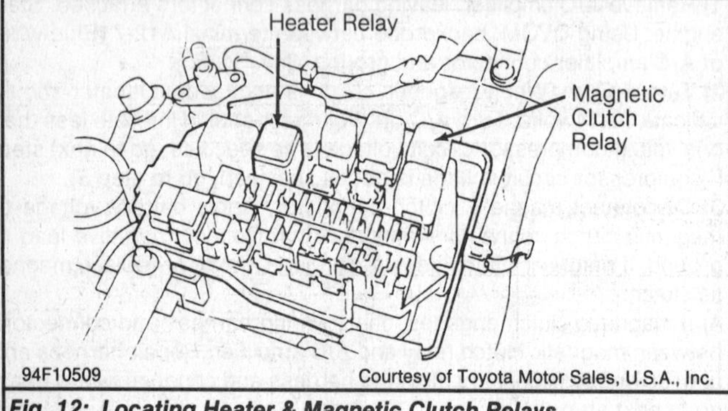
Heater Relay
Magnetic
Clutch
Relay

94F10509 Courtesy of Toyota Motor Sales, U.S.A., Inc.

Fig. 12: Locating Heater & Magnetic Clutch Relays

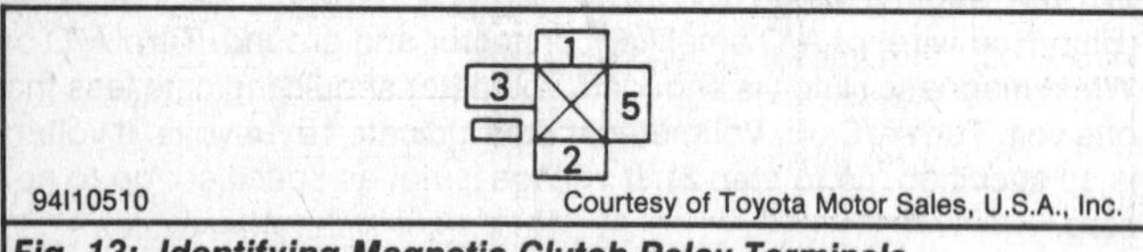
1
3
5
2

94I10510 Courtesy of Toyota Motor Sales, U.S.A., Inc.

Fig. 13: Identifying Magnetic Clutch Relay Terminals

COMPRESSOR LOCK SENSOR

Disconnect compressor lock sensor connector, located on compressor. Using an ohmmeter, measure resistance between sensor terminals. With ambient temperature of 68°F (20°C), resistance should be 160-210 ohms. If resistance is not as specified, replace sensor.

CONDENSER FAN

Disconnect negative battery cable. Disconnect condenser fan connector. Connect battery and ammeter in series to condenser fan connector. Condenser fan should rotate smoothly. Ammeter reading should be 6.0-7.4 amps. If operation is not as specified, replace condenser fan.

COOLANT TEMPERATURE SENSOR

1) Remove coolant temperature sensor. See COOLANT TEMPERATURE SENSOR under REMOVAL & INSTALLATION. Place sensor and a thermometer in a pan of water. Heat or cool water as necessary.

2) Using an ohmmeter, measure resistance between sensor terminals at indicated temperatures. See COOLANT TEMPERATURE SENSOR RESISTANCES table. If resistances are not as specified, replace sensor.

COOLANT TEMPERATURE SENSOR RESISTANCES

Ambient Temperature °F (°C)	Ohms
32 (0)	Less Than 50000
104 (40)	2400-2800
212 (100)	200-2400

[1] - As temperature increases, resistance should gradually decrease.

EVAPORATOR TEMPERATURE SENSOR

1) Remove evaporator temperature sensor. Submerge sensor at least 3.94" (100 mm) deep in cold water. *See Fig. 14*. Place thermometer in water.

2) Measure resistance of connector at specified temperatures. Use ice or hot water to vary water temperature. See EVAPORATOR TEMPERATURE SENSOR RESISTANCES table. If readings are not within specification, replace thermistor.

EVAPORATOR TEMPERATURE SENSOR RESISTANCES [1]

Ambient Temperature °F (°C)	Ohms
59 (15)	2000-2700
32 (0)	4500-5200

[1] - As temperature increases, resistance should gradually decrease.

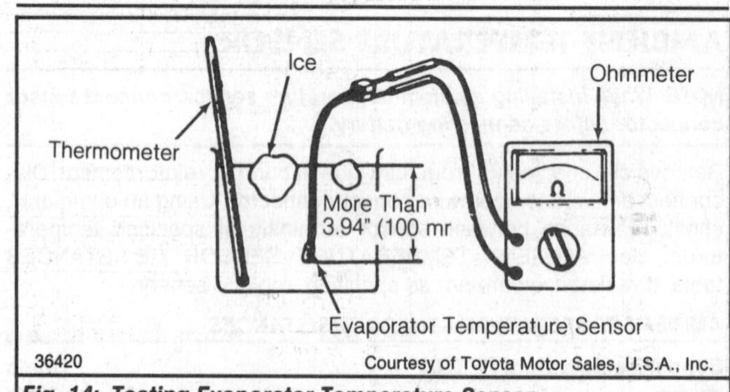
Ice
Ohmmeter
Thermometer
More Than
3.94" (100 mr
Evaporator Temperature Sensor

36420 Courtesy of Toyota Motor Sales, U.S.A., Inc.

Fig. 14: Testing Evaporator Temperature Sensor

EXPANSION VALVE

Ensure refrigerant quantity is sufficient (observe sight glass on receiver-drier). Connect manifold gauge set. Run engine at 2000 RPM for at least 5 minutes with A/C on. Ensure high side pressure is 199-228 psi (14-16 kg/cm²). If low side pressure drops to zero psi, expansion valve is clogged. Replace expansion valve. If low side pressure does not drop to zero psi, expansion valve is okay.

HEATER RELAY CIRCUIT

1) Remove A/C amplifier, leaving harness connectors attached. See A/C AMPLIFIER under REMOVAL & INSTALLATION. Using DVOM, backprobe between terminal A14-16 (Blue/White wire) of A/C amplifier connector and ground. *See Fig. 5*.

2) Turning ignition on and off, measure voltage as indicated in HEATER RELAY CIRCUIT SPECIFICATIONS table. If voltage is as specified, no problem is indicated at this time.

HEATER RELAY CIRCUIT SPECIFICATIONS

Ignition Switch Position	Volts
Off	0
On	
Blower On	Less Than 1
Blower Off	Battery Voltage

3) If voltage is not as specified, remove heater relay from junction block No. 2 (located on left side of engine compartment). *See Fig. 12*. Check for continuity between relay terminals. Continuity should exist between relay terminals No. 1 and 3, and between terminals No. 2 and 4. *See Fig. 15*. Continuity should not exist between terminals No. 4 and 5.

4) Apply positive battery lead to terminal No. 1, and negative lead to terminal No. 3. Continuity should exist between terminals No. 4 and 5. Continuity should not exist between terminals No. 2 and 4.

5) If continuity is not as specified, replace heater relay. If continuity is as specified, check HTR fuse in junction block No. 1 (located behind left kick panel). *See Fig. 4*. If fuse is okay, check wiring between A/C amplifier and battery. Repair wiring as necessary. If fuse is blown, check for short circuit and replace fuse.

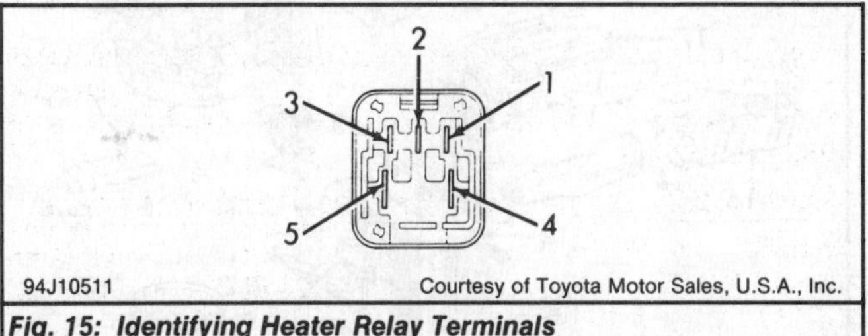

2
3
1
5
4

94J10511 Courtesy of Toyota Motor Sales, U.S.A., Inc.

Fig. 15: Identifying Heater Relay Terminals

IG POWER SOURCE CIRCUIT

1) Remove A/C amplifier, leaving harness connectors attached. See A/C AMPLIFIER under REMOVAL & INSTALLATION. Turn ignition on. Using DVOM, backprobe between terminals A14-8 (Red/Blue wire) and A14-9 (White/Black wire) of A/C amplifier connector. *See Fig. 5*.

2) If battery voltage is present, no problem is indicated at this time. If battery voltage is not present, turn ignition off. Check for continuity between A/C amplifier connector terminal A14-9 (White/Black wire) and ground. If continuity exists, go to next step. If continuity does not exist, repair wiring between terminal A14-9 and body ground.

3) Check HTR fuse in junction block No. 1, located behind left kick panel. *See Fig. 4*. If fuse is okay, check wiring harness and connector between A/C amplifier and battery. Repair wiring and connector as necessary. If fuse is blown, check for short circuit and replace fuse.

PRESSURE SWITCH

1) Disconnect pressure switch connector. *See Fig. 1*. Turn ignition on. Using an ohmmeter, check for continuity between terminals No. 1 and 2 (non-turbo) or terminals No. 1 and 4 (turbo). *See Fig. 16*.

2) With low side pressure of 28 psi (2.0 kg/cm²), there should be no continuity. With high side pressure of 455 psi (32 kg/cm²), there should be no continuity. If continuity is not as specified, replace switch.

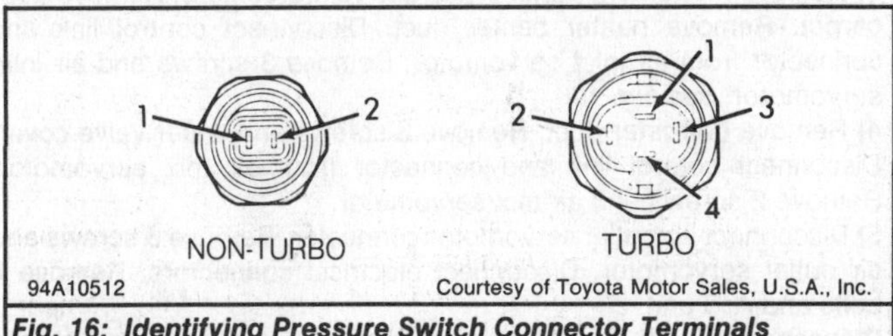

1
2
NON-TURBO
1
2
3
4
TURBO

94A10512 Courtesy of Toyota Motor Sales, U.S.A., Inc.

Fig. 16: Identifying Pressure Switch Connector Terminals

RADIATOR FAN

Disconnect negative battery cable. Disconnect fan connector. Connect battery and ammeter in series to fan connector. Radiator fan should rotate smoothly. Ammeter reading should be 2.5-4.5 amps. If operation is not as specified, replace radiator fan.

RADIATOR FAN RELAYS

Radiator Fan Relay No. 1 – 1) Remove radiator fan relay No. 1. *See Figs. 1 and 20*. Using an ohmmeter, check for continuity between terminals No. 3 and 4. *See Fig. 17*. Continuity should exist. Check for continuity between terminals No. 1 and 2. No continuity should exist.

2) Apply battery voltage across terminals No. 3 and 4. Check for continuity between terminals No. 1 and 2. Continuity should exist. If continuity is not as specified, replace relay.

Radiator Fan Relay No. 2 – 1) Remove radiator fan relay No. 2. *See Figs. 1 and 20*. Using an ohmmeter, check for continuity between terminals No. 1 and 6, and between terminals No. 3 and 5. *See Fig. 18*. Continuity should exist. Check for continuity between terminals No. 2 and 5. No continuity should exist.

2) Apply battery voltage across terminals No. 1 and 6. Check for continuity between terminals No. 3 and 5. Continuity should not exist. Check for continuity between terminals No. 2 and 5. Continuity should exist. If continuity is not as specified, replace relay.

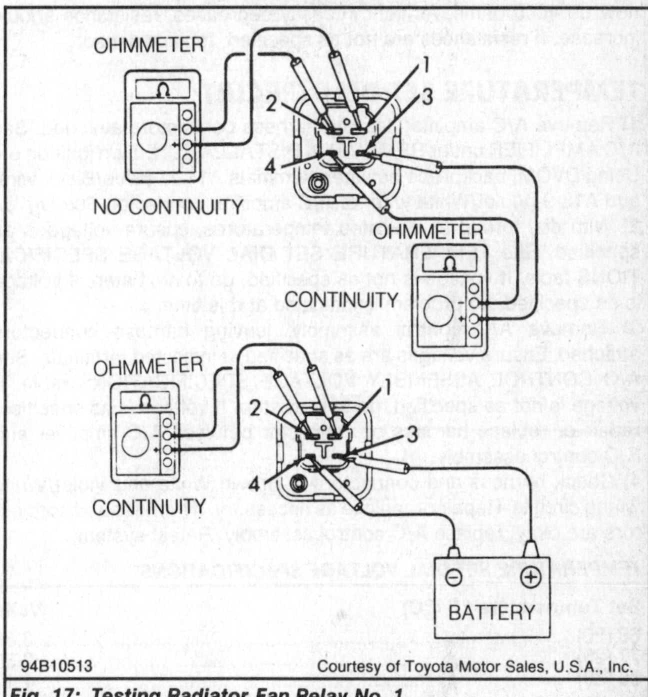

OHMMETER
1
2
3
4
NO CONTINUITY
OHMMETER
CONTINUITY
OHMMETER
1
2
3
4
CONTINUITY
BATTERY

94B10513 Courtesy of Toyota Motor Sales, U.S.A., Inc.

Fig. 17: Testing Radiator Fan Relay No. 1

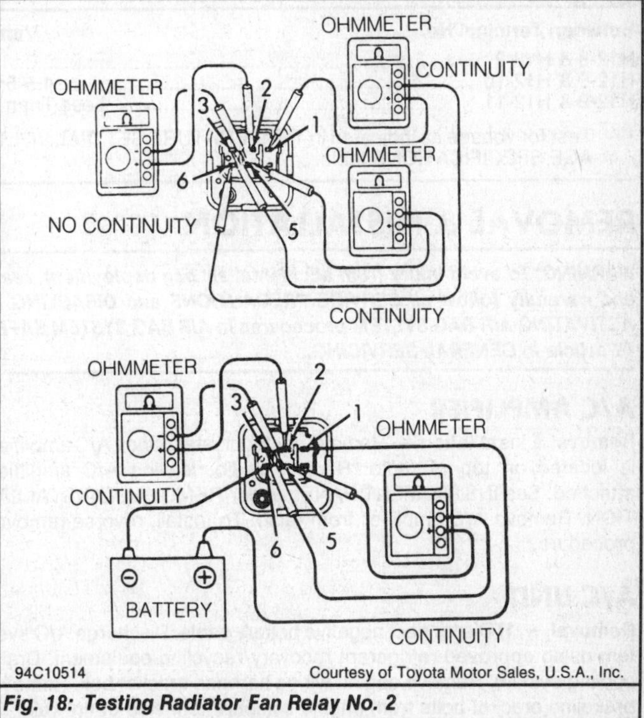

OHMMETER
CONTINUITY
OHMMETER
3
2
1
OHMMETER
6
NO CONTINUITY
5
CONTINUITY
OHMMETER
2
3
1
OHMMETER
CONTINUITY
6
5
BATTERY
CONTINUITY

94C10514 Courtesy of Toyota Motor Sales, U.S.A., Inc.

Fig. 18: Testing Radiator Fan Relay No. 2

ROOM TEMPERATURE SENSOR

Remove instrument panel. See INSTRUMENT PANEL under REMOVAL & INSTALLATION. Disconnect room temperature sensor connector. *See Fig. 1.* Using an ohmmeter, check resistance between sensor terminals. With ambient temperature of 77°F (25°C), resistance should be 1600-1800 ohms. If resistance is not as specified, replace sensor.

SOLAR SENSOR

1) Remove glove box. Remove solar sensor. Cover sensor with a cloth. Using an ohmmeter, connect positive lead to terminal No. 2 (Brown/White wire) and negative lead to terminal No. 1 (Yellow/Green wire). No continuity should be present.
2) Remove cloth, and expose sensor to bright light. Reading should now be 4000 ohms. As light intensity decreases, resistance should increase. If resistances are not as specified, replace sensor.

TEMPERATURE SET DIAL CIRCUIT

1) Remove A/C amplifier, leaving harness connectors attached. See A/C AMPLIFIER under REMOVAL & INSTALLATION. Turn ignition on. Using DVOM, backprobe between terminals A14-11 (Blue/Black wire) and A13-9 (Violet/White wire) of A/C amplifier connector. *See Fig. 5.*
2) With dial turned to indicated temperatures, ensure voltage is as specified. See TEMPERATURE SET DIAL VOLTAGE SPECIFICATIONS table. If voltage is not as specified, go to next step. If voltage is as specified, no problem is indicated at this time.
3) Remove A/C control assembly, leaving harness connectors attached. Ensure voltages are as specified at indicated terminals. See A/C CONTROL ASSEMBLY VOLTAGE SPECIFICATIONS table. If voltage is not as specified, go to next step. If voltage is as specified, repair or replace harness or connector between A/C amplifier and A/C control assembly.
4) Check harness and connectors in Brown/White and Violet/White wiring circuits. Repair or replace as necessary. If harness and connectors are okay, replace A/C control assembly. Retest system.

TEMPERATURE SET DIAL VOLTAGE SPECIFICATIONS

Set Temperature °F (°C)	Volts
68 (20)	3.88
77 (25)	2.50
86 (30)	1.12

A/C CONTROL ASSEMBLY VOLTAGE SPECIFICATIONS

Between Terminal No.	Volts
H12-9 & H12-2	[1]
H12-9 & H12-10	4.5-5.5
H12-9 & H12-11	Less Than 1

[1] – Test for voltage as indicated in TEMPERATURE SET DIAL VOLTAGE SPECIFICATIONS table.

REMOVAL & INSTALLATION

WARNING: To avoid injury from accidental air bag deployment, read and carefully follow all SERVICE PRECAUTIONS and DISABLING & ACTIVATING AIR BAG SYSTEM procedures in AIR BAG SYSTEM SAFETY article in GENERAL SERVICING.

A/C AMPLIFIER

Removal & Installation – Remove center cluster panel. A/C amplifier is located on top of radio. Remove radio, leaving A/C amplifier attached. See INSTRUMENT PANEL under REMOVAL & INSTALLATION. Remove A/C amplifier from radio. To install, reverse removal procedure.

A/C UNIT

Removal – **1)** Disconnect negative battery cable. Discharge A/C system using approved refrigerant recovery/recycling equipment. Drain cooling system. Remove engine wiring harness bracket bolt. Remove brakeline bracket bolts from engine compartment side of firewall.

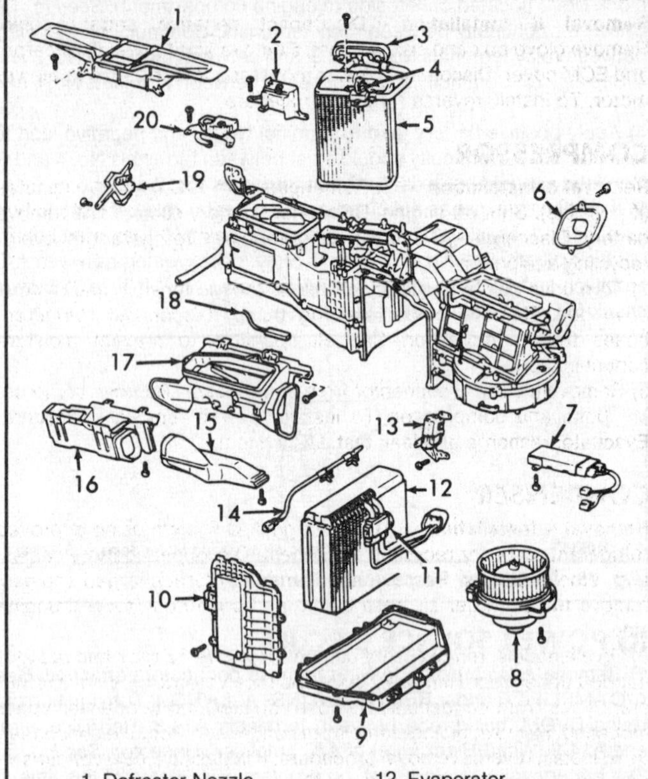

1. Defroster Nozzle
2. Water Valve Cover
3. Plate
4. Water Valve
5. Heater Core
6. A/C Unit Block Joint
7. Blower Motor Relay
8. Blower Motor
9. Lower Case
10. Evaporator Cover
11. Expansion Valve
12. Evaporator
13. Air Inlet Servomotor
14. Evaporator Temperature Sensor
15. Foot Air Duct
16. Heater Air Duct
17. Vent Air Duct
18. Coolant Temperature Sensor
19. Air Outlet Servomotor
20. Air Mix Servomotor

94D10515 Courtesy of Toyota Motor Sales, U.S.A., Inc.

Fig. 19: Exploded View Of A/C Unit Components

2) Remove heater core hoses. Remove 2 bolts and insulator retainer. Remove ABS actuator (if equipped). Remove refrigerant lines. Remove plate cover. Remove instrument panel. See INSTRUMENT PANEL.
3) Remove instrument panel brace and reinforcement. Remove floor carpet. Remove heater center duct. Disconnect control link and connector from air inlet servomotor. Remove 3 screws and air inlet servomotor. *See Fig. 19.*
4) Remove defroster duct. Remove 3 screws and water valve cover. Disconnect control link and connector from air mix servomotor. Remove 2 screws and air mix servomotor.
5) Disconnect air outlet servomotor connector. Remove 3 screws and air outlet servomotor. Disconnect electrical connectors. Remove 6 bolts and A/C unit.

Disassembly – **1)** Remove blower motor control relay and blower motor. *See Fig. 19.* Remove foot air duct. Remove A/C unit wiring harness and block joint. Remove lower case and evaporator cover. Remove evaporator.
2) Remove evaporator temperature sensor and expansion valve from evaporator. Remove heater core and water valve. Remove heater and vent air ducts. Remove coolant temperature sensor.

Reassembly & Installation – To reassemble and install, reverse disassembly and removal procedures. When installing A/C unit drain hose, pull hose forward until yellow paint mark on hose is visible in engine compartment. If installing a new evaporator, add 1.4 ounces of refrigerant oil. Evacuate, recharge and leak test system.

BLOWER MOTOR

Removal & Installation – Disconnect negative battery cable. Remove glove box and side air duct. Remove scuff plate, floor carpet and ECM cover. Disconnect blower motor connector. Remove blower motor. To install, reverse removal procedure.

COMPRESSOR

Removal & Installation – **1)** Run engine with A/C on for 10 minutes (if possible). Shut off engine. Disconnect battery cables, and remove battery. Discharge A/C system using approved refrigerant recovery/ recycling equipment.

2) Turn drive belt tensioner clockwise to loosen tension, and remove drive belt. Remove power steering pump. Disconnect refrigerant hoses from compressor. Cap all openings to prevent moisture contamination.

3) Remove electrical connector from compressor. Remove compressor bolts and compressor. To install, reverse removal procedure. Evacuate, recharge and leak test A/C system.

CONDENSER

Removal & Installation – **1)** Discharge A/C system using approved refrigerant recovery/recycling equipment. Disconnect battery cables, and remove battery. Remove air cleaner. On turbocharged engines, remove turbocharger air hose clamp and push hose toward engine side.

2) On all models, remove front bumper. Remove 12 clips and radiator support upper seal. Remove 2 bolts and receiver-drier. Remove refrigerant lines from condenser. Remove radiator and condenser upper mounting. Remove piping clamp from condenser. Remove condenser.

3) To install, reverse removal procedure. If installing a new condenser, add 1.4 ounces of refrigerant oil. Evacuate, recharge and leak test system.

COOLANT TEMPERATURE SENSOR

Removal & Installation – Disconnect negative battery cable. Remove engine undercover. Drain cooling system. Disconnect the coolant temperature sensor connector, located on left side of radiator. Remove sensor and "O" ring. To install, reverse removal procedure. Use a new "O" ring.

INSTRUMENT PANEL

CAUTION: Always store air bag assembly with air bag door pad facing upward. DO NOT dissemble air bag assembly.

Removal – **1)** Disable air bag system. See AIR BAG SYSTEM SAFETY article in GENERAL SERVICING. Disconnect negative battery cable. Remove steering wheel. Remove front pillar garnishes, foot rest and front door scuff inside plates. Remove steering column cover, upper console panel and parking brake hole cover. Remove console box.

2) Remove lower panels. Remove cluster finish panels. Remove instrument cluster. Remove instrument panel center duct heater. Remove combination switch, radio and computer cover.

3) Remove glove box door plates. Carefully disconnect air bag connector. Remove glove box. Remove 3 mounting brackets and air duct. Remove passenger air bag assembly.

4) Remove parking brake lever, right defroster nozzle and steering column. Disconnect instrument panel electrical connectors. Remove instrument panel. Remove 6 bolts, 6 nuts and instrument panel reinforcement.

Installation – To install, reverse removal procedure. Use new passenger air bag assembly bolts.

PRESSURE SWITCH

Removal & Installation – Discharge A/C system using approved refrigerant recovery/recycling equipment. Disconnect pressure switch connector. Pressure switch is located next to right strut tower. Using open end wrench, lock pressure switch mount on tube and remove switch. Use care to not deform tube. To install, reverse removal procedure. Evacuate, recharge and leak test system.

RADIATOR FAN RELAYS

Removal & Installation – Disconnect negative battery cable. On models without automatic spoiler, remove engine undercover. On models with automatic spoiler, remove left headlight. On all models, remove radiator fan relay. *See Figs. 1 and 20.* To install, reverse removal procedure.

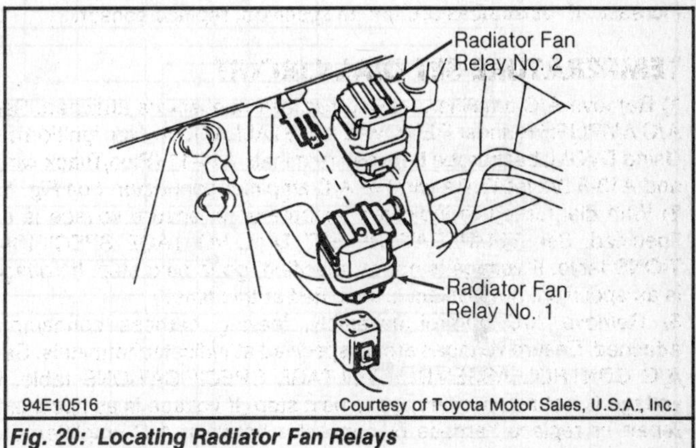
Radiator Fan Relay No. 2
Radiator Fan Relay No. 1
94E10516
Courtesy of Toyota Motor Sales, U.S.A., Inc.

Fig. 20: Locating Radiator Fan Relays

RECEIVER-DRIER

Removal & Installation – **1)** Discharge A/C system using approved refrigerant recovery/recycling equipment. Remove front bumper. Remove 12 clips and radiator support upper seal. Disconnect refrigerant lines from receiver-drier. Cap all openings to prevent moisture contamination. Remove receiver-drier from holder.

2) To install, reverse removal procedure. If receiver-drier is replaced, add 0.7 ounce of refrigerant oil to compressor. Evacuate, recharge and leak test A/C system.

TORQUE SPECIFICATIONS

TORQUE SPECIFICATIONS

Application	Ft. Lbs. (N.m)
Compressor Mounting Bolts	38 (52)
Compressor Stud Bolt	19 (26)
Passenger Air Bag-To-	
Instrument Panel Bolts	[1]
Instrument Panel Reinforcement Bolts	15 (21)
Power Steering Bolt	43 (58)
Steering Column Bolts	19 (25)
Steering Wheel Bolt	26 (35)
	INCH Lbs. (N.m)
Condenser Mounting Bolts	36 (4)
Coolant Temperature Sensor	65 (7.4)
Refrigerant Hoses	
Condenser	87 (10)
Compressor	87 (10)
Evaporator	87 (10)
Receiver-Drier	48 (5.4)
RPM Sensor	52 (6)
Steering Wheel Pad Bolts	62 (7)

[1] – Tighten bolts to 78 INCH lbs. (8.8 N.m).

WIRING DIAGRAM

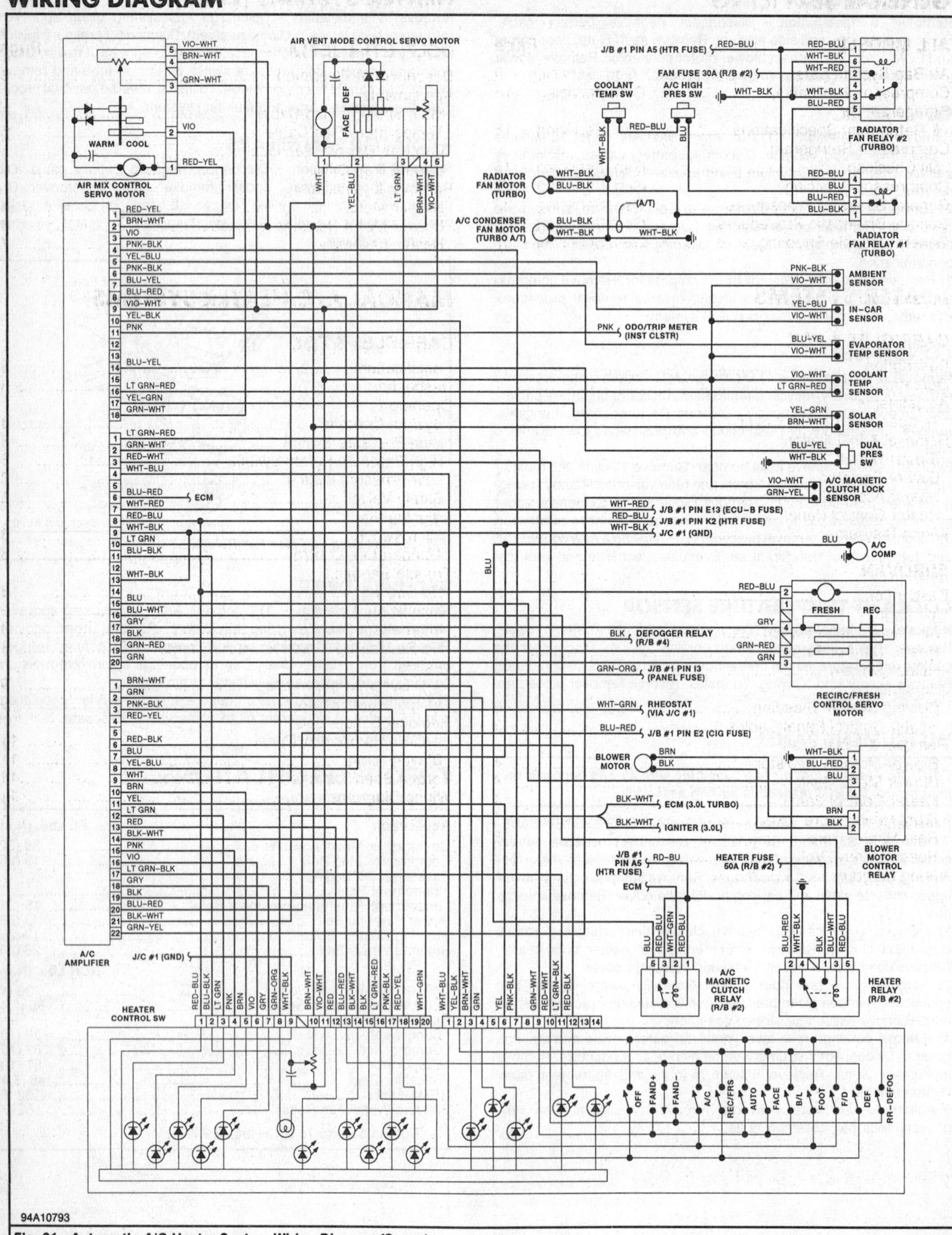
AIR VENT MODE CONTROL SERVO MOTOR
AIR MIX CONTROL SERVO MOTOR
WARM
COOL
FACE
DEF
J/B #1 PIN A5 (HTR FUSE)
FAN FUSE 30A (R/B #2)
COOLANT TEMP SW
A/C HIGH PRES SW
RADIATOR FAN RELAY #2 (TURBO)
RADIATOR FAN MOTOR (TURBO)
A/C CONDENSER FAN MOTOR (TURBO A/T)
RADIATOR FAN RELAY #1 (TURBO)
AMBIENT SENSOR
IN-CAR SENSOR
ODO/TRIP METER (INST CLSTR)
EVAPORATOR TEMP SENSOR
COOLANT TEMP SENSOR
SOLAR SENSOR
DUAL PRES SW
A/C MAGNETIC CLUTCH LOCK SENSOR
ECM
J/B #1 PIN E13 (ECU-B FUSE)
J/B #1 PIN K2 (HTR FUSE)
J/C #1 (GND)
A/C COMP
FRESH
REC
DEFOGGER RELAY (R/B #4)
J/B #1 PIN I3 (PANEL FUSE)
RECIRC/FRESH CONTROL SERVO MOTOR
RHEOSTAT (VIA J/C #1)
J/B #1 PIN E2 (CIG FUSE)
BLOWER MOTOR
ECM (3.0L TURBO)
IGNITER (3.0L)
BLOWER MOTOR CONTROL RELAY
J/B #1 PIN A5 (HTR FUSE)
HEATER FUSE 50A (R/B #2)
A/C MAGNETIC CLUTCH RELAY (R/B #2)
HEATER RELAY (R/B #2)
A/C AMPLIFIER
J/C #1 (GND)
HEATER CONTROL SW
OFF
FAN D+
FAN D-
A/C
REC/FRS
AUTO
FACE
B/L
FOOT
F/D
DEF
RR-DEFOG
94A10793

Fig. 21: Automatic A/C-Heater System Wiring Diagram (Supra)

1993 VOLKSWAGEN CONTENTS

GENERAL SERVICING

HEATER SYSTEMS

HEATER SYSTEMS (Cont.)

MANUAL A/C-HEATER SYSTEMS

1993 VOLKSWAGEN CONTENTS (Cont.)

MANUAL A/C-HEATER SYSTEMS (Cont.)

MANUAL A/C-HEATER SYSTEMS (Cont.)

1993 HEATER SYSTEMS
Cabriolet & Fox

WARNING: To avoid injury from accidental air bag deployment, read and carefully follow all SERVICE PRECAUTIONS and DISABLING & ACTIVATING AIR BAG SYSTEM procedures in AIR BAG SYSTEM SAFETY article in GENERAL SERVICING.

CAUTION: When battery is disconnected, radio will go into anti-theft protection mode. Obtain radio anti-theft protection code from owner prior to servicing vehicle.

DESCRIPTION

The heater is a water-valve type which combines heating, defrosting and ventilation into one unit. *See Figs. 1 and 2.* Controls include fan control knob, air distribution and temperature control levers/knobs. Blower fan control provides 3 speeds.

OPERATION

Two upper levers regulate airflow volume and distribution. To direct air to footwell vents, move upper left lever fully left. To direct air to defroster vents and side windows, move upper right lever fully right. To shut off air to both windshield and footwell, move both levers to center stop. To increase heat, move lower lever from left to right. As fan control knob is turned clockwise, fan motor turns on and can be switched to one of 3 speeds.

ADJUSTMENTS

TEMPERATURE CONTROL LEVER

1) Move temperature control lever to extreme left position. Loosen cable clip on heater control valve. Move heater control valve lever to fully closed position. Tighten cable with clip.

2) If control lever adjustment cannot be made, loosen control lever assembly in instrument panel (do not remove). Move temperature control lever to extreme left position. Ensure cable sheathing is against cable stop. Reposition cable as necessary.

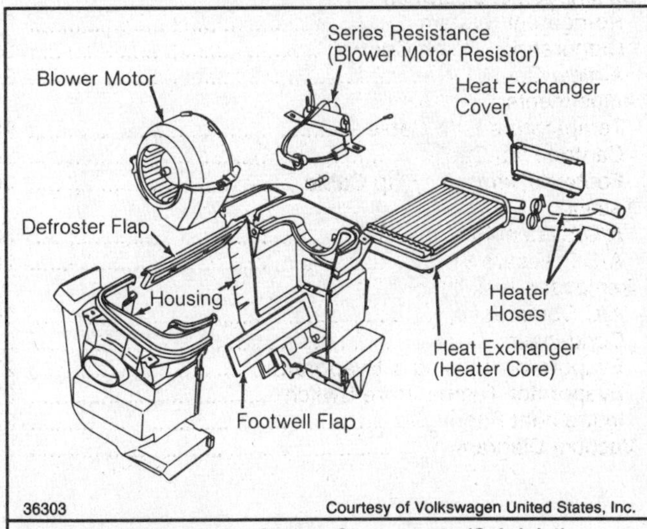
Series Resistance
(Blower Motor Resistor)
Blower Motor
Heat Exchanger
Cover
Defroster Flap
Housing
Heater
Hoses
Heat Exchanger
(Heater Core)
Footwell Flap
36303
Courtesy of Volkswagen United States, Inc.

Fig. 1: Identifying Heater System Components (Cabriolet)

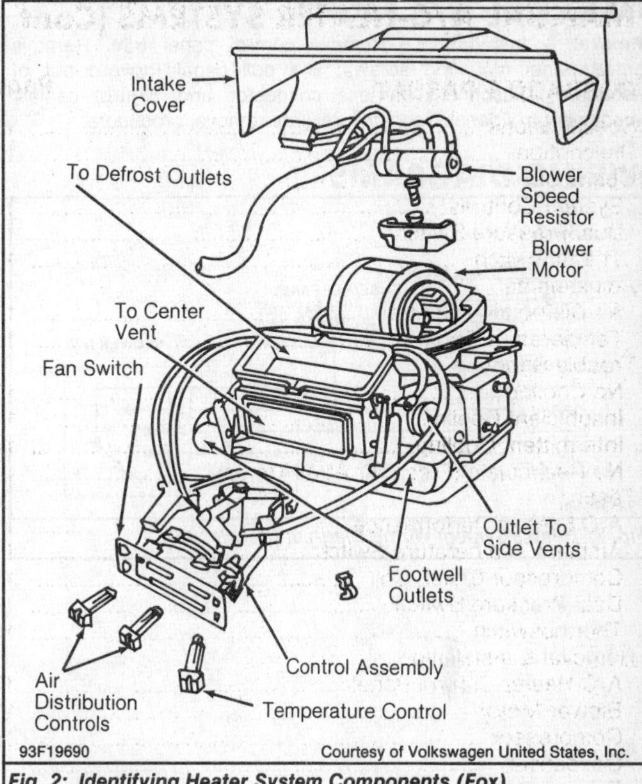
Intake
Cover
To Defrost Outlets
Blower
Speed
Resistor
Blower
Motor
To Center
Vent
Fan Switch
Outlet To
Side Vents
Footwell
Outlets
Control Assembly
Air
Distribution
Controls
Temperature Control
93F19690
Courtesy of Volkswagen United States, Inc.

Fig. 2: Identifying Heater System Components (Fox)

REMOVAL & INSTALLATION

WARNING: To avoid injury from accidental air bag deployment, read and carefully follow all SERVICE PRECAUTIONS and DISABLING & ACTIVATING AIR BAG SYSTEM procedures in AIR BAG SYSTEM SAFETY article in GENERAL SERVICING.

BLOWER MOTOR

Removal & Installation (Fox) – 1) Disconnect negative battery cable. Remove front cover gasket and water deflector. Release front fresh air housing cover clips, and remove front and rear fresh air housing covers.

2) Disconnect vacuum hoses. Disconnect blower resistor harness connector, and remove resistor. Loosen blower motor mounting screw. Disconnect blower motor harness connector.

3) Remove blower motor upper and lower housing covers. Rotate blower motor toward front of vehicle and remove motor. To install, reverse removal procedure.

BLOWER RESISTOR

Removal & Installation (Fox) – Remove blower housing cover. Disconnect blower resistor harness connector. Remove retaining screws and remove blower resistor. To install, reverse removal procedure.

HEATER ASSEMBLY

Removal – 1) Drain coolant from radiator. Loosen clamps and remove heater core hoses. Disconnect battery ground cable. Pull heater control knobs off. Remove trim plate and underdash access panels.

2) Disconnect wiring from blower motor, and remove cable from temperature control lever. Pry spring clamp off with screwdriver, and separate heater assembly halves. Remove heater core and blower motor.

Installation – To install, insert blower motor and heater core into right half of housing. Position left half, and install spring clips. To complete installation, reverse removal procedure.

1993 HEATER SYSTEMS
Cabriolet & Fox (Cont.)

HEATER CONTROL PANEL

Removal & Installation – Remove control panel trim. Remove control panel mounting screws, and pull panel forward out of dashboard. Disconnect harness connector and control cables. Remove control panel. To install, reverse removal procedure.

WIRING DIAGRAMS

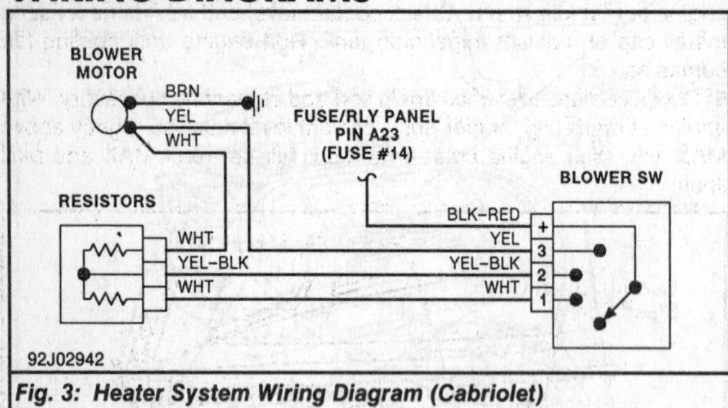
BLOWER MOTOR
BRN
YEL
WHT
FUSE/RLY PANEL PIN A23 (FUSE #14)
RESISTORS
BLOWER SW
BLK-RED
YEL
WHT
YEL-BLK
YEL-BLK
WHT
WHT
+
3
2
1
92J02942

Fig. 3: Heater System Wiring Diagram (Cabriolet)

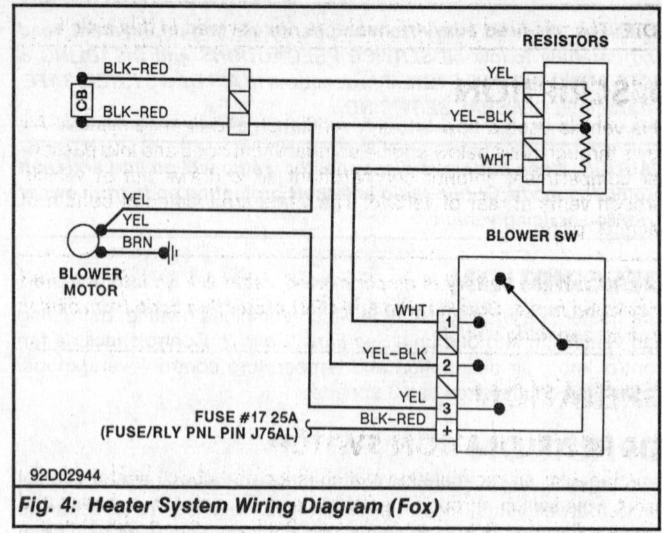
RESISTORS
BLK-RED
CB
BLK-RED
YEL
YEL-BLK
WHT
YEL
YEL
BRN
BLOWER MOTOR
BLOWER SW
WHT
1
YEL-BLK
2
YEL
3
FUSE #17 25A (FUSE/RLY PNL PIN J75AL)
BLK-RED
+
92D02944

Fig. 4: Heater System Wiring Diagram (Fox)

1993 HEATER SYSTEMS
EuroVan

NOTE: The gas-fired auxiliary heater is not covered in this article.

DESCRIPTION

This vehicle uses a flow-through ventilation and heating system. Air flows through grille below engine compartment hood and into passenger compartment. Interior compartment air is drawn out of vehicle through vents at rear of vehicle. The vents are located at bottom of each "D" pillar.

CAUTION: When battery is disconnected, radio will go into anti-theft protection mode. Obtain radio anti-theft protection code from owner prior to servicing vehicle.

OPERATION

AIR RECIRCULATION SWITCH

A rectangular air recirculation switch is located above heater control panel. This switch, through a solenoid and vacuum servo, opens and closes a flap that is located in air inlet duct. *See Fig. 3.* When flap is open, outside air enters vehicle. When flap is closed, the vehicle's interior compartment air is recirculated to help prevent exhaust or harmful fumes from entering vehicle.

HEATER CONTROL PANEL

Three slide levers and a fan switch rotary knob are used on control panel. Top left lever is used to control airflow to footwells. Top right lever is used to control airflow to head (upper body) area.

Bottom slide lever controls temperature. Depending on position of levers, fresh (cool) air or heated air flows out of vents.

A rear heater blower motor switch, located above heater control panel, has 3 fan speeds. *See Fig. 1.* Temperature setting for front heater is also the temperature setting for the rear heater.

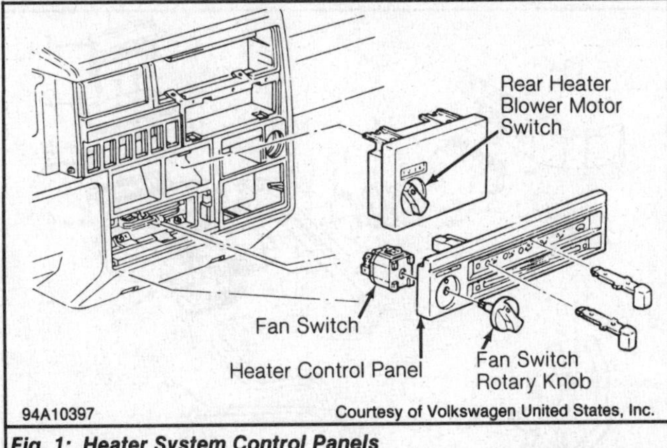
Rear Heater
Blower Motor
Switch
Fan Switch
Heater Control Panel
Fan Switch
Rotary Knob
94A10397
Courtesy of Volkswagen United States, Inc.

Fig. 1: Heater System Control Panels

HEATER SYSTEM

Front – The front heater system uses a heater control valve and is cable operated. The heater control valve is located on left side of engine compartment, below brake booster. *See Fig. 2.*

The cable-actuated heater control valve, controls temperature for both front and rear heater systems. Air distribution is controlled by defroster flap and footwell flap cables.

Rear – The rear heater, located underneath vehicle, is standard equipment on all models. Engine coolant is supplied to rear heater core by 2 heater hoses. The intake for the rear heater is located in the sliding door footwell, allows interior air to be recirculated through the heater core for greater efficiency.

A blower motor forces air through heater core, and out of an adjustable vent. On EuroVan CL, rear air outlet vent is located between middle row of seats. On EuroVan MV, rear air outlet vent is located underneath right jump seat.

ADJUSTMENTS

COOLING SYSTEM BLEEDING

1) Place heater control panel to maximum heat position. Remove cap from coolant expansion tank. Open cooling system bleed screw (on heater hose to heater control valve). *See Fig. 2.*

2) Fill coolant expansion tank to MAX line. Close bleed screw. Run engine at fast idle speed. Check coolant level and add as necessary. Install cap on coolant expansion tank. Run engine until cooling fan comes on.

3) Check coolant level once again and add coolant as necessary. With engine at operating temperature, coolant level must be slightly above MAX line. With engine cold, level must fall between MAX and MIN lines.

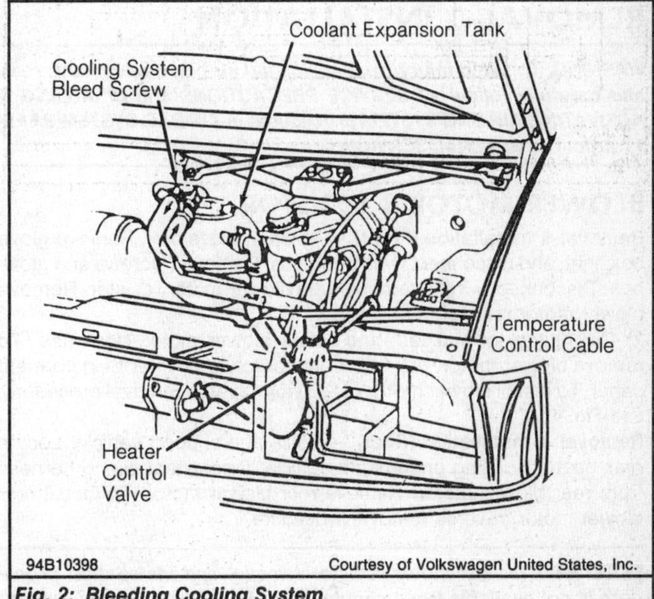
Coolant Expansion Tank
Cooling System
Bleed Screw
Temperature
Control Cable
Heater
Control
Valve
94B10398
Courtesy of Volkswagen United States, Inc.

Fig. 2: Bleeding Cooling System

HEATER CONTROL PANEL CABLES

1) Before installing heater control panel, attach cables onto panel. Position cable sleeves on stops, and secure cables with clips.

2) Push temperature control cable through firewall and into engine compartment. *See Fig. 2.* Slide temperature control lever to left stop. Slide control lever on heater control valve away from cable retaining clip (no coolant flow). Hold heater control valve lever in this position, and attach cable.

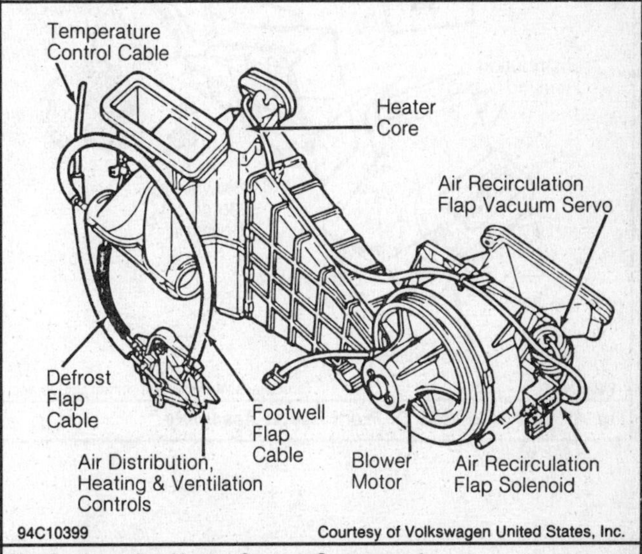
Temperature
Control Cable
Heater
Core
Air Recirculation
Flap Vacuum Servo
Defrost
Flap
Cable
Footwell
Flap
Cable
Air Distribution,
Heating & Ventilation
Controls
Blower
Motor
Air Recirculation
Flap Solenoid
94C10399
Courtesy of Volkswagen United States, Inc.

Fig. 3: Locating Heater System Component

1993 HEATER SYSTEMS
EuroVan (Cont.)

3) Slide defroster (top right) lever to left stop. Slide defroster flap lever toward cable retaining clip. Hold defroster flap lever in this position and attach cable.
4) Slide footwell (top left) lever to right stop. Slide footwell flap lever away from cable retaining clip. Hold footwell flap lever in this position and attach cable.
5) To complete adjustment, move control lever(s) from stop to stop. The cables for the defroster and footwell flaps are self-adjusting. *See Fig. 3.*

TESTING

Testing information is not available from manufacturer. Use wiring diagram as a guide. See WIRING DIAGRAM.

REMOVAL & INSTALLATION

WARNING: To avoid injury from accidental air bag deployment, read and carefully follow all SERVICE PRECAUTIONS and DISABLING & ACTIVATING AIR BAG SYSTEM procedures in AIR BAG SYSTEM SAFETY article in GENERAL SERVICING.

BLOWER MOTOR & RESISTOR

Removal & Installation (Front) – 1) Open glove box. Remove glove box light, and disconnect wiring harness. Remove 7 screws and glove box. Disconnect wiring harness from blower motor resistor. Remove blower motor resistor (if necessary).
2) Disengage locking tab, and rotate blower motor clockwise. To remove blower motor, pull blower motor toward center of instrument panel. To install blower motor or resistor, reverse removal procedure. *See Fig. 4.*
Removal & Installation (Rear) – Raise and support vehicle. Locate rear heater housing underneath vehicle. Disconnect wiring harness from rear blower motor. Remove rear blower motor. To install rear blower motor, reverse removal procedure.

NOTE: Rear blower motor resistor removal and installation procedure is not available from manufacturer. Rear blower motor resistor is located on left side of engine compartment.

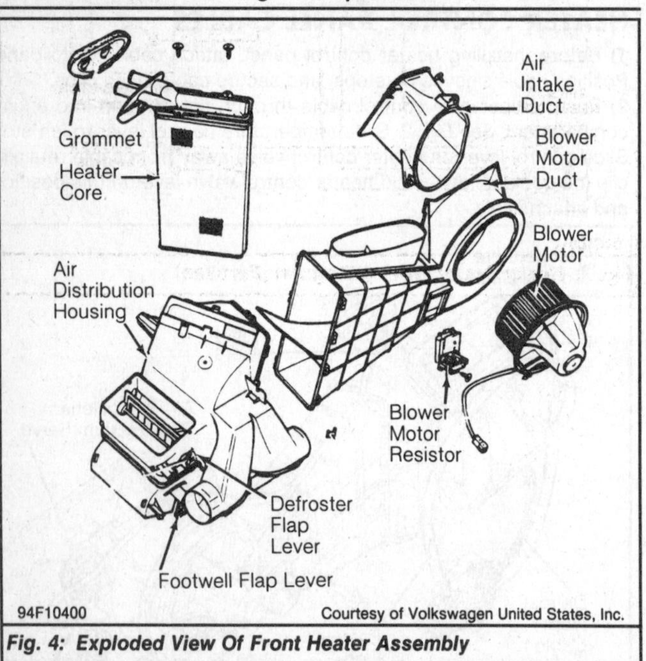
Air Intake Duct
Grommet
Heater Core
Blower Motor Duct
Blower Motor
Air Distribution Housing
Blower Motor Resistor
Defroster Flap Lever
Footwell Flap Lever
94F10400
Courtesy of Volkswagen United States, Inc.

Fig. 4: Exploded View Of Front Heater Assembly

BLOWER MOTOR SWITCH

Removal & Installation (Rear Heater) – Using a screwdriver, carefully pry blower motor switch (located above heater control panel) from instrument panel. Disconnect wiring harness and remove switch. To install switch, reverse removal procedure.

HEATER CONTROL PANEL

Removal – Remove fan switch rotary knob. *See Fig. 1.* Remove air distribution/temperature control levers. Remove heater control panel screws. Pull heater control panel away from instrument panel. Detach heater control panel cables.
Installation – Attach and adjust heater control cables. See HEATER CONTROL PANEL CABLES under ADJUSTMENTS. To complete installation, reverse removal procedure.

FRONT HEATER CORE

Removal (Front) – 1) Obtain radio anti-theft protection code from owner prior to servicing vehicle. Open hood. Disconnect negative battery cable. Remove 3 screws and air intake duct from engine compartment side of firewall.
2) Open glove box. Remove glove box light, and disconnect wiring harness. Remove 7 screws and glove box. Remove right air duct. Carefully remove vent from center air outlet. Remove screws, and carefully pry out center air outlet.
3) Remove center air duct (if equipped). Detach control cables from heater housing. Disconnect wiring harness form blower motor resistor. Remove footwell air outlet console and cover.
4) Disconnect temperature control cable from heater control valve (in engine compartment). Disconnect heater hoses, and plug openings. Remove screws, on engine compartment side of firewall, and remove heater assembly. Disassemble air distribution housing to remove heater core. *See Fig. 4.*
Installation – To install, reverse removal procedure. Install seal around entire circumference of heater core so there are no gaps.

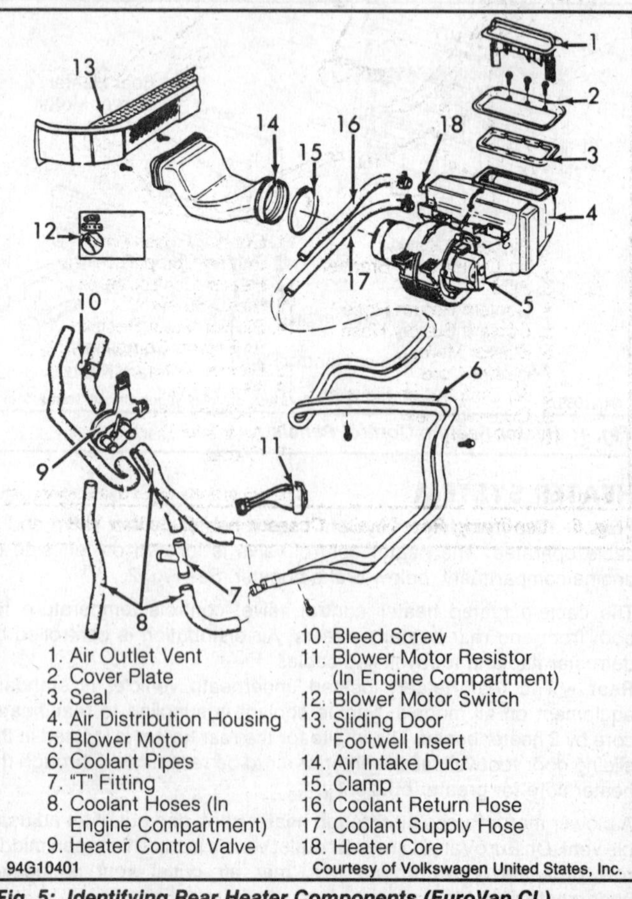
1. Air Outlet Vent
2. Cover Plate
3. Seal
4. Air Distribution Housing
5. Blower Motor
6. Coolant Pipes
7. "T" Fitting
8. Coolant Hoses (In Engine Compartment)
9. Heater Control Valve
10. Bleed Screw
11. Blower Motor Resistor (In Engine Compartment)
12. Blower Motor Switch
13. Sliding Door Footwell Insert
14. Air Intake Duct
15. Clamp
16. Coolant Return Hose
17. Coolant Supply Hose
18. Heater Core
94G10401
Courtesy of Volkswagen United States, Inc.

Fig. 5: Identifying Rear Heater Components (EuroVan CL)

REAR HEATER CORE

Removal - 1) On EuroVan CL, locate rear air outlet vent between middle row of seats. Pull up on rear air outlet vent to remove. Remove rear air outlet vent cover plate.

2) On EuroVan MV, locate rear air outlet vent underneath right jump seat. Remove screws from top of rear air outlet vent. Using a screwdriver, carefully unlock latch from bottom edge of rear air outlet vent. Remove rear air outlet vent bracket.

3) On all models, raise and support vehicle. Locate rear heater housing underneath vehicle. Disconnect wiring harness from rear heater housing. Detach heater hoses from heater core. *See Fig. 5 or 6.* Remove rear heater housing or heater core as necessary.

4) If air duct removal is necessary, remove sliding door footwell insert. Remove air duct screws. Loosen air duct clamp and remove air duct. If rear heater hose removal is necessary, remove fuel tank. Remove torsion bar. Remove rear heater hoses.

Installation - To install, reverse removal procedure. Install seal around entire circumference of heater core so there are no gaps.

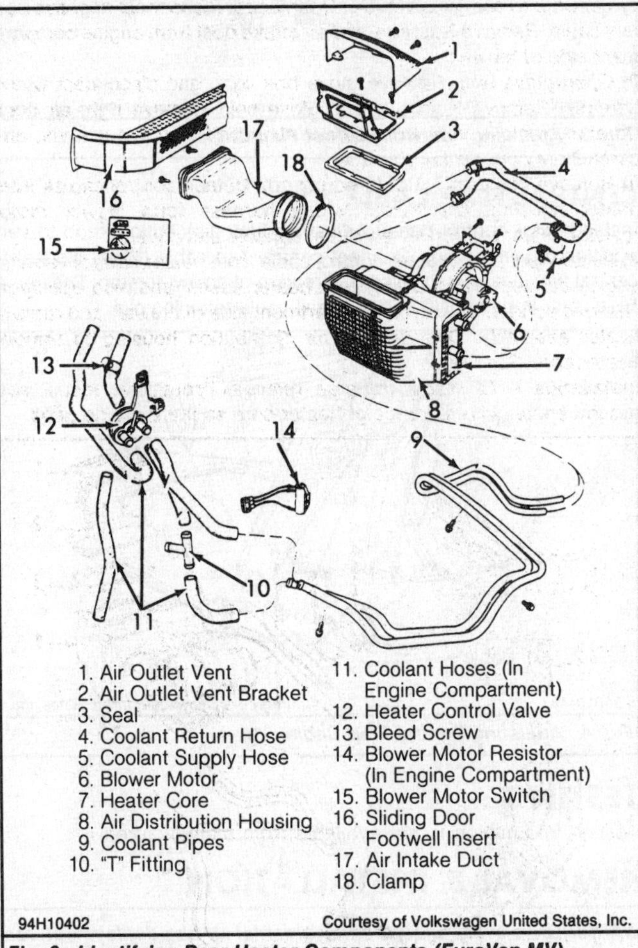

1
2
3
4
5
6
7
8
9
10
11
12
13
14
15
16
17
18
1. Air Outlet Vent
2. Air Outlet Vent Bracket
3. Seal
4. Coolant Return Hose
5. Coolant Supply Hose
6. Blower Motor
7. Heater Core
8. Air Distribution Housing
9. Coolant Pipes
10. "T" Fitting
11. Coolant Hoses (In Engine Compartment)
12. Heater Control Valve
13. Bleed Screw
14. Blower Motor Resistor (In Engine Compartment)
15. Blower Motor Switch
16. Sliding Door Footwell Insert
17. Air Intake Duct
18. Clamp
94H10402
Courtesy of Volkswagen United States, Inc.

Fig. 6: Identifying Rear Heater Components (EuroVan MV)

HEATER CONTROL VALVE

Removal & Installation (Front) - Detach temperature control cable from heater control valve. Clamp shut heater hoses at heater control valve. Detach hoses, and remove heater control valve. To install, reverse removal procedure.

Removal & Installation (Rear) - Detach temperature control cable from heater control valve. Clamp shut heater hoses at heater control valve. Detach hoses and remove heater control valve from expansion tank. To install, reverse removal procedure.

WIRING DIAGRAM

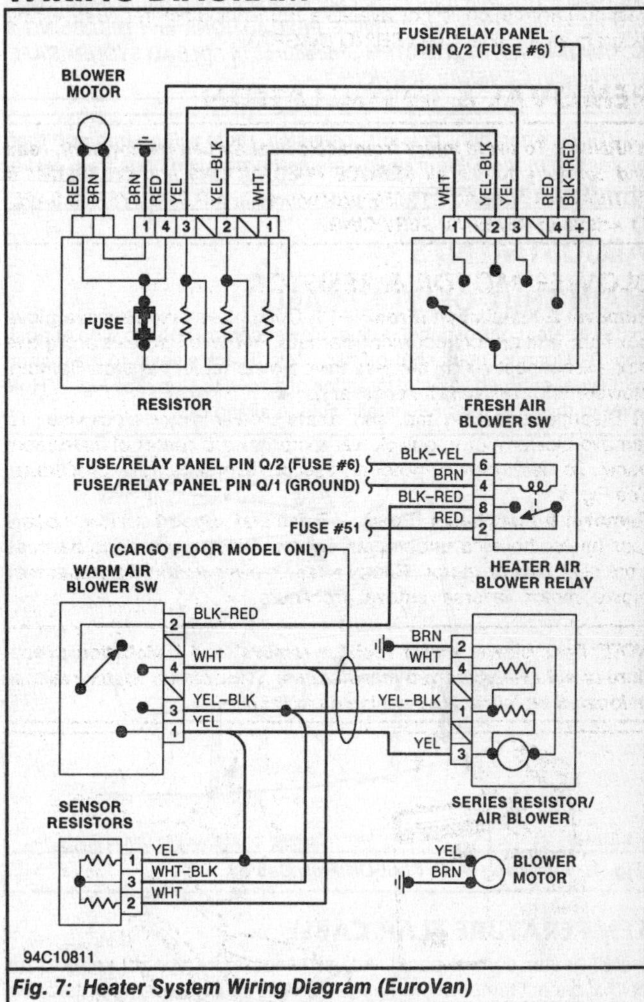

FUSE/RELAY PANEL PIN Q/2 (FUSE #6)
BLOWER MOTOR
RED
BRN
BRN
RED
YEL
YEL-BLK
WHT
WHT
YEL-BLK
YEL
RED
BLK-RED
FUSE
RESISTOR
FRESH AIR BLOWER SW
FUSE/RELAY PANEL PIN Q/2 (FUSE #6)
FUSE/RELAY PANEL PIN Q/1 (GROUND)
FUSE #51
(CARGO FLOOR MODEL ONLY)
BLK-YEL
BRN
BLK-RED
RED
HEATER AIR BLOWER RELAY
WARM AIR BLOWER SW
BLK-RED
WHT
YEL-BLK
YEL
BRN
WHT
YEL-BLK
YEL
SERIES RESISTOR/ AIR BLOWER
SENSOR RESISTORS
YEL
WHT-BLK
WHT
YEL
BRN
BLOWER MOTOR
94C10811

Fig. 7: Heater System Wiring Diagram (EuroVan)

1993 HEATER SYSTEMS
Golf, GTI & Jetta

DESCRIPTION & OPERATION

Heating and ventilation system is a blend type system. A heater control valve is not used. Coolant flows unrestricted through heater core. Interior temperature is regulated by a blend door which controls amount of air flowing through heater core. Blend door is operated by a cable connected to temperature control knob.

Three knobs are used to control blower speed, air temperature, and air distribution. Fresh air blower has 4 speeds. Blower motor resistor is located on blower motor housing.

WARNING: To avoid injury from accidental air bag deployment, read and carefully follow all SERVICE PRECAUTIONS and DISABLING & ACTIVATING AIR BAG SYSTEM procedures in AIR BAG SYSTEM SAFETY article in GENERAL SERVICING.

CAUTION: When battery is disconnected, radio will go into anti-theft protection mode. Obtain radio anti-theft protection code from owner prior to servicing vehicle.

ADJUSTMENTS

MAIN SHUT-OFF FLAP CABLE

Install heater control panel. Adjust blower control knob to stop at position "0". Connect main shut-off flap cable (Black sleeve) to main shut-off flap lever. Push lever, in direction of arrow, to stop. *See Fig. 1.* Hold lever in this position and install cable retaining clip.

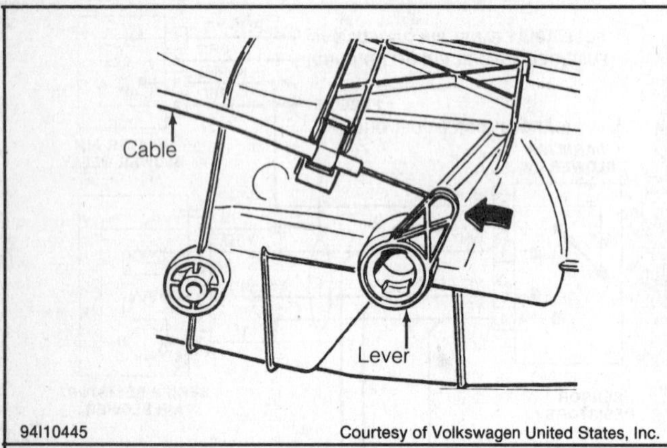
Cable
Lever
94I10445
Courtesy of Volkswagen United States, Inc.

Fig. 1: Adjusting Main Shut-Off Flap Cable

TEMPERATURE FLAP CABLE

Install heater control panel. Adjust temperature control knob to full cold. Connect temperature flap cable (Blue sleeve) to temperature flap lever. Push lever, in direction of arrow, to stop. *See Fig. 2.* Hold lever in this position and install cable retaining clip.

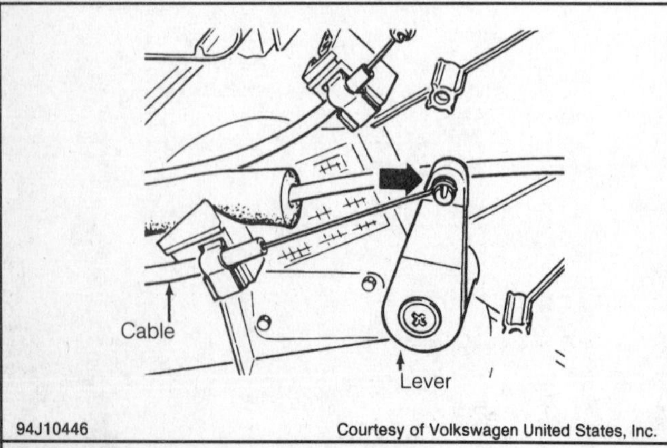
Cable
Lever
94J10446
Courtesy of Volkswagen United States, Inc.

Fig. 2: Adjusting Temperature Flap Cable

FOOTWELL/DEFROST FLAP CABLE

Install heater control panel. Adjust air flow distribution knob to defrost position (against stop). Connect footwell/defrost flap cable (Black sleeve) to footwell/defrost flap lever. Push lever, in direction of arrow, to stop. *See Fig. 3.* Hold lever in this position and install cable retaining clip.

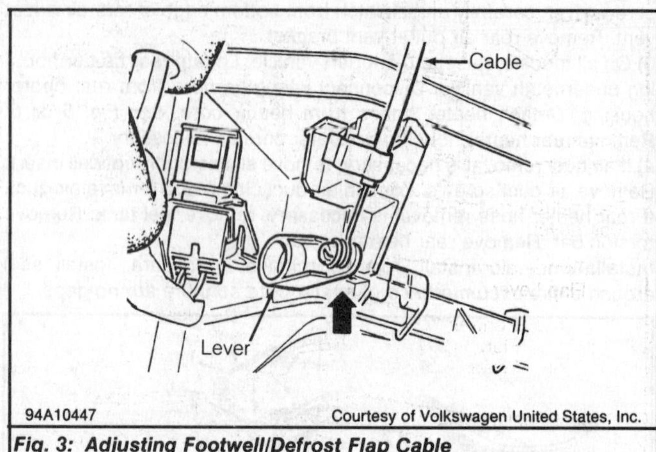
Cable
Lever
94A10447
Courtesy of Volkswagen United States, Inc.

Fig. 3: Adjusting Footwell/Defrost Flap Cable

CENTRAL FLAP CABLE

Install heater control panel. Adjust air flow distribution knob to vent position (against stop). Connect central flap cable (Black sleeve) to central flap lever. Push lever, in direction of arrow, to stop. *See Fig. 4.* Hold lever in this position and install cable retaining clip.

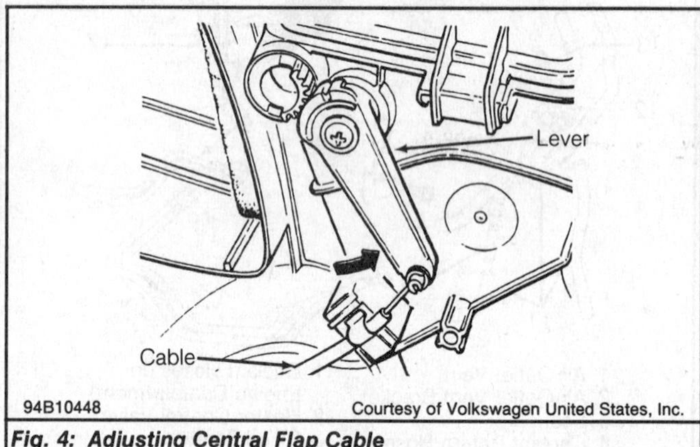
Lever
Cable
94B10448
Courtesy of Volkswagen United States, Inc.

Fig. 4: Adjusting Central Flap Cable

TESTING

Testing information is not available from manufacturer.

REMOVAL & INSTALLATION

WARNING: To avoid injury from accidental air bag deployment, read and carefully follow all SERVICE PRECAUTIONS and DISABLING & ACTIVATING AIR BAG SYSTEM procedures in AIR BAG SYSTEM SAFETY article in GENERAL SERVICING.

BLOWER MOTOR

Removal & Installation – Disconnect wiring harness from blower motor resistor. Remove clip and rotate blower motor clockwise. Remove blower motor. To install, reverse removal procedure.

BLOWER MOTOR RESISTOR

Removal & Installation – Disconnect wiring harness from blower motor resistor. Disengage locking tabs and remove blower motor resistor. To install, reverse removal procedure.

1993 HEATER SYSTEMS
Golf, GTI & Jetta (Cont.)

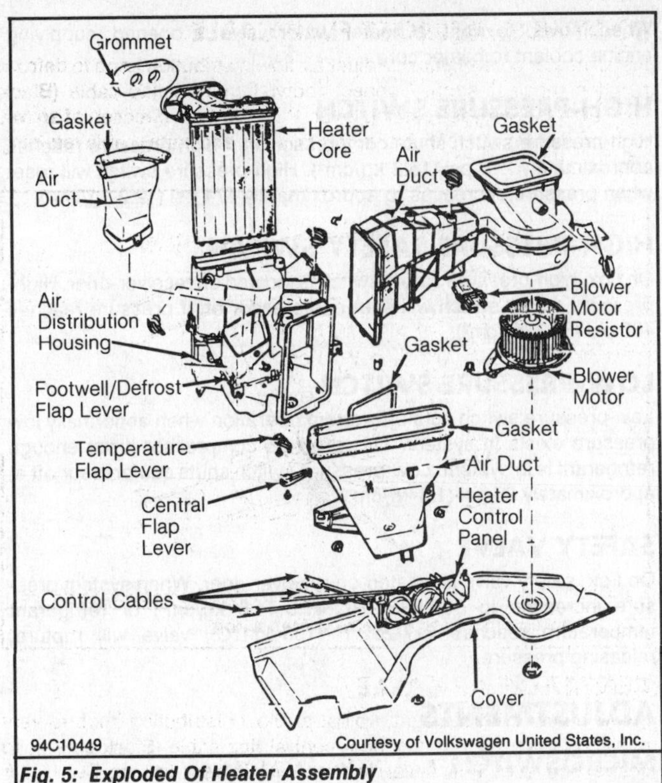
Grommet
Gasket
Heater Core
Gasket
Air Duct
Air Duct
Air Distribution Housing
Blower Motor Resistor
Gasket
Blower Motor
Footwell/Defrost Flap Lever
Gasket
Temperature Flap Lever
Air Duct
Central Flap Lever
Heater Control Panel
Control Cables
Cover
94C10449
Courtesy of Volkswagen United States, Inc.

Fig. 5: Exploded Of Heater Assembly

HEATER ASSEMBLY

Removal & Installation – Removal and installation procedure is not available from manufacturer. Exploded view of heater assembly is provided as a guide. *See Fig. 5.* Manufacturer recommends that air distribution housing not be disassembled.

WIRING DIAGRAM

NOTE: Information is not available from manufacturer.

1993 MANUAL A/C-HEATER SYSTEMS
Cabriolet & Fox

SPECIFICATIONS

Compressor Type	
Cabriolet	Sanden SD-508 5-Cyl. Or SD-709 7 Cyl.
Fox	Nipondenso 6-Cyl.
Compressor Belt Deflection	[1] 3/16-3/8" (5-10 mm)
System Oil Capacity	
Cabriolet	4.6 ozs.
Fox	5.7 ozs.
Refrigerant (R-12) Capacity	
Cabriolet	30.0-31.8 ozs.
Fox	41-42 ozs.
System Operating Pressures	
High Side	150-210 psi (10.5-19 kg/cm²)
Low Side	26-40 psi (1-2 kg/cm²)

[1] – Deflection is measured at center of belt, between A/C compressor pulley and crankshaft pulley, with thumb pressure.

WARNING: To avoid injury from accidental air bag deployment, read and carefully follow all SERVICE PRECAUTIONS and DISABLING & ACTIVATING AIR BAG SYSTEM procedures in AIR BAG SYSTEM SAFETY article in GENERAL SERVICING.

CAUTION: When battery is disconnected, radio will go into anti-theft protection mode. Obtain radio anti-theft protection code from owner prior to servicing vehicle.

DESCRIPTION

Air conditioning system is a cycling clutch type. Compressor is cycled on and off by a thermostatic switch to maintain constant cooling rate. System components include evaporator, expansion valve, receiver-drier, control panel, condenser, high-pressure switch and low-pressure switch. On Cabriolet, control panel includes a pair of levers and a 5-position fan control switch. Upper lever operates air distribution flap. Lower lever controls temperature selection. Rotary fan control switch controls fan speed selection.

On Fox, control panel has 5 air distribution buttons, a temperature control lever, and a rotary 4-speed fan switch.

OPERATION

SYSTEM CONTROLS

Air Distribution Control (Cabriolet) – With upper lever (air distribution control) in maximum cooling position, A/C is on and cooled air is recirculated, giving maximum cooling. Air is directed through dashboard vents. If lower lever (temperature control) is moved toward right, heated air is emitted from center dash vent and cooled air flows from side vents. With air distribution control in normal position, outside air is cooled and circulated. *See Figs. 1 and 2.*

In bi-level position, A/C is on, outside air is cooled and circulated, and air is emitted from dash and footwell vents. In ventilation position, A/C is off, and outside air is circulated. In heat position, A/C is off and fresh air is circulated through heater. Air is emitted from defogger, footwell and side dash vents. In defrost position, A/C is on and outside air is cooled and circulated. Air is emitted from windshield, side window and side dash vents. Lower lever (temperature control) is moved to extreme right and dash vents are closed for maximum defrosting.

Air Distribution Control (Fox) – From left to right, air distribution control buttons are: OFF, A/C, BI-LEV, HEAT and defrost position.

Fan Control Switch – On Cabriolet, 5-position fan control switch controls airflow. As knob is turned clockwise, fan operates in 4 different speeds, increasing speed as knob is moved to extreme right position.

On Fox, air volume is controlled by 4-speed fan control knob, located on left side of control panel. Fan operates when ignition is turned on and system is operated.

Temperature Control Lever – Temperature control lever controls heating and cooling. When moved to left, lever turns compressor on. When moved to right, a heater water valve is opened, supplying engine coolant to heater core.

HIGH-PRESSURE SWITCH

High-pressure switch shuts compressor off if high pressure reaches approximately 218 psi (15.3 kg/cm²). High-pressure switch will reset when pressure decreases to approximately 174 psi (12.2 kg/cm²).

HIGH-PRESSURE SAFETY SWITCH

On Fox, high-pressure safety switch is located on receiver-drier. High-pressure safety switch will shut compressor off if pressure reaches 436 psi (30.7 kg/cm²).

LOW-PRESSURE SWITCH

Low-pressure switch cuts off system operation when abnormally low pressure exists in system. This protects compressor if not enough refrigerant is in system. Low-pressure switch shuts compressor off at approximately 26 psi (1.8 kg/cm²).

SAFETY VALVE

On Fox, safety valve is located on receiver-drier. When system pressure increases to 590-635 psi (41.5-44.6 kg/cm²) or refrigerant temperature reaches 217-232°F (103-111°C), valve will rupture, releasing pressure.

ADJUSTMENTS

MICROSWITCH

Loosen microswitch mounting screw. Move microswitch so switch is on when air distribution control is at maximum A/C, NORM (normal), BI-LEV or extreme right position and off when lever is at VENT or HEAT position. Tighten microswitch mounting screw. Recheck operation.

TEMPERATURE CONTROL

Move temperature lever/knob to full cool position. Loosen temperature switch mounting screw. Move temperature switch counterclockwise to full stop position. Tighten temperature switch mounting screw.

TROUBLE SHOOTING

NO COOLING

1) Ensure fan motor operates in all speeds. Ensure air duct closes off outside air and heater water valve is closed. Adjust belt tension and clean condenser.

2) Inspect receiver-drier pressure seal. If seal is good, go to step **5)**. If seal is broken, replace seal, evacuate and recharge system. If system cools properly, testing is complete. If system does not cool, connect pressure gauges.

3) Set engine speed at 2000 RPM. Insert thermometer in left register and close all other ducts. Place controls on high blower and maximum cooling. With vehicle out of direct sunlight, close all windows. Radiator fan should come on with system pressure at 200 psi (14 kg/cm²).

4) If fan does not operate, replace pressure switch. Ensure system is okay. If fan does come on, turn engine off, and check for condenser obstructions and blocked airflow.

5) Turn air conditioner on and off with temperature control. Ensure compressor clutch engages. Push lever to extreme right position and back again. A click should be heard from compressor clutch. If a click is not heard, check for voltage at clutch coil wire with switch on. If voltage is present, replace clutch coil. If voltage is not present, check wiring or replace thermostatic switch.

6) If compressor clutch operates, check gauge readings. If both readings are low, locate leak and recharge system. If both readings are high, replace expansion valve. If low side is too high and high side is too low, replace or rebuild compressor.

INSUFFICIENT COOLING

1) Ensure fan motor operates at all speeds. Ensure air duct closes off outside air intake and heater water valve is closed. Adjust compressor belt tension and clean condenser.
2) Adjust engine speed to 2000 RPM. Position controls for maximum cooling and high blower. Insert thermometer in left register and close all other ducts. With vehicle out of direct sunlight, close all windows and doors. Connect pressure gauges and check readings.
3) If both gauges read too high, replace expansion valve. If both gauges read too low, recharge system after locating leak. If both readings are normal, go to next step. If pressure side is too high and suction side is normal, go to step **5)**. If pressure side is too low and suction side is too high, go to step **6)**. If pressure side is normal and suction side is too low, go to step **7)**.
4) Turn compressor off, and observe gauges. If readings equalize in 30 seconds, replace compressor. If readings take longer to equalize, ensure capillary tube installed length is 7" (178 mm).
5) If installation is correct, run system at maximum cooling for 15 minutes. If thermometer indicates temperature is less than 36°F (2°C) when compressor is turned off, or temperature is greater than 48°F (9°C) with compressor on, replace temperature switch.
6) Check condenser fins and clean or straighten. If operation is still not correct, discharge system until bubbles appear in sight glass. Recharge system until bubbles disappear, and recheck pressures. If still incorrect, locate leaks and tighten fittings. Discharge A/C system using approved refrigerant recovery/recycling equipment. Evacuate system to remove all air and recharge system.
7) Check for bubbles at sight glass. If present, repair leaks and recharge system. If no bubbles are present, check condenser-to-expansion valve line for kinks and repair if necessary. Feel along line from condenser to expansion valve. If there are no cold spots, replace expansion valve.
8) If cold spot is felt, remove and flush out lines and condenser. Check for bubbles at sight glass. If there are no bubbles, replace compressor. If bubbles are present, check for leaks. Repair and recharge system.

INTERMITTENT COOLING

1) Ensure fan motor operates in all 4 speeds. Ensure air duct closes off outside air and heater water valve is closed. Adjust belt tension and clean condenser.
2) Adjust engine speed to 2000 RPM. Set controls for maximum cooling and high fan. Insert thermometer in left air duct and close all other ducts. With vehicle in shade, close windows and doors, and connect pressure gauges. Operate system for 10 minutes.
3) Check for cool air at left duct. Low pressure gauge should read more than 16 psi (1.1 kg/cm²). If low pressure gauge is incorrect, place hands around expansion valve to warm valve. If pressure rises, moisture is present in system. Discharge A/C system using approved refrigerant recovery/recycling equipment. Evacuate and recharge system. If pressure does not rise, go to next step.
4) Check temperature on thermometer when thermostatic switch turns compressor off. If temperature is 39°F (4°C), system is okay. If temperature is lower than 39°F (4°C), ensure capillary tube installed length is 7" (178 mm). If installation is correct, replace thermostatic switch.

NO RECIRCULATE (FRESH AIR AT ALL TIMES)

1) Start engine. Turn blower motor off. Check fresh/recirculated air servomotor. Servomotor should be retracted. If servomotor is not as specified, check vacuum supply.
2) If vacuum does not exist, repair vacuum supply. If vacuum exists, check fresh/recirculated air door. If door is faulty, repair or replace as required. If door is okay, replace servomotor and retest.

TESTING

WARNING: To avoid injury from accidental air bag deployment, read and carefully follow all SERVICE PRECAUTIONS and DISABLING & ACTIVATING AIR BAG SYSTEM procedures in AIR BAG SYSTEM SAFETY article in GENERAL SERVICING.

A/C SYSTEM PERFORMANCE

1) Park vehicle out of direct sunlight. Install manifold gauge set. Press OFF button and move temperature control lever to left (cool) side. Open left, center, and right vents of instrument panel. Start engine and allow it to run at 2000 RPM.
2) Turn fresh air fan to fourth position (highest speed). Press A/C button and close doors and windows. After initial compressor cycling, measure temperature at left vent of instrument panel. Ensure temperature is as specified. See A/C SYSTEM PERFORMANCE TEMPERATURE SPECIFICATIONS table.

A/C SYSTEM PERFORMANCE TEMPERATURE SPECIFICATIONS

Vent Output Temperature °F (°C)	Ambient Temperature °F (°C)
39-46 (4.0-8.0)	104 (40)
40-47 (4.5-8.5)	95 (35)
41-48 (5.0-9.0)	86 (30)
42-49 (5.5-9.5)	77 (25)
45-52 (7.0-11.0)	66 (19)

VACUUM SERVOMOTORS

1) Ensure vacuum hoses are connected correctly. Connect vacuum gauge between vacuum check valve and vacuum reservoir "T" connection. Remove glove box or radio and control assembly cover.

VACUUM SERVOMOTOR TESTING

Application	Vacuum
Off	
Heat/Defrost	None
Mode Door	
1st Stage	Present
2nd Stage	Present
Recirculation	Present
Maximum	
Heat/Defrost	None
Mode Door	
1st Stage	Present
2nd Stage	Present
Recirculation	Present
Normal	
Heat/Defrost	None
Mode Door	
1st Stage	Present
2nd Stage	Present
Recirculation	None
Bi-Level	
Heat/Defrost	Present
Mode Door	
1st Stage	Present
2nd Stage	None
Recirculation	None
Vent	
Heat/Defrost	Present
Mode Door	
1st Stage	Present
2nd Stage	Present
Recirculation	None
Heat	
Heat/Defrost	Present
Mode Door	
1st Stage	None
2nd Stage	None
Recirculation	None
Defrost	
Heat/Defrost	None
Mode Door	
1st Stage	None
2nd Stage	None
Recirculation	None

1993 MANUAL A/C-HEATER SYSTEMS
Cabriolet & Fox (Cont.)

plate. Start engine and increase engine speed until vacuum gauge reads approximately 15 in. Hg.

2) Simultaneously move air distribution lever and temperature control lever to extreme right position. Stop engine and verify vacuum is present after at least one minute.

3) If vacuum drops, check vacuum check valve, grommet for vacuum reservoir, vacuum distributor, and vacuum reservoir for leaks. If any vacuum servomotor is pulled in, check vacuum distributor. Replace any faulty component and retest vacuum system.

4) Start engine. Connect vacuum gauge to appropriate servomotor vacuum line, and move A/C control to specified position. Compare vacuum reading to specification. See VACUUM SERVOMOTOR TESTING table.

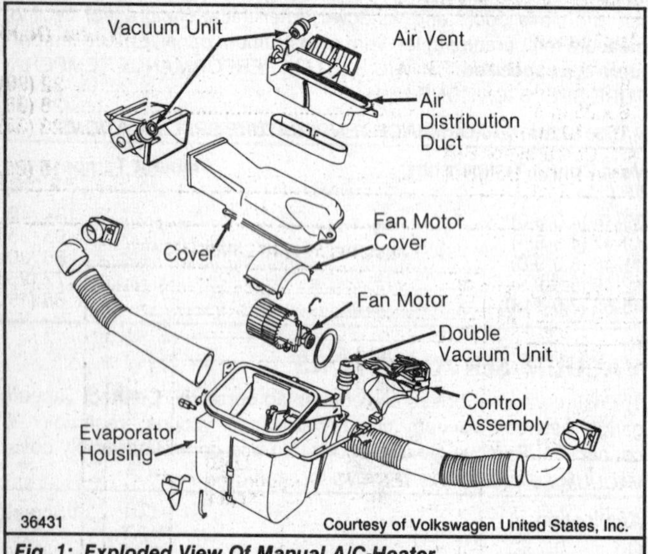
Vacuum Unit
Air Vent
Air Distribution Duct
Cover
Fan Motor Cover
Fan Motor
Double Vacuum Unit
Control Assembly
Evaporator Housing
36431
Courtesy of Volkswagen United States, Inc.

Fig. 1: Exploded View Of Manual A/C-Heater System Components (Cabriolet)

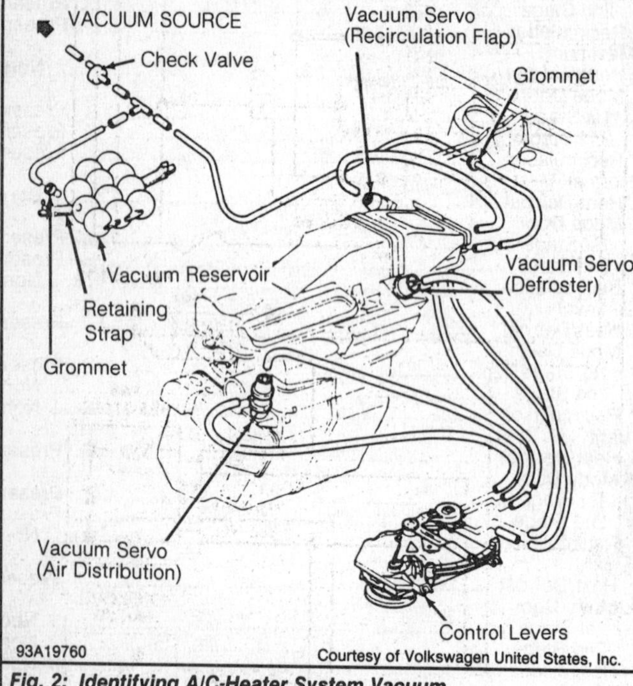
VACUUM SOURCE
Check Valve
Vacuum Servo (Recirculation Flap)
Grommet
Vacuum Reservoir
Retaining Strap
Grommet
Vacuum Servo (Defroster)
Vacuum Servo (Air Distribution)
Control Levers
93A19760
Courtesy of Volkswagen United States, Inc.

Fig. 2: Identifying A/C-Heater System Vacuum Controls & Components (Cabriolet)

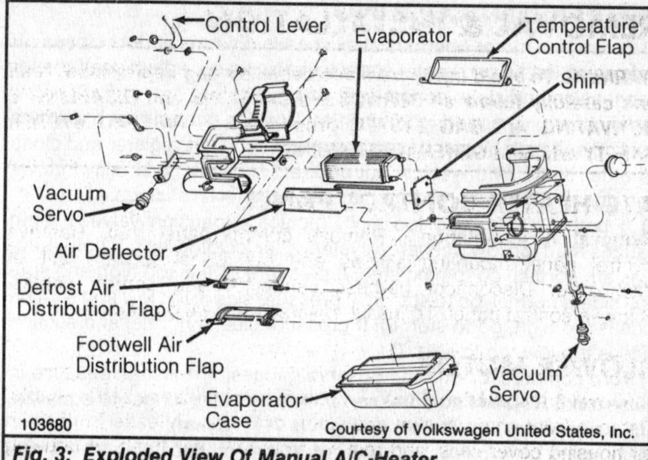
Control Lever
Evaporator
Temperature Control Flap
Shim
Vacuum Servo
Air Deflector
Defrost Air Distribution Flap
Footwell Air Distribution Flap
Evaporator Case
Vacuum Servo
103680
Courtesy of Volkswagen United States, Inc.

Fig. 3: Exploded View Of Manual A/C-Heater System Components (Fox)

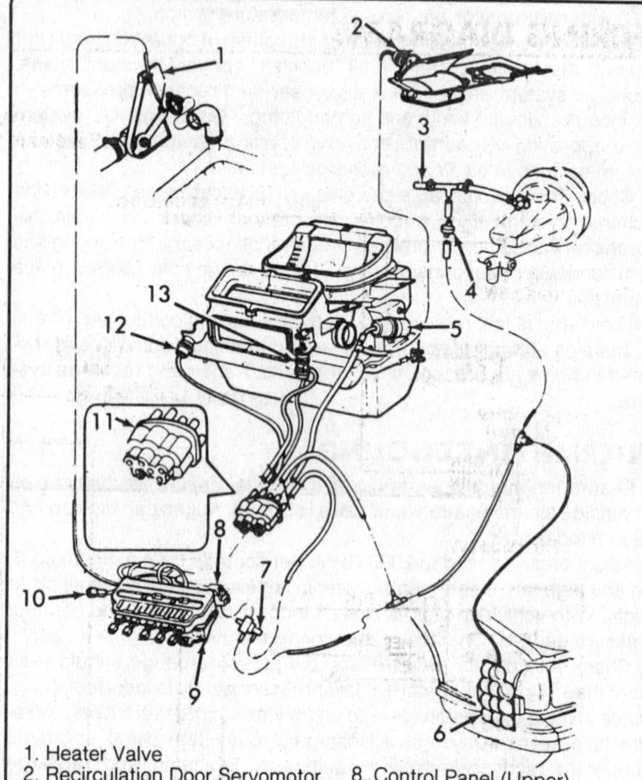
1. Heater Valve
2. Recirculation Door Servomotor
3. Vacuum Supply
4. Check Valve
5. Temperature Door Servomotor
6. Vacuum Reservoir
7. Recirculation Vacuum Switch
8. Control Panel (Upper)
9. Control Panel (Lower)
10. Heater Control Cable
11. Vacuum Harness Connector
12. Floor Door Servomotor
13. Defrost Door Servomotor
93B19761
Courtesy of Volkswagen United States, Inc.

Fig. 4: Identifying A/C-Heater System Vacuum Controls & Components (Fox)

REMOVAL & INSTALLATION

***WARNING:** To avoid injury from accidental air bag deployment, read and carefully follow all SERVICE PRECAUTIONS and DISABLING & ACTIVATING AIR BAG SYSTEM procedures in AIR BAG SYSTEM SAFETY article in GENERAL SERVICING.*

A/C-HEATER CONTROL PANEL

Removal & Installation – Remove control panel trim. Remove control panel mounting screws and pull panel forward out of dashboard. Disconnect harness connector and control cables. Remove control panel. To install, reverse removal procedure.

BLOWER MOTOR

Removal & Installation (Fox) – **1)** Disconnect negative battery cable. Remove front cover gasket and water deflector. Release front fresh air housing cover clips, and remove front and rear fresh air housing covers.

2) Disconnect vacuum hoses. Disconnect blower resistor harness connector, and remove resistor. Loosen blower mounting screw. Disconnect blower motor harness connector.

3) Remove blower motor upper and lower housing covers. Rotate blower motor toward front of vehicle and remove motor. To install, reverse removal procedure.

Removal & Installation (Cabriolet) – Disconnect blower motor harness connector. Depress blower motor retaining clip, and rotate motor clockwise to disengage lug on motor from clip. Remove motor. To install, reverse removal procedure.

TORQUE SPECIFICATIONS

TORQUE SPECIFICATIONS

Application	Ft. Lbs. (N.m)
Compressor Bracket Bolts	
8 x 25 mm	22 (30)
8 x 35 mm	28 (38)
10 x 40 mm	28 (38)
A/C Compressor Belt Idler Pulley Bolt/Nut	15 (20)

WIRING DIAGRAMS

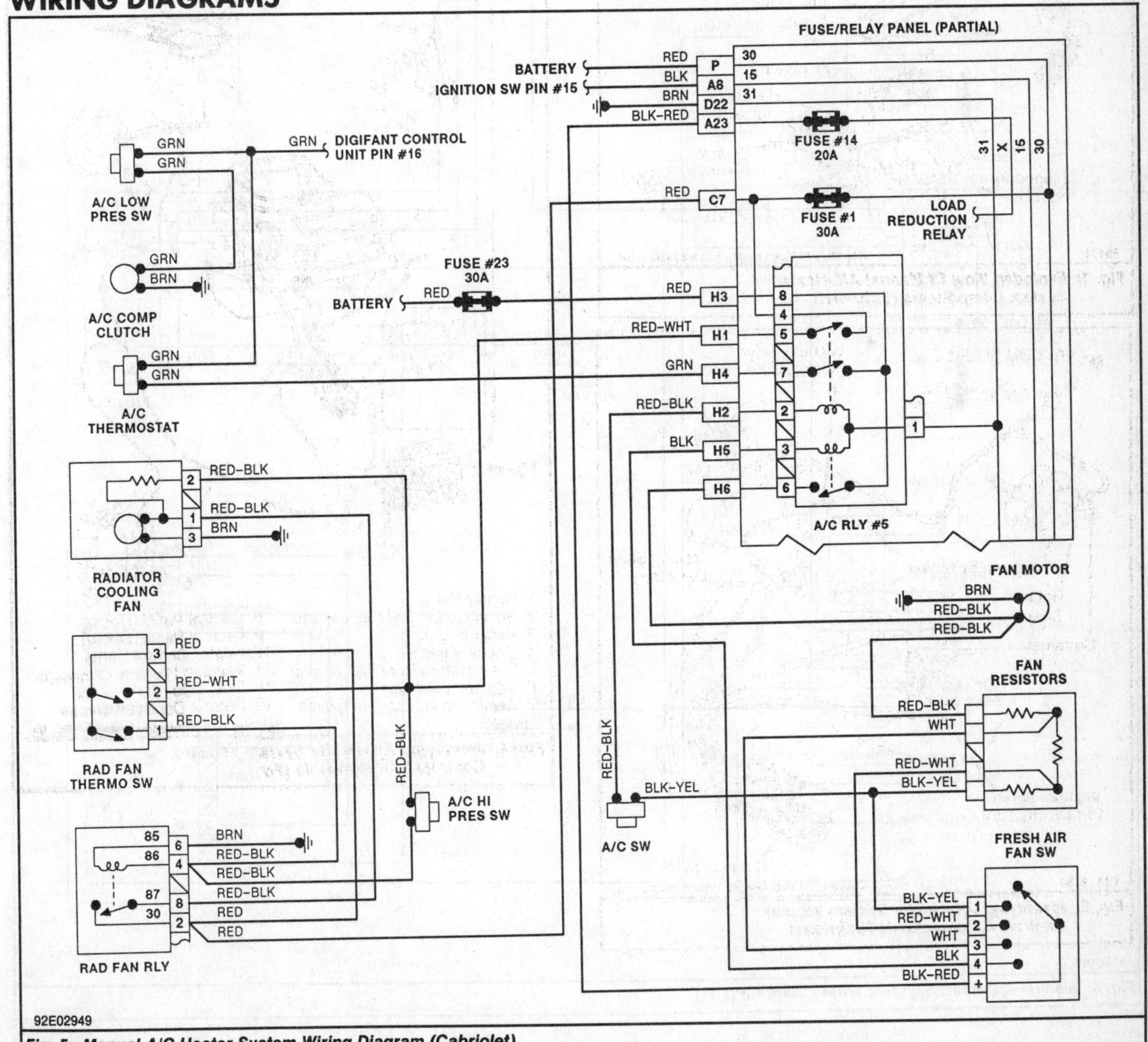

FUSE/RELAY PANEL (PARTIAL)
BATTERY
IGNITION SW PIN #15
RED
BLK
BRN
BLK-RED
P
A8
D22
A23
30
15
31
FUSE #14
20A
31
X
15
30
GRN
GRN
GRN
DIGIFANT CONTROL UNIT PIN #16
A/C LOW PRES SW
RED
C7
FUSE #1
30A
LOAD REDUCTION RELAY
GRN
BRN
A/C COMP CLUTCH
FUSE #23
30A
BATTERY
RED
RED
H3
RED-WHT
H1
GRN
H4
RED-BLK
H2
BLK
H5
H6
8
4
5
7
2
3
6
1
A/C RLY #5
GRN
GRN
A/C THERMOSTAT
RED-BLK
RED-BLK
BRN
2
1
3
RADIATOR COOLING FAN
FAN MOTOR
BRN
RED-BLK
RED-BLK
RED
RED-WHT
RED-BLK
3
2
1
RAD FAN THERMO SW
FAN RESISTORS
RED-BLK
WHT
RED-WHT
BLK-YEL
RED-BLK
RED-BLK
BLK-YEL
A/C HI PRES SW
A/C SW
85
86
87
30
6
4
8
2
BRN
RED-BLK
RED-BLK
RED-BLK
RED
RED
RAD FAN RLY
FRESH AIR FAN SW
BLK-YEL
RED-WHT
WHT
BLK
BLK-RED
1
2
3
4
+
92E02949

Fig. 5: Manual A/C-Heater System Wiring Diagram (Cabriolet)

1993 MANUAL A/C-HEATER SYSTEMS
Cabriolet & Fox (Cont.)

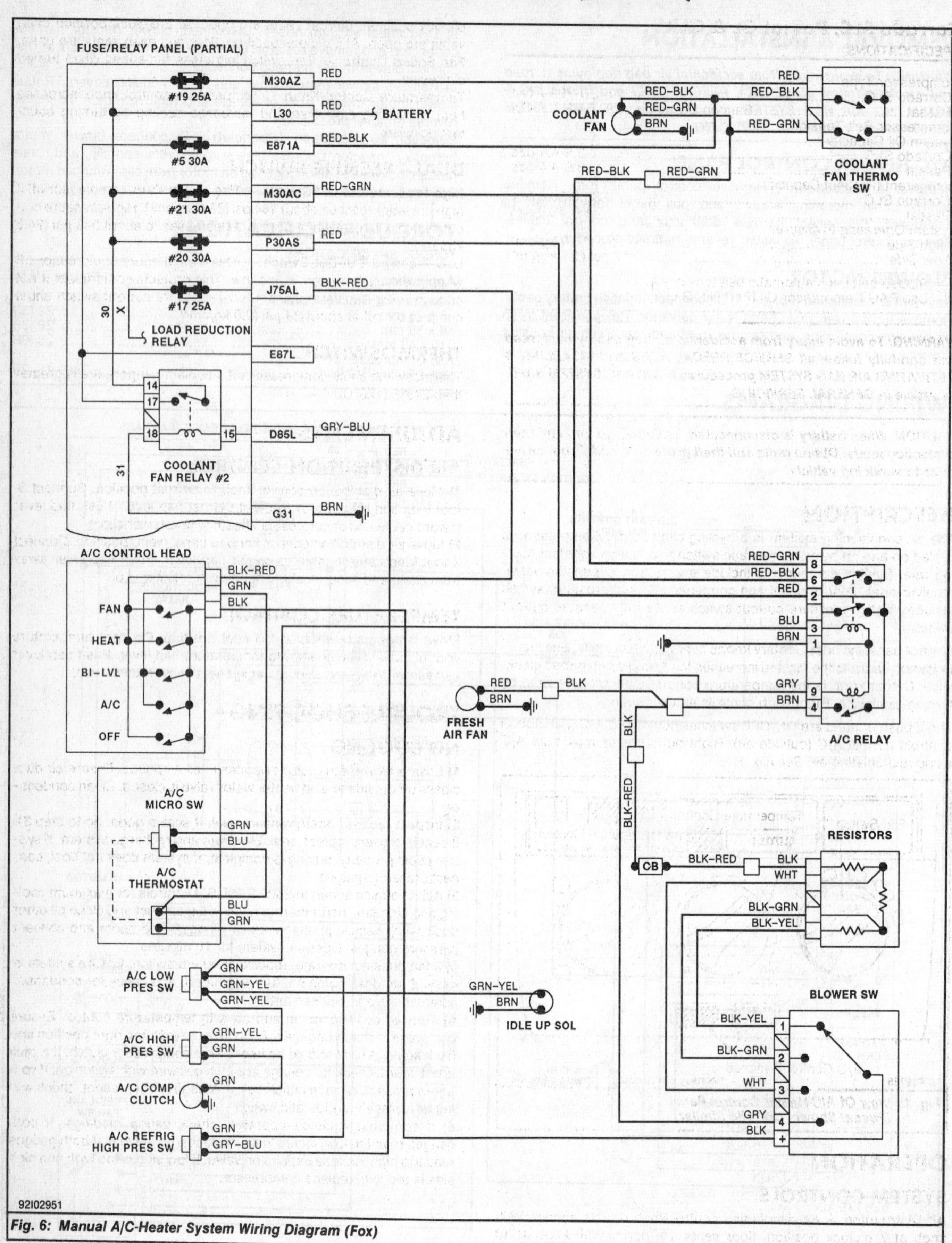
FUSE/RELAY PANEL (PARTIAL)
#19 25A
M30AZ
RED
L30
RED
BATTERY
#5 30A
E871A
RED-BLK
#21 30A
M30AC
RED-GRN
#20 30A
P30AS
RED
#17 25A
J75AL
BLK-RED
30
X
LOAD REDUCTION
RELAY
E87L
14
17
18
15
D85L
GRY-BLU
31
COOLANT
FAN RELAY #2
G31
BRN
RED
RED-BLK
RED-BLK
RED-GRN
COOLANT
FAN
BRN
RED-GRN
COOLANT
FAN THERMO
SW
RED-BLK
RED-GRN
A/C CONTROL HEAD
BLK-RED
GRN
BLK
FAN
HEAT
BI-LVL
A/C
OFF
RED-GRN
RED-BLK
RED
BLU
BRN
GRY
BRN
8
6
2
3
1
9
4
A/C RELAY
RED
BRN
BLK
FRESH
AIR FAN
BLK
BLK-RED
A/C
MICRO SW
GRN
BLU
A/C
THERMOSTAT
BLU
GRN
CB
BLK-RED
BLK
WHT
BLK-GRN
BLK-YEL
RESISTORS
A/C LOW
PRES SW
GRN
GRN-YEL
GRN-YEL
GRN-YEL
BRN
IDLE UP SOL
A/C HIGH
PRES SW
GRN-YEL
GRN
A/C COMP
CLUTCH
GRN
A/C REFRIG
HIGH PRES SW
GRN
GRY-BLU
BLOWER SW
BLK-YEL
1
BLK-GRN
2
WHT
3
GRY
4
BLK
+
92I02951

Fig. 6: Manual A/C-Heater System Wiring Diagram (Fox)

1993 MANUAL A/C-HEATER SYSTEMS
Corrado & Passat

Corrado SLC, Passat GL & GLX

SPECIFICATIONS

Compressor Type
Corrado SLC .... Sanden SD-709 7-Cyl.
Passat .... Sanden SD7-V16 or SD7-V16L 7-Cyl.
Compressor Belt Tension [1]
System Oil Capacity [2]
Corrado SLC .... 3.9-4.4 ozs.
Passat .... 3.9-4.4 ozs.
Refrigerant (R-134a) Capacity
Corrado SLC .... 35.0-36.6 ozs.
Passat .... 41.0-42.8 ozs.
System Operating Pressures
High Side .... 203 psi (13.8 kg/cm²)
Low Side .... 17 psi (1.1 kg/cm²)

[1] – Ribbed belt uses automatic belt tensioner.
[2] – Use PAG Compressor Oil (Part No. G 052 154 A2).

WARNING: To avoid injury from accidental air bag deployment, read and carefully follow all SERVICE PRECAUTIONS and DISABLING & ACTIVATING AIR BAG SYSTEM procedures in AIR BAG SYSTEM SAFETY article in GENERAL SERVICING.

CAUTION: When battery is disconnected, radio will go into anti-theft protection mode. Obtain radio anti-theft protection code from owner prior to servicing vehicle.

DESCRIPTION

The air conditioning system is a cycling clutch type. Compressor is cycled on and off by a thermostatic switch to maintain constant cooling rate. System components include evaporator, expansion valve, receiver-drier, control panel and condenser. A dual-pressure switch includes a high-pressure cut-out switch and a low-pressure cut-out switch.

Control panel includes 3 rotary knobs over 2 push buttons. *See Fig. 1.* Left knob controls the fan and increases fan speed when turned clockwise. Center knob is the temperature control and increases heat by turning clockwise. Right knob controls air distribution.

The 2 push buttons are ON/OFF switches controlling A/C. Left button controls normal A/C (outside air). Right button gives maximum A/C using recirculating air. *See Fig. 1.*

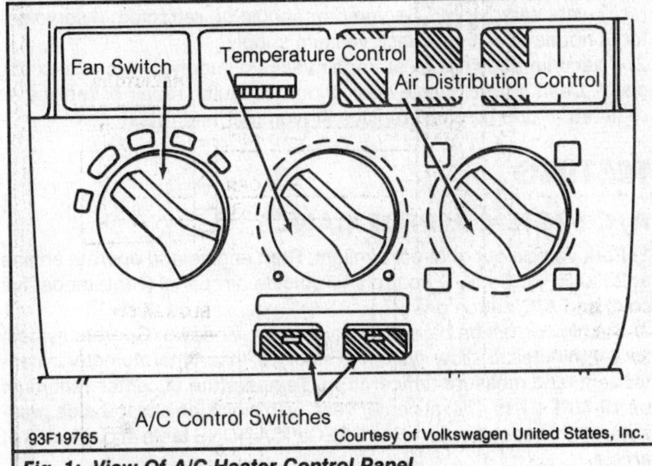
Fan Switch
Temperature Control
Air Distribution Control
A/C Control Switches
93F19765
Courtesy of Volkswagen United States, Inc.

Fig. 1: View Of A/C-Heater Control Panel (Passat Shown; Corrado Similar)

OPERATION

SYSTEM CONTROLS

Air Distribution – Air distribution control knob directs airflow. With knob at 7 o'clock position, floor vents are open. With knob at 10 o'clock position, defrost vents are open. At 2 o'clock position dash vents are open. At 5 o'clock position, floor and dash vents are open.

Fan Speed Control – Fan switch increases fan speed when turned clockwise.

Temperature Control Knob – Temperature control knob increases heat by turning clockwise and increases cooling by turning counterclockwise.

DUAL-PRESSURE SWITCH

High-Pressure Cut-Out Switch – This switch shuts compressor off if high pressure reaches about 464 psi (32.6 kg/cm²). High-pressure cut-out switch will reset when pressure decreases to about 348 psi (24.5 kg/cm²).

Low-Pressure Cut-Out Switch – This switch shuts compressor off when pressure in system is too low. This protects compressor if not enough refrigerant is in system. Low-pressure cut-out switch shuts compressor off at about 29 psi (2.0 kg/cm²).

THERMOSWITCH

Thermoswitch shuts compressor off if coolant temperature is greater than 248°F (120°C).

ADJUSTMENTS

AIR DISTRIBUTION CONTROL

1) Move air distribution control knob to defrost position. Connect 3-foot long control cable to footwell/defrost flap lever. Push flap lever toward cable and secure cable sheath with retainer clip.

2) Move air distribution control knob to panel (vent) position. Connect 2-foot long control cable to center flap lever. Push flap lever away from cable and secure cable sheath with retainer clip.

TEMPERATURE CONTROL

Move temperature knob to full cool position. Connect temperature control cable (Blue sheath) to temperature flap lever. Push flap lever away from cable and secure cable sheath with retainer clip.

TROUBLE SHOOTING

NO COOLING

1) Ensure blower fan motor operates in all 4 speeds. Ensure air duct closes off outside air and heater water valve is closed. Clean condenser.

2) Inspect receiver-drier pressure seal. If seal is good, go to step **3)**. If seal is broken, replace seal. Evacuate and recharge system. If system cools properly, testing is complete. If system does not cool, connect pressure gauges.

3) Adjust engine speed to 2500 RPM. Set controls for maximum cooling and high fan. Insert thermometer in left air duct and close all other ducts. With vehicle in shade, close windows and doors and connect pressure gauges. Operate system for 10 minutes.

4) If fan does not operate, replace pressure switch. Ensure system is okay. If fan does come on, turn engine off, and check for condenser obstructions and blocked airflow.

5) Turn air conditioner on and off with temperature control. Ensure compressor clutch engages. Push lever to extreme right position and back again. A click should be heard from compressor clutch. If a click is not heard, check for voltage at clutch coil wire with switch on. If voltage is present, replace clutch coil. If voltage is not present, check wiring or replace thermostatic switch.

6) If compressor clutch operates, check gauge readings. If both gauges read too low, locate leak and recharge system. If both gauges read too high, replace expansion valve. If low side is too high and high side is too low, replace compressor.

1993 MANUAL A/C-HEATER SYSTEMS
Corrado & Passat (Cont.)

INSUFFICIENT COOLING

1) Ensure blower fan motor operates at all 4 speeds. Ensure air duct closes off outside air intake and heater water valve is closed. Clean condenser.
2) Adjust engine speed to 2500 RPM. Set controls for maximum cooling and high fan. Insert thermometer in left air duct and close all other ducts. With vehicle in shade, close windows and doors and connect pressure gauges. Operate system for 10 minutes.
3) If both gauges read too high, replace expansion valve. If both gauges read low, locate leak and recharge system. If both gauge readings are normal, go to next step. If high side is too high and suction side is normal, go to step **5)**. If high side is too low and suction side is too high, go to step **6)**. If high side is normal and suction side is too low, go to step **7)**.
4) Turn compressor off and observe gauges. If readings equalize in 30 seconds, replace compressor. If readings take longer to equalize, ensure capillary tube installed length is 13" (330 mm).

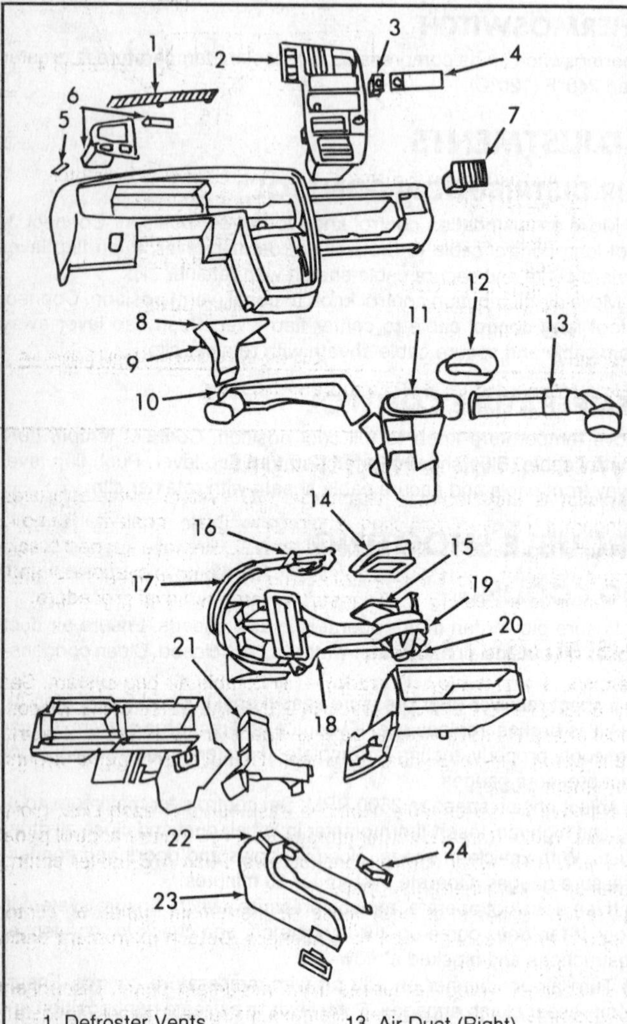
1
2
3
4
5
6
7
8
9
10
11
12
13
14
15
16
17
18
19
20
21
22
23
24
1. Defroster Vents
2. Instrument Panel Center
3. Fresh Air Blower Switch
4. Air Control Fascia
5. Side Window Air Vent
6. Air Outlet & Grille
7. Air Outlet
8. Seal
9. Defroster Air Duct
10. Air Duct (Left)
11. Air Distribution Housing
12. Center Air Outlet Duct
13. Air Duct (Right)
14. Air Intake Duct
15. Seal
16. Air Control Assembly
17. Control Cables
18. Air Distribution Housing With Heater Core
19. Blower Resistor
20. Blower
21. Footwell Air Outlets
22. Seal
23. Rear Footwell Air Duct
24. Rear Footwell Air Outlet
93A19695
Courtesy of Volkswagen United States, Inc.

Fig. 2: Exploded View Of A/C-Heater System (Corrado)

5) If capillary tube installation is correct, run system at maximum cooling for 15 minutes. If thermometer indicates temperature is less than 36°F (2°C) when compressor is turned off, or temperature is greater than 48°F (9°C) with compressor on, replace thermostatic switch.
6) Check condenser fins and clean or straighten. If operation is still not correct, discharge system until bubbles appear in sight glass. Recharge system until bubbles disappear, and recheck pressures. If operation is still incorrect, locate leaks and tighten fittings. Discharge A/C system using approved refrigerant recovery/recycling equipment. Evacuate system to remove all air and recharge system.
7) Check for bubbles at sight glass. If bubbles are present, repair leaks and recharge system. If no bubbles are present, check condenser-to-expansion valve line for kinks and repair if necessary. Check line (from condenser to expansion valve) for restrictions by feeling line for cold spots. If there are no cold spots, replace expansion valve.
8) If cold spot is felt, remove and flush out lines and condenser. Check for bubbles at sight glass. If there are no bubbles present, replace compressor. If bubbles are present, check for leaks. Repair and recharge system.

INTERMITTENT COOLING

1) Ensure blower fan motor operates in all 4 speeds. Ensure air duct closes off outside air and heater water valve is closed. Clean condenser.
2) Adjust engine speed to 2500 RPM. Set controls for maximum cooling and high fan. Insert thermometer in left air duct and close all other ducts. With vehicle in shade, close windows and doors and connect pressure gauges. Operate system for 10 minutes.
3) Check for cool air from left duct. Low pressure gauge should read more than 16 psi (1.1 kg/cm²). If low pressure gauge reading is incorrect, place hands around expansion valve to warm valve. If pressure rises, moisture is present in system. Discharge A/C system using approved refrigerant recovery/recycling equipment. Evacuate and recharge system. If pressure does not rise, go to next step.
4) Check temperature on thermometer when thermostatic switch turns compressor off. If temperature is 39°F (4°C), system is okay. If temperature is lower than 39°F (4°C), ensure capillary tube installed length is 13" (330 mm). If capillary tube installation is correct, replace thermostatic switch.

NO RECIRCULATE (FRESH AIR AT ALL TIMES)

Passat – 1) Start engine. Turn blower motor off. Check fresh air/recirculate servomotor. Servomotor should be retracted. If servomotor is not as specified, check vacuum supply.
2) If vacuum does not exist, repair vacuum supply. If vacuum exists, check fresh air/recirculate door. If door is faulty, repair or replace as required. If door is okay, replace servomotor and retest.

TESTING

A/C SYSTEM PERFORMANCE

1) Park vehicle out of direct sunlight. Start engine and operate engine at 2500 RPM. Set A/C controls to outside air, panel (vent) mode, full cold, and A/C button on.
2) Set blower/fan on high speed and open windows. Operate system for 6-7 minutes to allow system to stabilize. Insert thermometer in center vent, and measure temperature. Temperature at center vent must be 19-40°F (-7 to 4°C) at center vent, with high side and low side pressures within specification. See SPECIFICATIONS table at beginning of article.

AMBIENT TEMPERATURE SWITCH

1) Remove air intake grille from right side cowl. Remove switch from panel on right side of tray area. Place switch in freezer.
2) Using a DVOM, check switch resistance. Switch resistance must be infinite (no continuity) below 30°F (–1°C). Allow switch to warm above 45°F (7°C). Switch resistance must be zero ohms (continuity). Replace switch if necessary.

COMPRESSOR CLUTCH COIL

Disconnect compressor clutch harness connector. Check resistance between clutch connector terminals. Resistance reading should be 3.6 ohms. If resistance reading is not as specified, replace clutch coil.

DUAL-PRESSURE SWITCH

High-Pressure Cut-Out Switch – Locate dual-pressure switch on refrigerant line (right strut tower). Switch is identified by its 4 wires. Ensure switch opens at 464 psi (32 kg/cm²). Ensure switch closes at 348 psi (24 kg/cm²).

NOTE: Dual-pressure switch may be removed without discharging refrigerant from A/C system.

Low-Pressure Cut-Out Switch – Locate A/C pressure switch on refrigerant line (right strut tower). Switch is identified by its 4 wires. Ensure switch opens below 29 psi (2.0 kg/cm²). Ensure switch closes above 43.5 psi (3.0 kg/cm²). Replace switch if necessary.

THERMOSWITCH

Passat GLX – Locate thermoswitch on thermostat housing. Switch is identified by its Brown housing. Ensure switch turns radiator fan on high speed above 234°F (112°C). Radiator fan should go to medium speed below 226°F (108°C). Also check that thermoswitch opens circuit to A/C compressor relay above 246°F (119°C). Thermoswitch will allow A/C compressor relay operation below 234°F (112°C). Replace switch if necessary.

REMOVAL & INSTALLATION

WARNING: To avoid injury from accidental air bag deployment, read and carefully follow all SERVICE PRECAUTIONS and DISABLING & ACTIVATING AIR BAG SYSTEM procedures in AIR BAG SYSTEM SAFETY article in GENERAL SERVICING.

A/C-HEATER CONTROL PANEL

Removal & Installation – Remove control panel trim. Remove control panel mounting screws and pull cover forward out of dashboard. Disconnect harness connector and control cables. Remove A/C-heater control panel. To install, reverse removal procedures.

BLOWER MOTOR

Removal & Installation (Corrado) – Disconnect blower motor harness connector. Depress blower motor retainer clip and rotate blower motor clockwise to disengage lug on blower motor from clip. To install, reverse removal procedure.

Removal & Installation (Passat) – Remove glove box. Disconnect wiring and remove blower assembly. To install, reverse removal procedure.

COMPRESSOR

Removal & Installation – Remove ribbed belt. Discharge A/C system using approved refrigerant recovery/recycling equipment. Remove hoses and plug. Remove compressor. To install, reverse removal procedure.

CONDENSER

Removal & Installation (Passat) – Discharge A/C system using approved refrigerant recovery/recycling equipment. Remove hood lock assembly, front air intake grille, front bumper, air duct and A/C hoses. Remove A/C condenser. To install, reverse removal procedure.

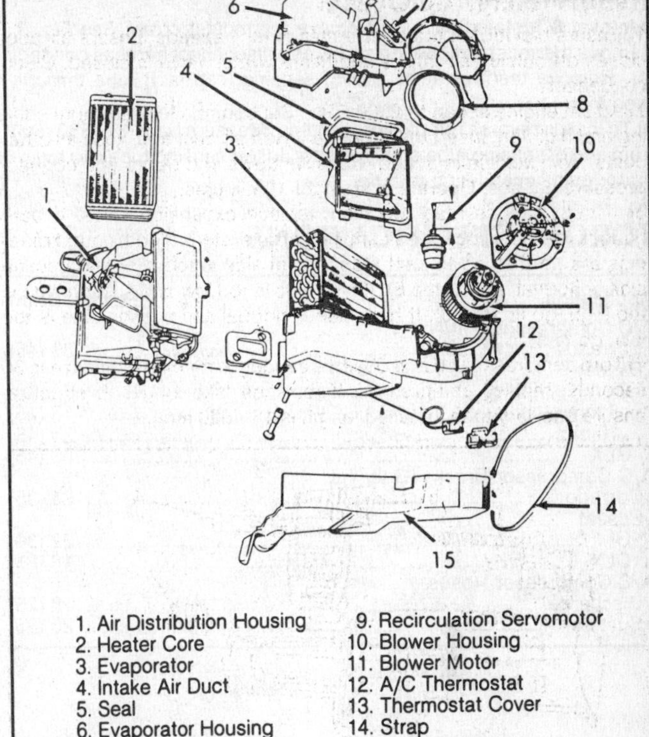
1
2
3
4
5
6
7
8
9
10
11
12
13
14
15
1. Air Distribution Housing
2. Heater Core
3. Evaporator
4. Intake Air Duct
5. Seal
6. Evaporator Housing
7. Blower Resistor
8. Air Ring
9. Recirculation Servomotor
10. Blower Housing
11. Blower Motor
12. A/C Thermostat
13. Thermostat Cover
14. Strap
15. Housing Cover
92C02905
Courtesy of Volkswagen United States, Inc.

Fig. 3: Exploded View Of Evaporator Housing (Corrado & Passat)

EVAPORATOR & HEATER CORE

Removal & Installation – Discharge A/C system using approved refrigerant recovery/recycling equipment. Drain coolant. Remove instrument panel. See INSTRUMENT PANEL. Remove support bracket and evaporator/heater housing assembly. Remove evaporator and/or heater core. *See Fig. 3.* To install, reverse removal procedure.

INSTRUMENT PANEL

Removal & Installation (Corrado) – **1)** Disable air bag system. See AIR BAG SYSTEM SAFETY article in GENERAL SERVICING. Disconnect battery. Remove storage trays and panel under left side of instrument panel. Remove steering wheel. Remove trim panel around instrument cluster.

2) Remove center console. Remove dash vents at each side, glove box and radio. Remove center storage box, A/C-heater control panel trim, and A/C-heater control panel screws. Push A/C-heater control panel away from instrument panel.

3) Remove screws at both sides of instrument panel, at center support, and 2 screws next to windshield. Detach instrument panel and pull part way out.

4) Disconnect wiring harnesses from instrument panel. Disconnect speedometer cable, if present. Remove instrument panel. To install, reverse removal procedure.

Removal & Installation (Passat) – **1)** Remove center console. Remove storage trays on both sides, A/C-heater control panel trim and control panel screws. Push control panel away from instrument panel.

2) Lower steering column. Disconnect wiring harnesses for instrument panel at fuse/relay panel. Disconnect speedometer cable. Remove screws at both sides of instrument panel and at center support.

3) Detach instrument panel retainers (2 at top and 2 at center support). Fold back support and remove instrument panel. To install, reverse removal procedure.

1993 MANUAL A/C-HEATER SYSTEMS
Corrado & Passat (Cont.)

THERMOSTAT

Removal & Installation – 1) Remove thermostat cover. *See Fig. 3.* Remove thermostat mounting screw and disconnect harness connector. Remove thermostat by pulling sensing (capillary) tube through grommet.

2) To install, reverse removal procedures. Measure back 13" (330 mm) from end of sensing tube and tape spot. Insert sensing tube into evaporator guide channel up to tape.

TORQUE SPECIFICATIONS

Application	Ft. Lbs. (N.m)
A/C Compressor Bolt/Nut	
Corrado	33 (45)
Passat	
GL	
8 mm	18 (25)
10 mm	33 (45)
GLX	33 (45)
A/C Compressor Bracket Bolt/Nut	
Corrado	25 (35)
Passat	
GL	22 (30)
GLX	18 (25)
A/C Compressor Hoses	
Discharge	18 (25)
Suction	25 (35)

VACUUM DIAGRAM

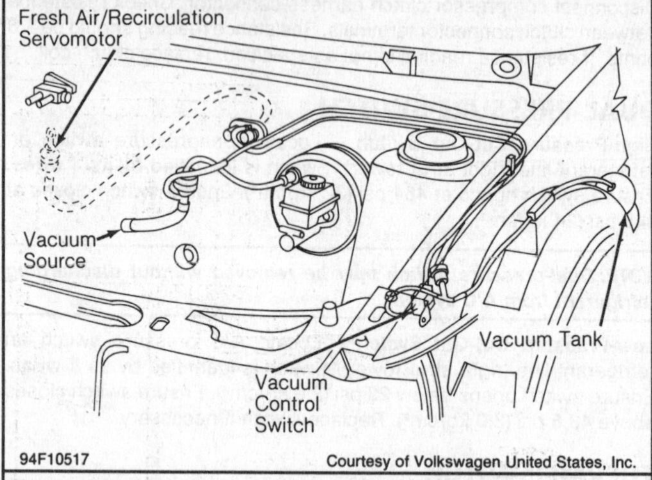
Fresh Air/Recirculation
Servomotor
Vacuum
Source
Vacuum Tank
Vacuum
Control
Switch
94F10517
Courtesy of Volkswagen United States, Inc.

Fig. 4: Manual A/C-Heater Vacuum Diagram (Passat)

1993 MANUAL A/C-HEATER SYSTEMS
Corrado & Passat (Cont.)

WIRING DIAGRAMS

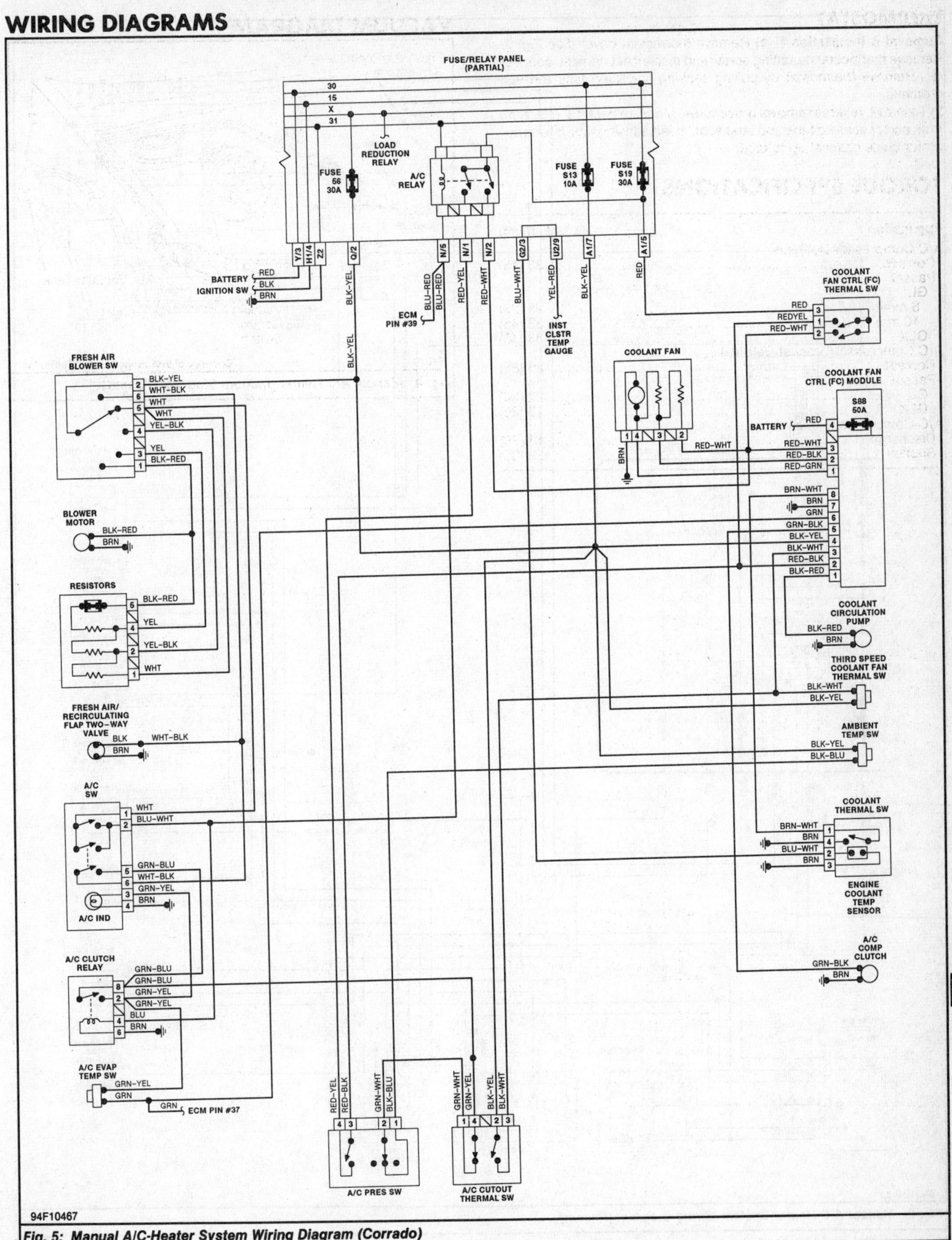
FUSE/RELAY PANEL
(PARTIAL)
30
15
X
31
LOAD
REDUCTION
RELAY
FUSE
56
30A
A/C
RELAY
FUSE
S13
10A
FUSE
S19
30A
Y/3
H1/4
Z2
Q/2
N/5
N/1
N/2
G2/3
U2/9
A1/7
A1/5
BATTERY
IGNITION SW
RED
BLK
BRN
BLK-YEL
BLU-RED
BLU-RED
RED-YEL
RED-WHT
BLU-WHT
YEL-RED
BLK-YEL
RED
ECM
PIN #39
INST
CLSTR
TEMP
GAUGE
COOLANT
FAN CTRL (FC)
THERMAL SW
REDYEL
RED-WHT
COOLANT FAN
COOLANT FAN
CTRL (FC) MODULE
S88
50A
FRESH AIR
BLOWER SW
WHT-BLK
WHT
YEL-BLK
YEL
BLK-RED
BLOWER
MOTOR
RESISTORS
FRESH AIR/
RECIRCULATING
FLAP TWO-WAY
VALVE
A/C
SW
BLU-WHT
GRN-BLU
GRN-YEL
A/C IND
A/C CLUTCH
RELAY
BLU
A/C EVAP
TEMP SW
GRN
ECM PIN #37
RED-BLK
GRN-WHT
BLK-BLU
BLK-WHT
A/C PRES SW
A/C CUTOUT
THERMAL SW
BRN-WHT
GRN-BLK
COOLANT
CIRCULATION
PUMP
THIRD SPEED
COOLANT FAN
THERMAL SW
AMBIENT
TEMP SW
BLK-BLU
COOLANT
THERMAL SW
ENGINE
COOLANT
TEMP
SENSOR
A/C
COMP
CLUTCH
94F10467

Fig. 5: Manual A/C-Heater System Wiring Diagram (Corrado)

1993 MANUAL A/C-HEATER SYSTEMS
Corrado & Passat (Cont.)

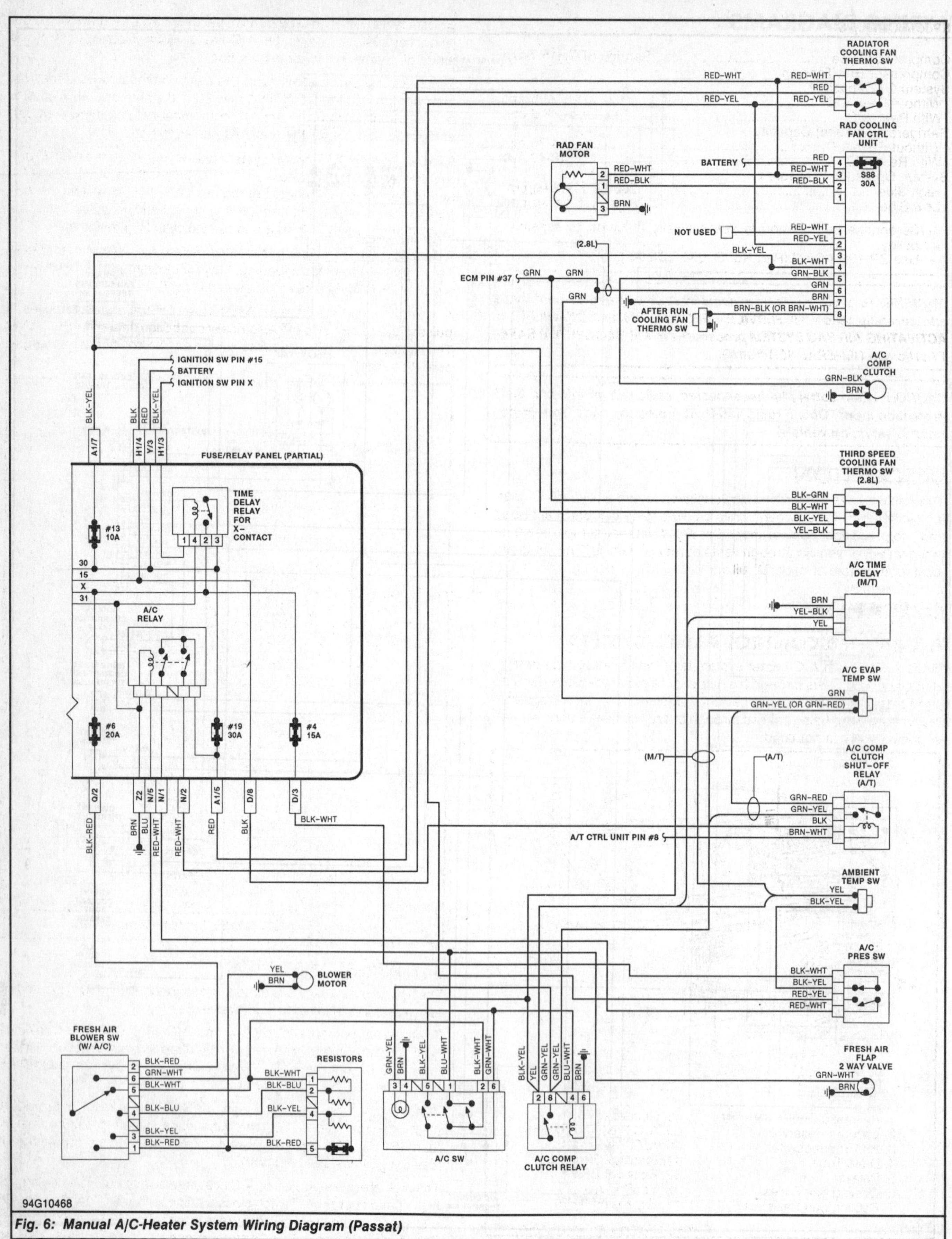
RADIATOR COOLING FAN THERMO SW
RED-WHT
RED
RED-YEL
RAD COOLING FAN CTRL UNIT
RAD FAN MOTOR
BATTERY
RED-BLK
S88 30A
BRN
NOT USED
(2.8L)
BLK-YEL
BLK-WHT
GRN-BLK
GRN
ECM PIN #37
AFTER RUN COOLING FAN THERMO SW
BRN-BLK (OR BRN-WHT)
A/C COMP CLUTCH
IGNITION SW PIN #15
IGNITION SW PIN X
FUSE/RELAY PANEL (PARTIAL)
TIME DELAY RELAY FOR X-CONTACT
A/C RELAY
#13 10A
#6 20A
#19 30A
#4 15A
THIRD SPEED COOLING FAN THERMO SW (2.8L)
BLK-GRN
YEL-BLK
A/C TIME DELAY (M/T)
YEL
A/C EVAP TEMP SW
GRN-YEL (OR GRN-RED)
(M/T)
(A/T)
A/C COMP CLUTCH SHUT-OFF RELAY (A/T)
GRN-RED
GRN-YEL
BLK
BRN-WHT
A/T CTRL UNIT PIN #8
AMBIENT TEMP SW
A/C PRES SW
BLOWER MOTOR
FRESH AIR BLOWER SW (W/ A/C)
BLK-RED
GRN-WHT
BLK-BLU
RESISTORS
A/C SW
BLU-WHT
BLU-YEL
A/C COMP CLUTCH RELAY
FRESH AIR FLAP 2 WAY VALVE
94G10468

Fig. 6: Manual A/C-Heater System Wiring Diagram (Passat)

SPECIFICATIONS

Compressor Type .... Sanden SD7H15 7-Cyl.
Compressor Belt Tension [1]
System Oil Capacity [2]
Without Rear A/C .... 4.6 ozs.
With Rear A/C .... 8.2 ozs.
Refrigerant (R-134a) Capacity
Without Rear A/C .... 34-35 ozs.
With Rear A/C .... 48-49 ozs.
System Operating Pressures
High Side .... 203 psi (14.3 kg/cm²)
Low Side .... 17-26 psi (1.2-1.8 kg/cm²)

[1] – Serpentine belt tension is automatically adjusted by tensioner pulley.
[2] – Use SP-10 PAG Oil (Part No. G 052 154 A2).

WARNING: To avoid injury from accidental air bag deployment, read and carefully follow all SERVICE PRECAUTIONS and DISABLING & ACTIVATING AIR BAG SYSTEM procedures in AIR BAG SYSTEM SAFETY article in GENERAL SERVICING.

CAUTION: When battery is disconnected, radio will go into anti-theft protection mode. Obtain radio anti-theft protection code from owner prior to servicing vehicle.

DESCRIPTION

This vehicle uses a flow-through ventilation, blend air-type A/C-heating system. Air flows through grille below engine compartment hood and into passenger compartment. *See Fig. 1*. Interior compartment air is drawn out of vehicle through vents at rear of vehicle. The vents are located at bottom of each "D" pillar.

OPERATION

A/C-HEATER CONTROL PANEL/SYSTEM

Front – The front A/C-heater system is of the blend-air type design. Heated coolant flows through the heater core at all times. Interior temperature is controlled by a temperature regulation flap which regulates the amount or air being passed through or around heater core. A heater control valve is not used.

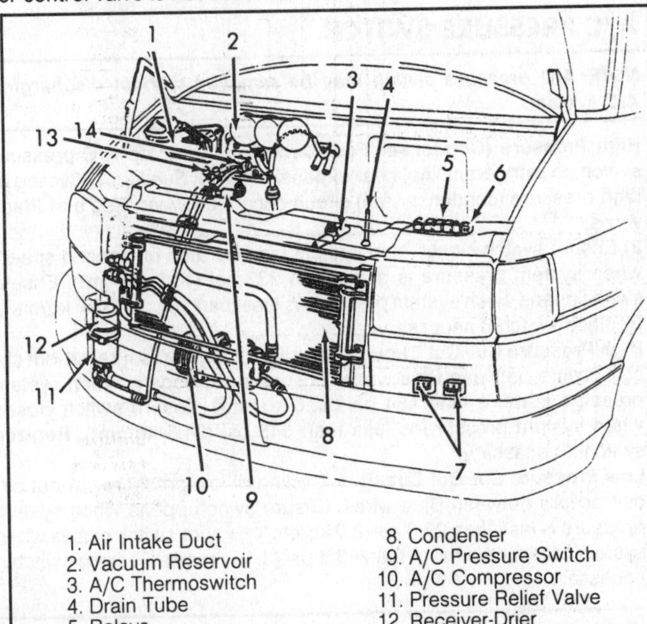
1
2
3
4
5
6
7
8
9
10
11
12
13
14
1. Air Intake Duct
2. Vacuum Reservoir
3. A/C Thermoswitch
4. Drain Tube
5. Relays
6. Cooling Fan Fuses
7. Cooling Fan Resistors
8. Condenser
9. A/C Pressure Switch
10. A/C Compressor
11. Pressure Relief Valve
12. Receiver-Drier
13. Service Valves
14. Expansion Valve
94F10558
Courtesy of Volkswagen United States, Inc.

Fig. 1: Identifying A/C-Heater System Components (Engine Compartment)

Bottom lever on A/C-heater control panel controls temperature regulation flap. The top lever on A/C-heater control panel determines mode of operation and air distribution.

This lever operates a combination vacuum/electrical switch. The vacuum portion of the switch determines air distribution. the electrical portion supplies power to the A/C compressor clutch, blower motor, and evaporator fan for the rear A/C-heater system.

Rear – The rear A/C-heater system only works when the main (front) A/C-heater system is switched on. The temperature of the rear A/C-heater system is independent of the main A/C-heater system. Air distribution is accomplished through 6 vents in headliner. The vents are located above each rear seat and are individually adjustable.

A temperature control knob is located next to fan switch rotary knob. To prevent windows from fogging, the rear blower motor will not operate when A/C or defrost modes are selected.

A potentiometer inside rear A/C-heater control panel supplies a pulsed voltage signal to the electrically controlled heater control valve. The heater control valve supplies heated engine coolant to rear heater core. *See Fig. 2.*

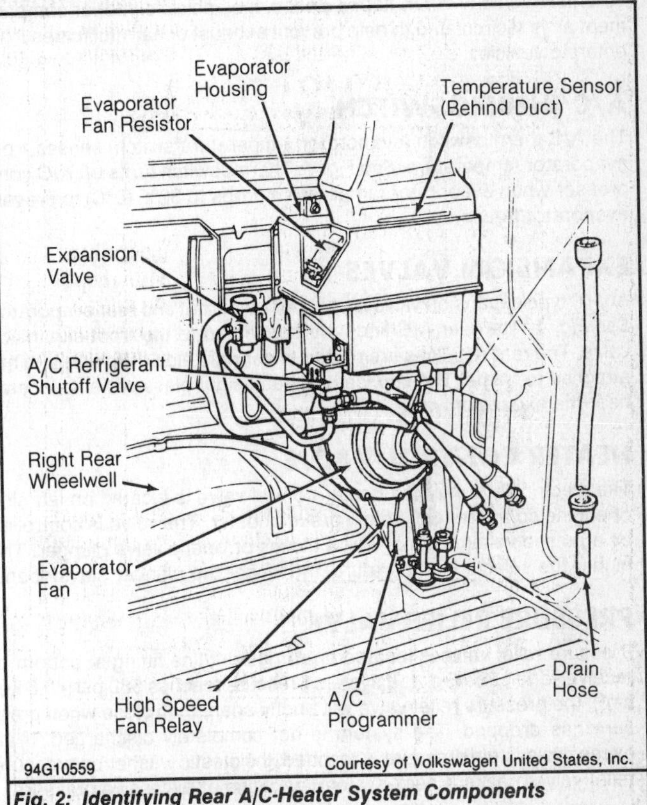
Evaporator Housing
Evaporator Fan Resistor
Temperature Sensor (Behind Duct)
Expansion Valve
A/C Refrigerant Shutoff Valve
Right Rear Wheelwell
Evaporator Fan
High Speed Fan Relay
A/C Programmer
Drain Hose
94G10559
Courtesy of Volkswagen United States, Inc.

Fig. 2: Identifying Rear A/C-Heater System Components

A/C PRESSURE SWITCH

The A/C pressure switch is a triple-pressure type. Switch is located on refrigerant line, near expansion valve. *See Fig. 1.*

If refrigerant pressure is too low, the A/C compressor is turned off (low pressure cutout). Switch opens when system pressure is less than 29.0 psi (2.0 kg/cm²). Switch closes when system pressure is more than 43.5 psi (3.1 kg/cm²).

If refrigerant pressure is too high, the A/C compressor is turned off (high pressure cutout). Switch opens when system pressure is more than 464 psi (32.6 kg/cm²). Switch closes when system pressure is less than 348 psi (24.5 kg/cm²).

The high pressure portion of A/C pressure switch controls cooling fan high speed operation. Switch closes, and cooling fan operates on second speed, when system pressure is more than 232 psi (16.3 kg/cm²). The switch opens when system pressure is less than 181 psi (12.7 kg/cm²).

1993 MANUAL A/C-HEATER SYSTEMS
EuroVan (Cont.)

A/C PROGRAMMER

The A/C programmer (temperature control unit) is located at bottom brace of rear evaporator (if equipped). *See Fig. 2.* The A/C programmer receives inputs from rear temperature control potentiometer and temperature sensor located at rear evaporator.

Depending on the temperature selected and the temperature of the air at rear evaporator, the A/C programmer will either open or close the A/C refrigerant shutoff valve.

A/C REFRIGERANT SHUTOFF VALVE

This valve, as controlled by A/C programmer, controls refrigerant flow to rear evaporator. *See Fig. 2.* The A/C programmer controls A/C refrigerant shutoff valve when evaporator temperature drops to 32°F (0°C) to prevent rear evaporator freeze-up.

AIR RECIRCULATION SWITCH

A rotary knob air recirculation switch is located above heater control panel. This switch, through a solenoid and vacuum servo, opens and closes a flap that is located in air inlet duct. When flap is open, outside air enters vehicle. When flap is closed, the vehicle's interior compartment air is recirculated to help prevent exhaust or harmful fumes from entering vehicle.

A/C THERMOSWITCH

The A/C thermoswitch (evaporator temperature switch) senses front evaporator temperature. *See Fig. 1.* Thermoswitch turns off A/C compressor when evaporator temperature drops to 32°F (0°C) to prevent evaporator freeze-up.

EXPANSION VALVES

An "H" type expansion valve is used for both front and rear evaporator. *See Fig. 1.* The rear A/C lines are connected to the front expansion valve. The rear A/C lines are routed under right side of vehicle and are attached to frame. The service ports and sight glass are also located near the expansion valve.

HEATER CONTROL VALVE

The electrically controlled heater control valve is located on left side of engine compartment, below brake booster. The valve is controlled by a pulsed voltage signal which closes or opens valve plunger. The higher the selected temperature, the longer the plunger stays open.

PRESSURE RELIEF VALVE

Pressure relief valve is located on refrigerant line fitting at bottom of receiver-drier. *See Fig. 1.* If system pressure reaches 580 psi (40.8 kg/cm²), the pressure relief valve will briefly open, then close when pressure has dropped. The system is not completely discharged. If an excessive system pressure is reached, the plastic washer on pressure relief valve breaks. Check system for cause of excessive pressure.

ADJUSTMENTS

TEMPERATURE FLAP CABLE

1) Attach temperature flap cable to lower control lever of A/C-heater control panel. Position cable sleeve on stop of A/C-heater control panel and secure with clip. Install A/C-heater control panel.

2) Slide temperature control lever fully left (cool position). Connect other end of temperature flap cable to temperature flap lever. Push lever away from cable until it stops. *See Fig. 3.*

3) Hold temperature flap lever in this position and secure cable with retaining clip. To check adjustment, slide temperature control lever back and forth from stop to stop. Temperature flap must audibly contact stops.

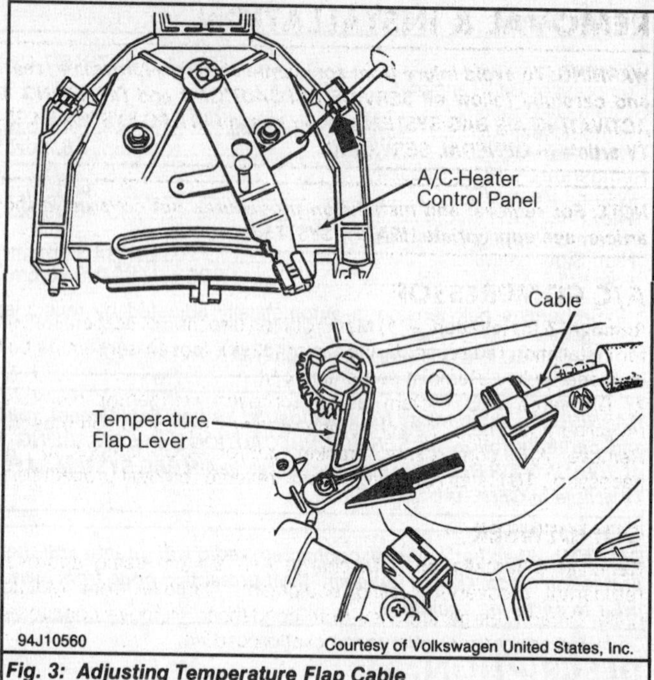
A/C-Heater
Control Panel
Cable
Temperature
Flap Lever
94J10560
Courtesy of Volkswagen United States, Inc.

Fig. 3: Adjusting Temperature Flap Cable

TESTING

WARNING: To avoid injury from accidental air bag deployment, read and carefully follow all SERVICE PRECAUTIONS and DISABLING & ACTIVATING AIR BAG SYSTEM procedures in AIR BAG SYSTEM SAFETY article in GENERAL SERVICING.

A/C SYSTEM PERFORMANCE

Park vehicle out of direct sunlight. Attach manifold gauge set to service valves. Start and run engine at 1500 RPM. Set A/C switch for maximum cooling. Set blower fan on high speed. Note low-side and high-side pressure readings. Service refrigerant system as necessary.

A/C PRESSURE SWITCH

NOTE: A/C pressure switch may be removed without discharging A/C system.

High Pressure (Condenser Fan) Circuit – 1) Locate A/C pressure switch on refrigerant line, near expansion valve. *See Fig. 1.* Cycling of high pressure (condenser fan) circuit occurs between Red and Black wires.

2) Ensure switch closes, and cooling fan operates on second speed, when system pressure is more than 232 psi (16.3 kg/cm²). Ensure switch opens when system pressure is less than 181 psi (12.7 kg/cm²). Replace switch if necessary.

High Pressure Cut-Out Circuit – Cycling of high pressure cut-out circuit occurs between Blue wires. Ensure switch opens when system pressure is more than 464 psi (32.6 kg/cm²). Ensure switch closes when system pressure is less than 348 psi (24.5 kg/cm²). Replace switch if necessary.

Low Pressure Cut-Out Circuit – Cycling of low pressure cut-out circuit occurs between Blue wires. Ensure switch opens when system pressure is less than 29.0 psi (2.0 kg/cm²). Ensure switch closes when system pressure is more than 43.5 psi (3.1 kg/cm²). Replace switch if necessary.

NOTE: Additional testing information is not available from manufacturer. Use wiring diagram as a guide. See WIRING DIAGRAMS.

1993 MANUAL A/C-HEATER SYSTEMS
EuroVan (Cont.)

REMOVAL & INSTALLATION

WARNING: To avoid injury from accidental air bag deployment, read and carefully follow all SERVICE PRECAUTIONS and DISABLING & ACTIVATING AIR BAG SYSTEM procedures in AIR BAG SYSTEM SAFETY article in GENERAL SERVICING.

NOTE: For removal and installation procedures not covered in this article, see appropriate HEATER SYSTEMS article.

A/C COMPRESSOR

Removal & Installation – 1) Mark rotation direction of serpentine belt for installation reference. Using Lever (3299), loosen serpentine belt tensioner pulley. Remove serpentine belt.

2) Discharge A/C system using approved refrigerant recovery/recycling equipment. Detach refrigerant lines from A/C compressor. Remove A/C compressor bracket and/or A/C compressor as necessary. To install A/C compressor, reverse removal procedure.

CONDENSER

Removal & Installation – Discharge A/C system using approved refrigerant recovery/recycling equipment. Remove front radiator grille. Detach refrigerant lines from condenser. Remove condenser. To install condenser, reverse removal procedure.

EVAPORATOR & HEATER CORE

Removal & Installation – 1) Evaporator and heater core removal and installation procedure is not available from manufacturer. If it is necessary to remove instrument panel, see INSTRUMENT PANEL.

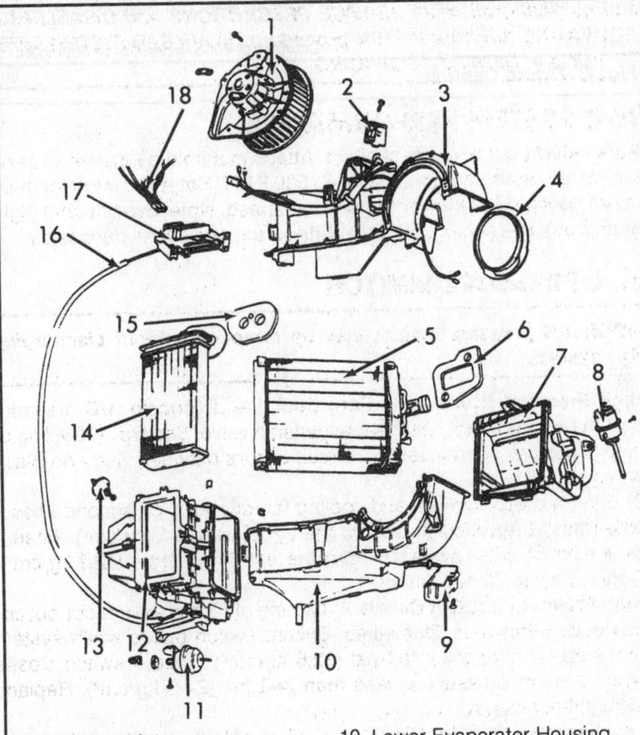
1
2
3
4
5
6
7
8
9
10
11
12
13
14
15
16
17
18
1. Blower Motor
2. Blower Motor Resistor
3. Upper Evaporator Housing
4. Air Intake Ring
5. Evaporator
6. Seal
7. Air Intake Duct
8. Fresh/Recirculated Air Flap Vacuum Servo
9. A/C Thermoswitch
10. Lower Evaporator Housing
11. Central Flap Vacuum Servo
12. Air Distribution Case
13. Footwell/Defroster Flap Vacuum Servo
14. Heater Core
15. Grommet
16. Temperature Flap Cable
17. A/C-Heater Control Panel
18. Vacuum Hoses
94A10561
Courtesy of Volkswagen United States, Inc.

Fig. 4: Exploded View Of Front Evaporator Assembly

2) Discharge A/C system using approved refrigerant recovery/recycling equipment. Use exploded view of evaporator assemblies as a guide. *See Figs. 4 and 5.* Manufacturer recommends that rear evaporator not be disassembled further than shown.

EVAPORATOR TEMPERATURE SWITCH

Removal & Installation – 1) Locate evaporator temperature switch along bottom of evaporator housing. Remove screw(s) and evaporator temperature switch from evaporator housing.

2) When installing evaporator temperature switch, apply tape 13" (330 mm) from end of sensor tube and install sensor tube into evaporator up to tape. DO NOT bend sensor tube.

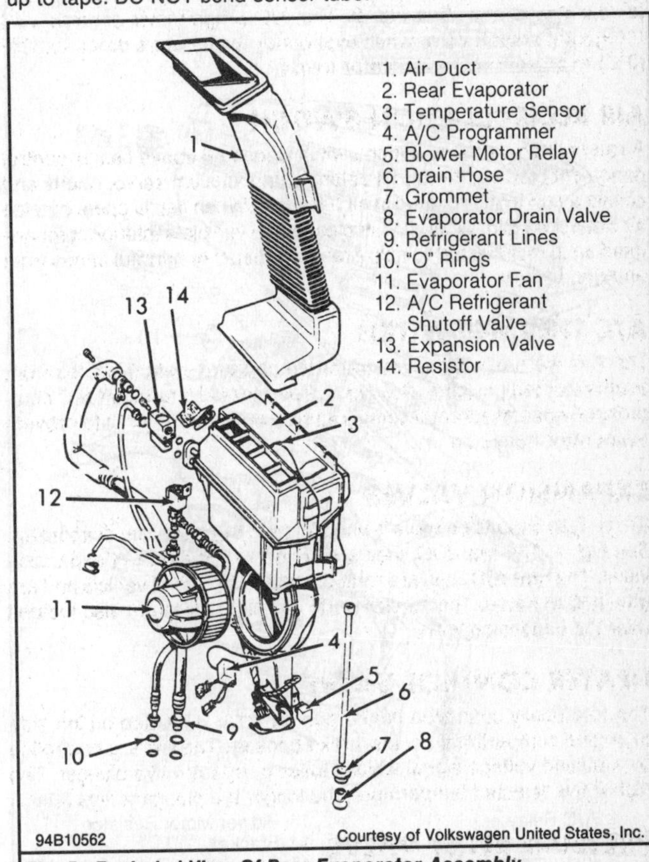
1. Air Duct
2. Rear Evaporator
3. Temperature Sensor
4. A/C Programmer
5. Blower Motor Relay
6. Drain Hose
7. Grommet
8. Evaporator Drain Valve
9. Refrigerant Lines
10. "O" Rings
11. Evaporator Fan
12. A/C Refrigerant Shutoff Valve
13. Expansion Valve
14. Resistor
1
2
3
4
5
6
7
8
9
10
11
12
13
14
94B10562
Courtesy of Volkswagen United States, Inc.

Fig. 5: Exploded View Of Rear Evaporator Assembly

FRESH/RECIRCULATING AIR FLAP VACUUM SERVO

Removal & Installation – Remove glove box. Remove screws, and rotate vacuum servo to disengage it from arm and lever. Remove vacuum servo. To install vacuum servo, reverse removal procedure.

INSTRUMENT PANEL

Removal – 1) Obtain radio anti-theft protection code from owner prior to servicing vehicle. Disconnect negative battery cable. Open engine compartment hood. Remove bolt from air duct and cross panel. Bolt is located on engine compartment side of firewall, near windshield wiper linkage.

2) Mark position of steering wheel for installation reference. Remove steering wheel. Remove steering column trim and combination switch. Remove instrument cluster trim. Disconnect speedometer cable from instrument cluster.

3) Carefully remove vent from left and right air outlets. Remove screw, and carefully pry out left and right air outlets. Remove switch panel located below air outlet on driver's side. Disconnect wiring from speakers.

4) Rotate knob on center of storage bin (fuse/relay panel cover) and open bin. Carefully disengage storage bin from pivot points and

1993 MANUAL A/C-HEATER SYSTEMS
EuroVan (Cont.)

remove bin. Carefully remove vent from center air outlet. Remove screws and carefully pry out center air outlet.

5) Remove A/C-heater control panel. *See Fig. 6.* Remove radio. Disconnect antenna, switches, and cigarette lighter wiring harness. Ensure all switches and/or harnesses are disconnected from center part of instrument panel.

6) Open glove box. Remove glove box light, and disconnect wiring harness. Remove 7 screws and glove box. Remove covers and bolts from ends of instrument panel. Remove remove instrument panel.

Installation – To install instrument panel, reverse removal procedure. Ensure wiring harnesses are not pinched during installation.

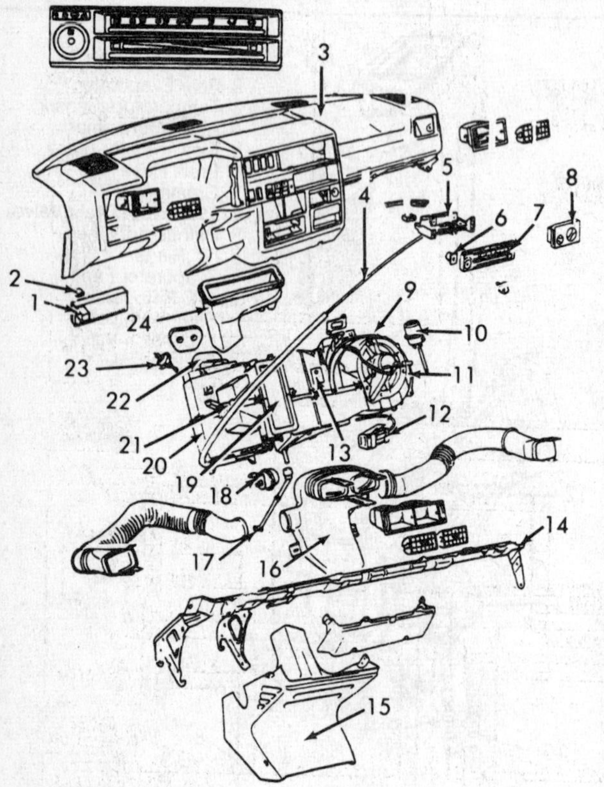
1
2
3
4
5
6
7
8
9
10
11
12
13
14
15
16
17
18
19
20
21
22
23
24

1. A/C Relay
2. A/C-Heater System Fuse
3. Instrument Panel
4. Temperature Flap Cable
5. A/C-Heater Control Panel
6. Blower Motor Switch (Front)
7. Trim Panel
8. Blower Motor Switch (Rear)
9. Air Intake Duct & Fresh/Recirculated Air Flap
10. Fresh/Recirculated Air Flap Vacuum Servo
11. Blower Motor
12. A/C Thermoswitch
13. Blower Motor Resistor
14. Bracket
15. Footwell Air Outlet Console
16. Center Air Duct
17. Drain Hose
18. Center Flap Vacuum Servo
19. Center Flap
20. Heater/Evaporator Housing
21. Footwell/Defroster Flap
22. Heater Core
23. Footwell/Defroster Flap Vacuum Servo
24. Defroster Duct

94C10563 Courtesy of Volkswagen United States, Inc.

Fig. 6: *Identifying A/C-Heater System Components (Passenger Compartment)*

VACUUM DIAGRAM

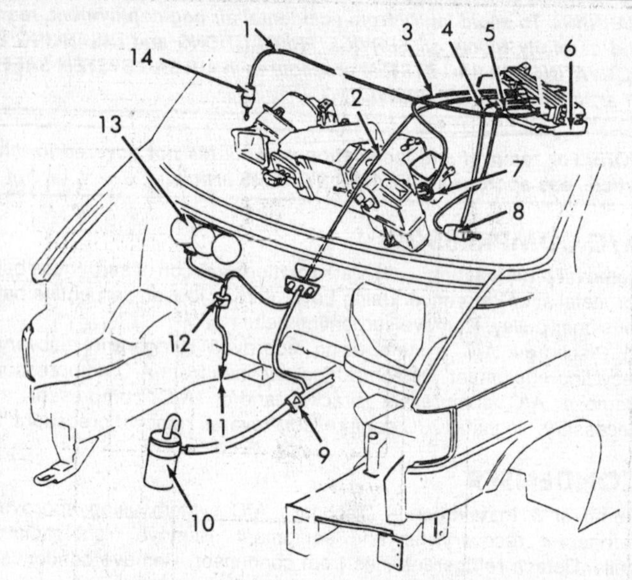
1
2
3
4
5
6
7
8
9
10
11
12
13
14

1. Vacuum Hose (White)
2. Vacuum Hose (Black)
3. Vacuum Hose (Red)
4. Vacuum Hose (Green)
5. Vacuum Hose (Yellow)
6. A/C-Heater Control Panel
7. Footwell/Defroster Flap Vacuum Servo
8. Central Flap Vacuum Servo
9. Check Valve (If Equipped)
10. Vacuum Pump (If Equipped)
11. Engine Vacuum Supply Hose
12. Check Valve
13. Vacuum Reservoir
14. Fresh/Recirculated Air Flap Vacuum Servo

94E10581 Courtesy of Volkswagen United States, Inc.

Fig. 7: *Figure Caption*

WIRING DIAGRAMS

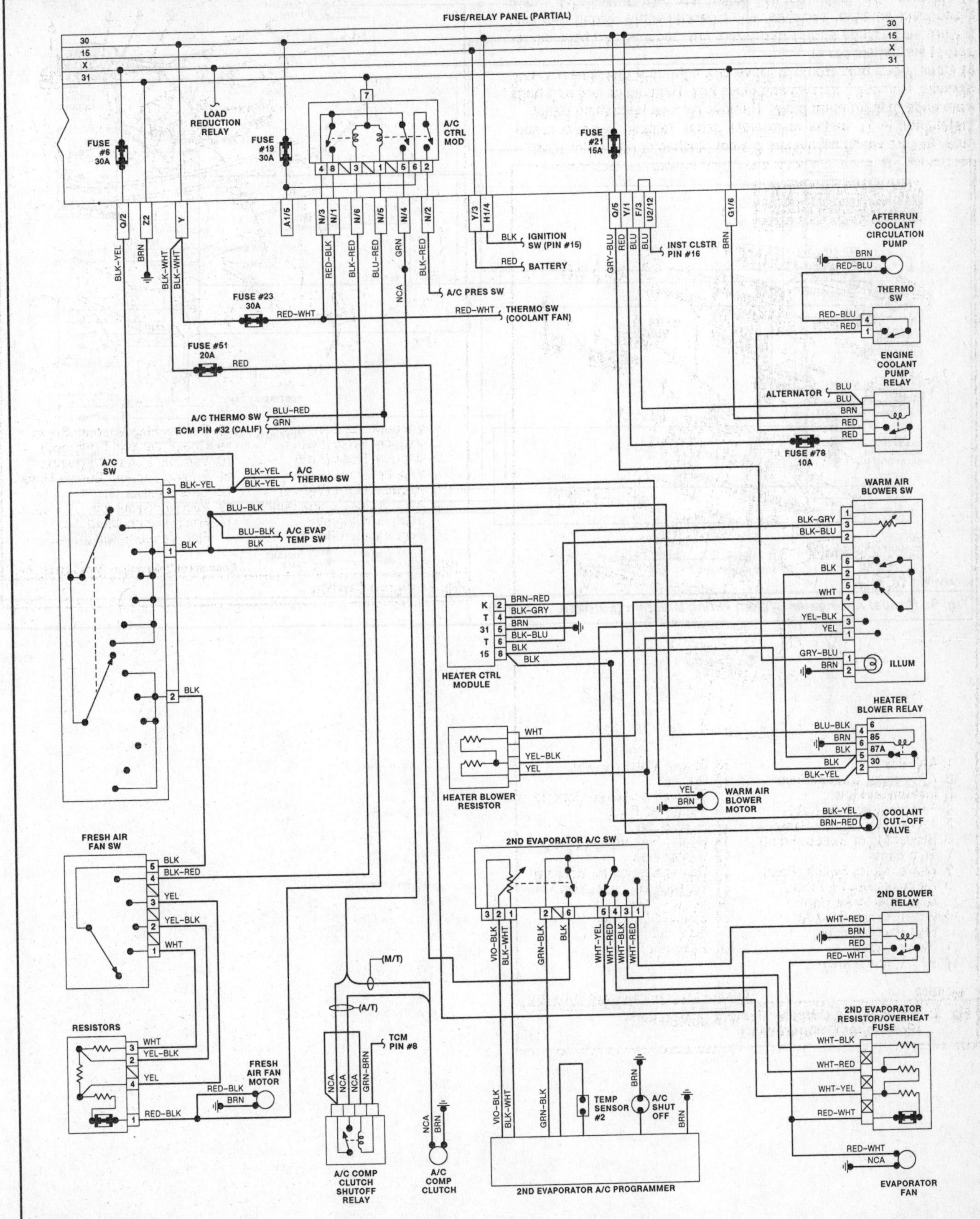

94I10809

Fig. 8: Manual A/C-Heater System Wiring Diagram (EuroVan – 1 Of 2)

1993 MANUAL A/C-HEATER SYSTEMS
EuroVan (Cont.)

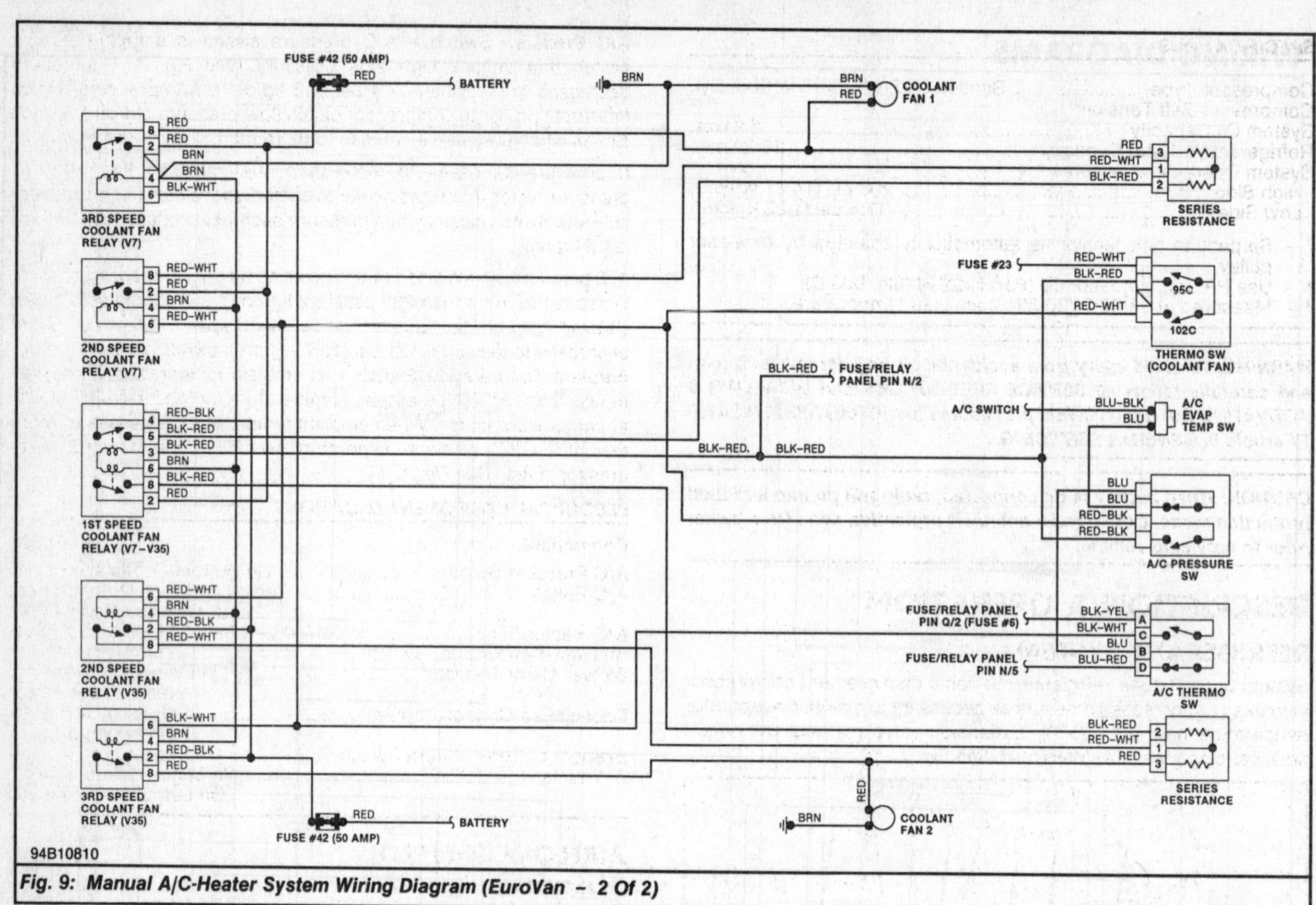
FUSE #42 (50 AMP)
RED
BATTERY
BRN
BRN
RED
COOLANT FAN 1
RED
RED
BRN
BRN
BLK-WHT
3RD SPEED COOLANT FAN RELAY (V7)
RED
RED-WHT
BLK-RED
SERIES RESISTANCE
RED-WHT
RED
BRN
RED-WHT
2ND SPEED COOLANT FAN RELAY (V7)
FUSE #23
RED-WHT
BLK-RED
95C
RED-WHT
102C
THERMO SW (COOLANT FAN)
BLK-RED
FUSE/RELAY PANEL PIN N/2
A/C SWITCH
BLU-BLK
BLU
A/C EVAP TEMP SW
RED-BLK
BLK-RED
BLK-RED
BRN
BLK-RED
RED
BLK-RED
BLK-RED
1ST SPEED COOLANT FAN RELAY (V7-V35)
BLU
BLU
RED-BLK
RED-BLK
A/C PRESSURE SW
RED-WHT
BRN
RED-BLK
RED-WHT
2ND SPEED COOLANT FAN RELAY (V35)
FUSE/RELAY PANEL PIN Q/2 (FUSE #6)
BLK-YEL
BLK-WHT
BLU
FUSE/RELAY PANEL PIN N/5
BLU-RED
A/C THERMO SW
BLK-WHT
BRN
RED-BLK
RED
3RD SPEED COOLANT FAN RELAY (V35)
BLK-RED
RED-WHT
RED
SERIES RESISTANCE
RED
BATTERY
FUSE #42 (50 AMP)
BRN
COOLANT FAN 2
94B10810

Fig. 9: Manual A/C-Heater System Wiring Diagram (EuroVan - 2 Of 2)

1993 MANUAL A/C-HEATER SYSTEMS
Golf, GTI & Jetta

SPECIFICATIONS

Compressor Type .... Sanden SD7-V16/SD7-V16L 7-Cyl.
Compressor Belt Tension [1]
System Oil Capacity .... 3.9 ozs.
Refrigerant (R-134a) Capacity [2] .... 28-30 ozs.
System Operating Pressures [3]
High Side .... 203 psi (14.27 kg/cm²)
Low Side .... 17.4 psi (1.22 kg/cm²)

[1] - Serpentine belt tension is automatically adjusted by tensioner pulley.
[2] - Use PAG Compressor Oil (Part No. 1H0 820 803 D).
[3] - Measured at 68-86°F (20-30°C) ambient temperature.

WARNING: To avoid injury from accidental air bag deployment, read and carefully follow all SERVICE PRECAUTIONS and DISABLING & ACTIVATING AIR BAG SYSTEM procedures in AIR BAG SYSTEM SAFETY article in GENERAL SERVICING.

CAUTION: When battery is disconnected, radio will go into anti-theft protection mode. Obtain radio anti-theft protection code from owner prior to servicing vehicle.

DESCRIPTION & OPERATION

REFRIGERANT SYSTEM

System uses R-134a refrigerant. Variable displacement compressor increases or decreases pressure as necessary to maintain evaporator temperature near 32°F (0°C). Expansion valve restricts refrigerant flow, causing pressure differential. *See Fig. 1*.

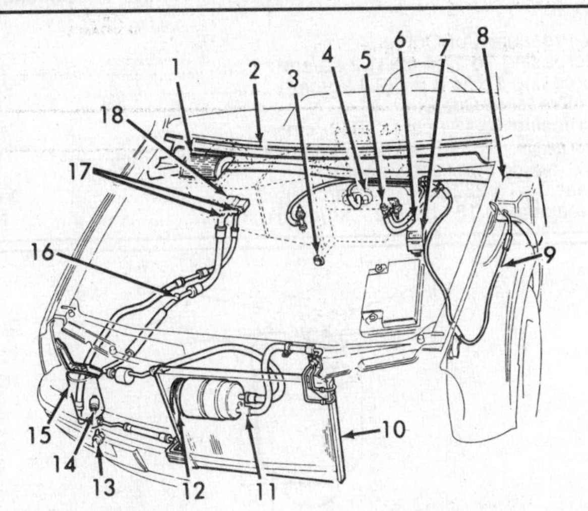
1. Dust & Pollen Filter
2. Plenum Cover
3. Evaporator Drain
4. Heater Core Connections & Vacuum Hose Entry
5. 2-Way Valve
6. Cooling Fan Control Module
7. Strip Fuse
8. Vacuum Reservoir
9. Vacuum Hose
10. Condenser
11. Pressure Relief Valve
12. Compressor Clutch
13. Ambient Temperature Switch
14. A/C Pressure Switch
15. Receiver-Drier
16. Sight Glass
17. Service Valves
18. Expansion Valve
94I10585
Courtesy of Volkswagen United States, Inc.

Fig. 1: View Of A/C-Heater System Components (Engine Compartment)

COMPRESSOR CLUTCH CONTROL

Evaporator Temperature Switch - Although compressor clutch does NOT normally cycle on and off, an evaporator temperature switch turns off the compressor clutch if evaporator temperature decreases to 32°F (0°C). This prevents evaporator icing. See ELECTRICAL COMPONENT LOCATIONS table. *See Fig. 6*.

A/C Pressure Switch - A/C pressure switch is a triple-pressure switch that senses high side pressure. *See Fig. 1*. If pressure decreases to less than 17.4 psi (1.2 kg/cm²), A/C pressure switch interrupts power to compressor clutch (low-pressure cut-out). Switch closes when pressure increases to more than 34.8 psi (2.4 kg/cm²).

If pressure increases to more than 464 psi (32.6 kg/cm²), A/C pressure switch interrupts power to compressor clutch (high-pressure cut-out). Switch closes when pressure decreases to less than 348 psi (24.5 kg/cm²).

A/C pressure switch also controls cooling fan high speed. If pressure increases to more than 232 psi (16.3 kg/cm²), switch contacts close, causing cooling fan to operate at high speed. When pressure decreases to less than 181 psi (12.7 kg/cm²), switch contacts open.

Ambient Temperature Switch - If ambient temperature decreases to less than 36°F (2°C), ambient temperature switch interrupts power to compressor clutch. When ambient temperature increases to more than 45°F (7°C), ambient temperature switch restores power to compressor clutch. *See Fig. 1*.

ELECTRICAL COMPONENT LOCATIONS

Component	Location
A/C Pressure Switch	On Bottom Of Receiver-Drier
A/C Relay	Behind Left Side Of Instrument Panel, On Fuse/Relay Block
A/C-Heater Fuse	Behind Left Side Of Instrument Panel
Ambient Temperature Switch	On Horn Bracket
Blower Motor Resistor	On Evaporator Housing, Near Blower Motor
Cooling Fan Control Module	Left Rear Corner Of Engine Compartment
Evaporator Temperature Switch	On Evaporator Housing
2-Way Valve	In Engine Compartment, On Left Side Of Firewall

AIRFLOW CONTROL

Fresh/Recirculated Air Flap - Fresh/recirculated air flap (door) above blower motor controls air entering ducting system. Flap is controlled by a vacuum servo. *See Fig. 6*. Vacuum supply to servo is controlled by a 2-way valve (electric solenoid) between vacuum reservoir and vacuum servo. When voltage signal from A/C-heater control panel is applied to the 2-way valve, the valve opens, allowing vacuum supply to vacuum servo.

Temperature Flap - Temperature flap (door) diverts air through or around heater core. Flap is controlled by a cable connected to the A/C-heater control panel.

Central Flap - Central flap (door) diverts air to face vents or to footwell and defrost vents (or a combination of all 3). Flap is controlled by a cable connected to the A/C-heater control panel.

Footwell/Defrost Flap - Footwell/defrost flap (door) diverts air to footwell or defrost vents (or a combination of both). Flap is controlled by a cable connected to the A/C-heater control panel.

ADJUSTMENTS

TEMPERATURE FLAP CABLE

Ensure cable is connected to A/C-heater control panel and panel is installed. Remove cable sleeve retaining clip (cable sleeve is Blue). *See Fig. 2*. Disconnect cable from temperature flap lever. Adjust temperature control knob to maximum cold position. Connect cable to temperature flap lever. Push lever in direction of arrow until it stops. Hold lever in position and install cable retaining clip.

1993 MANUAL A/C-HEATER SYSTEMS Golf, GTI & Jetta (Cont.)

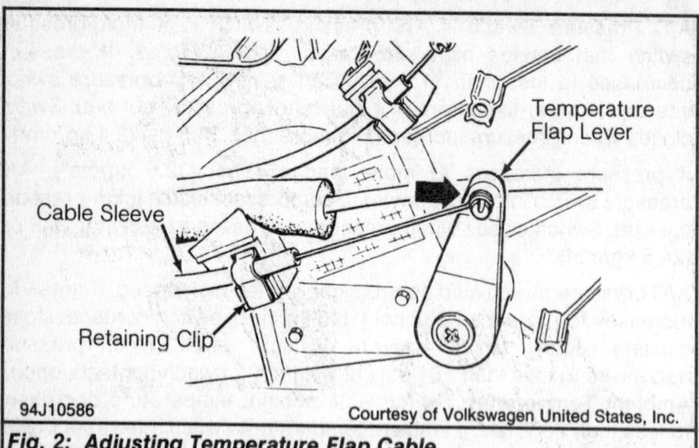
Temperature Flap Lever
Cable Sleeve
Retaining Clip
94J10586
Courtesy of Volkswagen United States, Inc.

Fig. 2: Adjusting Temperature Flap Cable

CENTRAL FLAP CABLE

Ensure cable is connected to A/C-heater control panel and panel is installed. Remove cable sleeve retaining clip (cable sleeve is Black). *See Fig. 3*. Disconnect cable from central flap lever. Adjust airflow distribution knob to defrost position. Connect cable to central flap lever. Push lever in direction of arrow until it stops. Hold lever in position and install cable retaining clip.

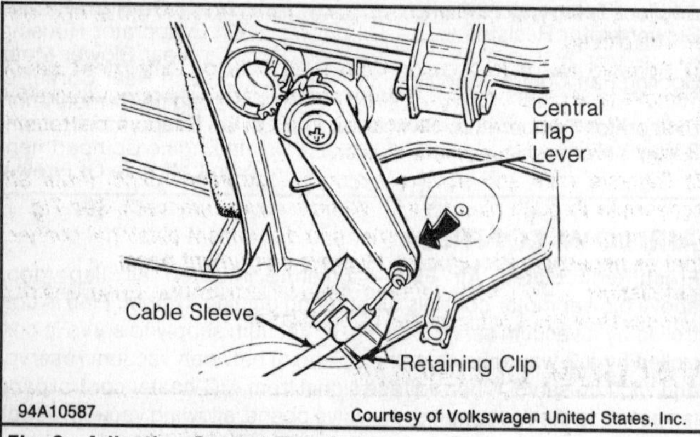
Central Flap Lever
Cable Sleeve
Retaining Clip
94A10587
Courtesy of Volkswagen United States, Inc.

Fig. 3: Adjusting Central Flap Cable

FOOTWELL/DEFROSTER FLAP CABLE

Ensure cable is connected to A/C-heater control panel and panel is installed. Remove cable sleeve retaining clip (cable sleeve is Black). *See Fig. 4*. Disconnect cable from footwell/defroster flap lever. Adjust airflow distribution knob to defrost position. Connect cable to footwell/defroster flap lever. Push lever in direction of arrow until it stops. Hold lever in position and install cable retaining clip.

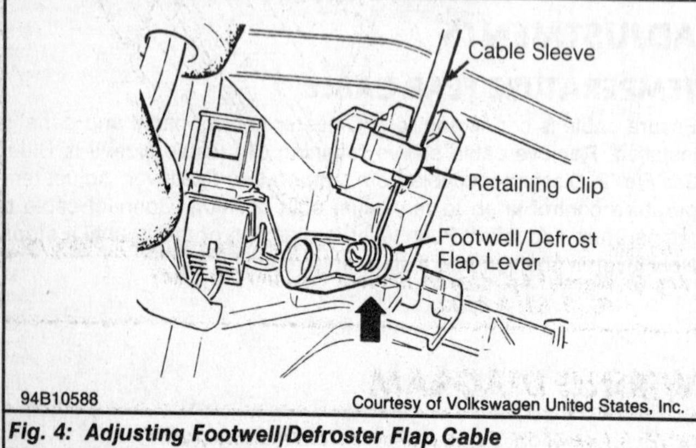
Cable Sleeve
Retaining Clip
Footwell/Defrost Flap Lever
94B10588
Courtesy of Volkswagen United States, Inc.

Fig. 4: Adjusting Footwell/Defroster Flap Cable

TESTING

WARNING: To avoid injury from accidental air bag deployment, read and carefully follow all SERVICE PRECAUTIONS and DISABLING & ACTIVATING AIR BAG SYSTEM procedures in AIR BAG SYSTEM SAFETY article in GENERAL SERVICING.

A/C SYSTEM PERFORMANCE

1) Ensure no bubbles are present in sight glass. *See Fig. 1*. Connect manifold gauge set to service valves. Run engine at 1500 RPM. Set air distribution knob to face vent position. Set temperature control knob to full cold position.

2) Press A/C NORM button. Set blower motor on 2nd speed. System is okay if air temperature at center vent is less than 50°F (10°C) after one minute and system operating pressures are within specification. See SPECIFICATIONS table at beginning of article.

A/C PRESSURE SWITCH

NOTE: A/C pressure switch may be removed without discharging A/C system.

Connect manifold gauge set to service valves. Disconnect A/C pressure switch connector. *See Fig. 5*. Check continuity between specified terminals of A/C pressure switch. See A/C PRESSURE SWITCH CONTINUITY table. Replace A/C pressure switch if continuity is not as specified.

A/C PRESSURE SWITCH CONTINUITY

Terminal No. & Pressure	Continuity
1 & 2	
Low-Pressure Cut-Out	
Decreasing To 17.4 psi (1.2 kg/cm²)	No
Increasing To 34.8 psi (2.4 kg/cm²)	Yes
High-Pressure Cut-Out	
Increasing To 464 psi (32.6 kg/cm²)	No
Decreasing To 348 psi (24.5 kg/cm²)	Yes
3 & 4 (Cooling Fan High Speed)	
Increasing To 232 psi (16.3 kg/cm²)	Yes
Decreasing To 181 psi (12.7 kg/cm²)	No

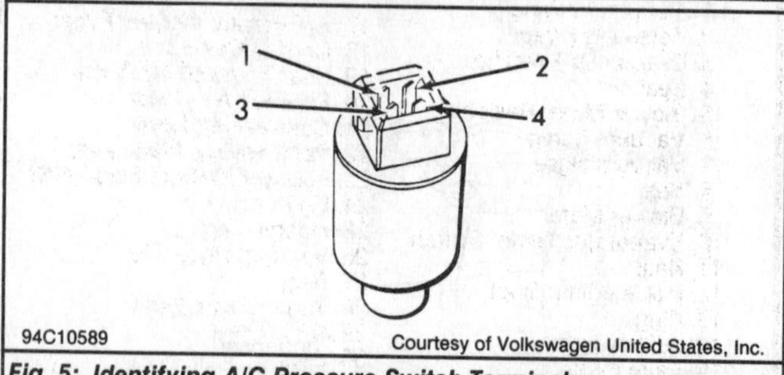
1
2
3
4
94C10589
Courtesy of Volkswagen United States, Inc.

Fig. 5: Identifying A/C Pressure Switch Terminals

REMOVAL & INSTALLATION

WARNING: To avoid injury from accidental air bag deployment, read and carefully follow all SERVICE PRECAUTIONS and DISABLING & ACTIVATING AIR BAG SYSTEM procedures in AIR BAG SYSTEM SAFETY article in GENERAL SERVICING.

NOTE: For removal and installation procedures not covered in this article, see HEATER SYSTEMS - GOLF, GTI & JETTA article.

A/C COMPRESSOR

Removal & Installation – 1) Mark rotation direction of serpentine belt for installation reference. Loosen serpentine belt tensioner pulley. Remove serpentine belt.

2) Discharge A/C system using approved refrigerant recovery/recycling equipment. Disconnect refrigerant lines from A/C compressor. Remove A/C compressor bracket and/or A/C compressor as necessary. To install, reverse removal procedure.

CONDENSER

Removal & Installation – Discharge A/C system using approved refrigerant recovery/recycling equipment. Remove front bumper. Remove bumper cross support. Disconnect refrigerant lines from condenser. Remove condenser. To install, reverse removal procedure.

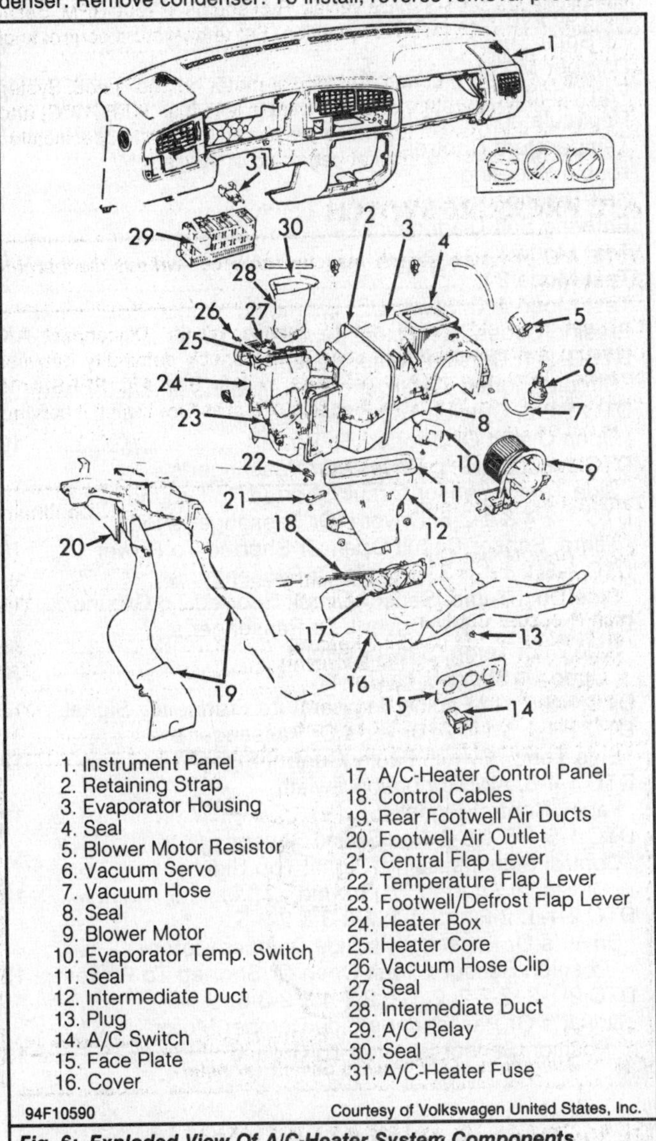
1. Instrument Panel
2. Retaining Strap
3. Evaporator Housing
4. Seal
5. Blower Motor Resistor
6. Vacuum Servo
7. Vacuum Hose
8. Seal
9. Blower Motor
10. Evaporator Temp. Switch
11. Seal
12. Intermediate Duct
13. Plug
14. A/C Switch
15. Face Plate
16. Cover
17. A/C-Heater Control Panel
18. Control Cables
19. Rear Footwell Air Ducts
20. Footwell Air Outlet
21. Central Flap Lever
22. Temperature Flap Lever
23. Footwell/Defrost Flap Lever
24. Heater Box
25. Heater Core
26. Vacuum Hose Clip
27. Seal
28. Intermediate Duct
29. A/C Relay
30. Seal
31. A/C-Heater Fuse
94F10590
Courtesy of Volkswagen United States, Inc.

Fig. 6: Exploded View Of A/C-Heater System Components (Passenger Compartment)

EVAPORATOR HOUSING & EVAPORATOR

Removal & Installation – Discharge A/C system using approved refrigerant recovery/recycling equipment. Drain coolant. Remove instrument panel and support bracket. See INSTRUMENT PANEL. Remove evaporator housing. *See Fig. 6*. Disassemble evaporator housing. *See Fig. 7*.

EVAPORATOR TEMPERATURE SWITCH

Removal & Installation – Remove screw(s) and evaporator temperature switch from bottom of evaporator housing. *See Fig. 6*. To install, apply tape 13" (330 mm) from end of sensor tube. Install sensor tube into evaporator until tape reaches grommet. DO NOT bend sensor tube.

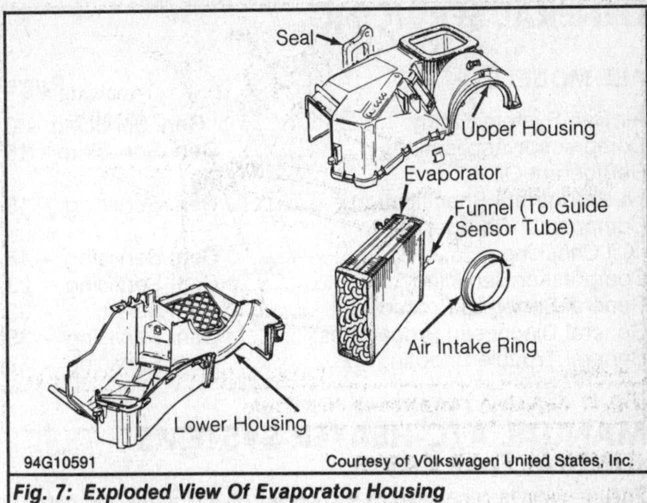
Seal
Upper Housing
Evaporator
Funnel (To Guide Sensor Tube)
Air Intake Ring
Lower Housing
94G10591
Courtesy of Volkswagen United States, Inc.

Fig. 7: Exploded View Of Evaporator Housing

INSTRUMENT PANEL

Removal – **1)** Obtain radio anti-theft protection code from vehicle owner. Disconnect negative battery cable. Remove center console and radio. Remove steering wheel and combination switch on steering column. On left side of instrument panel, remove lower cover and lower trim pieces.

2) Remove lower trim piece from right side of instrument panel. Remove face plate from A/C-heater control panel and remove screws. Push A/C-heater control panel back into cavity. Remove instrument cluster cover and instrument cluster.

3) Remove nuts and screws securing instrument panel (nuts are accessible through plenum with plenum cover removed). *See Fig. 1*. Pull instrument panel off of carrier and disconnect electrical connectors as necessary for removal. Remove instrument panel.

Installation – To install, reverse removal procedure. Ensure wiring harnesses are not pinched during installation.

VACUUM DIAGRAM

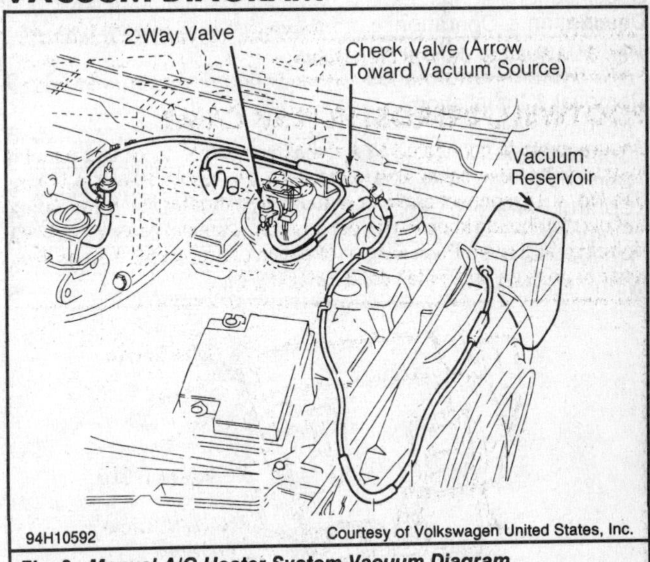
2-Way Valve
Check Valve (Arrow Toward Vacuum Source)
Vacuum Reservoir
94H10592
Courtesy of Volkswagen United States, Inc.

Fig. 8: Manual A/C-Heater System Vacuum Diagram (Golf, GTI & Jetta)

WIRING DIAGRAM

NOTE: Information is not available from manufacturer.

1993 VOLVO CONTENTS

GENERAL SERVICING

ALL MODELS

MANUAL A/C-HEATER SYSTEMS

240

940

AUTOMATIC A/C-HEATER SYSTEMS

850

1993 VOLVO CONTENTS (Cont.)

AUTOMATIC A/C-HEATER SYSTEMS (Cont.)

850 (Cont.) **Page**

AUTOMATIC A/C-HEATER SYSTEMS (Cont.)

960 **Page**

1993 MANUAL A/C-HEATER SYSTEMS
240

SPECIFICATIONS

Compressor Type	Seiko-Seiki SS-121DS5
Compressor Belt Deflection [1]	1/4-5/16" (6.3-8.0 mm)
Refrigerant (R-134a) Capacity	26 ozs.
Compressor Oil Capacity	[2] 7.4 ozs.
System Operating Pressures [3]	

[1] – With thumb pressure applied to center of longest belt run.
[2] – Use ZXL 100 PG Oil (Part No. 8708581-7).
[3] – Information not available from manufacturer.

WARNING: To avoid injury from accidental air bag deployment, read and carefully follow all SERVICE PRECAUTIONS and DISABLING & ACTIVATING AIR BAG SYSTEM procedures in AIR BAG SYSTEM SAFETY article in GENERAL SERVICING.

CAUTION: When battery or radio is disconnected, radio will go into anti-theft protection mode. Obtain radio code anti-theft protection code from owner prior to servicing vehicle.

DESCRIPTION

Vehicle is equipped with a cycling clutch system that uses an orifice tube in refrigerant line between condenser and evaporator. *See Fig. 1.*

A/C-heater unit, mounted under center of dash, contains heater core, evaporator core and blower motor. *See Fig. 2.* Blower resistor is inside A/C-heater unit, in blower chamber.

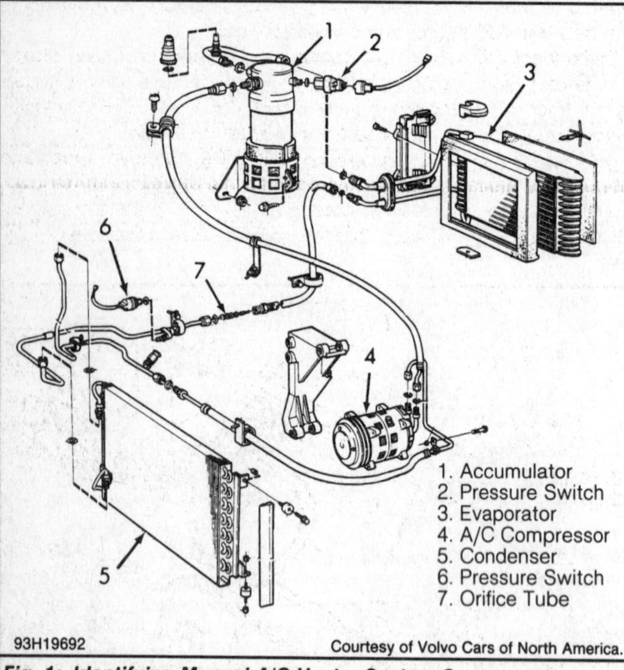
1
2
3
4
5
6
7
1. Accumulator
2. Pressure Switch
3. Evaporator
4. A/C Compressor
5. Condenser
6. Pressure Switch
7. Orifice Tube
93H19692
Courtesy of Volvo Cars of North America.

Fig. 1: Identifying Manual A/C-Heater System Components

OPERATION

Temperature lever on control panel operates a cable connected to coolant valve on left side of A/C-heater unit. System does not use a temperature blend (air mix) door. Instead, the amount of coolant flow through heater core regulates temperature.

Airflow modes and intake air (fresh or recirculated) are selected using buttons in center of control panel. Left button is for floor vents. Center button is for defrost vents. Right button controls intake air. These buttons control a vacuum valve on back of control panel. Vacuum valve controls vacuum to appropriate vacuum actuator, controlling door position.

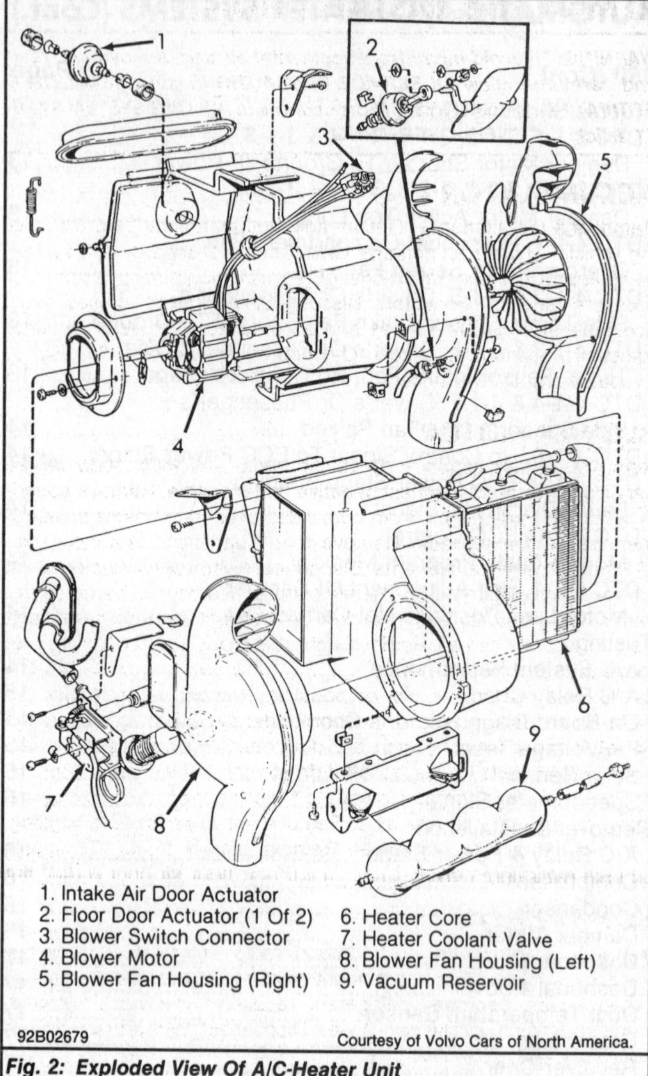
1
2
3
4
5
6
7
8
9
1. Intake Air Door Actuator
2. Floor Door Actuator (1 Of 2)
3. Blower Switch Connector
4. Blower Motor
5. Blower Fan Housing (Right)
6. Heater Core
7. Heater Coolant Valve
8. Blower Fan Housing (Left)
9. Vacuum Reservoir
92B02679
Courtesy of Volvo Cars of North America.

Fig. 2: Exploded View Of A/C-Heater Unit

TESTING

WARNING: To avoid injury from accidental air bag deployment, read and carefully follow all SERVICE PRECAUTIONS and DISABLING & ACTIVATING AIR BAG SYSTEM procedures in AIR BAG SYSTEM SAFETY article in GENERAL SERVICING.

A/C SYSTEM PERFORMANCE

1) Close hood and both front doors. Operate engine at 2000 RPM. Turn blower on third speed. Set temperature lever to cool setting. Close floor vents (left button not pressed). Close defrost vents (center button not pressed). Select recirculated air (right button pressed).

2) Open panel vents. Turn A/C on. After 5-10 minutes, ensure compressor cycles on and off. Ensure outlet temperature is as specified in A/C SYSTEM PERFORMANCE SPECIFICATIONS table.

A/C SYSTEM PERFORMANCE SPECIFICATIONS

Ambient Temp. °F (°C) [1]	Outlet Temp. °F (°C)
68 (20)	41-46 (5-8)
86 (30)	41-46 (5-8)
104 (40)	46-54 (8-12)

[1] – Ambient temperature measured in front of vehicle.

1993 MANUAL A/C-HEATER SYSTEMS
240 (Cont.)

REMOVAL & INSTALLATION

WARNING: To avoid injury from accidental air bag deployment, read and carefully follow all SERVICE PRECAUTIONS and DISABLING & ACTIVATING AIR BAG SYSTEM procedures in AIR BAG SYSTEM SAFETY article in GENERAL SERVICING.

ACCUMULATOR

Removal & Installation – Obtain radio anti-theft code before servicing vehicle. Disconnect negative battery cable. Discharge A/C system using approved refrigerant recovery/recycling equipment. Disconnect pressure switch connector. Disconnect refrigerant hoses from accumulator. Remove screws and accumulator. To install, reverse removal procedure. Use new "O" rings at connections. *See Fig. 3*. Evacuate and charge system.

BLOWER MOTOR

Removal & Installation – 1) Obtain radio anti-theft code before servicing vehicle. Disconnect negative battery cable. Remove soundproofing and side panels from both sides of center console at instrument panel. Remove radio. Remove control panel and center console.

2) Remove panel center vents. Disconnect electrical connectors from clock. Remove glove box. Remove ducts leading to panel center vents. Remove ducts leading to right defrost vent and right panel vent. Fold back floor carpet. Remove right rear floor air duct screw, and move duct slightly to one side.

3) Remove right outer blower housing. Remove right blower fan wheel. If necessary, remove support under glove box to remove fan wheel. Remove blower switch, and disconnect blower switch connector. Remove ducts leading to left defrost vent and left panel vent.

4) Fold back floor carpet. Remove left rear floor air duct screw, and move duct slightly to one side. Remove left outer blower housing. Remove left blower fan wheel. Remove blower motor. To install, reverse removal procedure.

COMPRESSOR

Removal & Installation – 1) Obtain radio anti-theft code before servicing vehicle. Disconnect negative battery cable. Discharge A/C system using approved refrigerant recovery/recycling equipment. Remove engine intake air hose. Disconnect compressor clutch connector and ground wire.

2) Disconnect refrigerant lines from compressor. Remove compressor bracket. Remove compressor. To install, reverse removal procedure. Evacuate and charge system.

CONDENSER

Removal & Installation – 1) Obtain radio anti-theft code before servicing vehicle. Disconnect negative battery cable. Discharge A/C system using approved refrigerant recovery/recycling equipment. Remove grille and both headlight rims. If necessary, remove right headlight. Remove center bracket and horn bracket.

2) Remove condenser cooling fan (if equipped). Disconnect refrigerant hoses from condenser. Remove condenser. To install, reverse removal procedure. Use new "O" rings. Evacuate and charge system.

CONTROL PANEL

Removal & Installation – Obtain radio anti-theft code before servicing vehicle. Disconnect negative battery cable. Remove screws on front of panel and screws from behind panel. Lift control panel upward and outward and disconnect electrical connectors and control cables. Remove control panel. To install, reverse removal procedure.

EVAPORATOR

Removal – Obtain radio anti-theft code before servicing vehicle. Disconnect negative battery cable. Discharge A/C system using approved refrigerant recovery/recycling equipment. Disconnect refrigerant lines from evaporator at firewall in engine compartment. Remove glove box. Remove panel under glove box. Remove right panel from center console. Remove end housing from right side of A/C-heater unit. Remove evaporator.

Installation – To install, reverse removal procedure. Apply sealing putty or insulating tape to evaporator outlet around hoses and connections. *See Fig. 3*. Evacuate and charge system.

HEATER CORE

Removal & Installation – 1) Obtain radio anti-theft code before servicing vehicle. Disconnect negative battery cable. Discharge A/C system using approved refrigerant recovery/recycling equipment. Disconnect refrigerant lines from evaporator at firewall in engine compartment.

2) Move temperature lever to cold setting. Remove soundproofing and left and right panels from sides of center console. Remove radio. Remove center console panel. Remove glove box. Using screwdriver, carefully pry out molding from below right panel vent. Remove steering column shroud.

3) Pry out molding from below left panel vent. Remove panel light adjusting knob and light switch knob. Remove instrument cluster. Remove storage box, center panel vents and instrument cluster frame. Disconnect windshield wiper switch connectors. Remove ducts from between A/C-heater unit and panel vents.

4) Disconnect glove box light connector. Disconnect rubber straps from defrost vents. Remove instrument panel. Remove screws securing rear floor ducts, and move ducts slightly out of way. Remove lower heater mount. Disconnect hose from vacuum reservoir.

5) Disconnect cable from heater coolant valve. Remove upper and lower screws from center console. Remove screws from center support beam. Disconnect blower motor ground wire. To prevent coolant spillage, crimp inlet hose of heater coolant valve. Disconnect inlet hose.

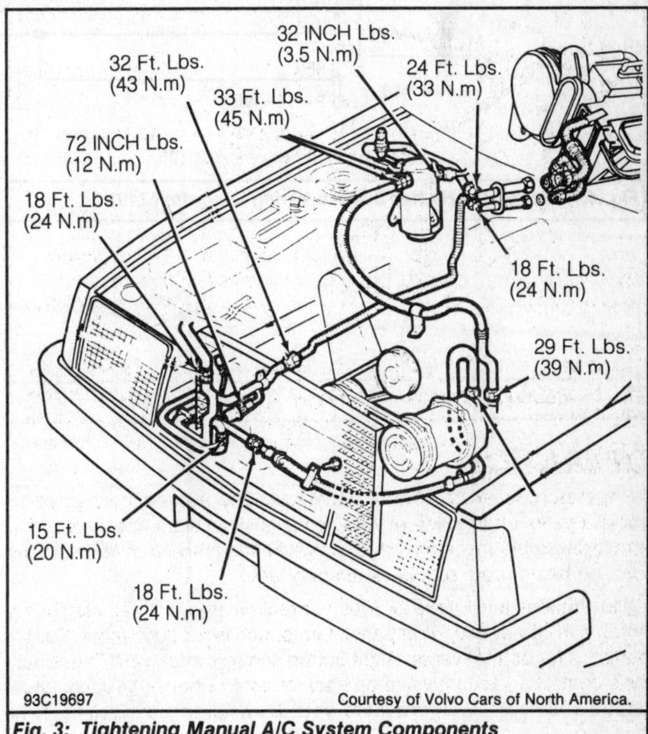
32 INCH Lbs.
(3.5 N.m)
32 Ft. Lbs.
(43 N.m)
24 Ft. Lbs.
(33 N.m)
33 Ft. Lbs.
(45 N.m)
72 INCH Lbs.
(12 N.m)
18 Ft. Lbs.
(24 N.m)
18 Ft. Lbs.
(24 N.m)
29 Ft. Lbs.
(39 N.m)
15 Ft. Lbs.
(20 N.m)
18 Ft. Lbs.
(24 N.m)
93C19697
Courtesy of Volvo Cars of North America.

Fig. 3: Tightening Manual A/C System Components

1993 MANUAL A/C-HEATER SYSTEMS 240 (Cont.)

6) Disconnect upper hose from heater core. Loosen heater upper screws. Remove left and right ducts. Disconnect other hose from vacuum reservoir. Disconnect rear floor ducts from A/C-heater unit, and move ducts slightly out of way.

7) Remove center console. Remove evaporator end cover from right side of A/C-heater unit. Remove A/C-heater unit upper screws and A/C-heater unit. Disassemble A/C-heater unit and remove heater core. To install, reverse removal procedure.

TORQUE SPECIFICATIONS

Tighten refrigerant line fitting to specifications. *See Fig. 3*. Additional torque specifications are not available from manufacturer.

WIRING DIAGRAM

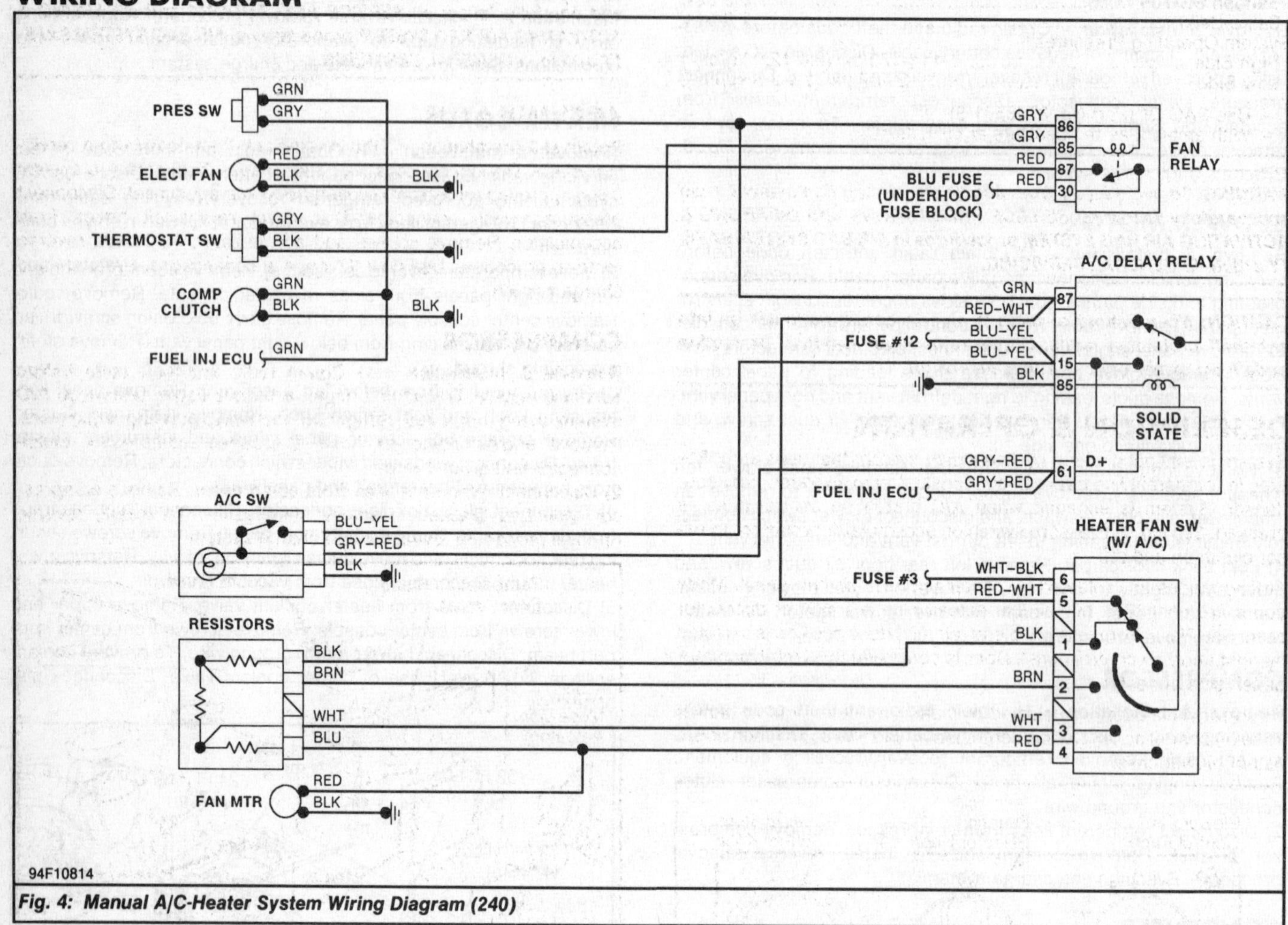
PRES SW
GRN
GRY
ELECT FAN
RED
BLK
BLK
THERMOSTAT SW
GRY
BLK
COMP CLUTCH
GRN
BLK
BLK
FUEL INJ ECU
GRN
A/C SW
BLU-YEL
GRY-RED
BLK
RESISTORS
BLK
BRN
WHT
BLU
FAN MTR
RED
BLK
GRY
GRY
RED
RED
86
85
87
30
FAN RELAY
BLU FUSE (UNDERHOOD FUSE BLOCK)
A/C DELAY RELAY
GRN
RED-WHT
BLU-YEL
BLU-YEL
BLK
87
15
85
FUSE #12
SOLID STATE
GRY-RED
GRY-RED
61
D+
FUEL INJ ECU
HEATER FAN SW (W/ A/C)
FUSE #3
WHT-BLK
RED-WHT
BLK
BRN
WHT
RED
6
5
1
2
3
4
94F10814
Fig. 4: Manual A/C-Heater System Wiring Diagram (240)

1993 MANUAL A/C-HEATER SYSTEMS 940

SPECIFICATIONS

Compressor Type	Sanden SD-510 5-Cyl., Sanden SD-709 7-Cyl. Or Seiko-Seiki SS-121DS5
Compressor Belt Deflection	13/64-25/64" (5-10 mm)
Refrigerant (R-134a) Capacity	32-34 ozs.
Compressor Oil Capacity [1]	
Sanden SD-510	4.8 ozs.
Sanden SD-709	8.5 ozs.
Seiko-Seiki	7.8 ozs.
System Operating Pressures [2]	
High Side	114-170 psi (8.0-12.0 kg/cm²)
Low Side	20-37 psi (1.4-2.6 kg/cm²)

[1] – Use PAG Oil (Part No. 8708581-9)
[2] – With ambient air temperature at 86°F (30°C).

WARNING: To avoid injury from accidental air bag deployment, read and carefully follow all SERVICE PRECAUTIONS and DISABLING & ACTIVATING AIR BAG SYSTEM procedures in AIR BAG SYSTEM SAFETY article in GENERAL SERVICING.

CAUTION: When battery or radio is disconnected, radio will go into anti-theft protection mode. Obtain radio code anti-theft protection code from owner prior to servicing vehicle.

DESCRIPTION & OPERATION

System is equipped with a cycling clutch system that uses an orifice tube in refrigerant line between condenser and evaporator, near condenser. System is engaged when A/C button on control panel is pressed. *See Fig. 1.* Pressure switch on accumulator cycles compressor clutch on and off.

Airflow modes are selected by center knob on control panel. Mode doors are controlled by vacuum actuator on left side of distributor case. *See Fig. 2.* Temperature blend (air mix) door position is selected by right knob on control panel. Door is controlled by electric actuator on left side of heater case.

Fresh/recirculated air is selected by button to lower right of blower knob on control panel. Door is controlled by vacuum actuator on upper half of blower case.

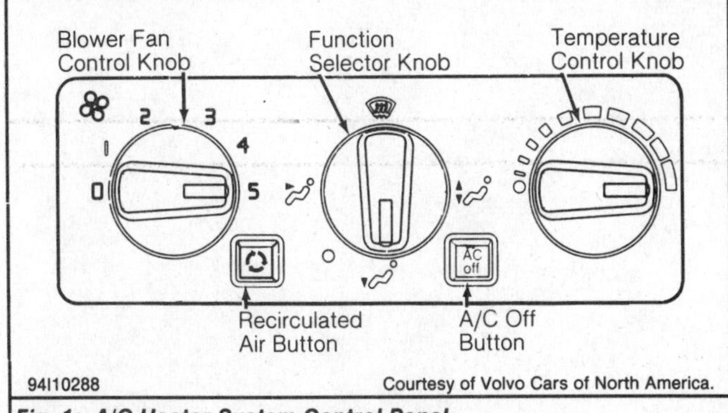
Blower Fan
Control Knob
Function
Selector Knob
Temperature
Control Knob
2
3
1
4
0
5
AC
off
Recirculated
Air Button
A/C Off
Button
94I10288
Courtesy of Volvo Cars of North America.

Fig. 1: A/C-Heater System Control Panel

TESTING

A/C SYSTEM PERFORMANCE

1) Close hood and front doors. Operate engine at 2000 RPM. Turn blower on third speed. Set temperature knob to cool setting. Select panel vent position on airflow mode control knob. Select recirculated air (button pressed).

2) Open panel vents. Turn on A/C. After 5-10 minutes, ensure compressor cycles on and off. Ensure duct temperature is 41-46°F (5-8°C) when ambient temperature is 68-86°F (20-30°C), or 46-54°F (8-12°C) when ambient temperature is 104°F (40°C).

REMOVAL & INSTALLATION

WARNING: To avoid injury from accidental air bag deployment, read and carefully follow all SERVICE PRECAUTIONS and DISABLING & ACTIVATING AIR BAG SYSTEM procedures in AIR BAG SYSTEM SAFETY article in GENERAL SERVICING.

ACCUMULATOR

Removal & Installation – Obtain radio anti-theft code before servicing vehicle. Disconnect negative battery cable. Discharge A/C system using approved refrigerant recovery/recycling equipment. Disconnect pressure switch connector. Disconnect refrigerant hoses from accumulator. Remove screws and accumulator. To install, reverse removal procedure. Use new "O" rings at connections. Evacuate and charge system.

COMPRESSOR

Removal & Installation – 1) Obtain radio anti-theft code before servicing vehicle. Disconnect negative battery cable. Discharge A/C system using approved refrigerant recovery/recycling equipment. Remove engine intake air hose. Disconnect compressor clutch connector and ground wire.

2) Disconnect refrigerant lines from compressor. Remove compressor mounting brackets. Remove compressor. To install, reverse removal procedure. Evacuate and charge system.

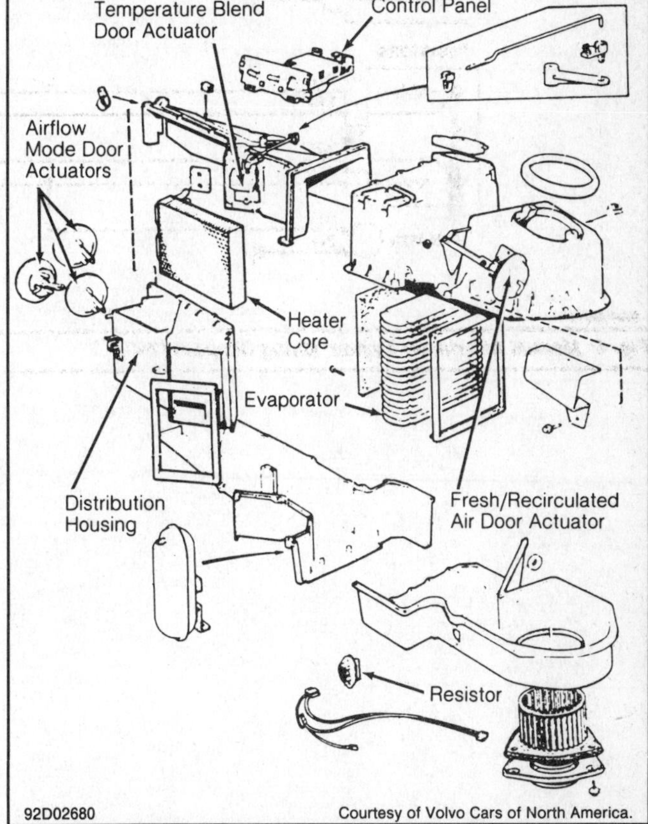
Temperature Blend
Door Actuator
Control Panel
Airflow
Mode Door
Actuators
Heater
Core
Evaporator
Distribution
Housing
Fresh/Recirculated
Air Door Actuator
Resistor
92D02680
Courtesy of Volvo Cars of North America.

Fig. 2: Exploded View Of Manual A/C-Heater System Case

1993 MANUAL A/C-HEATER SYSTEMS
940 (Cont.)

CONDENSER

Removal & Installation – Obtain radio anti-theft code before servicing vehicle. Disconnect negative battery cable. Discharge A/C system using approved refrigerant recovery/recycling equipment. Remove grille and grille center support. Remove upper radiator panel bolts. Disconnect refrigerant hoses from condenser. Remove condenser. To install, reverse removal procedure. Use new "O" rings. Evacuate and charge system.

CONTROL PANEL

Removal & Installation – Obtain radio anti-theft code before servicing vehicle. Disconnect negative battery cable. Remove screws on front of panel and screws from behind panel. Lift control panel upward and outward. Disconnect electrical connectors. Remove control panel. To install, reverse removal procedure.

EVAPORATOR

Removal & Installation – **1)** Obtain radio anti-theft code before servicing vehicle. Disconnect negative battery cable. Discharge A/C system using approved refrigerant recovery/recycling equipment. Disconnect refrigerant lines from evaporator at firewall in engine compartment. Remove panel under glove box. Remove glove box. Remove right door instep molding and right kick panel.

2) Remove electronic control unit and mounting bracket. Disconnect electrical connectors from blower resistor and blower motor. Remove lower half of blower/evaporator case with evaporator. To install, reverse removal procedure. Evacuate and charge system.

HEATER CORE

Removal & Installation – **1)** Obtain radio anti-theft code before servicing vehicle. Disconnect negative battery cable. Drain coolant, or clamp off hoses to heater core in engine compartment at firewall. Remove center console (floor part). Remove driver-side trim panel. Remove panel under glove box. Remove glove box.

2) Remove center console (panel part) and side panels. Remove necessary ducts. Remove distribution housing. Remove heater core. To install, reverse removal procedure.

WIRING DIAGRAM

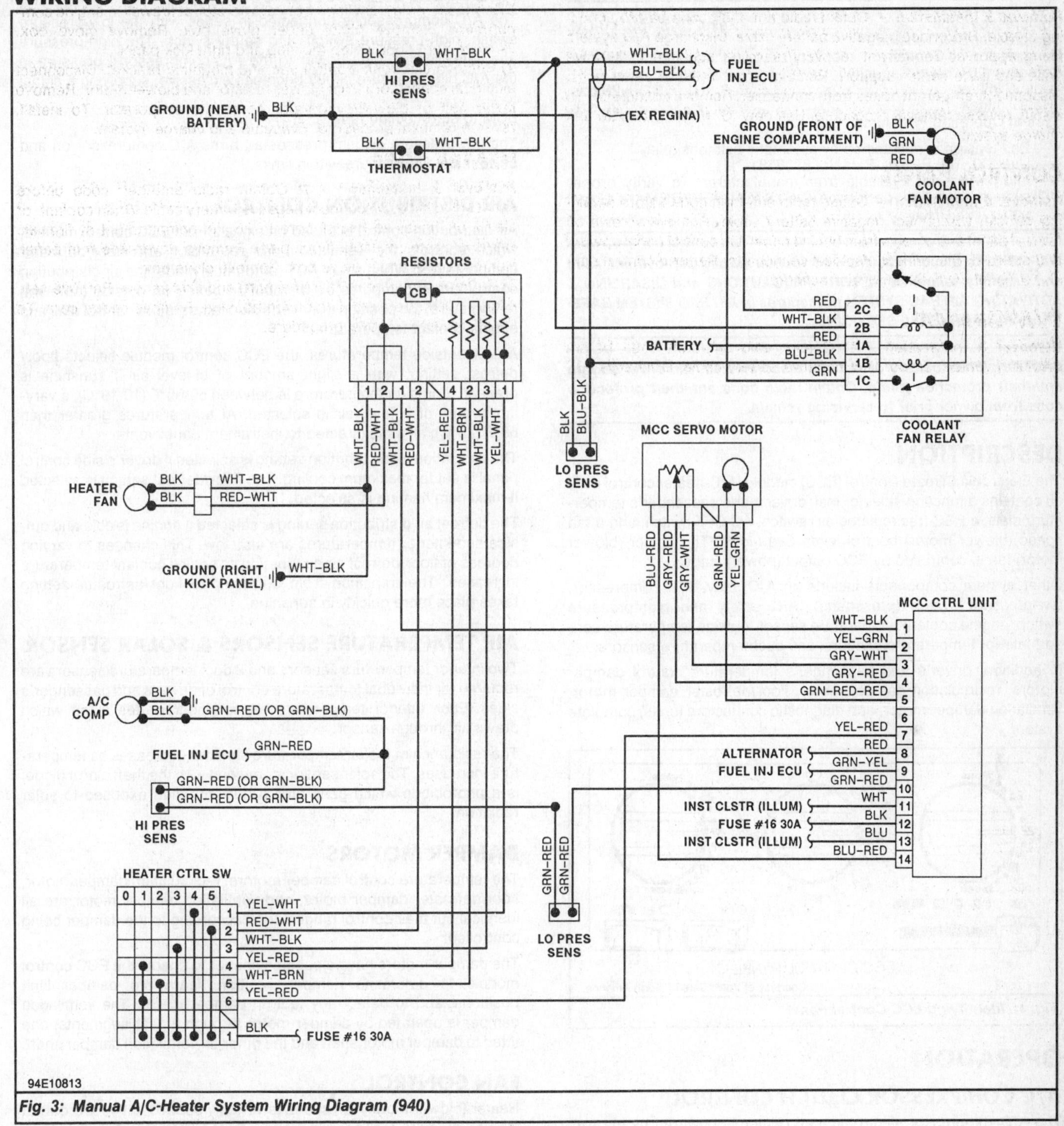
BLK
WHT-BLK
HI PRES SENS
GROUND (NEAR BATTERY)
BLK
WHT-BLK
THERMOSTAT
WHT-BLK
BLU-BLK
FUEL INJ ECU
(EX REGINA)
GROUND (FRONT OF ENGINE COMPARTMENT)
GRN
RED
COOLANT FAN MOTOR
RESISTORS
CB
RED
WHT-BLK
2C
2B
1A
1B
1C
BATTERY
BLU-BLK
GRN
COOLANT FAN RELAY
WHT-BLK
RED-WHT
YEL-RED
WHT-BRN
YEL-WHT
BLU-BLK
LO PRES SENS
MCC SERVO MOTOR
HEATER FAN
RED-WHT
GROUND (RIGHT KICK PANEL)
BLU-RED
GRY-RED
GRY-WHT
GRN-RED
YEL-GRN
MCC CTRL UNIT
YEL-GRN
GRY-WHT
GRY-RED
GRN-RED-RED
A/C COMP
GRN-RED (OR GRN-BLK)
FUEL INJ ECU
GRN-RED
ALTERNATOR
GRN-YEL
WHT
INST CLSTR (ILLUM)
FUSE #16 30A
BLU
BLU-RED
HI PRES SENS
HEATER CTRL SW
YEL-WHT
WHT-BRN
LO PRES SENS
FUSE #16 30A
94E10813

Fig. 3: Manual A/C-Heater System Wiring Diagram (940)

1993 AUTOMATIC A/C-HEATER SYSTEMS
850

SPECIFICATIONS

Compressor Type .... Zexel DKS-15CH 6-Cyl.
Compressor Belt Tension [1]
Compressor Oil Capacity .... [2] 7.0 ozs.
Refrigerant (R-134a) Capacity
 Cold Climates .... 29 ozs.
 Hot Climates .... 26 ozs.
System Operating Pressures [3]

[1] – Belt tension is maintained by automatic belt tensioner.
[2] – Use ZXL 100 PG Oil (Part No. 8708581-7).
[3] – Information not available from manufacturer. To verify proper system operation, perform A/C SYSTEM PERFORMANCE test under TESTING.

WARNING: To avoid injury from accidental air bag deployment, read and carefully follow all SERVICE PRECAUTIONS and DISABLING & ACTIVATING AIR BAG SYSTEM procedures in AIR BAG SYSTEM SAFETY article in GENERAL SERVICING.

CAUTION: When battery or radio is disconnected, radio will go into anti-theft protection mode. Obtain radio code anti-theft protection code from owner prior to servicing vehicle.

DESCRIPTION

The Electronic Climate Control (ECC) module (A/C-heater control panel) contains a function selector dial, driver's and passenger's temperature dials, a REC (recirculated air) switch, AC OFF switch, and a fan speed (blower motor) control lever. *See Fig. 1.* The heater (blower motor) fan is controlled by ECC output (power) stage.

Other system components include an A/C relay, A/C compressor, low-pressure switch (pressostat), A/C safety and high-pressure switch, engine coolant temperature sensor, outside temperature sensor, interior temperature sensors, and duct temperature sensors.

In addition, driver's and passenger's temperature control damper motors, recirculation damper motor, floor/defroster damper motor, ventilation damper motor, and diagnostic connectors (units) complete system.

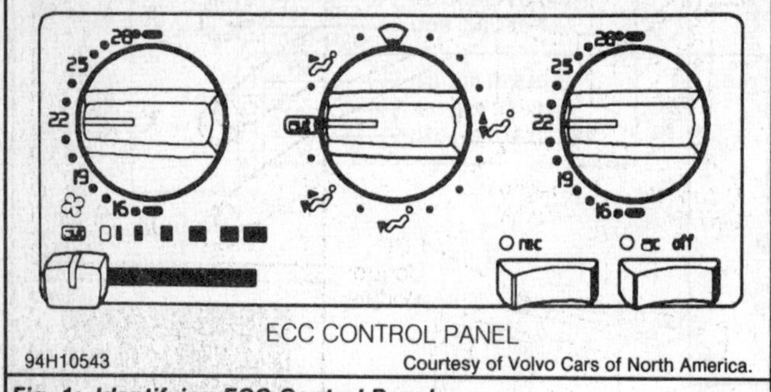
28
25
22
19
16
28
25
22
19
16
rec
ac off
ECC CONTROL PANEL
94H10543
Courtesy of Volvo Cars of North America.

Fig. 1: Identifying ECC Control Panel

OPERATION

A/C COMPRESSOR CLUTCH CONTROL

The A/C compressor electromagnetic clutch is powered by the A/C relay. Compressor operation requires that the A/C relay be activated by both Electronic Climate Control (ECC) module and Engine Control Module (ECM). The ECM turns A/C compressor off when engine is at full acceleration, at high engine temperature, and for 5-10 seconds after starting engine.

The ECC control module normally supplies voltage to A/C relay, except when heater (blower motor) fan is off and vehicle speed is less than 30 MPH; or when heater fan is off and recirculation is on.

If A/C is switched off using the AC OFF switch, ECC control module will cut supply voltage to relay, turning off compressor. However, this does not apply when air distribution control is in defrost setting, since A/C is always on in this case.

A/C PRESSURE SWITCHES

The A/C compressor is connected in series with the low-pressure switch, high-pressure switch, and safety switch. The high-pressure and safety switch cuts power to the A/C compressor if pressure in the A/C high-pressure circuit becomes excessive, supplying a signal to
ECM to start cooling fan.

The low-pressure switch (pressostat) turns A/C compressor on and off to maintain pressure within limits.

AIR DISTRIBUTION CONTROL

Air distribution control is based on signals from ECC control module, which controls the ventilation damper motor and floor/defroster damper motor. When set to AUT (automatic) mode, the air distribution control circuit computes air distribution based on outside (ambient) temperature, the position of driver's side temperature control dial, and engine coolant temperature.

At low outside temperatures, the ECC control module selects floor/defrost setting, with a slight amount of bi-level air if sunshine is present. If outside temperature is between 50-66°F (10-19°C), a varying degree of bi-level air is selected. At temperatures greater than 68°F (20°C), all air is directed to instrument panel vents.

The ventilation air distribution setting is selected if driver's side control panel is set for maximum cooling. The floor/defrost setting is selected if maximum heating is selected.

The defrost air distribution setting is selected if engine is cold and outside and interior temperatures are also low. This changes to varying degrees of floor/defrost air distribution as engine coolant temperature increases. The transition from defroster to floor/defroster setting takes place more quickly in sunshine.

AIR TEMPERATURE SENSORS & SOLAR SENSOR

Two interior temperature sensors and 2 duct temperature sensors are required for individual temperature control of driver's and passenger's sides. Each interior temperature sensor incorporates a fan which draws air through sensor.

The resistance of the air temperature sensors decreases as temperature increases. The solar sensor, combined with the theft alarm diode, is a photodiode which generates a current when exposed to solar radiation.

DAMPER MOTORS

The temperature control damper motors, recirculation damper motor, floor/defroster damper motor, and ventilation damper motor are all identical but their control range varies according to the damper being controlled.

The damper motors have a position sensor to enable the ECC control module to determine damper position, learn the damper limit positions, and to detect any fault in damper motor. The ventilation damper is operated by damper motor through 2 gear segments, one fitted to damper motor shaft and the other on ventilation damper shaft.

FAN CONTROL

Heater (blower motor) fan speed is variably controlled by ECC output (power) stage in response to signals from ECC control module. The ECC control module digital control signals vary in length according to required fan speed.

The ECC output stage has an electronic unit which receives the digital control signals and converts them to voltage. If there is no control signal or the fan is disabled, the ECC output stage sends a diagnostic signal to inform the ECC control module of the fault.

If fan speed control lever is set to AUT (automatic) mode, fan speed is influenced by the position of driver's side temperature control dial, driver's side interior temperature sensor, vehicle speed, and engine coolant temperature.

The highest fan speed is selected if driver's side temperature control dial is set to maximum or minimum cooling or heating. The greater the difference between the desired and actual temperatures, as sensed by the driver's side temperature sensor, the higher the fan speed.

As vehicle speed increases, the fan speed will be reduced to maintain a constant air flow throughout the passenger compartment. When heating the passenger compartment after starting a cold engine, the fan speed is gradually increased as engine coolant temperature rises.

RECIRCULATED AIR MODE

The ECC control module selects recirculated air mode only for a combination of cooling and high outside temperature, provided that:

- There is a considerable difference between the desired and actual temperature on driver's side. The quantity of recirculated air will vary between 70-100 percent, depending on difference in temperature.
- A high fan speed is manually selected. In this case, the recirculation damper will be set to a mid-position (50 percent of the air will be recirculated).

Recirculation Motor – This motor operates the recirculation damper by means of a mechanical linkage in response to signals from ECC control module.

Recirculation Switch – The off position of REC (recirculation) switch corresponds to automatic operation, the ECC control module determines whether recirculation is required.

Air Distribution Switch – With air distribution switch in defroster position, recirculated air mode always cuts out, as humidity in passenger compartment will normally be higher than that of outside air.

Recirculation Damper – In AUT (automatic) mode, recirculation damper movement is limited to fractions of a second. It takes about half a minute from full recirculation to take effect if outside temperature is high.

TEMPERATURE CONTROL

Individual temperature control is provided by the driver's and passenger's side temperature control damper motors in response to signals from ECC control module.

The ECC control module computes temperature control damper motors based on inputs from temperature dial settings, duct temperature sensors, interior temperature sensors, solar sensor, engine coolant temperature sensor, and outside (ambient) temperature sensor.

The air temperature is monitored downstream of temperature control dampers by the duct temperature sensors. The difference between the desired and actual interior temperature, as monitored by interior temperature sensors, has a direct effect on temperature control damper positions.

In direct sunlight, the temperature control dampers are positioned to provide a lower temperature, as determined by solar sensor input. If the engine is cold and outside temperature is low, the temperature control dampers are set for more heat to reach the desired temperature faster.

TROUBLE SHOOTING

SELF-DIAGNOSTICS

The Electronic Climate Control (ECC) control module can detect faults in the system and store Diagnostic Trouble Codes (DTC). If a fault is present, system informs driver by flashing the LEDs by the AC and REC switches for 20 seconds.

A fault warning is given when a fault is discovered or present, each time ignition is turned on, or engine started. DTCs will remain stored until cleared by an input code.

NOTE: Test Unit (981 3190) and Adapter (981 3194) are required for DTC diagnosis. The Volvo Diagnostic Key (998 8670) may be used to perform self-diagnostics. Follow tool manufacturer's instructions.

There are 3 different test modes/settings which can be selected for reading off DTCs. TEST MODE 1 may be used for reading off DTCs detected by control unit (up to 47 codes can be stored). TEST MODE 2 checks signals from speedometer and solar sensor.

TEST MODE 4 is used to check electrical circuits in A/C system, reset information on damper motor limit positions and change data transmission speed from ECC control module to on-board diagnostic unit.

NOTE: Ignition must be turned off before switching from one test mode to another.

ENTERING SELF-DIAGNOSTICS

1) Connect selector cable from diagnostic unit "A" to terminal No. 1 of diagnostic unit "B", located behind right headlight. *See Fig. 2.*

2) Turn ignition on. LED on diagnostic unit "A" should start flashing. Each DTC (3-digits) consists of a series of flashes with a short break between each series. DTCs are displayed in ascending order.

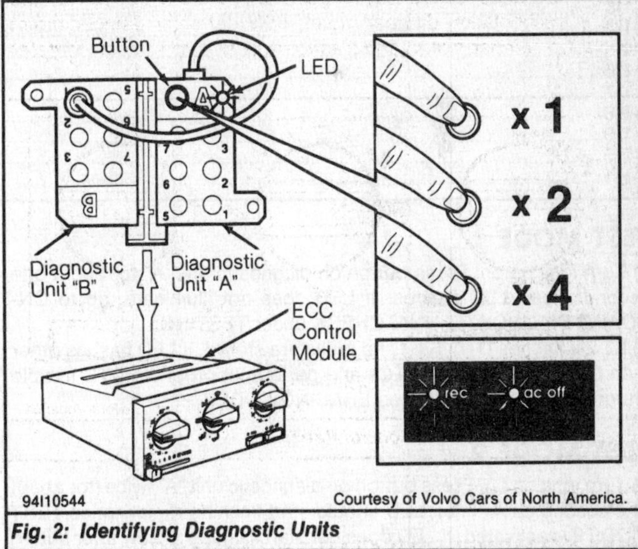
Button
LED
x 1
x 2
x 4
Diagnostic Unit "B"
Diagnostic Unit "A"
ECC Control Module
rec
ac off
94I10544
Courtesy of Volvo Cars of North America.

Fig. 2: Identifying Diagnostic Units

1993 AUTOMATIC A/C-HEATER SYSTEMS 850 (Cont.)

AUTOMATIC A/C-HEATER SYSTEM DIAGNOSTIC TROUBLE CODES

Code Number	Condition/Affected Circuit
1-1-1	No Fault Found By Diagnostic System
1-2-1	Outside Temp. Sensor Circuit Shorted To Ground
1-2-2	Outside Temp. Sensor Open Circuit Or Shorted To Power
1-2-3	Driver's Side Temp. Sensor Circuit Shorted To Ground
1-2-4	Driver's Side Temp. Sensor Circuit Open Or Shorted To Power
1-2-5	Passenger's Side Temp. Sensor Circuit Shorted To Ground
1-2-6	Passenger's Side Temp. Sensor Circuit Open Or Shorted To Power
1-3-1	Driver's Side Duct Temp. Sensor Shorted To Ground
1-3-2	Driver's Side Duct Temp. Sensor Open Circuit Or Shorted To Power
1-3-3	Passenger's Side Duct Temp. Sensor Shorted To Ground
1-3-4	Passenger's Side Duct Temp. Sensor Circuit Open Or Shorted To Power
1-3-5	No Engine Temp. Frequency Signal
1-4-1	Driver's Side Temp. Switch Faulty Control Signal
1-4-3	Passenger's Side Temp. Switch Faulty Control Signal
1-4-5	Air Distribution Switch Faulty Control Signal
1-5-1	Fan Speed Sensor Control Signal Missing Or Too High
1-5-2	Fan Speed Sensor Control Signal Shorted to Ground
2-1-1	Driver's Side Damper Motor Position Sensor Circuit Open Or Shorted To Power
2-1-2	Driver's Side Damper Motor Position Sensor Shorted To Ground
2-2-1	Passenger's Side Damper Motor Position Sensor Circuit Open Or Shorted To Power
2-2-2	Passenger's Side Damper Motor Position Sensor Shorted To Ground
2-3-1	Ventilation Damper Motor Position Sensor Circuit Open Or Shorted To Power
2-3-2	Ventilation Damper Motor Position Sensor Shorted To Ground
2-3-3	Floor/Defrost Damper Motor Position Sensor Circuit Open Or Short To Power
2-3-4	Floor/Defrost Damper Motor Position Sensor Shorted To Ground
2-3-5	Recirculation Damper Motor Position Sensor Circuit Open Or Short To Power
2-3-6	Recirculation Damper Motor Position Sensor Shorted To Ground
3-1-1	Driver's Side Damper Motor Shorted To Ground Or Power
3-1-2	Passenger's Side Damper Motor Shorted To Ground Or Power
3-1-3	Ventilation Damper Motor Shorted To Ground Or Power
3-1-4	Floor/Defrost Damper Motor Shorted To Ground Or Power
3-1-5	Recirculation Damper Motor Shorted To Ground Or Power
3-2-1	Driver's Side Damper Motor Active Too Long
3-2-2	Passenger's Side Damper Motor Active Too Long
3-2-3	Ventilation Damper Motor Active Too Long
3-2-4	Floor/Defrost Damper Motor Active Too Long
3-2-5	Recirculation Damper Motor Active Too Long
4-1-1	Passenger Compartment Fan Overcurrent Or Seized Fan
4-1-2	Driver's Side Temp. Sensor Intake Fan Shorted To Ground
4-1-3	Driver's Side Temp. Sensor Intake Fan, No Control Voltage
4-1-4	Driver's Side Temp. Sensor Intake Fan Seized
4-1-5	Passenger's Side Temp. Sensor Intake Fan Shorted To Ground
4-1-6	Passenger's Side Temp. Sensor Intake Fan, No Control Voltage
4-1-7	Passenger's Side Temp. Sensor Intake Fan Seized
4-1-8	No Control Signal To ECC Power Stage
4-1-9	ECC Power Stage Emitting Faulty Diagnostic Signal
4-2-0	ECC Control Module Fault, Program Memory
5-1-1	Self-Adjustment Of Damper Motor Limit Positions Not Carried Out

TEST MODE 1

1) Turn ignition on. Press button on diagnostic unit "A" for about one second. Read LED flashes. If LED does not illuminate, go to ON-BOARD DIAGNOSTIC UNIT CHECK under TESTING.

2) If LED flashes DTC 1-1-1, no faults are stored. If LED flashes other than DTC 1-1-1, display DTCs and perform appropriate DTC trouble shooting. To erase code, see ERASING CODES.

TEST MODE 2

1) Turn ignition on. Press button on diagnostic unit "A" twice (for about one second each time). LED should start flashing rapidly once TEST MODE 2 is activated. If LED does not start flashing rapidly after button is pressed, go to ON-BOARD DIAGNOSTIC UNIT CHECK under TESTING.

2) If LED flashes DTC 1-1-2, signal from solar sensor is okay. If LED flashes DTC 1-1-3, signal from speedometer is okay. If neither DTC is present, go to next step.

3) If DTC 1-1-2 is not present, check solar sensor. Go to SOLAR SENSOR under TESTING. If DTC 1-1-3 is not present, check speed sensor signal. Go to SPEEDOMETER SIGNAL under TESTING. To exit TEST MODE 2, turn ignition off.

TEST MODE 4

1) Turn ignition on. Press button on diagnostic unit "A" 4 times (for about one second each time). LED should illuminate. If LED illuminates, go to next step. If LED does not illuminate, go to ON-BOARD DIAGNOSTIC UNIT CHECK under TESTING.

2) Control codes must be entered one step at a time. See TEST MODE 4 CONTROL CODES table. LED should go off after each digit is entered. Entering each digit in a code must be made within 4 seconds as failure to do so will abort input and TEST MODE 4 must be restarted.

TEST MODE 4 CONTROL CODES

Code	Test
1-1-1	Controlling A/C Relay
3-1-1	[1] Normal Speed
3-1-2	[1] X2 Speed
3-1-3	[1 2] X10 Speed
9-9-9	Self-Adjustment Of Damper Motor Limit Positions

[1] – Changes data transmission speed/rate from ECC control module to on-board diagnostic unit.

[2] – Used only with Volvo Diagnostic Key (998 8670).

Controlling A/C Relay – Enter control code 1-1-1 by pressing button on diagnostic unit 3 times, with a short pause in between to allow LED to come on again. ECC control module will now switch A/C relay on and off 5 times (10 seconds on, 10 seconds off), switch A/C compressor on and off, and turn control panel A/C indicator on and off. If A/C relay does not respond as indicated, check A/C relay. See RELAY under TESTING.

Self-Adjustment Of Damper Motor Limit Positions – **1)** Turn ignition on. Place fan (blower motor) lever in manual mode. Turn function selector to AUT (automatic) mode. Ensure system is in TEST MODE 4.

2) Enter control code 9-9-9 by pressing button on diagnostic unit 9 times in quick succession. Enter each of the 9 series 3 times, with a short pause in-between to allow LED to come on again. ECC control module is now ready to adjust damper motor limit positions automatically.

3) Wait about 10 seconds for fan to start. Turn ignition off to exit TEST MODE 4. Turn ignition on. AC OFF and REC indicator on A/C control panel should flash. Drive car for a few minutes at speeds greater than 20 MPH.

4) Stop car and turn engine off, but leave ignition on for at least 2 minutes to enable ECC control module to store all values. Start TEST MODE 1 and record DTCs. If DTC 1-1-1 appears, self-adjustment is complete. If DTC 5-1-1 appears, self-adjustment is not complete.

Changing Data Transmission Speed/Rate From ECC Control Module To On-Board Diagnostic Unit – Enter desired control code (3-1-1 or 3-1-2) by pressing button on diagnostic unit "A", with a short pause in-between to allow LED to come on again. System always starts at normal speed unless another option is selected. If another option was selected, system will revert to normal speed each time ignition is turned off.

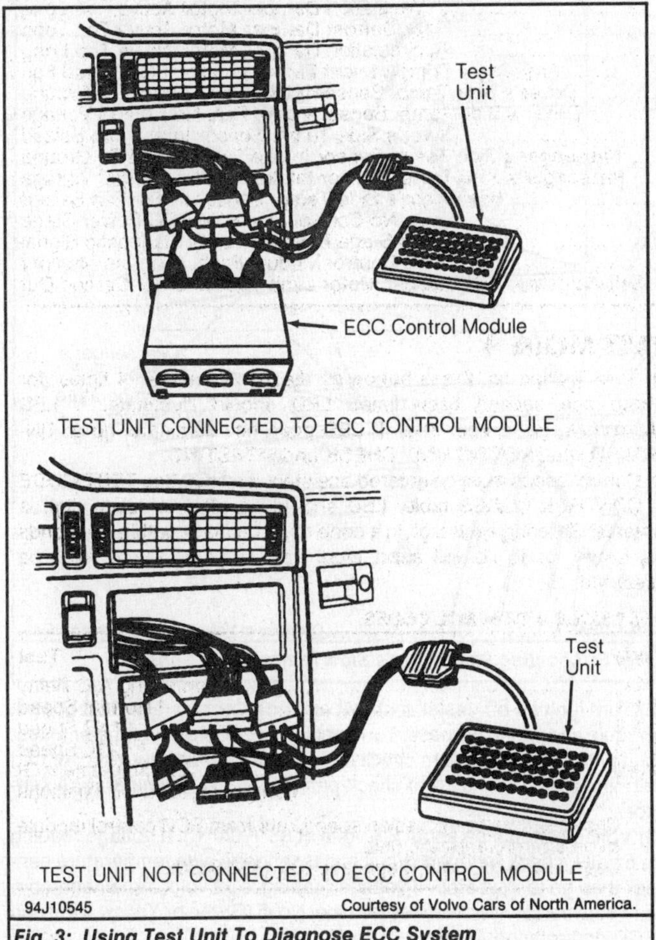

Test Unit
ECC Control Module
TEST UNIT CONNECTED TO ECC CONTROL MODULE
Test Unit
TEST UNIT NOT CONNECTED TO ECC CONTROL MODULE
94J10545
Courtesy of Volvo Cars of North America.

Fig. 3: Using Test Unit To Diagnose ECC System

ERASING CODES

1) All codes must be displayed at least once before they can be erased. To erase codes, ensure selector cable is connected to terminal No. 1 of diagnostic unit "B". *See Fig. 2.* Press and hold diagnostic button for at least 5 seconds. LED should illuminate 3 seconds after button is released.

2) Press and hold diagnostic button for a minimum of 5 seconds more. When button is released, LED should go out. Ensure codes have been erased by pressing diagnostic button once. If display shows 1-1-1, codes have been erased/cleared. If a DTC will not erase/clear, perform that particular code's diagnosis again.

DTC 1-2-1 OUTSIDE TEMP. SENSOR CIRCUIT SHORTED TO GROUND

1) Turn ignition off. Install Test Unit (981 3190) and Adapter (981 3194) between ECC control module and harness connector. *See Fig. 3.* Using ohmmeter, connect test leads between ground and test unit pins No. 6, 9, 10 and 56. Ohmmeter should read zero ohms in each terminal. If resistance is as specified, go to next step. If resistance is not as specified, check for open circuit.

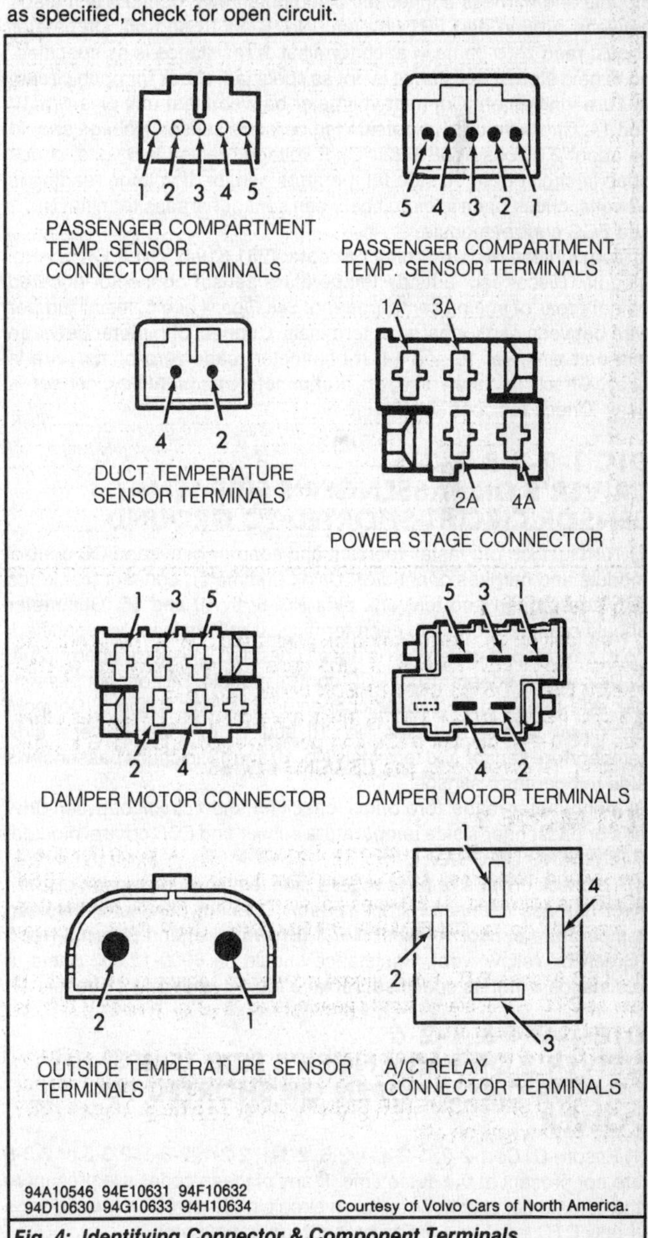

1 2 3 4 5
PASSENGER COMPARTMENT TEMP. SENSOR CONNECTOR TERMINALS
5 4 3 2 1
PASSENGER COMPARTMENT TEMP. SENSOR TERMINALS
4 2
DUCT TEMPERATURE SENSOR TERMINALS
1A 3A 2A 4A
POWER STAGE CONNECTOR
1 3 5 2 4
DAMPER MOTOR CONNECTOR
5 3 1 4 2
DAMPER MOTOR TERMINALS
2 1
OUTSIDE TEMPERATURE SENSOR TERMINALS
1 4 2 3
A/C RELAY CONNECTOR TERMINALS
94A10546 94E10631 94F10632
94D10630 94G10633 94H10634
Courtesy of Volvo Cars of North America.

Fig. 4: Identifying Connector & Component Terminals

2) Disconnect Adapter (981 3194) from ECC control module. Disconnect outside temperature sensor (located on right rear of engine compartment). *See Figs. 4 and 5.* Connect ohmmeter leads between test unit pins No. 10 and 14. Ohmmeter should read infinity. If reading is as specified, go to next step. If reading is not as specified, check for shorted circuit between sensor harness connector and ECC control module.

3) Connect ohmmeter leads between outside temperature sensor terminals. Resistance should be 8000-12,000 ohms. If resistance is not as specified, replace outside temperature sensor. Clear and recheck for codes.

DTC 1-2-2 OUTSIDE TEMP. SENSOR OPEN CIRCUIT OR SHORTED TO POWER

1) Ensure DTCs 1-2-2, 1-2-4, 1-2-6, 2-1-1, 2-2-1, 2-3-1, 2-3-3 or 2-3-5 are not present at the same time. If any of these codes are present at the same time, check for an open circuit in the common ground wire. If only DTC 1-2-2 is present, go to next step.

2) Turn ignition off. Install test unit and adapter between ECC control module and harness connector. Using ohmmeter, connect test leads between ground and test unit pins No. 6, 9, 10 and 56. Ohmmeter should read zero ohms in each terminal. If resistance is as specified, go to next step. If resistance is not as specified, check for open circuit.

3) Turn ignition on. Connect voltmeter between test unit pins No. 10 and 14. Check voltage to outside temperature sensor. Voltage should be about 2.6 volts at 68°F (20°C). If voltage reading is 5 volts, check open in circuit or in outside temperature sensor. If voltage reading is 12 volts, check open in circuit between sensor harness terminal No. 1 and ECC control module.

4) Turn ignition off. Disconnect Adapter (981 3194) from ECC control module. Disconnect outside temperature sensor connector (located on right rear of engine compartment). *See Figs. 4 and 5.* Install jumper wire between sensor harness terminals. Connect ohmmeter between test unit pins No. 10 and 14. If ohmmeter reads zero ohms, wire is okay. Check for faulty sensor. If ohmmeter reads infinity, sensor is okay. Check for open circuit.

DTC 1-2-3 & 1-2-5 DRIVER'S OR PASSENGER'S SIDE TEMP. SENSOR CIRCUIT SHORTED TO GROUND

1) Turn ignition off. Install test unit and adapter between ECC control module and harness connector. Using ohmmeter, connect test leads between ground and test unit pins No. 6, 9, 10 and 56. Ohmmeter should read zero ohms in each terminal. If resistance is as specified, go to next step. If resistance is not as specified, check for open circuit.

2) Disconnect adapter from ECC control module. Disconnect passenger side temperature sensor connector. *See Figs. 4 and 6.* Connect ohmmeter to test unit pins No. 10 and 12 to check driver's side temperature sensor and terminals No. 10 and 13 to check passenger's side temperature sensor.

3) If ohmmeter reads zero ohms, check for short circuit between driver's or passenger's side temperature sensor and ECC control module. See WIRING DIAGRAM.

4) To check driver's or passenger's side temperature sensor, disconnect harness connector from sensor. Connect ohmmeter between temperature sensor terminal No. 3 (Brown wire) and terminal No. 5 (Green or Yellow wire). Resistance should be 8000-12,000 ohms. If resistance is not as specified, replace faulty temperature sensor.

DTC 1-2-4 & 1-2-6 DRIVER'S OR PASSENGER'S SIDE TEMP. SENSOR CIRCUIT OPEN OR SHORTED TO POWER

1) Ensure DTCs 1-2-2, 1-2-4, 1-2-6, 2-1-1, 2-2-1, 2-3-1, 2-3-3 or 2-3-5 are not present at the same time. If any of these codes are present at the same time, check for an open circuit in the common ground wire. If only DTC 1-2-4 or 1-2-6 is present, go to next step.

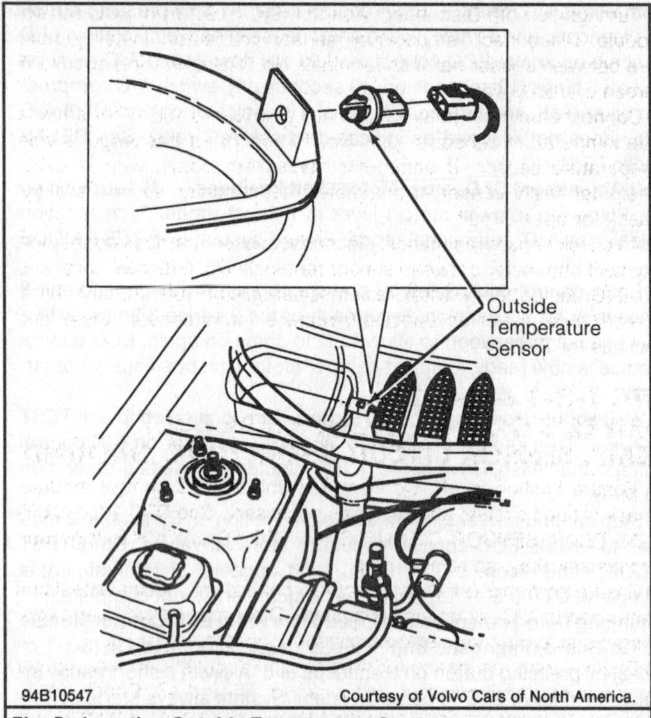
Outside
Temperature
Sensor
94B10547
Courtesy of Volvo Cars of North America.

Fig. 5: Locating Outside Temperature Sensor

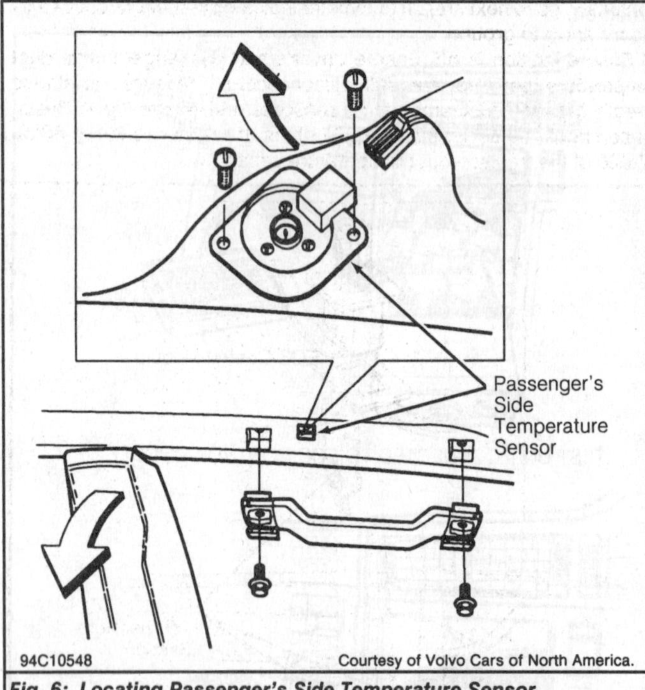
Passenger's
Side
Temperature
Sensor
94C10548
Courtesy of Volvo Cars of North America.

Fig. 6: Locating Passenger's Side Temperature Sensor

2) Turn ignition off. Install test unit and adapter between ECC control module and wiring harness. Turn ignition on. Connect voltmeter to test unit pins No. 10 and 12 to check driver's side temperature sensor and terminals No. 10 and 13 to check passenger's side temperature sensor.

3) Voltage should be about 2.6 volts at 68°F (20°C). If voltage reading is 5 volts, check for open circuit in passenger's side temperature sensor then go to next step. If voltage reading is 12 volts, repair short circuit between sensor harness terminal No. 5 (Green or Yellow wire) and ECC control module.

4) Turn ignition off. Disconnect Adapter (981 3194) from ECC control module. Disconnect temperature sensor connector. Install jumper wire between sensor harness terminals No. 3 (Brown wire) and No. 5 (Green or Yellow wire).

5) Connect ohmmeter between test unit pins No. 10 and 12 for driver's side temperature sensor or pins No. 10 and 13 for passenger's side temperature sensor. If ohmmeter reads zero ohms, wire is okay. Check for faulty sensor. If ohmmeter reads infinity, sensor is okay. Check for open circuit.

6) To check sensor resistance, disconnect sensor harness connector. Connect ohmmeter between sensor terminals No. 3 (Brown wire) and No. 5 (Green or Yellow wire), resistance should be 8000-12,000 ohms. If resistance is not as specified, replace faulty sensor. Clear and recheck for DTC.

DTC 1-3-1 & 1-3-3 DRIVER'S OR PASSENGER'S SIDE DUCT TEMP. SENSOR CIRCUIT SHORTED TO GROUND

1) Ensure ignition is off. Connect test unit to ECC control module. Check ground circuits and repair as necessary. See DTC 1-2-1 OUTSIDE TEMP. SENSOR CIRCUIT SHORTED TO GROUND. If ground circuits are okay, go to next step.

2) Ensure ignition is off. Disconnect A/C control unit, but leave test unit connected to A/C control unit connector. Disconnect driver's and passenger's side duct temperature sensor connectors. *See Fig. 7.*

3) Check wiring resistance for driver's side duct temperature sensor by measuring between test unit pins No. 56 and 47. Check wiring resistance for passenger's side duct temperature sensor by measuring between test unit pins No. 56 and 48. If ohmmeter indicates no continuity, go to next step. If ohmmeter indicates continuity, check wiring for short to ground.

4) Ensure ignition is off. Ensure driver's and passenger's side duct temperature sensors are still disconnected. Measure resistance directly between duct temperature sensor terminals. *See Fig. 4.* Resistance should be about 8000-12,000 ohms. If resistance is not 8000-12,000 ohms, replace duct temperature sensor(s).

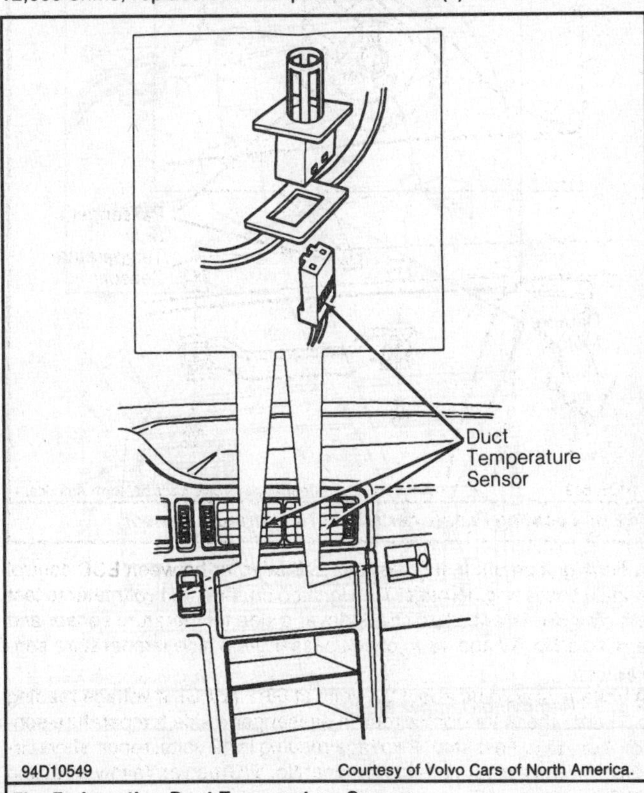
Duct
Temperature
Sensor
94D10549
Courtesy of Volvo Cars of North America.

Fig. 7: Locating Duct Temperature Sensor

DTC 1-3-2 & 1-3-4 DRIVER'S OR PASSENGER'S SIDE DUCT TEMP. SENSOR CIRCUIT OPEN OR SHORTED TO POWER

1) If DTC 1-3-2 and 1-3-4 are present, check for open circuit in duct temperature sensor common ground (Brown wire). IF DTC 1-3-2 and 1-3-4 are not present, there is an open or short circuit in wiring between ECC control module and duct temperature sensor. Go to next step.

2) Ensure ignition is off. Connect test unit between ECC control module and A/C system connector. Check ground circuit and repair as necessary. See DTC 1-2-1 OUTSIDE TEMP. SENSOR CIRCUIT SHORTED TO GROUND. If ground circuits are okay, go to next step.

3) Turn ignition on. Check driver's side duct temperature sensor wiring by checking voltage between test unit pins No. 56 and 47. Check passenger's side duct temperature sensor wiring by checking voltage between test unit pins No. 56 and 48. Voltage will vary with duct temperature, but generally should be in 0-3 volt range.

4) If voltmeter indicates 5 volts, check duct temperature sensor wiring for an open circuit. Go to next step. If voltmeter indicates 12 volts, check wiring for short to voltage between connector terminal No. 2 (Green or Yellow wire) and ECC control module terminal C1 (driver's side) or C2 (passenger's side). *See Figs. 7 and 8.*

5) Ensure ignition is off. Disconnect ECC control module, but leave test unit connected to control module connector. Disconnect connector from each duct temperature sensor. Connect jumper wire between duct temperature sensor connector terminals.

6) Check driver's side duct temperature sensor wiring by measuring resistance between test unit pins No. 56 and 47. Check passenger's side duct temperature sensor wiring by measuring resistance between test unit pins No. 56 and 48.

7) If continuity is present, wiring is okay but duct temperature sensor has an open circuit. Replace duct temperature sensor. If continuity is not present, duct temperature sensor is okay but an open circuit is present in wiring. Repair wiring for an open circuit.

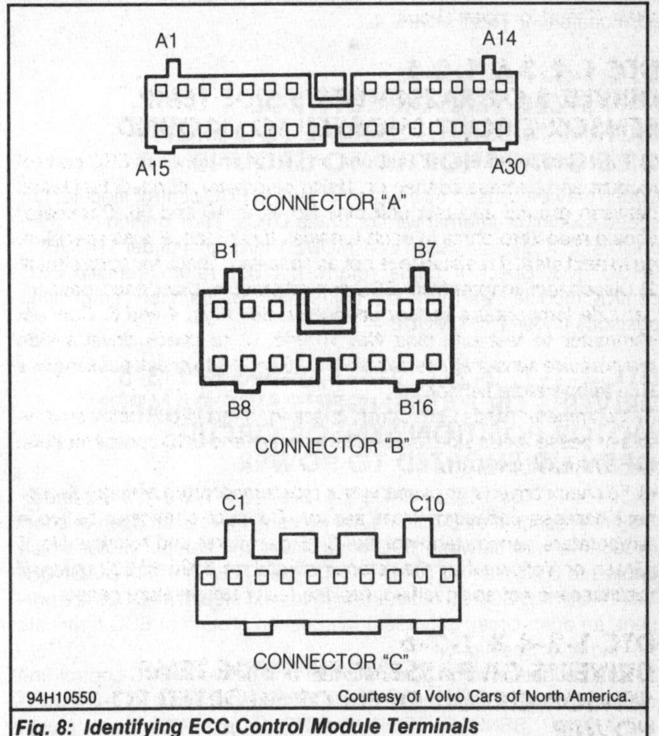
A1
A14
A15
A30
CONNECTOR "A"
B1
B7
B8
B16
CONNECTOR "B"
C1
C10
CONNECTOR "C"
94H10550
Courtesy of Volvo Cars of North America.

Fig. 8: Identifying ECC Control Module Terminals

1993 AUTOMATIC A/C-HEATER SYSTEMS
850 (Cont.)

DTC 1-3-5
NO ENGINE TEMPERATURE FREQUENCY SIGNAL

1) Run engine and check whether temperature gauge in instrument cluster works. If temperature gauge works, engine temperature signal is reaching instrument panel, but Green/Gray wire between ECC control module terminal A23 and instrument cluster has an open circuit. *See Fig. 8.*

2) If temperature gauge does not work, temperature sensor wiring may be shorted or engine temperature signal may be absent from engine management system.

3) To check wiring, turn ignition off. Check Green/Gray wire between ECC control module terminal A23 and instrument cluster for a short to ground or voltage. If no fault is found, problem may be in engine management system. See SELF-DIAGNOSTICS article in ENGINE PERFORMANCE of appropriate MITCHELL® manual.

DTC 1-4-1 & 1-4-3
DRIVER'S OR PASSENGER'S SIDE TEMP. SWITCH FAULTY CONTROL SIGNAL

These codes may be caused by an internal fault in ECC control module, temperature switch, or internal wiring. Erase DTCs. Turn ignition off, then on. Test ECC system. See TEST MODE 1 through 4 under TROUBLE SHOOTING. Check if DTCs return. If DTCs return, replace ECC control module. Perform self-adjustment of damper motor limit positions under TEST MODE 4.

DTC 1-4-5
AIR DISTRIBUTION SWITCH FAULTY CONTROL SIGNAL

Code may be caused by an internal fault in ECC control module, air distribution switch, or internal wiring. Erase DTCs. Turn ignition off, then on. Test ECC system. See TEST MODE 1 through 4 under TROUBLE SHOOTING. Check if DTCs return. If DTCs return, replace ECC control module. Perform self-adjustment of damper motor limit positions under TEST MODE 4.

DTC 1-5-1 & 1-5-2
FAN SPEED SENSOR CONTROL SIGNAL MISSING, SIGNAL TOO HIGH OR SIGNAL SHORTED TO GROUND

Codes may be caused by an internal fault in ECC control module, fan speed switch, or internal wiring. Erase DTCs. Turn ignition off, then on. Test ECC system. See TEST MODE 1 through 4 under TROUBLE SHOOTING. Check if DTCs return. If DTCs return, replace ECC control module. Perform self-adjustment of damper motor limit positions under TEST MODE 4.

DTC 2-1-1, 2-2-1, 2-3-1, 2-3-3 & 2-3-5
DRIVER'S OR PASSENGER'S SIDE DAMPER MOTOR POSITION SENSOR CIRCUIT OPEN OR SHORTED TO POWER

1) Check if DTCs 1-2-2, 1-2-4, 1-2-6, 2-1-1, 2-2-1, 2-3-1, 2-3-3 and 2-3-5 are present. If all DTCs are not present, there is an open or short circuit in a wire between ECC control unit and damper motor which applies to DTC. See AUTOMATIC A/C-HEATER SYSTEM DIAGNOSTIC TROUBLE CODES table, then go to next step. If all DTCs are present, an open circuit is present in common ground at ECC terminals A9 and A10. *See Fig. 8.*

2) Ensure ignition is off. Connect test unit between ECC control unit and control unit connector. Check ECC grounds. See DTC 1-2-1 OUTSIDE TEMP. SENSOR GROUND CIRCUIT test. Also check power supply to damper motor position sensor. See TEST MODE 2 under TROUBLE SHOOTING. If ECC grounds and power supply to damper motor position sensor are okay, go to next step.

3) Turn ignition on. Connect voltmeter between test unit pins No. 10 and No. 17 (driver's side damper motor), No. 18 (passenger's side damper motor), No. 20 (ventilation damper motor), No. 19 (floor/defrost damper motor), or No. 21 (recirculation damper motor).

4) If voltmeter indicates 12 volts, check wiring and ECC control unit terminals for a short to voltage. See PIN VOLTAGE TESTS under TESTING. If voltmeter indicates 5 volts, an open circuit is present in wire. Go to next step.

5) Ensure ignition is off. Disconnect ECC control module, but leave test unit connected to ECC connector. Disconnect 6-pin damper motor connector and install a jumper wire between connector terminals No. 1 and 2. *See Figs. 4 and 9.* Connect an ohmmeter between test unit pins No. 10 and 8. If ohmmeter indicates continuity, go to next step. If ohmmeter indicates no continuity, check for open circuit in Brown ground wire.

6) Connect jumper wire between damper motor connector terminals No. 2 and 3. Connect ohmmeter between test unit pins to test respective damper motor. See DAMPER MOTOR TEST UNIT PIN NUMBERS (RESISTANCE CHECK) table.

DAMPER MOTOR TEST UNIT PIN NUMBERS (RESISTANCE CHECK)

Pin No.	Damper Motor
8 & 17	Driver's Side
8 & 18	Passenger's Side
8 & 20	Ventilation
8 & 19	Floor/Defrost
8 & 21	Recirculation

7) If ohmmeter indicates continuity, wiring to damper motor terminal No. 3 is okay, but an open circuit is present in damper motor position sensor. Go to next step. If ohmmeter indicates no continuity, damper motor position sensor is okay, but open circuit is present in wire between damper motor connector terminal No. 3 and ECC control module connector "A".

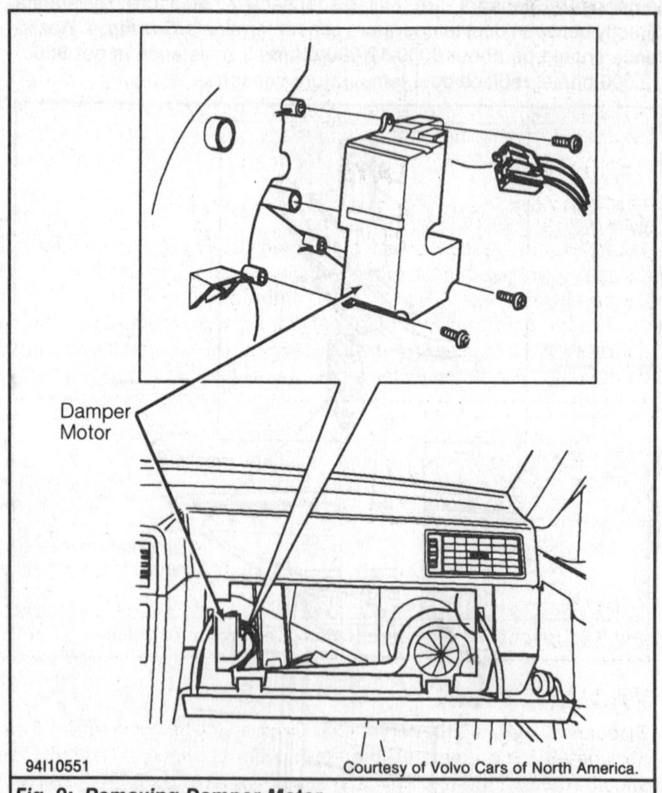
Damper
Motor
94I10551
Courtesy of Volvo Cars of North America.

Fig. 9: Removing Damper Motor

8) Ensure ignition is off. Disconnect damper motor connector. Connect ohmmeter between terminals No. 1 and 3. *See Fig. 4.* Turn damper motor output shaft. Ohmmeter should vary between 0-12,000 ohms. If resistance is to specification, go to next step. If resistance is not to specification, there is an open circuit in damper motor position sensor.

9) Connect ohmmeter between damper motor terminals No. 2 and 3. Turn damper motor output shaft. Ohmmeter should vary between 0-12,000 ohms. *See Fig. 4.* If ohmmeter indicates no continuity, there is an open circuit in damper motor position sensor. Replace damper motor.

DTC 2-1-2, 2-2-2, 2-3-2, 2-3-4 & 2-3-6 DRIVER'S OR PASSENGER'S SIDE DAMPER MOTOR POSITION SENSOR SHORTED TO GROUND

1) Check if DTCs 2-1-2, 2-2-2, 2-3-2, 2-3-4, and 2-3-6 are all present together. If all DTCs are not present, there is a short circuit in ground wire between ECC control unit and damper motor which applies to DTC. See AUTOMATIC A/C-HEATER SYSTEM DIAGNOSTIC TROUBLE CODES table, then go to next step. If DTCs are present, an open circuit is present in common voltage circuit at ECC terminal A8. *See Fig. 8.*

2) Ensure ignition is off. Connect test unit between ECC control module and control unit connector. Check ECC grounds. See DTC 1-2-1 OUTSIDE TEMP. SENSOR GROUND CIRCUIT test. Also check power supply to damper motor position sensor. See TEST MODE 2 under TROUBLE SHOOTING. If ECC grounds and power supply to damper motor position sensor are okay, go to next step.

3) Turn ignition off. Disconnect ECC control module, but leave test unit connected to ECC control module connector. Disconnect 6-pin damper motor connector. *See Figs. 4 and 9.* Connect ohmmeter between test unit pin No. 10 and pin indicated in DAMPER MOTOR TEST UNIT PIN NUMBERS (RESISTANCE CHECK) table.

DAMPER MOTOR TEST UNIT PIN NUMBERS (RESISTANCE CHECK)

Pin No.	Damper Motor
10 & 17	Driver's Side
10 & 18	Passenger's Side
10 & 20	Ventilation
10 & 19	Floor/Defrost
10 & 21	Recirculation

4) If ohmmeter indicates continuity, short circuit is present in wiring at terminal No. 3. If ohmmeter indicates no continuity, wiring is okay. Go to next step.

5) Ensure ignition is off. Disconnect damper motor connector. Connect ohmmeter between damper motor terminals No. 1 and 3. *See Fig. 4.* Turn damper motor output shaft. Ohmmeter reading should vary between 0-12,000 ohms.

6) If resistance is to specification, check voltage supply circuit between motor connector terminal No. 2 and ECC control module terminal A8. If resistance is a constant zero ohms, a short is present in damper motor position sensor. Replace damper motor.

DTC 3-1-1, 3-1-2, 3-1-3, 3-1-4 & 3-1-5 DAMPER MOTOR SHORTED TO GROUND OR POWER

1) Turn ignition off. Connect test unit between ECC control module and ECC control module connector. Check system ground circuits. See DTC 1-2-1 OUTSIDE TEMP SENSOR GROUND CIRCUIT. If ground circuits are okay, go to next step.

2) Turn ignition on. Connect one voltmeter lead to test unit pin No. 10 and other lead to test unit pin No. 31 (driver's damper motor), No. 33 (passenger's side damper motor), No. 37 (ventilation damper motor), No. 35 (floor/defrost damper motor), or No. 39 (recirculation damper motor). Voltmeter should vary from 0-4 volts.

3) If voltmeter indicates zero volts, wire is shorted to ground. If voltmeter indicates battery voltage, wire is shorted to voltage. Turn ignition off. Disconnect suspect damper motor connector. Check wiring between motor connector and EEC control module.

DTC 3-2-1, 3-2-2, 3-2-3, 3-2-4 & 3-2-5 DAMPER MOTOR ACTIVE TOO LONG

1) Check if DTCs 3-2-1, 3-2-2, 3-2-3, 3-2-4, and 3-2-5 are also present. If all DTCs are present, vehicle may be equipped with an EEC control module for a right-hand-drive vehicle, or vice versa. Check EEC terminal A28. *See Fig. 8.* ECC control module for left-hand-drive vehicles should not have terminal A28 grounded.

2) If terminal is okay, perform self-adjustment of damper motor limit positions under TEST MODE 4. If motor limit positions are adjusted correctly, check ECC system ground circuits. See DTC 1-2-1 OUTSIDE TEMP. SENSOR GROUND CIRCUIT. If ground circuits check okay, go to next step.

3) Ensure test unit is connected to ECC control module. Turn ignition on. Connect one voltmeter lead to test unit pin No. 10 and other lead to test unit pin No. 31 (driver's side damper motor), No. 33 (passenger's side damper motor), No. 37 (ventilation damper motor), No. 35 (floor/defrost damper motor), or No. 39 (recirculation damper motor).

4) Rotate air circulation knob to and from different settings while observing voltmeter. Voltmeter should show control voltage of about 0-12 volts while damper is moving to its new setting. If voltmeter shows about 0-12 volts for longer than about 12 seconds, check if damper is stuck in position. Replace damper if not stuck.

DTC 4-1-1 PASSENGER COMPARTMENT FAN OVERCURRENT OR SEIZED FAN

1) Turn ignition off. Disconnect passenger compartment (blower) fan electrical connector. Check if fan turns freely by hand. If not, replace fan. Check fan location for anything that could cause blockage and clear as necessary.

2) If fan is okay, erase DTC. If DTC returns, there may be a fault in power stage surge protector. See DTC 4-1-9 MISSING OR FAULTY DIAGNOSTIC SIGNAL FROM POWER STAGE.

DTC 4-1-2 & 4-1-5 DRIVER'S OR PASSENGER'S SIDE TEMP. SENSOR INTAKE FAN SHORTED TO GROUND

1) Ensure ignition is off. Connect test unit to ECC control module. Check ground circuits. See DTC 1-2-1 OUTSIDE TEMP. SENSOR GROUND CIRCUIT. If ground circuits are okay, turn ignition off. Disconnect test unit from ECC control module, but leave it connected to ECC control module connector. Disconnect passenger compartment temperature sensor connector.

2) Check driver's side fan by connecting an ohmmeter between test unit pins No. 6 and 45. Check passenger's side fan by connecting an ohmmeter between test unit pins No. 6 and 46. If ohmmeter indicates continuity, wiring is shorted to ground or voltage. If ohmmeter indicates no continuity, wiring is okay.

3) Ensure ignition is off. Disconnect passenger compartment temperature sensor connector. Connect an ohmmeter between passenger compartment temperature sensor connector terminals No. 4 and 2. *See Fig. 4.* Ohmmeter should indicate about 50,000 ohms. If ohmmeter indicates continuity, intake fan is shorted. Replace fan and temperature sensor.

DTC 4-1-3 & 4-1-6 DRIVER'S OR PASSENGER'S SIDE TEMP. SENSOR INTAKE FAN, NO CONTROL VOLTAGE

1) Ensure ignition is off. Connect test unit to ECC control module. Check ground circuits. See DTC 1-2-1 OUTSIDE TEMP. SENSOR GROUND CIRCUIT. If ground circuits are okay, go to next step.

2) Ensure ignition is off. Disconnect test unit from ECC control module, but leave it connected to ECC control module connector. Disconnect passenger compartment temperature sensor connector. Connect jumper wire between temperature sensor connector terminals No. 2 and 4.

1993 AUTOMATIC A/C-HEATER SYSTEMS 850 (Cont.)

3) Connect an ohmmeter between test unit pins No. 6 and 45 (driver's side), and between test unit pins No. 6 and 46 (passenger's side). If ohmmeter indicates continuity, wiring is okay but intake fan may have an open circuit. Go to next step. If ohmmeter indicates no continuity, intake fan is okay but wiring has an open circuit. Repair wiring as necessary.
4) Ensure ignition is off. Ensure connector from passenger compartment temperature sensor is disconnected. Connect an ohmmeter between temperature sensor terminals No. 2 and 4. *See Fig. 4.* Ohmmeter should indicate 50,000 ohms. If ohmmeter indicates no continuity, intake fan has an open circuit. Replace passenger compartment temperature sensor.

DTC 4-1-4 & 4-1-7 DRIVER'S OR PASSENGER'S SIDE TEMP. SENSOR INTAKE FAN SEIZED

Turn ignition off. Uncover passenger compartment temperature sensor. Check if fan turns freely by hand. If not, replace fan. Check fan for anything that could cause blockage and clear as necessary. If fan is okay, replace passenger compartment temperature sensor.

DTC 4-1-8 NO CONTROL SIGNAL TO ECC POWER STAGE

1) Ensure ignition is off. Connect test unit to ECC control module. Check ground circuits. See 1-2-1 OUTSIDE TEMP. SENSOR GROUND CIRCUIT. If ground circuits are okay, go to next step.
2) Turn ignition on. Place fan control lever to maximum speed. Connect voltmeter between test unit pins No. 6 and 42. If 6-8 volts are present, go to next step. If voltmeter indicates zero volts, wiring is shorted to ground. If voltmeter indicates 12 volts, wiring is shorted to voltage. Repair wiring as necessary.
3) Ensure ignition is off. Disconnect power stage 4-pin connector. *See Figs. 4 and 10.* Connect an ohmmeter between test unit pin No. 42 and power stage connector terminal 1A. Ohmmeter should indicate continuity. If no continuity is present, check wiring for an open circuit.

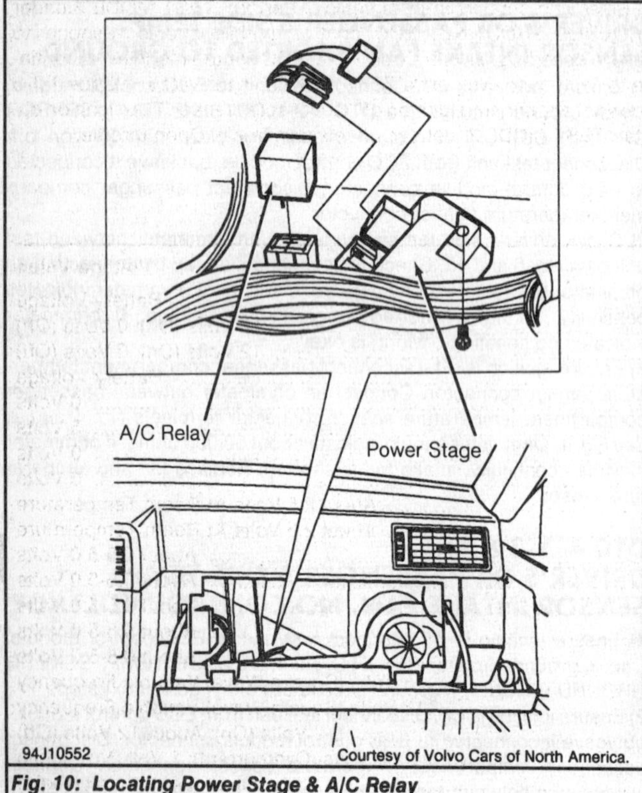
A/C Relay
Power Stage
94J10552
Courtesy of Volvo Cars of North America.
Fig. 10: Locating Power Stage & A/C Relay

DTC 4-1-9 ECC POWER STAGE EMITTING FAULTY DIAGNOSTIC SIGNAL

1) Ensure ignition is off. Connect test unit to ECC control module. Check ground circuits. See 1-2-1 OUTSIDE TEMP. SENSOR. If ground circuits are okay, go to next step.
2) Turn ignition on. Connect voltmeter between test unit pins No. 6 and 27. Voltmeter should indicate 3 volts. If voltmeter indicates one volt, there is no control signal to power stage. See DTC 4-1-8 NO CONTROL SIGNAL TO POWER STAGE. If voltmeter indicates 4 volts, there is excessive voltage from power stage. See DTC 4-1-1 BLOWER FAN OVERCURRENT OR SEIZED.
3) If voltmeter indicates 12 volts, check wire at ECC control module terminal A27 (Violet/White wire) for a short to voltage. *See Fig. 8.* If voltmeter indicates zero volts, wire has an open circuit or is shorted to ground. Go to next step.
4) Ensure ignition is off. Disconnect power stage 4-pin connector. *See Figs. 4 and 10.* Check Violet/White wire between power stage connector terminal 2A and ECC control module terminal A27 for a short to ground or open circuit. If wire is okay, go to next step.
5) Reconnect power stage 4-pin connector. Turn ignition on. Connect voltmeter between test unit pins No. 6 and 5. If battery voltage is present, go to next step. If zero volts are present, wire is shorted to ground.
6) Ensure ignition is off. Disconnect power stage 4-pin connector. Connect ohmmeter between test unit pin No. 5 and power stage connector terminal 3A. If ohmmeter indicates continuity, replace power stage. If ohmmeter indicates no continuity, check wiring for an open circuit and repair as necessary.

DTC 4-2-0 ECC CONTROL MODULE FAULT, PROGRAM MEMORY

Erase DTC. Start and run engine. Turn engine off, leaving ignition on. Check if DTC returns. If DTC returns, replace ECC control module. Perform damper motor limit self-adjustment under TEST MODE 4.

DTC 5-1-1 SELF-ADJUSTMENT OF DAMPER MOTOR LIMIT POSITIONS NOT CARRIED OUT

Erase DTC. ECC control module is programmed to carry out self-adjustment of damper motor limit positions. Drive vehicle over 20 MPH for a few minutes. ECC control module will carry out self-adjustment while driving. Stop vehicle and leave ignition on at least 2 minutes to enable ECC control module to store all values.

TESTING

WARNING: To avoid injury from accidental air bag deployment, read and carefully follow all SERVICE PRECAUTIONS and DISABLING & ACTIVATING AIR BAG SYSTEM procedures in AIR BAG SYSTEM SAFETY article in GENERAL SERVICING.

A/C SYSTEM PERFORMANCE

1) Ensure compressor drive belt is okay, fan motor runs at all speeds, and that temperature vents shut completely with temperature switch in full cooling position.
2) Ensure that all air comes from panel vents with mode control on vent position, recirculation motor is working, and condenser fan and cooling fan are working.
3) Start and warm engine to normal operating temperature. Ensure compressor clutch engages when A/C is turned on. Set temperature switch to full cold position, place mode control to vent position, turn on recirculate air switch and blower fan switch high speed.
4) Close engine hood, doors and windows. Run engine at 1500-1600 RPM. Place thermometer in one of the center panel vents. Allow system to stabilize for at least 8 minutes. Check temperature in center panel vent. See A/C SYSTEM PERFORMANCE SPECIFICATIONS table.

A/C SYSTEM PERFORMANCE SPECIFICATIONS [1]

Ambient Temperature °F (°C)	Outlet Air Temperature °F (°C)
68 (20)	41-48 (5-8)
86 (30)	41-48 (5-8)
104 (40)	46-54 (8-12)

[1] – Based on a relative humidity of 40-60 percent.

A/C RELAY CHECK

Remove relay. Connect battery positive lead to relay terminal No. 1 and negative lead to relay terminal No. 3. Continuity should be present between relay terminals No. 2 and 4. *See Fig. 10.* If continuity is not present, replace relay.

ON-BOARD DIAGNOSTIC UNIT CHECK

1) Turn ignition on. Press button on diagnostic unit "A". *See Fig. 2.* LED should illuminate. If LED does not illuminate, go to next step. If LED illuminates, but no code(s) is(are) present, go to step **4)**.

2) Turn ignition off. Remove connector from underside of diagnostic unit "A". Connect voltmeter between terminal No. 4 of diagnostic unit "A" and ground. Turn ignition on. Battery voltage should be present. If battery voltage is present, go to next step. If battery voltage is not present, check fuse No. 33 or open circuit between fuse block and terminal No. 4.

3) Turn ignition off. Connect ohmmeter between terminal No. 8 of diagnostic unit "A" and ground. Continuity should exist. If continuity exists, replace diagnostic unit and retest. If continuity does not exist, check ground connection.

4) Turn ignition off. Disconnect selector cable from diagnostic unit "B". Turn ignition on. Connect voltmeter between terminal No. 1 of diagnostic unit "B" and ground. Voltage should be about 10 volts. If voltage is as specified, replace diagnostic unit. If voltage is not as specified, check for open or shorted circuit between ECC control module and terminal No. 1 of diagnostic unit "B".

PIN VOLTAGE TESTS

NOTE: Perform all voltage tests using Digital Volt-Ohmmeter (DVOM) with a minimum 10-megohm input impedance.

Pin voltage chart is supplied to reduce diagnostic time. Checking pin voltage at ECC control module determines whether it is receiving or transmitting proper voltage signals. Charts may also help determine if control unit wiring harness has short or open circuit.

SOLAR SENSOR

1) Connect test unit to ECC control module. Check ground circuits. See DTC 1-2-1 OUTSIDE TEMP. SENSOR GROUND CIRCUIT. If ground circuits are okay, go to next step.

2) Turn ignition on. Aim a light source at solar sensor. Connect voltmeter between test unit pins No. 56 and 51 and record voltage. Cover solar sensor and read voltage again. *See Fig. 11.* Voltage should vary by a few millivolts. The higher the intensity, the lower the voltage. If sensor does not operate as specified, there is an open circuit or short to ground in wire or solar sensor.

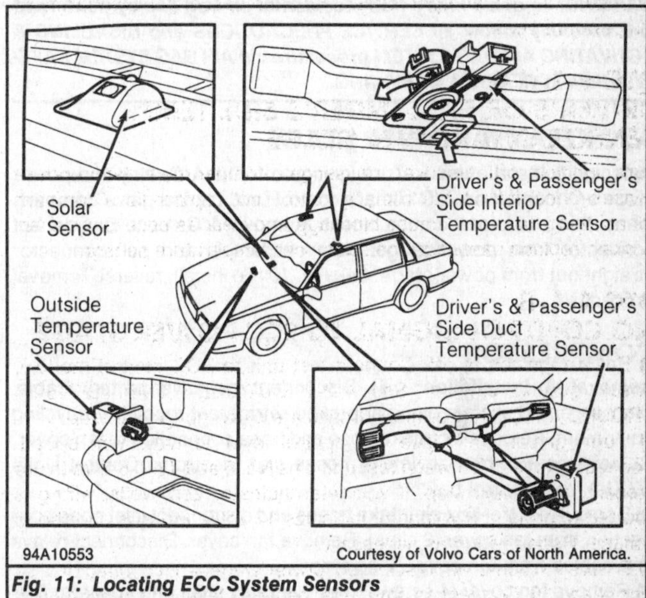

Solar Sensor
Driver's & Passenger's Side Interior Temperature Sensor
Outside Temperature Sensor
Driver's & Passenger's Side Duct Temperature Sensor
94A10553
Courtesy of Volvo Cars of North America.

Fig. 11: Locating ECC System Sensors

SPEEDOMETER SIGNAL

1) Raise and support front of vehicle. Perform TEST MODE 2 under TROUBLE SHOOTING. ECC control module should respond to vehicle speed signal with Code 1-1-3. ECC control module will continue to flash code even once TEST MODE 2 is activated. If Code 1-1-3 does not appear, turn ignition off. Cover solar sensor. Turn ignition on. Start TEST MODE 2. Let car wheels turn freely. Open throttle.

ECC CONTROL MODULE PIN ASSIGNMENTS [1]

Pin No.	Function/Description	Voltage Value
1	Power Supply To ECC Control Module	Battery Voltage
2	Digital Timer (Parking Heater)	12 Volts (On); 0 Volts (Off)
3	Rheostat	12 Volts (On); 0 Volts (Off)
5	Power Supply To Power Stage	Battery Voltage
6	Power Ground	0 Volts
8	Damper Motor Position Sensors	5 Volts
9	Signal Ground	0 Volts
10	Signal Ground	0 Volts
12	Driver's Side Temp. Sensor	About 2.5 Volts At Room Temperature
13	Passenger's Side Temp. Sensor	About 2.5 Volts At Room Temperature
17	Driver's Side Damper Motor Position Sensor	About 0.5-5.0 Volts
18	Passenger's Side Damper Motor Position Sensor	About 0.5-5.0 Volts
19	Floor/Defrost Damper Motor Position Sensor	About 0.5-5.0 Volts
20	Ventilation Damper Motor Position Sensor	About 0.5-5.0 Volts
21	Recirculation Damper Motor Position Sensor	About 0.5-5.0 Volts
23	Engine Coolant Temperature	5 Volts (Square Wave) Variable Frequency
24	Vehicle Speed Signal	12 Volts (Square Wave) Variable Frequency
25	A/C Relay Control Signal (From Ignition System)	0-2 Volts (On); About 12 Volts (Off)
27	Diagnostic Signal From Power Stage	3 Volts (Normal); 4 Volts (Overcurrent); 1 Volt (No Signal)
28	Logic Signal	Open (Left); 0 Volt (Right)
30	Signal To/From Diagnostic Unit	Battery Voltage

[1] – Pin assignments not listed are not used.

1993 AUTOMATIC A/C-HEATER SYSTEMS
850 (Cont.)

2) If no acknowledgment code appears after several attempts, there may be a problem with vehicle speed signal impulse sensor in ignition system, instrument panel, or wiring.
3) Check if speedometer operates. If speedometer does not operate, a fault may be present in vehicle speed signal impulse sensor, ignition system, instrument cluster, or wiring. If speedometer does operate, check for open circuit in instrument cluster wiring.

REMOVAL & INSTALLATION

WARNING: To avoid injury from accidental air bag deployment, read and carefully follow all SERVICE PRECAUTIONS and DISABLING & ACTIVATING AIR BAG SYSTEM procedures in AIR BAG SYSTEM SAFETY article in GENERAL SERVICING.

A/C RELAY & POWER STAGE

Removal & Installation – Turn ignition off. The A/C relay and power stage are located on A/C climate control unit, behind glove compartment. Remove glove compartment. Remove A/C relay. Disconnect connector from power stage. Hold catches in and pull connector straight out from power stage. *See Fig. 10.* To install, reverse removal procedure.

COMPRESSOR

Removal & Installation – 1) Disconnect negative battery cable. Discharge A/C system using approved refrigerant recovery/recycling equipment. Remove air intake hose and hose connection to fan cover. Remove control box air intake hoses and Electronic Control Units (ECUs) from control box.
2) Remove control box air intake hoses and disconnect inlet hose connection from fan cover (2 clips). Remove fan cover. Disconnect relays and cables from fan cover (2 tie strips).
3) Remove fan cover (4 screws), remove relay shelf and spacers. Disconnect 2-pin connector from fan relay and connector from fan motor. Remove fan cover. *See Fig. 12.*
4) Shield radiator. Disconnect harness connectors from compressor. Disconnect snap-on connectors on receiver-drier. Remove right side headlight casing. Remove receiver-drier bracket screw.
5) Remove air guide. With bracket hooked onto side member, lift receiver/drier out. Plug receiver-drier pipe ends. Disconnect drive belt.
6) Disconnect compressor connector and temperature sensor. Remove compressor. To install, reverse removal procedure. Lubricate new "O" rings with compressor oil.

CONDENSER

NOTE: When replacing condenser, always replace "O" rings and snap-on connections.

Removal & Installation – 1) Disconnect negative battery cable. Discharge A/C system using approved refrigerant recovery/recycling equipment. Disconnect air intake hose. Remove hose connector to fan cover.
2) Remove Electronic Control Units (ECUs) from control unit box. Disconnect control unit box air intake hoses. Remove inlet hose connector to fan cover (2 clips). Disconnect relays from relay casing. Disconnect fan cover (4 screws), fold cover back towards engine. Remove relay shelf and spacers. *See Fig. 12.*
3) Disconnect pipes from condenser. Disconnect high-pressure sensor connector. Remove high pressure sensor. Disconnect condenser screws. Lift condenser out.
4) To install, reverse removal procedure. Transfer high-pressure sensor and rubber gasket to new condenser. Lubricate new "O" rings with compressor oil.

DAMPER MOTOR

Removal & Installation – Turn ignition off. Remove soundproofing from center console. Remove glove compartment. Disconnect connector from damper motor (located on A/C control unit). Hold catches in on both sides of damper motor and pull motor straight out. *See Fig. 13.* To install, reverse removal procedure.

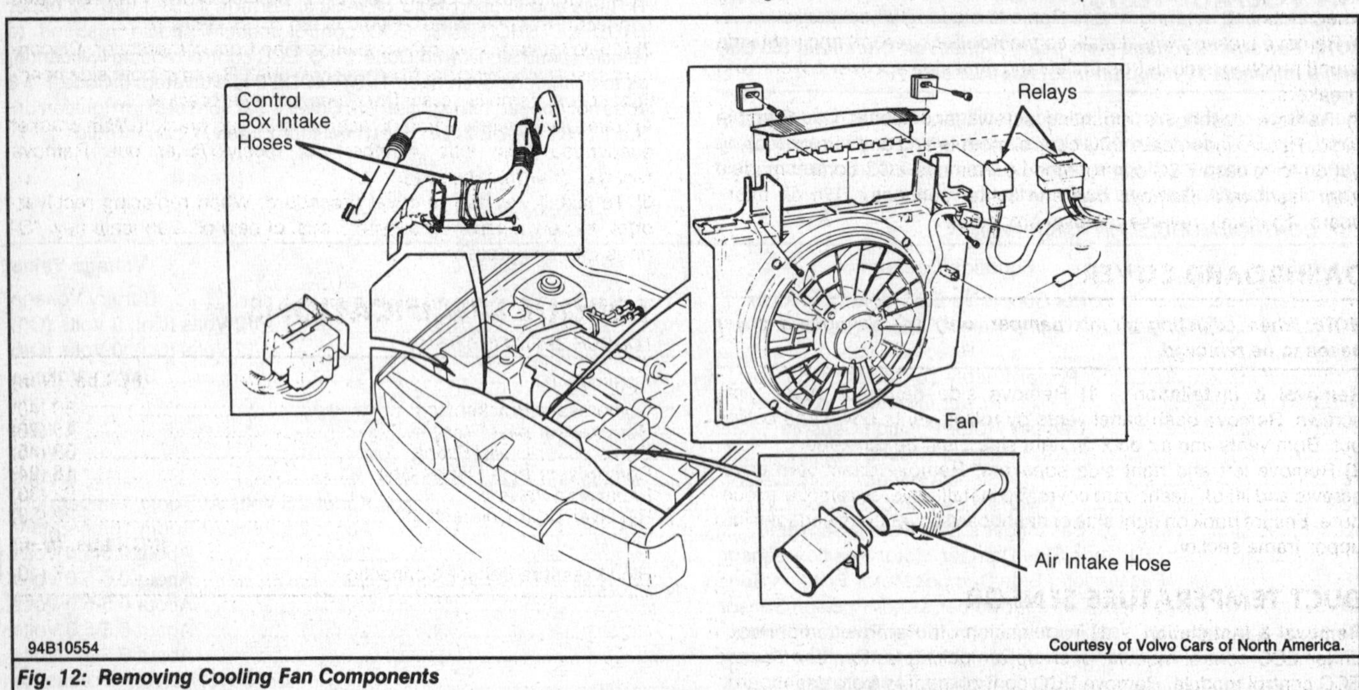
Control
Box Intake
Hoses
Relays
Fan
Air Intake Hose
94B10554
Courtesy of Volvo Cars of North America.

Fig. 12: Removing Cooling Fan Components

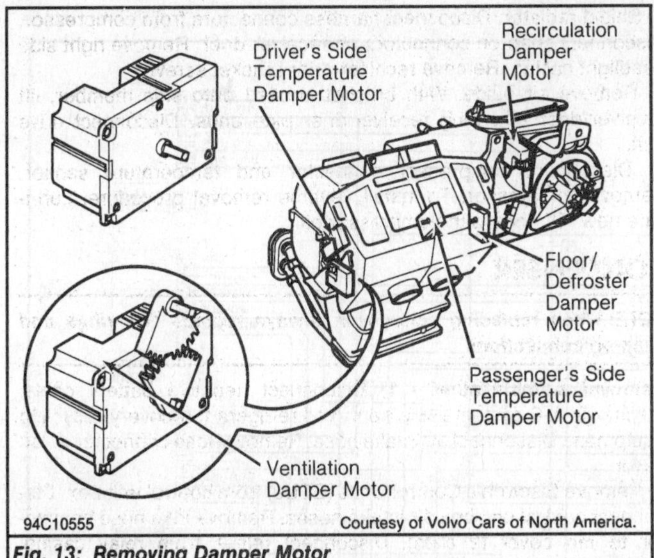
Driver's Side
Temperature
Damper Motor
Recirculation
Damper
Motor
Floor/
Defroster
Damper
Motor
Passenger's Side
Temperature
Damper Motor
Ventilation
Damper Motor
94C10555
Courtesy of Volvo Cars of North America.

Fig. 13: Removing Damper Motor

DASHBOARD

NOTE: Dashboard consists of 5 main sections: upper frame, lower frame (left and right), defroster duct and dashboard cover. Except for dashboard cover, all the main sections are glued together and cannot be separated.

Removal & Installation – 1) Disconnect negative battery cable. Disable air bag system. See AIR BAG SYSTEM SAFETY article in GENERAL SERVICING. From engine compartment, remove windshield wiper nuts, windshield wiper well cover panel screws and remove wiper well. Remove wiper motor mountings.

2) From passenger compartment, remove air bag module. Mark steering wheel position relative to steering wheel shaft. Remove steering wheel nuts and steering wheel. Remove steering wheel stalks.

3) Remove steering wheel stalk connector. Remove left and right side sound proofing, side defroster, left and right side speaker covers, and speakers.

4) Remove dashboard mounting screws and glove box. Remove radio. Reach underneath ECC control module and push up on locking button to release ECC control module. Remove ECC control module from dashboard. Remove cigarette lighter connector. Lift off dashboard. To install, reverse removal procedure.

DASHBOARD COVER

NOTE: When adjusting air-mix damper, only the dashboard cover needs to be removed.

Removal & Installation – 1) Remove side defroster cover plate screws. Remove dash panel vents by rolling vents down and pulling out. Both vents and air duct on right side must be removed.

2) Remove left and right side speakers. Remove dashboard cover screws and lift off dashboard cover. To install, reverse removal procedure. Ensure hook on right side of dashboard cover plate engages into upper frame section.

DUCT TEMPERATURE SENSOR

Removal & Installation – 1) Turn ignition off. Remove radio. Reach under ECC control module, push up on locking button, and release ECC control module. Remove ECC control module from dashboard.

2) Remove left and right side sound insulation from center console. Remove glove box. Remove duct temperature sensor connector and pull down on duct temperature sensor. To install, reverse removal procedure.

EVAPORATOR

Removal & Installation – Disconnect negative battery cable. Remove ECC control unit. Remove evaporator cover screws and clips. Lift out evaporator. *See Fig. 14.* To install, reverse removal procedure.

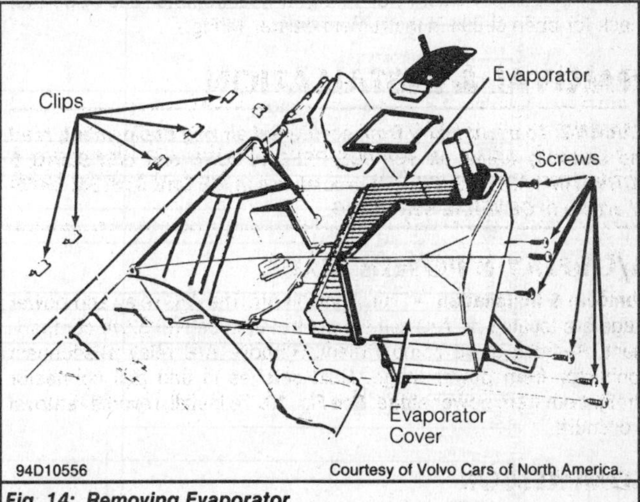
Clips
Evaporator
Screws
Evaporator
Cover
94D10556
Courtesy of Volvo Cars of North America.

Fig. 14: Removing Evaporator

RECEIVER-DRIER

Removal & Installation – 1) Disconnect negative battery cable. Discharge A/C system using approved refrigerant recovery/recycling equipment. Disconnect air intake hose and remove hose connector to fan cover. Remove control unit air intake hoses and Electronic Control Units (ECUs) from control unit box.

2) Remove control unit box air intake hoses and remove inlet hose connector to fan cover (2 clips). Remove fan cover. Disconnect relays and wires from fan cover. Remove fan cover (4 screws), remove relay casing and spacers. Disconnect 2-pin connector from fan relay and connector from fan motor. Remove fan cover. *See Fig. 12.*

3) Shield radiator. Disconnect suction pipe from compressor. Disconnect snap-on connectors from receiver-drier. Remove right side headlight cover. Remove screw from receiver-drier bracket.

4) Remove air guide. Remove receiver-drier and bracket. With bracket suspended from side member, lift receiver/drier out. Remove receiver-drier from bracket.

5) To install, reverse removal procedure. When replacing receiver-drier, fill new receiver-drier with 3 ozs. of new oil. Lubricate new "O" rings with compressor oil.

TORQUE SPECIFICATIONS

TORQUE SPECIFICATIONS

Application	Ft. Lbs. (N.m)
Compressor Bracket Bolt	30 (40)
Compressor Inlet Fitting	15 (20)
Compressor Outlet Fitting	33 (45)
Compressor Pipe Flange Bolt	18 (24)
Expansion Valve	22 (30)
Receiver-Drier Connection	22 (30)
	INCH Lbs. (N.m)
High Pressure Sensor Connection	7 (10)

1993 AUTOMATIC A/C-HEATER SYSTEMS
850 (Cont.)

WIRING DIAGRAM

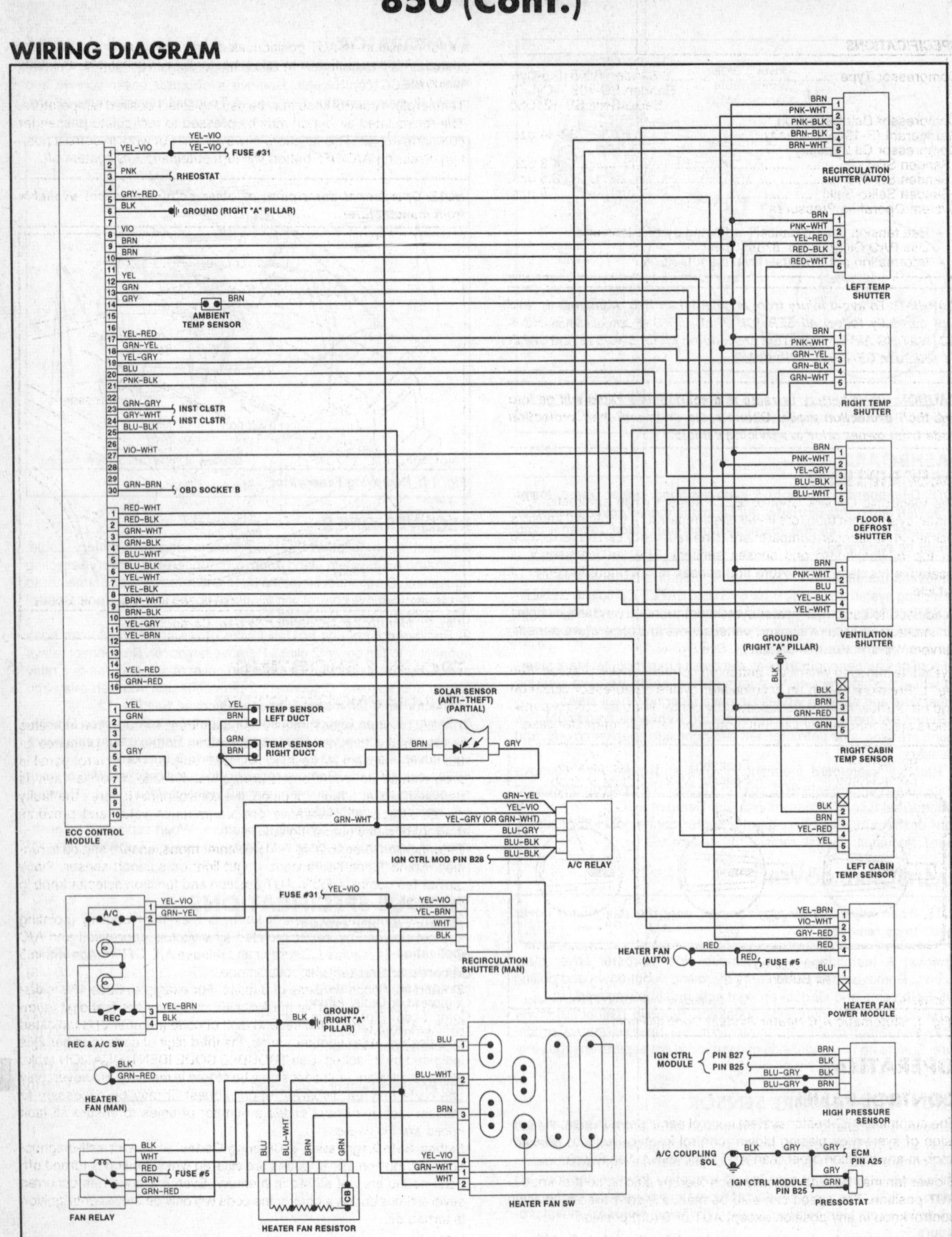
ECC CONTROL MODULE
YEL-VIO
FUSE #31
RHEOSTAT
GROUND (RIGHT "A" PILLAR)
AMBIENT TEMP SENSOR
INST CLSTR
OBD SOCKET B
TEMP SENSOR LEFT DUCT
TEMP SENSOR RIGHT DUCT
SOLAR SENSOR (ANTI-THEFT) (PARTIAL)
IGN CTRL MOD PIN B28
A/C RELAY
RECIRCULATION SHUTTER (MAN)
REC & A/C SW
HEATER FAN (MAN)
FAN RELAY
FUSE #5
HEATER FAN RESISTOR
HEATER FAN SW
RECIRCULATION SHUTTER (AUTO)
LEFT TEMP SHUTTER
RIGHT TEMP SHUTTER
FLOOR & DEFROST SHUTTER
VENTILATION SHUTTER
RIGHT CABIN TEMP SENSOR
LEFT CABIN TEMP SENSOR
HEATER FAN (AUTO)
HEATER FAN POWER MODULE
IGN CTRL MODULE
PIN B27
PIN B25
HIGH PRESSURE SENSOR
A/C COUPLING SOL
IGN CTRL MODULE PIN B25
ECM PIN A25
PRESSOSTAT
94J10735

Fig. 15: Automatic A/C-Heater System Wiring Diagram (850)

SPECIFICATIONS

Compressor Type	Sanden SD-510 5-Cyl., Sanden SD-709 7-Cyl. Or Seiko-Seiki SS-121DS5
Compressor Belt Deflection [1]	
Refrigerant (R-134a) Capacity	32-34 ozs.
Compressor Oil Capacity [2]	
Sanden SD-510	4.8 ozs.
Sanden SD-709	8.5 ozs.
Sanden Seiko-Seiki	7.8 ozs.
System Operating Pressures [3]	

[1] – Belt tension is automatically adjusted by belt tensioner.
[2] – Use PAG Oil (Part No. 8708581-9).
[3] – Information not available from manufacturer.

WARNING: To avoid injury from accidental air bag deployment, read and carefully follow all SERVICE PRECAUTIONS and DISABLING & ACTIVATING AIR BAG SYSTEM procedures in AIR BAG SYSTEM SAFETY article in GENERAL SERVICING.

CAUTION: When battery or radio is disconnected, radio will go into anti-theft protection mode. Obtain radio code anti-theft protection code from owner prior to servicing vehicle.

DESCRIPTION

The Electronic Climate Control (ECC) system is an automatic A/C-heater system that monitors in-vehicle temperature through 2 sensors located in passenger compartment. One (sunload) sensor is located on top of dashboard and senses sunlight. The second sensor is located in courtesy light fixture and senses temperature in center of vehicle.

In addition to basic A/C-heater system components, system includes air intake temperature sensor, water (coolant) temperature sensor, servomotor and vacuum actuators. *See Fig. 4.*

System is engaged when A/C button on control panel is pressed. *See Fig. 1.* Pressure switch on accumulator cycles compressor clutch on and off. Airflow modes are selected by center knob on control panel. Doors are controlled by vacuum motors on left side of heater case.

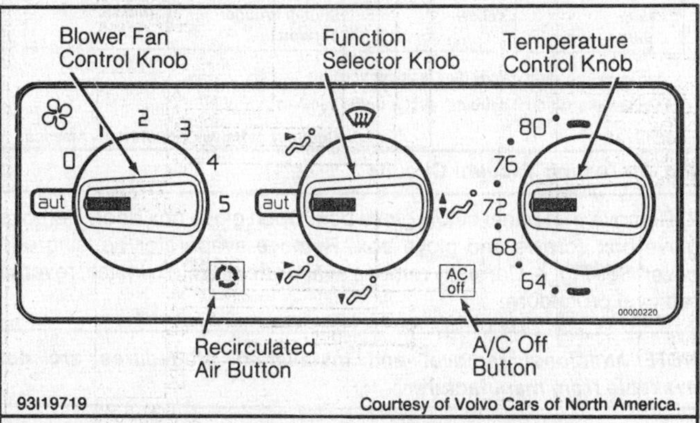
Blower Fan Control Knob
Function Selector Knob
Temperature Control Knob
1
2
3
0
4
5
aut
aut
80
76
72
68
64
AC off
Recirculated Air Button
A/C Off Button
93I19719
Courtesy of Volvo Cars of North America.

Fig. 1: Automatic A/C-Heater System Control Panel

OPERATION

CONTROL PANEL

The automatic A/C-heater system control panel permits manual operation of system by placing blower control knob or function selector knob in any position other than AUT (automatic). *See Fig. 1.*

Blower fan may be automatically controlled by placing control knob in AUT position. Fan speed can also be manually controlled by placing control knob in any position except AUT or 0 (off) position.

Function selector knob may be placed in defrost, vent, AUT, bi-level, or floor position. In AUT position, air distribution is automatically regulated. Air distribution may also be to floor, windshield and side windows.

Temperature control knob may be used to select desired temperature. The recirculated air button may be pressed to recirculate passenger compartment air. This function, however, will not work in defrost position. Pressing A/C OFF button will turn automatic A/C system off.

NOTE: Operational description of other components not available from manufacturer.

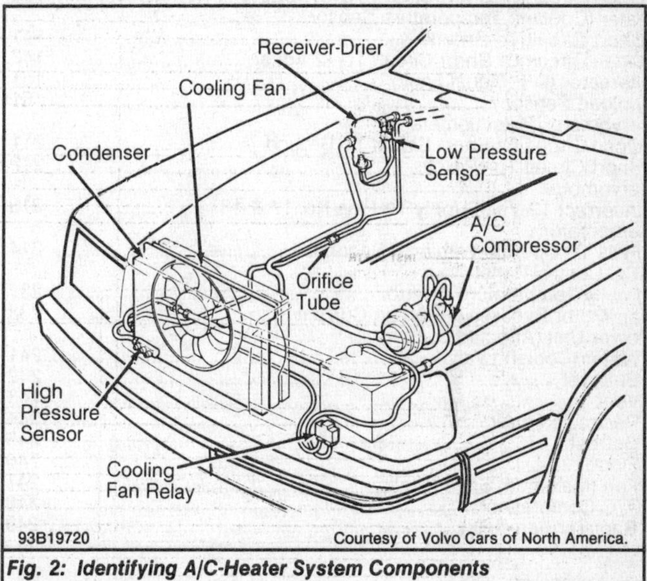
Receiver-Drier
Cooling Fan
Condenser
Low Pressure Sensor
A/C Compressor
Orifice Tube
High Pressure Sensor
Cooling Fan Relay
93B19720
Courtesy of Volvo Cars of North America.

Fig. 2: Identifying A/C-Heater System Components

TROUBLE SHOOTING

SELF-DIAGNOSTIC SYSTEM

The EEC system incorporates a self-diagnostic function that indicates system faults through a series of trouble codes. The presence of fault(s) is indicated by flashing A/C OFF button. The control panel is programmed to enter a pre-programmed mode when a fault is detected. Under a fault condition, the control panel ignores the faulty signal, selects an alternative pre-programmed value and prevents delivery of faulty output signals.

Entering Self-Diagnostics – 1) To enter mode, ensure engine is running. Shine a non-fluorescent, bright light on sunload sensor. Place blower fan control knob in AUT position and function selector knob in vent position.

2) Place temperature control knob to maximum cooling (pointing straight down). Ensure recirculated air switch is depressed and A/C OFF button is released. Depress and release A/C OFF button within 5 seconds to start self-diagnostic mode.

3) Each fault code consists of 3 digits. For example, Code 132 is displayed by a single flash of the A/C OFF button for the first digit (number 1). After a pause, the second digit of code (number 3) is indicated by 3 flashes. After another pause, the third digit of code (number 2) is indicated by 2 flashes. See TROUBLE CODE IDENTIFICATION table.

4) Three different fault codes may be stored in memory. However, only one code may be displayed upon request. It may be necessary to request display of fault codes a number of times to ensure all fault codes are displayed.

Exiting Self-Diagnostics & Clearing Codes – To exit self-diagnostics, turn ignition off. All codes are cleared when ignition is turned off. Fault codes are not stored in memory. Even if a code has occurred several times during a period, the code will only be stored until ignition is turned off.

1993 AUTOMATIC A/C-HEATER SYSTEMS
960 (Cont.)

TROUBLE CODE IDENTIFICATION

Affected Circuit/Sensor	Code
Fault Free System	111
Outside Temperature Sensor	
Short Circuit To Ground	121
Open Circuit Or Short Circuit To 12 Volts	122
In-Vehicle Temperature Sensor	
Short Circuit To Ground	131
Open Circuit Or Short Circuit To 12 Volts	132
In-Vehicle Temperature Sensor	
Short Circuit To Ground	131
Open Circuit Or Short Circuit To 12 Volts	132
Water (Coolant) Temperature Sensor	
Short Circuit To Ground	141
Open Circuit Or Short Circuit To 12 Volts	142
Alternator (D+ Signal Fault)	151
Sunload Sensor	161
Servomotor/Potentiometer	
Open Circuit Or Short Circuit To Ground	211
Short Circuit To 12 Volts	212
Servomotor	
Incorrect 12-Volt Supply To Pins No. 17 & 18	213
Servomotor	
Fails To Operate Within 10 Seconds	214
ECC Control Panel	
Faulty Temperature Control	231
Fan Motor Excessive Starting Current	233
Power Unit (Affected Output)	
Water (Coolant) Valve	241
Bi-Level	242
Vent	243
Recirculated Air	244
Defrost	245
Floor	246
Fan (Maximum Speed Relay)	247
A/C Compressor	248
Radiator Fan Relay	249

TESTING

VACUUM CIRCUITS

Using vacuum schematic and vacuum functions table, test for proper operation of vacuum circuits. *See Fig. 3.*

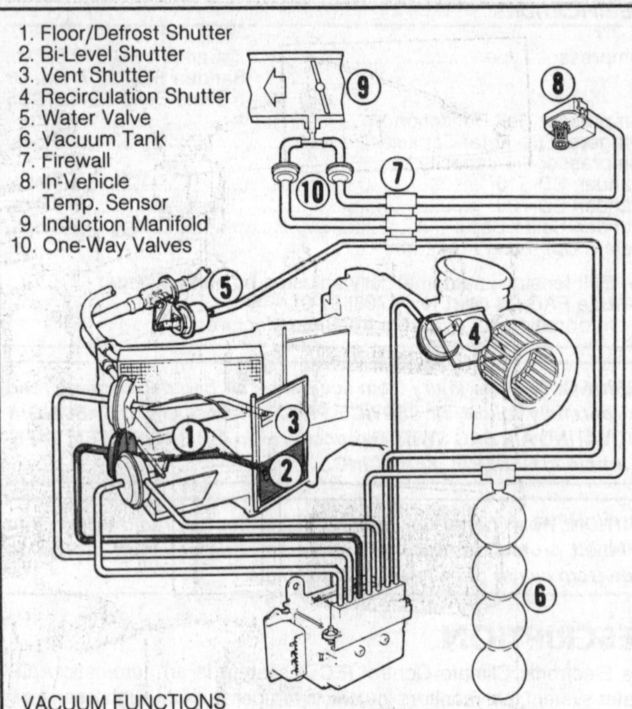
1. Floor/Defrost Shutter
2. Bi-Level Shutter
3. Vent Shutter
4. Recirculation Shutter
5. Water Valve
6. Vacuum Tank
7. Firewall
8. In-Vehicle Temp. Sensor
9. Induction Manifold
10. One-Way Valves

VACUUM FUNCTIONS

Component	Vacuum hose	Vacuum on	Vacuum off
Water valve	Grey	Closed (cold)	Open (warm)
Recirculation	Orange	Recirculation	Outside air
Vent shutter	Red	Open, also operates bilevel shutter mechanically	Closed
Bi-level	Transparent/ beige	Open	Closed
Defrost	Blue	Shutter in lower position	Middle* position
Floor shutter	Yellow	Shutter in upper position	Middle **

* In upper position if floor duct is under vacuum

** In lower position if defroster duct is under vacuum

93C19721 Courtesy of Volvo Cars of North America.

Fig. 3: Testing Vacuum Circuits

REMOVAL & INSTALLATION

WARNING: To avoid injury from accidental air bag deployment, read and carefully follow all SERVICE PRECAUTIONS and DISABLING & ACTIVATING AIR BAG SYSTEM procedures in AIR BAG SYSTEM SAFETY article in GENERAL SERVICING.

BLOWER MOTOR

Removal & Installation – 1) Obtain radio anti-theft code before servicing vehicle. Disconnect negative battery cable. Remove trim panel below glove box. Open glove box door. Remove glove box screws and glove box.

2) Detach wiring harness and bracket from blower motor housing. Disconnect blower motor. Remove blower motor screws and blower motor. To install, reverse removal procedure.

EVAPORATOR CORE

Removal & Installation – 1) Obtain radio anti-theft code before servicing vehicle. Disconnect negative battery cable. Discharge A/C system using approved refrigerant recovery/recycling equipment. Remove receiver-drier from engine compartment firewall. Remove cover plate and foam rubber seal from firewall.

2) Remove trim panel below glove box. Open glove box door. Remove glove box screws and glove box. Remove evaporator housing end cover. *See Fig. 4*. Carefully remove evaporator core. To install, reverse removal procedure.

NOTE: Additional removal and installation procedures are not available from manufacturer.

1993 AUTOMATIC A/C-HEATER SYSTEMS
960 (Cont.)

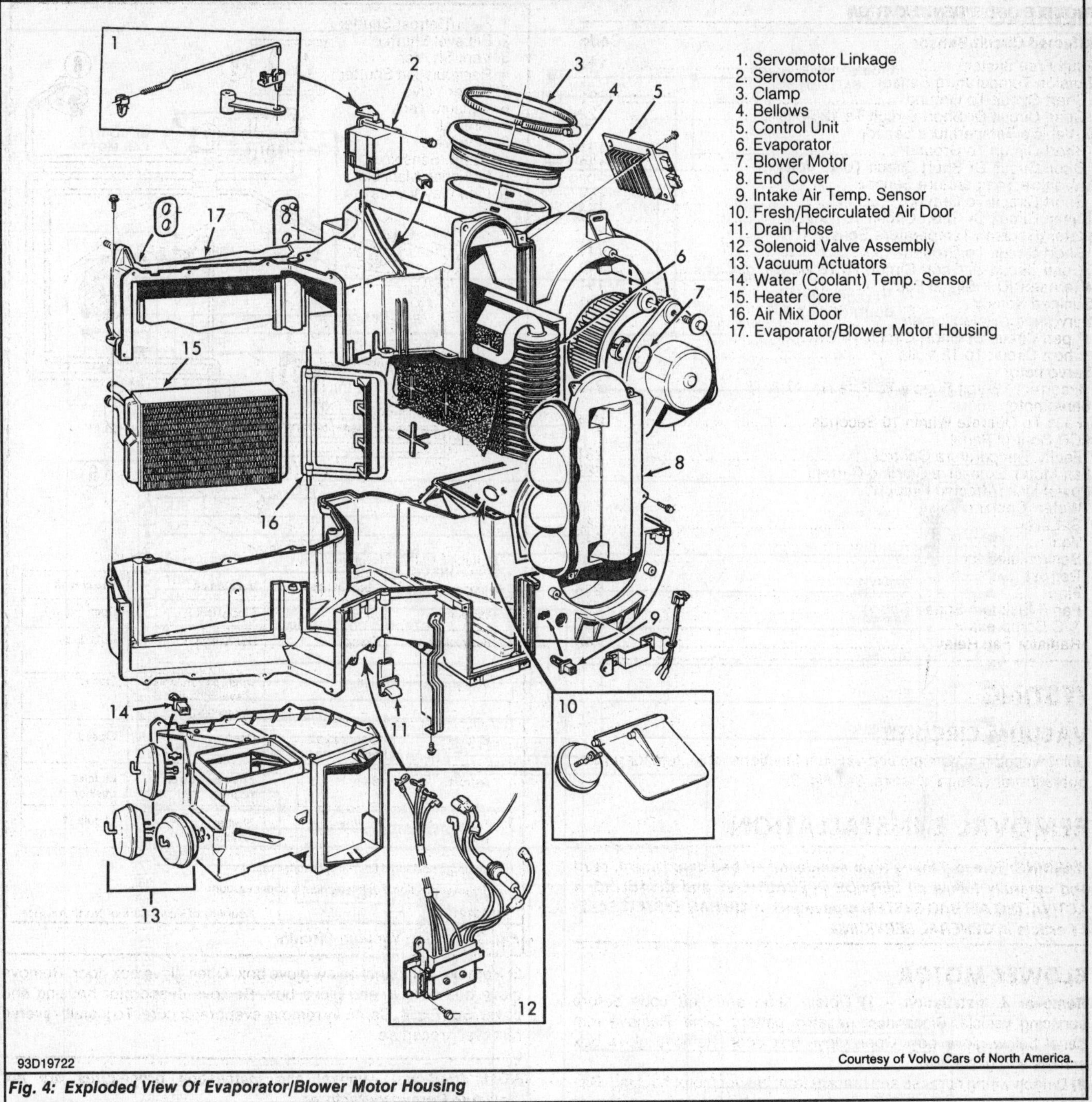
1. Servomotor Linkage
2. Servomotor
3. Clamp
4. Bellows
5. Control Unit
6. Evaporator
7. Blower Motor
8. End Cover
9. Intake Air Temp. Sensor
10. Fresh/Recirculated Air Door
11. Drain Hose
12. Solenoid Valve Assembly
13. Vacuum Actuators
14. Water (Coolant) Temp. Sensor
15. Heater Core
16. Air Mix Door
17. Evaporator/Blower Motor Housing
93D19722
Courtesy of Volvo Cars of North America.

Fig. 4: Exploded View Of Evaporator/Blower Motor Housing

1993 AUTOMATIC A/C-HEATER SYSTEMS
960 (Cont.)

WIRING DIAGRAM

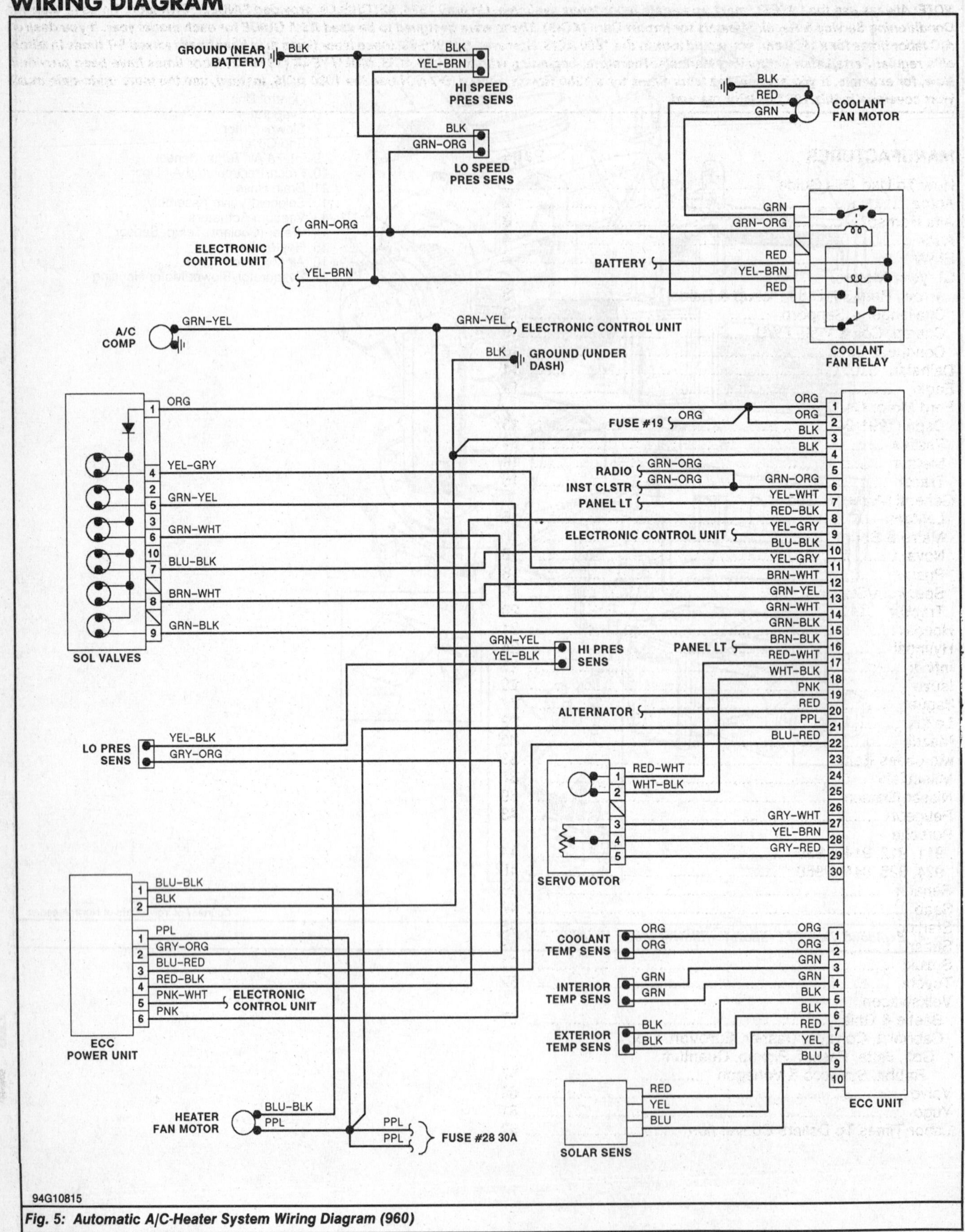
GROUND (NEAR BATTERY)
BLK
YEL-BRN
HI SPEED PRES SENS
GRN-ORG
LO SPEED PRES SENS
ELECTRONIC CONTROL UNIT
COOLANT FAN MOTOR
RED
GRN
BATTERY
COOLANT FAN RELAY
A/C COMP
GRN-YEL
GROUND (UNDER DASH)
SOL VALVES
ORG
YEL-GRY
GRN-WHT
BLU-BLK
BRN-WHT
GRN-BLK
FUSE #19
RADIO
INST CLSTR
PANEL LT
YEL-WHT
RED-BLK
HI PRES SENS
YEL-BLK
RED-WHT
WHT-BLK
PNK
PPL
BLU-RED
ALTERNATOR
LO PRES SENS
GRY-ORG
SERVO MOTOR
GRY-WHT
GRY-RED
ECC POWER UNIT
PNK-WHT
COOLANT TEMP SENS
INTERIOR TEMP SENS
EXTERIOR TEMP SENS
YEL
BLU
ECC UNIT
SOLAR SENS
HEATER FAN MOTOR
FUSE #28 30A
94G10815

Fig. 5: Automatic A/C-Heater System Wiring Diagram (960)

1993 TIME GUIDE CONTENTS

NOTE: Always use the LATEST, most up-to-date labor times available. Up until 1984, MITCHELL® provided SINGLE-YEAR labor times in their Air Conditioning Service & Repair Manuals for Import Cars (ACIS). These were designed to be used AS A GUIDE for each model year. If you desired A/C labor times for a 1980 car, you would look in the 1980 ACIS. However, by 1985-89, these labor times may have been revised 5-7 times in Mitchell's regular Parts/Labor Estimating Manuals. Therefore, beginning with the 1985 ACIS, MULTI-YEAR (1973-92) labor times have been provided. Now, for example, if you are seeking labor times for a 1980 Honda Accord, DO NOT use the 1980 ACIS. Instead, use the more up-to-date multi-year coverage in this 1993 or later manual.

AIR CONDITIONING TIME GUIDE
How To Use This Guide

COVERAGE

The Air Conditioning and Heating Labor Time Guide covers factory-installed air conditioning systems for most 1973-93 vehicles.

LABOR TIMES

The estimated labor times are given in hours and tenths of an hour in decimal form. For example, an hour and a half would be 1.5 hours.

Labor times generally reflect the time required for an average, trained mechanic to complete factory-recommended repair procedures. These should only be used as a guide and may need some adjustment to meet your shop's needs.

ADDITIONAL TIME

Additional time, highlighted by a bullet (•) or a tariff (¹), is the extra time it takes to replace/test a "buried" part.

The bullet (•) shows that additional time has a general application. An example is adding additional time for vehicles equipped with power steering. The tariff (¹) is a note for additional time added for a specific model or option.

COMBINATIONS

Combinations, indicated in text with a star (*), are labor times used to perform additional tasks, directly related to the original operation. An example is recharging A/C system after a performance test.

SKILL LEVEL CODE

The code letter, within parenthesis after the labor operation, suggests skill required for that specific procedure. The four skill levels are defined as follows:

(A) HIGHLY SKILLED – Requires precision measuring tools and specialized test equipment, plus a thorough knowledge of complicated systems and a strong diagnostic ability.

(B) SKILLED – Requires basic tools and simple measuring devices, plus accurate diagnostic abilities using special test equipment. Technician must have basic knowledge of complex systems.

(C) SEMI-SKILLED – Requires basic tools with diagnosis limited to a single possible problem. Technician must have basic knowledge of system operation.

(D) LOW SKILLED – Requires ability to replace parts and follow written/verbal instruction.

DEFINITIONS

The following abbreviations and/or terms appear throughout the Labor Time Guide:

- **O/H, O/HAUL, Overhaul:** Includes removing and installing (R&I) part/assembly unless noted otherwise. Also covers repairing or replacing parts, along with cleaning, inspection and adjustments.
- **R&I, Remove and Install:** This time is for removing another part/assembly for access to the part/assembly being repaired. An example is removing a dashboard for access to an evaporator. Includes any adjustments needed to reposition removed part/assembly.
- **R&R, Remove and Replace:** This time is for removing and replacing a part/assembly with a new part/assembly. Also includes transferring any attached part to a new part/assembly, installation and adjustments.

OVERLAPPING LABOR TIMES

When performing 2 or more repairs/procedures with overlapping labor operations, a reasonable deduction should be taken from the total time. Use your best judgment when this happens.

HOURLY RATES

Because labor rates vary throughout the country, local or individual rates must be computed for each job. To assist you, we have provided the convenient LABOR TIMES TO DOLLARS CONVERSION TABLE.

DIAGNOSTIC SERVICE RECOMMENDED TIMES

Before performing actual labor operations, diagnosis may be required to pinpoint the cause of the problem.

Subject or Complaint	Time (Hr.)
Air Conditioning	.8

(This procedure includes checking A/C system with gauge set and leak detector. Also includes checking outlet temperature, compressor and clutch operation, and drive belt condition.)

Subject or Complaint	Time (Hr.)
Overheating	.8

(This procedure includes inspecting/testing cooling system, radiator cap, belts and hoses. Add additional time if testing thermostat).

SPECIFIC TIME ADJUSTMENT

These are specific adjustments to the Mitchell labor time, indicated by numbers within a circle.

GENERAL NOTES & INCLUSION NOTES

These are self-explanatory. Be sure to look for these when preparing a labor estimate.

AIR CONDITIONING TIME GUIDE
How To Use This Guide (Cont.)

AIR CONDITIONING TIME GUIDE 553

COMBINATIONS

SPECIFIC TIME ADJUSTMENT

Acura Heating & Air Conditioning

NOTE 1: Times shown DO NOT include evacuate and charge system. If necessary to open refrigerant system or to evacuate, charge and test; refer to System Charge (Complete) for appropriate time.
NOTE 2: Times listed are for Factory and Dealer dash installed Integral Type air conditioning units only. Use necessary clock time for service of hang-on units.

HEATING & VENTILATION

GENERAL NOTE

HEATER HOSES - R&R *(D)*
NOTE: Deduct .2 when used in conjunction with Radiator Hoses - R&R.
One 8
Each Additional 3

CORE, HEATER - R&R *(A)*
Includes: R&I dash assembly.
DOES NOT include evacuate and charge system.
Integra
w/Air Cond 5.5
w/o Air Cond 5.0
Legend 6.0

VALVE, HEATER CONTROL - R&R *(B)*
All 7

MOTOR, BLOWER - R&R *(B)*
All 1.5

SWITCH, BLOWER MOTOR - R&R *(B)*
All 1.0

CONTROL ASSEMBLY, TEMPERATURE - R&R *(B)*
All 1.0

SWITCH, FUNCTION MODE - R&R *(B)*
All 1.0

SKILL LEVEL CODE

RESISTOR, BLOWER MOTOR - R&R *(B)*
All 6

CONTROL MOTOR - R&R *(B)*
Air Mix (Legend) 2.0
Function
Integra 5
Legend 8
Recirculation
Integra 8
Legend 2.5

ADDITIONAL TIME

AIR CONDITIONING

PERFORMANCE - TEST *(B)*
Includes: Gauge check, leak test and partial charge.
All 1.0

★ COMBINATIONS ★

★ System Charge (Complete)
Includes: Drain, evacuate and recharge.
All 4

SYSTEM CHARGE (PARTIAL) *(B)*
Includes: Performance test.
All 1.0

SYSTEM CHARGE (COMPLETE) *(B)*
Includes: Evacuate and recharge system.
NOTE: When performed in conjunction with other heating or air conditioning repairs, deduct .4.
All 1.4

BELT, COMPRESSOR - R&R *(D)*
Integra 5
Legend 3

IDLER PULLEY - R&R *(D)*
All 6

COMPRESSOR ASSEMBLY - R&R *(A)*
Includes: Transfer clutch assembly.
DOES NOT include evacuate and charge system.
Integra 2.2
Legend 2.4

SEAL, COMPRESSOR SHAFT - R&R *(A)*
DOES NOT include evacuate or charge system.
Integra 2.5
Legend 2.7

CLUTCH PLATE & HUB ASSEMBLY - R&R *(A)*
DOES NOT include evacurate and charge system.
Integra 2.2
Legend 2.4

● ADDITIONAL TIME ●

● Where Air Pump interferes add (.1) 1
● Where Pwr Strg interferes add (.1) 1

CONDENSER - R&R *(B)*
DOES NOT include evacuate and charge system.
Integra ① 1.6
Legend ② 1.9
① *Includes: R&I Bumper Assembly.*
② *Includes: R&I Grille and Tie Bar.*

RECEIVER DRIER - R&R *(B)*
DOES NOT include evacuate and charge system.
All 7

INCLUSION NOTES

CORE, EVAPORATOR - R&R *(B)*
DOES NOT include evacuate and charge system.
Integra 1.7
Legend 1.9

VALVE, EVAPORATOR EXPANSION - R&R *(B)*
DOES NOT include evacuate and charge system.
Integra 1.7
Legend 1.9

THERMOSTAT - R&R *(B)*
DOES NOT include evacuate and charge system.
Integra 1.7
Legend 1.9

MOTOR &/OR FAN, CONDENSER - R&R *(C)*
Integra 5
Legend 8

RELAY, FAN - R&R *(C)*
All 5

MOTOR, AIR MIX CONTROL - R&R *(B)*
Legend (Coupe) 2.0

MITCHELL LABOR TIME

SENSOR, AMBIENT TEMPERATURE - R&R *(B)*
Legend (Coupe) 6

SENSOR, SUNLIGHT LOAD - R&R *(B)*
Legend (Coupe) 3

SENSOR, IN-CAR TEMPERATURE - R&R *(B)*
Legend (Coupe) 1.3

HOSE, AIR CONDITIONING - R&R *(B)*
DOES NOT include evacuate and charge system.
One (Discharge or Suction) 7
Each Additional 3

Audi Heating & Air Conditioning

NOTE 1: Times shown DO NOT include evacuate and charge system. If necessary to open refrigerant system or to evacuate, charge and test; refer to System Charge (Complete) for appropriate time.
NOTE 2: Times listed are for Factory and Dealer dash installed Integral Type air conditioning units only. Use necessary clock time for service of hang on units.

HEATING & VENTILATION

CORE, HEATER - R&R *(A)*
DOES NOT include evacuate or charge system.
1973-88
Coupe,4000,4000 Quattro 3.5
Fox 1.7
80/90,80/90 Quattro 3.5
100 Ser 2.6
5000,5000 Quattro
(78-83) 2.7
(84-88) 3.6

WATER VALVE - R&R *(B)*
1973-77
Fox 5
100 Ser 1.0
1978-88 5

CONTROL, TEMPERATURE - R&R *(B)*
1979-88
Coupe,80/90,80/90 Quattro, 4000,4000 Quattro 9
Fox 7

AIR CONDITIONING TIME GUIDE

Acura Heating & Air Conditioning

NOTE 1: Times shown Do Not include recover, evacuate and charge system. If necessary to open refrigerant system or to recover, evacuate, charge and test, refer to System Charge (Complete) for appropriate time.
NOTE 2: Times listed are for Factory and Dealer dash installed Integral Type air conditioning units only. Use necessary clock time for service of hang-on units.

HEATING & VENTILATION

HEATER HOSES - R&R *(D)*
NOTE: Deduct .2 when used in conjunction with Radiator Hoses - R&R.

Integra,Legend,Vigor
One 8
Each Additional 3
NSX .... N.A.

CORE, HEATER - R&R *(B)*
Includes: R&I dash assembly.
DOES NOT include evacuate and charge system.

1986-93
Integra
w/Air Cond 5.5
w/o Air Cond 5.3
Legend
(86-90) 6.0
(91-93) 6.3
NSX 5.2
Vigor 7.2

VALVE, HEATER CONTROL - R&R *(B)*
Integra,Legend 7
NSX 8
Vigor 9

MOTOR, BLOWER - R&R *(B)*

1986-93
Integra
w/Air Cond 1.7
w/o Air Cond 1.5
Legend 1.5
NSX 9
Vigor 7.5

SWITCH, BLOWER MOTOR - R&R *(B)*

1986-93
Integra
w/Air Cond 1.3
w/o Air Cond 1.0
Legend 7

FUNCTION CONTROL PANEL - R&R *(B)*

1986-93
Integra
(86-89)
w/Climate Control 1.3
w/o Climate Control 9
(90-93)
w/Climate Control 3.0
w/o Climate Control 1.9
Legend
(86-90)
w/Climate Control 1.3
w/o Climate Control 1.0
(91-93) 9
NSX 8
Vigor 5

RESISTOR, BLOWER MOTOR - R&R *(B)*
Integra,Legend,Vigor 6
NSX 8

DOOR, CLIMATE CONTROL UNIT - R&R *(B)*
Legend 5

CONTROL MOTOR - R&R *(B)*

1986-93
Air Mix
Legend 2.0
NSX 1.5
Function
Integra 5
Legend 8
NSX 9
Vigor 1.5
Recirculation
Integra 8
Legend 2.5
NSX 9
Vigor 6

AMPLIFIER, HEATER CONTROL - R&R *(B)*
Vigor 5.4

AIR CONDITIONING

FREON - RECOVER *(B)*
NOTE: This operation is not to be used with any other operations.

All 3

PERFORMANCE - TEST *(B)*
Includes: Gauge check, leak test and partial charge.

All 1.0

SYSTEM CHARGE (PARTIAL) *(B)*
Includes: Pessure and leak test.

All 1.0

SYSTEM CHARGE (COMPLETE) *(B)*
Includes: Evacuate, recover and recharge system.

All 1.4

BELT, COMPRESSOR - R&R *(D)*

1986-93
Integra 5
Legend
(86-90) 3
(91-93) 6
NSX 3
Vigor 6

IDLER PULLEY - R&R *(D)*
1986-89 6
1990-93
Integra 8
Legend,NSX 6
Vigor 3

COMPRESSOR ASSEMBLY - R&R *(B)*
Includes: Transfer clutch assembly.
DOES NOT include evacuate and charge system.

1986-93
Integra 2.2
Legend
(86-90) 2.4
(91-93) 2.6
NSX 1.8
Vigor 2.0

SEAL, COMPRESSOR SHAFT - R&R *(B)*
DOES NOT include evacuate or charge system.

1986-93
Integra 2.5
Legend
(86-90) 2.7
(91-93) 2.9
NSX 2.1
Vigor 2.3

CLUTCH PLATE & HUB ASSEMBLY - R&R *(B)*
DOES NOT include evacurate and charge system.

1986-93
Integra 2.2
Legend
(86-90) 2.4
(91-93) 2.6
NSX 1.8
Vigor 2.0

CONDENSER - R&R *(B)*
DOES NOT include evacuate and charge system.

1986-89
Integra ① 1.6
Legend ② 1.9
1990-93
Integra 7
Legend
(86-90) 9
(91-93) 3.0
NSX ①
One Side 1.6
Both 2.1
Vigor 1.8

① *Includes: R&I Bumper Assembly.*
② *Includes: R&I Grille and Tie Bar.*

RECEIVER DRIER - R&R *(B)*
DOES NOT include evacuate and charge system.

1986-93
Integra 7
Legend
(86-90) 7
(91-93) 9
NSX 1.3
Vigor 3

CORE, EVAPORATOR - R&R *(B)*
DOES NOT include evacuate and charge system.

1986-89
Integra 1.7
Legend 1.9
1990-93
Integra 1.8
Legend
(86-90) 1.3
(91-93) 6.3
NSX 5.3
Vigor 7.5

VALVE, EVAPORATOR EXPANSION - R&R *(B)*
DOES NOT include evacuate and charge system.

1986-89
Integra 1.7
Legend 1.9
1990-93
Integra 1.1
Legend 1.3
NSX 1.0
Vigor 7.5

Cont.

AIR CONDITIONING TIME GUIDE

Acura Heating & Air Conditioning (Cont.)

THERMOSTAT - R&R *(B)*

DOES NOT include evacuate and charge system.

1986-89
Integra 1.7
Legend 1.9
1990-93
Integra 1.5
Legend 1.3
NSX 8
Vigor 3

MOTOR &/OR FAN, CONDENSER - R&R *(D)*

Integra 5
Legend 8
NSX
One Side 1.6
Both 2.1
Vigor 1.0

RELAY, FAN - R&R *(B)*

All 5

SENSOR, AMBIENT TEMP - R&R *(B)*

Legend 6
NSX 4

SENSOR, SUNLIGHT LOAD - R&R *(B)*

Legend 3
NSX 5

SENSOR, IN CAR TEMP - R&R *(B)*

1986-93
Legend
(86-90) 1.3
(91-93) 5
NSX 1.0

SENSOR, COOLANT TEMPERATURE - R&R *(B)*

Legend 8
NSX 6

HOSE, AIR CONDITIONING - R&R *(B)*

DOES NOT include evacuate and charge system.

1986-93 (Each)
Integra (Suction or Discharge) 6
Legend
(86-90) (Suction or Discharge) 6
(91-93)
Discharge 1.5
Suction 1.8
NSX
Condenser Pipe 1.1
Discharge Pipe
Pipe A 1.0
Pipe B 2.4
Pipe C 9
Receiver Pipe 1.6
Suction Pipe
Pipe A 3.4
Pipe B 9
Vigor
Discharge 8
Suction 9

★ **COMBINATIONS** ★

★ Make Up Hose From Stock 4

Alfa Romeo Heating & Air Conditioning

NOTE 1: Times shown Do Not include recover, evacuate and charge system. If necessary to open refrigerant system or to recover, evacuate, charge and test, refer to System Charge (Complete) for appropriate time.
NOTE 2: Times listed are for Factory and Dealer dash installed Integral Type air conditioning units only. Use necessary clock time for service of hang-on units.

HEATING & VENTILATION

HEATER HOSES - R&R *(D)*

1974-80 (Both)
Alfetta 2.4
Berlina,GTV,Spider 2.3
1981-93
GTV-6,Milano,164 .... 2.8
Spider 2.3

WATER VALVE - R&R *(B)*

1974-80
Alfetta 1.8
Berlina,GTV,Spider 1.3
1981-93
GTV-6 .... 1.9
Milano 3.5
Spider 1.3
164 .... N.A.

CABLE, WATER VALVE - R&R *(B)*

All 1.0

CORE, HEATER - R&R *(B)*

DOES NOT include System Charge.

1974-80
Alfetta 4.2
Berlina,GTV,Spider 5.3
1981-93
GTV-6 .... 4.4
Milano 5.6
Spider 5.3
164 .... 3.4

MOTOR, BLOWER - R&R *(B)*

1974-80
Alfetta
Air Cond
GT .... N.A.
Sedan 4.0
Heater 3.4
Berlina,GTV,Spider
Air Cond .... N.A.
Heater 4.5
1981-93
GTV-6
Air Cond 4.2
Heater 3.6
Milano
Air Cond 5.4
Heater 4.8
Spider
Air Cond 5.1
Heater 4.5
164
Air Cond 3.2
Heater 2.6

SWITCH, BLOWER MOTOR - R&R *(B)*

1974-80 3
1981-93
GTV-6 7
Milano,Spider 3
164 .... N.A.

RELAY, BLOWER MOTOR - R&R *(B)*

All 5

CONTROL ASSEMBLY, TEMPERATURE - R&R *(B)*

1974-80
Alfetta 9
Berlina,GTV,Spider 1.1
1981-93 .... 1.1

CABLE, VENTILATION CONTROL - R&R *(B)*

1974-93 (Each) 9

AIR CONDITIONING

FREON - RECOVER *(B)*

NOTE: This operation is not to be used with any other operations.

All 3

PERFORMANCE - TEST *(B)*

Includes: Gauge check, leak test and partial charge.

1974-93 .... 1.0

SYSTEM CHARGE (PARTIAL) *(B)*

Includes: Performance test.

1974-93 .... 1.0

SYSTEM CHARGE (COMPLETE) *(B)*

Includes: Recover, evacuate and recharge system.

1974-93 .... 1.4

BELT, COMPRESSOR - R&R *(D)*

All 5

COMPRESSOR ASSEMBLY - R&R *(B)*

DOES NOT include System Charge.

1974-80
Alfeta
GT .... N.A.
Sedan 1.0
Berlina,GTV,Spider .... N.A.
1981-93
GTV-6 (2.5L Eng) 2.4
Milano,Spider,164 .... N.A.

VALVE, EVAPORATOR EXPANSION - R&R *(B)*

DOES NOT include System Charge.

1974-80 .... N.A.
1981-93
Milano 1.1
164 6

Cont.

AIR CONDITIONING TIME GUIDE

Alfa Romeo Heating & Air Conditioning (Cont.)

RECEIVER DRIER - R&R *(B)*
DOES NOT include System Charge.

1974-93 .5

CONDENSER - R&R *(B)*
DOES NOT include System Charge.

1974-80
Alfetta
GT N.A.
Sedan 2.6
Berlina,GTV,Spider N.A.
1981-93
GTV-6 2.3
Milano 2.0
Spider
(81-82) 3.6
(83-93) 4.3
164 .6

CONDENSER FAN MOTOR - R&R *(B)*

1974-93 N.A.

RELAY, CONDENSER FAN - R&R *(B)*

1974-93 .3

CORE, EVAPORATOR - R&R *(B)*
DOES NOT include System Charge.

1974-80
Alfetta
GT N.A.
Sedan 4.0
Berlina,GTV,Spider N.A.
1981-93
GTV-6 4.2
Milano 5.4
Spider 5.1
164 3.2

HOSE, AIR CONDITIONING - R&R *(B)*
DOES NOT include System Charge.

One 1.0
Each Additional .5

★ COMBINATIONS ★

★ Make Up Hose From Stock .4

SWITCH, PRESSURE - R&R *(B)*

All .5

SWITCH, THREE WAY - R&R *(B)*

All .5

Audi Heating & Air Conditioning

NOTE 1: Times shown DO NOT include evacuate and charge system. If necessary to open refrigerant system or to evacuate, charge and test; refer to System Charge (Complete) for appropriate time.
NOTE 2: Times listed are for Factory and Dealer dash installed Integral Type air conditioning units only. Use necessary clock time for service of hang on units.

HEATING & VENTILATION

CORE, HEATER - R&R *(B)*
DOES NOT include evacuate or charge system.

1973-92
Coupe,4000,4000 Quattro 3.5
Coupe Quattro,80/90,80/90 Quattro 3.7
Fox 1.7
S4,100/200,100/200 Quattro 3.6
V8 Quattro 3.8
100 Ser (73-77) 2.6
5000,5000 Quattro
(78-83) 2.7
(84-88) 3.6

WATER VALVE - R&R *(B)*

1973-77
Fox .5
100 Ser 1.0
1978-92 .5

CONTROL, TEMPERATURE - R&R *(B)*

1979-92
Coupe,Coupe Quattro,80/90,
80/90 Quattro,100/200,100/200 Quattro,
4000,4000 Quattro .9
Fox .7
S4,V8 Quattro N.A.
100 Ser (73-77) 1.8
5000,5000 Quattro
(78-83) 1.5
(84-88) .9

CABLE, VENTILATION CONTROL - R&R *(B)*

1973-92
Coupe,4000,4000 Quattro (ea) .9
Coupe Quattro,80/90,80/90 Quattro 1.6
Fox,S4 (Heater Control) .7
V8 Quattro N.A.
100/200,100/200 Quattro
(89-91) 1.1
(92) .7
100 Ser (73-77)
Fresh Air .8
Heater Control 1.0
5000,5000 Quattro (ea)
(78-83) 1.3
(84-88) 1.1

HEATER HOSES - R&R *(D)*

One .4
Each Additional .2

FLAP, WARM AIR REGULATOR - R&R *(B)*

1973-77 (100 Ser) .6

MOTOR, BLOWER - R&R *(B)*

1973-92
Coupe,4000,4000 Quattro .6
Coupe Quattro,80/90,80/90 Quattro 1.1
Fox 1.8
S4 1.0
V8 Quattro 3.2
100/200,100/200 Quattro
(89-91) 3.5
(92) 1.0
100 Ser (73-77) 2.0
5000,5000 Quattro
(78-83) .9
(84-88) 3.5

RESISTOR, BLOWER MOTOR - R&R *(B)*
DOES NOT include R&I Blower Motor.

1973-92
Coupe,Fox,100 Ser,4000,4000 Quattro .3
Coupe Quattro,80/90,80/90 Quattro 1.0
S4,V8 Quattro .7
100/200,100/200 Quattro
(89-91) 3.5
(92) .7
5000,5000 Quattro
(78-83) .3
(84-88) 3.5

SWITCH, BLOWER MOTOR - R&R *(B)*

1973-92
Coupe,Coupe Quattro,80/90,
80/90 Quattro,4000,4000 Quattro,
5000,5000 Quattro .5
Fox 1.6
S4,V8 Quattro N.A.
100/200,100/200 Quattro .4
100 Ser .6

AIR CONDITIONING

FREON - RECOVER *(B)*
NOTE: This operation is not be used with any other operations.

All .3

PERFORMANCE - TEST *(B)*
Includes: Gauge check, leak test and partial charge.

1973-92 1.0

SYSTEM CHARGE (PARTIAL) *(B)*
Includes: Performance test.

1973-92 1.0

SYSTEM CHARGE (COMPLETE) *(B)*
Includes: Recover, evacuate and recharge system.
NOTE: When performed in conjunction with other heating or air conditioning repairs. deduct .2.

1973-92 1.4

BELT, COMPRESSOR - R&R *(D)*
Includes: Serpentine and V-Belt type.

1973-93
V-Belt .5
Serpentine .3

● ADDITIONAL TIME ●

- Where Alternator interferes add .2
- Where Air Pump interferes add .2
- Where Pwr Strg interferes add .2

Cont.

AIR CONDITIONING TIME GUIDE

Audi Heating & Air Conditioning (Cont.)

SEAL, COMPRESSOR SHAFT - R&R *(B)*
DOES NOT include System Charge.

1973-92
Coupe,4000,4000 Quattro **1.6**
Coupe Quattro,S4,V8 Quattro,80/90, 80/90 Quattro **2.3**
Fox,100 Ser **1.4**
100/200,100/200 Quattro
(89-91) **2.6**
(92) .... **N.A.**
5000,5000 Quattro
Diesel **1.8**
Gas **1.6**

COMPRESSOR ASSEMBLY - R&R *(B)*
DOES NOT include System Charge.

1973-92
Coupe,4000,4000 Quattro **1.1**
Coupe Quattro,S4,V8 Quattro,80/90, 80/90 Quattro **1.8**
Fox,100 Ser .... **.9**
100/200,100/200 Quattro
(89-91) **1.1**
(92) .... **N.A.**
5000,5000 Quattro
Diesel **1.3**
Gas **1.1**

CLUTCH PLATE & HUB ASSEMBLY - R&R *(B)*

1973-92
Coupe,Coupe Quattro,80/90, 80/90 Quattro,4000,4000 Quattro .... **.5**
Fox **2.0**
S4,V8 Quattro,100/200,100/200 Quattro, 5000,5000 Quattro .... **.9**
100 Ser (73-77) **1.9**

COIL, COMPRESSOR CLUTCH - R&R *(B)*

1973-92
Coupe,Coupe Quattro,80/90, 80/90 Quattro,4000,4000 Quattro .... **.7**
Fox,100 Ser (73-77) **2.2**
S4,V8 Quattro,100/200,100/200 Quattro, 5000,5000 Quattro **1.1**

SERVICE VALVE - R&R *(B)*
DOES NOT include System Charge.

Suction or Discharge (ea) .... **.5**

VALVE, EVAPORATOR EXPANSION - R&R *(B)*
DOES NOT include System Charge.

1973-87
Coupe,4000,4000 Quattro **2.5**
Fox **2.4**
100 Ser (73-77) .... **.8**

VALVE, V.I.R. - R&R *(B)*
DOES NOT include System Charge.

1978-83 (5000) **1.8**

VALVE, V.I.R. - R&I & O/H *(B)*
DOES NOT include System Charge.

1978-83 (5000) **2.3**

VALVE, RESTRICTOR (ORIFICE) - R&R *(B)*
DOES NOT include System Charge.

1984-92 .... **1.5**

CONDENSER - R&R *(B)*
DOES NOT include System Charge.

1973-92
Coupe,4000,4000 Quattro
(80-83)
Large .... **.8**
Small .... **.5**
(84-87) **1.5**
Coupe Quattro,80/90,80/90 Quattro **1.6**
Fox
Large .... **.9**
Small .... **.6**
S4 .... **1.8**
V8 Quattro **1.3**
100/200,100/200 Quattro
(89) **2.0**
(90-91) **1.1**
(92) **1.8**
100 Ser .... **.8**
5000,5000 Quattro
(78-83)
Large **1.1**
Small **1.0**
(84-88) **1.3**

FAN & MOTOR, CONDENSER - R&R *(B)*

1973-83
Coupe,4000,5000 .... **.7**
Fox .... **.3**
100 Ser .... **.8**
1984-92
w/ABS **1.2**
w/o ABS
Coupe,Coupe Quattro,80/90, 80/90 Quattro,4000,4000 Quattro .... **.7**
5000,5000 Quattro **2.0**

SWITCH, ELECTRIC FAN - R&R *(B)*

1973-92 .... **.5**

RELAY, ELECTRIC FAN - R&R *(B)*

1973-92 .... **.5**

ACCUMULATOR OR RECEIVER DRYER - R&R *(B)*
DOES NOT include Sytem Charge.

1973-92
Coupe,Fox,4000,4000 Quattro **1.1**
Coupe Quattro,80/90,80/90 Quattro
Accumulator **1.6**
Receiver Dryer .... **.5**
S4 .... **.6**
V8 Quattro **1.6**
100/200,100/200 Quattro
(89-91) **1.6**
(92) .... **.6**
100 Ser (73-77) .... **.8**
5000,5000 Quattro
(78-83) **1.9**
(84-88) **1.6**

CORE, EVAPORATOR - R&R *(B)*
DOES NOT include System Charge.

1973-92
Coupe,4000,4000 Quattro **1.9**
Coupe Quattro,80/90,80/90 Quattro **4.5**
Fox,100 Ser **2.0**
S4 .... **N.A.**
V8 Quattro,5000,5000 Quattro **1.8**
100/200,100/200 Quattro
(89-91) **1.8**
(92) .... **N.A.**

SENSOR, EVAPORATOR AIR TEMP - R&R *(B)*

1984-92 .... **.4**

MICRO SWITCH - R&R *(B)*

1973-92 .... **.5**

SWITCH, HIGH PRESSURE - R&R *(B)*
DOES NOT include System Charge.

1973-92 .... **.2**

SWITCH, LOW PRESSURE - R&R *(B)*
DOES NOT include System Charge.

1973-92 .... **.2**

SWITCH, THERMOSTATIC - R&R *(B)*

1973-92
Coupe,4000,4000 Quattro **1.1**
V8 Quattro,100/200,100/200 Quattro, 5000,5000 Quattro .... **.4**

CONTROL ASSEMBLY, A/C - R&R *(B)*

1984-92 .... **1.6**

CONTROL ASSEMBLY, VACUUM - R&R *(B)*

1984-92
Coupe,Coupe Quattro,80/90,80/90 Quattro **3.9**
S4,V8 Quattro,100/200,100/200 Quattro, 4000,4000 Quattro,5000,5000 Quattro ... **.5**

MOTOR, CONTROL ASSEMBLY - R&R *(B)*

1984-92
Coupe Quattro,S4,80/90,80/90 Quattro, 100/200,100/200 Quattro **1.0**
4000,4000 Quattro,5000,5000 Quattro .... **.7**

SENSOR, INTERIOR AIR TEMP - R&R *(B)*

1988-92
S4,V8 Quattro,100/200,100/200 Quattro
Roof .... **.2**
Lower
Upper (dash) **3.8**
Lower (console)
w/Air Bag **1.3**
w/o Air Bag **3.8**
5000,5000 Quattro **2.2**

BLOWER, INTERIOR TEMP SENSOR - R&R *(B)*

1989-92 .... **3.8**

POWER MODULE - R&R *(B)*

1984-92 .... **.4**

SENSOR, EXTERIOR AIR TEMP - R&R *(B)*

1984-92 .... **.6**

SENSOR, INST PANEL TEMP - R&R *(B)*

1988-92
S4,V8 Quattro,100/200,100/200 Quattro
w/Air Bag **1.3**
w/o Air Bag **3.8**
5000,5000 Quattro **2.2**

Cont.

AIR CONDITIONING TIME GUIDE

Audi Heating & Air Conditioning (Cont.)

HOSE, AIR CONDITIONING - R&R *(B)*
DOES NOT include System Charge.

1973-92
Coupe,4000,4000 Quattro
Discharge .4
Suction .6
Condenser to Evaporator .8
Compressor to Condenser .7

Coupe Quattro,80/90,80/90 Quattro
Discharge .8
Suction 1.1
Condenser to Evaporator 1.3
Drier to Evaporator 1.1
Fox
One .9
Each Additional .7

S4,V8 Quattro,100/200,100/200 Quattro
One .6
Each Additional .4
100 Ser,5000,5000 Quattro
One .7
Each Additional .5

★ COMBINATIONS ★

★ Make Up Hose From Stock .4

BMW Heating & Air Conditioning

***NOTE 1:** Times shown DO NOT include recover, evacuate and charge system. If necessary to open refrigerant system refer to System Charge (Complete) for appropriate time.*
***NOTE 2:** Times listed are for Factory and Dealer dash installed Integral Type air conditioning units only. Use necessary clock time for service of hang-on units.*

HEATING & VENTILATION

HEATER HOSES - R&R *(D)*

1973-93 (All)
L6,533i,535i,535is,635CSi .9
M3,M5,M6,325,325e,325es,325i,325iC, 325is,325iX 1.3
2002,2002tii,3.0 Bavaria,3.0CS,3.0S, 3.0Si,524td,525i 1.1
318i
(84-85) .7
(91-93) 1.8
318is,735i,735iL,740i,740iL 1.8
320i,528i,633CSi .8
528e 1.2
530i,630CSi .7
733i 1.4
750iL 2.8
850Ci,850i 2.2

PUMP, WATER (ADDITIONAL) - R&R *(B)*

1985-93
M5,525i,535i,735i,735iL 1.0
740i,740iL .9
750iL 1.3
850Ci,850i 1.4

CORE, HEATER - R&R *(B)*
DOES NOT include System Charge.

1973-93
L6,M3,M6,630CSi,633CSi,635CSi 7.7
M5
(87-88) 6.3
(91-93) 8.0
2002,2002tii,3.0S,3.0Si 4.1
3.0 Bavaria,3.0CS,325,325iC,325iX 7.2
318i
(84-85) 6.9
(91-93) 5.0
318is 5.0
320i 3.8
325e,325es 6.9
325i,325is
(87-91) 7.2
(92-93) 4.0
524td,530i 5.8
525i
(89-90) 7.0
(91-93) 7.5
528e,533i,535is,850Ci,850i 6.3
528i 9.3
535i
(85-88) 6.3
(89-93) 7.0
733i 9.0
735i,735iL,740i,740iL,750iL 8.5

● ADDITIONAL TIME ●

● w/Air Bag (SRS) add .5

WATER VALVE - R&R *(B)*

1973-93
L6,528e,533i,535is,635CSi .7
M3 2.0
M5,M6 .9
2002,2002tii 1.5
318i
(84-85) 1.8
(91-93) 1.3
318is,733i,735i,735iL,750iL,850Ci,850i 1.3
320i
(77-79) 1.8
(80-83) .8
325,325e,325es,325iC,325iX 1.8
325i,325is
(87-91) 1.8
(92-93) 1.0
524td .6
525i,740i,740iL 1.0
528i,530i 2.6
535i
(85-88) .7
(89-93) 1.0
630CSi 5.0
633CSi
(78-81) 5.0
(82-84) .7

MOTOR, BLOWER - R&R *(B)*
DOES NOT include System Charge.

1973-84
2002,2002tii
w/Air Cond 5.2
w/o Air Cond 4.7
3.0 Bavaria,3.0CS,3.0S,3.0Si,530i
w/Air Cond 6.7
w/o Air Cond 1.0
318i,325e .9
320i
w/Air Cond 3.2
w/o Air Cond .8
528e,533i,630CSi
w/Air Cond 2.7
w/o Air Cond .7
528i
w/Air Cond 3.9
w/o Air Cond .8
633CSi
w/Air Cond 2.7
w/o Air Cond
(78-81) 1.0
(82-84) .8
733i
w/Air Cond
(78-81) 8.0
(82-84) 9.0
w/o Air Cond 1.3

1985-93
exc M3,M5,525i,535i,733i,735i,735iL, 740i,740iL,750iL,850Ci,850i .9
M3 1.1
M5
(87-88) .9
(91-93) 3.2
525i
(89-90) 1.3
(91-93) 1.9
535i
(85-88) .9
(89-93) 1.5
733i,735i,735iL 1.5
740i,740iL 1.8
750iL 2.2
850Ci,850i 2.8

SWITCH, BLOWER MOTOR - R&R *(B)*

1973-93
w/Air Cond
exc M6,318i,325,325e,325es,325i, 325iC,325is,325iX .6
M6 1.1
318i,325,325e,325es,325iC,325iX .3
325i,325is
(87-91) .3
(92-93) .7
w/o Air Cond
2002,2002tii .9
3.0 Bavaria,3.0CS,3.0S,3.0Si,528i, 530i,733i .8
320i .6
524td,528e,533i .7
633CSi 1.1

RESISTOR, BLOWER MOTOR - R&R *(B)*

1973-93
exc M3,733i .7
M3 1.0
733i 1.2

AIR CONDITIONING

FREON - RECOVER *(B)*
***NOTE:** This operation is not to be used with any other operations.*

1973-93 .3

Cont.

AIR CONDITIONING TIME GUIDE

BMW Heating & Air Conditioning (Cont.)

PERFORMANCE - TEST *(B)*
Includes: Gauge check, leak test and partial charge.

1973-93 ... 1.0

SYSTEM CHARGE (PARTIAL) *(B)*
Includes: Performance test.

1973-93 ... 1.0

SYSTEM CHARGE (COMPLETE) *(B)*
Includes: Recover, evacuate and recharge system.

1973-93 ... 1.4

BELT, COMPRESSOR - R&R *(D)*
Includes: Serpentine and V-Belt type.

1973-93
- L6,M6,525i,533i,535i,535is,630CSi, 633CSi,635CSi,733i,735i,735iL 6
- M3,3.0 Bavaria,3.0CS,3.0S,3.0Si, 740i,740iL 8
- M5
  - (87-88) 6
  - (91-93) 8
- 318i
  - (84-85) 5
  - (91-93) 7
- 318is,325iX,524td,528e 7
- 320i,528i,750iL,850Ci,850i 5
- 325,325e,325es,325iC 9
- 325i,325is
  - (87-91) 9
  - (92-93) 5

SEAL, COMPRESSOR SHAFT - R&R *(B)*
DOES NOT include System Charge.

1973-84 ... 1.3

COMPRESSOR ASSEMBLY - R&R *(B)*
DOES NOT include System Charge.

1973-93
- exc 524td ... 2.1
- 524td ... 2.6

PULLEY, COMPRESSOR - R&R *(B)*

1973-84
- 3.0 Bavaria,3.0CS,3.0S,3.0Si ... 1.3
- 320i 7
- 528i,733i 8
- 630CSi,633CSi ... 1.0

CLUTCH OR COIL, COMPRESSOR - R&R *(B)*

1973-86 ... 1.3

1987-93
- M3,325,325i,325iC,325is,750iL, 850Ci,850i ... 1.5
- M5
  - (87-88) ... 1.1
  - (91-93) ... 1.5
- M6,325iX,525i,535i ... 1.1
- 318i,318is,735i,735iL,740i,740iL ... 1.0
- 528e,535is ... N.A.

VALVE, EVAPORATOR EXPANSION - R&R *(B)*
DOES NOT include System Charge.

1973-93
- L6,524td,525i,528e,533i,535i,535is, 633CSi,635CSi ... 3.9
- M3,318is,325,325i,325iC,325is ... 1.8
- M5
  - (87-88) ... 2.7
  - (91-93) ... 2.4
- M6,325e,325es,750iL ... 3.0
- 318i
  - (84-85) ... 3.0
  - (91-93) ... 1.8
- 733i ... 2.3
- 735i
  - (85-86) ... 2.3
  - (87-92) ... 2.6
- 735iL ... 2.6
- 740i,740iL,850Ci,850i ... 2.8

RECEIVER DRIER - R&R *(B)*
DOES NOT include System Charge.

1973-84
- exc 318i,325e,630CSi,633CSi,733i 7
- 318i,325e ... 1.8
- 630CSi 5
- 633CSi,733i
  - (78-81) 5
  - (82-84) 8

1985-86 ... 1.8

1987-93
- M3,318i,318is,325,325iC,325iX 6
- M5
  - (87-88) 7
  - (91-93) 9
- M6,740i,740iL 7
- 325i,325is
  - (87-91) 6
  - (92-93) ... 1.5
- 525i,528e,535i,535is ... 1.8
- 735i,735iL 8
- 750iL,850Ci,850i ... 1.0

CONDENSER - R&R *(B)*
DOES NOT include System Charge.

1973-86
- 2002,2002tii ... 3.8
- 3.0 Bavaria,3.0CS,3.0S,3.0Si ... 3.9
- 318i,528i,535i ... 2.4
- 320i ... 3.2
- 325e,325es,735i ... 2.6
- 524td ... 2.9
- 528e,533i,630CSi,633CSi,635CSi ... 1.8
- 733i ... 2.0

1987-93
- exc 325i,325is ... 2.0
- 325i,325is
  - (87-91) ... 2.0
  - (92-93)
    - Std Trans ... 2.4
    - Auto Trans ... 2.6

CORE, EVAPORATOR - R&R *(B)*
DOES NOT include System Charge.

1973-86
- 2002,2002tii ... 4.7
- 3.0 Bavaria,3.0CS,3.0S,3.0Si ... 6.4
- 318i,320i,325e,325es,535i ... 3.0
- 524td,528i ... 3.3
- 528e,533i,630CSi,633CSi,635CSi ... 2.9
- 733i,735i
  - (78-81) ... 7.8
  - (82-86) ... 10.9

1987-93
- L6,528e,535is,635CSi ... 3.4
- M3,318i,318is,325,325i,325iC, 325is,325iX ... 1.8
- M5 ... 2.7
- M6,735i,735iL ... 3.0
- 525i,750iL ... 8.5
- 535i
  - (87-88) ... 3.4
  - (89-93) ... 8.5
- 740i,740iL ... 3.2
- 850Ci,850i ... 3.8

AUXILIARY FAN - R&R *(B)*

1973-84
- exc 318i,320i,325e,528e,528i,533i,733i 8
- 318i,325e
  - Std Trans ... 1.3
  - Auto Trans ... 1.5
- 320i,528i ... 3.6
- 528e,533i ... 2.7
- 733i ... 1.1

1985-93
- L6,M5,M6,524td,525i,528e,533i,535i, 535is,635CSi,735i,735iL,740i, 740iL,750iL 8
- M3 ... 1.3
- 318i
  - (85)
    - Std Trans ... 1.3
    - Auto Trans ... 1.5
  - (91-93) ... 2.0
- 318is ... 2.0
- 325,325iC,325iX
  - Std Trans ... 2.2
  - Auto Trans ... 2.4
- 325e,325es
  - Std Trans ... 1.3
  - Auto Trans ... 1.5
- 325i,325is
  - (87-91)
    - Std Trans ... 2.2
    - Auto Trans ... 2.4
  - (92-93) ... 1.6

RELAY, AUXILIARY FAN - R&R *(B)*

All 3

Cont.

AIR CONDITIONING TIME GUIDE

BMW Heating & Air Conditioning (Cont.)

SWITCH, AUXILIARY FAN CONTROL - R&R *(B)*

All 4

SWITCH, TEMP CONTROL - R&R *(B)*

1973-93
exc M3,318i,318is,325,325e,325es,325i, 325iC,325is,325iX,733i 8
M3,318i,318is,325,325e,325es,325i, 325iC,325is,325iX 1.9
733i 1.3

SWITCH, ICING PROTECTION - R&R *(B)*

1973-93
M3,318is,325,325i,325iC,325is,325iX 3
318i
(84-85) 7
(91-93) 3
325e,325es 7
733i,735i,735iL 9

● ADDITIONAL TIME ●

● w/Air Bag (SRS) add 5

HOSE, AIR CONDITIONING - R&R *(B)*
DOES NOT include System Charge.

1973-93
One 5
Each Additional 3

★ COMBINATIONS ★

★ Make Up Hose From Stock 4

Chrysler Motors Heating & Air Conditioning

ARROW, RAM-50, D-50 PICKUP & RAIDER

NOTE 1: Times shown DO NOT include evacuate and charge system. If necessary to open refrigerant system or to evacuate, charge and test; refer to System Charge (Complete) for appropriate time.
NOTE 2: Times listed are for Factory and Dealer dash installed Integral Type air conditioning units only. Use necessary clock time for services of hang-on units.

HEATING & VENTILATION

HEATER HOSES - R&R *(D)*

All 9

WATER VALVE - R&R *(B)*

Arrow,D50,Ram 50
w/Air Cond *(.6)* 9
w/o Air Cond *(.5)* 7
Raider
Front 2.4
Rear 1.0

SWITCH, WATER PUMP - R&R *(B)*

All 5

CORE, HEATER - R&R *(B)*
DOES NOT include evacuate or charge system.

Arrow,D50,Ram 50 .... 4.9
Raider
Front 5.0
Rear 1.8

MOTOR, BLOWER - R&R *(B)*

Arrow,D50,Ram 50
w/Air Cond *(1.1)* 1.5
w/o Air Cond *(.4)* 9
Raider
Front 6
Rear 1.0

RESISTOR, BLOWER MOTOR - R&R *(B)*

Front *(.8)* 1.0
Rear *(.3)* 5

SWITCH, BLOWER MOTOR - R&R *(B)*

All *(.4)* 1.0

CONTROL ASSEMBLY, TEMP - R&R *(B)*

w/Air Cond *(1.0)* 1.3
w/o Air Cond *(.5)* 7

CABLES, VENTILATION - R&R *(B)*

Mode *(.4)* 8
Temp
w/Air Cond *(.5)* 9
w/o Air Cond *(.4)* 8
Vent *(.4)* 8

AIR CONDITIONING

FREON - RECOVER *(B)*

All 3

PERFORMANCE - TEST *(B)*
Includes: Gauge check, leak test and partial charge.

All *(.6)* 1.0

SYSTEM CHARGE (PARTIAL) *(B)*
Includes: Performance test.

All 1.0

SYSTEM CHARGE (COMPLETE) *(B)*
Includes: Recover, evacuate and recharge system.
NOTE: When performed in conjunction with other heating or air conditioning repairs, deduct .2.

All *(.8)* 1.4

BELT, COMPRESSOR - R&R *(D)*

All *(.2)* 4

COMPRESSOR ASSEMBLY - R&R *(B)*
DOES NOT include evacuate or charge system.

All *(1.0)* 1.9

CLUTCH OR COIL, COMPRESSOR - R&R *(B)*

Arrow,D50,Ram 50 .... 2.2
Raider 1.8

SEAL, COMPRESSOR SHAFT - R&R *(B)*
DOES NOT include evacuate and charge system.

Arrow,D50,Ram 50 .... 2.6
Raider 1.8

VALVE, EVAPORATOR EXPANSION - R&R *(B)*
DOES NOT include evacuate or charge system.

Arrow,D50,Ram 50 *(1.5)* 2.2
Raider
Front 2.2
Rear 1.3

RECEIVER DRIER - R&R *(B)*
DOES NOT include evacuate or charge system.

All *(.5)* 9

CONDENSER - R&R *(B)*
DOES NOT include evacuate or charge system.

Arrow,D50,Ram 50 *(.7)* 1.5
Raider 1.2

CORE, EVAPORATOR - R&R *(B)*
DOES NOT include evacuate or charge system.

Arrow,D50,Ram 50 *(2.0)* 2.7
Raider
Front 2.1
Rear 1.6

SWITCH, LOW PRESSURE CUTOFF - R&R *(B)*
DOES NOT include evacuate and charge system.

Arrow,D50,Ram 50 7
Raider 2.2

SWITCH, HIGH PRESSURE CUTOFF - R&R *(B)*

All *(.2)* 5

SWITCH, CLUTCH CYCLING - R&R *(B)*

All *(.6)* 9

SWITCH, COOLANT TEMP - R&R *(B)*

All 5

HOSE, AIR CONDITIONING - R&R *(B)*
DOES NOT include evacuate or charge system.

One 1.0
Each Additional 5

★ COMBINATIONS ★

★ Make Up Hose From Stock 4

MOTOR, CONDENSER FAN - R&R *(B)*

Arrow,D50,Ram 50 8
Raider 1.8

RELAY, CONDENSER FAN - R&R *(B)*

All 3

Chrysler Motors Heating & Air Conditioning (Cont.)

CHALLENGER & SAPPORO

NOTE 1: Times shown DO NOT include recover, evacuate and charge system. If necessary to open refrigerant system, refer to System Charge (Complete) for appropriate time.
NOTE 2: Times listed are for Factory and Dealer dash installed Integral Type air conditioning units only. Use necessary clock time for service of hang-on units.

HEATING & VENTILATION

HEATER HOSES - R&R *(D)*

Water Pump to Inlet Tube 6
Heater, Inlet or Outlet
One 7
Both 1.0

CORE, HEATER - R&R *(B)*
DOES NOT include System Charge.

w/Air Cond 3.1
w/o Air Cond 2.0

WATER VALVE - R&R *(B)*

w/Air Cond 2.0
w/o Air Cond 1.6

MOTOR, BLOWER - R&R *(B)*

w/Air Cond 2.0
w/o Air Cond 9

RESISTOR, BLOWER MOTOR - R&R *(B)*

w/Air Cond 1.1
w/o Air Cond 6

SWITCH, BLOWER MOTOR - R&R *(B)*

w/Air Cond 9
w/o Air Cond 7

CABLES, VENTILATION CONTROL - R&R *(B)*

All 9

AIR CONDITIONING

FREON - RECOVER *(B)*
NOTE: This operation is not to be used with any other operations.

All 3

PERFORMANCE - TEST *(B)*
Includes: Gauge check, leak test and partial charge.

All 1.0

SYSTEM CHARGE (PARTIAL) *(B)*
Includes: Performance test.

All 1.0

SYSTEM CHARGE (COMPLETE) *(B)*
Includes: Recover, evacuate and recharge system.

All 1.4

BELT, COMPRESSOR - R&R *(D)*

All 3

● ADDITIONAL TIME ●

● Where Alternator interferes add 1
● Where Air Pump interferes add 1
● Where Pwr Strg interferes add 1

COMPRESSOR ASSEMBLY - R&R *(B)*
DOES NOT include System Charge.

All 1.4

★ COMBINATIONS ★

★ Seal, Compressor - R&R 6
★ Clutch Assembly - R&R 4
★ Coil, Compressor Clutch - R&R 5

CLUTCH OR COIL, COMPRESSOR - R&R *(B)*
Use Compressor Assembly - R&R plus Combinations.

VALVE, EVAPORATOR EXPANSION - R&R *(B)*
DOES NOT include System Charge.

All 1.8

DISCHARGE VALVE - R&R *(B)*
DOES NOT include System Charge.

1978 6

SUCTION VALVE - R&R *(B)*
DOES NOT include System Charge.

1978 6

CONDENSER - R&R *(B)*
DOES NOT include System Charge.

All 1.4

RECEIVER DRIER - R&R *(B)*
DOES NOT include System Charge.

All 6

CORE, EVAPORATOR - R&R *(B)*
DOES NOT include System Charge.

All 2.4

SWITCH, HIGH PRESSURE CUTOFF - R&R *(B)*

All 3

SWITCH, LOW PRESSURE CUTOFF - R&R *(B)*
DOES NOT include System Charge.

All 8

SWITCH, CLUTCH CYCLING - R&R *(B)*

All 7

HOSE, AIR CONDITIONING - R&R *(B)*
DOES NOT include System Charge.

One 1.0
Each Additional 5

★ COMBINATIONS ★

★ Make Up Hose From Stock 4

Chrysler Motors Heating & Air Conditioning (Cont.)

CHAMP, COLT & VISTA FWD

NOTE 1: Times shown DO NOT include recover, evacuate and charge system. If necessary to open refrigerant system, refer to System Charge (Complete) for appropriate time.
NOTE 2: Times listed are for Factory and Dealer dash installed Integral Type air conditioning units only. Use necessary clock time for service of hang-on units.

HEATING & VENTILATION

HEATER HOSES - R&R *(D)*

All 9

WATER VALVE - R&R *(B)*

Champ
w/Air Cond 2.4
w/o Air Cond 1.3
Colt
H.B.
w/Air Cond 6.4
w/o Air Cond 6.2
S/W
w/Air Cond 2.6
w/o Air Cond 2.3
Vista S/W
w/Air Cond 3.7
w/o Air Cond 3.4

CORE, HEATER - R&R *(B)*
DOES NOT include System Charge.

1979-94
Champ,Colt
(79-88) 5.1
(89-94)
w/Air Cond 6.4
w/o Air Cond 6.2
Vista S/W
(84-91)
w/Air Cond 3.7
w/o Air Cond 3.4
(92-94) 4.3

Cont.

AIR CONDITIONING TIME GUIDE

Chrysler Motors Heating & Air Conditioning (Cont.)

CHAMP, COLT & VISTA FWD (Cont.)

MOTOR, BLOWER - R&R *(B)*

1979-94

Champ,Colt	
w/Air Cond	1.5
w/o Air Cond	1.0
Vista S/W	
(84-91)	
w/Air Cond	1.0
w/o Air Cond	.8
(92-94)	.6

RESISTOR, BLOWER MOTOR - R&R *(B)*

1979-94

Champ, Colt	
w/Air Cond	1.0
w/o Air Cond	.7
Vista S/W	
(84-91)	
w/Air Cond	1.0
w/o Air Cond	.7
(92-94)	.5

SWITCH, BLOWER MOTOR - R&R *(B)*

1979-94

Champ	
w/Air Cond	.7
w/o Air Cond	1.0
Colt	
w/Air Cond	1.3
w/o Air Cond	.7
Vista S/W	
(84-91)	.8
(92-94)	
w/Air Cond	1.3
w/o Air Cond	.7

CABLE, TEMP CONTROL - R&R *(B)*

Champ	.7
Colt	
H.B.	1.3
S/W	.7
Vista S/W	
(84-91)	.8
(92-94)	
w/Air Cond	.8
w/o Air Cond	.7

CABLE, HEATER MODE CONTROL - R&R *(B)*

Champ	.7
Colt	
H.B.	1.3
S/W	.7
Vista S/W	
(84-91)	.8
(92-94)	.9

CONTROL ASSEMBLY, TEMP - R&R *(B)*

1979-94

Champ	1.3
Colt	
(79-88)	1.5
(92-94)	.7
Vista S/W	1.5

AIR CONDITIONING

FREON - RECOVER *(B)*

NOTE: This operation is not to be used with any other operations.

All	.3

PERFORMANCE - TEST *(B)*

Includes: Gauge check, leak test and partial charge.

All	1.0

SYSTEM CHARGE (PARTIAL) *(B)*

Includes: Performance test.

All	1.0

SYSTEM CHARGE (COMPLETE) *(B)*

Includes: Recover, evacuate and recharge system.

All	1.4

BELT, COMPRESSOR - R&R *(D)*

Includes: Serpentine belts.

All	.5

● ADDITIONAL TIME ●

● Where Pwr Strg interferes add	.1
● Where Air Pump interferes add	.1
● Where Alt interferes add	.1

SEAL, COMPRESSOR SHAFT - R&R *(B)*

Use Compressor Assembly - R&R plus Combinations.

COMPRESSOR ASSEMBLY - R&R *(B)*

DOES NOT include System Charge.

All	1.3

★ COMBINATIONS ★

★ Seal, Compressor - R&R	.6
★ Clutch Assembly - R&R	.4
★ Coil, Compressor Clutch - R&R	.5

CLUTCH OR COIL, COMPRESSOR - R&R *(B)*

Use Compressor Assembly - R&R plus Combinations.

VALVE, EVAPORATOR EXPANSION - R&R *(B)*

DOES NOT include System Charge.

All	2.1

CONDENSER - R&R *(B)*

DOES NOT include System Charge.

All	1.1

RECEIVER DRIER - R&R *(B)*

DOES NOT include System Charge.

All	.8

SWITCH, LOW PRESSURE CUTOFF - R&R *(B)*

DOES NOT include System Charge.

All	.8

SWITCH, HIGH PRESSURE CUTOFF - R&R *(B)*

All	.5

CORE, EVAPORATOR - R&R *(B)*

DOES NOT include System Charge.

All	3.0

SWITCH, CLUTCH CYCLING - R&R *(B)*

All	1.2

HOSE, AIR CONDITIONING - R&R *(B)*

DOES NOT include System Charge.

One	1.0
Each Additional	.5

★ COMBINATIONS ★

★ Make Up Hose From Stock	.4

CONDENSER FAN MOTOR - R&R *(B)*

All	.8

RELAY, CONDENSER FAN - R&R *(B)*

All	.3

CONTROL SWITCH, AIR COND. - R&R *(B)*

All	.3

SWITCH, DUAL PRESSURE - R&R *(B)*

All	.9

SWITCH, TRIPLE PRESSURE - R&R *(B)*

All	.9

Chrysler Motors Heating & Air Conditioning (Cont.)

NOTE 1: Times shown DO NOT include evacuate and charge system. If necessary to open refrigerant system or to evacuate, charge and test; refer to System Charge (Complete) for appropriate time.
NOTE 2: Times listed are for Factory and Dealer dash installed Integral Type air conditioning units only. Use necessary clock time for service of hang-on units.

CONQUEST

HEATING & VENTILATION

HEATER HOSES - R&R *(D)*

NOTE: Deduct .2 when used in conjunction with Radiator Hose - R&R.

All	.9

CORE, HEATER - R&R *(B)*

DOES NOT include System Charge.

All	7.6

VALVE, TEMPERATURE CONTROL - R&R *(B)*

w/Air Cond	2.4
w/o Air Cond	2.1

SWITCH, WATER TEMP - R&R *(B)*

All	.5

Cont.

AIR CONDITIONING TIME GUIDE

Chrysler Motors Heating & Air Conditioning (Cont.)

CONQUEST (Cont.)

MOTOR, BLOWER - R&R *(B)*

w/Air Cond 9
w/o Air Cond 7

SWITCH, BLOWER MOTOR - R&R *(B)*

All 7

RESISTOR, BLOWER MOTOR - R&R *(B)*

All 6

CONTROL ASSEMBLY, TEMPERATURE - R&R *(B)*

w/Air Cond 2.6
w/o Air Cond 9

CABLE, TEMPERATURE CONTROL - R&R *(B)*

To Control Valve
w/Air Cond 2.4
w/o Air Cond 4
To Mode Control or Recirculation Door
One or Both 2.4

AIR CONDITIONING

FREON - RECOVER *(B)*

NOTE: This operation is not to be used with any other operations.

All 3

PERFORMANCE - TEST *(B)*

Includes: Gauge check, leak test and partial charge.

All 1.0

SYSTEM CHARGE (PARTIAL) *(B)*

Includes: Performance test.

All 1.0

SYSTEM CHARGE (COMPLETE) *(B)*

Includes: Recover, evacuate and recharge system.

All 1.4

BELT, COMPRESSOR - R&R *(D)*

All 3

• ADDITIONAL TIME •

• Where Air Pump interferes add 1
• Where Pwr Strg interferes add 1
• Where Alternator interferes add 1

SEAL, COMPRESSOR SHAFT - R&R *(B)*

Use Compressor Assembly - R&R plus Combinations.

COMPRESSOR ASSEMBLY - R&R *(B)*

DOES NOT include System Charge.

All 1.6

★ COMBINATIONS ★

★ Seal, Compressor - R&R 6
★ Valve Plates, Compressor - R&R 9
★ Clutch Assembly - R&R 4
★ Coil, Compressor Clutch - R&R 5

HEAD, GASKET &/OR VALVE PLATE - R&R *(A)*

Use Compressor Assembly - R&R plus Combinations..

PULLEY, BEARING &/OR COIL, CLUTCH - R&R *(B)*

Use Compressor Assembly - R&R plus Combinations.

CLUTCH ASSEMBLY - R&R *(B)*

Use Compressor Assembly - R&R plus Combinations.

VALVE, EVAPORATOR EXPANSION - R&R *(B)*

DOES NOT include System Charge.

All 2.5

CORE, EVAPORATOR - R&R *(B)*

DOES NOT include System Charge.

All 2.8

SWITCH, HIGH PRESSURE CUTOFF - R&R *(B)*

DOES NOT include System Charge.

All 7

SWITCH, LOW PRESSURE - R&R *(B)*

DOES NOT include System Charge.

All 8

SWITCH, CLUTCH CYCLING - R&R *(B)*

All 2.3

RECEIVER DRIER - R&R *(B)*

DOES NOT include System Charge.

All 9

CONDENSER - R&R *(B)*

DOES NOT include System Charge.

All 1.0

HOSE, AIR CONDITIONING - R&R *(B)*

DOES NOT include System Charge.

One 1.0
Each Additional 5

★ COMBINATIONS ★

★ Make Up Hose From Stock 4

CONDENSER FAN MOTOR - R&R *(B)*

All 6

Daihatsu Heating & Air Conditioning

***NOTE 1:* Times shown Do Not include recover, evacuate and charge system. If necessary to open refrigerant system or to recover, evacuate, charge and test, refer to System Charge (Complete) for appropriate time.**
***NOTE 2:* Times listed are for Factory and Dealer dash installed Integral Type air conditioning units only. Use necessary clock time for service of hang-on units.**

HEATING & VENTILATION

HEATER HOSES - R&R *(D)*

NOTE: Deduct .2 when used in conjunction with Radiator Hoses - R&R.

One 6
Both 8

CORE, HEATER - R&R *(B)*

Includes: R&I dash assembly and steering column.
DOES NOT include recover, evacuate and recharge system.

Charade 3.0
Rocky
Front 2.5
Rear 1.2

MOTOR, BLOWER - R&R *(B)*

All 5

SWITCH, BLOWER MOTOR - R&R *(B)*

All 6

CONTROL ASSEMBLY, TEMP - R&R *(B)*

Charade 6
Rocky 1.3

RESISTOR, BLOWER MOTOR - R&R *(B)*

All 5

AIR CONDITIONING

FREON - RECOVER *(B)*

NOTE: This operation is not to be used with any other operations.

All 3

PERFORMANCE - TEST *(B)*

Includes: Gauge check, leak test and partial charge.

All 1.0

SYSTEM CHARGE (PARTIAL) *(B)*

Includes: Performance test.

All 1.0

SYSTEM CHARGE (COMPLETE) *(B)*

Includes: Recover, evacuate and recharge system.

All 1.4

BELT, COMPRESSOR - R&R *(D)*

Charade 5
Rocky 6

IDLER PULLEY - R&R *(D)*

All 6

COMPRESSOR ASSEMBLY - R&R *(B)*

Includes: Transfer clutch assembly.
DOES NOT include System Charge.

Charade
1.0L Eng 2.0
1.3L Eng 2.6
Rocky 1.8

Cont.

AIR CONDITIONING TIME GUIDE

Daihatsu Heating & Air Conditioning (Cont.)

SEAL, COMPRESSOR SHAFT - R&R *(B)*
Includes: R&I compressor assembly.
DOES NOT include System Charge.

Charade
1.0L Eng 2.3
1.3L Eng 2.9
Rocky 2.0

CLUTCH ASSEMBLY - R&R *(B)*
DOES NOT include System Charge.

Charade
1.0L Eng 2.0
1.3L Eng 2.6
Rocky 1.0

CONDENSER - R&R *(B)*
DOES NOT include System Charge.

Charade
1.0L Eng 2.2
1.3L Eng 2.6
Rocky 2.2

RECEIVER DRIER - R&R *(B)*
DOES NOT include System Charge.

Charade
1.0L Eng 1.1
1.3L Eng 1.5
Rocky 1.5

CORE, EVAPORATOR - R&R *(B)*
DOES NOT include System Charge.

Charade 2.7
Rocky 2.0

VALVE, EVAPORATOR EXPANSION - R&R *(B)*
DOES NOT include System Charge.

Charade 2.7
Rocky 6

THERMOSTAT - R&R *(B)*
DOES NOT include System Charge.

Charade 2.7
Rocky .... N.A.

SWITCH, DUAL PRESSURE - R&R *(B)*
DOES NOT include System Charge.

Charade 2.7
Rocky .... N.A.

MOTOR &/OR FAN, CONDENSER - R&R *(D)*

Charade 1.3
Rocky .... N.A.

RELAY, CONDENSER FAN - R&R *(B)*

All 5

SWITCH, CONTROL - R&R *(B)*

All 7

SWITCH, ACCELERATING CUT-OFF - R&R *(B)*

All 3

AMPLIFIER, AIR CONDITIONER - R&R *(B)*

All 3

HOSE, AIR CONDITIONING - R&R *(B)*
DOES NOT include System Charge.

One (Discharge or Suction) 1.5
Each Additional 4

★ COMBINATIONS ★

★ Make Up Hose From Stock 4

Eagle Heating & Air Conditioning

NOTE 1: Times shown DO NOT include recover, evacuate and charge system. If necessary to open refrigerant system; refer to System Charge (Complete) for appropriate time.
NOTE 2: Times listed are for Factory and Dealer dash installed Integral Type air conditioning units only. Use necessary clock time for services of hang-on units.

HEATING & VENTILATION

HEATER HOSES (ALL) - R&R *(D)*

1989-94 9

WATER VALVE - R&R *(B)*

1989-94
w/Air Cond 2.4
w/o Air Cond 1.3

CORE, HEATER - R&R *(B)*
DOES NOT include System Charge.

1989-94
Summit
w/Air Cond 6.4
w/o Air Cond 6.2
Summit Wagon 4.3

MOTOR, BLOWER - R&R *(B)*

1989-94
Summit
w/Air Cond 1.5
w/o Air Cond 1.0
Summit Wagon 6

SUMMIT & SUMMIT WAGON

SWITCH, BLOWER MOTOR - R&R *(B)*

1989-94
w/Air Cond 1.3
w/o Air Cond 7

RESISTOR, BLOWER MOTOR - R&R *(B)*

1989-94 5

CONTROL ASSEMBLY, HEATER - R&R *(B)*

1989-94 .... 1.1

CABLES, VENTILATION CONTROL - R&R *(B)*

1988-94
Heater Mode 1.3
Temperature
w/Air Cond 1.3
w/o Air Cond 1.1
Vent 7

AIR CONDITIONING

FREON - RECOVER *(B)*
NOTE: This operation is not to be used with any other operations.

1989-94 3

PERFORMANCE - TEST *(B)*
Includes: Gauge check, leak test and partial charge.

1989-94 .... 1.0

SYSTEM CHARGE (PARTIAL) *(B)*
Includes: Performance test.

1989-94 .... 1.0

SYSTEM CHARGE (COMPLETE) *(B)*
Includes: Recover, evacuate and recharge system.

1989-94 .... 1.4

BELT, COMPRESSOR - R&R *(D)*

1989-94 5

• ADDITIONAL TIME •

• Where Alt interferes add 1
• Where Air Pump interferes add 1
• Where Pwr Strg interferes add 1

COMPRESSOR ASSEMBLY - R&R *(B)*
DOES NOT include System Charge.

1989-94 .... 1.3

★ COMBINATIONS ★

★ Seal, Compressor - R&R 6
★ Clutch Assembly - R&R 4

CLUTCH ASSEMBLY - R&R *(B)*
Use Compressor Assembly - R&R plus Combinations.

SEAL, COMPRESSOR SHAFT - R&R *(B)*
Use Compressor Assembly - R&R, plus Combinations.

VALVE, EVAPORATOR EXPANSION - R&R *(B)*
DOES NOT include System Charge.

1989-94 .... 2.1

CHECK VALVE, VACUUM - R&R *(B)*
DOES NOT include System Charge.

1989-94 5

Cont.

AIR CONDITIONING TIME GUIDE

Eagle Heating & Air Conditioning (Cont.)

SUMMIT & SUMMIT WAGON (Cont.)

CONDENSER - R&R *(B)*
DOES NOT include System Charge.
1989-94 .... 1.1

ACCUMULATOR OR RECEIVER DRIER - R&R *(B)*
DOES NOT include System Charge.
1989-94 8

CORE, EVAPORATOR - R&R *(B)*
DOES NOT include evacuate or charge system.
1989-94 .... 3.0

CONDENSER FAN MOTOR - R&R *(B)*
1989-94 8

RELAY, CONDENSER FAN - R&R *(B)*
1989-94 3

SWITCH, PRESSURE - R&R *(B)*
1989-94 9

SWITCH, CLUTCH CYCLING - R&R *(B)*
1989-94 7

SWITCH, HIGH PRESSURE - R&R *(B)*
1989-94 5

SWITCH, LOW PRESSURE - R&R *(B)*
DOES NOT include System Charge.
1989-94 7

HOSE, AIR CONDITIONING - R&R *(B)*
DOES NOT include System Charge.
1989-94
One 1.0
Each Additional 5

★ COMBINATIONS ★

★ Make Up Hose From Stock 4

Ford Motor Co. Heating & Air Conditioning

1991-94 CAPRI

NOTE 1: Times shown DO NOT include recover, evacuate and charge system. If necessary to open refrigerant system; refer to System Charge (Complete) for appropriate time.
NOTE 2: Times listed are for Factory and Dealer dash installed Integral Type air conditioning units only. Use necessary clock time for service of hang-on units.

HEATING & VENTILATION

HEATER HOSES - R&R *(D)*
NOTE: Deduct .2 when used in conjunction with Radiator Hose – R&R.
1991-94
One 8
Both 1.0

CORE, HEATER - R&R *(B)*
DOES NOT include evacuate or charge system.
1991-94 .... 3.4

MOTOR BLOWER - R&R *(B)*
1991-94 .... 1.3

CONTROL ASSEMBLY - R&R *(B)*
1991-94 .... 1.0

SWITCH, BLOWER MOTOR - R&R *(B)*
1991-94 .... 1.0

RESISTOR, BLOWER MOTOR - R&R *(B)*
1991-94 5

CABLE, TEMPERATURE - R&R *(B)*
1991-94 .... 1.1

CABLE, DEFROSTER - R&R *(B)*
1991-94 6

VACUUM MOTOR - R&R *(B)*
1991-94 .... 1.1

AIR CONDITIONING

FREON - RECOVER *(B)*
NOTE: This operation is not to be used with any other operations.
1991-94 3

PERFORMANCE - TEST *(B)*
Includes: Gauge check, leak test and partial charge.
1991-94 .... 1.0

SYSTEM CHARGE (PARTIAL) *(B)*
Includes: Performance test.
1988-94 .... 1.0

SYSTEM CHARGE (COMPLETE) *(B)*
Includes: Recover, evacuate and recharge system.
1991-94 .... 1.4

BELT, COMPRESSOR - R&R *(D)*
Includes: Serpentine type.
1991-94 6

SEAL, COMPRESSOR SHAFT - R&R *(B)*
DOES NOT include System Charge.
1991-94 .... 2.4

COMPRESSOR ASSEMBLY - R&R *(B)*
DOES NOT include System Charge.
1991-94 .... 1.3

PULLEY &/OR CLUTCH, COMPRESSOR - R&R *(B)*
DOES NOT include System Charge.
1991-94 .... 1.8

BEARING, COMP CLUTCH OR PULLEY - R&R *(B)*
DOES NOT include System Charge.
1991-94 – Use Pulley &/or Clutch - R&R

VALVE, EVAPORATOR EXPANSION - R&R *(B)*
DOES NOT include System Charge.
1991-94 .... 2.6

ACCUMULATOR OR RECEIVER DRIER - R&R *(B)*
DOES NOT include System Charge.
1991-94 6

CORE, EVAPORATOR - R&R *(B)*
DOES NOT include System Charge.
1991-94 .... 2.0

CONDENSER - R&R *(B)*
DOES NOT include System Charge.
1991-94 8

FAN &/OR MOTOR, CONDENSER - R&R *(B)*
1991-94 6

MODULE, COOLING FAN CONTROL - R&R *(B)*
1991-94 7

SWITCH, ELECTRIC FAN - R&R *(B)*
1991-94 5

HOSE, AIR CONDITIONING - R&R *(B)*
DOES NOT include evacuate or charge system.
Each 6

★ COMBINATIONS ★

★ Make Up Hose From Stock 2

Cont.

AIR CONDITIONING TIME GUIDE

Ford Motor Co. Heating & Air Conditioning (Cont.)

FESTIVA

NOTE 1: Times shown DO NOT include recover, evacuate and charge system. If necessary to open refrigerant system; refer to System Charge (Complete) for appropriate time.
NOTE 2: Times shown are for Factory and Dealer dash installed Integral Type air conditioning units only. Use necessary clock time for service of hang-on units.

HEATING & VENTILATION

HEATER HOSES - R&R *(D)*
NOTE: Deduct .2 when used in conjunction with Radiator Hoses - R&R.
One 6
Both 8

CORE, HEATER - R&R *(B)*
All 3.5

MOTOR, BLOWER - R&R *(B)*
w/Air Cond 8
w/o Air Cond 6

SWITCH, BLOWER MOTOR - R&R *(B)*
w/Air Cond 8
w/o Air Cond 7

CONTROL ASSEMBLY, TEMPERATURE - R&R *(B)*
w/Air Cond 7
w/o Air Cond 6

CABLE, TEMPERATURE CONTROL - R&R *(B)*
All 8

CABLE, DEFROSTER - R&R *(B)*
All 8

WATER VALVE - R&R *(B)*
All 9

AIR CONDITIONING

FREON - RECOVER *(B)*
NOTE: This operation is not to be used with any other operations.
All 3

PERFORMANCE - TEST *(B)*
Includes: Gauge check, leak test and partial charge.
All 1.0

SYSTEM CHARGE (PARTIAL) *(B)*
Includes: Pressure and leak test.
All 1.0

SYSTEM CHARGE (COMPLETE) *(B)*
Includes: Evacuate, recover and recharge system.
All 1.4

BELT, COMPRESSOR - R&R *(D)*
All 5

VALVE, PRESSURE RELIEF - R&R *(B)*
All 3

COMPRESSOR ASSEMBLY - R&R *(B)*
Includes: Transfer clutch and pulley.
DOES NOT include evacuate or charge system.
All 1.3

COMPRESSOR ASSEMBLY - R&I & O/H *(B)*
All 4.5

SEAL, COMPRESSOR SHAFT - R&R *(B)*
DOES NOT include evacuate or charge system.
All 2.2

CLUTCH ASSEMBLY - R&R *(B)*
All 1.3

★ **COMBINATIONS** ★

★ Bearing, Comp Clutch or Pulley - R&R 5

VALVE, EVAPORATOR EXPANSION - R&R *(B)*
DOES NOT include evacuate or charge system.
All 1.5

RECEIVER DRIER - R&R *(B)*
DOES NOT include evacuate or charge system.
All 7

CONDENSER - R&R *(B)*
DOES NOT include evacuate or charge system.
All 9

MOTOR, ELECTRIC FAN - R&R *(B)*
Front 3
Rear 7

SWITCH, ELECTRIC FAN - R&R *(B)*
All 5

RELAY, ELECTRIC FAN - R&R *(B)*
All 5

MODULE, COOLING FAN CONTROL - R&R *(B)*
All 7

CORE, EVAPORATOR - R&R *(B)*
DOES NOT include evacuate or charge system.
All 1.2

SWITCH, CLUTCH CYCLING - R&R *(B)*
All 9

HOSE, AIR CONDITIONING - R&R *(B)*
DOES NOT include evacuate or charge system.
Each 5

★ **COMBINATIONS** ★

★ Make Up Hose From Stock 4

Ford Motor Co. Heating & Air Conditioning (Cont.)

MERKUR

NOTE 1: Times shown DO NOT include recover, evacuate and charge system. If necessary to open refrigerant system; refer to System Charge (Complete) for appropriate time.
NOTE 2: Times listed are for Factory and Dealer dash installed Itegral Type air conditioning units only. Use necessary clock time for service of hang-on units.

HEATING & VENTILATION

HEATER HOSES - R&R *(D)*
NOTE: Deduct .2 when used in conjunction with radiator hose - R&R.
1985-89 8

WATER VALVE - R&R *(B)*
1985-89
Scorpio 7
XR4Ti 6

CORE, HEATER - R&R *(B)*
DOES NOT include evacuate or charge system.
1985-89
Scorpio 3.6
XR4Ti 3.4

MOTOR, BLOWER - R&R *(B)*
DOES NOT include evacuate or charge system.
1985-89 .... 5.4

SWITCH, BLOWER MOTOR - R&R *(B)*
1985-89
Heater 3
Air Cond 7

RESISTOR, BLOWER MOTOR - R&R *(B)*
1985-89
Scorpio 7
XR4Ti 5

CONTROL ASSEMBLY, TEMPERATURE - R&R *(B)*
1985-89
Scorpio 5
XR4Ti 2.0

CABLE, TEMPERATURE CONTROL - R&R *(B)*
1985-89
Scorpio 1.6
XR4Ti 2.0

Cont.

AIR CONDITIONING TIME GUIDE

Ford Motor Co. Heating & Air Conditioning (Cont.)

MERKUR (Cont.)

VACUUM MOTOR - R&R *(B)*

1985-89 6

AIR CONDITIONING

FREON - RECOVER *(B)*
NOTE: This operation is not to be used with any other operation.

All 3

PERFORMANCE - TEST *(B)*
Includes: Gauge check, leak test and partial charge.

1985-89 .... 1.0

SYSTEM CHARGE (PARTIAL) *(B)*
Includes: Pressure and leak test.

1985-89 .... 1.0

SYSTEM CHARGE (COMPLETE) *(B)*
Includes: Evacuate, recover and recharge system.

1985-89 .... 1.4

BELT, COMPRESSOR - R&R *(D)*

1985-89 5

SEAL, COMPRESSOR SHAFT - R&R *(B)*
DOES NOT include evacuate or charge system.

1985-89 .... 1.5

COMPRESSOR ASSEMBLY - R&R *(B)*
DOES NOT include evacuate or charge system.

1985-89
Scorpio 1.1
XR4Ti 1.0

PULLEY &/OR CLUTCH, COMPRESSOR - R&R *(B)*
DOES NOT include compressor - R&I, evacuate or charge system.

1985-89 8

★ COMBINATIONS ★

★ Field Assembly - R&R 3
★ Bearing, Compressor Clutch - R&R 1

VALVE, EVAPORATOR EXPANSION - R&R *(B)*
DOES NOT include evacuate or charge system.

1985-89
Scorpio 9
XR4Ti 7

RECEIVER DRIER - R&R *(B)*
DOES NOT include evacuate or charge system.

1985-89
Scorpio 1.5
XR4Ti 7

FAN & MOTOR, CONDENSER - R&R *(B)*

1985-89 7

RELAY, CONDENSER FAN - R&R *(B)*

1985-89 7

SWITCH, CONDENSER FAN - R&R *(B)*

1985-89 5

CONDENSER - R&R *(B)*
DOES NOT include evacuate or charge system.

1985-89
Scorpio 2.0
XR4Ti 1.3

CORE, EVAPORATOR - R&R *(B)*
Includes: R&I components necessary for access.
DOES NOT include evacuate or charge system.

1985-89
Scorpio 2.4
XR4Ti 5.4

SWITCH, A/C CLUTCH CYCLING - R&R *(B)*

1985-89 5

SWITCH, A/C BLOWER MOTOR - R&R *(B)*

1985-89 7

HOSE, AIR CONDITIONING - R&R *(B)*
DOES NOT include evacuate or charge system.

Each 5

★ COMBINATIONS ★

★ Make Up Hose From Stock 4

Ford Motor Co. Heating & Air Conditioning (Cont.)

TRACER

NOTE 1: Times shown DO NOT include recover, evacuate and charge system. If necessary to open refrigerant system; refer to System Charge (Complete) for appropriate time.
NOTE 2: Times listed are for Factory and Dealer dash installed Integral Type air conditioning units only. Use necessary clock time for service of hang-on units.

HEATING & VENTILATION

HEATER HOSES - R&R *(D)*
NOTE: Deduct .2 when used in conjunction with Radiator Hose - R&R.

One 6
Both 7

CORE, HEATER - R&R *(B)*
Includes: R&I instrument panel.
DOES NOT include evacuate and charge system.

1988-89 .... 4.5
1991-94
w/Air Cond 4.1
w/o Air Cond 3.5

MOTOR, BLOWER - R&R *(B)*

All 6

SWITCH, BLOWER MOTOR - R&R *(B)*

1988-89 8
1991-94 6

RELAY, BLOWER MOTOR - R&R *(B)*

All 3

CONTROL ASSEMBLY, HEATER - R&R *(B)*

All 9

CABLE, TEMP CONTROL - R&R *(B)*

1988-94 9

CABLE, DEFROSTER - R&R *(B)*

1988-94 9

AIR CONDITIONING

FREON - RECOVER *(B)*
NOTE: This operation is not to be used with any other operations.

All 3

PERFORMANCE - TEST *(B)*
Includes: Gauge check, leak test and partial charge.

All 1.0

SYSTEM CHARGE (PARTIAL) *(B)*
Includes: Pressure and leak test.

All 1.0

SYSTEM CHARGE (COMPLETE) *(B)*
Includes: Evacuate, recover and recharge system.

All 1.4

BELT, COMPRESSOR - R&R *(D)*

1988-89 3
1991-94 5

COMPRESSOR ASSEMBLY - R&R *(B)*
Includes: Transfer clutch assembly.
DOES NOT include evacuate and charge system.

1988-89 .... 1.8
1991-94 9

SEAL, COMPRESSOR SHAFT - R&R *(B)*
DOES NOT include evacuate and charge system.

1988-89 .... 2.2
1991-94 .... 1.3

CLUTCH PLATE & HUB ASSEMBLY - R&R *(B)*
DOES NOT include evacuate and charge system.

1988-89 .... 1.8
1991-94 .... 1.5

★ COMBINATIONS ★

★ Bearing, Clutch Pulley - R&R 4
★ Field Coil, Clutch - R&R 2

Cont.

AIR CONDITIONING TIME GUIDE

Ford Motor Co. Heating & Air Conditioning (Cont.)

TRACER (Cont.)

CONDENSER - R&R *(B)*
DOES NOT include evacuate and charge system.
1988-89 .... 1.0
1991-94 9

RECEIVER DRIER - R&R *(B)*
DOES NOT include evacuate and charge system.
1988-89 4
1991-94 .... 1.1

CORE, EVAPORATOR - R&R *(B)*
DOES NOT include evacuate and charge system.
1988-89 9
1991-94 .... 1.3

VALVE, EVAPORATOR EXPANSION - R&R *(B)*
DOES NOT include evacuate and charge system.
1988-89 9
1991-94 .... 1.5

BLOWER MOTOR - R&R *(B)*
All 6

SWITCH, BLOWER MOTOR - R&R *(B)*
1988-89 8
1991-94 6

RELAY, BLOWER MOTOR - R&R *(B)*
All 3

SWITCH, CLUTCH CYCLING - R&R *(B)*
All 8

FAN &/OR MOTOR, AIR COND COOLING - R&R *(B)*
All 4

SWITCH, ELECTRIC FAN - R&R *(B)*
All 6

RELAY, ELECTRIC FAN - R&R *(B)*
All 8

MODULE, COOLING FAN CONTROL - R&R *(B)*
All *(.3)* 5

HOSE, AIR CONDITIONING - R&R *(B)*
DOES NOT include evacuate and charge system.
Each 6

★ **COMBINATIONS** ★
★ Make Up Hose From Stock 4

GM & Geo Heating & Air Conditioning

LEMANS

NOTE 1: Times shown DO NOT include recover, evacuate and charge system. If necessary to open refrigerant system; refer to System Charge (Complete) for appropriate time.
NOTE 2: Times listed are for Factory and Dealer dash installed Integral Type air conditioning units only. Use necessary clock time for service of hang-on units.

HEATING & VENTILATION

HEATER HOSES (ALL) - R&R *(D)*
1988-93
w/Air Cond 8
w/o Air Cond 6

CORE, HEATER - R&R *(B)*
DOES NOT include System Charge.
1988-93
w/Air Cond 2.6
w/o Air Cond 2.0

★ **COMBINATIONS** ★
★ Heater Hoses - R&R 2

MOTOR BLOWER - R&R *(B)*
1988-93
w/Air Cond 5
w/o Air Cond 7

SWITCH, BLOWER MOTOR - R&R *(B)*
1988-93 6

RELAY, BLOWER MOTOR - R&R *(C)*
1988-93 3

RESISTOR, BLOWER MOTOR - R&R *(B)*
1988-93 5

CONTROL ASSEMBLY, HEATER - R&R *(B)*
1988-93 .... 1.1

CABLES, VENTILATION CONTROL - R&R *(B)*
1988-93
Defrost Cable 6
Temperature Cable
w/Air Cond 1.5
w/o Air Cond 6

DIAPHRAGM CONTROL (ACTUATOR) - R&R *(B)*
1988-93
Air Inlet (Recirculation) 7
Defroster 6
Mode/Diverter 7

AIR CONDITIONING

FREON - RECOVER *(B)*
NOTE: This operation is not to be used with any other operations.
1988-93 3

PERFORMANCE - TEST *(B)*
Includes: Gauge check, leak test and partial charge.
1988-93 .... 1.0

SYSTEM CHARGE (PARTIAL) *(B)*
Includes: Performance test.
1988-93 .... 1.0

SYSTEM CHARGE (COMPLETE) *(B)*
Includes: Recover, evacuate and recharge system.
1988-93 .... 1.4

BELT, COMPRESSOR - R&R *(D)*
1988-93 3

● **ADDITIONAL TIME** ●
● Where Air Pump interferes add 2
● Where Alternator interferes add 2
● Where Pwr Strg interferes add 2

SEAL, COMPRESSOR SHAFT - R&R *(B)*
Use Compressor Assembly - R&R plus Combinations.

COMPRESSOR ASSEMBLY - R&R *(B)*
DOES NOT include System Charge.
1988-93 .... 1.0

★ **COMBINATIONS** ★
★ Seal, Compressor Shaft - R&R 6
★ Pulley &/or Bearing - R&R 5
★ Clutch Coil - R&R 4
★ Clutch Plate or Hub - R&R 4
★ In-Line Filter - Installation
Spline in Filter 6
Tube with Filter 4

VALVE, COMPRESSOR CUTOFF - R&R *(B)*
DOES NOT include System Charge.
1988-93 6

PULLEY &/OR BEARINGS, COMPRESSOR - R&R *(B)*
Use Compressor Assembly - R&R plus Combinations.

CLUTCH PLATE & HUB ASSEMBLY - R&R *(B)*
Use Compressor Assembly - R&R plus Combinations.

COIL, COMPRESSOR CLUTCH - R&R *(B)*
Use Compressor Assembly - R&R plus Combinations.

SWITCH, COMPRESSOR CUTOFF - R&R *(B)*
DOES NOT include System Charge.
1988-93 5

Cont.

AIR CONDITIONING TIME GUIDE

GM & Geo Heating & Air Conditioning (Cont.)

LEMANS (Cont.)

CONDENSER - R&R *(B)*
DOES NOT include System Charge.
1988-93 .... 1.8

BLADE &/OR MOTOR, ELECTRIC FAN - R&R *(B)*
1988-93 6

SWITCH, COOLING FAN - R&R *(B)*
1988-93 5

RESISTOR, COOLING FAN - R&R *(B)*
1988-93 3

RELAY, COOLING FAN - R&R *(B)*
1988-93 3

ACCUMULATOR OR RECEIVER DRIER - R&R *(B)*
DOES NOT include System Charge.
1988-93 6

CORE, EVAPORATOR - R&R *(B)*
DOES NOT include System Charge.
1988-93 .... 2.7

HOSE, AIR CONDITIONING - R&R *(B)*
DOES NOT include System Charge.
1988-93
Condenser to Evaporator (Liquid Line) 7
Evaporator to Accumulator 6
Suction & Discharge Assy 7

★ COMBINATIONS ★

★ Make Up Hose From Stock 4

GM & Geo Heating & Air Conditioning (Cont.)

METRO & SPRINT

NOTE 1: Times shown DO NOT include recover, evacuate and charge system. If necessary to open refrigerant system, refer to System Charge (Complete) for appropriate time.
NOTE 2: Times listed are for Factory and Dealer dash installed Integral Type air conditioning units only. Use necessary clock time for service of hang-on units.

HEATING & VENTILATION

HEATER HOSES - R&R *(D)*
NOTE: Deduct .2 when used in conjunction with radiator hose R&R.
All 7

CORE, HEATER - R&R *(B)*
DOES NOT include System Charge.
1985-88
w/Air Cond 3.6
w/o Air Cond 2.3
1989-94
w/Air Cond 4.3
w/o Air Cond 3.1

● ADDITIONAL TIME ●

● Where Air Bag interferes add 2

MOTOR, BLOWER - R&R *(B)*
All 6

SWITCH, BLOWER MOTOR - R&R *(B)*
All 5

RESISTOR, BLOWER MOTOR - R&R *(B)*
All 5

CONTROL ASSEMBLY, TEMP - R&R *(B)*
All 5

CABLES, VENTILATION CONTROL - R&R *(B)*
All (ea) 5

MASTER SWITCH, CONTROL ASSY - R&R *(B)*
All 5

AIR CONDITIONING

FREON - RECOVER *(B)*
NOTE: This operation is not to be used with any other operations.
All 3

PERFORMANCE - TEST *(B)*
Includes: Gauge check, leak test and partial charge.
All 1.0

SYSTEM CHARGE (PARTIAL) *(B)*
Includes: Performance test.
All 1.0

SYSTEM CHARGE (COMPLETE) *(B)*
Includes: Recover, evacuate and recharge system.
All 1.4

BELT, COMPRESSOR - R&R *(D)*
All 7

SEAL, COMPRESSOR SHAFT - R&R *(B)*
DOES NOT include System Charge.
All 1.5

COMPRESSOR ASSEMBLY - R&R *(B)*
DOES NOT include System Charge.
All 1.5

CLUTCH PLATE & HUB ASSEMBLY - R&R *(B)*
All 1.5

COIL &/OR PULLEY, COMPRESSOR - R&R *(B)*
DOES NOT include System Charge.
All 1.0

HEAD &/OR REED ASSY, COMPRESSOR - R&R *(A)*
DOES NOT include System Charge.
All 1.3

VALVE, EVAPORATOR EXPANSION - R&R *(B)*
DOES NOT include System Charge.
All 2.3

CONDENSER - R&R *(B)*
DOES NOT include System Charge.
All 8

MOTOR, CONDENSER FAN - R&R *(D)*
All 8

RELAY, CONDENSER FAN - R&R *(B)*
All 3

SWITCH, CONDENSER FAN - R&R *(B)*
All 5

RECEIVER DRIER - R&R *(B)*
DOES NOT include System Charge.
All 3

VALVE, SUCTION THROTTLING - R&R *(B)*
DOES NOT include System Charge.
All 7

VALVE, COMPRESSOR DISCHARGE - R&R *(B)*
DOES NOT include System Charge.
All 7

CORE, EVAPORATOR - R&R *(B)*
DOES NOT include System Charge.
All 2.3

● ADDITIONAL TIME ●

● Where Air Bag interferes add 2

HOSE, AIR CONDITIONING - R&R *(B)*
DOES NOT include System Charge.
Compressor Discharge or Suction 6
Condenser to Filter Drier 3
Condenser Outlet 7
Evaporator or Filter Drier Outlet 5
Expansion Valve Inlet 1.8

★ COMBINATIONS ★

★ Make Up Hose From Stock 4

SWITCH, THERMOSTATIC - R&R *(B)*
All 1.6

SWITCH, COMPRESSOR CUTOFF - R&R *(B)*
DOES NOT include System Charge.
All (ea) 3

Cont.

AIR CONDITIONING TIME GUIDE

GM & Geo Heating & Air Conditioning (Cont.)

NOVA

NOTE 1: Times shown DO NOT include recover, evacuate and charge system. If necessary to open refrigerant system; refer to System Charge (Complete) for appropriate time.
NOTE 2: Times listed are for Factory and Dealer dash installed Integral Type air conditioning units only. Use necessary clock time for service of hang-on units.

HEATING & VENTILATION

HEATER HOSES (ALL) - R&R *(D)*

1985-88
w/Air Cond.......... 1.2
w/o Air Cond.......... 1.0

CORE, HEATER - R&R *(B)*
DOES NOT include System Charge.

1985-88
w/Air Cond.......... 3.3
w/o Air Cond.......... 2.5

★ COMBINATIONS ★

★ Heater Hoses - R&R.......... .2

VALVE, HEATER CONTROL - R&R *(B)*

1985-88.......... .7

MOTOR, BLOWER - R&R *(B)*

1985-88.......... .8

SWITCH, BLOWER MOTOR - R&R *(B)*

1985-88.......... 1.5

RELAY, BLOWER MOTOR - R&R *(B)*

1985-88.......... .3

CONTROL ASSEMBLY, HEATER - R&R *(B)*

1985-88.......... 1.5

CABLES, VENTILATION CONTROL - R&R *(B)*

1985-88
Temp Control.......... 1.1
Defroster.......... 1.1
Heater Air Inlet.......... 1.1

AIR CONDITIONING

FREON - RECOVER *(B)*
NOTE: This operation is not to be used with any other operations.

1985-88.......... .3

PERFORMANCE - TEST *(B)*
Includes: Gauge check, leak test and partial charge.

1985-88.......... 1.0

SYSTEM CHARGE (PARTIAL) *(B)*
Includes: Performance test.

1985-88.......... 1.0

SYSTEM CHARGE (COMPLETE) *(B)*
Includes: Recover, evacuate and recharge system.

1985-88.......... 1.4

BELT, COMPRESSOR - R&R *(D)*

1985-88.......... .6

● ADDITIONAL TIME ●

● Where Air Pump interferes add.......... .2
● Where Alternator interferes add.......... .2
● Where Pwr Strg interferes add.......... .2

SEAL, COMPRESSOR SHAFT - R&R *(B)*
Use Compressor Assembly - R&R plus Combinations.

COMPRESSOR ASSEMBLY - R&R *(B)*
DOES NOT include System Charge.

1985-88.......... .8

★ COMBINATIONS ★

★ Seal, Compressor Shaft - R&R.......... .6
★ Pulley &/or Bearing - R&R.......... .5
★ Clutch Coil - R&R.......... .4
★ Clutch Plate & Hub - R&R.......... .4
★ In-Line Filter - Installation
Splice in Filter.......... .6
Tube with Filter.......... .4

PULLEY &/OR BEARINGS, COMPRESSOR - R&R *(B)*
Use Compressor Assembly - R&R plus Combinations..

CLUTCH PLATE & HUB ASSEMBLY - R&R *(B)*
Use Compressor Assembly - R&R plus Combinations..

COIL, COMPRESSOR CLUTCH - R&R *(B)*
Use Compressor Assembly - R&R plus Combinations..

VALVE, EVAPORATOR EXPANSION - R&R *(B)*
DOES NOT include System Charge.

1985-88.......... 1.1

CONDENSER - R&R *(B)*
DOES NOT include System Charge.

1985-88.......... 1.1

BLADE &/OR MOTOR, ELECTRIC FAN - R&R *(B)*

1985-88
Right Side.......... .6
Left.......... 1.3
Both.......... 1.8

SWITCH, COOLING FAN - R&R *(B)*

1985-88.......... .5

RELAY, COOLING FAN - R&R *(B)*

1985-88.......... .3

ACCUMULATOR OR RECEIVER DRIER - R&R *(B)*
DOES NOT include System Charge.

1985-88.......... .6

CORE, EVAPORATOR - R&R *(B)*
DOES NOT include System Charge.

1985-88.......... 1.1

HOSE, AIR CONDITIONING - R&R *(B)*
DOES NOT include System Charge.

1985-88
Discharge.......... .7
Suction.......... .5

● ADDITIONAL TIME ●

● For Each additional hose add.......... .4

★ COMBINATIONS ★

★ Make Up Hose From Stock.......... .4

GM & Geo Heating & Air Conditioning (Cont.)

PRIZM

NOTE 1: Times shown DO NOT include recover, evacuate and charge system. If necessary to open refrigerant system; refer to System Charge (Complete) for appropriate time.
NOTE 2: Times listed are for factory and Dealer dash installed Integral Type air conditioning units only. Use necessary clock time for service of hang-on units.

HEATING & VENTILATION

HEATER HOSES - R&R *(D)*
NOTE: Deduct .2 when used in conjunction with Radiator Hose - R&R.

1989-94.......... 1.3

CORE, HEATER - R&R *(B)*
DOES NOT include System Charge.

1989-92
w/Air Cond.......... 3.6
w/o Air Cond.......... 2.3

1993-94
w/Air Cond.......... 6.0
w/o Air Cond.......... 5.0

Cont.

GM & Geo Heating & Air Conditioning (Cont.)

PRIZM (Cont.)

VALVE, HEATER CONTROL - R&R *(B)*
1989-94 .... 1.0

MOTOR, BLOWER - R&R *(B)*
1989-94 (.3) 5

SWITCH, BLOWER MOTOR - R&R *(B)*
1989-92
w/Air Cond 1.9
w/o Air Cond 1.5
1993-94
w/Air Cond 4
w/o Air Cond 1.1

RELAY, BLOWER MOTOR - R&R *(B)*
1989-94 3

RESISTOR, BLOWER MOTOR - R&R *(B)*
1989-94 5

CABLES, VENTILATION CONTROL - R&R *(B)*
1989-94
One (.6) 8
Each Additional 4

CONTROL ASSEMBLY, TEMP - R&R *(B)*
1989-92 .... 1.9
1993-94 .... 1.1

AIR CONDITIONING

FREON - RECOVERY *(B)*
NOTE: This operation is not to be used with any other operations.
1989-94 3

PERFORMANCE - TEST *(B)*
Includes: Gauge check, leak test and partial charge.
1989-94 .... 1.0

SYSTEM CHARGE (PARTIAL) *(B)*
Includes: Performance test
1989-94 .... 1.0

SYSTEM CHARGE (COMPLETE) *(B)*
Includes: Recover, evacuate and recharge system.
1989-94 .... 1.4

BELT, COMPRESSOR - R&R *(D)*
Includes: Serpentine and V-Belt type.
1989-92 7
1993-94 5

SEAL, COMPRESSOR SHAFT - R&R *(B)*
DOES NOT include System Charge.
1989-94 .... 1.6

COMPRESSOR ASSEMBLY - R&R *(B)*
DOES NOT include System Charge.
1989-94 .... 1.3

IDLER PULLEY - R&R *(D)*
1989-94 8

CLUTCH PLATE & HUB ASSEMBLY - R&R *(B)*
DOES NOT include System Charge.
1989-94 .... 1.5

COIL, COMPRESSOR CLUTCH - R&R *(B)*
DOES NOT include System Charge.
1989-94 .... 1.5

VALVE, EVAPORATOR EXPANSION - R&R *(B)*
DOES NOT include System Charge.
1989-92 .... 1.6
1993-94 .... 1.1

CONDENSER - R&R *(B)*
DOES NOT include System Charge.
1989-92 .... 1.6
1993-94 .... 1.8

BLADE &/OR MOTOR, ELECTRIC FAN - R&R *(B)*
1989-94 8

MODULE, COOLING FAN - R&R *(B)*
1989-94 (.3) 5

SWITCH, COOLING FAN - R&R *(B)*
1989-94 5

RESISTOR, COOLING FAN - R&R *(B)*
1989-94 (.2) 3

RELAY, COOLING FAN - R&R *(B)*
1989-94 4

ACCUMULATOR OR RECEIVER DRYER - R&R *(B)*
DOES NOT include System Charge.
1989-94 7

CORE, EVAPORATOR - R&R *(B)*
DOES NOT include System Charge.
1989-92 .... 1.6
1993-94 .... 1.2

HOSE, AIR CONDITIONING - R&R *(B)*
DOES NOT include System Charge.
1989-94
One 5
Each Additional 3

★ COMBINATIONS ★
★ Make Up Hose From Stock 4

SWITCH, PRESSURE CUT - R&R *(B)*
DOES NOT include System Charge.
1989-94 .... 1.1

GM & Geo Heating & Air Conditioning (Cont.)

SPECTRUM/STORM

NOTE 1: Times shown DO NOT include recover, evacuate and charge system. If necessary to open refrigerant system, refer to System Charge (Complete) for appropriate time.
NOTE 2: Times listed are for Factory and Dealer dash installed Integral Type air conditioning units only. Use necessary clock time for service of hang-on units.

HEATING & VENTILATION

HEATER HOSES - R&R *(D)*
NOTE: Deduct .2 when used in conjunction with radiator hose R&R.
All 7

CORE, HEATER - R&R *(B)*
1985-89 (Spectrum) 1.0
1990-93 (Storm)
w/Air Cond 4.4
w/o Air Cond 3.4

WATER VALVE - R&R *(B)*
All 3

MOTOR, BLOWER - R&R *(B)*
1985-89 (Spectrum) 5
1990-93 (Storm)
w/Air Cond 1.8
w/o Air Cond 8

SWITCH, BLOWER MOTOR - R&R *(B)*
1985-89 (Spectrum) 7
1990-93 (Storm) .... N.A.

RESISTOR, BLOWER MOTOR - R&R *(B)*
All 5

CONTROL ASSEMBLY, TEMPERATURE - R&R *(B)*
All 6

CABLES, VENTILATION CONTROL - R&R *(B)*
1985-89 (Spectrum) - Each 6
1990-93 (Storm) - Each 7

MASTER SWITCH, CONTROL ASSY - R&R *(B)*
All 7

Cont.

AIR CONDITIONING TIME GUIDE

GM & Geo Heating & Air Conditioning (Cont.)

SPECTRUM/STORM (Cont.)

AIR CONDITIONING

FREON - RECOVER *(B)*
NOTE: This operation is not to be used with any other operations.
All 3

PERFORMANCE - TEST *(B)*
Includes: Gauge check, leak test and partial charge.
All 1.0

SYSTEM CHARGE (PARTIAL) *(B)*
Includes: Performance test.
All 1.0

SYSTEM CHARGE (COMPLETE) *(B)*
Includes: Recover, evacuate and recharge system.
All 1.4

BELT, COMPRESSOR - R&R *(D)*
All 5

SEAL, COMPRESSOR SHAFT - R&R *(B)*
DOES NOT include System Charge.
1985-89 (Spectrum) 1.3
1990-93 (Storm)
1.6L Eng
w/Pwr Strg 1.4
w/o Pwr Strg 1.2
1.8L Eng 1.4

COMPRESSOR ASSEMBLY - R&R *(B)*
DOES NOT include System Charge.
1985-89 (Spectrum)
w/Turbocharger 1.1
w/o Turbocharger 9
1990-93 (Storm)
1.6L Eng
w/Pwr Strg 1.1
w/o Pwr Strg 9
1.8L Eng 1.1

COMPRESSOR ASSEMBLY - R&I & O/H *(B)*
DOES NOT include System Charge.
1985-89 (Spectrum)
w/Turbocharger 2.2
w/o Turbocharger 2.0
1990-93 (Storm)
1.6L Eng
w/Pwr Strg 2.2
w/o Pwr Strg 2.0
1.8L Eng 2.2

CLUTCH PLATE & HUB ASSEMBLY - R&R *(B)*
1985-89 (Spectrum) 1.2
1990-93 (Storm)
1.6L Eng
w/Pwr Strg 1.3
w/o Pwr Strg 1.1
1.8L Eng 1.3

COIL &/OR PULLEY, COMPRESSOR - R&R *(B)*
DOES NOT include System Charge.
1985-89 (Spectrum) 1.3
1990-93 (Storm)
1.6L Eng
w/Pwr Strg 1.3
w/o Pwr Strg 1.1
1.8L Eng 1.3

VALVE, EVAPORATOR EXPANSION - R&R *(B)*
DOES NOT include System Charge.
1985-89 (Spectrum) 1.8
1990-93 (Storm) 8

CONDENSER - R&R *(B)*
DOES NOT include System Charge.
All 1.0

MOTOR, CONDENSER FAN - R&R *(D)*
1985-89 (Spectrum) 7
1990-93 (Storm) 1.3

RELAY, CONDENSER FAN - R&R *(B)*
All 5

SWITCH, CONDENSER FAN - R&R *(B)*
All 5

RECEIVER DRIER - R&R *(B)*
DOES NOT include System Charge.
1985-89 (Spectrum) 8
1990-93 (Storm) 1.0

CORE, EVAPORATOR - R&R *(B)*
DOES NOT include System Charge.
All 1.8

HOSE, AIR CONDITIONING - R&R *(B)*
DOES NOT include System Charge.
One 1.0
Each Additional 5

★ **COMBINATIONS** ★

★ Make Up Hose From Stock 4

SWITCH, THERMOSTATIC - R&R *(B)*
1985-89 (Spectrum) 1.8
1990-93 (Storm) 1.6

SWITCH, LOW PRESSURE - R&R *(B)*
All 3

GM & Geo Heating & Air Conditioning (Cont.)

TRACKER

NOTE 1: Times shown DO NOT include recover, evacuate and charge system. If necessary to open refrigerant system, refer to System Charge (Complete) for appropriate time.
NOTE 2: Times listed are for Factory and Dealer dash installed Integral Type air conditioning units only. Use necessary clock time for service of hang-on units.

HEATING & VENTILATION

HEATER HOSES - R&R *(D)*
One 5
Two 7
All 1.0

CORE, HEATER - R&R *(B)*
Includes: R&I instrument panel assembly.
1989-93
w/Air Cond 6.1
w/o Air Cond 4.9

BLOWER MOTOR - R&R *(B)*
1989-93 .... 3.1

SWITCH, BLOWER MOTOR - R&R *(B)*
1989-93 5

RESISTOR, BLOWER MOTOR - R&R *(B)*
1989-93 5

CONTROL ASSEMBLY, TEMP & VENT - R&R *(B)*
1989-93 .... 3.0

CABLES, HEATER CONTROL - R&R *(B)*
1989-93 (All) 3.0

AIR CONDITIONING

NOTE: Times listed are for Factory and Dealer dash installed Integral Type air conditioning units only. Use necessary clock time for service of hang-on units.

FREON - RECOVER *(B)*
NOTE: This operation is not to be used with any other operations.
All 3

PERFORMANCE - TEST *(B)*
Includes: Gauge check, leak test and partial charge.
DOES NOT include electrical or vacuum circuit diagnosis.
1989-93 .... 1.0

SYSTEM CHARGE (PARTIAL) *(B)*
Includes: Performance test.
1989-93 .... 1.0

Cont.

AIR CONDITIONING TIME GUIDE

GM & Geo Heating & Air Conditioning (Cont.)

TRACKER (Cont.)

SYSTEM CHARGE (COMPLETE) *(B)*
Includes: Recover, evacuate and recharge system.
1989-93 .... 1.4

BELT, COMPRESSOR - R&R *(D)*
1989-93 3

● ADDITIONAL TIME ●
● Where Pwr Strg interferes add 1
● Where Alt interferes add 1

COMPRESSOR ASSEMBLY - R&R *(B)*
DOES NOT include System Charge.
1989-93 .... 1.5

★ COMBINATIONS ★
★ Seal, Compressor Shaft - R&R 6

CLUTCH ASSEMBLY - R&R *(B)*
DOES NOT include System Charge.
1989-93 .... 1.8

SEAL, COMPRESSOR SHAFT - R&R *(B)*
Use Compressor Assembly - R&R plus Combinations.

EXPANSION VALVE - R&R *(B)*
DOES NOT include System Charge.
1989-93 .... 3.3

CORE, EVAPORATOR - R&R *(B)*
DOES NOT include System Charge.
1989-93 .... 3.1

RECEIVER DRIER - R&R *(B)*
DOES NOT include System Charge.
1989-93 .... 1.1

CONDENSER - R&R *(B)*
DOES NOT include System Charge.
1989-93 .... 1.7

FAN, CONDENSER COOLING - R&R *(D)*
1989-93 8

SWITCH, CONDENSER FAN - R&R *(B)*
1989-93 7

RELAY, CONDENSER FAN - R&R *(B)*
1989-93 .... N.A.

HOSE, AIR CONDITIONING - R&R *(B)*
DOES NOT include System Charge.
One 1.0
Each Additional 6

★ COMBINATIONS ★
★ Make Up Hose From Stock 4

RELAY, POWER - R&R *(B)*
1989-93 3

SWITCH, CONTROL - R&R *(B)*
1989-93 6

THERMISTOR - R&R *(B)*
DOES NOT include System Charge.
1989-93 .... 3.2

Honda Heating & Air Conditioning

NOTE 1: Times shown Do Not include recover, evacuate and charge system. If necessary to open refrigerant system or to recover, evacuate, charge and test, refer to System Charge (Complete) for appropriate time.
NOTE 2: Times listed are for Factory and Dealer dash installed Integral Type air conditioning units only. Use necessary clock time for service of hang-on units.

HEATING & VENTILATION

HEATER HOSES - R&R *(D)*
NOTE: Deduct .2 when used in conjunction with Radiator Hoses - R&R.
1973-79
Accord,Prelude 7
Civic
w/Air Cond 1.2
w/o Air Cond 7
1980-93 7

CORE, HEATER - R&R *(B)*
DOES NOT include evacuate and charge system.
1973-81
Accord 2.8
Civic
(73-80)
CVCC,1200 .... 4.6
1300,1500 .... 2.1
(81) ① 4.5
Prelude 3.1
1982-85
Accord
w/Air Cond 6.8
w/o Air Cond 5.9
Civic,CRX
(82) ① 4.5
(83-85) 3.5
Prelude
(82) 3.1
(83-85)
w/Air Cond 2.4
w/o Air Cond 1.1

1986-87
Accord ①
w/Air Cond 6.8
w/o Air Cond 5.9
Civic,CRX 3.5
Prelude
w/Air Cond 2.4
w/o Air Cond 1.1
1988-93 ①
Accord
(88-89)
w/Air Cond 6.8
w/o Air Cond 5.9
(90-93)
w/Air Cond 5.8
w/o Air Cond 5.0
Civic,CRX,del Sol
w/Air Cond 6.2
w/o Air Cond 5.3
Prelude
(88-91)
w/Air Cond 6.8
w/o Air Cond 5.9
(92-93)
w/Air Cond 5.0
w/o Air Cond 4.0

① *Includes: R&I instrument panel.*

VALVE, HEATER CONTROL - R&R *(B)*
1973-79
Accord,Prelude 7
Civic
w/Air Cond 1.3
w/o Air Cond 8
1980-93 7

MOTOR, BLOWER - R&R *(B)*
1973-81
Accord 6
Civic
(73-80)
CVCC,1200 .... 3.1
1300,1500 8
(81) 8
Prelude 8
1982 8
1983
Accord,Civic 8
Prelude 1.1
1984-87
Accord 8
Civic,CRX 6
Prelude 1.1
1988-93
Accord
(88-89) 8
(90-93)
w/Air Cond 2.3
w/o Air Cond 1.3
Civic,CRX,del Sol
(88-91)
w/Air Cond 1.9
w/o Air Cond 9
(92-93)
w/Air Cond 4
w/o Air Cond 3
Prelude
(88-91)
w/Air Cond 1.9
w/o Air Cond 9
(92-93)
w/Air Cond 4
w/o Air Cond 3

Cont.

AIR CONDITIONING TIME GUIDE

Honda Heating & Air Conditioning (Cont.)

SWITCH, BLOWER MOTOR - R&R *(B)*

- **1973-79**
  - Accord .9
  - Civic .4
  - Prelude .7
- **1980-81**
  - Accord,Civic .9
  - Prelude .7
- **1982** .7
- **1983**
  - Accord,Civic .7
  - Prelude 1.5
- **1984-87**
  - Accord .7
  - Civic,CRX .9
  - Prelude 1.5
- **1988-93**
  - Accord
    - (88-89) .7
    - (90-93) 1.3
  - Civic,CRX,del Sol,Prelude .7

CONTROL ASSEMBLY - R&R *(B)*

Includes: Adjust cables.

- **1973-79**
  - Air Cond .4
  - Heater
    - Accord 1.5
    - Civic .6
    - Prelude .9
- **1980-82**
  - Air Cond .4
  - Heater
    - Accord 1.5
    - Civic,Prelude .9
- **1983-87**
  - Air Cond .4
  - Heater
    - Accord,Prelude 1.5
    - Civic,CRX 1.0
- **1988-93**
  - Accord 2.0
  - Civic,CRX,del Sol
    - (88-91) 2.0
    - (92-93) .8
  - Prelude
    - (88-91) 1.5
    - (92-93) .8

SWITCH, FUNCTION MODE - R&R *(B)*

- **1982-87**
  - Accord 1.0
  - Civic (CRX) .9
  - Prelude (83-87) 1.5
- **1988-93**
  - Accord 1.3
  - Civic,CRX,del Sol 1.0
  - Prelude
    - (88-91) .7
    - (92-93) .5

RESISTOR, BLOWER MOTOR - R&R *(B)*

- **1973-79**
  - Accord,Prelude .8
  - Civic
    - w/Air Cond .9
    - w/o Air Cond .4
- **1980-83** .8
- **1984-87**
  - Accord .8
  - Civic,CRX .6
  - Prelude 1.1
- **1988-93**
  - Accord
    - (88-89) .7
    - (90-93) 1.3
  - Civic,CRX,del Sol,Prelude
    - (88-91) .7
    - (92-93) .3

CABLE, TEMPERATURE CONTROL - R&R *(B)*

Includes: Adjustment.

- **1973-79**
  - Accord 1.1
  - Civic .4
  - Prelude .8
- **1980-81**
  - Accord 1.1
  - Civic,Prelude .8
- **1982**
  - Accord 1.5
  - Civic,Prelude .8
- **1983-87**
  - Accord 1.5
  - Civic,CRX .8
  - Prelude 1.0
- **1988-93** 1.3

DIAPHRAGM CONTROL (ACTUATOR) - R&R *(B)*

- **1982-87** (Heater Door)
  - Accord (Right or Left) 1.0
  - Prelude
    - Right Side 3.4
    - Left Side .7

CONTROL MOTOR (ACTUATOR) - R&R *(B)*

- **1982-87**
  - Accord,Prelude .8
  - Civic,CRX .5
- **1988-93**
  - Accord
    - (88-89) .8
    - (90-93)
      - Function .8
      - Recirculation
        - w/Air Cond 2.2
        - w/o Air Cond 1.1
  - Civic,CRX,del Sol .5
    - (88-91) .5
    - (92-93) .3
  - Prelude
    - (88-91) .7
    - (92-93)
      - w/Air Cond 2.2
      - w/o Air Cond 1.1

SENSOR, DOOR POSITION - R&R *(B)*

- **1982-87**
  - Accord .8
  - Prelude .5

AIR CONDITIONING

FREON - RECOVER *(B)*

NOTE: This operation is not to be used with any other operations.

- All .3

PERFORMANCE - TEST *(B)*

Includes: Gauge check, leak test and partial charge.

- **1979-93** 1.0

SYSTEM CHARGE (PARTIAL) *(B)*

Includes: Pressure and leak test.

- **1979-93** 1.0

SYSTEM CHARGE (COMPLETE) *(B)*

Includes: Evacuate, recover and recharge system.

- **1979-93** 1.4

BELT, COMPRESSOR - R&R *(D)*

- **1979-81**
  - Accord,Prelude
    - w/Pwr Strg .8
    - w/o Pwr Strg .5
  - Civic .8
- **1982-83**
  - Accord
    - w/Pwr Strg .7
    - w/o Pwr Strg .5
  - Civic .8
  - Prelude
    - w/Pwr Strg .8
    - w/o Pwr Strg .5
- **1984-87**
  - Accord,Prelude
    - w/Pwr Strg .7
    - w/o Pwr Strg .5
  - Civic,CRX
    - w/Pwr Strg .8
    - w/o Pwr Strg .5
- **1988-93**
  - Accord .6
  - Civic,CRX,del Sol
    - w/Pwr Strg .6
    - w/o Pwr Strg .3
  - Prelude .7

IDLER PULLEY - R&R *(D)*

- All .5

• **ADDITIONAL TIME** •

- Where Pwr Strg interferes add .3

COMPRESSOR ASSEMBLY - R&R *(B)*

Includes: Transfer clutch assembly.
DOES NOT include evacuate and charge system.

- **1979-83**
  - Accord
    - (79-81)
      - Man Strg 1.0
      - Pwr Strg 1.2
    - (82-83) .9
  - Civic .9
  - Prelude
    - Man Strg 1.0
    - Pwr Strg 1.6
- **1984-87**
  - Accord,Prelude
    - Man Strg .9
    - Pwr Strg 1.5
  - Civic,CRX ①
    - Man Strg 1.4
    - Pwr Strg 1.6
- **1988-93**
  - Accord 1.9
  - Civic,CRX,del Sol
    - Man Strg 1.5
    - Pwr Strg 1.9
  - Prelude 1.6

① *Includes: R&I Lower Bumper Extension.*

Cont.

Honda Heating & Air Conditioning (Cont.)

SEAL, COMPRESSOR SHAFT - R&R *(B)*
DOES NOT include evacuate or charge system.

1979-83
Accord
(79-81)
Man Strg 1.8
Pwr Strg 1.9
(82-83) 1.0
Civic 1.0
Prelude
Man Strg 1.1
Pwr Strg 2.0
1984-87
Accord,Prelude
Man Strg 1.0
Pwr Strg 1.6
Civic,CRX ①
Man Strg 1.5
Pwr Strg 1.7
1988-93
Accord 2.0
Civic,CRX,del Sol
Man Strg 1.6
Pwr Strg 2.0
Prelude 1.7
① *Includes: R&I Lower Bumper Extension.*

CLUTCH PLATE & HUB ASSEMBLY - R&R *(B)*
DOES NOT include evacuate or charge system.

1979-83
Accord
(79-81)
Man Strg 1.0
Pwr Strg 1.2
(82-83) 9
Civic 9
Prelude
Man Strg 1.0
Pwr Strg 1.6
1984-87
Accord,Prelude
Man Strg 9
Pwr Strg 1.5
Civic,CRX ①
Man Strg 1.4
Pwr Strg 1.6
1988-93
Accord 1.9
Civic,CRX,del Sol
Man Strg 1.5
Pwr Strg 1.9
Prelude 1.6
① *Includes: R&I Lower Bumper Extension.*

★ COMBINATIONS ★

★ Thermal Protector/Pick-up Sensor - R&R 2

CONDENSER - R&R *(B)*
DOES NOT include evacuate and charge system.

1979-93
Accord
(79-85) 7
(86-89) 1.0
(90-93) 7
Civic 8
CRX
(84-87) ① 1.5
(88-91) 8
del Sol 8
Prelude
(79-82) 6
(83-87) ② 1.0
(88-91) ① 1.1
(92-93) 8
① *Includes: R&I Front Bumper Assy.*
② *Includes: R&I Grille Assy.*

RECEIVER DRIER - R&R *(B)*
DOES NOT include evacuate and charge system.

1979-89 7
1990-93 5
Accord 5
Civic,CRX,del Sol
(90-91) 7
(92-93) 5
Prelude
(90-91) 7
(92-93) 1.0

CORE, EVAPORATOR - R&R *(B)*
DOES NOT include evacuate and charge system.

1979-93
Accord
(79-84) 8
(85-93) 1.1
Civic,CRX,del Sol
(79-83) 1.0
(84-93) 9
Prelude
(79-82) 1.0
(83-87) 1.5
(88-93) 1.0

VALVE, EVAPORATOR EXPANSION - R&R *(B)*
DOES NOT include evacuate and charge system.

1979-93
Accord
(79-84) 8
(85-93) 1.1
Civic,CRX,del Sol
(79-83) 1.0
(84-93) 9
Prelude
(79-82) 1.0
(83-87) 1.5
(88-93) 1.0

HOSE, AIR CONDITIONING - R&R *(B)*
DOES NOT include evacuate and charge system.

1979-89
One 7
Each Additional 5
1990-91
Accord
Discharge 6
Suction 5
Civic,CRX
Discharge 8
Suction 5
Prelude
Discharge 1.5
Suction 1.0
1992-93
Discharge
Accord,Prelude 6
Civic,CRX,del Sol 8
Suction (All) 5

★ COMBINATIONS ★

★ Make Up Hose From Stock 4

THERMOSTAT - R&R *(B)*
DOES NOT include evacuate and charge system.

1979-93
Accord
(79-84) 8
(85-93) 1.1
Civic,CRX,del Sol 1.0
Prelude
(79-82) 1.0
(83-87) 1.5
(88-93) 1.0

MOTOR &/OR FAN, CONDENSER - R&R *(D)*

1979-93 7

MICRO SWITCH, AIR COND CONTROL - R&R *(B)*

1979-81
Accord 1.1
Civic 8

SWITCH, AIR COND CONTROL - R&R *(B)*

1979-87
Accord 7
Civic
exc CRX (84-87) 5
CRX (84-87) 3
Prelude
(79-82) 7
(83-87) 1.0
1988-93 3

VALVE, IDLE SPEED SOLENOID - R&R *(B)*

1979-93 5

DIAPHRAGM, IDLE SPEED BOOST - R&R *(B)*

1979-82 7
1983-93
Accord,Civic,CRX,del Sol 7
Prelude 5

AIR CONDITIONING TIME GUIDE

Hyundai Heating & Air Conditioning

NOTE 1: Times shown DO NOT include recover, evacuate and charge system. If necessary to open refrigerant system; refer to System Charge (Complete) for appropriate time.
NOTE 2: Times listed are for Factory and Dealer dash installed Integral Type air conditioning units only. Use necessary clock time for service of hang-on units.

HEATING & VENTILATION

HEATER HOSES - R&R *(D)*
Elantra,Excel,Scoupe,Sonata 9

WATER VALVE - R&R *(B)*
Excel (86-89) 8

CORE, HEATER - R&R *(B)*
DOES NOT include System Charge.
1986-93
Elantra
w/Air Cond 4.0
w/o Air Cond 3.0
Excel
(86-89)
w/Air Cond 3.6
w/o Air Cond 2.0
(90-93)
w/Air Cond 3.8
w/o Air Cond 3.0
Scoupe
w/Air Cond 3.7
w/o Air Cond 2.7
Sonata
w/Air Cond 5.8
w/o Air Cond 4.8

MOTOR, BLOWER - R&R *(B)*
1986-93
Elantra,Scoupe,Sonata 5
Excel
(86-89) 9
(90-93) 5

SWITCH, BLOWER MOTOR - R&R *(B)*
1986-93
Elantra,Scoupe 6
Excel
(86-89) 8
(90-93) 6
Sonata 7

RESISTOR, BLOWER MOTOR - R&R *(B)*
Elantra,Excel,Scoupe,Sonata 5

CABLE, VENTILATION CONTROL - R&R *(B)*
Excel .... N.A.

CONTROL ASSEMBLY, TEMPERATURE - R&R *(B)*
Elantra .... N.A.
Excel,Scoupe 7
Sonata 5

ACTUATORS (DIAPHRAGM), VACUUM - R&R *(B)*
DOES NOT include evacuate or charge system.
1986-93
Blend Door (Sonata) 7
Defrost Door
Elantra 6
Excel,Scoupe,Sonata 5
Mode Door
Elantra 6
Excel,Scoupe,Sonata 5
Recirc Door
Elantra 1.4
Excel 1.1
Scoupe 8
Sonata 1.3

SENSOR, IN CAR - R&R *(B)*
Sonata 8

AIR CONDITIONING

FREON - RECOVER *(B)*
NOTE: This operation is not to be used with any other operations.
All 3

PERFORMANCE - TEST *(B)*
Includes: Gauge check, leak test and partial charge.
Elantra,Excel,Scoupe,Sonata 1.0

SYSTEM CHARGE (PARTIAL) *(B)*
Includes: Performance test.
Elantra,Excel,Scoupe,Sonata 1.0

SYSTEM CHARGE (COMPLETE) *(B)*
Includes: Recover, evacuate and recharge system.
Elantra,Excel,Scoupe,Sonata 1.4

BELT, COMPRESSOR - R&R *(D)*
Includes: Serpentine belts.
1986-93 5

● **ADDITIONAL TIME** ●
● Where Pwr Strg interferes add 1
● Where Alt interferes add 1

TENSIONER, COMPRESSOR BELT - R&R *(D)*
Use Compressor Belt - R&R.

COMPRESSOR ASSEMBLY - R&R *(B)*
DOES NOT include System Charge.
1986-93
Elantra,Excel,Scoupe 1.0
Sonata
Four 1.3
V6 (3.0L Eng) 9

★ **COMBINATIONS** ★
★ Seal, Compressor Shaft - R&R 6
★ Clutch Assembly - R&R 4

COMPRESSOR ASSEMBLY - R&I & O/H *(B)*
DOES NOT include System Charge.
1986-93
Elantra,Excel,Scoupe 2.3
Sonata
Four 2.6
V6 (3.0L Eng) 2.2

SEAL, COMPRESSOR SHAFT - R&R *(B)*
Use Compressor Assembly - R&R plus Combinations.

CLUTCH ASSEMBLY - R&R *(B)*
Use Compressor Assembly - R&R plus Combinations.

VALVE, EVAPORATOR EXPANSION - R&R *(B)*
DOES NOT include System Charge.
Excel (86-89) 2.5
Elantra 1.4

ACCUMULATOR ASSY - R&R *(B)*
DOES NOT include System Charge.
Excel,Scoupe,Sonata 3

RECEIVER DRIER - R&R *(B)*
DOES NOT include System Charge.
Elantra,Excel (86-89) 6

CONDENSER - R&R *(B)*
DOES NOT include System Charge.
1986-93
Elantra,Excel 1.0
Scoupe,Sonata 1.3

CORE, EVAPORATOR - R&R *(B)*
DOES NOT include System Charge.
Elantra 1.9
Excel 1.8
Scoupe 1.6
Sonata 5.8

MOTOR, CONDENSER FAN - R&R *(D)*
Elantra 5
Excel,Scoupe 4
Sonata 6

RESISTOR, CONDENSER FAN - R&R *(B)*
Excel,Sonata 4

SWITCH, FAN PRESSURE - R&R *(B)*
Sonata 4

HOSE, AIR CONDITIONING - R&R *(B)*
DOES NOT include System Charge.
One 1.0
Each Additional 5

★ **COMBINATIONS** ★
★ Make Up Hose From Stock 4

RELAY, POWER - R&R *(B)*
Elantra,Excel,Scoupe,Sonata 5

THERMOSTAT ASSEMBLY - R&R *(B)*
DOES NOT include System Charge.
Elantra 2.1
Excel (86-89) 1.5

SOLENOID VALVE - R&R *(B)*
Excel (86-89) 3

SWITCH, LOW PRESSURE - R&R *(B)*
Excel,Scoupe,Sonata 4

VALVE, COMPRESSOR RELIEF - R&R *(B)*
Elantra,Excel,Scoupe,Sonata 4

MANIFOLD ASSY - R&R *(B)*
DOES NOT include System Charge.
Sonata (Four or Six) 6

SENSOR, AMBIENT - R&R *(B)*
Sonata 4

Infiniti Heating & Air Conditioning

NOTE: Times shown DO NOT include recover, evacuate and charge system. If necessary to open refrigerant system; refer to System Charge (Complete) for appropriate time.

HEATING & VENTILATION

HEATER HOSES - R&R *(D)*
NOTE: Deduct .2 when used in conjunction with Radiator Hose - R&R.
1990-93 (All)
G20 9
J30,M30 .... 1.0
Q45 .... 1.8

WATER VALVE - R&R *(B)*
DOES NOT include System Charge.
1990-93
G20,J30 .... 5.0
M30 .... 5.5
Q45 .... 7.0

ACTUATOR, WATER VALVE - R&R *(B)*
DOES NOT include System Charge.
1990-93
G20,J30 .... 5.2
M30 .... 5.7
Q45 .... 7.2

CORE, HEATER - R&R *(B)*
DOES NOT include System Charge.
1990-93
G20,J30 .... 5.0
M30 .... 5.5
Q45 .... 7.0

MOTOR, BLOWER - R&R *(B)*
1990-93
G20 5
J30 .... 1.0
M30 6
Q45 .... 1.6

SWITCH, BLOWER MOTOR - R&R *(B)*
1990-93
G20 .... 1.3
J30,Q45 6
M30 .... 1.0

RELAY, BLOWER MOTOR - R&R *(B)*
1990-93
G20,J30,Q45 4
M30 3

AMPLIFIER, BLOWER MOTOR CONTROL - R&R *(B)*
1990-93
J30 6
M30 3
Q45 4

CONTROL ASSEMBLY, TEMPERATURE - R&R *(B)*
1990-93
G20 .... 1.3
J30,Q45 6
M30 .... 1.0

DIAPHRAM CONTROL (ACTUATOR) - R&R *(B)*
1990-93
G20
Air Intake Door 7
Mode Door 4
J30
Air Intake Door 5
Air Mix Door 8
Mode Door 8
M30
Air Intake Door 5
Mode Door 6
Q45
Air Intake Door 1.6
Air Mix Door 7
Mode Door 9

AIR CONDITIONING

FREON - RECOVER *(B)*
NOTE: This operation is not to be used with any other operations.
1990-93 3

PERFORMANCE - TEST *(B)*
Includes: Gauge check, leak test and partial charge.
1990-93 .... 1.0

SYSTEM CHARGE (PARTIAL) *(B)*
Includes: Performance test.
1990-93 .... 1.0

SYSTEM CHARGE (COMPLETE) *(B)*
Includes: Recover, evacuate and recharge system.
1990-93 .... 1.4

BELT, COMPRESSOR - R&R *(D)*
1990-93
G20 6
J30,M30,Q45 8

IDLER PULLEY, AIR CONDITIONING - R&R *(D)*
1990-93
J30,M30 7
Q45 6

COMPRESSOR ASSEMBLY - R&R *(B)*
DOES NOT include System Charge.
1990-93
G20 .... 1.0
J30 .... 1.4
M30 8
Q45 .... 2.5

CLUTCH, COMPRESSOR - R&R *(B)*
Includes: R&I compressor.
DOES NOT include System Charge.
1990-93
G20 .... 1.8
J30 .... 1.7
M30 .... 1.1
Q45 .... 2.8

VALVE, EVAPORATOR EXPANSION - R&R *(B)*
Includes: R&I evaporator assembly.
DOES NOT include System Charge.
1990-93
G20,J30 8
M30 .... 1.0
Q45 .... 1.3

CORE, EVAPORATOR - R&R *(B)*
DOES NOT include System Charge.
1990-93
G20,J30 8
M30 .... 1.0
Q45 .... 1.3

VALVE, SUCTION THROTTLE - R&R *(B)*
Includes: R&I evaporator assembly.
DOES NOT include System Charge.
1990-93
G20,J30 8
M30 .... 1.0
Q45 .... 1.3

RECEIVER DRIER - R&R *(B)*
DOES NOT include System Charge.
1990-93
G20 8
J30,M30,Q45 6

CONDENSOR - R&R *(B)*
DOES NOT include System Charge.
1990-93
G20 .... 1.5
J30 7
M30,Q45 .... 2.2

MOTOR &/OR FAN, CONDENSER - R&R *(B)*
1990-93
G20 9
J30 .... 1.0
M30 .... 1.1
Q45 .... 1.8

SWITCH, ELECTRIC FAN TEMP - R&R *(B)*
1990-93 5

RELAY, CONDENSER FAN - R&R *(B)*
1990-93 4

SWITCH, LOW PRESSURE - R&R *(B)*
DOES NOT include System Charge.
1990-93 5

CONTROL ASSEMBLY, A.T.C. - R&R *(B)*
1990-93
J30,Q45 7
M30 .... 1.1

AUTO AMPLIFIER, A.T.C. - R&R *(B)*
1990-93
J30,Q45 5
M30 .... 1.1

SENSOR, IN-VEHICLE ASPIRATOR - R&R *(B)*
1990-92 (M30) 1.0

AMBIENT SENSOR (A.T.C.) - R&R *(B)*
1990-93 5

Cont.

AIR CONDITIONING TIME GUIDE

Infiniti Heating & Air Conditioning (Cont.)

SENSOR, COOLANT TEMP (A.T.C.) - R&R *(B)*

1990-93
- M30 .5
- Q45 6.3

SENSOR, SUNLOAD (A.T.C.) - R&R *(B)*

1990-93 .4

SENSOR, ROOF IN-CAR (A.T.C.) - R&R *(B)*

1990-93 .4

SENSOR, FOOT IN-CAR (A.T.C.) - R&R *(B)*

1990-93 .4

SENSOR, VENTILATOR DUCT (A.T.C.) - R&R *(B)*

1990-93 .4

SENSOR, FLOOR DUCT (A.T.C.) - R&R *(B)*

1990-93 .4

SENSOR, GRILLE (A.T.C.) - R&R *(B)*

1990-93 .4

SENSOR, IN-VEHICLE - R&R *(B)*

1990-93 .8

HOSE, AIR CONDITIONING - R&R *(B)*

DOES NOT include System Charge.

1990-93
- One .5
- Each Additional .3

★ COMBINATIONS ★

- ★ Make Up Hose From Stock .4

Isuzu Heating & Air Conditioning

NOTE 1: Times shown DO NOT include recover, evacuate and charge system. If necessary to open refrigerant system; refer to System Charge (Complete) for appropriate time.
NOTE 2: Times listed are for Factory and Dealer dash installed Integral Type air conditioning units only. Use necessary clock time for service of hang-on units.

HEATING & VENTILATION

HEATER HOSES - R&R *(D)*

1981-93 (All) .7

CORE, HEATER - R&R *(B)*

DOES NOT include System Charge.

1981-93
- Amigo,Pickup,Rodeo 4.0
- I-Mark
  - F.W.D. (85-89) 1.0
  - R.W.D. (81-85) 4.3
- Impulse,Stylus
  - F.W.D. (90-93)
    - w/Air Cond 4.4
    - w/o Air Cond 3.4
  - R.W.D.
    - (83-87) 4.6
    - (88-89) 4.8
- Trooper,Trooper II
  - (84-91)
    - Front 4.0
    - Rear N.A.
  - (92-93)
    - w/Air Cond 4.9
    - w/o Air Cond 4.2

WATER VALVE - R&R *(B)*

1981-89
- I-Mark .3
- Impulse (R.W.D.) .6

MOTOR, BLOWER - R&R *(B)*

1981-93
- Amigo,Pickup,Rodeo,Trooper,Trooper II 1.6
- I-Mark
  - F.W.D. (85-89) .5
  - R.W.D. (81-85)
    - Diesel 1.6
    - Gas 1.3
- Impulse,Stylus
  - F.W.D. (90-93)
    - w/Air Cond 1.8
    - w/o Air Cond .8
  - R.W.D. (83-89) 2.7

SWITCH, BLOWER MOTOR - R&R *(B)*

1981-93
- Amigo,Pickup,Rodeo,Trooper,Trooper II .5
- I-Mark
  - F.W.D. .7
  - R.W.D. .5
- Impulse,Stylus
  - F.W.D. (90-93) N.A.
  - R.W.D. (83-89) 1.9

RESISTOR, BLOWER MOTOR - R&R *(B)*

1981-93 .5

CONTROL ASSEMBLY, TEMPERATURE - R&R *(B)*

1981-93
- Amigo,Pickup,Rodeo,Trooper,Trooper II .8
- I-Mark,Impulse,Stylus .6

CABLE'S, VENTILATION CONTROL - R&R *(B)*

1983-93 (ea)
- Amigo,Pickup,Rodeo .5
- I-Mark
  - F.W.D. (85-89) .6
  - R.W.D. (81-85) .5
- Impulse,Stylus .7
- Trooper,Trooper II
  - (84-91) .5
  - (92-93) .7

DIAPHRAGM CONTROL (ACTUATOR) - R&R *(B)*

1981-93 (ea) .6

SOLENOID (ACTUATOR) - R&R *(B)*

1981-93 (ea) .3

AIR CONDITIONING

FREON - RECOVER *(B)*

NOTE: This operation is not to be used with any other operations.

All .3

PERFORMANCE - TEST *(B)*

Includes: Gauge check, leak test and partial charge.

1981-93 1.0

SYSTEM CHARGE (PARTIAL) *(B)*

Includes: Performance test.

1981-93 1.0

SYSTEM CHARGE (COMPLETE) *(B)*

Includes: Recover, evacuate and recharge system.

1981-93 1.4

BELT, COMPRESSOR - R&R *(D)*

1981-93
- F.W.D. .3
- R.W.D. .5

● ADDITIONAL TIME ●

- ● Where Alt interferes add .1
- ● Where Pwr Strg interferes add .1
- ● Where Air Pump interferes add .1

SEAL, COMPRESSOR SHAFT - R&R *(B)*

Use Compressor Assembly - R&R plus Combinations.

COMPRESSOR ASSEMBLY - R&R *(B)*

DOES NOT include System Charge.

1981-93
- Amigo 1.0
- I-Mark
  - F.W.D. (85-89)
    - w/Turbocharger 1.1
    - w/o Turbocharger .9
  - R.W.D. (81-85) 1.5
- Impulse,Stylus
  - F.W.D. (90-93)
    - 1.6L Eng
      - w/Pwr Strg 1.1
      - w/o Pwr Strg .9
    - 1.8L Eng 1.1
  - R.W.D. (83-89)
    - w/Turbocharger 1.3
    - w/o Turbocharger .8
- Pickup
  - (81-87) 1.4
  - (88-93) 1.0
- Rodeo 1.4
- Trooper,Trooper II
  - Four 1.4
  - V6
    - 2.8L Eng .8
    - 3.2L Eng 1.3

★ COMBINATIONS ★

- ★ Seal, Compressor Shaft - R&R .6
- ★ Coil, Compressor Clutch - R&R .8
- ★ Clutch, Compressor Drive - R&R .2

COMPRESSOR ASSEMBLY - R&I & O/H *(B)*

DOES NOT include System Charge.

1981-93
- Amigo 2.4

Cont.

Isuzu Heating & Air Conditioning (Cont.)

I-Mark
F.W.D. (85-89)
w/Turbocharger 2.2
w/o Turbocharger 2.0
R.W.D. (81-85) 2.5
Impulse,Stylus
F.W.D. (90-93)
1.6L Eng
w/Pwr Strg 2.2
w/o Pwr Strg 2.0
1.8L Eng 2.2
R.W.D. (83-89)
w/Turbocharger 2.3
w/o Turbocharger 1.8
Pickup
(81-87) 2.0
(88-93) 2.4
Rodeo 2.4
Trooper,Trooper II
Four 3.0
V6
2.8L Eng 2.4
3.2L Eng .... N.A.

PULLEY &/OR BEARINGS, COMPRESSOR - R&R *(B)*
Use Compressor Assembly - R&R plus Combinations.

CLUTCH, COMPRESSOR DRIVE - R&R *(B)*
Use Compressor Assembly - R&R plus Combinations.

COIL, COMPRESSOR CLUTCH - R&R *(B)*
Use Compressor Assembly - R&R plus Combinations.

VALVE, EVAPORATOR EXPANSION - R&R *(B)*
DOES NOT include System Charge.
1981-93
Amigo,Pickup,Rodeo 1.9
I-Mark 1.8
Impulse,Stylus
F.W.D. (90-93) 8
R.W.D. (83-89) 1.8
Trooper,Trooper II
(84-91) 1.9
(92-93) 1.3

CONDENSER - R&R *(B)*
DOES NOT include System Charge.
1981-93
Amigo,Pickup,Rodeo 1.4
I-Mark
F.W.D. (85-89) 1.0
R.W.D. (81-85) 1.5
Impulse,Stylus
F.W.D. (90-93)
w/Turbocharger 1.3
w/o Turbocharger 1.0
R.W.D. (83-89) 9
Trooper,Trooper II
(84-91) 1.4
(92-93) 1.1

MOTOR, CONDENSER FAN - R&R *(D)*
1985-93
I-Mark (F.W.D.) 7
Impulse (F.W.D.),Stylus 1.3

RELAY, CONDENSER FAN - R&R *(B)*
All 5

SWITCH, CONDENSER FAN - R&R *(B)*
All 5

RECEIVER DRIER - R&R *(B)*
DOES NOT include System Charge.
1981-93
Amigo,I-Mark,Pickup,Rodeo 8
Impulse,Stylus
F.W.D. (90-93) 1.0
R.W.D. (83-89) 8
Trooper,Trooper II
(84-91) 8
(92-93) 9

CORE, EVAPORATOR - R&R *(B)*
DOES NOT include System Charge.
1981-93
Amigo,Pickup,Rodeo 1.9
I-Mark
F.W.D. (85-89) 1.8
R.W.D. (81-85) 2.2
Impulse,Stylus 1.8
Trooper,Trooper II
(84-91) 1.9
(92-93) 1.2

HOSE, AIR CONDITIONING - R&R *(B)*
DOES NOT include System Charge.
1981-93
One 1.0
Each Additional 5

★ COMBINATIONS ★

★ Make Up Hose From Stock 4

THERMOSTATIC SWITCH - R&R *(B)*
DOES NOT include System Charge.
1981-93
Amigo,Pickup,Rodeo 1.3
I-Mark
F.W.D. (85-89) 1.8
R.W.D. (81-85) 3.1
Impulse,Stylus
F.W.D. (90-93) 1.6
R.W.D. (83-89) 2.3
Trooper,Trooper II
(84-91) 1.3
(92-93) 4

SWITCH, LOW PRESSURE - R&R *(B)*
DOES NOT include System Charge.
All 3

SWITCH, TRIPLE PRESSURE - R&R *(B)*
DOES NOT include System Charge.
All 9

SWITCH, CONDENSER PRESSURE - R&R *(B)*
DOES NOT include System Charge.
All 1.1

SWITCH, DUAL PRESSURE - R&R *(B)*
DOES NOT include System Charge.
1985-89 (I-Mark F.W.D.) 1.1

SENSOR, SUN - R&R *(B)*
All 6

SENSOR, AMBIENT TEMP - R&R *(B)*
All 4

SENSOR, INSIDE TEMP - R&R *(B)*
All 1.3

Jaguar Heating & Air Conditioning

***NOTE 1:** Times shown DO NOT include evacuate and charge system. If necessary to open refrigerant system or to evacuate, charge and test; refer to System Charge (Complete) for appropriate time.*
***NOTE 2:** Times listed are for Factory and Dealer dash installed Integral Type air conditioning units only. Use necessary clock time for service of hang-on units.*

HEATING & VENTILATION

HEATER HOSES - R&R *(D)*
NOTE: Deduct .2 hours when used in conjunction with Radiator Hose - R&R.
1973-87
E Series III
One 6
All 1.0
XJS,XJSC (ea) 1.0
XJ6
Series I
One 6
All 1.0
Series II
Pressure 7
Return 6
Series III (ea) 9
XJ12 (ea)
Series I 9
Series II
Pressure 7
Return 6
1988-93 (ea) 1.0

CORE, HEATER - R&R *(B)*
1973-87
E Series III 1.0
XJS,XJSC 14.8
XJ6
Series I 11.2
Series II & III 9.5
XJ12 .... 11.8
1988-93
XJRS,XJS,XJSC 2.8
XJ6 .... 2.4

WATER VALVE - R&R *(B)*
1973-87
E Series III,XJ12 9
XJS,XJSC 1.5
XJ6
Series I & II 8
Series III 1.0

Cont.

AIR CONDITIONING TIME GUIDE

Jaguar Heating & Air Conditioning (Cont.)

1988-92
XJS,XJSC 1.5
XJ6 .... 1.0
1993
XJRS 1.5
XJS,XJ6 .... 1.0

CABLE, TEMP CONTROL - R&R *(B)*

XJ6 Series II,XJ12 Series II 2.7

MOTOR, BLOWER - R&R *(B)*

1973-87
E Series III
w/Air Cond 1.2
w/o Air Cond 9
XJS,XJSC
w/Air Cond (ea) 2.4
w/o Air Cond 9
XJ6
Series I 9
Series II
w/Air Cond
Right Side 1.3
Left 2.0
w/o Air Cond 9
Series III
w/Air Cond
Right Side 2.7
Left 2.3
w/o Air Cond 2.0
XJ12
Series I 9
Series II
w/Air Cond
Right Side 1.3
Left 2.0
w/o Air Cond 9
1988-93
XJRS,XJS,XJSC (ea) 2.4
XJ6
Right Side 2.0
Left
Thru V.I.N. #629286 .... 1.1
V.I.N. #629287 & Up 1.8

SWITCH, BLOWER MOTOR - R&R *(B)*

1973-87
E Series III,XJ12 5
XJS,XJSC 2.6
XJ6
Series I & II 5
Series III 2.6
1988-93
XJRS,XJS,XJSC 2.6
XJ6 7

RESISTOR, BLOWER MOTOR - R&R *(B)*

E Series III 5
XJRS,XJS,XJSC
w/Air Cond 1.8
w/o Air Cond 1.0
XJ6,XJ12
w/Air Cond 1.5
w/o Air Cond 1.0

RELAY, BLOWER MOTOR - R&R *(B)*

1973-87
XJS,XJSC
w/Air Cond 1.6
w/o Air Cond 1.0
XJ6,XJ12 .... 1.0
1988-93
XJRS,XJS,XJSC 1.6
XJ6
High Speed (ea) 8
Isolation
Right Side 1.6
Left 8

AIR CONDITIONING

FREON - RECOVER *(B)*

NOTE: This operation is not to be used with any other operations.

All 3

PERFORMANCE - TEST *(B)*

Includes: Gauge check, leak test and partial charge.

All 1.0

SYSTEM CHARGE (PARTIAL) *(B)*

Includes: Performance test.

All 1.0

SYSTEM CHARGE (COMPLETE) *(B)*

Includes: Recover, evacuate and recharge system.

All 1.4

BELT, COMPRESSOR - R&R *(D)*

Includes: Serpentine belts.

1973-93
V-Belt 5
Serpentine 3

● **ADDITIONAL TIME** ●

- Where Alternator interferes add 2
- Where Air Pump interferes add 2
- Where Pwr Strg interferes add 2

RELAY, COMPRESSOR CLUTCH - R&R *(B)*

1988-93 6

CLUTCH OR COIL, COMPRESSOR - R&R *(B)*

DOES NOT include System Charge.

1974-87
XJS,XJSC,XJ12
Clutch 1.4
Coil 1.8
XJ6
Series I & II 9
Series III
Clutch 1.7
Coil 2.1
1988-92
XJS,XJSC
Clutch 1.4
Coil 1.8
XJ6
Clutch 1.6
Coil 2.0
1993
XJRS
Clutch 1.4
Coil 1.8
XJS,XJ6
Clutch 1.6
Coil 2.0

SEAL, COMPRESSOR SHAFT - R&R *(B)*

DOES NOT include System Charge.

1974-87
XJS,XJSC,XJ12 .... 2.0
XJ6
Series I & II 1.0
Series III 2.2
1988-92
XJS,XJSC 2.0
XJ6 .... 2.2
1993
XJRS 2.0
XJS,XJ6 .... 2.2

COMPRESSOR ASSEMBLY - R&R *(B)*

DOES NOT include System Charge.

1973-87
E Series III 1.0
XJS,XJSC,XJ12 .... 1.9
XJ6
Series I 1.0
Series II & III 1.9
1988-92
XJS,XJSC 1.9
XJ6 .... 2.1
1993
XJRS 1.9
XJS,XJ6 .... 2.1

SENSOR, AMBIENT (AUTOMATIC AIR) - R&R *(B)*

1973-87
XJS,XJSC 1.3
XJ6 Series II & III,XJ12 Series II 2.6
1988-93
XJRS,XJS,XJSC 1.3
XJ6 .... 2.0

SENSOR (IN CAR) - R&R *(B)*

1973-87
XJS,XJSC 2.7
XJ6
Series II 1.5
Series III 6
XJ12 Series II 1.5
1988-93
XJRS,XJS,XJSC 2.7
XJ6 .... 1.3

FAN & MOTOR, CONDENSER - R&R *(B)*

1973-87
E Series III 8
XJS,XJSC 1.5
XJ6
Series I & II 8
Series III 1.6
XJ12
Series I 1.3
Series II 3.0
1988-92
XJS,XJSC 1.5
XJ6 .... 1.0
1993
XJRS 1.5
XJS .... N.A.
XJ6 .... 1.0

RELAY, CONDENSER FAN - R&R *(B)*

E Series III 8
XJS,XJSC
exc H.E. 8
H.E. 5
XJ6,XJ12 5

Cont.

AIR CONDITIONING TIME GUIDE

Jaguar Heating & Air Conditioning (Cont.)

SWITCH, CONDENSER FAN - R&R *(B)*

1973-92
- E Series III 8
- XJS,XJSC 1.0
- XJ6,XJ12 7

1993
- XJRS 1.0
- XJS,XJ6 7

CONDENSER - R&R *(B)*
DOES NOT include System Charge.

1973-87
- E Series III 1.0
- XJS,XJSC 2.7
- XJ6
  - Series I 2.2
  - Series II 2.6
  - Series III 1.3
- XJ12
  - Series I 1.3
  - Series II 2.6

1988-93
- XJRS,XJS,XJSC 1.5
- XJ6 .... 1.0

RECEIVER DRIER - R&R *(B)*
DOES NOT include System Charge.

1973-87
- E Series III 7
- XJS,XJSC 4
- XJ6
  - Series I 7
  - Series II & III 4
- XJ12
  - Series I 7
  - Series II 4

1988-93 4

CORE, EVAPORATOR - R&R *(B)*
DOES NOT include System Charge.

1973-87
- E Series III 5.3
- XJS,XJSC 15.0
- XJ6
  - Series I 13.5
  - Series II & III 14.0
- XJ12
  - Series I 13.5
  - Series II 14.0

1988-93
- XJRS,XJS,XJSC 15.0
- XJ6 .... 13.0

VALVE, EVAPORATOR EXPANSION - R&R *(B)*
DOES NOT include System Charge.

1973-87
- E Series III 9
- XJS,XJSC 3.4
- XJ6 Series II & III 1.3
- XJ12 Series II 5.3

1988-93
- XJRS,XJS,XJSC 3.4
- XJ6 .... 2.4

HOSE, AIR CONDITIONING - R&R *(B)*
DOES NOT include System Charge.

1973-87 (ea)
- E Series III,XJ12 .... 1.3
- XJS,XJSC 2.2
- XJ6
  - Series I & II 1.3
  - Series III 1.0

1988-93 (ea) 2.2

★ **COMBINATIONS** ★

★ Make Up Hose From Stock 4

SOLENOID, AIR COND VACUUM - R&R *(B)*

1976-93
- XJRS,XJS,XJSC 1.1
- XJ6
  - (80-87 - Series III) 9
  - (88-93)
    - Center Vent or Defroster 5
    - Recirculation or Water Valve 1.5

RESERVOIR, AIR COND VACUUM - R&R *(B)*

1988-93 (XJ6) 7

CONTROL, AIR DISTRIBUTION - R&R *(B)*

1976-93
- XJRS,XJS,XJSC (ea) 2.7
- XJ6
  - (80-87)
    - Demister Flap Servo 9
    - Main Unit (w/Vacuum Switches) 1.3
  - (88-93)
    - Center Flap Servo 3.6
    - Demister Flap Servo 2.6
    - Lower or Upper Flap
      - Gearbox and Motor Assy (ea) 1.0
      - Potentiometer (ea) 5

SENSOR, EVAPORATOR TEMP - R&R *(B)*

1988-89 (XJ6) 5

1990-93
- XJRS,XJS,XJSC 1.0
- XJ6 7

SENSOR, SOLAR - R&R *(B)*

1988-93 (XJ6) 6

MODULE, ELECTRONIC CONTROL - R&R *(B)*

1988-89 (XJ6) 1.0

1990-93
- XJRS,XJS,XJSC 1.1
- XJ6 .... 1.4

Lexus Heating & Air Conditioning

NOTE: Times shown DO NOT include recover, evacuate and charge system. If necessary to open refrigerant system; refer to System Charge (Complete) for appropriate time.

HEATING & VENTILATION

HEATER HOSES - R&R *(D)*

1990-93 (All)
- ES 250,ES 300,GS 300,SC 300,SC 400 .... 1.4
- LS 400 7

WATER VALVE - R&R *(B)*

1990-93
- ES 250 8
- ES 300,GS 300,SC 300,SC 400 .... 1.0
- LS 400 7

CORE, HEATER - R&R *(B)*
DOES NOT include System Charge.

1990-93
- ES 250 .... 5.0
- ES 300 .... 1.8
- GS 300 .... 7.0
- LS 400 .... 8.0
- SC 300 ①
  - Std Trans 17.2
  - Auto Trans 16.7
- SC 400 ① 17.0

① *Includes: R&I engine.*

MOTOR, BLOWER - R&R *(B)*
DOES NOT include System Charge.

1990-93
- ES 250,ES 300,GS 300 6
- LS 400 .... 1.8
- SC 300,SC 400 .... 1.0

SWITCH, BLOWER MOTOR - R&R *(B)*

1990-93
- ES 250 9
- ES 300,GS 300,LS 400 6
- SC 300,SC 400 8

RELAY, BLOWER MOTOR - R&R *(B)*

1990-93 5

RESISTOR, BLOWER MOTOR - R&R *(B)*

1990-93
- ES 250,ES 300,GS 300 5
- LS 400 .... 1.1
- SC 300,SC 400 7

CONTROL ASSEMBLY, TEMP - R&R *(B)*

1990-93
- ES 250 .... 1.0
- ES 300,GS 300,LS 400 6
- SC 300,SC 400 8

AIR CONDITIONING

FREON - RECOVER *(B)*
NOTE: This operation is not to be used with any other operations.

1990-93 3

PERFORMANCE - TEST *(B)*
Includes: Gauge check, leak test and partial charge.

1990-93 .... 1.0

Cont.

AIR CONDITIONING TIME GUIDE

Lexus Heating & Air Conditioning (Cont.)

SYSTEM CHARGE (PARTIAL) *(B)*
Includes: Performance test.
1990-93 .... 1.0

SYSTEM CHARGE (COMPLETE) *(B)*
Includes: Recover, evacuate and recharge system.
1990-93 .... 1.4

BELT, COMPRESSOR - R&R *(D)*
Includes: Serpentine and V-Belt type.
1990-93 5

COMPRESSOR ASSEMBLY - R&R *(B)*
DOES NOT include System Charge.
1990-93
ES 250 .... 1.2
ES 300 .... 2.0
GS 300 .... 1.8
LS 400,SC 300 .... 1.4
SC 400 .... 1.1

CLUTCH PLATE & HUB ASSEMBLY - R&R *(B)*
DOES NOT include System Charge.
1990-93
ES 250,SC 400 .... 1.4
ES 300 .... 2.2
GS 300 .... 2.1
LS 400 .... 1.7
SC 300 .... 1.8

VALVE, EVAPORATOR EXPANSION - R&R *(B)*
DOES NOT include System Charge.
1990-93
ES 250 .... 1.1
ES 300 .... 1.4
GS 300 .... 1.5
LS 400 .... 2.2
SC 300,SC 400
w/Traction Control System 4.0
w/o Traction Control System 2.4

REGULATOR, EVAPORATOR PRESSURE - R&R *(B)*
DOES NOT include System Charge.
1990-93
GS 300,LS 400 7
SC 300,SC 400
w/Traction Control System 3.2
w/o Traction Control System 1.4

CONDENSER - R&R *(B)*
DOES NOT include System Charge.
1990-93
ES 250 8
ES 300 ① 3.0
GS 300 .... 2.9
LS 400 ② 2.6
SC 300,SC 400 ③ 2.2
① *Includes: R&I headlamps, front bumper and hood lock support.*
② *Includes: R&I headlamps, front bumper and horns.*
③ *Includes: R&I battery.*

FAN & MOTOR, CONDENSER - R&R *(B)*
1990-93
ES 250 8
LS 400 ①
One 2.1
Both 2.3
① *Includes: R&I headlamps, front bumper and horns.*

RELAY, ELECT FAN MOTOR - R&R *(B)*
1990-93 3

RECIEVER DRIER - R&R *(B)*
DOES NOT include System Charge.
1990-93
ES 250,ES 300,GS 300 5
LS 400 ① 9
SC 300,SC 400 ② 1.3
① *Includes: R&I right side headlamp.*
② *Includes: R&I left side headlamp.*

CORE, EVAPORATOR - R&R *(B)*
DOES NOT include System Charge.
1990-93
ES 250,ES 300 .... 1.4
GS 300 .... 1.5
LS 400 .... 2.2
SC 300,SC 400
w/Traction Control System 4.0
w/o Traction Control System 2.4

HOSE, AIR CONDITIONING - R&R *(B)*
DOES NOT include System Charge.
1990-93 (All)
ES 250,ES 300,GS 300,SC 300,SC 400 8
LS 400 .... 3.2

★ COMBINATIONS ★

★ Make Up Hose From Stock 4

SWITCH, PRESSURE CUT - R&R *(B)*
DOES NOT include System Charge.
1990-93
ES 250 .... 1.1
ES 300,GS 300,LS 400,SC 300,SC 400 9

Mazda Heating & Air Conditioning

NOTE 1: Times shown Do Not include recover, evacuate and charge system. If necessary to open refrigerant system or to recover, evacuate, charge and test, refer to System Charge (Complete) for appropriate time.
NOTE 2: Times listed are for Factory and Dealer dash installed Integral Type air conditioning units only. Use necessary clock time for service of hang-on units.

HEATING & VENTILATION

HEATER HOSES - R&R *(D)*
NOTE: Deduct .2 when used in conjunction with Radiator Hose - R&R.
1979-93
exc 929
One 6
Both 7
929
(88-91)
One 5
Both 9
(92-93)
One 7
Both 1.1

WATER VALVE - R&R *(B)*
1979-93
B2000,B2200,B2600,GLC 6
MX6,626
(79-82) 8
(83-85) 2.5
RX7
(79-84) 6
(85-91) 2.6

HEATER ASSEMBLY - R&R *(B)*
For models not listed use Heater Core - R&R.
1979-93
B2000,B2200,B2600
(79-84) 1.0
(85-93) 3.2
GLC
F.W.D. 2.7
R.W.D.
w/Air Cond 3.0
w/o Air Cond 8
Miata 4.7
MPV
Front 2.2
Rear 1.1
MX3 .... 4.2
MX6,626
(79-82) 3.4
(83-92) 3.9
(93) 2.7
Protege,323 .... 3.9
RX7
(79-91) 3.9
(93) 3.1
929 .... 4.5

★ COMBINATIONS ★

★ Core, Heater - R&R 5

CORE, HEATER - R&R *(B)*
For models not listed use Heater Assembly - R&R.
Navajo 9

SWITCH, BLOWER MOTOR - R&R *(B)*
1979-81 .... **N.A.**
1982-93
B2000,B2200,B2600,Miata,MPV,RX7 7
GLC
F.W.D. 5
R.W.D. 7
MX6,Protege,323,626 6
Navajo 7

Cont.

Mazda Heating & Air Conditioning (Cont.)

RESISTOR, BLOWER MOTOR - R&R *(B)*
1979-93
B2000,B2200,B2600,GLC,Miata,RX7,929 .. .6
MPV
Front .3
Rear .9
MX3 .7
MX6,Navajo,Protege,323,626 .5

MOTOR, BLOWER - R&R *(B)*
1979-93
B2000,B2200,B2600 .8
GLC
Air Cond Blower .9
Heater Blower .7
Miata,MX3,Navajo .8
MPV
Front .5
Rear .9
MX6,Protege,323,626 .6
RX7
(79-91) .8
(93) .5
929
(88-91) .5
(92-93) 4.2

FAN ASSEMBLIES, SOLAR VENTILATION - R&R *(B)*
1992-93 (929)
One Side .3
Both .5

SWITCH, SOLAR VENTILATION - R&R *(B)*
1992-93 (929) .3

AMPLIFIER, SOLAR VENTILATION - R&R *(B)*
1992-93 (929) .8

CONTROL ASSEMBLY, TEMP - R&R *(B)*
1979-93
B2000,B2200,B2600
(79-80) .7
(81-82) 1.5
(83-84) 1.3
(86-93) .7
GLC
F.W.D. .8
R.W.D. 1.0
Miata,MX3 .6
MPV .7
MX6,626
w/Logic Control .7
w/o Logic Control .5
Navajo .8
Protege,RX7,323 .9
929
(88-91)
w/Logic Control .9
w/o Logic Control .6
(92-93) 1.9

CABLES, TEMP CONTROL - R&R *(B)*
1979-93 (One or All)
B2000,B2200,B2600
(79-82) 1.3
(83-84) 1.5
(86-93) .6
GLC
F.W.D. .9
R.W.D. 1.1

MPV .8
MX6,626
(79-82) 1.1
(83-92) .8
Navajo,Protege,323 .9
RX7 .8

AIR CONDITIONING

FREON - RECOVER *(B)*
NOTE: This operation is not to be used with any other operations.
All .3

PERFORMANCE - TEST *(B)*
Includes: Gauge check, leak test and partial charge.
1979-93 1.0

SYSTEM CHARGE (PARTIAL) *(B)*
Includes: Pressure and leak test.
1979-93 1.0

SYSTEM CHARGE (COMPLETE) *(B)*
Includes: Evacuate, recover and recharge system.
1979-93 1.4

SEAL, COMPRESSOR SHAFT - R&R *(B)*
Includes: R&I compressor.
DOES NOT include evacuate or charge system.
1979-93
B2000
(80-82) 2.3
(83-86) .9
B2200
(82-84) 1.1
(87-93) .8
B2600 1.0
GLC
(77-80) 1.6
(81-84) 1.4
(85) 1.8
MPV 1.1
MX3 2.5
MX6 1.3
Navajo 1.3
Protege,323
w/Turbocharger 1.5
w/o Turbocharger 1.3
RX7
(79-84) 1.4
(85) 2.1
(86-91) 1.1
(93) 1.3
323 1.3
626
(79-82) 1.6
(83-84) 1.4
(85)
Diesel 1.5
Gas 2.0
(86-93) 1.3
929
(88-91) 1.5
(92-93) 3.2

CLUTCH OR COIL, COMPRESSOR - R&R *(B)*
DOES NOT include evacuate or charge system.
1979-93
B2000
(80-82) 2.2
(83-86) 1.2

B2200
(82-84) 1.4
(87-93) .9
B2600 1.1
GLC
(79-80) 1.5
(81-84) 1.2
(85) 1.6
Miata 1.0
MPV 1.0
MX3 2.3
MX6 1.5
Navajo 1.1
Protege,323
w/Turbocharger 1.7
w/o Turbocharger 1.5
RX7
(79-84) 1.2
(85) 1.8
(86-91) 1.1
(93) 1.5
626
(79-82) 1.5
(83-84) 1.2
(85)
Diesel 1.3
Gas 1.8
(86-93) 1.5
929
(88-91) 1.6
(92-93) 3.0

BELT, COMPRESSOR - R&R *(D)*
Includes: Serpentine.
1979-93
exc Navajo .5
Navajo .7

COMPRESSOR ASSEMBLY - R&R *(B)*
DOES NOT include evacuate or charge system.
1979-93
B2000
(80-82) 1.9
(83-86) .9
B2200
(82-84) 1.1
(87-93) .7
B2600 .9
GLC
(79-80) 1.2
(81-84) .9
(85) 1.3
Miata .8
MPV .9
MX3 1.9
MX6 1.1
Navajo 1.4
Protege,323
w/Turbocharger .9
w/o Turbocharger .8
RX7
(79-84) .9
(85) 1.5
(86-91) .9
(93) 1.1
626
(79-82) 1.2
(83-84) .9
(85)
Diesel 1.0
Gas 1.6
(86-93) 1.1
929
(88-91) 1.0
(92-93) 2.7

Cont.

AIR CONDITIONING TIME GUIDE

Mazda Heating & Air Conditioning (Cont.)

VALVE, EVAPORATOR EXPANSION - R&R *(B)*
DOES NOT include evacuate or charge system.

1979-93
B2000
(80-82) 5
(83-86) 1.2
B2200
(82-84) 1.2
(87-93) 9
B2600 9
GLC
F.W.D. 1.2
R.W.D. 5
Miata,MPV,MX6 .... 1.5
MX3 .... 2.0
Protege,323 .... 1.5
RX7
(79-85) 1.5
(86-93) 1.0
626
F.W.D. 1.5
R.W.D. 5
929
(88-91) 1.5
(92-93) 2.3

ORIFICE, EVAPORATOR CORE - R&R *(B)*
DOES NOT include evacuate or charge system.
Navajo 5

CONDENSER - R&R *(B)*
DOES NOT include evacuate or charge system.

1979-93
B2000
Std Trans 6
Auto Trans 1.1
B2200
(82-84) 1.1
(87-93) 8
B2600 8
GLC
F.W.D. 5
R.W.D. 1.2
Miata,MPV 7
MX3 .... 1.3
MX6,626
(79-82) 9
(83-92) 7
(93) 1.1
Navajo 6
Protege,323 9
RX7
(79-80) 9
(81-84) 7
(85) 1.1
(86-93) 8
929
(88-91) 6
(92-93) 1.6

RECEIVER DRIER - R&R *(B)*
DOES NOT include evacuate or charge system.

1979-93
B2000,B2200,B2600,GLC,MPV,Protege,323 6
MX3 .... 1.3
MX6,626
(79-92) 8
(93) 6
Navajo 7
RX7
(79-91) 6
(93) 4
929
(88-91) 6
(92-93) 1.3

VALVE, THREE-WAY - R&R *(B)*
DOES NOT include evacuate or charge system.
1988-93 (B2200,B2600) 5

SWITCH, PRESSURE - R&R *(B)*
DOES NOT include evacuate or charge system.

1979-93
exc MX3,RX7 5
MX3 .... 1.5
RX7
(79-91) 5
(93) 7

FAN, CONDENSER - R&R *(D)*
DOES NOT include evacuate or charge system.

1979-93
B2200,323 5
B2600,MX3 7
Miata 5
MPV 6
MX6,626 9
RX7 7

SENSOR, SUN - R&R *(B)*
1988-93 (929) 3

SENSOR, INSIDE TEMP - R&R *(B)*
1988-93 (929) 5

SENSOR, WATER TEMP - R&R *(B)*
1988-93 (929) 6

SENSOR, AMBIENT - R&R *(B)*
1988-93 (929) 3

SENSOR, DUCT - R&R *(B)*
DOES NOT include evacuate or charge system.
1988-93 (929)
(88-91) 1.3
(92-93) 2.2

HOSE, AIR CONDITIONING - R&R *(B)*
DOES NOT include evacuate or charge system.

1979-93
B2000
Suction 7
Discharge 5
B2200,B2600
Suction 4
Suction and Discharge Assembly 7
GLC
Suction 6
Discharge 1.0
Miata (ea) 8
MPV (ea) 5
MX3
Suction 1.1
Discharge 1.3
MX6,626 (ea)
(79-92) 6
(93) 9
Navajo,Protege,323 (ea) 6
RX7
(79-91)
Suction 4
Suction and Discharge Assembly 9
(93)
Suction 1.1
Discharge 8
929
(88-91)
Suction 5
Discharge 1.0
(92-93)
Suction 1.8
Discharge 1.6

★ **COMBINATIONS** ★

★ Make Up Hose From Stock 4

CORE, EVAPORATOR - R&R *(B)*
Includes: R&I blower assembly and console.
DOES NOT include evacuate or charge system.

1979-93
B2000,B2200
(79-82) 1.0
(83-84) 1.2
(86-93) 9
B2600 9
GLC 1.4
Miata 1.0
MPV 1.0
MX3 .... 2.0
MX6,626
(79-92) 1.3
(93) 1.1
Navajo 1.1
Protege,323 .... 1.3
RX7
(79-80) 1.5
(81-84) 1.2
(85) 1.6
(86-93) 1.0
929
(88-91) 1.5
(92-93) 2.2

Mercedes-Benz Heating & Air Conditioning

NOTE 1: Times shown DO NOT include recover, evacuate and charge system. If necessary to open refrigerant system; refer to System Charge (Complete) for appropriate time. NOTE 2: Times listed are for Factory and Dealer dash installed Integral Type air conditioning units only. Use necessary clock time for service of hang-on units.

HEATING & VENTILATION

HEATER HOSES - R&R *(D)*

1973-80 .... 2.5
1981-85
190D,190E 1.8
240D,280CE,280E,300CD,300D,300TD 1.3
300SD,380SE,380SEC,380SEL,500SEC,500SEL 2.4
380SL,380SLC 2.7
1986-91
190D,190E
Four 1.8
Six 2.6
260E,300CE,300D,300E,300SDL,300TD, 300TE 2.6
300SE,300SEL 4.0
350SD,350SDL,420SEL,560SEC,560SEL 2.3
560SL .... N.A.
1992-93
190E 1.8
300CE,300D,300E,300TE,400E,500E 2.6
300SD,300SE,400SE,500SEC,500SEL,600SEC, 600SEL .... N.A.
300SL,500SL,600SL 7.2

CORE, HEATER - R&R *(B)*

NOTE: For applications not listed, use Heater Housing Assembly - R&I plus Combinations. DOES NOT include R&I heater housing or evacuate and charge system.

1973-80
220,220D 6.3
230,240D (74-76) 6.3
280,280C 9.5
280S,280SE (76-80) 11.3
300SD,300TD (78-80) 11.3
450SE,450SEL,6.9 (76-80) 14.4

● **ADDITIONAL TIME** ●

● Where Air Cond interferes add
220,220D,230,240D 3.8

★ **COMBINATIONS** ★

★ Control Cable, Heater - R&R
One 3
Both 5
★ Control Valve, Heater - R&R
One 3
Both 5

HEATER HOUSING ASSEMBLY - R&I *(B)*

1973-80
220,220D,280,280C 4.4
230,240D
(74-76) 4.4
(77-80)
w/Air Cond 9.8
w/o Air Cond 6.3
280CE,280E,300CD,300D,300TD 10.9
280S,280SE,300SD,450SE,450SEL,6.9
(73-75) 14.6
(76-80) 15.6
450SL,450SLC
(73-75) 17.3
(76-80) 18.3
1981-85
190D,190E 6.9
240D
w/Air Cond 9.8
w/o Air Cond 6.3
280CE,280E,300CD,300D,300TD 10.9
300SD,380SE,380SEC,380SEL,500SEC,500SEL 13.2
380SL,380SLC 18.3
1986-91
190D,190E 7.1
260E,300CE,300D,300E,300TD,300TE 9.5
300SDL,300SE,300SEL,350SD,350SDL, 420SEL,560SEC,560SEL 13.2
300SL,500SL 11.6
560SL 14.5
1992-93
190E 7.1
300CE,300D,300E,300TE,400E,500E 9.5
300SD,300SE,400SE,400SEL,500SEC,500SEL, 600SEC,600SEL 17.3
300SL,500SL,600SL 11.6

★ **COMBINATIONS** ★

★ Core, Heater - R&R
73-85
190D,190E 1.0
220,220D,280,280C 1.9
230,240D
w/Air Cond 1.5
w/o Air Cond 9
280CE,280E,300CD,300D,300TD 1.5
280S,280SE,300SD 1.1
380SE,380SEC,380SEL,500SEC,500SEL 1.1
380SL,380SLC,450SL,450SLC 9
450SE,450SEL,6.9 .... 1.1
86-91
190D,190E 1.3
260E,300CE,300D,300E,300TD,300TE, 300SDL,300SE,300SEL,350SD,350SDL, 420SEL,560SEC,560SEL 1.0
300SL,500SL 4
560SL 8
92-93
190E 1.3
300CE,300D,300E,300TE,400E,500E 1.0
300SD,300SE,400SE,400SEL,500SEC,500SEL, 600SEC,600SEL 5
300SL,500SL,600SL 4
★ Control Cable, Heater - R&R
One 3
Both 5
★ Control Valve, Heater - R&R
exc 380SL,380SLC,450SL,450SLC 5
380SL,380SLC,450SL,450SLC 8
★ Motor, Blower - R&R 3
★ Housing, Blower - R&R 8
★ Resistor, Blower Motor - R&R 5

SWITCH, BLOWER MOTOR - R&R *(B)*

1973-85
190D,190E 6
220,220D,230,240D,280,280C,6.9 9
280CE,280E,300CD,300D,300TD 9
280S,280SE 1.8
300SD
(78-80) 9
(81-85) 1.1
380SE,380SEC,380SEL,500SEC,500SEL 1.1
380SL,380SLC,450SE,450SEL,450SL,450SLC 1.8
1986-91
190D,190E 6
260E,300CE,300D,300E,300TD,300TE,560SL 7
300SDL,300SE,300SEL,420SEL,560SEC, 560SEL 1.1
1992-93 6

RESISTOR, BLOWER MOTOR - R&R *(B)*

1973-80
220,220D,280,280C .... N.A.
230,240D
(74-76) .... N.A.
(77-80)
w/Air Cond 6.8
w/o Air Cond 10.3
280CE,280E,300CD,300D,300TD 7.9
280S,280SE,450SE,450SEL,6.9
w/Climate Control 9
w/o Climate Control 1.5
300SD 9
450SL,450SLC
w/Climate Control 8
w/o Climate Control 1.8
1981-85
190D,190E 5
240D
w/Air Cond 6.8
w/o Air Cond 10.3
280CE,280E,300CD,300D,300TD 7.9
300SD,380SE,380SEC,380SEL,500SEC,500SEL 2.6
380SL,380SLC 1.8
1986-91
190D,190E 3
260E,300CE,300D,300E,300TD,300TE 6
300SDL,300SE,300SEL,420SEL,560SEC, 560SEL 2.6
300SL,500SL 1.0
560SL 1.8
1992-93
190E,300CE,300D,300E,300TE,400E,500E. 3
300SD,300SE,400SE,400SEL,500SEC,500SEL, 600SEC,600SEL 6
300SL,500SL,600SL 1.0

MOTOR, BLOWER - R&R *(B)*

1973-76
220,220D 1.6
230,240D
w/Air Cond 8.8
w/o Air Cond 5.6
280,280C,300D 8.7
280S,450SE,450SEL 2.7
450SL,450SLC 1.8
1977-85
190D,190E 2.4
230,240D,280CE,280E,300CD,300D,300TD 1.1
280SE 2.7
300SD
(78-80) 2.7
(81-85) 1.3
380SE,380SE,380SEL,500SEC,500SEL 1.3
380SL,380SLC,450SL,450SLC 1.8
450SE,450SEL,6.9 .... 2.7
1986-91
190D,190E 2.4
260E,300CE,300D,300E,300SL,300TD,300TE, 500SL 2.8
300SDL,300SE,300SEL,420SEL,560SEC,560SEL 1.3
560SL 1.8

Cont.

AIR CONDITIONING TIME GUIDE

Mercedes-Benz Heating & Air Conditioning (Cont.)

1992-93
190E **2.4**
300CE,300D,300E,300SL,300TE,400E,500E, 500SL,600SL **2.8**
300SD,300SE,400SE,400SEL,500SEC,500SEL, 600SEC,600SEL .... **.9**

WATER VALVE - R&R *(B)*

1973-80
220,220D **1.1**
230,240D
(74-76) .... **.6**
(77-80) **1.5**
280,280C,300SD,300TD .... **.8**
280CE,280E,300CD,300D **1.5**
280S,280SE,450SE,450SEL **1.8**
450SL,450SLC **2.2**
1981-85
190D,190E .... **.9**
240D,280CE,280E,300CD,300D,300TD .... **.8**
300SD,380SE,380SEC,380SEL,500SEC,500SEL **1.6**
380SL,380SLC **2.2**
1986-91
190D,190E .... **.9**
260E,300CE,300D,300E,300TD,300TE,400E, 500E .... **.7**
300SDL,,300SE,300SEL,420SEL,560SEC, 560SEL **1.8**
300SL,500SL,560SL .... **.8**
1992-93
190E,300SD,300SE,400SE,400SEL,500SEC, 500SEL,600SEC,600SEL .... **.9**
300CE,300D,300E,300TE,400E,500E .... **.7**
300SL,500SL,600SL .... **.8**

CABLE, VENTILATION CONTROL - R&R *(B)*

1973-85
190D,190E,220,220D,280,280C .... **N.A.**
230,240D
Air Volume
w/Air Cond **3.9**
w/o Air Cond **1.5**
Heating/Ventilation
w/Air Cond **2.3**
w/o Air Cond **1.1**
Rotary Knob
w/Air Cond
Right Side .... **.9**
Left **1.5**
w/o Air Cond
Right Side **3.6**
Left **2.3**
280CE,280E,300CD,300D,300TD
Air Volume **3.9**
Rotary Knob
Right Side **3.6**
Left **2.3**
280S,280SE,450SE,450SEL (Air Volume) .. **1.9**
300SD
(78-80) .... **N.A.**
(81-85)
Front (Air Outlet)
Right Side .... **.9**
Left .... **.7**
Rear (Air Outlet) **1.9**
380SE,380SEC,380SEL,500SEC,500SEL
Front (Air Outlet)
Right Side .... **.9**
Left .... **.7**
Rear (Air Outlet) **1.9**
380SL,380SLC,450SL,450SLC
Air Duct (Right or Left) **1.9**
Defroster **1.8**

CONTROL PANEL - R&R *(B)*
With auto climate control.

1976-80
exc 280CE,280E,300CD,300D,300TD .... **.9**
280CE,280E,300CD,300D,300TD **3.8**
1981-85
exc 190D,190E **1.4**
190D,190E .... **.8**
1986-91
190D,190E,260E,300CE,300D,300E,300TD, 300TE .... **.8**
300SDL,300SE,300SEL,350SD,350SDL, 420SEL,560SEC,560SEL .... **.9**
300SL,500SL .... **.4**
560SL .... **.5**
1992-93
190E .... **.8**
300CE,300D,300E,300SL,300TE,400E,500E, 500SL,600SL .... **.7**
300SD,300SE,400SE,400SEL,500SEC,500SEL, 600SEC,600SEL **1.0**

★ **COMBINATIONS** ★

★ Switch, Blower Motor - R&R .... **.3**
★ Switch, Push Button - R&R .... **.3**
★ Switch, Compressor - R&R .... **.2**
★ Selector Wheel, Temp - R&R .... **.3**

CONTROL ASSEMBLY, VENTILATION - R&R *(B)*
Without auto climate control.

220,220D,280,280C .... **N.A.**
230,240D
Air Outlet
w/Air Cond **1.6**
w/o Air Cond .... **.8**
Air Volume
w/Air Cond **1.9**
w/o Air Cond .... **.9**
Heater Control
w/Air Cond
Right Side **3.2**
Left **2.0**
w/o Air Cond (ea) .... **.9**
280CE,280E,300CD,300D,300TD **1.6**
280S,280SE,450SE,450SEL
One Side **5.2**
Both **7.3**
450SL,450SLC
One Side **5.9**
Both **8.0**

CONTROL, AUTO CLIMATE - R&R *(B)*

1973-85 .... **.4**
1986-91
190D,190E,260E,300D,300TD,300TE .... **.8**
300SDL,300SE,300SEL,420SEL,560SEC, 560SEL .... **.5**
560SL .... **.9**
1992-93 .... **.8**

SENSOR, AUTO CLIMATE TEMP - R&R *(B)*

1976-80 (ea) .... **.7**
1981-85
190D,190E .... **.7**
240D,280CE,280E,300CD,300D,300TD
Ambient (In Car) .... **.8**
Evaporator or Heater (ea) .... **.7**
300SD,380SE,380SEC,380SEL,500SEC,500SEL
Ambient (In Car) .... **.7**
Evaporator **1.9**
Heater .... **.8**
380SL,380SLC (ea) .... **.7**

1986-91
190D,190E
In Car .... **.7**
Heater Core .... **.7**
Evaporator **1.1**
Outside Air .... **.7**
260E,300CE,300D,300E,300TD,300TE
In Car .... **.3**
Heater Core .... **.6**
Evaporator **1.0**
Outside Air .... **.7**
300SDL,300SE,300SEL,350SD,350SDL 420SEL,56CSEL
In Car .... **.7**
Heater Core .... **.6**
Evaporator **1.9**
300SL,500SL (One) .... **.5**
560SEC,560SL
In Car .... **.5**
Heater Core .... **.6**
Evaporator **1.9**
1992-93
190E
Evaporator **1.1**
In Car .... **.7**
Outside .... **.7**
300CE,300D,300E,300TE,400E,500E
Evaporator .... **.7**
Heater Core .... **.6**
In Car .... **.3**
Outside **2.0**
300SD,300SE,400SE,400SEL,500SEC,500SEL, 600SEC,600SEL (One) **1.0**
300SL,500SL (One) .... **.5**

AIR CONDITIONING

FREON - RECOVER *(B)*

All .... **.3**

PERFORMANCE - TEST *(B)*
Includes: Gauge check, leak test and partial charge.

All **1.0**

SYSTEM CHARGE (PARTIAL) *(B)*
Includes: Performance test.

All **1.0**

SYSTEM CHARGE (COMPLETE) *(B)*
Includes: Recover, evacuate and recharge system.

All **1.4**

COMPRESSOR ASSEMBLY - R&R *(B)*
DOES NOT include evacuate or charge system

1973-80
220,220D **2.7**
230 .... **2.9**
240D,300CD,300D,300SD,300TD **2.3**
280,280C,280S,280SE **2.6**
280CE,280E **1.5**
450SE,450SEL,6.9 .... **4.5**
450SL,450SLC **4.9**
1981-85
190D,280CE,280E **1.5**
190E,240D,300CD,300D,300SD,300TD **2.3**
380SE,380SEC,380SEL,500SEC,500SEL, . **2.9**
380SL,380SLC **4.9**

Cont.

Mercedes-Benz Heating & Air Conditioning (Cont.)

1986-91
190D,420SEL,560SEC,560SEL ... 1.9
190E
Four ... 2.8
Six ... 2.0
260E,300CE,300D,300E,300SE,300SEL, 300SL,300TD,300TE,350SD,350SDL,500SL ... 2.0
300SDL ... 3.1
560SL ... 2.4

1992-93
190E
Four ... 2.8
Six ... 2.0
300CE,300D,300E,300SD,300SL,300TE,400E, 000E,500SL,600SL ... 2.0
300SE,400SE,400SEL,500SEC,500SEL, 600SEC,600SEL ... 1.8

CLUTCH OR COIL, COMPRESSOR - R&R *(B)*

Includes: R&I compressor where necessary.

1973-85
190D ... 2.3
190E ... 3.1
220,220D,230,240D ... 1.1
280,280C,280DE,280E ... 1.1
280S,280SE ... 1.5
300CD,300D,300TD
w/Turbocharger ... 3.1
w/o Turbocharger ... 1.1
300SD ... 3.1
380SE,380SEC,380SEL,500SEC,500SEL ... 2.4
380SL,380SLC,450SL,450SLC ... 4.4
450SE,450SEL,6.9 ... 4.0

1986-91
190D,420SEL,560SEC,560SEL ... 2.4
190E
Four ... 3.3
Six ... 2.5
260E,300CE,300D,300E,300SE,300SEL, 300SL,300TD,300TE,350SD,350SDL,500SL ... 2.5
300SDL ... 3.6
560SL ... 2.9

1992-93
190E
Four ... 3.3
Six ... 2.5
300CE,300D,300E,300SD,300SL,300TE,400E, 500E,500SL,600SL ... 2.5
300SE,400SE,400SEL,500SEC,500SEL, 600SEC,600SEL ... 2.3

PULLEY, COMPRESSOR - R&R *(B)*

Includes: R&I compressor where necessary.

1973-85
380SE,380SEC,380SEL,500SEC,500SEL ... 2.1
380SL,380SLC,450SL,450SLC ... 4.1
450SE,450SEL,6.9 ... 3.7

1986-93
exc 190D,190E 9
190D 8
190E
Four
8 Valve Eng 9
16 Valve Eng ... 1.0
Six 9

SEAL, COMPRESSOR SHAFT - R&R *(B)*

DOES NOT include charge system.

1973-85
190D ... 2.2
190E ... 3.0
220,220D,230,240D ... 1.5
280,280C,280CE,280E ... 1.5
280S,280SE ... 2.0
300CD,300D,300SD,300TD ... 1.5
380SE,380SEC,380SEL,380SL,380SLC ... 2.0
450SE,450SEL,450SL,450SLC,500SEC,500SEL ... 2.0

1986-91
190D,420SEL,560SEC,560SEL ... 2.6
190E
Four ... 3.5
Six ... 2.7
260E,300SE,300D,300E,300SE,300SEL, 300SL,300TD,300TE,350SD,350SDL,500SL ... 2.7
300SDL ... 3.8
560SL ... 3.1

1992-93
190E
Four ... 3.5
Six ... 2.7
300CE,300D,300E,300SD,300SL,300TE,400E, 500E,500SL,600SL ... 2.7
300SE,400SE,400SEL,500SEC,500SEL, 600SEC,600SEL ... 2.5

BELT, COMPRESSOR - R&R *(D)*

Includes: Serpentine type.

1973-85
190D,190E,220,220D,280,280C 8
230
w/Air Pump ... 1.6
w/o Air Pump 9
240D,300CD,300D,300SD,300TD 8
280CE,280E
w/Air Pump ... 1.1
w/o Air Pump 6
280S,280SE,450SE,450SL,450SLC,6.9
w/Air Pump 8
w/o Air Pump 3
380SE,380SEC,380SEL,500SEC,500SEL 7
380SL,380SLC 3

1986-91
190D 8
190E
Four
8 Valve Eng 8
16 Valve Eng ... 1.0
Six 9
260E,300CE,300D,300E,300SDL,300SE, 300SEL,300SL,300TD,300TE,350SD,350SDL, 420SEL,500SL,560SEC,560SEL 9
560SL ... 1.1

1992-93
190E
Four 8
Six 9
300CE,300E,300SD,300SE,300TE 9
300D,300SL,400E,400SE,400SEL,500E 500SEC,500SEL,500SL 7
600SEC,600SEL,600SL ... 10.

TENSIONER, BELT - R&R *(D)*

1973-91
V-Belt Type 7
Serpentine Type
190D ... 1.4
190E
Four ... 1.4
Six ... 3.2

300CE,300D,300E,300SE,300SEL,300SL, 300TE,300TD ... 2.4
300SD ... 1.4

1992-93
190E
Four ... 1.3
Six ... 4.0
300CE,300E,300SL,300TE,600SEC,600SEL, 600SL ... 2.4
300D,300SD ... 1.3
300SE ... 2.0
400E,500E,500SL ... 1.1
400SE,400SEL,500SEC,500SEL 9

★ **COMBINATIONS** ★

★ Support Bracket - Replace 2
★ Pulley Bearing - Replace 2

CONDENSER - R&R *(B)*

DOES NOT include evacuate or charge system.

1973-85
190D ... 1.0
190E ... 1.6
220,220D,230 ... 2.3
240D
Std Trans ... 2.0
Auto Trans ... 2.3
280,280C,280CE,280E,280S,280SE ... 2.3
300CE,300D,300TD ... 2.3
300SD
(78-80) ... 2.3
(81-85) ... 1.9
380SE,380SEC,380SEL,500SEC,500SEL ... 1.9
380SL,380SLC ... 3.1
450SE,450SEL,450SL,450SLC,6.9 ... 3.1

1986-91
190D,560SL ... 2.3
190E
Four
8 Valve Eng ... 1.6
16 Valve Eng ... 2.2
Six ... 1.6
260E,300CE,300D,300E,300SDL,300SE, 300SEL,300TD,300TE,350SD,350SDL, 420SEL,560SEC,560SEL ... 2.0
300SL,500SL ... 3.4

1992-93
190E ... 1.6
300CE,300D,300E,300TE,400E,500E ... 2.0
300SD,300SE,400SE,400SEL,500SEC,500SEL, 600SEC,600SEL ... 1.3
300SL,500SL,600SL ... 3.4

RECEIVER DRIER - R&R *(B)*

DOES NOT include evacuate or charge system.

1973-80
exc 450SL,450SLC 5
450SL,450SLC 7

1981-85
190D,190E,240D,300CD,300D,300TD 5
280CE,280E,300SD 7
380SE,380SEC,380SEL,380SLC, 500SEC,500SEL 7

1986-91
190D,190E,260E,300CE,300D,300E,300TD, 300TE 5
300SDL,300SE,300SEL,350SD,350SDL, 420SEL,560SEC,560SEL,560SL 7
300SL,500SL ... 1.0

1992-93
190E,300CE,300D,300E,300TE,400E 5
300SD,300SE,400SE,500SEL,600SEL ... N.A.
300SL,500E,500SL,600SL ... 1.0

Cont.

AIR CONDITIONING TIME GUIDE

Mercedes-Benz Heating & Air Conditioning (Cont.)

VALVE, EVAPORATOR EXPANSION - R&R *(B)*
DOES NOT include evacuate or charge system.

1973-80
220,220D,230,240D,280,280C,280CE,280E . 1.1
280S,280SE,300SD ... 2.3
300CD,300D,300TD ... 1.1
450SE,450SEL,6.9 ... 2.3
450SL,450SLC ... 3.5
1981-85
190D,190E ... 1.0
240D,280CE,280E,300CD,300D,300TD ... 1.1
300SD,380SE,380SEC,380SEL ... 2.3
380SL,380SLC ... 3.5
500SEC,500SEL ... 2.3
1986-91
190D,190E ... 1.0
260E,300CE,300D,300E,300TD,300TE ... 1.3
300SDL,300SE,300SEL,350SD,350SDL, 420SEL,560SEC,560SEL ... 2.6
300SL,500SL ... 2.4
560SL ... 2.7
1992-93
190E ... 1.0
300CE,300D,300E,300TE,400E,500E ... 1.3
300SD,300SE,300SL,400SE,400SEL,500SEC, 500SEL,500SL,600SEC,600SEL,600SL .. 2.4

CORE, EVAPORATOR - R&R *(B)*
DOES NOT include evacuate or charge system.

1973-80
220,220D,280,280C ... 5.1
230,240D
(74-76) ... 5.1
(77-80) ... 8.7
280CE,280E,300CD,300D,300TD ... 14.3
280S,280SE,450SE,450SEL,6.9
w/Climate Control ... 16.5
w/o Climate Control ... 16.0
300SD ... 16.5
450SL,450SLC
w/Climate Control ... 19.5
w/o Climate Control ... 19.9
1981-85
190D,190E ... 2.8
240D ... 11.3
280CE,280E,300CD,300D,300TD ... 13.9
300SD,380SE,380SEC,380SEL ... 17.7
380SL,380SLC ... 19.9
500SEC,500SEL ... 17.7
1986-91
190D,190E ... 3.3
260E,300CE,300D,300E,300TD,300TE ... 11.9
300SDL,300SE,300SEL,350SD,350SDL, 420SEL,560SEC,560SEL ... 16.2
300SL,500SL ... 12.3
560SL ... 15.5
1992-93
190E ... 3.3
300CE,300D,300E,300TE,400E,500E ... 11.9
300SD,300SE,400SE,400SEL,500SEC,500SEL, 600SEC,600SEL ... 20.8
300SL,500SL,600SL ... 12.3

★ COMBINATIONS ★

★ Valve, Evaporator Expansion - R&R 4

HOSE, AIR CONDITIONING - R&R *(B)*
DOES NOT include evacuate or charge system.

1973-80
Compressor to Evaporator
220,220D,230,240D 8
280,280C,280CE,280E 8
280S,280SE ... 1.7
300CD,300D,300SD,300TD 8
450SE,450SEL,6.9 ... 1.8
450SL,450SLC ... 2.2
Condenser to Receiver 8
Evaporator to Suction Valve
220,220D ... N.A.
230,240D ... 1.1
280,280C,280CE,280E ... 1.1
280S,280SE ... 1.8
300CD,300D,300SD,300TD ... 1.1
450SE,450SEL,6.9 ... 1.8
450SL,450SLC ... 2.4
Receiver to Expansion Valve
220,220D,230,240D,280,280C 8
280CE,280E ... 1.3
280S,280SE ... 1.8
300CD,300D,300SD,300TD ... 1.3
450SE,450SEL,6.9 ... 1.8
450SL,450SLC ... 2.4
1981-85
Compressor to Condenser ① ... 3.0
Expansion Valve to Condenser 7
Expansion Valve to Connector
380SE,380SEC,380SEL,500SEC,500SEL. 2.7
Receiver to Expansion Valve or Tank
190D,190E 9
240D,280CE,280E,300CD,300D,300SD, 300TD ... 1.3
380SE,380SEC,380SEL,500SEC,500SEL. 2.7
380SL,380SLC ... 2.4
Evaporator to Suction Valve
exc 300SD,380SL,380SLC ... 1.1
300SD,380SL,380SLC ... 2.4
1986-91
190D,190E
Condenser to Receiver Drier 5
Receiver Drier to Expansion Valve 9
Tubing & Hose Assembly at Compressor
190D ... 2.7
190E
Four
8 Valve Eng ... 4.4
16 Valve Eng ... 5.6
Six ... 2.2
260E,300CD,300D,300E,300TD,300TE
Condenser to Receiver Drier 5
Receiver Drier to Expansion Valve 9
Expansion Valve to Connector 9
Tubing & Hose Assembly at Compressor. 1.6
300SDL,350SD,350SDL
Pressure Valve to Condenser 7
Condenser to Receiver Drier 6
Expansion Valve to Evaporator ... 2.7
To Expansion Valve ... 1.3
Tubing & Hose Assembly at Compressor. 2.7
300SE,300SEL,420SEL,560SEC,560SEL
Condenser to Receiver Drier 6
Receiver Drier to Expansion Valve ... 2.7
Expansion Valve to Connector ... 2.7
300SL,500SL
Condenser to Receiver Drier 8
To Expansion Valve (High Pressure) ... 4.8
From Expansion Valve to Evap (Suction). 4.5
Receiver Drier to Hose to Expansion Valve 8
Tubing & Hose Assembly at Comp 6
560SL
Pressure Valve to Condenser 7
Receiver Drier to Expansion Valve ... 2.4
Evaporator to Suction Valve ... 2.7
1992-93
190E,300CE,300D,300TE
Condenser to Receiver Drier 5
To Expansion Valve (High Pressure) 9
From Expansion Valve to Evap (Suction) . .9
Tubing/Hose Assy - At Comp ... 4.0
300SE,300SE,400SE,400SEL,500SEC,500SEL, 600SEC,600SEL
Compressor Tubing to Condenser 6
Condenser to Receiver Drier ... 1.0
From Expansion Valve (Suction) ... 5.0
Receiver Drier to Hose to Expansion Valve ... 1.3
To Expansion Valve (High Pressure) .. 5.0
Tubing & Hose Assembly at Compressor. 1.3
300SL,500SL
Condenser to Receiver Drier 8
To Expansion Valve (High Pressure) ... 4.8
From Expansion Valve to Evap (Suction). 4.5
Receiver Drier to Hose to Expansion Valve 8
Tubing & Hose Assembly at Compressor. .6
400E,500E
Compressor Tubing to Condenser 6
Condenser to Receiver Drier 5
From Expansion Valve (Suction) 9
To Expansion Valve (High Pressure) 9

① *Tubing with suction hose and pressure valve (Frigidair Compressor).*

★ COMBINATIONS ★

★ Make Up Hose From Stock 4

RELAY, AIR CONDITIONING - R&R *(B)*
w/Auto Climate 6
w/o Auto Climate 3

PRESSURE SWITCH - R&R *(B)*
DOES NOT include evacuate or charge system.
All 3

SWITCH, TEMPERATURE CONTROL - R&R *(B)*
DOES NOT include charge system.

1974-76
exc 450SL,450SLC 6
450SL,450SLC ... 2.8
1977-85 9
1986-91 - Refer to E.T.R. Switch - R&R.

WATER PUMP (AUXILIARY) - R&R *(B)*
1973-85 8
1986-91
190D,190E,560SL 7
260E,300CE,300D,300E,300TD,300TE 5
300SDL,300SE,300SEL,350SD,350SDL, 420SEL,560SEC,560SEL ... 1.9
300SL,500SL ... 3.1
1992-93
exc 300SL,500SL,600SL 8
300SL,500SL,600SL ... 3.1

ASPIRATOR - R&R *(B)*
1973-85 9
1986-91
300SDL,300SE,300SEL,420SEL,560SEC, 560SEL ... 1.6
560SL ... 1.1
1992-93 7

★ COMBINATIONS ★

★ Valve, Switch Over - R&R ... 1.2

Cont.

AIR CONDITIONING TIME GUIDE

Mercedes-Benz Heating & Air Conditioning (Cont.)

SWITCH, E.T.R. - R&R *(B)*
With auto climate control.

1976-85
190D,190E,240D 8
280CE,280E,300CD,300D,300TD 6
280S,280SE,450SE,450SEL,6.9 .... 9.0
300SD
(78-80) 9.0
(81-85) 9
380SE,380SEC,380SEL,500SEC,500SEL 9
380SL,380SLC,450SL,450SLC 2.4
1986-91
300SDL,300SE,300SEL,420SEL,560SEL,
560SEL 9
560SL 1.8

SWITCH, COLD ENG LOCKOUT - R&R *(B)*
With auto climate control.

1976-85
280CE,280E,300CD,300D,300TD
(76-80) 1.9
(81-85) 3
280S,280SE,450SE,450SEL,6.9 .... 1.5
300SD
(78-80) 1.5
(81-85) 3
380SE,380SEC,380SEL,500SEC,500SEL 3
380SL,380SLC,450SL,450SLC 2.0
1986-91 3

SWITCH, AUXILIARY FAN TEMP - R&R *(B)*
1973-93 3

AUXILIARY FAN - R&R *(B)*
1973-85
190D,190E,220,220D 8
230,240D,280S,280SE 7
280CE,280E,300CD,300D,300TD
w/Climate Control 9
w/o Climate Control 7
300SD,380SE,380SEC,380SEL 7
380SL,380SLC,450SL,450SLC 1.9
450SE,450SEL,500SEC,500SEL,6.9 7
1986-93
Single
190D,190E,300SDL,300E,300SEL,420SEL,
560SEC,560SEL 7
260E,300CE,300D,300E,300TD,300TE 1.0
560SL 1.9
Dual (Both)
190D,190E 1.6
300CE,300E,300TE,400E,500E 2.4
300SD,400SE,400SEL,500SEC,500SEL,
600SEC,600SEL 1.0
300SE
(88-91) 2.2
(92-93) 1.0
300SEL,350SD,350SDL,420SEL,560SEL 2.2
300SL,500SL,600SL 3.4

RELAY, AUXILIARY FAN - R&R *(B)*
1973-93 3

VALVE, SWITCH-OVER - R&R *(B)*
1976-85 (ea) 5
1986-91
190D,190E 1.0
260E,300CE,300D,300E,300TD,300TE,
350SD,350SDL,560SL 7
300SDL,300SEL,420SEL,560SEC,560SEL 9
300SL,500SL 4
1992-93
190E 1.0
300CE,300D,300E,300TE,400E,500E 7
300SD,300SE,400SE,400SEL,500SEC,500SEL
600SEC,600SEL 5
300SL,500SL,600SL 4

SERVO ASSEMBLY - R&R *(B)*
With auto climate control.

1976-80
exc 450SL,450SLC 1.6
450SL,450SLC 1.9
1981-85
exc 380SL,380SLC 1.3
380SL,380SLC 1.9

Mitsubishi Heating & Air Conditioning

NOTE 1: Times shown DO NOT include recover, evacuate and charge system. If necessary to open refrigerant system; refer to System Charge (Complete) for appropriate time.
NOTE 2: Times listed are for Factory and Dealer dash installed Integral Type air conditioning units only. Use necessary clock time for service of hang-on units.

HEATING & VENTILATION

HEATER HOSES - R&R *(D)*
All 9

WATER VALVE - R&R *(B)*
1983-93
Cordia,Tredia 2.7
Galant,Precis,Sigma 8
Mirage
w/Air Cond 2.4
w/o Air Cond 1.3
Montero
Front 2.4
Rear 1.0
Pickup
w/Air Cond 9
w/o Air Cond 7
Starion
w/Air Cond 2.4
w/o Air Cond 2.1

SWITCH, WATER TEMP - R&R *(B)*
All 5

CORE, HEATER - R&R *(B)*
DOES NOT include System Charge.

1983-93
Cordia,Tredia 4.6
Diamante,Eclipse,3000GT
w/Air Cond 7.6
w/o Air Cond 6.8
Expo,Expo LRV 4.3
Galant 6.1
Mirage
(85-88) 5.1
(89-93)
w/Air Cond 6.4
w/o Air Cond 6.2
Montero
Front 5.0
Rear 1.8
Pickup 4.9
Precis
(87-89)
w/Air Cond 3.6
w/o Air Cond 2.0
(90-93)
w/Air Cond 3.8
w/o Air Cond 3.0
Starion (84-89) 7.6
Tredia 5.4
Van
Front 4.9
Rear 1.3

MOTOR, BLOWER - R&R *(B)*
1983-93
Cordia,Galant,Starion,Tredia
w/Air Cond 9
w/o Air Cond 7
Diamante 7
Eclipse,3000GT
w/Air Cond 8
w/o Air Cond 5
Expo,Expo LRV,Sigma 6
Mirage
w/Air Cond 1.5
w/o Air Cond 1.0
Montero
Front 6
Rear 1.0
Pickup
w/Air Cond 1.5
w/o Air Cond 9
Precis
(87-89) 9
(90-93) 3
Van
Front 6
Rear 5

SWITCH, BLOWER MOTOR - R&R *(B)*
1983-93
Cordia,Tredia (83-88) 1.0
Diamante 9
Eclipse,Expo,Expo LRV,Mirage
w/Air Cond 1.3
w/o Air Cond 7
Galant,Sigma,Starion,3000GT 7
Montero,Pickup,Van 1.0
Precis
(87-89) 8
(90-93) 6

Cont.

AIR CONDITIONING TIME GUIDE

Mitsubishi Heating & Air Conditioning (Cont.)

RESISTOR, BLOWER MOTOR - R&R *(B)*

1983-93
Cordia,Tredia (83-88) .6
Diamante,Sigma,Starion .6
Eclipse,Expo,Expo LRV,3000GT .5
Galant
(85-87) .7
(89-93) .3
Mirage
w/Air Cond 1.0
w/o Air Cond .7
Montero,Van
Front .6
Rear .5
Pickup .7
Precis .5

CABLE, VENTILATION CONTROL - R&R *(B)*

Air Cond Recirculation
exc Starion .8
Starion 2.4
Mode Control
exc Starion .9
Starion 2.4
Temp Control
w/Air Cond
exc Starion .8
Starion 2.4
w/o Air Cond
exc Pickup,Starion .7
Pickup .6
Starion .8
Defroster & Heat
Pickup .7
Vent Control
Cordia,Montero,Tredia .6
Pickup .7

CONTROL ASSEMBLY, TEMPERATURE - R&R *(B)*

1983-93
Cordia .9
Diamante,Eclipse,3000GT .9
Expo,Expo LRV N.A.
Galant
(85-87) .9
(89-93) .7
Mirage
(85-88) 1.5
(89-93) .7
Montero,Pickup .8
Precis,Van .7
Sigma .9
Starion
w/Air Cond 2.6
w/o Air Cond .9
Tredia 1.3

AIR CONDITIONING

FREON - RECOVER *(B)*

NOTE: *This operation is not to be used with any other operations.*

All .3

PERFORMANCE - TEST *(B)*

Includes: Gauge check, leak test and partial charge.

1983-93 1.0

SYSTEM CHARGE (PARTIAL) *(B)*

Includes: Performance test.

1983-93 1.0

SYSTEM CHARGE (COMPLETE) *(B)*

Includes: Recover, evacuate and recharge system.

1983-93 1.4

BELT, COMPRESSOR - R&R *(D)*

Includes: Serpentine belts.

1983-93
F.W.D. .5
R.W.D. .3

● **ADDITIONAL TIME** ●

● Where Pwr Strg interferes add .1
● Where Alt interferes add .1

CONTROL UNIT, AIR CONDITIONING - R&R *(B)*

1983-93
Cordia,Tredia 2.4
Diamante
Full Air 1.0
Compressor Lock Up .6
Eclipse,Mirage,Pickup,Starion .6
Expo,Expo LRV
Air Compressor Controller .5
Compressor Lock Up 1.3
Galant,Sigma .9
Montero
Air Conditioning Controller (83-91) 1.6
Air Compressor Controller(92-93) .5
Precis N.A.
Van 1.8
3000GT
Full Air .8
Compressor Lock Up .9

COMPRESSOR ASSEMBLY - R&R *(B)*

DOES NOT include System Charge.

1983-93
Cordia,Tredia (83-88) 1.8
Diamante 1.5
Eclipse 1.2
Expo,Expo LRV,Mirage 1.3
Galant
(85-87) 2.4L Eng 1.3
(89-93) 2.0L Eng
S.O.H.C. 1.3
D.O.H.C. 1.5
Montero,Pickup 1.9
Precis 1.0
Starion (83-89) 1.6
Sigma,Van 1.5
3000GT
w/Turbocharger 2.7
w/o Turbocharger 1.7

★ **COMBINATIONS** ★

★ Seal, Compressor Shaft - R&R .6
★ Clutch Assembly - R&R .4

CLUTCH ASSEMBLY - R&R *(B)*

Use Compressor Assembly - R&R plus Combinations.

SEAL, COMPRESSOR SHAFT - R&R *(B)*

Use Compressor Assembly - R&R plus Combinations.

VALVE, EVAPORATOR EXPANSION - R&R *(B)*

DOES NOT include System Charge.

1983-93
Cordia,Tredia (83-88) 2.2
Diamante 1.5
Eclipse 3.9
Expo,Expo LRV,Mirage 2.1
Galant
(85-87) 2.4L Eng 1.8
(89-93) 2.0L Eng 1.5
Montero
Front 2.2
Rear 1.3
Pickup,Sigma,3000GT 2.2
Precis,Starion 2.5
Van
Front 1.5
Rear 1.1

RECEIVER DRIER - R&R *(B)*

DOES NOT include System Charge.

1983-93
Cordia,Montero,Pickup,Starion,Tredia .9
Diamante N.A.
Eclipse,3000GT 1.0
Expo,Expo LRV,Mirage .8
Galant,Precis,Sigma,Van .6

CONDENSER - R&R *(B)*

DOES NOT include System Charge.

1983-93
Cordia,Tredia (83-88) 1.2
Diamante 1.2
Eclipse 1.4
Expo,Expo LRV,Mirage,3000GT 1.1
Galant
(85-87) 1.4
(89-93) 1.2
Montero
Front 1.5
Sub 1.2
Pickup 1.5
Precis,Sigma,Starion 1.0
Van
Front 1.9
Rear 1.1

CONDENSER FAN MOTOR - R&R *(B)*

All .8

RELAY, CONDENSER FAN - R&R *(B)*

All .3

CORE, EVAPORATOR - R&R *(B)*

DOES NOT include System Charge.

1983-93
Cordia,Tredia (83-88) 2.8
Diamante,Eclipse,3000GT 5.0
Expo,Expo LRV, 3.0
Galant
(85-87) 1.9
(89-93) 1.5
Mirage 3.0
Montero
Front 2.1
Rear 1.6
Pickup 2.7
Precis 1.8
Sigma 1.9
Starion (83-89) 2.8
Van
Front 1.9
Rear 1.1

Cont.

Mitsubishi Heating & Air Conditioning (Cont.)

HOSE, AIR CONDITIONING - R&R *(B)*
DOES NOT include System Charge.

One 1.0
Each Additional 5

★ COMBINATIONS ★

★ Make Up Hose From Stock 4

SWITCH, LOW PRESSURE CUTOFF - R&R *(B)*
DOES NOT include System Charge.

1983-93
- Cordia,Tredia (83-88) 2.2
- Galant (85-87) 1.0
- Precis 4
- Starion (83-89) 8

SWITCH, HIGH PRESSURE CUTOFF - R&R *(B)*
DOES NOT include System Charge.

1983-93 5

SWITCH, DUAL PRESSURE - R&R *(B)*
Diamante,3000GT 1.0
Eclipse,Galant,Mirage 9
Montero
- (83-91) 9
- (92-93) 1.1

SWITCH, TRIPPLE PRESSURE - R&R *(B)*
All 9

RELAY, POWER - R&R *(B)*
1983-93 3

SWITCH, TEMPERATURE - R&R *(B)*
1983-93 5

RELAY, THERMO - R&R *(B)*
1983-93 5

SOLENOID VALVE - R&R *(B)*
1983-93 (Front or Rear) 3

THERMISTOR (SENSOR) - R&R *(B)*
1983-93
- One 7
- Each Additional 4

Nissan/Datsun Heating & Air Conditioning

NOTE 1: Times shown DO NOT include recover, evacuate and charge system. If necessary to open refrigerant system; refer to System Charge (Complete) for appropriate time.
NOTE 2: Times listed are for Factory and Dealer dash installed Integral Type air conditioning units only. Use necessary clock time for service of hang-on units.

HEATING & VENTILATION

HEATER HOSES - R&R *(D)*
NOTE: Deduct .2 when used in conjunction with Radiator Hose - R&R.

1973-79 (All)
- exc 240Z,260Z,280Z,280ZX 1.3
- 240Z,260Z,280Z,280ZX 1.1

1980-93 (All)
- Altima 9
- Axxess,240SX 1.4
- Maxima
  - (81-84) 7
  - (85-93) 1.4
- NX 1.0
- Pathfinder 2.6
- Pickup
  - Diesel 6
  - Gas
    - D21 Series 2.6
    - 720 Series
      - w/Air Cond 1.3
      - w/o Air cond 8
- Pulsar
  - (83-86) 8
  - (87-90) 1.2
- Quest
  - Front Heater 8
  - Rear Heater 2.5
- Sentra
  - (82-86) 8
  - (87-90) 1.4
  - (91-93) 1.0
- Stanza
  - (82-86) 8
  - (87-89)
    - exc S/W 1.4
    - S/W 1.2
  - (90-92) 1.4
- Van
  - Front Heater 3.1
  - Rear Heater 7

- 200SX
  - (80-83) 1.4
  - (84-88) 1.1
- 210,510,810 8
- 280ZX 1.2
- 300ZX
  - (84-89) 1.8
  - (90-93) 1.2
- 310 6

WATER VALVE - R&R *(B)*
1973-78
- exc 260Z,280Z 7
- 260Z,280Z 2.2

1979-83
- exc Pickup,200SX,280ZX,810 .... 2.4
- Pickup
  - w/Air Cond 1.3
  - w/o Air Cond 7
- 200SX ① 6.4
- 280ZX
  - w/Air Cond 4.0
  - w/o Air Cond 2.4
- 810 .... 1.3

1984-93
- Altima 6
- Axxess
  - w/Air Cond 3.8
  - w/o Air Cond 3.5
- Maxima
  - (84-88)
    - w/Air Cond 4.3
    - w/o Air Cond 4.0
  - (89-93) 6
- NX
  - w/Air Cond 5.4
  - w/o Air Cond 5.0
- Pathfinder
  - w/Air Cond 4.7
  - w/o Air Cond 2.3
- Pickup
  - D21 Series
    - w/Air Cond 4.7
    - w/o Air Cond 2.3
  - 720 Series
    - w/Air Cond 1.3
    - w/o Air Cond 7
- Pulsar
  - (84-86) 2.0
  - (87-90)
    - w/Air Cond 4.3
    - w/o Air Cond 4.0
- Quest
  - w/Air Cond 3.8
  - w/o Air Cond 3.6
- Sentra
  - (84-86) 2.2
  - (87-90)
    - w/Air Cond 3.5
    - w/o Air Cond 3.2
  - (91-93)
    - w/Air Cond 5.4
    - w/o Air Cond 5.0
- Stanza
  - (84-86) 2.0
  - (87-89)
    - exc S/W
      - w/Air Cond 4.3
      - w/o Air Cond 4.0
    - S/W
      - w/Air Cond 3.6
      - w/o Air Cond 3.3
  - (90-92)
    - w/Air Cond 4.2
    - w/o Air Cond 3.8
- Van
  - w/Air Cond 3.3
  - w/o Air Cond 3.0
- 200SX ① 6.4
- 300ZX 2.0

① *Includes: R&I instrument panel.*

CORE, HEATER - R&R *(B)*
DOES NOT include System Charge.

1973-93
- Altima 4.5
- Axxess
  - w/Air Cond 3.6
  - w/o Air Cond 3.3
- B210 .... 2.8
- F10,510 .... 3.0
- Maxima
  - (81-84) ① 6.5
  - (85-88) ② 6.0
  - (89-93) ① 4.5
- NX
  - w/Air Cond 5.4
  - w/o Air Cond 5.0
- Pathfinder
  - w/Air Cond 6.0
  - w/o Air Cond 3.5

Cont.

AIR CONDITIONING TIME GUIDE

Nissan/Datsun Heating & Air Conditioning (Cont.)

- Pickup
  - (73-79) 1.0
  - (80-84) ② 3.0
  - (85-93)
    - D21 Series
      - w/Air Cond 6.0
      - w/o Air Cond 3.5
    - 720 Series ② 3.0
- Pulsar
  - (83-86)
    - w/Air Cond 3.5
    - w/o Air Cond 2.7
  - (87-90)
    - w/Air Cond 4.2
    - w/o Air Cond 3.9
- Quest
  - Front 3.7
  - Rear 3.8
- Sentra
  - (82-90)
    - w/Air Cond 3.5
    - w/o Air Cond 3.2
  - (91-93)
    - w/Air Cond 5.4
    - w/o Air Cond 5.0
- Stanza
  - (82-86) 2.8
  - (87-89)
    - exc S/W
      - w/Air Cond 4.5
      - w/o Air Cond 3.7
    - S/W
      - w/Air Cond 3.3
      - w/o Air Cond 3.0
  - (90-92)
    - w/Air Cond 4.0
    - w/o Air Cond 3.7
- Van
  - Front
    - w/Air Cond 3.0
    - w/o Air Cond 2.7
  - Rear 1.5
- 200SX ② 6.4
- 210 3.2
- 240SX
  - w/Air Cond 2.9
  - w/o Air Cond 2.6
- 240Z,260Z,280Z 5.0
- 280ZX,810 4.0
- 300ZX
  - (84-89) 4.5
  - (90-93) 6.0
- 310 ② 6.0
- 610,710 2.0
- 1200 1.0

① *Includes: R&I instrument panel, front seats and carpet.*

② *Includes: R&I instrument panel.*

MOTOR, BLOWER - R&R *(B)*

1973-79

- B210,F10,510,610,710 1.5
- Pickup
  - Air Cond .6
  - Heater .9
- 200SX 3.1
- 210,240Z,260Z,280Z,310,1200
  - Air Cond .8
  - Heater .6
- 810 1.3

1980-93

- Altima,Axxess,210,280ZX,300ZX,510 .6
- Maxima,200SX,240SX,310 .8
- NX .5
- Pathfinder 2.6
- Pickup
  - D21 Series 2.6
  - 720 Series .6
- Pulsar .7
- Quest
  - Front .7
  - Rear 2.1
- Sentra
  - (82-90) .7
  - (91-93) .5
- Stanza
  - (82-86) 1.0
  - (87-89)
    - exc S/W 1.0
    - S/W .8
  - (90-92) .7
- Van
  - Front 1.0
  - Rear 1.3
- 810 1.4

SWITCH, BLOWER MOTOR - R&R *(B)*

1973-79

- B210,F10,Pickup,200SX,610,710,810,1200 1.0
- 210 1.8
- 240Z,260Z,280Z 1.5
- 280ZX 1.1
- 310 .9
- 510 1.3

1980-93

- Altima .6
- Axxess,Van .7
- Maxima
  - (81-84) 1.1
  - (85-88) 1.6
  - (89-93) 1.0
- NX
  - w/Air Cond 1.8
  - w/o Air Cond 1.4
- Pathfinder,510 1.3
- Pickup
  - D21 Series 1.3
  - 720 Series .8
- Pulsar .9
- Quest
  - Front .8
  - Rear .6
- Sentra
  - (82-90) .9
  - (91-93)
    - w/Air Cond 1.8
    - w/o Air Cond 1.4
- Stanza
  - (82-89)
    - exc S/W .8
    - S/W 1.8
  - (90-92) .9
- 200SX
  - (80-83) 1.0
  - (84-88) 1.6
- 210 1.8
- 240SX 1.6
- 280ZX,310,810 1.1
- 300ZX
  - (84-89) 1.3
  - (90-93) .7

RESISTOR, BLOWER MOTOR - R&R *(B)*

1973-93

- exc Van .6
- Van
  - Front .6
  - Rear 1.3

RELAY, BLOWER MOTOR - R&R *(B)*

1973-93

- exc Axxess .5
- Axxess 1.5

AMPLIFIER, BLOWER MOTOR - R&R *(B)*

1984-89 .5

CONTROL ASSEMBLY, TEMPERATURE - R&R *(B)*

1973-79

- B210,F10,200SX,610,710,810 1.0
- Pickup,310 .9
- 210 1.8
- 240Z,260Z,280Z 1.5
- 280ZX 1.1
- 510 1.3

1980-93

- Altima .7
- Axxess,Van .8
- Maxima
  - (81-84) 1.2
  - (85-88) 1.7
  - (89-93) 1.1
- NX
  - w/Air Cond 1.9
  - w/o Air Cond 1.5
- Pathfinder,510 1.4
- Pickup
  - D21 Series 1.4
  - 720 Series .9
- Pulsar 1.0
- Quest
  - Front .7
  - Rear .6
- Sentra
  - (82-90) 1.0
  - (91-93)
    - w/Air Cond 1.9
    - w/o Air Cond 1.5
- Stanza
  - (82-89)
    - exc S/W .9
    - S/W 1.9
  - (90-92) 1.0
- 200SX
  - (80-83) 1.1
  - (84-88) 1.7
- 210 1.9
- 240SX 1.7
- 280ZX,310,810 1.2
- 300ZX
  - (84-89) 1.4
  - (90-93) .8

CABLE, TEMPERATURE CONTROL - R&R *(B)*

Use Temperature Control Assembly - R&R.

SOLENOID (ACTUATOR) - R&R *(B)*

1973-93

- Air Intake Door
  - exc Maxima,Pulsar,Sentra,300ZX,310,810 .5
  - Maxima
    - (81-84) .7
    - (85-88) .9
    - (89-93) .5
  - Pulsar,Sentra,310 .3
  - 300ZX
    - (84-89) .8
    - (90-93) 5.0
  - 810 .7

Cont.

Nissan/Datsun Heating & Air Conditioning (Cont.)

Air Mix Door
Altima,Quest .8
300ZX 3.1
Mode Door
exc 300ZX .7
300ZX
(84-89) .8
(90-93) 5.0

DIAPHRAGM CONTROL (ACTUATOR) - R&R *(B)*

1973-93
Air Intake Door
exc Maxima,Stanza,300ZX .5
Maxima
(85-88) 1.2
(89-93) .5
Stanza .9
300ZX
(84-89) .6
(90-93) 1.4
Air Mix Door
Maxima .9
300ZX
(84-89) 3.1
(90-93) 1.5
Mode Door
Maxima
(85-88) .7
(89-93) .5
Stanza,240SX .5
200SX .6
300ZX
(84-89) .8
(90-93) 5.0

AIR CONDITIONING

FREON - RECOVER *(B)*
NOTE: This operation is not to be used with any other operations.
All .3

PERFORMANCE - TEST *(B)*
Includes: Gauge check, leak test and partial charge.
All 1.0

SYSTEM CHARGE (PARTIAL) *(B)*
Includes: Performance test.
All 1.0

SYSTEM CHARGE (COMPLETE) *(B)*
Includes: Recover, evacuate and recharge system.
All 1.4

BELT, COMPRESSOR - R&R *(D)*

1973-93
exc Stanza,Van,310 .7
Stanza
(82-86) .8
(87-89)
exc S/W .6
S/W .7
(90-92) .6
Van .8
310 .5

● ADDITIONAL TIME ●

● Where Air Pump interferes add .2
● Where Alternator interferes add .2
● Where Pwr Strg interferes add .2

IDLER PULLEY - R&R *(D)*

1973-93
exc Stanza,240SX .7
Stanza
(82-89) .7
(90-92) .5
240SX .5

COMPRESSOR ASSEMBLY - R&R *(B)*
DOES NOT include System Charge.

1973-79
B210,310 2.5
F10 2.7
Pickup,240Z,260Z,280Z,280ZX 1.8
200SX,210,510,610,710,810 2.1

1980-93
Altima,240SX 1.5
Axxess 2.0
Maxima
(81-84) 2.0
(85-88) 1.6
(89-93) 1.3
NX 1.4
Pathfinder,Van 1.6
Pickup
D21 Series 1.6
720 Series 2.0
Pulsar
(83-86)
w/Turbocharger 2.6
w/o Turbocharger 2.0
(87-90) 1.6
Quest .8
Sentra
(82-90) 2.0
(91-93) 1.4
Stanza
(82-86) 2.0
(87-89)
exc S/W 1.6
S/W 2.0
(90-92) 1.5
200SX
(80-83) 2.0
(84-88) 2.4
210,510 2.1
280ZX
w/Turbocharger 2.5
w/o Turbocharger 2.0
300ZX
(84-89)
w/Turbocharger 1.9
w/o Turbocharger 1.6
(90-93)
w/Turbocharger 2.1
w/o Turbocharger 1.8
310
(80-81) 2.5
(82) 1.9

★ COMBINATIONS ★

★ Seal, Compressor Shaft - R&R
exc Maxima .7
Maxima .6
★ Bearing or Magnetic Clutch - R&R
exc 260Z,280ZX .4
260Z .8
280ZX .3

COMPRESSOR ASSEMBLY - R&I & O/H *(B)*
DOES NOT include System Charge.

1973-79
B210,310 4.5
F10 4.7
Pickup,240Z,260Z,280Z,280ZX 3.8
200SX,210,510,610,710,810 4.1

1980-93
Altima,240SX 3.5
Axxess 4.0
Maxima
(81-84) 4.0
(85-88) 3.6
(89-93) 3.3
NX 3.4
Pathfinder,Van 3.6
Pickup
D21 Series 3.6
720 Series 4.0
Pulsar
(83-86)
w/Turbocharger 4.6
w/o Turbocharger 4.0
(87-90) 3.6
Quest 2.8
Sentra
(82-90) 4.0
(91-93) 3.4
Stanza
(82-86) 4.0
(87-89)
exc S/W 3.6
S/W 4.0
(90-92) 3.5
200SX
(80-83) 4.0
(84-88) 4.4
210,510 4.1
280ZX
w/Turbocharger 4.5
w/o Turbocharger 4.0
300ZX
(84-89)
w/Turbocharger 3.9
w/o Turbocharger 3.6
(90-93)
w/Turbocharger 4.1
w/o Turbocharger 3.8
310
(80-81) 4.5
(82) 3.9

SEAL, COMPRESSOR SHAFT - R&R *(B)*
Use Compressor Assembly - R&R plus Combinations.

CLUTCH, COMPRESSOR - R&R *(B)*
Includes: R&I Compressor.
DOES NOT include System Charge.

1973-79
B210,310 3.0
F10 3.2
Pickup,240Z,280Z 2.3
200SX,210,510,610,710,810 2.6
260Z 2.1

Cont.

AIR CONDITIONING TIME GUIDE

Nissan/Datsun Heating & Air Conditioning (Cont.)

1980-93
Altima,240SX 1.9
Axxess 2.4
Maxima
(81-84) 2.4
(85-88) 2.0
(89-93) 1.7
NX 1.8
Pathfinder,Van 2.0
Pickup
D21 Series 2.1
720 Series 2.5
Pulsar
(83-86)
w/Turbocharger 3.1
w/o Turbocharger 2.5
(87-90) 2.1
Quest 1.2
Sentra
(82-90) 2.4
(91-93) 1.8
Stanza
(82-86) 2.5
(87-89)
exc S/W 2.1
S/W 2.5
(90-92) 1.9
200SX
(80-83) 2.5
(84-88) 2.9
210,510 .... 2.6
280ZX
w/Turbocharger 2.8
w/o Turbocharger 2.3
300ZX
(84-89)
w/Turbocharger 2.4
w/o Turbocharger 2.0
(90-93)
w/Turbocharger 2.5
w/o Turbocharger 2.2
310
(80-81) 3.0
(82) 2.4

SENSOR, COMPRESSOR REVOLUTION - R&R *(B)*

All 4

VALVE, EVAPORATOR EXPANSION - R&R *(B)*

DOES NOT include System Charge.

1973-79
exc 200SX,240Z,260Z,280Z,280ZX,310 .... 1.9
200SX 2.2
240Z,260Z,280Z 3.1
280ZX 2.7
310 .... 2.6
1980-93 - Use Evaporator Core - R&R.

RECEIVER DRIER - R&R *(B)*

DOES NOT include System Charge.

All 6

CONDENSER - R&R *(B)*

DOES NOT include System Charge.

1973-79
B210,510,610,710,810 .... 1.8
F10,210,310 .... 1.3
Pickup 1.9
200SX,240Z,260Z,280Z,280ZX 1.4

1980-93
Altima 6
Axxess 1.8
Maxima
(81-84) 1.5
(85-88) 1.8
(89-93) 1.6
NX 1.6
Pathfinder,310 .... 1.4
Pickup
D21 Series 1.4
720 Series 1.6
Pulsar,280ZX,510,810 .... 1.5
Quest 1.3
Sentra
(82-90) 1.5
(91-93) 1.6
Stanza
(82-86)
exc S/W 1.2
S/W 1.9
(87-89) 1.9
(90-92) 1.7
Van 1.2
200SX
(80-83) 1.2
(84-88) 2.2
240SX 2.5
300ZX
(84-89) 1.6
(90-93) 1.9

CORE, EVAPORATOR - R&R *(B)*

DOES NOT include System Charge.

1973-79
B210,F10,Pickup,210,510 .... 2.3
200SX 2.7
240Z,260Z,280Z 3.6
280ZX 3.2
310 .... 2.8
610,710,810 .... 2.5
1980-93
Altima,NX 1.9
Axxess,240SX 1.8
Maxima
(81-88) 2.5
(89-93) 1.9
Pathfinder 3.4
Pickup
D21 Series 3.4
720 Series 2.3
Pulsar
(83-86) 2.8
(87-90) 2.0
Quest
Front 8
Rear 3.1
Sentra
(82-86) 2.8
(87-90) 2.3
(91-93) 1.9
Stanza
w/Fuel Injection
exc S/W
(82-86) 3.8
(87-89) 2.3
(90-92) 2.0
S/W 2.8
w/o Fuel Injection 2.8
Van
Front 1.9
Rear 2.0

200SX,210,510 .... 2.3
280ZX 3.2
300ZX
(84-89) 3.7
(90-93) 2.2
310 .... 2.8
810 .... 2.5

MOTOR &/OR FAN, CONDENSER - R&R *(B)*

1973-86 8
1987-93
Axxess 1.2
Maxima,Pulsar,Quest,Stanza,200SX 8
NX 5
Sentra
(87-90) 8
(91-93) 5
Van ①
Main Condenser 1.8
Sub Condenser 2.6
240SX ① 2.7
300ZX
(87-89) 8
(90-93) 1.0

① *Includes: Recover, evacuate and charge system.*

RELAY, CONDENSER FAN - R&R *(B)*

All 3

SWITCH, LOW PRESSURE - R&R *(B)*

DOES NOT include System Charge.

All 5

SWITCH, ACCELERATION CUT - R&R *(B)*

All 3

THERMO SWITCH - R&R *(B)*

exc Pulsar,Sentra 1.1
Pulsar,Sentra 1.3

RELAY, AIR CONDITIONING - R&R *(B)*

Each 3

CONTROL ASSEMBLY, A.T.C. - R&R *(B)*

1979-93
Altima 7
Maxima 1.0
Pathfinder 1.3
280ZX 1.1
300ZX
(84-89) 1.3
(90-93) 4

SENSOR, IN-VEHICLE ASPIRATOR - R&R *(B)*

Maxima w/A.T.C. 6
300ZX w/A.T.C. 7

FEEDBACK RHEOSTAT (A.T.C.) - R&R *(B)*

1984-89 (300ZX) 3.2

POWER SERVO (A.T.C.) - R&R *(B)*

Maxima 2.4
300ZX 3.2

SENSOR, AMBIENT (A.T.C.) - R&R *(B)*

All 5

Cont.

AIR CONDITIONING TIME GUIDE

Nissan/Datsun Heating & Air Conditioning (Cont.)

SWITCH, VACUUM PROGRAM (A.T.C.) - R&R *(B)*

280ZX 2.4
300ZX 3.2

SWITCH, VACUUM LOCKOUT (A.T.C.) - R&R *(B)*

Maxima 6

AMPLIFIER, RADIATOR FAN (A.T.C.) - R&R *(B)*

Maxima 6

SENSOR, SUNLOAD (A.T.C.) - R&R *(B)*

All 6

AMPLIFIER, SUNLOAD SENSOR (A.T.C.) - R&R *(B)*

All 1.4

SENSOR, DEFROSTER (A.T.C.) - R&R *(B)*

1984-89 (300ZX) 2.5
1990-93 (300ZX) 4.0

RESISTOR, PONTENTIO BALANCE - R&R *(B)*

Maxima 5
300ZX 6

HOSE, AIR CONDITIONING - R&R *(B)*

DOES NOT include System Charge.

1973-93
exc Van,300ZX
One (Pressure or Suction) 8
Each Additional 3
Van
Pressure 1.2
Suction 9
300ZX
(84-89)
One (Pressure or Suction) 8
Each Additional 3
(90-93)
Pressure 2.0
Suction 5

★ COMBINATIONS ★

★ Make Up Hose From Stock 4

Peugeot Heating & Air Conditioning

***NOTE 1:** Times shown DO NOT include recover, evacuate and charge system. If necessary to open refrigerant system; refer to System Charge (Complete) for appropriate time.*
***NOTE 2:** Times listed are for Factory and Dealer dash installed Integral Type air conditioning units only. Use necessary clock time for service of hang-on units.*

HEATING & VENTILATION

HEATER HOSES - R&R *(D)*

NOTE: Deduct .2 when used in Conjunction with Radiator Hose - R&R

405
Inlet 6
Return 8
Both 1.0
504,505,604 (ea) ① 1.4
① *Includes: Glove Box - R&R*

CORE, HEATER - R&R *(B)*

DOES NOT include recover, evacuate and recharge system.

405 .... 7.9
504
w/Air Cond 4.0
w/o Air Cond 3.0
505,604 .... 3.0

MOTOR, BLOWER - R&R *(B)*

1973-84
504 .... 5.1
505 .... 3.5
604 .... 7.2
1985-91
405 6
505
Diesel 3.8
Gas
w/Turbocharger 4.4
w/o Turbocharger 3.8

SWITCH, BLOWER MOTOR - R&R *(B)*

405 .... N.A.
504 .... 1.3
505 .... 1.6
604 .... 1.2

AIR CONDITIONING

FREON - RECOVER *(B)*

NOTE: This operation is not to be used with any other operations.

All 3

PERFORMANCE - TEST *(B)*

Includes: Gauge check, leak test and partial charge.

All 1.0

★ COMBINATIONS ★

★ System Charge (Complete) 4

SYSTEM CHARGE (PARTIAL) *(B)*

Includes: Performance test.

All 1.0

SYSTEM CHARGE (COMPLETE) *(B)*

Includes: Evacuate,recover and recharge system.

All 1.4

VALVE, EVAPORATOR EXPANSION - R&R *(B)*

DOES NOT include System Charge.

405 .... 2.4
504 .... 3.0
505 .... 2.0
604 .... 4.8

COMPRESSOR ASSEMBLY - R&R *(B)*

DOES NOT include System Charge.

405 .... 4.3
504
Diesel 3.0
Gas 2.5
505
Four
Diesel 2.5
Gas
w/Turbocharger
w/Intercooler 3.0
w/o Intercooler 2.5
w/o Turbocharger 2.0
V6 .... 1.5
604 .... 3.5

CONDENSER - R&R *(B)*

DOES NOT include System Charge.

405 .... 3.5
504
Diesel 3.5
Gas 2.6
505 .... 2.5
604 .... 3.2

FAN & MOTOR, CONDENSER - R&R *(D)*

1989-91 (405)
One 6
Both 8

SWITCH, ELECTRIC FAN - R&R *(B)*

1989-91 (405) 5

RELAY, ELECTRIC FAN - R&R *(B)*

1989-91 (405) 3

RECEIVER DRIER - R&R *(B)*

DOES NOT include System Charge.

All 1.2

CORE, EVAPORATOR - R&R *(B)*

DOES NOT include System Charge.

405 .... 9.1
504 .... 2.8
505 .... 5.8
604 .... 4.8

E.C.U., CLIMATE CONTROL - R&R *(B)*

1989-91 (405) 5

SENSOR, EVAPORATOR - R&R *(B)*

1989-91 (405) 3

SENSOR, INSIDE TEMP - R&R *(B)*

1989-91 (405) 6

SENSOR, OUTSIDE TEMP - R&R *(B)*

1989-91 (405) 5

SWITCH, PRESSURE - R&R *(B)*

1989-91 (405 - Three Way Switch) 3

HOSE, AIR CONDITIONING - R&R *(B)*

DOES NOT include System Charge.

One 5
Each Additional 4

★ COMBINATIONS ★

★ Make Up Hose From Stock 4

AIR CONDITIONING TIME GUIDE

Porsche Heating & Air Conditioning

911, 912, 914 & 930

NOTE 1: Times shown Do Not include recover, evacuate and charge system. If necessary to open refrigerant system or to recover, evacuate, charge and test, refer to System Charge (Complete) for appropriate time.
NOTE 2: Times listed are for Factory and Dealer dash installed Integral Type air conditioning units only. Use necessary clock time for service of hang-on units.

HEATING & VENTILATION

HEAT EXCHANGER - R&R *(C)*

1973-88
Four
912
One Side 1.0
Both 2.0
914
One Side 9
Both 1.6
Six
One Side 8
Both 1.4
1989-93
w/Turbocharger
Right Side 1.3
Left 1.5
Both 2.3
w/o Turbocharger
Right Side 1.1
Left 1.6
Both 2.6

CONTROL BOX, HEATER - R&R *(C)*
Includes: Adjust Control Cable.

1973-88
w/Air Cond
Right Side 9
Left 3.0
Both 3.6
w/o Air Cond
Right Side 7
Left 9
Both 1.3
1989-93
w/Turbocharger
Right Side 9
Left 8
Both 1.3
w/o Turbocharger
One Side 7
Both 1.1

SENSOR, TEMP (IN CAR) - R&R *(B)*
1973-93 3

SENSOR, TEMP (CONTROL BOX) - R&R *(B)*
1973-93 3

CONTROL, AUTO TEMP - R&R *(B)*
1973-93 6

CABLE, TEMPERATURE CONTROL - R&R *(B)*

1973-93
911,930 .... 1.0
912 8
914 5

MOTOR, BLOWER - R&R *(B)*

1973-93
Air Cond ① 1.2
Fresh Air/Heater 4
Heater Booster 8
① *Includes: R&I evaporator housing*

HEATER HOSES - R&R *(D)*

1973-93
Four 5
Six 8

VALVE, HEATER CONTROL - R&R *(B)*
Use Control Box, Heater - R&R

BLOWER SWITCH, HEATER BOOSTER - R&R *(B)*
1973-93 5

SWITCH, BOOSTER TEMP REGULATING - R&R *(B)*
1973-93 4

SWITCH, HEATER BOOSTER CONTROL - R&R *(B)*
1973-93 5

RELAY, HEATER BOOSTER CONTROL - R&R *(B)*
1973-93 3

VALVE, HEATER BOOSTER CONTROL - R&R *(B)*
1973-93 5

PUMP, HEATER BOOSTER - R&R *(B)*
With Metering Unit.
1973-93 4

PUMP, HEATER BOOSTER MIXTURE - R&R *(B)*
1973-93 6

AIR CONDITIONING

FREON - RECOVER *(B)*
NOTE: This operation is not to be used with any other operations.
All 3

PERFORMANCE - TEST *(B)*
Includes: Gauge check, leak test and partial charge.
1973-93 .... 1.0

SYSTEM CHARGE (PARTIAL) *(B)*
Includes: Pressure and leak test.
1973-93 .... 1.0

SYSTEM CHARGE (COMPLETE) *(B)*
Includes: Evacuate, recover and recharge system.
1973-93 .... 1.4

SEAL, COMPRESSOR SHAFT - R&R *(B)*
DOES NOT include recharge.
1973-93 .... 1.8

CLUTCH OR COIL, COMPRESSOR - R&R *(B)*
1973-93 8

BELT, COMPRESSOR - R&R *(D)*
1973-93 5

RELAY, COMPRESSOR CLUTCH - R&R *(B)*
1989-93 5

COMPRESSOR ASSEMBLY - R&R *(B)*
DOES NOT include recharge.
1973-88 .... 2.2
1989-93 7

VALVE, EVAPORATOR EXPANSION - R&R *(B)*
DOES NOT include recharge.
1973-88 6
1989-93 .... 1.3

CORE, EVAPORATOR - R&R *(B)*
DOES NOT include recharge.
1973-88 .... 1.0
1989-93 .... 4.9

SENSOR, EVAP TEMP - R&R *(B)*
1989-93 3

CONDENSER - R&R *(B)*
DOES NOT include recharge.
1973-88
Front 5
Rear 6
1989-93 .... 2.3

FAN, FRONT CONDENSER - R&R *(B)*
1973-88 6
1989-93 .... N.A.

VALVE, SERVICE - R&R *(B)*
DOES NOT include recharge.
1973-93
One 4
Both 7

RECEIVER DRIER - R&R *(B)*
DOES NOT include recharge.
1973-93 8

HOSE, AIR CONDITIONING - R&R *(B)*
DOES NOT include recharge.
1973-93
Discharge
(73-88) ea 8
(89-93)
Compressor to Condenser 3
Condenser to Condenser 1.9
Condenser to Receiver Dryer 9
Receiver Dryer to Evaporator 7
Suction ① 1.8
① *Includes: Loosen evaporator.*

★ **COMBINATIONS** ★

★ Make Up Hose From Stock 4

Cont.

Porsche Heating & Air Conditioning (Cont.)

924, 928, 944 & 968

NOTE 1: Times shown Do Not include recover, evacuate and charge system. If necessary to open refrigerant system or to recover, evacuate, charge and test, refer to System Charge (Complete) for appropriate time.
NOTE 2: Times listed are for Factory and Dealer dash installed Integral Type air conditioning units only. Use necessary clock time for service of hang-on units.

HEATING & VENTILATION

HEATER HOSES - R&R *(D)*

1977-81
Heater Core to Valve
924
w/Turbocharger 1.6
w/o Turbocharger 1.3
928 .... 1.8
Heater Core to Engine
924
w/Turbocharger 1.5
w/o Turbocharger 1.1
928 .... 1.8
Water Pump to Valve
924
w/Turbocharger 1.1
w/o Turbocharger 9
928 .... 1.3

1982-84
Heater Core to Valve or Engine
924,944
w/Air Cond 8.1
w/o Air Cond 7.3
928,928S 1.8
Engine to Valve
924,944
w/Turbocharger 1.1
w/o Turbocharger 9
928,928S 1.3

1985-93
Heater Core to Valve or Engine
924S
w/Air Cond 8.1
w/o Air Cond 7.3
928GT,928GTS,928S,928S4 .... 1.8
Heater Core to Flange
944,944S,944S2
w/Air Cond 8.9
w/o Air Cond 8.7
968 .... 9.2
Engine to Valve or Flange
924S 9
928GT,928GTS,928S,928S4 .... 1.8
944,944S,944S2 .... 1.6
968 .... 1.8

CORE, HEATER - R&R *(B)*
DOES NOT include evacuate or charge system.

1977-81
924
w/Air Cond 6.4
w/o Air Cond 5.9
928
w/Air Cond
Auto 9.0
Man 8.6
w/o Air Cond 8.3

1982-84
924
w/Air Cond 8.3
w/o Air Cond 7.5
928,928S
w/Air Cond
Auto 9.0
Man 8.6
w/o Air Cond 8.3
944
w/Air Cond 8.3
w/o Air Cond 7.5

1985-93
924S
w/Air Cond 8.3
w/o Air Cond 7.5
928GT,928GTS,928S,928S4
w/Air Cond
Auto 9.0
Man 8.6
w/o Air Cond 8.3
944,944S,944S2
w/Air Cond 9.2
w/o Air Cond 8.7
968 .... 9.5

VALVE, HEATER CONTROL - R&R *(B)*

924
w/Turbocharger 1.3
w/o Turbocharger 1.0
924S,944 .... 1.8
928,928GT,928GTS,928S,928S4,944S,944S2 .... 1.3
968 .... 1.6

CABLE, VENTILATION CONTROL - R&R *(B)*

924,924S
Defrost Control 1.9
Fresh Air Regulator 2.0
Heater Control
w/Turbocharger
w/Air Cond 5.9
w/o Air Cond 2.6
w/o Turbocharger
w/Air Cond 5.9
w/o Air Cond 2.3
944
Defrost Control 1.9
Fresh Air Regulator 2.0
Heater Control
w/Air Cond 5.6
w/o Air Cond 2.3

MOTOR, BLOWER - R&R *(B)*
DOES NOT include evacuate or charge system.

1977-93
924,924S,944,944S,944S2
w/Air Cond 6.4
w/o Air Cond 5.9
928,928GT,928GTS,928S,928S4
Main
(78-80) 2.7
(81-93) 1.8
Aux
(78-86) 2.6
(87-93) 1.9
968 .... 1.1

SWITCH, BLOWER MOTOR - R&R *(B)*

1977-93
924,924S 6
928,928GT,928GTS,928S,928S4 8
944,944S,944S2
(83-84) 6
(85-91) 5
968 5

CONTROL ASSEMBLY, TEMPERATURE - R&R *(B)*

1977-93
924,924S
w/Turbocharger 2.9
w/o Turbocharger 2.7
944,944S,944S2
(83-84) 2.7
(85-91) 5
968 5

AIR CONDITIONING

FREON - RECOVER *(B)*
NOTE: This operation is not to be used with any other operation.

All 3

PERFORMANCE - TEST *(B)*
Includes: Gauge check, leak test and partial charge.

All 1.0

SYSTEM CHARGE (PARTIAL) *(B)*
Includes: Pressure and leak test.

All 1.0

SYSTEM CHARGE (COMPLETE) *(B)*
Includes: Evacuate, recover and recharge system.

All 1.4

BELT, COMPRESSOR - R&R *(D)*
Includes: Serpentine type.

924
w/Turbocharger 8
w/o Turbocharger 6
924S,944,944S,944S2
Man Strg 7
Pwr Strg 9
928,928GT,928GTS,928S,928S4 .... 1.1
968 (Serpentine) 9

SEAL, COMPRESSOR SHAFT - R&R *(B)*
DOES NOT include evacuate or charge system.

All 1.8

COMPRESSOR ASSEMBLY - R&I *(B)*
DOES NOT include evacuate or charge system.

924 .... 1.5
924S,928,928GT,928GTS,928S,928S4,968 .... 1.1
944,944S,944S2
w/Turbocharger 1.5
w/o Turbocharger 1.1

Cont.

AIR CONDITIONING TIME GUIDE

Porsche Heating & Air Conditioning (Cont.)

924, 928, 944 & 968 (Cont.)

★ COMBINATIONS ★

★ Compressor - R&R 2
★ Valve Plate &/or Cylinder Head - R&R .. .7
★ Service Plate - R&R 5
★ Bracket, Compressor - R&R 5
★ Clutch, Compressor - R&R 2
★ Pulley, Compressor - R&R 2

COMPRESSOR ASSEMBLY - R&R *(B)*
Use Compressor - R&I plus Combinations.

PULLEY, COMPRESSOR - R&R *(B)*
Use Compressor - R&I plus Combinations.

CLUTCH, COMPRESSOR - R&R *(B)*
Use Compressor - R&I plus Combinations.

CONDENSER - R&R *(B)*
DOES NOT include evacuate or charge system.

1977-93
924 .... 2.0
924S
w/Fog Lamps 4.3
w/o Fog Lamps 3.0
928,928GT,928GTS,928S,928S4 .... 1.9
944,944S,944S2
(83-84)
w/Fog Lamps 4.3
w/o Fog Lamps 3.0
(85-91)
w/Turbocharger 1.3
w/o Turbocharger 1.1
968 .... 1.1

FAN, CONDENSER - R&R *(D)*
924 .... 1.8
924S 1.0
928,928GT,928GTS,928S,928S4 8
944,944S,944S2
w/Turbocharger 2.7
w/o Turbocharger 1.0
968
One 1.1
Both 1.3

SWITCH, FAN THERMOSTATIC - R&R *(D)*
Includes: Drain and refill coolant.
924
w/Turbocharger 7
w/o Turbocharger 5
924S 1.5
928GT,928GTS,928S4 9
944
w/Turbocharger 2.8
w/o Turbocharger 1.5
944S,944S2 .... 1.5
968 .... 1.0

RESISTOR, FAN - R&R *(B)*
924,924S,928GT,928GTS,928S4 3
944,944S,944S2 7
968
One 5
Both 6

RECEIVER DRIER - R&R *(B)*
DOES NOT include evacuate or charge system.
924,924S,944,944S,944S2,968 7
928,928GT,928GTS,928S,928S4 9

CORE, EVAPORATOR - R&R *(B)*
DOES NOT include evacuate or charge system.
1977-93
924,924S 2.0
928,928GT,928GTS,928S,928S4
Main
Auto Air Cond 9.2
Man Air Cond 8.8
Aux
(78-86) 1.8
(87-93) 1.1
944,944S,944S2
(83-84) 2.0
(85-91) 9.8
968 .... 9.9

VALVE, EVAPORATOR EXPANSION - R&R *(B)*
DOES NOT include evacuate or charge system.
924,924S,944,944S,944S2 .... 1.9
928,928S
Main 1.8
Aux 2.0
928GT,928GTS,928S4
Main 1.8
Aux 1.5
968 .... 9.2

HOSE, AIR CONDITIONING - R&R *(B)*
DOES NOT include evacuate or charge system.
Suction 1.3
Discharge 1.0

★ COMBINATIONS ★

★ Make Up Hose From Stock 4

CONTROL ASSEMBLY, TEMPERATURE - R&R *(B)*
1977-93
924,924S
w/Turbocharger 6.8
w/o Turbocharger 6.5

928,928GT,928GTS,928S,928S4
(78-79) 3.0
(80-82) 1.8
(83-93)
Auto Air Cond 6
Man Air Cond 9
968 6

CONTROL UNIT - R&R *(B)*
928GT,928GTS,928S4 (Auto Air Cond) 1.0
928S (Auto Air Cond) 1.6

SENSOR, INSIDE TEMP - R&R *(B)*
924S,944,944S,944S2,968 7
928GT,928GTS,928S,928S4 .... 2.4

SENSOR, OUTSIDE TEMP - R&R *(B)*
924S,944,944S,944S2,968 3
928GT,928GTS,928S,928S4 7

SWITCH, TEMPERATURE - R&R *(B)*
1977-93
924,924S
(77-81) 3
(82-91) 8
928,928GT,928GTS,928S,928S4 6
944,944S,944S2,968 .... 1.3

SWITCH, PRESSURE - R&R *(B)*
924,924S,944,944S,944S2,968 5
928,928GT,928GTS,928S,928S4 6

RELAY, AIR CONDITIONING - R&R *(B)*
All 3

TANK, VACUUM - R&R *(C)*
924,924S,944,944S,944S2,968 3
928,928GT,928GTS,928S,928S4 9

SERVO, TEMPERATURE CONTROL - R&R *(B)*
924,924S,944,944S,944S2,968 .... 1.8
928,928GT,928GTS,928S,928S4 .... N.A.

SERVO, DEFROST VENT - R&R *(B)*
924,924S,944,944S,944S2,968 .... 2.4
928,928GT,928GTS,928S,928S4 .... 5.0

SERVO, FLOOR VENT - R&R *(B)*
924,924S,944,944S,944S2,968 .... 1.8
928,928GT,928GTS,928S,928S4 .... 5.0

Renault Heating & Air Conditioning

NOTE 1: Times shown DO NOT include recover, evacuate and charge system. If necessary to open refrigerant system; refer to System Charge (Complete) for appropriate time. NOTE 2: Times listed are for Factory and Dealer dash installed Integral Type air conditioning units only. Use necessary clock time for service of hang-on units.

HEATING & VENTILATION

HEATER HOSES - R&R *(D)*
NOTE: Deduct .2 when used in conjunction with radiator hose R&R.
Fuego,R5 (Le Car),Sportwagon,18i 1.6
R12 .... 1.0
R15,R17 .... 1.3

VALVE, TEMPERATURE CONTROL - R&R *(B)*
Fuego,Sportwagon,18i 7
R5 (Le Car) 9
R12,R15,R17 8

Cont.

Renault Heating & Air Conditioning (Cont.)

CORE, HEATER - R&R *(B)*
DOES NOT include System Charge.

Fuego,Sportwagon,18i
- w/Air Cond 5.0
- w/o Air Cond 2.8

R5 (Le Car),R12 .... 2.2
R15,R17 .... 6.0

MOTOR, BLOWER - R&R *(B)*

Fuego,Sportwagon,18i
- w/Air Cond 4.0
- w/o Air Cond 2.5

R5 (Le Car) 1.0
R12 .... 1.8
R15,R17 .... 2.0

SWITCH, BLOWER MOTOR - R&R *(B)*

All 5

CONTROL ASSEMBLY, TEMPERATURE - R&R *(B)*

Fuego,Sportwagon,18i 1.6
R5 (Le Car) 7
R12,R15,R17 .... 1.5

CABLE, TEMPERATURE - R&R *(B)*

Fuego,R12,R15,R17,Sportwagon,18i 1.0
R5 (Le Car) 1.9

AIR CONDITIONING

FREON - RECOVER *(B)*
NOTE: This operation is not ot be used with any other operations.

All 3

PERFORMANCE - TEST *(B)*
Includes: Gauge check, leak test and partial charge.

All 1.0

SYSTEM CHARGE (PARTIAL) *(B)*
Includes: Performance test.

All 1.0

SYSTEM CHARGE (COMPLETE) *(B)*
Includes: Recover, evacuate and recharge system.

All 1.4

COMPRESSOR ASSEMBLY - R&R *(B)*
DOES NOT include System Charge.

Fuego,Sportwagon,18i 3.4
R5 (Le Car) 2.0
R12,R15 .... 1.0
R17
- exc Gordini 1.5
- Gordini 2.4

SEAL, COMPRESSOR SHAFT - R&R *(B)*
DOES NOT include System Charge. With compressor removed.

All 8

BELT, COMPRESSOR - R&R *(D)*

All 5

CONDENSER - R&R *(B)*
DOES NOT include System Charge.

Fuego,Sportwagon,18i 2.3
R5 (Le Car) 2.2
R12,R15,R17 .... 1.1

CLUTCH ASSEMBLY - R&R *(B)*

All 9

IDLER PULLEY - R&R *(D)*

All 6

VALVE, EVAPORATOR EXPANSION - R&R *(B)*
DOES NOT include System Charge.

Fuego,Sportwagon,18i 9
R5 (Le Car) 5
R12 .... 1.1
R15,R17 .... 1.3

CORE, EVAPORATOR - R&R *(B)*
DOES NOT include System Charge.

Fuego,Sportwagon,18i 4.5
R5 (Le Car) 1.6
R12 .... 1.1
R15,R17 .... 1.3

MOTOR, EVAPORATOR - R&R *(B)*
DOES NOT include System Charge.

Fuego,Sportwagon,18i 1.5
R5 (Le Car),R12,R15,R17 .... 1.0

RECEIVER DRIER - R&R *(B)*
DOES NOT include System Charge.

Fuego,R5 (Le Car),Sportwagon,18i 8
R12,R15,R17 5

HOSE, AIR CONDITIONING - R&R *(B)*
DOES NOT include System Charge.

Fuego,Sportwagon,18i
- Compressor to Condenser 7
- Compressor to Evaporator 2.2
- Condenser to Drier 7
- Drier to Evaporator 7

R5 (Le Car),R12,R15,R17
- One 6
- Each Additional 5

★ **COMBINATIONS** ★

★ Make Up Hose From Stock 4

THERMOSTAT, TEMPERATURE CONTROL - R&R *(B)*
DOES NOT include System Charge.

Fuego,Sportwagon,18i 1.6
Medallion 1.1
R5 (Le Car),R12,R15,R17 8

Saab Heating & Air Conditioning

NOTE 1: Times shown DO NOT include recover, evacuate and charge system. If necessary to open refrigerant system; refer to System Charge (Complete) for appropriate time.
NOTE 2: Times listed are for Factory and Dealer dash installed Integral Type air conditioning units only. Use necessary clock time for service of hang-on units.

HEATING & VENTILATION

HEATER HOSES - R&R *(D)*

1973-85 (Both) 6
1986-93 (Both)
- 900,900S,900 Turbo 6
- 9000,9000CD,9000CDE,9000CS,9000CSE, 9000S,9000 Turbo,9000CD Turbo 9

CORE, HEATER - R&R *(B)*
DOES NOT include evacuate or charge system.

1973-85
- Sonett,95,96 .... N.A.
- 99 .... 2.3
- 900
  - w/Console 2.2
  - w/o Console 1.8

1986-91
- 900,900S,900 Turbo
  - w/Console 2.2
  - w/o Console 1.8
- 9000,9000CD,9000S 3.4

1992-93 .... 2.2

MOTOR, BLOWER - R&R *(B)*
DOES NOT include evacuate or charge system.

1973-78
- Sonett 5
- 95,96
  - w/Air Cond 3.4
  - w/o Air Cond 5
- 99 .... 1.3

1979-80
- 99 .... 1.3
- 900 .... 2.4

1981-85 .... 2.4
1986-91
- 900,900S,900 Turbo 2.4
- 9000,9000CD,9000S 3.5

1992-93 .... 2.0

SWITCH, BLOWER MOTOR - R&R *(B)*

1973-78 3
1979-85
- 99 3
- 900 .... 1.1

1986-93
- 900,900S,900 Turbo 1.1
- 9000,9000CD,9000CDE,9000CS,9000CSE, 9000S,9000 Turbo,9000CD Turbo 3

WATER VALVE - R&R *(B)*

1973-78
- Sonett,95,96 .... 1.1
- 99 .... 2.3

1979-85 .... 1.8
1986-93 (900,900S,900 Turbo) 1.8

Cont.

AIR CONDITIONING TIME GUIDE

Saab Heating & Air Conditioning (Cont.)

AIR CONDITIONING

FREON - RECOVER *(B)*
NOTE: This operation is not to be used with any other operations.
All 3

PERFORMANCE - TEST *(B)*
Includes: Gauge check, leak test and partial charge.
All 1.0

SYSTEM CHARGE (PARTIAL) *(B)*
Includes: Performance test.
All 1.0

SYSTEM CHARGE (COMPLETE) *(B)*
Includes: Recover, evacuate and recharge system.
All 1.4

BELT, COMPRESSOR - R&R *(D)*
1973-78 5
1979-80
99 5
900 3
1981-85 5
1986-93 3

COMPRESSOR ASSEMBLY - R&R *(B)*
DOES NOT include evacuate or charge system.
1973-80
Sonett 3.2
95,96 .... 1.3
99 9
900 .... 1.1
1981-85 7
1986-90
900,900S,900 Turbo 7
9000,9000CD,9000S 1.5
1991-93
900,900S,900 Turbo 7
9000,9000CD,9000CDE,9000CS,9000CSE, 9000S,9000 Turbo,9000CD Turbo 8

COMPRESSOR ASSEMBLY - R&I & O/H *(B)*
DOES NOT include evacuate or charge system.
1973-80
Sonett 4.4
95,96 .... 2.6
99 .... 2.2
900 .... N.A.
1981-93 .... N.A.

CLUTCH, COMPRESSOR - R&R *(B)*
Includes: Loosen compressor.
DOES NOT include evacuate or charge system.
1973-80
Sonett 3.4
95,96,99 9
900 9
1981-85 .... 1.6
1986-93
900,900S,900 Turbo 1.6
9000,9000CD,9000CDE,9000CS,9000CSE, 9000S,9000 Turbo,9000CD Turbo 2.3

IDLER PULLEY - R&R *(D)*
1973-80
Sonett 3.1
95,96,99 7
900 5
1981-85 5
1986-93
900,900S,900 Turbo 5
9000,9000CD,9000CDE,9000CS,9000CSE, 9000S,9000 Turbo,9000CD Turbo 3

CONDENSER - R&R *(B)*
DOES NOT include evacuate or charge system.
1973-78
Sonett 3.2
95,96,99 .... 1.4
1979-80
99 9
900 7
1981-93 .... 1.3

MOTOR, ELECTRIC FAN - R&R *(B)*
1973-74 .... N.A.
1975-85
99 .... 1.2
900 7
1986-93 (One or Both) 7

VALVE, EVAPORATOR EXPANSION - R&R *(B)*
DOES NOT include evacuate or charge system.
1973-78 .... 2.8
1979 6
1980-85 5
1986-93
900,900S,900 Turbo 8
9000,9000CD,9000CDE,9000CS,9000CSE, 9000S,9000 Turbo,9000CD Turbo 9

CORE, EVAPORATOR - R&R *(B)*
DOES NOT include evacuate or charge system.
1973-78 .... 1.7
1979-80
99 .... 1.0
900 .... 1.6
1981-84 .... 1.6
1985
w/Turbocharger 9
w/o Turbocharger 1.6
1986-93
900
(86-88) 1.6
(89-92) 9
900S,900 Turbo 9
9000,9000CD,9000CDE,9000CS,9000CSE, 9000S,9000 Turbo,9000CD Turbo 1.3

RECEIVER DRIER - R&R *(B)*
DOES NOT include evacuate or charge system.
1973-93 9

HOSE, AIR CONDITIONING - R&R *(B)*
DOES NOT include evacuate or charge system.
1973-85 4
1986-93
900,900S,900 Turbo 4
9000,9000CD,9000CDE,9000CS,9000CSE, 9000S,9000 Turbo,9000CD Turbo
Compressor to Condenser 4
Condenser to Receiver Drier 8
Evaporator to Condenser 8

★ **COMBINATIONS** ★
★ Make Up Hose From Stock 4

Sterling Heating & Air Conditioning

NOTE 1: Times shown Do Not include recover, evacuate and charge system. If necessary to open refrigerant system or to recover, evacuate, charge and test, refer to System Charge (Complete) for appropriate time.
NOTE 2: Times listed are for Factory and Dealer dash installed Integral Type air conditioning units only. Use necessary clock time for service of hang-on units.

HEATING & VENTILATION

HEATER HOSES - R&R *(D)*
NOTE: Deduct .2 when used in conjunction with Radiator Hoses - R&R.
1987-91
One 8
Each Additional 3

CORE, HEATER - R&R *(B)*
DOES NOT include System Charge.
1987-91 .... 6.0

VALVE, HEATER CONTROL - R&R *(B)*
1987-91 7

MOTOR, BLOWER - R&R *(B)*
1987-91 .... 1.5

SWITCH, BLOWER MOTOR - R&R *(B)*
1987-91 8

CONTROL ASSEMBLY, TEMPERATURE - R&R *(B)*
1987-91 .... 1.0

RELAY, BLOWER MOTOR - R&R *(B)*
1987-91 3

RESISTOR, BLOWER MOTOR - R&R *(B)*
1987-91 .... 1.0

CONTROL MOTOR - R&R *(B)*
1987-91
Air Mix
825 .... 1.3
827 .... 2.8
Function 5
Recirculation 1.5

Cont.

AIR CONDITIONING TIME GUIDE

Sterling Heating & Air Conditioning (Cont.)

AIR CONDITIONING

FREON - RECOVER *(B)*
NOTE: This operation is not to be used with any other operations.
All 3

PERFORMANCE - TEST *(B)*
Includes: Gauge check, leak test and partial charge.
1987-91 .... 1.0

SYSTEM CHARGE (PARTIAL) *(B)*
Includes: Performance test.
1987-91 .... 1.0

SYSTEM CHARGE (COMPLETE) *(B)*
Includes: Recover, evacuate and recharge system.
1987-91 .... 1.4

BELT, COMPRESSOR - R&R *(D)*
1987-91 3

IDLER PULLEY - R&R *(D)*
1987-91 6

COMPRESSOR ASSEMBLY - R&R *(B)*
Includes: Transfer clutch assembly.
DOES NOT include System Charge.
1987-91 .... 2.4

SEAL, COMPRESSOR SHAFT - R&R *(B)*
DOES NOT include System Charge.
1987-91 .... 2.7

CLUTCH, COMPRESSOR - R&R *(B)*
DOES NOT include System Charge.
1987-91 .... 2.4

CONDENSER - R&R *(B)*
DOES NOT include System Charge.
1987-91 9

RECEIVER DRIER - R&R *(B)*
DOES NOT include System Charge.
1987-91 9

CORE, EVAPORATOR - R&R *(B)*
DOES NOT include System Charge.
1987-91
w/Passive Restraint 4.0
w/o Passive Restraint 1.9

VALVE, EVAPORATOR EXPANSION - R&R *(B)*
DOES NOT include System Charge.
1987-91
w/Passive Restraint 4.5
w/o Passive Restraint 2.3

CONTROL ASSEMBLY, A.T.C. - R&R *(B)*
1990-91 (827) 7

SENSOR, AMBIENT TEMP (A.T.C.) - R&R *(B)*
1990-91 (827) 6

SENSOR, COOLANT TEMP (A.T.C.) - R&R *(B)*
1990-91 (827) 1.6

SENSOR, EVAPORATOR TEMP (A.T.C.) *(B)*
1990-91 (827) 4.7

HOSE, AIR CONDITIONING - R&R *(B)*
DOES NOT include System Charge.
1987-91
One (Discharge or Suction) 7
Each Additional 3

★ COMBINATIONS ★

★ Make Up Hose From Stock 4

MOTOR &/OR FAN, CONDENSER - R&R *(D)*
1987-91 .... 1.3

RELAY, CONDENSER FAN - R&R *(B)*
1987-91 5

RELAY, COMPRESSOR CLUTCH - R&R *(B)*
1987-91 3

SWITCH, HIGH PRESSURE - R&R *(B)*
1987-91 6

SWITCH, DUAL PRESSURE - R&R *(B)*
1987-91 6

Subaru Heating & Air Conditioning

NOTE 1: Times shown Do Not include recover, evacuate and charge system. If necessary to open refrigerant system or to recover, evacuate, charge and test, refer to System Charge (Complete) for appropriate time.
NOTE 2: Times listed are for Factory and Dealer dash installed Integral Type air conditioning units only. Use necessary clock time for service of hang-on units.

HEATING & VENTILATION

HEATER HOSES - R&R *(D)*
NOTE: Deduct .2 when used in conjunction with Radiator Hoses - R&R.
1973-77 8
1978-84 .... 1.0
1985-93 6

CORE, HEATER - R&R *(B)*
DOES NOT include evacuate or charge system.
1973-78 .... 3.0
1979-84
w/Air Cond 4.3
w/o Air Cond 3.7
1985-93
Brat ①
w/Air Cond 3.1
w/o Air Cond 2.3
Impreza,Legacy ①
w/Air Cond 3.1
w/o Air Cond 2.7
Justy ①
w/Air Cond 2.3
w/o Air Cond 1.9
Loyale,Subaru
w/Air Cond 4.2
w/o Air Cond 3.8
SVX ① 4.7
XT,XT6 ①
w/Air Cond 3.5
w/o Air Cond 3.1
① *Includes: R&I dash assembly.*

VALVE, TEMP CONTROL - R&R *(B)*
1973-76 6
1977-78 9
1979-93 .... 1.0

MOTOR, BLOWER - R&R *(B)*
1973-74 .... 1.1
1975-76 .... 2.2
1977
Stage 1 .... 2.2
Stage 2 9
1978 9
1979-81
w/Air Cond
Brat 2.2
Subaru 1.3
w/o Air Cond 9
1982-84
w/Air Cond 1.3
w/o Air Cond 9
1985-93
Brat,Justy 1.1
Impreza,Legacy,Loyale 7
Subaru
Cpe,Sed,S/W 6
Hatchback 1.1
SVX 8
XT,XT6 6

SWITCH, BLOWER MOTOR - R&R *(B)*
1973-77 8
1978-93
Brat,Loyale,Subaru,XT,XT6 .... 1.0
Impreza,Justy 9
Legacy 1.5

RESISTOR, BLOWER MOTOR - R&R *(B)*
1973-93 6

RELAY, BLOWER MOTOR - R&R *(B)*
Brat,Subaru 6
Impreza,Legacy,Loyale,XT,XT6 7
Subaru 6
SVX 3

CONTROL ASSEMBLY, TEMP - R&R *(B)*
1975-77 .... 1.0
1978-81
Brat
w/Air Cond 2.3
w/o Air Cond 1.9
Subaru
w/Air Cond 2.6
w/o Air Cond 2.0

Cont.

AIR CONDITIONING TIME GUIDE

Subaru Heating & Air Conditioning (Cont.)

1982-84
w/Air Cond 2.6
w/o Air Cond 2.0
1985-93
Brat
w/Cruise Control 8
w/o Cruise Control 6
Impreza,Justy 9
Legacy,Loyale,XT,XT6 .... 1.3
Subaru
Cpe,Sed,S/W 1.1
Hatchback
w/Cruise Control 8
w/o Cruise Control 6
SVX 8

AIR CONDITIONING

FREON - RECOVER *(B)*
NOTE: *This operation is not to be used with any other operations.*
All 3

PERFORMANCE - TEST *(B)*
Includes: Gauge check, leak test and partial charge.
1979-93 .... 1.0

SYSTEM CHARGE (PARTIAL) *(B)*
Includes: Pressure and leak test.
1979-93 .... 1.0

SYSTEM CHARGE (COMPLETE) *(B)*
Includes: Evacuate, recover and recharge system.
1979-93 .... 1.4

SEAL, COMPRESSOR SHAFT - R&R *(B)*
DOES NOT include evacuate or charge system.
1979-82
Hitachi (80-82) .... N.A.
Lonestar
(79) 1.6
(80-81)
Brat 1.6
Subaru 1.3
(82) 1.3

CLUTCH OR COIL, COMPRESSOR - R&R *(B)*
1979-84
Hitachi (80-84) 6
Lonestar
(79-82) 6
(83-84) - Not Serviced.
1985-93
Calsonic,Diesel Kiki (90-93) 1.5
Hitachi (85-93) 1.3
Lonestar (85-86) - Not Serviced.
Panasonic (85-93) 1.5
Wynn's (87-93) 9
Zexel 1.3

BELT, COMPRESSOR - R&R *(D)*
1979-84 3
1985-93
Calsonic,Diesel Kiki (90-93) 5
Hitachi (85-93) 6
Lonestar (85-86) 3
Panasonic (85-93) 5
Wynn's (87-93)
Justy 5
Loyale 6
Subaru
Cpe,Sed,S/W 6
Hatchback 4
Zexel 5

COMPRESSOR ASSEMBLY - R&R *(B)*
DOES NOT include evacuate or charge system.
1979-84
Hitachi (80-84) 1.5
Lonestar
(79-81)
Brat 1.5
Subaru 9
(82-84) 9
1985-93
Calsonic,Diesel Kiki (90-93) 9
Hitachi (85-93)
Justy 7
Subaru,XT,XT6 9
Lonestar (85-86) 7
Panasonic (85-93) 9
Wynn's (87-93) 8
Zexel 8

VALVE PLATE, COMPRESSOR - R&R *(B)*
DOES NOT include evacuate or charge system.
1979 .... 1.3
1980-81 (Lonestar)
Brat 1.3
Subaru 1.1
1982 (Lonestar) 1.1

VALVE, EVAPORATOR EXPANSION - R&R *(B)*
DOES NOT include evacuate or charge system.
1979-81
Hitachi (80-81) 1.5
Lonestar
(79) 1.7
(80-81)
Brat 1.7
Subaru 1.5
1982-84 .... 1.5
1985-93 .... 1.3

CORE, EVAPORATOR - R&R *(B)*
DOES NOT include evacuate or charge system.
1979-81
Hitachi (80-81) 1.5
Lonestar (79-81)
Brat 2.0
Subaru 1.5
1982-84 .... 1.5
1985-93 .... 1.3

CONDENSER - R&R *(B)*
Includes: R&I fan.
DOES NOT include evacuate or charge system.
1979-84
Hitachi
w/Turbocharger 9
w/o Turbocharger 8
Lonestar
(79-81)
Brat 1.0
Subaru
Man Strg 8
Pwr Strg 9
(82-84) 1.0
1985-93
Calsonic,Diesel Kiki (90-93) 6
Hitachi (85-93)
Justy,Loyale,Subaru 7
XT,XT6 8
Lonestar,Panasonic 7
Wynn's (87-93)
Justy 7
Loyale 6
Subaru
Cpe,Sed,S/W 7
Hatchback 8
Zexel
Legacy 6
SVX 1.1

MOTOR, CONDENSER FAN - R&R *(D)*
exc SVX 6
SVX 1.0

HOSE, AIR CONDITIONING - R&R *(B)*
DOES NOT include evacuate or charge system.
1979-84
Hitachi (80-84)
Discharge 5
Suction 6
Lonestar
(79)
Discharge 8
Suction 1.5
(80-81)
Brat
Discharge 8
Suction 1.5
Subaru (ea) 5
(82-84) (ea) 5
1985-93
One 5
Each Additional 3

★ **COMBINATIONS** ★

★ Make Up Hose From Stock 4

RECEIVER DRIER - R&R *(B)*
DOES NOT include evacuate or charge system.
1979-93 5

THERMOSTAT, TEMP CONTROL - R&R *(B)*
1979-93
Calsonic,Diesel Kiki,Hitachi,Panasonic, Wynn's 1.3
Lonestar 1.0

RELAY, AIR CONDITIONING - R&R *(B)*
1979-93 (ea) 5

SWITCH, FAN PRESSURE - R&R *(B)*
DOES NOT include evacuate or charge system.
1979-93 3

SWITCH, LOW PRESSURE - R&R *(B)*
DOES NOT include evacuate or charge system.
1979-93 3

SWITCH, HIGH PRESSURE - R&R *(B)*
DOES NOT include evacuate or charge system.
1980-82 (Hitachi) Fuse Bolt 8
1983-93 (Hitachi) 3

SWITCH, MICRO - R&R *(B)*
1985-93 5

Cont.

AIR CONDITIONING TIME GUIDE

Subaru Heating & Air Conditioning (Cont.)

DIAPHRAGM CONT (ACTUATOR) - R&R *(B)*

1979-93 (ea) .5

SWITCH OR SOLENOID, VACUUM - R&R *(B)*

1979-93 .5

AMPLIFIER, PULSER - R&R *(B)*

1983-93 (Hitachi,Panasonic) .9

SENSOR, PULSER - R&R *(B)*

1983-93 (Hitachi,Panasonic) .7

AUTOMATIC CLIMATE CONTROL - DIAGNOSIS *(B)*

SVX .8

SENSOR, AIR INTAKE - R&R *(B)*

DOES NOT include evacuate or charge system.

SVX 1.3

SENSOR, REFRIGERANT TEMPERATURE - R&R *(B)*

SVX 1.9

SENSOR, SUNLOAD - R&R *(B)*

SVX 3.4

CONTROL UNIT - R&R *(B)*

SVX .8

SENSOR, AMBIENT - R&R *(B)*

SVX .5

FAN CONTROL AMPLIFIER - R&R *(B)*

SVX .6

IDLER PULLEY - R&R *(D)*

1979-84 .7

1985-93

- Calsonic,Diesel Kiki,Hitachi,Zexel .6
- Panasonic .8

Suzuki Heating & Air Conditioning

NOTE 1: Times shown DO NOT include recover, evacuate and charge system. If necessary to open refrigerent system, refer to System Charge (Complete) for appropriate time.
NOTE 2: Times listed are for Factory and Dealer dash installed Integral Type air conditioning units only. Use necessary clock time for service of hang-on units.

HEATING & VENTILATION

HEATER HOSES - R&R *(D)*

One .5
Two .7
All 1.0

WATER VALVE - R&R *(B)*

Samurai .8
Sidekick,Swift N.A.

CORE, HEATER - R&R *(B)*

Includes: R&I instrument panel assembly.

Samurai 5.0
Sidekick
- w/Air Cond 6.1
- w/o Air Cond 4.9

Swift 2.6

BLOWER MOTOR - R&R *(B)*

Samurai 4.8
Sidekick 3.1
Swift .6

SWITCH, BLOWER MOTOR - R&R *(B)*

Samurai 1.0
Sidekick .6
Swift N.A.

RESISTOR, BLOWER MOTOR - R&R *(B)*

Samurai 4.7
Sidekick .5
Swift .6

CONTROL ASSEMBLY, TEMP & VENT - R&R *(B)*

Samurai 3.1
Sidekick 3.0
Swift 1.9

CABLES, HEATER CONTROL - R&R *(B)*

Samurai (All) 2.2
Sidekick (All) 3.0
Swift 1.9

AIR CONDITIONING

FREON - RECOVER *(B)*

NOTE: This operation is not to be used with any other operation.

All .3

PERFORMANCE - TEST *(B)*

Includes: Gauge check, leak test and partial charge.

Samurai,Sidekick,Swift 1.0

SYSTEM CHARGE (PARTIAL) *(B)*

Includes: Performance test.

All 1.0

SYSTEM CHARGE (COMPLETE) *(B)*

Includes: Recover, evacuate and recharge system.

Samurai,Sidekick,Swift 1.4

BELT, COMPRESSOR - R&R *(D)*

Samurai,Sidekick .5
Swift 1.3

• **ADDITIONAL TIME** •

- Where Pwr Strg interferes add
  Sidekick .1
- Where Alt interferes add
  Samurai,Sidekick .1

COMPRESSOR ASSEMBLY - R&R *(B)*

DOES NOT include System Charge.

Samurai 1.2
Sidekick 1.5
Swift 2.2

★ **COMBINATIONS** ★

★ Seal, Compressor Shaft - R&R .6

CLUTCH ASSEMBLY - R&R *(B)*

DOES NOT include System Charge.

Samurai 1.5
Sidekick 1.8
Swift 2.4

SEAL, COMPRESSOR SHAFT - R&R *(B)*

Use Compressor Assembly - R&R plus Combinations.

VALVE, SUCTION - R&R *(B)*

DOES NOT include System Charge.

Samurai 1.0
Sidekick,Swift N.A.

VALVE, DISCHARGE - R&R *(B)*

DOES NOT include System Charge.

Samurai .7
Sidekick,Swift N.A.

EXPANSION VALVE - R&R *(B)*

DOES NOT include System Charge.

Samurai 1.9
Sidekick 3.3
Swift 2.6

CORE, EVAPORATOR - R&R *(B)*

DOES NOT include System Charge.

Samurai 1.6
Sidekick 3.1
Swift 2.5

RECEIVER DRIER - R&R *(B)*

DOES NOT include System Charge.

Samurai 1.0
Sidekick 1.1
Swift 2.2

CONDENSER - R&R *(B)*

DOES NOT include System Charge.

Samurai 1.6
Sidekick 1.7
Swift 2.5

FAN, CONDENSER COOLING - R&R *(D)*

Samurai,Sidekick .8
Swift 3.0

SWITCH, CONDENSER FAN - R&R *(B)*

All .7

RELAY, CONDENSER FAN - R&R *(B)*

All N.A.

HOSE, AIR CONDITIONING - R&R *(B)*

DOES NOT include System Charge.

One 1.0
Each Additional .6

★ **COMBINATIONS** ★

★ Make Up Hose From Stock .4

RELAY, POWER - R&R *(B)*

Samurai,Sidekick .3
Swift N.A.

SWITCH, CONTROL - R&R *(B)*

Samurai .7
Sidekick,Swift .6

Cont.

AIR CONDITIONING TIME GUIDE

Suzuki Heating & Air Conditioning (Cont.)

AMPLIFIER ASSEMBLY - R&R *(B)*

Samurai 5

THERMISTOR - R&R *(B)*

DOES NOT include System Charge.

Samurai 1.7
Sidekick 3.2
Swift 3.5

Toyota Heating & Air Conditioning

NOTE 1: Times shown DO NOT include recover, evacuate and charge system. If necessary to open refrigerant system; refer to System Charge (Complete) for appropriate time.
NOTE 2: Times listed are for Factory and Dealer dash installed Integral Type air conditioning units only. Use necessary clock time for service of hang-on units.

HEATING & VENTILATION

HEATER HOSES - R&R *(D)*

1973-81 (All)
Carina,Celica,Corolla,Starlet,Supra 1.0
Corona
(73-74) 1.3
(75-81) 1.0
Cressida
(78-80) 9
(81) 1.1
Land Cruiser
(73-80) 9
(81)
exc S/W 9
S/W 1.1
Pickup
(73-74) 1.2
(75-81) 1.0
1982-93 (All)
Camry,Celica,Supra 1.4
Corolla
(83) 1.1
(84-93) 1.3
Corona,Cressida,Paseo,Starlet,Tercel 1.1
Land Cruiser
(82-90)
exc S/W 9
S/W 1.1
(91-93) 1.2
MR2,Previa 1.2
Pickup,T100,4Runner 9
Van 1.9

WATER VALVE - R&R *(B)*

1973-93
Camry
(83-91) 8
(92-93) 1.0
Carina 6
Celica (exc Supra)
(73-81) 7
(82-89) 9
(90-93) 1.0
Corolla,Tercel
(73-74) 7
(75-77) 9
(78-79) 1.6
(80-93) 1.0
Corona
(73) 7
(74-78) 9
(79-82) 8
Cressida
(78-80) 6
(81-92) 9
Land Cruiser
(73-80) 6
(81-90)
exc S/W 6
S/W 9
(91-93) 1.0
MR2,Previa 1.0
Pickup
(73-88) 6
(89-93) 8
Starlet 9
Supra
(79-81) 7
(82-92) 9
T100 8
Van 1.1
4Runner
(84-89) 6
(90-93) 8

CORE, HEATER - R&R *(B)*

1973-93
Camry
(83-86)
w/Air Cond 4.0
w/o Air Cond 2.7
(87-91)
w/Air Cond 5.0
w/o Air Cond 3.9
(92-93) 1.8
Carina 1.0
Celica (exc Supra)
(73-75) 1.0
(76-77) 1.8
(78-81) 3.2
(82-85) 4.4
(86-89)
w/Air Cond 3.6
w/o Air Cond 2.3
(90-93)
w/Air Cond 5.0
w/o Air Cond 4.0
Corolla (exc Tercel)
(73-74) 9
(75-79) 1.9
(80-83) 3.7
(84-92)
w/Air Cond 3.6
w/o Air Cond 2.3
(93)
w/Air Cond 6.0
w/o Air Cond 5.0
Corona
(73-78)
exc RT104,114,118 .... 3.2
RT104,114,118 .... 2.6
(79-82) 4.2
Cressida
(78-80) 3.1
(81-84) 7.5
(85-88)
w/Air Cond 5.6
w/o Air Cond 4.7
(89-92)
w/Air Cond 5.1
w/o Air Cond 4.0
Land Cruiser
(73-80) 1.0
(81-90)
exc S/W 1.3
S/W
w/Air Cond 4.5
w/o Air Cond 3.2
(91-93)
w/Air Cond 4.6
w/o Air Cond 3.6
MR2
(85-89)
w/Air Cond 4.2
w/o Air Cond 2.6
(91-93)
w/Air Cond 6.3
w/o Air Cond 5.4
Paseo
w/Air Cond 5.9
w/o Air Cond 4.9
Pickup
(73-78) 1.0
(79-93)
w/Air Cond 3.2
w/o Air Cond 1.9
Previa
w/Air Cond 5.3
w/o Air Cond 4.7
Starlet 3.8
Supra
(79-81) 3.4
(82-92)
w/Air Cond 5.4
w/o Air Cond 4.4
Tercel
(80-86)
w/Air Cond 4.4
w/o Air Cond 3.2
(87-90)
exc S/W
w/Air Cond 3.6
w/o Air Cond 2.2
S/W
w/Air Cond 4.4
w/o Air Cond 3.2
(91-93)
w/Air Cond 5.9
w/o Air Cond 4.9
T100,4Runner
w/Air Cond 3.2
w/o Air Cond 1.9
Van
w/Air Cond 3.9
w/o Air Cond 2.2

Cont.

Toyota Heating & Air Conditioning (Cont.)

MOTOR, BLOWER - R&R *(B)*

1973-93

- Camry (Air Cond or Heater)
  - (83-86) .9
  - (87-93) .6
- Carina .5
- Celica (exc Supra)
  - w/Air Cond
    - (73-81) .9
    - (82-85) .8
    - (86-93) .5
  - w/o Air Cond
    - (73-81) .8
    - (82-85) 1.0
    - (86-93) .5
- Corolla (exc Tercel)
  - w/Air Cond
    - (73) .7
    - (74-79) 2.3
    - (80-83) .7
    - (84-87)
      - F.W.D. .8
      - R.W.D. .7
    - (88-93)
      - exc FX,FX16 .5
      - FX,FX16 .8
  - w/o Air Cond
    - (73-74) 1.0
    - (75-79) .6
    - (80-83) .7
    - (84-87)
      - F.W.D. .8
      - R.W.D. .7
    - (88-93)
      - exc FX,FX16 .5
      - FX,FX16 .8
- Corona
  - w/Air Cond
    - exc MX13/29 .9
    - MX13/29 .7
  - w/o Air Cond
    - (73) .8
    - (74-78) .6
    - (79-82) .7
- Cressida
  - w/Air Cond
    - (78-80) 2.4
    - (81-82) .9
    - (83-88) 2.0
    - (89-92) .7
  - w/o Air Cond
    - (78-80) .6
    - (81-82) .9
    - (83-92) .7
- Land Cruiser
  - (73-90)
    - w/Air Cond 1.9
    - w/o Air Cond .6
  - (91-93) Air Cond or Heater .6
- MR2 (Air Cond or Heater)
  - (85-89) .8
  - (91-93) .5
- Paseo (Air Cond or Heater) .5
- Pickup
  - w/Air Cond
    - (73-82) 1.9
    - (83-88) .8
    - (89-93) 1.6
  - w/o Air Cond
    - (73-78) 1.1
    - (79-82) .6
    - (83-88) .8
    - (89-93) .5
- Previa (Air Cond or Heater) 1.1
- Supra
  - (79-81)
    - w/Air Cond .9
    - w/o Air Cond .8
  - (82-92) Air Cond or Heater 1.0
- Tercel (Air Cond or Heater)
  - (80-83) .7
  - (84-90) .8
  - (91-93) .5
- T100
  - w/Air Cond 1.6
  - w/o Air Cond .5
- Van
  - w/Air Cond 3.9
  - w/o Air Cond 1.3
- 4Runner
  - (84-89) Air Cond or Heater .8
  - (90-93)
    - w/Air Cond 1.6
    - w/o Air Cond .5

SWITCH, BLOWER MOTOR - R&R *(B)*

1973-93

- Camry
  - (83-86)
    - w/Air Cond .6
    - w/o Air Cond 1.8
  - (87-91) Air Cond or Heater .9
  - (92-93) Air Cond or Heater .6
- Carina .5
- Celica (exc Supra)
  - (73-77) .5
  - (78-81)
    - w/Air Cond .6
    - w/o Air Cond .8
  - (82-85)
    - w/Air Cond .5
    - w/o Air Cond 2.0
  - (86-93) Air Cond or Heater 1.0
- Corolla (exc Tercel)
  - (73)
    - w/Air Cond .7
    - w/o Air Cond .5
  - (74-79) .6
  - (80-83)
    - w/Air Cond .6
    - w/o Air Cond .8
  - (84-87)
    - w/Air Cond
      - F.W.D. .8
      - R.W.D. .9
    - w/o Air Cond
      - F.W.D. .9
      - R.W.D. 1.1
  - (88-92)
    - exc FX,FX16
      - w/Air Cond 1.9
      - w/o Air Cond 1.5
    - FX,FX16
      - w/Air Cond .8
      - w/o Air Cond .9
  - (93)
    - w/Air Cond .4
    - w/o Air Cond 1.1
- Corona
  - (73-78)
    - exc MX13/29
      - w/Air Cond 1.0
      - w/o Air Cond .5
    - MX13/29 .8
  - (79-82)
    - w/Air Cond .5
    - w/o Air Cond .7
- Cressida
  - w/Air Cond
    - (78-82) .5
    - (83-84) 1.6
    - (85-88) .3
    - (89-92) 1.1
  - w/o Air Cond
    - (78-81) .6
    - (82-84) 1.6
    - (85-88) .3
    - (89-92) 1.3
- Land Cruiser
  - (73-80) .5
  - (81-90)
    - exc S/W .5
    - S/W
      - w/Air Cond .7
      - w/o Air Cond .6
  - (91-93)
    - w/Air Cond .4
    - w/o Air Cond 1.0
- MR2 (Air Cond or Heater) .7
- Paseo
  - w/Air Cond .4
  - w/o Air Cond 1.0
- Pickup (Air Cond or Heater)
  - (73-78) .5
  - (79-88) .6
  - (89-93) .8
- Previa
  - w/Air Cond .7
  - w/o Air Cond 2.8
- Starlet
  - w/Air Cond .8
  - w/o Air Cond
    - (81-82) .5
    - (83-84) .9
- Supra
  - (79-81)
    - w/Air Cond .6
    - w/o Air Cond .8
  - (82-92)
    - 2.8L (12 Valve) Eng
      - w/Air Cond .5
      - w/o Air Cond 2.0
    - 3.0L (24 Valve) Eng
      - w/Air Cond .5
      - w/o Air Cond .7
- Tercel
  - (80-82) Air Cond or Heater .7
  - (83-86)
    - w/Air Cond .6
    - w/o Air Cond 1.0
  - (87-90)
    - exc S/W (Air Cond or Heater) .7
    - S/W
      - w/Air Cond .6
      - w/o Air Cond 1.0
  - (91-93)
    - w/Air Cond .4
    - w/o Air Cond 1.0
- T100
  - w/Air Cond .4
  - w/o Air Cond 1.5
- Van (Air Cond or Heater) .5
- 4Runner (Air Cond or Heater)
  - (84-89) .6
  - (90-93) .8

Cont.

AIR CONDITIONING TIME GUIDE

Toyota Heating & Air Conditioning (Cont.)

RELAY, BLOWER MOTOR - R&R *(B)*

1973-93
Camry,Carina,Celica (exc Supra), Corolla,Corona,Paseo,Pickup,Previa, Starlet,Tercel,T100,Van,4Runner 5
Land Cruiser
(73-90) 6
(91-93) 4
MR2
(85-89) 6
(91-93) 1.8
Supra
(79-81) 5
(82-92)
2.8L (12 Valve) Eng 5
3.0L (24 Valve) Eng 7

RESISTOR, BLOWER MOTOR - R&R *(B)*

1973-93
Camry
(83-86) 3
(87-93) 5
Celica (exc Supra)
w/Air Cond
(73-85) 7
(86-89) 3
(90-93) 5
w/o Air Cond
(73-77) 5
(78-81) 8
(82-85) 9
(86-89) 3
(90-93) 5
Corolla (exc Tercel)
w/Air Cond
(73-79) 2.2
(80-87)
F.W.D. 5
R.W.D. 7
(88-92)
exc FX,FX16 6
FX,FX16 3
(93) 5
w/o Air Cond
(73) 8
(74-79) 5
(80-87)
F.W.D. 3
R.W.D. 6
(88-92)
exc FX,FX16 6
FX,FX16 3
(93) 5
Corona,Paseo 5
Cressida
w/Air Cond
(78-88) 5
(89-92) 3
w/o Air Cond
(78-80) 5
(81-86) 7
(87-88) 5
(89-92) 3
Land Cruiser
(73-80)
w/Air Cond 2.2
w/o Air Cond 7
(81-90)
w/Air Cond 7
w/o Air Cond
exc S/W 7
S/W 3
(91-93) 3
MR2
(85-89) 5
(91-93) 3.9
Pickup,4Runner
w/Air Cond
(73-80) 2.2
(81-84) 6
(85-93) 3
w/o Air Cond
(73-84) 6
(85-93) 3
Previa 1.1
Starlet
(81-82) 5
(83-84) 8
Supra 9
Tercel
w/Air Cond
(80-86) 5
(87-93)
exc S/W 5
S/W 1.0
w/o Air Cond
(83-86) 1.0
(87-93)
exc S/W 5
S/W 1.0
T100 3
Van 8

CONTROL ASSEMBLY, TEMP - R&R *(B)*

1973-93
Camry
(83-86) 1.6
(87-91) 1.0
(92-93) 6
Carina,Pickup,4Runner 9
Celica (exc Supra)
(73-79) 1.0
(80-85) 1.9
(86-89) 1.3
(90-93) 9
Corolla (exc Tercel)
(73-74) 9
(75-87)
F.W.D. 8
R.W.D. 1.0
(88-92)
exc FX,FX16 .... 1.9
FX,FX16 8
(93) 1.1
Corona
(73) 1.1
(74-78) 9
(79-82) 7
Cressida
(78-80) 1.0
(81-84) 1.6
(85-88) 5
(89-92) 1.1
Land Cruiser
(73-80) 1.0
(81-90)
exc S/W 1.0
S/W 8
(91-93) 1.1
MR2
(85-89) 1.6
(91-93) 7
Paseo,Tercel 1.0
Previa 2.7
Starlet
(81-82) 1.3
(83-84) 8
Supra 1.9
T100 .... 1.5
Van 7

CABLE, TEMP CONTROL - R&R *(B)*

1973-82
Celica,Corolla 9
Corona
exc MX13/29 9
MX13/29 5
Cressida 5
Land Cruiser
exc S/W 5
S/W 9
Pickup 7

1983-93 (Defroster)
Camry
(83-86) 1.6
(87-91) 1.0
Celica (exc Supra)
(83-85) 1.9
(86-89) 1.3
(90-93) 9
Corolla
(83) 7
(84-87)
F.W.D. 8
R.W.D. 1.0
(88-92)
exc FX,FX16 .... 1.0
FX,FX16 8
(93) 1.1
Cressida,MR2 .... 1.6
Land Cruiser
(83-90) 8
(91-93) 1.1
Paseo,Tercel 1.0
Pickup,Starlet,4Runner 9
Previa 2.7
Supra 1.9
T100 .... 1.5
Van 5

AIR CONDITIONING

FREON - RECOVER *(B)*

NOTE: *This operation is not to be used with any other operations.*

All 3

PERFORMANCE - TEST *(B)*

Includes: Guage check, leak test and partial charge.

1973-93 .... 1.0

SYSTEM CHARGE (PARTIAL) *(B)*

Includes: Performance test.

1973-93 .... 1.0

SYSTEM CHARGE (COMPLETE) *(B)*

Includes: Recover, evacuate and recharge system.

1973-93 .... 1.4

Cont.

Toyota Heating & Air Conditioning (Cont.)

BELT, COMPRESSOR - R&R *(D)*

1973-82
Carina,Corolla,Cressida,Pickup,Starlet .5
Celica,Supra
(73-81) .7
(82) .5
Corona
(73-74) .5
(75-78) .7
(79-82) .5
Land Cruiser .6
1983-93
Camry
(83-86) .3
(87-93) .5
Celica,Cressida,Paseo,Supra .5
Corolla
(83-87) .5
(88-92)
exc FX,FX16 .7
FX,FX16 .5
(93) .5
Land Cruiser,MR2,Pickup,Starlet, T100,4Runner .7
Previa 1.3
Tercel
(83-86) .5
(87-90)
exc S/W .7
S/W .5
(91-93) .5
Van 1.0

ADDITIONAL TIME

- Where Air Pump interferes add .2
- Where Alternator interferes add .2
- Where Pwr Strg interferes add .2

IDLER PULLEY - R&R *(D)*

1973-79
exc Celica,Corolla,Supra .5
Celica,Supra
(73-74) .3
(75-79) .5
Corolla .4
1980-82 .5
1983-93
Camry,Pickup,Starlet,T100,4Runner .6
Celica (exc Supra)
(83-89) .5
(90-93) .9
Corolla
(83-87)
F.W.D. .9
R.W.D. .3
(88-92)
exc FX,FX16,GT-S .5
FX,FX16,GT-S .9
(93) .8
Cressida,Land Cruiser,MR2,Supra,Tercel .5
Van 1.1

COMPRESSOR ASSEMBLY - R&R *(B)*

DOES NOT include System Charge.

1973-82
Carina,Cressida,Land Cruiser .7
Celica,Supra
(73-74) .7
(75-82) .9
Corolla .9
Corona
(73-74) 1.4
(75-78) .9
(79-82) 1.1
Land Cruiser,Starlet .8
Pickup 1.1
1983-93
Camry
(83-91)
Four .9
V6 1.2
(92-93)
Four .8
V6 2.0
Celica (exc Supra)
(83-85) .9
(86-89)
F.W.D. 1.2
4 W.D. (88-89) 1.6
(90-93) .8
Corolla
(83) 1.2
(84-93)
Diesel 1.1
Gas
F.W.D. 1.3
R.W.D. 1.0
Cressida
(83-88) 1.2
(89-92) 1.0
Land Cruiser
(83-90)
exc S/W 1.2
S/W 1.0
(91-93) 1.1
MR2
(85-89) 1.3
(91-93) 1.1
Paseo 1.1
Pickup
(83-84)
Diesel 1.2
Gas 1.6
(85-88) 1.0
(89-93) .8
Previa,Van 1.6
Starlet,T100 .8
Supra 1.0
Tercel
(83-86) 1.0
(87-90)
exc S/W 1.2
S/W 1.0
(91-93) 1.0
4Runner
(84) 1.6
(85-89) 1.0
(90-93) .8

CLUTCH PLATE & HUB ASSEMBLY - R&R *(B)*

DOES NOT include System Charge.

1973-82
Carina,Land Cruiser .7
Celica (exc Supra)
(73-74) .7
(75-81) .9
(82) 1.0
Corolla
exc Tercel .7
Tercel .8
Corona
(73-74) .6
(75-82)
exc RT105,115,119 .6
RT105,115,119 .9
Cressida
(78-80) 1.2
(81-82) .9
Pickup .6
Starlet .9
Supra
(79-81) .6
(82) 1.0
1983-93
Camry
(83-91)
Four 1.1
V6 1.4
(92-93)
Four 1.0
V6 2.2
Celica (exc Supra)
(83-85) 1.1
(86-89)
F.W.D. 1.4
4 W.D. (88-89) 1.8
(90-93) 1.0
Corolla
Diesel 1.3
Gas
F.W.D. 1.5
R.W.D.
w/Twin Cam Eng 1.5
w/o Twin Cam Eng .8
Cressida
(83-88) 1.4
(89-92) 1.2
Land Cruiser
(83-90)
exc S/W .8
S/W .7
(91-93) 1.3
MR2
(85-89) 1.5
(91-93) 1.3
Paseo 1.3
Pickup
(83-88)
Diesel .7
Gas .6
(89-93) 1.0
Previa 1.9
Starlet .8
Supra,T100 1.0
Tercel
(83-86) .9
(87-90)
exc S/W 1.5
S/W .9
(91-93) 1.2
Van 1.8
4Runner
(84-89) .6
(90-93) 1.0

VALVE, EVAPORATOR EXPANSION - R&R *(B)*

DOES NOT include System Charge.

1973-82
Carina,Land Cruiser,Starlet .7
Celica (exc Supra)
(73-77) .8
(78-81) 1.0
(82) 1.4
Corolla .6

Cont.

AIR CONDITIONING TIME GUIDE

Toyota Heating & Air Conditioning (Cont.)

Corona
(73-78)
exc RT85/95 .8
RT85/95 1.2
(79-82) 1.0
Cressida .9
Pickup 1.0
Supra
(79-81) 1.6
(82) 2.0
1983-93
Camry
(83-91) 1.1
(92-93) 1.4
Celica (exc Supra)
(83-85) 1.6
(86-93) 1.1
Corolla
(83) 1.4
(84-87) 1.2
(88-92)
exc FX,FX16 1.6
FX,FX16 1.2
(93) 1.1
Cressida
(83-88) 1.8
(89-92) 1.1
Land Cruiser
(83-90)
exc S/W 1.0
S/W 1.4
(91-93) 1.1
MR2
(85-89) 1.5
(91-93) 1.2
Paseo 1.1
Pickup
(83-88) 1.4
(89-93) 1.2
Previa 1.3
Starlet 1.5
Supra 2.2
Tercel
(83-86) 1.4
(87-93)
exc S/W 1.1
S/W 1.4
T100 1.2
Van 2.3
4Runner
(84-89) 1.4
(90-93) 1.2

CONDENSER - R&R *(B)*

DOES NOT include System Charge.

1973-82
Carina .6
Celica (exc Supra)
(73-74) .6
(75-77) .9
(78-81) 1.0
(82) 1.2
Corolla
exc Tercel 1.0
Tercel .7
Corona
(73-74) 1.1
(75-78) 1.0
(79-82) .7
Cressida
(78-80) .9
(81-82) 1.2
Land Cruiser
exc S/W .7
S/W 1.0
Pickup 1.1
Starlet .8
Supra
(79-81) 1.0
(82) 1.4
1983-93
Camry
(83-91) .8
(92-93)
Four 1.7
V6 3.0
Celica (exc Supra)
(83-85) 1.2
(86-89) 1.4
(90-93) 1.3
Corolla
(83) 1.9
(84-87)
exc FX 1.2
FX 1.5
(88-92)
exc FX,FX16 1.6
FX,FX16 1.5
(93) 1.8
Cressida
(83-85) 1.2
(86-88) 1.6
(89-92) 1.9
Land Cruiser
(83-90)
exc S/W .7
S/W 1.4
(91-93) 1.1
MR2,Paseo 1.3
Pickup,Previa,T100,4Runner 1.1
Starlet .8
Supra 1.4
Tercel
(83-86) .8
(87-90)
exc S/W 1.2
S/W .8
(91-93) 1.3
Van 1.8

FAN & MOTOR, CONDENSER - R&R *(B)*

1980-93
Camry
(83-86) .9
(87-93) .6
Celica
(86-89)
F.W.D. .6
4 W.D. (88-89) 1.0
(90-93)
F.W.D. .7
4 W.D. 1.1
Corolla
(84-87) 1.0
(88-93)
exc FX,FX16 .8
FX,FX16 1.0
Cressida
(85-88) 2.0
(89-92) 1.5
MR2,Starlet .7
Paseo .8
Tercel
(83-86) .8
(87-90)
exc S/W .8
S/W .6
(91-93) .9

RELAY, ELECT FAN MOTOR - R&R *(B)*

All .3

RECEIVER DRIER - R&R *(B)*

DOES NOT include System Charge.

1973-82
Carina,Celica,Supra .6
Corolla
(75-79) 1.1
(80-82) .9
Corona
(73-74) 1.2
(75-78) .8
(79-82) .6
Cressida
(78-80) .9
(81-82) 1.3
Land Cruiser,Pickup .7
Starlet .8
1983-93
Camry,Paseo,Starlet,Tercel .5
Celica,Cressida,Previa,Supra .8
Corolla,Land Cruiser,MR2,Pickup,
T100,4Runner .7
Van 1.2

CORE, EVAPORATOR - R&R *(B)*

DOES NOT include System Charge.

1973-82
Carina .9
Celica (exc Supra)
(73-77) .9
(78-81) 1.3
(82) 2.0
Corolla
(75-79)
exc KE30 1.3
KE30 1.7
(80-82)
exc Tercel 1.6
Tercel 1.3
Corona
(73-74) 1.6
(75-78) 2.3
(79-82) 1.9
Cressida 1.6
Land Cruiser,Starlet 1.7
Pickup 1.3
Supra
(79-81) 2.4
(82) 2.2
1983-93
Camry,MR2 1.4
Celica (exc Supra)
(83-85) 1.8
(86-93) 1.3
Corolla
(83) 1.5
(84-87) 1.3
(88-92)
exc FX,FX16 1.6
FX,FX16 1.3
(93) 1.2
Cressida
(83-88) 1.8
(89-92) 1.4
Land Cruiser
(83-90)
exc S/W 1.2
S/W 1.6
(91-93) 1.3
Paseo,Tercel 1.3
Pickup
(83-88) 1.4
(89-93) 1.2
Previa,Starlet 1.5

Cont.

Toyota Heating & Air Conditioning (Cont.)

Supra 2.2
T100 .... 1.2
Van 2.3
4Runner
(84-89) 1.4
(90-93) 1.2

HOSE, AIR CONDITIONING - R&R *(B)*
DOES NOT include System Charge.

1973-77
Carina,Land Cruiser (ea) 5
Celica,Corolla,Supra (ea) 7
Corona
exc MX13/29
(73) (ea) 1.9
(74-77) (ea) 7
MX13/29
Suction 1.4
Discharge 1.1
Pickup
Suction 8
Discharge 6
1978-93
One 5
Each Additional 3

★ **COMBINATIONS** ★

★ Make Up Hose From Stock 4

SWITCH, PRESSURE CUT - R&R *(B)*
DOES NOT include System Charge.

1973-82
Celica (exc Supra)
(73-77) 1.4
(78-81) 1.2
(82) 1.6
Corolla
(73-79) 1.4
(80-82)
exc Tercel 1.1
Tercel 1.2
Corona
(75-78)
RT105/119 .... 2.0
MX13/29 .... N.A.
(79-82) 1.8
Cressida
(78-80) 1.4
(81-82) 1.8
Land Cruiser 1.1
Pickup 1.2
Starlet 1.4
Supra 2.0
1983-93
Camry
(83-91) 1.1
(92-93) 9
Celica (exc Supra)
(83-85) 1.6
(86-89) 7
(90-93) 9
Corolla
(83-92)
F.W.D. 1.1
R.W.D. 1.2
(93) 9
Cressida
(83-84) 1.8
(85-88) 7
(89-92) 1.0
Land Cruiser
(83-90) 1.1
(91-92) 8
(93) 1.0
MR2
(85-89) 1.1
(91-93) 9
Paseo 1.1
Pickup
(83-88) 1.2
(89-93) 1.0
Previa 1.3
Starlet 1.6
Supra 2.0
Tercel
(83-90) 1.6
(91-93) 1.1
T100 .... 1.0
Van 2.2
4Runner
(84-89) 1.2
(90-93) 1.0

Volkswagen Heating & Air Conditioning

BEETLE & GHIA

HEAT EXCHANGER - R&R *(C)*
Each 1.0

CABLE, TEMPERATURE CONTROL - R&R *(B)*
All 1.0

SWITCH, BLOWER MOTOR - R&R *(B)*
All 8

BLOWER MOTOR, FRESH AIR - R&R *(B)*
All 7

Volkswagen Heating & Air Conditioning (Cont.)

CABRIOLET, CORRADO, DASHER, EUROVAN, FOX, GOLF, JETTA PASSAT, PICKUP, QUANTUM, RABBIT, SCIROCCO & VANAGON

NOTE 1: Times shown DO NOT include recover, evacuate and charge system. If necessary to open refrigerant system or to recover, evacuate, charge and test; refer to System Charge (Complete) for appropriate time.
NOTE 2: Times listed are for Factory and Dealer dash installed Integral Type air conditioning units only. Use necessary clock time for service of hang-on units.

HEATING & VENTILATION

HEATER HOSES - R&R *(D)*
NOTE: Deduct .2 when used in conjunction with Radiator Hose - R&R.

1974-93 (ea)
Cabriolet,Corrado,Dasher,Eurovan,Fox, Golf,Jetta,Passat,Pickup,Rabbit, Scirocco 6
Quantum
w/Air Cond 1.8
w/o Air Cond 6
Vanagon 8

VALVE, HEATER CONTROL - R&R *(B)*
1974-93 6

CORE, HEATER - R&R *(B)*
DOES NOT include recover, evacuate or recharge system.

1974-93
Cabriolet
w/Air Cond 4.1
w/o Air Cond 1.9
Corrado,Passat ① 6.8

Cont.

AIR CONDITIONING TIME GUIDE

Volkswagen Heating & Air Conditioning (Cont.)

CABRIOLET, CORRADO, DASHER, EUROVAN, FOX, GOLF, JETTA PASSAT, PICKUP, QUANTUM, RABBIT, SCIROCCO & VANAGON (Cont.)

Dasher,Quantum
- w/Air Cond 2.9
- w/o Air Cond 1.9

Eurovan 6.6

Fox ①
- w/Air Cond 5.8
- w/o Air Cond 4.8

Golf ①
- w/Air Cond 6.0
- w/o Air Cond 3.9

Jetta
- (80-84)
  - w/Air Cond 3.4
  - w/o Air Cond 1.9
- (85-93) ①
  - w/Air Cond 6.0
  - w/o Air Cond 3.9

Pickup,Rabbit
- w/Air Cond 3.4
- w/o Air Cond 1.9

Scirocco
- (75-84)
  - w/Air Cond 3.4
  - w/o Air Cond 1.9
- (85-88)
  - w/Air Cond 4.1
  - w/o Air Cond 1.9

Vanagon
- Front 4.3
- Rear
  - Diesel 8
  - Gas 1.0

① *Includes: R&I Inst Panel and Console.*

MOTOR, BLOWER - R&R *(B)*

1974-93

Cabriolet
- w/Air Cond 2.4
- w/o Air Cond 1.6

Corrado
- w/Air Cond 1.2
- w/o Air Cond 6

Dasher,Fox,Quantum 1.0

Eurovan 6

Golf
- w/Air Cond 1.0
- w/o Air Cond 5

Jetta
- (80-84)
  - w/Air Cond 2.4
  - w/o Air Cond 1.3
- (85-93)
  - w/Air Cond 1.0
  - w/o Air Cond 5

Passat 1.2

Pickup,Rabbit
- w/Air Cond 2.4
- w/o Air Cond 1.3

Scirocco
- w/Air Cond 2.4
- w/o Air Cond
  - (75-84) 1.3
  - (85-88) 1.6

Vanagon
- Diesel (82-83) 3.9
- Gas
  - w/Air Cond 2.7
  - w/o Air Cond 3.4

SWITCH, BLOWER MOTOR - R&R *(B)*

1974-93

Cabriolet,Corrado,Eurovan,Fox,Golf, Jetta,Passat,Pickup,Quantum,Rabbit, Scirocco 7

Dasher 1.6

Vanagon 5

RESISTOR, BLOWER MOTOR - R&R *(B)*

1974-93

Cabriolet,Corrado,Dasher,Fox,Golf, Passat,Pickup,Quantum,Rabbit,Scirocco ①

Jetta
- (80-84) ① 3
- (85-92)
  - w/Air Conditioning 1.1
  - w/o Air Conditioning 3
- (93) 3

Eurovan .... N.A.

Vanagon 3.1

① *DOES NOT include R&I Blower Motor.*

CONTROL ASSEMBLY, TEMP - R&R *(B)*

1974-93

Cabriolet,Corrado,Golf
- w/Air Cond 8
- w/o Air Cond 1.0

Dasher 9

Eurovan,Passat 1.0

Fox
- w/Air Cond 2.0
- w/o Air Cond 7

Jetta
- (80-84)
  - w/Air Cond 7
  - w/o Air Cond 9
- (85-93)
  - w/Air Cond 8
  - w/o Air Cond 1.0

Pickup,Rabbit
- w/Air Cond 7
- w/o Air Cond 9

Quantum
- w/Air Cond 8
- w/o Air Cond 1.6

Scirocco
- (75-84)
  - w/Air Cond 7
  - w/o Air Cond 9
- (85-88)
  - w/Air Cond 8
  - w/o Air Cond 1.0

Vanagon 1.3

CABLE, TEMP &/OR HEATER CONTROL - R&R *(B)*

DOES NOT include System Charge.

1974-93

Cabriolet,Dasher,Pickup,Rabbit,Scirocco 1.1

Fox
- (87-90) 1.1
- (91-93)
  - w/Air Cond 3.7
  - w/o Air Cond 3.6

Golf,Jetta
- (80-89) 1.1
- (90-93)
  - w/Air Cond 2.6
  - w/o Air Cond 1.1

Quantum 1.8

Vanagon
- Diesel 9
- Gas
  - One 1.1
  - Both 1.9

CONTROL UNIT, TEMP VACUUM - R&R *(B)*

1974-93

Cabriolet,Golf 3.0

Corrado,Passat 4.8

Fox 1.8

Jetta
- (80-84) 6
- (85-93) 3.0

Pickup,Rabbit 6

Quantum 4

Scirocco
- (75-84) 6
- (85-88) 3.0

AIR CONDITIONING

FREON - RECOVER *(B)*

NOTE: *This operation is not be used with any other operations.*

All 3

PERFORMANCE - TEST *(B)*

Includes: Gauge check, leak test and partial charge.

1974-93 .... 1.0

SYSTEM CHARGE (PARTIAL) *(B)*

Includes: Performance Test.

1974-93 .... 1.0

SYSTEM CHARGE (COMPLETE) *(B)*

Includes: Recover, evacuate and recharge system.
NOTE: *When performed in Conjunction with other heating or air conditioning repairs, deduct .2.*

1974-93 .... 1.4

BELT, COMPRESSOR - R&R *(D)*

Includes: Serpentine belts.

1974-93
- V-Belt 5
- Serpentine 3

• ADDITIONAL TIME •

- Where Alternator interferes add 2
- Where Air Pump interferes add 2
- Where Pwr Strg interferes add 2

Cont.

AIR CONDITIONING TIME GUIDE

Volkswagen Heating & Air Conditioning (Cont.)

CABRIOLET, CORRADO, DASHER, EUROVAN, FOX, GOLF, JETTA PASSAT, PICKUP, QUANTUM, RABBIT, SCIROCCO & VANAGON (Cont.)

CLUTCH, COMPRESSOR - R&R *(B)*
Includes: R&I compressor.
DOES NOT include System Charge.

1974-93
Cabriolet,Pickup,Rabbit, Scirocco 2.1
Corrado 3.3
Dasher,Eurovan 2.0
Fox 2.6
Golf,Jetta,Passat 1.9
Quantum 1.5
Vanagon
(84-85) 2.6
(86-91) 2.9

★ COMBINATIONS ★

★ Holding Coil - R&R 2

SEAL, COMPRESSOR SHAFT - R&R *(B)*
DOES NOT include System Charge.

1974-93
Cabriolet,Pickup,Rabbit,Scirocco
exc Sanko Comp 2.2
Sanko Comp 6
Dasher
Abacus Comp 2.4
York Comp 2.2
Eurovan 2.1
Fox 2.0
Golf,Jetta,Passat 2.0
Quantum 1.8

COMPRESSOR ASSEMBLY - R&R *(B)*
DOES NOT include System Charge.

1974-93
Cabriolet,Pickup,Rabbit,Scirocco 1.8
Corrado 3.0
Dasher,Eurovan 1.7
Fox 2.3
Golf,Jetta,Passat 1.6
Quantum 1.2
Vanagon
(84-85) 2.3
(86-91) 2.6

RELAY, CONTROL - R&R *(B)*
All 3

CORE, EVAPORATOR - R&R *(B)*
Includes: R&I evaporator assembly.
DOES NOT include System Charge.

1974-93
Cabriolet 4.4
Corrado,Passat ① 7.1
Dasher,Quantum 2.2
Eurovan 6.6
Fox ① 5.8
Golf ① 6.0
Jetta
(80-84) 2.8
(85-93) 6.0
Pickup,Rabbit,Scirocco 2.8
Vanagon
(84-85) 2.7
(86-91) 3.8

① *Includes: R&I Inst panel and console.*

VALVE, EVAPORATOR EXPANSION - R&R *(B)*
Includes: Evaporator Core removal on Dasher, Fox, Quantum and Vanagon models.
DOES NOT include System Charge.

1974-93
Cabriolet,Golf,Jetta,Pickup, Rabbit,Scirocco 1.0
Corrado,Passat 8
Dasher,Quantum 2.5
Eurovan .... N.A.
Fox ① 6.4
Vanagon
(84-85) 2.7
(86-91) 3.8

① *Includes: R&I instrument panel.*

MOTOR, EVAPORATOR BLOWER - R&R *(B)*

1984-93
Cabriolet 1.5
Corrado,Passat 1.2
Dasher,Pickup,Quantum,Rabbit 3
Eurovan 6
Fox 1.1
Golf,Jetta
(79-84) 3
(85-93) 1.0
Scirocco
(79-84) 3
(85-88) 1.5
Vanagon 2.7

SWITCH, THERMOSTAT - R&R *(B)*

1974-93
Cabriolet,Pickup,Rabbit,Scirocco 9
Dasher,Quantum 1.6
Fox 1.9
Golf 2.7
Jetta
(80-84) 9
(85-93) 2.7
Vanagon
(84-85) 1.1
(86-91) 2.7

SWITCH, PRESSURE - R&R *(B)*
DOES NOT include System Charge.

1974-93 (High or Low) 3

SWITCH, COMP CLUTCH CUT-OUT - R&R *(B)*

1974-93 4

CONDENSER - R&R *(B)*
DOES NOT include System Charge.

1974-93
Cabriolet 1.0
Corrado 1.9
Dasher,Quantum 9
Eurovan 1.6
Fox 1.1
Golf,Jetta
(80-92) 1.0
(93) 2.0
Passat 1.7
Pickup,Rabbit,Scirocco 1.5
Vanagon 1.6

FAN & MOTOR, CONDENSER - R&R *(B)*

1984-93
Cabriolet,Eurovan,Scirocco 9
Corrado,Passat 1.0
Dasher,Fox,Pickup,Quantum,Rabbit 7
Golf,Jetta
(80-84) 7
(85-92) 9
(93) 1.2
Vanagon 1.6

RELAY, ELECTRIC FAN - R&R *(B)*
All 4

RESISTOR, ELECTRIC FAN - R&R *(B)*
All 4

RECEIVER DRIER - R&R *(B)*
DOES NOT include System Charge.

1974-93
Cabriolet,Eurovan,Fox,Golf,Jetta, Passat,Pickup,Rabbit,Scirocco 6
Corrado,Dasher 1.0
Quantum 1.5
Vanagon 7

HOSE, AIR CONDITIONING - R&R *(B)*
DOES NOT include System Charge.

1974-93
Cabriolet,Passat,Pickup,Rabbit,Scirocco
One 5
Each Additional 2
Corrado,Eurovan,Golf
One 8
Each Additional 2
Dasher
Condenser to Evaporator 9
Discharge 5
Small to Large Condenser 5
Suction 9
Fox
Condenser to Evaporator 1.0
Discharge 7
Suction 8
Jetta
One
(80-84) 5
(85-93) 8
Each Additional 2
Quantum
Condensor to Evaporator 8
Discharge or Suction 5
Vanagon
Discharge 2.3
Reciever Drier
(84-85) 1.0
(86-91) 3.4
Suction
(84-85) 3.5
(86-91) 3.1

★ COMBINATIONS ★

★ Make Up Hose From Stock 4

AIR CONDITIONING TIME GUIDE

Volvo Heating & Air Conditioning

NOTE 1: Times shown DO NOT include recover, evacuate and charge system. If necessary to open refrigerant system; refer to System Charge (Complete) for appropriate time. NOTE 2: Times listed are for Factory and Dealer dash installed Integral Type air conditioning units only. Use necessary clock time for service of hang-on units.

HEATING & VENTILATION

HEATER HOSES - R&R *(D)*

All 5

VALVE, HEATER CONTROL - R&R *(B)*

1973-93
- Coupe,740,760,780,940,960 Series 3
- 140,160,180 Series 8
- 240,260 Series 7
- 850 Series .... N.A.

CORE, HEATER - R&R *(B)*

1973-74 .... 6.9

1975-80
- 160 Series 5.9
- 240,260 Series 6.8

1981-93
- Coupe,960 Series 8.0
- 240,260 Series 5.8
- 740,760,780,940 Series
  - w/ECC 8.0
  - w/o ECC 2.7
- 850 Series 2.0

MOTOR, BLOWER - R&R *(B)*

1973-80 .... 4.5

1981-93
- Coupe,740,760,780,960 Series 7
- 240,260 Series ① 6.0
- 850 Series 6
- 940 Series
  - GL,GLE 7
  - SE 6

① *Includes necessary modifications needed to install O.E.M. replacement motor.*

SWITCH, BLOWER MOTOR - R&R *(B)*

1973-93 7

CONTROL SWITCH, VACUUM MOTOR - R&R *(B)*

1973-93 .... 1.0

TANK, VACUUM - R&R *(C)*

1973-93 3

DIAPHRAGM CONTROL (ACTUATOR) - R&R *(B)*

1973-93
- Coupe,740,760,780,940,960 Series 2.6
- 140,160,180,240,260 Series (ea)
  - Defroster 5
  - Floor
    - Front 3
    - Rear 1.0
- 850 Series .... N.A.

CONTROL ASSEMBLY, TEMPERATURE - R&R *(B)*

1973-93 9

CABLE, TEMPERATURE CONTROL - R&R *(B)*

1973-93 (ea) 6

AIR CONDITIONING

FREON - RECOVER *(C)*

NOTE: This operation is not to be used with any other operations.

All 3

PERFORMANCE - TEST *(B)*

Includes: Gauge check, leak test and partial charge.

1973-93 .... 1.0

SYSTEM CHARGE (PARTIAL) *(B)*

Includes: Performance test.

1973-93 .... 1.0

SYSTEM CHARGE (COMPLETE) *(B)*

Includes: Recover, evacuate and recharge system.

1973-93 .... 1.4

CONTROL UNIT, ECC - R&R *(B)*

1990-93 (Coupe,760,780,940,960 Series) 3

PROGRAMMER (ECC ECU) - R&R *(B)*

1988-93 (Coupe,760,780,940,960 Series) 8

VALVE, ECC SOLENOID - R&R *(B)*

1988-93 (Coupe,760,780,940,960 Series) 4

POWER UNIT, ECC - R&R *(B)*

1988-93 (Coupe,760,780,940,960 Series) 7

MOTOR, ECC AIR MIX SERVO - R&R *(B)*

1988-93 (Coupe,760,780,940,960 Series) 7

SENSOR, AMBIENT TEMP - R&R *(B)*

1988-93 (Coupe,760,780,940,960 Series) 3

SENSOR, WATER TEMP - R&R *(B)*

1988-93 (Coupe,760,780,940,960 Series) 3

SENSOR, ECC SUN - R&R *(B)*

1988-93 (Coupe,760,780,940,960 Series) 6

SENSOR, IN-CAR TEMP - R&R *(B)*

1988-93
- Coupe,780,940,960 Series 3
- 760 Series 6

BELT, COMPRESSOR - R&R *(D)*

Includes: Serpentine type.

1973-93
- Coupe,780,850,940,960 Series 3
- 140,160,180 Series 5
- 240,260 Series 6
- 740,760 Series
  - Diesel 6
  - Gas 3

• **ADDITIONAL TIME** •

• w/Shimmed Air Cond Belt add 5

IDLER PULLEY - R&R *(D)*

1973-85
- 140,180 Series 1.0
- 160 Series 1.3
- 240 Series
  - Diesel 1.8
  - Gas 7

SEAL, COMPRESSOR SHAFT - R&R *(B)*

DOES NOT include System Charge.

1973-75 .... 1.1

1976-85
- 240 Series
  - Diesel ① 2.8
  - Gas 1.0
- 260 Series 1.5
- 740,760,780 Series
  - Diesel ① 2.8
  - Gas 1.2

1986-93
- Coupe,740,760,780,940 Series 1.2
- 240,260 Series
  - Diesel ① 2.8
  - Gas 1.0
- 850 Series ① 1.8

① *Includes: R&I Compressor.*

CLUTCH, COMPRESSOR - R&R *(B)*

DOES NOT include System Charge.

1973-75 6

1976-93
- 240 Series
  - Diesel ① 2.6
  - Gas 1.0
- 260 Series 9
- 740,760,780,940 Series
  - Diesel ① 2.6
  - Gas 1.2
- 850 Series ① 1.7
- 960 Series 1.0

① *Includes: R&I Compressor.*

PULLEY, COMPRESSOR - R&R *(B)*

1973-87 5

SENSOR, PRESSURE - R&R *(B)*

1983-93 3

COMPRESSOR ASSEMBLY - R&R *(B)*

DOES NOT include System Charge.

1973-75 6

1976-93
- Coupe,240,740,760,780,940 Series
  - Diesel 2.0
  - Gas
    - Four 1.6
    - V6 .... 1.0
- 260 Series 1.0
- 850 Series 1.5
- 960 Series 8

Cont.

AIR CONDITIONING TIME GUIDE

Volvo Heating & Air Conditioning (Cont.)

VALVE PLATES, COMPRESSOR - R&R *(B)*
DOES NOT include System Charge.

1973-93
140,180 Series 1.3
240 Series
(75) 1.3
(76-93) 2.6

VALVE, EVAPORATOR EXPANSION - R&R *(B)*
DOES NOT include System Charge.

1973-93
Coupe,740,760,780,940,960 Series 2
140,160,180,260 Series 9
240 Series
(76-90) 9
(91-93) 2
850 Series 5

RECEIVER DRIER - R&R *(B)*
DOES NOT include System Charge.

1973-93
Coupe,140,160,180,740,780,940, 960 Series 5
240,260 Series 6
850 Series 9

★ COMBINATIONS ★

★ Receiver Drier - O/H
73-76 7

CONDENSER - R&R *(B)*
DOES NOT include System Charge.

1973-93
Coupe,140,180,740,760,780,940, 960 Series 8
160,240,260 Series 7
850 Series 1.0

FAN, CONDENSER - R&R *(B)*
1983-93 6

RELAY, CONDENSER FAN - R&R *(B)*
1983-93 4

SWITCH, CONDENSER FAN - R&R *(B)*
1983-93 4

CORE, EVAPORATOR - R&R *(B)*
DOES NOT include System Charge.

1973-93
Coupe 1.0
140,160,180,240,260 Series 1.3
740,760,940,960 Series 1.2
780 Series
(87) 1.2
(88-90) 1.0
850 Series 7.0

THERMOSTAT, TEMPERATURE CONTROL - R&R *(B)*
DOES NOT include System Charge.

1973-93 .... 1.5

HOSE, AIR CONDITIONING - R&R *(B)*
DOES NOT include System Charge.

1973-93 (ea) 5

★ COMBINATIONS ★

★ Make Up Hose From Stock 4

Yugo Heating & Air Conditioning

NOTE 1: Times shown DO NOT include recover, evacuate and charge system. If necessary to open refrigerant system; refer to System Charge (Complete) for appropriate time.
NOTE 2: Times listed are for Factory and Dealer dash installed Integral Type air conditioning units only. Use necessary clock time for service of hang-on units.

HEATING & VENTILATION

HEATER HOSES - R&R *(D)*
All 6

WATER VALVE - R&R *(B)*
All 8

CORE, HEATER - R&R *(B)*
DOES NOT include System Charge.
All 1.3

MOTOR, BLOWER - R&R *(B)*
All 8

SWITCH, BLOWER MOTOR - R&R *(B)*
All 3

CONTROL ASSEMBLY, TEMPERATURE - R&R *(B)*
All 2.0

AIR CONDITIONING

FREON - RECOVER *(B)*
NOTE: This operation is not to be used with any other operations.
All 3

PERFORMANCE - TEST *(B)*
Includes: Gauge check, leak test and partial charge.
All 1.0

SYSTEM CHARGE (PARTIAL) *(B)*
Includes: Performance test.
All 1.0

SYSTEM CHARGE (COMPLETE) *(B)*
Includes: Recover, evacuate and recharge system.
All 1.4

BELT, COMPRESSOR - R&R *(D)*
All 1.1

COMPRESSOR ASSEMBLY - R&R *(B)*
DOES NOT include System Charge.
All 2.0

CONDENSER - R&R *(B)*
DOES NOT include System Charge.
All 1.3

CONDENSER FAN MOTOR - R&R *(B)*
All 7

SWITCH, CONDENSER FAN - R&R *(B)*
All 4

RELAY, CONDENSER FAN - R&R *(B)*
All 3

RECEIVER DRIER - R&R *(B)*
DOES NOT include System Charge.
All 7

EVAPORATOR ASSY - R&R *(B)*
DOES NOT include System Charge.
All 1.3

★ COMBINATIONS ★

★ Expansion Valve - Replace 4
★ Blower Assembly - Replace 7
★ Resistor, Fan Switch - Replace 7

EXPANSION VALVE - R&R *(B)*
Use Evaporator Assembly - R&R plus Combinations.

BLOWER ASSEMBLY - R&R *(B)*
Use Evaporator Assembly - R&R plus Combinations.

RESISTOR, FAN SWITCH - R&R *(B)*
Use Evaporator Assembly - R&R plus Combinations.

SWITCH, TEMP CONTROL - R&R *(B)*
All 5

SWITCH, FAN CONTROL - R&R *(B)*
Includes: Remove console.
All 1.3

HOSE, AIR CONDITIONING - R&R *(B)*
DOES NOT include System Charge.
One 1.0
Each Additional 5

★ COMBINATIONS ★

★ Make Up Hose From Stock 4

AIR CONDITIONING TIME GUIDE

Labor Times To Dollars Conversion Table

FOR DOLLAR RATES ENDING WITH 50 CENTS, ADD THIS COLUMN TO YOUR RATE COLUMN.

Time	$10	$11	$12	$13	$14	$15	$16	$17	$18	$19	$20	.50	$21	$22	$23	$24	$25	$26	$27	$28	$29	$30
0.1	1.00	1.10	1.20	1.30	1.40	1.50	1.60	1.70	1.80	1.90	2.00	.05	2.10	2.20	2.30	2.40	2.50	2.60	2.70	2.80	2.90	3.00
0.2	2.00	2.20	2.40	2.60	2.80	3.00	3.20	3.40	3.60	3.80	4.00	.10	4.20	4.40	4.60	4.80	5.00	5.20	5.40	5.60	5.80	6.00
0.3	3.00	3.30	3.60	3.90	4.20	4.50	4.80	5.10	5.40	5.70	6.00	.15	6.30	6.60	6.90	7.20	7.50	7.80	8.10	8.40	8.70	9.00
0.4	4.00	4.40	4.80	5.20	5.60	6.00	6.40	6.80	7.20	7.60	8.00	.20	8.40	8.80	9.20	9.60	10.00	10.40	10.80	11.20	11.60	12.00
0.5	5.00	5.50	6.00	6.50	7.00	7.50	8.00	8.50	9.00	9.50	10.00	.25	10.50	11.00	11.50	12.00	12.50	13.00	13.50	14.00	14.50	15.00
0.6	6.00	6.60	7.20	7.80	8.40	9.00	9.60	10.20	10.80	11.40	12.00	.30	12.60	13.20	13.80	14.40	15.00	15.60	16.20	16.80	17.40	18.00
0.7	7.00	7.70	8.40	9.10	9.80	10.50	11.20	11.90	12.60	13.30	14.00	.35	14.70	15.40	16.10	16.80	17.50	18.20	18.90	19.60	20.30	21.00
0.8	8.00	8.80	9.60	10.40	11.20	12.00	12.80	13.60	14.40	15.20	16.00	40	16.80	17.60	18.40	19.20	20.00	20.80	21.60	22.40	23.20	24.00
0.9	9.00	9.90	10.80	11.70	12.60	13.50	14.40	15.30	16.20	17.10	18.00	.45	18.90	19.80	20.70	21.60	22.50	23.40	24.30	25.20	26.10	27.00
1.0	10.00	11.00	12.00	13.00	14.00	15.00	16.00	17.00	18.00	19.00	20.00	.50	21.00	22.00	23.00	24.00	25.00	26.00	27.00	28.00	29.00	30.00
1.1	11.00	12.10	13.20	14.30	15.40	16.50	17.60	18.70	19.80	20.90	22.00	.55	23.10	24.20	25.30	26.40	27.50	28.60	29.70	30.80	31.90	33.00
1.2	12.00	13.20	14.40	15.60	16.80	18.00	19.20	20.40	21.60	22.80	24.00	.60	25.20	26.40	27.60	28.80	30.00	31.20	32.40	33.60	34.80	36.00
1.3	13.00	14.30	15.60	16.90	18.20	19.50	20.80	22.10	23.40	24.70	26.00	.65	27.30	28.60	29.90	31.20	32.50	33.80	35.10	36.40	37.70	39.00
1.4	14.00	15.40	16.80	18.20	19.60	21.00	22.40	23.80	25.20	26.60	28.00	.70	29.40	30.80	32.20	33.60	35.00	36.40	37.80	39.20	40.60	42.00
1.5	15.00	16.50	18.00	19.50	21.00	22.50	24.00	25.50	27.00	28.50	30.00	.75	31.50	33.00	34.50	36.00	37.50	39.00	40.50	42.00	43.50	45.00
1.6	16.00	17.60	19.20	20.80	22.40	24.00	25.60	27.20	28.80	30.40	32.00	.80	33.60	35.20	36.80	38.40	40.00	41.60	43.20	44.80	46.40	48.00
1.7	17.00	18.70	20.40	22.10	23.80	25.50	27.20	28.90	30.60	32.30	34.00	.85	35.70	37.40	39.10	40.80	42.50	44.20	45.90	47.60	49.30	51.00
1.8	18.00	19.80	21.60	23.40	25.20	27.00	28.80	30.60	32.40	34.20	36.00	.90	37.80	39.60	41.40	43.20	45.00	46.80	48.60	50.40	52.20	54.00
1.9	19.00	20.90	22.80	24.70	26.60	28.50	30.40	32.30	34.20	36.10	38.00	.95	39.90	41.80	43.70	45.60	47.50	49.40	51.30	53.20	55.10	57.00
2.0	20.00	22.00	24.00	26.00	28.00	30.00	32.00	34.00	36.00	38.00	40.00	1.00	42.00	44.00	46.00	48.00	50.00	52.00	54.00	56.00	58.00	60.00
2.1	21.00	23.10	25.20	27.30	29.40	31.50	33.60	35.70	37.80	39.90	42.00	1.05	44.10	46.20	48.30	50.40	52.50	54.60	56.70	58.80	60.90	63.00
2.2	22.00	24.20	26.40	28.60	30.80	33.00	35.20	37.40	39.60	41.80	44.00	1.10	46.20	48.40	50.60	52.80	55.00	57.20	59.40	61.60	63.80	66.00
2.3	23.00	25.30	27.60	29.90	32.20	34.50	36.80	39.10	41.40	43.70	46.00	1.15	48.30	50.60	52.90	55.20	57.50	59.80	62.10	64.40	66.70	69.00
2.4	24.00	26.40	28.80	31.20	33.60	36.00	38.40	40.80	43.20	45.60	48.00	1.20	50.40	52.80	55.20	57.60	60.00	62.40	64.80	67.20	69.60	72.00
2.5	25.00	27.50	30.00	32.50	35.00	37.50	40.00	42.50	45.00	47.50	50.00	1.25	52.50	55.00	57.50	60.00	62.50	65.00	67.50	70.00	72.50	75.00
2.6	26.00	28.60	31.20	33.80	36.40	39.00	41.60	44.20	46.80	49.40	52.00	1.30	54.60	57.20	59.80	62.40	65.00	67.60	70.20	72.80	75.40	78.00
2.7	27.00	29.70	32.40	35.10	37.80	40.50	43.20	45.90	48.60	51.30	54.00	1.35	56.70	59.40	62.10	64.80	67.50	70.20	72.90	75.60	78.30	81.00
2.8	28.00	30.80	33.60	36.40	39.20	42.00	44.80	47.60	50.40	53.20	56.00	1.40	58.80	61.60	64.40	67.20	70.00	72.80	75.60	78.40	81.20	84.00
2.9	29.00	31.90	34.80	37.70	40.60	43.50	46.40	49.30	52.20	55.10	58.00	1.45	60.90	63.80	66.70	69.60	72.50	75.40	78.30	81.20	84.10	87.00
3.0	30.00	33.00	36.00	39.00	42.00	45.00	48.00	51.00	54.00	57.00	60.00	1.50	63.00	66.00	69.00	72.00	75.00	78.00	81.00	84.00	87.00	90.00
3.1	31.00	34.10	37.20	40.30	43.40	46.50	49.60	52.70	55.80	58.90	62.00	1.55	65.10	68.20	71.30	74.40	77.50	80.60	83.70	86.80	89.90	93.00
3.2	32.00	35.20	38.40	41.60	44.80	48.00	51.20	54.40	57.60	60.80	64.00	1.60	67.20	70.40	73.60	76.80	80.00	83.20	86.40	89.60	92.80	96.00
3.3	33.00	36.30	39.60	42.90	46.20	49.50	52.80	56.10	59.40	62.70	66.00	1.65	69.30	72.60	75.90	79.20	82.50	85.80	89.10	92.40	95.70	99.00
3.4	34.00	37.40	40.80	44.20	47.60	51.00	54.40	57.80	61.20	64.60	68.00	1.70	71.40	74.80	78.20	81.60	85.00	88.40	91.80	95.20	98.60	102.00
3.5	35.00	38.50	42.00	45.50	49.00	52.50	56.00	59.50	63.00	66.50	70.00	1.75	73.50	77.00	80.50	84.00	87.50	91.00	94.50	98.00	101.50	105.00
3.6	36.00	39.60	43.20	46.80	50.40	54.00	57.60	61.20	64.80	68.40	72.00	1.80	75.60	79.20	82.80	86.40	90.00	93.60	97.20	100.80	104.40	108.00
3.7	37.00	40.70	44.40	48.10	51.80	55.50	59.20	62.90	66.60	70.30	74.00	1.85	77.70	81.40	85.10	88.80	92.50	96.20	99.90	103.60	107.30	111.00
3.8	38.00	41.80	45.60	49.40	53.20	57.00	60.80	64.60	68.40	72.20	76.00	1.90	79.80	83.60	87.40	91.20	95.00	98.80	102.60	106.40	110.20	114.00
3.9	39.00	42.90	46.80	50.70	54.60	58.50	62.40	66.30	70.20	74.10	78.00	1.95	81.90	85.80	89.70	93.60	97.50	101.40	105.30	109.20	113.10	117.00
4.0	40.00	44.00	48.00	52.00	56.00	60.00	64.00	68.00	72.00	76.00	80.00	2.00	84.00	88.00	92.00	96.00	100.00	104.00	108.00	112.00	116.00	120.00
4.1	41.00	45.10	49.20	53.30	57.40	61.50	65.60	69.70	73.80	77.90	82.00	2.05	86.10	90.20	94.30	98.40	102.50	106.60	110.70	114.80	118.90	123.00
4.2	42.00	46.20	50.40	54.60	58.80	63.00	67.20	71.40	75.60	79.80	84.00	2.10	88.20	92.40	96.60	100.80	105.00	109.20	113.40	117.60	121.80	126.00
4.3	43.00	47.30	51.60	55.90	60.20	64.50	68.80	73.10	77.40	81.70	86.00	2.15	90.30	94.60	98.90	103.20	107.50	111.80	116.10	120.40	124.70	129.00
4.4	44.00	48.40	52.80	57.20	61.60	66.00	70.40	74.80	79.20	83.60	88.00	2.20	92.40	96.80	101.20	105.60	110.00	114.40	118.80	123.20	127.60	132.00
4.5	45.00	49.50	54.00	58.50	63.00	67.50	72.00	76.50	81.00	85.50	90.00	2.25	94.50	99.00	103.50	108.00	112.50	117.00	121.50	126.00	130.50	135.00
4.6	46.00	50.60	55.20	59.80	64.40	69.00	73.60	78.20	82.80	87.40	92.00	2.30	96.60	101.20	105.80	110.40	115.00	119.60	124.20	128.80	133.40	138.00
4.7	47.00	51.70	56.40	61.10	65.80	70.50	75.20	79.90	84.60	89.30	94.00	2.35	98.70	103.40	108.10	112.80	117.50	122.20	126.90	131.60	136.30	141.00
4.8	48.00	52.80	57.60	62.40	67.20	72.00	76.80	81.60	86.40	91.20	96.00	2.40	100.80	105.60	110.40	115.20	120.00	124.80	129.60	134.40	139.20	144.00
4.9	49.00	53.90	58.80	63.70	68.60	73.50	78.40	83.30	88.20	93.10	98.00	2.45	102.90	107.80	112.70	117.60	122.50	127.40	132.30	137.20	142.10	147.00
5.0	50.00	55.00	60.00	65.00	70.00	75.00	80.00	85.00	90.00	95.00	100.00	2.50	105.00	110.00	115.00	120.00	125.00	130.00	135.00	140.00	145.00	150.00
5.1	51.00	56.10	61.20	66.30	71.40	76.50	81.60	86.70	91.80	96.90	102.00	2.55	107.10	112.20	117.30	122.40	127.50	132.60	137.70	142.80	147.90	153.00
5.2	52.00	57.20	62.40	67.60	72.80	78.00	83.20	88.40	93.60	98.80	104.00	2.60	109.20	114.40	119.60	124.80	130.00	135.20	140.40	145.60	150.80	156.00
5.3	53.00	58.30	63.60	68.90	74.20	79.50	84.80	90.10	95.40	100.70	106.00	2.65	111.30	116.60	121.90	127.20	132.50	137.80	143.10	148.40	153.70	159.00
5.4	54.00	59.40	64.80	70.20	75.60	81.00	86.40	91.80	97.20	102.60	108.00	2.70	113.40	118.80	124.20	129.60	135.00	140.40	145.80	151.20	156.60	162.00
5.5	55.00	60.50	66.00	71.50	77.00	82.50	88.00	93.50	99.00	104.50	110.00	2.75	115.50	121.00	126.50	132.00	137.50	143.00	148.50	154.00	159.50	165.00
5.6	56.00	61.60	67.20	72.80	78.40	84.00	89.60	95.20	100.80	106.40	112.00	2.80	117.60	123.20	128.80	134.40	140.00	145.60	151.20	156.80	162.40	168.00
5.7	57.00	62.70	68.40	74.10	79.80	85.50	91.20	96.90	102.60	108.30	114.00	2.85	119.70	125.40	131.10	136.80	142.50	148.20	153.90	159.60	165.30	171.00
5.8	58.00	63.80	69.60	75.40	81.20	87.00	92.80	98.60	104.40	110.20	116.00	2.90	121.80	127.60	133.40	139.20	145.00	150.80	156.60	162.60	168.20	174.00
5.9	59.00	64.90	70.80	76.70	82.60	88.50	94.40	100.30	106.20	112.10	118.00	2.95	123.90	129.80	135.70	141.60	147.50	153.40	159.30	165.20	171.10	177.00
6.0	60.00	66.00	72.00	78.00	84.00	90.00	96.00	102.00	108.00	114.00	120.00	3.00	126.00	132.00	138.00	144.00	150.00	156.00	162.00	168.00	174.00	180.00
6.1	61.00	67.10	73.20	79.30	85.40	91.50	97.60	103.70	109.80	115.90	122.00	3.05	128.10	134.20	140.30	146.40	152.50	158.60	164.70	170.80	176.90	183.00
6.2	62.00	68.20	74.40	80.60	86.80	93.00	99.20	105.40	111.60	117.80	124.00	3.10	130.20	136.40	142.60	148.80	155.00	161.20	167.40	173.60	179.80	186.00
6.3	63.00	69.30	75.60	81.90	88.20	94.50	100.80	107.10	113.40	119.70	126.00	3.15	132.30	138.60	144.90	151.20	157.50	163.80	170.10	176.40	182.70	189.00
6.4	64.00	70.40	76.80	83.20	89.60	96.00	102.40	108.80	115.20	121.60	128.00	3.20	134.40	140.80	147.20	153.60	160.00	166.40	172.80	179.20	185.60	192.00

AIR CONDITIONING TIME GUIDE

Labor Times To Dollars Conversion Table

FOR DOLLAR RATES ENDING WITH 50 CENTS, ADD THIS COLUMN TO YOUR RATE COLUMN.

Time	$10	$11	$12	$13	$14	$15	$16	$17	$18	$19	$20	.50	$21	$22	$23	$24	$25	$26	$27	$28	$29	$30
6.5	65.00	71.50	78.00	84.50	91.00	97.50	104.00	110.50	117.00	123.50	130.00	3.25	136.50	143.00	149.50	156.00	162.50	169.00	175.50	182.00	188.50	195.00
6.6	66.00	72.60	79.20	85.80	92.40	99.00	105.60	112.20	118.80	125.40	132.00	3.30	138.60	145.20	151.80	158.40	165.00	171.60	178.20	184.80	191.40	198.00
6.7	67.00	73.70	80.40	87.10	93.80	100.50	107.20	113.90	120.60	127.30	134.00	3.35	140.70	147.40	154.10	160.80	167.50	174.20	180.90	187.60	194.30	201.00
6.8	68.00	74.80	81.60	88.40	95.20	102.00	108.80	115.60	122.40	129.20	136.00	3.40	142.80	149.60	156.40	163.20	170.00	176.80	183.60	190.40	197.20	204.00
6.9	69.00	75.90	82.80	89.70	96.60	103.50	110.40	117.30	124.20	131.10	138.00	3.45	144.90	151.80	158.70	165.60	172.50	179.40	186.30	193.20	200.10	207.00
7.0	70.00	77.00	84.00	91.00	98.00	105.00	112.00	119.00	126.00	133.00	140.00	3.50	147.00	154.00	161.00	168.00	175.00	182.00	189.00	196.00	203.00	210.00
7.1	71.00	78.10	85.20	92.30	99.40	106.50	113.60	120.70	127.80	134.90	142.00	3.55	149.10	156.20	163.30	170.40	177.50	184.60	191.70	198.80	205.90	213.00
7.2	72.00	79.20	86.40	93.60	100.80	108.00	115.20	122.40	129.60	136.80	144.00	3.60	151.20	158.40	165.60	172.80	180.00	187.20	194.40	201.60	208.80	216.00
7.3	73.00	80.30	87.60	94.90	102.20	109.50	116.80	124.10	131.40	138.70	146.00	3.65	153.30	160.60	167.90	175.20	182.50	189.80	197.10	204.40	211.70	219.00
7.4	74.00	81.40	88.80	96.20	103.60	111.00	118.40	125.80	133.20	140.60	148.00	3.70	155.40	162.80	170.20	177.60	185.00	192.40	199.80	207.20	214.60	222.00
7.5	75.00	82.50	90.00	97.50	105.00	112.50	120.00	127.50	135.00	142.50	150.00	3.75	157.50	165.00	172.50	180.00	187.50	195.00	202.50	210.00	217.50	225.00
7.6	76.00	83.60	91.20	98.80	106.40	114.00	121.60	129.20	136.80	144.40	152.00	3.80	159.60	167.20	174.80	182.40	190.00	197.60	205.20	212.80	220.40	228.00
7.7	77.00	84.70	92.40	100.10	107.80	115.50	123.20	130.90	138.60	146.30	154.00	3.85	161.70	169.40	177.10	184.80	192.50	200.20	207.90	215.60	223.30	231.00
7.8	78.00	85.80	93.60	101.40	109.20	117.00	124.80	132.60	140.40	148.20	156.00	3.90	163.80	171.60	179.40	187.20	195.00	202.80	210.60	218.40	226.20	234.00
7.9	79.00	86.90	94.80	102.70	110.60	118.50	126.40	134.30	142.20	150.10	158.00	3.95	165.90	173.80	181.70	189.60	197.50	205.40	213.30	221.20	229.10	237.00
8.0	80.00	88.00	96.00	104.00	112.00	120.00	128.00	136.00	144.00	152.00	160.00	4.00	168.00	176.00	184.00	192.00	200.00	208.00	216.00	224.00	232.00	240.00
8.1	81.00	89.10	97.20	105.30	113.40	121.50	129.60	137.70	145.80	153.90	162.00	4.05	170.10	178.20	186.30	194.40	202.50	210.60	218.70	226.80	234.90	243.00
8.2	82.00	90.20	98.40	106.60	114.80	123.00	131.20	139.40	147.60	155.80	164.00	4.10	172.20	180.40	188.60	196.80	205.00	213.20	221.40	229.60	237.80	246.00
8.3	83.00	91.30	99.60	107.90	116.20	124.50	132.80	141.10	149.40	157.70	166.00	4.15	174.30	182.60	190.90	199.20	207.50	215.80	224.10	232.40	240.70	249.00
8.4	84.00	92.40	100.80	109.20	117.60	126.00	134.40	142.80	151.20	159.60	168.00	4.20	176.40	184.80	193.20	201.60	210.00	218.40	226.80	235.20	243.60	252.00
8.5	85.00	93.50	102.00	110.50	119.00	127.50	136.00	144.50	153.00	161.50	170.00	4.25	178.50	187.00	195.50	204.00	212.50	221.00	229.50	238.00	246.50	255.00
8.6	86.00	94.60	103.20	111.80	120.40	129.00	137.60	146.20	154.80	163.40	172.00	4.30	180.60	189.20	197.80	206.40	215.00	223.60	232.20	240.80	249.40	258.00
8.7	87.00	95.70	104.40	113.10	121.80	130.50	139.20	147.90	156.60	165.30	174.00	4.35	182.70	191.40	200.10	208.80	217.50	226.20	234.90	243.60	252.30	261.00
8.8	88.00	96.80	105.60	114.40	123.20	132.00	140.80	149.60	158.40	167.20	176.00	4.40	184.80	193.60	202.40	211.20	220.00	228.80	237.60	246.40	255.20	264.00
8.9	89.00	97.90	106.80	115.70	124.60	133.50	142.40	151.30	160.20	169.10	178.00	4.45	186.90	195.80	204.70	213.60	222.50	231.40	240.30	249.20	258.10	267.00
9.0	90.00	99.00	108.00	117.00	126.00	135.00	144.00	153.00	162.00	171.00	180.00	4.50	189.00	198.00	207.00	216.00	225.00	234.00	243.00	252.00	261.00	270.00
9.1	91.00	100.10	109.20	118.30	127.40	136.50	145.60	154.70	163.80	172.90	182.00	4.55	191.10	200.20	209.30	218.40	227.50	236.60	245.70	254.80	263.90	273.00
9.2	92.00	101.20	110.40	119.60	128.80	138.00	147.20	156.40	165.60	174.80	184.00	4.60	193.20	202.40	211.60	220.80	230.00	239.20	248.40	257.60	266.80	276.00
9.3	93.00	102.30	111.60	120.90	130.20	139.50	148.80	158.10	167.40	176.70	186.00	4.65	195.30	204.60	213.90	223.20	232.50	241.80	251.10	260.40	269.70	279.00
9.4	94.00	103.40	112.80	122.20	131.60	141.00	150.40	159.80	169.20	178.60	188.00	4.70	197.40	206.80	216.20	225.60	235.00	244.40	253.80	263.20	272.60	282.00
9.5	95.00	104.50	114.00	123.50	133.00	142.50	152.00	161.50	171.00	180.50	190.00	4.75	199.50	209.00	218.50	228.00	237.50	247.00	256.50	266.00	275.50	285.00
9.6	96.00	105.60	115.20	124.80	134.40	144.00	153.60	163.20	172.80	182.40	192.00	4.80	201.60	211.20	220.80	230.40	240.00	249.60	259.20	268.80	278.40	288.00
9.7	97.00	106.70	116.40	126.10	135.80	145.50	155.20	164.90	174.60	184.30	194.00	4.85	203.70	213.40	223.10	232.80	242.50	252.20	261.90	271.60	281.30	291.00
9.8	98.00	107.80	117.60	127.40	137.20	147.00	156.80	166.60	176.40	186.20	196.00	4.90	205.80	215.60	225.40	235.20	245.00	254.80	264.60	274.40	284.20	294.00
9.9	99.00	108.90	118.80	128.70	138.60	148.50	158.40	168.30	178.20	188.10	198.00	4.95	207.90	217.80	227.70	237.60	247.50	257.40	267.30	277.20	287.10	297.00
10.0	100.00	110.00	120.00	130.00	140.00	150.00	160.00	170.00	180.00	190.00	200.00	5.00	210.00	220.00	230.00	240.00	250.00	260.00	270.00	280.00	290.00	300.00
10.5	105.00	115.50	126.00	136.50	147.00	157.50	168.00	178.50	189.00	199.50	210.00	5.25	220.50	231.00	241.50	252.00	262.50	273.00	283.50	294.00	304.50	315.00
11.0	110.00	121.00	132.00	143.00	154.00	165.00	176.00	187.00	198.00	209.00	220.00	5.50	231.00	242.00	253.00	264.00	275.00	286.00	297.00	308.00	319.00	330.00
11.5	115.00	126.50	138.00	149.50	161.00	172.50	184.00	195.50	207.00	218.50	230.00	5.75	241.50	253.00	264.50	276.00	287.50	299.00	310.50	322.00	333.50	345.00
12.0	120.00	132.00	144.00	156.00	168.00	180.00	192.00	204.00	216.00	228.00	240.00	6.00	252.00	264.00	276.00	288.00	300.00	312.00	324.00	336.00	348.00	360.00
12.5	125.00	137.50	150.00	162.50	175.00	187.50	200.00	212.50	225.00	237.50	250.00	6.25	262.50	275.00	287.50	300.00	312.50	325.00	337.50	350.00	362.50	375.00
13.0	130.00	143.00	156.00	169.00	182.00	195.00	208.00	221.00	234.00	247.00	260.00	6.50	273.00	286.00	299.00	312.00	325.00	338.00	351.00	364.00	377.00	390.00
13.5	135.00	148.50	162.00	175.50	189.00	202.50	216.00	229.50	243.00	256.50	270.00	6.75	283.50	297.00	310.50	324.00	337.50	351.00	364.50	378.00	391.50	405.00
14.0	140.00	154.00	168.00	182.00	196.00	210.00	224.00	238.00	252.00	266.00	280.00	7.00	294.00	308.00	322.00	336.00	350.00	364.00	378.00	392.00	406.00	420.00
14.5	145.00	159.50	174.00	188.50	203.00	217.50	232.00	246.50	261.00	275.50	290.00	7.25	304.50	319.00	333.50	348.00	362.50	377.00	391.50	406.00	420.50	435.00
15.0	150.00	165.00	180.00	195.00	210.00	225.00	240.00	255.00	270.00	285.00	300.00	7.50	315.00	330.00	345.00	360.00	375.00	390.00	405.00	420.00	435.00	450.00
15.5	155.00	170.50	186.00	201.50	217.00	232.50	248.00	263.50	279.00	294.50	310.00	7.75	325.50	341.00	356.50	372.00	387.50	403.00	418.50	434.00	449.50	465.00
16.0	160.00	176.00	192.00	208.00	224.00	240.00	256.00	272.00	288.00	304.00	320.00	8.00	336.00	352.00	368.00	384.00	400.00	416.00	432.00	448.00	464.00	480.00
16.5	165.00	181.50	198.00	214.50	231.00	247.50	264.00	280.50	297.00	313.50	330.00	8.25	346.50	363.00	379.50	396.00	412.50	429.00	445.50	462.00	478.50	495.00
17.0	170.00	187.00	204.00	221.00	238.00	255.00	272.00	289.00	306.00	323.00	340.00	8.50	357.00	374.00	391.00	408.00	425.00	442.00	459.00	476.00	493.00	510.00
17.5	175.00	192.50	210.00	227.50	245.00	262.50	280.00	297.50	315.00	332.50	350.00	8.75	367.50	385.00	402.50	420.00	437.50	455.00	472.50	490.00	507.50	525.00
18.0	180.00	198.00	216.00	234.00	252.00	270.00	288.00	306.00	324.00	342.00	360.00	9.00	378.00	396.00	414.00	432.00	450.00	468.00	486.00	504.00	522.00	540.00
18.5	185.00	203.50	222.00	240.50	259.00	277.50	296.00	314.50	333.00	351.50	370.00	9.25	388.50	407.00	425.50	444.00	462.50	481.00	499.50	518.00	536.50	555.00
19.0	190.00	209.00	228.00	247.00	266.00	285.00	304.00	323.00	342.00	361.00	380.00	9.50	399.00	418.00	437.00	456.00	475.00	494.00	513.00	532.00	551.00	570.00
19.5	195.00	214.50	234.00	253.50	273.00	292.50	312.00	331.50	351.00	370.50	390.00	9.75	409.50	429.00	448.50	468.00	487.50	507.00	526.50	546.00	565.50	585.00
20.0	200.00	220.00	240.00	260.00	280.00	300.00	320.00	340.00	360.00	380.00	400.00	10.00	420.00	440.00	460.00	480.00	500.00	520.00	540.00	560.00	580.00	600.00
30.0	300.00	330.00	360.00	390.00	420.00	450.00	480.00	510.00	540.00	570.00	600.00	15.00	630.00	660.00	690.00	720.00	750.00	780.00	810.00	840.00	870.00	900.00
40.0	400.00	440.00	480.00	520.00	560.00	600.00	640.00	680.00	720.00	760.00	800.00	20.00	840.00	880.00	920.00	960.00	1000.00	1040.00	1080.00	1120.00	1160.00	1200.00

AIR CONDITIONING TIME GUIDE

Labor Times To Dollars Conversion Table

FOR DOLLAR RATES ENDING WITH 50 CENTS, ADD THIS COLUMN TO YOUR RATE COLUMN.

Time	$31	$32	$33	$34	$35	$36	$37	$38	$39	$40	.50	$41	$42	$43	$44	$45	$46	$47	$48	$49	$50
0.1	3.10	3.20	3.30	3.40	3.50	3.60	3.70	3.80	3.90	4.00	.05	4.10	4.20	4.30	4.40	4.50	4.60	4.70	4.80	4.90	5.00
0.2	6.20	6.40	6.60	6.80	7.00	7.20	7.40	7.60	7.80	8.00	.10	8.20	8.40	8.60	8.80	9.00	9.20	9.40	9.60	9.80	10.00
0.3	9.30	9.60	9.90	10.20	10.50	10.80	11.10	11.40	11.70	12.00	.15	12.30	12.60	12.90	13.20	13.50	13.80	14.10	14.40	14.70	15.00
0.4	12.40	12.80	13.20	13.60	14.00	14.40	14.80	15.20	15.60	16.00	.20	16.40	16.80	17.20	17.60	18.00	18.40	18.80	19.20	19.60	20.00
0.5	15.50	16.00	16.50	17.00	17.50	18.00	18.50	19.00	19.50	20.00	.25	20.50	21.00	21.50	22.00	22.50	23.00	23.50	24.00	24.50	25.00
0.6	18.60	19.20	19.80	20.40	21.00	21.60	22.20	22.80	23.40	24.00	.30	24.60	25.20	25.80	26.40	27.00	27.60	28.20	28.80	29.40	30.00
0.7	21.70	22.40	23.10	23.80	24.50	25.20	25.90	26.60	27.30	28.00	.35	28.70	29.40	30.10	30.80	31.50	32.20	32.90	33.60	34.30	35.00
0.8	24.80	25.60	26.40	27.20	28.00	28.80	29.60	30.40	31.20	32.00	.40	32.80	33.60	34.40	35.20	36.00	36.80	37.60	38.40	39.20	40.00
0.9	27.90	28.80	29.70	30.60	31.50	32.40	33.30	34.20	35.10	36.00	.45	36.90	37.80	38.70	39.60	40.50	41.40	42.30	43.20	44.10	45.00
1.0	31.00	32.00	33.00	34.00	35.00	36.00	37.00	38.00	39.00	40.00	.50	41.00	42.00	43.00	44.00	45.00	46.00	47.00	48.00	49.00	50.00
1.1	34.10	35.20	36.30	37.40	38.50	39.60	40.70	41.80	42.90	44.00	.55	45.10	46.20	47.30	48.40	49.50	50.60	51.70	52.80	53.90	55.00
1.2	37.20	38.40	39.60	40.80	42.00	43.20	44.40	45.60	46.80	48.00	.60	49.20	50.40	51.60	52.80	54.00	55.20	56.40	57.60	58.80	60.00
1.3	40.30	41.60	42.90	44.20	45.50	46.80	48.10	49.40	50.70	52.00	.65	53.30	54.60	55.90	57.20	58.50	59.80	61.10	62.40	63.70	65.00
1.4	43.40	44.80	46.20	47.60	49.00	50.40	51.80	53.20	54.60	56.00	.70	57.40	58.80	60.20	61.60	63.00	64.40	65.80	67.20	68.60	70.00
1.5	46.50	48.00	49.50	51.00	52.50	54.00	55.50	57.00	58.50	60.00	.75	61.50	63.00	64.50	66.00	67.50	69.00	70.50	72.00	73.50	75.00
1.6	49.60	51.20	52.80	54.40	56.00	57.60	59.20	60.80	62.40	64.00	.80	65.60	67.20	68.80	70.40	72.00	73.60	75.20	76.80	78.40	80.00
1.7	52.70	54.40	56.10	57.80	59.50	61.20	62.90	64.60	66.30	68.00	.85	69.70	71.40	73.10	74.80	76.50	78.20	79.90	81.60	83.30	85.00
1.8	55.80	57.60	59.40	61.20	63.00	64.80	66.60	68.40	70.20	72.00	.90	73.80	75.60	77.40	79.20	81.00	82.80	84.60	86.40	88.20	90.00
1.9	58.90	60.80	62.70	64.60	66.50	68.40	70.30	72.20	74.10	76.00	.95	77.90	79.80	81.70	83.60	85.50	87.40	89.30	91.20	93.10	95.00
2.0	62.00	64.00	66.00	68.00	70.00	72.00	74.00	76.00	78.00	80.00	1.00	82.00	84.00	86.00	88.00	90.00	92.00	94.00	96.00	98.00	100.00
2.1	65.10	67.20	69.30	71.40	73.50	75.60	77.70	79.80	81.90	84.00	1.05	86.10	88.20	90.30	92.40	94.50	96.60	98.70	100.80	102.90	105.00
2.2	68.20	70.40	72.60	74.80	77.00	79.20	81.40	83.60	85.80	88.00	1.10	90.20	92.40	94.60	96.80	99.00	101.20	103.40	105.60	107.80	110.00
2.3	71.30	73.60	75.90	78.20	80.50	82.80	85.10	87.40	89.70	92.00	1.15	94.30	96.60	98.90	101.20	103.50	105.80	108.10	110.40	112.70	115.00
2.4	74.40	76.80	79.20	81.60	84.00	86.40	88.80	91.20	93.60	96.00	1.20	98.40	100.80	103.20	105.60	108.00	110.40	112.80	115.20	117.60	120.00
2.5	77.50	80.00	82.50	85.00	87.50	90.00	92.50	95.00	97.50	100.00	1.25	102.50	105.00	107.50	110.00	112.50	115.00	117.50	120.00	122.50	125.00
2.6	80.60	83.20	85.80	88.40	91.00	93.60	96.20	98.80	101.40	104.00	1.30	106.60	109.20	111.80	114.40	117.00	119.60	122.20	124.80	127.40	130.00
2.7	83.70	86.40	89.10	91.80	94.50	97.20	99.90	102.60	105.30	108.00	1.35	110.70	113.40	116.10	118.80	121.50	124.20	126.90	129.60	132.30	135.00
2.8	86.80	89.60	92.40	95.20	98.00	100.80	103.60	106.40	109.20	112.00	1.40	114.80	117.60	120.40	123.20	126.00	128.80	131.60	134.40	137.20	140.00
2.9	89.90	92.80	95.70	98.60	101.50	104.40	107.30	110.20	113.10	116.00	1.45	118.90	121.80	124.70	127.60	130.50	133.40	136.30	139.20	142.10	145.00
3.0	93.00	96.00	99.00	102.00	105.00	108.00	111.00	114.00	117.00	120.00	1.50	123.00	126.00	129.00	132.00	135.00	138.00	141.00	144.00	147.00	150.00
3.1	96.10	99.20	102.30	105.40	108.50	111.60	114.70	117.80	120.90	124.00	1.55	127.10	130.20	133.30	136.40	139.50	142.60	145.70	148.80	151.90	155.00
3.2	99.20	102.40	105.60	108.80	112.00	115.20	118.40	121.60	124.80	128.00	1.60	131.20	134.40	137.60	140.80	144.00	147.20	150.40	153.60	156.80	160.00
3.3	102.30	105.60	108.90	112.20	115.50	118.80	122.10	125.40	128.70	132.00	1.65	135.30	138.60	141.90	145.20	148.50	151.80	155.10	158.40	161.70	165.00
3.4	105.40	108.80	112.20	115.60	119.00	122.40	125.80	129.20	132.60	136.00	1.70	139.40	142.80	146.20	149.60	153.00	156.40	159.80	163.20	166.60	170.00
3.5	108.50	112.00	115.50	119.00	122.50	126.00	129.50	133.00	136.50	140.00	1.75	143.50	147.00	150.50	154.00	157.50	161.00	164.50	168.00	171.50	175.00
3.6	111.60	115.20	118.80	122.40	126.00	129.60	133.20	136.80	140.40	144.00	1.80	147.60	151.20	154.80	158.40	162.00	165.60	169.20	172.80	176.40	180.00
3.7	114.70	118.40	122.10	125.80	129.50	133.20	136.90	140.60	144.30	148.00	1.85	151.70	155.40	159.10	162.80	166.50	170.20	173.90	177.60	181.30	185.00
3.8	117.80	121.60	125.40	129.20	133.00	136.80	140.60	144.40	148.20	152.00	1.90	155.80	159.60	163.40	167.20	171.00	174.80	178.60	182.40	186.20	190.00
3.9	120.90	124.80	128.70	132.60	136.50	140.40	144.30	148.20	152.10	156.00	1.95	159.90	163.80	167.70	171.60	175.50	179.40	183.30	187.20	191.10	195.00
4.0	124.00	128.00	132.00	136.00	140.00	144.00	148.00	152.00	156.00	160.90	2.00	164.00	168.00	172.00	176.00	180.00	184.00	188.00	192.00	196.00	200.00
4.1	127.10	131.20	135.30	139.40	143.50	147.60	151.70	155.80	159.90	164.00	2.05	168.10	172.20	176.30	180.40	184.50	188.60	192.70	196.80	200.90	205.00
4.2	130.20	134.40	138.60	142.80	147.00	151.20	155.40	159.60	163.80	168.00	2.10	172.20	176.40	180.60	184.80	189.00	193.20	197.40	201.60	205.80	210.00
4.3	133.30	137.60	141.90	146.20	150.50	154.80	159.10	163.40	167.70	172.00	2.15	176.30	180.60	184.90	189.20	193.50	197.80	202.10	206.40	210.70	215.00
4.4	136.40	140.80	145.20	149.60	154.00	158.40	162.80	167.20	171.60	176.00	2.20	180.40	184.80	189.20	193.60	198.00	202.40	206.80	211.20	215.60	220.00
4.5	139.50	144.00	148.50	153.00	157.50	162.00	166.50	171.00	175.50	180.00	2.25	184.50	189.00	193.50	198.00	202.50	207.00	211.50	216.00	220.50	225.00
4.6	142.60	147.20	151.80	156.40	161.00	165.60	170.20	174.80	179.40	184.00	2.30	188.60	193.20	197.80	202.40	207.00	211.60	216.20	220.80	225.40	230.00
4.7	145.70	150.40	155.10	159.80	164.50	169.20	173.90	178.60	183.30	188.00	2.35	192.70	197.40	202.10	206.80	211.50	216.20	220.90	225.60	230.30	235.00
4.8	148.80	153.60	158.40	163.20	168.00	172.80	177.60	182.40	187.20	192.00	2.40	196.80	201.60	206.40	211.20	216.00	220.80	225.60	230.40	235.20	240.00
4.9	151.90	156.80	161.70	166.60	171.50	176.40	181.30	186.20	191.10	196.00	2.45	200.90	205.80	210.70	215.60	220.50	225.40	230.30	235.20	240.10	245.00
5.0	155.00	160.00	165.00	170.00	175.00	180.00	185.00	190.00	195.00	200.00	2.50	205.00	210.00	215.00	220.00	225.00	230.00	235.00	240.00	245.00	250.00
5.1	158.10	163.20	168.30	173.40	178.50	183.60	188.70	193.80	198.90	204.00	2.55	209.10	214.20	219.30	224.40	229.50	234.60	239.70	244.80	249.90	255.00
5.2	161.20	166.40	171.60	176.80	182.00	187.20	192.40	197.60	202.80	208.00	2.60	213.20	218.40	223.60	228.80	234.00	239.20	244.40	249.60	254.80	260.00
5.3	164.30	169.60	174.90	180.20	185.50	190.80	196.10	201.40	206.70	212.00	2.65	217.30	222.60	227.90	233.20	238.50	243.80	249.10	254.40	259.70	265.00
5.4	167.40	172.80	178.20	183.60	189.00	194.40	199.80	205.20	210.60	216.00	2.70	221.40	226.80	232.20	237.60	243.00	248.40	253.80	259.20	264.60	270.00
5.5	170.50	176.00	181.50	187.00	192.50	198.00	203.50	209.00	214.50	220.00	2.75	225.50	231.00	236.50	242.00	247.50	253.00	258.50	264.00	269.50	275.00
5.6	173.60	179.20	184.80	190.40	196.00	201.60	207.20	212.80	218.40	224.00	2.80	229.60	235.20	240.80	246.40	252.00	257.60	263.20	268.80	274.40	280.00
5.7	176.70	182.40	188.10	193.80	199.50	205.20	210.90	216.60	222.30	228.00	2.85	233.70	239.40	245.10	250.80	256.50	262.20	267.90	273.60	279.30	285.00
5.8	179.80	185.60	191.40	197.20	203.00	208.80	214.60	220.40	226.20	232.00	2.90	237.80	243.60	249.40	255.20	261.00	266.80	272.60	278.40	284.20	290.00
5.9	182.90	188.80	194.70	200.60	206.50	212.40	218.30	224.20	230.10	236.00	2.95	241.90	247.80	253.70	259.60	265.50	271.40	277.30	283.20	289.10	295.00

AIR CONDITIONING TIME GUIDE

Labor Times To Dollars Conversion Table

FOR DOLLAR RATES ENDING WITH 50 CENTS, ADD THIS COLUMN TO YOUR RATE COLUMN.

Time	$31	$32	$33	$34	$35	$36	$37	$38	$39	$40	.50	$41	$42	$43	$44	$45	$46	$47	$48	$49	$50
6.0	186.00	192.00	198.00	204.00	210.00	216.00	222.00	228.00	234.00	240.00	3.00	246.00	252.00	258.00	264.00	270.00	276.00	282.00	288.00	294.00	300.00
6.1	189.10	195.20	201.30	207.40	213.50	219.60	225.70	231.80	237.90	244.00	3.05	250.10	256.20	262.30	268.40	274.50	280.60	286.70	292.80	298.90	305.00
6.2	192.20	198.40	204.60	210.80	217.00	223.20	229.40	235.60	241.80	248.00	3.10	254.20	260.40	266.60	272.80	279.00	285.20	291.40	297.60	303.80	310.00
6.3	195.30	201.60	207.90	214.20	220.50	226.80	233.10	239.40	245.70	252.00	3.15	258.30	264.60	270.90	277.20	283.50	289.50	296.10	302.40	308.70	315.00
6.4	198.40	204.80	211.20	217.60	224.00	230.40	236.80	243.20	249.60	256.00	3.20	262.40	268.80	275.20	281.60	288.00	294.40	300.80	307.20	313.60	320.00
6.5	201.50	208.00	214.50	221.00	227.50	234.00	240.50	247.00	253.50	260.00	3.25	266.50	273.00	279.50	286.00	292.50	299.00	305.50	312.00	318.50	325.00
6.6	204.60	211.20	217.80	224.40	231.00	237.60	244.20	250.80	257.40	264.00	3.30	270.60	277.20	283.80	290.40	297.00	303.60	310.20	316.80	323.40	330.00
6.7	207.70	214.40	221.10	227.80	234.50	241.20	247.90	254.60	261.30	268.00	3.35	274.70	281.40	288.10	294.80	301.50	308.20	314.90	321.60	328.30	335.00
6.8	210.80	217.60	224.40	231.20	238.00	244.80	251.60	258.40	265.20	272.00	3.40	278.00	285.60	292.40	299.20	306.00	312.80	319.60	326.40	333.20	340.00
6.9	213.90	220.80	227.70	234.60	241.50	248.40	255.30	262.20	269.10	276.00	3.45	282.90	289.80	296.70	303.60	310.50	317.40	324.30	331.20	338.10	345.00
7.0	217.00	224.00	231.00	238.00	245.00	252.00	259.00	266.00	273.00	280.00	3.50	287.00	294.00	301.00	308.00	315.00	322.00	329.00	336.00	343.00	350.00
7.1	220.10	227.20	234.30	241.40	248.50	255.60	262.70	269.80	276.90	284.00	3.55	291.10	298.20	305.30	312.40	319.50	326.60	333.70	340.80	347.90	355.00
7.2	223.20	230.40	237.60	244.80	252.00	259.20	266.40	273.60	280.80	288.00	3.60	295.20	302.40	309.60	316.80	324.00	331.20	338.40	345.60	352.80	360.00
7.3	226.30	233.60	240.90	248.20	255.50	262.80	270.10	277.40	284.70	292.00	3.65	299.30	306.60	313.90	321.20	328.50	335.80	343.10	350.40	357.70	365.00
7.4	229.40	236.80	244.20	251.60	259.00	266.40	273.80	281.20	288.60	296.00	3.70	303.40	310.80	318.20	325.60	333.00	340.40	347.80	355.20	362.60	370.00
7.5	232.50	240.00	247.50	255.00	262.50	270.00	277.50	285.00	292.50	300.00	3.75	307.50	315.00	322.50	330.00	337.50	345.00	352.50	360.00	367.50	375.00
7.6	235.60	243.20	250.80	258.40	266.00	273.60	281.20	288.80	296.40	304.00	3.80	311.60	319.20	326.80	334.40	342.00	349.60	357.20	364.80	372.40	380.00
7.7	238.70	246.40	254.10	261.80	269.50	277.20	284.90	292.60	300.30	308.00	3.85	315.70	323.40	331.10	338.80	346.50	354.20	361.90	369.60	377.30	385.00
7.8	241.80	249.60	257.40	265.20	273.00	280.80	288.60	296.40	304.20	312.00	3.90	319.80	327.60	335.40	343.20	351.00	358.80	366.60	374.40	382.20	390.00
7.9	244.90	252.80	260.70	268.60	276.50	284.40	292.30	300.20	308.10	316.00	3.95	323.90	331.80	339.70	347.60	355.50	363.40	371.30	379.20	387.10	395.00
8.0	248.00	256.00	264.00	272.00	280.00	288.00	296.00	304.00	312.00	320.00	4.00	328.00	336.00	344.00	352.00	360.00	368.00	376.00	384.00	392.00	400.00
8.1	251.10	259.20	267.30	275.40	283.50	291.60	299.70	307.80	315.90	324.00	4.05	332.10	340.20	348.30	356.40	364.50	372.60	380.70	388.80	396.90	405.00
8.2	254.20	262.40	270.60	278.80	287.00	295.20	303.40	311.60	319.80	328.00	4.10	336.20	344.40	352.60	360.80	369.00	377.20	385.40	393.60	401.80	410.00
8.3	257.30	265.60	273.90	282.20	290.50	298.80	307.10	315.40	323.70	332.00	4.15	340.30	348.60	356.90	365.20	373.50	381.80	390.10	398.40	406.70	415.00
8.4	260.40	268.80	277.20	285.60	294.00	302.40	310.80	319.20	327.60	336.00	4.20	344.40	352.80	361.20	369.60	378.00	386.40	394.80	403.20	411.60	420.00
8.5	263.50	272.00	280.50	289.00	297.50	306.00	314.50	323.00	331.50	340.00	4.25	348.50	357.00	365.50	374.00	382.50	391.00	399.50	408.00	416.50	425.00
8.6	266.60	275.20	283.80	292.40	301.00	309.60	318.20	326.80	335.40	344.00	4.30	352.60	361.20	369.80	378.40	387.00	395.60	404.20	412.80	421.40	430.00
8.7	269.70	278.40	287.10	295.80	304.50	313.20	321.90	330.60	339.30	348.00	4.35	356.70	365.40	374.10	382.80	391.50	400.20	408.90	417.60	426.30	435.00
8.8	272.80	281.60	290.40	299.20	308.00	316.80	325.60	334.40	343.20	352.00	4.40	360.80	369.60	378.40	387.20	396.00	404.80	413.60	422.40	431.20	440.00
8.9	275.90	284.80	293.70	302.60	311.50	320.40	329.30	338.20	347.10	356.00	4.45	364.90	373.80	382.70	391.60	400.50	409.40	418.30	427.20	436.10	445.00
9.0	279.00	288.00	297.00	306.00	315.00	324.00	333.00	342.00	351.00	360.00	4.50	369.00	378.00	387.00	396.00	405.00	414.00	423.00	432.00	441.00	450.00
9.1	282.10	291.20	300.30	309.40	318.50	327.60	336.70	345.80	354.90	364.00	4.55	373.10	382.20	391.30	400.40	409.50	418.60	427.70	436.80	445.90	455.00
9.2	285.20	294.40	303.60	312.80	322.00	331.20	340.40	349.60	358.80	368.00	4.60	377.20	386.40	395.60	404.80	414.00	423.20	432.40	441.60	450.80	460.00
9.3	288.30	297.60	306.90	316.20	325.50	334.80	344.10	353.40	362.70	372.00	4.65	381.30	390.60	399.90	409.20	418.50	427.80	437.10	446.40	455.70	465.00
9.4	291.40	300.80	310.20	319.60	329.00	338.40	347.80	357.20	366.60	376.00	4.70	385.40	394.80	404.20	413.60	423.00	432.40	441.80	451.20	460.60	470.00
9.5	294.50	304.00	313.50	323.00	332.50	342.00	351.50	361.00	370.50	380.00	4.75	389.50	399.00	408.50	418.00	427.50	437.00	446.50	456.00	465.50	475.00
9.6	297.60	307.20	316.80	326.40	336.00	345.60	355.20	364.80	374.40	384.00	4.80	393.60	403.20	412.80	422.40	432.00	441.60	451.20	460.80	470.40	480.00
9.7	300.70	310.40	320.10	329.80	339.50	349.20	358.90	368.60	378.30	388.00	4.85	397.70	407.40	417.10	426.80	436.50	446.20	455.90	465.60	475.30	485.00
9.8	303.80	313.60	323.40	333.20	343.00	352.80	362.60	372.40	382.20	392.00	4.90	401.80	411.60	421.40	431.20	441.00	450.80	460.60	470.40	480.20	490.00
9.9	306.90	316.80	326.70	336.60	346.50	356.40	366.30	376.20	386.10	396.00	4.95	405.90	415.80	425.70	435.60	445.50	455.40	465.30	475.20	485.10	495.00
10.0	310.00	320.00	330.00	340.00	350.00	360.00	370.00	380.00	390.00	400.00	5.00	410.00	420.00	430.00	440.00	450.00	460.00	470.00	480.00	490.00	500.00
10.5	325.50	336.00	346.50	357.00	367.50	378.00	388.50	399.00	409.50	420.00	5.25	430.50	441.00	451.50	462.00	472.50	483.00	493.50	504.00	514.50	525.00
11.0	341.00	352.00	363.00	374.00	385.00	396.00	407.00	418.00	429.00	440.00	5.50	451.00	462.00	473.00	484.00	495.00	506.00	517.00	528.00	539.00	550.00
11.5	356.50	368.00	379.50	391.00	402.50	414.00	425.50	437.00	448.50	460.00	5.75	471.50	483.00	494.50	506.00	517.50	529.00	540.50	552.00	563.50	575.00
12.0	372.00	384.00	396.00	408.00	420.00	432.00	444.00	456.00	468.00	480.00	6.00	492.00	504.00	516.00	528.00	540.00	552.00	564.00	576.00	588.00	600.00
12.5	387.50	400.00	412.50	425.00	437.50	450.00	462.50	475.00	487.50	500.00	6.25	512.50	525.00	537.50	550.00	562.50	575.00	587.50	600.00	612.50	625.00
13.0	403.00	416.00	429.00	442.00	455.00	468.00	481.00	494.00	507.00	520.00	6.50	533.00	546.00	559.00	572.00	585.00	598.00	611.00	624.00	637.00	650.00
13.5	418.50	432.00	445.50	459.00	472.50	486.00	499.50	513.00	526.50	540.00	6.75	553.50	567.00	580.50	594.00	607.50	621.00	634.50	648.00	661.50	675.00
14.0	434.00	448.00	462.00	476.00	490.00	504.00	518.00	532.00	546.00	560.00	7.00	574.00	588.00	602.00	616.00	630.00	644.00	658.00	672.00	686.00	700.00
14.5	449.50	464.00	478.50	493.00	507.50	522.00	536.50	551.00	565.50	580.00	7.25	594.50	609.00	623.50	638.00	652.50	667.00	681.50	696.00	710.50	725.00
15.0	465.00	480.00	495.00	510.00	525.00	540.00	555.00	570.00	585.00	600.00	7.50	615.00	630.00	645.00	660.00	675.00	690.00	705.00	720.00	735.00	750.00
15.5	480.50	496.00	511.50	527.00	542.50	558.00	573.50	589.00	604.50	620.00	7.75	635.50	651.00	666.50	682.00	697.50	713.00	728.50	744.00	759.50	775.00
16.0	496.00	512.00	528.00	544.00	560.00	576.00	592.00	608.00	624.00	640.00	8.00	656.00	672.00	688.00	704.00	720.00	736.00	752.00	768.00	784.00	800.00
16.5	511.50	528.00	544.50	561.00	577.50	594.00	610.50	627.00	643.50	660.00	8.25	676.50	693.00	709.50	726.00	742.50	759.00	775.50	792.00	808.50	825.00
17.0	527.00	544.00	561.00	578.00	595.00	612.00	629.00	646.00	663.00	680.00	8.50	697.00	714.00	731.00	748.00	765.00	782.00	799.00	816.00	833.00	850.00
17.5	542.50	560.00	577.50	595.00	612.50	630.00	647.50	665.00	682.50	700.00	8.75	717.50	735.00	752.50	770.00	787.50	805.00	822.50	840.00	857.50	875.00
18.0	558.00	576.00	594.00	612.00	630.00	648.00	666.00	684.00	702.00	720.00	9.00	738.00	756.00	774.00	792.00	810.00	828.00	846.00	864.00	882.00	900.00
18.5	573.50	592.00	610.50	629.00	647.50	666.00	684.50	703.00	721.50	740.00	9.25	758.50	777.00	795.50	814.00	832.50	851.00	869.50	888.00	906.50	925.00
19.0	589.00	608.00	627.00	646.00	665.00	684.00	703.00	722.00	741.00	760.00	9.50	779.00	798.00	817.00	836.00	855.00	874.00	893.00	912.00	931.00	950.00
19.5	604.50	624.00	643.50	663.00	682.50	702.00	721.50	741.00	760.50	780.00	9.75	799.50	819.00	838.50	858.00	877.50	897.00	916.50	936.00	955.50	975.00
20.0	620.00	640.00	660.00	680.00	700.00	720.00	740.00	760.00	780.00	800.00	10.00	820.00	840.00	860.00	880.00	900.00	920.00	940.00	960.00	980.00	1000.00
30.0	930.00	960.00	990.00	1020.00	1050.00	1080.00	1110.00	1140.00	1170.00	1200.00	15.00	1230.00	1260.00	1290.00	1320.00	1350.00	1380.00	1410.00	1440.00	1470.00	1500.00
40.0	1240.00	1280.00	1320.00	1360.00	1400.00	1440.00	1480.00	1520.00	1560.00	1600.00	20.00	1640.00	1680.00	1720.00	1760.00	1800.00	1840.00	1880.00	1920.00	1960.00	2000.00

LATEST CHANGES & CORRECTIONS CONTENTS

MANUFACTURER **Page**

LATEST CHANGES & CORRECTIONS For 1993 & Earlier Models

NOTE: Latest Changes and Corrections represents a collection of last minute information and relevant technical service bulletins. Read this section and make notations in the appropriate manuals for easy reference later.

BMW

1 *1988-93 325i, 525i, 535i, 735i, 735iL, 740i, 740iL, 750i & 850i A/C-HEATER SYSTEM: DELAYED HEATER OUTPUT (TSB 64 05 93 3750)* – During 10-15 minute period of operation after cold start in low ambient temperatures, output from heater may be at reduced temperatures. This condition occurs primarily on V8 (M60) engines. Changes to internal coating may cause water valve to stick. Ensure IHKA (or IHKR) control module and cooling system are operating properly. If necessary, replace water valves with new modified parts (64 11 1 387 319 for 325i, and 64 11 1 391 958 for all others). New parts can be identified by White paint dot next to date code.

2 *1989-93 318i, 325e, 325is, 525i, 535i WITH 2.5L ENGINE A/C-HEATER SYSTEM: A/C BELT TENSION (TSB 64 01 93 3721)* – On 2.5L engines, incorrect A/C belt tension may allow belt to rub coolant hose. Over an extended period, this could cause wear on coolant hose sidewall. Using Belt Tension Tester (11 5 021), ensure belt tension is correct. If belt is stretched, replace belt. Ensure a gap of at least 0.39" (10 mm) exists between coolant hose and A/C compressor belt pulley. *See ADJUSTING A/C BELT TENSION.*

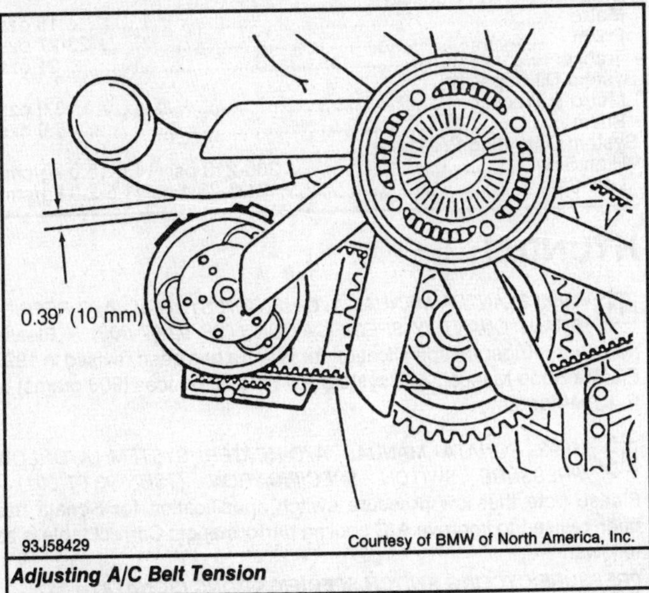
0.39" (10 mm)
93J58429
Courtesy of BMW of North America, Inc.
Adjusting A/C Belt Tension

3 *1993 740 & 740iL A/C-HEATER SYSTEM: WHISTLING FROM A/C SYSTEM WITH SUNROOF OR WINDOW SLIGHTLY OPEN (TSB 64 03 93 3744)* – When blower is turned completely off and sunroof or window is slightly open, a whistling noise from windshield defroster ducts may be heard. Noise is most noticeable at fast highway speeds. If blower switch is turned just past the OFF detent, noise will stop. To decrease amount of air passing flap seal, defroster flap linkage can be tightened. Correct procedure is as follows:

1) Remove trim below steering column. Remove knee bolster. Remove carpeted trim panel on right side driver's side footwell. Locate "L" shaped defroster control rod on left side of IHKA housing.
2) A rectangular White plastic clip threaded on end of control rod is used to secure rod to defroster flap lever. Carefully pry clip from Black flap lever. *See ADJUSTING DEFROSTER FLAP LINKAGE.* Turn clip approximately 5 times to tighten.
3) Snap clip into Black flap lever. Ensure there is no play in flap operation. Ensure flap linkage and lever are snug, and lever is not bent. To complete installation, reverse removal procedure.

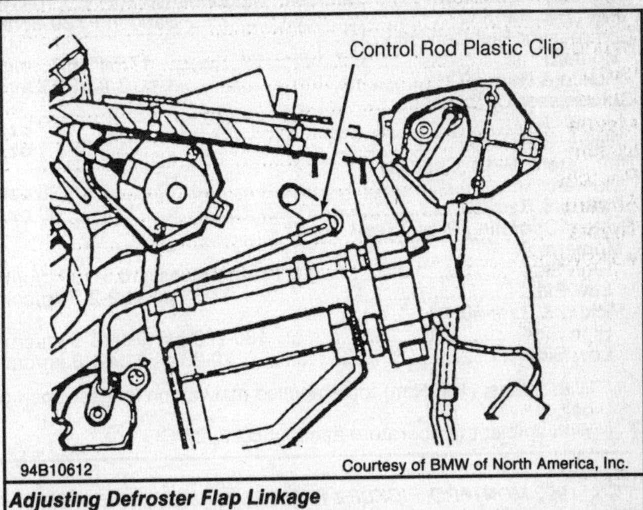
Control Rod Plastic Clip
94B10612
Courtesy of BMW of North America, Inc.
Adjusting Defroster Flap Linkage

CHRYSLER/MITSUBISHI

4 *ALL MODELS A/C-HEATER SYSTEM: AIR CONDITIONER ODOR (TSB 93-55-001)* – Some models may experience a musty odor from bacterial and fungal growth forming in A/C evaporator condensation when A/C system is turned on. To eliminate the bacterial and fungal growths and leave a protective film for a one year period, Mitsubishi Air Conditioner Treatment (A993ZC1X01) is available. Using shop air, air gun or product's applicator nozzle, air conditioner treatment is installed into evaporator area through fresh air inlet. Two treatments will be necessary for dual-A/C systems (one for front evaporator and one for rear evaporator). To use air conditioner treatment, follow instructions and video provided with kit.

5 *1992 STEALTH & 3000GT HEATER SYSTEM: REMOVAL & INSTALLATION – HEATER CONTROL PANEL* – Please note that HEATER CONTROL PANEL removal and installation procedure on page CHRYSLER/MITSUBISHI 16 has been revised. Correct procedure is as follows:

HEATER CONTROL PANEL

Removal & Installation – 1) Disconnect negative battery cable. Drain coolant. Remove cup holder and plug from rear floor console. Remove rear console. Remove radio panel, radio and switch panel from front floor console. Remove front console side covers and trim plates. Remove shift lever knob (M/T models) and front floor console. Remove glove box door stops. Remove glove box upper cover.
2) Disconnect air selector cable. Remove hood release handle, light dimmer and rear wiper/washer switch from knee bolster plate. Remove knee bolster plate and foot shower duct. Disconnect mode selector cable and temperature control cable. Using screwdriver, disengage center air outlet panel clips. Remove panel using trim stick. Remove heater control panel. To install, reverse removal procedure. Adjust heater control cables during installation.

6 *1992 MONTERO, PICKUP & RAM-50 MANUAL A/C-HEATER SYSTEM: SPECIFICATIONS* – Please note that COMPRESSOR OIL CAPACITY and SYSTEM OPERATING PRESSURES in SPECIFICATIONS table on page CHRYSLER/MISTSUBISHI 35 of 1992 AIR CONDITIONING & HEATING SERVICE & REPAIR manual have been revised. Correct table is as follows:

LATEST CHANGES & CORRECTIONS For 1993 & Earlier Models (Cont.)

SPECIFICATIONS

Compressor Type	
Montero	Nippondenso 10PA15 10-Cyl.
Pickup & Ram-50	Sanden FX80 Scroll
Compressor Belt Deflection [1]	
Montero	17/64" (6.75 mm)
Pickup & Ram-50	3/8" (9.53 mm)
Compressor Oil Capacity	
Montero	2.7 ozs.
Pickup & Ram-50	4.4-5.1 ozs.
Refrigerant (R-12) Capacity	
Montero	28 ozs.
Pickup & Ram-50	30 ozs.
System Operating Pressures [2]	
Montero	
High Side	149-185 psi (10.5-13 kg/cm²)
Low Side	17-33 psi (1.2-2.3 kg/cm²)
Pickup & Ram-50	
High Side	130-220 psi (9.1-15.5 kg/cm²)
Low Side	20-26 psi (1.4-1.8 kg/cm²)

[1] – With 22 lbs. (100 N.m) force applied midway on longest span of belt.
[2] – With ambient temperature at about 80°F (27°C).

7 *1992 MONTERO, PICKUP & RAM-50 MANUAL A/C-HEATER SYSTEM: TESTING – BLOWER RESISTOR* – Please note that specifications for Montero in testing procedure for BLOWER RESISTOR on page CHRYSLER/MITSUBISHI 37 of 1992 AIR CONDITIONING & HEATING SERVICE & REPAIR manual has been revised. Correct table is as follows:

BLOWER RESISTOR RESISTANCE

Terminal No.	Approximate Ohms
Montero	
1 & 2	0.95
2 & 3	0.33
2 & 4	1.96
Pickup & Ram-50	
1 & 2	1.19
1 & 3	0.50
1 & 4	2.33
1 & 5	0

8 *1992 STEALTH & 3000GT AUTOMATIC A/C-HEATER SYSTEM: SPECIFICATIONS* – Please note that COMPRESSOR BELT DEFLECTION and SYSTEM OPERATING PRESSURES in SPECIFICATIONS table on page CHRYSLER/MISTSUBISHI 59 of 1992 AIR CONDITIONING & HEATING SERVICE & REPAIR manual have been revised. Correct table is as follows:

SPECIFICATIONS

Compressor Type	Sanden FX105VS Scroll
Compressor Belt Deflection	
DOHC	5/32 - 7/32" (4.0-5.5 mm)
SOHC	19/64 - 3/8" (7.5-9.5 mm)
Compressor Oil Capacity	4.6-6.0 ozs.
Refrigerant Capacity	34 ozs.
System Operating Pressures [1]	
High Side	111-118 psi (7.8-8.3 kg/cm²)
Low Side	18.5-27.5 psi (1.3-1.9 kg/cm²)

[1] – With ambient temperature at 80°F (27°C).

GEO

9 *1992 LEMANS & STORM HEATER SYSTEM: TESTING – BLOWER SWITCH TEST* – Please note that wire colors for LeMans in testing procedure for BLOWER SWITCH on page GM/GEO 3 of 1992 AIR CONDITIONING & HEATING SERVICE & REPAIR manual have been revised. Correct table is as follows:

BLOWER SWITCH CONTINUITY

Switch Position	Continuity Between Terminals
LeMans	
Low	White/Blue & Yellow
Medium	White/Green & Yellow
High	White/Brown & Yellow
Storm	
1	Blue/White & Black
2	Blue/Yellow & Black
3	Blue/Orange & Black
4	Blue/Red & Black

10 *1992 METRO, PRIZM & TRACKER MANUAL A/C-HEATER SYSTEM: SPECIFICATIONS* – Please note that REFRIGERANT (R-12) CAPACITY for Metro in SPECIFICATIONS table on page GM/GEO 17 of 1992 AIR CONDITIONING & HEATING SERVICE & REPAIR manual has been revised. Correct table is as follows:

SPECIFICATIONS

Compressor Type	
Metro & Tracker	Nippondenso 10-Cyl.
Prizm	Matsushita Rotary Vane
Compressor Belt Deflection	
New	1/4" (6.4 mm)
Used	1/2" (12.7 mm)
Refrigerant (R-12) Capacity	
Metro	18 ozs.
Prizm	23-27 ozs.
Tracker	21 ozs.
System Oil Capacity	
Metro & Tracker	3.0 ozs.
Prizm	6.0 ozs.
System Operating Pressure	
High Side	206-213 psi (14.5-15.0 kg/cm²)
Low Side	21.3-28.4 psi (1.5-2.0 kg/cm²)

HYUNDAI

11 *1992 ELANTRA MANUAL A/C-HEATER SYSTEM: A/C REFRIGERANT QUANTITY SPECIFICATION (TSB 92-97-003)* – Please note that refrigerant specification for Elantra has been revised in 1992 Elantra Shop Manual. A/C system will hold 32 ounces (900 grams) of R-12 refrigerant.

12 *1993 SONATA MANUAL A/C-HEATER SYSTEM: A/C LOW PRESSURE SWITCH SPECIFICATION (TSB 93-97-001)* – Please note that low pressure switch specification for Sonata has been revised to improve A/C cooling performance. Correct table is as follows:

PRESSURE/CYCLING SWITCH SPECIFICATIONS (SONATA)

Application	Pressure
Low Pressure Switch [1]	
On	21 psi (1.5 kg/cm²)
Off	47 psi (3.3 kg/cm²)

[1] – Sonata uses low pressure switch only.

ISUZU

13 *1991-92 PICKUP & RODEO WITH V6 ENGINES MANUAL A/C-HEATER SYSTEM: A/C SEALING WASHERS (TSB 92-12-001)* – As a running production change, sealing washers are now used at compressor-to-hose block connections instead of "O" rings. A compressor with sealing washers can be used on "O" ring type hoses. DO NOT use a compressor with "O" rings on a sealing washer type hose. Compressor type can be identified by number printed on end of compressor housing label ("005" indicates compressor uses sealing washers, and "616" indicates compressor uses "O" rings). The following compressors use sealing washers:

- Compressor with clutch (8-01134-005-0).
- Compressor without clutch (8-02724-618-0).
- Zexel A/C kits with lot number 09199101 or higher.

LATEST CHANGES & CORRECTIONS For 1993 & Earlier Models (Cont.)

If manifold is separated from compressor, use new sealing washers. Sealing Washer Kit (8-02724-655-0) includes thin and thick sealing washers. Thin sealing washers are used on sealing washer type compressors using sealing washer type hoses. Thick sealing washers are used on sealing washer type compressors using "O" ring type hoses. When using sealing washers, an intentional gap will occur between manifold and compressor during manifold installation. *See LOCATING SEALING WASHERS and INSTALLING SEALING WASHERS*. DO NOT overtighten fitting to eliminate gap.

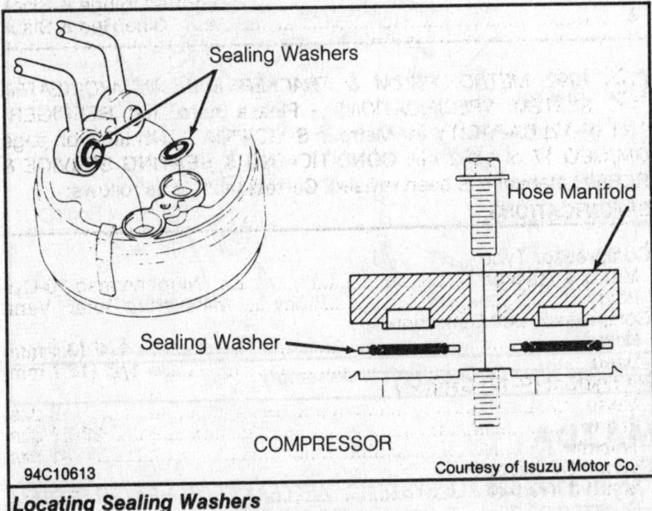
Sealing Washers
Hose Manifold
Sealing Washer
COMPRESSOR
94C10613
Courtesy of Isuzu Motor Co.

Locating Sealing Washers

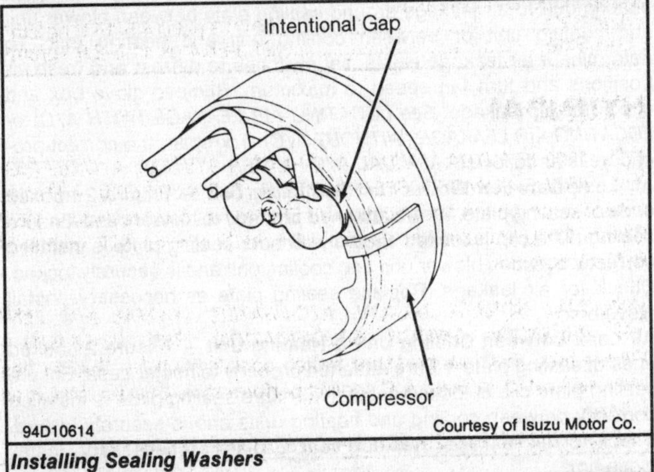
Intentional Gap
Compressor
94D10614
Courtesy of Isuzu Motor Co.

Installing Sealing Washers

14 *1992 RODEO MANUAL A/C-HEATER SYSTEM: A/C OVERCHARGE TEST (TSB 92-12-002)* – Some 1992 Rodeo with factory- or port-installed A/C systems produced prior to 12/16/91 may experience a knocking noise in A/C system when it is running. To determine if A/C system is overcharged, perform the following procedure:

1) Start engine. Turn A/C on and put blower fan lever in medium-high (#3) position. Move mode lever to vent position and air intake lever to recirculated air position. Open vehicle doors. Warm engine to normal operating temperature, then idle for 5 minutes.

2) Check sight glass on receiver-drier. Sight glass should be clear. Disconnect lead wire from compressor clutch. Measure amount of time it takes for bubbles to appear in sight glass (liquid level "drop time").

3) Repeat step **2)** 3 more times. Allow A/C system to run for approximately 30 seconds between each test. If average drop time for all 4 tests is more than 50 seconds or if drop times in all 4 tests are more than 30 seconds, A/C system is overcharged.

4) If A/C system is overcharged, discharge A/C system using approved refrigerant recovery/recycling equipment. Evacuate, recharge and leak test system. Reconnect A/C compressor clutch lead wire.

15 *1993 AMIGO, PICKUP & RODEO MANUAL A/C-HEATER SYSTEM: A/C EVAPORATOR FREEZING UP (TSB 93-12-003)* – Some vehicles may experience reduced airflow from panel vents, visible mist coming from panel vents, or insufficient cooling after extended drive with proper cooling after a 15-20 minute rest period. These conditions are due to evaporator freezing up, which may be caused by an improperly positioned A/C thermosensor in evaporator case. Some vehicles have had thermosensor relocated prior to delivery. This will be indicated by a round Blue sticker or White part number label affixed to bottom of evaporator case. To install A/C Thermosensor Relocation Kit (2-90050-346-0) on other vehicles, perform following procedure:

1) Disconnect negative battery cable. Remove glove box. Remove rubber grommet from evaporator case. Gently pull thermosensor probe wire from case just enough to create a slight tension in wire. Cut probe wire as close to case as possible. *See CUTTING THERMOSENSOR PROBE WIRE*.

2) Remove and discard thermosensor. Install new thermosensor (included in kit) in same location as original thermosensor. Using plastic bracket with probe and screw provided in kit, install bracket into existing hole in side of evaporator case. *See INSTALLING BRACKET WITH PROBE*. Ensure bracket is properly aligned.

3) Route thermosensor wires through clips on evaporator case. Store excess wire behind resistor harness. *See INSTALLING THERMOSENSOR WIRES*. To install, reverse removal procedure. Start engine, and verify compressor clutch engagement.

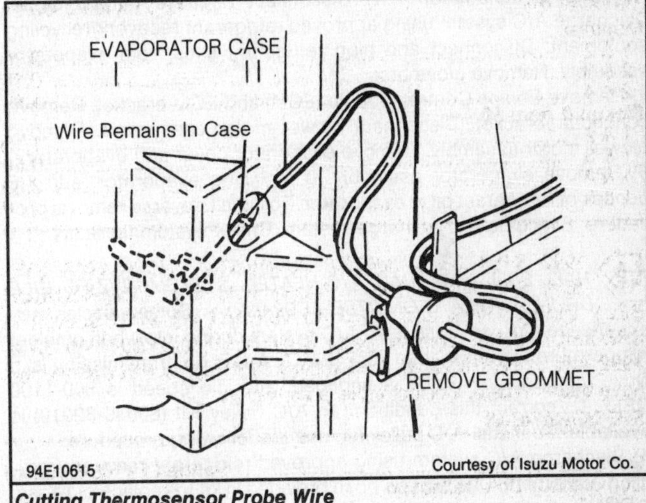
EVAPORATOR CASE
Wire Remains In Case
REMOVE GROMMET
94E10615
Courtesy of Isuzu Motor Co.

Cutting Thermosensor Probe Wire

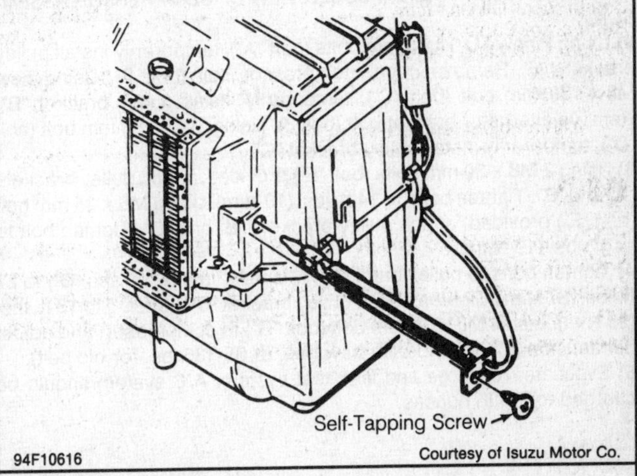
Self-Tapping Screw
94F10616
Courtesy of Isuzu Motor Co.

Installing Bracket With Probe

LATEST CHANGES & CORRECTIONS For 1993 & Earlier Models (Cont.)

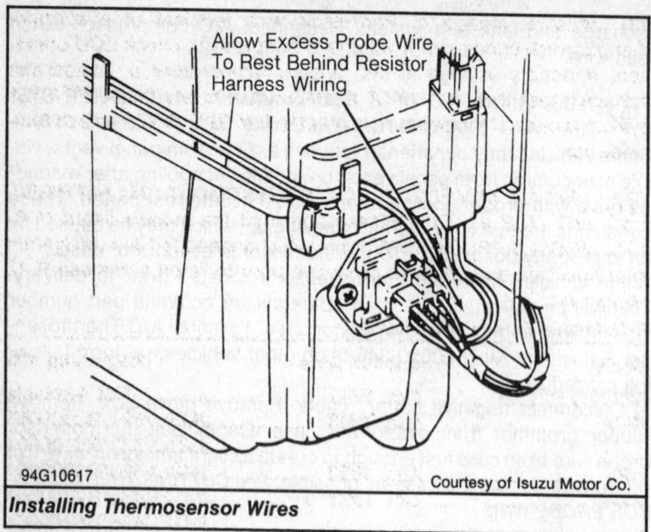
Allow Excess Probe Wire
To Rest Behind Resistor
Harness Wiring
94G10617
Courtesy of Isuzu Motor Co.

Installing Thermosensor Wires

LEXUS

16 *1992 ES300 AUTOMATIC A/C-HEATER SYSTEM: REMOVAL & INSTALLATION - HEATER CONTROL PANEL* - Please note that EVAPORATOR ASSEMBLY removal and installation procedure on page LEXUS 8 has been revised. Correct procedure is as follows:

EVAPORATOR ASSEMBLY

Removal & Installation - 1) Disconnect negative battery cable. Discharge A/C system using approved refrigerant recovery/recycling equipment. Disconnect and plug refrigerant lines from evaporator assembly. Remove glove box.

2) Remove Engine Control Module (ECM) and ECM bracket. Remove connector bracket. Disconnect blower motor connectors. Remove blower motor assembly. Remove evaporator cover and evaporator.

3) Remove evaporator assembly. If replacing evaporator, add 1.6 ounces of refrigerant oil to evaporator. To install, reverse removal procedure. Evacuate and recharge system. Check system for leaks.

17 *1992 ES250 MANUAL A/C-HEATER SYSTEM: 2VZ-FE IDLE DRONE WITH A/C ON ((TSB AC92-002)* - Some vehicles may experience a drone noise from A/C system during idle when ambient temperature is greater than 75°F (24°C), A/C is on, transmission is in Drive, compressor clutch is engaged, and idle speed is 800-1100 RPM. To correct this condition, an A/C Pulley Kit (88039-32010) is available. To install A/C pulley kit, use the following procedure:

1) Discharge A/C system using approved refrigerant recovery/recycling equipment. Use suction hose provided in kit to replace old hose. Remove alternator adjusting bolt. Remove 2 bolts at front of compressor bracket (bolt 1). *See EXPLODED VIEW OF COMPRESSOR ASSEMBLY.*

2) Using 2 new M10 x 70 mm bolts (bolt "A"), temporarily install pulley bracket "A". Remove upper compressor bolt (bolt 2). Using new M8 x 120 mm bolt (bolt "C"), temporarily install pulley bracket "B". Remove alternator bracket bolt (bolt 3). Using M10 x 55 mm bolt (bolt "D"), temporarily install pulley bracket "C".

3) Using 2 M8 x 30 mm bolts (bolt "E") provided, attach pulley brackets "A" and "B". Tighten bolts to 14 ft. lbs. (19 N.m). Using M6 x 25 mm bolt (bolt "F") provided, attach pulley brackets "B" and "C". Tighten bolt to 14 ft. lbs. (19 N.m).

4) Tighten bolts to pulley brackets "A" and "C" (bolts "A" and "D") to 27 ft. lbs. (37 N.m). Tighten bolt to pulley bracket "B" (bolt "C") to 18 ft. lbs. (25 N.m). Install M8 x 90 mm bolt (bolt "B") to compressor, and adjust belt tension (170-180 lbs. for new belt, or 95-135 lbs. for old belt).

5) Evacuate, recharge and leak test system. A/C system should be charged to 21-26 ounces.

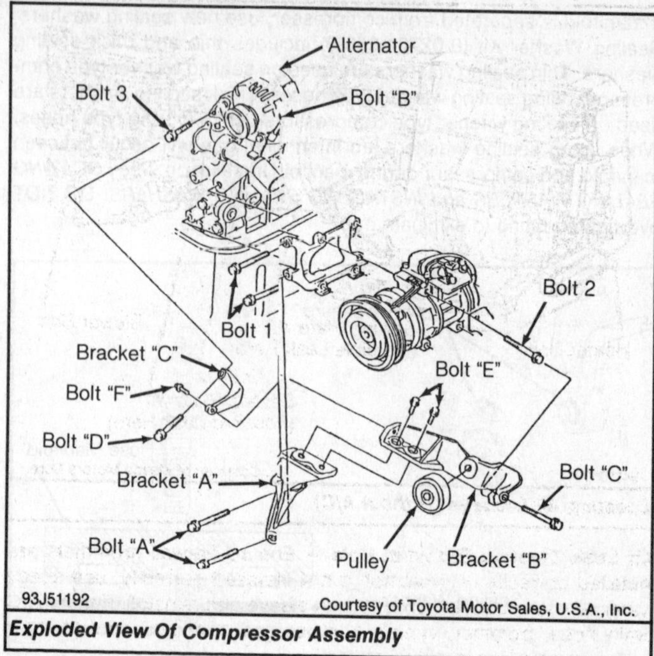
Alternator
Bolt 3
Bolt "B"
Bolt 2
Bolt 1
Bracket "C"
Bolt "E"
Bolt "F"
Bolt "D"
Bracket "A"
Bolt "C"
Bolt "A"
Pulley
Bracket "B"
93J51192
Courtesy of Toyota Motor Sales, U.S.A., Inc.

Exploded View Of Compressor Assembly

MAZDA

18 *1989-92 626 ALL SYSTEMS: AIR LEAK FROM HEATER SYSTEM (TSB 93-03)* - Some vehicles may be experiencing insufficient heating due to air leakage around sealing plate between blower unit and cooling unit or between cooling unit and heating unit. To determine if air leakage exists, set switches to defrost and fresh air positions and turn fan speed to maximum. Remove glove box and check for air leakage. *See LOCATING AIR LEAKAGE (WITH A/C) or LOCATING AIR LEAKAGE (WITHOUT A/C).* To repair, the correct procedure is as follows:

Air Leak Between Blower Unit & Cooling Unit - Ensure 2 hooked ends of sealing plate #1 are attached properly to blower case. Ensure sealing plate clip is locked securely. Ensure sealing plate is installed correctly between blower unit and cooling unit and is securely locked. Check for air leakage. Replace sealing plate as necessary. Install glove box.

Air Leak Between Cooling Unit & Heating Unit - Ensure 2 hooked ends of sealing plate #2 are attached properly to heater case. Ensure sealing plate clip is locked securely. Ensure sealing plate is installed correctly between cooling and heating units and is securely locked. Check for air leakage. Replace sealing plate as necessary. Install glove box.

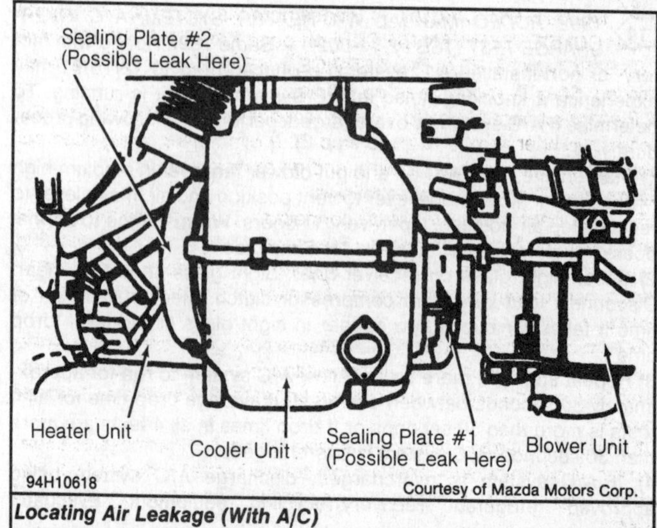
Sealing Plate #2
(Possible Leak Here)
Heater Unit
Cooler Unit
Sealing Plate #1
(Possible Leak Here)
Blower Unit
94H10618
Courtesy of Mazda Motors Corp.

Locating Air Leakage (With A/C)

LATEST CHANGES & CORRECTIONS For 1993 & Earlier Models (Cont.)

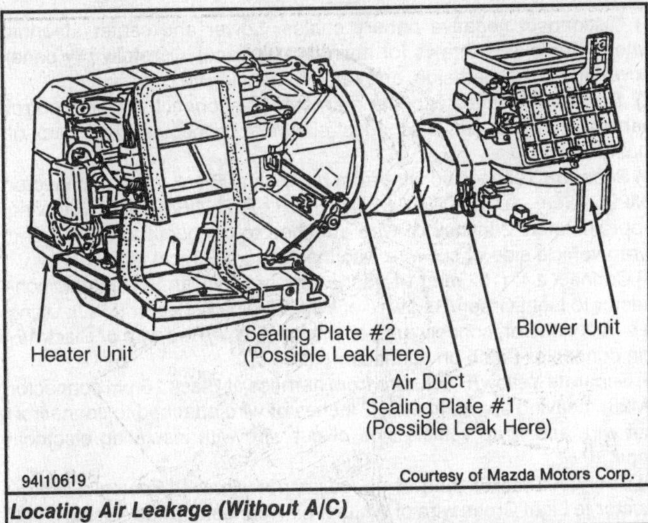
Heater Unit
Sealing Plate #2
(Possible Leak Here)
Blower Unit
Air Duct
Sealing Plate #1
(Possible Leak Here)
94I10619
Courtesy of Mazda Motors Corp.

Locating Air Leakage (Without A/C)

Air Leak Through Grommet Hole – Ensure firewall grommets are installed correctly. If grommet is not installed correctly, use soapy water or spray lubricant on grommet sleeve and reinstall. Ensure A/C drain hose grommet, vehicle harness grommet and speedometer cable grommet are installed correctly.

19 *1992 MPV MANUAL A/C-HEATER SYSTEM: SPECIFICATIONS* – Please note that COMPRESSOR BELT DEFLECTION in SPECIFICATIONS table on page MAZDA 25 of 1992 AIR CONDITIONING & HEATING SERVICE & REPAIR manual has been revised. Correct table is as follows:

SPECIFICATIONS

Application	Specification
Compressor Type	Nippondenso 10-Cyl.
Compressor Belt Deflection [1]	
2.6L	
New Belt	11/32-25/64" (8.5-10.0 mm)
Used Belt	25/64-29/64" (10.0-11.5 mm)
3.0L	
New Belt	5/32-3/16" (4.0-4.5 mm)
Used Belt	3/16-7/32" (4.5-5.5 mm)
Compressor Oil Capacity	2.7-3.3 ozs.
Refrigerant (R-12) Capacity	
With Rear A/C	51 ozs.
Without Rear A/C	37 ozs.
System Operating Pressures	
High Side	171-235 psi (12.0-16.5 kg/cm²)
Low Side	21-43 psi (1.5-3.0 kg/cm²)

[1] – Measure belt deflection between longest belt run.

20 *1992 MPV MANUAL A/C-HEATER SYSTEM: TESTING – CONDENSER FAN CIRCUIT* – Please note that steps **3)** and **10)-13)** under CONDENSER FAN CIRCUIT on page MAZDA 25 of 1992 AIR CONDITIONING & HEATING SERVICE & REPAIR manual have been revised. **Step 3) should read as follows:**

3) Reconnect negative battery cable. If condenser fan(s) operates, disconnect jumper wire, and go to step **6)**. If condenser fan(s) does not operate, disconnect jumper wire, and go to next step.

Steps 10)-13) should read as follows:

10) Reconnect pressure switch connector. Turn ignition off. Check refrigerant high-side pressure. Pressure switch normal operating range is 33.4-299 psi (2.35-21.0 kg/cm²). If pressure is not within range, service refrigerant system. If pressure is within range, replace pressure switch.

11) Turn ignition and blower on. Measure voltage at Green wire terminal of A/C switch connector. If no voltage is present, go to next step. If battery voltage exists, repair circuit between A/C switch and blower switch.

12) Measure voltage at Blue/White wire terminal of thermoswitch connector. If no voltage is present, go to next step. If battery voltage exists, repair circuit between evaporator thermoswitch and A/C switch.

13) Measure voltage at Red/Black wire terminal of evaporator thermoswitch connector. If voltage is not present, check ECU operation. If battery voltage exists, ensure temperature at evaporator surface is less than 32°F (0°C). If temperature is less than 32°F (0°C), system is okay. If temperature is greater than 32°F (0°C), replace thermoswitch.

21 *1993 ALL MODELS A/C-HEATER SYSTEM: R-134a REFRIGERANT (TSB 93-05)* – Please note that the models listed in R-134a MODEL APPLICATIONS table will change to R-134a refrigerant after specified date. Models produced prior to listed dates use R-12 refrigerant.

R-134a MODEL APPLICATIONS

Model	Production Date	Beginning VIN
B2200 & B2600i	Oct. 1993	Not Available
MPV	Aug. 1993	JM3LV521*R0600001
		JM3LV522*R0600001
MPV	Aug. 1993	JM3LV523*R0600001
MX-3	Oct. 1993	JM1EC435*R0300001
		JM1EC436*R0300001
MX-5	Aug. 1993	JM1NA353*R*500001
MX-6	Aug. 1993	1YVGE31C*R5100001
		1YVGE31D*R5100001
Protege & 323	1995 Model	Not Available
RX-7	Aug. 1993	JH1FD333*R0300001
616	June 1993	1YVGE22C*R5100001
		1YVGE22D*R5100001
929	Aug. 1993	JM1HD461*R0300001

NISSAN

22 *1991-92 NX & SENTRA MANUAL A/C-HEATER SYSTEM: A/C COMPRESSOR CLUTCH COUNTERMEASURE PART (TSB NTB93-027)* – Some models may experience smoke from compressor clutch, a burnt smell, noise from engine compartment or no A/C operation when A/C is turned on. Replace original compressor with new compressor using a heavy-duty clutch (92600-65Y01 for 1.6L engines, and 92600-69Y01 for 2.0L engines).

23 *1991-92 300ZX AUTOMATIC A/C-HEATER SYSTEM: TROUBLE SHOOTING – DIAGNOSTIC PROCEDURE 6* – Please note that DIAGNOSTIC PROCEDURE 6 on page NISSAN 196 of 1991 AIR CONDITIONING & HEATING SERVICE & REPAIR manual and on page NISSAN 157 of 1992 AIR CONDITIONING & HEATING SERVICE & REPAIR manual has been revised. See DIAGNOSTIC PROCEDURE 6 in 1993 AUTOMATIC A/C-HEATER SYSTEMS TROUBLE SHOOTING – 300ZX article.

24 *1992-93 MAXIMA A/C-HEATER SYSTEM: A/C SERVICE ON MODELS WITH AIR BAG (TSB NTB93-012)* – Due to the obstruction of air bag harness clamp bracket on steering member, removal and installation procedure for cooling unit has been revised. Correct procedure is as follows:

1) Remove 8 glove box screws. Remove glove box. Remove instrument panel reinforcement. Remove clip, and disconnect fresh vent shaft control cable. Remove fresh vent duct.

2) Disconnect connectors from resistor or fan control amplifier and thermo control amplifier. From engine compartment side, remove high and low side tubes on cooling unit. Remove 5 screws to cooling unit.

3) Using a screwdriver inserted between cooling unit and steering member, pry down to remove cooling unit. *See REMOVING COOLING UNIT*. Cap all openings to prevent damage and contamination. To install, reverse removal procedure.

25 *1992 NX, PATHFINDER, PICKUP, SENTRA, STANZA & 240SX HEATER SYSTEM: TESTING – BLOWER SPEED CONTROL SWITCH* – Please note that captions for Figs. 11 and 12 under BLOWER SPEED CONTROL SWITCH on page NISSAN 3 of 1992 AIR CONDITIONING & HEATING SERVICE & REPAIR manual were transposed. Captions for Figs. 11 and 12 should read as follows:

LATEST CHANGES & CORRECTIONS For 1993 & Earlier Models (Cont.)

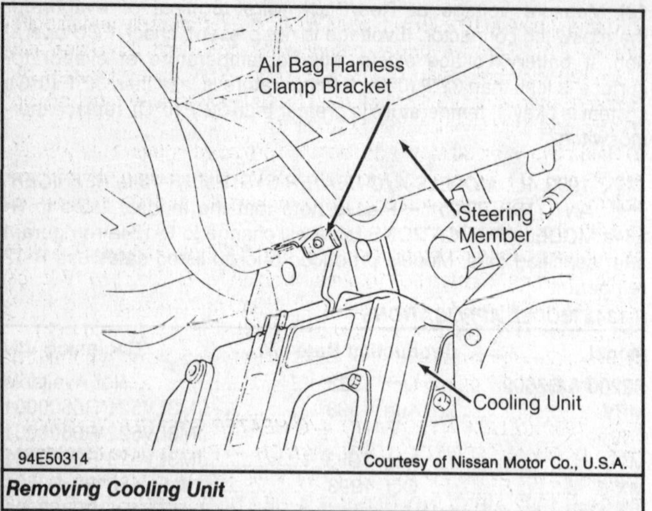
Air Bag Harness
Clamp Bracket
Steering
Member
Cooling Unit
94E50314
Courtesy of Nissan Motor Co., U.S.A.

Removing Cooling Unit

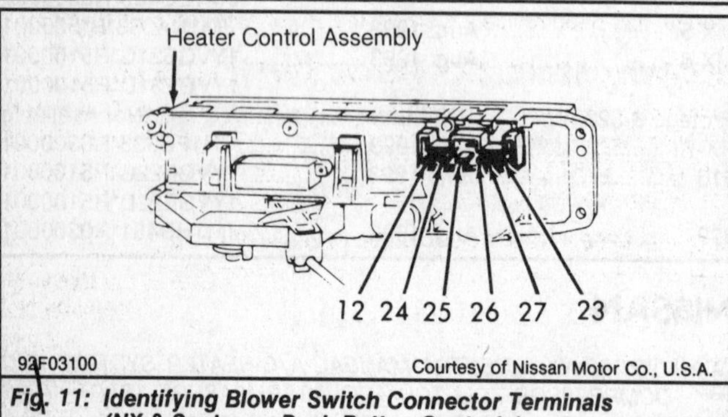
Heater Control Assembly
12 24 25 26 27 23
92F03100
Courtesy of Nissan Motor Co., U.S.A.

Fig. 11: Identifying Blower Switch Connector Terminals (NX & Sentra - Push Button Controls)

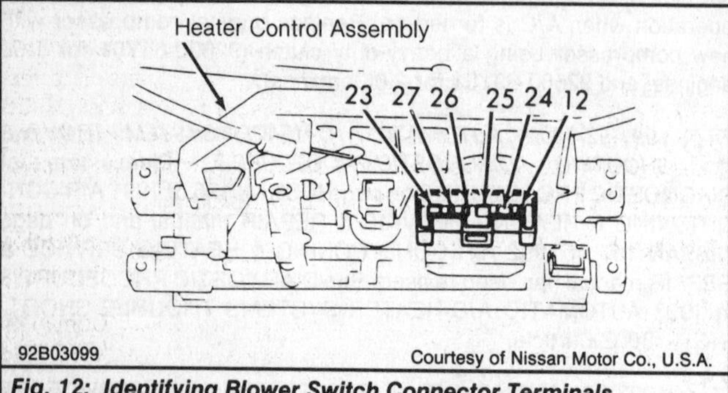
Heater Control Assembly
23 27 26 25 24 12
92B03099
Courtesy of Nissan Motor Co., U.S.A.

Fig. 12: Identifying Blower Switch Connector Terminals (NX & Sentra - Lever Type Controls)

26 *1993 ALTIMA A/C-HEATER SYSTEM: EVAPORATOR ICING ON VIN 1N4BU31*PC100000-1N4BU31*PC108000 (TSB NTB93-054)* – Some models may experience poor A/C performance due to evaporator icing if A/C is used for an extended period with a low blower speed during long drives in high humidity. To prevent evaporator icing, a countermeasure Thermal Control Unit (TCU) is available for models with VIN 1N4BU31*PC100000-1N4BU31*108000.

Determine TCU manufacture date (stamped in White) on TCU control box, located on cooling unit under dash behind glove box. If manufacture date is prior to 8/14/92, use new TCU (27675-D9000). To install new TCU, remove control box and thermistor probe screws. Reusing old screws, install new TCU.

27 *1993 ALTIMA (VIN 1N4BU31FX*PC17007) MANUAL A/C-HEATER SYSTEM: A/C COMPRESSOR OPERATION DURING DEFROST MODE (TSB NTB93-059)* – Models produced prior to 2/15/93 (VIN 1N4BU31FX*PC17007) do not automatically engage A/C compressor when defrost mode is selected. If increased defroster performance in defrost mode (due to compressor operation) is desired, the correct modification is as follows:

1) Disconnect negative battery cables. Lower and center steering wheel. Remove 5 screws for main cluster panel. Carefully pry panel down and out on left side, and remove panel from clips.
2) Disconnect mirror control harness. Disconnect cruise control harness (if equipped). Disconnect electrical connectors from back of cluster panel.
3) Separate Yellow/Red wire from harness at Black 12-pin connector (M29). *See ADJUSTING DEFROSTER PERFORMANCE*. Leaving approximately 2 inches of wire attached to connector, cut wire and wrap vehicle side of cut wire with insulating electrical tape.
4) Connect a 4" (102 mm) 14-gauge jumper wire with Scotchlok® connector to Light Green/Red wire of White 3-pin connector (M30). Using a butt connector, connect jumper wire to Yellow/Red wire of Black 12-pin connector (M29) on connector side.
5) Separate Yellow/Black wire from harness at Black 16-pin connector (M28). Leaving approximately 2 inches of wire attached to connector, cut wire and wrap vehicle side of cut wire with insulating electrical tape.
6) Connect a 4" (102 mm) 14-gauge jumper wire with Scotchlok® connector to Light Green wire of White 3-pin connector (M30). Using a butt connector, connect jumper wire to Yellow/Black wire of Black 12-pin connector (M29) on connector side.
7) Reconnect M28, M29 and M30 connectors to control head. Reconnect negative battery cable. Turn fan speed to third or fourth position, A/C button off, recirculated air button on, and face mode on. Turn on ignition.
8) Depress defrost button. A/C compressor clutch should engage, and system should adjust to fresh air position. To complete procedure, reverse removal procedure.

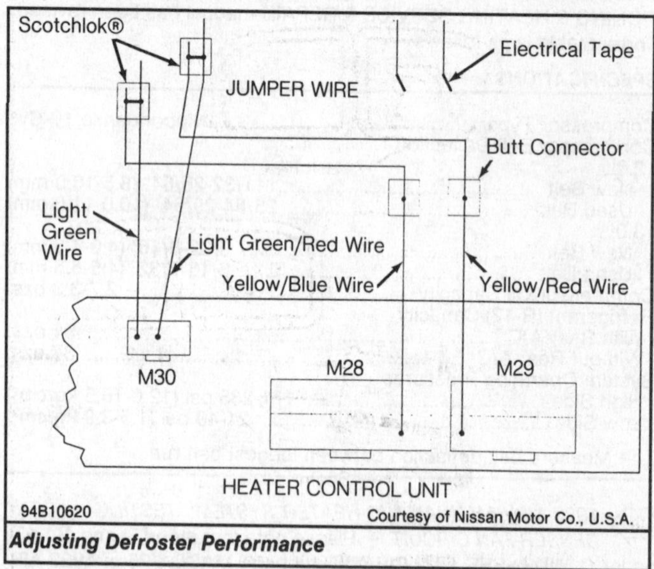
Scotchlok®
JUMPER WIRE
Electrical Tape
Butt Connector
Light
Green
Wire
Light Green/Red Wire
Yellow/Blue Wire
Yellow/Red Wire
M30
M28
M29
HEATER CONTROL UNIT
94B10620
Courtesy of Nissan Motor Co., U.S.A.

Adjusting Defroster Performance

PORSCHE

28 *1989-92 911 CARRERA AUTOMATIC A/C-HEATER SYSTEM: SPECIFICATIONS* – Please note that SYSTEM OPERATING PRESSURES in SPECIFICATIONS table on page PORSCHE 0 of 1992 AIR CONDITIONING & HEATING SERVICE & REPAIR manual has been revised. Correct table is as follows:

SPECIFICATIONS

Compressor Type	Nippondenso 10-Cyl.
Compressor Belt Deflection [1]	13/64 - 25/64" (5-10 mm)
Refrigerant (R-12) Capacity	33 ozs.
System Oil Capacity	[2] 2.6-4.0 ozs.
System Operating Pressures [3]	
High Side	254-297 psi (17.9-20.9 kg/cm²)
Low Side	12-17 psi (0.8-1.2 kg/cm²)

[1] – With light pressure applied to center of belt.
[2] – Compressor refrigerant oil capacity is 1.3 ounces.
[3] – Specifications are with ambient temperature at about 77°F (25°C).

LATEST CHANGES & CORRECTIONS For 1993 & Earlier Models (Cont.)

29 *1989-92 911 CARRERA AUTOMATIC A/C-HEATER SYSTEM: WIRING DIAGRAMS* – Please note that some pin numbers on page PORSCHE 4 of 1992 AIR CONDITIONING & HEATING SERVICE & REPAIR manual have been revised. Pin K5 (Blue/White wire) should be pin K6. Pin G2 (White wire) should be pin G27. Pin G3 (Yellow/Gray wire) should be pin G31. Pin K12 (Blue/White wire) should be pin G1.

SUBARU

30 *1993 IMPREZA ALL SYSTEMS: HEATER VENT DOOR BINDING OR LEAKING AIR (TSB 10-64-93)* – Some vehicles may experience air coming from center vent when in heat mode or binding of vent door due to deformation of center duct. This condition can be corrected by installing a clip/bracket (available through Technical Service Helpline) in left side opening of center vent. Correct procedure is as follows:

1) Remove 2 screws from bottom of center vent grille. Carefully pull out center vent in order not to damage side lock tabs.

2) Slide small curved end of clip over outer edge of left duct. Snap clip into place on inner side. Slide clip toward right side of left duct. *See INSTALLING CLIP/BRACKET IN CENTER VENT.*

3) Check operation of vent door. To complete installation, reverse removal procedure.

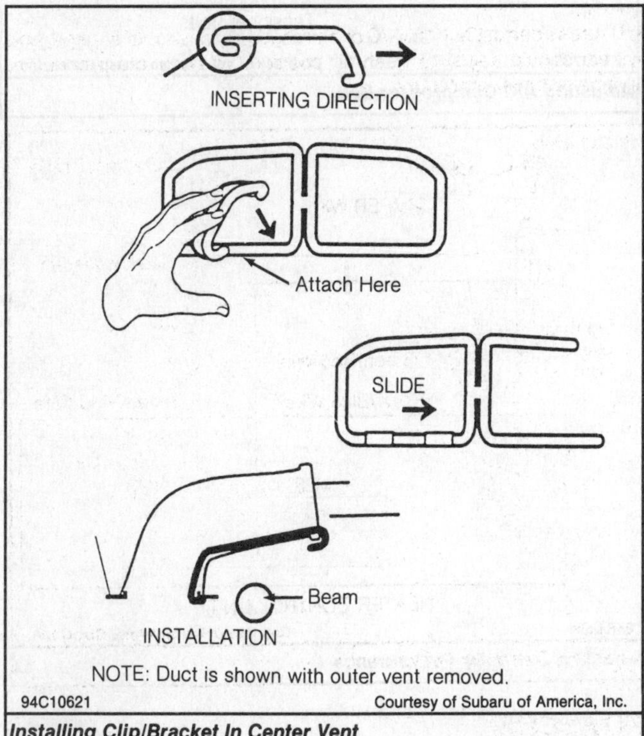
INSERTING DIRECTION
Attach Here
SLIDE
Beam
INSTALLATION
NOTE: Duct is shown with outer vent removed.
94C10621
Courtesy of Subaru of America, Inc.

Installing Clip/Bracket In Center Vent

TOYOTA

31 *1988-91 CAMRY MANUAL A/C-HEATER SYSTEM: 2VZ-FE IDLE DRONE WITH A/C ON (TSB AC92-002)* – Some vehicles may experience a drone noise from A/C system during idle when ambient temperature is greater than 75°F (24°C), A/C is on, transmission is in Drive, compressor clutch is engaged, and idle speed is 800-1100 RPM. To correct this condition, an A/C Pulley Kit (88039-32020 for serial numbers up to 0028864, and 88039-32010 for serial number 0028865) is available. To install A/C pulley kit, use the following procedure:

1) Discharge A/C system using approved refrigerant recovery/recycling equipment. Use suction hose provided in kit to replace old hose. Remove alternator adjusting bolt. Remove 2 bolts at front of compressor bracket (bolt 1). *See EXPLODED VIEW OF COMPRESSOR ASSEMBLY under LEXUS.*

2) Using 2 new M10 x 70 mm bolts (bolt "A"), temporarily install pulley bracket "A". Remove upper compressor bolt (bolt 2). Using new M8 x 120 mm bolt (bolt "C"), temporarily install pulley bracket "B". Remove alternator bracket bolt (bolt 3). Using M10 x 55 mm bolt (bolt "D"), temporarily install pulley bracket "C".

3) Using two M8 x 30 mm bolts (bolt "E") provided, attach pulley brackets "A" and "B". Tighten bolts to 14 ft. lbs. (19 N.m). Using M6 x 25 mm bolt (bolt "F") provided, attach pulley brackets "B" and "C". Tighten bolt to 14 ft. lbs. (19 N.m).

4) Tighten bolts to pulley brackets "A" and "C" (bolts "A" and "D") to 27 ft. lbs. (37 N.m). Tighten bolt to pulley bracket "B" (bolt "C") to 18 ft. lbs. (25 N.m). Install M8 x 90 mm bolt (bolt "B") to compressor, and adjust belt tension (170-180 lbs. for new belt, or 95-135 lbs. for old belt).

5) Evacuate, recharge and leak test system. A/C system should be charged to 21-26 ounces.

32 *1992 CELICA AUTOMATIC A/C-HEATER SYSTEM: TESTING – BLOWER SPEED CONTROL SWITCH* – Please note that testing procedure for BLOWER SPEED CONTROL SWITCH on page TOYOTA 64 of 1992 AIR CONDITIONING & HEATING SERVICE & REPAIR manual has been revised. Correct testing procedure is as follows:

BLOWER SPEED CONTROL SWITCH TEST

Disconnect connector "B" from A/C-heater control panel. Check continuity between specified terminals of connector "B". See BLOWER SPEED CONTROL SWITCH CONTINUITY TEST table. If continuity is not as specified, replace A/C-heater control panel.

BLOWER SPEED CONTROL SWITCH CONTINUITY TEST

Switch Position	Continuity Between Terminals No.
OFF	None
AUTO	1, 3 & 7
LO	2, 3 & 6
■	2, 3 & 4
HI	2, 3 & 5

33 *1992 LAND CRUISER, PICKUP & 4RUNNER MANUAL A/C-HEATER SYSTEM: TESTING – A/C AMPLIFIER* – Please note that table for Pickup and 4Runner in testing procedure for A/C AMPLIFIER on page TOYOTA 35 of 1992 AIR CONDITIONING & HEATING SERVICE & REPAIR manual has been revised. Correct table is as follows:

A/C AMPLIFIER CIRCUIT TEST (PICKUP & 4RUNNER)

Terminals & Test Condition [1]	Specification
2 & 5	Continuity
7 & 8	
Pickup	Continuity
8 & Ground	Continuity
3 & 8	
A/C Switch On	Battery Voltage
A/C Switch Off	Battery Voltage
4 & 8	
A/C Switch On	Battery Voltage
A/C Switch Off	No Voltage
6 & 8	
Start Engine	About 10-14 Volts
Stop Engine	No Voltage
8 & 9	
A/C Switch On	Battery Voltage
A/C Switch Off	Battery Voltage
5 & 8 [2]	About 1500 Ohms
7 & 8	
4Runner	About 3.6 Ohms

[1] – Ensure ignition switch is on (if required), temperature control lever is at the maximum cool position, and blower switch is on HI position.

[2] – Test with air temperature at 77°F (25°C).

LATEST CHANGES & CORRECTIONS For 1993 & Earlier Models (Cont.)

34 *1992 LAND CRUISER, PICKUP & 4RUNNER MANUAL A/C-HEATER SYSTEM: TESTING – A/C SWITCH* – Please note that terminals for Pickup and 4Runner in testing procedure for A/C SWITCH on page TOYOTA 36 of 1992 AIR CONDITIONING & HEATING SERVICE & REPAIR manual may be incorrect. Correct table is as follows:

A/C SWITCH CONTINUITY

Switch Position	Continuity Between Terminals
Land Cruiser	
OFF	[1]
ON	2 & 3
Pickup & 4Runner	
OFF	[2]
ON	5 & 6

[1] – No continuity with switch in the OFF position.
[2] – No continuity between terminals No. 5 and 6.

VOLKSWAGEN

35 *1990-92 CABRIOLET MANUAL A/C-HEATER SYSTEM: ADJUSTING A/C COMPRESSOR BELT (TSB 92-02)* – Procedure to adjust A/C compressor belt using toothed rack tensioner has been revised due to restricted space in engine compartment. Correct procedure is as follows:

1) Remove generator "V" belt. Remove power steering reservoir. Remove reservoir bracket. Loosen compressor bracket Allen-head bolts. Loosen toothed rack tensioner bolts. *See ADJUSTING A/C COMPRESSOR BELT*.

2) After bolts are loosened, compressor will drop down under its own weight. If necessary, knock back spring sleeves on compressor bracket.

3) Using torque wrench, turn tensioning nut (4.5 ft.lbs. (6 N.m) for new belts, and 3 ft. lbs. (4 N.m) for used belts). Tighten toothed rack tensioner bolts to 22 ft. lbs. (30 N.m). To complete installation, reverse removal procedure.

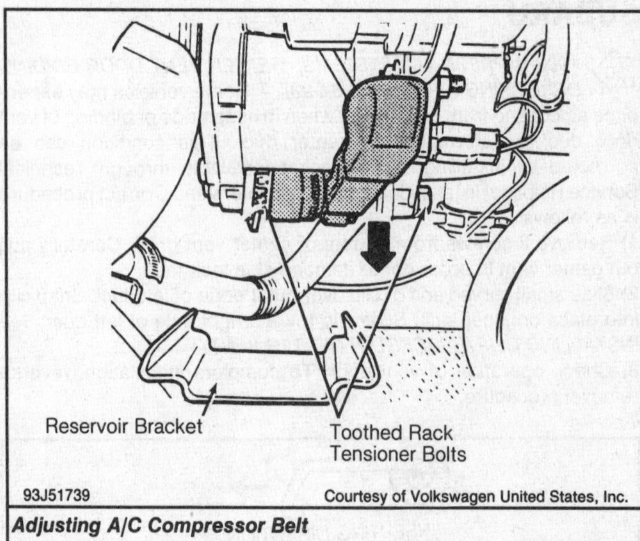
Reservoir Bracket
Toothed Rack Tensioner Bolts
93J51739
Courtesy of Volkswagen United States, Inc.

Adjusting A/C Compressor Belt

NOTES

NOTES

NOTES

NOTES

NOTES

NOTES

NOTES

NOTES

NOTES

NOTES